C000280036

THE OFFICIAL FOOTBALL ASSOCIATION

NON-LEAGUE CLUB DIRECTORY 2001

(23rd Edition)

EDITOR TONY WILLIAMS

Copyright
Non League Club Directory Ltd. All rights reserved.
No part of this publication may be reproduced, stored in a
retrieval system or transmitted, in any form or by any means,
electronic material, photocopying, recording or otherwise,
without the permission of the copyright holder.

ISBN 0.9539111-0.1

Published by Non-League Club Directory Ltd
Printed by Biddles of Guildford
Typesetting by Nina Whatmore and George Brown
All distributing queries to Pat Vaughan
Tel: 01823 490080 or 01458 241592

INTRODUCTION

The past year has seen the birth of an exciting new company called 'Non-League Media plc'.

Inspired by the introduction of a new non-League Sunday national newspaper 'The Non-League Paper' edited by ex-Daily Express Sports Editor Dave Emery, the company also invited Team Talk and the F.A. Non League Club Directory to link with a new website nlfootball.com and give the level of football that I personally love, the best publicity, general coverage and promotion it has ever received.

This Directory is obviously the twenty-three year 'old timer' amongst the newcomers and will act as an annual review and record of the year gone by.

We know there are over four million football enthusiasts linked with football outside the Premier and Nationwide football League every weekend and hopefully we will be able to cover all aspects of the game to which they are dedicated.

Every year when published, the Directory features well up the sports book ratings published in the national press. It has even reached No. 1 in recent years, so hopefully you, the readers will find it useful and enjoyable once again as you get into another busy and exciting season.

Editorial Team

Tony Williams (Editor)
George Brown (House Editor)
Steve Whitney, Jenny Gullick and Nina Whatmore

Editorial Address: Non League Directory Ltd.,
Helland, North Curry, Taunton, Somerset, TA3 6DU.
Tel: 01823 490080 - Fax: 01823 490281
Email: tony.williams12@virgin.net

ACKNOWLEDGEMENTS

There has been so much going on this year with the development of The Non-League Media plc, the compilation of the Directory just followed on in a prolonged rush!

The compilation of the pages by House Editor George Brown, (normal hours of work 6.00am - 6.00pm) unless suffering from an abcess of the gums, when he goes home at 5.00pm, and Nina Whatmore, who just works through the night, has been appreciated more this year than ever.

The majority of League and County Secretaries and Club Chairmen, Secretaries and Press Officers are really helpful and cannot do enough to help. One League Secretary who will remain nameless failed to help after the usual letter and two promises over the phone, but we hope you won't notice this in his league's section. Thanks to the vast majority and our best wishes for the rest of the season.

No where could anyone find more helpful and knowledgable experts than Steve Clark and his team in the Competitions Department of The Football Association and David Barber in the Library. They all obviously enjoy their work!

Many thanks too, to the hardy team of photographers who brave all weathers to cover the non-League season for us. They have become a cult of their own and will always accept a drink if you spot them around the grounds. Thanks to:-

Paul Barber, Peter Barnes, Graham Brown, Paul Carter, Andrew Chitty, Keith Clayton, Alan Coomes, Graham Cotterill, Paul Dennis, Tim Edwards, Keith Gillard, Ken Gregory, Tim Lancaster, Garry Letts, Peter Lirettoc, Eric Marsh, Ian Morsman, Dennis Nicholson, Ray Pruden, Mark Sandon, Francis Short, Peter Singh, Colin Stevens, Neil Thaler, Darren Thomas, Roger Turner, Alan Watson, Bill Wheatcroft, Gordon Whittington and Martin Wray. What stars!

Other contributors who have given valuable help other than the club statisticians and historians are:

Mike Amos, John Anderson, Jeremy Biggs, Bill Berry, Drian Buns, Albert Cole, Stewart Davidson (editor of the Scottish Non League Review - Contact 0141 5662 5721), Arthur Evans, Mike Ford, Rob Grillo, Wally Goss, William Hughes, Tony Incenzo, Tina Lightening, Alan Meadows, Dave Phillips, Mike Simmonds and Mike Wilson.

The expertise and impressive knowledge of Non-League players that Steve Whitney brings to the Directory is always much appreciated and hopefully as the different aims of our company are extended during this year we will all collect more and more knowledge for future editions of the Directory.

My thanks to everyone who has so willingly helped with the compilation of our twenty-third effort. The common denomination for us all is we do really care for the game as it is played and supported at non-League level.

Tony Williams

CONTENTS

Editorial

The Football Conference, originally 'The Alliance', is celebrating its 21st anniversary this season, so it is appropriate that seven member clubs are being accepted into the Auto Windscreen Trophy, and there appears to be a very good chance of at least two promoted clubs being accepted by Division Two in the 2001-2002 season.

Membership of the top semi-professional league (now including eight full time clubs) has certainly seen some changes over the years from Redditch United and Trowbridge Town to new boys Leigh RMI and star pyramid climbers Forest Green Rovers.

The quality of the play, the facilities and the attendances cannot be doubted, but, just at the time they are celebrating their coming of age, their immediate level of support in the pyramid is in disarray.

At the time of writing the Conference plus the Northern Premier League (Unibond) and Southern League (Dr. Martens) have turned on the Isthmian (Ryman) and decided they are not wanted as feeders to the Conference.

Whether they can make this decision without the Football Association's blessing is in doubt, but the action was taken following a meeting between the three feeder leagues, after a session at the F.A. had failed to solve the over-lapping of leagues in the South East.

It would have appeared that one Northern, one Midland/West and one South Eastern League would have fed nicely into the Conference, if the Dr. Martens and the Ryman League officials could have agreed a compromise for the South Eastern clubs. But they couldn't!

So the Conference have agreed to accept promotion from just two leagues - Northern Premier and Southern Premier - but will allow two up from each, thus relegating four each season. If the two up, two down link with Division Three is also agreed, it will mean a change of six clubs a season, and would certainly keep the Conference fresh!

As this problem boiled over, The Football Association were introducing a fresh administrative structure under their new chief executive, Adam Crozier. 'The National Game Board' are to look after the huge section of the game outside The Premier and Nationwide Football Leagues, and their full time Director, Steve Parkin, takes on mammoth responsibilities at The Football Association, while Frank Pattison is the chairman of the Game Board's executive.

Certainly a new and exciting concept, with a huge challenge ahead. At much the same time our own organisation changed significantly as 'The Non-League Media' was floated on the AIM market in the City, introducing 'The Non-League Paper', a national Sunday newspaper, a non-League website - nlfootball.com - and Team Talk, the national non-League monthly that celebrated its 100th issue last April, and the Directory, which is now in its 23rd year.

For one company to dedicate itself to promote the massive world of non-League football is a dream come true for me, as readers of the Directory and Team Talk will have been aware of the struggle to develop the publications over the years.

Hopefully, our level of the game will have the best publicity ever and we hope you will enjoy and appreciate our efforts.

After the disappointment of Euro 2000, as far as English football fans were concerned, the start of the new season may have offered less excitement than usual. The F.A. very sensibly threatened strong action against the ill discipline that brought the game into disrepute, but, no sooner had the Charity

Shield and the first week's games been played, then the Premier League was awash with bad temper, retribution, general criticism of referees and once again a sinking feeling of despair to those who love the game the way the vast majority of those not in the glare of publicity, play it up and down the country, week in and week out.

The trouble with the stars behaving so badly (and at £30,000 plus a week, why should they care about anything?) is that lesser players and certainly youngsters will copy them and then referees at lower levels will very soon be leaving the game in droves.

So the good news is that many leagues set up their own sportsmanship awards last season, many with sponsorship, and this season we are pleased to welcome Burtons Menswear not only as sponsors for our Directory, but also as sponsors for a national sportsmanship award to cover all leagues who compete in F.A. Trophy and Vase.

The more chairmen, managers and club captains emphasis the importance of keeping eleven men on the field and enjoying disciplined football, then the more the supporters, certainly at our levels, will enjoy their football and will keep coming back.

The reason why four million people are involved with grass roots football every weekend is because they enjoy the club spirit, the comradeship, the game and they find it fun.

That is also why attendances are going up and more and more youngsters want to play.

Hopefully, the TV money procured by Kate Hoey, the Minister for Sport, for our level of the sport, will enable more youngsters to get a game, but once again Burtons Menswear will be helping by handing over vouchers for all non-League, youth or schools members who buy clothes at Burtons. These vouchers can be collected by their respective football teams and exchanged for football kit or training aids. So when shopping at Burtons please remember to ask for your football vouchers and hand them in to your clubs.

Last season produced some wonderful finishes to the league campaigns, and it was good to see The F.A. Umbro Trophy Final produce such a brilliant game. The lead changed hands three times and a five goal thriller brought yet another triumph for Geoff Chapple. He has managed five winning Trophy clubs (Woking three, Kingstonian two) and must have written himself into football history with the latest thrilling performance. It was tough luck on a very well supported and plucky Kettering Town side, but it was a great day to remember.

Interestingly, The F.A. Carlsberg Vase attracted just 49 more supporters to the final than the Trophy and here most credit must go to the town of Chippenham, who masterminded a superb 'Wembley promotion' and seemed to bring most of the town to the final.

Once again the best supported finalists lost, but, with this special spirit in the club, who is to say where they will end up in the year ahead? After all, little Forest Green Rovers won the Vase in 1982 and only two years ago reached the Trophy Final.

The F.A. Challenge Vase, energetically supported and sponsored by Carlsberg, is a wonderful competition as it offers such exciting rewards as travelling the country, attracting big crowds, hitting the headlines and making many new contacts and good friends for very small clubs used to playing in regional leagues.

It is a joy to watch and fascinating to see the season's stories unfold as Cinderella clubs do actually go to the ball and they do sometimes attract more than their big Trophy brothers. This is all about spirit of the game!

Every year the Directory brings us all a very real satisfaction. We realise from the replies we receive from clubs, leagues and counties that the publication is enjoyed and hopefully our efforts this year will again be useful. I suspect that the support thar will be given by 'The Non-League Media' will help it reach many more readers and consequently may bring more football fans in touch with what we enjoy referring to as the 'Football Family'. Have a good season.

TW

TEAM TALK's
100th Birthday

Team Talk celebrated its 100th edition in March with a party on `The Elizabethan' a riverboat on the Thames.

A good time was had by all and I must say the battle to keep the magazine going over ten years has been helped greatly by the enthusiasm and support of all our loyal readers. It has all been well worth while.   TW

Above: "The Elizabethan". Photo: Eric Marsh
Below: It's a Riverboat Shuffle. Photo: Andrew Chitty

Non-League Football

welcomes

BURTON MENSWEAR

It is refreshing to see a company such as Burtons, a valued Football Association Associate, investing so much time and money in helping more youngsters to take up the game.

The scheme will help schools and youth clubs as well as senior clubs by supplying a new source of kit, equipment and training aids, all of which are vital if the game is to be enjoyed by our youngsters all over the country.

So often lack of funds is blamed for the relatively small number of youth teams, but the Burtons' scheme will give the chance to clubs to help themselves and hopefully they will seize their opportunities.

I am also impressed by the sportsmanship awards which can only be good for the game and, of course, their involvement with the non-League game's own treasured Directory which will, I am sure, be mutually appreciated by Publishers and Sponsors alike in the year ahead.

Congratulations and good luck for this season.

KATE HOEY M.P
Minister for Sport.

Burton Menswear are launching a unique initiative, the Kits for Clubs scheme - one of the biggest ever give-aways to support the future of non-League football.

Created by official F.A. sponsor Burton Menswear, KITS FOR CLUBS is dedicated to giving something back to the football community at grass roots level by investing in the people who play football across the pitches in the UK. By helping non-League, school and youth club teams across the county to obtain vital football kit and training equipment KITS FOR CLUBS hopes to invest in a new generation of world class footballers.

The initiative will allow the entire nation to help make a difference to their local team or school. A purchase made at any Burton Menswear store across the UK means a direct contribution to the club of personal choice for top quality kit and equipment.

Burton Menswear hopes to redress the lack of funds experienced by so many non-League clubs and schools by providing a simple and effective scheme, which will invest in the kids of today and the footballers of the future.

KITS FOR CLUBS is a logical step for a company with such a strong football heritage as Burton Menswear. An England sponsor - Burton also has a long history as the official suit-maker for the England team. The Burton suit was most ecently sported by the England squad at Euro 2000, but the association goes as far back as 1966 when Burton suited the likes of Bobby Charlton and Geoff Hurst in the victorious World Cup Final against Germany.

Burton Menswear will send participating non-League clubs and schools further information about the scheme, including posters and the best methods of harnessing support to help invest in the future of the club.

KITS FOR CLUBS launches in October 2000 and will be supported through national and local media.

Proud to be associated with the national game

BURTON
MENSWEAR

Official Sponsor of The Football Association

www.burtonsoccer.co.uk

BURTON
MENSWEAR

Official Sponsor of The Football Association

A major sponsorship deal has been struck with 'Burton Menswear', an official Associate of The Football Association.

They are going to sponsor our F.A. Non League Club Directory and also nationwide sportsmanship awards, apart from their truly outstanding offer of 'Kits for Clubs' of which you will read about on these pages.

At a time when hardly a week during the football season goes by without a sickening example of bad behaviour or bad sportsmanship being thrust at us through the national media, it is perhaps time to realise that in general the huge majority of footballers and their clubs do play the game in the right spirit.

Some leagues published their sponsored sportsmanship competitions last season and the Liverpool based Marine club won the Unibond Award and finished fourth in their Premier League, while Nigel Clough, obviously following his father's attitude to talking back to referees, took Burton Albion to the Dr Martens Premier Award and finished second in their Premier Division.

Disciplined players don't have to be 'soft' losers. Look back over the years and imagine playing against Gerry Byrne, John Charles, Dave Mackay, Nat Lofthouse, the 'new' Tony Adams or Stuart Pearce. You would know you had been in a game as all those players were (or are) out and out winners and 'hard men', but also disciplined. Can you remember any of these characters chasing referees around, showing the opposition they had lost their tempers and their control or letting their team mates and supporters down by getting sent off for petty offences?

You don't have to be loud mouthed or quick tempered to be a 'winner'.

There is nothing better in team sport such as football, rugby or even boxing than a full blooded physical battle after which you finish up with respect for your opponents, whether you have won or lost. That surely is one of the rewards for getting fit and playing your sport at a competitive level.

Burton Menswear are sponsoring awards that will highlight the sportsmanship standard of all clubs at F.A. Umbro Trophy and F.A. Carlsberg Vase levels.

We will highlight the disciplinary records of clubs during the season and at the half way stage the club with the best disciplinary record will receive a special Christmas present from Burton.

Then at the end of the season not only will the club with the best record receive another special prize from the sponsors, but the league whose clubs have the best average sportsmanship record for the season will also receive a spectacular award.

The sportsmanship records will be gauged by adding the cautions (one point) and dismissals (three points) for the league season and then divided by the number of league games played. In the case of a tie, the club record in their cup ties will be taken into account in the same way.

Hopefully, this Award will encourage all clubs to emphasise the fact that tackling must continue, but dissent, retaliation and general petulance must be eliminated. The referees will certainly enjoy themselves more, the football will be better to watch, better to play and the game will be all the better for this very encouraging and worthwhile sponsorship.

Thank you Burton Menswear!

Tony Williams

The Non-League Club Directory

1999-2000
AWARDS

ROLL OF HONOUR

FOOTBALLER OF THE YEAR
Gary Abbott

MANAGER OF THE YEAR
Jan Molby

ENGLAND PLAYER OF THE YEAR
Gary Patterson

INDIVIDUAL MERIT AWARDS
Geoff Chapple
Jimmy Conway
Max Griggs
Ken Jarvis
Anthony Lynch
Ken Marsden

REGIONAL AWARDS
Bedlington Terriers
Vauxhall Motors
Rushden & Diamonds
Boston United
Langney Sports
Dagenham & Redbridge
Chippenham Town
Hereford United

INDIVIDUAL MERIT AWARDS 1999-2000

Geoff Chapple (Kingstonian)
So much has been written and said about Geoff's managerial skills, especially in the F.A. Umbro Challenge Trophy competition that it is difficult to be original. He won our poll for Manager of the 21 Year Non League Directory era 1977-98 and now, of course, he has produced four Trophy winning squads. Geoff, who is a director of his club and also sits on the Management Committee of the Conference is always available to help and co-operate in non-League football matters and has proved an ideal role model for new managers at our level of the game.

Anthony Lynch, Taunton Town
Photo: Stuart Ferguson

Jimmy Conway
(Kidderminster Harriers Physiotherapist)
In every successful dressing room there needs to be a good talker and, of course, a quality physio, Kidderminster Harriers and the England semi-professional squad have both in the form of Jimmy Conway. He has given great support to Graham Allner and past England managers, before linking successfully with Jan Molby and John Owens. His very presence lightens up many a tough situation and his experience has proved invaluable. Jimmy will be sorely missed on the non-League circuit.

Max Griggs (Chairman, Rushden & Diamonds)
When you are such a high profiled personality, it brings its own very different problems compared to the normal club official. Transfer fees are scorned with envy, everyone wants to beat your club, there is gloating when things go wrong. But in Max's case he has always put the club first, and their facilities are beautiful and useful, not flashy. His success has been accepted with modesty and 'The Diamonds' and their home, Nene Park, are a wonderful advertisement for what can be done with taste and love for the game. Just think of the Chairmen we all know without the humble touch!

Ken Jarvis (Croydon)
The steady rise of Croydon F.C. from a very quiet period outside the top level of the pyramid, has been inspired by the incredible work rate, initiative and ambition of Ken Jarvis. He has virtually built a new club and has justifiably had the satisfaction of seeing all his teams successful - even the sadly now departed women's team. It was a shame club president Jack Milstead didn't live to see Ken lead the club back to the Ryman Premier, but the town itself know how much they owe to him.

Anthony Lynch (Taunton Town)
Those involved with Senior level clubs have often overlooked the achievements of the Vase level players as standards are obviously not so high. But if you look at Anthony's record at Screwfix Western League Champions, Taunton Town, when he scored 62 goals in the season, you will also note that he finished the season second top scorer in the AXA sponsored F.A. Cup with seven and also the top scorer in the F.A. Carlsberg Vase with ten. Here is a really special goalscorer!

Ken Marsden (Chairman, Unibond League)
Ken celebrates fifty years of involvement with non-League football. He has served with Gainsborough Trinity, The Northern Premier League and as an F.A. Councillor who, at present, is the chairman of the F.A. Representative Committee which administers the England Semi-Professional international squad. Officials such as Ken are lucky to be involved with a labour of love, but all the hours given to the game add up to a terrific service to our level of the game.

REGIONAL CLUB AWARDS 1999-2000

North East
BEDLINGTON TERRIERS - It is very easy to fall away after a special season, but Terriers not only fought hard to return to Wembley, losing after a replay in the Quarter Final, but kept up the pressure in the Arnott Insurance Northern League and retained their title by nine points and a goal difference of sixty three in the cups.

North West
VAUXHALL MOTORS - The football produced by the Motors' young side was suitably stylish and smart to grace the superb facilities enjoyed by this progressive club in the Wirral. All season they looked likely North West Trains Champions and, despite a glamourous F.A. Vase run which finished in the semi-final, they won their championship and promotion in real style.

Midlands
RUSHDEN & DIAMONDS - No doubt missing their main aim of promotion was disappointing, but The Diamonds still had a great season by anyone else's standards. Runners-up in the Conference, The Quarter Rounds of the Trophy and the scalp of Scunthorpe United and two great games with Sheffield United in the F.A. Cup all added up to an excellent campaign which will be hard to beat. The facilities and ground atmosphere at the club is a wonderful tribute to non-League football.

East of England
BOSTON UNITED - took over at the top of the Dr. Martens Premier table mid way through the season and shook off all their challengers with an impressive consistency that eventually gave them a fourteen point winning margin. This famous non-League club deserves to be at the top of the pyramid and they are determined to consolidate before challenging for another surge upwards.

Home Counties South
LANGNEY SPORTS - One of the fairy stories of regional football has come true in Sussex where constant ground developments and steady improvements on the field have brought Langney Sports through the three divisions of the Sussex League to membership of the Dr. Martens League. Their story shows that progress can be made without huge cash injections or big attendances - just spirit, determination, hard work and common sense.

Home Counties North
DAGENHAM & REDBRIDGE - There's a special football atmosphere at Victoria Road, Dagenham and even when re-building a Conference squad, they reached a Trophy Final, so with new manager Gary Hill at the helm you sensed the Daggers meant business. Their very professional approach to last season league programme proved just that and they are now back in the Conference where they belong.

South West
CHIPPENHAM TOWN - An early season F.A. Cup run alerted their supporters of the things to come and their larger than life manager Tommy Saunders, certainly used the press well to build the club's reputation. So when their Vase campaign ran and ran all the way to Wembley, the way the club, the town and the supporters responded to show a very special spirit indeed.

F.A. Cup
HEREFORD UNITED - are one of the most famous non-League giant killers, but since their Newcastle experience they have enjoyed a spell in The Football League and now their modern players have made a name for themselves in their own right. Victories over York City and Hartlepool United preceded two very closely fought Third Round ties with Premier Division Leicester City. Congratulations to everyone involved.

ENGLAND PLAYER OF THE YEAR

GARY PATTERSON

Photo: Keith Clayton

Gary must have been disappointed to miss the Trophy Final through suspension, but he had enjoyed a superb season once again both with Kingstonian and the England Semi-Professional team. In Gary Butterworth's absence he had taken over as England's captain against Holland (1-0) and Wales (1-1). His absence through injury in the last few minutes at Llanelli probably gave the Welsh their opportunity to score an equaliser from a set piece, as his covering, marking and defensive organisation was greaty valued by England manager John Owens, who has selected him as England Player of the Season.

NON LEAGUE MANAGER OF THE YEAR

JAN MOLBY
(Kidderminster Harriers)

Photo: Peter Barnes

Jan proved many doubters completely wrong by steadily building his Harriers squad into an excellent winning combination thanks to simple passing football, good organisation and faith in each other. Lifting youngsters to standards they had not considered and inspiring older players to regain their love for, and dedication to the game. Jan has shown that with sensible application, famous international players can understand the non-League scene and succeed within it.

PAST WINNERS

1998-99	Brendan Phillips	Nuneaton Borough
1997-98	Steve Cotterill	Cheltenham Town
1996-97	Paul Futcher	Southport
1995-96	Paul Fairclough	Stevenage Borough
1994-95	Sammy McIlroy	Macclesfield Town
1993-94	Bill Punton	Diss Town
1992-93	Martin O'Neill	Wycombe Wanderers

NON LEAGUE FOOTBALLER OF THE YEAR
GARY ABBOTT
(Aldershot Town)

Photo: Eric Marsh

Photo: Ian Morsman

At the age of 33 Gary's move to Aldershot was considered by many to be just a case of a short swan song. Two seasons and over 100 goals later he has displayed some of his best football and last season's superb form brought him the Adidas Predator Award for most goals by a senior player in his Premier Division. The AXA sponsored F.A. Cup and the F.A. Umbro Trophy and he also scored in eleven consecutive league games. Gary's attitude and consistant success provides an excellent example to all young players at semi-professional level.

PAST WINNERS

1998-99	Neil Grayson	(Cheltenham Town)
1997-98	Phil Everett	(Tiverton Town)
1996-97	Howard Forinton	(Yeovil Town)
1995-96	Barry Hayes	(Stevenage Borough)
1994-95	Kevan Brown	(Woking)
1993-94	Chris Brindley	(Kidderminster Harriers)
1992-93	Steve Guppy	(Wycombe Wanderers)
1991-92	Tommy Killick	(Wimborne Town)
1990-91	Mark West	(Wycombe Wanderers)
1989-90	Phil Gridelet	(Barnet)
1988-89	Steve Butler	(Maidstone United)
1987-88	David Howell	(Enfield)
1986-87	Mark Carter	(Runcorn)
1985-86	Jeff Johnson	(Altrincham)
1984-85	Alan Cordice	(Wealdstone)
1983-84	Brian Thompson	(Maidstone United)

Non-League Media plc

Aims to give non-League football the very best media coverage it has ever received

Through:-

⚽ The daily use of our Website - **www.nlfootball.com**

⚽ The weekly paper **THE NON-LEAGUE PAPER** (already over 40,000 weekly sales), published nationally on Sundays.

⚽ The monthly magazine **'ON THE BALL'** which promotes Womens Football

⚽ The monthly magazine **TEAM TALK** (over 100 editions), published nationally each month
(12 months subscription £29.00 - 6 months subscription £15.00)

⚽ The best selling **F.A. NON LEAGUE CLUB DIRECTORY** (now in its 23rd year)

For subscription enquiries only please contact the
Subscribers Hotline - 0800 424 567
(For the Non-League Paper, On The Ball or Team Talk)

Any general enquiries regarding Team Talk or the Directory contact
01823 490080 or Email: tony.williams12@virgin.net

Any general enquiries regarding The Non-League Paper or On the Ball to -
Non-League Media Plc., Elvin House, Stadium Way, Wembley, Middlesex, HA9 0DW.
Tel: 0208 900 9021

PECKING ORDER 1999-2000
A J Sarnecki

96-7	97-8	98-9	99-00	Code	League	FA Cup ext	FA Cup xmt	FA Cup won	FA Trophy ent	FA Trophy xmt	FA Trophy won	FA Vase ent	FA Vase xmt	FA Vase won	C pts	T pts	V pts	Total pts
1	1	1	1	ap	CONFERENCE	22	176	18	22	44	53	0	0	0	216	185	0	401
2	3	2	2	npp	NORTHERN PREMIER Premier	23	92	30	23	0	36	0	0	0	145	128	0	273
4	4	3	3	sop	SOUTHERN Premier	22	88	34	22	0	20	0	0	0	144	108	0	252
4	2	4	4	isp	ISTHMIAN Premier	22	88	29	22	0	22	0	0	0	139	110	0	249
8	7	5	5	is1	ISTHMIAN First	22	0	44	22	0	14	0	0	0	66	102	0	168
(5	6)	6	6	soe	SOUTHERN Eastern	22	0	36	22	0	13	0	0	0	58	101	0	159
6=	5	5	7	np1	NORTHERN PREMIER First	22	0	36	22	0	8	0	0	0	58	96	0	154
10	9	9	8	is2	ISTHMIAN Second	22	0	21	0	0	0	22	54	28	43	0	104	147
(6=	9	8)	9	sow	SOUTHERN Western	22	0	25	22	0	10	0	0	0	47	98	0	145
13	11=	11=	10	nwc1	NORTH WEST COUNTIES First	19	0	12	0	0	0	22	30	40	31	0	92	123
9	10	10	11	nor1	NORTHERN First	20	0	22	0	0	0	20	30	27	42	0	77	119
11	11=	11=	12	ecop	EASTERN COUNTIES Premier	20	0	12	0	0	0	22	34	30	32	0	86	118
12	13=	13=	13	ncep	NORTHERN COUNTIES EAST Premier	18	0	18	0	0	0	19	28	25	36	0	72	108
20	20	20	14	wsx1	WESSEX	18	0	14	0	0	0	20	26	27	32	0	73	105
17	15	15	15	is3	ISTHMIAN Third	21	0	13	0	0	0	21	14	23	34	0	58	92
15	13=	13=	16=	wesp	WESTERN Premier	15	0	17	0	0	0	17	10	32	32	0	59	91
14	16	19	16=	mda	MIDLAND ALLIANCE	20	0	9	0	0	0	21	14	27	29	0	62	91
19	21	21	18	ken1	KENT	16	0	11	0	0	0	18	20	25	27	0	63	90
16	20	17=	19	ssx1	SUSSEX COUNTY First	17	0	17	0	0	0	19	14	17	34	0	50	84
18	17	16	20	ssmp	SPARTAN SOUTH MIDLANDS Premier	14	0	9	0	0	0	20	4	17	23	0	41	64
24	17=	17=	21	ucop	UNITED COUNTIES Premier	18	0	8	0	0	0	17	18	12	26	0	36	62
22	24	22	22	help	HELLENIC Premier	7	0	6	0	0	0	15	4	11	13	0	46	59
25	26	23	23	cocp	COMBINED COUNTIES	12	0	7	0	0	0	16	4	10	19	0	30	49
23	22	28=	24	nce1	NORTHERN COUNTIES EAST First	10	0	6	0	0	0	15	0	17	16	0	32	48
21	25	24	25=	esxs	ESSEX Senior	9	0	4	0	0	0	11	6	5	13	0	22	35
29	21	25=	25=	nor2	NORTHERN Second	11	0	3	0	0	0	15	6	6	14	0	21	35
28	31=	30=	27	nwc2	NORTH WEST COUNTIES Second	7	0	2	0	0	0	12	4	6	9	0	22	31
27	28	30=	28	eco1	EASTERN COUNTIES First	2	0	1	0	0	0	17	0	6	3	0	25	28
35	31=	28=	29	wes1	WESTERN First	7	0	3	0	0	0	11	6	6	10	0	17	27
30	30	26	30	lesp	LEICESTERSHIRE SENIOR Premier	0	0	0	0	0	0	11	12	12	0	0	23	23
32	29	27	31	swe	SOUTH-WESTERN	2	0	1	0	0	0	5	6	7	3	0	18	21
33	24=	32	32	cmsu	CENTRAL MIDLANDS Supreme	0	0	0	0	0	0	9	6	8	0	0	17	17
34	33	34=	33=	ssx2	SUSSEX COUNTY Second	5	0	1	0	0	0	6	3	3	6	0	9	15
38	34	34	33=	wmrp	WEST MIDLAND REGIONAL Premier	0	0	0	0	0	0	12	8	6	0	0	15	15
37	36	35	33=	ssms	SPARTAN SOUTH MIDLANDS Senior	0	0	0	0	0	0	7	0	3	0	0	15	15
36	39=	38=	36	mdcp	MIDLAND COMBINATION Premier	0	0	0	0	0	0	9	3	8	0	0	12	12
39=	36	38=)	37=	nalp	NORTHERN ALLIANCE Premier	0	0	0	0	0	0	1	0	3	0	0	2	2
(43=)	38=	41=	37=	hamp	HAMPSHIRE Premier	0	0	0	0	0	0	2	0	1	0	0	2	2
	38=	38=	37=	dvc	DEVON COUNTY LEAGUE	0	0	0	0	0	0	1	0	0	0	0	2	2
36	37	37	40=	wch1	WEST CHESHIRE First	0	0	0	0	0	0	1	0	1	0	0	2	2
46=	43=	38=	40=	ntas	NOTTS ALLIANCE Senior	0	0	0	0	0	0	1	0	0	0	0	1	1
44=	39=	41=	40=	manp	MANCHESTER Premier	0	0	0	0	0	0	1	0	0	0	0	1	1
	39=		40=	hel1	HELLENIC First	0	0	0	0	0	0	0	0	1	0	0	1	1
42			40=	smsp	SOMERSET SENIOR Premier	0	0	0	0	0	0	0	0	0	0	0	1	1

(figures in parentheses refer to slightly different leagues: SOUTHERN South and Midland, HAMPSHIRE First). With apologies to the current year's sponsors.

F.A. CHALLENGE CUP

sponsored by AXA

1999 - 2000 REVIEW

NON LEAGUE HONOURS BOARD 1999-2000

FIRST ROUND PROPER

NATIONWIDE CONFERENCE (12)	DR MARTENS (7)	RYMANS (cont)
Doncaster Rovers	Bath City	Oxford City
Forest Green Rovers	Burton Albion	St Albans City
Hayes	Cambridge City	Whyteleafe
Hednesford Town	Chelmsford City	Worthing
Hereford United	Ilkeston Town	
Kettering Town	Merthyr Tydfil	**UNIBOND (6)**
Kingstonian	Tamworth	
Morecambe		Bamber Bridge
Rushden & Diamonds	**RYMANS (7)**	Eastwood Town
Southport		Gateshead
Welling United	Aldershot Town	Guiseley
Yeovil Town	Enfield	Runcorn
	Hendon	Stalybridge Celtic

SECOND ROUND

Aldershot
Bamber Bridge
Enfield
Forest Green Rovers
Hayes
Hendon
Hereford United
Ilkeston Town
Rushden & Diamonds
Stalybridge Celtic

THIRD ROUND

Hereford United	v	Leicester City	0-0, 2-1	7,795, 12,157
Rushden & Diamonds	v	Sheffield United	1-1, 1-1, 5p6	10,104, 6,101

PRELIMINARY ROUND

1	Shildon	1 v 3	Thornaby-on-Tees	*123
	Chapman 27		*Harrison 46, Newell 47, 73*	
2	Glasshoughton Welf.	0 v 1	Hebburn	75
			Scott 51	
3	Brandon United	0 v 3	Ossett Town	64
			Stabb 41, 85, Brooke 50	
4	Bradford (P A)	1 v 0	Prescot Cables	178
	Maxwell 44			
5	Workington	1 v 2	Burscough	751
	Swailes 26		*Birch 82, Talbot 84*	
6	Garforth Town	0 v 4	Armthorpe Welfare	192
			Johnson 51, 84, Erskine 6, Ridley 90	
7	Dunston Fed. Brewery	1 v 0	Maine Road	89
	Fletcher 19			
8	Atherton Collieries	1 v 2	Ramsbottom United	90
	Little 41		*Brierley 20, Westhead 81*	
9	Marske United	1 v 1	Ashington	120
	Norminton 78		*Robson (og) 59*	
r	Ashington	1 v 2	Marske United	
	Purvis		*James 42, Sankey 76*	
10	Cheadle Town	0 v 3	Warrington Town	80
			Holden 8, Burnell 55, Lee 89	
11	Morpeth Town	2 v 1	Harrogate Town	98
	Smithson 37, 58		*Denney 57*	
12	Tow Law Town	6 v 0	Tadcaster Albion	174
	Pickering 27, 74, Bolton 42, 47, Nash 66, 77			
13	Chester-Le-Street T	1 v 3	St Helens Town	108
	Mawson 86p		*Bickerstaffe 60, O'Niell 82, 87*	
14	Hallam	1 v 2	Liversedge	107
	Pearson 71		*Carter 65, O'Hara 88*	
15	Billingham Town	1 v 2	Fleetwood Freeport	108
	Woodhouse 30		*Walsh 50, 55*	
16	Farsley Celtic	1 v 1	Guisborough Town	78
	Blackstone 84		*Hutchinson*	
r	Guisborough Town	0 v 1	Farsley Celtic	
			Whellans 90p	
17	Accrington Stanley	3 v 0	Peterlee Newtown	221
	O'Callaghan 22, Ceraolo 69, Payne 71			
18	Rossendale United	2 v 1	Chadderton	181
	Sargeson 7, Grimshaw 58		*Bennett 65*	
19	Netherfield Kendal	3 v 0	Oldham Town	98
	Phil Brown 3 (34, 38, 50)			
20	Harrogate Railway	1 v 0	Willington	105
	Hart 70			
21	Bootle	0 v 0	Jarrow Roofing Boldon CA	
r	Jarrow Roofing Bdn CA	1 v 1	Harrogate Railway	
	Chow 15			
		Jarrow won 5-3 on penalties		
22	Crook Town	2 v 0	Yorkshire Amateur	134
	Moan 63, og 42			
23	Louth United	2 v 1	Kennek Ryhope CA	72
	Blake 29, Elkington 85		*Griffiths 55*	
24	Flixton	2 v 1	Northallerton Town	98
	Hogan 46, Bromley 65		*Ramm 88*	
25	Ashton United	2 v 1	Clitheroe	168
	France 79, og 86		*Pilkington 50*	
26	Goole	1 v 1	Trafford	210
			McCartney 60p	
r	Trafford	6 v 3	Goole	
	Lowe 11, 61 Shaughnessey 14, 25 Burns 37, Murray 35		*Brown 15, Miller 53, Elton 58*	
27	Woodley Sports	2 v 1	Ossett Albion	151
	Weardon 63, McNeil 33		*Gomersal 78*	
28	Pickering Town	4 v 1	Horden CW	164
	Joe Conner 3 (20p, 71, 83p)		*Cowley 75*	
29	Denaby United	0 v 2	Chorley	128
			Kay 15, Mitchell 31	

30	Darwen	0 v 1	Billingham Synthonia	55
			Barker 87	
31	Brodsworth	1 v 0	South Shields	92
	Smith 20			
32	Mossley	2 v 1	Atherton LR	189
	Brennan 17, Willcock 83		*Bradshaw 31*	
33	Parkgate	1 v 5	Eccleshill United	42
	Adams 44p		**Stuart Taylor 4 (14, 25, 62, 75),** *Cochrane 48*	
34	Thackley	0 v 1	Consett	101
			McGinley 10	
35	North Ferriby Utd	1 v 0	Witton Albion	227
	Perrin 58			
36	Penrith	4 v 0	Shotton Comrades	91
	Walker 3, Bell 12 Cowperthwaite 48, Stewart 68			
37	Salford City	2 v 0	Evenwood Town	120
	og 67, Taylor 83			
38	Radcliffe Borough	2 v 1	Durham City	175
	Bean 12, Mullen 90		*Rooke 33*	
39	Selby Town	0 v 3	Bedlington Terriers	170
			Milner 20, Ludlow 60, Cameron 89	
40	Bacup Borough	2 v 2	Sheffield	71
	Betts 3, Taylor 68		*Godber 54, Wood 88*	
r	Sheffield	4 v 0	Bacup Borough	
	Wood 50, 69, Cartledge 41 Godber 58			
41	Curzon Ashton	0 v 1	Brigg Town	97
			Ward 28	
42	Skelmersdale Utd	5 v 2	Whitley Bay	132
	McBride 20, 39 Rudi 63, 72, Cowley 50		*McLabe 16, 71*	
43	Easington Colliery	2 v 2	Newcastle Blue Star	55
	Davis 56, Milborne 83		*Hollier 52, Bell 60*	
r	Newcastle Blue Star	4 v 0	Easington Colliery	
	Hurst 27, Smith 53 Bell 58, Beech 61			
44	Seaham Red Star	2 v 1	West Auckland Tn	110
	Taylor 35, 75		*Elliott 80*	
45	Gretna	5 v 0	Rossington Main	51
	Ross Milligan 3 (57, 75, 85) *Dobie 8, Armstrong 90*			
46	Brackley Town	2 v 1	Long Buckby	120
	Jenkins 3, Clarke 6		*McLeary 73*	
47	Stourbridge	3 v 1	Bromsgrove Rovers	417
	Banks 17, Rhodes 71, 74		*Jinks 18*	
48	Blackstone	0 v 0	Willenhall Town	77
r	Willenhall Town	4 v 2	Blackstone	
	Grosvenor 4, Barnes 35, 45 Chester 90		*Harrald 25, Fogg 75*	
49	Rocester	2 v 3	Spalding United	140
	Owen 18, Bott 28			
50	Stamford	3 v 1	Corby Town	202
	Staff 55, Garman 81, Rhule 84		*Hollis 13*	
51	Belper Town	2 v 2	Stourport Swifts	146
	Brady 74, og 87		*Marsh 77, Booth 79*	
r	Stourport Swifts	1 v 2	Belper Town	
	Mountford 40		*Weston 44, Cunningham 95*	
52	Boston Town	1 v 0	Boldmere St Michaels	98
	Scotney 70			
53	Stratford Town	4 v 1	Leek CSOB	65
	Darrock 6, 13, Brant 59 Kelly 86		*Bourne 53*	

Top: Ray Stanger in action for Durham City.
Photo: Colin Stevens

Middle: Marske's Simon Kasonali gets in a shot at goal.
Photo: Alan Watson

Bottom: Penrith's Ross Cowperthwaite vaults the Shotton Comrades' keeper after shooting the home side 3-0 ahead.
Photo: Bill Wheatcroft

54	Borrowash Victoria	0 v 1	Sutton Coldfield Tn	97
			Howells 90	
55	Matlock Town	1 v 0	Chasetown	235
	Campbell 90			
56	Moor Green	3 v 0	Paget Rangers	180
	Hall 31, 37, Casey 88			
57	Barwell	1 v 1	Staveley MW	105
	Lyne 90		*Thomson 20*	
r	Staveley MV	5 v 3	Barwell	
	K Leatherday 3 (74, 83, 90)		***M Rosegreen 3 (4, 27, 74)***	
	Schofield 68, White 71			
58	Redditch United	1 v 0	Kings Norton Town	175
	Nicholls 5			
59	Stafford Rangers	2 v 0	Glossop North End	493
	Shaw 39, Swain 88			
60	Lincoln United	1 v 2	Mickleover Sports	149
	Gray 14		*Briscoe 16, Parking 74*	
61	Alfreton Town	1 v 2	Congleton Town	144
	Hopkinson 61		*Thornley 44, 45*	
62	Ford Sports Daventry	1 v 2	Nantwich Town	80
			Borthwick 28, Gayle 70	
63	Racing Club Warwick	1 v 2	Blakenall	121
	Hepburn 43		*Street 18, Palmer 62*	
64	Shepshed Dynamo	0 v 3	Raunds Town	151
			Hornby 9, 30, Harrisen 67	
65	Bilston Town	2 v 4	Oadby Town	141
	Yates 46, Burton 76		*Walker 14, 63, Jackson 50,*	
			Tiday 90	
66	Wednesfield	1 v 6	Oldbury United	64
	Bellingham 39		*Banner 11,88, Richards 27,47,*	
			Hesson 21, Nightingale 79	
67	Desborough Town	2 v 3	Northampton Spencer	112
	Chong 69, McPolin 88		*Coleman 35, Pepperall 59,*	
			Richardson 77	
68	Glapwell	3 v 1	Stapenhill	90
	Scott 56, Morgan 76		*Eaton 20*	
	Gamble 87			
69	Bridgnorth Town	1 v 3	Hinckley United	177
	Hemstock 27		*Ricketts 52, Stadler 89,*	
			McGlinchey	
70	Wellingborough Tn	3 v 0	Kidsgrove Athletic	26
	Knight 24, 78, Gent 70			
71	Gresley Rovers	0 v 1	Eastwood Town	387
			Tomlinson 67	
72	Holbeach United	2 v 0	Pelsall Villa	82
	Barnes 32, Rowley 34			
73	Newcastle Town	1 v 0	Sandwell Borough	141
	Pesteridge 54			
74	VS Rugby	1 v 2	Solihull Borough	251
	Green 83		*Nesbitt 32, Dowling 80*	
75	Bourne Town	0 v 2	Stewarts & Lloyds	76
			Fraser 15, 55	
76	Knypersley Victoria	v	Bedworth United	
	Walkover for Bedworth United			
77	Shifnal Town	3 v 3	Rushall Olympic	120
	Hull 14, Treharne 22		*Palmer 20, Charlton 52,*	
	Ashley 71		*Blakemore 85*	
	Rushall Olympic	0 v 1	Shifnal Town	
			Treharne 118	
78	Arnold Town	2 v 2*	Yaxley	123
	Whitman 34, Baxter 19		*Ward 75, MacCallum 108*	
	Yaxley	1 v 2	Arnold Town	
	George 38		*Baxter 10, Waitman 37*	
79	Halesowen Harriers	4 v 0	West Midlands Police	83
	L. Smith 35, Clark 65			
	Jones 68, N. Smith 88			

80	St Neots Town	2 v 1	Hornchurch	92
	Gale 32, Carby 80		*Wolff 71*	
81	Potters Bar Town	3 v 3	Flackwell Heath	80
	Harris 10, 70p, Martin 13		*Bartlett 40, 90, Watson 12*	
r	Flackwell Heath	1 v 0	Potters Bar Town	
	Watson 68			
82	Great Wakering Rrs	0 v 0	Staines Town	147
r	Staines Town	5 v 0	Great Wakering Rrs	
	Butler 37, 76, Glynn 59			
	Jansen 72, Walters 81			
83	Chalfont St Peter	0 v 6	Barking	126
			Kevin Hoddy 3 (34, 45, 88),	
			Hughes 43, Aransibia 45, 62	
84	Stotfold	0 v 0	Wembley	121
r	Wembley	2 v 1	Stotfold	
	Hayle 13, McCarthy 38		*Davidson 85*	
85	Grays Athletic	7 v 1	Basildon United	192
	J Vincent 4 (20, 60, 75, 88)		*og 67*	
	Hayzelden 34, Risley 86			
	Nesling 88			
86	Diss Town	1 v 6	Sudbury	343
	Mayes 65		***Gary Bennett 3 (28, 47, 53),***	
			Norfolk 4, Devereux 27, 50	
87	Ely City	2 v 3	Witham Town	89
	Wilkinson 4, 87			
88	Berkhamsted Town	2 v 2	Bishop's Stortford	176
	Morgan 32, Richardson 49		*Benstock 68, Paxton 77*	
r	Bishop's Stortford	3 v 3*	Berkhamsted Town	
	Ibe 15, Campbell 34		*Fannon, Benstock, Hayes (p)*	
	Nightingale 41			
	Bishop's Stortford won 4-3 on penalties			
89	Tiptree United	2 v 0	London Colney	81
	Parnell 62, 85			
90	Wealdstone	1 v 0	Clacton Town	286
	Holmes 66			
91	Fakenham Town	3 v 2	Brook House	177
	Metcalfe 51, Coe 85, 90		*Hibbert 20, Seymour 80*	
92	Southend Manor	4 v 0	Ilford	85
	Taylor 43 secs			
	Barnett 22, 73, Danson 53			
93	Southall	2 v 5	Witney Town	70
	Zazzera 32, Alvite 66		*Merritt 3, Redknap 17,*	
			Neville 19, Henry 8, 75	
94	Felixstowe Port & Tn	1 v 3	Wingate & Finchley	100
	Ewers 76		*Brady 15, 26, Sawyer 35*	
95	Watton United	0 v 1	Arlesey Town	95
			Jarrett 9	
96	Saffron Walden Tn	5 v 0	Kempston Rovers	158
	Das 15, King 40, Miles 60			
	Riley 70, Haupt 88			
97	Romford	1 v 0	Maldon Town	208
	Rose 53			
98	Burnham	0 v 1	Wisbech Town	107
			Furnell 15	
99	Harwich & Parkeston	2 v 3	Harlow Town	179
	Mann 54, Carmichael 65		*Cort 2, Salmon 29, Samuel 87*	
100	Warboys Town	3 v 3	Bury Town	132
	Clarke 54, Randle 37, 74		*Layton 16, Debenham 39, 61*	
r	Bury Town	2 v 2*	Warboys Town	
	Watson 33, Foreman 114		*Coles 6, Neville 109*	
	Warboys won 4-3 after extra time on penalties			
101	Concord Rangers	2 v 2	East Thurrock United	90
	Jenkins 52, Grayburn 85		*Cockayne 3, 53*	
r	East Thurrock United	4 v 2	Concord Rangers	
	L Baulkham 3 (41, 61, 89)		*Jenkins 9, Grayburn 39*	
	Mahon 5			

Top: Redhill's Zak Newman, left, and Jay Westwood of Slade Green tussle for the ball.
Photo: D Nicholson

Middle: Tilbury's goalkeeper James Nicholls fails to stop this shot from going to a corner.
Photo: Neil Thaler

Bottom: Bognor's Rob Ackroyd just fails with this attempt on the Didcot goal much to the relief of keeper Simon Reeve and Paul Noble.
Photo: Andrew Chitty

102	Uxbridge	0 v 1	Wroxham	116	
			Terrington 36		
103	Ruislip Manor	2 v 0	Leighton Town	50	
	Williams 33, Flaherty 90				
104	Gorleston	1 v 1	Lowestoft Town	376	
	Gordon 57		*Smith 50*		
r	Lowestoft Town	1 v 2*	Gorleston		
	og 4		*Fleck 37, Gordon 98*		
105	Wivenhoe Town	0 v 1	Bedford Town	228	
			Jaggard 19		
106	Banbury United	2 v 0	Milton Keynes City	271	
	Preedy 6, McKay 31				
107	Burnham Ramblers	1 v 2	Hoddesdon Town	81	
	Down 96		*Cross 88, Hughton 95*		
108	Great Yarmouth Tn	5 v 3	Tilbury	148	
	Stuart Roach 3 (59, 85, 90)		*Fielding 7, Engwell 33,*		
	McIntosh 82, Horais 89		*Quartell 57*		
109	Braintree Town	1 v 1	Leyton Pennant	174	
	Adams 72		*Allen 75*		
r	Leyton Pennant	1 v 2	BraintreeTown		
	Allen 80		*Caldon 5, Keen 59*		
110	Hemel Hempstead T	4 v 0	Harpenden Town		
	Price 6, Butler 23				
	Ravenscroft 48, Moore 86				
111	Soham Town Rngrs	7 v 0	Buckingham Town	137	
	Moye 9, Nebimoull 17, 33				
	Rutter 27, Green 50				
	Braybrooke 67, Collins 74				
112	Aveley	0 v 1	Stansted	101	
			Rogers 10		
113	Histon	1 v 0	Hullbridge Sports	91	
	Potter 84				
114	Wootton Blue Cross	0 v 2	Cheshunt		
			Koulamanoli 52, Boyce 89		
115	Waltham Abbey	1 v 1	Yeading	95	
	Milton		*Vrhouski 50*		
r	Yeading	1 v 3	Waltham Abbey		
	Lord 70		*Milton 50, Obeney 75,*		
			Tickner 77		
116	Ware	3 v 0	Newmarket Town	152	
	Dean Callcut 3 (50, 53, 89)				
117	Stowmarket Town	3 v 0	Welwyn Garden City	98	
	Platt 17, Yeomans 35				
	Langham 88				
118	Baldock Town	6 v 0	Potton United	138	
	Lee 19, Grant 18, 39				
	Chattle 58, Behan 65, Kilby 69				
119	Bowers United	4 v 0	Hanwell Town	37	
	Scawthorn 29, Hobden 63				
	Hope 73, Martin 81				
120	Ford United	5 v 1	Edgware Town	82	
	Ben Willis 3 (22, 25, 88)				
	Wood 55, Allen 77				
121	Woodbridge Town	1 v 5	Chelmsford City	320	
	Dearsley 63		*Fuller 63, 78,*		
			Berquez 67p, 81, 1 og		
122	Halstead Town	1 v 3	Royston Town	128	
	Schultz 65		*Bluck, Pugh, Miles*		
123	Beaconsfield SYCOB	3 v 0	Eynesbury Rovers	35	
	Jarvis 42, Keadell 60				
	Jones 80				
124	Hertford Town	v	Barkingside		
	(Walkover for Hertford Town – Barkingside removed)				
125	Northwood	8 v 0	Clapton	122	
	L Yaru 3 (39, 47, 48)				
	og 17, Fitzgerald 20, 44				
	Gell 52, Watkins 63				

126	Marlow	2 v 2	Barton Rovers	151	
	Brannan 13, Bradley 84		*Guile 74, Whelan 90*		
r	Barton Rovers	1 v 3	Marlow		
	Turner 42		*Pritchard 16, 18, Gibson 58*		
127	Kingsbury Town	2 v 1	Tring Town		
	Hughes 34, Dunning 36		*Simpson 50*		
128	East Cowes Victoria	0 v 1	Sittingbourne	56	
			Berry 53		
129	Folkestone Invicta	4 v 2	Croydon Athletic	277	
	Manuel 59, Ayling 74, 86		*Fowler 26, Baines 90*		
	Dent 79				
130	Bracknell Town	2 v 2	Camberley Town	177	
	Kettle 45, Oliphant 81		*Cooke 15, Whiddets 17*		
r	Camberley Town	1 v 3	Bracknell Town		
	Tomsett 80		*Oliphant 19, 72p, Haverhant 43*		
131	Cobham	1 v 1	Farnham Town	54	
	Tilbury 11		*Warton 79*		
r	Farnham Town	3 v 2	Cobham		
	Warton 39, 67, May 89		*Tilbury 25, 70*		
132	Ashford T (Middx)	1 v 2	Langney Sports	118	
	Lyons 31		*Badham 18, Pearce 43*		
133	Saltdean United	1 v 0	Beckenham Town	119	
	Essam 53				
134	Eastbourne Town	0 v 0	Three Bridges	211	
r	Three Bridges	1 v 1*	Eastbourne Town		
	Cook 72		*Brockwell 88*		
	Eastbourne Town won 4-3 on penalties after extra time				
135	Ash United	1 v 2	Chatham Town	87	
	Calvert 82		*Mitchell 73, Utsava 78*		
136	Newport (IW)	2 v 0	North Leigh	334	
	Price 59, Leigh 79				
137	Erith & Belvedere	0 v 2	Wick	119	
			Elliott 2, Smith 84		
138	Abingdon Town	6 v 0	Peacehaven/Telscombe	110	
	Charles 13, Wyatt 23				
	Carlisle 21, 28, Smith 81p				
	Connell 85				
139	Thamesmead Tn	2 v 2	Reading Town	45	
	Wilkinson 77, Saunders 83		*Treves 20, Deadman 65*		
r	Reading Town	1 v 0	Thamesmead Town		
	Saunders 53				
140	Chipstead	0 v 5	Tonbridge Angels	130	
			David Arter 3 (37, 43, 77),		
			Bates 55, Milling 84		
141	Hillingdon Borough	0 v 0	St Leonards	58	
r	St. Leonards	4 v 1	Hillingdon Borough		
	Keith Miles 3 (7, 30, 63)		*Bissah 20*		
	Ruddy 88				
142	Leatherhead	0 v 1	Cowes Sports	168	
			Sampson 60		
143	Merstham	1 v 5	Corinthian Casuals	75	
			Naghorn 18, Griffiths 30, 65,		
			West 84, Froeborough 90		
144	Hailsham Town	5 v 4*	Littlehampton Town	100	
	P. Richardson 40		*Whitehouse 37, Barrett 58,*		
	French 49, 91, March 52		*Thornton 74, Chester 69*		
	M. Richardson 63				
145	Molesey	3 v 1	Ringmer		
	og 52, Musgrove 75, 78		*Hapman 85*		
146	Bedfont	4 v 0	Tunbridge Wells	75	
	Read, Jenkins, Williams (2)				
147	Raynes Park Vale	1 v 2	Fisher Athletic	75	
	Cooper 68		*og 61, Aris 75*		
148	Viking Greenford	3 v 2	Whitstable Town	87	
	Stockwell 30, Haley 38		*Maxted 52, Forbes 90*		
	Smith 40				
149	Erith Town	0 v 0	Dorking	105	
r	Dorking	1 v 2	Erith Town		
	Moses 13		*Barrett 65, Powell 69*		

150	Ashford Town	2 v 1	East Preston	347
	McRobert 15, 55p		Withers 37	
151	Shoreham	1 v 2	Abingdon United	65
	Hudson 12		Brown 47, Odhiambo 30	
152	Windsor & Eton	0 v 0	Bromley	146
r	Bromley	3 v 0	Windsor & Eton	
	Cooksey 11, Tompkins 13			
	Woolf 55			
153	Oxford City	5 v 1	Gosport Borough	177
	Whitehead 23, Smith 33		Diprose 30	
	Davy 64, Hayward 71			
	Emsden 82			
154	Herne Bay	1 v 0	Canterbury City	201
	Malyon 87			
155	Epsom & Ewell	0 v 3	Worthing	
			Rice 4, Holden 39, Miles 73	
156	Redhill	2 v 0	Slade Green	86
	Newman 20, Otway 85			
157	Deal Town	5 v 0	Greenwich Borough	224
	Graham 6, Miles 35			
	Marshall 14, 38, Lovell 72			
158	Fleet Town	1 v 3	Lewes	64
	Jones 76		Lockhart 34, 52, Reed 67	
159	Hastings Town	6 v 1	Southwick	334
	White 4, Simmon 13		O'Donnell 50	
	Myah 17, 38, Mintham 35			
	Jones 64			
160	Bognor Regis Tn	2 v 1	Didcot Town	261
	Marriott 52		Blake 5, Martin 90	
161	Sandhurst Town	0 v 0	Newbury	86
r	Newbury	5 v 2	Sandhurst Town	
	Packer 9, Alleyne 14, 45		Blake 37, 41	
	Voller 75, Angell 85			
162	Thatcham Town	4 v 2	Lordswood	71
	Keepax 15, Norris 22		Derrall 82, Skinner 92	
	Maskell 44, Whorriskey 88			
163	Chichester City	2 v 2	Selsey	165
	og 73, Stephens 43		og 5, Bristow 40	
r	Selsey	4 v 2	Chichester City	
	Lowery 3, 68, Rishman 15		Romasz 48p, Thorpe 71	
	Loe 38p			
164	Wokingham Town	1 v 4	Sheppey United	92
	Puckett 79		Dickens 18,	
			Matt Toms 3 (62, 78, 90)	
165	Cray Wanderers	2 v 2	Portfield	73
	Godfrey 33, Heaslewood 68		Poulton 33, Hopkins 76	
r	Portfield	2 v 3	Cray Wanderers	
	Chambers 8, Woods 61		Heaslewood 14, Wood 20,	
			Jenkins 57	
166	Whyteleafe	4 v 3	Lancing	101
	Paul Scott 3 (16, 44, 47)		Hall 53, Brunton 88, 89	
	Hancock 8			
167	Whitehawk	0 v 1	Maidenhead United	120
			Agudosi 61	
168	Egham Town	2 v 0	Croydon	40
	Harrison 43, 88			
169	Metropolitan Police	2 v 1	Chertsey Town	120
	Derby 15, Jones 64		Ashe 89p	
170	Horsham	0 v 1	Hassocks	239
			French 30	
171	Fareham Town	0 v 1	Carterton Town	126
			Sharkey 45	
172	Godalming\Guildford	1 v 2	Horsham YMCA	116
	Keeley 62		Butcher 12, Russell 67	
173	Hythe United	0 v 0	Burgess Hill Town	141
r	Burgess Hill Town	3 v 0	Hythe United	
	Newman 75, Cable 80, 90			

174	Arundel	1 v 2	Portsmouth R N	35
	Wincell 33		Young 24, Whitcombe 41	
175	Banstead Athletic	0 v 2	Thame United	71
			Louis 12, 19	
176	Ramsgate	2 v 1	Dartford	198
	Davey 49, Love 90		Guiver 40	
177	Christchurch	1 v 1	Bridport	170
	Town 23		McAuley 83	
r	Bridport	2 v 4	Christchurch	
	Diaz 38, Evans 45		Collins 25, 64, Town 67,	
			Gardner 74	
178	Frome Town	0 v 4	Cinderford Town	95
			Bevan 22, Toomey 24, 41,	
			Lewis 50	
179	Mangotsfield Utd	3 v 0	Hungerford Town	183
	Edwards 46, Boyle 49			
	O'Sullivan 55			
180	Falmouth Town	1 v 2	Bideford	210
	Rapsey 35		Collings 55, Christie 80	
181	Bridgwater Town	0 v 5	Lymington/New Milton	146
			Oldbury 5, Phillips 38. 50,	
			Stone 45, Cuffie 75	
182	Minehead Town	1 v 3	Elmore	110
	McKenna 23		Stansfield 8, Symonds 13,	
			Rowlands 71	
183	Totton	1 v 2	Weston Super Mare	109
	Murphy 53		Wharton 61, Rogers 64	
184	Bashley	6 v 1	Calne Town	183
	R Morse 4 (5, 10, 57, 81)		Colbourne 75	
	Andrews 59,			
	Chavezmunez 73			
185	Chippenham Town	1 v 0	Bournemouth	269
	James 15			
186	Street	0 v 1	Eastleigh	132
			Bundy 56	
187	Walton Rovers	4 v 0	Warminster Town	63
	Evans 55, Porter 60			
	Ford 70, 78			
188	Yate Town	0 v 3	Taunton Town	239
			Lynch 7, 64, Laight 21	
189	Tiverton Town	7 v 1	Pershore Town	640
	Pears 50, 64, Ovens 58		Thomas 87	
	Daly 63, 74, Everett 73			
	Conning 78			
190	Bemerton Heath H	0 v 1	Brislington	72
			Sweeney 55	
191	Melksham Town	1 v 3	Evesham United	229
	Brooks 23		Coppin 16, McCartan 23,	
			Yates 89	
192	Downton	3 v 6	Barnstaple Town	75
	Witheridge 12, 72		Bonaparte 10, Chapman 12,	
	O'Hagan 35		Bedler 51, Rollason 68,	
			Gough 85, Calderhead 88	
193	St Blazey	3 v 1	Brockenhurst	129
	Andy Waddell 3 (4, 9, 18)		Leah 27	
194	Backwell United	5 v 1	Andover	260
	Gould 1, King 35, 75		Luscombe 63	
	Penny 60, Parry 70			
195	Westbury United	0 v 1	Devizes Town	124
			Kilmurray 55	
196	Paulton Rovers	1 v 2	Odd Down	150
	Byrne 43		Witts 75, Pike 90	
197	Cirencester Town	3 v 0	BAT Sports	108
	Marshall 65, Harris 70			
	Corcoran 86			

Byes: Stocksbridge Park Steels, Tooting & Mitcham Utd, Torrington, Tuffley Rvrs. & Wimborne Town.

FIRST QUALIFYING ROUND

1	Crook Town	5 v 0	Armthorpe		128

Bellamy 23, Tallentire 28
Eccles 45, 87, Vasey 76

2   Rossendale United   1 v 1   Ossett Town   137
Barker 6   *Borland 20*

r   Ossett Town   2 v 0   Rossendale Utd
Annan 46, 52

3   Consett   0 v 2   Accrington Stanley   149
Williams 30, Carragher 83

4   Liversedge   3 v 2   Woodley Sports   113
Thomas 49, Carter 53   *Seddon 26, McNeill 28*
Teronczar 76

5   Bradford (Park Ave)   2 v 1   Skelmersdale Utd   261
Maxwell 56, Hancock 64   *Cowley 31p*

6   Thornaby-on-Tees   1 v 5   Tow Law Town   137
Bolton 44, 56, Pickering 50,
Moorhead 55, Cullen 65

7   Brigg Town   4 v 0   Harrogate Railway   117
Buckley 5, Ward 19, 41
Thompson 66

8   St Helens Town   1 v 1   Pickering Town   138
O'Neill 40   *Gaughan 53*

r   Pickering Town   3 v 2*   St Helens Town   142
Morton 78, Sturdy 90   *O'Niell 35, Pennington 88*
Thornton 95

9   Trafford   3 v 3   Jarrow R B CA   155
Burns 18, Lowe 44   *Hodgson 16, Thompson 28,*
Murray 74   *Bangura 81*

r   Jarrow R B CA   1 v 3   Trafford
Thompson 78   *Lowe 17, Simms 68, Shepley 70*

10   Hebburn   2 v 2   Louth United
Hallway 79, 81   *Blake 30, Jones 38*

r   Louth United   4 v 2   Hebburn
Elkington, Hay, Pitchers   *Donnelly 44, 65*
Rockhill

11   Ramsbottom Utd   1 v 2   Fleetwood Freeport   211
Clarke 65   *Mainds 37, Ludlow 50*

12   Farsley Celtic   1 v 1   Burscough   96
Stimpson 67   *McMullen 90*

r   Burscough   0 v 3   Farsley Celtic   144
Blackstone 23, 58, Reagan 57

13   Mossley   0 v 2   Gretna   249
Milligan 88, Bird 90

14   Eccleshill United   4 v 0   Marske United   68
S Taylor 4 (4, 12, 74p, 90)

15   Ashton United   2 v 0   Flixton   120
Comley-Excell 15, Dogherty 33

16   Radcliffe Borough   8 v 1   Warrington Town   169
Ian Lunt 3 (44, 53, 90)   *Tickle 57*
Cardew 27, 70
Mullin 43, 55, Parker 73

17   Chorley   3 v 0   Seaham Red Star   220
Mitchell 14, Corcoran 36
Fleming 47

18   Penrith   0 v 2   Morpeth Town   82
Bibby 24, Symonds 26

19   Sheffield   1 v 0   Brodsworth (5/0)
Godber 64

20   North Ferriby Utd   3 v 2   Netherfield Kendal   199
Flounders 21, Perrin 65   *Hodgson 49, Foster 69*
France 83

21   Newcastle Blue Star   1 v 1   Billingham Synthonia   77
Bell 22   *Lowes 31*

r   Billingham Synthonia   3 v 2   Newcastle B. Star   135
Butler 59, Lowes 77, Wood 90   *Fuller 75, Weatherson 80*

22   Dunston F. Brewery   1 v 0   Salford City   135
Forbes 16

---

23   Bedlington Terriers   2 v 0   Stocksbridge P Steels   301
Milner 50, 80

24   Stourbridge   0 v 2   Belper Town   186
Mays 61, Cunningham 68

25   Stafford Rangers   2 v 2   Matlock Town   487
Mitchell 4, Shaw 19   *Bochenski 35, Heath 80*

r   Matlock Town   0 v 4   Stafford Rangers   485
   Mitchell 24, Smith 36, og 47,
   Shaw 90

26   Northampton Spncr   1 v 1   Boston Town   90
Dunckley 38   *Don-Duncan 88*

r   Boston Town   4 v 6   Northampton Spncr   102
Shooter 53, Price 70   **Peter Green 3 (17, 35, 77),**
Lovelace 80, Parkinson 87   *Dunckley 20, Pepperill 22,*
   Mann 50

27   Hinkley United   1 v 0   Glapwell   210
Hunter 36

28   Solihull Borough   1 v 0   Sutton Coldfield T.   122
Brown 21

29   Wellingborough T.   2 v 2   Newcastle Town   47
Jameson 12, Downes 29   *Myatt 9, Bates 88*

r   Newcastle Town   1 v 2   Wellingborough T   107
Twigg 58

30   Oldbury Utd   2 v 0   Stratford Town   71
Hesson 32, McCarthy 41

31   Willenhall Town   1 v 1   Oadby Town   164
Long 51   *Kee 30*

r   Oadby Town   3 v 1   Willenhall Town   142

32   Stamford   3 v 1   Brackley Town   152
Batley 12, Tallems 19, Staff 28   *og*

33   Shifnal Town   2 v 3   Congleton Town   120
Ashley 66, Tremayne 67   *Thornley 10, 45, Bermionous 63*

34   Bedworth United   1 v 3   Redditch United   234
McKenzie 70   *Nicholls 3, Knight 18, Cope 85*

35   Moor Green   3 v 2   Mickleover Sports   170
Hall 17, 56, Pountney 80   *Baxter 49, Parkins 90*

36   Staveley MW   1 v 3   Blakenall   151
Wells 80   *Dodd 16, Street 23, Worsey 90*

37   Eastwood Town   3 v 0   Holbeach United   141
Morgan 72, 85, Worboys 76

38   Halesowen Harriers   1 v 4   Arnold Town   115
Clarke 49   *Baxter 16, Whitman 42,*
   Hurst 43, Heverin 90

39   Nantwich Town   3 v 0   Stewarts & Lloyd   92
Gayle 33, 85, Williamson 88

40   Spalding United   1 v 0   Raunds Town   228
Barrass 17

41   Bishop's Stortford   4 v 2   Hemel Hempstead T.   251
Harding 56, Paxton 74   *Price 10, Somers 60*
Willock 84, Hayes 90

42   Banbury United   6 v 3   Gorleston   298
og 10, Preedy 15, Gooderick 21   **Gary McGee 3 (47, 65, 74)**
McKay 40, 56, Sherlock 87

43   Cheshunt   1 v 0   Waltham Abbey   64

44   Wingate & Finchley   3 v 2   Braintree Town
Sawter 5, Nyman 66, Baum 73   *Reinelt 45p, Brown 60*

45   Great Yarmouth T.   2 v 3   Warboys Town   175
McIntosh 35, Vinconi 48   *Benjamin 19, Clarke 60, 68*

46   East Thurrock Utd   1 v 2   Baldock Town   64
Greaves 80   *Spencer 8, 20*

47   Romford   4 v 1   Southend Manor   215
Rose 24,79, Miller 74, Pitcher 90p   *Cox 87*

48   Fakenham Town   1 v 3   Staines Town   201
Ward 45   *Glynn 37, Kerr 84, 90*

49   Saffron Walden T.   3 v 1   Hoddesdon Town   122
Saggers 40, Miles 65, 75   *Conner 41*

Top: Steve Pyle (Morpeth) and Anthony Rayson (Penrith) on the right. Photo: Alan Watson

Middle: Leroy Griffiths tussles with a Sheppey United defender during Corinthian Casuals' 4-0 victory at Tolworth. Photo: Peter Lirettoc

Bottom: Time stands still at Kingsbury. Gavin Child (in net) heads off his own line and onto the top of the bar to deny Chelmsford a goal. Photo: Francis Short

50	Wisbech Town	3 v 1	Wroxham	505
	Furnell 80, Robertson 87		Rauling 12	
	Korkmaz 88			
51	Ruislip Manor	0 v 1	Beaconsfield SYCOB	90
			Clements 57	
52	Barking	0 v 2	Grays Athletic	183
			Hazle 86	
53	Sudbury	1 v 0	Flackwell Heath	242
	(at Priory Stadium)			
	Day 36			
54	Hertford Town	0 v 2	Royston Town	88
			Hardy 16, Crate 7	
55	Arlessey Town	4 v 1	Bowers United	115
	Pike 75, 86, Campbell 65, 84		Warner 81	
56	Wealdstone	1 v 1	Ford United	254
	Sterling 81		Wood 37	
r	Ford United	2 v 3	Wealdstone	
	Parish 40, Wood 62		Rocky Baptiste 3 (28, 54, 80)	
57	Marlow	7 v 2	Histon	142
	Gary Wiltshire 3 (16, 44, 61)		Barker 33, Goddard 45	
	Gibson 40, 90, Cooper 8			
	Pritchard 83			
58	Kingsbury Town	0 v 1	Chelmsford City	138
			Sennex 90	
59	Tiptree United	1 v 2	Witney Town	86
	Brady 29		Henry 47, 78	
60	Ware	1 v 1	Soham Tn Rangers	115
	Hart 1		Nedimovic 87	
r	Soham Town Rangers	2 v 1	Ware	206
	Nedimovic 14, Rutter 70			
61	Wembley	3 v 1	Harlow Town	102
	Keane 11, 71, McCarthy 18		Salmon 6	
62	Bedford Town	0 v 0	Aveley	498
r	Aveley	1 v 2*	Bedford Town	167
	Bass 117		Jaggard 105, 115	
63	Northwood	2 v 0	Stowmarket Town	144
	Hart 77, Yaki 81			
64	St Neots Town	0 v 4	Witham Town	72
			Pearce, Braybrook, Nash, Poole	
65	Ashford Town	0 v 2	Fisher Athletic	346
			Charles 41, Gamble 26	
66	Farnham Town	3 v 0	Selsey	100
	Bridger 16, Moors 45			
	Wharton 52			
67	Hailsham Town	1 v 3	Sittingbourne	150
	Overton 37		Owen 7, 48, Hodge 85	
68	Bedfont	5 v 1	Reading Town	48
	Jones 28, Stewart 11		Stacey 90	
	Williams 65, King 80, Logie 90			
69	Worthing	2 v 1	Saltdean United	231
	Knee, Rice		Townsend	
70	Maidenhead United	5 v 0	Viking Greenford	121
	Channell 37, Agudesi 45, 55			
	Nesbeth 87, Clark 91			
71	Horsham YMCA	3 v 0	Cray Wanderers	95
	Tilley 53, Fitzgerald 60			
	McCall 56			
72	Folkestone Invicta	1 v 3	Ramsgate	335
	Dent 87		Davey 16, Munday 21, Hansen 86	
73	St Leondards	0 v 1	Bognor Regis T.	306
			Pickering 91	
74	Eastbourne Town	0 v 4	Langney Sports	421
			Allen 36, Barham 48,	
			Snellgrave 78, 83	
75	Lewes	3 v 3	Erith Town	122
	og 34, Lockhart 61, Stokes 85		Reeves 89 s, Adeniyi 27, og 63	
r	Erith Town	3 v 4	Lewes	230
	Coburn 25, Reeves 66		Pattenden 32, Reed 53,	
	Fennimore 70		Johnson 60, 90	

76	Tonbridge Angles	3 v 0	Abingdon Town	294
	Arter 67, Morgan 78			
	Gooding 85			
77	Molesey	0 v 3	Hastings Town	91
			White 81, Simmonds 78,	
			Harrison 90	
78	Thame United	3 v 1	Wick	68
	Louis 30, 68, Walker 87		More 59	
79	Abingdon United	0 v 6	Oxford City	222
			Pierson 6, Davy 35, Strong 49,	
			Smith 55, Emsden 67, Lee 71	
80	Deal Town	2 v 0	Metropolitan Police	246
	Bennett 78, Fox 89			
81	Thatcham Town	4 v 6	Cowes Sports	137
	Norris 46		J O'Rourke 4 (44, 45, 76, 81),	
	Richard Grist 3 (6, 66, 79)		Stevens 74, Arnold 90	
82	Carterton Town	1 v 4	Herne Bay	35
	Rodney 45		Ware, Malyon, Henry 2	
83	Corinthian Casuals	4 v 0	Sheppey United	64
	Owen 15, Murtin 67			
	West 76, Griffith 89			
84	Hassocks	1 v 1	Bromley	202
	French 75		Cooksey 64	
r	Bromley	2 v 1	Hassocks	247
	Kyte 4, Woolf 60		Kitchin 85	
85	Redhill	1 v 1	Burgess Hill Town	
	Newman 47		Francis	
r	Burgess Hill Town	3 v 0	Redhill	226
	Francis 45, Head 64, Pook 70			
86	Newbury	3 v 1	Portsmouth RN	63
	Caswell 12, Curran 33		Whitcombe 27	
	Myers 63			
87	Chatham Town	2 v 3	Newport (IW)	80
	Jones 10, 86p		Leigh 30, White 40, Riley 85	
88	Egham Town	1 v 3	Whyteleafe	190
	Boateng 32		Mckay 10, Scott 23, Hancock 50	
89	Bracknell Town	2 v 4	Tooting & Mitcham U	146
	Tallentire 9, Bonaventura 62		R Bhola 4 (1, 10, 50, 90)	
90	Elmore	0 v 3	Welton Rovers	105
			Porter 35, Ford 60, Perrett 75	
91	Lymington & N M	3 v 0	Bideford	191
	Phillips 42, Sims 53, Barnes 73			
92	Devizes Town	0 v 2	Weston super Mare	169
			Pritchard 50, Gibbins 67	
93	Mangotsfield Utd	1 v 1	Odd Down	183
	Rosslee 40		Willis 43	
r	Odd Down	1 v 2	Mangotsfield Utd	127
	Hare 35		Wilson 48, Elsey 54	
94	Backwell United	5 v 0	Bashley	85
	Sullivan 10, Fowler 38			
	Gould 43, King 47, 65			
95	Cinderford	0 v 1	Barnstaple Town	120
			Rollason 21	
96	Tiverton Town	4 v 3	Evesham United	699
	Daly 37, Harvey 47		og 39, Yates 53, Heaton 89	
	Ovens 48, Rogers 69			
97	Christchurch	1 v 0	Brislington	84
	Nickler 54			
98	Cirencester Town	2 v 2	Taunton Town	218
	Griffen 50, Corcoran 81		Laight 10, Cann 87	
r	Taunton Town	4 v 0	Cirencester T	454
	Tony Lynch 3 (6, 47, 85)			
	Laight 87			
99	Torrington	0 v 2	Wimborne Town	91
			og 29, Turner 86	
100	Chippenham Town	2 v 1	St Blazey	253
	Campbell 43, Tweedle 52		Barton 58	
101	Tuffley Rovers	2 v 1	Eastleigh	67
	Radcliffe 52, 84		McAllister 20	

SECOND QUALIFYING ROUND

1	Guiseley	6 v 0	Pickering Town	387
	Agana 14, Poole 18			
	Reid 30 (og), Parke 66, 75			
	Daly 69			
2	Gateshead	3 v 0	Winsford United	226
	Hall 35, Anderson 52			
	Fletcher 67			
3	Ossett T	2 v 1	Spennymoor Utd	127
	Warburton 60, Ryder 90		*Ramsey 78*	
4	Morpeth Town	2 v 1	Tow Law Town	145
	Pyle 43, Symonds 90		*Cullen 55*	
5	Worksop Town	2 v 3	Bishop Auckland	351
	Clark 52, 67		*Callagher 59,*	
			Holmshaw 81 og, Irvine 90	
6	Lancaster City	v	Fleetwood Freeport	
	Walkover for Lancaster City – Fleetwood removed			
7	Gainsborough Trinity	2 v 0	Eccleshill United	340
	Lacey 16, Bennett 90			
8	Leigh RMI	5 v 3	Blyth Spartans	197
	Ian Monk 3 (42, 45, 68)		**Gary Robson 3 (9p, 75, 87)**	
	Matthews 86, 89			
9	Hyde United	1 v 1	Crook Town	411
	Taylor 4p		*Bell 70*	
r	Crook Town	2 v 1	Hyde United	240
	Bellamy 49, Bell 75		*Taylor 11p*	
10	Barrow	2 v 2	Marine	1218
	Peverill 4, Whittle 18		*Townsend 44, Price 60*	
r	Marine	3 v 2	Barrow	425
	Morgan 3 (17, 49, 86p)		*Doherty 13, Peverell 77*	
11	Ashton United	0 v 2	Brigg Town	170
			Roach 35, Thompson 84	
12	Accrington Stanley	0 v 2	Whitby Town	357
			Featherstone 27, Goodchild 78	
13	Trafford	2 v 2	Bamber Bridge	215
	Vaughan 39p, Feeney 57		*Smith 50, Greenwood 60*	
r	Bamber Bridge	2 v 1	Trafford	233
	Vickers 62, Smith 65		*McCartney 24*	
14	Billingham Synthonia	1 v 2	North Ferriby United	176
	O'Brien 57		*Flounders 81, 83*	
15	Liversedge	1 v 2	Dunston F. B.	147
	Dyson 65		*Scaife 16, og 84*	
16	Stalybridge Celtic	1 v 0	Colwyn Bay	435
	Burgess 17			
17	Emley	2 v 0	Louth United	244
	Robshaw 50, David 63			
18	Sheffield	0 v 0	Farsley Celtic	115
r	Farsley Celtic	2 v 0	Sheffield	114
	Surtees 44, Whellans 90			
19	Runcorn	2 v 0	Gretna	313
	Moseley 52, Watson 82			
20	Bradford (Park A.)	2 v 2	Droylsden	251
	Ball 32p, Lee 56		*Whalley 72, Kinnet 82*	
r	Droylsden	2 v 1	Bradford (Park A.)*	
	Wright 99, Kinnet 121			
21	Radcliffe Borough	0 v 1	Chorley	312
			Evans 87	
22	Frickley Athletic	0 v 1	Bedlington Terriers	206
			Milner 87	
23	Nantwich Town	1 v 0	Hucknall Town	98
	Borthwick 81			
24	Solihull Borough	3 v 4	Ilkeston Town	230
	Judd 29, Dowling 46		*White 3, Eshelby 9, Raynor 16,*	
	Saunders 88 (og)		*Moore 65*	
25	Moor Green	2 v 1	Atherstone United	298
	Softley 15, Shepherd 72		*Storer 9*	
26	Redditch United	0 v 1	Burton Albion	608
			George 50	
27	Tamworth	6 v 2	Spalding United	527
	Hallam 33, Batchelor 34		*Gibson 40, Leach 81*	
	Smith 38, 66			
	Mutchell 62, Haughton 87			
28	Boston United	3 v 1	Oldbury United	938
	Wilson 9p, Norris 33		*Hesson 54*	
	Rennie 38			
29	Oadby T	2 v 1	Halesowen Town	259
	Boyles 58, Tiday 70		*Rowland 20*	
30	Leek Town	0 v 2	Blakenall	306
			Myers 46, Bennett 64	
31	Belper Town	4 v 2	Arnold Town	218
	Cunningham 8, 70		*Whitman 54p, Mitchell 88*	
	Payne 10, Cope 44			
32	Grantham Town	6 v 0	Northampton Spncr	298
	Gilbert 6p, Bogan 22			
	Featherstone 47			
	Wicks 49, 67, Rogers 77			
33	Hinckley United	2 v 0	Wellingborough Tn	212
	Sadler 30, Hunter 33			
34	Stamford	1 v 1	Congleton Town	183
	Polland 77		*Thornley 2*	
r	Congleton Town	2 v 0	Stamford	159
35	Stafford Rangers	1 v 3	Eastwood Town	463
	Mitchell 2		*Kennerdale 49, 77, Tomlinson 85*	
36	Wisbech Town	1 v 3	Billericay Town	554
	Henderson 56		*Game 17, Gentle 32,*	
			Simpson 50	
37	Bishop's Stortford	1 v 1	Wingate & Finchley	469
	Hayes 54		*Brady 68*	
r	Wingate & Finchley	3 v 2	Bishop's Stortford	285
	Brady 12, Baum 15, Nyman 38			
38	Warboys Town	0 v 2	Witney Town	185
			Miller 10, Henry 90	
39	Sudbury	1 v 2	Dagenham/Redbridge	522
	(at Priory Stadium)			
	Bennett 72		*Cobb 26, McDougald 34*	
40	Canvey Island	3 v 1	Boreham Wood	245
	Jones 35, 50, Brazier 88		*Ferguson 55*	
41	Heybridge Swifts	1 v 2	Romford	288
	Adcock 73		*Paul 15, Abraham 65*	
42	Purfleet	0 v 0	Banbury United	176
r	Banbury United	0 v 1	Purfleet	405
			Carthy 82	

43	Northwood	3 v 3	Rothwell Town	147	
	Yeomans 6, Fitzgerald 51		*Machin 45, Moore 55,*		
	Sargent 87		*Vallence 90*		
r	Rothwell Town	2 v 0	Northwood		
	Moore, Jowett				
44	Cambridge City	3 v 1	Arlesey Town	296	
	l Cambridge 3 (29, 80, 85p)		*Pike 57*		
45	Beaconsfield SYCOB	0 v 3	Kings Lynn	139	
			Turner 25, Robinson 28,		
			Wilson 50		
46	Saffron Walden Tn	1 v 4	Hitchin Town	261	
	Miles 20		*Dixon 20, 89, Parker 64, 90*		
47	Aylesbury United	1 v 3	Chelmsford City	602	
	Hercules 7		*Fuller 12, Bramble 66, 79*		
48	Bedford Town	0 v 2	St Albans City	851	
			Piper 31, 76		
49	Chesham United	1 v 3	Baldock Town	236	
	Mitchell 75		*Cook 43, Chattoe 45, Walker 78*		
50	Royston Town	1 v 3	Wembley	96	
	Moulding		*Harrack 68, Haule 18,*		
			Woodruffe 21		
51	Soham Town Rngrs	1 v 3	Enfield	512	
	Nedimuvic 12		*Protheroe 41, 48, Dunwell 42*		
52	Staines Town	0 v 3	Wealdstone		
			Rocky Baptiste 3 (8, 23, 52)		
53	Marlow	1 v 4	Harrow Borough	250	
	McDonnell 73		*Ottis Roberts 3 (54, 65, 85),*		
			Bates 90		
54	Hendon	2 v 0	Grays Athletic	201	
	Whitmarsh 23, 70				
55	Cheshunt	0 v 0	Witham Town	66	
r	Witham Town	0 v 2	Cheshunt	110	
56	Aldershot Town	6 v 1	Lewes	1396	
	Gary Abbott 3 (39, 45p, 76)		*Hill 66*		
	Sugrue 18, Bentley 35				
	Hathaway 63				
57	Thame United	0 v 1	Whyteleafe	78	
			Thornton 77		
58	Hampton/Richmond B	1 v 1	Bognor Regis Town	243	
	Carter 58		*Scammell 2*		
r	Bognor Regis Town	0 v 0	Hampton & Richmond B		
	(Bognor won 5-4 after penalties)				
59	Ramsgate	0 v 3	Margate	1502	
			O'Brien 12, Sykes 35, Collins 75		
60	Burgess Hill Town	2 v 2	Bedfont	197	
	Thomsett 47, Francis 43p		*Biggins 35, Logie 80*		
r	Bedfont	0 v 2	Burgess Hill Town	130	
			Williams 50, Flower 67		
61	Walton & Harsham	0 v 2	Maidenhead United	209	
			Agudosi 20, 38		
62	Tooting & Mitcham U	0 v 2	Oxford City	127	
			Thorpe 41, Wimble 36		
63	Farnham Town	2 v 2	Herne Bay	95	
			Trewinnard 8, Jeffreys 15		
r	Herne Bay	2 v 1	Farnham		
64	Hastings Town	3 v 1	Newbury	401	
	Elford 59, White 72p, 80p		*Clarkson 10*		

65	Carshalton Athletic	2 v 2	Sittingbourne	293	
	Elberson 89, 90		*King 36, Hodge 77p*		
r	Sittingbourne	0 v 1	Carshalton Athletic	278	
			Newbury 47		
66	Tonbridge Angels	0 v 2	Farnborough Town	606	
			Darlington 14, Ansall 53		
67	Horsham YMCA	4 v 0	Corinthian Casuals	105	
	Russell 25, 38, Francis 32				
	Butcher 90				
68	Newport (IW)	1 v 1	Dulwich Hamlet	569	
	Laidlaw 88		*Garland 51*		
69	Slough Town	3 v 1	Cowes Sports	461	
	Hall 45, Deaner 65		*O'Rourke 59*		
	Rainford 72				
70	Havant & Water.	2 v 2	Langney Sports	240	
	Wyatt 20, Taylor 32		*Colbran 71, Phillips 79*		
r	Langney Sports	2 v 1	Havant & Waterlooville	377	
	Snelgrove 31, 73		*Elley 42*		
71	Bromley	4 v 1	Crawley Town	334	
	Woolf 3 (24, 79, 90), Kyte 90		*Lovett 78*		
72	Gravesend & Nor.	1 v 1	Fisher Athletic	316	
	Wilkins 58		*Newson 66*		
r	Fisher Athletic	2 v 1	Gravesend\Northfleet	183	
73	Deal Town	2 v 2	Worthing	330	
	Graham 63, Lovell 29				
r	Worthing	3 v 0	Deal Town	245	
74	Christchurch	2 v 3	Worcester City	296	
	Town 41p, Keeler 73		*Davies 19, Bowen 24, 81p*		
75	Clevedon Town	2 v 1	Tiverton Town	619	
	Rollo 5, Rawlings 30		*Rogers 30*		
76	Taunton Town	3 v 0	Dorchester Town	663	
	Laight 36, Lynch 65, 83				
77	Newport County	1 v 1	Wimborne Town	659	
	Hill 42		*Smith 85*		
r	Wimborne Town	0 v 3	Newport County	364	
			Dare 3 (11, 54, 84p)		
78	Barnstaple Town	2 v 3	Backwell United	175	
			King 80, Gould 50, 53		
79	Weymouth	0 v 0	Gloucester City	642	
r	Gloucester City	2 v 1	Weymouth	491	
	Smith 66p, Fergusson 87				
80	Bath City	4 v 0	Weston Super Mare	744	
	Davis 10, Tisdale 46				
	Paul 50p, Bird 60 (og)				
81	Lymington & New M	1 v 1	Tuffley Rovers	131	
	Huxford 75		*Freeman 4*		
r	Tuffley Rovers	0 v 5	Lymington & New M	119	
			Mottashed 57, 90, Strong 77,		
			Sims 55, Stone 70		
82	Welton Rovers	1 v 3	Salisbury City	234	
	Ford 39		*Shepherd 3 (13, 44, 90)*		
83	Chippenham Town	2 v 0	Mangotsfield United	354	
	Tiley 55, Bennett 40				
84	Basingstoke Town	0 v 0	Merthyr Tydfill	540	
r	Merthyr Tydfill	2 v 1	Basingstoke Town	523	
	Griffiths 86, Ramasut 39p				

Top: Leon Gatzmore of Aldershot (left) is tackled by Lewes defender Sandy Brown.
Photo: Ian Morsman

Middle: James Featherstone scores for Whitley Town against Accrington Stanley.
Photo: Neil Thaler

Bottom: Runcorn 2 Gretna 0. Panic stations in the Gretna goalmouth.
Photo: Alan Watson

THIRD QUALIFYING ROUND

1	Dunston Federation B	0 v 2	Runcorn
			Att: 239 Moseley 33, Carter 55
2	Bamber Bridge	3 v 0	Morpeth Town
	Greenwood 20, Maddock 31 Att: 271		
	Smith 63		
3	Stalybridge Celtic	4 v 2	Farsley Celtic
	Bauress 9 (p), Jones 30 Att: 447 Learoyd 26 (p), 67		
	Marginson 85, Steele 89		
4	Bishop Auckland	1 v 1	Bedlington Terriers
	Bayles 85 Att: 413 Cross 46		
r	Bedlington Terriers	0 v 1	Bishop Auckland
		Att: 430 Shaw 10 (p)	
5	Lancaster City	2 v 2	Whitby Town
	Ward 66, Kilbane 87 Att: 295 Goodchild 17, Skedd 71		
r	Whitby Town	2 v 2	Lancaster City
	Goodchild 35, Williams 64 Att: 418 Ward 30, 80		
	Lancaster won 4-2 on penalties		
6	Marine	2 v 0	Chorley
	Townsend 61, Price 89 Att: 414		
7	North Ferriby United	1 v 3	Guiseley
	Evans 51 Att: 429 Shuttleworth 34, 40,		
	Williams 35		
8	Droylsden	2 v 2	Gainsborough Trinity
	Holmes 63 (p), Kinney 69 Att: 289 Sharman 14, Saville 83		
r	Gainsborough Trinity	1 v 2	Droylsden
	Saville 34 Att: 468 Jones 64, Stannard 80		
9	Leigh RMI	1 v 1	Crook Town
	Black 3 Att: 301 Nicholson 74		
r	Crook Town	2 v 1	Leigh RMI
	Nicholson 15, Clough 70 Att: 445 Jones 24		
10	Gateshead	4 v 0	Brigg Town
	Preen 10, Raitt 68 Att: 237		
	Thompson 85, 89		
11	Ossett Town	0 v 0	Emley
		Att: 590	
r	Emley	4 v 1	Ossett Town
	Day 18, 39, Robshaw 36 Att: 425		
	Haran 87		
12	Enfield	2 v 0	Billericay Town
	Cooper, Brown Att: 358		
13	Wembley	0 v 3	Canvey Island
		Att: 153 Readings (og), Jones,	
	Bartley		
14	Chelmsford City	1 v 0	Moor Green
	Berquez 22 Att: 858		
15	Belper Town	1 v 2	Tamworth
	Mays 46 Att: 641 Haughton 25, 29		
16	Wingate & Finchley	0 v 5	Ilkeston Town
		Att: 275 Eshelby 16, Hemmings 36, 73,	
	Raynor 44, Middleton 62		
17	Hitchin Town	2 v 1	Grantham Town
	Meah 53, Dixon 68 Att: 430 Wilkes 2		
18	Eastwood Town	3 v 0	Oadby Town
	Tomlinson 23, 55, Kennerdale 29 Att: 360		
19	Romford	6 v 0	Congleton Town
	Paul 4 (30, 60, 75, 80) Att: 303		
	Stanbrook 88, 90		

20	Cambridge City	1 v 0	Kings Lynn
	Taylor 25 Att: 812		
21	Baldock Town	5 v 1	Cheshunt
	Lee 13, Deller 32, Walker 34 Att: 145 Gregorio 56		
	Cook 75, Pratt 86		
22	Wealdstone	1 v 1	Rothwell Town
	Baptiste 65 Att: 397 Machin 83		
r	Rothwell Town	2 v 0	Wealdstone
	Dunlop 55, Keast 59 Att: 425		
23	Dagenham/Redbridge	0 v 2	Burton Albion
		Att: 919 Cole 6 (og), Anderson 59	
24	St. Albans City	4 v 2	Nantwich Town
	Clark (3), Andrews Att: 504 Gayle (2)		
25	Hendon	2 v 1	Blakenall
	Hyatt, Gentle Att: 302 Palmer		
26	Boston United	4 v 0	Purfleet
	Stanhope 18, Rawle 28, 45 Att: 1024		
	Wilson 54 (p)		
27	Witney Town	2 v 1	Hinckley United
	Miller 51, Henry 86 Att: 223 Ricketts 26		
28	Chippenham Town	1 v 1	Worthing
		Att: 496	
r	Worthing	3 v 1	Chippenham Town
	Burt, Kennett, Miles Att: 349 Charity		
29	Dulwich Hamlet	2 v 1	Hastings Town
	Garland 41, Stephens 74 Att: 437 Ball 89		
30	Bath City	3 v 1	Farnborough Town
	Paul 3 (6, 15, 81p) Att: 890 Ansah 72		
31	Maidenhead United	0 v 1	Salisbury City
		Att: 345 Sales 16	
32	Gloucester City	2 v 3	Merthyr Tydfil
	Wyatt 7, Smith 89 Att: 729 Gannaway (og) 27,		
	Ramasut 54, Lima 70		
33	Whyteleafe	1 v 0	Langney Sports
	Thornton Att: 348		
34	Backwell United	2 v 4	Oxford City
	Gould, King Strong, Smith,		
	Sweeney, Lee		
35	Bognor Regis Town	1 v 0	Bromley
	Bermingham Att: 564		
36	Fisher Athletic	1 v 2	Aldershot Town
	McEntegart 85 Att: 832 Gutzmore 43, Hathaway 51		
37	Herne Bay	v	Horsham YMCA
38	Worcester City	3 v 2	Harrow Borough
	Bowen 3 (26, 42, 58) Att: 767 Barry-Bates 70, Gavin 75		
39	Slough Town	1 v 0	Carshalton Athletic
	Deaner Att: 620		
40	Newport County	1 v 2	Burgess Hill Town
	Thomas 8 Att: 723 Carr 22, Moore 80		
41	Lymington & New M.	3 v 1	Clevedon Town
	Stone 38, 75, Simms 70 Att: 313 Rollo 85		
42	Taunton Town	0 v 3	Margate
		Att: 720 Munday 29, Porter 35,	
	Dixon 56		

Top: Moor Green's Derek Hall (right) out-jumps Chelmsford's Kevin Dobinson but puts his header wide. (Chelmsford City's ground is shared with Billericay Town)
Photo: Alan Coomes

Middle: An aerial dual as Cheshunt keeper Brian Sealey gets the better of Baldock Town's Gary Walker.
Photo: Gordon Whittington

Bottom: Elliott Jackson in control for Bath City against Farnborough Town.
Photo: Mark Sandom

FOURTH QUALIFYING ROUND

Altrincham 0 v 0 Stalybridge Celtic
Att: 1,186

r Stalybridge Celtic 2 v 1† Altrincham
Att: 791
† after 2-1 Stalybridge victory, disallowed for ineligible player

r **Stalybridge Celtic** 3 v 2 Altrincham
Filson 50, 78 Steele 107 Att: 791 *Ellison 26 Ellender 28*

Bognor Regis Town 0 v 1 **Whyteleafe** (Div 1)
Att: 702 *Scott 14*

Canvey Island 3 v 3 St Albans City
Tilson 65, Cheltham 75 Att: 711 *McMenamin 17,*
Jones 85 *Clark 37, 74*

r **St Albans City** 2 v 1 Canvey Island
Randall, Pollard Att: 678 *Tilsen (pen)*

Doncaster Rovers 7 v 0 Crook Town
Newell 1 Att: 2240
Kirkwood 4 (6,11,16,66)
Cauldwell 63, McIntyre 73

Droylsden 0 v 2 **Eastwood Town**
Att: 524 *Kennerdale 83,*
Tomlinson 84

Dulwich Hamlet 0 v 0 Hayes
Att: 830

r **Hayes** 3 v 0 Dulwich Hamlet
Bunce, Charles, Spencer Att: 602

Enfield 1 v 1 Baldock Town
Jones 73 Att: 650 *Cook 18*

r Baldock Town 2 v 2* Enfield
Cook 15, 58 Att: 610 *Bunn 16, Lleyne 45*
Enfield won 4-3 after penalties

Hendon 1 v 0 Margate
Hyatt 11 Att: 531

Hereford United 4 v 1 Burgess Hill Town
Williams 3, Fewings 25 Att: 1611 *Moore 21*
Parry 76, Piearce 86

Horsham Y.M.C.A. 2 v 3 **Chelmsford City**
Grim 2, Butcher 68 Att: 790 *Bramble 13, Fuller 17, 75*

Ilkeston Town 3 v 0 Romford
Knapper 5(p) Att: 780
Hemmings 55, 88

Kingstonian 0 v 0 Boston United
Att: 1108

r Boston United 0 v 3 **Kingstonian**
Att: 2120 *Bastock 41, Leworthy 52,*
Wingfield 79

Lancaster City 0 v 0 Bamber Bridge
Att: 64

r **Bamber Bridge** 4 v 3* Lancaster City
Vickers 24, Whittaker 96, Att: 699 *Mayers 19, Haddow 99,*
Aspinall 113(p), Turner 120 *Burnes 115*

Lymington/N. Milton 1 v 3 **Aldershot Town**
Stone 38 Att: 1524 *Bentley 16, Abbott 70, 81*

Marine 1 v 1 Runcorn
Townsend 56 Att: 665 *Burke 75*

r **Runcorn** 3 v 2* Marine
McNally 7, 53 Watson 120 Att: 603 *Morgan 19, 37*

Merthyr Tydfil 2 v 0 Hitchin Town
Sloan 45, Salton 58(og) Att: 726

Morecambe 1 v 0 Bishop Auckland
Lyons 5 Att: 868

Northwich Victoria 2 v 2 Hednesford Town
Owen 67, West 85 Att: 1651 *Twynham 74, Blades 83*

r **Hednesford Town** 1 v 0 Northwich Victoria
Davis 76 Att: 930

Nuneaton Borough 2 v 3 **Guiseley**
Williams 62, Hanson 68 Att: 2175 *Parke 3, 74, Gallagher 26*

Oxford City 2 v 1 Salisbury City
Smith 30, McCleary 47 Att: 409 *Shepherd 52*

Rothwell Town 1 v 1 Kettering Town
Vallance 47 Att: 1437 *McNamara 23*

r **Kettering Town** 2 v 1 Rothwell Town
Banya 72, Adams 76 Att: 1611 *Machin 74*

Rushden & Diamonds 4 v 1 Sutton United
McElhatton 11, 45 Att: 2525 *Rowlands 53*
Brady 13, Collins 74

Scarborough 0 v 1 **Tamworth**
Att: 1374 *Foy 19*

Top: Tamworth's Rob Mutchell (left) and Micky Gray (right) get into action early in the first half against Scarborough.
Photo: Paul Barber

Middle: Horsham apply the pressure as YMCA's Lee Butcher (6) and Peter Durrant challenge Kevin Dobinson and John Girling (right).
Photo: Kevin Rolfe

Bottom:
Hayes 3 Dulwich Hamlet 0. Matt Hodson makes a fine save to thwart a Dulwich attack.
Photo: Paul Dennis

Slough Town 1 v 1 Cambridge City
Deaner 39 Att: 771 *McCann 90*

r **Cambridge City** 3 v 2 Slough Town
Newby 45 (p), McCann 85 Att: 650 *Deaner 44*
Coburn 90

Southport 1 v 1 Emley
Guyett 50 Att: 1310 *Robshaw 13*

r Emley 0 v 2 **Southport**
Att: 872 *Arnold 68 (p), Ellison 81*

Stevenage Borough 1 v 1 Bath City
Strouts 45 Att: 1603 *Colbourne 58*

r **Bath City** 1 v 0 Stevenage Borough
Trott 77 (og) Att: 1,427

Telford United 0 v 0 Gateshead
Att: 611

r **Gateshead** 2 v 1 Telford United
Bowey 73, Thompson 76 Att: 318 *Murphy 52*

Welling United 2 v 0 Kidderminster Harriers
Braithwaite 44, Rutherford 70 Att: 780

Woking 1 v 1 Burton Albion
Payne 58 Att: 2015 *Stride 67*

r **Burton Albion** 3 v 1* Woking
Thomas 12, Blount 103 Att: 2081 *Hayes 44*
Anderson 113

Worcester City 2 v 5 **Forest Green Rovers**
Bowen 5, Owen 20 Att: 1301 *Hodges 15, Cook 19,*
Sykes 59, Mehew 76,
Randall 81

Worthing 1 v 1 Dover Athletic
Carrington 88 Att: 1010 *Leberl 74*

r Dover Athletic 0 v 1* **Worthing**
Att: 1077 *Holden*

Yeovil Town 2 v 1 Witney Town
Chandler 70, Foster 78 Att: 2092 *Swann 90*

Top: David Foy's shot beats the Scarborough keeper to put Tamworth one goal up after eighteen minutes.
Photo: Paul Barber

Left: Worcester City 2 Forest Green Rovers 5. Rovers goalkeeper Steve Perrin gathers the ball from City's Sam Bowen.
Photo: Tim O'Grady

*Top: Whyteleafe 0
Chester City Reserves 0.
City keeper Wayne Brown
takes the ball under pressure
from his own defender, while
Steve Lunn looks to pick up
the scraps.
Photo: Kevin Rolfe*

*Middle: The top crowd of the
Round was at Reading where
8,032 saw this Yeovil attack in
a torrential downpour, but the
League club won quite
comfortably 4-2.
Photo: Andrew Chitty*

*Bottom: Mark Hallam
(Tamworth) heads home the
equaliser against Bury.
Photo: Keith Clayton*

FIRST ROUND

Aldershot Town 1 v 1 **Hednesford Town**
Abbott 56 Att: 3269 *Robinson 51*

Hednesford Town 1 v 2 *Aldershot Town*
Lake 44 Att: 1719 *Chewings 68, Abbott 87*

Bath City 0 v 2 *Hendon*
Att: 1690 *Gentle 87, Guentchev 90*

Burton Albion 0 v 0 Rochdale
Att: 3103

Rochdale 3 v 0 **Burton Albion**
Platt 5, Peeke 47, Dowe 81 Att: 2633

Cambridge City 0 v 2 Wigan Athletic
Att: 4024 *Barlow 30, 44*

Cambridge United 1 v 0 **Gateshead**
Taylor 79 Att: 2970

Chesterfield 1 v 2 *Enfield*
Lomas 49 Att: 2506 *Bunn 23, Brown 67*

Darlington 2 v 1 **Southport**
Tutill 35, Gabbiadini 77p Att: 4313 *Bolland 52*

Doncaster Rovers 0 v 2 Halifax Town
Att: 5588 *Tate 51, Paterson 82*

Exeter City 2 v 1 **Eastwood Town**
Flack 40, Gale 47 Att: 2441 *Smith 56*

Forest Green Rovers 6 v 0 Guiseley
Hunt 3 (1, 31, 62) Att: 1047
McGregor 25
Drysdale 38, Sykes 51

Hayes 2 v 1 **Runcorn**
Bunce 25, Charles 90p Att: 890 *McDonald 45*

Hereford United 1 v 0 York City
May 77 Att: 2787

Ilkeston Town 2 v 1 Carlisle United
Moore 39, Raynor 62 Att: 1748 *Harries 18*

Lincoln City 1 v 0 **Welling United**
Smith 30 Att: 2766

Luton Town 4 v 2 **Kingstonian**
Gray 11, George 66 Att: 4682 *Crossley 35, Leworthy 47*
Spring 76, Taylor 79

Merthyr Tydfil 2 v 2 **Stalybridge Celtic**
Mitchell 50, 84 Att: 871 *Parr 9, Sullivan 42*

Stalybridge Celtic 3 v 1 **Merthyr Tydfil**
Bauress 1 (p), Pickford 24 Att: 1399 *Lima 4*
Sullivan 86

Oldham Athletic 4 v 0 **Chelmsford City**
Dudley 28, Sheridan 29 Att: 4392
Duxbury 70, Whitehall 83

Oxford United 3 v 2 **Morecambe**
Lilley 12, Powell 58 Att: 3504 *Wright 28, Jackson 47*
Abbey 87

Reading 4 v 2 **Yeovil Town**
Bernall 31, Caskey 63p Att: 8032 *Foster 36, Eaton 90*
Hunter 80, Williams 87

Rotherham United 3 v 0 **Worthing**
Thompson 31, Garner 81 Att: 3716
Martindale 90p

Rushden & Diamonds 2 v 0 Scunthorpe United
Warburton 47, Hamsher 76p Att: 4112

St Albans City 0 v 2 *Bamber Bridge*
Att: 1127 *Whittaker 45, Carroll 89*

Tamworth 2 v 2 Bury
Haughton 8, Hallam 75 Att: 2743 *Bullock 1, Littlejohn 68*

Bury 2 v 1* **Tamworth**
Dilley 87, James 95 Att: 2531 *Haughton 15* *aet*

Whyteleafe 0 v 0 Chester City
Att: 2164

Chester City 3 v 1 **Whyteleafe**
Cross 25, 52, Beckett 48 Att: 2183 *Lunn 8*

Wrexham 1 v 1 **Kettering Town**
Roberts 85p Att: 2701 *Brown 48*

Kettering Town 0 v 2 Wrexham
Att: 2611 *Roberts 11, Williams 21*

Wycombe Wanderers 1 v 1 **Oxford City**
Simpson 67 Att: 2963 *Pierson 87*

Oxford City 1 v 1* Wycombe Wanderers
Strong 40 Att: 2586 *Simpson 59*
* After extra time. Abandoned after 120 minutes

Oxford City 0 v 1 Wycombe Wanderers
Att: 4004 *Brown 51*

Top: Alan Foster of Oxford City makes a fine save to foil a Wycombe attack.
Photo: Paul Dennis

Middle: The scoreboard tells the story. Ray Warburton (6) and Gary Butterworth watch the progress of Scunthorpe striker Guy Ipoua with only eight minutes left.
Photo: Peter Barnes

Bottom: It's there! Paul Raynor's wind-assisted corner kick finds the top corner of Carlisle's net for Ilkeston's winner.
Photo: D Nicholson

SECOND ROUND

Blackpool 2 v 0 **Hendon**
Clarkson 69, Durnin 73   Att: 2,975

Hendon – McCann, White, Clarke, Daly, Towler, Fitzgerald, Guentchev, Hyatt Whitmarsh, (sub 80 mins Sakala), McKoy (sub 75 mins Maran), Gentle. Subs not used: Howard, Baker, Watson

Cambridge Utd 1 v 0 **Bamber Bridge**
Butler 72 (pen)   Att: 3,303

Bamber Bridge – Dootson, Brown, Bryson, Jones, Baldwin, Cliff, Smith (sub 90 mins Turner), Aspinall, Greenwood, Whittaker, Carroll (sub 75 mins Vickers). Subs not used Senior, Woodward, Spencer.

Exeter City 2 v 0 **Aldershot Town**
Alexander 32, Flack 35   Att: 4,151

Aldershot Town – Pape, Colt, Adedeji, Pearce (sub 68 mins Nartey), Chewins, Fielder, Sugreu (sub 72 mins Bell), Bentley, Gell, Abbott, Hathaway. Subs not used Bassey, Harte, Champion.

Hayes 2 v 2 Hull City
Charles (2)   Att: 2,749   *D'Avria 4, Edwards 56*

Hayes – Gothard, Boyce, Flynn, Watts, Bunce, Goodliffe, McKimm, Charles, Trebble (sub 88 mins Spencer), Moore (sub 81 mins Telemarque), Roddis. Subs not used Gallen, Hodson, M. Coppard.

r   Hull City 3 v 2 **Hayes**
Brown 49, Edwards 97   *Gallen, Charles*
Wood 112

Hayes - Gothard, Boyce, Flynn (sub 17 mins Gallen), Watts, Bunce, Goodliffe, McKimm (sub 90 mins Onwere), Charles, Trebble, Moore, Spencer (sub 104 mins Telemarque). Subs not used: Hodson, M Coppard.

Ilkeston Town 1 v 1 **Rushden & Diamonds**
Eshelby 18   Att: 4151   *De Souza 51*

Ilkeston Town – Beattie, Fairclough, Wright, Middleton, Fearon, Knapper, Eshelby (sub 73 mins Hurst), Clifford, Helliwell, Moore, Raynor (sub 86 mins Ludlum). Subs not used White, Gorden, Clark.

Rushden & Diamonds - Turley, Wooding, Rodwell, McElhatton, Peters, Warburton, Butterworth, Brady (sub 73 mins Town), De Souza, Collins Underwood. Subs not used Smith M, Hamsher, Mison, Cramman.

r   **Rushden & Dia.** 3 v 0 **Ilkeston Town**
Wooding, Town, Collins   Att: 4226

Rushden & Diamonds - Turley, Wooding, Burgess, McElhatton, Rodwell, Warburton, Butterworth, Brady, Town (sub 82 mins Heggs), Collins, Underwood. Subs not used: De Souza, Smith, M Cramman, Mison.

Ilkeston Town - Beattie, Fairclough, Wright (sub 63 mins Clifford), Middleton, Fearon, Knapper, Eshelby, Hemmings, Helliwell, Moore, Raynor. Subs not used: O'Reilly, Hurst, Baker, Bishop.

Preston North E. 0 v 0 **Enfield**
Att: 11,566

Enfield – John, Annon, Morgan, Cooper (sub 84 mins Southgate), Witter (sub 62 mins Protheroe), Brown, Deadman, Jones, Bunn, Moran, Dunwell. Subs not used Hall, Morris, Alleyne.

r   **Enfield** 0 v 3 Preston North End
Att: 1,808   *Eyres 53, Alexander 60p*
Gunnlaugsson 83

Enfield - John, Annon, Morgan, G Cooper (sub 36 mins Tomlinson), Protheroe, Brown (sub 80 mins Southgate), Deadman, Jones, Bunn (sub 83 mins Alleyne), Rattray, Dunwell. Subs not used: Moran, Hall.

Stalybridge Celtic 1 v 2 Chester City
Scott 8   Att: 3,312   *Cross 45, Beckett 69*

Stalybridge Celtic – Ingram, Ward, Scott, Ogley, Johnston, Bauress, Pickford (sub 80 mins Mason), Parr, Steele, Jones (sub 69 mins Filson), Williamson (sub 60 mins Sullivan). Subs not used Marginson, Stratford.

Forest Green Rovers 0 v 3 Torquay United
Att: 2,962   *Brandon 77, Hill 81*
Donaldson 87

Forest Green Rovers – Perrin, Hedges, Hatswell, Clark, Kilgour (sub 88 mins Randall), Burns, Daley, Sykes, MacGregor, Mehew (sub 63 mins Hunt), Cook (sub 82 mins Bailey). Subs not used Forbes.

Hereford United 1 v 0 Hartlepool United
Elmes   Att: 4,914

Hereford – Jones, Lane, Sturgess, Snape, Wright, James, Parry, Taylor, Elms (sub 86 mins May), Williams (sub 71 mins Rodgerson), Fewings. Subs not used Wall, Siddaway, Clarke.

Above: Rushden & Diamonds goalscorer Miguel de Souza (9) crosses despite close attention from Ilkeston's Dale Wright.   Photo: Bill Wheatcroft.

Top:
Exeter City 2
Aldershot 0.
Aldershot clear under pressure at
St James Park
Photo: Ian Morsman

Middle:
Enfield 0
Preston North End 3.
Enfield's John Morgan fends off a
challenge from Graham Alexander.
Photo: Gary Letts

Bottom:
Cambridge United 1
Bamber Bridge 0.
Cambridge United's Paul Wanless
just beats Stephen Aspinall in the
first half at the Abbey Stadium.

THIRD ROUND

Hereford United 0 v 0 Leicester City
Att: 7,795

Hereford United: Jones, Lane, Sturgess, *Snaps, Wright, James, Parry, Taylor, Elms, Williams, Fewings (sub 79 mins Rodgerson). Subs not used: Wall, Siddaway, Clarke, May.
Leicester City: Flowers, Sinclair (sub 7 mins Walsh), Taggart, Izzet, Lennon, Heskey, Guppy, Savage, Elliott, Impey, Cottee. Subs not used Zagorakia, Gilchrist, Oakes, Hodges.

Replay

Leicester City 2 v 1 **Hereford United**
Elliott 78, Izzett 104   aet   *Fewings 38*
Att: 12,157

Leicester City: Pegguy, Arphexad, Gerry Taggart, Matt Elliott, Phil Gilchrist, Robbie Savage, Theo Zagoraskis (sub Stuart Campbell 59th min.), Muzzy Izzet, Stefan Oakes, Arnar Gunnlaugsson (sub Graham Fenton 69th min.), Tony Cottee, Steve Walsh (sub Andrew Impey 46th min.). Subs (not used): John Hodges and Danny Thomas.

Hereford United: Mark Jones, Chris Lane, Ian Wright, Tony James, Paul Sturgess, Gavin Williams, Mark Taylor, John Snape, Paul Parry, Robin Elmes (sub Leroy May 94th min.), Paul Fewings (sub Ian Rodgerson 70th min.). Subs (not used): James Wall, Lee Ruddal and Matthew Clark.

Sheffield United 1 v 1 **Rushden & Diamonds**
Bent Att: 10,104   *Brady*

Sheffield United: Tracey, Devlin, Woodhouse, *Murphy, Quinn, Hunt (sub 80 mins Smeets), Derry, Ribeiro (sub 46 mins Hamilton), Ford, Bent, Smith (sub 80 mins Kachouro). Subs not used: Cullen, Duke.
Rushden & Diamonds: Turley, Wooding, Burgess (sub 67 mins De Souza), McElhatton, *Rodwell, Butterworth, Brady, Town (sub 89 mins Heggs), Collins, Underwood, Warburton. Subs not used: Smith, M, Hamsher, Mison.

Replay

Rushden & Diamonds 1 v 1 Sheffield United
aet, Sheffield United won 6-5 on penalties
Brady 105 Att: 6,010 *Devlin 102*

Rushden & Diamonds - Billy Turley, Tim Wooding, Andy Burgess (sub John Hamsher 118th min.), Michael McElhatton, Jim Rodwell, Ray Warburton, Gary Butterworth, Jon Brady, David Town (sub Mequel de Souza 65th min.), Darren Collins, Paul Underwood. Subs (not used): Mark Smith, Carl Heggs and Michel Mison.

Sheffield United - Simon Tracey, Lee Sandford, Shaun Derry, Shaun Murphy, Wayne Quinn, Curtis Woodhouse, Jonathan Hunt (sub Peter Kathouro 79th min), Paul Devlin, Marcus Bent, Martin. Subs (not used): Matt Duke, David Gysbrechts, Ben Doane.

F. A. CUP THIRD ROUND: HEREFORD UNITED 0 LEICESTER CITY 0

Everyone at Hereford was making it quite clear that a cup tie against a Premier club was exciting and a great experience, but three points on the next Conference games and possible promotion was far more important.

At the end of the game however everyone looked very happy and thrilled and there's no doubt that the confidence gained by their cup performances will do no harm to that overall ambition of promotion.

Edgar Street has a lovely atmosphere when packed on F.A. Cup day. The club presented the match well and when Paul Parry struck the Leicester City upright in the 66th minute perhaps supporters' hearts were broken, but the directors could see the chance of vital financial help from a possible replay.

An excellent all round battling performance brought that vital money raiser and the players, while accepting Leicester City shirts at the end of the game, were threatened with a fine of a week's wages if they gave theirs away!

Arthur Evans

F.A. CUP THIRD ROUND: SHEFFIELD UNITED 1 RUSHDEN & DIAMONDS 1

Having played Leeds United twice in the F.A. Cup last season, perhaps the Diamonds' supporters were disappointed by a less glamourous trip to Bramall Lane.

The players, however, fancied their chances although they suffered from a shaky start as Wayne Quinn was just thwarted by excellent goalkeeper Billy Turley and then Marcus Bent headed a simple goal.

These were followed by a Paul Davidson right wing cross after fourteen minutes from which United could have extended their lead - but they didn't!

Diamonds settled down, realising they had nothing to lose; they seemed to be holding their own and were only one down. As half time loomed, a simple cross from Jon Brady, probably meant for Darren Collins, confused keeper Simon Tracey and squirmed in off the far post.

Before the interval Turley survived a possible dismissal for handball outside the penalty area and also received a nasty cut that needed five stitches above an eye.

It says a lot for the Diamonds' defence who protected their goalkeeper in the second half and he repaid them with an excellent penalty save from Jonathan Hunt after Paul Underwood had been adjudged to have handled by an alert linesman.

A replay had been deservedly gained and back in the Conference none of Diamonds' challengers seemed keen to take advantage of the favourites' absence.

Arthur Evans

THIRD ROUND REPLAY: LEICESTER CITY 2 HEREFORD UNITED 1

Chairman, Manager and Director of Football - none of Graham Turner's personae will have been let down by the performance of the Bulls on the field, or by the vociferous 3,400 travelling supporters who roared them on at rain driven Filbert Street, where the Premier Division side found their playing resources stretched by injury. On a day when the Pierpoint saga had apparently at last been put to bed it looked for some time as if Leicester's Cup hopes would be similarly sent to rest. Manager Martin O'Neill looked desparate as he raged round his allotted area like a caged lion, pausing every few seconds to stoop for the comfort of a sip from his overworked water bottle. He admitted afterwards, "Hereford were fantastic". As so they were.

United took the lead in the 38th minute. Strange goal it was too. Young Paul Parry centred from the left byeline. The home defence hesitated fatally. Paul Fewings crept in front of keeper Pegguy Arphexhad who had come to his near post. Stooping low, Fewings backheaded and the ball looped into the net to send the Hereford contingent delirious. Up to that point Arphexhad had been untested. His counterpart, Mark Jones, similarly unused, could have stayed on his Shropshire farm until called on, in injury time of the first half, to rush out and grab a hoisted ball, knocking out big Steve Walsh in the process. The defender, turned emergency attacker did not appear for the second half.

Walsh had been the first to shoot in the opening minutes, but most of the forward movement had come from the Bulls. Mark Taylor and John Snape had largely controlled midfield so that Fewings and Robin Elmes were given opportunities to run at the Leicester defence. At the other end Tony Cottee looked sharp and Muzzy Issett grew more belligerent.

The introduction of Andrew Impey enlivened the homesters in the second half. Straightaway Taylor had to clear from a corner, and Cottee missed the target completely with a header when left unmarked. Leicester surged forward, knocking balls into the box in increasing desparation. Matt Elliott was pushed up alongside Cottee. And the ploy worked, for Elliott was on hand at the post to touch home Jones's parry of Graham Fenton's header in the 78th minute. How relieved were the Blues. Hereford broke out for a couple of runs, the best by Parry, dribbling past three defenders before being blocked as he shaped to shoot.

Down to ten men, following an injury to Impey, and having already used their substitue allocation, Leicester kept Elliott forward as extra time began. The increasingly influential Izzet presented Elliott with a chance which the indefatigable Chris Lane raced back to clear off the line. But then came the killer. Minute 104, Robbie Savage, who had shown tremendous spirit, picked up the ball in his own half, sprinted away down the right, found Cottee whose cross went unerringly to Izzet's head, thence powerfully between Jones legs to clinch an Arsenal trip for the home team.

Elliott was now restored to defence. Hereford regrouped. From somewhere they found renewed energy to mount another attack at goal. Leicester were not too proud to boot clear, anywhere to use up time. Gavin Williams' header was cleared from the goal line with two minutes left before impressive referee Dean signalled the end of another chapter in the Hereford Cup Story.

Significantly, Martin O'Neill went firstly to congratulate the visiting players, no doubt his congratulations mixed consisderably with relief. Graham Turner and his warriors received the accolades of their travelling support before turning for the dressing rooms to find the generous home supporters had remained to honour the conference representatives with a thoroughly deserved standing ovation. A fitting sporting end to a memorably sporting contest.

Match report by Arthur Evans

Hereford first half attack against Leicester City in front of nearly 8,000 fans. Photo: Eric Marsh

Top left: Billy Turley makes an excellent save despite the close attention of Blades striker Marcus Bent. Photo: Peter Barnes

Top right: Sheer delight on the Diamonds' faces as they level the score. Photo: Peter Barnes

Bottom left: Tim Wooding keeps his eye firmly on the ball despite Martin Smith in possession. Photo: Peter Barnes

Bottom right: Diamonds' physio Simon Parsell and Referee Barry Knight repair Diamonds' keeper Billy Turley with a head bandage in the first half at Bramall Lane. Photo: Peter Barnes

THIRD ROUND REPLAY: RUSHDEN & DIAMONDS 1   SHEFFIELD UNITED 1

Hero at one moment, crestfallen the next. Visiting keeper Simon Tracey and home midfielder Jon Brady suffered these conflicting feelings at the end of this elongated tie, but it was Brady who left the field needing consoling arms when his penalty miss proved the only one of the night. Ironically he had been the hero in the first tie at Brammall Lane, when scoring the goal which had given Diamonds a second chance. Then Tracey's mistake had contributed. Last night the keeper did the same, failing to hold Brady's corner and allowing the ball to slip to Ray Warburton who headed the equaliser gleefully home. However Tracey was able to redeem himself with that crucial parry which denied Brady and left marcus Bent needing to score United's first penalty of the sudden death part of the shoot out. He duly obliged before setting off on a victory weave prior to being immersed by his relieved colleagues.

And relieved they were since Diamonds had certainly edged the contest on the night but just failing, like their opponents, to carve out too many scoring chances. Barely a month into his managerial seat at Bramall Lane, Neil Warnock acknowledged the lack of chances but said United had had plenty in the first tie and he knew there would be few in the replay. He was delighted for Tracey whose two mistakes were now behind him and recalled that, as a manager, he had now completed 10-11 ties against non-leaguers and was still to lose one, although Bury had come mighty close to it against Tamworth in an earlier round.

Although admitting disappointment, Brian Talbot was delighted by his Diamonds. He said it had not looked as if there was a three division gap between the teams. They had matched Sheffield for fitness and proved there were good players in the Conference. When asked if he thought exit from the Cup might allow them to concentrate on the League, and not falter as they had during the second half of last season, he said, "Tonight we're just disappointed. We won't fold like we did last year, we've got stronger characters in the team." He felt sorry for Brady. Like all his players, Brady could not have given more.

In their fluorescent strip and baggy shorts Sheffield could well have claimed Motorway Maintenance as their sponsors. They dominated the opening minutes, Paul Devlin's 25 yarder saw Billy Turley, in confident form and justifying his expensive tag, fingertip over, his third save in the first five minutes. A Jonathan Hunt volley found the keeper also well positioned. Surging down the left, reminiscent of Stuart Pearce, but able to use both feet, Andy Burgess impressed for Diamonds, deserving his sponsored man of the match award. David Town, sent clear, should have done better than allow Tracey to smother. Town's striking partner, Darren Collins, was disappointing. Substitute de Souza was more threatening while Michael McElhatton thrust forward well from midfield, where Gary Butterworth was, as ever, energetic and immaculate in his passing.

Rob Kozluk's long throws were a source of visiting danger although Warburton and Jim Rodwell were never beaten in the air. One fell to Marcus Bent but Rodwell just nicked it from his toecap. Turley made the save of the match in the 87th minute, diving to his left to turn aside Shaun Derry's scorcher. Four bookings for United against one for Diamonds showed where the tension was greater. All that pent up emotion was released by visiting players and supporters twelve minutes into extra time. Put away by Devlin, Shaun Derry sidefooted past Turley and Rodwell's desperate lunge could not prevent the ball crossing the line. Three minutes later emotions were reversed as jubilation hit Northants, following Tracey's failure to deal with Brady's corner. After 100 scoreless minutes two goals in three minutes.

Mequel de Souza and Bent brought both keepers into action in the second period of extra time. Right at the death Turley grabbed the ball from Peter Kathouro's foot after another Kozluk throw in, sending the tie to penalties.

Ten accurate and powerful shots later, at five all, up stepped Brady. Though his drive was forceful, Tracey managed to beat it away, leaving Bent, who had already missed during the season, under pressure. The former Port Vale man did the necessary and so it will be United to assume the underdog role which had been so capably filled by Diamonds. Their Cup run once again brought publicity for their superb stadium, accomplished team and sound organisation. Come next May, as Brian Talbot conceded, the disappointment of Cup exit, may be seen in a different light.

Match report by Arthur Evans

Bottom: Jon Brady beats Simon Tracey to equalise the scores at Bramall Lane. Photo: Peter Barnes

Top: Two Hereford heroes: Mark Jones, keeper, 10th clean sheet of the season, and Paul Sturgess, a vital goal line clearance in the first half against Leicester City. Photo: Eric Marsh
Middle: Hereford players clap fans at the end of the 0-0 match against Leicester City. Photo: Eric Marsh
Bottom: Diamonds' players applaud their 3,000 plus fans at Bramall Lane. Photo: Peter Barnes

AXA F.A. CUP TOP INDIVIDUAL GOALSCORERS

		P	1Q	2Q	3Q	4Q	1st	
Stuart Taylor	Eccleshill United	4	4	-	-	-	-	= 8
Anthony Lynch	Taunton Town	2	3	2	-	-	-	= 7
Rocky Baptiste	Wealdstone	-	3	3	1	-	-	= 7
Gary Abbott	Aldershot	-	-	3	0	2	1	= 6
Sam Bowen	Worcester City	-	-	2	3	1	-	= 6
Steve Clark	St Albans City	-	-	-	-	2	-	= 5
John Morgan	Marine	-	-	3	0	2	-	= 5
Nicky Kennerdale	Eastwood Town	-	-	2	2	1	-	= 5

HAT TRICK SCORERS

PRELIMINARY ROUND

4	Richard Morse	Bashley
	Stuart Taylor	Eccleshill Utd
3	Phil Brown	Netherfield Kendal
	Joe Connor	Pickering Town
	Ross Milligan	Gretna
	Kevin Leatherday	Staveley MW
	Mark Rosegreen	Barwell
	Kevin Hoddy	Barwell
	Gary Bennett	Sudbury
	Luke Baulkham	East Thurrock United
	Stuart Roach	Great Yarmouth Town
	Ben Willis	Ford United
	Lawrence Yaru	Northwood
	Dave Arter	Tonbridge Angels
	Keith Miles	St Leonards
	Matt Toms	Sheppey United
	Paul Scott	Whyteleafe
	Andy Waddell	St Blazey

FIRST QUALIFYING ROUND

4	Stuart Taylor	Eccleshill United
	Ricardo Bhola	Tooting & Mitcham
	James O'Rourke	Cowes Sports

FIRST QUALIFYING ROUND cont.

3	Peter Green	Northampton Spencer
	Rocky Baptiste	Wealdstone
	Richard Grist	Thatcham
	Gary McGee	Gorleston
	Gary Wiltshire	Marlow
	Tony Lynch	Taunton Town

SECOND QUALIFYING ROUND

3	Gary Abbott	Aldershot Town
	Ottis Roberts	Harrow Borough
	Ian Cambridge	Cambridge City
	Martin Shepherd	Salisbury City
	Ian Monk	Leigh RMI
	Gary Robson	Gateshead
	Matt Woolf	Bromley
	John Morgan	Marine

THIRD QUALIFYING ROUND

4	Trevor Paul	Romford
3	Sam Bowen	Worcester City
	Steve Clark	St Albans City
	Martin Paul	Bath City

AXA F.A. CUP SPECIAL AWARDS

REGIONAL AWARDS

FIRST QUALIFYING ROUND

North East — Bedlington Terriers
(Arnott Insurance Northern League)

North West — Radcliffe Borough
(Unibond Division One)

Midlands — Stafford Rangers
(Dr Martens - Western)

South East — Ramsgate
(Bass Brewers Kent)

South West — Backwell
(Screwfix Direct Western)

THIRD QUALIFYING ROUND

North East — Crook Town
(Arnott Insurance Northern)

North West — Droylsden
(Unibond Premier Division)

Midlands — Burton Albion
(Dr Martens Premier Division)

South East — Burgess Hill Town
(Unijet Sussex Division One)

South West — Lymington & New Milton
(Screwfix Wessex)

SECOND QUALIFYING ROUND

North East — Crook Town
(Arnott Insurance Northern League)

North West — Marine
(Unibond Premier Division)

Midlands — Oadby Town
(Midland Alliance)

South East — Langney Sports
(Unijet Sussex Division One)

South West — Taunton Town
(Screwfix Western Premier Division)

FOURTH QUALIFYING ROUND

North East — Guiseley
(Unibond Premier)

North West — Stalybridge Celtic
(Unibond Premier)

Midlands — Tamworth
(Dr Martens Premier)

South East — Worthing
(Ryman Division One)

South West — Bath City
(Dr Martens Premier)

LAST MAN IN AWARD

An award and cheque for £8,000 was offered to the last
remaining non-exempt team in the competition.

Last season's winners:
Oxford City, Whyteleafe, Worthing, Chelmsford City and Eastwood Town
will all share the prize money for reaching the First Round Proper.
None of the teams reached the Second Round.

SPECIAL AXA AWARDS

NON-LEAGUE LEADING SCORER
Stuart Taylor (Eccleshill United), 8

AXA F.A. CUP NON-LEAGUE TEAM OF THE SEASON
Hereford United

F.A. UMBRO TROPHY

1999-2000 REVIEW

FIRST ROUND

1 Bromsgrove Rovers 2 v 5 Halesowen Town 517
Ball 12, 53 *Crisp 3, Thomas 13,89, Rowland 46, Ulfig (og) 81*

2 Guiseley 2 v 0 Flixton 306
Hazel 38, Parke 49

3 Leigh RMI 1 v 0 Boston United 377
Jones 80

4 Gresley Rovers 0 v 1 Redditch United 316
Cross 15

5 Solihull Borough 1 v 2 Runcorn 155
Judd 75 *McNally 83, Griffiths 87*

6 Atherstone United 0 v 3 Ossett Town 208
Smithard 15, Slater 68, Shaw 90 (og)

7 Lincoln United 2 v 3 Hucknall Town 238
McDaid 2, Simmons 90 *Gray 9 (og), Roberts 24, Martin 90*

8 Blyth Spartans 3 v 0 Stourbridge 419
Stewart 55, Robson 69, og 90

9 Burscough 2 v 6 Ilkeston Town 183
Knowles 2, Wilde 55 *Knapper 60 (p), Fearon 41, Hemmings 71, Manners 82, Helliwell 53, 61*

10 Hinckley United 5 v 1 Congleton Town 194
Sadler 10, 35, Ricketts 66 Allcock 23, Hunter 90 *Dodd 30*

11 Grantham Town 1 v 3 Matlock Town 298
Ramshaw 2 *Davies 42, Simpson 47, Campbell 88*

12 Corby Town 2 v 1 Belper Town 120
Hollis 12, 69 *Cunningham 70*

13 Barrow 4 v 0 Netherfield Kendal 1059
Bullimore 11, Peverell 19 O'Keefe 29, 30

14 Frickley Athletic 1 v 1 Ashton United 142
Beckett 90 *Conley-Excell 63*

r Ashton United 2 v 4* Frickley Athletic 142
Phillips 22, Shaw 52 *Hatto 75, 107 (p), Thompson 90, Hayward 115*

15 Emley 2 v 0 Colwyn Bay 280
Robshan 18, 31

16 Rocester 1 v 1 Farsley Celtic 105
Francis 42 *Blackstone 67 (pen)*

r Farsley Celtic 0 v 2 Rocester 74
Bourne 5, Ede 49 (pen)

17 Chorley 0 v 1 Moor Green 219
Hall 33

18 Spalding United 2 v 1 Shepshed Dynamo 205
Leach 12, 86 *McLarnow 61*

19 Paget Rangers 0 v 1 Spennymoor United 107
Williams 70

20 Burton Albion 1 v 1 Trafford 795
Smith 71 *Murray 68*

r Trafford 1 v 3 Burton Albion 305
Simms 66 *George 14, Stride 25, 86*

21 Leek Town 2 v 2 Accrington Stanley 302
Dundass 15, 80 *Coleman 36, Howard 75*

r Accrington Stanley 5 v 4 Leek Town 221
Coleman 1, Baxter 18, Carregher 40, Hollis 41 Shirley 77 *Hobby 19, 44, Callan 45, Dundass 84*

22 Gateshead 4 v 1 Braford (Pk Ave) 254
Alderson 5, Preen 31 Thompson 82, 89 *Maxwell 89*

23 Romford 1 v 1 Bashley 228
Emmanuel 28 *Morse 41*

r Bashley 2 v 1 Romford 147
Elliott 55, McCarthy 85 *Paul 87 (pen)*

24 Bishop's Stortford 1 v 3 Gravesend & North. 372
Bartley *Cooper (2) Powell*

25 Salisbury City 2 v 0 Tonbridge Angels 471
Housley 18, Sales 26

26 Racing Club Warwick 1 v 3 Harlow Town 148
Samuel 90 (og) *Falana 7, 21, Kelly 61*

27 Hitchin Town 1 v 1 Harrow Borough 291
Falton *Thomas*

r Harrow Borough 2 v 1* Hitchin Town 153
Gusavac, Towle *Dixon*

28 Purfleet 2 v 0 Dagenham & Red. 536
Coombs, Georgiou

29 Basingstoke Town 1 v 1 Bognor Regis Town 359
Dean *Rake*

r Bognor Regis Town 2 v 0 Basingstoke Town 263
Young, Birmingham

30 Sittingbourne 1 v 3 Chelmsford City 361
Berry 84 *Berquez 8, Lakin 9, Bramble 65*

31 Gloucester City 4 v 2 Chesham United 513
Chenowith 20, Cox 31, 50 Smith 78 *Fox 56, Boothe 90*

32 Bath City 1 v 0 Baldock Town 547
Paul 35

33 Raunds Town 0 v 0 Maidenhead United 102

r Maidenhead United 0 v 1 Raunds Town 154
Carr 19

34 Heybridge Swifts 2 v 0 Weston Super Mare 182
McLean, Streetley

35 Cinderford Town 1 v 2 Merthyr Tydfil 225
Toomey 50 *Griffiths 22, Sloan 66*

36 Cirencester Town 3 v 2 Cambridge City 160
Harris 6, Griffin 21, 74 (p) *Newby 40, Cambridge 53*

Burton Albion v Trafford 1-1. Man of the Match Jim O'Donnell stops yet another Burton attack. His confident handling and shot stopping helped the Unibond side to a well earned draw. Photo: Bill Wheatcroft

37	Braintree Town	3 v 2	Clevedon Town	303
	Adams 72, Rideout 85		Ford 2, Jefferies 75	
	Poulson 90			

38	Newport County	2 v 1	Yeading	349
	Smart 54, Brown 86		Thompson 47	

39	Rothwell Town	0 v 0	Boreham Wood	182

r	Boreham Wood	3 v 5*	Rothwell Town	63
	Howard 75, Lamine 85, 89		Gould 14, Grime 29 (og),	
			Machin 70, Foley 108,	
			Hough 117	

40	Fisher Athletic	1 v 3	Burnham	65
	Charles 9		Small 45 (p), Tomlinson 49, 65	

41	Worthing	5 v 1	Fleet Town	226
	Carrington, Gatehouse (og)		Lewis	
	Weston (2), Kennett			

42	Leatherhead	2 v 0	Kings Lynn	177
	Warrilow, Papa			

43	Chertsey Town	1 v 2	Hampton & Rich. B.	241
	Line		Charles, Burton	

44	Slough Town	0 v 2	Hendon	461
			Hyatt, Gentle	

45	St Albans City	1 v 2	Thame United	373
	Pratt		Louis (2)	

46	Havant & W.	0 v 0	Aylesbury United	289

r	Aylesbury United	2 v 4	Havant & W.	250
	Gallagher, King		O'Rourke (2), Wakefield,	
			Wyatt	

47	Croydon	0 v 0	Margate	150

r	Margate	5 v 0	Croydon	324
	Munday 56, 62 (p)			
	Utterson 71, 81, Collins 83			

48	Oxford City	2 v 0	Hastings Town	133
	Wimble, Strong			

49	Tiverton Town	1 v 1	Dorchester Town	773
	Richarson 60		O'Hagan (pen) 49	

r	Dorchester Town	2 v 2	Tiverton Town	490
	Groves 28, Sullivan 79		Nancekivell 43, Daly 56	
	(Tiverton Town won 5-3 on kicks from the penalty mark)			

FIRST ROUND STATISTICS

Home Victories 25

Away Victories 24

Replays 12

Best Attendance
1059 - Barrow v Netherfield Kendal
Average Attendance 289

Best Home Victory
Margate 5 v 0 Croydon

Best Away Victory
Burscough 2 v 6 Ilkeston Town

Top Right: Bath City's Colin Towler is foiled by Baldock 'keeper Adam Wheeler. The home side won the tie 1-0.
Photo: Ken Gregory

Above: Dagenham's Steve Heffer blasts over against Purfleet. Photo: Alan Coomes

SECOND ROUND

1	Barrow	2 v 3	Southport		1334
	Furlong 7, Rush 35		Doherty 12, Arnold 65, 67		
2	Stocksbridge Park	1 v 1	Redditch United		219
	Fiddler 12		Smith 9		
r	Redditch United	3 v 4	Stocksbridge Pk Stls		225
3	Rochester	1 v 2	Tamworth		361
	Woolley 87		Foy 12, Hallam 86		
4	Leigh RMI	1 v 1	Worksop Town		232
	Ridings 85		Whitehead 90		
r	Worksop Town	3 v 1	Leigh RMI		335
	Stafford 2, 35, Johnson 53		Ridings 59		
5	Accrington Stanley	2 v 2	Spalding United		401
	Flannery 16, Williams 41		Wilson 54, Beech 90		
r	Spalding United	1 v 0	Accrington Stanley		260
6	Morecambe	6 v 1	Hucknall Town		
	Hardy 3, Jackson 12		Martin 61		
	Lyons 41, Eastwood 71, 82				
7	Wisbech Town	1 v 2	Bishop Auckland		420
	Salmon 90 (og)		Naylor 40, Shaw 65		
8	Kidderminster Harr.	2 v 4	Telford United		1618
	Pope 11, Clarkson 67		Davies 42, Simpson 47,		
			Campbell 88		
9	Hyde United	6 v 0	Whitley Bay		398
	Yeo 5 (22, 36, 40, 42, 80)				
	Banim 83				
10	Stafford Rangers	1 v 4	Emley		605
	Mitchel 43		Robshaw 60, Calcutt 79,		
			Boughly 90 (og), Day 90		
11	Ilkeston Town	2 v 4	Scarborough		840
	Knapper 80, 82		Betts 75, Morris 80		
			Brodie 90, Brogan 90		
12	Blakenall	3 v 1	Eastwood Town		164
	Palmer 30, 80, Myers 88		Bonsell 43		
13	Runcorn	2 v 0	Northwich Victoria		875
	Moseley 25, 31				

14	Spennymoor Utd	2 v 1	Gretna		199
	Brown 71, Fairhurst 86		Dobie 42		
15	Bedworth United	0 v 2	Hednesford Town		308
			Kimmings 43, Davies 47(p)		
16	Matlock Town	0 v 1	Harrogate Town		384
			Dunn 73		
17	Hinckley United	1 v 1	Marine		322
	Thompson 29		Thompson 21		
r	Marine	1 v 0	Hinckley United		259
	Scott 40				
18	Halesowen Town	3 v 1	Sutton Coldfield Tn		375
	Smith 21, Birch 60, 72		Hole 69		
19	Frickley Athletic	4 v 3	Droylsden		173
	Haywood 3 (39, 62, 80)		Carroll 9, Whalley 34		
	Thompson 54		Hennigan 45		
20	Ossett Town	0 v 1	Doncaster Rovers		1310
			Kirkwood 57		
21	Stalybridge Celtic	1 v 1	Gainsborough Trinity		429
	Sullivan 68		Fothersill 33		
r	Gainsborough Trinity	1 v 3	Stalybridge Celtic		429
	Saville 76		Steele 9, Bauress 39 (p)		
			Filson 61		
22	Bilston Town	2 v 2	Workington		151
	Jackson 46, Voice 66		Irvine 51, Stewart 81		
r	Workington	3 v 2	Bilston Town		
	Borge 5, Wilson 74		Rollason 15, Jackson 84		
	Dawson 108				
23	Winsford United	1 v 1	VS Rugby		161
	Mussin 33		John 21		
r	VS Rugby	2 v 0*	Winsford United		197
	Jones 91, Ross 120				
24	Lancaster City	3 v 0	Corby Town		197
	Ward 32, 77, Barnes 71				
25	Radcliffe Borough	1 v 6	Moor Green		190
	Whealing 79		Hall 28, 66, Softley 46, 72,		
			Casey 84, Shepherd 89		

Darren Hay heads Woking's second goal against Ashford in the F.A. Challenge Trophy. Photo: Alan Coomes

Guiseley striker Simon Parks fires the ball through the legs of a Nuneaton defender and into the net to put his side 2-0 up and knock Borough out of the FA Umbro Trophy. Photo: Darren Thames

26	Guiseley	2 v 0	Nuneaton Borough	597	
	Poole 27, Parke 29				
27	Bamber Bridge	0 v 2	Burton Albion	402	
			Stride 14, Anderson 56		
28	Whitby Town	4 v 1	Stamford	391	
	Dixon 45, 49, Robinson 79		*Bailey 32*		
	Uru 87				
29	Blyth Spartans	2 v 0	Witton Albion	375	
	West 44 (og), Edgecumbe 52				
30	Altrincham	1 v 0	Gateshead	578	
	Power 73				
31	Rothwell Town	4 v 1	Evesham United	174	
	West 10 (og), Bullimore 42		*Yates 90*		
	Preston 47, Aitkens 54				
32	Hereford United	1 v 0	Barton Rovers	1501	
	Rogerson 59				
33	Heybridge Swifts	3 v 2	Witney Town	204	
	Parker 48, 90, Simpson 57		*Merriot 21, Neville 74*		
34	Enfield	2 v 2	Newport (IoW)	273	
	Dunwell 21, 48		*Protheroe 40 (og), Leigh 63*		
	At St Albans City FC				
r	Newport (IoW)	1 v 0*	Enfield		
	Wright 94				
35	Hayes	0 v 2	Worcester City	671	
			Owen 23, 34		
36	Rushden & Dia.	1 v 0	Havant & W.	1835	
	Collins 50				
37	Purfleet	5 v 0	Raunds Town	113	
	Keeling 12, Coombs 21, 80				
	Georgiou 33, Dorrell 82				
38	Harlow Town	2 v 3	Dover Athletic	451	
	Salmon, Rideout		*Vansittart 37, Beard 82,*		
			Brown 83		
39	Bromley	2 v 0	Chelmsford City	379	
	Watts 15, Kyte 35				

40	Cirencester Town	0 v 3	Forest Green Rovers	496	
			McGregor 9, Mehew 62,		
			Cook 86		
41	Folkestone Invicta	0 v 1	Kingstonian	727	
			Basford 65		
42	Leatherhead	0 v 0	Bedford Town	258	
r	Bedford Town	2 v 0	Leatherhead	369	
	Shorlock 2, 11				
43	Bath City	5 v 0	Erith & Belvedere	634	
	Davis 19, 63, Harrington 65				
	Colbourne 47, 75				
44	Hendon	1 v 0	Grays Athletic	237	
	Gentle 26				
45	Weymouth	0 v 0	Yeovil Town	4053	
r	Yeovil Town	2 v 1	Weymouth	3196	
	Patmore 76, Tisdale 85		*Laws 88*		
46	Merthyr Tydfil	0 v 0	Stevenage Borough	583	
r	Stevenage Borough	4 v 0	Merthyr Tydfil	1098	
47	Yate Town	0 v 2	Billericay Town	142	
			Brown 11, Simpson 21		
48	Dulwich Hamlet	1 v 1	Burnham	304	
	Carroll 58		*Lockhart 10*		
r	Burnham	1 v 0	Dulwich Hamlet	125	
	Lockhart				
49	Bashley	1 v 2	Newport County	257	
	Elliott 56		*Hill 7, Bayliss 85*		
50	Ashford Town	0 v 5	Woking	826	
			Akrour 3 (1, 30, 65),		
			Hay 9, 57		
51	Harrow Borough	0 v 0	Oxford City	127	
r	Oxford City	3 v 2	Harrow Borough		
	Smith, McCleary, Strong		*Markham, Nwao Kold*		

52	Tiverton Town 0 v 4 Farnborough Town	842
		Mendonca 57, 79	
		Darlington 59, 90	
53	Hampton & Rich. B. 1 v 2 Carshalton Athletic	249
	Charles 26	McKinlay 32, Newbury 37	
54	Bognor Regis Town 1 v 2 Walton & Hersham	379
	Masson 82	Blackman 45, Coates 48	
55	Crawley Town 0 v 2 Wealdstone	712
		Bircham 55, Jones 62	
56	Uxbridge 0 v 2 Canvey Island	140
		Tilson 4, Britnell 65	
57	Welling United 2 v 1 Gloucester City	425
	Hanlon 14, Braithwaite 90	Smith 38 (p)	
58	Gravesend & N'fleet 2 v 0 Worthing	371
	Campbell 25, Stanchart 29		
59	Whyteleafe 4 v 2 St Leonards	126
	Elliott 12, McKay 62	Hogg 84 (p), Tate 90	
	Milton 83, 86		

60	Leyton Pennant 0 v 3 Staines Town	87
		Jenson 12, Haywood 35,	
		Butter 40	
61	Margate 0 v 0 Dartford	400
r	Dartford 2 v 2 Margate	149
	Dartford won 4-2 after penalties		
62	Kettering Town 2 v 2 Thame United	127
	Watkins 50, Storer 87	Joe 65, 69	
r	Thame United 0 v 1 Kettering Town	412
		Watkin	
63	Aldershot Town 3 v 1 Braintree Town	1878
	Abbott 16, Dell 80, Poyne 86	Teineit 88	
64	Salisbury City 2 v 5 Sutton United	643
	Shepherd 57, Sales 83	Winston 6, Watson 33,	
		Ekoku 68, Rowlands 87,	
		Harlow 88	

SECOND ROUND STATISTICS

Home Victories 37

Away Victories 27

Replays 5

Best Attendance
4053 - Weymouth v Yeovil Town

Average Attendance 571

Best Home Victory
Hyde United 6 v 0 Whitley Bay

Best Away Victory
Radcliffe Borough 1 v 6 Moor Green
Ashford Town 0 v 5 Woking

Hat Tricks
5 Yeo (Hyde United)
3 Haywood (Frickley Athletic)
3 Akrour (Woking)

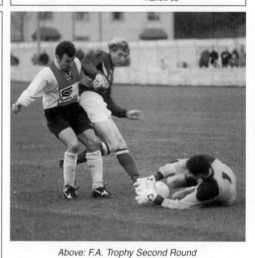

Above: F.A. Trophy Second Round
Lancaster City 3 Corby Town 0.
Corby Skipper Dougie Keast holds off City's Chris Ward
as his keeper Kevin Fox gathers.   Photo: Alan Watson

Left: F.A. Trophy Third Round. In a crowded area, Yeovil Town's Warren Patmore gets in a shot during his side's 2-1 win over Stevenage.
Photo: Ken Gregory

THIRD ROUND

1	V.S. Rugby *John 43 (p)*	1 v 4	Moor Green 452 *Shepherd 3, Softley 66 Hayde 75, Round 86*
2	Emley *Robshaw 25, Day 45*	2 v 1	Frickley Athletic 416 *Hayward 33*
3	Blakenall *Muir 63, Palmer 75*	2 v 1	Morecambe 375 *McKearney 89*
4	Tamworth	0 v 1	Runcorn 894 *McDonald 48*
5	Stalybridge Celtic *Stratford 22*	1 v 0	Blyth Spartans 579
6	Doncaster Rovers *Watson 60*	1 v 1	Halesowen Town 2103 *Olney 52*
r	Halesowen Town *Wright 69, Crisp 100*	2 v 3*	Doncaster Rovers 724 *Duerden 50, Minett 104 Walling 113*
7	Stocksbridge P.S.	0 v 0	Scarborough 634
r	Scarborough **Betts 3 (4, 29, 65)** *Brodie 34, 44*	5 v 0	Stocksbridge P.S. 964
8	Worksop Town *Johnson 90*	1 v 1	Lancaster City 440 *Martin 86*
r	Lancaster City	0 v 3	Worksop Town 260 *Townsend 38, Johnson 42 Ludlam 66*
9	Workington *Henney 84*	1 v 1	Burton Albion 440 *Blount 16*
r	Burton Albion	0 v 0	Workington 830 *Workington won 4-2 after penalties*
10	Spennymoor United *Bowes 5*	1 v 1	Harrogate Town 218 *Nesovic 16*
r	Harrogate Town *Ryan 51, Elliott 61, 73*	3 v 2	Spennymoor Utd 282 *Moat 20, 58* *(Game void as Harrogate played an ineligible player)*

r	Harrogate Town	0 v 2	Spennymoor United *Moat 45, Bowes 75*
11	Whitby Town *Ludlow 76*	1 v 3	Telford United 547 *Edwards 28, 42, Travis 75*
12	Marine *Gautrey 42, Bainbridge 90*	2 v 1	Guiseley 397 *Parke 59*
13	Southport	0 v 0	Altrincham 1387
r	Altrincham *Landon 61*	1 v 1	Southport 766 *Pell 90* *Southport won 4-3 after penalties*
14	Spalding United *Dolby 89, Keeble 90*	2 v 2	Bishop Auckland 275 *Appleby 27 (og), Mellanby 52*
r	Bishop Auckland	2 v 0	Spalding United 232
15	Hednesford Town *Davies 88*	1 v 1	Hyde United 710 *Taylor 90*
r	Hyde United *Walker 20, Banim 81*	2 v 0	Hednesford Town 518
16	Sutton United *Winston*	1 v 0	Canvey Island 719
17	Rothwell Town *Preston 45*	1 v 1	Walton & Hersham 207 *Dowling 34*
r	Walton & Hersham *Pickett*	1 v 0	Rothwell Town 204
18	Purfleet *Georgiou 87*	1 v 1	Newport (IoW) 203 *Wilson 65*
r	Newport (IoW) *Wright (2)*	2 v 1	Purfleet 404 *Marsden*
19	Forest Green Rovers *Sykes (2), Daley, Clark*	4 v 1	Hendon 583 *Daly*
20	Gravesend & North. *Restarick*	1 v 1	Dover Athletic 1265 *Vansittart*
r	Dover Athletic *Brown, Vansittart*	2 v 1	Gravesend & North. 1059 *Stadhart*

Sutton v Canvey Island. Sutton's Dave Harlow turns Steve Tilson as Paul Harford looks on.   Photo: Garry Letts

21	Oxford City	1 v 5	Burnham	176	
	Thorp		***Jarvis (3)**, Bunce, Sampson*		
22	Billericay Town	3 v 1	Hereford United	757	
	Browne, Gentle, Simpson		*Elmes*		
23	Aldershot Town	4 v 1	Staines Town	2050	
	Bentley (2), Payne (2)		*Driscoll*		
24	Wealdstone	0 v 5	Kingstonian	639	
			Wingfield, Pitcher (p),		
			Akuamoah, O'Connor, Taylor		
25	Carshalton Athletic	0 v 1	Farnborough Town	392	
			Warner		
26	Kettering Town	2 v 0	Welling United	1031	
27	Bath City	1 v 2	Rushden & Dia.	2034	
	Paul 24		*Rodwell 66, Aldridge 72*		
28	Worcester City	2 v 1	Bromley	783	
	Carty 61, Owen 84 (p)		*Gray 43*		
29	Woking	4 v 2	Whyteleafe	1550	
	Hay (2), West, Akrour		*Lunn, Arkright*		
30	Yeovil Town	2 v 1	Stevenage Borough	2604	
	Foster 8, 51		*Kirby 71*		
31	Dartford	1 v 2	Heybridge Swifts	542	
	Guiver 27		*Roberts 35 (og), Simpson 86*		
32	Bedford Town	0 v 0	Newport County	944	
r	Newport County	0 v 1	Bedford Town	669	
			Payne 40		

Billericay keeper Gavin King punches clear from Hereford's Ian Wright in their FA Trophy Third Round match. Photo: Alan Coomes

THIRD ROUND STATISTICS

Home Victories 19

Away Victories 13

Replays 12

Best Attendance
2604 - Yeovil Town v Stevenage Borough

Average Attendance 756

Best Home Victory
Scarborough 5 v 0 Stocksbridge Park Steels

Best Away Victory
Wealdstone 0 v 5 Kingstonian

Hat Tricks
3 Betts (Scarborough)
3 Jarvis (Burnham)

Left: Telford's keeper Justin Bray collects the ball from Whitby Town's Lee Ludlow. Photo: Neil Thaler

FOURTH ROUND

Bedford Town 0 v 4 Yeovil Town
Att: 2010 *Covington 6 (og),*
Patmore 14, Eaton 56,
Cousins 60
Bedford Town: Heeps, Daniels, Joyce (Cobb 90), P Covington, Williams, Searle, G Covington (Gutzmore 62), Sherlock, Payne, Jaggard (Cooper 67), Lawley. Subs not used: Lomas, Bone.
Yeovil Town: Pennock, Piper (Pounder 68), Poole, Skiverton, Brown, Cousins (Wilmot 78), Pitman, Chandler, Patmore (Foster 68), Eaton, Smith. Subs not used: Thompson, Steele.

Billericay Town 0 v 0 Rushden & Dia.
Att: 2027
Billericay Town: King, Game, Moore, Culverhouse, Williams, Parratt, Penn, Linger, Simpson, Browne, Gentle. Subs not used: Jordan, Scott, Henty, Trainer, Blaney.
Rushden & Diamonds: Turley, Wooding, Cramman, Cooper, Rodwell, Warburton, Brady, Butterworth, Lowe (De Souza 63), Collins, Underwood. Subs not used: Burgess, Smith, Bradshaw, Mills

r Rushden & Dia. 2 v 1 Billericay Town
Lowe 46, De Souza 71 *Att: 2132* *Browne 86*
Rushden & Diamonds: Turley, Wooding, Cramman, Mills, Rodwell, Warburton, Butterworth, Brady (De Souza 46), Lowe, Collins, Underwood. Subs not used: Smith, Burgess, Cooper, Peters.
Billericay Town: King, Game, Moore, Culverhouse, Williams, Parratt, Penn (Henty), Linger, Simpson, Browne, Jordan (Gentle 41). Subs not used: Scott, Trainer, Blaney.

Blakenall 0 v 1 Marine
Att: 407 *Seams 35*
Blakenall: Lowe, Simkin, Hillman, Richards, Jackson (Jones 59), Palmer (Bennett 65), Worsey (Swann 59), Myers, Muir, Street, Dodd. Subs not used: Smith, Olden.
Marine: Clarke, Fearns, Randles, Price, Schofield, Gautrey, Morgan, Gamble, Rigoglioso, Nulty, Baines. Subs not used: Smith, England, Powell, Scott, McHale.

Burnham 1 v 1 Scarborough
Howell 62 *Att: 469* *Brodie 56*
Burnham: Stallard, Potter, Brett, O'Sullivan, Furmage, Jarvis, Clarke (Small 58), Lockhart, Sampson, Howell, Walsh (Rowley 85). Subs not used: Johnson, Tillson, Shepherd.
Scarborough: Woods, Betts, Williams, Harriott, Ellender, Sinnott, Jones, Stoker (Bass 45), Tate, Brodie, Russell. Subs not used: Roberts, Martin, McNaughton, Alkhatib.

r Scarborough 6 v 0 Burnham
Williams 4, Tate 9 *Att: 887*
Russell 31, Roberts 36
Jones 61, Stoker 76
Scarborough: Woods, Russell, Betts, Harriott, Ellender, Sinnott (Bass 65), Jones, Stoker, Tate, Brodie (Roberts 15), Williams (Alkhatib 65). Subs not used: Martin, McNaughton.
Burnham: Stallard, Potter, Johnson (Rowley 65), O'Sullivan, Furmage, Sampson, Clarke, Lockhart, Small, Howell (Shepherd 54), Nesbeth (Tillson 90).

Dover Athletic 1 v 0 Doncaster Rovers
Vansittart 58 *Att: 1683*
Dover Athletic: Hyde, Browne, Virgo, Munday (Daniels 89), Shearer, Beard, Clarke, Wormall, Vansittart (Hynes 65), Brown (Carruthers 46), Norman. Subs not used: Hudson, Livett.
Doncaster Rovers: Warrington, Marples (Warren 78), Maxfield, Minett, Walling, Barnard, Watson (Wright 82), Penney (Duerdon 68), Maamria, Newell, McIntyre. Subs not used: Foster, Illman.

Heybridge Swifts 1 v 0 Newport (IoW)
McClean 65 *Att: 2010*
Heybridge Swifts: Banks, Cranfield, Wiles, Haydon, Lewis, Gillespie, Simpson, Parker, Taylor, Streetley, McClean. Subs not used: Fiddes, Morden, Warwick, Bond, Grice.
Newport (I-W): Hards, Wilson, White (Husbands 74), Riley, Price, Buckman, Leigh, Green, Quirke (Laidlaw 56), Sperry (Youngs 74), Betteridge. Subs not used: Cole, Lloyd.

Left: Bedford Town v Yeovil Town. James Heeps in the Bedford goal, sadly for him beaten four times by the Yeovil attack. Photo: Steve Ayre
Right: Ben Smith (Yeovil) halts the progress of Bedford midfielder, Eddie Lawley.

Hyde United 0 v 0 Runcorn
Att: 764

Hyde United: Bennett, Foster, Robertson, Wilson, Taylor, Band, McDonald, Walker, Yeo, Banim, Critchley. Subs: Tobin, McConnell, Esdaille, Aspinall.

Runcorn: Acton, Rose, Ness, Nolan, Burke, Ruffer, Brunskill, Robinson, McNally, Smith, Watson (Moseley 68). Subs not used: Tomlinson, McMahon, Carter, McDonald.

r Runcorn 3 v 2* Hyde United
Smith 11, 119, Burke 95   Att: 649   Aspinall 22, Wilson 96

Kettering Town 2 v 2 Walton & Hersham
Norman 24p, 54p   Att: 1128   Dowling 46p,
Blackman 65

Kettering Town: Sollitt, Diuk (Hudson 45), Adams, Doane, Vanden, Norman, Fisher, McNamara, Shutt, Watkins, Ridgway. Subs not used: Setchell, Hopkins, Paul, Wilson.

Walton & Hersham: Blake, Humphrey, Dowling, Dowson, Whelan, Craker, Williams (Rose 76), Holloway, Harrison (Tilbury 62), Coates (Blackman 45), Pickett. Subs not used: Ball, Gregory.

r Walton & Hersham 0 v 2 Kettering Town
Att: 490   Watkins 4, 64

Walton & Hersham: Blake, Humphrey, Dowling, Dowson, Whelan, Craker, Blackman, Holloway, Cory, Rose, Pickett. Subs: Williams, Harrison, Tilbury, Gregory, Harris.

Kettering Town: Sollitt, Diuk, Adams, McNamara, Vowden, Norman, Fisher, Doane, Shutt, Watkins, Setchell . Subs: Hudson, Hopkins, Banya, Paul, Wilson.

Kingstonian 2 v 1 Moor Green
Taylor 44, Pitcher 80   Att: 623   Shepherd 33

Kingstonian: Farrelly, Mustafa (Lester 90), Luckett, Allan, Stewart, Harris, Patterson, Pitcher, Akuamoah, Leworthy (O'Connor 82), Taylor (Wingfield 72). Subs not used: Hurst, Crossley.

Moor Green: Arnold, Mulholland, Brighton, Gillard, Smith, Round (Casey), Softley, Crisp, Hall (Russell), Shepherd, Petty. Subs not used: Hamilton, Cope, Hayde.

Southport 2 v 0 Emley
Pell 39, Elam 46   Att: 1272

Southport: Dickinson, Guyett, Stuart, Morley, Bolland, Ryan, Clark, Grayston, Arnold (Ellison 59), Pell (Mike 89), Elam. Subs not used: O'Hanlon, Formby, Furlong.

Emley: Rhodes, Nicholson, Jones, Haran, Fee (Hamlet 51), David, Tonks (Day 79), Thorpe, Robshaw, Calcutt, Wood. Subs not used: Wilson, Sykes, Robinson.

Spennymoor Utd 0 v 3 Bishop Auckland
Att: 422   Brunskill 19, Shaw 29, 31

Spennymoor United: Campbell, Nelson, Bates, Crosby, Taylor, Howarth, Ramsay, Holloway, Moat, Bowes, Rowe. Subs: Williams, Sweeney, Lowe.

Bishop Auckland: Jones, Roulston, Dunn, Brightwell, Hutt, Mellanby, Gallacher, Bayles, Shaw, Brunskill, Naylor. Subs: Adams, Smith, Croft, Veart.

Stalybridge Celtic 0 v 1 Worcester City
Att: 747   Bowen 27

Stalybridge Celtic: Ingham, Ward, Scott (Sullivan 58), Ogley, Johnston (Marginson 86), Bauress, Pickford, Parr, Steele, Jones (Mason 58), Williamson. Subs not used: Robinson, Higgins.

Worcester City: Watson, Sandeman, Willetts, Tucker, Heeley, Carty, Knight, Bowen, Owen, Lutz, Jukes. Subs: Frost, Wyatt, Purdie, Deakin, Upton.

Left: Burnham v Scarborough 1-1. Charlie Stallard collects the ball to foil the visitors.   Photo: Gordon Whittington
Right: The red shirts of Hyde United clear the ball during their 0-0 draw against Runcorn at Ewen Fields.
Photo: Colin Stevens

Sutton United   3   v   0   Forest Green Rvrs
Brooker 25   *Att: 711*
Newhouse 41, Winston 62
Sutton United: Howells, Brooker, Skelly, Brodrick, Laker (Sears 63), Harlow, Dack (Ekoku 79), Harford, Newhouse, Winston (Watson 74), Riley. Subs not used: Rowlands, Hutchinson.
Forest Green Rovers: Perrin, Hedges, Forbes (Mings 57), Bailey (Cook 80), Clark, Burns, Daley, Drysdale, McGregor, Hunt, Sykes. Subs not used: Domm, Smith, Kilgour.

Telford United   2   v   1   Farnborough Town
Murphy 51, 84   *Att: 944*   *Darlington 59*
Telford United: Price, Macauley, Travis, Naylor, Ford, Albrighton, Doyle, Palmer, Edwards, McGorry, Murphy. Subs: Malkin, Bray, Fowler, Bridgwater.
Farnborough Town: MacKenzie, Corbett, Wye, Kuhl, Harper, Dublin (Carruth 27), Watson, Warner, Darlington, Bennetts, Endersby. Subs not used: Cheesman, Codner, Omigie, Smart.

Woking   0   v   0   Aldershot Town
Att: 4973
Woking: Flahauan, Girdler, Hollingdale, West, Smith, Danzey, Perkins, Wilkinson, Akrour, Hay, Steele (Bolt 67). Subs not used: Gridlet, Goddard, Alighier, Batty.
Aldershot Town: Pape, Gell, Gugwins, Adedeji, Coll, Baker, Champion, Bentley, Abbott, Payne, Fielder. Subs: Hathaway, Bassey, Sucrue, Achamfour, Searle.

r   Aldershot Town   0   v   1   Woking
Att: 5307   *Hay 31*
Aldershot Town: Pape, Gell, Bassey, Adedeji, Coll, Baker (Sugrue 46), Fielder, Bentley, Abbott, Payne, Hathaway. Subs not used: Champion, Searle, Flinn, Achamfour.
Woking: Flahavan, Girdler, Alighieri, West, Smith, Danzey, Perkins, Wilkinson, Akrour, Hay (Panter 89), Smith. Subs not used: Gridlet, Bolt, Batty, Goddard.

Worksop Town   1   v   1   Workington
Jackson 64   *Att: 657*   *Irvine 14*
Worksop Town: Kennedy, Ludlam, Mason, Davis, Hobson, Johnson, Smith, Whitehead, Townsend, Goddard, Smith (Jackson 60). Subs not used: Stafford, Clark, Field, Norwood.
Workington: Armfield, Kay, Green, Gray, Johnson, Carr, Borg, Henney, Dawson, Stewart, Irving. Subs: Wilson, Jones, Millar, Hoggeth.

r   Workington   1   v   0   Worksop Town
Wilson 51   *Att: 1029*
Workington: Armfield, Kay, Green, Gray, Johnson, Carr, Borg, Henney, Dawson (Henderson 29), Irving, Wilson. Subs not used: Jones, Harrison, Thornthwaite, Hoggeth.
Worksop Town: Kennedy, Field (Clark 61), Mason, Davis, Hobson, Johnson, Smith, Whitehead, Townsend, Goddard, Reeve (Stafford 45). Subs not used: Norwood, Jackson, Smith.

* after extra time

FOURTH ROUND STATISTICS

Home Victories 10

Away Victories 6

Replays 6

Best Attendance
4973 - Woking v Aldershot

Average Attendance 1303

Best Home Victory
Sutton Utd 3 v 0 Forest Green Rovers

Best Away Victory
Bedford Town 0 v 4 Yeovil Town

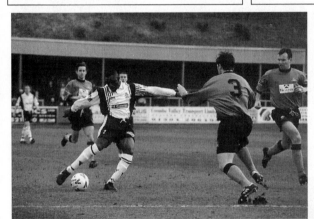

Top: Dave Clarke (Dover Athletic) steadies himself, closely watched by Doncaster Rovers' Scott Maxfield and Mark Barnard. Photo: Roger Turner
Bottom: Large crowd in Tennis Court Terrace from Aldershot Town. Photo: Eric Marsh

FIFTH ROUND

Bishop Auckland   2   v   1   Scarborough
Shaw 11p, Mallanby 44   Att: 747   Jones 61
Bishop Auckland: Jones, Salmon, Lee, Smith, Hutt, Downey (Roulston 69), Mellanby, Bayles, Shaw (Adams 44), Brunskill, Naylor. Subs not used: Croft, Hughes, Foster.
Scarborough: Woods, Russell, Betts, Rennison (Tyrell 86), Ellender, Sinnott, Jones, Stoker, Tate, Bass (McNiven 45), Roberts (Morris 45). Subs not used: Martin, Naughton.

Runcorn   2   v   1   Heybridge Swifts
McDonald 37, Griffiths 76   Att: 759   Gillespie 89
Runcorn: Acton, Ward, Ness, Nolan, Burke, Ruffer, Brunskill, Tomlinson, McNally, McDonald (Griffith 67), Smith. Subs not used: Ellis, McMahon, Carter, Langton.
Heybridge Swifts: Banks, Cranfield (Heasman 90), Wiles, Haydon, Lewis, Waters, Streetley (Warwick 61), Parker, Taylor, Gillespie, McClean. Subs not used: Morden, Fiddes, Caton.

Rushden & Diamonds   1   v   0   Marine
Lowe 32   Att: 3094
Rushden & Diamonds: Turley, Wooding, Cramman, McElhatton (Hamsher 82), Rodwell, Warburton, Butterworth, Brady, Lowe, Town (Heggs 58), Underwood. Subs not used: Burgess, Smith, Peters.
Marine: Clarke, Scott, Randles, Bainbridge, Schofield, Gautrey, Morgan, Gamble, Rigoglioso, Nulty, Baines. Subs: Robinson, Gillies, England, McHale, Smith.

Southport   3   v   0   Woking
Arnold 25p   Att: 1560
Grayston 70, Pell 90
Southport: Dickinson, Guyett, Stuart, Morley, Grayston, Ryan, Clark, Gouck, Arnold, Pell, Elam. Subs not used: Mike, Formby, Ellison, Furlong, Trundle.
Woking: Flahauan, Smith (Akrour 50), Alighieri, West, Hollingdale (Bolt 75), Smith, Perkins, Wilkinson, Goddard, Hay, Girdler. Subs not used: Smith, Batty, Gridlet.

Top: Kingstonian enter the fray for one of their toughest ties at Yeovil led by Matt Crossley. This match attracted the biggest attendance before the Final. Photo: Keith Clayton.
Bottom: Both "benches" look on anxiously in a tight game at Nene Park. Diamonds v Marine. Photo: Peter Barnes.

Sutton United	2
v	
	1 Dover Athletic

Winston 13   Att: 1207   Lebihan 40
Newhouse 86

Sutton United: Howells, Brooker, Skelly, Riley, Laker, Harlow, Dack, Newhouse, Winston (Forrester 88), Watson (Ekoku 76), Brodrick. Subs not used: Berry, Rowlands, Sears.

Dover Athletic: Hyde, Browne, Norman, Virgo (Hynes 90), Shearar, Beard, Clarke, Wormull, Vansittart, Brown, Le Biham (Carruthers 81). Subs not used: Hudson, Holmes, Godden.

Telford United	4	v	1	Worcester City

Ford 17, Palmer 52   Att: 2085   Lutz 88
Malkin 77, 85

Telford United: Price, Travis, Fitzpatrick, MacAuley, Ford, Fowler, Hartfield (Naylor 67), Palmer (Bridgwater 75), Malkin, McGorry, Edwards (Murphy 52). Subs not used: Bray.

Worcester City: Watson, Sandeman, Willetts, Tucker, Weir, Carty, Lutz, bowen, Owen, Cottrill (Deakin 75), Purdie. Subs not used: Heeley, Wyatt, Jukes, Frost.

Workington	0	v	1	Kettering Town

Att: 1643   Brown 71

Workington: Armfield, Kay, Green, Gray, Johnson, Carr, Borg, Henney, Irving, Dawson, Wilson (Goulding 67). Subs not used: Moffat, Jones, thornthwaite, Hoggeth.

Kettering Town: Sollitt, Kiuk, Adams, Cox, Vowden, Norman, Ridgway, Brown, Shutt, Watkins, McNamara. Subs not used: Doane, Williams, Setchell, Mark, Wilson.

Yeovil Town	0	v	1	Kingstonian

Att: 3330   Leworthy 40

Yeovil Town: Pennock, Piper (Eaton 85), Poole, Skiverton, Brown, Cousins, Pitman (Tisdale 61), Chandler (Hayfield 72), Patmore, Foster, Smith. Subs not used: Steele, Pounder.

Kingstonian: Fareelly, Mustafa, Luckett, Crossley, Stewart (Harris 64), Allan, Patterson, Pitcher, Akuamoah, Leworthy (Boylan 72), Wingfield. Subs not used: O'Connor, Hurst, Taylor.

Top: Sutton's Mark Watson holds off Dover's Steve Norman. Photo: Garry Letts
Bottom: David Lowe (white) heads the only goal of the game for Rushden & Diamonds against Marine at Nene Park.
Photo: Peter Barnes.

FIFTH ROUND STATISTICS

Home Victories 6

Away Victories 2

Best Attendance
3330 - Yeovil Town v Kingstonian

Average Attendance 1803

Best Home Victory
Southport 3 v 0 Woking
Telford 4 v 1 Worcester City

Best Away Victory
Workington 0 v 1 Kettering Town
Yeovil Town 0 v 1 Kingstonian

Top: David Gamble (Marine) sprints away with the ball from Diamonds' substitute Carl Heggs. Photo: Peter Barnes
Bottom: Warren Patmore (Yeovil) heads the ball on, but Steve Farrelly (Kingstonian) is well placed to catch.
Photo: Keith Clayton.

QUARTER-FINALS

Kingstonian 0 v 0 Southport
Att: 1201

Kingstonian: Farrelly, Mustafa, Luckett, Crossley, Allan, Harris, Basford, Pitcher, Akuamoah, Leworthy, Boylan (Wingfield 81). Subs not used: O'Corror, Hurst, Kadi, Green.

Southport: Dickinson, Guyett, Formby, Morley, Bolland, Grayston, Clark, Gouck, Arnold, Furlong, Elam. Subs: Pell, Mike, Trundle, Connolly, Croxton.

r
Southport 0 v 1 **Kingstonian**
Att: 1576   *Leworthy 86*

Southport: Dickinson, Guyett, Stuart (Elam 53), Morley, Bolland, Ryan, Clark, Gouck, Arnold, Mike (Furlong 55), Grayston. Subs not used: Formby, Trundle, Croxton.

Kingstonian: Farrelly, Mustafa, Luckett, Crossley, Allan, Harris, Patterson, Pitcher, Akuamoah, Leworthy, Wingfield (Boylan 78). Subs not used: O'Connor, Hurst, Green, Basford.

Gareth Howells makes a superb catch despite pressure from Darren Collins. Photo: Peter Barnes

Sutton United   1 v 1   Rushden & Diamonds

Winston 12   Att: 1586   Burgess 63

Sutton United: Howells, Brocker, Skelly, Riley, Laker, Harlow, Dack, Harford, Winston, Newhouse, Ekoku. Subs not used: Berry, Rowlands, Hutchinson, Sears, Forrester.

Rushden & Diamonds: Turley, Wooding, Ozamman, Hamshel, Rodwell, Warburton, Butterworth, Brady, De Souza, Collins, Underwood. Subs not used: Lowe, Bertocchi, Peters, Burgess, Mills.

r   Rushden & Diamonds   1 v 3   **Sutton United**

Coper 85   Att: 2703   Winston 35, Newhouse 51, Ekoku 67

Rushden & Diamonds: Turley, Wooding (Cooper 59), Cramman (Burgess 46), Hamsher, Rodwell, Warburton, Butterworth, Brady (De Souza 59), Lowe, Collins, Underwood. Subs not used: Bertocchi, Peters.

Sutton United: Howells, Brooker, Skelly, Riley, Laker, Harlow, Dack, Harford, Winston (Watson 88), Newhouse, Ekoku (Hutchinson 80). Subs not used: Sears, Berry, Rowlands.

Kettering Town   2 v 2   Bishop Auckland

Norman 34, 51   Att: 2071   Shaw 18, Downey 21

Kettering Town: Sollitt, Ridgway (Diuk 70), Adams (Setchell 70), Doane, Vowden, Norman, Fisher, Brown, Williams (Shutt 45), Watkins, McNamara. Subs not used: Paul, Wilson.

Bishop Auckland: Jones, Salmon, Lee, Downey, Hutt, Gallacher (Milroy 80), Mellanby (Adams 82), Bayles, Shaw, Brunskill, Naylor. Subs not used: Croft, Dunn, Smith.

r   Bishop Auckland   1 v 2   **Kettering Town**

Att: 1087   Norman 37(p), McNamara 38

Bishop Auckland: Jones, Salmon, Lee, Downey, Hutt (Milroy 45), Gallacher, Mellanby, Bayles, Shaw, Brunskill, Naylor (Smith 65). Subs not used: Adams, Croft, Dunn.

Kettering Town: Sollitt, Ridgway, Adams, Diuk, Vowden, Norman, Fisher, Brown, Shutt, Watkins (Setchell 89), McNamara. Subs not used: Williams, Paul, Hopkins, Wilson.

Please, don't shoot. Photo: Peter Lirettoc

Telford United 2 v 0 Runcorn
Palmer 18, Murphy 85   Att: 1557

Telford United: Price, Macauley, Travis, Fitzpatrick, Ford, Fowler, Doyle, Palmer, Malkin, Hartfield, Edwards (Murphy 70). Subs not used: Sandwith, Bray, Bridgewater
Runcorn: Acton, Rose, Callaghan (Ness 83), Nolan, Burke, Ruffer, Brunskill, Robinson, McNally, McDonald (Griffiths 56), Smith. Subs not used: Ellis, Carter, McMahon.

QUARTER FINAL STATISTICS

Home Victories 1

Away Victories 3

Replays 3

Best Attendance
2703 - Rushden & Diamonds v Sutton United

Average Attendance 1611

Best Home Victory
Telford United 2 v 0 Runcorn

Best Away Victory
Rushden & Diamonds 1 v 3 Sutton United

Left: Sutton's Sammy Winston and Rushden & Diamonds' Ray Warburton.
Photo: Garry Letts

Below: Kingstonian's Eddie Akuamoah closely watched by a Southport defender.
Photo: Peter Lirettoc.

SEMI-FINALS

Sutton United 1 v 1 Kingstonian
Att: 2384

Sutton United: Howells, Brooker (Sears 80), Skelly, Riley, Laker, Harlow, Dack, Harford, Winston, Newhouse, Ekoku (Hutchinson 78). Subs not used: Watson, Iga, Broderick.

Kingstonian: Farrelly, Mustafa, Luckett, Crossley, Allan, Harris, Patterson, Pitcher, Akuamoah, Boylan (Green 74), Simba. Subs not used: Hurst, Lester, O'Connor, Saunders.

Kingstonian 6 v 0 Sutton United
Att: 2309

Kingstonian: Farrelly, Mustafa, Luckett, Crossley, Saunders, Harris, Patterson, Pitcher, Akuamoah (Green 82), Simba (Boylan 82), Wingfield (O'Connor 82). Subs not used: Hurst, Basford.

Sutton United: Howells, Rowlands (Dack 59), Skelly, Riley, Laker (Ekoku 46), Harlow, Hutchinson, Brodrick, Winston, Newhouse (Forrester 59), Watson. Subs not used: Iga, Berry.

Left: Kingstonian defender Tarkan Mustafa fails to prevent Nko Ekoku centering. Photo Peter Lirettoc.

Below: Sutton's Andy Riley v Kingstonian's Tarkan Mustafa. Photo: Eric Marsh.

Kettering Town 1 v 0 Telford United
Att: 2915

Kettering Town: Sollitt, Ridgway, Adams, Cox, Vowden, Norman, Fisher, Brown, Shutt, Watkins (McNamara 87), Setchell. Subs not used: Perkins, Diuk, Paul, Wilson.

Telford United: Price, Travis, Sandwith, Moore, Ford, Gayle, Preece, McGorry, Malkin (Murphy 74), Edwards, Hartfield (Palmer 58). Subs not used: Bray, Macauley, Martindale.

Telford United 0 v 0 **Kettering Town**
Att: 2165

Telford United: Price, Travis, Sandwith (Murphy 56), Moore, Gayle, Fowler, Preeece, Palmer, Martindale, Edwards, McGorry. Subs not used: Bray, Macauley, Ford, Hartfield.

Kettering Town: Sollitt, McNamara, Adams, Perkins, Vowden, Norman, Fisher (Diuk 80), Brown, Shutt, Watkins (Ridgway 63), Setchell (Hudson 85). Subs not used: Wilson, Paul.

Top: Ryan Price (Telford keeper) gathers the ball safely late in the game at Rockingham Road. Photo: Peter Barnes
Bottom: Phil Brown and Chris Malkin contest the ball in midfield with Carl Adams and Roger Preece looking on.
Photo: Peter Barnes

Top: Kingstonian book their visit to the Twin Towers again. Photo: Eric Marsh

Left: Telford's Jake Edwards (left) challenges Kettering Town. Photo: Andy Benson

FA UMBRO TROPHY AT A GLANCE

THIRD ROUND

Sutton United 1
Canvey Island 0

Forest Green R. 4
Hendon 1

Gravesend & N. 1, 1
Dover Athletic 1, 2

Doncaster Rvrs 1, 3*
Halesowen Tn 1, 2*

Billericay Town 3
Hereford United 1

Bath City 1
Rushden & Dia. 2

Blakenall 2
Morecambe 1

Marine 2
Guiseley 1

Bedford Town 0, 1
Newport County 0, 0

Yeovil Town 2
Stevenage Boro 1

Wealdstone 0
Kingstonian 5

V.S. Rugby 1
Moor Green 4

Southport 0, 1, 4p
Altrincham 0, 1, 3p

Emley 2
Frickley Athletic 1

Woking 4
Whyteleafe 2

Aldershot Town 4
Staines Town 1

Worksop Town 1, 3
Lancaster City 1, 0

Workington 1, 0, 4p
Burton Albion 1, 0, 2p

Kettering Town 2
Welling United 0

Rothwell Town 1, 0
Walton & Hersh. 1, 1

Spennymoor U 1
Harrogate Town 1

Spalding United 2, 0
Bishop Auckland 2, 2

Oxford City 1
Burnham 5

Stocksbridge P.S. 0, 0
Scarborough 0, 5

Whitby Town 1
Telford United 3

Carshalton Athletic 0
Farnborough Town 1

Stalybridge Celtic 1
Blyth Spartans 0

Worcester City 2
Bromley 1

Hednesford T 1, 0
Hyde United 1, 2

Tamworth 0
Runcorn 1

Dartford 1
Heybridge Swifts 2

Purfleet 1, 1
Newport (IoW) 1, 2

FOURTH ROUND

Sutton United 3
Forest Green Rvrs 0

Dover Athletic 1
Doncaster Rovers 0

Billericay Town 0
Rushden & Dia. 0

Blakenall 0
Marine 1

Bedford Town 0
Yeovil Town 4

Kingstonian 2
Moor Green 1

Southport 2
Emley 0

Woking 0
Aldershot 0

Worksop 1
Workington 1

Kettering Town 2
Walton & Hersham 2

Spennymoor Utd 0
Bishop Auckland 3

Burnham 1
Scarborough 1

Telford United 2
Farnborough Town 1

Stalybridge Celtic 0
Worcester City 1

Hyde United 0
Runcorn 0

Heybridge Swifts 1
Newport (IoW) 0

FIFTH ROUND

Sutton United 2

Dover Athletic 1

Rushden & Diamonds 1

Marine 0

Yeovil Town 0

Kingstonian 1

Southport 3

Woking 0

Workington 0

Kettering Town 1

Bishop Auckland 2

Scarborough 1

Telford 4

Worcester City 1

Runcorn 2

Heybridge Swifts 1

SIXTH ROUND

Sutton United 1, 3

Rushden & Dia. 1, 1

Kingstonian 0, 1

Southport 0, 0

Kettering Town 2, 2

Bishop Auckland 2, 1

Runcorn 0

Telford United 2

SEMI FINALS

Sutton United 1, 0

Kingstonian 1, 6

Kettering Town 2

Kettering Town 1, 0

Telford United 0, 0

FINAL

Kingstonian 3

PAST F.A. TROPHY FINALS

1970   MACCLESFIELD TOWN 2 (Lyond, B Fidler)   TELFORD UNITED 0   Att: 28,000
Macclesfield: Cooke, Sievwright, Bennett, Beaumont, Collins, Roberts, Lyons, B Fidler,Young, Corfield, D Fidler.
Telford: Irvine, Harris, Croft, Flowers, Coton, Ray,Fudge, Hart, Bentley, Murray, Jagger.   Ref: K Walker

1971   TELFORD UTD 3 (Owen, Bentley, Fudge)   HILLINGDON BORO. 2 (Reeve, Bishop)
Telford: Irvine, Harris, Croft, Ray, Coton, Carr, Fudge, Owen, Bentley, Jagger ,Murray.   Att: 29,500
Hillingdon B.: Lowe, Batt, Langley, Higginson, Newcombe, Moore, Fairchild,Bishop, Reeve, Carter, Knox.   Ref: D Smith

1972   STAFFORD RANGERS 3 (Williams 2, Cullerton)   BARNET 0   Att: 24,000
Stafford R.: Aleksic, Chadwick, Clayton, Sargeant, Aston, Machin, Cullerton, Chapman,Williams, Bayley, Jones.
Barnet: McClelland, Lye, Jenkins, Ward, Embrey, King,Powell, Rerry, Flatt, Easton, Plume .   Ref: P Partridge

1973   SCARBOROUGH 2 (Leask, Thompson)   WIGAN ATHLETIC 1 (Rogers) aet   Att:23,000
Scarborough: Garrow, Appleton, Shoulder, Dunn, Siddle, Fagan, Donoghue, Franks,Leask (Barmby), Thompson, Hewitt.
Wigan: Reeves, Morris, Sutherland, Taylor,Jackson, Gillibrand, Clements, Oats (McCunnell), Rogers, King, Worswick.   Ref: H Hackney

1974   MORECAMBE 2 (Richmond, Sutton)   DARTFORD 1 (Cunningham)   Att: 19,000
Morecambe: Coates, Pearson, Bennett, Sutton, Street, Baldwin, Done, Webber,Roberts (Galley), Kershaw, Richmond.
Dartford: Morton, Read, Payne, Carr, Burns,Binks, Light, Glozier, Robinson (Hearne), Cunningham, Halleday.   Ref: B Homewood

1975   MATLOCK TOWN 4 (Oxley, Dawson, T Fenoughty, N Fenoughy)   SCARBOROUGH 0   Att: 21,000
Matlock: Fell, McKay, Smith, Stuart, Dawson, Swan, Oxley, N Fenoughy, Scott, T Fenoughty, M Fenoughty.
Scarborough: Williams, Hewitt, Rettitt, Dunn, Marshall, Todd, Houghton, Woodall, Davidson, Barnby, Aveyard.   Ref: K Styles

1976   SCARBOROUGH 3 (Woodall, Abbey, Marshall(p))   STAFFORD R. 2 (Jones 2) aet   Att: 21,000
Scarborough: Barnard, Jackson, Marshall, H Dunn, Ayre (Donoghue), HA Dunn, Dale,Barmby, Woodall, Abbey, Hilley.
Stafford: Arnold, Ritchie, Richards, Sargeant,Seddon, Morris, Chapman, Lowe, Jones, Hutchinson, Chadwick.   Ref: R Challis

1977   SCARBOROUGH 2 (Dunn(p), Abbey)   DAGENHAM 1 (Harris)   Att: 21,500
Scarborough: Chapman, Smith, Marshall (Barmby), Dunn, Ayre, Deere, Aveyard,Donoghue, Woodall, Abbey, Dunn.
Dagenham: Hutley, Wellman, P Currie, Dunwell,Moore, W Currie, Harkins, Saul, Fox, Harris, Holder.   Ref: G Courtney

1978   ALTRINCHAM 3 (King, Johnson, Rogers)   LEATHERHEAD 1 (Cook)   Att: 20,000
Altrincham: Eales, Allan, Crossley, Bailey, Owens, King, Morris, Heathcote,Johnson, Rogers, Davidson (Flaherty).
Leatherhead: Swannell, Cooper, Eaton, Davies,Reid, Malley, Cook, Salkeld, Baker, Boyle (Bailey).   Ref: A Grey

1979   STAFFORD RANGERS 2 (A Wood 2)   KETTERING TOWN 0   Att: 32,000
Stafford: Arnold, F Wood, Willis, Sargeant, Seddon, Ritchie, Secker, Chapman, AWood, Cullerton, Chadwick (Jones).
Kettering: Lane, Ashby, Lee, Eastell, Dixey,Suddards, Flannagan, Kellock, Phipps, Clayton, Evans (Hughes).   Ref: D Richardson

1980   DAGENHAM 2 (Duck, Maycock)   MOSSLEY 1 (Smith)   Att : 26,000
Dagenham: Huttley, Wellman, Scales, Dunwell, Mooore, Durrell, Maycock, Horan,Duck, Kidd, Jones (Holder).
Mossley: Fitton, Brown, Vaughan, Gorman, Salter,Polliot, Smith, Moore, Skeete, O'Connor, Keelan (Wilson).   Ref: K Baker

1981   BISHOP'S STORTFORD 1 (Sullivan)   SUTTON UNITED 0   Att:22,578
Bishop's Stortford: Moore, Blackman, Brame, Smith (Worrell), Bradford, Abery, Sullivan,Knapman, Radford, Simmonds, Mitchell.
Sutton Utd.: Collyer, Rogers, Green, J Rains,T Rains, Stephens (Sunnucks), Waldon, Pritchard, Cornwell, Parsons.   Ref: J Worrall

1982   ENFIELD 1 (Taylor)   ALTRINCHAM 0   Att:18.678
Enfield: Jacobs, Barrett, Tone, Jennings, Waite, Ironton, Ashford, Taylor,Holmes, Oliver (Flint), King.   Ref: B Stevens
Altrincham: Connaughton, Crossley, Davison, Bailey,Cuddy, King (Whitbread), Allan, Heathcote, Johnson, Rogers, Howard.

1983   TELFORD UTD 2 (Mather 2)   NORTHWICH VICTORIA 1 (Bennett)   Att: 22,071
Telford: Charlton, Lewis, Turner, Mayman (Joseph), Walker, Easton, Barnett,Williams, Mather, Hogan, Alcock.
Northwich: Ryan, Fretwell, Murphy, Jones,Forshaw, Ward, Anderson, Abel (Bennett), Reid, Chesters, Wilson.   Ref: B Hill

1984   NORTHWICH VICTORIA 1 (Chester)   BANGOR CITY 1 (Whelan)   Att: 14,200
Replay   NORTHWICH 2 (Chesters(p), Anderson)   BANGOR 1 (Lunn)   Att: 5,805 (at Stoke)
Northwich: Ryan, Fretwell, Dean, Jones, Forshaw (Power 65), Bennett, Anderson,Abel, Reid, Chesters, Wilson.   Ref: J Martin
Bangor: Letheren, Cavanagh, Gray, Whelan, Banks,Lunn, Urqhart, Morris, Carter, Howat, Sutcliffe (Westwood 105) . Same in replay.

1985   WEALDSTONE 2 (Graham, Holmes)   BOSTON UNITED 1 (Cook)   Att: 20,775
Wealdstone: Iles, Perkins, Bowgett, Byatt, Davies, Greenaway, Holmes, Wainwright,Donnellan, Graham (N Cordice 89), A Cordice.
Boston: Blackwell, Casey, Ladd,Creane, O'Brien, Thommson, Laverick (Mallender 78), Simpsom, Gilbert, Lee, Cook.   Ref: J Bray

1986   ALTRINCHAM 1 (Farrelly)   RUNCORN 0   Att: 15,700
Altrincham: Wealands, Gardner, Densmore, Johnson, Farrelly, Conning, Cuddy,Davison, Reid, Ellis, Anderson. Sub: Newton.
Runcorn: McBride, Lee, Roberts,Jones, Fraser, Smith, S Crompton (A Crompton), Imrie, Carter, Mather, Carrodus.   Ref: A Ward

1987   KIDDERMINSTER HARRIER S 0   BURTON ALBION 0   Att: 23,617
Replay   KIDDERMINSTER 2 (Davies 2)   BURTON 1 (Groves)   Att: 15,685 (at West Brom)
Kidderminster: Arnold, Barton, Boxall, Brazier (sub Hazlewood in rep), Collins (subPearson 90 at Wembley), Woodall, McKenzie, O'Dowd, Tuohy, Casey, Davies. sub:Jones.
Burton: New, Essex, Kamara, Vaughan, Simms, Groves, Bancroft, Land, Dorsett, Redfern, (sub Wood in replay), Gauden.
Sub: Patterson.   Ref: D Shaw

1988   ENFIELD 0   TELFORD UNITED 0   Att: 20,161, Ref: L Dilkes
Replay   ENFIELD 3 (Furlong 2, Howell)   TELFORD 2 (Biggins, Norris(p))   Att: 6,912 (at W Brom)
Enfield: Pape, Cottington, Howell, Keen (sub Edmonds in rep), Sparrow (subHayzleden at Wembley), Lewis (sub Edmonds at Wembley), Harding, Cooper, King,Furlong, Francis.
Telford: Charlton, McGinty, Storton, Nelson, Wiggins, Mayman (sub Cunningham inrep (sub Hancock)), Sankey, Joseph, Stringer (sub Griffiths at Wembley,Griffiths in rep), Biggins, Norris.

1989   TELFORD UNITED 1 (Crawley)   MACCLESFIELD TOWN 0   Att: 18,102
Telford: Charlton, Lee, Brindley, Hancock, Wiggins, Mayman, Grainger, Joseph,Nelson, Lloyd, Stringer. Subs: Crawley, Griffiths.
Macclesfield: Zelem, Roberts, Tobin, Edwards, Hardman, Askey, Lake, Hanton,Imrie, Burr, Timmons. Subs: Devomshire, Kendall.
    Ref: T Holbrook

1990   BARROW 3 (Gordon 2, Cowperthwaite)   LEEK TOWN 0   Att: 19,011
Barrow: McDonnell, Higgins, Chilton, Skivington, Gordon, Proctor, Doherty(Burgess), Farrell (Gilmore), Cowperthwaite, Lowe, Ferris.
Leek: Simpson, Elsby (Smith), Pearce, McMullen, Clowes, Coleman (Russell),Mellor, Somerville, Sutton, Millington   Ref: T Simpson

1991   WYCOMBE W. 2 (Scott, West)   KIDDERMINSTER H. 1 (Hadley)   Att: 34,842
Wycombe: Granville, Crossley, Cash, Kerr, Creaser, Carroll, Ryan, Stapleton,West, Scott, Guppy (Hutchinson). Ref: J Watson
Kidderminster: Jones, Kurila, McGrath, Weir, Barnett, Forsyth, Joseph (Wilcox), Howell (Whitehouse), Hadley, Lilwall, Humphries

1992   COLCHESTER UTD 3 (Masters, Smith, McGavin)   WITTON ALBION 1 (Lutkevitch)   Att: 27,806
Colchester: Barrett, Donald, Roberts, Knsella, English, Martin, Cook, Masters,McDonough (Bennett 65), McGavin, Smith. Ref: K P Barratt
Witton: Mason, Halliday, Coathup, McNeilis, JimConnor, Anderson, Thomas, Rose,Alford, Grimshaw (Joe Connor), Lutkevitch (McCluskie)

1993   WYCOMBE W. 4 (Cousins, Kerr, Thompson, Carroll) RUNCORN 1 (Shaughnessy)   Att: 32,968
Wycombe: Hyde, Cousins, Cooper, Kerr, Crossley, Thompson (Hayrettin 65),Carroll, Ryan, Hutchinson, Scott, Guppy. Sub: Casey.
Runcorn: Williams, Bates, Robertson, Hill, Harold (Connor 62), Anderson, Brady(Parker 72), Brown, Shaughnessy, McKenna, Brabin
    Ref: I J Borritt

1994   WOKING 2 (D Brown, Hay)   RUNCORN 1 (Shaw (pen))   Att: 15,818
Woking: Batty, Tucker, L Wye, Berry, Brown, Clement, Brown (Rattray 32), Fielder, Steele, Hay (Puckett 46), Walker.   Ref: Paul Durkin
Runcorn: Williams, Bates, Robertson, Shaw, Lee, Anderson, Thomas, Connor, McInerney (Hill 71), McKenna, Brabin. Sub: Parker

1995   WOKING 2 (Steele, Fielder)   KIDDERMINSTER H. 1 aet (Davies)   Att: 17,815
Woking: Batty, Tucker, L Wye, Fielder, Brown, Crumplin (Rattray 42), S Wye, Ellis, Steele, Hay (Newberry 112), Walker. Sub: Read(gk)
Kidderminster: Rose, Hodson, Bancroft, Webb, Brindley (Cartwright 94), Forsyth, Deakin, Yates, Humphreys (Hughes 105), Davies, Purdie. Sub: Dearlove (gk)   Ref: D J Gallagher

1996   MACCLESFIELD TOWN 3 (Payne, OG, Hemmings) NORTHWICH VICTORIA 1 (Williams)   Att: 8,672
Macclesfield: Price, Edey, Gardiner, Payne, Howarth(C), Sorvel, Lyons, Wood (Hulme 83), Coates, Power, Hemmings (Cavell 88).
Northwich: Greygoose, Ward, Duffy, Burgess (Simpson 87), Abel (Steele), Walters, Williams, Butler (C), Cooke, Humphries, Vicary.   Ref: M Reed

1997   DAGENHAM & REDBRIDGE 0   WOKING 1 (Hay 112)   Att: 24,376
Dagenham: Gothard, Culverhouse, Connor, Creaser, Jacques (sub Double 75), Davidon, Pratt (Naylor 81), Parratt, Broom, Rogers, Stimson (John 65).
Woking: Batty, Brown, Howard, Foster, Taylor, S Wye, Thompson (sub Jones 115), Ellis, Steele (L Wye 108), Walker, Jackson (Hay 77).   Ref: J Winter

1998   CHELTENHAM TOWN 1 (Eaton 74)   SOUTHPORT 0   Att: 26,387
Cheltenham: Book, Duff, Freeman, Banks, Victory, Knight (Smith 78), Howells, Bloomer, Walker (sub Milton 78), Eaton, Watkins. Sub: Wright.
Southport: Stewart, Horner, Futcher, Ryan, Farley, Kielty, Butler, Gamble, Formby (sub Whittaker 80), Thompson (sub Bollard 88), Ross. Sub: Mitten.   Ref: G S Willard

1999   FOREST GREEN ROVERS 0   KINGSTONIAN 1 (Mustafa 49)   Att: 20,037
Forest Green Rovers: Shuttlewood, Hedges, Forbes, Bailey (Smart 76), Kilgour, Wigg (Cook 58), Honor (Winter 58), Drysdale, McGregor, Mehew, Sykes. Subs (not used): Perrin, Coupe
Kingstonian: Farrelly, Mustafa, Luckett, Crossley, Stewart, Harris, Patterson, Pitcher, Rattray, Leworthy (Francis 87), Akuamoah. Subs (not used): John, Corbett, Brown, Tranter   Ref: A B Wilkie

FINAL

KETTERING TOWN (0)2 v 3 (1) KINGSTONIAN

Vowden 55
Norman 64 (pen)

Att: 20,034

Akuamoah 40, 69
Simba 75

Kettering Town	Kingstonian
Adam Sollit	Steve Farelly
Brett McNamara	Takan Mustafa
Carl Adams	Colin Luckett
Chris Perkins	Matt Crossley
Colin Vowden	Simon Stewart
Craig Norman	(sub Eddie Saunders 77th min)
(sub Wayne Duik 76th min)	Mark Harris
Matt Fisher	Junior Kadi
Phil Brown	(sub David Leworthy 83rd min)
Carl Shutt	Geoff Pitcher
Dale Watkins	Ronnie Green
(sub Lee Hudson 46th min)	(sub Luke Basford 86th min)
Gary Setchell	Amara Smiba
(sub Craig Hopkins 81st min)	Eddie Akuamoah

Subs not used:
Ian Ridgway
Steve Wilson

Subs not used:
Richard Hurst
Derek Allan

Referee: Mr S W Dunn (Gloucestershire FA)

The reports as first published in Team Talk

What a joy - an F.A. Umbro Trophy final which was a real thriller. The game came to life when Eddie Akuamoah scored in the first half and the respective managers did the rest in the dressing rooms at half time.

Instead of a battle of attrition and a late single winner, Kettering Town needed to score and Kingstonian were ready and very capable of counter attacking through the blistering pace of Tarkan Mustafa, Ronnie Green and the inspired scorer himself.

The Northamptonshire supporters were magnificent, they sensed that their side could be lifted and indeed the glorious set piece goal, headed home by Colin Vowden also encouraged a massive roar which momentarily shook Steve Farrelly.

The giant goalkeeper had faultlessly played one and a half Trophy finals and must have been feeling on top of the world when a perfect free kick was headed home and suddenly he found himself losing the ball, and what appeared to be another goal, after a suicidal dribble.

The linesman's flag temporarily saved K's, but the luck then reversed to give Kettering a penalty and the lead. The noise was the loudest at a Trophy final in recent years. Could Geoff Chapple's Trophy spell be broken? His team had never had to fight back at Wembley before but how they took up the challenge.

Long serving 'Eddie A' did it again and amidst near hysteria at the Kingstonian end, Mustafa, last year's match winner, raced at the Kettering defence and unleashed a shot that Adam Sollitt couldn't hold and as the French can do no wrong on the football field these days, it was natural that Amara Simba delicately lifted the rebound in off the post for a winner which gave his manager a fifth success, his captain, Matt Crossley, a fourth and a medal for himself on his first visit to Wembley.

Kettering Town had helped make this final the best for years, it was a great example of senior semi-professional football, televised live on Sky TV and enjoyed by 20,034 (just 49 less that The Vase final!).

A big thank you to both clubs, some superb supporters and what is there left to say about Geoff Chapple?

Just what is his secret?

Tony Williams

If you're going to win a national trophy five times within seven seasons then you just have to be someone extra special. Step forward Geoff Chapple, the already selected non-League manager of the era, a selection fully vindicated by this victory at a sunny Wembley. Ironically "extra special" was Geoff's description of his side's triumph, "Since we did not play particularly well. I've gone through every feeling you can get out of your body today. Of the five I've been involved with that's the hardest I've earned. 1-0 up at half time, I was reasonably confident but we got lethargic. For some reason their second goal was a kick start for us."

"Some way to start," was Peter Morris, Kettering manager's retort when told of the quip.

Yet how true was Chapple's remark. Kettering had shaded the first half, been unlucky to go behind just before half time, and then begun the second half in fine form, to equalise and then go one ahead, only to see Kingstonian reinvigoratedly level, before snatching the lead, and the victory, with fifteen minutes still to go.

In a relatively poor first half, reminiscent of previously disappointing finals, the first fifteen minutes were the brightest. Kingstonian, in blue and yellow, having magnanimously volunteered to change from the red normal for both teams, had the first shot, Tarkan Mustafa firing past Adam Sollitt's right post, a reminder of his goal in last year's final. Dale Watkins and Brett McNamara were lively up front for the Poppies, the former shooting just over from Gary Setchell's pull back, and then repeating the flight path with a curler. Sollitt found himself in the back of the net with the ball in his clutches, courtesy of Mark Harris' re-enactment of challenges last legal in the fifties. Steve Farrelly distinguished himself with a low dive to his right to catch Phil Brown's dipping shot. With five minutes to go to the interval Amara Simba put Eddie Akuamoah away. Racing clear, he drew Sollitt from his line and then slipped the ball under him to put K's one up. Only a last ditch hack away by Chris Perkins prevented Simba doubling the lead, Akuamoah this time the provider.

Having seen their youngsters win the half time penalty competition, Kingstonian, despite being outnumbered two to one in supporters, seemed to have everything going their way but Brown's early shot showed that the Poppies, having made a tactical change by taking off Watkins, were not going to submit easily. McNamara's twenty yard left footer underlined their determination, and they deservedly drew level in the 56th minute. Carl Adams' free kick was met by skipper Colin Vowden's head as the K's defence stood like sightseers lost in awe. Four minutes later Lee Hudson thought he had secured the lead. Farrelly dribbled out complacently, was robbed by McNamara and Hudson touched his pass home. After seconds of shirt waving gesticulation by the corner flag nearest his fans, Hudson turned to find Steve Dunn had accepted his assistant's flag

Key to photos:
Top: Kingstonian's Tarkan Mustafa (Man of the Match) slides in ahead of Gary Setchell of Kettering.
Photo: D Nicholson
Centre: Dale Watkins (Kettering) sends a volley just over the bar. Photo: Keith Clayton
Bottom: Eddie Akuamoah scores Kingstonian's first goal. Photo: Peter Lirettoc

and given offside. Hudson's cup of glory was dashed from his lips but moments later Kettering were sipping success. McNamara, trailed by Mustafa, ran into the box and tripped over his own feet. Mr Dunn saw it as a trip by Mustafa and gave the penalty from which Craig Norman needed no second invitation to smash the Northants men into a 2-1 lead.

"Kick started", Kingstonian roared back. A long, high ball from Matt Crossley was not cleared and there was Akuamoah again to net left footed. Simba shot wide before, another five minutes having elapsed, Mustafa when striding through from his own half. Reaching the edge of the penalty box he shot low and hard. Sollitt, looking below his usual confident form ("I've never seen him spill it before" said manager Morris later, "I think it's the poorest game he's had for us."), fumbled and French full international Simba was at hand to scoop into the net.

Geoff Pitcher, outstanding with his prompting and support play, had two chances to put the tie beyond doubt. However, Kettering were beaten by now and the final minutes were like a practice game, Kingstonian playing for time and the Poppies spent and energyless. No wonder after 90 minutes in the hot London sun.

Named Man of the Match, Mustafa smiled, "Getting the award this year was a greater achievement than scoring in last year's final." Long serving Akuamoah declared his second goal had given him more pleasure than the first as it had brought his team back into the game. Looking back reflectively, he said, "Colin Luckett and I have come through some bad times at Kingston. I can remember getting beaten 5-1 at Yeading." He seemed very much cast in the modest mould of his manager who concluded, "I get a buzz out of coming to Wembely, even if it's empty so I was glad to win this last one." Asked then were he though the next final should be played he suggested Old Trafford.

It seemed pointless to ask if he intended to be there, but tempting to conjecture who will be there as his opponents! They will need to be extra special to beat him.

Arthur Evans

Top: Past Trophy winners march past at Wembley. Photo: Paul Carter
Bottom: Victorious Kingstonian and 'young'. Photo: Paul Carter

FA TROPHY OVERALL RECORDS

The table is a record of the performance of the top 110 teams that have played in the Trophy since its inception in 1970. During that time we have seen many teams enjoying successful periods in the competition and this is an attempt to reward teams for their consistency during the various rounds as well as whether they actually win the Trophy or not. The points are calculated as follows: Last 64 = 1point; Last 32 = 2 points; Last 16 = 3 points; Last 8 = 4 points; Last 4 = 5 points; Finalists = 6 points; Winners = 7 points.   *John Anderson*

	1999	2000		S	P	W	L	%	Pts	Best
+	2	1	Telford United	31	91	63	28	69.23	85	W x 3
-	1	2	Altrincham	31	92	63	29	68.48	81	W x 2
=	3	3	Runcorn	31	93	62	31	66.67	76	F x 3
=	4	4	Enfield	26	80	56	24	70.00	70	W x 2
=	5	5	Northwich Victoria	31	82	52	30	63.41	69	W 1984
=	6	6	Kidderminster Harriers	31	75	45	30	60.00	66	W 1987
=	7	7	Stafford Rangers	31	76	47	29	61.84	65	W x 2
=	8	8	Macclesfield Town	28	74	48	26	64.86	62	W x 2
+	13	9	Kettering Town	31	70	39	31	55.71	61	F x 2
+	12	10	Scarborough	19	58	42	16	72.41	58	W x 3
-	9	11	Boston United	31	73	42	31	57.53	58	F 1985
+	14	12	Yeovil Town	31	67	36	31	53.73	58	SF x 2
-	10	13	Cheltenham Town	29	85	57	28	67.06	57	W 1998
-	11	14	Dagenham	18	67	50	17	74.63	55	W 1980
+	16	15	Dartford	27	66	39	27	59.09	52	F 1974
+	19	16	Woking	26	73	50	23	68.49	51	W x 3
-	15	17	Wycombe Wanderers	19	52	35	17	67.31	51	W x 2
-	17	18	Morecambe	31	78	48	30	61.54	51	W 1974
-	18	19	Burton Albion	31	77	46	31	59.74	50	F 1987
=	20	20	Bangor City	22	53	31	22	58.49	47	F 1984
=	21	21	Weymouth	31	64	33	31	51.56	47	last 8 x 2
=	22	22	Barrow	28	62	35	27	56.45	46	W 1990
=	23	23	Bromsgrove Rovers	31	69	38	31	55.07	46	last 8 x 2
+	28	24	Bishop Auckland	26	68	42	26	61.76	45	last 8 x 3
-	24	25	Merthyr Tydfil	31	70	39	31	55.71	45	last 8 1978
+	27	26	Worcester City	30	66	36	30	54.55	45	last 8 x 4
-	25	27	Bath City	31	71	40	31	56.34	43	last 8 1990
+	30	28	Marine	26	59	33	26	55.93	42	SF x 2
+	34	29	Sutton United	26	58	32	26	55.17	42	F 1981
-	26	30	Slough Town	26	56	30	26	53.57	42	SF x 2
-	29	31	Witton Albion	31	80	49	31	61.25	40	F 1992
+	35	32	Dover Athletic	31	63	32	31	50.79	40	SF 1998
+	32	33	Hyde United	31	79	48	31	60.76	39	SF x 3
-	31	34	Nuneaton Borough	31	62	31	31	50.00	38	last 8 x 3
-	33	35	Barnet	22	52	30	22	57.69	37	F 1972
+	39	36	Bedford Town	14	41	27	14	65.85	36	SF 1975
-	36	37	Chorley	31	68	37	31	54.41	36	SF 1996
-	37	38	Gateshead	30	63	33	30	52.38	36	last 8 x 3
-	38	39	Blyth Spartans	26	53	27	26	50.94	36	last 8 x 2
=	40	40	Matlock Town	31	74	44	30	59.46	34	W 1975
=	41	41	Grantham	31	68	37	31	54.41	33	last 8 x 2
=	42	42	Welling United	18	39	21	18	53.85	32	last 8 1989
=	43	43	Chelmsford City	31	64	33	31	51.56	30	SF 1970
=	44	44	Maidstone United	17	43	26	17	60.47	29	last 8 x 2
=	45	45	Mossley	26	59	33	26	55.93	29	F 1980
+	52	46	Southport	22	54	32	22	59.26	28	F 1998
=	47	47	Wigan Athletic	9	27	18	9	66.67	27	F 1973
-	46	48	Dagenham & Redbridge	11	31	20	11	64.52	27	F 1997
+	65	49	Kingstonian	26	65	41	24	63.08	27	W x 2
-	48	50	Wealdstone	25	58	34	24	58.62	27	W 1985
+	53	51	Spennymoor United	26	51	25	26	49.02	26	SF 1978

-	49	52	Hillingdon Borough	16	40	24	16	60.00	25	F 1971
-	50	53	Aylesbury United	22	48	26	22	54.17	25	last 8 1981
-	51	54	Bishops Stortford	26	54	29	25	53.70	25	W 1981
=	55	55	Frickley Athletic	31	66	35	31	53.03	24	last 8 1985
=	56	56	Stalybridge Celtic	31	66	35	31	53.03	24	last 16 1992
-	54	57	Gloucester City	31	75	44	31	58.67	23	SF 1997
+	62	58	Farnborough Town	21	44	23	21	52.27	23	last 8 1993
-	57	59	Hendon	26	53	27	26	50.94	23	last 16 x 3
-	59	60	Stevenage Borough	11	35	24	11	68.57	22	SF 1997
-	60	61	Lancaster City	23	49	26	23	53.06	22	last 16 x 2
-	58	62	Hastings United	17	34	17	17	50.00	22	last 16 x 2
-	61	63	Buxton	29	60	31	29	51.67	21	last 8 x 2
-	63	64	Dulwich Hamlet	26	52	26	26	50.00	21	last 8 1980
-	64	65	Harrow Borough	25	65	39	26	60.00	20	SF 1983
=	66	66	Leatherhead	19	43	24	19	55.81	20	F 1978
+	73	67	Whitby Town	24	49	25	24	51.02	19	last 8 1984
-	67	68	Gainsborough Trinity	31	56	25	31	44.64	19	last 32 x 5
-	68	69	Tooting & Mitcham Utd	23	52	29	23	55.77	18	last 8 1976
-	69	70	Wimbledon	8	18	10	8	55.56	18	last 8 1975
-	70	71	Leek Town	28	60	32	28	53.33	18	F 1990
=	72	72	Winsford United	31	63	32	31	50.79	18	last 8 1978
-	71	73	Romford	12	24	12	12	50.00	18	last 16 x 4
+	75	74	Guiseley	9	25	16	9	64.00	17	SF 1994
-	75	74	St Albans City	26	57	31	26	54.39	17	SF 1999
=	76	76	Emley	20	53	33	20	62.26	16	last 8 x 2
+	102	77	Rushden & Diamonds	9	23	14	9	60.87	15	SF 1995
-	77	78	Goole Town	26	63	37	26	58.73	15	last 8 1975
-	78	79	Colwyn Bay	23	54	31	23	57.41	15	last 8 1997
-	79	80	Wokingham Town	24	55	31	24	56.36	15	SF 1988
+	84	81	Carshalton Athletic	26	55	29	26	52.73	15	last 16 x 2
-	80	82	Stourbridge	31	51	20	31	39.22	15	last 8 1971
-	81	83	Dorchester Town	31	69	38	31	55.07	14	last 16 x 2
-	82	84	Hitchin Town	26	57	31	26	54.39	14	last 16 x 3
-	83	85	Hayes	26	56	30	26	53.37	14	last 8 x 2
-	85	86	South Liverpool	22	46	24	22	52.17	14	last 32 x 3
-	86	87	Margate	31	56	25	31	44.64	14	last 16 1979
+	90	88	Hednesford Town	31	55	24	31	43.64	14	last 16 1998
+	91	89	Hereford United	6	17	11	6	64.71	13	SF 1971
-	87	90	Ashton United	23	48	25	23	52.08	13	last 8 1997
-	88	91	Banbury United	22	42	20	22	47.62	13	last 16 x 2
-	89	92	Fisher Athletic	17	30	13	17	43.33	13	last 16 x 3
-	92	93	Atherstone Town	10	26	16	10	61.54	12	last 16 x 2
-	93	94	Windsor & Eton	11	24	13	11	54.17	12	last 16 1989
-	94	95	South Bank	19	40	21	19	52.50	12	last 8 1986
+	103	96	Gravesend & Northfleet	31	65	34	31	52.31	12	last 16 1989
-	95	97	Boreham Wood	26	53	27	26	50.94	12	last 16 x 3
-	97	98	Corby Town	30	60	30	30	50.00	12	last 16 1987
-	98	99	Minehead	19	38	19	19	50.00	12	last 32 x 3
-	99	100	Gretna	16	32	16	16	50.00	12	last 32 x 4
-	100	101	Ilkeston Town	22	40	18	22	45.00	12	last 16 x 2
-	99	102	Kings Lynn	26	47	21	26	44.68	12	last 32 1979
-	101	103	Colchester United	2	10	9	1	90.00	11	W 1992
+	111	104	Forest Green Rovers	15	36	21	15	58.33	11	F 1999
-	104	105	Worthing	16	32	16	16	50.00	11	last 16 1986
-	105	106	Ashford Town	31	57	26	31	45.61	11	SF 1973
-	106	107	Burscough	19	28	9	19	32.14	11	last 32 x 3
+	112	108	Staines Town	26	58	32	26	55.17	10	last 32 x 2
-	108	109	Halifax Town	5	10	5	5	50.00	10	last 16 1994
-	107	110	Chesham United	26	51	25	26	49.02	10	last 16 1993

F.A. CARLSBERG VASE

1999-2000 REVIEW

Terry Martin, captain of the eventual winners Deal Town receives a Carlsberg Man of the Match award from John Christopher, Chairman of the FA Challenge Vase Committee.   *Photo: Peter Barnes*

FIRST QUALIFYING ROUND

Saturday 11th September 1999

1	Chadderton	0 v 4	Fleetwood Freeport	95
2	Squires Gate	2 v 1	Sheffield	114
3	Bridlington Town	2 v 1	Newcastle Blue Star	145
4	Atherton Collieries	3 v 1	Shildon	
5	Nelson	0 v 6	Skelmersdale Utd	100
6	Woodley Sports	0 v 3	Billingham Synthonia	103
7	Evenwood Town	2 v 1	Poulton Victoria	29
8	Eccleshill United	10 v 1	Blackpool Mechanics	
9	Hallam	1 v 3	Thackley	169
10	Easington Coll.	0 v 3	Brandon United	36
11	Louth United	3 v 2	Salford City	56
12	Worsborough Bridge	1 v 2	Shotton Comrades	99
13	Denaby United	1 v 0	Baccup Borough	77
14	Rossington Main	1 v 3	Liversedge	64
15	Knypersley Victoria	3 v 0	Boston	62
16	Bridgnorth Town	2 v 1	Alvechurch	90
17	Stafford Town	0 v 0*	Birstall United	
r	Birstall United	1 v 0	Stafford Town	
18	Wednesfield	1 v 2	Stratford Town	40
19	Halesowen Harriers	0 v 7	Quorn	98
20	Holbeach United	1 v 0	Bourne Town	
21	Barwell	1 v 3	Holwell Sports	103
22	Blackstone	5 v 4*	Stewarts & Lloyds	60
23	Shifnal Town	3 v 1	Kings Heath	102
24	Highfield Rangers	2 v 3	Cradley Town	40
25	Long Eaton Utd	6 v 2	Southam United	74
26	Kingsbury Town	0 v 1	Letchworth	84
27	Chalfont St. Peter	3 v 1	Brache Sparta	35
28	Harpenden Town	0 v 2	Cornard United	44
29	Saffron Walden T.	1 v 3	Downham Town	94
30	Cockfosters	1 v 0	Dereham Town	74
31	March Town Utd	2 v 0	Norwich United	65
32	Lowestoft Town	5 v 0	Haverhill Rovers	168
33	Marlow	6 v 0	Brightlingsea Utd.	
34	Cheshunt	3 v 0	Brimsdown Rvrs	52
35	Mildenhall Town	3 v 1	Brentwood	122
36	Harwich & Parkeston	2 v 4	Wallingford	119
37	Hullbridge Sports	3 v 0	Witham Town	138
38	St. Margaretsbury	4 v 2	Royston Town	44
39	Buckingham Town	0 v 2	Gorleston	

40	Leverstock Green	2 v 1	Hadleigh United	62
41	Portsmouth RN	2 v 4	Faversham Town	70
42	Moneyfields	7 v 2	Godalming/Guildford	42
43	Beckenham Town	0 v 1*	Chatham Town	
44	Gosport Boro	0 v 4	Totton	84
45	Arundel	1 v 2	Eastbourne Town	36
46	Langney Sports	1 v 2	Redhill	224
47	Hillingdon Borough	4 v 1	Raynes Park Vale	
48	Fareham Town	7 v 0	Peacehaven & Tel.	118
49	VCD Athletic	3 v 2	Lewes	85
50	Whitehawk	1 v 0	Cove	45
51	Sandhurst Town	0 v 1	Abingdon United	76
52	BAT Sports	2 v 0*	Eastbourne United	81
53	Wick	2 v 0	Ashford T. (Middx)	100
54	Wimborne Town	7 v 0	Warminster Town	151
55	Minehead	1 v 2	Tuffley Rovers	60
56	Almondsbury Tn	v	Newquay	
	(Walkover for Almondsbury Town – Newquay withdrawn)			
57	Bodmin Town	2 v 1	Keynsham Town	57
58	Chard Town	2 v 1	Street	79
59	Bideford	3 v 2	Downton	120
60	Cirencester Acad.	0 v 1	Devizes Town	61
61	Elmore	1 v 0	Shortwood United	96
62	Ilfracombe Town	2 v 1	Melksham	88

*(*After extra time)*

FIRST QUALIFYING ROUND STATISTICS

Home Victories 36

Away Victories 26

Replays 1

W/O 1

Best Attendance 224
Langney Sports v Redhill

Average Attendance 85

Best Home Victory
Eccleshill United 10 v 1 Blackpool Mechanics

Best Away Victory
Halesowen Harriers 0 v 7 Quorn

Top: Stuart Ogilvie (Mildenhall Town) puts the Bedford United defence under pressure.
Photo: Peter Barnes

Centre: Northampton Spencer's Wayne Richardson supported by Russell Dunkley pressurise the Malvern defence in the FA Vase Second Qualifying Round at The Mill.
Photo: Peter Barnes

Bottom: Dan Barber (Holwell) makes a fine save from Neil Lyne (Barwell).
Photo: Keith Clayton

SECOND QUALIFYING ROUND

Saturday 25th September 1999

1	Crook Town	5 v 0	Bootle	142
2	Selby Town	4 v 1	St Helens Town	86
3	Shotton Comrades	0 v 2	Skelmersdale Utd	70
4	Peterlee Newtown	1 v 1*	Darwen	
	Darwen	2 v 4	Peterlee Newton	
5	Thackley	3 v 0	Hebburn	121
6	Abbey Hey	1 v 0	Pontefract Collieries	90
7	Harrogate Railway	1 v 6	Marske United	81
8	Liversedge	0 v 1	Armthorpe Welfare	115
9	Thornaby-on-Tees	3 v 0	Holker Old Boys	
10	Evenwood Town	1 v 4	Parkgate	21
11	Rossendale United	2 v 3*	Curzon Ashton	182
12	Eccleshill United	4 v 2	Prudhoe Town	54
13	Washington I.H.	0 v 7	Ramsbottom Utd	42
14	Prescot Cables	2 v 1	West Auckland T.	120
15	Penrith	3 v 4	Consett	97
16	Pickering Town	3 v 1	Fleetwood Freeport	64
17	Louth United	1 v 1*	Hall Road Rangers	37
r	Hall Road Rangers	6 v 3	Louth United	
18	Kennek Ryhope CA	3 v 1	East Manchester	45
19	Glasshoughton Wel.	2 v 1	Ashington	55
20	Brandon United	5 v 1	Denaby United	39
21	Horden CW	1 v 6	Billingham Synthonia	50
22	Morpeth Town	3 v 2	Jarrow Rfg Boldon CA	92
23	Oldham Town	0 v 3	Castleton Gabriels	25
24	Guisborough Town	2 v 0*	Tadcaster Albion	100
25	Yorkshire Amateur	1 v 1*	Squires Gate	62
r	Squires Gate	2 v 1	Yorkshire Amateur	119
26	Durham City	7 v 1	Hatfield Main	88
27	Cheadle Town	6 v 0	Esh Winning	62
28	Northallerton Tn	0 v 4	West Allotment Ctc	80
29	Bridlington Town	3 v 1	Brodsworth	147
30	Whickham	2 v 1	South Shields	60
31	Atherton LR	1 v 3	Atherton Collieries	83
32	Willington	3 v 0	Maine Road	52
33	Goole	4 v 0	Garforth Town	273
34	Holwell Sports	0 v 1	Nettleham	90
35	Rainworth MW	2 v 3	Barrow Town	
36	Sandiacre Town	0 v 1	Nantwich Town	32
37	Sandwell Borough	2 v 1*	Wolverhampton Cas.	
38	Bridgnorth Town	0 v 2	West Mids Police	96
39	Arnold Town	3 v 1	Kington Town	186
40	Ludlow Town	0 v 6	Cogenhoe United	79
41	Heanor Town	1 v 0	Dunkirk	96
42	Bugbrooke St M.	1 v 0	Cradley Town	74
43	St Andrews	3 v 4*	Quorn	58
44	Sth Normanton Ath	1 v 2*	Gornal Athletic	88
45	Pelsall Villa	2 v 0	Cheslyn Hay	78
46	Star	1 v 2	Holbeach United	58
47	Shirebrook Town	0 v 2	Knypersley Victoria	103
48	Tividale	4 v 5*	Anstey Nomads	
49	Gedling Town	6 v 4*	Downes Sports	45
50	Long Eaton Utd	3 v 0	Kimberley Town	100
51	Long Buckby	1 v 6	Chasetown	69
52	Stourport Swifts	1 v 0	Glapwell	93
53	Shifnal Town	2 v 0	Rushall Olympic	95
54	Northampton Spncr	2 v 3	Malvern Town	62
55	Blackstone	0 v 2	Glossop North End	50
56	Willenhall Town	2 v 0	Stapenhill	139
57	Ford Spts Daventry	1 v 3	Bolehall Swifts	
58	Ibstock Welfare	1 v 1*	Handrahan TImbers	79
r	Handrahan Timbers	0 v 2	Ibstock Welfare	45
59	Stratford Town	5 v 1	Birstall United	65
60	Friar Lane OB	5 v 1	Walsall Wood	82
61	Mickleover Sports	4 v 3	Leek CSOB	
62	Boldmere St M.	2 v 0	Highgate United	78
63	Westfields	0 v 3	Kirby Muxloe	32
64	Wellingborough T	0 v 4	Meir KA	35
65	Borrowash Victoria	3 v 1	Lye Town	62
66	Blidworth MW	v	Studley BKL	
	(Walkover for Studley BKL – Blidworth MW withdrawn)			
67	Newcastle Town	4 v 0	Dudley Town	101
68	Clacton Town	2 v 1	Basildon United	136
69	Thetford Town	1 v 2	Hanwell Town	66
70	Brook House	v	Barkingside	
	(Walkover for Brook House – Barkingside removed)			
71	Bury Town	1 v 0	Wivenhoe Town	
72	Wootton Blue Cross	2 v 0	Gorleston	
73	Leighton Town	5 v 1	Swaffham Town	
74	Tring Town	2 v 1	March Town Utd	
75	Stowmarket Town	2 v 0	Tiptree United	63
76	Ely City	3 v 0	Hullbridge Sports	95
77	Somerset Am. V&E	3 v 4	Letchworth	
78	Arlesey Town	2 v 4	Banbury United	154
79	Barking	3 v 3*	Chalfont St Peter	87
r	Chalfont St Peter	v	Barking	
80	Beaconsfield SYCOB	3 v 0	Southall	66
81	Hoddesdon Town	1 v 4	WIngate & Finchley	91
82	Tilbury	3 v 1	St Neots Town	74
83	Kempston Rovers	5 v 2	Southend Manor	27
84	Felixstowe Port & T	0 v 3	Warboys Town	83
85	Milton Keynes City	6 v 2	Downham Town	68

86	Newmarket Town	1 v 2	Harefield United	98
87	Laverstock Green	1 v 4	Flackwell Heath	
88	Lowestoft Town	0 v 1	Ware	172
89	Welwyn Garden C	2 v 3	Somersham Town	51
90	Langford	1 v 1*	Wallingford	
r	Wallingford	3 v 0	Langford	140
91	Sawbridgeworth T	1 v 2	Marlow	60
92	Cockfosters	2 v 3	Watton United	52
93	Needham Market	1 v 3	Whitton United	172
94	Stanway Rovers	4 v 3	Haringey Borough	
95	Halstead Town	3 v 1	Edgware Town	133
96	St Margaretsbury	2 v 4	Holmer Green	38
97	Ipswich Wanderers	0 v 2	London Colney	70
98	Chatteris Town	0 v 4	Hertford Town	47
99	Hornchurch	1 v 2	Burnham Ramblers	72

(at Burnham Ramblers FC)

100	Soham Tn Rgrs	4 v 1	East Thurrock U	143
101	Concord Rangers	1 v 5	Ilford	44
102	Bedford United	2 v 3*	Mildenhall Town	
103	Clapton	1 v 5	Cheshunt	103
104	Yaxley	3 v 1*	Eynesbury Rovers	55
105	Aveley	7 v 0	Potton United	58
106	Maldon Town	5 v 1	Bicester Town	33
107	Stotfold	3 v 1	Cornard United	51
108	Waltham Abbey	4 v 1	Ruislip Manor	
109	Biggleswade T	4 v 2	Stansted	48
110	Corinthian Casuals	3 v 0	Littlehampton Tn	54
111	Kintbury Rangers	v	Oakwood	

(Walkover for Oakwood – Kintbury Rangers removed)

112	Whitehawk	1 v 1*	Didcot Town	
r	Didcot Town	3 v 0	Whitehawk	132
113	Thamesmead T	2 v 0	Farnham Town	51
114	Erith Town	3 v 1	Three Bridges	62
115	BAT Sports	3 v 2*	Hassocks	55
116	Sidley United	0 v 2	Eastleigh	136
117	Abingdon United	4 v 1	Chessington & H. U	101
118	Hailsham Town	1 v 0	Viking Greenford	105
119	Ringmer	1 v 3*	Hythe United	66
120	Walton Casuals	1 v 0	Selsey	51
121	Ash United	5 v 1	Shoreham	103
122	Fareham Town	1 v 0	East Cowes Victoria	111
123	Southwick	2 v 1	Lancing	132
124	Croydon Athletic	4 v 0	Romsey Town	77
125	Reading Town	5 v 0	Lordswood	44
126	Whitstable Town	0 v 2	Chatham Town	138
127	Faversham Town	3 v 2	Blackfield & Langley	33
128	Merstham	1 v 4	Egham Town	45
129	North Leigh	3 v 4	Cobham	92
130	Totton	3 v 1	Horsham	100

131	Metropolitan Police	3 v 3*	Sheppey United	
r	Sheppey United	0 v 2	Metropolitan Police	52
132	Dorking	3 v 1	Canterbury City	73
133	Tunbridge Wells	1 v 2	Epsom & Ewell	109
134	Wick	1 v 1*	VCD Athletic	144
r	VCD Athletic	v	Wick	
135	Eastbourne Town	2 v 0*	Slade Green	96
136	Cray Wanderers	1 v 2	Hillingdon Borough	
137	Windsor & Eton	3 v 0	Redhill	116
138	Cowes Sports	8 v 1	Portfield	96
139	Brockenhurst	2 v 4	East Preston	72
140	Moneyfields	0 v 1	Bracknell Town	72
141	Bedfont	4 v 0	Wantage Town	42
142	Chichester City	2 v 0	Whitchurch United	90
143	Willand Rovers	1 v 0	Tuffley Rovers	100
144	Almondsbury T	1 v 3	Dawlish Town	34
145	Bideford	6 v 2*	Wellington Town	60
146	Ilfracombe Town	3 v 2	Fairford Town	83
147	Christchurch	3 v 1	Backwell United	67
148	Mangotsfield Utd	2 v 1	Barnstaple Town	176
149	Bishop Sutton	2 v 0	Torrington	63
150	Falmouth Town	2 v 0	Bodmin Town	162
151	Bridgwater Town	4 v 1	Welton Rovers	146
152	Bournemouth	2 v 0	Hallen	27
153	Odd Down	4 v 0	Ross Town	52
154	Chard Town	0 v 3	Devizes Town	87
155	Westbury United	1 v 1*	St Blazey	125

(Walkover for St Blazey – Westbury Utd withdrawn)

156	Glastonbury	v	Elmore	
157	Harrow Hill	1 v 3	Wimborne Town	92
158	Brislington	2 v 1	Pershore Town	60
159	Paulton Rovers	2 v 0	Calne Town	120
160	Frome Town	1 v 0	Bridport	75

2nd QUALIFYING ROUND STATISTICS

Home Victories 88

Away Victories 58

Replays 9

W/O 4

Best Attendance 273
Goole 4 v 0 Garforth Town

Average Attendance 84

Best Home Victory
Aveley 7 v 0 Potton United
Cowes Sports 8 v 1 Portfield

Best Away Victory
Washington I.H. 0 v 7 Ramsbottom United

FIRST ROUND
Saturday 23rd October 1999

1   Hall Road Rangers   3 v 2   Armthorpe Welfare   40
Richards 59, Palmer 93, 102   *Smith 72, 103*

2   Curzon Ashton   3 v 3*   Warrington Town   120
McLennon 77, Garrick 78, 96

r   Warrington Town   3 v 1   Curzon Ashton   97
McDonald 36, Holden 67   *Garrick 9*
Bushell 86

3   Bridlington Town   0 v 1   Eccleshill United   147
   Sutcliffe 104 (p)

4   Abbey Hey   3 v 0   Parkgate   80
Hunt 7, Pickering 23
Hipkin 37

5   Morpeth Town   4 v 1   Durham City   84
   MacDonald 74

6   Thornaby-On-Tees   2 v 3*   North Ferriby Utd   105
   Flounders 9, Morris 71
   Nikaladis 93

7   *West Allotment Ctc*   1 v 2   *Peterlee Newtown*   101
Graham 70   *Outhwake 30, 70*

8   Whickham   0 v 1   Pickering Town   82
   1 og

9   Consett   1 v 0   Kennek Ryhope CA   65
McLeod 58

10   Billingham Synthonia   0 v 3   Guisborough Tn   208
   Banks 50, Mowbray 76, Ward 78

11   Crook Town   3 v 1   Cheadle Town   147
Burns 5, Torr 7, 73   *Bailey 71*

12   Goole AFC   1 v 0   Castleton Gabriele   206
Gibson 4

13   Brandon United   0 v 1   Prescot Cables   90
   Lynch 104

14   Skelmersdale Utd   2 v 0   Glasshoughton Welf.   140
Cowley 25, Rudd 42

15   Atherton Collieries   4 v 1   Thackley
Jones 13, 14, Maloney 17   *Muller 1*
Lomas 51

16   Marske United   2 v 0   Seaham Red Star   144

17   Chester-le-Street T   1 v 3   Billingham Town   103
Ryan 24   *Rowntree 71, 75, Southall 90*

18   Squires Gate   3 v 3*   Ramsbottom Utd   118
Burgess 43, Longnorth 71   *Brierley 82, O'Shaughnessey 85*
Rushton 110   *Yorke-Robinson 117*

r   Ramsbottom Utd   5 v 3*   Squires Gate
Orrell 5, Yorke -Robinson 15   *Shaw, Skeock (p), McKenna*
Brierley 98, 113, Goodall 120

19   Willington   1 v 3   Selby Town   100
Spayne 80   *Cygan 5, Young 54, Hart 88*

20   Nantwich Town   2 v 2*   Meir KA   95
Gayle 88, Cannon 110   *Moran 4, Wiltshire 116*

r   Meir KA   2 v 4   Nantwich Town   120
Wood 15, Moran 44   *Smith 3, Gayle 31*
   Williamson 74, Dawson 85

21   Chasetown   2 v 1   Sandwell Borough   84
Bradbury 36, Oldaker 87   *Prince 25*

22   West Mids Police   3 v 2*   Cogenhoe United   71
Speed 44, Reece 72   *Goodacre 2, Gilmour 54*
Burton 109

23   Long Eaton Utd   0 v 5   Newcastle Town   97
   Haddrell 3 (35, 49, 65)
   Myatt 31, Pesteridge 34

24   Brigg Town   5 v 2   Barrow Town   144
Evans 9, Ward 11, 46   *Pitman 75, Wardman 88*
Buckley 26, Roach 36

25   Friar Lane OB   0 v 0*   Anstey Nomads   128

r   Anstey Nomads   2 v 0   Friar Lane OB
Conelly 27, Chambers 42

26   Borrowash Victoria   4 v 1   Boldmere St Michaels   62
Gary Briscoe 3 (34, 45, 90)   *Hanson 83*
Carruthers 75

27   Mickleover Sports   8 v 1   Bugbrooke St Michaels   148
Parkins 2, 59, Yeomans 7   *Shelswell 20*
Mighty 28, Mable 43
Hudson 64, 82

28   Shifnal Town   4 v 2   Studley BKL   73
Lane 19, Treharne 79   *Powell 12, 25*
Kiernan 87, Phillips 89

29   Quorn   1 v 1*   Kirby Muxloe   105
Culpin 22   *Tansley 41*

r   Kirby Muxloe   2 v 5   Quorn
Tansley 55, Mason 65   *Culpin 10, 20*
   Darren Hannighan 3 (15, 49, 80)

30   Arnold Town   6 v 1   Pelsall Villa   208
Baxter 43, 47, Williams 60   *Lovett 30*
Whitman 51, 75, Mitchell 67

31   Knypersley Victoria   2 v 1   Gornal Athletic   71
Palin 3, Redgate 65   *Burgess*

32   Glossop North End   4 v 2   Bolehall Swifts   130
Ringland 38, Sweet 48   *Derry 5, Phillips 44*
Robinson 87, Levendis 90

33   Stourport Swifts   2 v 0   Staveley MW   84
Hacketts 48, Shaw 88

34   Willenhall Town   1 v 2   Gedling Town   110
Chester 20   *Marshall 84, Goodwin 90*

35   Stratford Town   4 v 1   Holbeach United   73
Hamill9, Martin 33   *Rowley 25*
Darroch 41, Brant 87

36   Buxton   1 v 2*   Desborough Town   185
Hodginson 67   *Maddox 17, 108*

37   Malvern Town   4 v 2   Ibstock Welfare   92
Taffy 30, 54, Wade 63   *Emery 30, 48*
Walker 78

38   Nettleham   0 v 1   Heanor Town   47
   Froggatt 51

39   Oldbury United   3 v 2   Kings Norton Town   49
Clark 59, McCarthy 33   *Lamorte 75, Pippard 80*
Nightingale 115

40   Harefield United   0 v 4   Great Wakering Rvrs   28
   Arlitt 13, Flack 44, 46
   Hampshire 55

Top Left: FA Vase First Round action from Curzon Ashton versus Warrington Town, with home side player Danny Warner on the ball during the teams' 3-3 draw. Photo: Colin Stevens

Top right: Nick Barden, Eastbourne Town (left) attempts to control the ball as Gary Clifford, Reading Town, moves in. Photo: Roger Turner

Bottom: Friar Lane Old Boys v Anstey Nomads. No shortage of effort from both sides in a keenly contested Vase First Round tie. Photo: Peter Barnes

41　　　　Hertford Town　2 v 0　Warboys Town
Glynn 17, Raisborough 90

42　Beaconsfield SYCOB　0 v 2　Potters Bar Town　47
　　　　　　　　　　　　Jordan 22, Talbot 87

43　　　Whitton United　0 v 3　Hemel Hempstead T　134
　　　　　　　　　　　　Somers 24, Kelly 56
　　　　　　　　　　　　Ravenscroft 84

44　　　　　　　Ware　2 v 3　Stotfold　103
Gildersleve 46, Beattie 67　*Chellew 40, Byrne 55, Drury 88*

45　　　　Bury Town　4 v 1　Flackwell Heath　142
Deers 32, Gaston 59, og 81　*Bartlett 39*
Debenham 90

46　　Banbury United　2 v 1*　Ely City　248
Jenkins 78, Gooderick 106　*Egan 60*

47　　Maldon Town　1 v 2　Burnham Ramblers　107
　　　Coe 24　*Hewey 4, Huttley 38*

48　　　　　Marlow　4 v 0　Waltham Abbey　130
Murray 16, McDonnell 36
Cooper 53, Brannan 90

49　　Fakenham Town　6 v 1　Kempston Rovers　135
Coe 45, 90, Gallagher 60
Haynes 80, McLaughlin 81, 85

50　　　　Cheshunt　2 v 1　Leighton Town　45
Obeng 16, Panayiotou 48　*Dyer 90*

51　Somersham Town　1 v 2　Great Yarmouth T　104
　　　　　　　　　　　　Vincent 65, Roach 73

52　　Hanwell Town　1 v 2　Sohem Town Rngrs　80
　　　Holmes 82　*Nedinovic 65, 75*

53　　Letchworth　2 v 1　Yaxley　53
　Webb 73, Coley 86　*MacCallum 41*

54　　Tring Town　0 v 0　Clacton Town　60

r　　Clacton Town　1 v 1*　Tring Town
　　Hepburn 50　*McKane 65*
　Tring Town won 4-1 after penalties

55　Mildenhall Town　0 v 2　Diss Town　248
　　　　　　　　　　　　Hayes 6, Hardy 70

56　　　　Histon　3 v 2　Stowmarket Town　82
Martin 1, 65, Kennedy 75　*Platt 10, og 25*

57　Milton Keynes City　2 v 0　Biggleswade Town
Hirst 61p, Brown

58　　　　Aveley　0 v 2*　Ilford　95
　　　　　　　　　Emmanuel 101, McGillicuddy 113

59　Halstead Town　1 v 3　Tilbury
　Wareham 25　*Mully 18, 53, Francois 40*

60　Wootton Blue Cross　0 v 1　London Colney　63
　　　　　　　　　　　　Sweetman 8

61　Wallingford AFC　0 v 1　Barking　160
　　　　　　　　　　　Hibberd 7

62　Holmer Green　1 v 1*　Watton United　34
　Roscoe 14　*White 50*

r　Watton United　3 v 1　Holmer Green
Coe 55, Spallis 85, Reeve 88　*Moffatt 41*

63　　Brook House　3 v 1*　Wingate & Finchley　80
D Warner 89p, Hibbert 96　*Myers 75*
K Warner 95

64　Stanway Rovers　3 v 1　Abingdon Town　72
Clarke 59, Caldon 11, 56　*Smith 55*

65　　Hythe United　1 v 0　Walton Casuals　106
　　Brazier 81

66　Hillingdon Borough　0 v 4　East Preston　43
　　　　　　　　　　　Brackley 19, 57
　　　　　　　　　　　Pearce 49, Withers 80

67　　　　Bedfont　2 v 0　Southwick　45
Jenkins 47, McAvoy 89

68　Eastbourne Town　5 v 2　Reading Town　180
Barden 12, Fuller 31　*Bolger 30, Wilkinson 57*
Brockwell 55, 57, Wallis 77

69　　　Chipstead　5 v 2　Greenwich Borough　27
Mike Nolan 3 (35, 40, 69)　*Robert 28, Eagle 44*
Oakins 51, Berry 76

70　　　Erith Town　5 v 0　Oakwood　67
　Godley 21, 63
Sillence 64, 79, Coburn 90

71　　Didcot Town　1 v 0　Hailsham Town　123
　　Marriets 86

72　Wokingham Town　2 v 5　Metropolitan Police
　　Odey 14, 63　*Derby 7, Pring 21, 79*
　　　　　　　　　　　Service 29, Cormack 46

73　　　Ash United　2 v 5　Epsom & Ewell　75
　Everland 5, og　**Barry Stevens 3 (11, 39, 51)**
　　　　　　　　　　Grant 26, 30

74　Corinthian Casuals　3 v 0　Dorking　100
Owen 6, Griffiths 68
　Liddle 87

75　Saltdeen United　2 v 1　Chichester City　93
Dobbyn 36, Essam 72　*Sibley 45*

76　Horsham YMCA　5 v 3*　Thatcham Town　69
Butcher 2, Russell 57, 108　*Green 16, McCall 75og*
Grim 63, 105　*Crisp 90*
　(at Broadbridge Heath FC)

77　Bracknell Town　1 v 4*　Cowes Sports
　Havermans 36　*og 81, Barsdell 100,*
　　　　　　　　　Stevens 116, O'Rourke 117

78　　Totton AFC　2 v 1　Egham Town　83
　1 og, Gray 59　*Moody 55*

79　Chatham Town　5 v 2　Faversham Town　67
Utsaja 37, Jones 68, 90　*O'Sullivan 1, West 53*
Ward 65, Bourne 75

80　Windsor & Eton　5 v 2　Croydon Athletic　120
Duffy 12, Greene 22　*Dutfield 70, Evans 85*
Theodosiou 43, Franks 70
Glynn 90

81　Fareham Town　0 v 0†　Abingdon United
　　† *Abandoned at half time*

　Fareham Town　2 v 3　Abingdon United　125
　Clark 60, Fitt 62　*Morton 9, Simms 15, Odhiam 89*

82　Thamesmead Tn　3 v 0　VCD Athletic　78
Kearley 15, Hesolden 60, 88

83　　　Eastleigh　3 v 4　Deal Town　129
McAlister 15, Colvin 36　*Ribbens 8, Marshall 60*
　Kenna 40　*Graham 64, Best 87*

84	Cobham	2 v 4	B.A.T. Sports	59	

84   Cobham   2 v 4   B.A.T. Sports   59
Goldie 5, 60   *Brown 33, 70, Hodder 75,*
                 Chance 79

85   Christchurch   1 v 0   Bridgwater Town   111
           King 89

86   Ilfracombe Town   0 v 2   Glastonbury   92
                  Sargent 5, Rowlend 18

87   St Blazey   2 v 2*   Swindon S.marine   134
Clarke 52, Hooper 86   *Wilkinson 84, Saye 89*

r   Swindon S.marine   3 v 2*   St Blazey   101
Silvanus 70, Matthews 81   *Hooper 10, Smith 90*

88   Brislington   3 v 1   Bishop Sutton   71
Coleman 47, Dempsey 70   *Day 38*
       Weeks 84

89   Highworth Town   2 v 3   Carterton Town   103
     Day 48, Walker 83   *Lewis 15, Foggarty 17, 23*

90   Odd Down   3 v 4   Bideford   27
        Hart 20   *Howarth 60, Hadley 63*

91   Devizes Town   0 v 2*   Mangotsfield Utd   167
                  Rosslee 85, 87

92   Frome Town   1 v 6   Paulton Rovers   122
                  Winstone 5, Buxton 13, 38
                  Cheesman 22, James 66
                  Clark 72

93   Newbury AFC   2 v 1   Hungerford Town   204
   Veller 16, Clarkson 37   *Wollen 14*

94   Dawlish Town   1 v 0   Bournemouth   65
        Stocker 60

95   Wimborne Town   1 v 3   Chippenham Tn   212
       Barham 67   *Campbell 12, Collier 42*
                  Charity 63

96   Willand Rovers   0 v 3   Falmouth Town   170
                  Hodge 37, Morris 75

(after extra time)*

FIRST ROUND STATISTICS

Home Victories 54

Away Victories 42

Replays 8

Best Attendance 248
Banbury United v Ely City
Mildenhall Town v Diss Town

Average Attendance 105

Best Home Victory
Mickleover Sports 8 v 1 Bugrooke St Michaels

Best Away Victory
Long Eaton United 0 v 5 Newcastle Town
Frome Town 1 v 6 Paulton Rovers

Hat Tricks
3 Haddrell (Newcastle Town)
3 Darren Hannighan (Quorn)
3 Barry Stevens (Epsom & Ewell)
3 Mike Nolan (Chipstead)

Aron Rutter (Soham Town Rangers) leaves Hanwell's Warren Williams trailing during their Vase First Round encounter. Photo: Francis Short

SECOND ROUND
Saturday 13th November 2000

1	Morpeth Town 1 v 2* Clitheroe	77	
	Heron 58	*Norman 3, Greenwood 115*	

2 Great Harwod Town 0 v 4 Crook Town 126
Nicholson 26, Clover 27
Key 62, Loughrey 72

3 Prescot Cables 2 v 3 Consett 93
O'Callaghan 5, Childhay 35   *Cowley 59, McFinley 66*
Halliday 90

4 Tow Law Town 1 v 1* Ramsbottom Utd 168
Bolton 80   *Brierley 78*

r Ramsbottom Utd 1 v 2* Tow Law Town 214
Brierley 69   *McGarrigle 28, Nash 105*

5 Ossett Albion 0 v 0* Marske United 133

r Marske United 1 v 2 Ossett Albion 244
Thompson 47   *Cornelly 12, 89*

6 Dunston Fed. B. 1 v 2 Warrington Town 82
Scaife 26   *Taney 38, Tyrell 81*

7 North Ferriby Utd 3 v 0 Pickering Town 220

8 Mossley 2 v 1 Billingham Town 192
Willcock 12, Porter 41   *Wintersgill 1*

9 Hall Road Rangers 1 v 0 Peterlee Newtown 45
1 og

10 Vauxhall 2 v 0 Atherton Collieries 43
Blundell 10, 22

11 Guisborough Town 3 v 4 Eccleshill United 104
Fuller 8, Ward 60, 95   *Taylor 43, Dolan 85*
Newsome 103, Sutcliffe 118p

12 Selby Town 1 v 1* Bedlington Terriers 194
Oygan 51   *Boon 43*

r Bedlington Terriers 3 v 3* Selby Town 312
(3-0 to Bedlington Terriers after penalties)
Gibb 3 (18, 72, 78), Dean   *Oygan 55, Cygan 58, Wilson 78*

13 Abbey Hey 1 v 2 Skelmersdale Utd 85
Pickering 35   *Cowley 10, Sloan 86*

14 Shifnal Town 2 v 3 Stourport Swifts 76
Treharne 41, Powell 79p   *Hackett 16, Meenan 44*
Conway 89

15 Gedling Town 0 v 3 Anstey Nomads 44
Chambers 30, Morning 48
Capell 73

16 West Mids Police 3 v 1 Oldbury United 77
Burton 5, 31, Goss 69   *Wilkinson 84*

17 Alfreton Town 4 v 0 Knypersley Victoria 156
Cheetham 12
Hopkinson 15, 54p, Kerry 51

18 Arnold Town 1 v 3* Brigg Town 141
Whitman 10   *Grocock 16, Ward 100, 110*

19 Oadby Town 0 v 2 Chasetown 210
OlDarker 62, Bradbury 89

20 Nantwich Town 4 v 0 Kidsgrove Athletic 101
Gayle 8, 68, Scarlett 74
Grant 84

21 Newcastle Town 2 v 1 Desborough Town 101
Myatt 50, Twigg 78   *Maddox 35*

22 Malvern Town 2 v 2* Glossop North End
Brain 38, Tarry 119   *Heaton 73, Power 110*

r Glossop North End 3 v 0 Malvern Town 126
Heaton 3, Davies 23
Levendis 48

23 Borrowash Victoria 2 v 1 Stratford Town 73
Moran 34, McGovern 60   *Darroch 40p*

24 Heanor Town 2 v 0 Goole 148
Johnson 9, 50

25 Mickleover Sports 1 v 0 Quorn 110
Parkins 50

26 London Colney 4 v 0 Potters Bar Town 60
Ross 8, Anderson 13
Dean 31, 41

27 Watton United 2 v 1 Ilford 215
(at Dereham Town FC)
Reeve 53, S Pauls 85   *Emmanuel 64*

28 Sudbury 3 v 4* Northwood 286
Devereux 40, 90, Norfolk 110

29 Burnham Ramblers 0 v 0* Letchworth 111

r Letchworth 2 v 0 Burnham Ramblers 99
Howell 33, Dixon 68

30 Great Wakering R 2 v 0 Clacton Town 105
Flack 15, Hampshire 52

31 Banbury United 0 v 1 Histon 230
Kennedy 14

32 Brook House 4 v 4* Berkhamsted Town 50
Yeardley 5, 82   *Foley 11, Nightingale 3, 57*
Bird 72, Day 118   *Osborne 111*

r Berkhamsted Town 1 v 0 Brook House 94
Richardson 110

33 Marlow 4 v 1* Hertford Town 138
Bradley 37, Gibson 93   *Knapman 48*
McDinnell 105, Young 118

34 Stanway Rovers 3 v 3* Barking 90
Ball 60, Clarke 116, Bate 119   *Rogan 67, 111, Sharland 94*

r Barking 2 v 1 Stanway Rovers 107
O'Sullivan 46, Buffone 53   *Ball 20*

35 Wembley 3 v 1 Brackley Town 70
Mitchell 51, Woodruffe 53   *Milner 14*
Kellman 71

36 Ford United 1 v 4 Hemel Hempstead T 119
Somers 70, 89
Ravenscroft 74, Butler 80

37 Bury Town 2 v 2* Tilbury 214
Vince 36, Foreman 112   *Mully 46, Rees 96*

r Tilbury 3 v 2 Bury Town 40
Martin 57, 107, Deakin 101   *Debenham 15, Barber 97*

38 Fakenham Town 2 v 1 Soham Tn Rngrs 201
Gallagher 15, Moore 90   *Green 60*

Top: Stratford's Matthew Collinson gets his foot in first to thwart Borrowash Victoria's Gary Briscoe (stripes).
Photo: Bill Wheatcroft

Centre: Des Elliott (Desborough) dominates his area against Newcastle in the FA Vase Second Round.
Photo: Keith Clayton

Bottom: Ashley Carr of Burgess Hill Town has the ball taken away by Camberley Town's Ricky McNamara.
Photo: Neil Thaler

91

39	Bowers United	1 v 3	Wroxham	61	
	Hope 38		*Edridge 20, 1 og, Johnson 90*		
40	Great Yarmouth T	2 v 2*	Woodbridge Town	99	
	Wooldridge 47, Roach 60		*Keeley 35, Burgess 69*		
r	Woodbridge Town	2 v 0	Great Yarmouth T	157	
	Curtis 14, Smith 90				
41	Cheshunt	0 v 2	Stotfold	77	
			Griffith 30, 80		
42	Milton Keynes City	0 v 3	Diss Town	128	
			Key 34, Harry 71, Mayes 78		
43	Saltdean United	3 v 1	Windsor & Eton	143	
	Townsend 4, Allen 14, og 66		*Duffy 68*		
44	Deal Town	3 v 0	East Preston	150	
	og 9, Seager 45, Marshall 84				
45	Chipstead	1 v 2	Metropolitan Police	50	
			Cormack 34, 88		
46	Banstead Athletic	3 v 2*	Molesey	76	
			Allen 30, 44p		
47	Chatham Town	2 v 3*	BAT Sports	146	
	Utsaja 76, Tilley 103		*Elliott 32, Chalke 92, Pegler 119*		
48	Burgess Hill Town	3 v 1	Camberley Town	207	
	Williams 46, Davies 62		*Greene 43*		
	Moore 80				
49	Tooting & Mitcham U	2 v 0	Thamesmead Tn	132	
	Pace 16, Hazel 85				
50	Totton	4 v 0	Didcot Town	64	
	Gray 36, Ross 48				
	Reacord 72, Harrington 88				
51	Bedfont	2 v 1	Hythe United	60	
	Jones 11, Fossey 36				
52	Epsom & Ewell	1 v 1*	Cowes Sports	101	
	Latuske 63		*O'Rourke 74*		
r	Cowes Sports	1 v 0	Epsom & Ewell	108	
	Stevens 70				
53	Corinthian Casuals	3 v 1	Erith Town	89	
	Waghorn 18		*Griffin 89*		
	Freeborough 37, West 69				
54	Ramsgate	4 v 2	Herne Bay	199	
	Davey 20, 84, Court 42p		*Malton 25, Moore 40*		
	Bowey 65				
55	Horsham YMCA	4 v 3	Eastbourne Town	125	
	Tilley 2, Price 24		*Austin 64, Wallis 87*		
	Russell 31, Janson 47		*Donovan 90*		
56	Newbury	2 v 1*	Mangotsfield Utd	160	
	Alleyne 24, Whormskey 100		*Rudge 2*		

57	Chippenham Town	3 v 0	Swindon S.marine	256	
	Tweddle 75, 80, Cutler 70				
58	Abingdon United	0 v 1	Paulton Rovers	65	
			Buxton 56		
59	Bideford	1 v 0	Dawlish Town	62	
	Downing 80				
60	Bemerton Heath H.	0 v 2	Taunton Town	268	
			Parker 18, Cann 67		
61	Christchurch	0 v 3	Elmore	97	
			Rowland 1, Stansfield 46, 49		
62	Falmouth Town	7 v 2	Brislington	275	
	Andrew Morris 3 (20, 25, 60)		*Haines 29, Morrissey 43*		
	Luke Hodge 3 (4, 7, 48)				
	Street 68				
63	Carterton Town	0 v 4	Porthleven	58	
			Bannister 25, Legg 35, 37		
			Harrington 81		
64	Andover	1 v 2*	Lymington & New M.	106	
	Forsey 74		*Sims 48, Jones 100*		

(* after extra time)

SECOND ROUND STATISTICS

Home Victories 30

Away Victories 24

Replays 10

Best Attendance 312
Bedlington Terriers v Selby Town

Average Attendance 129

Best Home Victory
Falmouth Town 7 v 2 Brislington

Best Away Victory
Great Harwood Town 0 v 4 Crook Town
Carterton Town 0 v 4 Porthleven

Hat Tricks
Andrew Morris (Falmouth Town)
Luke Hodge (Falmouth Town)
Dean Gibb (Bedlington Terriers)

THIRD ROUND

1   Glossop North End 3 v 2 Brigg Town   87
Malone 21, Heaton 55   *Bartlett 70, Evans 82*
Hamilton 60

2   Skelmersdale Utd 3 v 2 Hall Road R.   143
Borland 1, Cowley 10, 70   *Barrass 54, Lewis 85*

3   Tow Law Town 0 v 0* Consett   266

r   Consett 1 v 0 Tow Law Town   271
McLeod 47

4   Mossley 5 v 1 Nantwich Town   149
Wolstenholme 26   *Borthwick 13*
Brennan 58, Dicken 65
Wilcock 73, Thomas 83

5   Chase Town 1 v 0 Mickleover Sports   150

6   Vauxhall 2 v 1 Warrington Town   83
Nesbitt 34, Riley 87   *Bushell 40*

7   Bedlington Terriers 3 v 1 North Ferriby Utd   410
Kirkby 34, og 45, Boon 77   *Nikolaidis 26*

8   Ossett Albion 5 v 1 Anstey Nomads   138
Craig Gomershall 3 (15, 35, 72)   *Connolly 46*
Bradley 89, Braime 90

9   Crook Town 3 v 1 West Mids Police   184
Harnett 3, 15, Rose 37   *Latchiford 28*

10   Eccleshill Utd 2 v 1 Heanor Town   68
Heddinstall 29, Taylor 63   *Johnson 80*

11   Newcastle Town 2 v 1 Clitheroe Town   139
Cunningham 23, 82   *Hart 35*

12   Alfreton Town 2 v 1 Borrowash Victoria   122
Anson 8, Phelan 51   *Moran 7*

13   Porthleven 1 v 0 Bedfont   316
Legg 80

14   Deal Town 2 v 1 Watton   230
Ribbens 49, Turner 89   *Taylor 54*

15   Cowes (IoW) 3 v 1 Banstead Athletic   143
Jamie O'Rourke 3 (54, 63, 86)   *Burton 16*

16   Histon 4 v 1 Wembley   159
Harrington 12, Saddington 13   *Kellman 76*
Kennedy 42, 44

17   Totton 2 v 0 Barring   149
Reacord 20, 90

18   Berkhamsted T 2 v 0 Stourport Swifts   109
Richardson 10, Swales 85

19   Hemel Hempstead T 0 v 1 Gt Wakering Rvrs   135
   Hampshire 71

20   Fakenham Town 2 v 3* Saltdean United   143
Delicay 6, Williams 72   *Cooper 44, Randell 75*
   Bagnall 112

21   Bideford 1 v 2* Woodbridge Town   135
Collings 38   *Wallis 10, Oxbrow 118*

22   Letchworth 3 v 1 Stotfold   289
Coley 18, 24, Keane 60   *Byrne 64*

23   Chippenham Tn 2 v 0 Northwood   258
Tweddle 35, Hubbs 43

24   Taunton Town 4 v 1 Tooting & Mitcham U   608
Antony Lynch 4 (48,50,63,77)   *Whelan 60*

25   Horsham YMCA 4 v 2 Diss Town   146
Russell 14, 52, McCall 16   *Hardy 80, Kev 90*
Tilley 42

26   Marlow 1 v 1* Metropolitan Police   179
Gibson 92   *Derby 102*

r   Metropolitan Police 1 v 0 Marlow   105
Prins 90

27   Lymington & New M 1 v 2 Ramsgate   237
Phillips 82   *Bowey 87, 90*

28   Burgess Hill Tn 3 v 0 Newbury Town   263
Moore 36, 89, Newman 44

29   Paulton Rovers 2 v 0 Corinthian Casuals   141
Winstone 39, Buxton 70

30   Tilbury 1 v 1* Falmouth Town   231
og 29   *Tomlinson 84*

r   Falmouth Town 0 v 0* Tilbury   343
   Tilbury won 2-0 after penalties

31   London Colney 7 v 0 Elmore   98
Simon Dean 4 (20, 47, 65, 70)
Sweetman 2
Anderson 55, Ross 80

32   Wroxham 0 v 0* BAT Sports   133

r   BAT Sports 1 v 1* Wroxham   127
   Wroxham won 4-2 after penalties
Peglar 100   *Carter 100*

(* after extra time)

THIRD ROUND STATISTICS

Home Victories   26

Away Victories   6

Replays   4

Best Attendance   608
Taunton Town v Tootam & Mitcham United

Average Attendance   191

Best Home Victory
London Colney 7 v 0 Elmore

Hat Tricks
4   Anthony Lynch (Taunton Town)
4   Simon Dean (London Colney)
3   Craig Gomershall (Ossett Albion)
3   Jamie O'Rourke (Cowes Sports)

Top: Justin Fox, Diss Town (left) takes a run as Horsham YMCA captain Wayne Potter gets ready to make a challenge in the FA Vase Third Round. Photo: Roger Turner

Centre: SaltdeanUnited's Sean Randell avoids a challenge from Phil Porter of Mossley., who proved too strong for their Southern visitors running out 5-1 winners.
Photo: Colin Stevens

Bottom: First to the ball is Great Wakering Rovers' Hickton (right) as he clears from Craig Ravenscroft of Hemel Hempstead.
Photo: D Nicholson

FOURTH ROUND

1   Metropolitan Police   3   v   2   Burgess Hill Town
Prins 12, Cormack 31   *Att: 244*   *Davies 5, Hutchings 76*
Batten 56

2   Crook Town   0   v   3   Deal Town
Att: 397   *Marshall 58, 88, Graham 88*

3   Letchworth   0   v   2   Newcastle Town
Att: 445   *Pesteridge 12, Twigg 44*

4   Cowes Sports   1   v   0   Tilbury
O'Rourke 84   *Att: 248*

5   Bedlington Terriers   1   v   0   Histon
Milner 55   *Att: 470*

6   Gt Wakering Rvrs   1   v   2*   Vauxhall
Hampshire 53   *Att: 345*   *Young 46, 120*

7   Woodbridge Town   3   v   0   Ossett Albion
Burgess 29, Bailey 75   *Att: 292*
Smith 90

8   Glossop North End   0   v   1*   Chippenham Town
Att: 325   *Tweddle 99*

9   Consett   0   v   1   Alfreton Town
Att: 276   *Kerry 67*

10   Wroxham   3   v   2   Paulton Rovers
Johnson 69, Metcalf 79, 90   *Att: 189*   *Cook 4, Crawdon 54*

11   AFC Totton   1   v   0   Horsham YMCA
Murphy 49   *Att: 198*

12   Ramsgate   0   v   0*   Berkhamstead Tn
Att: 265

r   Berkhamsted Town   0   v   0*   Ramsgate
Att: 237
(Ramsgate won after penalties)

13   Mossley   5   v   1   Saltdean United
Brennan 16, 64   *Att: 273*   *Fletcher 27*
Welstenholme 14, 34
Wilkinson 57

14   Skelmersdale U.   2   v   3*   Taunton Town
Cowley 21, Holcroft 27   *Att: 602*   *Lynch 12, 114, Laight 28*

15   Chasetown   0   v   0*   Porthleven
Att: 576

r   Porthleven   1   v   2*   Chasetown
og 80   *Att: 410*   *Reyner 15, Rawlinson 107*

16   London Colney   3   v   4   Eccleshill United
Ross 20, 53, Dean 15   *Att: 210*   *Newsome 3, Taylor 30, 79*
Ward 66

(* after extra time)

FOURTH ROUND STATISTICS

Home Victories   7

Away Victories   9

Replays   2

Best Attendance   602
Skelmersdale United v Taunton Town

Average Attendance   333

Best Home Victory
Mossley 5 v 1 Saltdean United

Best Away Victory
Crook Town 0 v 3 Deal Town

John Burrows (Porthleven) left, and John Jackson (Chasetown)

Top: Met Police v Deal. Deal keeper, Craig Tucker gathers safely. Photo: Eric Marsh

Centre: Airborne Chasetown keeper Ryan Young makes a splendid catch in the FA Vase Fifth Round tie with Newcastle Town. Photo: Peter Barnes

Bottom: Richard Morton (Newcastle) is tackled by John Jackson (Chasetown). Photo: Keith Clayton

FIFTH ROUND

1 Bedlington Terriers 5 v 0 AFC Totton
John Milner 3 (49, 72, 78)   *Att: 555*
Pike 47, Boon 89

2 Chasetown 0 v 0* Newcastle Town
Att: 715

r Newcastle Town 0 v 0* Chasetown
Newcastle Town won 3-1 on penalties

3 Ramsgate 2 v 1 Woodbridge Town
Court 10p, 52   *Att: 339*   *Burgess 75*

4 Mossley 1 v 0* Alfreton Town
Murray 115   *Att: 414*

5 Chippenham Town 3 v 1 Wroxham
Charity 32, Brown 38   *Att: 948*   *Johnson 50*
Tweddle 52

6 Cowes Sports 0 v 7 Taunton Town
Att: 928   *Antony Lynch 4 (5,28, 45,90)*
Loram 68, Thompson 79
Parkers 89

7 Vauxhall GM 2 v 0 Eccleshill United
Blundell 25, 61   *Att: 305*

8 Metropolitan Police 2 v 5 Deal Town
Prins 17, Scott 66   *Att: 332*   *Lovell 2, Graham 25*
Marshall 51, 87
Monteith 89

(after extra time)*

FIFTH ROUND STATISTICS

Home Victories 6

Away Victories 2

Replays 1

Best Attendance 948
Chippenham Town v Wroxham

Average Attendance 544

Best Home Victory
Bedlington Terriers 5 v 0 AFC Totton

Best Away Victory
Cowes Sports 0 v 7 Taunton Town

Hat Tricks
4 Antony Lynch (Taunton Town)
3 John Milner (Bedlington Terriers)

All eyes are on Mossley's goalkeeper Martin White as he clutches the ball after saving an Alfreton shot
Photo: Bill Wheatcroft

Top: FA Vase 6th Round. Taunton Town v Vauxhall. Taunton's Ian Down gains possession to set up a Taunton raid during the FA Vase Quarter Final tie.
Photo: Ken Gregory

Centre: Deal Town's Roly Graham steadies himself as he sends over a cross, as Mossley's captain Jimmy Birch comes in to challenge.
Photo: Roger Turner

Bottom: John Milner scores for Bedlington to send the tie into extra time.
Photo: Peter Barnes

SIXTH ROUND

Chippenham Town (1) 2 v 2 (1) Bedlington Terriers
Pike 38, Cross 69   *Att: 1924*   *Tweddle 4, Murphy 62*

Chippenham Town: Jones, James (sub Jackson 75), Andrews, Murphy, Burns, Woods, Brown (sub Tiley 118), Charity, Tweddle, Godley (sub Cutler 80), Collier. Subs not used: Godwin, Beaverstock.

Bedlington Terriers: O'Connor, Bowes (Hildreth 75), Locker, Teasdale, Melrose, Kirkby, Cross (sub Boyle 60), Walker (sub Bond 52), Gibb, Milner, Pike. Subs not used: Harminson.

r

Bedlington Terriers (0) 0 v 2 (2) Chippenham Town
Att: 1,543   *Brown 7, Charity 30*

Bedlington Terriers: O'Connor, Boyle (sub Boon 65), Locker, Teasdale, Melrose, Kirkby, Cross, Bond, Gibb (sub Hildreth 78), Milner, Pike (sub Walker 65). Subs not used: Harminson, Egan.

Chippenham Town: Jones, James, Andrews, Murphy, Burns, Woods, Brown, Charity, Tweddle, Godley, Beaverstock.

Deal Town (1) 3 v 1 (0) Mossley
Kempster 3, Marshall 58, 90   *Att: 936*   *Oldham 89*

Deal Town: Tucker, Kempster, Best, Ash, Martin, Seager, Monteith, Graham, Lovell (sub Warden 63), Marshall, Ribbens. Subs not used: P Turner, Lakin, Fox, J Turner.

Mossley: White, Oldham, Birch, Paver, Taylor, Murray, Porter (sub Murray 64), Brennan, Wilkinson, Wolstenholme (sub Wilcock 67), Dicken. Subs not used: Connor, Cain, Bates.

Ramsgate (0) 0 v 1 (0) Newcastle Town
Att: 577   *Myatt 112*

Ramsgate: Simmons, Harrop, E Vahid, Foley (sub Summers 100), Coatham, Brown, Davey, Love, Court, Hansen (sub Whittaker 90), S Vahid (sub Bowey 60). Subs not used: Stacey, Wild.

Newcastle Town: Holmes, Gillick, Banks, Bates, Buckle, Talbot, Morton (sub Cunningham 65 (sub Myatt 110)), Brown (sub Woodvine 60), Haddrell, Twigg, Pesteridge. Subs not used: Weston, Wakefield.

Taunton Town (0) 1 v 5 (0) Vauxhall Motors
Myers 70   *Att: 1204*   *Young 48, 72, Blundell 56*
Briggs 68, Daley 89

Taunton Town: Coombe, Edwards, Down (sub Bastow 79), West, Cann, Kelly, Rowe (sub Thompson 70), Laight, Loram (sub Parker 57), Myers, Lynch. Subs not used: Fowler, Whisler.

Vauxhall Motors: Hilton, Brazier, Clarke, Lawton, Lacy, Daley, Nesbitt, Williams, Blundell (sub Riley 73), Young, Briggs (sub Schumacker 82). Subs not used: Clynch, Odger, McDiarmid.

Top: Steve Tweddle, Chippenham (right) and Paul Lacey, Vauxhall (centre).   Photo: Andrew Chitty
Bottom: Chris Holmes, Newcastle Town's goalkeeper collects safely in front of a big crowd at Deal.
Photo: Roger Turner

SEMI-FINALS

1st LEG

Vauxhall Motors 0 v 0 Chippenham Town
Attendance: 900

Vauxhall Motors: Hilton, Brazier, Thompson, Lawton, Lacy, Daley, Nesbitt, Williams, Blundell, Odger, Clarke. Subs: Riley, Briggs, Schumacker, MacDiarmid.

Chippenham Town: Jones, James, Andrews, Murphy, Burns, Woods, Brown, Charity, Tweedle, Godley, Beaverstock. Subs: Cutler, Tiley, Jackson.

Referee: Mr P J Joslin assisted by Messrs. P McGuffog (Stretford) and B T Ward (Rossendale). Fourth official: Mr D Leyland (Denton)

2nd LEG

Chippenham Town 1 v 0 Vauxhall Motors
(after extra time, Chippenham win 1-0 on aggregate)
Attendance: 3,008

Chippenham Town: Ian Jones, Lea James (sub Nick Tiley 63rd min), Shane Andrews, Ian Murphy, Lee Burns, John Woods, Steve Brown, Simon Charity, Steve Tweddle, Dave Godley (sub Mark Cutler 91st min), Richard Bourne. Subs (not used): Toby Jackson, Lee Collier and Ian Harris (g/k).

Vauxhall Motors: Steve Hilton, Phil Brazier, Kevin Thompson, Robbie Lawton, Paul Lacy, Carl Spellman (sub Peter Daley 106th min), Carl Nesbitt, Leigh Williams, Gregg Blundell (sub Mike Riley 99th min), Nicky Young, Neil Clarke. Subs (not used) Gregg Briggs, Steve Walsh, Andy Clynch (g/k).

Referee: Mr S Tomlin (Lewes) assisted by Messrs R Maynard (Bristol) and H Singh (West Bromwich). Fourth official, Mr S Cook (Yate)

Vauxhall's Robbie Lawton (white) clears from Chippenham captain Lee Burns. Photo: Andrew Chitty

It's different at Vase Semi-Finals . . .

Top left: "Deal for Wembley" flag flying from bedroom window over looking ground.
Photo: Eric Marsh

Top right: Fireworks greeted the players.
Photo: Peter Barnes

Centre left: Match officials lead out teams at Vauxhall.
Photo: Andrew Chitty

Centre right: Lee Burns, Chippenham Town, in his post match interview with BBC local radio.
Photo: Andrew Chitty

Bottom left: Decorative physio for Chippenham Town, Steve Lodge.
Photo: Peter Barnes

SEMI-FINALS

1st LEG

Newcastle Town 0 v 2 Deal Town
Attendance: 811

Newcastle Town: Chris Holmes, Dean Gillick, Ian Banks, Michael Bates, Anthony Buckle (sub Richard Morton 58th min), Dave Talbot, Dave Woodvine (Dean Cunningham 72nd min), Ray Walker, Matt Hadrell, Rob Myatt (sub Marc Hawkes 82nd min), Neil Pestridge. Subs (not used):- John Brown and Paul Wakefield (g/k).

Deal Town: Craig Tucker, Jamie Kempster, Steve Best, Jason Ash, Terry Martin Marc Seager, Dave Monteith, Roly Graham, Steve Lovell (sub John Warden 69th min), Steve Marshall, Paul Ribbens. Subs (not used):- Liam Fox, Paul Roberts, Jamie Turner and Ricky Bennett (g/k).

Referee: Mr P Walton (Long Buckby) assisted by Messrs. G T Stott (Middleton) and P N Gibbs (Solihull). Reserve Official, Mr D Shipp (Oldham).

2nd LEG

Deal Town 1 v 1 Newcastle Town
(Deal win 3-1 on aggregate)
Attendance 2,495

Deal Town: Craig Tucker, Jamie Kempster, Steve Best, Jason Ash, Terry Martin, Marc Seager, Dave Monteith, Roly Graham (sub Phil Turner 88th min), Steve Lovell (sub Jon Warden 54th min), Steve Marshall, Paul Ribbens. Subs (not used)- Barry Lakin, Paul Roberts and Jamie Turner (g/k).
Newcastle Town: Chris Holmes, Dean Gillick, Ian Banks, Michael Bates, Anthony Buckle (sub Dave Woodvine 55th min), Dave Talbot (sub Dean Cunningham 80th min), Richard Morton, Ray Walker (sub Matt Haddrell 68th min), Rob Myatt, Darren Twigg, Neil Pestridge. Subs (not used)- Peter Weston and Paul Wakefield (g/k).

Referee: Mr L E Cable (Woking) assisted by Messrs I F Bentley (West Wickham) and A R Legg (East Grinstead). 4th official Mr P Sleat (Horsham).

All action at the Lyme Valley Stadium. Newcastle Town v Deal Town. Photo: Peter Barnes

THIRD ROUND

Deal Town 2
Watton Utd 1

Crook Town 3
W Midlands Police 1

Burgess Hill Tn 3
Newbury 0

Marlow 1, 0
Met. Police 1, 1

Tow Law Town 0, 0
Consett 0, 1

Alfreton T 2
Borrowash Vic. 1

Fakenham Town 2
Saltdean United 3

Mossley 5
Nantwich Town 1

Lymington 1
Ramsgate 2

Berkhamsted T 2
Stourport Swifts 0

Bideford 1
Woodbridge Town 2

Ossett Albion 5
Anstey Nomads 1

Portleven 1
Bedfont 0

Chasetown 1
Mickleover Sports 0

Letchworth 3
Stotfold 1

Newcastle Town 2
Clitheroe 1

Vauxhall 2
Warrington Town 1

H Hempstead T 0
Gt Wakering R 1

London Colney 7
Elmore 0

Eccleshill United 2
Heanor Town 1

Tilbury 1
Falmouth Town 1

Cowes Sports 3
Banstead Athletic 1

Skelmersdale Utd 3
Hall Road R 2

Taunton Town 4
Tooting & Mitcham 1

Horsham YMCA 4
Diss Town 2

Totton 2
Barking 0

Histon 4
Wembley 1

Bedlington Terriers 3
North Ferriby Utd 1

Paulton Rovers 2
Corinthian Casuals 0

Wroxham 0
BAT Sports 0

Glossop NE 3
Brigg Town 2

Chippenham Town 2
Northwood Town 0

FOURTH ROUND

Deal Town 3

Crook Town 0

Burgess Hill Town 2
Metropolitan Police 3

Consett 0
Alfreton Town 1

Saltdean United 1
Mossley 5

Ramsgate 0, 0, 4p
Berkhamstead T 0, 0, 3p

Woodbridge Town 3
Ossett Albion 0

Porthleven 0, 1
Chasetown 0, 2

Letchworth 0
Newcastle Town 2

Vauxhall 2
Gt Wakering T 4

London Colney 3
Eccleshill Utd 4

Tilbury 0
Cowes Sports 1

Skelmersdale Utd 2
Taunton Town 3

Horsham YMCA 0
Totton 1

Histon 0
Bedlington Terriers 1

Paulton Rovers 2
Wroxham 3

Glossop North End 0
Chippenham Town 1

FIFTH ROUND

Deal Town 5

Metropolitan Police 2

Alfreton Town 0
Mossley 1

Ramsgate 2
Woodbridge Town 1

Chasetown 0, 0, 1p
Newcastle T 0, 0, 3p

Vauxhall 2
Eccleshill United 0

Cowes Sports 0
Taunton Town 7

Totton 0
Bedlington Terriers 5

Wroxham 1
Chippenham Town 3

SIXTH ROUND

Deal Town 3

Mossley 1

Ramsgate 0
Newcastle Town 1

Vauxhall 5
Taunton Town 1

Bedlington Terr. 2, 0
Chippenham T 2, 2

FA CARLSBERG VASE AT A GLANCE

SEMI FINALS

Deal Town 2, 1

Newcastle Town 0, 1

Chippenham Town 0, 1

FINAL

Deal Town 1

Chippenham Town 0

FINAL

Chippenham Town   0   v   1   **Deal Town**

Att: 20,000   Graham 87

Chippenham Town: Ian Jones, Lea James, Shane Andrews, Ian Murphy, Lee Burns, John Woods, Steve Brown, Simon Charity, Steve Tweddle, Lee Collier, Dave Godley. Subs: Nick Tiley, Mark Cutler

Deal Town: Craig Tucker, Jamie Kempster, Steve Best, Jason Ash, Terry Martin Marc Seager, Dave Monteith, Roly Graham, Steve Lovell, Steve Marshall, Paul Ribbens. Subs: Paul Roberts, John Warden, Phil Turner

F.A. Vase Finals have been dour affairs for three years now. Competing clubs at this level used to be unable to defend for ninety minutes without making a few mistakes, but lately the defences have certainly prevailed, and on this occasion the heat and the importance of the match seemed to stifle any possibility of flair.

When you are better than your local rivals, clubs and their officials are often resented. In Kent, their own League refused to change the date of Deal's League Cup Final fixture to link in with their Vase Final plans and the local council were not at all thrilled with the club's ground development plans. It really is sad that this so often happens when small clubs become successful - no doubt there are many reasons, but from an outsider's point of view these squabbles can appear very petty.

Over in Wiltshire, the West either loved or hated Chippenham Town's extrovert manager, but the club had terrific support from their local council, the town authorities, sponsors, the media and a huge number of supporters.

They came from the same league as Tiverton Town, Vase winners for the previous two seasons, and they had beaten favourites Bedlington Terriers away.

On a very hot day, Chippenham Town with the greater support did dominate most of the play, but as the game drifted towards the full ninety minutes there was no sign of a spark to light up the game for either side.

Suddenly, with three minutes to go Steve Marshall, the Deal top scorer, tiring in sweltering heat, looked as if he had just enjoyed a helping of magic mushrooms, striding forward at a pace we hadn't seen before he rounded his marker, tore down the right, looked up and chipped perfectly for Roly Graham to sidefoot a volley into the roof of the net from the edge of the penalty area!

It was a goal, so good we didn't mind seeing it over three hundred times on a big screen at a special launching party for 'Non-League Media Plc' in London on the following Thursday!

The dedication of manager Tommy Sampson had been rewarded and my best memory was seeing the injured David Montieth, who had been helped off after ten minutes, being carried onto the pitch in his plaster by team mates to join in the after match celebrations.

Another excellent football occasion lifted by the Chippenham supporters and that Deal Town magnificent goal.

Tony Williams

FA Vase Final 2000 - the Chippenham Army. Photo: Keith Clayton

Tommy Sampson proved that age and experience is the most important ingredient as his Deal Town side grabbed a last-ditch goal to snatch the FA Carlsberg Vase at Wembley Stadium.

The famous Twin Towers have witnessed many historic moments during a sporting century overshadowing football's most hallowed turf but the fans of Deal Town will never forget Roly Graham's rasping volley just three minutes from time.

Chippenham were marched out of the tunnel by the youngest manager in the stadium's history but his brash promises were destroyed in a single moment of Deal brilliance. At just 28 Tom Saunders possesses the perfect frame for a football boss. He shunned the traditional Wembley suit for a replica Bluebirds strip but his portly girth explained why he quit playing early to take a place in the dug out.

Saunders spent the afternoon shrouded against the sun by a beach towel whilst his troops sweated it out on the pitch, but his confidence did not appear misplaced. For what he lacks in athleticism he appeared to make up for in tactical know-how as Chippenham threatened to swamp the famous Cinque ports town with a neat brand of flowing football.

Deal never looked close to troubling Bluebirds keeper Ian Jones until Steve Marshall broke clear on 87 minutes and delivered a killer cross into the heart of the area. Roly Graham seized his chance and crashed a blazing volley into the roof of the net past a despairing Jones.

Big match nerves dominated scrappy opening exchanges as both sides adjusted to the wide expanses and billiard table surface at the doomed venue of legends.

Steve Brown's dancing run and cross presented the Bluebirds with their first really gilt-edged chance but Steve Tweedle - whose goals have underpinned Chippenham's road to Wembley - failed to test Deal's Craig Tucker from close range.

Moments later Steve Chantry's defence splitting pass put Tweedle within range again, but his shot lacked power and Dave Godley steered the resulting loose ball into the side netting.

Top: Chippenham's Mark Cutler (left) and Steve Brown try to fight their way through the Deal defence.
Photo: D Nicholson
Bottom left: Terry Martin of Deal (hoops) challenges for the ball. Photo: Peter Lirettoc
Bottom right: Chippenham's keeper Ian Jones scrambles the ball clear from Deal Town's Steve Marshall.
Photo: D Nicholson

Deal, who suffered an early blow when midfielder David Monteith was carried off from the field, may have lacked the youthful ambition of their final opponents, but age and experience is just as valuable on the big stage.

Convention dictates that most grandfathers should participate in nothing more taxing that back garden kickarounds but Steve Lovell is no respecter of tradition. Just two months shy of his 40th birthday the former Football League professional, whose career with Millwall, Crystal Palace and Gillingham spanned 500 games, was absolutely determined to hang up his boots alongside a Wembley winners medal. He worked tirelessly to rally Deal, who finally shifted out of first gear with a speculative Steve Marshall header and Mark Seager shot, after a clumsy spell of Bluebirds defending.

But Chippenham always seemed to have control with Brown and Shane Andrews both causing headaches with probing runs down the wings.

Lovell's Wembley dreams were ended on 58 minutes when the dreaded substitution board signalled his removal and the end of a 20-year career. With Deal increasingly ineffective up front, the former Welsh international had struggled to break down the Bluebirds watertight defence, but his day was destined to finish with a smile.

Chippenham should have taken the lead when Lee Collier's pinpoint cross found Brown alone and unmarked but he also failed to trouble Tucker form six yards out.

Fairy tales are made for this famous old stadium and, on a vintage warm May afternoon, Mark Cutler's introduction had Chippenham's majority support on their feet. Cutler is twelve months younger than his manager, but arthritis in both knees means doctors advised this should be his last game of football. Football can be both cruel and kind.

With the clock creeping closer to added time Deal finally surged forward and Marshall's pinpoint cross and Graham's brutal execution had Deal headed home for a wild night of seaside celebrations.

Saunders had spent the week promising his Screwfix Western league side would have little difficulty overcoming their rivals form the kent League. Sampson, a knowledgeable non-League figure with 30 years pedigree to his name, just sat back and listened.

That night he had the final laugh.

by James Tovey. First published in The Non League Paper

Top: Deal Town matchwinner Roly Graham is carried aloft at Wembley. Photo: D Nicholson
Bottom: Deal Town - FA Vase Winners. Photo: Garry Letts

PAST F.A. VASE FINALS

1975 HODDESDON TOWN 2 EPSOM & EWELL 1 Att: 9,500
Sedgwick 2 Wales Ref: Mr R Toseland
Hoddesdon: Galvin, Green, Hickey, Maybury, Stevenson, Wilson, Bishop, Picking, Sedgwick, Nathan, Schofield
Epsom & Ewell: Page, Bennett, Webb, Wales, Worby, Jones, O'Connell, Walker, Tuite, Eales, Lee

1976 BILLERICAY TOWN 1 STAMFORD 0 (aet) Att: 11,848
Aslett Ref: Mr A Robinson
Billericay: Griffiths, Payne, Foreman, Pullin, Bone, Coughlan, Geddes, Aslett, Clayden, Scott, Smith
Stamford: Johnson, Kwiatowski, Marchant, Crawford, Downs, Hird, Barnes, Walpole, Smith, Russell, Broadbent

1977 BILLERICAY TOWN 1 SHEFFIELD 1 (aet) Att: 14,000
Clayden Coughlan og Ref: Mr J Worrall
Billericay: Griffiths, Payne, Bone, Coughlan, Pullin, Scott, Wakefield, Aslett, Clayden,Woodhouse, McQueen. Sub: Whettell
Sheffield: Wing, Gilbody, Lodge, Hardisty, Watts, Skelton, Kay, Travis, Pugh, Thornhill,Haynes. Sub: Strutt

Replay BILLERICAY TOWN 2 SHEFFIELD 1 Att: 3,482
Aslett, Woodhouse Thornhill at Nottingham Forest
Billericay: Griffiths, Payne, Pullin, Whettell, Bone, McQueen, Woodhouse, Aslett, Clayden, Scott, Wakefield
Sheffield: Wing, Gilbody, Lodge, Strutt, Watts, Skelton, Kay, Travis, Pugh, Thornhill, Haynes

1978 NEWCASTLE BLUE STAR 2 BARTON ROVERS 1 Att: 16,858
Dunn, Crumplin Smith Ref: Mr T Morris
Newcastle: Halbert, Feenan, Thompson, Davidson, S Dixon, Beynon, Storey, P Dixon, Crumplin, Callaghan, Dunn. Sub: Diamond
Barton Rovers: Blackwell, Stephens, Crossley, Evans, Harris, Dollimore, Dunn, Harnaman, Fossey, Turner, Smith. Sub: Cox

1979 BILLERICAY TOWN 4 ALMONDSBURY GREENWAY 1 Att: 17,500
Young 3, Clayden Price Ref: Mr C Steel
Billericay: Norris, Blackaller, Bingham, Whettell, Bone, Reeves, Pullin, Scott, Clayden,Young, Groom. Sub: Carrigan
Almondsbury: Hamilton, Bowers, Scarrett, Sulllivan, Tudor, Wookey, Bowers, Shehean, Kerr,Butt, Price. Sub: Kilbaine

1980 STAMFORD 2 GUISBOROUGH TOWN 0 Att: 11,500
Alexander, McGowan Ref: Neil Midgeley
Stamford: Johnson, Kwiatowski, Ladd, McGowan, Bliszczak I, Mackin, Broadhurst, Hall,Czarnecki, Potter, Alexander. Sub: Bliszczak S
Guisborough: Cutter, Scott, Thornton, Angus, Maltby, Percy, Skelton, Coleman, McElvaney,Sills, Dilworth. Sub: Harrison

1981 WHICKHAM 3 WILLENHALL 2 (aet) Att: 12,000
Scott, Williamson, Peck og Smith, Stringer Ref: Mr R Lewis
Whickham: Thompson, Scott, Knox, Williamson, Cook, Ward, Carroll, Diamond, Cawthra,Robertson, Turnbull. Sub: Alton
Willenhall: Newton, White, Darris, Woodall, Heath, Fox, Peck, Price, Matthews, Smith,Stringer. Sub: Trevor

1982 FOREST GREEN ROVERS 3 RAINWORTH M.W 0 Att: 12,500
Leitch 2, Norman Ref: Mr K Walmsey
Forest Green: Moss, Norman, Day, Turner, Higgins, Jenkins, Guest, Burns, Millard, Leitch, Doughty. Sub: Dangerfield
Rainworth M.W: Watson, Hallam, Hodgson, Slater, Sterland, Oliver, Knowles, Raine, Radzi, Reah, Comerford. Sub: Robinson

1983 V.S. RUGBY 1 HALESOWEN TOWN 0 Att: 13,700
Crawley Ref: Mr B Daniels
VS Rugby: Burton, McGinty, Harrison, Preston, Knox, Evans, ingram, Setchell, Owen,Beecham, Crawley. Sub: Haskins
Halesowen Town: Coldicott, Penn, Edmonds, Lacey, Randall, Shilvock, Hazelwood, Moss, Woodhouse,P Joinson, L Joinson. Sub: Smith

1984 STANSTED 3 STAMFORD 2 Att: 8,125
Holt, Gillard, Reading Waddicore, Allen Ref: Mr T Bune
Stanstead: Coe, Williams, Hilton, Simpson, Cooper, Reading, Callanan, Holt, Reevs,Doyle, Gillard. Sub: Williams
Stamford: Parslow, Smitheringate, Blades, McIlwain, Lyon, Mackin, Genovese, Waddicore,Allen, Robson, Beech. Sub: Chapman

1985 HALESOWEN TOWN 3 FLEETWOOD TOWN 1 Att: 16,715
L Joinson 2, Moss Moran Ref: Mr C Downey
Halesowen: Coldicott, Penn, Sherwood, Warner, Randle, Heath, Hazlewood, Moss (Smith),Woodhouse, P Joinson, L Joinson
Fleetwood Town: Dobson, Moran, Hadgraft, Strachan, Robinson, Milligan, Hall, Trainor, Taylor(Whitehouse), Cain, Kennerley

1986 HALESOWEN TOWN 3 SOUTHALL 0 Att: 18,340
Moss 2, L Joinson Ref: Mr D Scott
Halesowen: Pemberton, Moore, Lacey, Randle (Rhodes), Sherwood, Heath, Penn, Woodhouse, P.Joinson, L Joinson, Moss
Southall: Mackenzie, James, McGovern, Croad, Holland, Powell (Richmond), Pierre,Richardson, Sweales, Ferdinand, Rowe

1987 ST. HELENS 3 WARRINGTON TOWN 2 Att: 4,254
Layhe 2, Rigby Reid, Cook Ref: Mr T Mills
St Helens: Johnson, Benson, Lowe, Bendon, Wilson, McComb, Collins (Gledhill), O'Neill,Cummins, Lay, Rigby. Sub: Deakin
Warrington: O'Brien. Copeland, Hunter, Gratton, Whalley, Real, Brownville (Woodyer), Cook,Kinsey, Looker (Hill), Hughes

1988 COLNE DYNAMOES 1 EMLEY 0 Att: 15,000
Anderson Ref: Mr A Seville
Colne Dynamoes: Mason, McFafyen, Westwell, Bentley, Dunn, Roscoe, Rodaway, Whitehead (Burke),Diamond, Anderson, Wood (Coates)
Emley: Dennis, Fielding, Mellor, Codd, Hirst (Burrows), Gartland (Cook), Carmody,Green, Bramald, Devine, Francis

F.A. CARLSBERG VASE

1989   TAMWORTH 1   SUDBURY TOWN 1   aet   Att: 26,487
Devaney   Hubbick   Ref: Mr C Downey
Tamworth: Bedford, Lockett, Atkins, Cartwright, McCormack, Myers, Finn, Devaney, Moores,Gordon, Stanton. Subs: Rathbone, Heaton
Sudbury Town: Garnham, Henry, G Barker, Boyland, Thorpe, Klug, D Barker, Barton, Oldfield,Smith, Hubbick. Subs: Money, Hunt

Replay   TAMWORTH 3   SUDBURY TOWN 0   Att: 11,201
Stanton 2, Moores   at Peterborough
Tamworth: Bedford, Lockett, Atkins, Cartwright, Finn, Myers, George, Devaney, Moores,Gordon, Stanton. Sub: Heaton
Sudbury Town: Garnham, Henry, G Barker, Boyland, Thorpe, Klug, D Barker, Barton, Oldfield,Smith, Hubbick. Subs: Money, Hunt

1990   YEADING 0   BRIDLINGTON TOWN 0   aet   Att: 7,932
                                                Ref: Mr R Groves
Yeading: Mackenzie, Wickens, Turner, Whiskey (McCarthy), Croad, Denton, Matthews, James(Charles), Sweates, Impey, Cordery
Bridlington: Taylor, Pugh, Freeman, McNeill, Warburton, Brentano, Wilkes (Hall), Noteman,Gauden, Whiteman, Brattan (Brown)

Replay   YEADING 1   BRIDLINGTON TOWN 0   Att: 5,000
Sweales   at Leeds Utd FC
Yeading: Mackenzie, Wickens, Turner, Whiskey, Croad (McCarthy), Schwartz, Matthews,James, Sweates, Impey (Welsh), Cordery
Bridlington: Taylor, Pugh, Freeman, McNeill, Warburton, Brentano, Wilkes (Brown), Noteman,Gauden (Downing), Whiteman, Brattan

1991   GRESLEY ROVERS 4   GUISELEY 4 aet   Att: 11,314
Rathbone, Smith 2, Stokes   Tennison 2, Walling, A Roberts   Ref: Mr C Trussell
Gresley: Aston, Barry, Elliott (Adcock), Denby, Land, Astley, Stokes, K Smith, Acklam,Rathbone, Lovell (Weston)
Guiseley: Maxted, Bottomley, Hogarth, Tetley, Morgan, McKenzie, Atkinson (Annan),Tennison, Walling, A Roberts, B Roberts

Replay   GUISELEY 3   GRESLEY ROVERS 1   Att: 7,585
Tennison, Walling, Atkinson   Astley   at Bramall Lane
Guiseley: Maxted, Annan, Hogarth, Tetley, Morgan, McKenzie (Bottomley), Atkinson,Tennison (Noteman), Walling, A Roberts, B Roberts
Gresley: Aston, Barry, Elliott, Denby, Land, Astley, Stokes (Weston), K Smith, Acklam, Rathbone, Lovell (Adcock)

1992   WIMBORNE TOWN 5   GUISELEY 3   Att: 10,772
Richardson, Sturgess 2, Killick 2   Noteman 2, Colville   Ref: Mr M J Bodenham
Wimborne: Leonard, Langdown, Wilkins, Beacham, Allan, Taplin, Ames, Richardson, Bridle,Killick, Sturgess (Lovell), Lynn
Guiseley: Maxted, Atkinson, Hogarth, Tetley (Wilson), Morgan, Brockie, A Roberts,Tennison, Noteman (Colville), Annan, W Roberts

1993   BRIDLINGTON TOWN 1   TIVERTON TOWN 0   Att: 9,061
Radford   Ref: Mr R A Hart
Bridlington: Taylor, Brentano, McKenzie, Harvey, Bottomley, Woodcock, Grocock, A Roberts, Jones, Radford (Tyrell), Parkinson. Sub: Swailes
Tiverton Town: Nott, J Smith, N Saunders, M Saunders, Short (Scott), Steele, Annunziata, KSmith, Everett, Daly, Hynds (Rogers)

1994   DISS TOWN 2   TAUNTON TOWN 1   Att: 13,450
Gibbs (p), Mendham   Fowler   Ref: Mr K. Morton
Diss Town: Woodcock, Carter, Wolsey (Musgrave), Casey (Bugg), Hartle, Smith, Barth, Mendham, Miles, Warne, Gibbs
Taunton Town: Maloy, Morris, Walsh, Ewens, Graddon, Palfrey, West (Hendry), Fowler, Durham, Perrett (Ward), Jarvis

1995   ARLESEY TOWN 2   OXFORD CITY 1   Att: 13,670
Palma, Gyalog   S Fontaine   Ref: Mr G S Willard
Arlesey: Young, Cardines, Bambrick, Palma (Ward), Hull, Gonsalves, Gyalog, Cox, Kane,O'Keefe, Marshall (Nicholls). Sub: Dodwell
Oxford: Fleet, Brown (Fisher), Hume, Shepherd, Muttock, Hamilton (Kemp), Thomas, Spittle, Sherwood, S Fontaine, C Fontaine. Sub: Torres

1996   BRIGG TOWN 3   CLITHEROE 0   Att: 7,340
Stead 2, Roach   Ref: Mr S J Lodge
Brigg: Gawthorpe, Thompson, Rogers, Greaves (Clay), Buckley (Mail), Elston, C Stead, McLean, N Stead (McNally), Flounders, Roach
Clitheroe: Nash, Lampkin, Rowbotham (Otley), Baron, Westwell, Rovine, Butcher, Taylor (Smith), Grimshaw, Darbyshire, Hill (Dunn)

1997   NORTH FERRIBY UTD. 0   WHITBY TOWN 3   Att: 11,098
                             Williams, Logan, Toman   Ref: Graham Poll
North Ferriby: Sharp, Deacey, Smith, Brentano, Walmsley, M Smith, Harrison (Horne), Phillips (Milner), France (Newman), Flounders, Tennison
Whitby Town: Campbell, Williams, Logan, Goodchild, Pearson, Cook, Goodrick (Borthwick), Hodgson, Robinson, Toman (Pyle), Pitman (Hall)

1998   TIVERTON TOWN 1   TOW LAW TOWN 0   Att: 13,139
Varley   Ref: M A Riley
Tiverton: Edwards, Felton, Saunders, Tatterton, Smith J, Conning, Nancekivell (Rogers), Smith K (Varley), Everett, Daly, Leonard (Waters)
Tow Law: Dawson, Pickering, Darwent, Bailey, Hague, Moan, Johnson, Nelson, Suddick, Laidler (Bennett), Robinson.

1999   BEDLINGTON TERRIERS 0   TIVERTON TOWN 1   Att: 13, 878
                             Rogers 88   Ref: W. C. Burns
Bedlington Terriers: O'Connor, Bowes, Pike, Boon (Renforth), Melrose, Teasdale, Cross, Middleton (Ludlow), Gibb, Milner, Bond. Subs:
Pearson, Cameron, Gowans
Tiverton Town: Edwards, Fallon, Saunders, Tatterton, Tallon, Conning (Rogers), Nancekivell (Pears), Varley, Everett, Daly, Leonard. Subs:
Tucker, Hynds, Grimshaw

F.A. CARLSBERG VASE CLUB RECORDS

The table is a record of the performance of the top 50 teams that have played in the Vase since its inception in 1975, a period of 26 years. During that time we have seen many teams enjoying successful periods in the competition and this is an attempt to reward teams for their consistency during the various rounds as well as whether they actually win the Vase or not. The various columns of the table represent the following:

1	1999	the position of the team in the table at the end of the 1999 season.
2	2000	the position of the team in the table at the end of the 2000 season.
3.	S	the number of seasons that the team has played in the competition
4.	P	number of rounds the team has played in, ie, if a team had to replay it is counted as one match
5.	W	the number of matches the team has won in the Vase
6.	L	number of matches the team lost, usually one per season unless the team won the Competition
7.	%	the percentage success rate of the team calculated by dividing wins by matches played x 100
8.	Pts	points are calculated as follows: 1st Rnd - 1 point, 2nd Rnd - 2 points, 3rd Rnd - 3 points, 4th Rnd - 4 points, 5th Rnd - 5 points, 6th Rnd - 6 points, Semis - 7 points, Final - 8 points, Winner - 9 points.
9.	Best	best performance in the competition by that team and the year. 'x' a number means that they reached that stage more than once, ie, 3rd x 3 means they reached the Third Round 3 times

Although I have tried my best to ensure that the information is as accurate as possible it is inevitable that an error or two (or three!) will be present. I would be very grateful if anyone who spots a mistake would contact me via the Team Talk address so that I can correct the table.

John Anderson

Positions									
1999	2000		S	P	W	L	%	Pts	Best
1	1	Hungerford Town	26	78	52	26	66.67	78	SF x 3
2	2	Stamford	24	69	46	23	66.67	73	W 80
6	3	North Ferriby United	26	75	49	26	65.33	66	F 97
3	4	Buckingham Town	22	57	35	22	61.40	66	6th x 2
4	5	Guiseley	17	63	47	16	74.60	64	W 91
5	6	Barton Rovers	20	63	43	20	68.25	64	F 78
7	7	Burnham	17	47	30	17	63.83	60	SF 83
8	8	Tiverton Town	18	65	49	16	75.38	59	W x 2
9	9	Irthingborough Diamonds	15	53	38	15	71.70	58	SF x 2
10	10	Hinckley Athletic	23	60	37	23	61.67	58	5th x 2
14	11	Brigg Town	26	65	40	25	61.54	58	W 96
11	12	Newcastle Blue Star	16	50	35	15	70.00	57	W 78
12	13	Whickham	20	57	38	19	66.67	57	W 81
13	14	Wisbech Town	16	48	32	16	66.67	54	SF x 2
18	15	Warrington Town	20	57	37	20	64.91	54	F 87
15	16	Sudbury Town	11	46	35	11	76.09	53	F 89
17	17	Friar Lane Old Boys	26	65	39	26	60.00	53	SF x 2
21	18	Banstead Athletic	26	63	37	26	58.73	53	SF 97
16	19	Billericay Town	9	44	38	6	86.36	52	W x 3
19	20	Lincoln United	21	50	29	21	58.00	51	6th 75
22	21	Harefield United	25	55	30	25	54.55	51	6th 90
20	22	Halesowen Town	12	45	35	10	77.78	50	W x 2
26	23	Clitheroe	24	57	33	24	57.89	50	F 96
23	24	Hucknall Town	17	53	36	17	67.92	49	6th 86
29	25	Paulton Rovers	20	55	35	20	63.64	49	5th 90
24	26	Bridgnorth Town	24	58	34	24	58.62	48	5th x 2
28	27	Molesey	16	46	30	16	65.22	47	6th 82
32	28	Diss Town	23	57	35	22	61.40	47	W 94
25	29	Newport IOW	18	46	28	18	60.87	47	5th x 2
27	30	Gresley Rovers	19	53	34	19	64.15	46	F 91
60	31	Chippenham Town	24	63	39	24	61.90	46	F 00
53	32	Taunton Town	8	40	32	8	80.00	45	F 94
36	33	Guisborough Town	14	38	24	14	63	16	45 F 80
31	34	Eastleigh	25	66	41	25	62.12	45	4th x 3
45	35	Burgess Hill Town	23	59	36	23	61.02	45	5th 98
30	36	Arlesey Town	26	57	32	25	56.14	45	W 95
39	37	Windsor & Eton	15	48	33	15	68.75	44	SF 81
33	38	Almondsbury Town	24	58	34	24	58.62	44	F 79
34	39	Tunbridge Wells	26	60	34	26	56.67	44	4th x 5
35	40	Newbury Town	20	45	25	20	55.56	44	6th 94
38	41	Abingdon Town	19	42	23	19	54.76	44	5th x 3
40	42	Wimborne Town	18	50	33	17	66.00	43	W 92
41	43	Thackley	22	61	39	22	63.93	43	5th 81
47	44	Great Yarmouth Town	20	48	28	20	58.33	43	SF 83
37	45	Rainworth MW	21	48	27	21	56.25	43	F 82
42	46	Basildon United	21	49	28	21	57.14	42	6th x 2
43	47	Sheffield	26	60	34	26	56.67	42	F 77
44	48	Hallam	25	56	31	25	55.36	42	5th 81
63	49	Ossett Albion	24	49	25	24	51.02	42	4th x 3
55	50	Mangotsfield United	16	47	31	16	65.96	41	SF 96

ENGLAND SEMI-PROFESSIONAL REPRESENTATIVE FOOTBALL

Another semi-professional international season started for England after disappointing F.A. XI trial games.

The match against the Unibond League was called off for the second consecutive year at Stalybridge because of bad weather. The dour 0-0 draw with many of the original selection having been withdrawn was played in front of a sparse crowd at Rugby and an injury after all substitutions had been used by the Ryman XI gave the game a lop sided second half in which it was difficult to gauge form or class.

Yes, it was a frustrating time for manager John Owens, his assistant Steve Avory and long serving physio from Kidderminster Harriers, Jim Conway.

The names that emerged as England potentials were:

Goalkeepers - Paul Gothard (Hayes), *Adam Sollitt (Kettering Town), *Steve Farrelly (Kingstonian), Ryan Price (Telford United) and Billy Turley (Rushden & Diamonds).

Wing Backs - Simon Wormhull (Dover Athletic) *Simon Marples and Kevin McIntyre (Doncaster Rovers), *Paul Underwood (Rushden & Diamonds) and Simon Travis (Telford United).

Centre Backs - *Mark Smith (Stevenage Borough), Michael Danzey and Steve West (Woking), *Tim Ryan (Southport), *Adie Smith (Kidderminster), Andy Comyn (Hednesford Town), Paul Ellender (Scarborough), Ian Wright (Hereford United), *Rob Cousins (Yeovil Town) and *Jason Goodliffe (Hayes).

Mid Field - *Gary Butterworth (Rushden & Diamonds), *Stuart Drumond (Morecambe), *Gary Patterson and *Geoff Pitcher (Kingstonian), Steve Perkins (Woking), Barry Williams (Nuneaton Borough) and Michael McElhatton (Rushden & Diamonds).

Strikers - *Warren Patmore (Yeovil Town), Darren Collins (Rushden & Diamonds), Lee Charles (Hayes), *Marc MacGregor (Forest Green Rrovers), *Dale Watkins (Kettering Town), Carl Alford (Stevenage Borough), Dean Bennett (Kidderminster Harriers) and Steve Brodie (Scarborough).

Those with asterisks travelled for the first international which was in Italy at Padova in a huge new stadium. The town was about an hour's drive from Venice and the team settled into a comfy hotel and were given a run out at the stadium on the day of arrival.

Cap Presentation
Martin Peters, Chairman Ken Marsden, Tim Ryan, Gary Butterworth, Adie Smith, Mark Smith, Stuart Drummond, Marc MacGregor, Jason Goodliffe, Warren Patmore, Kevin McIntyre, Chief Coach John Owens, and Assistant Coach Steve Avery. Photo: Eric Marsh

As usual John Owens concentrated on getting the team comfortable with its shape and a 3-5-2 line up with the emphasis on a passing game developing from the back, and using a mobile midfield with prominence on width, giving the front two a variety of support.

But the best made plans can be ruined, and sure enough the traditional torrential rain that follows England semi-professionals in their first match each season (v Wales at Crawley 1998 and v Italy at Hayes 1999) arrived during an afternoon's cloudburst in which the referee did well to get the game completed.

England dominated the first half with excellent passing and movement straight from the training ground and led through a neat Dale Watkins goal following good work by Garry Patterson on the left.

However, the quagmire struck and claimed a back pass leaving England 'keeper Steve Farrelly stranded and an equaliser for Simon Cavelli before half time brought the teams level. In the second half perhaps neither side deserved to lose the beach football contest.

England's first half football had been impressive, however, and only two enforced changes were made at Northwich for the visit of the Dutch "Amateur" XI.

The two Rushden & Diamond's players, skipper Gary Butterworth and Paul Underwood, were injured and their places were taken by Morecambe's Stuart Drummond in midfield and Kevin McIntyre of Doncaster Rovers at left wing back. Kingstonian's midfield 'power house', Gary Patterson, took over as skipper, but the game was a dour affair that only brought a late and rather lucky winner from Dale Watkins. However, no one complains about a victory and a clean sheet, so spirits were high and the season's new caps were particularly pleased with life.

The last game was played at Llanelli's lovely stadium the week after the excellent F.A. Umbro Trophy Final. Kidderminster Harriers' great season was also rewarded withAdie Smith being selected to start in the back three, and Dean Bennett and Ian Foster winning their first caps, whileit was good to see that Wembley's losing 'keeper, Adam Sollitt, who was selected as the Conference's best, but experienced his worst game of the season at Wembley, was picked to start his first international. Showing great character he played immaculately.

Another excellent first half saw Dale Watkins complete a 'hat-trick' of goals - over three games - as England's only scorer this season, when he coolly put England ahead from the penalty spot after debutant Justin Jackson had been tripped.

The Welsh played better and better as the game developed, but it was probably John Owens' commendable policy (as the games are only friendlies) of ensuring that any uncapped members of his squad do get the chance to wear an England shirt, which may have unhinged the system that looked to be about to achieve another clean sheet.

The Welsh free kicks from Gary Lloyd had been superb and their very last effort was headed home by Glyndwr Hughes to produce a deserved draw.

John Owens' third season in charge left his England squad still undefeated, but in each year it is getting more difficult for anyone to coach, play, report on or administer these games as they are really are just low key friendly matches with very little support from the terraces or the headquarters.

Let's hope all this changes very soon and a lively competitive tournament is set up for the England squad that does after all represent 97 per cent of our adult male footballers.

Below: Final words from John Owens in Padova before the international against Italy.   Photo: Andrew Chitty

ENGLAND ACTION

v Italy: Jason Goodliffe forms the attack but is outnumbered. Photo: Andrew Chitty

v Holland: Warren Patmore rises to power in a header. Photo: Keith Clayton

v Wales: Dale Watkins scores his third England goal of the season from the penalty spot past Tony Pennock.
Photo: Keith Clayton

ITALY SERIE C UNDER 21   1   v   1   ENGLAND SEMI PROFESSIONAL
Cavalli   Watkins
(at Padova. Att: 1,150)

ENGLAND SQUAD (3-5-2): Steve Farrelly (Kingstonian), Simon Marples (Doncaster Rovers), Paul Underwood (Rushden & Diamonds), Jason Goodliffe (Hayes), Mark Smith (Stevenage Borough), Tim Ryan (Southport), Geoff Pitcher (Kingstonian), Garry Butterworth (Rushden & Diamonds) (captain), Warren Patmore (Yeovil Town), Dale Watkins (Kettering Town), Gary Patterson (Kingstonian), Adam Sollitt (Kettering Town).
SUBSTITUTES: Marc McGregor (Forest Green Rovers) for Warren Patmore, Adie Smith (Kidderminster Harriers) for Jason Goodliffe, Rob Cousins (Yeovil Town) for Simon Marples, Stuart Drummond (Morecambe) for Geoff Pitcher, Adam Sollitt (Kettering Town).

ITALY: Alessandre Ruggini, Simone Puleo, Mirko Savini, Paolo Gobba, Mattia Notarg, Bruni Emanuele, Durio Serra, Andrew Stampetta, Simone Cavalli, Vincento De Liguori, Vincento la Quinta, Luca Formica, Vonni Chiarotto, Vosco Morelli, Federico Coppola, Leonardo Coppola.

ENGLAND SEMI PROFESSIONAL   1   v   0   HOLLAND AMATEURS
Watkins
(at The Drill Field. Att: 1,150)

ENGLAND: Steve Farrelly (Kingstonian), Simon Marples (Doncaster Rovers), Simon Wormull (Rushden & Diamonds), Jason Goodliffe (Hayes), Mark Smith (Stevenage Borough), Tim Ryan (Southport), Geoff Pitcher (Kingstonian), Stewart Drummond (Morecambe), Warren Patmore (Yeovil Town), Dale Watkins (Kettering Town), Gary Patterson (Kingstonian).
SUBSTITUTES: Adam Sollitt (Kettering Town) for Steve Farrelly, Kevin McIntyre (Doncaster Rovers) for Simon Marples, Rob Cousins (Yeovil Town) for Jason Goodliffe, Adrian Smith (Kidderminster Harriers) for Mark Smith, Marc McGregor (Forest Green Rovers) for Warren Patmore.

HOLLAND: Schoemaker, Venterink, Knijn, van de Homberg, van Rijswijk, Boots, Hoffman, Thies, Wissink, Bierstekers, Linger.
SUBSTITUTES: Pak, van Haagen, Sepp, Dreuze.
Referee: A N Butler   **Assistants:** T Massey, R A Pashley   **Fourth Official:** L Higgins

They're still trying to look cheerful, but it was very cold and very wet.
Back Row: Jimmy Conway, John Owens, Rob Cousins, Warren Patmore, Stuart Drummond, Gary Patterson, Mark Smith, Jason Goodliffe, Simon Marples, Tim Ryan, Marc MacGregor, Adam Sollitt, Tour Doctor, Steve Avery
Front Row: Adie Smith, Paul Underwood, Dale Watkins, Geoff Pitcher, Gary Butterworth, Steve Farrelly.

Photo: Andrew Chitty

WALES SEMI PROFESSIONAL 1 v 1 ENGLAND SEMI PROFESSIONAL

Hughes   Watkins

(at Llanelli. Att: 1200)

WALES: Tony Pennock (Yeovil Town), Mike Flynn (Newport County), Gary Lloyd (Barry Town), Andrew York (Barry Town), Neil O'Brien (Cwmbran Town), Dave Barnhouse (Carmarthen Town), Chris Summers (Cwmbran Town), Anthony Wright (Llanelli), Adrian Needs (Merthyr Tydfil), Ricky Evans (Total Network Solutions), Mark Dickeson (Llanelli).

SUBSTITUTES: Glyndwr Hughes (Aberystwyth Town) for Anthony Wright, Aneurin Thomas (Aberystwyth Town) for Neil O'Brien, Mark Hughes for Mark Dickeson, Gareth Evans (Newtown) for Ricky Evans, Glyn Garner (Llanelli) for Tony Pennock.

ENGLAND: Adam Sollitt (Kettering Town), Simon Wormull (Rushden & Diamonds), Jason Goodliffe (Hayes), Adrian Smith (Kidderminster Harriers), Tim Ryan (Southport), Kevin McIntyre (Doncaster Rovers), Geoff Pitcher (Kingstonian), Gary Patterson (Kingstonian), Dale Watkins (Kettering Town), Justin Jackson (Morecambe), Stewart Drummond (Morecambe).

SUBSTITUTES: Dean Bennett (Kidderminster Harriers) for Dale Watkins, Ian Foster (Kidderminster Harriers) for Justin Jackson, Rob Cousins (Yeovil Town) for Geoff Pitcher, Steve Farrelly (Kingstonian) for Adam Sollitt, Mark Smith (Stevenage Borough) for Gary Patterson.

Above: Dale Watkins. Photo: Keith Clayton

NEW "CAPS" 1999-2000

Rob Cousins
(Yeovil Town, now Forest Green Rovers)
Photo: Andrew Chitty

Jason Goodliffe
(Hayes)
Photo: Andrew Chitty

Marc MacGregor
(Forest Green Rovers, now Nuneaton Borough)
Photo: Andrew Chitty

Stuart Drummond
(Morecambe)

ENGLAND SEMI-PRO CAPS 1979-2000

KEY TO COUNTRY CODES:
E - Eire; I - Italy; F - Finland; G - Gibralter; H - Holland; N - Norway; S - Scotland; W - Wales.
Players capped for the first time during season 1999-2000 are in bold.

Gary Abbott (Welling) 87 I(s), S(s), 92 W(s)	(3)
David Adamson (Boston Utd) 79 SH, 80 ISH	(5)
Tony Agana (Weymouth) 86 E	(1)
Carl Alford (Kettering T. & Rushden & Ds) 96 EH	(2)
Ian Arnold (Kettering Town) 95.W(s)H	(2)
Jim Arnold (Stafford Rangers) 79 SH	(2)
Nick Ashby (Kettering & Rushden & Ds) 94 FN, 95 G 96 EH	(5)
Noel Ashford (Enfield & Redbridge For.) 82 GHS, 83 IHS, 84 WHSI, 85 WI(s), 86 EE,87 W(s), IHS, 90 WE, 91 I(s)	(21)
John Askey (Macclesfield) 90 W	(1)
Paul Bancroft (Kidderminster H.) 89 IW, 90 IWE, 91 W	(6)
Chris Banks (Cheltenham T.) 98 H, 99 W	(2)
Keith Barrett (Enfield) 81 HSI, 82 GIHS, 83 IHS, 84 W(s)HS, 85 IHS	(16)
Laurence Batty (Woking) 93 F(s), 95 WHG	(4)
Mark Beeney (Maidstone) 89 I(s)	(1)
Dean Bennett (Kidderminster H) 00 W(s)	**(1)**
Graham Benstead (Kettering) 94 WFN(s)	(3)
Kevin Betsy (Woking) 98 H(s)	(1)
Marcus Bignot (Kidderminster H) 97 H	(1)
Jimmy Bolton (Kingstonian) 95 G	(1)
Steve Book (Cheltenham Town) 99 IHW	(3)
Gary Brabin (Runcorn) 94 WFN	(3)
Mark Bradshaw (Halifax T.) 98 H	(1)
Colin Brazier (Kidderminster) 87 W	(1)
Stewart Brighton (Bromsgrove) 94 W	(1)
Steve Brooks (Cheltenham) 88 W(s), 90 WE	(3)
Derek Brown (Woking) 94 F(s)N	(2)
Kevan Brown (Woking) 95 WHG 96 H 97 E	(5)
Corey Browne (Dover) 94 F(s)N(s), 95 H(s)	(3)
David Buchanan (Blyth) 86 E(s)E	(2)
Brian Butler (Northwich) 93 F	(1)
Gary Butterworth (Rushden & Diamonds) 97 EH, 98 H, 99 IHW, 00 I	(7)
Steve Butler (Maidstone) 88 W, 89 IW	(3)
Chris Byrne (Macclesfield T.) 97 H	(1)
Mark Carter (Runcorn & Barnet) 87 WIHS, 88 W, 89 IW, 90 IE, 91 IW(s)	(11)
Kim Casey (Kidderminster) 86 WEE(s), 87 WI	(5)
Paul Cavell (Redbridge) 92 W, 93 F	(2)
Kevin Charlton (Telford) 85 WI	(2)
Lee Charles (Hayes) 99 I(s) H(s) W(s)	(3)
Andrew Clarke (Barnet) 90 EE	(2)
David Clarke (Blyth Spartans) 80 IS(s)H, 81 HSI, 82 IHS, 83 HS, 84 HSI	(14)
Gary Clayton (Burton) 86 E	(1)
Robert Codner (Barnet) 88 W	(1)
John Coleman (Morecambe) 93 F(s)	(1)
Darren Collins (Enfield) 93 F(s), 94 WFN	(4)
Andy Comyn (Hednesford T.) 98 H(s), 99 I(s)H(s)W(s)	(4)
Steve Conner (Dartford, Redbridge & Dagenham & R) 90 I, 91 IW, 92 W, 93 F	(5)
David Constantine (Altrincham) 85 IHS, 86 W	(4)
Robbie Cooke (Kettering) 89 W(s), 90 I	(2)
Scott Cooksey (Hednesford T.) 97 E 98 H(s)	(2)
Alan Cordice (Wealdstone) 83 IHS, 84 WS(s), I(s), 85 IHS	(9)
Rob Cousins (Yeovil Town) 00 I(s)HW	**(3)**
Ken Cramman (Gateshead & Rushden & Diamonds) 96 E 97 EH	(3)

Paul Cuddy (Altrincham) 87 IHS (3)

Paul Culpin (Nuneaton B) 84 W, 85 W(s) IHS (5)

Michael Danzey (Woking) 99 IH (2)

Paul Davies (Kidderminster H.) 86 W, 87 WIS, 88 W, 89 W (6)

John Davison (Altrincham)
79 SH, 80 IS, 81 HSI, 82 GIHS, 83 IHS,
84 WHIS, 85 IHS, 86 WEE (24)

John Denham (Northwich Victoria) 80 H (1)

Peter Densmore (Runcorn) 88 W, 89 I (2)

Phil Derbyshire (Mossley) 83 H(s)S(s) (2)

Mick Doherty (Weymouth) 86 W(s) (1)

Neil Doherty (Kidderminster H.) 97 E (1)

Stuart Drummond (Morecambe) 00 I(s)HW **(3)**

Lee Endersby (Harrow Bor.) 96 H (1)

Mick Farrelly (Altrincham) 87 IHS (3)

Steve Farrelly (Macclesfield & Kingstonian) 95 H(s)G(s),
00 IHW(s) (5)

Trevor Finnegan (Weymouth) 81 HS (2)

Murray Fishlock (Yeovil Town) 99 H(s) (1)

Richard Forsyth (Kidderminster) 95 WHG (3)

Ian Foster (Kidderminster H) 00 W(s) **(1)**

Paul Furlong (Enfield) 90 IEE, 91 IW (5)

Mark Gardiner (Macclesfield T.) 97 E (1)

Jerry Gill (Yeovil T.) 97 E (1)

John Glover (Maidstone Utd) 85 WIHS (4)

Mark Golley (Sutton Utd.) 87 H(s)S, 88 W, 89 IW, 92 W (6)

Jason Goodliffe (Hayes) 00 IHW **(3)**

Paul Gothard (Dagenham & Redb.) 97 E(s), 99 I(s)W(s) (3)

Neil Grayson (Cheltenham T.) 98, H 99 IHW (4)

Phil Gridelet (Hendon & Barnet) 89 IW, 90 WEE (5)

Steve Guppy (Wycombe W.) 93 W (1)

Steve Hancock (Macclesfield) 90 W (1)

David Harlow (Farnborough T.) 97 E(s)H (2)

Barry Hayles (Stevenage Bor.) 96 EH (2)

Brian Healy (Morecambe) 98 H (1)

Tony Hemmings (Northwich) 93 F (1)

Andy Hessenthaler (Dartford) 90 I (1)

Kenny Hill (Maidstone Utd) 80 ISH (3)

Mark Hine (Gateshead) 95 W(s)H (2)

Simeon Hodson (Kidderminster) 94 WFN (3)

Colin Hogarth (Guiseley) 95 WH (2)

Steven Holden (Kettering) 94 WFN(s), 95 HG (5)

Mark Hone (Welling) 90 I, 93 F, 94 W(s)F(s)N (5)

Gary Hooley (Frickley) 85 W (1)

Dean Hooper (Kingstonian) 98 H (1)

Keith Houghton (Blyth Spartans) 79 S (1)

Barry Howard (Altrincham) 81 HSI, 82 GIHS (7)

Neil Howarth (Macclesfield) 95 H(s) 97 E (2)

David Howell (Enfield) 85 H(s)S(s), 86 WEE, 87 WIHS,
88 W, 89 IW, 90 IEE (14)

Lee Howells (Cheltenham T.) 98, H 99 W (1)

Lee Hughes (Kidderminster) 96 EH 97 EH (4)

Delwyn Humphreys (Kidderminster H.) 91 W(s), 92 W,
94 WFN, 95 WH (7)

Steve Humphries (Barnet) 87 H(s) (1)

Nicky Ironton (Enfield) 83 H(s), 84 W (2)

Justin Jackson (Morecambe) 00 W **(1)**

Tony Jennings (Enfield) 79 SH, 80 ISH, 81 HSI, 82 GIHS (12)

Jeff Johnson (Altrincham) 81 SI, 82 GIHS, 83 IHS,
84 HSI, 84 IHS, 86 W(s)EE (18)

Tom Jones (Weymouth) 87 W (1)

Anton Joseph (Telford Utd. & Kidderminster H.) 84 S(s),
85 WIHS, 86 W(s), 87 WI(s)H, 88 W, 89 IW, 90 IEE (14)

Andy Kerr (Wycombe) 93 W (1)

Ged Kimmins (Hyde Utd.) 96 E(s)H(s) 97 E(s) (3)

Mike Lake (Macclesfield) 89 I (1)

Andy Lee (Telford U. & Witton A.) 89 I(s), 91 IW (3)

David Leworthy (Farnborough & Rushden & Diamonds)
93 W, 94 W 97 EH (4)

Kenny Lowe (Barnet) 91 IW (2)

Martin McDonald (Macclesfield) 95 G(s) (1)

Mark McGregor (Forest Green Rovers) 00 I(s)H(s) **(2)**

Kevin McIntyre (Doncaster Rovers) 00 H(s)W **(2)**

John McKenna (Boston Utd) 88 W(s), 90 IEE,
91 IW, 92 W (7)

Simon Marples (Doncaster Rovers) 00 IH **(2)**

Leroy May (Stafford R.) 95 G(s) (1)

"OLD BOYS" CORNER

Garry Brabin

Andy Pape
Photo: Dave West

Neil Grayson
Photo: Andrew Chitty

John Watson
Photo: Bob Thomas

Bobby Mayes (Redbridge) 92 W	(1)
Paul Mayman (Northwich Vic) 80 IS	(2)
Stewart Mell (Burton) 85 W	(1)
Neil Merrick (Weymouth) 80 I(s)S	(2)
Russell Milton (Dover) 94 FN	(2)
Trevor Morley (Nuneaton) 84 WHSI, 85 WS(s)	(6)
Les Mutrie (Blyth Spartans) 79 SH, 80 ISH	(5)
Mark Newson (Maidstone U) 84 WHSI, 85 W	(5)
Doug Newton (Burton) 85 WHS	(3)
Paul Nicol (Kettering T) 91 IW, 92 W	(3)
Steve Norris (Telford) 88 W(s)	(1)
Joe O'Connor (Hednesford T.) 97 EH(s)	(2)
Eamon O'Keefe (Mossley) 79 SH	(2)
Frank Ovard (Maidstone) 81 H(s)S(s)I(s)	(3)
Andy Pape (Harrow Bor. & Enfield) 85 W(s)HS, 86 W(s)E, 87 WIHS, 88 W, 89 IW, 90 IWE	(15)
Brian Parker (Yeovil Town) 80 S	(1)
Warren Patmore (Yeovil Town) 99 IHW, 00 IH	(5)
Gary Patterson (Kingstonian) 99 IH, 00 IHW	(5)
Steve Payne (Macclesfield T.) 97 H	(1)
Trevor Peake (Nuneaton Bor) 79 SH	(2)
David Pearce (Harrow Bor) 84 I(s)	(1)
Brendan Phillips (Nuneaton Bor. & Kettering T.) 79 SH, 80 S(s)H	(4)
Gary Philips (Barnet) 82 G	(1)
Owen Pickard (Yeovil T.) 98 H(s)	(1)
Geoff Pitcher (Kingstonian) 99W, 00 IHW	(1)
Phil Power (Macclesfield T.) 96 E(s)H(s)	(2)
Ryan Price (Stafford R. & Macclesfield) 92 W(s) 93 WF 96 EH 97 H	(6)
Steve Prindiville 98 H(s)	(1)
Simon Read (Farnborough) 92 W(s)	(1)
Andy Reid (Altrincham) 95 W	(1)
Carl Richards (Enfield) 86 E	(1)
Derek Richardson (Maidstone U) 83 I, 84 W, 86 E	(4)
Ian Richardson (Dagenham & Red) 95 G	(1)
Kevin Richardson (Bromsgrove) 94 WFN	(3)
Paul Richardson (Redbridge) 92 W, 93 WF	(3)
Terry Robbins (Welling) 92 W, 93 WF, 94 WFN	(6)
Peter Robinson (Blyth S) 83 IHS, 84 WI, 85 W	(6)
John Rogers (Altrincham) 81 HSI, 82 I(s)S	(5)
Paul Rogers (Sutton) 89 W, 90 IE(2), 91 IW	(6)
Colin Rose (Witton Alb.) 96 E(s)H	(2)
Kevin Rose (Kidderminster) 94 F(s)N	(2)
Brian Ross (Marine) 93 W(s)F(s), 94 W(s) 95 WH	(5)
Tim Ryan (Southport) 98 H, 99 IHW, 00 IHW	(7)
Neil Sellars (Scarboro) 81 HSI, 82 GH(s)S, 83 IHS	(9)
Mark Shail (Yeovil T.) 93 W	(1)
Simon Shaw (Doncaster Rovers) 99 IH	(2)
Peter Shearer (Cheltenham) 89 I(s)	(1)
Paul Shirtliff (Frickley A. & Boston U.) 86 EE, 87 WIH, 88 W, 89 IW, 90 IWEE, 92 W, 93 WF	(15)
Paul Showler (Altrincham) 91 I(s)W	(2)
Gordon Simmonite (Boston Utd.) 79 S(s)H(s), 80 ISH	(5)
Gary Simpson (Stafford R.) 86 EE, 87 IHS, 90 IWEE	(9)
Wayne Simpson (Stafford) 94 FN(s)	(2)
Glenn Skivington (Barrow) 90 IWE, 91 IW	(5)
Adrian Smith (Kidderminster H) 00 I(s)H(s)W	**(3)**
Alan Smith (Alvechurch) 82 GIS	(3)
Ian Smith (Mossley) 80 ISH(s)	(3)
Mark Smith (Stevenage Bor.) 96 EH 98 H, 99 IHW, 00 IHW(s)	(9)
Ossie Smith (Runcorn) 84 W	(1)
Tim Smithers (Nuneaton), 85 W(s)I, 86 W	(3)
Adam Sollitt (Kettering Town) 00 I(s)H(s)W	**(3)**
Simon Stapleton (Wycombe) 93 W	(1)
Mickey Stephens (Sutton), 82 GS(s), 86 WEE(s)	(5)
Billy Stewart (Southport) 98 H	(1)
Bob Stockley (Nuneaton Bor) 80 H	(1)
Steve Stott (Kettering T., Rushden & Ds & Yeovil T.) 95 WH(s)G, 96 EH, 99 HW(s)	(7)
Peter Taylor (Maidstone) 84 HSI	(3)
Steve Taylor (Bromsgrove R.) 95 G	(1)
Shaun Teale (Weymouth) 88 W	(1)
Stuart Terry (Altrincham) W	(1)

Brian Thompson (Yeovil & Maidstone) 79 SH, 81 HSI, 82 IHS, 83 IHS, 84 WHSI (15)

Steve Thompson (Wycombe) 93 W (1)

Kevin Todd (Berwick Rangers) 91 W (1)

Mark Tucker (Woking) 96 E (1)

Tony Turner (Telford) 85 W (1)

Paul Underwood (Rushden & Diamonds) 99 IH, 00 I (3)

David Venables (Stevenage Bor.) 94 W(s), 95 HG 96 EH(s) (5)

Jamie Victory (Cheltenham T.) 98 H(s) (1)

David Waite (Enfield) 82 G (1)

Paul Walker (Blyth) 86 WEE(s), 87 S(s) (4)

Steve Walters (Northwich Victoria) 97 H (1)

Mark Ward (Northwich Victoria) 83 S(s) (1)

Dale Watkins (Cheltenham T.) 98 H, 99 I(s), 00 IHW (5)

John Watson (Wealdstone, Scarborough & Maidstone) 79 S(s)H, 80 ISH, 81 HSI, 82 IHS, 83 IHS, 84 W(s)HSI (18)

Liam Watson (Marine) 95 WH(s) (2)

Paul Watts (Redbridge Forest) 89 W, 90 IEE, 91 I, 92 W, 93 WF (8)

Paul Webb (Bromsgrove R & Kidderminster H) 93 F, 94 WFN(s) 95 WHG 96 EH 97 EH (11)

Mark West (Wycombe W) 91 W (1)

Barry Whitbread (Runcorn & Altrincham) 79 SH, 80 ISH, 81 I (6)

Russ Wilcox (Frickley) 86 WE (2)

Barry Williams (Nuneaton Borough) 99 H(s)W (2)

Colin Williams (Scarborough & Telford Utd.) 81 HS, 82 IHS (5)

Roger Willis (Barnet) 91 I(s) (1)

Paul Wilson (Frickley) 86 W (1)

Simon Wormull (Dover Athletic) 99 I(s)W (2)

Mark Yates (Cheltenham Town) 99 IW (2)

Pre-Match Tension
Stuart Drummond, Adam Sollitt, Mark Smith and Tim Ryan before the International in Italy
Photo: Andrew Chitty

ENGLAND ON TOUR
Photos by Andrew Chitty

Top: The coach has to be loaded at Venice airport . . .

. . . and unloaded in Padova.

Below: Off to the game before the rain really sets in.

ENGLAND ON TOUR

Photos by Andrew Chitty

Top left: At least John Owens has eleven men on the field.

Top right: Guess who was a 'sub' (Gary Butterworth or Stuart Drummond).

Centre right: Post match relaxation for the Yeovil connection (Warren Patmore and Rob Cousins).

Below: Relaxation with Italian pasta.

FA XI REPRESENTATIVE MATCHES 1999-2000

FA XI 3 v 1 RYMAN LEAGUE XI
Akuamoah, Patmore, West   Watson
(At Dulwich Hamlet FC)

FA SQUAD: Steve Farrelly (Kingstonian), Lew Watts (Welling United), Rob Hollingdale (Woking), Matt Crossley (Kingstonian), Jason Goodliffe (Hayes), Michael Danzey (Woking), Ritchie Hanlon (Welling United), Steve Perkins (Woking), Warren Patmore (Yeovil Town), Lee Charles (Hayes), Gary Patterson (Kingstonian).
SUBSTITUTIONS: Paul Wilkerson (Welling United) for Steve Farrelly, Steve West (Woking) for Matt Crossley, Jamie Pitman (Yeovil Town) for Lew Watts, Eddie Akuamoah (Kingstonian) for Lee Charles, Phil Wingfield (Kingstonian) for Rob Hollingdale.

RYMAN LEAGUE SQUAD: Tony Roberts (St Albans City), Justin Gregory (Dulwich Hamlet), Jason Chewins (Aldershot Town), Tim Cole (Dagenham & Redbridge), Jimmy McFarlane (Purfleet), Ashley Vickers (St Albans City), Greg Berry (Purfleet), Steve Watson (Farnborough Town), Gary Abbott (Aldershot Town), Paul Whitmarsh (Hendon), Grant Payne (Aldershot Town).
SUBSTITUTIONS: Paul Newell (Dagenham & Redbridge) for Tony Roberts, Boncho Guentchev (Hendon) for Ashley Vickers, Dave McEwan (Dulwich Hamlet) for Greg Berry, Dave Stevens (Dulwich Hamlet) for Gary Abbott.

FA XI 0 v 0 DR MARTENS LEAGUE XI
(At VS Rugby FC)

FA SQUAD: Adam Sollitt (Kettering Town), Ian Clarkson (Kidderminster Harriers), Steve Hollis (Accrington Stanley), Scott Guyett (Southport), Colin Vowden (Kettering Town), Tim Ryan (Southport), Barry Williams (Nuneaton Borough), Iain Brunskill (Runcorn), Mark Druce (Kidderminster Harriers), Ian Foster (Kidderminster Harriers), Jimmy Kelly (Hednesford Town).
SUBSTITUTIONS: Adie Smith (Kidderminster Harriers) for Colin Vowden, Tim Clarke (Kidderminster Harriers) for Adam Sollitt, Dean Bennett (Kidderminster Harriers) for Jimmy Kelly, Lee Elam (Southport) for Ian Clarkson.

DR MARTENS LEAGUE SQUAD: Danny McDonnell (Halesowen), Rob Warner (Tamworth), Jason Burnham (Atherstone), Richard Lavery (Atherstone), Dave Robinson (Kings Lynn), Paul Hatton (Tamworth), Ian Cambridge (Cambridge City), Mark Turner (Kings Lynn - captain), Mark Hallam (Tamworth), Christian Moore (Ilkeston Town), Jon Holloway (Bath City).
SUBSTITUTES: David Foy (Tamworth), Nick Colley (Tamworth), Darren Acton (Tamworth), Leon Kelly (Atherstone United).

FA XI 4 v 0 COMBINED SERVICES
Elmes, McGregor, Thackeray, Moore
(at Worcester City FC)

FA SQUAD: Chris Mackenzie (Nuneaton Borough), Thackeray (Nuneaton Borough), Simon Travis (Telford United), Ian Wright (Hereford United), Rob Cousins (Yeovil Town), Andy Comyn (Hednesford Town), Taylor (Hereford United), Stuart Drummond (Morecambe), Rob Elmes (Hereford United), Mark MacGregor (Forest Green Rovers), Durcross (Nuneaton Borough).
SUBSTITUTES: Shuttlewood (Forest Green Rovers) for Chris Mackenzie, Angus (Nuneaton Borough) for Thackeray, Gary Twynham (Hednesford Town) for Taylor, Moore (Ilkeston Town) for Rob Elmes.

FA XI 0 v 1 BRITISH STUDENTS
(at Taunton Town FC)

FA SQUAD: Mark Coombe (Taunton Town), Paul Edwards (Tiverton Town), Roy O'Brien (Dorchester Town), Nick Marker (Tiverton Town), Alex Brown (Weymouth), Gary Thorne (Gloucester City), Matthew Hale (Weymouth), John Holloway (Bath City), Steve Daley (Tiverton Town), Mike Davies (Bath City), Mark Robinson (Weymouth), Matthew Rose (Gloucester City), Martin Sullivan (Dorchester Town), Ellis Laight (Taunton Town), Anthony Lynch (Taunton Town), Martin Paul (Bath City).
SUBSTITUTES: Robinson (Weymouth) for Anthony Lynch, Hare (Weymouth) for Martin Sullivan, Dungey (Dorchester Town) for Paul Edwards, Loram (Taunton Town), Nancekivell (Tiverton Town) for Mike Davis.

THE NATIONWIDE CONFERENCE

FOOTBALL CONFERENCE

Founded 1979

President: J C Thompson MBIM, Minst.M, FID

Chairman: W J King   **Chief Executive:** J A Moules

Secretary: M A Annett, The Nationwide Conference, Collingwood House, Schooner Court, Crossways, Dartford, Kent DA2 6QQ
Tel: 01322 303120   Fax: 01322 303121

Rushden & Diamonds have everything a senior non-League (or probable Division 2 & 3 clubs) could want, but they also got the tag of `favourites' at the beginning of the season and this not only inspires their opponents each week, but also give their supporters very high expectations.

Diamonds started brilliantly last season, especially in comparison to Jan Molby's Kidderminster Harriers. Yeovil Town and Nuneaton Borough also gave their supporters hopes which were not to be fulfiled and Scarborough although obviously strong at the start didn't seem to be consistent enough.

As usual most clubs were good enough to beat any opponent on their day, but only one or two clubs either had the technique and skill, or the strength in depth to see their challenge through to the end of the season.

The F.A. Cup produced its heroes as usual with the big guns from Hereford and Rushden, both reaching the Third Round. This, of course, may have taken the edge off the Diamond's Conference run-in, but in the F.A. Trophy they didn't have the same problem as lowly Sutton United beat them 3-0 at Nene Park in a Sixth Round replay.

Geoff Chapple produced yet another Trophy winning squad for Kingstonian and won a superb final against a plucky Kettering Town side, despite the absence of England star Gary Patterson.

Sutton United and Telford United were the unlucky semi-finalists, but both had more important battles at the other end of the table. Telford surviving, but the Surrey club made a quick return to the Ryman League and was relegated with Welling United who finally dropped after years of battling and unlucky Altrincham who were only in the bottom three on the final day of the season!

The new season sees seven full time clubs, the top section of the Conference accepted onto the Auto Windscreen competition and the very confident talk of at least two up to Division Three in a years time.

Attendances are up and facilities improved by the month so let's hope that increased competitiveness also brings increased excitement and quality.

THE **NON-LEAGUE** PAPER

CONFERENCE & PYRAMID LEAGUES SOCCER / £1.00

NATIONWIDE CONFERENCE FINAL LEAGUE TABLE 1999-2000

		P	Home					Away					Pts	gd
			W	D	L	F	A	W	D	L	F	A		
1	Kidderminster Harriers	42	16	3	2	47	16	10	4	7	28	24	85	35
2	Rushden & Diamonds	42	11	8	2	37	18	10	5	6	34	24	76	29
3	Morecambe	42	10	7	4	46	29	8	9	4	24	19	70	22
4	Scarborough	42	10	6	5	36	14	9	6	6	24	21	69	25
5	Kingstonian	42	9	4	8	30	24	11	3	7	28	20	67	14
6	Dover Athletic	42	10	7	4	43	26	8	5	8	22	30	66	9
7	Yeovil Town	42	11	4	6	37	28	7	6	8	23	35	64	-3
8	Hereford United	42	9	6	6	43	31	6	8	7	18	21	59	9
9	Southport	42	10	5	6	31	21	5	8	8	24	35	58	-1
10	Stevenage Borough	42	8	5	8	26	20	8	4	9	34	34	57	6
11	Hayes	42	7	3	11	24	28	9	5	7	33	30	56	-1
12	Doncaster Rovers	42	7	5	9	19	21	8	4	9	27	27	54	-2
13	Kettering Town	42	8	10	3	25	19	4	6	11	19	31	52	-6
14	Woking	42	5	6	10	17	27	8	7	6	28	26	52	-8
15	Nuneaton Borough	42	7	6	8	28	25	5	9	7	21	28	51	-4
16	Telford United	42	12	4	5	34	21	2	5	14	22	45	51	-10
17	Hednesford Town	42	10	3	8	27	23	5	3	13	18	45	51	-23
18	Northwich Victoria	42	10	8	3	33	25	3	4	14	20	53	51	-25
19	Forest Green Rovers	42	11	2	8	35	23	2	6	13	19	40	47	-9
20	Welling United	42	6	5	10	27	32	7	3	11	27	34	47	-12
21	Altrincham	42	6	8	7	31	26	3	11	7	20	34	46	-9
22	Sutton United	42	4	8	9	23	32	4	2	15	16	43	34	-36

THE MAIL ON SUNDAY GOALSCORER OF THE YEAR

Conf.			FAC	ECT	FAUT
29	Justin Jackson (Morecambe)	+	1	-	1
24	Carl Alford (Stevenage Borough)	+	-	1	1
18	Neil Davis (Hereford United)	+	1	-	2
17	Ian Foster (Kidderminster Harriers)	+	-	-	-
15	Joff Vansittart (Dover Athletic)	+	-	-	4
14	Ian Arnold (Southport)	+	1	-	3
	Kevin Ellison (Altrincham)	+	1	-	-
13	Steve Brodie (Scarborough)	+	-	1	2
	Lee Charles (Hayes)	+	5	-	-
	Robin Elmes (Hereford United)	+	1	-	1
	Paul Fewings (Hereford United)	+	2	-	-
	Warren Patmore (Yeovil Town)	+	-	2	2
12	Nassim Akrour (Woking)	+	-	2	3
	Stewart Hadley (Kidderminter H.)	+	-	-	-
	Ritchie Hanlon (Welling United)	+	-	1	1
	Richard Landon (Altrincham)	+	1	-	1
	David Leworthy (Kingstonian)	+	2	1	2
	Marc McGregor (Forest Green Rovers)	+	1	-	1
	Val Owen (Northwich Victoria)	+	1	-	-
11	Darren Collins (Rushden & Diamonds)	+	2	-	2
	Phil Eastwood (Morecambe)	+	-	-	2
	Lee Elam (Southport)	+	-	-	1
	Mike McElhatton (Rushden & Diam.)	+	2	-	-
	Zeke Rowe (Welling United)	+	-	-	-
	Dave Stevens (Hayes)	+	-	-	-
	Mark Watson (Sutton United)	+	-	-	1

NATIONWIDE CONFERENCE RESULTS 1999-2000

Bold = Best Attendances

Each cell shows the result (score) and the attendance for the home team (row) against the away team (column).

Home Team \ Away	Altrincham	Doncaster	Dover A	Forest G	Hayes	H'ford	Hereford	Kettering	Kidd. H.	Kingst'n	M'combe	Northwich	Nuneaton	Rushden	S carboro	Southport	Stevenage	Sutton U	Telford U	Welling U	Woking	Yeovil T
Altrincham	X	1-2 1066	3-0 938	1-1 853	1-2 657	0-1 851	0-1 1006	1-1 939	0-0 **1761**	1-3 779	2-2 1159	2-0 1713	2-2 765	1-2 1114	2-1 761	3-0 1226	0-1 853	3-0 889	3-3 720	0-1 839	1-1 1006	2-2 792
Doncaster Rovers	0-1 2978	X	0-1 1976	3-2 4302	0-0 3546	2-1 3021	2-2 2767	2-1 3544	1-2 2723	1-0 2548	0-1 2009	2-0 1865	0-1 3407	0-1 4187	0-1 **4706**	1-1 4285	1-2 2631	3-0 2447	2-0 1871	1-1 3497	0-0 1960	0-3 2498
Dover Athletic	2-2 1015	0-1 876	X	3-0 967	2-2 1011	3-0 669	2-0 840	2-0 693	3-2 1314	1-0 1070	3-1 1471	4-1 740	1-2 1087	1-0 **2904**	0-1 945	1-0 773	4-2 1001	1-2 1056	5-2 704	1-2 1658	2-2 780	3-0 1442
Forest Green Rovers	1-1 901	3-0 646	3-1 876	X	2-1 962	1-0 1006	1-1 1129	1-0 1795	3-3 5301	0-1 931	1-1 1016	0-0 911	2-3 1929	3-2 3195	5-0 1626	1-1 1241	1-1 1419	3-2 607	2-0 830	1-0 765	1-0 1505	1-0 3028
Hayes	1-1 642	2-1 851	1-2 612	2-1 962	X	1-1 1655	1-0 1252	2-1 2636	2-1 1183	1-4 1240	0-0 1002	2-1 2186	2-1 2434	4-1 1295	1-0 1097	1-0 1617	2-2 1058	1-2 811	0-3 815	2-4 2041	2-4 2603	2-4 676
Hednesford Town	5-0 1193	3-4 1087	1-0 797	1-0 1006	2-1 962	X	1-1 1189	4-2 1980	0-1 1522	1-0 1708	0-2 664	3-2 1768	0-0 1104	1-1 1947	3-0 4022	1-2 1242	0-3 1287	3-0 1940	1-1 1386	3-1 824	1-0 648	1-0 **1837**
Hereford United	2-2 1789	2-1 1383	2-0 2003	1-1 1129	1-1 1655	1-1 1189	X	4-2 1980	4-3 **4437**	2-3 1527	1-1 1808	1-0 1812	2-1 2551	1-1 1724	4-4 1886	2-1 2810	2-2 2143	4-1 1432	2-2 1910	1-2 1390	2-4 2216	0-1 972
Kettering Town	0-0 1170	5-3 1690	1-2 1026	1-0 1795	1-0 1252	4-2 1980	0-1 716	X	3-1 1815	0-2 1485	1-1 1409	0-1 1267	1-1 2598	4-0 3744	0-0 1270	0-3 1209	1-0 1575	1-0 1328	X X	X X	X X	4-4 1329
Kidderminster Harriers	1-1 3054	2-2 1279	1-2 2175	3-3 5301	2-1 1183	0-1 1522	2-0 635	1-0 1708	X	1-0 1933	2-0 2189	3-1 1779	1-2 3152	2-0 **6254**	2-0 1784	5-0 1404	3-1 2832	1-0 2818	2-0 3138	4-1 2073	3-2 1729	4-0 1769
Kingstonian	2-2 984	1-0 2382	4-1 1106	0-1 931	1-4 1183	1-0 1708	2-3 1527	0-2 1485	0-1 1523	X	2-0 834	5-0 1003	1-1 985	0-0 1772	0-1 952	3-3 1027	1-0 1034	4-2 1527	4-2 1026	2-1 1023	0-2 **2467**	0-1 1421
Morecambe	3-3 1230	0-1 1407	2-0 1127	1-1 1016	1-4 1240	0-2 664	0-1 676	1-1 1409	1-1 1411	2-0 834	X	5-0 1024	1-1 1620	0-0 1797	0-1 2301	3-3 1027	3-3 1518	2-0 1460	2-1 1280	3-2 1046	3-1 1208	1-1 1490
Northwich Victoria	1-1 **1814**	2-1 1346	1-1 1049	0-0 911	0-0 1002	3-2 1768	2-1 616	0-1 1267	0-1 2596	5-0 1003	5-0 1024	X	3-1 1024	3-1 1231	1-1 1036	0-1 1127	3-3 1010	2-0 805	2-1 663	4-3 904	3-1 831	3-0 1011
Nuneaton Borough	3-1 2205	2-1 1688	0-2 1608	2-3 1929	2-1 2186	0-0 1104	3-0 703	1-1 2598	1-2 3152	1-1 985	1-1 1620	3-1 1024	X	4-1 **4490**	2-0 2641	4-0 2519	0-1 1250	2-0 1766	2-2 2203	2-0 2007	0-1 1355	1-1 2216
Rushden & Diamonds	1-0 2731	0-2 1723	1-1 3037	3-2 3195	2-1 2434	1-1 1947	1-2 901	4-0 3744	2-0 6254	0-0 1772	0-0 1797	3-1 1231	4-1 4490	X	1-1 2641	4-2 2619	2-1 1250	4-0 2749	1-1 2729	6-0 2805	1-3 2699	2-2 3611
Scarborough	1-0 1274	3-1 3177	1-2 **3510**	5-0 1626	4-1 1295	3-0 4022	0-1 506	0-0 1270	2-0 1784	0-1 952	0-1 2301	1-1 1036	2-0 2641	1-1 2641	X	3-0 1002	1-3 2291	3-0 1395	2-0 1317	0-0 1310	3-2 1345	5-0 2005
Southport	2-0 1427	0-0 1376	3-1 1015	1-1 1241	1-0 1097	1-2 1242	0-2 637	0-3 1209	5-0 1404	3-3 1027	3-3 1027	0-1 1127	4-0 2519	4-2 2619	3-0 1002	X	4-2 2291	1-0 1122	1-3 1010	3-2 1003	4-1 1378	1-1 1343
Stevenage Borough	1-1 1762	3-0 1156	3-1 1853	1-1 1419	1-0 1617	0-3 1287	1-2 906	1-0 1575	3-1 2832	1-0 1034	3-3 1518	3-3 1010	0-1 1250	2-1 1250	1-3 2291	4-2 2291	X	3-0 **5721**	1-3 1010	0-0 1310	4-1 1378	0-0 1452
Sutton United	3-0 805	3-3 3361	0-1 601	3-2 607	2-2 1058	3-0 1940	1-0 1006	1-0 1328	1-0 2818	4-2 1527	2-0 1460	2-0 805	2-0 1766	4-0 2749	3-0 1395	1-0 1122	0-2 1151	X	2-0 1011	2-3 814	0-1 935	0-1 1010
Telford United	0-1 1017	1-0 1077	1-1 838	2-0 830	0-3 815	1-1 1386	1-2 591	X X	2-0 3138	4-2 1026	2-1 1280	2-1 663	2-2 2203	1-1 2729	2-0 1317	1-3 1010	2-1 2191	1-0 825	X	2-0 921	1-2 1019	3-1 1002
Welling United	2-2 607	0-2 1157	2-1 1054	1-0 765	2-4 815	3-1 824	1-0 706	X X	4-1 2073	2-1 1023	3-2 1046	4-3 904	2-0 2007	6-0 2805	0-0 1310	3-2 1003	2-3 1581	2-0 1485	2-3 825	X	1-1 **1828**	2-3 1550
Woking	0-1 1565	1-3 789	2-0 1560	1-0 1505	2-4 2041	1-0 648	3-0 834	X X	3-2 1729	0-2 1023	3-1 1208	3-1 831	0-1 1355	1-3 2699	3-2 1345	4-1 1378	2-3 2992	1-0 935	1-0 1019	2-3 1550	X	0-3 2340
Yeovil Town	3-0 2214	1-3 2079	3-0 2420	1-0 **3028**	2-4 2603	1-0 1622	1-0 2632	1-3 2347	1-0 2473	3-2 1593	2-0 2042	3-2 2239	1-3 2029	5-1 2180	1-2 2031	1-1 2217	2-2 2604	1-2 1455	2-1 2174	1-1 1812	0-3 2727	X

MACMILLAN TROPHY 1999-2000

FIRST ROUND

Altrincham	1	v	0	Kidderminster Harriers
Forest Green Rovers	1	v	2	Telford United
Hednesford Town	1	v	2	Nuneaton Borough
Hereford United	2	v	0*	Sutton United
Morecambe	1	v	2	Southport
Welling United	3	v	0	Dover Athletic

SECOND ROUND

Doncaster Rovers	4	v	0	Nuneaton Borough
Kettering Town	0	v	1	Hayes
Northwich Victoria	1	v	6	Altrincham
Rushden & Diamonds	0	v	1	Telford United
Southport	1	v	2	Scarborough
Welling United	0	v	1	Kingstonian
Woking	3	v	1	Stevenage Borough
Yeovil Town	3	v	0	Hereford United

QUARTER-FINALS

Altrincham	1	v	3	Telford United
Hayes	2	v	1	Yeovil Town
Kingstonian	2	v	0	Woking
Scarborough	1	v	2	Doncaster Rovers

SEMI-FINALS 1st LEG

Hayes	0	v	0	Kingstonian
Telford United	1	v	2	Doncaster Rovers

SEMI-FINALS 2nd LEG

Doncaster Rovers	1	v	0	Telford United
Kingstonian	1	v	0	Hayes

FINAL

DONCASTER ROVERS	2	v	0	KINGSTONIAN

at Doncaster Rovers FC

For up to the minute news, results, fixtures,
and general facts and figures
from the world of non-league football
log on to

www.nlfootball.com

Brought to you by The Non-League Newspaper in conjunction with e-comsport

MANAGER OF THE YEAR 1999-2000

JAN MOLBY
Kidderminster Harriers
Photo: Peter Barnes

GOALKEEPER OF THE YEAR 1999-2000

ADAM SOLLITT
Kettering Town
(now Northampton Town)
Photo: Peter Barnes

WING BACKS OF THE YEAR 1999-2000

(Right)
RIGHT BACK
TARKAN MUSTAFA
Kingstonian

Photo: Paul Carter

(Left)
LEFT BACK
PAUL UNDERWOOD
Rushden & Diamonds

Photo: Andrew Chitty

CENTRE BACK

IAN WRIGHT
Hereford United

CENTRE BACK

ADIE SMITH
Kidderminster Harriers
Photo: Andrew Chitty

MIDFIELD COLLEAGUES FOR ENGLAND 1999-2000

(Left)
STEWART DRUMMOND
Morecambe

(Right)
GEOFF PITCHER
Kingstonian

Photo: Keith Clayton

MIDFIELD AND PLAYER OF THE YEAR 1999-2000

CONFERENCE PLAYER OF THE YEAR
MIKE MARSH
Kidderminster Harriers
(now Southport)
With Kidderminster Harriers midfield colleague and ex-England Captain, Paul Webb

Photo: Peter Barnes

STRIKER

CARL ALFORD
Stevenage Borough
(now Doncaster Rovers)
Photo: Peter Barnes

STRIKER

WARREN PATMORE
Yeovil Town
Photo: Andrew Chitty

STRIKER

JUSTIN JACKSON
Morecambe
(now Rushden & Diamonds)

Photo: Keith Clayton

BOSTON UNITED

It was a season the likes of which Boston United supporters had not seen for more than two decades. Not since they lifted the old Northern Premier League title in 1978 had the Pilgrims been able to celebrate a championship success.

But, inspired by the astute managership of Steve Evans, Boston were at last able to toast a return to the glory stakes.

When Evans was appointed to the United hot seat in October 1998, the club sat joint third bottom of the Dr. Martens Premier Division. Eighteen months, 73 league games and 42 wins later Boston were remarkably holding aloft the coveted Dr. Martens championship shield.

The 1999/2000 campaign was largely a tale of consistent success, particularly on home soil with the York Street faithful seeing their favourites drop points in just three league matches - draws against Bath and Newport plus one solitary loss, against King's Lynn over the festive period.

Eighteen home wins and a goals ratio of 64-15 laid the foundations for the title glory. On away soil, Boston were equally hard to beat with only three reverses being inflicted.

Arguably the decisive run which tipped the title race in Boston's favour came from the start of the new Millennium. A 3-0 win at Grantham on January 3 was the starting point of a stunning sequence of results which yielded fifteen wins, four draws and just one loss for a points harvest of 49 out of a possible 60 to burn off all potential challengers.

A string of six straight victories during January earned Evans the manager of the month award and the run also featured a 6-1 away demolition of Crawley, a result which became the division's biggest away win of the season.

In that match, teenage midfielder David Norris grabbed a hat-trick - goals which were to p,rove an apt sign-off before he was snapped up by Nationwide League First Division outfit Bolton Wanderers.

Goal-grabbing, in fact, was never really a problem for Boston throughout the season with the club breaking through the league century mark in their final day 4-3 win at Dorchester. Midfielder Adie Hayes was the man who `hit the ton,' a goal which was also - by coincidence - the 200th competitive strike during the eighteen month Evans regime.

Boston's leading scorer during the season, when a total of eighteen different players got their names on the score-sheet, was striker Mark Rawle with 22 to his credit.

During the season there were disappointing edits from the main knockout competitions, in particular at the hands of Leigh (FA Trophy) and Wisbech (League Cup) while Kingstonian ended United's interest in the FA Cup. But the eventual league triumph more than made up for those setbacks.

Rob Singleton

Boston United display the Dr. Martens Championship Trophy with the club's "Young Pilgrims' in front of the team.   Photo courtesy of the Lincolnshire Standard Group

BOSTON UNITED

GROUND DETAILS

York Street,
Boston,
Lincs. PE21 6HN

TELEPHONE: 01205 364406 office,
01205 365524/5 matchday no.,
Fax: 01205 354063
email: ????????????
Website: ?????

Directions:
A1 to A17 Sleaford-Boston, over rail crossing,
bear right at Eagle pub to lights over Haven Bridge,
through the lights opposite New Store,
then right intoYork Street.
Ground just off town centre

Capacity: 8,771
Cover: 8,771
Seats: 1,826

Clubhouse: (01205 362967) Open every day except
Tuesday. Live entertainmentSaturday, pool, darts, dominoes, Sunday football teams

Club Shop: At club office (as secretary's address).
A new shop is being built in ground for later this season

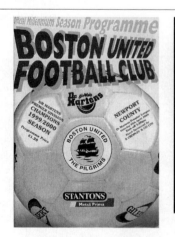

Pages: 44   Price: £1
Editor: John Blackwell (Secretary)
Tel: 01205 364406 (office)

Founded:	1934
Nickname:	The Pilgrims
Sponsors:	"Finn Forest"
Colours:	Black & amber striped shirts, black shorts with amber stripes
Change colours:	Purple and grey
Midweek matchday:	Wednesday
Newsline:	0898 121 539
Reserve League:	Lincolnshire League

CLUB OFFICIALS

Chairman:	P Malkinson
President:	Mr A E Bell
Vice-Chairman:	S Burgess

Directors: S Burgess, P Malkinson, S J Malkinson,
A Malkinson, T Ruck, R Hackford,
R Carrington, C Woodcock

General Manager / Secretary /
/ Comm. Manager: John Blackwell,
14-16 Spain Place, Boston,
Lincs PE26 6HN
Tel: 01205 364406 (office)

FOOTBALL MANAGEMENT TEAM

MANAGER   STEVE EVANS

Date of Appointment	October 1998
Date of Birth:	30th October 1962
Place of Birth:	Glasgow

PREVIOUS CLUBS

As manager	Holbeach Utd., Stamford AFC
As asst. manager/coach	-
As player	St. Johnstone, Ayr United, Bolton Wanderers

HONOURS

As manager	United Counties 97-98 (Stamford) Southern Lge. Prem. Div. 99-00
As player	-

*   *   *

Asst Manager: Trevor Quow
Physiotherapist: Peter Jellett

Season	League	Div.	Pos.	P	Home					Away					A	Pts	Manager
					W	D	L	F	A	W	D	L	F				
99-00	Southern	Premier	1	42	18	2	1	64	15	9	9	3	38	24	92		Steve Evans
98-99	Southern	Premier	2	42	12	5	4	42	21	5	11	5	27	30	67		Steve Evans
97-98	N.P.L.	Premier	2	42	11	6	4	29	23	11	6	4	26	17	78		Greg Fee
96-97	N.P.L.	Premier	6	44	12	7	3	43	25	10	6	6	31	22	79		Greg Fee

Season	League	Div.	Pos.	P	W	D	L	F	A	Pts	Manager
95-96	N.P.L.	Premier	2	42	23	6	13	86	59	75	Mel Sterland
94-95	N.P.L.	Premier	5	42	20	11	11	80	43	71	Mel Sterland
93-94	N.P.L.	Premier	3	42	23	9	10	90	43	78	Peter Morris
92-93	Conference	-	22	42	9	13	20	50	69	40	Peter Morris
91-92	Conference	-	8	42	18	9	15	71	66	63	Dave Cusack
90-91	Conference	-	18	42	12	11	19	55	69	47	George Kerr/Dave Cusack

HONOURS

Southern Lge. Premier Div. 99-00; R-up 98-99.
Northern Premier Lge 72-73 73-74 76-77 77-78
(R-up 71-72 95-96)
Lge Cup 73-74 75-76(R-up 77-78),
Challenge Shield 73-74 74-75 76-77 77-78;
Lincs Senior Cup (12);
East Anglian Cup 60-61;
Central Alliance 61-62 (Lg Cup 61-62);
Utd Counties Lge 65-66 (Lg Cup 65-66);
West Midlands (Reg) Lg 66-67 67-68,
Eastern Professional F'loodlit Cup 71-72 (R-up 76-77);
Midland Lg R-up 55-56.
Non-League Champion of Champions Cup
72-73 73-74 76-77 77-78
Lincolnshire Lge 99-00 (Res.)

PREVIOUS

Leagues: Midland 21-58 62-64;
Southern League 58-61 98-00;
Central Alliance 61-62;
United Counties 65-66;
West Midlands (Regional) 66-68;
Northern Premier 68-79, 93-98;
Alliance Premier (Conference) 79-93

Names: Boston Town; Boston Swifts
Grounds: None

CLUB RECORDS

Attendance: 10,086
v Corby Tn, floodlit inauguration 1955

Goalscorer: Chris Cook (181)

Appearances: Billy Howells, 500+

Win: 12-0
v Spilsby Tn, Grace Swan Cup, 92-93

Fee Paid: £14,000
for Micky Nuttell (Wycombe Wanderers)

Fee Received: £50,000
for David Norris to Bolton W. (2000)

Past Players who progressed to the Football League

Jim Smith (Colchester), Steve Thompson(Lincoln),
Brendon Phillips (Mansfield),
Gordon Simmonite (Blackpool), Simon Garner (Blackburn),
John Froggatt & Bobby Svarc (Colchester),
David Gilbert, Neil Grayson, Jamie Pascoe,
Robbie Curtis, Dean Trott (Northampton),
Tim Dalton(Bradford C.), Gary Jones (Southend)
David Norris (Bolton W.)

BEST SEASON

FA Trophy: Runners-up 84-85

FA Cup: Third Round replay 73-74,
1-6 V Derby County (H), after 0-0
League clubs defeated: Derby 55-56,
Southport 70-71,Hartlepool 71-72, Crewe 82-83

League: 3rd Conference 1988-89

LAST SEASON

F.A. Cup: 4th Qualifying Round
F.A. Trophy: First Round
League: Southern League Champions
Top Goalscorer: Mark Rawle
Player of the Year: Peter Costello
Captain: David Rennie

David Rennie (right) and Paul Bastock with the Trophy.
Photo courtesy of Lincolnshire Standard Group

BOSTON UNITED

	Date	Comp.	H/A	Opponents	Gate	Result & Score	Goalscorers	League Position
1	14.08	DM-P	H	Salisbury City	1,228	W 6 - 0	Stanhope 18, Nuttell 46, 52, Wilson 49[p], Hoyle 66, Rawle 85	
2	16.08	DM-P	A	Cambridge City	545	W 2 - 0	Wilson 14[p], Hoyle 85	
3	21.08	DM-P	A	Tamworth	721	W 2 - 1	Rawle 10, 42	1
4	25.08	DM-P	H	Rothwell Town	1,434	W 2 - 0	Norris 45, Watts 84	1
5	28.08	DM-P	H	Clevedon Town	1,423	W 5 - 1	Hoyle 20, Rawle 44, Watts 62, Norris 81, Kiwomya 89	1
6	30.08	DM-P	A	Ilkeston Town	1,120	L 0 - 1		2
7	04.09	DM-P	H	Atherstone United	1,210	W 3 - 0	Norris 38, 67, Rawle 50	2
8	07.09	DMP	A	Burton Albion	1,920	D 1 - 1	Nuttell 55	
9	11.09	DMP	A	Halesowen Town	465	D 1 - 1	Wilson 89[p]	
10	25.09	DMP	H	Weymouth	1,247	W 3 - 0	Stanhope 5, 37, Wilson 67[p]	
11	23.10	DM P	H	Bath City	1,731	D 1 - 1	Rawle 79	
12	27.10	DM P	H	Cambridge City	957	W 5 - 0	Pincher 21[og], Nuttell 61, Rennie 71, Rawle 77, Watts 84	
13	30.10	DM P	A	Gloucester City	507	D 2 - 2	Noteman 61, Nuttell 73	
14	06.11	DM P	H	Dorchester Town	1,164	W 3 - 0	Nuttell 32, Power 61, Norris 65	
15	09.11	DM P	A	Rothwell Town	345	W 2 - 0	Rennie 7, Norris 13	
16	13.11	DM P	H	Tamworth	1,159	W 1 - 0	Wilson 33	
17	20.11	DM P	A	Newport County	907	D 2 - 2	Childs 14, Power 43	
18	27.11	DM P	A	Clevedon Town	407	D 0 - 0		
19	04.12	DM P	H	Burton Albion	2,090	W 3 - 1	Power 40, Nuttell 52, Noteman 71	
20	11.12	DM P	A	Atherstone United	435	D 1 - 1	Stanhope 15	
21	18.12	DM P	A	Bath City	1,658	L 0 - 2		
22	27.12	DM P	H	King's Lynn	3,119	L 1 - 2	Costello 68[p]	
23	03.01	DM P	A	Grantham Town	1,265	W 3 - 0	Costello 32[p], Rawle 59 75	
24	08.01	DM P	A	Salisbury City	593	W 2 - 1	Norris 59, Charles 74	
25	15.01	DM P	H	Margate	1,558	W 3 - 0	Rawle 44, Costello 88[p], Stanhope 89	
26	19.01	DM P	H	Ilkeston Town	1,467	W 3 - 2	Nuttell 13, Hoyle 31, Rennie 34	
27	22.01	DM P	A	Crawley Town	1,037	W 6 - 1	Rawle 24, Hoyle 36, Childs 45, **Norris 3** (53 64 87)	
28	29.01	DM P	H	Merthyr Tydfil	1,584	W 4 - 1	Rennie 19, Rawle 21, Stanhope 36, Nuttell 51	1
29	05.02	DM P	A	Margate	953	L 1 - 2	Stanhope 44	1
30	12.02	DM P	H	Havant & Waterlooville	1,514	W 4 - 2	Costello 14[p] 57, Keeble 45 83	1
31	19.02	DM P	H	Halesowen Town	1,614	W 4 - 1	Hoyle 18, Power 33, Stanhope 40, Rawle 90	1
32	26.02	DM P	A	Merthyr Tydfil	594	W 2 - 0	Keeble 49, Nuttell 78	1
33	04.03	DM P	H	Worcester City	1840	W 2 - 1	Costello 18, Keeble 30	1
34	11.03	DM P	A	Havant & Waterlooville	675	D 3 - 3	Keeble 22, Stanhope 64, Power 67	1
35	25.03	DM P	H	CRAWLEY TOWN	2022	W 1-0	Hoyle 72	1
36	27.03	DM P	A	Worcester City	1151	W 2-1	Rawle 28, Little 43	1
37	01.04	DM P	A	Weymouth	922	D 2-2	OG (Bradford) 45, Rennie 77	1
38	08.04	DM P	H	GLOUCESTER CITY	2063	W 6-1	**Costello 3** (20, 37, 49), Rawle 29, 52, Allardyce 79	1
39	22.04	DM P	H	GRANTHAM TOWN	4137	W 3-1	Rawle 27, 66, Childs 81	1
40	24.04	DM P	A	King's lynn	1960	D 0-0		1
41	29.04	DM P	H	NEWPORT COUNTY	2596	D 1-1	Nuttell 25	1
42	06.05	DM P	A	Dorchester Town	904	L 3-4	Rawle 21, 80, Hayes 63, Watts 67	1

CUP COMPETITIONS

F.A. CUP

18.09	2Q	H	OLDBURY UNITED	938	W 3 - 1	Wilson 9[p], Norris 32, Rawle 39
02.10	3Q	H	PURFLEET	1,024	W 4 - 0	Stanhope 18, Rawle 28 45, Wilson 54[p]
16.10	4Q	A	Kingstonian	1,108	D 0 - 0	
20.10	4Q R	H	KINGSTONIAN	2,120	L 0 - 3	

F.A. TROPHY

09.10	1	A	Leigh RMI	377	L 0 - 1	

LEAGUE CUP

03.11	1	H	WISBECH TOWN	508	L 2 - 3	Childs 38, Charles 61

LINCS. SENIOR CUP

09.02	SF	H	GRIMSBY TOWN	388	L 1 - 2	Charles 43

	1	2	3	4	5	6	7	8	9	10	11	Substitutes	
1	Bastock	Gowshall	Wilson	Hoyle	Costello	Rennie	Stanhope	Porter	Nuttell	Watts	Norris	Rawle, A Taylor & L Taylor	1
2	Bastock	Gowshall	Wilson	Hoyle	Costello	Rennie	Stanhope	Porter	Nuttell	Watts	Norris	A Taylor, Burnham & Dack	2
3	Bastock	Gowshall	Wilson	Hoyle	Costello	Rennie	Stanhope	Porter	Nuttell	Rawle	Norris	Watts, A Taylor & Burnham	3
4	Bastock	Gowshall	Wilson	Hoyle	Costello	Rennie	Stanhope	Porter	Nuttell	Rawle	Norris	Watts, A Taylor & Burnham	4
5	Bastock	Gowshall	Wilson	Hoyle	Costello	Rennie	Stanhope	Childs	Watts	Rawle	Norris	Kiwomya, Melson & Taylor	5
6	Bastock	Gowshall	Wilson	Hoyle	Costello	Rennie	Stanhope	Childs	Nuttell	Rawle	Norris	Appleby, Kiwomya & Burnham	6
7	Bastock	Gowshall	Wilson	Hoyle	Costello	Rennie	Stanhope	Childs	Nuttell	Rawle	Norris	Watts, Porter & Burnham	7
8	Bastock	Gowshall	Wilson	Hoyle	Costello	Rennie	Stanhope	Porter	Nuttell	Rawle	Norris	Watts, Hardy & Childs	8
9	Bastock	Gowshall	Wilson	Hoyle	Costello	Rennie	Stanhope	Porter	Nuttell	Watts	Norris	Kiwomya, Childs & Appleby	9
10	Bastock	Gowshall	Wilson	Curtis	Costello	Rennie	Stanhope	Childs	Noteman	Rawle	Norris	Slinn, Dobbin & Nichols	10
11	Bastock	Gowshall	Wilson	Hoyle	Childs	Rennie	Stanhope	Walker	Nuttell	Rawle	Norris	Nichols, Dubbin & Noteman	11
12	Bastock	Gowshall	Wilson	Hoyle	Noteman	Rennie	Stanhope	Walker	Nuttell	Rawle	Norris	Childs, Watts & Appleby	12
13	Bastock	Gowshall	Wilson	Hoyle	Noteman	Rennie	Stanhope	Walker	Nuttell	Rawle	Norris	Charles, Childs & Watts	13
14	Bastock	Gowshall	Wilson	Hoyle	Costello	Rennie	Stanhope	Childs	Nuttell	Power	Norris	Rawle, Charles & Noteman	14
15	Bastock	Gowshall	Wilson	Hoyle	Charles	Rennie	Stanhope	Childs	Nuttell	Power	Norris	Rawle, Noteman & Appleby	15
16	Bastock	Gowshall	Wilson	Hoyle	Appleby	Rennie	Stanhope	Childs	Nuttell	Power	Norris	Rawle, Noteman & Walker	16
17	Bastock	Gowshall	Wilson	Hoyle	Costello	Rennie	Stanhope	Childs	Nuttell	Power	Norris	Watts, Noteman & Charles	17
18	Bastock	Gowshall	Wilson	Hoyle	Curtis	Rennie	Stanhope	Childs	Nuttell	Power	Norris	Walker, Watts & Costello	18
19	Bastock	Gowshall	Wilson	Hoyle	Costello	Rennie	Stanhope	Childs	Nuttell	Power	Kiwomya	Watts, Noteman & Charles	19
20	Bastock	Gowshall	Wilson	Hoyle	Costello	Rennie	Stanhope	Childs	Nuttell	Power	Noteman	Norris, Elding & Charles	20
21	Bastock	Gowshall	Wilson	Hoyle	Costello	Rennie	Stanhope	Childs	Nuttell	Power	Noteman	Norris, Charles & Rawle	21
22	Bastock	Gowshall	Wilson	Rawle	Costello	Rennie	Stanhope	Kiwomya	Nuttell	Power	Norris	Nichols, Noteman & Taylor	22
23	Bastock	Gowshall	Wilson	Hoyle	Costello	Rennie	Stanhope	Charles	Nuttell	Rawle	Norris	Kiwomya, Noteman & Childs	23
24	Bastock	Gowshall	Wilson	Hoyle	Costello	Rennie	Stanhope	Charles	Noteman	Rawle	Norris	Melson, Lodge & Kiwomya	24
25	Bastock	Gowshall	Wilson	Hoyle	Costello	Rennie	Stanhope	Charles	Nuttell	Rawle	Norris	Kiwomya, Melson & Lodge	25
26	Bastock	Gowshall	Wilson	Hoyle	Costello	Rennie	Stanhope	Charles	Nuttell	Rawle	Norris	Kiwomya, Melson & Lodge	26
27	Bastock	Gowshall	Wilson	Hoyle	Childs	Rennie	Stanhope	Charles	Nuttell	Rawle	Norris	Kiwomya, Appleby & Lodge	27
28	Bastock	Gowshall	Wilson	Hoyle	Childs	Rennie	Stanhope	Charles	Nuttell	Rawle	Kiwomya	Power, Curtisi & Lodge	28
29	Bastock	Gowshall	Wilson	Hoyle	Costello	Rennie	Stanhope	Charles	Nuttell	Kiwomya	Childs	Watts, Power & Lodge	29
30	Bastock	Gowshall	Wilson	Hoyle	Costello	Rennie	Stanhope	Charles	Nuttell	Keeble	Hayes	Power, Raynor & Lodge	30
31	Bastock	Gowshall	Wilson	Hoyle	Costello	Rennie	Stanhope	Charles	Power	Keeble	Raynor	Rawle, Lodge & Hayes	31
32	Bastock	Gowshall	Wilson	Hoyle	Costello	Rennie	Stanhope	Charles	Nuttell	Keeble	Raynor	Power, Rawle & Hayes	32
33	Bastock	Gowshall	Wilson	Hoyle	Costello	Rennie	Stanhope	Charles	Nuttell	Keeble	Raynor	Power, Hayes & Watts	33
34	Bastock	Gowshall	Wilson	Hoyle	Costello	Rennie	Stanhope	Charles	Power	Keeble	Raynor	Watts, Hayes & Curtis	34
35	Bastock	Gowshall	Wilson	Hoyle	Costello	Rennie	Stanhope	Charles	Power		Hayes	Watts, Rawle & Curtis	35
36	Bastock	Gowshall	Curtis	Hoyle	Costello	Rennie	Stanhope	Childs	Nuttell	Rawle	Raynor	Hayes, Watts & Power	36
37	Bastock	Gowshall	Curtis	Hoyle	Costello	Rennie	Stanhope	Childs	Nuttell	Rawle	Raynor	Power, Allardyce & Hayes	37
38	Bastock	Gowshall	Curtis	Hoyle	Costello	Rennie	Stanhope	Childs	Nuttell	Rawle	Raynor	Power, Allardyce & Hayes	38
39	Bastock	Gowshall	Curtis	Hoyle	Costello	Rennie	Stanhope	Childs	Nuttell	Rawle	Raynor	Watts, Allardyce & Wilson	39
40	Bastock	Gowshall	Wilson	Hoyle	Costello	Allardyce	Stanhope	Stringfellow	Nuttell	Keeble	Raynor	Watts, Lodge & Hayes	40
41	Bastock	Gowshall	Curtis	Hoyle	Costello	Rennie	Stanhope	Childs	Nuttell	Rawle	Raynor	Watts, Allardyce & Power	41
42													42

	1	2	3	4	5	6	7	8	9	10	11	Substitutes
	Bastock	Gowshall	Wilson	Hoyle	Costello	Rennie	Stanhope	Childs	Nuttell	Slinn	Norris	Hardy, Timby & Sedlan
	Bastock	Gowshall	Wilson	Curtis	Costello	Rennie	Stanhope	Childs	Noteman	Rawle	Norris	Hardy, Dubbin & Melson
	Bastock	Gowshall	Wilson	Hoyle	Costello	Rennie	Stanhope	Noteman	Nuttell	Rawle	Childs	Norris, Nichols & Hardy
	Bastock	Gowshall	Wilson	Hoyle	Costello	Rennie	Stanhope	Childs	Nuttell	Rawle	Norris	Nichols, Hardy & Watts
	Bastock	Gowshall	Wilson	Hardy	Costello	Rennie	Stanhope	Childs	Noteman	Rawle	Norris	Slinn, Dubbin & Melson
	Bastock	Gowshall	Wilson	Hoyle	Charles	Rennie	Childs	Walker	Nuttell	Noteman	Melson	Stanhope, Rawle & Appleby
	Bastock	Gowshall	Wilson	Melson	Childs	Rennie	Stanhope	Charles	Power	Keeble	Lodge	Nuttell, Eldin & Appleby

PLAYING SQUAD

BOSTON UNITED

Player   **Birthplace**   *D.O.B.*   *Previous Clubs*
Bold print indicates an England Semi-Professional

GOALKEEPERS

Paul Bastock	Leamington	19.05.70	Coventry, Cambridge U, Kettering T

DEFENDERS

Tim Wooding DMP	Wellingborough	05.07.73	Norwich, Bournemouth, Rushden & D
Job Gowshall DMP	Louth	07.08.75	Grimsby, Lincoln C
David Rennie SY, DMP	Edinburgh	29.08.64	Leicester, Leeds, Bristol C, Birmingham, Coventry, Northampton, Peterborough
Colin Hoyle DMP	Derby	15.01.72	Arsenal, Barnsley, Bradford C, Notts Co, Mansfield, King's Lynn
Kenny Cramman ESP	Gateshead	17.08.69	Hartlepool, Bishop Auckland, Gateshead, Rushden & D
Richard Lucas	Sheffield	22.09.70	Sheffield U, Preston, Scarborough, Hartlepool, Halifax
Andy Lodge	Whittlesey		Whittlesey U, Bury T, Spalding U, Stamford, Wisbech T, Stamford
Lee Howarth	Bolton	03.01.68	Chorley, Peterborough, Mansfield, Barnet, Stevenage B

MIDFIELDERS

Peter Costello DMP	Halifax	31.10.69	Bradford C, Rochdale, Peterborough, Lincoln, Dover Ath., Nuneaton B, Kettering T, South Africa
Paul Raynor DMP	Nottingham	29.04.66	Nottingham F, Huddersfield, Swansea, Camb.U, Preston, Camb.U, Guang Dong, Leyton O, Stevenage B, Kettering T, Ilkeston T
Jason Minett	Peterborough	12.08.71	Norwich, Exeter, Lincoln, Exeter, Kettering T, Doncaster R
Adie Hayes DMP	Norwich	22.05.78	Camb.U, Kettering T, Diss T, £4,000 to Boston U
Simon Livett	Plaistow	08.01.69	West Ham, Leyton O, Camb.U, Billericay T, Southend, Enfield
Andy Stanhope DMP	Peterborough		Peterborough, King's Lynn
Jimmy Dick	Scotland		Airdrie

FORWARDS

Paul Fewings	Hull	18.02.78	Hull C, Hereford U
Lee Power Eire Y, u-21, B Int DMP	Lewisham	30.06.72	Norwich, Bradford C, Hibernian, Plymouth, Halifax, £25k to Boston U
Miguel De Souza	Newham	11.02.70	Dag & Red, Birmingham, Wycombe, Peterborough, Rushden & D
Mark Rawle DMP	Leicester		Leicester YMCA, Rushden & D
Micky Nuttell DMP	Boston	22.11.68	Peterborough, Cheltenham T, Wycombe, Boston U, Kettering T, Dag & Red, Rushden & D, Burton Alb., Kettering T, King's Lynn

CHESTER CITY

It is an old cliche that life can be cruel and this applies very much to Chester City as they face the immediate future outside the Football League which they have graced since 1931, but in a way they were architects of their own destruction as they faced their final match of the season - at home to Peterborough United - needing only a draw to stay up, but as had happened the previous Saturday at Cheltenham they lost by a single goal to leave Carlisle United (for a second successive season) as lucky survivors along with Shrewsbury Town.

Perhaps it is a blessing in disguise as the team spent the whole season in one or other of the last two places in the table and the fact that they failed to score in sixteen of their matches reveals one of the main problems; at one stage they went five matches without scoring a goal. Both `six-pointers' against Carlisle United were lost, but they did manage to win at Shrewsbury, and then could only produce a goalless draw in the return.

Stability was not improved by backroom and administrative problems and the cups brought little joy despite brave efforts against Aston Villa in the Worthington Cup, when they lost on aggregate after beating higher rated Port Vale in the First Round (2-1 and 4-4), and versus Manchester City (1-4 at home) in the F.A. Cup following victories in the First Round after a replay over Whyteleafe and in the Second round at Stalybridge Celtic (2-1).

Worse fates have befallen other clubs than a spell in The Conference, as the most recent revival of Halifax Town shows, and there is no lack of talent in the squad for the 2000-01 season, although there have been a large number of personnel changes, and manager Graham Barrow will hope that the directors will keep cool heads and allow him enough time to rebuild for a potentially decent future.

Bill Mitchell

Back Row: Neil Fisher, David Kerr, Martyn Lancaster, Dean Greygoose, Mattie Woods, Wayne Brown, Paul Beesley, Paul Carden, Neil Fitzhenry. **Middle:** Gordon Hill (Youth Coach), Mark Beesley, Andy Shelton, Dean Spink, Scott Ruscoe, Nick Richardson, Darren Moss, Chrsi Blackburn, Craig Gaunt, Graham Vile (Centre of Excellence Director). **Front:** Darren Wright, Paul Berry, Terry Smith (Chairman), Graham Barrow (Manager), Joe Hinnegan (Physio), Matt Doughty, Steve Finney

GROUND DETAILS

Deva Stadium,
Bumpers Lane,
Chester
CH1 4LT

Tel: 01244 371376 or 371809
Fax: 01244 390243
email: chesterfc@The Deva.FSBusiness.co.uk
Web site: http://www.chesterfc.co.uk

SIMPLE DIRECTIONS:
Follow signs to Chester , into Town Centre, then follow signs to Queensferry (A548) onto Sealand Road. Turn into Bumpers Lane, signed Chester City F.C.
British Rail, Chester (01244 340170). Car Parking at ground

CAPACITY:	6,000
SEATED:	3,094
COVERED TERRACING:	2,640

Clubhouse: Open matchdays & for private bookings
Contact: The club office on 01244 371376
Function/Banqueting facilities: Yes

CLUB SHOP: Yes

Founded:	1884
Nickname:	The Blues
Club Sponsors:	Gap Recruitment
Club colours:	Blue & white striped shirts blue shorts, white socks
Change colours:	All white
Midweek home matchday:	Tuesday
Reserves' League:	None
Clubcall	0891 121633

CLUB OFFICIALS

President	C Thompson
Honory Vice Presidents	
	J Kane, L Lloyd, M Swallow
Chairman	Terry Smith
Directors	G Smith, M Smith, M Fair
Secretary	Michael Fair
Commercial Manager	Rodney Buxton

MATCHDAY PROGRAMME

Pages: 36   Price: £2.00

Editor: Norman Spencer
chesterfc@The Deva.FSBusiness.co.uk

Local Press: Chester Chronicle, Evening Leader
Local Radio: Radio Merseyside, Marcher Sound

FOOTBALL MANAGEMENT TEAM

MANAGER	GRAHAM BARROW
Date of Appointment:	June 2000
Date of Birth:	13th June 1954
Place of Birth:	Chorley

PREVIOUS CLUBS
As manager	Chester C.
As player	Altrincham, Wigan Ath., Chester C.

HONOURS
As manager	R-up Div. 3 93-94
As player	

Assistant Manager:	Paul Beesley
Physiotherapist:	Joe Hinnigan
Community Officer:	Brian Croft

Season	League	Div.	Pos.	P	Home					Away					Pts	Manager
					W	D	L	F	A	W	D	L	F	A		
99-00	Football Lge	3	24	46	5	5	13	20	36	5	4	14	24	43	39	Kevin Ratcliffe / Ian Atkins
98-99	Football Lge	3	14	46	6	12	5	28	30	7	6	10	29	36	57	Kevin Ratcliffe
97-98	Football Lge	3	14	46	12	7	4	34	15	5	3	15	26	46	61	Kevin Ratcliffe
96-97	Football Lge	3	6	46	11	8	4	30	16	7	8	8	25	27	70	Kevin Ratcliffe
95-96	Football Lge	3	8	46	11	9	3	45	22	7	7	9	27	31	70	Kevin Ratcliffe
94-95	Football Lge	2	23	46	5	6	12	23	42	1	5	17	14	42	29	Mike Pejic/Derek Mann*/Kevin Ratcliffe*
93-94	Football Lge	3	2	42	13	5	3	35	18	8	6	7	34	28	74	Graham Barrow
92-93	Football Lge	2	24	46	6	2	15	30	47	2	3	18	19	55	29	Harry McNally/Graham Barrow

Premiership formed, Div. 2 became Div. 1 etc.

Season	League	Div.	Pos.	P	Home					Away					Pts	Manager
91-92	Football Lge	3	18	46	10	6	7	34	29	4	8	11	22	30	56	Harry McNally
90-91	Football Lge	3	19	46	10	3	10	27	27	4	6	13	19	31	51	Harry McNally

HONOURS

League Division 3N Cup 35-36 36-37
Debenhams Cup 77
Welsh Cup Winners 07-08 32-33 46-47
R-up 08-09 09-10 34-35 35-36
52-53 53-54 54-55 57-58 65-66 69-70

PREVIOUS

Leagues:
The Combination 1890-1910
Lancashire Combination 1910-1914
Cheshire County League 1919-1931
Football League 1931-2000

Grounds:
The Stadium, Sealand Rd. 1906-1990
Moss Rose, Macclesfield (ground share) 90-92

Names:
Chester F.C. until 1983

Past Players who progressed to the Football League

not applicable

CLUB RECORDS

Attendance:
5,538
v Preston N.E., Div. 3, 2.4.1994
(Sealand Rd.) 20,500 v Chelsea, FAC 16.1.52

Record win:
12-0
v York City, Div. 3N, 1.2.1936

Record defeat:
0-9
v Barrow, Div. 3N, 19.1.1952

Career goalscorer: Stuart Rimmer 121 (85-88 & 91-93)

Career appearances: Trevor Storton 453

Transfer fee paid:
£94,000
for Stuart Rimmer, to Barnsley, Aug. 1991

Transfer fee received:
£300,000
for Ian Rush from Liverpool, May 1980

BEST SEASON

FA Cup:
5th Round replay
76-77, 79-80

League:
5th, League Div. 3 77-78

League Cup:
Semi-Final 74-75
4-5 (agg) v Aston Villa

LAST SEASON

F.A. Cup: Third Round
League Cup: Second Round
League: 24th League Division 3
Top Goalscorer: Luke Beckett 18
Player of the Year: Luke Beckett
Captain: Nick Richardson

CHESTER CITY

Match Facts 1999-00

	Date	Comp.	H/A	Opponents	Gate	Result & Score	Goalscorers	League Position
1	07.08	Div. 3	H	Barnet	2,234	L 0-2		
2	14.08	Div. 3	A	Rotherham United	2,966	L 0-4		
3	18.08	Div. 3	H	Northampton Town	1,904	L 0-2		23
4	28.08	Div. 3	A	Torquay United	2,345	D 2-2	Beckett 12, Berry 81	23
5	30.08	Div. 3	H	Rochdale	2,307	L 0-2		23
6	03.09	Div. 3	A	Hull City	6,137	L 1-2	Richardson 23	24
7	11.09	Div. 3	H	Exeter City	1,855	D 1-1	Beckett 48	24
8	18.09	Div. 3	A	Brighton & Hove Albion	5,810	W 3-2	Beckett 70, OG (Watson) 73, Agogo 90	24
9	25.09	Div. 3	H	Lincoln City	2,161	L 1-3	Blackwood 13	24
10	02.10	Div. 3	A	York City	2,052	D 2-2	Blackwood 55, Agogo 79	24
11	09.10	Div. 3	A	Peterborough United	4,965	L 1-2	Beckett 14	24
12	16.10	Div. 3	H	Macclesfield Town	2,506	L 1-2	Agogo 16	24
13	19.10	Div. 3	H	Cheltenham Town	2,963	W 2-1	Agogo 61, 66	24
14	23.10	Div. 3	A	Lincoln City	3,790	L 1-4	Agogo 41	24
15	02.11	Div. 3	A	Shrewsbury Town	2,523	W 1-0	Richardson 72	23
16	06.11	Div. 3	H	Plymouth Argyle	2,027	L 0-1		23
17	13.11	Div. 3	A	Hartlepool United	2,266	L 0-1		24
18	23.11	Div. 3	H	Southend United	1,906	D 0-0		24
19	27.11	Div. 3	H	Swansea City	2,713	L 0-1		24
20	04.12	Div. 3	A	Barnet	2,252	L 0-2		24
21	15.12	Div. 3	A	Darlington	3,553	L 1-3	OG (Samways) 74	24
22	18.12	Div. 3	H	Halifax Town	2,037	W 2-1	Laird 26, Eve 29	23
23	26.12	Div. 3	A	Mansfield Town	3,234	L 1-2	Doughty 68	23
24	28.12	Div. 3	H	Leyton Orient	3,160	L 1-5	Wright 66	24
25	03.01	Div. 3	A	Carlisle United	4,565	L 1-4	Eve 89	24
26	08.01	Div. 3	H	Darlington	2,067	L 1-2	Beckett 37	24
27	15.01	Div. 3	H	Rotherham United	2,398	L 0-2		24
28	22.01	Div. 3	A	Northampton Town	5,332	L 1-3	Pickering 2	24
29	29.01	Div. 3	H	Torquay United	2,229	W 2-1	Eyjolfsson 47	24
30	05.02	Div. 3	A	Rochdale	3,093	L 1-2	Beckett 83	24
31	12.02	Div. 3	H	Hull City	2,802	D 0-0		24
32	18.02	Div. 3	A	Swansea City	6,336	L 1-2	Eyjolfsson 22	24
33	26.02	Div. 3	H	Brighton & Hove Albion	2,743	L 1-7	Beckett 77	24
34	04.03	Div. 3	A	Exeter City	2,391	W 2-0	Eyjolfsson 7, Beckett 22	24
35	07.03	Div. 3	A	Plymouth Argyle	4,140	D 0-0		24
36	11.03	Div. 3	H	Shrewsbury Town	4,002	D 0-0		23
37	18.03	Div. 3	A	Southend United	3,483	L 1-3	Beckett 45	24
38	21.03	Div. 3	H	Hartlepool United	1,816	D 1-1	Hemmings 24	24
39	25.03	Div. 3	H	Mansfield Town	1,953	W 5-0	Heggs 17, Beckett 20, Hemmings 29, Eve 59, 68	24
40	01.04	Div. 3	A	Halifax Town	2,431	W 1-0	Beckett 14 (p)	24
41	08.04	Div. 3	H	Carlisle United	5,507	L 0-1		24
42	15.04	Div. 3	A	Leyton Orient	4,123	W 2-1	Heggs 15, Fisher 57	23
43	22.04	Div. 3	A	Macclesfield Town	3,456	D 1-1	Beckett 49	24
44	24.04	Div. 3	H	York City	3,503	W 2-0	OG (Bower) 61, Beckett 62	23
45	29.04	Div. 3	A	Cheltenham Town	5,391	L 0-1		23
46	06.05	Div. 3	H	Peterborough United	4,905	L 0-1		24

CUP COMPETITIONS

Worthing ton Cup

Date	Round	H/A	Opponents	Gate	Result	Goalscorers
10.08	1-1	H	Port Vale	2,100	W 2-1	Richardson 7, Beckett 72 (p)
24.08	1-2	A	Port Vale	2,625	D 4-4	Beckett 5 (p), 13, Shelton 71, Jones 77
14.09	2-1	H	Aston Villa	4,364	L 0-1	
28.09	2-2	A	Aston Villa	22,613	L 0-5	

F.A. Cup

Date	Round	H/A	Opponents	Gate	Result	Goalscorers
30.10	1	A	Whyteleafe	2,164	D 0-0	
09.11	1R	H	Whyteleafe	2,183	W 3-1	Cross 25, 53, Beckett 49
20.11	2	A	Stalybridge Celtic	3,312	W 2-1	Cross 45, Beckett 69
12.12	3	H	Manchester City	5,469	L 1-4	Richardson 27

1	2	3	4	5	6	7	8	9	10	11	Substitutes Used	
Brown	Davidson	Lancaster	Woods	Cross	Shelton	Reid	Richardson	Fisher	Beckett	Wright	Moss (6), Doughty (11)	1
Brown	Jones	Cross	Reid	Lancaster	Woods	Shelton	Richardson	Beckett	Fisher	Moss	Doughty (7), Blackburn (4), Berry (2)	2
Brown	Davidson	Cross	Reid	Lancaster	Woods	Shelton	Richardson	Beckett	Jones	Fisher	Wright (10)	3
Brown	Moss	Davidson	Woods	Fisher	Shelton	Wright	Richardson	Jones	Beckett	Cross	Berry (9)	4
Brown	Moss	Cross	Shelton	Davidson	Woods	Wright	Richardson	Jones	Beckett	Fisher	Berry (9), Doughty (11)	5
Brown	Davidson	Cross	Lancaster	Woods	Fisher	Shelton	Richardson	Beckett	Agogo	Blackwood	Berry (6), Wright (2)	6
Brown	Davidson	Doughty	Agogo	Lancaster	Blackwood	Wright	Richardson	Moss	Beckett	Woods	Cross (3), Shelton (7), Fisher (4)	7
Brown	Davidson	Doughty	Lancaster	Woods	Wright	Richardson	Milosavaijevic	Agogo	Beckett	Blackwood	Shelton (8), Fisher (11)	8
Brown	Davidson	Doughty	Lancaster	Woods	Wright	Blackwood	Nash	Agogo	Beckett	Fisher	Milosavaijevic (5), Berry (11), Jones (7)	9
Brown	Moss	Doughty	Richardson	Lancaster	Woods	Milosavaijevic	Blackwood	Agogo	Beckett	Wright	No subs used	10
Brown	Moss	Doughty	Davidson	Lancaster	Woods	Wright	Richardson	Agogo	Beckett	Blackwood	Carver (11), Cross (6), Nash (3)	11
Brown	Wright	Cross	Carver	Lancaster	Richardson	Nash	Fisher	Agogo	Beckett	Blackwood	Moss (3), Berry (4)	12
Brown	Moss	Doughty	Wright	Lancaster	Woods	Milosavaijevic	Richardson	Agogo	Beckett	Blackwood	No subs used	13
Brown	Moss	Doughty	Nash	Lancaster	Woods	Milosavaijevic	Richardson	Agogo	Beckett	Blackwood	Fisher (4), Finney (7)	14
Brown	Moss	Woods	Milosavaijevic	Fisher	Doughty	Wright	Richardson	A Shelton	Agogo	Beckett	Berry (3), Nash (6), Finney (9)	15
Brown	Moss	Doughty	Fisher	Milosavaijevic	Wright	Spooner	A Shelton	Finney	Beckett	Richardson	Nash (6), Cross (9)	16
Brown	Nash	Spooner	Milosavaijevic	Fisher	Doughty	Wright	Richardson	A Shelton	Cross	Beckett	Berry (8), Finney (4)	17
Brown	Moss	Doughty	Reid	Woods	Spooner	Richardson	Nash	Beckett	Cross	Fisher	Finney (8), Berry (4)	18
Brown	Moss	Doughty	Reid	Spooner	Woods	Richardson	Nash	Beckett	Cross	Fisher	Finney (4)	19
Brown	Reid	Woods	Richardson	Beckett	Fisher	Wright	Doughty	Spooner	Nash	Finney	No subs used	20
Brown	Moss	Doughty	Reid	Milosavaijevic	Woods	Nash	Richardson	Cross	Beckett	Fisher	Lancaster (5), Wright (8), Jones (7)	21
Brown	Moss	Doughty	Eve	Spooner	Milosavaijevic	Nash	Richardson	Beckett	Laird	Fisher	Wright (10), Woods (6)	22
Brown	Moss	Cross	Eve	Spooner	Nash	Richardson	Beckett	Fisher	Woods	Milosavaijevic	Doughty (3), Laird (5), Wright (6)	23
Brown	Moss	Doughty	Eve	Spooner	Woods	Nash	Richardson	Beckett	Laird	Fisher	Reid (4), Wright (10)	24
Brown	Richardson	Milosavaijevic	Beckett	Fisher	Moss	Wright	Doughty	Spooner	Nash	Eve	Woods (9), Finney (7), Reid (10)	25
Brown	Hobson	Woods	Fisher	Keister	Doughty	Moss	Reid	Beckett	Richardson	Elyjolfsson	Wright (8), Cross (10)	26
Brown	Pickering	Cross	Hobson	Woods	Lancaster	Keister	Eve	Richardson	Beckett	Elyjolfsson	Moss (2), Nash (9), Wright (11)	27
Brown	Hodson	Reid	Woods	Richardson	Beckett	Fisher	Robinson	Elyjolfsson	Hemmings	Pickering	Wright (3), Lancaster (11), Doughty (9)	28
Brown	Hobson	Pickering	Woods	Robinson	Reid	Keister	Fisher	Hemmings	Beckett	Elyjolfsson	Richardson (6), Eve (11)	29
Brown	Pickering	Hobson	Robinson	Woods	Fisher	Porter	Keister	Elyjolfsson	Beckett	Hemmings	Moss (6), Doughty (2), Eve (11)	30
Brown	Pickering	Woods	Robinson	Hobson	Moss	Keister	Hemmings	Elyjolfsson	Beckett	Porter	Doughty (8), Richardson (7)	31
Brown	Hobson	Pickering	Woods	Robinson	Keister	Moss	Porter	Hemmings	Beckett	Elyjolfsson	Richardson (6), Fisher (9)	32
Brown	Hobson	Pickering	Hicks	Lancaster	Keister	Porter	Beckett	Elyjolfsson	Hemmings	Moss	Doghty (10), Fisher 93), Finney (7)	33
Brown	Woods	Robinson	Hicks	Doughty	Moss	Fisher	Porter	Hemmings	Beckett	Elyjolfsson	Keister (6)	34
Brown	Woods	Hicks	Robinson	Hobson	Porter	Hemmings	Moss	Fisher	Beckett	Finney	Doughty (11), Richardson (8), Berry (7)	35
Brown	Woods	Fisher	Robinson	Hobson	Moss	Keister	Hemmings	Richardson	Beckett	Heggs	Eve (9), Carden (11)	36
Brown	Woods	Hicks	Robinson	Hobson	Porter	Hemmings	Moss	Fisher	Beckett	Heggs	Doughty (4), Carden (9), Eve (7)	37
Brown	Woods	Hicks	Hobson	Moss	Porter	Hemmings	Eve	Carden	Beckett	Heggs	Fisher (8), Doughty (11)	38
Brown	Woods	Hicks	Hobson	Moss	Hemmings	Porter	Eve	Carden	Beckett	Heggs	Finney (10), Fisher (11), Reid (9)	39
Brown	Moss	Hicks	Woods	Hobson	Fisher	Carden	Porter	Hemmings	Beckett	Heggs	No subs used	40
Brown	Woods	Hicks	Hobson	Fisher	Hemmings	Porter	Eve	Carden	Beckett	Heggs	Finney (11)	41
Brown	Hobson	Woods	Richardson	Beckett	Fisher	Carden	Heggs	Hicks	Hemmings	Porter	Doughty (4), Keister (10)	42
Brown	Woods	Hicks	Hobson	Fisher	Hemmings	Porter	Carden	Richardson	Beckett	Heggs	No subs used	43
Brown	Woods	Hicks	Hobson	Fisher	Hemmings	Porter	Carden	Eve	Beckett	Heggs	Doughty (9), Richardson (6)	44
Brown	Woods	Hicks	Hobson	Fisher	Hemmings	Porter	Richardson	Carden	Beckett	Heggs	Moss (8), Eve (5), Doughty (6)	45
Brown	Woods	Hicks	Hobson	Fisher	Hemmings	Porter	Carden	Beckett	Heggs	Finney	Moss (11), Wright (5), Lancaster (6)	46

Brown	Davidson	Reid	Lancaster	Cross	Woods	Shelton A	Richardson	Beckett	Fisher	Moss		
Brown	Moss	Cross	Reid	Davidson	Woods	Shelton	Richardson	Wright	Beckett	Fisher	Jones (4)	
Brown	Davidson	Doughty	Shelton	Lancaster	Woods	Wright	Richardson	Milos'vic	Beckett	Fisher	Berry (9)	
Brown	Shelton	Davidson	Lancaster	Woods	Doughty	Richardson	Milos'vic	Fisher	Wright	Beckett	Berry (2), Jones (8), Carson (9)	

Brown	Moss	Doughty	Nash	Lancaster	Woods	Milos'vic	Richardson	Wright	Beckett	Fisher	Jones (4), Shelton (11)	
Brown	Moss	Doughty	Fisher	Milos'vic	Malone	Wright	Richardson	Cross	Beckett	Shelton A	Lancaster (6), Nash (2)	
Brown	Moss	Doughty	Reid	Milos'vic	Spooner	Richardson	Nash	Cross	Beckett	Fisher	Woods (5), Shelton A (7)	
Brown	Reid	Woods	Richardson	Beckett	Fisher	Moss	Wright	Doughty	Spooner	Nash	Cross (8), Berry (11)	

PLAYING SQUAD

CHESTER CITY

Bold print denotes England semi-professional international.

Player Honours	*Birthplace*	*D.O.B.*	*Previous Clubs*

GOALKEEPERS

Wayne Brown	Southampton	14.01.77	Bristol C, Weston-S-Mare
Dean Greygoose Altrincham	Thetford	18.12.64	Camb.U, Leyton O, Crystal Palace, Crewe, Holywell T, Northwich V,

DEFENDERS

Phil Robinson	Manchester	28.09.80	Blackpool
Matt Woods	Gosport	09.09.76	Everton
Paul Beesley	Liverpool	21.07.65	Marine, Wigan, Leyton O, Sheffield U, Leeds, Manchester C, Port Vale, Blackpool
Craig Gaunt BLT	Sutton	31.03.73	Arsenal, Scarborough, Bromsgrove R, Kettering T, Singapore, Ilkeston T, Grantham T, Singapore
Neil Fitzhenry	Billinge	24.09.78	Wigan
Martin Lancaster	Wigan	10.11.80	From Trainee
Carl Ruffer	Chester	20.12.74	Everton, Runcorn

MIDFIELD

Chris Blackburn	Chester		From Trainee
David Kerr	Dumfries	06.09.74	Manchester C, Mansfield
Darren Moss	Wrexham	24.05.81	From Trainee
Nick Richardson	Halifax	11.04.67	Emley, Halifax. Cardiff, Bury
Mark Beesley	Lancaster		Preston
Andy Shelton	Sutton Coldfield	19.06.80	From Trainee
Paul Carden	Liverpool	29.03.79	Blackpool, Rochdale
Michael Quigley	Manchester	02.10.70	Manchester C, Hull

FORWARDS

Dean Spink	Halesowen	22.01.67	Halesowen T, Aston Villa, Shrewsbury, Wrexham
Darren Wright	Warrington	07.09.79	From Trainee
Scott Ruscoe	Stoke		Stoke, Port Vale, Newtown
Steve Finney	Hexham	31.10.73	Preston, Manchester C, Swindon, Carlisle, Leyton O

DAGENHAM & REDBRIDGE

The old cliche, "the league championship is a marathon not a sprint" became more like a comfortable jog for Dagenham & Redbridge as they won the Ryman League title by an incredible 24 points from nearest challengers Aldershot Town. After the Daggers claimed the top spot, on September 25th with a 4-0 victory over then leaders Enfield, the Ryman League championship became a one-horse race with only brief challenges from St. Albans City and Aldershot Town.

During the close season, the Daggers installed former Heybridge Swifts and St. Albans City manager Garry Hill into the hot seat. His brief was straight forward - to take the Daggers back to the Conference and build a solid platform for the future.

Named as pre-season favourites by bookmakers William Hill their first game away to Harrow Borough saw them hiccup as they could only draw 1-1, but, with only one defeat in their first twenty league games, they began to pull away from the other sides in the league. Cup results suffered though and they went out of both the FA Cup and FA Umbro Trophy competitions early on to Burton Albion and Purfleet respectively.

The first crunch game came at the end of January with a visit to Clarence Park, home of St. Albans City who were eight points behind them. A 3-1 victory for the visitors stretched their lead at the top and blew away the Hertfordshire side's challenge.

February proved to be the Dagger's poorest month of results as they picked up only one point from three games, but any hopes the chasing pack may have had of catching them were dismissed as the Essex side then went on a tremendous run of results, dropping only four points from their remaining fourteen matches.

The title was won on April 22nd when they came from behind to win 3-2 at Hampton & Richmond Borough despite having been reduced to nine men whilst nearest challengers Aldershot Town lost at home to Enfield.

By the end of the season they had made Victoria Road a fortress with only Chesham United departing with a point as they recorded twenty victories and a draw from their 21 home league games. The average crowd rose over 40 per cent compared to the previous season and topped the thousand mark for only the third time in the club's history with their following outnumbering the home side at a number of away fixtures during the season.

The 101 points recorded was the joint second highest ever in the Ryman Premier Division and of goals. They were presented with the League Championship on the final day of the season as they defeated Slough 2-0 to record their tenth consecutive league victory.

The Ryman League title together with the required ground grading means the Daggers return to the Conference after a four year absence.

Dave Simpson

Back Row: Tim Cole, Ashley Vickers, Lee Matthews, Paul Dennis, Stve Forbes, Tony Roberts, Rob Haworth, Danny Shipp, Mark Keen.
Front: Mark Brennan, Derek Payne, Junior McDougald, Dominic Naylor, Lee Goodwin, Matt Jones, Paul Cobb, Mark Janney, Paul Terry

DAGENHAM & REDBRIDGE

GROUND DETAILS

Victoria Road,
Dagenham
RM10 7XL

Tel: 0181 592 1549
Fax: 0181593 7227
email: info@daggers.co.uk
web site: http://www.daggers.co.uk

DIRECTIONS: On A112 between A12 & A13.
Buses 103 & 174,
Dagenham East tube station, turn left and after approximately
500 yards take 5th turning left into Victoria Road.

CAPACITY: 6,000
SEATS: 700
COVERED: 3,000

CLUBHOUSE: Open 7 days 11am-11pm.
Hot & cold food available.
For Functions: Tony Manhood (0181 592 7194)
Shop Contact: SteveThompson 0181 5927194

CLUB SHOP: Open on matchdays
for enquiries on other days contact Steve, above.

Formed:	1992
Nickname:	Daggers
Colours:	Red shirts, white shorts, red socks
Change colours:	Blue & white stries
Midweek matchday:	Tuesday
Reserves Lge:	Capital League
Sponsors Main:	Compass Plumbing Supplies
Kit:	Vandanell
Programme:	Recorder Group Newspapers
Match Reports:	0930 555840

CLUB OFFICIALS

Chairman:	Dave Andrews
Joint Presidents:	John & Brian East
Vice Chairman:	David Ward
Secretary:	Derek Almond,
	149 Kings Head Hill, Chingford,
	London E4 7JG
	Tel: 0181 524 2689
Press Officer:	Dave Simpson
	Tel: 0860 119430

MATCHDAY PROGRAMME

Pages: 48   **Price:** £1.50

Editor: Dave Simpson Tel: 0860 119430

Other Club Publications: None

Local Press: Dagenham Post,
Waltham Forest Guardian, Ilford Recorder

Local Radio: Breeze AM, BBC Radio Essex,
Capital Radio, Active FM.

FOOTBALL MANAGEMENT TEAM

MANAGER: GARRY HILL

Date of appointment: 7th May 1999
Date of Birth: 15th October 1959
Place of Birth: Essex

PREVIOUS CLUBS
As manager: St. Albans, Haybridge Swifts
As player: None

HONOURS
As manager: Isthmian Prem. League 99-00
As player: N.A.

Asst Manager: Terry Harris
Chief Scout: Mick Loughton
Safety Officer: Bill Doig
Physio: Richard Harper

Season	League	Div.	Pos.	Home						Away						Manager	
				P	W	D	L	F	A	W	D	L	F	A	Pts		
99-00	Isthmian	Prem.	1	42	20	1	0	58	13	12	4	5	39	22	101	Garry Hill	
98-99	Isthmian	Prem.	3	42	10	8	3	40	15	10	5	6	31	29	73	Ted Hardy	
97-98	Isthmian	Prem.	4	42	11	6	4	43	25	10	4	7	30	25	73	Ted Hardy	
96-97	Isthmian	Prem.	4	42	11	3	7	32	21	7	8	6	25	22	65	Ted Hardy	

Season	League	Div.	Pos.	P	W	D	L	F	A	Pts	Manager	
95-96	Conference	-	21	42	7	12	23	43	73	33	Graham Carr	
94-95	Conference	-	15	42	13	13	16	56	69	52	Dave Cusack	
93-94	Conference	-	6	42	15	14	13	62	54	59	John Still	
92-93	Conference	-	3	42	19	11	12	75	47	67	John Still	
91-92	Conference	-	7	42	18	9	15	69	56	63	John Still	as Redbridge
90-91	Isthmian	Prem.	1	42	29	6	7	74	43	93	John Still	Forest

HONOURS

(Ryman) Isthmian League Prem. Div. 99-00

F.A. Trophy Runners-up 96-97

Essex Senior 97-98

PREVIOUS

Names:
Ilford FC (1881) & Leytonstone (1886) merged in 1979 to form Leytonstone-Ilford.
They & Walthamstow Avenue (1900) merged in 1988 to form Redbridge Forest
who in turn merged with Dagenham (1949) in 1992 to form Dagenham & Redbridge.

Grounds: None

Leagues: GMV Conference 92-96; Isthmian Lge 96-2000

Past Players who progressed to the Football League

Warren Barton (via Maidstone Utd '89 to Wimbledon '90)
Andy Hessenthaler (Watford '91)
Juan Mequel DeSouza (Birmingham C. '94)
Ian Richardson (Birmingham City '95)

CLUB RECORDS

Attendance: 5,500
v Leyton Orient - FA Cup 1st Rnd - 14.11.92

Career goalscorer all competitions): Paul Cobb 75
(Danny Shipp - 69 Paul Cavell - 49)

Career appearances (all competitions): Jason Broom - 266
(Steve Corner - 257. Paul Watts - 174)

Win: 8-1 v Woking (A)
GMV Conference 19/4/94
7-0 v Oxford (H) Isthmian Lge1/11/97

Defeat: 0-5
v Stalybridge Celtic (A) GMV Conference 31/4/94
v Northwich Victoria, GMV Conference 3/9/94 &
v Hyde Utd (H) FA Trophy 2nd Rd.

Transfer fee paid £50,000
to Boston United for Paul Cavell & Paul Richardson -1991

Transfer fee received: £85,000
from Watford for Andy Hessenthaler - 1991

BEST SEASON

FA Cup: 2nd Rd Proper
v Peterborough 2-3, 97-98

FA Trophy: Runners-up 96-97

League: 3rd Conference 92-93

LAST SEASON

F.A. Cup: 3rd Qualifying Round
F.A. Trophy: 1st Round
League: Isthmian League Champions
Joint Top Goalscorer: Danny Shipp 17
Paul Cobb 17

Player of the Year: Tom Cole
Captain: Mick Bodley

DAGENHAM & REDBRIDGE

Match Facts 1999-00

	Date	Comp.	H/A	Opponents	Gate	Result & Score		Goalscorers	League Position
1	14.08	RYM P	A	Harrow Borough	443	D	1-1	Cobb 28	
2	17.08	RYM P	H	Carshalton Athletic	673	W	3-1	Matthews 35, Heffer 50, Jones 53	
3	21.08	RYM P	H	Aylesbury United	838	W	4-1	Cobb 38 56, Jones 40, McDougald 79	2
4	24.08	RYM P	A	Farnborough Town	616	L	1-2	Rush 4	
5	28.08	RYM P	A	Hendon	410	W	1-0	Cobb 52	4
6	30.08	RYM P	H	Heybridge Swifts	912	W	2-0	Jones 16 20	
7	03.09	RYM P	H	Billericay Town	1102	W	2-1	Heffer 45, McDougald 79	2
8	06.09	RYM P	A	Dulwich Hamlet	489	D	0-0		
9	11.09	RYM P	A	Boreham Wood	354	W	1-0	Cole 83	3
10	25.09	RYM P	H	Enfield	1200	W	4-0	McDougald 14, Cole 21, 49, Protheroe 66[og]	1
11	23.10	RYM P	H	Walton & Hersham	776	W	2-0	Jones 77, Shipp 88	1
12	30.10	RYM P	A	Basingstoke Town	507	W	4-0	Shipp 9 34, Woolsey 15, Cole 47	1
13	06.11	RYM P	A	Hitchin Town	504	W	2-0	Cobb 64, Shipp 71	1
14	13.11	RYM P	H	Hampton & Richmond Borough	894	**W**	**5-0**	Cobb 34, Terry 35 59, Heffer 68, Janney 69	1
15	20.11	RYM P	A	Slough Town	592	W	3-2	Broom 22, Jones 46, Janney 79	1
16	27.11	RYM P	H	Chesham United	907	D	1-1	Shipp 66	1
17	30.11	RYM P	H	Aldershot Town	1150	W	3-1	Cole 21, Shipp 57, 65	1
18	04.12	RYM P	H	Hendon	802	W	4-0	Broom 12, Nabil 52, McDougald 88, Shipp 90	1
19	18.12	RYM P	H	Hitchin Town	774	W	4-1	Shipp 43 75, McDougald 71, Broom 90	1
20	27.12	RYM P	A	Canvey Island	2003	**L**	**1-3**	Cobb 55	1
21	03.01	RYM P	H	Gravesend & Northfleet	1332	W	2-1	Bodley 18, Shipp 78	1
22	08.01	RYM P	H	Billericay Town	1182	W	4-0	Nabil 6, Shipp 12[p] 54[p], McDougald63	1
23	15.01	RYM P	A	Aylesbury United	729	W	2-0	Bodley 16, McDougald 64	1
24	22.01	RYM P	H	Harrow Borough	971	W	4-1	Janney 33, **Cobb 3** (38 59 86[p])	1
25	24.01	RYM P	A	St Albans City	1264	W	3-1	Terry 8, Cobb 24, Bodley 77	1
26	29.01	RYM P	A	Carshalton Athletic	482	D	1-1	Elverson 68[og]	1
27	04.02	RYM P	A	Purfleet	1173	L	0-2		1
28	12.02	RYM P	A	Heybridge Swifts	604	L	4-5	McDougald 17 82, Payne 38, Heffer 45	1
29	19.02	RYM P	H	Dulwich Hamlet	1141	W	3-0	Cole 13, McDougald 26, Matthews 86	1
30	26.02	RYM P	H	St Albans City	1582	W	2-1	Cole 78, Terry 86	1
31	04.03	RYM P	A	Aldershot Town	2439	L	0-1		1
32	12.03	RYM P	A	Enfield	482	D	1-1	Goodwin 38 at Boreham Wood	1
33	18.03	RYM P	H	Boreham Wood	1028	W	2-0	Cole 6, Samuels 44	1
34	25.03	RYM P	H	Basingstoke Town	1040	W	1-0	Heffer 12	1
35	01.04	RYM P	A	Walton & Hersham	402	W	2-0	Cobb 30 (p), Shipp 88	1
36	04.04	RYM P	H	Farnborough Town	844	W	3-2	Cobb 65, Keen 88, 90	1
37	08.04	RYM P	A	Gravesend & Northfleet	836	W	2-1	Samuels 51, Shipp 65	1
38	15.04	RYM P	H	Purfleet	1440	W	3-1	Goodwin 43, Shipp 54, 79	1
39	22.04	RYM P	A	Hampton & Richmond Borough	453	W	3-2	Broom 5, McDougald 55 (p), Samuels 90	1
40	24.04	RYM P	H	Canvey Island	1,722	W	2-0	Terry 28, Cobb 68	1
41	29.04	RYM P	A	Chesham United	548	W	3-0	Goodwin 2, Cobb 57, 65 (p)	1
42	06.05	RYM P	H	Slough Town	1,540	W	2-1	Terry 21, Cobb 64	1

CUP COMPETITIONS

FA Cup

18.09	2Q	A	Sudbury	522	W	2 - 1	Cobb 27, McDougald 33
02.10	3Q	H	Burton Albion	919	L	0 - 2	

FA Trophy

09.10	1	A	Purfleet	532	L	0 - 2

Full Members Cup

16.11	2	H	Romford		W	2 - 0	
11.01	3	A	Leyton Pennant	109	W	5 - 1	Bodley 38 56, Heffer 42, Janney 44, Terry 70
14.02	QF	A	Purfleet		L	2 - 5	

Ryman League Cup

15.09	1	A	Croydon		L	0 - 5

Essex Senior Cup

26.10	3	A	Braintree Town		L	0 - 2

1	2	3	4	5	6	7	8	9	10	11	Substitutes Used	
Newell	Woolsey	Broom	Bodley	Conner	Payne	St. Hilaire	Cobb	McDougald	Jones	Cole	Terry (5), Shipp (7)	1
Newell	Cole	Broom	Bodley	Matthews	Payne	St. Hilaire	Cobb	McDougald	Jones	Heffer	Shipp (8), Kimble (10)	2
Newell	Cole	Broom	Bodley	Matthews	Payne	St. Hilaire	Cobb	McDougald	Jones	Heffer	Woolsey (3), Kimble (7), Shipp (8)	3
Newell	Cole	Broom	Bodley	Matthews	Payne	Rush	Cobb	McDougald	Jones	Heffer	Shipp (5)	4
Newell	Cole	Broom	Bodley	Matthews	Payne	Rush	Cobb	McDougald	Jones	Terry	Shipp (8)	5
Newell	Cole	Broom	Bodley	Matthews	Payne	Rush	Cobb	McDougald	Jones	Heffer	Shipp (8)	6
Newell	Cole	Broom	Bodley	Matthews	Payne	Rush	Cobb	McDougald	Jones	Heffer	Shipp (5)	7
Newell	Cole	Broom	Bodley	Matthews	Payne	Rush	Cobb	McDougald	Jones	Heffer	Terry (5), Kimble (7), Shipp (8)	8
Newell	Cole	Broom	Bodley	Woolsey	Payne	Rush	Shipp	McDougald	Jones	Heffer	Terry (4), Kimble (10), Cobb (7)	9
Newell	Cole	Broom	Woolsey	Goodwin	Payne	St. Hilaire	Cobb	McDougald	Jones	Heffer	Terry (7), Kimble (10), Shipp (8)	10
Newell	Cole	Broom	Woolsey	Bodley	Terry	St. Hilaire	Cobb	McDougald	Jones	Heffer	Shipp (7), Kane (6)	11
Newell	Cole	Naylor	Bodley	Terry	Woolsey	Janney	Cobb	Shipp	Jones	Heffer	Holding (10), Goodwin (3)	12
Newell	Cole	Naylor	Bodley	Goodwin	Terry	Janney	Cobb	Shipp	Jones	Heffer	Kane (6)	13
Newell	Cole	Naylor	Bodley	Goodwin	Terry	Janney	Cobb	Shipp	Broom	Heffer	Kane (6), Payne (9), Woolsey (2)	14
Newell	Cole	Naylor	Bodley	Goodwin	Terry	Janney	Cobb	Broom	Jones	Heffer	McDougald (10)	15
Newell	Goodwin	Naylor	Bodley	Conner	Terry	Janney	Cobb	Shipp	Broom	Heffer	McDougald (8), Nabil (7)	16
Newell	Cole	Naylor	Bodley	Goodwin	Terry	Janney	McDougald	Shipp	Broom	Heffer	Nabil (6), Cobb (8)	17
Newell	Cole	Naylor	Bodley	Goodwin	Nabil	Janney	McDougald	Shipp	Broom	Heffer	Conner (2), Payne (10)	18
Newell	Cole	Naylor	Bodley	Goodwin	Terry	Janney	McDougald	Shipp	Nabil	Heffer	Broom (10)	19
Newell	Conner	Naylor	Bodley	Goodwin	Terry	Janney	McDougald	Shipp	Matthews	Heffer	Cobb (10)	20
Newell	Cole	Naylor	Bodley	Goodwin	Terry	Janney	Cobb	Shipp	Nabil	Heffer	Matthews (5), McDougald (8)	21
Newell	Cole	Naylor	Bodley	Matthews	Terry	Janney	McDougald	Shipp	Nabil	Heffer	Cobb (8), Jones (10), Kane (2)	22
Newell	Matthews	Naylor	Bodley	Goodwin	Terry	Janney	McDougald	Shipp	Nabil	Heffer	Cobb (7), Jones (10), Woolsey (6)	23
Newell	Goodwin	Naylor	Bodley	Matthews	Terry	Janney	Cobb	Shipp	Nabil	Heffer	Keen (10), Broom (6)	24
Newell	Cole	Naylor	Bodley	Matthews	Terry	Janney	Cobb	Shipp	Broom	Heffer	Keen (10), McDougald (8)	25
Newell	Cole	Naylor	Bodley	Keen	Terry	Janney	Cobb	Shipp	Jones	Broom	Payne (10), Nabil (7), McDougald (8)	26
Newell	Cole	Naylor	Bodley	Matthews	Terry	Payne	Cobb	Shipp	Jones	Heffer	Nabil (6), McDougald (4)	27
Newell	Cole	Naylor	Bodley	Woolsey	Terry	Nabil	Payne	Shipp	McDougald	Heffer	Keen (4), Jones (5), Cobb (6)	28
Newell	Cole	Naylor	Goodwin	Matthews	Terry	Nabil	Payne	McDougald	Shipp	Heffer	No subs used	29
Newell	Cole	Naylor	Goodwin	Matthews	Terry	Nabil	Payne	Shipp	McDougald	Heffer	Keen (8)	30
Newell	Cole	Naylor	Goodwin	Matthews	Terry	Nabil	Payne	Shipp	McDougald	Heffer	Cobb (10), Keen (7)	31
Newell	Cole	Naylor	Goodwin	Matthews	Terry	Janney	Cobb	Nabil	Jones	Heffer	Ken (10), Payne (6)	32
Newell	Cole	Naylor	Goodwin	Matthews	Payne	Janney	Nabil	Shipp	Samuels	Heffer	Cobb (10), Keen (9), Jones (7)	33
Newell	Cole	Naylor	Goodwin	Matthews	Terry	Nabil	Cobb	Shipp	Jones	Heffer	Janney (7), Samuels (8), Vickers (4)	34
Newell	Vickers	Naylor	Goodwin	Matthews	Terry	Janney	Cobb	Shipp	Jones	Heffer	Keen (9), Samuels (8)	35
Newell	Vickers	Naylor	Goodwin	Matthews	Terry	Janney	Cobb	Shipp	Jones	Heffer	Keen (10), Samuels (9), Payne (6)	36
Newell	Vickers	Naylor	Goodwin	Matthews	Payne	Janney	Samuels	Shipp	Jones	Heffer	Terry (10), Keen (9), McDougald (8)	37
Newell	Vickers	Naylor	Goodwin	Matthews	Broom	Janney	Payne	Shipp	McDougald	Heffer	Samuels (10), Terry (6)	38
Newell	Vickers	Naylor	Goodwin	Matthews	Broom	Janney	Payne	Shipp	McDougald	Heffer	Terry (8), Samuels (9), Keen (7)	39
Newell	Cole	Vickers	Goodwin	Bodley	Broom	Janney	Cobb	McDougald	Terry	Heffer	Keen (3), Jones (4), Nabil (7)	40
Newell	Cole	Vickers	Goodwin	Matthews	Broom	Terry	Cobb	Nabil	McDougald	Heffer	Keen (7), Janney (9), Keen (3)	41
												42

1	2	3	4	5	6	7	8	9	10	11	Substitutes Used
Newell	Cole	Broom	Woolsey	Goodwin	Payne	Rush	Cobb	McDougald	Jones	Heffer	Shipp (8), St. Hilaire (7)
Newell	Cole	Broom	Woolsey	Goodwin	Payne	St. Hilaire	Cobb	McDougald	Kimble	Heffer	Terry (4), Shipp (7), Jones (10)
Newell	Cole	Broom	Goodwin	Conner	Payne	Woolsey	Shipp	McDougald	Jones	Heffer	St. Hilaire (3), Cobb (7)
Newell	Woolsey	Broom	Goodwin	Bodley	Terry	Heffer	Kane	Janney	Cobb	Jones	Cole (5), Holding (7), Obierio (10)
Newell	Woolsey	Naylor	Bodley	Matthews	Kane	Janney	Cobb	Shipp	Jones	Heffer	Terry (11), McDougald (9), Holding (3)
Boyle	Matthews	Naylor	Keen	Woolsey	Terry	Goodwin	Payne	Shipp	McDougald	Jones	Holding (2), Cobb (10)
Dennis	Rolfe	Kimble	Fielder	Shaw	David	Janney	Terry	Obierio	Resterick	Holding	Kane (8)
Newell	Cole	Broom	Kane	Goodwin	Terry		McDougald	Shipp	Jones	Heffer	St. Hilaire (4), Holding (7), Dyer (3)

155

PLAYING SQUAD

Player Honours	Birthplace	D.O.B.	Previous Clubs

GOALKEEPERS

Tony Roberts Wales Int.	Holyhead	04.08.69	QPR, Millwall, St.Albans C

DEFENDERS

Lee Matthews RP	Southend		Southend, Purfleet, £3,000 to Dag & Red
Dominic Naylor RP	Watford	12.08.70	Watford, Halifax, Barnet, Plymouth, Gillingham, Leyton O, Stevenage B
Ashley Vickers RP	Sheffield	14.06.72	Sheffield U, Worcester C, Malvern T, 61 Club, Heybridge S, Peteborough, St.Albans C
Lee Goodwin RP	Stepney	05.09.78	West Ham
Tim Cole RP	London		Walthamstow Pennant, Leyton Pennant
Mark Keen RP	Essex	23.07.64	Witham T, Dartford, Enfield, Chelmsford C, Heybridge S, St.Albans C, Braintree T, Heybridge S

MIDFIELDERS

Jason Broom RP, FA XI	Essex	15.10.69	Eton Manor, Billericay T, £3,000 to Dag & Red
Mark Brennan EY, u-21 Int	Rossendale	04.10.65	Ipswich, Middlesbrough, Manchester C, Oldham, Australia
Derek Payne Conf., RP	Edgware	26.04.67	Kingsbury T, Burnham, Hayes, Barnet, Southend, Watford, Peterborough
Matt Jones ES, RP	Chiswick	09.10.70	Arsenal, Souhend, Chelmsford C, Heybridge S, St.Albans C
Steve Heffer RP	London	11.01.73	West Ham, Southend, Swindon, Grays Ath., Hendon, Boreham Wood
Mark Janney RP	Romford	02.12.77	Spurs

FORWARDS

Junior McDougald RP	Big Spring	12.01.75	Spurs, Brighton, Rotherham, FC Toulon, Camb.C., Millwall, Camb.C., Leyton O
Rob Haworth	Edgware	21.11.75	Fulham, Millwall, Kettering T, Aylesbury U, St.Albans C
Paul Terry RP	London		Charlton, Bromley
Danny Shipp RP	Romford	25.09.76	West Ham, Coleraine
Paul Cobb RP	Essex	13.12.72	Purfleet, Leyton O, Purfleet, Enfield, Purfleet, £14,000 to Dag & Red

DONCASTER ROVERS

Doncaster Rovers played some memorable football last season, especially in the early part of the season, and left nine clubs leaving Belle View wondering how on earth they had come away with maximum points. Teams were played off the park, as they say, but the end product that seals a victory, a goal or several goals, were in short supply.

In 21 home league games Rovers only scored nineteen goals and shipped in 21 while away from home, where they registered some superb away victories, they scored 27 and let in 27.

But for a full time team with some expensive and experienced players on board to finish in twelfth place only seven points above the trap door is inexcusable and I'm afraid the local management from day one in the Nationwide Conference, Ian and Glynn Snodin, paid the price and left with half a dozen fixtures to play.

Dave Penney and Mark Atkins, two experienced players on the club staff and Mike Newell had left for Backpool in February, took over as acting player-managers to hopefully see the club to league safety.

This was achieved and then with two fixtures remaining committed chairman John Ryan and equally committed deputy chairman Peter Wetzel brought in Steve Wignall and Alan Lewer as his assistant.

The attendances, which had once again started in the 4,000 bracket, soon started to dwindle as the goal famine and charity handouts commenced. The high sport of the season again was the club retaining the Conference League Cup - this past season named the Macmillan Trophy after the now well known cancer trust - lifted the spirits of the fans after a most disappointing season.

They beat Kingstonian 2-0 with second half goals from Jason Minett and David Penney before a crowd of 3,837, the second highest crowd ever recorded in the competition, the previous best being 7,200 when Rovers beat Farnborough Town at the end of the 1998-99 season.

At the start of the season Rovers won a round robin event at Scarborough and with season ticket sales the highest for fifteen years fans were really relishing a great season ahead. It was not be, but they did with the Macmillan success see their beloved club lift its third piece of silverware in three decades, adding the honour to last season's success and the old Fourth Division championship in 1969. Mr. Ryan summed up the trophy success when he said "Another marvellous evening for our very supportive fans and I just hope that we can achieve similar success in the league next season - this sleeping giant needs awakening."

Doncaster Rovers 1999-2000 **Back Row:** Lee Warren (now Barrow), Simon Shaw, Jason Minett (now Boston Utd), Glenn Kirkwood (now Ilkeston), Mark Hulme (now Barrow), Colin Sutherland (now Clydebank), Ian Duerden, Mike Newell (now Blackpool). **Middle:** Dave Penney, Dean Walling, Dino Maamria (now Southport), Mark Barnard, Andy Warrington, Kevin McIntyre, Matt Caudwell, Andy Watson, Tommy Wright (now King's Lynn). **Front:** Scott Maxfield (now Barrow), John Ryan (chairman), Shaun Goodwin (now Frickley Ath.), Glynn Snodin coach (now reserve team coach at Charlton Athletic), Ian Snodin, manager (now pursuing a business career), Martin Foster, Peter Wetzel (vice-chairman), David Jones (now Hatfield Main).

DONCASTER ROVERS

GROUND DETAILS

Belle Vue Ground,
Doncaster,
S. Yorks. DN4 5HT

TELEPHONE
01302 539441
Fax 01302 539679
Website: www.doncasterroversfc.co.uk
email: info@doncasterroversfc.co.uk

SIMPLE DIRECTIONS:
From north & west
Into Doncaster town centre and follow signs
to Bawtry (A638) and after 1.2 miles take 3rd exit
at roundabout into BawtryRoad.
From east
M18, then A630, A18 and A638 (Bawtry Road)
From south
M18 junct 3, A6182, then A18 and A638 (Bawtry Road)

CAPACITY: 7,219
SEATED: 1,252
COVERED TERRACING: 4,753

SOCIAL FACILITIES: No Clubhouse.
Food outlets on ground on matchdays

CLUB SHOP: Open on matchdays, and Mon - Fri 1-4.30pm

MATCHDAY PROGRAMME

Pages: 40 **Price:** £2.00
Editor: Miles Cartwright, c/o the club

Other club publications:
Supporters' Club Handbook
Two fanzines
Local Press: Doncaster Star; Yorkshire Post
Local Radio: Radio Hallam; Radio Sheffield

For up to the minute news,
results, fixtures,
plus general facts & figures
from the world of
non-league football

log on to

www.nlfootball.com

Founded:	1879
Nickname:	The Rovers
Sponsors:	Beazer Homes
Club Colours:	Red shirts with navy insert, navy shorts, white socks with navytrim
Change Colours:	All yellow
Midweek matchday:	Tuesday
Reserve Team's League:	No reserve team

CLUB OFFICIALS

President Alick Jeffrey

Chairman John Ryan

Vice Chairman Peter Wetzel

Club Secretary Mrs K Joan Odale
c/o the club
Tel: 01302 539441 Fax: 01302 539679

Commercial Executive Miles Cartwright/Alick Jeffrey
c/o the club
Tel: 01302 539441 Fax: 01302 539679

FOOTBALL MANAGEMENT TEAM

MANAGER STEVE WIGNALL
Date of Appointment 3rd Mayl 2000
Date of Birth: 17th September 1954
Place of Birth: Liverpool

PREVIOUS CLUBS
As manager Aldershot, Colchester Utd.,
Stevenage Borough
As asst. manager/coach Aldershot
As player Doncaster Rovers, Colchester Utd.,
Brentford, Aldershot
HONOURS
As manager Football Lge - AutoWindscreen R-up,
2 playoffs -1 promotion
Isthmian Lge - 2 promotions
As player AutoWindscreen R-up

* * *

Assistant Manager/Coach: Alan Lewer
Reserve / Youth team Manager: Micky Walker
Physio: Jon Bowden

Season	League	Div.	Pos.	Home						Away						Manager
				P	W	D	L	F	A	W	D	L	F	A	Pts	
99-00	Conference	-	12	42	7	5	9	19	21	8	4	9	27	27	54	Ian Snodin / Steve Wignall
98-99	Conference	-	16	42	7	5	9	26	26	5	7	9	25	29	48	Ian Snodin

Season	League	Div.	Pos.	P	W	D	L	F	A	Pts	Manager
97-98	F. League	3	24	46	4	8	34	30	113	20	Kerry Dixon
96-97	F. League	3	19	46	14	10	22	52	66	52	Ian Atkins
95-96	F. League	3	13	46	16	11	19	49	60	59	Sammy Chung
94-95	F. League	3	9	42	17	10	15	58	64	58	Sammy Chung
93-94	F. League	3	15	42	14	10	18	44	57	52	Steve Beaglehole
92-93	F. League	3	16	42	11	14	17	42	57	47	Steve Beaglehole
91-92	F. League	4	21	42	9	8	25	40	65	35	Billy Bremner
90-91	F. League	4	11	46	17	14	15	56	46	65	Billy Bremner

HONOURS

Division 3 N 1934-35, 46-47, 49-50;
Division 4 1965-66, 68-69;
Sheffield County Cup 1890-91, 1911-12,
35-36, 37-38, 55-56, 67-68, 75-76, 85-86;
Yorkshire Electricity Cup 1995-96;
Midland Counties League 1896-97, 98-99;
Northern Intermediate Lge Cup 1984-95, 86-87
Nationwide McMillan Trophy (Conf. Lge Cup) 98-99, 99-00

PREVIOUS

Leagues: Midland Alliance Lge 1890-91;
Midland League 1891-1901, 03-04 & 05-15,20-23;
Football League 1901-3, 04-05, 23-Sept 39, 42-44, 45-98;
Midland Comb. 1915-16; E Midlands War Lge Oct 1939-40;
War Lge North 1940-42, 44-45

Names: None

Ground: 1880-1916 Intake Ground;
1920-22 Benetthorpe Ground;
1922 > Belle Vue (formerly known as Low Pasture)

Past Players

who progressed to the Football League

CLUB RECORDS

Attendance: 37,149 v Hull City, Div. 3N, 2.10.1948

Career Goalscorer: Tom Keetley, 180, 1923-29

Career Appearances: Fred Emery, 417, 1925-36

Win: 10-0 v Darlington (H), Div. 4, 25.01.64

Defeat: 0-12 v Small Heath (A), Division 2, 11.04.03

Transfer Fee Paid: £62,500
to Torquay United for Darren Moore, July 1995

Transfer Fee Received: £350,000
from Bradford City for Darren Moore, 1997

BEST SEASON

FA Trophy: 4th Rd 99-00 (2nd season)

FA Cup: 5th Rd 1951-52, 53-54, 54-55 & 55-56

League Cup: 5th Round 1975-76

League: 7th , League Div. 2, 1901-02

LAST SEASON

FA Trophy:	Fourth Round
FA Cup:	First Round
League:	12th Conference
Leading Goalscorer	Dino Maamria 11
Players' Player of the Year	Kevin McIntyre
Captain	Dean Walling
Club Captain	Dave Penney

DONCASTER ROVERS

Match Facts 1999-00

	Date	Comp.	H/A	Opponents	Gate	Result & Score		Goalscorers	League Position
1	14.08	N.C.	H	Forest Green Rovers	4,302	W	3-2	Duerden 3 (2,58,77)	
2	16.08	N.C.	A	Stevenage Borough	3,361	L	0-3		
3	21.08	N.C.	A	Woking	2,358	W	3-1	Maamria 45,90 Newell 84	5
4	24.08	N.C.	H	Southport	4,285	D	1-1	Hume 73	
5	28.08	N.C.	H	Hayes	3,546	D	0-0		11
6	30.08	N.C.	A	Northwich Victoria	1,688	L	1-2	Walling 64	
7	04.09	N.C.	A	Hereford United	1,690	L	3-5	McIntyre 5 Newell 29 Sturgess 77 (o.g.)	14
8	07.09	N.C.	H	Altrincham	2,978	L	0-1		
9	11.09	N.C.	A	Dover Athletic	1,065	W	3-1	McIntyre 26, Hume 27, Penney 84	13
10	14.09	N.C.	H	Hednesford Town	3,021	W	2-1	McIntyre 1, Penney 10.	10
11	18.09	N.C.	H	Kettering Town	3,544	W	2-1	Maamria 71, Penney 77	7
12	25.09	N.C.	A	Kidderminster H.	2,382	L	0-1		7
13	02.10	N.C.	H	Welling United	3,497	D	1-1	Minett 76 (pen)	10
14	09.10	N.C.	H	Nuneaton Borough	3,407	L	0-1		12
15	22.10	N.C.	A	Telford United	1,157	W	2-0	Cauldwell 38, Maamria 90	11
16	06.11	N.C.	A	Sutton United	1,097	L	0-1		12
17	13.11	N.C.	A	Woking	1,960	D	0-0		13
18	20.11	N.C.	A	Kingstonian	1,407	W	1-0	Duerden 59	10
19	04.12	N.C.	H	Stevenage Borough	2,631	L	1-2	Atkins 26	11
20	18.12	N.C.	A	Welling United	789	W	1-0	Barnard 11	13
21	27.12	N.C.	H	Scarborough	4,706	L	0-1		13
22	03.01	N.C.	A	Scarborough	3,510	D	0-0		13
23	08.01	N.C.	H	Sutton United	2,447	W	1-0	Kirkwood 23	12
24	22.01	N.C.	H	Kingstonian	2,548	W	1-0	Maamria 29	9
25	29.01	N.C.	H	Hayes	1,087	W	4-3	Mamria 9, Minett 20, 80 (p), McIntyre 58	7
26	12.02	N.C.	H	Hereford United	2,767	D	2-2	McIntyre 4, Maamria 72	9
27	19.02	N.C.	H	Rushden & Diamonds	4,187	L	0-1		10
28	04.03	N.C.	A	Hednesford Town	1,383	L	1-2	Penney 49	13
29	07.03	N.C.	A	Kidderminster H.	2,723	L	1-2	Penney 45	13
30	11.03	N.C.	A	Yeovil Town	2,079	W	3-1	Penney 26, Maamria 54, OG (Tomkin) 57	10
31	18.03	N.C.	H	Yeovl Town	2,498	L	0-3		13
32	21.03	N.C.	A	Southport	1,156	L	0-1		13
33	25.03	N.C.	A	Nuneaton Borough	1,723	D	0-0		14
34	08.04	N.C.	H	Morecambe	2,009	L	0-1		15
35	11.04	N.C.	A	Kettering Town	1,279	D	2-2	Kirkwood 7, Atkins 69	14
36	15.04	N.C.	A	Morecambe	1,346	L	1-2	Williams 80	15
37	22.04	N.C.	H	Dover Athletic	1,976	L	0-1		
38	24.04	N.C.	A	Altrincham	1,066	W	2-1	Campbell 36, Warren 76	16
39	26.04	N.C.	H	Telford United	1,871	W	2-0	Atkins 67, Kirkwood 87	
40	29.04	N.C.	A	Forest Green Rovers	851	L	0-1		
41	01.05	N.C.	H	Northwich Victoria	1,865	W	2-0	Maamria 79, 82	11
42	06.05	N.C.	A	Rushden & Diamonds	3,177	D	0-0		12

CUP COMPETITIONS

F.A. Cup
16.10	FAC 4Q	H	Crook Town	2,240	W	7-0	Newell 1, Kirkwood 4 (6,11,16,66), Cauldwell 65, McIntyre 70
30.10	FAC 1	H	Halifax Town	5,588	L	0-2	

Nationwide McMillan Trophy
09.11	2	H	Nuneaton Bor.	1,245	W	4-0	Foster 7, Walling 41, Duerden 77, Maamria 87
02.02	4	A	Scarborough	1,188	W	2-1	Wright 64, Williams 83
14.03	SF 1	A	Telford United	735	W	2-1	Williams 8, Warren 22
28.03	SF 2	H	Telford United	1,867	W	1-0	Penney 82 (p)
08.05	Final	H	Kingstonian	3,837	W	2-0	Minett 64, Penney 80

F.A. Trophy
27.11	2	A	Ossett Town	1,310	W	1-0	Kirkwood 57
15.01	3	H	Halesowen Town	2102	D	1-1	Watson 60
18.01	3R	A	Halesowen Town	724	W	*3-2	Duerden 50, Minett 104, Walling 113
05.02	4	A	Dover Athletic	1,682	L	0-1	

No.	1	2	3	4	5	6	7	8	9	10	11	Substitutes Used
1	Shaw	Barnard	Foster	Walling	Warren	Penney	Goodwin	Duerden	Newell	McIntyre		Sutherland (2), Minett (4)
2	Minett	Barnard	Warren	Walling	Sutherland	Penney	Goodwin	Duerden	Newell	McIntyre		Foster (3), Maamria (9), Hume (2)
3	Warren	Barnard	Foster	Walling	Sutherland	Minett	Penney	Duerden	Newell	McIntyre		Maamria (9)
4	Warren	Barnard	Foster	Walling	Sutherland	Minett	Penney	Maamria	Newell	McIntyre		Hume (9), Watson (4), Cauldwell (8)
5	Warren	Barnard	Minett	Walling	Sutherland	Watson	McIntyre	Maamria	Newell	Cauldwell		Penney (6), Goodwin (9), Wright (7)
6	Warren	Barnard	Foster	Walling	Minett	Wright	Goodwin	Watson	McIntyre	Cauldwell		Kirkwood(3) sub Hume, Maamria (11)
7	Warren	McIntyre	Snodin I	Walling	Minett	Maamria	Goodwin	Newell	Foster	Cauldwell		Penney (4), Watson (7), Hume (11)
8	Futcher	Barnard	Warren	Walling	Minett	Watson	Goodwin	Newell	McIntyre	Cauldwell		Foster (8), Bubalovic (6), Hume (11)
9	Futcher	Barnard	Warren	Walling	Minett	Penney	Goodwin	Newell	McIntyre	Watson		Hume (8), Cauldwell (11) sub Foster
10	Futcher	Barnard	Warren	Walling	Minett	Penney	Hume	Newell	McIntyre	Watson		Maamria (11), Foster (8)
11	Futcher	Barnard	Warren	Walling	Minett	Penney	Hume	Newell	Foster	Watson		Maamria (8), Wright (11)
12	Futcher	Barnard	Warren	Walling	Minett	Watson	Penney	Duerden	Newell	McIntyre		Maamria (9), Hume (2), Wright (3)
13	Marples	Maxfield	Foster	Walling	Sutherland	Watson	Penney	Duerden	Newell	Minett		Wright (4), Maamria (7), Barnard (8)
14	Marples	Maxfield	McIntyre	Walling	Sutherland	Penney	Minett	Duerden	Newell	Cauldwell		Kirkwood (9), Maamria (8), Goodwin (10)
15	Marples	Maxfield	Foster	Walling	Sutherland	Cauldwell	Goodwin	Kirkwood	Newell	McIntyre		Minett (4), Maamria (7), Warren (8)
16	Marples	Cauldwell	Atkins	Walling	Warren	Penney	Goodwin	Kirkwood	Duerden	Maxfield		Maamria (9), Snodin I (9)
17	Marples	Cauldwell	Atkins	Walling	Warren	Minett	Foster	Duerden	Newell	Maxfield		Barnard (11), Kirkwood (10), Maamria (9)
18	Marples	Barnard	Atkins	Walling	Warren	Minett	Foster	Duerden	Maamria	McIntyre		Kirkwood (10), Penney (8)
19	Marples	Barnard	Atkins	Walling	Cauldwell	Minett	Foster	Duerden	Maamria	McIntyre		Newell (9), Sutherland (8)
20	Marples	Barnard	Atkins	Walling	Warren	Minett	Foster	Duerden	Maamria	Maxfield		Penney (9)
21	Marples	Barnard	Atkins	Walling	Warren	Minett	Foster	Maamria	Newell	Maxfield		Cauldwell (8), Watson (11)
22	Marples	Barnard	Atkins	Walling	Warren	Minett	Penney	Maamria	Newell	McIntyre		Kirkwood (9), Cauldwell (3)
23	Marples	Barnard	Atkins	Walling	Cauldwell	Minett	Penney	Kirkwood	Newell	McIntyre		Warren (4), Illman (9), Maxfield (8)
24	Marples	Maxfield	Penney	Walling	Barnard	Watson	Minett	Duerden	Maamria	McIntyre		Foster (4), Warren (11), Kirkwood (9)
25	Marples	Maxfield	Minett	Walling	Barnard	Watson	Penney	Kirkwood	Maamria	McIntyre		Williams (7)
26	Minett	Cauldwell	Atkins	Walling	Barnard	Watson	Penney	Duerden	Maamria	McIntyre		Williams (9), Maxfield (3)
27	Warren	Cauldwell	Warren	Walling	Barnard	Minett	Penney	Duerden	Maamria	McIntyre		Watson (2), Williams (9)
28	Marples	Warren	Atkins	Walling	Barnard	Minett	Penney	Kirkwood	Maamria	Maxfield		Foster (9), Watson (3), Duerden (10)
29	Marples	Cauldwell	Atkins	Walling	Barnard	Foster	Penney	Duerden	Maamria	McIntyre		Minett (7), Williams (3)
30	Marples	Cauldwell	Atkins	Walling	Barnard	Foster	Penney	Williams	Maamria	McIntyre		Warren (4), Kirkwood (9)
31	Marples	Cauldwell	Atkins	Walling	Barnard	Foster	Penney	Williams	Maamria	McIntyre		Whitman (3), Warren (4), Minett (10)
32	Shaw	Barnard	Atkins	Walling	Warren	Watson	Minett	Campbell	Maamria	McIntyre		Foster (7), Cauldwell (2), Whitman (4)
33	Marples	Barnard	Atkins	Walling	Warren	Minett	Penney	Campbell	Wliams	McIntyre		Maamria (10), Cauldwell (3)
34	Marples	Cauldwell	Atkins	Warren	Barnard	Penney	Foster	Campbell	Duerrden	McIntyre		Williams (3), Maamria (10), Watson (11)
35	Marples	Barnard	Atkins	Walling	Shaw	Penney	Campbell	Kirkwood	Maxfield	Foster		Williams (2) sub Watson,
36	Shaw	Maxfield	Atkins	Walling	Barnard	Foster	Penney	Campbell	Kirkwood	McIntyre		Minett (8), Watson (7), Williams (2)
37	Marples	Barnard	Atkins	Walling	Warren	Minett	Penney	Campbell	Kirkwood	Wright		McIntyre (2), Maamria (11), Duerden (9)
38	Shaw	Maxfield	Atkins	Walling	Warren	Minett	Penney	Campbell	Maamria	McIntyre		Watson (8), Williams (10), Kirkwood (9)
39	Shaw	Maxfield	Atkins	Barnard	Warren	Minett	Penney	Campbell	Maamria	McIntyre		Kirkwood (9), Williams (10)
40	Shaw	Maxfield	Atkins	Barnard	Warren	Minett	Penney	Campbell	Maamria	Cauldwell		Walling (6), Kirkwood (10), Watson (11)
41	Shaw	Maxfield	Foster	Walling	Barnard	Watson	Minett	Duerden	Kirkwood	Wright		Maamria (9), Campbell (10), Penney (11)
42	Marples	Maxfield	Atkins	Walling	Barnard	Minett	Foster	Duerden	Kirkwood	Wright		Penney (4), Watson (11), Campbell (10)

THE NON-LEAGUE PAPER

CONFERENCE & PYRAMID LEAGUES SOCCER / £1.00

AVAILABLE AT A NEWSAGENT NEAR YOU EVERY SUNDAY

PLAYING SQUAD

Bold print denotes England semi-professional international.

Player	Birthplace	D.O.B.	Previous Clubs
Honours			

GOALKEEPERS

Barry Richardson	Wallsend	05.08.69	Sunderland, Scarborough, Northampton, Preston, Lincoln
Andy Warrington	Sheffield	10.0676	York City

DEFENDERS

Mark Barnard	Sheffield	27.1175	Darlington
Colin Hawkins			St.Patricks Ath.
Simon Marples ESP	Sheffield		Sheffield Wed., Rotherham, Stocksbridge Park Steels, £12,000 to Doncaster
Tim Ryan ESP	Stockport	10.12.74	Doncaster R, Buxton, Scunthorpe, Southport
Simon Shaw ESP	Middlesbrough	21.09.73	Darlington
Dean Walling	Leeds	17.04.69	Lincoln City £25,000

MIDFIELD

Mark Atkins ES	Doncaster	14.98.68	Scunthorpe, Blackburn, Wolves, York
Matthew Caldwell	Chesterfield	16.10.78	Hallam
Martin Foster	Rotherham	29.10.77	Greenock Morton
Jimmy Kelly	Liverpool	14.02.73	Wrexham, Wolves, Hednesford T, £15,000 to Doncaster R
Chris Newton	Leeds	05.11.79	Huddersfield, Halifax
David Penney	Wakefield	17.08.64	Pontefract Coll., Derby, Oxford U, Swansea, Cardiff
Andy Watson	Leeds	13.11.78	Garforth Town

FORWARDS

Carl Alford ESP, DMP	Denton	11.02.72	Rochdale, Stockport, Burnley, Witton Alb., Macclesfield, Kettering T, Rushden & D, Stevenage B, £55K to Doncaster R
Neil Campbell	Middlesbrough	26.01.77	York, Scarborough, Southend, £10,000 to Doncaster R
Ian Duerden	Burnley	27.03.78	Burnley, Halifax Town
Stephen Halliday	Sunderland	03.05.76	Charlton, Hartlepool, Motherwell
Tristam Whitman	Nottingham		Arnold T, £10,000 to Doncaster R
Gary Williams	Lancashire		Morecambe, Ashton U, Accrington Stanley, £60K to Doncaster R

DOVER ATHLETIC

Dover Athletic are currently into their seventh Nationwide Conference season and, following the dual appointment of manager Bill Williams and coach Clive Walker in February 1997, they have now firmly established themselves at this level.

Promotion to the Conference in 1993 saw a solid debut season of eighth position being followed by three years of struggle against relegation under a succession of managers. Long standing boss Chris Kinnear departed in February 1995 with John Ryan, Peter Taylor and Joe O'Sullivan all failing to arrest the clu's lowly progress until Mr. Williams' appointment in 1997.

Dover Athletic originally took over the Southern League position of the old Dover F.C. in 1983. After a steady start the `golden years' under Chris Kinnear saw the Whites win promotion in 1988 with the Premier Division Championship then being won twice in both 1990 and 1993. They were also Southern League Cup Winners in 1992, although the club has still to reach the First Round Proper of the F.A. Cup after seventeen successive attempts.

Off the field, major stadium improvements during the last decade has seen the club secure Grade A status for their picturesque Crabbles Athletic ground. Last season saw them finish in eleventh position, although they were holding down third spot for a time in February 1999.

Optimism is high that Mr. Williams' Conference Championship winning experience at Maidstone United will satisfy the club's ambitions in the not too distant future.

Back Row: J Moore, James Virgo, R Godden, Matt Carruthers, Tony Browne, Lee McRobert. **Middle:** Frank Brookes (Physio), Jake Leberl, Anthony Hogg, Joff Vansittart, Lee Shearer, Simon Beard, James Strouts, R Hastie (Kit Man). **Front:** Stuart Munday, Steve Brown, Bill Williams (Manager), Paul Hyde, Clive Walker (Asst. Manager), Steve Norman, Neil Lebihan

DOVER ATHLETIC

GROUND DETAILS

Crabble Athletic Ground
Lewisham Road
River, Dover,
Kent. CT17 0JB

Telephone Number: 01304 822373

Simple Directions: Follow the A2 from Canterbury until you pass the Forte Posthouse on your left and approach a r-about with McDonalds & petrol station on your left. Turn right signed 'Town Centre' & follow down the hill.

Capacity: 6,500
Seated: 1,000
Terracing - **Covered:** 4,900
Uncovered: None

SOCIAL FACILITIES:
Social Club open 7 days a week. Meals available.
Steward: Gavin Hughes 01304 822306.

CLUB SHOP:
At the ground. Open matchdays for general souvenirs.
Also at Worthington Street in town, open daily.
Contact Jean Haves 01304 240041.

Founded:	1983
Nickname:	The 'Whites'
Club Sponsors:	Jenkins & Pain
Club colours:	White shirts
	Black shorts, white socks
Change colours:	Red shirts
	red shorts, red socks
Reserve team's league:	Kent League Div. 1
Midweek home matchday:	Tuesday

CLUB OFFICIALS

Chairman	**John Husk**
Directors	**J T Husk, A G Husk,**
	J Gleeson, G A Goodacre,
Associate Directors	**J F Durrant, K F Stamp,**
	D Hammond, C J Harman
Secretary	**John Durrant**
	Tel: 01304 823429 (H)
	01304 240041 (Club)
Commercial Manager	**Jean Haves**
& Press Officer	Tel: 01304 240041

MATCHDAY PROGRAMME

Yeovil Town
Saturday August 29th 1998
Kick Off 3.00pm
Official Matchday Programme £1.50 No.6

Pages: 40   Price: £1.50

Editor: Martin Burke, 01797 230572
e mail: nicework@compuserve.com
m.burke9857@aol.com

Local Press: Dover Express; Dover Mercury

Local Radio: Radio Kent; Invicta FM

FOOTBALL MANAGEMENT TEAM

MANAGER: **BILL WILLIAMS**
Date of Appointment 24.01.97
Date of Birth: 23rd August 1942
Place of Birth: Esher, Surrey.
PREVIOUS CLUBS
As manager   Durban City (SA), Sacramento Gold (ASL),
              Atlanta Chiefs (NASL), Maidstone Utd.
As coach   None
As player   Portsmouth, West Brom. A., Q.P.R.,
              Gillingham, Maidstone Utd.
HONOURS
As manager   Championships with Durban City (x2),
              Sacramento (x2), Atlanta.
              GMVC & F.Lge 4 with Maidstone U.
As player   England: Youth (8).
              *   *   *

Assistant Manager	Clive Walker
Coach	Paul Hyde
Reserve Team Managers	Les Hall & Julian Holmes
Youth Team Managers	Steve Nolan, Jim Gleeson,
	John Spencer, Savas Pavlou,
	Tom Smyth
Physiotherapist	Frank Brooks
Club Doctor	Dr. S F Hodnett MBBCH BAO

Season	League	Div.	Pos.	Home						Away						Pts	Manager
				P	W	D	L	F	A	W	D	L	F	A			
99-00	Conference	-	6	42	10	7	4	43	26	8	5	8	22	30	66	Bill Williams
98-99	Conference	-	11	42	7	9	5	27	21	8	4	9	27	27	58	Bill Williams
97-98	Conference	-	13	42	10	4	7	34	29	5	6	10	26	41	55	Bill Williams
96-97	Conference	-	17	42	7	9	5	32	30	5	5	11	25	38	50	Joe O'Sullivan/ Bill Williams

Season	League	Div.	Pos.	P	W	D	L	F	A	Pts	Manager
95-96	Conference	-	20	42	11	7	24	51	74	40	Peter Taylor
94-95	Conference	-	16	42	11	16	15	48	55	49	Chris Kinnear
93-94	Conference	-	8	42	17	7	18	48	49	58	Chris Kinnear
92-93	Southern Lge	Prem.	1	40	25	11	4	65	23	86	Chris Kinnear
91-92	Southern Lge	Prem.	2	42	23	15	4	66	30	84	Chris Kinnear
90-91	Southern Lge	Prem.	4	42	21	11	10	56	37	74	Chris Kinnear

HONOURS

Southern League   Premier Division 89-90, 92-93
Southern Division 87-88
Championship Match 1990, 1993
Premier Inter League Cup 90-91
Challenge Cup 91-92

Kent Senior Cup 90-91, R-up 93-94, 96-97

PREVIOUS

Leagues: Kent League, Southern League

Grounds: None

Names: Dover FC

Bill Williams

Past Players who progressed to the Football League

Ricky Reina (Brentford) 1997

CLUB RECORDS

Attendance: 4,035 v Bromsgrove Rovers
Southern League April 92

Win: 7-0 v Weymouth 03.04.1990

Defeat: 1-7 v Poole Town

Career Goalscorer: Lennie Lee 160

Career Appearances: Jason Bartlett 539

Transfer Fees Paid: £50,000 for David Leworthy (Farnborough Town) Aug. 93

Received: £50,000 for Ricky Reina (Brentford) '97

BEST SEASON

FA Cup: 1st Round 81-82 0-2 v Oxford Utd (H)

FA Trophy: Semi-Final 97-98

FA Amateur Cup: Did not compete

League: 6th Conference 99-00

LAST SEASON

F.A. Cup: 4th Qualifying Round
F.A. Trophy: 5th Round
Conference: 6th Conference
Top Goalscorer: Joff Vansittart
Player of the Year: Jake Leberl
Captain: Paul Hyde

DOVER ATHLETIC

Match Facts 1999-00

	Date	Comp.	H/A	Opponents	Gate	Result & Score	Goalscorers	League Position
1	14.08	N.C.	A	Kidderminster Harriers	2,175	W 2-1	Hynes 9 Vansittart 45	
2	18.08	N.C.	A	Kingstonian	1,106	L 1-4	Hynes 72	
3	21.08	N.C.	H	Nuneaton Borough	1,078	W 3-1	Wormull 30 Shearer 35(Pen) Clarke 40	5
4	24.08	N.C.	H	Hayes	1,011	D 2-2	Shearer 25 (Pen) Flynn 48 (o.g.)	
5	28.08	N.C.	A	Telford United	838	D 1-1	Coates 53	10
6	30.08	N.C.	H	Sutton United	1,066	D 1-1	Leberl 75	10
7	04.09	N.C.	A	Altrincham	938	L 0-3		13
8	11.09	N.C.	H	Doncaster Rovers	1,065	L 1-3	Vansittart 23	18
9	18.09	N.C.	A	Northwich Victoria	1,049	D 1-1	Vansittart 2	17
10	25.09	N.C.	H	Hereford United	840	W 2-0	Hynes 13, 14	14
11	02.10	N.C.	A	Yeovil Town	2,420	D 1-1	Brown 84	14
12	09.10	N.C.	H	Scarborough	945	D 1-1	Shearer 65 (pen)	14
13	23.10	N.C.	H	Hednesford Town	669	W 4-1	Brown 15, Wormull 27, Carruthers 82, Shearer 86	13
14	30.10	N.C.	H	Stevenage Borough	1,001	W 4-2	Vansittart 27, Leberl 45, Dunne 48, Brown 54	11
15	06.11	N.C.	A	Rushden & Diamonds	3,037	D 1-1	Clarke 51	10
16	14.11	N.C.	H	Forest Green Rovers	967	W 4-0	**Vansittart 3** (1, 17, 71), Brown 21	8
17	20.11	N.C.	A	Southport	1,015	W 2-1	Norman 37, Vansittart 40	7
18	04.12	N.C.	H	Altrincham	1,015	D 2-2	Dunne 9, Carruthers 76	8
19	11.12	N.C.	A	Stevenage Borough	1,853	L 1-3	Vansittart 5	8
20	18.12	N.C.	A	Kettering Town	1,026	W 2-1	Shearer 73, Hynes 89.	8
21	27.12	N.C.	H	Welling United	1,658	W 2-1	Hynes 38, Norman 41	5
22	03.01	N.C.	A	Welling United	1,054	D 1-1	Vansittart 89	5
23	08.01	N.C.	H	Yeovil Town	1442	W 3-0	Leberl 22, Wormull 72, Brown 83	3
24	22.01	N.C.	A	Nuneaton Borough	1608	W 2-0	Vansittart 7, 22	2
25	29.01	N.C.	H	Morecambe	1471	W 3-1	Morrison 16, 69, Shearer 50 (p)	2
26	12.02	N.C.	H	Rushden & Diamonds	2,904	L 0-4		4
27	19.02	N.C.	A	Hereford United	2,003	L 0-2		4
28	04.03	N.C.	A	Scarborough	1,376	W 2-1	Morrison 75, Brown 84	3
29	11.03	N.C.	A	Forest Green Rovers	876	L 1-3	Brown 37	4
30	18.03	N.C.	A	Morecambe	1,127	L 0-2		6
31	21.03	N.C.	A	Hayes	612	W 2-1	Le Bihan 60, Shearer 90	4
32	25.03	N.C.	H	Kingstonian	1,025	L 0-1		5
33	28.03	N.C.	H	Woking	780	D 2-2	Shearer 15 (p), Norman 37	5
34	01.04	N.C.	A	Hednesford Town	797	L 0-1		5
35	08.04	N.C.	H	Northwich Victoria	740	W 4-1	Vansittart 31, 85, Leberl 38, S Brown 75	4
36	18.04	N.C.	H	Kettering Town	693	D 1-1	Norman 51	
37	22.04	N.C.	A	Doncaster Rovers	1,976	W 1-0	Le Bihan 22	
38	24.04	N.C.	H	Kidderminster Harriers	1,314	L 0-1		6
39	29.04	N.C.	H	Southport	773	D 1-1	Shearer 64	
40	01.05	N.C.	A	Sutton United	601	W 1-0	OG (Berry) 57	5
41	03.05	N.C.	A	Woking	1,560	L 0-2		6
42	06.05	N.C.	H	Telford United	704	W 3-0	Le Bihan 2, Hynes 70, Vansittart 80	6

CUP COMPETITIONS

F.A. Cup

16.10	4Q	A	Worthing	1,010	D 1-1	Leberl 74	
19.10	4Q R	H	Worthing	1,077	L 0-1*		

Nationwide McMillan Trophy

05.10	1	A	Welling United	361	L 0-3	

F.A. Trophy

27.11	2	A	Harlow Town	451	W 3-2	
15.01	3	A	Gravesend & N'fleet	1265	D 1-1	Vansittart
18.01	3R	H	Gravesend & N'fleet	1059	W 2-1	Brown, Vansittart
05.02	4	H	Doncaster Rovers	1,682	W 1-0	Vansittart 58
26.02	5	A	Sutton United	1,207	L 1-2	Le Bihan 40

1	2	3	4	5	6	7	8	9	10	11	Substitutes Used	
Hyde	Browne	Norman	Munday	Shearer	Beard	Clarke D	Leberl	Vansittart	Hynes	Wormull	Coates (10)	1
Hyde	Browne	Norman	Munday	Shearer	Beard	Clarke D	Leberl	Vansittart	Coates	Wormull	Hynes (6)	2
Hyde	Browne	Norman	Munday	Shearer	Beard	Clarke D	Leberl	Vansittart	Hynes	Wormull	No subs used	3
Hyde	Browne	Norman	Munday	Shearer	Beard	Clarke D	Leberl	Coates	Hynes	Wormull	Clarke M (7)	4
Hyde	Browne	Norman	Munday	Shearer	Beard	Carruthers	Leberl	Vansittart	Hynes	Coates	Clarke M (2), Manning (10)	5
Hyde	Browne	Norman	Munday	Shearer	Beard	Carruthers	Leberl	Vansittart	Hynes	Coates	Clarke M (7), Manning (4)	6
Hyde	Browne	Norman	Munday	Shearer	Beard	Carruthers	Leberl	Vansittart	Hynes	Coates	Brown (10), Manning (11)	7
Mitten	Wormull	Norman	Munday	Shearer	Beard	Carruthers	Leberl	Vansittart	Hynes	Coates	Dunne (6), Browne (10) sub Brown	8
Hyde	Browne	Virgo	Munday	Shearer	Leberl	Dunne	LeBihan	Vansittart	Brown	Wormull	Carruthers (9) sub Hynes, Godden (2)	9
Hyde	Wormull	Virgo	Munday	Shearer	Leberl	Clarke D	Dunne	Hynes	Brown	LeBihan	Carruthers (10), Norman (3)	10
Hyde	Wormull	Virgo	Munday	Shearer	Leberl	Clarke D	Dunne	Hynes	Brown	LeBihan	Carruthers (10), Norman (3)	11
Hyde	Daniels	Virgo	Leberl	Shearer	Wormull	Clarke D	Dunne	Hynes	Brown	LeBuhan	Beard (2)	12
Hyde	Browne	Virgo	Munday	Shearer	Wormull	Clarke D	Dunne	Vansittart	Brown	LeBuhan	Hynes (8), Carruthers (9)	13
Hyde	Browne	Virgo	Munday	Shearer	Wormull	Clarke D	Dunne	Vansittart	Brown	LeBuhan	Leberl (4), Carruthers (6)	14
Hyde	Browne	Virgo	Leberl	Beard	Wormull	Clarke D	Dunne	Vansittart	Brown	LeBuhan	Norman (11), Carruthers (6), Daniels (7)	15
Hyde	Browne	Virgo	Leberl	Shearer	Dunne	Clarke D	Wormull	Vansittart	Brown	Norman	Carruthers (8)	16
Hyde	Browne	Virgo	Leberl	Shearer	Dunne	Clarke D	Wormull	Vansittart	Brown	Norman	Carruthers (8)	17
Hyde	Browne	Virgo	Leberl	Shearer	Dunne	Beard	Wormull	Carruthers	Brown	Norman	Hynes (3)	18
Hyde	Browne	Norman	Beard	Shearer	Dunne	Clarke D	Wormull	Vansittart	Carruthers	Bolt	Hynes (10), Godden (8)	19
Hyde	Browne	Norman	Leberl	Shearer	Beard	Clarke D	Wormull	Vansittart	Brown	Bolt	Carruthers (9), Hynes (11), Godden (10)	20
Hyde	Browne	Virgo	Leberl	Shearer	Beard	Clarke D	Wormull	Hynes	Brown	Bolt	Virgo (3), Carruthers (9)	21
Hyde	Browne	Virgo	Leberl	Shearer	Beard	Norman	Wormull	Vansittart	Brown	Bolt	Carruthers (3), Hynes (11)	22
Hyde	Browne	Norman	Leberl	Shearer	Beard	Clarke D	Wormull	Carruthers	Brown	LeBihan	Hynes (9), Bolt (11)	23
Hyde	Browne	Norman	Leberl	Shearer	Beard	Clarke D	Wormull	Vansittart	Brown	LeBihan	Morrison (11)	24
Hyde	Browne	Norman	Leberl	Shearer	Beard	Munday	Wormull	Vansittart	Brown	Morrison	Livett (7), Carruthers (10)	25
Hyde	Browne	Norman	Munday	Shearer	Beard	Clarke D	Wormull	Strouts	Brown	Morrison	Carruthers (4), LeBihan (11), Hynes (10)	26
Hyde	Browne	Shearer	Virgo	Norman	Clarke D	Strouts	Carruthers	LeBihan	Vansittart	Brown	Morrison (4), Hynes (2)	27
Hyde	Browne	Norman	Leberl	Shearer	Beard	Clarke D	Carruthers	Vansittart	Brown	Morrison	No subs used	28
Hudson	Browne	Norman	Leberl	Reina	Beard	Carruthers	Strouts	Vansittart	Brown	Morrison	LeBihan (6), Wormull (7), Hynes (10)	29
Hyde	Munday	Norman	Leberl	Shearer	Strouts	Carruthers	Morrison	Vansittart	Brown	LeBihan	Hynes (10), Beard (4)	30
Hyde	Munday	Norman	Leberl	Shearer	Beard	Clarke D	Morrison	Vansittart	Carruthers	LeBihan	Hynes (10)	31
Hyde	Munday	Norman	Leberl	Shearer	Beard	Clarke D	Morrison	Vansittart	Carruthers	LeBihan	Brown (10), Hynes (6)	32
Hyde	Munday	Norman	Leberl	Shearer	Beard	Clarke D	Morrison	Vansittart	Brown	LeBihan	Strouts (8), Browne (2)	33
Hyde	Munday	Norman	Leberl	Shearer	Beard	Clarke D	Morrison	Vansittart	Brown	LeBihan	Strouts (8) sub Hynes, Virgo (11)	34
Hyde	Munday	Norman	Leberl	Shearer	Beard	Clarke D	Virgo	Vansittart	Brown	LeBihan	Hynes (3), Strouts (4)	35
Hyde	Munday	Norman	Leberl	Shearer	Beard	Clarke D	Browne	Vansittart	Brown	LeBihan	Strouts (7)	36
Hyde	Munday	Norman	Leberl	Shearer	Beard	Clarke D	Browne	Vansittart	Brown	LeBihan	Strouts (6)	37
Hyde	Munday	Norman	Leberl	Shearer	Beard	Clarke D	Browne	Vansittart	Brown	LeBihan	Hynes (6), Virgo (11), Strouts (2)	38
Hyde	Munday	Norman	Leberl	Shearer	Beard	Clarke D	Browne	Vansittart	Brown	LeBihan	Strouts (2), Hynes (8), Daniels (9)	39
Hyde	Browne	Virgo	Leberl	Shearer	Beard	Clarke D	Strouts	Godden	Hynes	Hogg	Norman (11)	40
Hyde	Godden	Norman	Leberl	Shearer	Beard	Clarke D	Strouts	Vansittart	Brown	Hogg	Hynes (10), Virgo (11), Browne (2)	41
Hyde	Munday	Norman	Leberl	Shearer	Beard	Godden	Strouts	Vansittart	Brown	LeBihan	Hynes (7), Hogg (6)	42
Hyde	Dunne	Virgo	Daniels	Shearer	Leberl	Clarke D	Wormull	Hynes	Brown	LeBuhan	Vansittart, Munday	
Hyde	Dunne	Virgo	Munday	Shearer	Leberl	Clarke D	Wormull	Vansittart	Carruthers	LeBuhan	Brown, Norman, Hynes	
Mitten	Munday	Virgo	Wormull	Daniels	Dunne	Clarke D	Leberl	Carruthers	Brown	Norman	Shearer, Hynes	
Hyde	Browne	Virgo	Leberl	Shearer	Dunne	Clarke D	Wormull	Vansittart	Brown	Norman	Hynes, Beard	
Hyde	Browne	Norman	Leberl	Shearer	Beard	Clarke D	Wormull	Carruthers	Brown	LeBihan	Vansittart, Munday	
Hyde	Browne	Norman	Leberl	Shearer	Beard	Clarke D	Wormull	Vansittart	Brown	LeBihan	Hynes, Virgo	
Hyde	Browne	Virgo	Munday	Shearer	Beard	Clarke D	Wormull	Vansittart	Brown	Norman	Carruthers, Hynes, Daniels	
Hyde	Browne	Shearer	Beard	Virgo	Wormull	Clarke D	LeBihan	Norman	Vansittart	Brown	Carruthers, Hynes	

PLAYING SQUAD

Player Honours	Birthplace	D.O.B.	Previous Clubs

GOALKEEPERS

Paul Hyde FAT, GMVC	Hayes	07.04.63	Hayes, Hillingdon, Wycombe, Leicester, Leyton O

DEFENDERS

Lee Shearer	Rochford	23.10.77	Leyton O
Stuart Munday British Univ.	Newham	28.09.72	Brighton
David Clarke	Nottingham		Notts Co., Eastwood T, Harrow B, £5,000 to Dover Ath.
Simon Beard	Bromley	08.09.72	West Ham, Sittingbourne, Hastings T
Jake Leberl	Manchester		Crewe
Tony Browne	Sheppey	28.09.72	West Ham, Gravesend, Brighton

MIDFIELD

Neil Le Bihan British Univ.	Croydon	14.03.76	Spurs, Peterborough
James Virgo	Brighton	21.12.76	Brighton, Sutton U
Anthony Hogg	Kent		From Youth team
James Strouts Combined Services	Kent		Harrogate RA, Frickley Ath., Harrogate T, Sittingbourne, Dover Ath., Stevenage B
Steve Norman	Harold Wood	30.01.79	Gillingham, St.Leonards

FORWARDS

Lee McRobert	Bromley	04.10.72	Ashford T, Sittingbourne, Millwall, Hastings T, Ashford T
Joff Vansittart	Sussex	12.09.74	Brighton, Crawley T, Sutton U, £10,000 to Dover Ath.
Steve Brown	Rochford	06.12.73	Southend, Scunthorpe, Colchester, Gillingham, Lincoln, Macclesfield
Matt Carruthers	Dover	22.07.76	Dover Ath., Ashford T, Folkestone Invicta

FOREST GREEN ROVERS

For Forest Green Rovers to have made it through another Conference season will have been satisfactory enough, but they did leave it very late, needing to beat visitors Kettering Town on the final day of the season, and even then they still left it late - winning the match with two goals in the last six minutes!

Manager Frank Gregan did exceptionally well to persuade ex-England star Tony Daley to join the club and his partnership in attack with the experienced Dennis Bailey and England semi-professional international Marc McGregor was a major factor in Rovers' survival.

They did manage to achieve some notable victories during the season including the scalps of Kidderminster Harriers, Rushden & Diamonds, Dover Athletic, Yeovil Town and they beat both the Trophy Finalists in the last few weeks of the campaign, but they were unable to string together a run of victories and this created the exciting end to the season.

Sadly for Rovers fans, Marc McGregor has now left to join rivals Nuneaton Borough and that will leave a big hole for Frank Gregan to fill. Fortunately, Daley and Bailey are still around, and hopefully the arrival of another ex-England man in veteran goalkeeper Nigel Spink and Yeovil Town's Rob Cousins will help strengthen things at the back for the Gloucestershire outfit.

I have a feeling that although Rovers will start as many people's favourites for the drop, if they can get off to a reasonable start, they will be celebrating another Conference season come next May.

Steve Whitney

Back Row: Frankie Bennett, Bradley Thomas, Steve Campbell, Rob Cousins, Wayne Hatswell, Nigel Spink, Alex Meecham, Steve Perrin, Billy Clarke, Dean Birkby, Ian Hedges, Nathan Lightbody, Paul Hunt.
Front: Darren Perrin (Coach), Jason Drysdale, David Norton, Chris Burns, Chris Smith (Coach), Frank Gregan (Manager), Mike Kilgour (Asst. Manager), Dennis Bailey, Tony Daley, Martyn Sullivan, Bob Baird (Physio)

FOREST GREEN ROVERS

GROUND DETAILS

'The Lawn',
Nympsfield Road,
Forest Green,
Nailsworth,
Glos. GL6 0ET

TELEPHONE NUMBERS:

01453 834860
(Matchday & Club AdministrationCentre)
Fax: 01453 835291
Lawnside Fitness Suite: 01453 832268
Social Club: 01453 833295

SIMPLE DIRECTIONS:
About 4 miles south of Stroud on the A46 towards Bath.
InNailsworth turn into Spring Hill from the mini roundabout
and the ground is approx. half a mile up the hill on the left.
The nearest BR station is Stroud

CAPACITY: 3,030
COVERED TERRACING: 1050
SEATED: 526

SOCIAL FACILITIES: Clubhouse open every evening.
Bar and lounge. Open before and after Saturday matches.

CLUB SHOP: Open only on matchdays
selling souvenirs and programmes. ContactAndy Whiting.

Founded:	1890
Nickname:	Rovers
Sponsors:	Sheffield Insulations
Club Colours:	Black & white striped shirts, black shorts, red socks.
Change Colours:	All Yellow.
Midweek matchday:	Wednesday
Reserves' League:	College Academy
Youth League:	Glos. CountyYouth Lge

CLUB OFFICIALS

President E G Smith

Chairman Trevor Horsley

Secretary David Honeybill

c/o The lawn, Nympsfield Road,
Forest Green, Nailsworth, Glos. GL6 0ET
Tel: 01453 834860 Fax: 01453 835291

Press Officer Heather Cook
Tel: 01453 823281 Mobile 07775 603287

Managing Director Colin Peake

Pages: 52   Price: £1.50

Editor: Julie Davis Tel: 01453 834860

Other club publications: None

Local Press: Stroud News & Journal
Gloucester Citizen

Local Radio: Severn Sound
BBC Radio Gloucestershire

FOOTBALL MANAGEMENT TEAM
MANAGER: FRANK GREGAN

Date of Appointment   01.01.94
Date of Birth: 09.08.57
Place of Birth: Newcastle-upon-Tyne
PREVIOUS CLUBS
As manager   None
As player   None
HONOURS
As manager   Southern League -
Southern Div. Championship 96-97
Premier Div. Championship 97-98
FA Trophy Runners-up 98-99

Assistant Manager: Mike Kilgour
Coach: Chris Smith
Scout: Darren Perrin
Physio: Bob Baird
College Academy: Billy Clark &
Frank Gregan

Season	League	Div.	Pos.	P	W	D	L	F	A	W	D	L	F	A	Pts	Manager
						Home					*Away*					
99-00	Conference	-	19	42	11	2	8	35	23	2	6	13	19	40	47	Frank Gregan
98-99	Conference	-	12	42	9	5	7	28	22	6	8	7	27	28	58	Frank Gregan
97-98	Southern	Prem	1	42	16	3	2	51	20	11	5	5	42	35	89	Frank Gregan

Season	League	Div.	Pos.	P	W	D	L	F	A	Pts	Manager
96-97	Southern	Southern	1	42	27	10	5	87	40	91	Frank Gregan
95-96	Southern	Southern	8	42	22	8	12	85	55	74	Frank Gregan
94-95	Southern	Midland	18	42	11	13	18	56	76	46	Frank Gregan
93-94	Southern	Midland	15	42	12	12	18	61	84	48	Pat Casey / Frank Gregan
92-93	Southern	Midland	19	42	12	6	24	61	97	42	Geoff Medcroft
91-92	Southern	Midland	19	42	14	4	24	66	88	46	Bobby Jones
90-91	Southern	Midland	18	42	11	14	17	51	64	47	Bobby Jones

HONOURS

FA Trophy R-up 98-99,
FA Vase 81-82,
Southern League - Premier Div . 97-98,
Southern Div . 96-97;
Hellenic Lg 81-82,
Gloucs Nthn Sen Lg 37-38 49-50 50-51,
Gloucs Sen Cup 84-85 85-86 86-87,
Gloucs Sen Amat Cup (N) 26-27 45-46 71-72 75-76 77-78,
Gloucs Sen Prof Cup 84-85 85-86 86-87.

PREVIOUS

Leagues: Stroud & Dist. 1890-1921,
Glos Northern Snr 22-67,
Glos Co. 67-73,
Hellenic 73-82,
Southern League 82-98,
Conference 98-.

Name: Stroud FC, 1989-92

Ground: None

Past Players who progressed to the Football League

G Rogers (Newport Co. 85)
K Gill (Newport Co. 85),
M England (Bristol Rov 85).

CLUB RECORDS

Attendance: 3,002
v St. Albans City, FA Umbro Trophy 18.04.99

Win: 8-0
v Fareham Town Southern Lge. Southern Div. 96-97

Defeat: 0-7
v Moor Green, Southern Lge. Midland Div. 85-86.

Career Goalscorer: Karl Bayliss

Career Appearances: Tommy Callinan

Transfer Fee paid: Adrian Randall from Salisbury City

Transfer Fee Received: £35,000
for Marc McGregor to Nuneaton Borough (July 2000)

BEST SEASON

FA Cup: 2nd Round 99-00
0-3 v Torquay Utd. (H)

FA Trophy: Runners-up 98-99

FA Vase: Winners 81-82.

League: 12th Conference 98-99

LAST SEASON

F.A. Cup: Second Round
F.A. Trophy: Fourth Round
Conference: 19th
Top Goalscorer: Marc McGregor 14
Player of the Year: Billy Clark
Captain: Billy Clark

FOREST GREEN ROVERS

Match Facts 1999-00

	Date	Comp.	H/A	Opponents	Gate	Result & Score	Goalscorers	League Position
1	14.08	N.C.	A	Doncaster Rovers	4,302	L 2-3	McGregor 14, 43	
2	21.08	N.C.	H	Scarborough	863	L 0-1		
3	24.08	N.C.	A	Telford United	830	L 0-2		
4	28.08	N.C.	H	Southport	1,241	L 1-2	Sykes 37	
5	30.08	N.C.	H	Kidderminster Harriers	919	W 3-2	Bailey 23, Hatswell 38, Randall 68	
6	04.09	N.C.	H	Nuneaton Borough	910	L 1-2	Sykes 18	20
7	11.09	N.C	A	Kettering Town	1,264	L 0-1		21
8	14.09	N.C.	A	Hereford Utd.	1,795	L 0-1		21
9	18.09	N.C.	H	Kingstonian	803	L 0-3		22
10	25.09	N.C.	A	Welling United	765	D 1-1	Burns 7	22
11	29.09	N.C.	H	Northwich Victoria	486	W 5-1	McGregor 4 (6, 17, 39, 61), Sykes 75	22
12	02.10	N.C.	H	Stevenage Borough	963	W 3-2	Hunt 27, 43, Bailey 72	22
13	09.10	N.C.	A	Hednesford Town	1,006	L 0-1		22
14	23.10	N.C.	A	Woking	1,505	L 1-2	McGregor 6	22
15	06.11	N.C.	H	Morecambe	705	L 1-2	Hedges 68	22
16	14.11	N.C.	A	Dover Athletic	967	L 0-4		22
17	04.12	N.C.	A	Nuneaton Borough	1,929	W 3-2	Daley 15, Bailey 27, 39	22
18	11.12	N.C.	H	Hednesford Town	701	W 3-0	Burns 6, Drysdale 36, Cook 90.	22
19	15.12	N.C.	H	Sutton United	586	L 1-2	Drysdale 25 (pen)	22
20	18.12	N.C.	A	Altrincham	853	D 1-1	Thomas 79	22
21	27.12	N.C.	H	Yeovil Town	1,837	W 3-0	McGregor 20, 36, Norton 77	20
22	03.01	N.C.	A	Yeovil Town	3,028	L 0-1		21
23	08.01	N.C.	H	Altrincham	901	D 1-1	Daley 60	21
24	22.01	N.C.	H	Rushden & Diamonds	1302	W 1-0	Clark 18	21
25	26.01	N.C.	H	Hayes	676	L 0-1		21
26	12.02	N.C.	H	Telford United	851	W 5-2	Sykes 25, Bailey 3 (26, 39, 67), Daley 90	19
27	15.02	N.C.	A	Rushden & Diamonds	3,195	L 2-3	Sykes 2, Bailey 21	
28	19.02	N.C.	H	Southport	903	W 1-0	Bailey 44	18
29	26.02	N.C.	A	Northwich Vics	911	D 0-0		18
30	04.03	N.C.	A	Morecambe	1,016	D 1-1	Daley 13	18
31	11.03	N.C.	H	Dover Athletic	876	W 3-1	Clark 10, Hatswell 55, McGregor 90	17
32	18.03	N.C.	H	Hereford United	1,509	L 0-1		17
33	25.03	N.C.	A	Hayes	646	L 0-3		18
34	01.04	N.C.	H	Woking	1,102	D 0-0		18
35	08.04	N.C.	A	Stevenage Borough	1,478	D 1-1	Clark 2	19
36	11.04	N.C.	A	Sutton United	607	L 2-3	Bennett 27, Hunt 75	19
37	15.04	N.C.	A	Scarborough	1,636	L 0-5		20
38	22.04	N.C.	A	Kingstonian	935	W 1-0	Burns 38	
39	24.04	N.C.	H	Welling United	1,107	L 1-2	Burns 58	21
40	29.04	N.C.	H	Doncaster Rovers	851	W 1-0	Sykes 82	
41	01.05	N.C.	A	Kidderminster Harriers	5,301	D 3-3	Burns 70, Sykes 71, McGregor 84 (p)	20
42	06.05	N.C.	H	Kettering Town	1,382	W 2-0	Hunt 84, McGregor 86	19

CUP COMPETITIONS

F.A. Cup

	Date		H/A	Opponents	Gate	Result & Score	Goalscorers
	16.10	4Q	A	Worcester City	1,301	W 5-2	Hedges 14, Cook 18, Sykes 59, Mehew 76, Randall 81
	30.10	1	H	Guiseley	1,047	W 6-0	Hunt 3 (1, 31, 62), McGregor 25 Drysdale 38, Sykes 51
	21.11	2	H	Torquay United	2,962	L 0-3	

Nationwide McMillan Trophy

	Date		H/A	Opponents	Gate	Result & Score	Goalscorers
	06.09	1	H	Telford United	424	L 1-2	Mehew 44

F.A. Trophy

	Date		H/A	Opponents	Gate	Result & Score	Goalscorers
	01.12	2	A	Cirencester Town	490	W 3-0	McGregor 9, Mehew 62, Cook 86
	15.01	3	H	Hendon	583	W 4-1	Sykes 2, Daley, Clark
	05.02	4	A	Sutton United	711	L 0-3	

1	2	3	4	5	6	7	8	9	10	11	Substitutes Used	
Shuttlewood	Hedges	Hatswell	Honor	Kilgour	Randall	Winter	Sykes	McGregor	Bailey	Forbes	Chapple (11), Mings (3), Mehew (8)	1
Shuttlewood	Hedges	Hatswell	Chapple	Kilgour	Randall	Winter	Sykes	McGregor	Bailey	Forbes	Hunt (9) sub Mehew, Mings (4)	2
Shuttlewood	Hedges	Hatswell	Clark	Kilgour	Randall	Winter	Sykes	Mehew	Bailey	Forbes	Mings (9), Chapple (3), Hunt (6)	3
Perrin	Hedges	Hatswell	Clark	Honor	Randall	Cook	Sykes	Chapple	Bailey	Forbes	Kilgour (3), Winter (7), Mehew (8)	4
Perrin	Hedges	Hartswell	Honor	Clark	Randall	Cook	Sykes	Mehew	Bailey	Burns	Mings (9), Kilgour (4), Winter (11)	5
Perrin	Hedges	Hartswell	Honor	Clark	Randall	Cook	Sykes	Mings	Bailey	Burns	Winter (4), Hunt (6), Mehew (9)	6
Perrin	Hedges	Forbes	Honor	Clark	Randall	Burns	Drysdale	Hunt	Sykes	Bailey	Catley (6), Hatswell (9), Mings (8)	7
Perrin	Hedges	Forbes	Honor	Clark	Burns	Cook	Bailey	Mings	Hunt	Sykes	Mehew (10), Hatswell (11), Kilgour (6)	8
Perrin	Hedges	Forbes	Honor	Clark	Burns	Cook	Hunt	Mings	Bailey	Sykes	Hatswell (4), Mehew (7), Catley (9)	9
Perrin	Hedges	Hatswell	Honor	Kilgour	Clark	Burns	Mehew	McGregor	Bailey	Drysdale	Forbes (5), Sykes (11), Hunt (8)	10
Perrin	Hedges	Drysdale	Honor	Kilgour	Clark	Burns	Mehew	McGregor	Bailey	Sykes	Forbes (3)	11
Perrin	Hedges	Drysdale	Honor	Kilgour	Hunt	Burns	Mehew	McGregor	Bailey	Sykes	Hatswell (2), Forbes (3)	12
Perrin	Hedges	Drysdale	Honor	Kilgour	Hunt	Burns	Mehew	McGregor	Bailey	Sykes	Randall (11), Smith (6), Cook (2)	13
Perrin	Hedges	Forbes	Burns	Kilgour	Randall	Daley	Sykes	McGregor	Bailey	Drysdale	Mehew (9), Hunt (11), Clark (3)	14
Perrin	Hedges	Forbes	Honor	Clark	Randall	Daley	Sykes	Bailey	Hunt	Drysdale	Mehew (9), Cook (6)	15
Perrin	Hedges	Hatswell	Clark	Kilgour	Burns	Daley	Cook	McGregor	Mehew	Drysdale	Sykes (11), Randall (4), Hunt (10)	16
Perrin	Hedges	Hatswell	Clark	Kilgour	Burns	Daley	Drysdale	McGregor	Bailey	Cook	Domm (8), Hunt (9)	17
Perrin	Hedges	Forbes	Clark	Kilgour	Burns	Daley	Drysdale	McGregor	Bailey	Cook	Honor (7), Mehew (9)	18
Perrin	Hedges	Forbes	Clark	Kilgour	Burns	Daley	Drysdale	McGregor	Bailey	Cook	Sykes (5), Hunt (11), Mehew (3)	19
Perrin	Hedges	Forbes	Clark	Hatswell	Burns	Daley	Drysdale	Mehew	Bailey	Cook	Hunt (9), Sykes (10), Thomas (3)	20
Perrin	Hedges	Hatswell	Norton	Clark	Burns	Daley	Drysdale	McGregor	Bailey	Cook	Thomas (11), Hunt (9)	21
Perrin	Hedges	Hatswell	Norton	Clark	Burns	Daley	Drysdale	McGregor	Bailey	Cook	Mehew (10), Thomas (11), Sykes (8)	22
Perrin	Hedges	Hatswell	Norton	Clark	Burns	Daley	Drysdale	McGregor	Thomas	Sykes	Bailey (11)	23
Shuttlewood	Hedges	Forbes	Norton	Clark	Burns	Daley	Drysdale	Bailey	Hunt	Sykes	Mehew (7)	24
Shuttlewood	Hedges	Forbes	Norton	Clark	Burns	Daley	Drysdale	McGregor	Hunt	Sykes	Bailey (3), Mehew (4)	25
Shuttlewood	Hedges	Hatswell	Norton	Clark	Burns	Daley	Drysdale	McGregor	Bailey	Sykes	Thomas (11), Mings (9)	26
Perrin	Hedges	Hatswell	Norton	Clark	Burns	Daley	Drysdale	McGregor	Bailey	Sykes	Hunt (9), Thomas (11)	27
Shuttlewood	Hedges	Hatswell	Norton	Clark	Barnett	Daley	Drysdale	Hunt	Bailey	Sykes	Mings (9), Forbes (11)	28
Shuttlewood	Hedges	Hatswell	Norton	Barnett	Cook	Daley	Drysdale	McGregor	Bailey	Sykes	Forbes (11)	29
Shuttlewood	Thomas	Hatswell	Norton	Clark	Forbes	Daley	Drysdale	Mings	Hunt	Sykes	Cook (4), Smith (7), McGregor (10)	30
Shuttlewood	Hedges	Hatswell	Clark	Barnett	Burns	Thomas	Drysdale	McGregor	Bailey	Sykes	Forbes (11)	31
Shuttlewood	Hedges	Hatswell	Norton	Clark	Burns	Daley	Drysdale	McGregor	Bailey	Sykes	Mings (2), Hunt (9)	32
Shuttlewood	Hedges	Hatswell	Norton	Clark	Burns	Daley	Drysdale	McGregor	Bailey	Sykes	Thomas (11), Forbes (4), Mings (10)	33
Shuttlewood	Hedges	Hatswell	Clark	Forbes	Burns	Daley	Drysdale	Bennett	Bailey	Sykes	Thomas (11), McGregor (7)	34
Shuttlewood	Hedges	Hatswell	Clark	Forbes	Thomas	Bennett	Drysdale	McGregor	Mings	Sykes		35
Shuttlewood	Hedges	Hatswell	Clark	Forbes	Burns	Daley	Drysdale	Bennett	Mings	Sykes	Hunt (5), Bailey (10), Perrin (1)	36
Shuttlewood	Hedges	Hatswell	Norton	Clark	Burns	Daley	Drysdale	Bennett	Bailey	Thomas	Hunt (4), Mings (10), Forbes (5)	37
Perrin	Hedges	Hatswell	Norton	Clark	Burns	Daley	Drysdale	Bennett	Bailey	Thomas	Sykes (8), Forbes (7)	38
Perrin	Hedges	Hatswell	Norton	Clark	Burns	Daley	Drysdale	Bennett	Bailey	Thomas	Sykes (8), McGregor (11), Mings (10)	39
Perrin	Hedges	Hatswell	Norton	Clark	Burns	Daley	Drysdale	McGregor	Mings	Bennett	Hunt (7), Sykes (8), Bailey (9)	40
Perrin	Hedges	Hatswell	Norton	Clark	Burns	Thomas	Sykes	McGregor	Mings	Bennett	Hunt (7), Bailey (10)	41
Perrin	Hedges	Hatswell	Norton	Clark	Burns	Daley	Bennett	McGregor	Bailey	Sykes	Hunt (10), Drysdale (2)	42

THE NON-LEAGUE PAPER
CONFERENCE & PYRAMID LEAGUES SOCCER / £1.00
AVAILABLE AT A NEWSAGENT NEAR YOU EVERY SUNDAY

PLAYING SQUAD

(Bold print indicates an England Semi-Professional International)

Player Honours	Birthplace	D.O.B.	Previous Clubs

GOALKEEPERS

Nigel Spink England Int., EC, Div.1	Chelmsford	08.08.58	Chelmsford C, Aston Villa, WBA, Millwall
Steve Perrin	Wiltshire		Melksham T, Trowbridge T

DEFENDERS

Mike Kilgour DMP	Dartford	25.05.65	Bath C, Larkhall Ath., Melksham T, Trowbridge T, Salisbury C, Stroud, Trowbridge T, Gloucester C, Dorchester T, Salisbury C
Billy Clark	Christchurch	19.05.67	Bournemouth, Bristol R, Bristol C
Wayne Hatswell	Swindon	08.02.75	Cinderford T, Witney T
Martyn Sullivan	Plymouth		Plymouth, Torrington, Dorchester T
Jason Drysdale	Bristol	17.11.70	Watford, Newcastle, Swindon, Northampton
Rob Cousins	Bristol	09.01.71	Bristol C, Bath C, Yeovil T

MIDFIELDERS

David Norton	Cannock	03.03.65	Aston Villa, Notts Co., Hull, Northampton, Cheltenham T, Yeovil T
Chris Burns	Manchester	09.01.67	Gloucester C, Cheltenham T, Portsmouth, Swansea, Northampton
Graeme Little	Gloucester		From Reserves
Lee McMullen	Gloucester		From Reserves
Chris Smith DMP	Christchurch	28.03.66	Cheltenham T, Bristol R, Gloucester C, Bath C, Newport AFC, Cinderford T
Bradley Thomas	Gloucester		Sharpness, Cinderford T, New Plymouth, Cinderford T, Newport Co

FORWARDS

Tony Daley England Int.	Birmingham	18.11.67	Aston Villa, Wolves, Watford, Walsall
Dennis Bailey	Lambeth	13.11.65	Barking, Fulham, Farnborough T, Crystal Palace, Bristol R, Birmingham, Bristol R, QPR, Farnborough T, Cheltenham T
Frankie Bennett	Birmingham	13.01.69	Halesowen T, Southampton, Bristol R, Exeter
Paul Hunt DMP	Swindon	08.10.70	Swindon, Charlton, Cardiff, Bristol R, Brann Bergen, Cirencester T
Streve Campbell	Wiltshire		Devizes T
Dean Birkby	Bristol	03.03.71	Mangotsfield U, Clevedon T, Yate T, Bath C, Yeovil T, Forest Green R, Paulton R, Clevedon T, Merthyr Tydfil

HAYES

After the previous season's third place finish expectations for the season were high, but Hayes came down to earth with a bump, from their disappointing opening day defeat at newly promoted Nuneaton they made a terrible start to the season.

Hayes were let down by their dismal home form - Church Road had been a fortress the previous season, no one in the league had won more at home, this season hardly anyone had won less at home. Away from home however, Terry Brown's side were surprisingly stubborn and they won more away than they did at home.

A mini revival in form during October, which included a great win at home against eventual league champions Kidderminster, coincided with the F.A. Cup. Dulwich in a replay and Runcorn were beaten in the Fourth Qualifying and First Round respectively, before Hull were drawn in the Second Round. A good 2-2 draw in front of the Match of the Day cameras was achieved, Lee Charles scoring twice, before being narrowly beaten 3-2, after extra time in a replay with the prospect of Chelsea in the next round snatched away.

A quick exit, yet again from the F.A. Trophy and a disappointing drop in form saw Hayes fall back into the bottom two in the league. A week before Christmas they faced the daunting prospect of travelling to league leaders Yeovil with reserve `keeper Matt Hodson in goal and key defender and Captain Nathan Bunce missing. Trailing 2-1 at half time another defeat seemed on the cards before a stunning 45 minutes saw the West Country side beaten 4-2.

Manager Terry Brown engineered a typical second half season recovery which saw his side move into a more mid table position, even if they did have to look nervously over their shoulder at the chasing pack sometimes. The two main factors for this recovery were the return to form of `keeper Paul Gothard and the signing from Dulwich, for a club record fee, of Dave Stevens who set the Conference alight in the closing months of the season.

A 4-1 destruction of Morecambe at Christie Park followed by a narrow victory at Forest Green kick started the second half of the season.

The good progress in the Cups was continued when the League Cup Southern Section Final was reached and the Middlesex Senior Cup was won with a romp over Ryman League Northwood in the Final. Kingstonian stopped progress to the League Cup Final with a single goal victory over a tight two-legged affair.

A late season surge which included tough 2-1 away wins at Altrincham and Welling before avenging the League Cup Semi Final defeat at home by winning at Kingstonian 3-1 with a performance more convincing than the scoreline suggested. The Lee Charles, David Stevens partnership was largely instrumental in these victories. The season ended where it started with Nuneaton, this time a good 3-0 victory was secured to help Hayes end up in a comfortable and very respectable eleventh place given the start made to the season.

Back Row: Ben Hodson, Alvin Watts, Dominic Sterling, Paul Gothard, Matt Hodson, Dean Coppard, Jason Tucker, Rocky Baptiste.
Middle Row: Mark Molesley, Barry Moore, Ryan Spencer, Mark Preston, Brendon Gallen, Danny Tilbury.
Front Row: Dave Killick (Chief Scout), Steve Barnes, Steve McKimm, Jason Goodliffe (Captain), Derek Goodall (Chairman), Lee Flynn, Dave Stevens, Errol Telemaque, Terry Brown (Manager)

HAYES

GROUND DETAILS

Townfield House
Church Road
Hayes
Middx. UB3 2LE

Telephone Number: 0208 573 2075
email:
Web: www:

Simple Directions: M25, M4, A312 (Hayes By-Pass), A4020 (Uxbridge Road) and Church Rd. is on the left.

Capacity: 6,500
Seated: 450
Terracing - **Covered:** 2,000
Uncovered: 4,050

SOCIAL FACILITIES:
Clubhouse open Sat 12 - 11pm.
Sun 12 - 3pm, 7 - 11pm. Midweek 6.30 - 11pm.
Hot and cold snacks are available.

CLUB SHOP:
Wide range of programmes & souvenirs.
Contact Lee Hermitage, c/o the club.

Terry Brown

MATCHDAY PROGRAMME

Pages: 32   Price: £1.50

Editor: Ken Green

Other club publications: None

Local Press: Hayes Gazette

Local Radio: Capital Radio

Founded: 1909
Nickname: The Missioners
Club Sponsors: Taylor Woodrow

Club colours: Red & white shirts
black shorts, black socks

Change colours: Blue shirts
blue shorts, blue socks

Reserve team's league: Suburban Premier
Midweek home matchday: Tuesday
Local Newspapers: Hayes Gazette
Local Radio: Capital Radio

CLUB OFFICIALS

President Les Lovering

Chairman Derek Goodall

Vice Chairman Trevor Griffith

Financial Director Charles Mackintosh

Directors D Goodall, C Porter, E Stevens,
T Griffith, C Mackintosh, A Bond, J Bond,
N Griffith, T Gorman.

Football Secretary John Bond Jnr.

Press Officer Trevor Griffith
c/o the club Tel: 0208 573 2075

FOOTBALL MANAGEMENT TEAM

MANAGER: **TERRY BROWN**
Date of Appointment November 1993
Date of Birth 5th August 1952
Place of Birth Hillingdon

PREVIOUS CLUBS
As manager None
As coach Wokingham Town
As player Hayes, Slough Town, Hayes,
Wokingham Town
HONOURS
as manager Isthmian League Championship 95-96
As player None

*   *   *

Assistant Manager Willy Wordsworth

Coach Dave Killick

Physio Karl Ballard

176

Season	League	Div.	Pos.	Home						Away					Pts	Manager
				P	W	D	L	F	A	W	D	L	F	A		
99-00	Conference	-	11	42	7	3	11	24	28	9	5	7	33	30	56	Terry Brown
98-99	Conference	-	3	42	12	3	6	34	25	10	5	6	29	25	74	Terry Brown
97-98	Conference	-	12	42	10	4	7	36	25	6	6	9	26	27	58	Terry Brown
96-97	Conference	-	15	42	7	7	7	27	21	5	7	9	27	34	50	Terry Brown

Season	League	Div.	Pos.	P	W	D	L	F	A	Pts	Manager
95-96	Isthmian	Prem	1	42	24	14	4	76	32	86	Terry Brown
94-95	Isthmian	Prem	3	42	20	14	8	66	47	74	Terry Brown
93-94	Isthmain	Prem	13	42	15	8	19	63	72	53	Clive Griffiths
92-93	Isthmian	Prem	10	42	16	13	13	64	59	61	Clive Griffiths
91-92	Isthmian	Prem	19	42	10	14	18	52	63	44	Harry Manoe
90-91	Isthmian	Prem	8	42	20	5	17	60	57	65	Harry Manoe

HONOURS

Isthmian League 95-96
Athenian League 56-57
Spartan League 27-28
Great Western Suburban League 1920-24 (4 times)
Middlesex Senior Cup 19-20, 20-21, 25-26,
30-31, 35-36, 39-40, 49-50, 81-82, 95-96, 99-00
London Senior Cup 31-32, 80-81
Middlesex Charity Cup - 15 Times
London Charity Cup 60-61

PREVIOUS

Leagues:
Local leagues 1909-14;
Gt. Western Suburban 19-22;
London 22-24;
Spartan 24-30;
Athenian 30-71;
Isthmian 71-96.

Names: Bokwell Mission

Ground: Botwell Common

Past Players who progressed to the Football League

Cyril Bacon (Orient 46), Phil Nolan (Watford 47),
Dave Groombridge (Orient 51),
Jimmy Bloomfield (Brentford 52),
Derek Neate & Les Champleover(Brighton 56 & 57),
Gordon Phillips (Brentford 63), Robin Friday (Reading 74),
Les Smith (A Villa), Cyrille Regis (WBA 1977),
Les Ferdinand (QPR 87),Derek Payne (Barnet 88),
Paul Hyde (Wycombe 91), Dean Hooper (Swindon95),
Jason Roberts (Wolverhampton W. 97)

CLUB RECORDS

Attendance: 15,370 v Bromley
FA Amateur Cup, 10.2.51

Win: Unknown
Defeat: Unknown
Career Goalscorer: Unknown

Career Appearances: Reg Leather 701

Transfer Fees
Paid: £6,000 for
Gary Keen (Hendon) 1990
Joe Francis (Enfield) 1996

Received: £30,000 for Les Ferdinand
(Q.P.R.) 1987

BEST SEASON

FA Cup: 2nd Round (replay)
72-73: 0-1 v Reading (H) after 0-0
99-00: 2-3 aet v Hull City (A) after 2-2
also 2nd Round 90-91 & 91-92
League clubs defeated:
Fulham, Bristol Rov., Cardiff C.

FA Trophy: Quarter Final
78-79, 1-2 v Runcorn (A)
97-98, 0-1 v Cheltenham Town (A)

FA Amateur Cup: Runners Up 1930-31

LAST SEASON

F.A. Cup: Second Round replay
F.A. Trophy: Second Round
Conference: 11th
Top Goalscorer: Lee Charles 17
Player of the Year: Jason Goodliffe
Captain: Nathan Bunce

HAYES

	Date	Comp.	H/A	Opponents	Gate	Result & Score		Goalscorers	League Position
1	14.08	N.C.	A	Nuneaton Borough	2,186	L	1-2	Flynn 65	
2	17.08	N.C.	H	Welling United	706	W	1-0	Hodson 78	
3	21.08	N.C.	H	Morecambe	676	L	0-1		15
4	24.08	N.C.	A	Dover Athletic	1,011	D	2-2	Bunce 76, Hodson 87	
5	28.08	N.C.	A	Doncaster Rovers	3,546	D	0-0		15
6	30.08	N.C.	H	Kingstonian	829	L	1-2	Treble 68	
7	04.09	N.C.	H	Southport	637	L	0-2		16
8	07.09	N.C.	A	Rushden & Diamonds	2,434	L	0-1		
9	11.09	N.C.	A	Telford United	811	W	2-1	Charles 40 Bunce 45	19
10	14.09	N.C.	H	Yeovil Town	747	L	2-3	Ansell 3, Trebble 13	19
11	18.09	N.C.	A	Hednesford Town	962	L	1-2	Ansell 19	20
12	25.09	N.C.	A	Scarborough	1,295	L	1-4	McKimm 52	21
13	02.10	N.C.	H	Kidderminster Harriers	635	W	2-0	Charles 61, 89	21
14	09.10	N.C.	A	Kettering Town	1,252	D	1-1	Telemaque 9	19
15	23.10	N.C.	A	Hereford United	1,665	W	2-0	Telemaque 48, Charles 62	16
16	06.11	N.C.	H	Northwich Victoria	616	W	2-1	Moore 33, 75	17
17	14.11	N.C.	H	Stevenage Borough	906	L	1-2	Charles 75	18
18	04.12	N.C.	H	Rushden & Diamonds	901	L	0-5		20
19	18.12	N.C.	A	Yeovil Town	2,603	W	4-2	Goodliffe 33, Charles 68, McKimm 71, Flynn 87	19
20	27.12	N.C.	H	Sutton United	1,006	W	1-0	Charles 67	16
21	03.01	N.C.	A	Sutton United	1,058	D	2-2	Charles 41, McKimm 51	18
22	08.01	N.C.	H	Kettering Town	716	L	0-1		18
23	15.01	N.C.	A	Kidderminster Harriers	2,636	L	1-2	Stevens 39	18
24	22.01	N.C.	A	Morecambe	1,240	W	4-1	OG (Fensome) 10, Roddis 19, Moore 21, Stevens 60	17
25	26.01	N.C.	A	Forest Green Rovers	676	W	1-0	Roddis 39	16
26	29.01	N.C.	H	Doncaster Rovers	1,087	L	3-4	Moore 18, Stevens 35, Flynn 69	16
27	12.02	N.C.	A	Northwich Vics	1,002	D	0-0		16
28	19.02	N.C.	H	Hednesford Town	607	W	2-1	Spencer 32, Stevens 45	14
29	26.02	N.C.	H	Hereford United	849	D	0-0		15
30	04.03	N.C.	A	Southport	1,097	L	1-4	Moore 65	16
31	11.03	N.C.	A	Woking	2,041	W	3-0	Stevens 27, 44, Charles 71	14
32	18.03	N.C.	H	Altrincham	642	D	1-1	D Stevens	15
33	21.03	N.C.	H	Dover Athletic	612	L	1-2	Flynn 77	15
34	25.03	N.C.	H	Forest Green Rov.	646	W	3-0	Moore 10, Stevens 22, OG (Hartswell) 78	13
35	01.04	N.C.	A	Stevenage Borough	1,617	L	0-3		15
36	08.04	N.C.	H	Woking	1,067	D	0-0		14
37	11.04	N.C.	H	Scarborough	506	L	0-1		16
38	18.04	N.C.	A	Altrincham	657	W	2-1	Charles 1, Stevens 46	
39	22.04	N.C.	A	Welling United	815	W	2-1	Charles 23, McKimm 28	11
40	29.04	N.C.	H	Telford United	591	L	1-2	Stevens 48	14
41	01.05	N.C.	A	Kingstonian	1,183	W	3-1	Flynn 68, 86, Charles 70	12
42	06.05	N.C.	H	Nuneaton Borough	703	W	3-0	Preston 21, Stevens 44, Charles 90	11

CUP COMPETITIONS

F.A. Cup

	Date		H/A	Opponents	Gate		Score	Goalscorers
	16.10	4Q	A	Dulwich Hamlet	830	D	0-0	
	19.10	4Q R	H	Dulwich Hamlet	602	W	3-0	Bunce 4, Charles 45(p), Spencer 73
	30.10	1	H	Runcorn	890	W	2-1	Bunce 25, Charles 90 (pen)
	20.11	2	H	Hull City	2,749	D	2-2	Charles 21, 63 (p)
	30.11	2R	A	Hull City	5,947	L	*2-3	Gallen 77, Charles 114

F.A. Trophy

	Date		H/A	Opponents	Gate		Score	
	27.11	2	H	Worcester City	671	L	0-2	

Nationwide McMillan Trophy

	Date		H/A	Opponents	Gate		Score	Goalscorers
	08.02	4	H	Yeovil Town	364	W	2-1	Roddis 24, Trebble 90
	28.03	SF1	H	Kingstonian	531	D	0-0	
	20.04	SF2	A	Kingstonian	306	L	0-1	

1	2	3	4	5	6	7	8	9	10	11	Substitutes Used	
Gothard 1	Bunce	Flynn	Watts	Bunce	Witter	McKimm	Charles	Patton	Spencer	Trebble	Roddis (9), Hodson B (10)	1
Gothard 2	Watts	Flynn	Bunce	Goodliffe	Witter	Roddis	Charles	Hodson B	McKimm	Trebble	Patton (10)	2
Gothard 3	Watts	Flynn	Patton	Bunce	Goodliffe	Roddis	Charles	Boyce	Metcalfe	Trebble	Spencer (10), Hodson B (9)	3
Gothard 4	Roddis	Flynn	Watts	Bunce	Goodliffe	McKimm	Charles	Hodson B	Patton	Trebble	Spencer (7)	4
Gothard 5	Patton	Flynn	Watts	Bunce	Goodliffe	Roddis	Charles	Hodson B	McKimm	Trebble	Spencer (2), Sparks (11)	5
Gothard 6	Watts	Flynn	Roddis	Bunce	Goodliffe	McKimm	Charles	Hodson B	Patton	Trebble	Spencer (4), Sparks (2), Boyce (10)	6
Wilkerson 7	Watts	Flynn	Boyce	Bunce	Goodliffe	Onwere	Charles	Spencer	McKimm	Trebble	Patton (9), Hodson B (4)	7
Wilkerson 8	Spencer	Flynn	Watts	Bunce	Goodliffe	McKimm	Charles	Hodson B	Patton	Trebble	Sullivan (9), Boyce (2)	8
Wilkerson 9	Boyce	Flynn	Watts	Bunce	Goodliffe	McKimm	Charles	Ansell	Patton	Trebble	Spencer (10)	9
Wilkerson 10	Boyce	Flynn	Watts	Bunce	Goodliffe	McKimm	Charles	Ansell	Roddis	Trebble	Spencer (10), Patton (2), Witby (8)	10
Gothard 11	Boyce	Flynn	Watts	O'Brien	Goodliffe	McKimm	Charles	Ansell	Patton	Trebble	Hodson (4), Spencer (7)	11
Gothard 12	Boyce	Flynn	Coppard	O'Brien	Goodliffe	McKimm	Charles	Ansell	Onwere	Trebble	Roddis (8), Telemarque (9), Patton (10)	12
Gothard 13	Boyce	Flynn	Watts	Moore	Goodliffe	McKimm	Charles	Telemarque	Roddis	Trebble	Patton (5), Ansell (9), Coppard (11)	13
Hodson 14	O'Brien	Flynn	Watts	Coppard	Goodliffe	McKimm	Charles	Telemarque	Moore	Trebble	Spencer (10), Witby (9)	14
Hodson 15	Boyce	Flynn	Coppard	Bunce	Goodliffe	McKimm	Charles	Telemarque	Moore	Spencer	Trebble (9), Roddis (11)	15
Hodson 16	Boyce	Flynn	Watts	Bunce	Goodliffe	McKimm	Charles	Telemarque	Moore	Roddis	Trebble (9)	16
Gothard 17	Boyce	Flynn	Watts	Bunce	Goodliffe	McKimm	Charles	Telemarque	Moore	Roddis	Trebble (9), Spencer (7)	17
Gothard 18	Boyce	Gallen	Watts	Bunce	Goodliffe	Onwere	Charles	Trebble	Moore	Spencer	Telemarque (7), Coppard (4), Carter (9)	18
Hodson 19	Boyce	Flynn	Watts	Smith	Goodliffe	McKimm	Charles	Trebble	Moore	Roddis		19
Hodson 20	Boyce	Flynn	Watts	Broad	Smith	McKimm	Charles	Trebble	Moore	Roddis	Spencer (11), Gallen (7), Hodson B (9)	20
Hodson 21	Boyce	Flynn	Gallen	Coppard	Smith	McKimm	Charles	Trebble	Moore	Spencer	Gothard (1), Hodson B (9)	21
Gothard 22	Boyce	Flynn	Smith	Bunce	Goodliffe	Roddis	Charles	Stevens	Moore	Spencer	McKimm (7), Gallen (4)	22
Gothard 23	Spencer	Gallen	Broad	Bunce	Goodliffe	McKimm	Charles	Stevens	Moore	Roddis	Smith (4), Boyce (5), Telemarque (10)	23
Gothard 24	Spencer	Flynn	Broad	Bunce	Goodliffe	McKimm	Charles	Stevens	Moore	Roddis	Watts (10), Trebble (8), Boyce (2)	24
Gothard 25	Spencer	Flynn	Watts	Bunce	Goodliffe	McKimm	Charles	Stevens	Moore	Roddis	Coppard (10), Trebble (9)	25
Gothard 26	Boyce	Flynn	Watts	Bunce	Goodliffe	McKimm	Charles	Stevens	Moore	Spencer	Trebble (2)	26
Gothard 27	Roddis	Gallen	Watts	Bunce	Goodliffe	McKimm	Charles	Stevens	Moore	Spencer	Carter (10), Trebble (9), Coppard (2)	27
Gothard 28	Spencer	Gallen	Watts	Bunce	Goodliffe	McKimm	Charles	Stevens	Moore	Roddis	Coppard (11), Boyce (10)	28
Gothard 29	Boyce	Gallen	Watts	Bunce	Goodliffe	McKimm	Charles	Stevens	Spencer	Roddis	McKimm (10), Trebble (11)	29
Gothard 30	Boyce	Flynn	Watts	Bunce	Goodliffe	McKimm	Charles	Stevens	Moore	Roddis	Trebble (2), Spencer (10), Gallen (3)	30
Gothard 31	Boyce	Flynn	Watts	Metcalfe	Bunce	Goodliffe	Charles	Stevens	Moore	Roddis	Boyce (7)	31
Gothard 32	Metcalfe	Flynn	Coppard	Bunce	Goodliffe	Boyce	Charles	Stevens	Moore	Roddis	Trebble (2)	32
Gothard 33	Metcalfe	Flynn	Watts	Bunce	Coppard	McKimm	Charles	Stevens	Moore	Roddis	Spencer ((11), Preston (2)	33
Gothard 34	Metcalfe	Flynn	Watts	Coppard	Goodliffe	McKimm	Charles	Stevens	Moore	Trebble	Hodson (11), Boyce (8)	34
Gothard 35	Metcalfe	Flynn	Watts	Bunce	Goodliffe	McKimm	Charles	Stevens	Moore	Trebble	Coppard (4), Preston (8), Roddis (10)	35
Gothard 36	Metcalfe	Flynn	Coppard	Bunce	Goodliffe	McKimm	Charles	Stevens	Moore	Roddis	Watts (4), Boyce (10), Preston (11)	36
Gothard 37	Metcalfe	Flynn	Watts	Bunce	Goodliffe	McKimm	Charles	Stevens	Boyce	Roddis	Preston (8), Trebble (10), Moore (11)	37
Gothard 38	Boyce	Flynn	Watts	Bunce	Goodliffe	McKimm	Charles	Stevens	Moore	Roddis	Coppard (10), Trebble (9)	38
Gothard 39	Boyce	Flynn	Watts	Bunce	Goodliffe	McKimm	Charles	Stevens	Metcalfe	Roddis	Coppard (2), Trebble (10)	39
Gothard 40	Carter	Flynn	Coppard	Bunce	Goodliffe	McKimm	Tilbury	Stevens	Metcalfe	Preston	Charles (2), Watts (6), Gallen (4)	40
Gothard 41	Boyce	Flynn	Coppard	Tucker	Goodliffe	McKimm	Charles	Stevens	Metcalfe	Roddis	Preston (11), Moore (7)	41
Gothard 42	Moore	Flynn	Coppard	Tucker	Goodliffe	Preston	Telemarque	Stevens	Metcalfe	Molesey	Charles (8), McKimm (10), Boyce (2)	42

THE NON-LEAGUE PAPER

CONFERENCE & PYRAMID LEAGUES SOCCER / £1.00

AVAILABLE AT A NEWSAGENT NEAR YOU EVERY SUNDAY

PLAYING SQUAD

(Bold print indicates an England Semi-Professional International)

Player *Honours*	*Birthplace*	*D.O.B.*	*Previous Clubs*

GOALKEEPERS

Paul Gothard ESP	Essex	24.06.74	Colchester, Chelmsford C, Grays Ath., Dag & Red

DEFENDERS

Jason Goodliffe RP	Hillingdon	07.03.74	Brentford
Ryan Spencer British Univ.	London	03.01.79	Tottenham H, Ruislip Manor
Lee Flynn RP	London	04.09.73	Romford, Boreham Wood, Hendon
Mark Boyce	Hammersmith	11.08.80	Watford
Dominic Sterling	London		Wimbledon, Wealdstone
Matt Coppard			From Youth team

MIDFIELDERS

Jason Tucker	London	03.02.73	Aldershot, Yeading, Chertsey T, Aldershot T, Enfield, Aldershot T, Chertsey T, B.Stortford, Yeading
Steve McKimm	London	30.07.75	Hendon, Molesey, Dulwich Hamlet, Farnborough T, £4,000 to Hayes
Barry Moore	London	04.02.77	Hampton
Mark Preston	London		From Youth team
Steve Barnes	Harrow	05.01.76	Welling U, Birmingham, Barnet

FORWARDS

Alvin Watts	London	17.06.79	Yeading
Dave Stevens	Ashford	29.04.79	Crystal Palace, Bromley, Dulwich Hamlet, £35,000 to Hayes
Rocky Baptiste	London		Willesden Constantine, Wealdstone, Staines T
Mark Molesley			From Youth team

HEDNESFORD TOWN

After five seasons in the Conference, during which time a steady improvement and a couple of good FA cup runs had been enjoyed, perhaps a start of three straight victories gave supporters natural, but unrealistic, expectations last season.

Consistancy just could not be achieved and throughout the campaign, goals were in short supply. In fact eight in the last eleven Conference matches, with Neil Davis scoring most of them, underlined the need for a settled and balanced attack, while at the back although Chris Brindley only missed one game, his defensive colleagues changed regularly and no less than five goalkeepers were used during the Conference campaign.

The arrival of Neil Pointon as player-coach may help reorganise the side as the new signings settle in but this coming season will probably see 'the Pitmen' happy to settle for a mid table position.

Since their promotion from the Dr Martens league the club has given Keys Park a wonderful new look and their supporters must be proud of the club's achievements.

Last season's disappointing FA Cup and FA trophy defeats at the hands of clubs lower down the pyramid were suffered but this season these competitions could be where the highlights are most likely to be achieved.

Looking at Hednesford Town's record over the last ten years one has to admire their steady development on and off the field with only one manager, John Baldwin, so it must be reasonable to suggest the club will be aiming to consolidate sensibly before moving forward again to challenge for honours

T.W.

Back Row: Tom Griffiths, Adam Shakespeare, Ross Rhodes, Keith Russell, Scott Bonsall, Ian Robinson, Stuart Tapper, Stewart Airdrie, Leon Brown. **Middle:** Don Drakeley, Jake Sedgemore, Russell Bradley, Mark Haram, Andy Carney, Mark Gayle, Stuart Ford, Stuart Lake, Noel Malcolm, Stuart Evans, Pete Windsor (Kit Manager). **Front:** Paul Bagshaw, Val Owen, Mark Cooper, Neil POinton, John Baldwin (Manager), Colin Lamber (Asst. Manager), Mick Norbury, Neil Davis, Lee Colkin, Scott Goodwin.

HEDNESFORD TOWN

GROUND DETAILS

Keys Park,
Hednesford,
Cannock,
Staffordshire WS12 5DW

COMMUNICATION   Tel: 01543 422870
                          Fax: 01543 428180
                          Hotline: 0930 555880
Web site: www.hednesfordtownfc.co.uk

SIMPLE DIRECTIONS: M6 J11 to Cannock,
through traffic lights to island , 3rd exit,
next island, 2nd exit onto Lichfield Rd.
Next island 1st exit, next island straight on,
next island 3rd exit, continue to mini-island.
Keys Park is straight on (signposted from 2nd island.)

CAPACITY: 6,000
SEATED: 1,000
COVERED TERRACING: 1,000

CLUB SHOP: Open throughout the week

SOCIAL FACILITIES: Strikers Bar
Open matchdays and every evening 7-11 except Sunday
No food available. Chase Suite hold functions

HEDNESFORD TOWN v HAYES

Pages: 32   Price: £2.00
Editor: Terry Brumpton

Other club publications: None

Local Press: Express & Star; Sporting Star; Chase Post;
Cannock Mercury; Birmingham Evening Mail; Sports
Argus; The Chronicle
Local Radio: Radio WM; BRMB; WABC; Beacon; Signal;
BBC Radio Stoke

Founded: 1880

Nickname: The Pitmen

Club Sponsors: Jewson

Club colours: White shirts & black & red trim,
                              black shorts, white trim

Change colours: Navy blue shirts with sky blue band,
                          navy blue shorts & sky blue socks

Midweek home matchday: Monday

Reserve team league: Central Conference, and
                          Midland Combination (Reserve Div.)

CLUB OFFICIALS

Directors   John Baldwin, Steve Price &
                                      Carole Price
President   Nigel Tinsley
Chairman   Steve Price
General Manager   David Degg
Football Secretary   Richard Munning
Club Secretary   Sue Thomas
Commercial Manager   Terry Brumpton
Press Officer   Neil Holden

FOOTBALL MANAGEMENT TEAM
MANAGER   JOHN BALDWIN

Date of Appointment   January 1990
Date of Birth: 05.05.54
Place of Birth: London

PREVIOUS CLUBS
As manager   Electricity, Harrisons.
As coach
As player   Walsall, Darlaston & Hednesford Town

HONOURS
As manager   Southern League Prem Div. 94-95
As player   England: Youth.
               British Universities

*   *   *

Assistant Manager   Colin Lambert
Club Physiothapist   Don Drakeley
2nd Team Manager   Colin Lambert
Chief Scout   Steve Griffiths
Youth Team Co-ordinator   James Thomas

Season	League	Div.	Pos.	P	Home W	D	L	F	A	Away W	D	L	F	A	Pts	Manager
99-00	Conference	-	17	42	10	3	8	27	23	5	3	13	18	45	51	John Baldwin
98-99	Conference	-	10	42	9	8	4	30	24	6	8	7	19	20	61	John Baldwin
97-98	Conference	-	7	42	14	4	3	28	12	4	8	9	31	38	66	John Baldwin
96-97	Conference	-	8	42	10	7	4	28	17	6	5	10	24	33	60	John Baldwin

Season	League	Div.	Pos.	P	W	D	L	F	A	Pts	Manager
95-96	Conference	-	3	42	23	7	12	71	46	76	John Baldwin
94-95	Southern	Premier	1	42	28	9	5	99	49	93	John Baldwin
93-94	Southern	Premier	13	42	15	9	18	67	66	54	John Baldwin
92-93	Southern	Premier	4	40	21	7	12	72	52	70	John Baldwin
91-92	Southern	Midland	2	42	26	13	3	81	37	91	John Baldwin
90-91	Southern	Midland	3	42	25	7	10	79	47	82	John Baldwin

HONOURS

Welsh Cup R-up 91-92;

Southern League   Prem. Div. 94-95;

Midland Div. R-up 91-92,

Lge. Cup R-up 86-87;

West Midlands. Lge 77-78, R-up 83-84; Lge. Cup 83-84;

Birmingham Combination 09-10 50-51, R-up 12-13 52-53;

Staffs Senior Cup 69-70, 73-74; R-up 92-93;

Birmingham Senior Cup 35-36; R-up 93-94.

PREVIOUS

Leagues: Walsall & District;
Birmingham Combination 08-15, 45-53;
West Midlands 19-39, 53-72, 74-84;
Midland Counties 72-74;
Southern League 84-95;
Conference 95-.

Grounds: The Tins (behind Anglesey Hotel) until 1904,
Cross Keys until 1995.

Names: None

Past Players

who progressed to the Football League

(Post War)   Brian Horton (Port Vale 1970)
Vernon Allatt (Halifax Town 1979)
Chris Brindley (Wolverhampton W. 1986)
Scott Cooksey (Shrewsbury Town 1998)
Dave Hanson (Leyton Orient)
Paul Ware (Macclesfield Town)
Keith Russell (Blackpool 1997)

CLUB RECORDS

Attendance: 10,000 v Walsall F.A.Cup 1919-20

Win: 12-1 v Birmingham City,
Birmingham Wartime League cup 40-41
12-1 v Redditch United,
Birmingham Cambination 52-53

Defeat: 0-15 v Burton,
Birmingham Combination 52-53

Career goalscorer: Tosh Griffiths
Joe O'Connor (post-war)

Career appearances: Kevin Foster

Transfer fee paid: £12,000
for Steve Burr (Macclesfield Town 1991)

Transfer fee received: £50,000
for Dave Hanson (Leyton Orient)

BEST SEASON

FA Cup: 1996-97, 4th Round
2-3 v Middlesbrough (A)

League clubs defeated: Blackpool, York City,
Hull City and Barnet

FA Trophy: 1997-98, 3rd Round
1-2 v Grantham Town (A)

League: 3rd, Conference 95-96

LAST SEASON

F.A. Cup: First Round replay
F.A. Trophy: Third Round
Conference: 17th
Top Goalscorer: Neil Davis 21
Player of the Year: Neil Davis
Captain: James Kelly

HEDNESFORD TOWN

	Date	Comp.	H/A	Opponents	Gate	Result & Score		Goalscorers	League Position
1	14.08	N.C.	A	Welling United	731	W	2-1	Robinson 26, Davis 52	
2	17.08	N.C.	A	Altrincham	851	W	1-0	Mike 75	
3	21.08	N.C.	H	Sutton United	1,062	W	1-0	Kimmins 27	2
4	24.08	N.C.	A	Scarborough	2,198	D	1-1	Mike 40	
5	28.08	N.C.	H	Morecambe	1,289	L	1-3	Norman 7	4
6	30.08	N.C.	H	Nuneaton Borough	1,622	D	0-0		5
7	04.09	N.C.	A	Woking	1,622	W	1-0	Brindley 90	3
8	06.09	N.C.	H	Kettering Town	1,189	D	1-1	Kimmins 65 (pen)	
9	11.09	N.C.	H	Stevenage Borough	1,525	D	2-2	Davis 33 (pen) Mike 44	3
10	14.09	N.C.	A	Doncaster Rovers	3,021	L	1-2	Kimmins 24	4
11	18.09	N.C.	H	Hayes	962	W	2-1	Kimmins 23, 58 (pen)	4
12	25.09	N.C.	H	Rushden & Diamonds	1,638	L	1-2	Robinson 2	6
13	02.10	N.C.	A	Northwich Victoria	1,308	L	2-3	Robinson 86, Szewezyk 87	8
14	09.10	N.C.	H	Forest Green Rovers	1,006	W	1-0	Norman 60	7
15	23.10	N.C.	A	Dover Athletic	669	L	1-4	Davis 45	7
16	01.11	N.C.	H	Kidderminster H.	1,522	L	0-2		5
17	06.11	N.C.	A	Yeovil Town	972	W	1-0	Davies 69	5
18	14.11	N.C.	A	Morecambe	1,247	**L**	**0-4**		10
19	04.12	N.C.	H	Woking	978	W	3-0	Kimmins 4, 48, Davies 78	10
20	11.12	N.C.	A	Forest Green Rovers	701	L	0-3		10
21	18.12	N.C.	A	Kingstonian	903	W	2-0	Davis 22, 67.	9
22	27.12	N.C.	H	Telford United	1,550	W	2-1	Lake 43, Davis 45 (pen)	7
23	03.01	N.C.	A	Telford United	1,714	L	2-6	Albrighton 29 (OG), Davis 35	8
24	08.01	N.C.	H	Scarborough	1057	L	0-3		10
25	22.01	N.C.	A	Southport	1122	L	0-2		11
26	29.01	N.C.	H	Hereford United	1129	L	0-1		13
27	05.02	N.C.	H	Altrincham	1,193	**W**	**5-0**	Kimmins 16, Davis 39, Norbury 59, Robinson 78, 90	10
28	12.02	N.C.	A	Kidderminster Harriers	2,964	L	0-3		10
29	19.02	N.C.	A	Hayes	607	L	1-2	Robinson 74	13
30	22.02	N.C.	A	Rushden & Diamonds	3,714	D	1-1	Davis 54	
31	04.03	N.C.	H	Doncaster Rovers	1,383	W	2-1	Davis 43, Twynham 64	11
32	11.03	N.C.	A	Hereford United	2,122	L	0-3		12
33	18.03	N.C.	A	Stevenage Borough	1,213	W	1-0	Colkin 60	10
34	25.03	N.C.	H	Northwich Victoria	867	W	1-0	Davis 26	8
35	28.03	N.C.	A	Sutton United	642	D	0-0		8
36	01.04	N.C.	H	Dover Athletic	797	W	1-0	Davis 62	6
37	08.04	N.C.	A	Kettering Town	1,021	L	2-4	Davis 3, 43	9
38	22.04	N.C.	A	Yeovil Town	2,012	L	0-3		
39	24.04	N.C.	H	Southport	850	L	1-2	Lake 19	11
40	29.04	N.C.	H	Kingstonian	683	L	2-3	Davis 34, 89	
41	01.05	N.C.	A	Nuneaton Borough	1,369	L	0-3		16
42	06.05	N.C.	H	Welling United	834	L	0-1		17

CUP COMPETITIONS

F.A. Cup

	Date	Comp.	H/A	Opponents	Gate	Result & Score		Goalscorers
	16.10	4Q	A	Northwich Victoria	1,651	D	2-2	Twynham 73, Bates 83 (og)
	18.10	4Q R	H	Northwich Victoria	930	W	1-0	Davis 76
	30.10	1	A	Aldershot Town	3,267	D	1-1	Robinson 51
	08.11	1R	H	Aldershot Town	1,719	L	1-2	Lake 44

Nationwide McMillan Trophy

	Date	Comp.	H/A	Opponents	Gate	Result & Score		Goalscorers
	04.10	1	H	Nuneaton Borough	456	L	1-2	Szewczyk 63

F.A. Trophy

	Date	Comp.	H/A	Opponents	Gate	Result & Score		Goalscorers
	27.11	2	A	Bedworth United	308	W	2-0	Kimmins 43, Davis 47 (p)
	15.01	3	H	Hyde United	710	D	1-1	Davis 88
	17.01	3R	A	Hyde United	518	L	0-2	

1	2	3	4	5	6	7	8	9	10	11	Substitutes Used	
Morgan	Evans	Colkin	Lake	Brindley	Robinson	Airdrie	Kelly	Davis	Mike	Kimmins	Norman (7), Twynham (9)	1
Morgan	Evans	Colkin	Lake	Brindley	Robinson	Kimmins	Kelly	Davis	Mike	Airdrie	Hunter (11)	2
Morgan	Evans	Colkin	Lake	Brindley	Robinson	Kimmins	Kelly	Davis	Mike	Norman	Twynham (9)	3
Morgan	Evans	Colkin	Lake	Brindley	Robinson	Kimmins	Kelly	Norman	Mike	Airdrie		4
Morgan	Evans	Colkin	Lake	Brindley	Robinson	Kimmins	Kelly	Norman	Mike	Airdrie	O'Connor (9), Twynham (6), Hunter (11)	5
Morgan	Evans	Colkin	Lake	Brindley	Robinson	Airdrie	Kelly	Kimmins	Mike	Goodwin		6
Morgan	Evans	Colkin	Lake	Brindley	Robinson	Goodwin	Kelly	Kimmins	Mike	Hunter	Airdrie (11)	7
Morgan	Evans	Colkin	Lake	Brindley	Robinson	Kimmins	Kelly	Goodwin	Mike	Hunter	Airdrie (11)	8
Morgan	Evans	Colkin	Lake	Brindley	Robinson	Kimmins	Kelly	Davis	Mike	Goodwin	Airdrie (9), Amos (4), Norman (11)	9
Morgan	Evans	Colkin	Lake	Brindley	Robinson	Twynham	Kelly	Kimmins	Mike	Goodwin	Airdrie (7), Norman (4)	10
Morgan	Evans	Colkin	Lake	Brindley	Robinson	Goodwin	Kelly	Airdrie	Mike	Kimmins		11
Morgan	Evans	Colkin	Lake	Brindley	Robinson	Goodwin	Kelly	Airdrie	Mike	Kimmins	Hunter (11), Norman (10)	12
Morgan	Evans	Colkin	Lake	Brindley	Robinson	Goodwin	Lampkin	Airdrie	Mike	Norman	Twynham (8), Hunter (11), Szewczyk (2)	13
Morgan	Evans	Colkin	Lake	Brindley	Robinson	Twynham	Kelly	Norman	Goodwin	Hunter	O'Connor (7), Mike (9), Reece (3)	14
Hayward	Evans	Colkin	Lake	Brindley	Robinson	Rhodes	Twynham	Davis	Goodwin	Hunter	Sedgemore (2), O'Connor (7), Mike (11)	15
Morgan	Evans	Colkin	Comyn	Brindley	Robinson	Lake	Twynham	Davis	Goodwin	Kimmins	Hunter (8), Rhodes (10), Norman (4)	16
Morgan	Evans	Colkin	Comyn	Brindley	Robinson	Kimmins	Norman	Davis	Mike	Szewczyk	O'Connor (11)	17
Morgan	Comyn	Robinson	Lake	Norman	Sedgemore	Kimmins	O'Connor	Mike	Goodwin	Davis	Airdrie (8) sub Hunter	18
Morgan	Evans	Reece	Lake	Brindley	Twynham	Kelly	Comyn	Davis	Kimmins	O'Connor	Mike (11), Goodwin (7)	19
Morgan	Evans	Reece	Lake	Brindley	Twynham	Goodwin	Comyn	Davis	Mike	O'Connor	Norman (10)	20
Morgan	Evans	Colkin	Lake	Brindley	Comyn	Twynham	Kelly	Davis	Kimmins	O'Connor	Robinson (7), Reece (3)	21
Stewart	Evans	Reece	Lake	Brindley	Comyn	Robinson	Goodwin	Davis	Szewczyk	O'Connor	Rhodes (4), Norman (10)	22
Stewart	Evans	Colkin	Lake	Brindley	Comyn	Twynham	Kelly	Davis	Szewczyk	O'Connor	Robinson (7), Airdrie (10), Goodwin (4)	23
Stewart	Evans	Colkin	Comyn	Brindley	Robinson	Airdrie	Kelly	Goodwin	Szewczyk	O'Connor	Reece (3), Norman (11), O'Connor (2)	24
Stewart	Robinson	Comyn	Bradley	Brindley	Bettney	Tipton	Goodwin	Davis	Kimmins	O'Connor	Airdrie (11), Twynham (10)	25
Stewart	Bradley	Comyn	Brindley	Bettney	Kimmins	Goodwin	Davis	Norman	Airdrie	Hibbins	Szewczyk (8), Twynham (7), Evans (11)	26
Wilson	Evans	Comyn	Lake	Brindley	Robinson	Kimmins	Norbury	Davis	Goodwin	Airdrie	O'Connor (7), Reece (4), Twynham (10)	27
Wilson	Evans	Comyn	Lake	Brindley	Bettney	Hibbins	Norbury	Davis	Goodwin	Airdrie	O'Connor (4)	28
Wilson	Evans	Bradley	Comyn	Brindley	Robinson	Bettney	Norbury	Davis	Kelly	Airdrie	Twynham (4), Hickey (7)	29
Ford	Evans	Colkin	Bradley	Brindley	Robinson	Bettney	Kelly	Davis	Norbury	Twynham		30
Ford	Evans	Colkin	Kimmins	Brindley	Bradley	Robinson	Kelly	Davis	Goodwin	Twynham	Lake (4)	31
Ford	Evans	Colkin	Bradley	Brindley	Robinson	Kelly	Norbury	Davis	Goodwin	Twynham	Kimmins (11), Airdrie (6), Lake (10)	32
Ford	Evans	Colkin	Lake	Brindley	Bradley	Kelly	Norbury	Davis	Goodwin	Kimmins		33
Ford	Evans	Colkin	Lake	Brindley	Bradley	Robinson	Norbury	Davis	Goodwin	Bagshaw	Twynham (11)	34
Ford	Evans	Colkin	Lake	Brindley	Bradley	Robinson	Norbury	Davis	Kelly	Bagshaw	Twynham (11)	35
Ford	Evans	Colkin	Lake	Brindley	Bradley	Robinson	Twynham	Davis	Kelly	Bagshaw	Hickey (4), Kimmins (3)	36
Ford	Robinson	Colkin	Comyn	Brindley	Bradley	Twynham	Kelly	Davis	Hickey	Bagshaw	Norbury (4), Rhodes (3), Airdrie (7)	37
Ford	Evans	Colkin	Lake	Bradley	Robinson	Bagshaw	Kelly	Davis	Norbury	Airdrie	Kimmins (3), Szewczyk (10)	38
Ford	Evans	Colkin	Lake	Bradley	Bagshaw	Airdrie	Kelly	Davis	Norbury	Twynham	Brindley (4), Kimmins (7)	39
Ford	Evans	Colkin	Lake	Bradley	Robinson	Kelly	Norbury	Davis	Goodwin	Bagshaw	Twynham (10), Airdrie (8)	40
Ford	Sedgemore	Colkin	Evans	Bradley	Robinson	Airdrie	Kelly	Davis	Norbury	Bagshaw		41
Ford	Evans	Colkin	Lake	Bradley	Robinson	Hickey	Szewczyk	Davis	Kelly	Bagshaw	Airdrie (8), Shakespeare (2) Norbury (8)	42

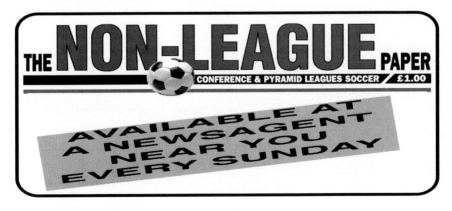

THE NON-LEAGUE PAPER
CONFERENCE & PYRAMID LEAGUES SOCCER / £1.00

AVAILABLE AT A NEWSAGENT NEAR YOU EVERY SUNDAY

PLAYING SQUAD

HEDNESFORD TOWN

(Bold print indicates an England Semi-Professional International)

Player Honours	Birthplace	D.o.B.	Previous Clubs

GOALKEEPERS

Andy Carney	Sheffield		Stocksbridge Park Steels
Mark Gayle	Bromsgrove	21.10.69	Leicester, Blackpool, Worcester C, Walsall, Crewe, Rushden & D, Chesterfield

DEFENDERS

Stuart Evans	Birmingham		Wolves, Gresley R, Halesowen T, Hereford U
Mark Haran	Rotherham	21.01.77	Rotherham, Eastwood T, Frickley Ath, Emley
Lee Colkin	Nuneaton	15.07.74	Northampton
Jake Sedgemore	Birmingham		WBA
Neil Pointon	Warsop Vale	28.11.64	Scunthorpe, Everton, Manchester C, Oldham, Hearts, Walsall, Chesterfield
Russell Bradley	Birmingham	28.03.66	Dudley T, Nottingham F, Hereford U, Halifax, Scunthorpe, Hartlepool
Neil Broadhurst	Birmingham		Birmingham

MIDFIELDERS

Scott Goodwin	Hull	13.09.78	Coventry, Grantham T
Ian Robinson	Nottingham	25.08.78	Mansfield, Ilkeston T, £10,000 to Hednesford T
Scott Bonsall	Nottingham		Goole T, Eastwood T
Val Owen	Manchester	11.02.71	Hyde U, Northwich V
Mark Cooper	Wakefield	18.12.68	Bristol C, Exeter, Birmingham, Fulham, Wycombe, Exeter, Hartlepool, Leyton O, Rushden & D
Paul Bagshaw	Sheffield	25.09.79	Barnsley

FORWARDS

Neil Davis	Bloxwich	15.08.73	Redditch U, Aston Villa, Wycombe
Stewart Airdrie	Bradford		Bradford C, Guiseley, £2,000 to Hednesford T
Keith Russell	Aldridge	31.01.74	Walsall, Tamworth, Atherstone U, Hednesford T, Blackpool, Altrincham
Sean O'Connor	Birmingham		Youth team
Paul Szewczyk	Birmingham		Youth team
Leon Brown	Birmingham		Lye T

HEREFORD UNITED

With mainly a young, developing side, the Bulls enjoyed a relatively good 1999/2000 season and, but for a poor end of term run which saw them win just one game in the last eight, they would surely have finished much higher than eighth.

They did however have a very good FA Cup run disposing of York City and Hartlepool United before losing out in extra time of their replay against Leicester City at Filbert Street. However it obviously gave them a lot of confidence as they then went eleven Conference games without defeat, although they did disappointingly lose to Billericay Town away in the Third Round of the FA Umbro Trophy during that run.

Manager Graham Turner's policy of using young players appears to be paying dividends. The likes of Paul Parry, Chris Lane and Gavin Williams all caught the eye and created interest when the club featured on TV during their FA Cup run.

It looks as though Turner is building a solid foundation at Edgar Street and the Bulls could well be amongst the leading candidates for the new season. Turner's acquisition of another legendary Bull, former Wolves and England star Steve, as a member of the club's coaching staff could also prove to be a smart move, and with a handful of useful-looking signings, Hereford look well set for a challenge to return to the Nationwide Third Division.

Steve Whitney

Back Row: Paul Sturgess, Matthew Clarke, Chris Lane, Ian Wright (Captain), Scott Cooksey, James Wall, Paul Parry, Tony James, Matthew gardiner. Middle: John Shirley, Matthew Beale(released), John Snape, Michael McIndoe, Gavin Williams, Steve Piearce, Crag Hanson. Front: Tony Ford (Coach), Ian Rodgerson, Steve Bull (Coach), Graham Turner (Chairman/Director of Football), Phil Robinson (Player/Coach), Simon Thompson (Physio).

HEREFORD UNITED

GROUND DETAILS

Edgar Street,
Hereford.
HR4 9JU

Telephone

Tel: 01432 276666
Fax 01432 341359
Club Call 0891 121645

E-mail HUFC@msn.com
Website: http://www.hufc.demon.co.uk

SIMPLE DIRECTIONS: From Hereford city centre
follow signs to Leominster (A49) into Edgar Street.
Car parking for 1000 (approx.) available near the ground.
Nearest railway station Hereford

CAPACITY:	8,843
SEATED:	2,761
COVERED TERRACING:	6,082

SOCIAL FACILITIES: Clubhouse open on matchdays

CLUB SHOP: Yes

Founded: 1924

Nickname: The Bulls

Sponsors: Sun Valley

Club Colours: Black & White Halves
black shorts, white trim; black socks,white tops

Change Colours: Red & black quarters;
black shorts; black socks

Midweek matchday: Tuesday

Reserve League: Central Conference

CLUB OFFICIALS

Chairman/Director of Football
Graham Turner

Company Secretary Joan Fennessy

Directors Tristram Richmond-Sterry
Sam Lodh, George Hyde
Ron Jukes, Grenville Smith&
Steve Bayliss

Club Secretary Joan Fennessy
c/o the club
Tel: 01432 276666   Fax: 01432 341359

MATCHDAY PROGRAMME

Pages: 32   Price: £1.50

Editor: Lee Symonds

Other club publications: None

Local Press: Hereford Journal; Hereford Times;
Evening News

Local Radio: BBC Hereford & Worcester

FOOTBALL MANAGEMENT TEAM

MANAGER: **GRAHAM TURNER**

Date of Appointment   August 1995
Date of Birth: 5th October 1947
Place of Birth: Ellesmere Port

PREVIOUS CLUBS
As manager   Shrewsbury T., Aston Villa,
Wolverhampton W.
As player   Wrexham, Chester City, Shrewsbury T.
HONOURS
As manager   League: Div.3 78-79 (Shrewsbury),
Div.4 87-88, Div.3 88-89; S.V.T. 87-88 (Wolves)
As player   England - Youth cap.

*   *   *

Coaches: Steve Bull, Tony Ford &
Phil Robinson (player-coach)

Chief Scout: Ron Jukes

Physio: Simon Thompson

Season	League	Div.	Pos.	P	Home W	D	L	F	A	Away W	D	L	F	A	Pts	Manager
99-00	Conference	-	8	42	9	6	6	43	31	6	8	7	18	21	59	Graham Turner
98-99	Conference	-	13	42	9	5	7	25	17	6	5	10	24	29	55	Graham Turner
97-98	Conference	-	6	42	11	7	3	30	19	7	6	8	26	30	67	Graham Turner

Season	League	Div.	Pos.	P	W	D	L	F	A	Pts	Manager
96-97	F. League	3	24	46	11	14	21	50	65	47	Graham Turner
95-96	F. League	3	6	46	20	14	12	65	47	74	Graham Turner
94-95	F. League	3	16	42	12	13	17	45	62	49	Graham Turner
93-94	F. League	3	20	42	12	6	24	60	79	42	Greg Downs & John Layton
92-93	F. League	3	17	42	10	15	17	47	60	45	Greg Downs & John Layton
91-92	F. League	4	17	42	12	8	22	44	57	44	John Sillett
90-91	F. League	4	17	46	13	14	19	53	58	53	Colin Addison

HONOURS

Football League Div. 3 75-76, Div. 4 R-up 72-73;

Southern League R-up 45-46 50-51 71-72
NW Championship 58-59
Div. 1 58-59,
Cup Winners 52 57 59

Welsh Cup Winners 89-90,
R-up 3 times;

PREVIOUS

Leagues: Birmingham League;
Birmingham Combination;
Southern League 39-72;
Football League 72-97

Names: None

Ground: None

Past Players who progressed to the Football League

Since joining the Conference: Gavin Mahon (Brentford)

CLUB RECORDS

Attendance: 18,114
v Sheffield Wed., FA Cup 3rd Rd, 4.1.58

Career Goalscorer: Unknown
Career Appearances: unknown

Win: 6-0 v Burnley (A), Div. 4 24.1.87

Defeat: 0-6 v Rotherham Utd (A), Div. 4 29.4.89

Transfer Fee Paid: £75,000
to Walsall for Dean Smith, 7.94
Transfer Fee Received: £250,000
for Darren Peacock from Q.P.R., 3.91
+ a further £240,000
when he moved to Newcastle Utd. 3.91

BEST SEASON

FA Trophy: 3rd Round 99-00,
1-3 v Billericay Town (A)

FA Cup: 4th Rd 71-72 (as Southern League side),
76-77, 81-82, 89-90, 91-92

League: 22nd Football League Div. 2

LAST SEASON

F.A. Cup: Third Round replay
F.A. Trophy: Third Round
Conference: 8th
Top Goalscorer: Robin Elmes & Paul Fewings 13
Player of the Year: John Snape
Captain: Ian Wright

HEREFORD UNITED

Match Facts 1999-00

	Date	Comp.	H/A	Opponents	Gate	Result & Score		Goalscorers	League Position
1	14.08	N.C.	A	Sutton United	1,386	D	1-1	James 82	
2	17.08	N.C.	H	Nuneaton Borough	2,551	D	1-1	Piearce 45	
3	21.08	N.C.	H	Kettering Town	1,980	W	4-2	Wright 11, Williams 56, Elmes 63, 85	8
4	24.08	N.C.	A	Morecambe	1,768	L	2-3	Williams 27 (Pen), Elmes 34	
5	28.08	N.C.	A	Welling United	743	L	1-3	Wright 64	13
6	30.08	N.C.	H	Telford United	1,910	D	2-2	Piearce 30, Elmes 66	15
7	04.09	N.C.	A	Doncaster Rovers	1,690	W	5-3	Elmes 1,83, Wall 49, Williams 58(p), Hanson 89	
8	07.09	N.C.	A	Yeovil Town	2,632	L	0-1		11
9	11.09	N.C.	A	Southport	1,286	W	1-0	Fewings 84	8
10	14.09	N.C.	H	Forest Green R.	1,795	W	1-0	Fewings 90	7
11	18.09	N.C.	H	Stevenage Borough	2,143	L	1-2	Fewings 16	9
12	25.09	N.C.	A	Dover Athletic	840	L	0-2		12
13	28.09	N.C.	H	Rushden & Ds	1,724	W	4-0	Wright 2, 61, Fewings 63, 68	
14	02.10	N.C.	H	Scarborough	1,886	D	4-4	Fewings 10,12, Elmes 44, Snape 88	6
15	09.10	N.C.	A	Woking	2,128	W	2-0	Fewings 38, May 86	6
16	23.10	N.C.	H	Hayes	1,665	L	0-2		6
17	06.11	N.C.	A	Altrincham	1,006	L	1-2	May 17	9
18	14.11	N.C.	H	Northwich Victoria	1,812	W	3-0	Parry 2, Williams 77 (p), Taylor 84	9
19	04.12	N.C.	H	Southport	2,610	W	2-1	Fewings 45, Wright 89	9
20	18.12	N.C.	A	Scarborough	1,242	L	0-3		12
21	27.12	N.C.	H	Kidderminster Harriers	4,437	D	1-1	Fewings 6	12
22	03.01	N.C.	A	Kidderminster Harriers	4,606	D	1-1	May 4	11
23	22.01	N.C.	H	Altrincham	1789	D	2-2	Parry 51, Rodgerson 56	14
24	29.01	N.C.	A	Hednesford Town	1129	W	1-0	Elmes 77	11
25	05.02	N.C.	A	Northwich Victoria	1,104	D	0-0		12
26	12.02	N.C.	H	Doncaster Rovers	2767	D	2-2	Fewings 66, May 81	12
27	19.02	N.C.	H	Dover Athletic	2,003	W	2-0	Fewings 45, 54	9
28	26.02	N.C.	A	Hayes	849	D	0-0		9
29	28.02	N.C.	A	Stevenage Borough	1,940	W	3-0	Parry 35, Rodgerson 37, Elmes 90	8
30	04.03	N.C.	A	Nuneaton Borough	1,947	W	1-0	Elmes 65	4
31	11.03	N.C.	H	Hednesford Town	2,122	W	3-0	Elmes 4, 90, Williams 87	3
32	14.03	N.C.	H	Woking	2,216	L	2-4	OG (West) 61, Parry 67	3
33	18.03	N.C.	A	Forest Green Rovers	1,509	W	1-0	James 59	3
34	25.03	N.C.	A	Rushden & Diamonds	4,022	D	0-0		3
35	01.04	N.C.	H	Morecambe	1,808	D	1-1	Norman 77	3
36	06.04	N.C.	A	Kingstonian	664	D	0-0		3
37	08.04	N.C.	H	Yeovil Town	1,819	L	0-1		3
38	20.04	N.C.	A	Telford United	908	D	1-1	Williams 43	
39	22.04	N.C.	A	Kettering Town	1,617	L	0-2		7
40	24.04	N.C.	H	Kingstonian	1,527	L	0-2		8
41	29.04	N.C.	H	Welling United	1,390	L	1-2	Elmes 27	9
42	06.05	N.C.	H	Sutton United	1,432	W	4-1	Piearce 31, 77, Snape 72, Taylor 90	8

CUP COMPETITIONS

F.A. Cup

Date	Round	H/A	Opponents	Gate	Result & Score		Goalscorers
16.10	4Q	H	Burgess Hill	1,611	W	4-1	Williams 3, Fewings 26, Parry 76, Piearce 86
30.10	1	H	York City	2,787	W	1-0	May 77
21.11	2	H	Hartlepool United	4,914	W	1-0	Elmes 54
11.12	3	H	Leicester City	7,795	D	0-0	
22.12	3R	A	Leicester City	12,157	L	*1-2	Fewings 40

Nationwide Mcmillan Trophy

Date	Round	H/A	Opponents	Gate	Result & Score		Goalscorers
05.10	1	H	Sutton United	625	W	2-0*	May 97, 104
09.11	2	A	Yeovil Town	823	L	0-3	

F.A. Trophy

Date	Round	H/A	Opponents	Gate	Result & Score		Goalscorers
27.11	2	H	Barton Rovers	1,501	W	1-0	Rodgerson 59
15.01	3	A	Billericay Town	757	L	1-3	Elmes

Substitutes Used

1	2	3	4	5	6	7	8	9	10	11	Substitutes Used	
Quy	Clarke	Wall	Snape	Wright	James	Williams	Taylor	May	Piearce	Rodgerson	Fewings (4), Elmes (9), Hanson (10)	1
Quy	Clarke	Sturgess	Rodgerson	Wright	James	Williams	Taylor	May	Piearce	Fewings	Snape (11), Elmes (9), Hanson (4)	2
Quy	Clarke	Sturgess	Rodgerson	Wright	James	Williams	Taylor	Elmes	Hanson	Snape	May (10)	3
Quy	Clarke	Sturgess	Lane	Wright	Wall	Williams	Taylor	Elmes	Hanson	Snape	May (10)	4
Quy	Clarke	Sturgess	Lane	Wright	James	Williams	Taylor	Elmes	Piearce	Snape	Hanson (4), Wall (5)	5
Quy	Clarke	Sturgess	Hanson	Wall	James	Williams	Taylor	Elmes	Piearce	Snape	May (10)	6
Quy	Clarke	Sturgess	Hanson	Wright	Wall	Williams	Taylor	Elmes	Piearce	Rodgerson	Jones (1)	7
Jones	Lane	Sturgess	Hanson	Wright	Wall	Williams	Taylor	Elmes	Piearce	Rodgerson	James (5), Snape (4), Cotterill (11)	8
Jones	Lane	Sturgess	Snape	James	Wall	Williams	Taylor	Elmes	Piearce	Rodgerson	Fewings (10)	9
Jones	Clarke	Sturgess	Snape	Wright	Wall	Williams	Taylor	Elmes	Piearce	Rodgerson	James (5), Fewings (10), Parry (7)	10
Jones	Clarke	Sturgess	Snape	James	Wall	Williams	Taylor	Elmes	Fewings	Rodgerson	Hanson (10), Parry (4)	11
Jones	Clarke	Sturgess	Snape	Wright	Wall	Williams	Taylor	Elmes	Fewings	Rodgerson	James (6), Parry (7), Beale (4)	12
Jones	Clarke	Sturgess	Snape	Wright	James	Parry	Taylor	Elmes	Fewings	Rodgerson	Williams (7)	13
Jones	Clarke	Sturgess	Snape	Wright	James	Parry	Taylor	Elmes	Fewings	Rodgerson	Williams (7)	14
Jones	Clarke	Sturgess	Snape	Wright	James	Parry	Taylor	Elmes	Fewings	Rodgerson	Williams (7), May (10)	15
Jones	Clarke	Sturgess	Snape	Wright	James	Parry	Taylor	Elmes	Williams	Rodgerson	May (10)	16
Jones	Clarke	Sturgess	Snape	Wright	James	Parry	Taylor	May	Williams	Rodgerson	Lane (3)	17
Jones	Lane	Sturgess	Snape	Wright	James	Parry	Taylor	Elmes	Williams	Fewings	Cotterill (7)	18
Jones	Lane	Snape	Sturgess	Wright	James	Parry	Taylor	Elmes	Williams	Fewings	Rogerson (7), May (11)	19
Jones	Clarke	Snape	Sturgess	Wright	James	Rogerson	Wall	Elmes	Williams	May	Fewings (5), Parry (8)	20
Jones	Lane	Sturgess	Snape	Wright	James	Parry	Taylor	Elmes	Williams	Fewings	Wall (6), Rogerson (7), May (11)	21
Jones	Lane	Sturgess	Snape	Wright	Clarke	Rogerson	Taylor	May	Williams	Fewings	Shirley (3), Wall (11), Elmes (9)	22
Jones	Lane	Sturgess	Snape	Wall	James	Rogerson	Taylor	Elmes	Williams	Parry	No subs used	23
Cooksey	Lane	Sturgess	Snape	White	James	Rogerson	Taylor	Elmes	Williams	Parry	May (11), Fewings (10)	24
Cooksey	Lane	Sturgess	Snape	Wright	White	Rogerson	Taylor	Elmes	Williams	Parry	May (9), Fewings (10)	25
Cooksey	Lane	Sturgess	Snape	Wright	White	Rogerson	Taylor	May	Williams	James	Fewings (3), Parry (10)	26
Cooksey	Lane	James	Snape	Wright	White	Rogerson	Taylor	May	Fewings	Parry	Williams (11)	27
Cooksey	Lane	James	Clark	Wright	White	Rogerson	Taylor	May	Fewings	Williams	Sturgess (5), Parry (11), Elmes (9)	28
Cooksey	Lane	Sturgess	Clark	James	White	Rogerson	Snape	May	Fewings	Parry	Williams (11), Elmes (10)	29
Cooksey	Lane	Sturgess	Clark	James	White	Rogerson	Snape	May	Fewings	Parry	Elmes (10), Williams (11)	30
Quy	Lane	Sturgess	Clark	James	White	Rogerson	Snape	May	Elmes	Parry	Williams (11)	31
Quy	Lane	Sturgess	Clark	James	White	Rogerson	Snape	May	Elmes	Parry	Williams (11)	32
Cooksey	Lane	James	Clark	Wright	White	Rogerson	Snape	May	Elmes	Parry	Fewings (9), Taylor (4), Williams (11)	33
Cooksey	Lane	James	Taylor	Wright	White	Rogerson	Snape	May	Elmes	Parry	Williams (9), Fewings (9), Sturgess (8)	34
Cooksey	Lane	James	Wright	Rogerson	Williams	Snape	Taylor	Parry	Fewings	May	Elmes (10)	35
Cooksey	Lane	James	Taylor	Wright	White	Rogerson	Snape	May	Elmes	Parry	Williams (7), Clarke (9)	36
Cooksey	Lane	Sturgess	Taylor	Wright	White	Clarke	Snape	May	Elmes	Parry	Hanson (10)	37
Cooksey	Lane	James	Taylor	Wright	White	Clarke	Snape	May	Fewings	Williams	Hanson (10), Parry (4)	38
Cooksey	Lane	James	Sturgess	Wright	White	Clarke	Snape	May	Hanson	Williams	Cotterill (10), Shirley (7)	39
Cooksey	Lane	James	Taylor	Wright	White	Rogerson	Snape	May	Parry	Williams	Elmes (9), Clarke (2), Piearce (10)	40
Cooksey	Clarke	Sturgess	Taylor	Wright	James	Rogerson	Snape	Elmes	Williams	Parry	Lane (11)	41
Cooksey	Lane	Clarke	Taylor	Wright	James	Rogerson	Snape	Elmes	Piearce	Williams	No subs used	42

THE **NON-LEAGUE** PAPER

CONFERENCE & PYRAMID LEAGUES SOCCER / £1.00

AVAILABLE AT A NEWSAGENT NEAR YOU EVERY SUNDAY

PLAYING SQUAD (Bold print indicates an England Semi-Professional International)   HEREFORD UNITED

Player Honours	Birthplace	Signed From	Previous Clubs

GOALKEEPERS

Scott Cooksey ESP	Birmingham	24.06.72	Derby, Shrewsbury, Bromsgrove R, Peterborough, Hednesford T, Shrewsbury

DEFENDERS

Tony James	Birmingham		WBA
Paul Sturgess	Dartford	04.08.75	Charlton, Millwall, Brighton
Ian Wright	Lichfield	10.03.72	Stoke, Bristol R, Stoke
James Wall	Carshalton	21.03.80	Derby
Matt Gardiner	Birmingham	28.03.74	Torquay, Moor Green, Stourbridge, Halesowen T
Matthew Clarke British Univ.	Cardiff		Cradley T, Halesowen H, Halesowen T, Kidderminster H
Paul Parry	Hereford		Youth team

MIDFIELDERS

Chris Lane	Liverpool	24.05.79	Everton
Gavin Williams	Hereford		Youth team
John Snape	Birmingham		WBA, Bromsgrove R, Northfield T, Stourbridge, Halesowen T
Ian Rodgerson	Hereford	09.04.66	Pegasus Jun., Hereford U., Cardiff C., Birmingham C., Sunderland, Cardiff C.
Phil Robinson	Stratford	06.01.67	Aston Villa, Wolves, Notts Co., Huddersfield, Chesterfield, Notts Co., Stoke
Michael McIndoe	Edinburgh	02.12.79	Luton

FORWARDS

Steve Piearce	Sutton Coldfield	29.09.76	Wolves, Doncaster R, Halesowen T
Rob Elmes	Birmingham		Boldmere St.Michaels, Bromsgrove R, Halesowen T
Craig Hanson	Derby		Derby

KETTERING TOWN

The high expectations, following last season's runners up spot, were not quite fulfilled, at least in League terms, as a lack of goals and too many drawn matches saw the Poppies struggling for much of the season. A final placing of 13th was ,in the end, respectable, but it was not until the final couple of games that their Conference status was guaranteed for a 22nd successive campaign.

Peter Morris had kept faith with the nucleus of the squad which had performed such heroics last term, although long term injuries to Martin Matthews, who did not play a game all season, and Lee Hudson proved to be a significant handicap. It needed the experience and quality of players such as Carl Shutt and striker Dale Watkins to bring the stability, coupled with a great team spirit, which eventually saw them to safety. A solid defence was the backbone of the side, with Adam Sollitt proving himself to be just about the best goalkeeper in the Conference and justifiably forcing his way into the England semi- professional squad. Skipper Colin Vowden was a rock in the centre of the defence, while, paradoxically for a defender, Craig Norman ended up as leading scorer.

But, it was in the Trophy where the season was made. Not since 1979 had Kettering got to Wembley, when they lost to Stafford Rangers. A Final appeerence seemed highly unlikely, as the Poppies trailed Thame, with two minutes of the 2nd Round left, before Stuart Storer forced an equaliser to keep them in the Competition. Subsequent draws at home against Walton & Hersham and Bishop Auckland meant an arduous route to the semi's, even ignoring a long trip to Workington.

Telford were the semi- final opponents. A solid defensive display at Bucks   Head in the second leg protected Kettering's hard earnt victory at Rockingham Road, through Gary Setchell's solitary goal.

Nearly 14000 made the trip to the Twin Towers to see Kettering take on Kingstonian in the Final. Although going down by the odd goal in five, in a thrilling match, they could be proud of their performance, while their achievement in reaching the Final was amply recognised by the thousands who took to the streets of Kettering to welcome them home the day after the match.

If offered at the start of the season, most fans would have accepted a mid table finish and a trip to Wembley, but they will hope, now, that the Club will build from that and move on. Most would agree that the squad is 3 or 4 quality players short. If Peter Morris is able to capture them, there is the possibility that Kettering might just be the surprise package next year.

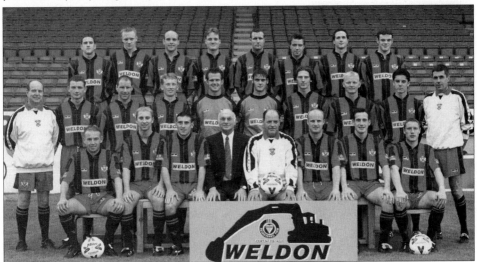

Back Row: Ian Ridgway, Andy Wayte, Dale Watkins, Craig Norman, Carl Shutt, Lee Cowling, Paul Cox, Wayne Diuk.
Middle: Peter Lake (Physio), Steve Kennedy, Steve Wilkinson, Brett McNamara, Steve Wilson, Kevin Tye, Steve Lenagh, Colin Vowden (Captain), Jason Lee, Ernie Moss (Asst. Manager).   **Front:** Phil Brown, Martin Matthews, Mark Paul, Peter Mallinger (Chairman), Peter Morris (Manager), Carl Adams, Lee Hudson, Matt Fisher.
Photo courtesy of Kappa Sports Pictures 01536 511595

KETTERING TOWN

GROUND DETAILS

Rockingham Road,
Kettering,
Northants, NN16 9AW

COMMUNICATION Tel: 01536 83028/410815 (Office)
01536 410962 (Social Club)
Fax: 01536 412273
email: info@ketteringtownafc.co.uk
web site: http://www.ketteringtownafc.co.uk

SIMPLE DIRECTIONS:
From south - M1 junction 15, A43 to Kettering use A14 exit
Junct. 7, follow A43 to Corby/Stamford to 1st roundabout, turn
right A6003, ground half a mile.
From north - M1 or M6 use junction 19 then A14 to Kettering.
Exit Junct. 7 then as above.
British Rail - Inter-City Midland - 50 mins from London
(St.Pancras), 20 mins from Leicester

CAPACITY: 6,170
COVERED SEATING: 1,800
COVERED TERRACING: 2,200

CLUB SHOP: Open before and after matches, & office staff
will open on request on non-match days. Situated in front of
main stand. Also Alex Elmores in town centre

SOCIAL FACILITIES: Social Club (Poppies),
Vice-Presidents Bar & Sponsor's Lounge

Pages: 32   Price: £1.50

Editor: Fox Design to Print 0116 222 8500

Other club publications:
"Poppies at the Gates of Dawn" (Fanzine)

Local Press: Evening Telegraph;
Chronicle & Echo; Herald & Post; Citizen
Local Radio: Radio Northampton; Northants 96; KCBC

Founded:	1872
Nickname:	Poppies
Club Sponsors:	Weldon Plant Ltd.
Club colours:	Red & black shirts, red shorts, black socks
Change colours:	Yellow shirts, shorts & socks
Midweek home matchday:	Tuesday

CLUB OFFICIALS

President	Sid Chapman
Chairman	Peter Mallinger
Vice Chairman	Michael Leech
Directors	Peter Oliver, Peter Webb
Club Secretary/ Press Officer	Graham Starmer c/o the club
Tel: 01536 483028/410815 Fax: 01536 412273	
Assistant Secretary	Andy Thomas

FOOTBALL MANAGEMENT TEAM

MANAGER: **PETER MORRIS**

Date of Appointment: May 1998
Date of Birth: 8th November 1943
Place of Birth: New Houghton, Mansfield

PREVIOUS CLUBS
As manager   Mansfield T., Peterborough U., Crewe A.,
              Southend U., Nuneaton B., Kettering T.,
              King's Lynn.
As asst. man./coach Newcastle U., Leicester C.
As player   Mansfield T., Ipswich T., Norwich C.,
              Mansfield T., Peterborough U.
HONOURS
As manager   Conference R-up 88-89, 98-99
              FA Trophy R-up 99-00

*   *   *

Assistant Manager: Ernie Moss
Physio: Peter Lake
Youth & Comunity development: Dominic Genovese

Season

League	Div.	Pos.	P	Home W	D	L	F	A	Away W	D	L	F	A	Pts	Manager
99-00 Conference	-	13	42	8	10	3	25	19	4	6	11	19	31	52	Peter Morris
98-99 Conference	-	2	42	11	5	5	31	16	11	5	5	27	21	76	Peter Morris
97-98 Conference	-	14	42	8	6	7	29	29	5	7	9	24	31	52	Steve Berry
96-97 Conference	-	14	42	9	4	8	30	28	5	5	11	23	34	51	Gary Johnson/Steve Berry

League	Div.	Pos.	P	W	D	L	F	A	Pts	Manager
95-96 Conference	-	16	42	13	9	20	68	84	48	Gary Johnson
94-95 Conference	-	6	42	19	10	13	73	56	67	Graham Carr
93-94 Conference	-	2	42	19	15	8	46	42	72	Graham Carr
92-93 Conference	-	13	42	14	13	15	61	63	55	Dave Cusack/Graham Carr
91-92 Conference	-	3	42	20	13	9	72	50	73	Peter Morris
90-91 Conference	-	4	42	23	11	8	67	45	80	Peter Morris

HONOURS

Premier Inter League Cup;
FA Trophy Runners-up 78-79;
Alliance Premier League (Conference) R-up x 4;
Southern League Winners,
County Cup Winners,
Daventry Charity Cup Winners x 2;
Northants Senior Cup x 28;
Maunsell Cup Winners x 12

PREVIOUS

Leagues: Southern League,
Northants League,
Midland League,
Birmingham League
Central Alliance,
United Counties League

Grounds   North Park; Green Lane

Past Players who progressed to the Football League

Billy Kellock(Peterborough), Gary Wood (Notts Co.),
Dave Longhurst (Nott'm Forest), Scott Endersby (Ipswich),
Steve Fallon (Cambridge U.), Andy Rogers (Plymouth),
MartynFoster (Northampton), Cohen Griffith (Cardiff C.),
Andy Hunt (Newcastle), Richard Brown (Blackburn R.)
Ben Wright (Bristol C.), Kofi Nyamah (Stoke C.)

CLUB RECORDS

Attendance: 11,536
Kettering v Peterborough (pre-Taylor report)

Win: 16-0
v Higham YMCI (FA Cup 1909)
Defeat: 0-13
v Mardy (Southern League Div. 2, 1911/12)

Transfer fee paid: £25,000
to Macclesfield for Carl Alford, 1994
Transfer fee received: £150,000
from Newcastle United for Andy Hunt

Career goalscorer: Roy Clayton 171 (1972 - 1981)
Career appearances: Roger Ashby

BEST SEASON

FA Trophy: Runners-up 78-79 99-00

FA Cup: 4th Round
1988-89, 1-2 v Charlton Ath.
91-92, 1-4 v Blackburn R
League clubs defeated: Swindon T., Millwall,
Swansea C., Halifax T., Maidstone & Bristol Rovers

League: Conference Runners-up
1980-81; 88-89; 93-94; 98-99

LAST SEASON

FA. Trophy: Runners-up
F.A. Cup: 1st Rd replay, 0-2 v Wrexham (H)
Conference: 13th
Top Goalscorer: Craig Norman
Player of the Year: Craig Norman
Captain: Colin Vowden

KETTERING TOWN

Match Facts 1999-00

	Date	Comp.	H/A	Opponents	Gate	Result & Score		Goalscorers	League Position
1	14.08	N.C.	H	Northwich Victoria	1,779	D	1-1	Robertson 90 (og)	
2	17.08	N.C.	A	Woking	2,205	D	1-1	Steele 70 (pen)	
3	21.08	N.C.	A	Hereford United	1,980	L	2-4	Banya 15, Fisher 31	16
4	24.08	N.C.	H	Kingstonian	1,485	W	2-1	Diuk 50, Norman 59	
5	28.08	N.C.	A	Yeovil Town	2,347	L	0-2		16
6	30.08	N.C.	A	Stevenage Borough	4,017	L	0-3		16
7	04.09	N.C.	H	Sutton Un ited	1,328	W	1-0	Abrahams 40	15
8	06.09	N.C.	A	Hednesford Town	1,189	D	1-1	Norman 13 (pen)	
9	11.09	N.C.	H	Forest Green Rovers	1,264	W	1-0	Norman 87 (pen)	10
10	14.09	N.C.	H	Rushden & Diamonds	3,744	D	1-1	Norman 34 (pen)	11
11	18.09	N.C.	A	Doncaster Rovers	3,544	L	1-2	Setchell 90	11
12	25.09	N.C.	H	Morecambe	1,409	D	1-1	Vowden 74	13
13	02.10	N.C.	A	Kingstonian	1,252	L	0-2		15
14	09.10	N.C.	H	Hayes	1,252	D	1-1	Fisher 75	15
15	23.10	N.C.	A	Kidderminster Harriers	1,708	L	0-1		17
16	02.11	N.C.	A	Welling United	1,032	W	2-1	Shutt 72, Norman 77 (p)	
17	06.11	N.C.	A	Southport	1,032	W	1-0	Perkins 81	13
18	14.11	N.C.	H	Altrincham	1,170	D	0-0		14
19	20.11	N.C.	A	Scarborough	1,462	D	0-0		14
20	04.12	N.C.	H	Telford United	1,267	D	0-0		13
21	11.12	N.C.	A	Sutton United	716	D	1-1	Brown 54	14
22	18.12	N.C.	H	Dover Athletic	1,026	L	1-2	Watkins 46	14
23	27.12	N.C.	H	Nuneaton Borough	3,602	W	2-1	Watkins 47	19
24	03.01	N.C.	A	Nuneaton Borough	2,598	D	1-1	Chambers 69	14
25	08.01	N.C.	A	Hayes	716	W	1-0	Brown 45	13
26	22.01	N.C.	H	Woking	1282	D	0-0		13
27	29.01	N.C.	H	Yeovil Town	1329	L	1-2	Brown 72	14
28	12.02	N.C.	H	Scarborough	1,270	D	0-0		15
29	19.02	N.C.	H	Kidderminster Harriers	1,815	W	3-1	Fisher 23, Shutt 27, Brown 46	12
30	04.03	N.C.	A	Welling United	648	L	0-1		15
31	18.03	N.C.	H	Southport	1,209	L	0-3		16
32	25.03	N.C.	A	Altrincham	939	D	1-1	Shutt 63	17
33	28.03	N.C.	A	Rushden & Diamonds	4,752	L	0-2		17
34	04.04	N.C.	A	Telford United	824	L	1-3	Watkins 5	17
35	08.04	N.C.	H	Hednesford Town	1,021	W	4-2	Fisher 4, Norman 32(p), McNamara 40, Duik 47	
36	11.04	N.C.	H	Doncaster Rovers	1,279	D	2-2	Setchell 48, Adams 59	18
37	18.04	N.C.	A	Dover Athletic	693	D	1-1	McNamara 48	
38	22.04	N.C.	H	Hereford United	1,617	W	2-0	Norman 26 (p), McNamara 49	15
39	24.04	N.C.	A	Northwich Victoria	919	W	6-2	McNamara 40, Norman 59 (p), 81, Watkins 73, Vowden 86, Shutt 87	13
40	29.04	N.C.	A	Morecambe	1,250	L	1-2	Hudson 80	15
41	01.05	N.C.	H	Stevenage Borough	1,575	W	1-0	Hudson 75	13
42	06.05	N.C.	A	Forest Green Rovers	1,382	L	0-2		13

CUP COMPETITIONS

F.A. Cup

	Date		H/A	Opponents	Gate	Result & Score		Goalscorers
	16.10	4Q	A	Rothwell Town	1,437	D	1-1	McNamara 23
	19.10	4Q R	H	Rothwell Town	1,611	W	2-1	Banya 72, Adams 76
	30.10	1	A	Wrexham	2,701	D	1-1	Brown 48
	10.11	1R	H	Wrexham	2,611	L	0-2	

Nationwide McMillan Trophy

	Date		H/A	Opponents	Gate	Result & Score	
	18.01	2	H	Hayes	302	L	0-1

F.A. Trophy

	Date		H/A	Opponents	Gate	Result & Score		Goalscorers
	27.11	2	H	Thame United	919	D	2-2	Watkins 50, Storer 87
	30.11	2R	A	Thame United	413	W	1-0	Watkins
	15.01	3	H	Welling United	1,031	W	2-0	Watkins, Shutt
	05.02	4	H	Walton & Hersham	1,128	D	2-2	Norman 24, 54
	08.02	4R	A	Walton & Hersham	490	W	2-0	Watkins 4, 64
	26.02	5	A	Workington	1,643	W	1-0	Brown 70
	11.03	6	H	Bishop Auckland	2,074	D	2-2	Norman 34, 51
	14.03	6R	A	Bishop Auckland	1,087	W	2-0	McNamara 38, Norman 87 (p)
	01.04	SF 1	H	Telford United	2,915	W	1-0	Setchell 28
	15.04	SF 2	A	Telford United	2,165	D	0-0	
	13.05	FINAL	Wembley	Kingstonian	20,034	L	2-3	Vowden 55, Norman 64 (p)

1	2	3	4	5	6	7	8	9	10	11	Substitutes Used	
Sollitt 1	Setchell	Cox	Vowden	Norman	Fisher	Brown	McNamara	Adams	Abrahams	Haydon	Banya (8), Hudson (11), Diuk (2)	1
Sollitt 2	Diuk	Adams	Cox	Vowden	Norman	Fisher	Brown	Banya	McNamara	Setchell	Hudson (11), Abrahams (8), Haydon (2)	2
Sollitt 3	Diuk	Adams	Cox	Vowden	Norman	Fisher	Brown	Banya	McNamara	Setchell	Hudson (11), Abrahams (8), Haydon (9)	3
Sollitt 4	Diuk	Abrahams	Cox	Vowden	Norman	Fisher	Hudson	Banya	McNamara	Adams	Wilson (1), Haydon (9)	4
Sollitt 5	Diuk	Adams	Haydon	Vowden	Norman	Fisher	Brown	Banya	McNamara	Abrahams	Hudson (7), Setchell (9), Hopkins (11)	5
Sollitt 6	Diuk	Haydon	Cox	Vowden	Norman	Abrahams	Fisher	Hudson	McNamara	Adams	Banya (6), Brown (7), Setchell (9)	6
Sollitt 7	Diuk	Setchell	Haydon	Vowden	Cox	Fisher	Brown	Hudson	Abrahams	Adams	Banya (7), Ridgway (10)	7
Sollitt 8	Diuk	Adams	Cox	Vowden	Norman	Fisher	Brown	Hudson	McNamara	Setchel	Abrahams (11), Hopkins (10)	8
Sollitt 9	Diuk	Adams	Cox	Vowden	Norman	Hopkins	Brown	Hudson	McNamara	Abrahams	Setchel (9), Banya (2), Fisher (11)	9
Sollitt 10	Diuk	Adams	Cox	Vowden	Norman	Hopkins	Brown	Banya	Lock	McNamara	Fisher (3), Abrahams (10), Ridgway (8)	10
Sollitt 11	Diuk	McNamara	Cox	Vowden	Norman	Fisher	Brown	Banya	Lock	Hopkins	Setchel (9), Ridgway (10)	11
Sollitt 12	Diuk	Setchel	Cox	Vowden	Norman	Adams	Brown	Banya	McNamara	Hopkins	Shutt (9), Ridgway (10), Fisher (11)	12
Sollitt 13	Diuk	Adams	Cox	Vowden	Ridgway	Fisher	Setchel	Shutt	McNamara	Storer	Hudson (8), Brown (2), Banya (9)	13
Sollitt 14	Diuk	Adams	Cox	Vowden	Norman	Brown	Storer	Hudson	McNamara	Ridgway	Shutt (10), Banya (7), Fisher (8)	14
Sollitt 15	Diuk	Adams	Cox	Vowden	Norman	Fisher	Ridgway	Banya	Hudson	Setchel	Storer (4), Brown (3), Shutt (10)	15
Sollitt 16	Diuk	Adams	Ridgway	Vowden	Norman	Fisher	Storer	Tomlinson	Hudson	Setchel	McNamara (9), Perkins (11)	16
Sollitt 17	Diuk	Ridgway	Adams	Cox	Vowden	Norman	Fisher	Shutt	Hudson	McNamara	Setchel	Brown (8), Banya (10), Perkins (9)	17
Sollitt 18	Diuk	Adams	Cox	Vowden	Norman	Storer	Brown	Shutt	McNamara	Setchel	Banya (9), Hudson (10), Ridgway (11)	18
Sollitt 19	Diuk	Hopkins	Perkins	Vowden	Norman	Storer	Dyer	McNamara	Watkins	Setchel	Hudson (10), Shutt (11)	19
Sollitt 20	Diuk	Adams	Perkins	Vowden	Norman	McNamara	Ridgway	Shutt	Watkins	Dyer	Hudson (9), Hopkins (11), Banya (7)	20
Sollitt 21	Diuk	Adams	Perkins	Vowden	Norman	Ridgway	Brown	Banya	Watkins	McNamara	Hudson (9), Hopkins (7), Storer (8)	21
Sollitt 22	Fisher	Adams	Cox	Vowden	Norman	McNamara	Ridgway	Banya	Watkins	Brown	Hudson (9), Hopkins (6)	22
Sollitt 23	Diuk	Adams	Cox	Vowden	Norman	Ridgway	Brown	Chambers	Watkins	Fisher	Hopkins (2)	23
Sollitt 24	Diuk	Adams	Cox	Setchell	Norman	Fisher	Ridgway	Chambers	Watkins	Brown	Hopkins (5), Hudson (2)	24
Sollitt 25	Diuk	Adams	Cox	Vowden	Norman	Fisher	Brown	Chambers	Watkins	Ridgway	Hopkins (6), Hudson (10)	25
Sollitt 26	Diuk	Adams	Cox	Vowden	Norman	Fisher	Brown	Shutt	Watkins	Doane	McNamara (2), Hudson (11)	26
Sollitt 27	Diuk	Adams	Doane	Vowden	Norman	Fisher	Hudson	Shutt	Watkins	Setchell	Brown (11), McNamara (8)	27
Sollitt 28	Diuk	Adams	Doane	Vowden	Brown	Fisher	McNamara	Shutt	Watkins	Ridgway	Banya (9)	28
Sollitt 29	Diuk	Ridgway	Adams	Cox	Vowden	Norman	Brown	Fisher	Shutt	Watkins	McNamara	No subs used	29
Sollitt 30	Ridgway	Adams	Cox	Vowden	Norman	Brown	Fisher	Shutt	Watkins	McNamara	Williams (9), Diuk (11), Paul (2)	30
Sollitt 31	Ridgway	Diuk	Cox	Vowden	Norman	Fisher	Brown	Shutt	Watkins	McNamara	Williams (2), Setchell (5), Adams (11)	31
Sollitt 32	Ridgway	Adams	Cox	Vowden	Norman	Fisher	Brown	Shutt	Watkins	Setchell	Hudson (10)	32
Sollitt 33	Ridgway	Adams	Cox	Vowden	Norman	Fisher	Brown	Shutt	Watkins	Diuk	Setchell (6), Hudson (10)	33
Sollitt 34	Diuk	Adams	Cox	Vowden	Norman	Fisher	Brown	Shutt	Watkins	Setchell	Ridgway (7), McNamara (2), Paul 4)	34
Sollitt 35	Ridgway	Adams	Cox	Vowden	Norman	Fisher	Brown	Shutt	Watkins	Setchell	McNamara (4), Diuk (7)	35
Sollitt 36	Diuk	Adams	Perkins	Vowden	Norman	McNamara	Brown	Shutt	Watkins	Setchell	Hudson (10)	36
Sollitt 37	McNamara	Adams	Perkins	Vowden	Norman	Fisher	Brown	Shutt	Watkins	Setchell	Diuk (9), Ridgway (11), Hudson (10)	37
Sollitt 38	McNamara	Adams	Perkins	Vowden	Norman	Fisher	Brown	Ridgway	Watkins	Setchell	Hudson (10), Shutt (11)	38
Sollitt 39	McNamara	Adams	Perkins	Vowden	Norman	Fisher	Brown	Ridgway	Watkins	Setchell	Hudson (11), Shutt (10), Diuk (7)	39
Sollitt 40	McNamara	Adams	Perkins	Vowden	Norman	Fisher	Brown	Ridgway	Watkins	Setchell	Diuk (5), Hudson (11), Shutt (10)	40
Sollitt 41	Ridgway	Adams	Perkins	Vowden	Norman	Fisher	Brown	McNamara	Shutt	Setchell	Hudson (9), Cox (6),	41
Sollitt 42	Diuk	Adams	Perkins	Vowden	Cox	Fisher	Hopkins	Hudson	Watkins	Setchell	Broomes (10), Wilson (1), Hailstone (2)	42

Sollitt	Diuk	Adams	Cox	Vowden	Norman	Fisher	Brown	Hudson	McNamara	Shutt	Ridgway (11), Setchell (9), Banya (2)	
Sollitt	Diuk	Adams	Ridgway	Vowden	Norman	Brown	Fisher	Hudson	McNamara	Setchell	Hopkins (8), Banya (9), Shutt (10(	
Sollitt	Diuk	Adams	Brown	Vowden	Norman	Fisher	Ridgway	McNamara	Hudson	Setchel	Hopkins (10), Banya (7)	
Sollitt	Diuk	Adams	Cox	Vowden	Norman	Fisher	Brown	Hudson	McNamara	Setchel	Shutt (2), Ridgway (6)	

Wilson	Doane	Adams	Hopkins	Vowden	Shutt	McNamara	Ridgway	Banya	Hudson	Brown	No subs used	

SUBSTITUTES

Sollitt	Diuk	Adams	Perkins	Vowden	Norman	Storer	Brown	McNamara	Watkins	Dyer	Hudson,Ridgway,Cox,Banya,Wilson	
Sollitt	Diuk	Adams	Cox	Vowden	Norman	Dyer	Brown	Banya	Watkins	McNamara	Shutt,Hudson,Ridgway,Hopkins,Wilson	
Wilson	Diuk	Adams	Cox	Vowden	Norman	McNamara	Brown	Banya	Watkins	Ridgway	Hudson, Setchell, Shutt, Hopkins	
Sollitt	Diuk	Adams	Doane	Vowden	Norman	Fisher	McNamara	Shutt	Watkins	Ridgway	Hudson,Setchell,Hopkins,Paul,Wilson	
Sollitt	Diuk	Adams	McNamara	Vowden	Norman	Fisher	Doane	Shutt	Watkins	Setchell	Hudson,Hopkins,Banya,Paul,Wilson	
Sollitt	Diuk	Adams	Cox	Vowden	Norman	Ridgway	Brown	Shutt	Watkins	McNamara	Doane,Williams,Setchell,Paul,Wilson	
Sollitt	Ridgway	Adams	Doane	Vowden	Norman	Fisher	Brown	Williams	Watkins	McNamara	Shutt,Diuk,Setchell,Paul,Wilson	
Sollitt	Ridgway	Adams	Diuk	Vowden	Norman	Fisher	Brown	Shutt	Watkins	McNamara	Williams,Setchell,Paul,Hopkins,Wilson	
Sollitt	Ridgway	Adams	Cox	Vowden	Norman	Fisher	Brown	Shutt	Watkins	Setchell	McNamara,Perkins,Diuk,Paul,Wilson	
Sollitt	McNamara	Adams	Perkins	Vowden	Norman	Fisher	Brown	Shutt	Watkins	Setchell	Ridgway,Diuk,Hudson,Paul,Wilson	
Sollitt	McNamara	Adams	Perkins	Vowden	Norman	Fisher	Brown	Shutt	Watkins	Setchell	Hudson (10), Diuk (6), Hopkins (11)	

PLAYING SQUAD

KETTERING TOWN

(Bold print indicates an England Semi-Professional International)

Player Honours	*Birthplace*	*D.O.B.*	*Previous Clubs*

GOALKEEPERS

Kevin Tye	Nottingham		Mansfield
Steve Wilson	Leicester	29.11.78	Leicester

DEFENDERS

Colin Vowden	Newmark et	13.09.71	Newmarket T, Cambridge C, Cambridge U
Craig Norman	Perivale	21.03.75	Chelsea
Paul Cox	Nottingham	06.01.72	Notts Co., Kettering T, Gresley R, Ilkeston T, Halifax T
Lee Cowling	Doncaster	22.09.77	Nottingham F, Mansfield
Chris Perkins	Stepney	01.03.08	Southend
Steve Lenagh	Durham	21.03.79	Sheffield Wed., Chesterfield
Martin Matthews	Peterborough	22.12.75	Derby, Northampton, King's Lynn

MIDFIELDERS

Ian Ridgway	Nottingham	28.12.75	Notts Co
Wayne Duik	Nottingham	26.05.80	Notts Co., Gedling T
Matt Fisher	Mansfield		Army, Ashfield U, Gedling T
Carl Adams	Birmingham	13.03.74	Birmingham C, Weymouth, Stevenage B
Craig Hopkins	Nottingham		Shirebrook Coll., King's Lynn, Spalding U

FORWARDS

Brett McNamara	Peterborough		Stamford., Northampton, King's Lynn
Phil Brown GMVC, Div.4	Sheffield	16.01.66	Chesterfield, Stockport, Lincoln, Kettering T, Boston U, Gainsborough T
Le Hudson	Peterborough		Moulton Harrox, Spalding U, Boston T, King's Lynn
Steve Wilkinson	Lincoln	01.09.68	Leicester, Mansfield, Preston, Chesterfield
Dale Watkins ESP, NC	Sheffield	04.11.71	Sheffield U, Grimsby, Rotherham, Peterborough, G rantham T, Rushden & D, Gloucester C, Cheltenham T
Carl Shutt	Sheffield	10.10.61	Spalding U, Sheffield Wed., Bristol C, Leeds, Birmingham, Bradford C, Darlington

KINGSTONIAN

The K's and their outstanding manager Geoff Chapple ended the season in fifth spot - three places higher than the previous campaign - and also retained the FA Umbro Trophy with an exciting 3-2 win over Kettering Town in the last-ever final at the 'old' Wembley Stadium.

Kingstonian, in common with several other clubs, hit the top of the table twice during the campaign but suffered the same immediate drop in form or attack of nerves as the others did having hit the top. They had an incredibly difficult run in, in part due to their Trophy success, playing eight league games in fifteen days - and lost only two.

They possess an outstanding midfield trio in Geoff Pitcher, Gary Patterson and Phil Wingfield, so it was an even greater achievement to retain the Trophy without two of them on the day of the Final.

The performance of teenager Ronnie Green towards the end of the season and the permanent arrival of Frenchman Amara Simba has allowed star striker Dave Leworthy to persue his coaching ambitions at Havant & Waterlooville and Chapple has also managed to secure a number of other interesting signings for the new campaign.

My only hope foR the K's is that they are able to attract more paying customers through the Kingsmeadow turnstiles. With such an exciting young side to watch, it was very disappointing that Kingstonian could only average 1,193 for league games.

Steve Whitney

KINGSTONIAN

GROUND DETAILS

Kingsmeadow Stadium,
Kingston Road,
Kingston-upon-Thames,
Surrey. KT13PB

Tel: 0208 547 3335/6
Fax: 0208 974 5713

DIRECTIONS:
From town centre - Cambridge Rd on to Kingston Rd (A2043)
toMalden Rd. From A3, turn off at New Malden, turn left on to
A2043 - grd 1 mile on left. Half mile from Norbiton (BR)

CAPACITY:	9,000
COVERED TERRACING:	3,500
SEATED:	690

SOCIAL FACILITIES:
Banqueting centre, open 7 days. 3 bars capacity 400. Contact
Chris Kelly (0208 547 3335).

CLUB SHOP: Sells programmes, shirts, badges etc.
Contact Chris Dickinson Tel: 0208 747 3336

Founded:	1885
Nickname:	The Ks
Sponsors:	Bass Brewers
Club Colours:	Red & white hooped shirts, white shorts, white socks
Change Colours:	Yellow shirts, royal blue shorts, white socks
Midweek matchday:	Tuesday
Reserves' League:	Suburban
Geoff Chapple's Buzz Line:	09066 555 965

CLUB OFFICIALS

Chairman	Alan Kingston
General Manager	Chris Kelly

Directors : G Chapple, L Cooley, T Dixon, M Grant,
C Kelly, A Kingston,P Claiden, B Gold, N Verbruggen,

Football Secretary Derek Powell
30 Warwick Rd., Ash Vale, Aldershot GU12 5PL
Tel: 01252 675007

Commercial Chris Richardson

Press Officer Alan Kingston
Tel: 01737 210032

Pages: 28   Price: £1.50

Editor: Brian Giffard Tel: 0870 442 5003

Other club publications: None

Local Press: Surrey Comet 0181 546 2261

Local Radio: County Sound; Southern Counties

FOOTBALL MANAGEMENT TEAM

MANAGER: GEOFF CHAPPLE
Date of Appointment   May 1997
Date of Birth: 7th November 1945
Place of Birth: Farnham, Surrey
PREVIOUS CLUBS
As manager   Windsor & Eton, Woking.
As player   Woking, Guildford City, Windsor & Eton
HONOURS
As manager   FA Trophy 93-94, 94-95, 96-97, 98-99, 99-00
Isthmian League - Premier Div. 91-92, 97-98,
Div. 1 R-up 89-90, Div. 2 S 86-87,
League Cup 90-91, Charity Shield 91-92;
Conference - R-up 94-95, 95-96,
Championship Shield 94-95, R-up 95-96.

Assistant Manager/Coach	Ian McDonald
Physio	Jim Pearce
Reserve Team Manager	Steve Chamberlain
Academy Coach:	Martin Spong

Season	League	Div.	Pos.	P	Home W	D	L	F	A	Away W	D	L	F	A	Pts	Manager
99-00	Conference	-	5	42	9	4	8	30	24	11	3	7	28	20	67	Geoff Chapple
98-99	Conference	-	8	42	9	7	5	25	19	8	6	7	25	30	64	Geoff Chapple
97-98	Isthmian	Prem.	1	42	14	4	3	51	18	11	8	2	33	17	87	Geoff Chapple
96-97	Isthmian	Prem.	11	42	10	4	7	46	34	6	4	11	33	45	56	Bill Smith

Season	League	Div.	Pos.	P	W	D	L	F	A	Pts	Manager
95-96	Isthmian	Prem	8	42	20	11	11	62	38	71	Bill Smith
94-95	Isthmian	Prem.	13	42	16	8	18	62	57	56	Richard Parkin
93-94	Isthmian	Prem.	10	42	18	9	15	101	64	63	Chris Kelly
92-93	Isthmian	Prem.	13	42	14	10	18	59	58	52	Chris Kelly
91-92	Isthmian	Prem.	10	42	17	8	17	71	65	59	Chris Kelly
90-91	Isthmian	Prem.	10	42	17	8	17	71	65	59	Chris Kelly

HONOURS

FA Trophy 98-99 99-00;
Isthmian League 33-34, 36-37, 97-98,
R-up 47-48 62-63,
Div 1 R-up 84-85,
League Cup 95-96;
Athenian Lge 23-24 25-26, R-up 26-27;
London Senior Cup 62-63 64-65 86-87,
R-up x 5;
Surrey Senior Cup x 9,
R-up 90-91.

PREVIOUS

Leagues: Kingston & Dist.; West Surrey; Southern Suburban; Athenian 1919-29; Isthmian League 29-98

Names: Kingston & Surbiton YMCA 1885-87, Saxons 87-90, Kingston Wanderers 1893-1904, Old Kingstonians 08-19

Grounds: Several to 1921; Richmond Rd 21-89

Past Players who progressed to the Football League

C Nastri (C Palace), H Lindsay (Southampton 65), G Still (Brighton 79), D Byrne (Gillingham 1985), J Power(Brentford 87), Jamie Ndah (Torquay) Gavin Holligan (West Ham '99)

CLUB RECORDS

Attendance: 4,582 v Chelsea (Friendly) 22.7.95

Goalscorer: Johnny Whing 295
Appearances: Micky Preston 555

Win: 15-1 v Delft, friendly 5/9/51
Competitive 10-0 v Hitchin (H) Isthmian Lge 19/3/66)
Defeat: 0-11 v Ilford (A) Isthmian Lge 13/2/37

Transfer Fee Paid: £18,000
for David Leworthy to Rushden & Diamonds '97
Transfer Fee Received: £150,000
for Gavin Holligan from West Ham Utd. '99

BEST SEASON

FA Amateur Cup: Winners 32-33
R-up 59-60

FA Trophy: Winners 98-99 99-00

FA Cup: 2nd Rd Proper 94-95, v Aylesbury U 95-96, v Plymouth A.
League clubs defeated: Brighton & H.A. 94-95 1-0

League: 5th Conference 99-00

LAST SEASON

F.A. Cup: First Round
F.A. Trophy: Winners
Conference: 5th
Top Goalscorer: David Leworthy
Player of the Year: Geoff Pitcher
Captain: Matt Crossley

KINGSTONIAN   Match Facts 1999-00

	Date	Comp.	H/A	Opponents	Gate	Result & Score	Goalscorers	League Position
1	14.08	N.C.	A	Telford United	920	L 0-1		
2	18.08	N.C.	H	Dover Athletic	1,106	W 4-1	Leworthy 3 (20, 27, 56), Luckett 60	
3	21.08	N.C.	H	Southport	1,027	W 4-2	Marshall 20, Leworthy 71, 75, Luckett 79	4
4	24.08	N.C.	A	Kettering Town	1,485	L 1-2	Leworthy 61	
5	28.08	N.C.	H	Altrincham	984	D 2-2	Leworthy 32, Pitcher 41	6
6	30.08	N.C.	A	Hayes	829	W 2-1	Akuamoah 32, 77	6
7	04.09	N.C.	A	Scarborough	1,671	W 1-0	Akuamoah 14	4
8	11.09	N.C.	H	Northwich Vic.	1.004	D 3-3	Wingfield 15, Leworthy 69, Stewart 88	6
9	18.09	N.C.	A	Forest Green Rovers	803	W 3-0	Pitcher 33, 51, Akuamoah 56	6
10	25.09	N.C.	A	Stevenage Borough	2,775	W 1-0	Pitcher 57	5
11	28.09	N.C.	A	Welling United	605	W 1-0	Leworthy 40	1
12	02.10	N.C.	H	Kettering Town	1,252	W 2-0	Akuamoah 49, Leworthy 84	1
13	09.10	N.C.	A	Rushden & Diamonds	3,764	L 0-1		2
14	13.10	N.C.	H	Yeovil Town	1,421	L 0-1		2
15	23.10	N.C.	A	Morecambe	1,384	W 2-1	Allan 24, Leworthy 40	2
16	02.11	N.C.	A	Sutton United	1,422	D 2-2	Berry 16 (OG), Laker 64 (OG)	2
17	06.11	N.C.	H	Welling United	1,023	W 1-0	Wingfield 54	1
18	12.11	N.C.	A	Nuneaton Borough	3,203	L 0-2		1
19	20.11	N.C.	H	Doncaster Rovers	1,407	L 0-1		2
20	04.12	N.C.	A	Kidderminster Harriers	1,933	L 0-2		4
21	18.12	N.C.	H	Hednesford Town	903	L 0-2		5
22	27.12	N.C.	A	Woking	3,614	D 1-1	Pitcher 66	6
23	03.01	N.C.	H	Woking	2,467	L 0-2		7
24	08.01	N.C.	H	Telford United	1026	W 4-2	Pitcher 1, Akuamoah 16, 61, Stewart 69	6
25	22.01	N.C.	A	Doncaster Rovers	2548	L 0-1		7
26	29.01	N.C.	H	Kidderminsterr Harriers	1523	L 0-1		8
27	12.02	N.C.	H	Sutton United	1,527	W 4-2	Wingfield 5, 90, Crossley 47, Leworthy 87	7
28	16.02	N.C.	H	Stevenage Borough	1,034	W 1-0	Wingfield 59	5
29	04.03	N.C.	H	Rushden & Diamonds	1,772	L 0-1		9
30	18.03	N.C.	H	Nuneaton Borough	985	W 2-0	Harris 80, J O'Connor 83	7
31	25.03	N.C.	A	Dover Athletic	1.025	W 1-0	OG (Shearer) 47	7
32	06.04	N.C.	H	Hereford United	664	D 0-0		
33	08.04	N.C.	H	Scarborough	983	W 2-0	Simba 38, 45	7
34	11.04	N.C.	A	Yeovil Town	1,593	L 2-3	O'Connor 34, Harris 78	8
35	22.04	N.C.	H	Forest Green Rovers	935	L 0-1		8
36	24.04	N.C.	A	Hereford United	1,527	W 2-0	Harris 42, Pitcher 81	7
37	26.04	N.C.	H	Morecambe	834	D 0-0		
38	29.04	N.C.	A	Hednesford Town	683	W 3-2	Pitcher 27, Drewett 36, Harris 62	6
39	01.05	N.C.	H	Hayes	1,183	L 1-3	Simba 8	7
40	03.05	N.C.	A	Altrincham	779	W 3-1	Pitcher 16, Akuamoah 17, Simba 77	5
41	04.05	N.C.	A	Southport	1,039	D 0-0		
42	06.05	N.C.	A	Northwich Victoria	976	W 3-0	Simba 16, 48, Wingfield 88	5

CUP COMPETITIONS

	Date	Comp.	H/A	Opponents	Gate	Result & Score	Goalscorers	
	05.10		A	Cheltenham Town	896	W 1-0	Marshall 45	Championship Shield
	16.10	4Q	H	Boston United	1,108	D 0-0		F.A. Cup
	20.10	4Q R	A	Boston United	2,120	W 3-0	OG 41, Leworthy 52, Wingfield 79	
	30.10	1	A	Luton Town	4,682	L 2-4	Crossley 35, Leworthy 47	
	09.11	2	A	Welling United	206	W 1-0	Mustafa 85	Nationwide McMillan Trophy
	26.01	3	H	Woking	416	W 2-0	Patterson 6, Leworthy 27	
	28.03	SF1	A	Hayes	531	D 0-0		
	20.04	SF2	H	Hayes	306	W 1-0	Green 64	
	08.05	Final		Doncaster Rovers				
	27.11	2	A	Folkestone Invicta	727	W 1-0	Basford 65	F.A. Trophy
	15.01	3	A	Wealdstone	639	W 5-0	Wingfield, Pitcher (p), Akuamoah, O'Connor, Taylor.	
	05.02	4	H	Moor Green	623	W 2-1	Taylor 45, Pitcher 80	
	26.02	5	A	Yeovil Town	3,330	W 1-0	Leworthy 40	
	11.03	6	H	Southport	1,201	D 0-0		
	14.03	6R	A	Southport	1,576	W 1-0	Leworthy 86	
	01.04	SF 1	A	Sutton United	2,384	D 1-1	Harris 78	
	18.04	SF 2	H	Sutton United	2,309	W 6-0	Luckett 12, 38, Simba 51, 64, Wingfield 67, Pitcher 85	
	13.05	FINAL	Wembley	Kettering Town	20,034	W 3-2	Akuamoah 40, 69, Simba 75	

1	2	3	4	5	6	7	8	9	10	11	Substitutes Used	
Farrelly	Mustafa	Luckett	Crossley	Stewart	Harris	Patterson	Pitcher	Akuamoah	Marshall	Wingfield	Basford (3), Leworthy (10), Newman (11)	1
Farrelly	Mustafa	Luckett	Crossley	Stewart	Harris	Patterson	Pitcher	Marshall	Leworthy	Wingfield	Basford (9), Akuamoah (11)	2
Farrelly	Mustafa	Luckett	Crossley	Stewart	Harris	Patterson	Pitcher	Marshall	Leworthy	Wingfield	Basford (6), Akuamoah (11), Kadi (7)	3
Farrelly	Mustafa	Luckett	Crossley	Stewart	Harris	Patterson	Pitcher	Marshall	Leworthy	Wingfield	Akuamoah (11), Basford (8)	4
Farrelly	Marshall	Luckett	Crossley	Stewart	Harris	Patterson	Pitcher	Mustafa	Leworthy	Wingfield	Akuamoah (11), Basford (6) sub Kadi	5
Farrelly	Mustafa	Luckett	Crossley	Stewart	Alan	Patterson	Pitcher	Akuamoah	Leworthy	Wingfield	No subs used	6
Farrelly	Mustafa	Luckett	Crossley	Stewart	Allan	Patterson	Pitcher	Akuamoah	Leworthy	Wingfield	Marshall (11), Smith (7)	7
Farrelly	Mustafa	Luckett	Crossley	Stewart	Allan	Patterson	Pitcher	Akuamoah	Leworthy	Wingfield	No subs used	8
Farrelly	Mustafa	Luckett	Crossley	Stewart	Allan	Patterson	Pitcher	Akuamoah	Leworthy	Wingfield	Harris (2), Marshall (10), Kadi (11)	9
Farrelly	Mustafa	Luckett	Crossley	Stewart	Allan	Patterson	Pitcher	Kadi	Leworthy	Wingfield	Harris (9), Marshall (11)	10
Farrelly	Mustafa	Luckett	Crossley	Stewart	Allan	Patterson	Pitcher	Akuamoah	Leworthy	Wingfield	No subs used	11
Farrelly	Mustafa	Luckett	Crossley	Stewart	Allan	Patterson	Pitcher	Akuamoah	Leworthy	Wingfield	Harris (5)	12
Farrelly	Mustafa	Luckett	Crossley	Harris	Allan	Patterson	Pitcher	Akuamoah	Marshall	Wingfield	No subs used	13
Farrelly	Mustafa	Luckett	Crossley	Harris	Allan	Patterson	Pitcher	Kadi	Marshall	Thompson	Walker (9)	14
Farrelly	Mustafa	Luckett	Crossley	Harris	Allan	Patterson	Pitcher	Marshall	Leworthy	Wingfield	Kadi (9)	15
Farrelly	Mustafa	Luckett	Crossley	Harris	Allan	Patterson	Pitcher	Akuamoah	Leworthy	Wingfield	No subs used	16
Farrelly	Mustafa	Luckett	Crossley	Harris	Allan	Patterson	Pitcher	Akuamoah	Leworthy	Wingfield	Thompson (9) sub Marshall	17
Farrelly	Mustafa	Luckett	Crossley	Harris	Allan	Patterson	Pitcher	Taylor	Leworthy	Wingfield	No subs used	18
Farrelly	Mustafa	Luckett	Crossley	Harris	Allan	Patterson	Pitcher	Taylor	Leworthy	Wingfield	Kadi (3), Stewart (6), Drewett (11)	19
Farrelly	Mustafa	Brown	Crossley	Stewart	Allan	Patterson	Lyttle	Akuamoah	Leworthy	Harris	Kadi (8), Wingfield (11), Drewett (10)	20
Farrelly	Mustafa	Brown	Crossley	Stewart	Allan	O'Connor	Pitcher	Akuamoah	Leworthy	Wingfield	Basford (11), Kadi (5)	21
Farrelly	Mustafa	Basford	Crossley	Stewart	Harris	Patterson	Pitcher	O'Connor	Akuamoah	Wingfield		22
Farrelly	Mustafa	Basford	Crossley	Stewart	Harris	Patterson	Pitcher	O'Connor	Akuamoah	Wingfield	Leworthy (3)	23
Farrelly	Mustafa	Basford	Allan	Stewart	Harris	Patterson	Pitcher	Akuamoah	Leworthy	Wingfield	O'Connor (10)	24
Farrelly	Mustafa	Taylor	Crossley	Allan	Harris	Patterson	Pitcher	Akuamoah	Leworthy	Wingfield	O'Connor (10), Basford (11)	25
Farrelly	Mustafa	Taylor	Harris	Stewart	Allan	Patterson	Pitcher	O'Conner	Akuamoah	Wingfield	Drewett (2), Basford (5)	26
Farrelly	Mustafa	Luckett	Crossley	Stewart	Allan	Patterson	Pitcher	Akuamoah	Leworthy	Wingfield	Taylor (7), O'Conner (10)	27
Farrelly	Mustafa	Luckett	Crossley	Stewart	Allan	Patterson	Pitcher	Akuamoah	Leworthy	Wingfield	Taylor (6), Boylan (10)	28
Farrelly	Mustafa	Luckett	Crossley	Allan	Harris	Taylor	Pitcher	Akuamoah	Leworthy	Wingfield	Boylan (10), O'Conner (6)	29
Farrelly	Mustafa	Luckett	Crossley	Saunders	Harris	Patterson	Pitcher	Akuamoah	Boylan	Wingfield	O'Conner (9), Hendrie (11)	30
Farrelly	Mustafa	Luckett	Crossley	Allan	Harris	Patterson	Pitcher	O'Conner	Simba	Boylan	Green (9), Hendrie (10)	31
Farrelly	Mustafa	Luckett	Crossley	Allan	Saunders	Patterson	Pitcher	Boylan	Green	Simba	O'Conner (9)	32
Farrelly	Mustafa	Luckett	Crossley	Saunders	Harris	Patterson	Green	Akuamoah	Simba	Basford	Allan (4), O'Conner (8), Boylan (10)	33
Hurst	Lester	Luckett	Hendrie	Allan	Harris	Kadi	Drewett	O'Conner	Boylan	Basford	Wingfield (5), Saunders (8), Mustafa (2)	34
Farrelly	Mustafa	Luckett	Crossley	Saunders	Harris	Patterson	Pitcher	Akuamoah	Simba	Wingfield	Green (11) sub Boylan, O'Conner (10)	35
Farrelly	Mustafa	Luckett	Allan	Saunders	Harris	Patterson	Pitcher	O'Conner	Kadi	Boylan	Hendrie (9), Basford (10)	36
Farrelly	Mustafa	Luckett	Crossley	Saunders	Harris	Patterson	Pitcher	Kadi	Simba	Drewett	Lester (2), Leworthy (10), O'Conner (11)	37
Farrelly	Mustafa	Luckett	Crossley	Saunders	Harris	Patterson	Pitcher	O'Conner	Drewett	Akuamoah	Leworthy (9), Boylan (10), Hendrie (8)	38
Farrelly	Basford	Luckett	Crossley	Saunders	Harris	Kadi	Pitcher	Akuamoah	Simba	Drewett	Wingfield (11), Boylan (9), Leworthy (10)	39
Farrelly	Lester	Luckett	Crossley	Stewart	Harris	Patterson	Pitcher	Akuamoah	Simba	Green	O'Conner (9), Leworthy (10), Drewett (11)	40
Hurst	Hendrie	Basford	Crossley	Saunders	Allan	Patterson	Kadi	Green	Leworthy	Wingfield	Pitcher (11)	41
Farrelly	Mustafa	Basford	Allan	Stewart	Harris	Patterson	Pitcher	Simba	Leworthy	Kadi	Saunders(6),Akuamoah(9), Wingfield(10)	42

| Farrelly | Mustafa | Luckett | Crossley | Stewart | Harris | Kadi | Pitcher | Green | Simba | Akuamoah | Saunders (5), Leworthy (7), Basford(9) |

PLAYING SQUAD

(Bold print indicates an England Semi-Professional International)

Player Honours	Birthplace	D.O.B.	Previous Clubs

GOALKEEPERS

Player Honours	Birthplace	D.O.B.	Previous Clubs
Steve Farrelly ESP, FAT	Liverpool	27.03.65	Chester, Macclesfield, Rotherham, Barrow
Richard Hurst	Hammersmith	23.12.76	QPR

DEFENDERS

Player Honours	Birthplace	D.O.B.	Previous Clubs
Eddie Saunders FAT	London		Civil Service, Sutton U, Yeading, Carshalton Ath., Woking
Colin Luckett FAT, RP	London	19.01.76	Millwall
Derek Allan Scottish u-21 FAT	Irvine	24.12.74	Ayr U, Southampton, Brighton
Simon Stewart FAT	Leeds	01.11.73	Sheffield Wed., Fulham
Mark Harris FAT	Reading	15.07.63	Wokingham T, Crystal Palace, Swansae, Gillingham, Cardiff
Mark Beard	Roehampton	08.10.74	Millwall, Sheffield U, Southend
Luke Basford FAT	Lambeth	06.01.80	Bristol R

MIDFIELDERS

Player Honours	Birthplace	D.O.B.	Previous Clubs
Gary Patterson ESP, FAT, RP	Newcastle	27.11.72	Notts Co., Shrewsbury, Wycombe
Geoff Pitcher ESP, FAT, RP	Carshalton	15.08.75	Millwall, Watford, Carshalton Ath., Kingstonian, Colchester
Junior Kadi FAT	London	16.08.79	Coventry, Whyteleafe
Phil Wingfield	London	11.03.69	Walton & Hersham, Kingstonian, Hayes, Kingstonian, Farnboough T
Robin Taylor FAT, British Univ.	Leicester		Camb.C, Kettering T, Port Vale, Dag & Red, Woking
Richard O'Connor	Wandsworth	30.08.78	Wimbledon

FORWARDS

Player Honours	Birthplace	D.O.B.	Previous Clubs
Sammy Winston	London	06.08.78	Norwich, Leyton O, Yeovil T, Chesham U, Sutton U, £5,000 to Kingstonian
Ronnie Green FAT	London		Youth team
Eddie Akuamoah FAT, RP	London	20.11.72	Bedfont, Carshalton Ath.
Neville Roach	Reading	29.09.78	Reading, Southend
David Bass	Frimley	29.11.74	Reading, Rotherham, Carlisle, Scarborough
Joe O'Connor ESP	Birmingham	20.10.67	Lye T, Stafford R, Hednesford T, Nuneaton B, £10,.000 to Kingstonian
Amara Simba France Int., FAT	Paris	23.12.61	Jeanne D'Arc, Houdan, Versailles, Paris St.Germain, AS Cannes, Paris St.Germain, Monaco, Caen, Lille, Leyton O

LEIGH R.M.I.

Before the 1999/2000 season began it would have been difficult to predict the winners of the UniBond League Premier Division.

However, a closer inspection of Leigh's credentials might have given a hint of the success to come. Manager Steve Waywell had led the Lancastrians to an exciting FA Cup run the previous season, culminating in the first round proper against Fulham at Craven Cottage. They drew magnificently in London and then lost at their own Hilton Park in front of more than 7,000 fans.

The nucleus of that side was still in place when the 1999/2000 season kicked off and Waywell also shrewdly added England men Brian Ross, Brian Butler and Mark Ward to his squad. They all played a major part in Leigh's league triumph, as did 40-year-old goalkeeper David Felgate.

The only disappointment for the club was the attendance figures at Hilton Park. Bordered by a number of Nationwide League clubs, it is hard for Leigh to attract decent crowds but to average only 284 on their way to the championship was disappointing.

Leigh will no doubt start the new season as favourites to go straight back down again, but they have an astute manager and I have a feeling they will survive.

I only hope the Lancashire public support them in their efforts.

Steve Whitney

Leigh RMI celebrate with the Unibond Trophy - **Back Row**: Derek Miles, Mick Higgins, Ian Bold, Peter Cumiskey, Dave Ridings, Dave Felgate, Ged Kielty, Rick Harris, Eddie Turkington, Mark O'Connor, Andy Mason. **Front Row:** Gerry Luska, Tony Black, Dave German, Ian Monk, Brian Butler, Mark Ward, Steve Jones, Brian Ross, Mick Wallace, Steve Wallace.

LEIGH R.M.I.

GROUND DETAILS

**Hilton Park,
Kirkhall Lane,
Leigh WN7 1RN**

Tel: 01942 743743 (Office)
Fax: 01942 768856
Web site: http://www.leigh-rmi.co.uk

DIRECTIONS:
From M61 junction 5, follow the Westhoughton sign to r'about, then follow signs to Leigh. Keep on main road to the traffic lights, left into Leigh Road, carry on about 3 miles to the traffic lights. Turn left and first right to the next set of lights. Right onto Atherleigh Way, A579 at the first set of traffic lights, turn left (B & Q on right), at the next set of lights turn right into Kirkhall Lane (Leigh town centre), at the 2nd opening on right turn into Prescott St., carry on to top, turn right, ground on left.

CAPACITY: 8000
COVER: 4,000
SEATS: 2,000

CLUBHOUSE: Open matchdays with food available. Pre-match meals can be arranged.
2 separate function facilities for 200 and 100.

CLUB SHOP: At the ground & open most days. Contact club.

Formed:	1896
Nickname:	Railwaymen
Sponsors:	TBA
Colours:	Red & white striped shirts
	black shorts and white socks
Change colours:	All Yellow
Midweek home matchday:	Tuesday
Reserve Team	None

CLUB OFFICIALS

Chairman:	Chris Healey
Vice Chairman:	Alan Leach
Directors:	A Kirkman, L Berry, A Marshall, K Freer, W Taylor, T Leece, A Blakeney, G Culshaw, Mrs Y Clarke
President:	G H Fisher
Secretary:	Alan Robinson 55 Janice Drive, Fulwood, Preston, Lancs. PR2 9TY. Tel: 01772 719266 (H) 01942 743743 (Club)
Press Officer:	Secretary

FOOTBALL MANAGEMENT TEAM

MANAGER: STEVE WAYWELL

Date of Appointment	November 1996
Date of Birth:	4th June 1954
Place of Birth:	Bury

PREVIOUS CLUBS
As manager	Curzon Ashton
As asst. manager	Ashton United
As player	Burnley, Stalybridge C., Chorley, Hyde U., Stalybridge C.

HONOURS
As manager	N.P.L. - Prem. Div. 99-00; Div. 1 R-up 96-97
As asst. manager	None
As player	None

*   *   *

Asst Manager: Dave Miller
First Team Coach: Gerry Luczka
Physiotherapist: TBA
Chief Scout: TBA

MATCHDAY PROGRAMME

LEIGH RMI FC
at HILTON PARK
Premier Division

Pages: 32   Price: £1.50

Editor: Secretary

Local Press: Bolton Evening News

Local Radio: Radio Lancs, Red Rose Radio, G.M.R.

Season	League	Div.	Pos.	Home P	W	D	L	F	A	Away W	D	L	F	A	Pts	Manager
99-00	N.P.L.	Premier	1	44	15	3	4	42	17	13	5	4	49	28	92	Steve Waywell
98-99	N.P.L.	Premier	8	42	6	10	5	30	26	10	5	6	33	28	63	Steve Waywell
97-98	N.P.L.	Premier	3	42	12	6	3	32	15	9	7	5	31	26	76	Steve Waywell

Season	League	Div.	Pos.	P	W	D	L	F	A	Pts						Manager
96-97	N.P.L.	One	2	42	24	1	7	65	33	83						Steve Waywell
95-96	N.P.L.	One	14	40	14	7	19	53	59	49						Mick Holgate
94-95	N.P.L.	Premier	22	42	9	4	29	49	94	31						Mick Holgate
93-94	N.P.L.	Premier	20	42	8	12	22	50	75	*35						Mick Holgate
92-93	N.P.L.	Premier	13	42	14	10	18	72	79	52						Ken Wright
91-92	N.P.L.	Premier	13	42	13	14	15	44	52	53						Ken Wright
90-91	N.P.L.	Premier	16	40	13	6	21	62	81	45						Alan Kirkman

HONOURS

Northern Premier League Champions 1999-2000
Division 1 R-up 96-97;
Premier Inter League (GMAC) Cup 87-88;
Cheshire County Lg 78-79,
Challenge Shield 78-79;
Lancs Combination 57-58
R-up 29-30 55-56 66-67;
Lg Cup 28-29 53-54 56-57 65-66,
Div 2 R-up 48-49 50-51;
West Lancs League 10-11 11-12;
Lancs Junior Cup 24-25 29-30 (R-up x 4);
Lancs Floodlit Trophy 84-85 (R-up 83-84);
Lancs FA Cup 84-85

PREVIOUS

Leagues: Lancashire Alliance 1891-97;
Lancashire League 1897-1900;
Lancashire Combination 17-18, 19-39, 46-68;
Cheshire County League 68-82;
North West Counties League 82-83;
Northern Premier League 83-2000

Name: Horwich R.M.I. until 1995

Ground: Grundy Hill, Horwich until 1994

Past Players who progressed to the Football League

Harold Lea (Stockport 58),
David Holland (Stockport 59),
Jim Cunliffe (Stockport 60),
Frank Wignall (Everton 58),
Gary Cooper (Rochdale73),
Tony Caldwell (Bolton 83),
Raymond Redshaw (Wigan 84),
Tony Ellis (Oldham 86).
Paul Jones (Oldham , Nov. 99)

CLUB RECORDS

Attendance:
(at Horwich)   8,500 v Wigan Ath Lancs Jnr Cup 54
(at Leigh)   7,125 v Fulham, FAC 98-99

Win: Unknown

Career Appearances: Neil McLachlan

Career Goalscorer: Neil McLachlan

Defeat: 2-9 v Brandon Utd (H)
FA Cup 1998-99

Transfer fee paid: £4,000
to Hyde Utd for Keith Evans 95-96

Transfer fee received: £10,000
from Bolton W. for Marcus Hallows 1995

BEST SEASON

FA Trophy: Quarter Final 90-91

FA Cup: 1st Rd
28-29, 82-83, 98-99 (replay)

FA Vase: N/A

League: 1st, Northern Premier League 99-00

LAST SEASON

F.A. Cup: 3rd Qualifying Round
F.A. Trophy: Second Round replay
League: Champions, N.P.L.
Top Goalscorer: Steve Jones 25
Player of the Year: Steve Jones
Captain: Brian Butler

LEIGH R.M.I.

Match Facts 1999-00

	Date	Comp.	H/A	Opponents	Gate	Result & Score	Goalscorers	League Position
1	14.08	UNIB P	A	Blyth Spartans	401	W 1-0	Matthews 61	
2	17.08	UNIB P	A	Lancaster City	260	W 3-1	Patterson 34, S Jones 62, Monk 73	
3	21.08	UNIB P	H	Gateshead	215	W 3-1	Butler 32, S jones 42, 65	
4	24.08	UNIB P	H	Bamber Bridge	260	W 3-0	Black 1, Matthews 50, S Jones 84	
5	28.08	UNIB P	A	Leek Town	325	L 0-2		
6	30.08	UNIB P	H	Guiseley	247	L 0-1		
7	04.09	UNIB P	A	Emley	316	L 1-3	Black 60	
8	07.09	UNIB P	A	Frickley Athletic	151	W 4-2	Black 11, 72, Matthews 35, S Jones 86	
9	11.09	UNIB P	H	Whitby Town	202	W 2-1	Black 2, Monk 60	
10	25.09	UNIB P	H	Barrow	331	W 1-0	Black 63	
11	28.09	UNIB P	H	Marine	266	W 2-1	Locke 44[p], Black 85	
12	16.10	UNIB P	A	Hucknall Town	259	W 2-1	Black 44, Ross 50	
13	26.10	UNIB P	A	Bamber Bridge	406	D 2-2	Ross 32, 75	
14	30.10	UNIB P	H	Hucknall Town	209	W 1-0	Monk 90	
15	06.11	UNIB P	H	Gainsborough Trinity	201	D 1-1	Wallace 45	
16	09.11	UNIB P	A	Droylsden	193	W 2-0	Ridings 46, S Jones 78	
17	13.11	UNIB P	H	Colwyn Bay	211	L 1-2	Ross 7	
18	04.12	UNIB P	A	Winsford United	101	W 5-0	**Black 3** (33 46 90), Ridings 51, Ross 69	
19	14.12	UNIB P	H	Runcorn	161	W 2-0	Ridings 4, Harris 17	
20	27.12	UNIB P	A	Marine	663	D 1-1	S Jones 23	
21	03.01	UNIB P	H	Emley	419	W 1-0	S Jones 15	1
22	08.01	UNIB P	H	Hyde United	427	D 0-0		2
23	15.01	UNIB P	H	Leek Town	228	L 0-2		2
24	18.01	UNIB P	A	Stalybridge Celtic	423	W 3-1	Ward 24[p], Ross 55, Ridings 71	1
25	29.01	UNIB P	A	Gateshead	408	D 1-1	Ross 51	1
26	04.02	UNIB P	H	Winsford United	255	W 3-2	Black 25 63, S Jones 81	1
27	12.02	UNIB P	A	Bishop Auckland	226	D 1-1	Black 55	1
28	19.02	UNIB P	H	Frickley Athletic	241	W 5-0	Ridings 8, S Jones 40 73, Ross 48, Harris 82	1
29	25.02	UNIB P	H	Lancaster City	401	W 2-1	Ross 30 51	1
30	29.02	UNIB P	A	Barrow	900	D 2-2	Ross 20 70	1
31	11.03	UNIB P	A	Whitby Town	489	L 0-2		
32	13.03	UNIB P	A	Hyde United	903	W 2-1	Black 28, Cumiskey 47	
33	18.03	UNIB P	H	Worksop Town	275	D 2-2	S Jones 36 77	
34	25.03	UNIB P	H	Guiseley	274	W 3-0	Ross 13, S Jones 38, Kielty 48	
35	28.03	UNIB P	H	Spennymoor United	253	W 4-0	Wallace 5, Ward 28(p), Matthews 35, 62	
36	01.04	UNIB P	A	Gainsborough Trinity	341	L 3-4	Ward 21(p), Ross 24, Matthews 60	
37	08.04	UNIB P	H	Droylsden	235	L 1-2	Ward 15(p)	
38	11.04	UNIB P	H	Bishop Auckland	203	W 4-1	Black 14, Ridings 17, Ross 30, Ward 52 (p)	1
39	18.04	UNIB P	A	Runcorn	254	W 2-0	Black 57, S Jones 87	1
40	22.04	UNIB P	H	Stalybridge Celtic	304	W 2-0	Black 49, S Jones 79	1
41	24.04	UNIB P	A	Colwyn Bay	280	W 5-3	Ross 9, Kielty 19, S Jones 31, OG (Jones) 26, OG (Price) 57	1
42	29.04	UNIB P	A	Spennymoor United	235	W 3-1	Kielty 20, Ward 58 (p), S Jones 70	1
43	01.05	UNIB P	H	Blyth Spartans	695	W 2-0	Harris 73, Matthews 75	1
44	06.05	UNIB P	A	Worksop Town	449	W 3-0	Matthews 40, 86, Ridings 50	1

CUP COMPETITIONS

	Date	Comp.	H/A	Opponents	Gate	Result & Score	Goalscorers	
	18.09	Q2	H	Blyth Spartans	197	W 5-3	**Monk 3** (42 45 68), Matthews 85, 89	**F.A. Cup**
	02.10	Q3	H	Crook Town	301	D 1-1	Black 3	
	06.10	Q3 r	A	Crook Town	445	L 1-2	S Jones 24	
	09.10	1	H	Boston United	377	W 1-0	S Jones 80	**F.A. Trophy**
	27.11	2	H	Worksop Town	232	D 1-1	Ridings 85	
	30.11	2R	A	Worksop Town	335	L 1-3	Ridings 59	
	14.09	G4	H	Ashton United	107	W 2-1	Carr 28, S Jones 73	**N.P.L. League Cup**
	12.10	G4	A	Radcliffe Borough	180	W 2-0	Black 10, 65	
	02.11	GA	H	Lancaster City	161	D 2-2	Eatock 10, Locke 80[p]	
	23.11	GA	A	Workington	312	D 0-0		
	22.01	QF	H	Eastwood Town	120	W 1-0	Quayle 55	**N.P.L. Presidents Cup**
	04.03	SF	H	Whitby Town	159	L 1-3	S Jones 79	
	16.11	1	A	Nelson	212	W 2-1	Wallace 30, Ross 87	**Lancs. Mars Trophy**
	11.01	2	A	Southport	294	W 2-1	Ross 75, Wallace 107	
	01.02	QF	A	Accrington Stanley	303	W 2-1	Ridings 5, Matthews 34	
	07.03	SF	H	Marine	179	L 2-4	Black 44, S Jones 45	

1	2	3	4	5	6	7	8	9	10	11	Substitutes Used	
Felgate	Locke	Wallace	P Jones	Turkington	Butler	Monk	Ridings	Ross	Matthews	S Jones	Carr (9)	1
Felgate	Locke	Wallace	P Jones	Turpin	Patterson	German	Ridings	Matthews	Monk	S Jones	Carr (6)	2
Felgate	Locke	Patterson	P Jones	Turkington	Butler	Monk	Ridings	Matthews	Black	S Jones	Carr (3), German (7), Tobin (9)	3
Felgate	Locke	Wallace	P Jones	Turkington	Butler	Monk	Ridings	Matthews	Black	S Jones	German (10)	4
Felgate	Locke	Wallace	P Jones	Turkington	Butler	German	Ridings	Matthews	Black	S Jones	Tobin (3)	5
Felgate	Locke	Wallace	P Jones	Turkington	Butler	Pryor	Ridings	Matthews	Black	S Jones	Carr (3(, Pryers (7)	6
Felgate	Locke	Wallace	P Jones	Turkington	Butler	German	Ridings	Matthews	Black	S Jones	Carr (3), Smyth (8), Tobin (9)	7
Felgate	Locke	Wallace	P Jones	Turpin	Turkington	Monk	Butler	Matthews	Black	S Jones	German (7), Smyth (8)	8
Felgate	Locke	Wallace	P Jones	Turpin	Turkington	Monk	Smyth	S Jones	Black	Pryers	Carr (9), Tobin (10), German (11)	9
Felgate	Locke	Wallace	P Jones	Turpin	Butler	Monk	Smyth	Matthews	Black	S Jones	Ross (9)	10
Felgate	Locke	Smyth	P Jones	Turpin	Butler	Matthews	Ridings	Ross	Black	S Jones	German (8), Wallace (9)	11
Felgate	Locke	Butler	P Jones	German	Ward	Monk	Ridings	Ross	Black	S Jones	Wallace (7), Carr (9)	12
Felgate	Locke	Butler	P Jones	German	Ward	Monk	Ridings	Ross	Black	S Jones	Carr (10), Wallace (8)	13
Felgate	Locke	German	P Jones	Turkington	Butler	Monk	Ward	Ross	Black	S Jones	Ridings (5), Carr (9)	14
Felgate	Locke	German	P Jones	Turkington	Ward	Monk	Butler	Eatock	Wallace	S Jones		15
Felgate	Locke	German	P Jones	Turkington	Ward	S Jones	Ridings	Ross	Black	Wallace		16
Felgate	Locke	German	Ward	Turkington	Wallace	Eatock	Butler	Ross	Black	S Jones	Ridings (6)	17
Felgate	Butler	Wallace	German	Turkington	Ward	S Jones	Ridings	Ross	Black	Harris	Smyth (6), Matthews (7), Quinn (9)	18
Felgate	Butler	Wallace	German	Turkington	Ward	S Jones	Ridings	Ross	Black	Harris	Smyth (6), Matthews (9), Quinn (11)	19
Felgate	Locke	German	Butler	Turkington	Harris	Ward	Ridings	Ross	Black	S Jones	Monk (6)	20
Felgate	Locke	German	Butler	Turkington	Harris	Ward	Ridings	Ross	Black	S Jones	Monk (6), Matthews (7), Smyth (11)	21
Felgate	Locke	German	Butler	Turkington	Harris	Monk	Ridings	Ross	Black	Patterson	Quinn (4) sub Matthews	22
Felgate	Locke	Wallace	German	Harris	Ward	Monk	Ridings	Ross	Black	Patterson	Smyth (2), Matthews (5), Bold (9)	23
Felgate	Locke	Wallace	German	Turkington	Ward	Monk	Ridings	Ross	Black	Harris	Matthews (4), Smyth (10)	24
Felgate	Locke	Wallace	Butler	Harris	Patterson	Monk	Ridings	Ross	Black	S Jones		25
Felgate	Locke	Wallace	Butler	Turkington	Harris	Patterson	Ridings	Ross	Black	S Jones	Smyth (9), Quinn (11)	26
Felgate	Locke	Wallace	German	Turkington	Ward	Patterson	Harris	Ross	Black	S Jones		27
Felgate	German	Wallace	Butler	Swan	Harris	Ward	Ridings	Ross	Black	S Jones	Locke (5), Bold (7), Christie (10)	28
Felgate	German	Wallace	Butler	Swan	Harris	Ward	Ridings	Ross	Black	S Jones	Cumiskey	29
Felgate	Locke	Wallace	German	Swan	Harris	Ward	Matthews	Ross	Christie	Cumiskey	Bold (5), Turpin (10), Black (11)	30
Felgate	Locke	Wallace	Swan	Turkington	Harris	Butler	Ridings	Ross	Cumiskey	S Jones	German (3), Matthews (7)	31
O'Connor	German	Wallace	Swan	Turkington	Harris	S Jones	Ridings	Ross	Black	Cumiskey	Matthews (10), Locke (11)	32
Felgate	Locke	Wallace	Butler	Turkington	German	Ward	Ridings	Matthews	Cumiskey	S Jones		33
Felgate	German	Wallace	Butler	Turkington	Kielty	Ward	Ridings	Ross	Cumiskey	S Jones	Matthews (5), Locke (9), Monk (10)	34
Felgate	German	Wallace	Butler	Turkington	Kielty	Ward	Ridings	Ross	Monk	S Jones	Matthews (5), Harris (7), Locke (10)	35
Felgate	German	Wallace	Butler	Turkington	Kielty	Ward	Ridings	Ross	Matthews	S Jones	Locke (3), Harris (4), Monk (6)	36
Felgate	German	Harris	Butler	Turkington	Kielty	Ward	Ridings	Ross	Matthews	S Jones	Monk (6), Mason (10)	37
Felgate	Locke	German	Butler	Harris	Ward	S Jones	Ridings	Ross	Black	Kielty	Mason (6), Monk (9), Cumiskey (10)	38
Felgate	Locke	German	Butler	Turkington	Harris	Ward	Ridings	Ross	Black	S Jones	Kielty (8), Cumiskey (10)	39
Felgate	Locke	German	Butler	Turkington	Kielty	Ward	Ridings	Ross	Black	S Jones	Monk (9), Cumiskey (10)	40
Felgate	Locke	German	Butler	Turkington	Kielty	Ward	Ridings	Ross	Black	S Jones		41
Felgate	Locke	German	Butler	Turkington	Kielty	Ward	Ridings	Ross	Black	S Jones		42
												43
												44

1	2	3	4	5	6	7	8	9	10	11	Substitutes Used
Felgate	Locke	Wallace	P Jones	Turpin	Butler	Monk	Smyth	Matthews	Black	S Jones	Ross (10)
Felgate	Butler	Pryers	P Jones	Turpin	Smyth	Monk	Ridings	Matthews	Black	Wallace	Carr (10)
Felgate	German	Wallace	P Jones	Carr	Butler	Monk	Ridings	Matthews	Black	S Jones	Pryers (5), Smyth (6), Ross (7)
Felgate	Locke	Wallace	P Jones	German	Butler	Monk	Ridings	Ross	Black	S Jones	Matthews (10)
Felgate	Locke	German	Butler	Wallace	Ward	Monk	Ridings	Ross	Black	S Jones	Eatock (7)
Felgate	Smyth	German	Locke	Wallace	Ward	Monk	Ridings	Ross	Black	S Jones	Butler (8), Matthews (10)
Felgate	Locke	German	P Jones	Turpin	Smyth	S Jones	Tobin	Carr	Black	Pryers	Wallace (2), McNair (11)
Felgate	Locke	Butler	P Jones	German	Ward	Monk	Ridings	Ross	Black	S Jones	Wallce (3), Carr (8), Pryers (9)
Felgate	Locke	German	P Jones	Turkington	Ward	Monk	Ridings	Eatock	Wallace	S Jones	Ross (4), Carr (7), Pryers (8)
Felgate	Smyth	Pryers	German	Turkington	Wallce	Ward	Ridings	Ross	Black	S Jones	Eatock (11)
Felgate	Smyth	Wallace	Butler	Culshaw	Ward	Quinn	Bold	Matthews	Quayle	Patterson	Black (7)
Felgate	Bold	Wallace	German	Swan	Harris	Butler	Ward	Ross	Christie	S Jones	Black ((2)
Felgate	Locke	German	Ward	Carr	Wallace	S Jones	Ridings	Ross	Black	Pryers	Eatock (7)
Felgate	Locke	German	Butler	Turkington	Harris	Patterson	Ridings	Ross	Black	Matthews	Monk (4), Wallace (10)
Felgate	Locke	Wallace	Butler	Turkington	Patterson	Monk	Ridings	Matthews	Black	Quinn	Smyth (7), Ross (10), Harris (11)
Felgate	Locke	Wallace	Butler	Culshaw	German	Quinn	harris	Ross	Black	S Jones	Bold (5), Mollenux ((10)

PLAYING SQUAD

LEIGH R.M.I.

(Bold print indicates an England Semi-Professional International)

Player Honours	Birthplace	D.O.B.	Previous Clubs

GOALKEEPERS

Craig Dootson	Preston		Preston, Morecambe, Bamber Bridge, £4,000 to Leigh
David Felgate Wales Int., UP	Blaenau Ffestiniog	04.03.60	Blaenau Ffestiniog, Bolton, Lincoln, Grimsby, Bolton, Bury, Chester C, Wigan

DEFENDERS

David German UP	Sheffield	16.10.73	Sheffield U, Halifax, Macclesfield, Winsford U
Neil Critchley	Crewe	18.10.78	Crewe
Iain Swan	Glasgow	04.07.80	Oldham, Partick Thistle
Stuart Locke UP	Manchester		Manchester C, Northwich V, Stalybridge C, Macclesfield, Leek T
Richard Harris UP	Manchester	12.07.67	Ashton U, Altrincham, Hyde U, Runcorn, Hyde U, Altrincham
Craig Allardyce	Bolton	09.06.75	Preston, Blackpool, Chorley, Chesterfield, Peterborough, Mansfield, Boston U
Jamie Udall	Blackpool		Morecambe, Lancaster C
Andy Farrell	Colchester	07.10.65	Colchester, Burnley, Wigan, Rochdale, Morecambe
Gary Scott	Liverpool	03.02.78	Tranmere, Rotherham, Barrow, Marine

MIDFIELDERS

Tony Black UP	Barrow	15.07.69	Burnley U, Bamber Bridge, Wigan, Accrington Stanley, Chorley
Ged Kielty UP	Manchester	01.09.76	Manchester C, Cobh Ramblers, Southport, Barrow, Altrincham
Dave Ridings UP	Farnworth	27.02.70	Bury, Curzon Ashton, Halifax, Lincoln, Ashton U, Crewe
Andy Patterson UP	Kirkaldy	26.11.80	Bradford C
Clayton Blackmore Wales Int., Premiership, FAC, ECWC, ESC	Neath	23.09.64	Manchester U, Middlesbrough, Barnsley, Notts Co.

FORWARDS

Brian Ross ESP, UP	Rochdale	02.07.66	Manchester U, Rochdale, Winsford U, Chorley, Marine, Chorley, Southport
Steve Jones	Manchester		Chorley
Neil Matthews UP	Grimsby	19.09.66	Grimsby, Halifax, Stockport, Lincoln, Dag & Red, Gainsborough T, Guiseley
Ian Monk GMVC, UP	Burnley	30.06.68	Clitheroe, Ashton U, Macclesfield, Morecambe
Andy Mason	Bolton	22.11.74	Bolton, Hull, Chesterfield, Macclesfield, Kettering T, Stalybridge C
Mike Morrell	Yorkshire		Guiseley, Harrogate T, Altrincham

MORECAMBE

Morecambe deserve enormous credi for finishing in third place - even though it was a distant third.

Manager Jimmy Harvey made one of the shrewdest moves of the season when he re-signed striker Justin Jackson. His 29 goals earned him the *Mail on Sunday* Goalscorer of the Year award and was a major factor in the Shrimps' rise. His subsequent record-breaking move to Rushden & Diamonds will be a massive blow to the club.

Morecambe ended the 1999/2000 season with a 17-match unbeaten run which was one of the best performances in the Conference for over a decade.

What makes Morecambe's future all the more exciting is that they possess a tremendous crop of very talented youngsters waiting in the wings. Some have already tasted first-team action and certainly didn't disappoint.

Harvey has also added some impressive new signings during the close season, including breaking their own record by bringing in England midfielder Steve Walters from Northwich Victoria.

Dark horses for the title? That may be pushing it a little too far for this season but they undoubtedly will be serious challengers within a year or two.

Steve Whitney

Back Row: Claudia Manfredi (Physio), Lew Dewhurst (Kit Man), Andy Lyons, Andy Heald, Mark Wright, Paul McGuire, John Hardiker, Nick Coyle, Phil Eastwood, Chris Price, Tom Sawyer (Kit Man), Vicky Bright (Physio).
Middle Row: Alan Keeling (Asst. Manager), Dave Edge (Physio), Barrie Keeling, Stewart Drummond, Adriano Rigoglioso, Peter Summerfield, Andy Banks, Steve McIlhargey, Michael Stringfellow, Stephen Alty, Garry Thompson, Jeff Udall (Reserve Team Manager), Tony Gibbins (Reserve Team Asst. Manager).
Front: Russell McKenna, Andy Fensome, Greg Brown, David Swanick, Leon Smith, Jim Harvey (Manager), Dave McKearney, Steve Walters, John Norman, Keisuke Takano, David Perkins.   **Photo:** Neil Marsdin

MORECAMBE

GROUND DETAILS

Christie Park,
Lancaster Road,
Morecambe,
Lancashire LA4 5TJ

TELEPHONE 01524 411797
Fax: 01524 411797
email: nmarsdin@aol.com
Web site: http://www.morecambefc.com

DIRECTIONS:
From south leave M6 motorway at junction 34. Follow signs
for Morecambe through Lancaster, on A589, go straight
across the first 2roundabouts, and at the third (with the
Shrimp pub on your left), follow thesigns for Town Centre -
Christie Park is approx. 600 metres on your left

CAPACITY:	6,300
SEATED:	1,200
COVERED TERRACING:	4,300

CLUB SHOP: On ground and open on matchdays.
Also commercial office open Monday to Friday
9.00 - 5.00 selling the same goods

SOCIAL FACILITIES: J B's open normal licensing hours

SEASIDER
The Official Matchday Magazine Of Morecambe F.C.
£1.50

MATCHDAY PROGRAMME

MORECAMBE
VS
RUSHDEN & DIAMONDS
Saturday 14th August
Kick Off 3pm

Pages: 48   Price: £1.50
Editor: Martin Shaw

Other club publications: "Gazetta de la Shrimpa"

Local Press: Morecambe Visitor; Morecambe
Guardian; Lancashire Evening Post; The Citizen

Local Radio: Radio Lancashire;
Red Rose Radio; Bay Radio

Founded: 1920
Nickname: The Shrimps
Club sponsor:
Club colours: Red shirts,
black shorts, black & white socks
Change colours: Yellow shirts,
Blue shorts, yellow & blue socks
Midweek home matchday: Tuesdays,
7.45pm kick-off
Reserve Team's League: Lancashire Lge Div. A
& North West All. Yth Div.

CLUB OFFICIALS

Honorary President	Jim Bowen
Chairman	Peter McGuigan
Vice Chairman	Graham Hodgson
Directors	David Derham, Stuart Forrest, Mark Hallam, Stuart Redman, Rod Taylor
Company & Club Secretary	Neil Marsdin
Commercial Manager	Peter Howard

FOOTBALL MANAGEMENT TEAM

MANAGER   JIM HARVEY

Date of Appointment	June 1994
Date of Birth:	2nd May 1958
Place of Birth:	Lurgan, Northern Ireland
PREVIOUS CLUBS	
As manager	None
As asst. manager	Morecambe (Jan - June 1994)
As player	Glenavon, Arsenal, Hereford Utd., Bristol C., Tranmere Rov., Crewe Alex.
HONOURS	
As manager	Spalding Cup 97-98; NPL R-up 94-95
As player	N. Ireland - u23., Leyland Daf Cup, Mercantile Trophy Promotion from Division 4 & Division 3

*   *   *

Assistant Manager	Alan Keeling
Second Team Manager	Jeff Udall
2nd Team Asst. Manager	Tony Gribbins
Football in the Community	Derek Quinn
Sports Therapist	David Edge

Season	League	Div.	Pos.	P	W	D	L	F	A	W	D	L	F	A	Pts	Manager
						Home					Away					
99-00	Conference	-	3	42	10	7	4	46	29	8	9	4	24	19	70	Jim Harvey
98-99	Conference	-	14	42	9	5	7	31	29	6	3	12	29	47	53	Jim Harvey
97-98	Conference	-	5	42	11	4	6	35	30	10	6	5	42	34	73	Jim Harvey
96-97	Conference	-	4	42	10	5	6	34	23	9	4	8	35	33	66	Jim Harvey

Season	League	Div.	Pos.	P	W	D	L	F	A	Pts	Manager
95-96	Conferece	-	9	42	17	8	17	78	72	59	Jim Harvey
94-95	N.P.L.	Premier	2	42	28	10	4	99	34	94	Jim Harvey
93-94	N.P.L.	Premier	7	42	20	7	15	90	56	67	Bryan Griffiths
92-93	N.P.L.	Premier	3	42	25	11	6	93	51	86	Bryan Griffiths
91-92	N.P.L.	Premier	2	42	23	9	10	64	32	78	Bryan Griffiths
90-91	N.P.L.	Premier	3	42	19	16	5	72	44	73	Bryan Griffiths

HONOURS

F.A. Trophy 73-74,
Spalding Cup 97-98,
Northern Premier Lge R-up 91-92 94-95,
Presidents Cup 91-92,
Lancs Combination 24-25 61-62 62-63 66-67 67-68
R-up 25-26,
Lg Cup 26-27 45-46 64-65 66-68;
Lancashire Junior Cup (now ATS Trophy) x8
25-27 61-63 68-69 85-87 92-93, 95-96;
Lancashire Senior Cup 67-68,
(Reserves) Lancashire League Div 2 83-84

PREVIOUS

Leagues: Lancs Combination 1920-68,
Northern Premier 1968-1995

Grounds: Woodhill Lane 1920-25,
shared with cricket club who still play there

Past Players who progressed to the Football League

Fred Blondel (Bury 1946),
Herbert Harrison (Accrington 1947),
Gordon Milne (Preston 1956),
Ray Charnley (Blackpool 1957),
Geoff Slack (Stockport 1958),
Ron Mitchell (Leeds 1958), Derek Armstrong (Carlisle 1961),
Alan Taylor(Rochdale 1973),
John Coates (Southport via Burscough & Skelmersdale 1975),
Keith Galley (Southport 1975),
Brian Thompson (West Ham 1977),
Malcolm Darling (Bury 1978)
David Eyres (Blackpool), Kenny Lowe (Barnet via Barrow),
Steve Gardner (Bradford City), Dave Lancaster (Chesterfield)

Semi-Professional Capped Players

John Coleman, Mike Bignall, Brian Healy, Stewart Drummond, Justin Jackson

CLUB RECORDS

Attendance: 9,324 v Weymouth FA Cup 4.1.62

Win: 16-0 v Rossendale Utd,
Lancs Combination Sept 1967
(Arnold Timmins scored 8)

Defeat: 0-7 v Darwen,
November 7th 1953

Transfer fee paid: £25,000
to Northwich V. for Steve Walters, July 2000
Transfer fee received: £180,000
from Rushden & Diamonds for Justin Jackson, July 2000

Career Goalscorer: Keith Borrowdale 289
1956-68, 78-79 Lancashire Combination
John Coleman 130
1990-1995 (Northern Premier League)
Career Appearances: Steve Done 523 + 7 sub
1968-78

BEST SEASON

FA Cup: 3rd Round 1961-62,
0-1 v Weymouth
League clubs defeated: Chester City

FA Trophy: Winners 73-74,
Q-final 72-73, 77-78, 93-94

League: 3rd Conference 1999-2000

LAST SEASON

F.A. Cup: 1st Round
F.A. Trophy: 3rd Round
Conference: 3rd
Top Goalscorer: Justin Jackson 31
Player of the Year: Stewart Drummond
Captain: Dave McKearney

MORECAMBE

Match Facts 1999-00

	Date	Comp.	H/A	Opponents	Gate	Result & Score		Goalscorers	League Position
1	14.08	N.C.	H	Rushden & Diamonds	1,797	D	0-0		
2	17.08	N.C.	A	Northwich Victoria	1.030	D	0-0		
3	21.08	N.C.	A	Hayes	676	W	1-0	Jackson 43	11
4	24.08	N.C.	A	Hereford United	1.768	W	3-2	**Eastwood 3** (14, 30, 32)	
5	28.08	N.C.	A	Hednesford Town	1,289	W	3-1	Burns 11, 89 Jackson 36	2
6	30.08	N.C.	H	Scarborough	2,301	L	0-1		3
7	04.09	N.C.	H	Telford United	1,280	W	5-2	Eastwood 20, **Jackson 3** (54, 57, 71pen), Gardner 77	2
8	11.09	N.C.	A	Yeovil Town	2,642	L	0-2		7
9	18.09	N.C.	H	Kidderminster Harriers	1,411	L	0-1		10
10	25.09	N.C.	A	Kettering Town	1,409	D	1-1	Hardy 27	10
11	02.10	N.C.	H	Woking	1,218	W	1-0	Jackson 15 (pen)	
12	09.10	N.C.	A	Stevenage Borough	2,039	W	2-1	Jackson 50 (pen), Knowles 74	8
13	23.10	N.C.	H	Kingstonian	1,384	L	1-2	Lyons 27	9
14	06.11	N.C.	A	Forest Green Rovers	705	W	2-1	Hardy 13, Jackson 90	7
15	14.11	N.C.	A	Hednesford Town	1,247	W	4-0	Burns 19, Lyons 21, Jackson 24, Hardy 82	6
16	20.11	N.C.	A	Altrincham	1,159	D	2-2	Drummond 18, 73	6
17	04.12	N.C.	H	Sutton United	1,460	W	6-2	Eastwood 29, 45, Jackson 70, Drummond 80, Smith 83, Lyons 88	5
18	11.12	N.C.	A	Woking	1,517	D	0-0		5
19	18.12	N.C.	A	Kidderminster Harriers	2,189	L	1-2	Jackson 40	6
20	27.12	N.C.	H	Southport	3,583	D	3-3	Burns 24(p), Jackson 28, Eastwood 80	8
21	03.01	N.C.	A	Southport	2,202	D	1-1	Hardy 42	6
22	08.01	N.C.	H	Stevenage Borough	1,518	D	3-3	Hardy 4, 52, McGuire 35	7
23	18.01	N.C.	A	Telford	914	L	2-3	Jackson 6, 72	7
24	22.01	N.C.	H	Hayes	1,240	L	1-4	Hardy 51	8
25	29.01	N.C.	A	Dover Athletic	1471	L	1-3	Hardy 85	10
26	12.02	N.C.	A	Nuneaton Boough	1,411	D	1-1	Jackson 75	11
27	19.02	N.C.	A	Welling United	626	D	0-0		11
28	26.02	N.C.	H	Altrincham	1,240	D	0-0		11
29	04.03	N.C.	H	Forest Green Rovers	1,016	D	1-1	Eastwood 23 (p)	12
30	18.03	N.C.	H	Dover Athletic	1,127	W	2-0	Jackson 19, 34	12
31	25.03	N.C.	H	Welling United	1,045	W	2-1	Brown 70, Jackson 73	10
32	01.04	N.C.	A	Hereford United	1,808	D	1-1	Norman 77	
33	04.04	N.C.	A	Rushden & Diamonds	2,533	W	2-0	Norman 71, Jackson 86 (p)	8
34	08.04	N.C.	A	Doncaster Rovers	2,009	W	1-0	Jackson 62	8
35	11.04	N.C.	H	Northwich Victoria	1,024	W	5-0	Jacksn 30, 90, Norman 43, Thompson 50, Drummond 55	5
36	15.04	N.C.	H	Doncaster Rovers	1,346	W	2-1	Jackson 15 (p), Eastwood 66	4
37	22.04	N.C.	A	Sutton United	659	W	1-0	Norman 66	
38	24.04	N.C.	H	Nuneaton Borough	1,620	D	1-1	Eastwood 61	4
39	26.04	N.C.	A	Kingstonian	834	D	0-0		
40	29.04	N.C.	H	Kettering Town	1,250	W	2-1	Eastwood 60, Jackson 88	
41	01.05	N.C.	A	Scarborough	1,505	W	2-0	Jackson 19, 42 (p)	3
42	06.05	N.C.	H	Yeovil Town	1,490	D	1-1	Jackson 78	3

CUP COMPETITIONS

F.A. Cup

Date		H/A	Opponents	Gate	Result & Score		Goalscorers
16.10	4Q	H	Bishop Auckland	868	W	1-0	Lyons 5
30.10	1	A	Oxford United	3,504	L	2-3	Wright 28, Jackson 47

Nationwide McMillan Trophy

Date		H/A	Opponents	Gate	Result & Score		Goalscorers
05.10	1	H	Southport	468	L	1-2	Milner 81

F.A. Trophy

Date		H/A	Opponents	Gate	Result & Score		Goalscorers
27.11	2	H	Hucknall Town	735	W	6-1	Hardy 3, 56, Jackson 12, Lyons 41, Eastwood 75, 82
15.01	3	A	Blakenall	375	L	1-2	McKearney 89

Lancs Trophy

Date		H/A	Opponents	Gate	Result & Score		Goalscorers
27.01	2	H	Barrow	576	L	0-2	

Substitutes Used

1	2	3	4	5	6	7	8	9	10	11	Substitutes Used	#
Banks	Rushton	Wright	McKearney	Farrell	Burns	Lyons	Drummond	Morton	Eastwood	Takano	Hardy (9), Black (11)	1
Banks	Fensome	Wright	McKearney	Farrell	Burns	Lyons	Drummond	Morton	Eastwood	Takano	Hardy (9), Keeling (10), Rushton (11)	2
Banks	Fensome	Wright	McKearney	Farrell	Burns	Lyons	Drummond	Eastwood	Takano	Jackson	Hardy (10), Morton (9)	3
Banks	Fensome	Wright	McKearney	Farrell	Burns	Lyons	Drummond	Jackson	Eastwood	Takano	Hardy (9), Keeling (10)	4
Banks	Fensome	Wright	McKearney	Farrell	Burns	Lyons	Drummond	Jackson	Eastwood	Takano	Keeling (8), Hardy (10), Gardner (7)	5
Banks	Fensome	Wright	McKearney	Farrell	Burns	Lyons	Drummond	Jackson	Eastwood	Takano	Garder (11), Keeling (8), (10)	6
Banks	Fensome	Wright	McKearney	Farrell	Burns	Lyons	Drummond	Jackson	Eastwood	Takano	Keeling (6), Gardner (7), McGuire (3)	7
Banks	Fensome	Hardiker	McKearney	Farrell	Burns	Lyons	Drummond	Keeling	Eastwood	Gardner	Thompson (7), Hardy (9)	8
Banks	Fensome	Takano	McKearney	Farrell	Burns	Thompson	Drummond	Jackson	Eastwood	Gardner	Hardy (9), Hardiker (7), Knowles (6)	9
Banks	Fensome	Wright	McKearney	Farrell	Burns	Gardner	Drummond	Jackson	Hardy	Takano	Keeling (10), Hardiker (11), Knowles (6)	10
Banks	Fensome	Hardiker	McKearney	Farrell	Knowles	Gardner	Drummond	Jackson	Hardy	Takano	Thompson (7), Keeling (9)	11
Banks	Fensome	Wright	McKearney	Farrell	Burns	Lyons	Drummond	Jackson	Hardy	Knowles	Milner (9), Keeling (10)	12
Banks	Fensome	Brown	McKearney	Farrell	Ward	Lyons	Drummond	Jackson	Hardy	Knowles	Keeling (10), Takano ((7)	13
Banks	Fensome	Wright	McKearney	Farrell	Burns	Lyons	Drummond	Jackson	Hardy	Takano	Brown (3), Thompson (7), Keeling (10)	14
Banks	Fensome	Brown	McKearney	Farrell	Burns	Lyons	Drummond	Jackson	Hardy	Takano	Eastwood (11), Smith(6), Thompson (7)	15
Banks	Fensome	Takano	McKearney	Farrell	Burns	Lyons	Drummond	Jackson	Hardy	Eastwood	McGuire (3), Heald (11), Smith (6)	16
Banks	Fensome	McGuire	McKearney	Farrell	Smith	Lyons	Drummond	Jackson	Eastwood	Takano	Heald (11), Milner (9), Keeling (7)	17
Banks	Fensome	McGuire	McKearney	Farrell	Smith	Lyons	Drummond	Jackson	Eastwood	Takano	Heald (11) sub Keeling, Hardy (10)	18
Banks	Fensome	Wright	McKearney	Farrell	Burns	Lyons	Drummond	Jackson	Hardy	Heald	Knowles (6), Eastwood (7), Thompson (10)	19
Banks	Fensome	Wright	McGuire	Farrell	Burns	Lyons	Drummond	Jackson	Hardy	Heald	Smith (6), Eastwood (11), Thompson (10)	20
Banks	Fensome	Hardiker	McKearney	Farrell	Knowles	Lyons	Drummond	Eastwood	Hardy	Takano	Keeling (6), Milner (7), McGuire (3)	21
Banks	Fensome	Hardiker	McKearney	McGuire	Smith	Lyons	Drummond	Jackson	Hardy	Takano	Eastwood (9), Keeling (7), Heald (11)	22
Banks	Fensome	Hardiker	McKearney	Farrell	Burns	Lyons	McGuire	Jackson	Hardy	Takano	Thompson (6), Swanick (11), Milner (9)	23
Banks	Fensome	Wright	McKearney	Farrell	Smith	Lyons	Drummond	Jackson	Hardy	Thompson	Eastwood (2), Takano (11), Hardiker (3)	24
Banks	Fensome	Wright	McKearney	Farrell	Burns	Lyons	Drummond	Jackson	Hardy	Brown	Takano (3), Eastwood (6), Smith (7)	25
Banks	Swanick	Brown	McKearney	Farrell	Burns	Lyons	Drummond	Jackson	Hardy	Takano	Smith (11), McGuire (5), Thompson (6)	26
McIlhargey	Fensome	Brown	McKearney	Farrell	McGuire	Thompson	Drummond	Jackson	Hardy	Heald	Hardiker (5), Keeling (10), Lyons (7)	27
Banks	Fensome	Brown	McKearney	Hardiker	McGuire	Thompson	Drummond	Jackson	Keeling	Heald		28
Banks	Fensome	Brown	McKearney	Farrell	Knowles	Thompson	Drummond	Jackson	Eastwood	Heald	Smith (6), Hardy (10), Lyons (7)	29
McIlhargey	Fensome	Wright	McKearney	Farrell	Knowles	Thompson	Drummond	Eastwood	Eastwood	Heald	Hardy (10), Brown (3), Smith (8)	30
McIlhargey	Fensome	Wright	McKearney	Hardiker	Knowles	Thompson	Drummond	Jackson	Hardy	Heald	Brown (11), Norman (10), McGuire (7)	31
McIlhargey	Fensome	Wright	McKearney	Hardiker	Knowles	Thompson	Drummond	Jackson	Norman	Brown	Eastwood (3), Smith (6), Hardy (10)	32
McIlhargey	Fensome	Brown	McKearney	Hardiker	Knowles	Thompson	Drummond	Jackson	Norman	Eastwood	McGuire (11), Hardy (10), Burns (7)	33
McIlhargey	Fensome	Brown	McKearney	Hardiker	Knowles	Keeling	Drummond	Jackson	Norman	Eastwood	Banks (1), McGuire (11), Hardy (7)	34
Banks	Fensome	Brown	McKearney	Hardiker	Knowles	Thompson	Drummond	Jackson	Norman	Eastwood	Black (10), Keeling (7), McGuire (5)	35
McIlhargey	Fensome	Brown	McKearney	Hardiker	Knowles	Thompson	Drummond	Jackson	Norman	Eastwood	Keeling (8), Black (7), McGuire (5)	36
McIlhargey	Fensome	Wright	McKearney	Hardiker	Burns	Thompson	Knowles	Jackson	Norman	Eastwood	Smith (6), McGuire (11)	37
McIlhargey	Fensome	Wright	McKearney	Hardiker	Knowles	Thompson	Drummond	Jackson	Norman	Eastwood	Banks (1), McGuire (3), Burns (8)	38
Banks	Fensome	McGuire	McKearney	Hardiker	Knowles	Thompson	Drummond	Jackson	Norman	Eastwood	Black (7), Farrell (3), Burns (10)	39
Banks	Fensome	Hardiker	McKearney	Farrell	Burns	Knowles	Drummond	Jackson	Norman	Eastwood	Smith (8), Curtis (7), Keeling (11)	40
Banks	Fensome	Hardiker	McKearney	Farrell	Burns	Knowles	Smith	Jackson	Norman	Eastwood	Brown (11), Keeling (8), Hardy (6)	41
Banks	Fensome	Brown	McKearney	Hardiker	Burns	Knowles	Drummond	Jackson	Norman	Eastwood	Black (6), Heald (11), Smith (7)	42

1	2	3	4	5	6	7	8	9	10	11	Substitutes Used
Banks	Fensome	Takano	McKearney	Farrell	Burns	Lyons	Drummond	Jackson	Hardy	Knowles	
Banks	Fensome	Wright	McKearney	Farrell	Burns	Lyons	Drummond	Jackson	Hardy	Knowles	Eastwood (10), Smith (11), Keeling (7)
Banks	Fensome	Hardiker	McKearney	Farrell	Knowles	Gardner	Drummond	Jackson	Hardy	Takano	Milner (9), Lyons (7)
Banks	Fensome	McGuire	McKearney	Farrell	Smith	Lyons	Drummond	Jackson	Hardy	Takano	Heald (11), Eastwood (10), Keeling (9)
Banks	Fensome	Wright	McKearney	McGuire	Burns	Lyons	Keeling	Eastwood	Hardy	Takano	Hardiker (3), Milner (9), Thompson (11)
Banks	Fensome	Hardiker	McKearney	Farrell	Smith	Lyons	Drummond	Jackson	Hardy	Takano	Eastwood (7), Milner (9), Wright (11)

PLAYING SQUAD

(Bold print indicates an England Semi-Professional International)

Player Honours	Birthplace	D.O.B.	Previous Clubs

GOALKEEPERS

Andy Banks	Preston	26.04.76	Preston, Bury
Mark Smith	Birmingham	02.01.73	Nottingham F, Crewe, Walsall, Rushden & D, Bedford T

DEFENDERS

Greg Brown	Wythenshawe	31.07.78	Chester C, Macclesfield
Andy Fensome	Northampton	18.02.68	Norwich, Camb.U, Preston, Rochdale, Barrow
Mark Wright Scot.S & Y	Manchester	29.01.70	Everton, Huddersfield, Wigan, Chorley
John Hardiker	Preston	07.07.82	Youth Team
David Swannick	Bebbington	16.05.79	Youth team
David McKearney	Liverpool	20.06.68	Prescot Cables, Bolton, Northwich V, Crewe, Wigan, Chorley
Paul Maguire	Manchester	17.11.79	Youth team

MIDFIELDERS

Steve Walters EY, ESP	Plymouth	09.01.72	Crewe, Northwich V, £25,000 to Morecambe
Leon Smith	Bolton	18.02.80	Youth team
Chris Price	Liverpool	24.10.75	Everton, Oxford U, Chester C, Clitheroe, Marine
Stuart Drummond ESP	Preston	11.12.75	Youth team
Barrie Keeling	Oldham	20.08.77	Manchester C

FORWARDS

Andy Lyons	Blackpool	10.10.66	Morecambe, Fleetwood T, Crewe, Wigan, Partick Thistle, Ayr U
Gary Thompson	Kendal	24.11.80	Youth team
Phil Eastwood	Whalley	06.04.78	Burnley
Wayne Curtis	Barrow	06.03.80	Holker OB
Adriano Rigoglioso	Liverpool	28.05.79	Liverpool, Marine
John Norman	Birkenhead	26.06.71	Tranmere, Mold Alex., Morecambe, Hednesford T
Andy Heald	Manchester	26.07.80	Youth team
Ken Takano	Japan		Morecambe, Southport

NORTHWICH VICTORIA

Vics' 21st consecutive season in the top-flight of the semi-professional game will not go down as one of their most memorable. The Greens failed to win a single cup match in a sorry season, which saw them just about survive their nearest brush with relegation yet, Conference status being retained with just a week of the season remaining. Yet there were mitigating circumstances.

The club's financial position had become so desperate that in November they were forced to pay off five contract players and their historic Drill Field ground was put up for sale in March.

On the footballing front, manager Mark Gardiner was also hampered by one of the worst injury crises the club had ever seen. Citing a long list for the treatment table may be the oldest excuse in the footballing book, but the fact remained that Bates, Birch, Cooke, Devlin, Ellis, Fletcher, Illman, Owen, Robertson, Simpson, Terry and Walters all spent chunks of their season on the sidelines.

In the end, it was only their excellent home record - the Vics were not defeated on home soil until April - that helped them survive.

Merely maintaining their Conference membership might not sound like much of an achievement, but considering the relegations of Cheshire rivals Chester City and Altrincham Vics had several reasons to be satisfied. Not least among them was the fact they had survived despite finishing the season with the dubious honour of holding the worst defensive record in the league, a statistic which came courtesy of being hit for six at Rushden and, for the first time in their conference career at home, when Kettering won 6-2 at the Drill Field on Easter Monday.

On the plus side, the performances of Val Owen, who netted thirteen goals from midfield on his way to claiming the Player of the Year award, and youngsters Gary Fletcher and Lee Poland gave Vics fans a much needed fillip.

Extra interest in the Greens' FA Cup Fourth Qualifying Round tie with Hednesford was created by the goalkeeping position. With regular custodian Lance Key suspended, Vics drafted in Liverpool legend Bruce Grobbelaar. The Zimbabwean helped swell the gate but Vics could only draw 2-2 and went out of the competition in the Keys Park replay.

The 2000/01 season looks set to be another tough one for the Vics, with an uncertain future off the pitch and financial pressures necessitating the summer sale of captain and midfield playmaker Steve Walters.

Yet the importance of football, or lack of it, was put into perspective by two tragedies which occurred during the 1999/2000 campaign.

In September, Vauxhall player Mark Pearson collapsed and died during a Cheshire Senior cup match at the Drill Field. Three months later, Rushden striker Martin Aldridge was killed in a car crash on his way home from Diamonds' match against Vics at Nene Park.

These incidents served as reminders that, for all football's ups and downs, it is only a game.

William Hughes

Back Row: Mark Devlin, Adie Mike, Lance Key, Malcolm Rigby, Gary Burke, Steve Davies. **Middle:** Lee Poland, Mark Bailey, Neil Ellis, Wes Simpson, John Robertson, Ian Cooke, Gary Fletcher, Ged Kimmins, Steve Walsh, Richard Norris, Darren Vicary. **Front:** Dave Gillett (asst. kit man.), Peter Holcroft, Carl Laurie, Mark Gardiner (player-manager), Phil Lea (physio), Colin Rose, Jamie Bates, Jason Avison (kit manager)

NORTHWICH VICTORIA

GROUND DETAILS

The Drill Field,
Drill Field Road,
Northwich,
Cheshire. CW9 5HN

TELEPHONE: 01606 41450
Fax: 01606 330577.
Club Newsline: 0930 30 122 713
Web site: www.nvfc.co.uk

SIMPLE DIRECTIONS: Leave M6 at Junc.19 and follow A556 towards Chester. At second roundabout (approx. 6 miles), turn right onto A533. Ground on right behind Volunteer Public House

CAPACITY:	6,000
SEATED:	660
COVERED TERRACING:	3,500

CLUB SHOP: Located inside ground. Open match days. Manager: Andy Dakin
SOCIAL FACILITIES:
Large social club with members lounge and separate functionroom - both available for hire Tel: 01606 43120. Food available on matchdayswith prior notice. Bass beers, Pool, Darts, TV. New suite now available offering matchday & midweek catering

Celebrating 20 Seasons in the Nationwide Conference

DrillFielder

Saturday 6th May 2000, Kick off 3.00pm
NATIONWIDE CONFERENCE
NORTHWICH VICS v KINGSTONIAN
Match Sponsor: CARLSBERG TETLEY
Matchball Sponsor: WALTON BOWYER / MID CHESHIRE CONSTRUCTION
Official Matchday Magazine of Northwich Victoria FC • Price £1.50

Nationwide   HARVEY'S TYRE & EXHAUST

MATCHDAY PROGRAMME

Pages: 48   Price: £1.50

Editor: William Hughes & James Wood

Other club publications: 'Distant Vics'
(a bi-monthly magazine for exiled Vics' fans)

Local Press: Northwich Guardian (Wed.);
Northwich Chronicle (Wed.); Daily Post;
Manchester Evening News Pink (Sat.)
Local Radio: GMR (BBC Manchester);
Piccadilly Radio; Signal Radio

Founded:	1874
Nickname:	The Vics, Greens, Trickies
Club Sponsors:	Harvey's Tyres
Club colours:	Green shirts, white shorts and black socks
Change colours:	TBA
Midweek home matchday:	Tuesday
Reserve Team's league:	Lancashire League

CLUB OFFICIALS

Chairman	Rod J Stitch
Vice Chairman	Dave Stone
Company Secretary	Graham Cookson
Chief Executive	John Stitch
Directors	Dave Price, Jim Rafferty

Associate Directors
Graham Cookson, Dave Edgeley,
Dave Bush, dave Thomas.
President &
Football Secretary Derek Nuttall
c/o the club
Tel: 01606 41450 Fax: 01606 330577

FOOTBALL MANAGEMENT TEAM

MANAGER:	MARK GARDINER
Date of Appointment	December 1998
Date of Birth	25th December 1966
Place of Birth	Cirencester
PREVIOUS CLUBS	
As manager	none
As coach	none
As player	Crewe Alexandra, Chester City, Macclesfield T., Swindon Town, Torquay United
HONOURS	
As manager	MCSC
As coach	
as player	GMV Conference; F.A. Trophy

* * *

Physio:	Phil Lea
Fitness Trainer:	Peter Everson
Reserve & Youth Team Manager	Ted Carthy

League   Div.   Pos.

Season	League	Div.	Pos.	P	W	D	L	F	A	W	D	L	F	A	Pts	Manager
						Home						Away				
99-00	Conference	-	18	42	10	8	3	33	25	3	4	14	20	53	51	Mark Gardiner
98-99	Conference	-	7	42	11	3	7	29	21	8	6	7	31	30	66	Phil Wilson/Mark Gardiner
97-98	Conference	-	9	42	8	9	4	34	24	7	6	8	29	35	60	Phil Wilson
96-97	Conference	-	6	42	11	5	5	31	20	6	7	8	30	34	63	Mark Hancock/ Phil Wilson

Season	League	Div.	Pos.	P	W	D	L	F	A	Pts	Manager
95-96	Conference	-	8	42	16	12	14	72	64	60	Brian Kettle
94-95	Conference	-	10	42	14	15	13	77	66	57	John Williams
93-94	Conference	-	15	42	11	19	12	44	45	52	John Williams
92-93	Conference	-	11	42	16	8	18	68	55	56	Sammy McIlroy/John Williams
91-92	Conference	-	11	42	16	6	20	63	58	54	Sammy McIlroy
90-91	Conference	-	12	42	13	13	16	65	75	52	Cliff Roberts

HONOURS

Welsh Cup R-up 1881/82,1888-89;
FA Trophy 1983/84, R-up 1982/83 & 1995/96;
Bob Lord Trophy 1979/80, 92/93;
Northern Premier Lge R-up 1976/77;
Northern Premier Lge Cup 1972/73, R-up 1978/79;
Cheshire County Lge 1956/57, R-up 1924/25, 47/48;
Cheshire County Lge Cup 1925/35;
Manchester Lge 1902/03, R-up 1900/01, 03/04, 07/08, 08/09,
11/12; The Combination R-up 1890/91;
Cheshire Senior Cup 1880-81, 81/82, 82/83, 83/84, 84/85,
85/86,1928/29, 36/37, 49/50, 54/55, 71/72, 76/77, 78/79,
83/84, 93/94. R-up 1891/92,96/97, 1905/06, 08/09, 47/48,
50/51, 63/64, 65/66, 69/70, 70/71, 77/78, 85/86; 98/99
Staffordshire Senior Cup 1978/79, 79/80, 89/90,
R-up 1986/87, 90/91;
CheshireAmateur Cup 1901/02, R-up 1898/99, 02/93,
Northwich Senior Cup 1948/49, 58/59,59/60, 63/64, 64/65,
65/66, 67/68, 68/69, 69/70, 71/72, 74/75, R-up x7;
Mid Cheshire Senior Cup 1984/85, 85/86, 87/88, 89/90,
91/92, 93/94, 94/95, 96/97,98/99; R-up 1982/83, 83/84,
90/91, 92/93;
North-West Floodlit Lge 1966/67, 75/76;
Cheshire Lge Lancs. Comb. Inter-Lge Cup 1961/62;
Guardian Charity Shield 1985/86, 86/87, 87/88

PREVIOUS

Leagues: The Combination 1890-1892,
Football League Div.2 1892-94,
The Combination 1894-1898,
The Cheshire League 1898-1900,
Manchester League 1900-12,
Lancashire 1912-19,
Cheshire County League 1919-68,
Northern Premier League 1968-79

Grounds: None

Past Players who progressed to the Football League

Tony Hemmings (Wycombe W.), Tony Bullock (Barnsley),
Darren Tinson(Macclesfield), Lee Steele (Shrewsbury T.)
Paul Tait (Crewe Alex.),
Shaun Teale (Tranmere R., A Villa, Carlisle)

CLUB RECORDS

Attendance: 11,290 v Witton Albion,
Cheshire League, Good Friday 1949

Win: 17-0 v Marple Ass. 15.12.1883
Defeat: 3-10 v Port Vale 7.2.1931

Career Goalscorer: Peter Burns 160 - 1955-65
Career Appearances: 970 by Ken Jones 1969-85

Transfer Fee paid: £12,000
to Hyde United for Malcolm O'Connor - August 1988

Transfer Fee received: £50,000
from Chester City for Neil Morton - October1990

BEST SEASON

FA Cup: Quarter Finals 1883-84
League clubs defeated: Rochdale, Peterborough,
Watford, Chester C., Crewe Alexandra

FA Trophy: Winners 83-84
R-up 82-83 95-96

League: 4th Conference 80-81

LAST SEASON

F.A. Cup: 4th Qualifying Round
F.A. Trophy: 2nd Round
Conference: 18th
Top Goalscorer: Val Owen 13
Player of the Year: Val Owen
Captain: Steve Walters

	Date	Comp.	H/A	Opponents	Gate	Result & Score		Goalscorers	League Position
1	14.08	N.C.	A	Kettering Town	1.779	D	1-1	Walters 11	
2	17.08	N.C.	H	Morecambe	1,030	D	0-0		
3	21.08	N.C.	H	Welling United	904	W	3-2	Cooke 18, Walters 45 (Pen) Ellis 89	10
4	28.08	N.C.	A	Nuneaton Borough	2,084	L	1-3	Robertson 51	14
5	30.08	N.C.	H	Doncaster Rovers	1,688	W	2-1	Devlin 13 Cooke 17	11
6	04.09	N.C.	H	Rushden & Diamond	1,231	W	2-1	Devlin 76, Walters 89	10
7	11.09	N.C.	A	Kingstonian	1,004	D	3-3	Robinson 36, Vicary 81, Walters 90	9
8	14.09	N.C.	H	Scarborough	1,036	W	2-0	Simpson 44, Robinson 84 (pen)	6
9	18.09	N.C.	H	Dover Athletic	1,049	D	1-1	Owen 5	8
10	29.09	N.C.	A	Forest Green Rovers	486	L	1-5	Owen 80	9
11	02.10	N.C.	H	Hednesford Town	1,308	W	3-2	Simpson 13, Robertson 21, Owen 52	7
12	09.10	N.C.	A	Sutton United	803	D	2-2	OG (Howells) 24, Owen 78	8
13	23.10	N.C.	H	Stevenage Borough	1,010	D	3-3	Ellis 17, Owen 24, Fletcher 60	10
14	30.10	N.C.	A	Woking	1,606	D	1-1	Bates 90	7
15	06.11	N.C.	A	Hayes	616	L	1-2	Owen V 5	11
16	14.11	N.C.	A	Hereford United	1,812	L	0-3		13
17	20.11	N.C.	H	Kidderminster Harriers	1,310	D	1-1	Simpson 90	13
18	04.12	N.C.	A	Yeovil Town	2,239	L	2-3	Pell 52, Owen 66	14
19	11.12	N.C.	H	Nuneaton Borough	1,024	W	3-1	Ellis 4, Cooke 40, Owen 53	11
20	18.12	N.C.	A	Southport	1,352	W	1-0	Owen 21	10
21	27.12	N.C.	H	Altrincham	1,814	D	1-1	Gray 89	11
22	03.01	N.C.	A	Altrincham	1,713	L	0-2		12
23	08.01	N.C.	A	Welling United	502	W	3-1	Bailey 16, Gray 48, Vicary 90	11
24	22.01	N.C.	A	Scarborough	1502	L	0-3		12
25	29.01	N.C.	A	Rushden & Diamonds	3468	**L**	**0-6**		15
26	05.02	N.C.	H	Hereford United	1,104	D	0-0		14
27	12.02	N.C.	H	Hayes	1,002	D	0-0		14
28	19.02	N.C.	A	Stevenage Borough	1,586	L	1-3	Devlin 15	16
29	26.02	N.C.	H	Forest Green Rovers	911	D	0-0		16
30	04.03	N.C.	H	Yeovil Town	1,011	W	3-0	Cooke 14, 63, Owen 19	14
31	18.03	N.C.	A	Telford United	1,015	W	1-0	Walters 90	14
32	25.03	N.C.	A	Hednesford Town	867	L	0-1		15
33	01.04	N.C.	H	Southport	1,127	L	0-1		16
34	08.04	N.C.	A	Dover Athletic	740	L	1-4	Devlin 41	16
35	11.04	N.C.	A	Morecambe	1,024	L	0-5		17
36	18.04	N.C.	H	Woking	831	W	3-1	Fletcher 21, Owen 23, Cooke 59	
37	22.04	N.C.	A	Kidderminster H.	3,443	L	1-3	Poland 90	
38	24.04	N.C.	H	Kettering Town	919	L	2-6	Fletcher 27, Gray 68	17
39	29.04	N.C.	H	Sutton United	805	W	2-0	Cooke 50, Owen 67	
40	01.05	N.C.	A	Doncaster Rovers	1,865	L	0-2		18
41	03.05	N.C.	H	Telford United	663	W	2-1	Poland 49, 69	17
42	06.05	N.C.	H	Kingstonian	976	L	0-3		18

CUP COMPETITIONS

F.A. Cup

16.09	4Q	H	Hednesford Town	1,651	D	2-2	Owen 67, West 85
18.10	4Q R	A	Hednesford Town	930	L	0-1	

F.A. Trophy

27.11	2	A	Runcorn	875	L	0-2	

Nationwide McMillan Trophy

15.12	2	H	Altrincham	402	L	1-6	Cooke 70

Cheshire Senior Cup

16.11		H	Altrincham	414	L	1-3	Cooke

	1	2	3	4	5	6	7	8	9	10	11	Substitutes Used	#
Key	Birch	Crookes	Robertson	Devlin	Simpson	Walters	Cooke	Vicary	Robinson	Prendergast		Illman (10), Ellis (9)	1
Key	Birch	Prendergast	Simpson	Robertson	Devlin	Terry	Walters	Cooke	Robinson	Vicary		Ellis (11), Illman (10), Peel (9)	2
Key	Birch	Prendergast	Simpson	Robertson	Devlin	Terry	Walters	Cooke	Robinson	Vicary		Ellis (11), Bates (3), Illman (10)	3
Key	Birch	Bates	Crookes	Robertson	Devlin	Ellis	Walters	Cooke	Robinson	Vicary		Peel ((9), Illman (10), Owen V (11)	4
Key	Birch	Bates	Simpson	Robertson	Devlin	Terry	Walters	Cooke	Robinson	Vicary		Ellis (11), Peel (9), Owen V (8)	5
Key	Birch	Bates	Simpson	Robertson	Devlin	Terry	Walters	Cooke	Robinson	Vicary		Ellis (3), Illman (11), Peel (9)	6
Key	Birch	Crookes	Simpson	Robertson	Devlin	Illman	Walters	Cooke	Robinson	Ellis		Terry (7), Vicary (9), Owen V (10)	7
Key	Birch	Ellis	Simpson	Robertson	Devlin	Terry	Walters	Peel	Robinson	Vicary		Owen V (8), Fletcher (9)	8
Key	Birch	Ellis	Simpson	Robertson	Devlin	Terry	Owen V	Peel	Robinson	Vicary		Fletcher (9), Crookes (10)	9
Key	Birch	Ellis	Simpson	Robertson	Devlin	Terry	Owen V	Peel	Robinson	Vicary		Fletcher (10) Prendergast (11) Bates (2)	10
Key	Bates	Prendergast	Simpson	Robertson	Devlin	Terry	Owen V	Fletcher	Robinson	Ellis		Walters (6), Gann (9), C-Pearson (10)	11
Key	Bates	Prendergast	Simpson	Robertson	Owen V	Terry	Walters	Robinson	Ellis	West		C-Pearson (7) sub Fletcher, Devlin (3)	12
Key	Birch	Bates	Simpson	Robertson	Owen V	Ellis	Walters	West	Fletcher	Vicary		Gardiner (7) Robinson (6) Prendergast (10)	13
Key	Birch	Bates	Simpson	Robertson	Devlin	Owen V	Walters	Fletcher	Robinson	Crookes		Cooke (9), Vicary (4)	14
Key	Birch	Bates	Simpson	Robertson	Owen V	Crookes	Walters	Fletcher	Robinson	Vicary		Cooke (10), Thomas (11), Poland (5)	15
Key	Birch	Prendergast	Simpson	Crookes	Owen V	Thomas	Walters	Cooke	Poland	Vicary		Robertson (2), Gardiner (10)	16
Key	Bates	Crookes	Simpson	Robertson	Owen V	Devlin	Walters	Cooke	Poland	Vicary		Ellis (10), Thomas (6)	17
Key	Bates	Ellis	Walker	Robertson	Owen V	Gardiner	Walters	Cooke	Vicary	Pell		Terry (8)	18
Game	Bates	Ellis	Walker	Robertson	Owen V	Devlin	Walters	Cooke	Pell	Vicary		Terry (9)	19
Rigby	Bates	Ellis	Walker	Robertson	Devlin	Devlin	Walters	Cooke	Pell	Vicary		Crookes (9), Birch (8)	20
Rigby	Bates	Crookes	Walker	Robertson	Devlin	Ellis	Walters	Cooke	Pell	Vicary		Eatock (3), Gray (9)	21
Rigby	Bates	Crookes	Walker	Robertson	Devlin	Ellis	Bailey	Cooke	Gray	Vicary		Eatock (9), Terry (11)	22
Rigby	Bates	Ellis	Walker	Robertson	Devlin	Bailey	Terry	Cooke	Gray	Vicary		Birch (7)	23
Rigby	Bates	Simpson	Walker	Robertson	Devlin	Gardiner	Bailey	Gray	Vicary	Holt		Crookes (5), Birch (3), Terry (7)	24
Rigby	Birch	Bates	Crookes	Simpson	Devlin	Bailey	Walters	Milner	Holt	Vicary		Gray (10), Terry (9)	25
Rigby	Birch	Bates	Walker	Robertson	Devlin	Bailey	Owen V	Milner	Holt	Vicary		Cooke (9), Simpson (5), Gray (10)	26
Rigby	Birch	Bates	Walker	Simpson	Owen V	Bailey	Walters	Cooke	Holt	Vicary		Milner (10),Terry (2), Gray (9)	27
Rigby	Birch	Bates	Walker	Simpson	Devlin	Bailey	Walters	Cooke	Holt	Vicary		Gray (10), Terry (9), Doherty (11)	28
Rigby	Birch	Bates	Simpson	Robertson	Devlin	Terry	Walters	Cooke	Owen V	Vicary		Milner (7), Gray (10), Bailey (9)	29
Rigby	Birch	Bates	Simpson	Robertson	Devlin	Terry	Walters	Cooke	Owen V	Vicary		Crookes (5), Gray (9), Fletcher (10)	30
Rigby	Birch	Bates	Simpson	Robertson	Devlin	Terry	Walters	Cooke	Owen V	Vicary			31
Rigby	Birch	Bates	Simpson	Robertson	Devlin	Terry	Walters	Cooke	Owen V	Vicary		Gray (7), Fletcher (8)	32
Rigby	Birch	Bates	Simpson	Robertson	Devlin	Terry	Walters	Cooke	Owen V	Vicary		Gray (4), Fletcher (11)	33
Rigby	Birch	Bates	Simpson	Crookes	Devlin	Terry	Walters	Gray	Owen V	Vicary		Fletcher (7), Bailey (8)	34
Rigby	Birch	Bates	Simpson	Robertson	Devlin	Crookes	Bailey	Gray	Fletcher	Vicary		Poland (10), Burke (9), Royle (5)	35
Rigby	Birch	Bates	Simpson	Robertson	Devlin	Terry	Owen V	Cooke	Fletcher	Vicary		Crookes (3), Bailey (7)	36
Rigby	Birch	Gardiner	Crookes	Bailey	Devlin	Burke	Owen V	Gray	Poland	Vicary		Ellis (11), Royle (7)	37
Rigby	Birch	Crookes	Simpson	Robertson	Devlin	Terry	Owen V	Cooke	Fletcher	Vicary		Gray (9), Gardiner (4), Poland (7)	38
Rigby	Birch	Bates	Crookes	Robertson	Devlin	Terry	Owen V	Cooke	Fletcher	Vicary			39
Rigby	Birch	Bates	Crookes	Robertson	Bailey	Terry	Owen V	Gray	Fletcher	Vicary		Ellis (3), Terry (7), Poland (9)	40
Rigby	Birch	Gardiner	Crookes	Cooke	Walsh	Bailey	Fletcher	Gray	Poland	Vicary		Ellis (6), Terry (4)	41
Rigby	Birch	Walsh	Bailey	Cooke	Devlin	Fletcher	Owen V	Gray	Poland	Vicary		Williams P (1), Terry (9), Ellis (10)	42

	1	2	3	4	5	6	7	8	9	10	11	Substitutes Used
Grobbelaar	Bates	Prendergast	Simpson	Crookes	Owen	Logan	Walters	West	Robinson	Ellis		Vicary (7), Fletcher (10)
Key	Birch	Bates	Simpson	Robertson	Owen	Ellis	Walters	West	Robinson	Vicary		Gardiner (5), Fletcher (10)
Key	Bates	Crookes	Simpson	Robertson	Devlin	Thomas	Walters	Cooke	Poland	Vicary		Ellis (4), Heverin (7), Gann (10)
Key	Bates	Birch	Walker	Robertson	Owen	Devlin	Walters	Terry	Pell	Vicary		Thomas (7), Cooke (10), Crookes (5)
Key	bates	Predergast	Simpson	Robertson	Owen	Crookes	Thomas	Cooke	Robinson	Vicary		Gardiner (3), Poland (10)

PLAYING SQUAD

NORTHWICH VICTORIA

(Bold print indicates an England Semi-Professional International)

Player *Honours*	*Birthplace*	*D.O.B.*	*Previous Clubs*

GOALKEEPERS

Lance Key	Kettering	13.05.68	Histon, Sheffield Wed, Dundee U, Sheffield U, Rochdale
Malcolm Rigby	Nottingham	13.03.76	Nottingham F, Ilkeston T, Yeovil T, Emley, Stafford R

DEFENDERS

Jamie Bates	Manchester		Maine Road, Runcorn, Stalybridge C
John Robertson	Liverpool	08.01.74	Wigan, Lincoln
Mark Gardiner ESP, GMVC, FAT	Cirencester	25.12.66	Swindon, Torquay, Crewe, Macclesfield
Garry Burke	Manchester		Woodley Sports, Runcorn
Mark Bailey	Stoke	12.08.76	Stoke, Rochdale

MIDFIELDERS

Mark Devlin	Irvine	08.01.73	Stoke, Exeter
Colin Rose ESP	Winsford	22.01.72	Crewe, Witton Alb, Macclesfield, Runcorn
Darren Vicary	Liverpool		Vauxhall GM, Cammell Laird
Richard Norris	Birkenhead	05.01.78	Marine, Crewe
Peter Holcroft	Liverpool	03.01.76	Everton, Swindon
Martin Doherty			Boston U, Altrincham

FORWARDS

Ian Cooke	Bebington	01.11.73	Cammell Laird
Adie Mike ES, EY	Manchester	16.11.73	Manchester C, Stockport, Bury, Hartlepool, Doncaster R, Leek T, Hednesford T, Southport
Ged Kimmins ESP	Manchester		Salford C, Hyde U, Hednesford T

NUNEATON BOROUGH

Jekyll & Hyde Boro finished fifteenth in the Nationwide Conference at the end of the 1999-2000 season - a position most of their fans would have happily accepted back at the start of the season, but whether that was the case at the end is open to argument.

The Manor Park club's vastly contrasting fortunes in racing to the top of the table just before Christmas and then undergoing lingering relegation fears inside the last month of a topsy turvy campaign left them neither smiling or crying.

For a club who had been demoted - not relegated - from the Conference in the late 80s, to return and power to the head of affairs in late November and early December, the outlook looked rosy but manager Brendan Phillips was wary of all the hype and expectation being aroused.

And his anxieties almost turned into a nightmare as a woeful run of eleven home games without a win and just two victories in the same five month period suddenly saw Nuneaton free-falling towards the drop zone.

Just fifteen points from 23 league outings saw panic take over from panache and it was only in their final home game in the last week of the campaign did Boro confirm their survival with maximum points at the expense of Hednesford Town.

And though it was a traumatic start to the new century for Nuneaton, it was one that manager Brendan Phillips feels will hold his side in good stead during the 2000-2001 season.

Some will say Boro were lucky not to have made a rapid return back to the Dr. Martens Premier as did the league's other two newcomers from the lower ranks - Altrincham and Sutton United - but on reflection the club's excellent early form, in which they suffered just one defeat in their opening eleven outings, earned them the right to a second bite of the cherry.

Phillips said: "We have to be satisfied with what we achieved. It doesn't need saying how difficult it was to adapt to the Conference from winning the Dr. Martens Premier Division. This is a quality league with no bad teams."

He continued: "We have got another opportunity and I think we have to be thankful for that although probably the biggest disappointment for me was our early exits from the two F.A. competitions at the hands of Guiseley, those defeats hit me hard. They certainly helped the rot set in."

Phillips added: "for all that went on last season in the league you are only as good as your final position. We finished fifteenth and that was about right. No complaints from me on that score, but I would like to think we can improve quite a bit this time around."

Derek Brown (Nuneaton Telegraph)

Back Row: Ian King, Jon Gittens, Krystof Kotylo, Andy Thackeray, Alex Sykes, Wayne Simpson, Mark Taylor, Lee Charles.
Middle: Brian Clarke (Kit Man), Shaun Wray, Nathan Thompson, Carl Bacon, Chris MacKenzie, Barry Williams, Ryan Young, Bobby Stevenson, Karl Brennan, Simon Weaver, Kevin Shoemake.
Front: Richie Norman (Physio), Terry Angus, Richard Mitchell, Delton Francis, Brendan Phillips (Manager), Steve Burr (Coach), Marc McGregor, Michael Love, David Crowley, Paul Egan (Physio).

NUNEATON BOROUGH

GROUND DETAILS

Manor Park,
Beaumont Road,
Nuneaton,
Warks. CV11 5HD

Telephone Number: 02476 385738
Fax: 02476 342690

Simple Directions:
A444 to Nuneaton from M6 junction 3, 2nd exit at 1st round-about, 2nd exit at 2nd r'about, left at 3rd r'bout, 2nd right into Greenmoor Rd, turn right at the end, grd on left.
Parking 100 cars at Manor Park School, Beaumont Rd, 50p each.   Ground 1 mile from Nuneaton Trent Valley (BR)

Capacity: 6,500
Seated: 520
Terracing - **Covered:** 3,000
Uncovered: 3,500

SOCIAL FACILITIES: Clubhouse open every evening, weekend lunchtimes & matchdays.

CLUB SHOP: Sells souvenirs, programmes & replica kits
Contact Commercial department

Pages: 48   **Price:** £1.50
Editorial Team:
Rod Grubb, John Moore, Andy Pace
Steve Packer, Martin Renshaw & Scott Renshaw

Other club publications: None

Local Press:
Nuneaton Telegraph & Weekly Tribune
Local Radio: Mercia Sound, BBC CWR

Formed: 1937

Nickname: The Boro

Club colours: Blue & white stripes,blue shorts

Change colours: All purple

Reserve team's league: Central Conference

Midweek home matchday: Tuesday 7.45pm

Club Sponsors: Pailton Steering Systems

CLUB OFFICIALS

Chairman: Phil Clayton

Executive Directors:
Gordon Chislett, Phil Clayton, Graham Cooper,
Howard Kerry, David Lee, Ralph Nollett, Dave Radburn,
Roger Stanford, Trevor Wooley

Secretary: Peter Humphreys
29 Amington Rd, Shirley, Solihull,
West Midlands B90 2RF
Tel: 0121 745 2031 (H) 07946 273692 (M)

Commercial Director: Phil Clayton
c/o the club

Press Officers: Phil Clayton/Brendon Phillips
c/o the club

FOOTBALL MANAGEMENT TEAM

MANAGER: BRENDAN PHILLIPS
Date of Appointment June 1995
Date of Birth: 16th July 1954
Place of Birth: West Indies
PREVIOUS CLUBS
As manager: Bedworth Utd.,
Stafford Rangers
As player: Leicester C., Peterborough U.,
Mansfield T.,Boston Utd.

HONOURS
As manager Southern Lge 98-99
As player England Semi-Pro

1st Team Coach: Steve Burr
Physio: Paul Miller
Reserve Team Manager: Ron Bradbury
Youth Team Manager: Ron Bradbury
Coaches: Mick Dennis
Mark Taylor
Chief Scout: John Halford

Season	League	Div.	Pos.	Home						Away					Pts	Manager
				P	W	D	L	F	A	W	D	L	F	A		
99-00	Conference	-	15	42	7	6	8	28	25	5	9	7	21	28	51	Brendal Phillips
98-99	Southern	Premier	1	42	16	3	2	52	15	11	6	4	39	18	90	Brendan Phillips
97-98	Southern	Premier	12	42	12	3	6	39	22	5	3	13	29	39	57	Brendan Phillips
96-97	Southern	Premier	7	42	15	2	4	44	20	4	7	10	17	32	65	Brendan Phillips

Season	League	Div.	Pos.	P	W	D	L	F	A	Pts	Manager
95-96	Southern	Midland	1	42	30	5	7	82	35	95	Brendan Phillips
94-95	Southern	Midland	7	42	19	11	12	76	55	68	Elwyn Roberts
93-94	Southern	Premier	22	42	11	8	23	42	66	41	John Barton
92-93	Southern	Midland	1	42	29	5	8	102	45	92	George Rooney/John Barton
91-92	Southern	Midland	6	42	17	11	14	68	53	62	Les Green
90-91	Southern	Midland	5	42	21	11	10	74	51	70	Les Green

HONOURS

Alliance Prem Lge R-up (2) 83-85
Southern Lg Premier Div. 98-99, R-up 66-67 74-75
League Cup Win 95-96
Midland Div 81-82 92-93, Champ 95-96
Lg Cup R-up 62-63, Merit Cup 92-93 (jt)
Birmingham Lg 55-56 (Nth Div 54-55)
Birmingham Comb. R-up 3
Birmingham Snr Cup 6, R-up 3

PREVIOUS

Leagues: Central Amateur 37-38; B'ham Comb 38-52; West Mids (B'ham) 52-58;Southern 58-79 81-82 88-99. GM Conference (Alliance Premier & Gola) 79-81 82-8

Names: None

Ground: None

Past Players who progressed to the Football League

A Morton (Fulham 70), R Edwards (Port Vale 72),
K Stephens (Luton 78), T Peake (Lincoln C. 79),
P Sugrue (Man City 80),
M Shotton & T Smithers (Oxford U. 80),
D Thomas (Wimbledon 81), P Richardson (Derby C. 84),
P Culpin (Coventry 85),
R Hill/T Morley/E McGoldrick/A Harris
(Northampton 85/86),
D Bullock (Huddersfield 93)
M Christie (Derby Co. 98)
A Ducros (Kidderminster Harriers) 2000

CLUB RECORDS

Attendance:	22,114 v Rotherham, FA Cup 3rd Rd 1967	
Defeat:	1-8 (55-56 & 68-69)	
Win:	11-1 (45-46 & 55-56)	
Goalscorer:	Paul Culpin	201 (Career)
		55 (Season - 92/93)
Career Appearances:	Alan Jones 545 (62-74)	
Transfer Fee Paid:	£35,000	
	for Marc McGregor from Forest Green R. 2000	
Transfer Fee Received:	£80,000	
	for Andy Ducros to Kidderminster H. 2000	

BEST SEASON

FA Cup: 3rd Rd replay 66-67
1st Rd 19 times

FA Trophy: Quarter final- 76-77(rep),
79-80, 86-87

League: Runners-up Conference 83-84, 84-85

LAST SEASON

F.A. Cup: 4th Qualifying Round
F.A. Trophy: 2nd Round
Conference: 15th
Top Goalscorer: Andy Ducros 9
Player of the Year: Andy Thackeray
Captain: Terry Angus

NUNEATON BOROUGH

Match Facts 1999-00

	Date	Comp.	H/A	Opponents	Gate	Result & Score		Goalscorers	League Position
1	14.08	N.C.	H	Hayes	2,186	W	2-1	Ducros 45, 78	
2	17.08	N.C.	A	Hereford United	2,551	D	1-1	O'Connor 33	
3	21.08	N.C.	A	Dover Athletic	1,078	L	1-3	Thackeray 70	13
4	24.08	N.C.	H	Yeovil Town	2,216	D	1-1	Hanson 59	
5	28.08	N.C.	H	Northwich Victoria	2,084	W	3-1	O'Connor 53, Hanson 78, Prindiville 83 (Pen)	8
6	30.08	N.C.	A	Hednesford Town	1,622	D	0-0		8
7	04.09	N.C	A	Forest Green R	910	W	2-1	Muir 57, 77 (2 pens)	6
8	11.09	N.C.	H	Welling United	2,007	W	4-3	**Williams B. 3** (8, 10, 48) Ducros 33	4
9	13.09	N.C.	A	Kidderminster H.	3,152	W	2-1	Ryder 73, Ducross 86	3
10	18.09	N.C.	A	Scarborough	1,662	D	1-1	Hanson 43	3
11	25.09	N.C.	H	Altrincham	2,205	W	3-1	Ducros 24, Francis 45, 79	2
12	02.10	N.C.	H	Southport	2,519	L	0-2		5
13	09.10	N.C.	A	Doncaster Rovers	3,407	W	1-0	O'Connor 19	3
14	23.10	N.C.	H	Sutton United	1,799	W	2-0	Muir 33 (p), Ducros 44	3
15	30.10	N.C.	A	Telford United	1,217	L	0-1		3
16	02.11	N.C.	H	Rushden & Diamonds	4,490	D	1-1	Angus 18	3
17	06.11	N.C.	A	Woking	1,711	D	1-1	Francis 64	3
18	12.11	N.C.	H	Kingstonian	3,203	W	2-0	Crossley 19, Ducros 85	2
19	20.11	N.C.	H	Telford United	2,203	D	1-1	Ford 26 (og)	1
20	30.11	N.C.	A	Altrincham	765	D	2-2	Wray 33, Ducros 34	1
21	04.12	N.C.	H	Forest Green Rovers	1,929	L	2-3	Prindiville 86, Straw 90	3
22	11.12	N.C.	A	Northwich Victoria	1,024	L	1-3	Francis 9	3
23	18.12	N.C.	A	Sutton United	749	W	2-1	Ware 43, 84	1
24	27.12	N.C.	H	Kettering Town	3,602	L	0-1		2
25	03.01	N.C.	A	Kettering Town	2,598	D	1-1	Ware 32	2
26	08.01	N.C.	H	Kidderminster Harriers	2,596	L	2-3	Thackeray 25, McDermott 77	4
27	22.01	N.C.	H	Dover Athletic	1,608	L	0-2		5
28	29.01	N.C.	A	Welling United	708	D	0-0		5
29	05.02	N.C.	A	Stevenage Borough	1,711	L	1-2	Thackeray 74	5
30	12.02	N.C.	H	Morecambe	1,411	D	1-1	Ducros 12	6
31	19.02	N.C.	A	Yeovil Town	2,629	W	3-1	Broughton 43, Murphy 68, Reed 87	6
32	04.03	N.C.	H	Hereford Utd.	1,947	L	0-1		8
33	11.03	N.C.	H	Scarborough	1,351	D	1-1	McDermott 57	7
34	18.03	N.C.	A	Kingstonian	985	L	0-2		8
35	25.03	N.C.	H	Doncaster Rovers	1,723	D	0-0		9
36	01.04	N.C.	A	Rushden & Diamonds	4,144	D	1-1	Wray 84	10
37	04.04	N.C.	A	Southport	1,064	L	0-2		11
38	22.04	N.C.	H	Woking	1,355	L	0-1		
39	24.04	N.C.	A	Morecambe	1,620	D	1-1	Broughton 65	14
40	29.04	N.C.	H	Stevenage Borough	1,250	L	0-1		
41	01.05	N.C.	H	Hednesford Town	1,369	W	3-0	Francis 32, 60, Wray 34	14
42	06.05	N.C.	A	Hayes	703	L	0-3		15

CUP COMPETITIONS

Dr Martens Championship

07.08		H	Sutton Coldfield Town.	744	W	1 - 0	Reed 84

F.A. Cup

16.10	4Q	H	Guiseley	2,175	L	2-3	Williams 62, Hanson 68

Nationwide McMillan Trophy

04.10	1	A	Hednesford Town	456	W	2-1	O'Connor 23, 75
09.11	2	A	Doncaster Rovers	1,245	L	0-4	

F.A. Trophy

27.11	FAT 2	A	Guiseley	597	L	0-2	

1	2	3	4	5	6	7	8	9	10	11	Substitutes Used	
McKenzie	Thackeray	Prindiville	Simpson	Crowley	Angus	Wray	Williams	Hanson	Ducros	Reed	O'Connor (9)	1
McKenzie	Thackeray	Prindiville	Simpson	Crowley	Angus	Wray	Williams	O'Connor	Ducros	Reed	Blake (10)	2
McKenzie	Thackeray	Prindiville	Simpson	Crowley	Angus	Wray	Williams	Hanson	Ducros	Reed	Hanson (7), Muir (8), Brown (10)	3
McKenzie	Thackeray	Prindiville	Simpson	Crowley	Angus	Williams	O'Connor	Hanson	Muir	Reed	Wray (7), Ducros (10), Brown (11)	4
McKenzie	Thackeray	Prindiville	Simpson	Brown	Angus	Crowley	O'Connor	Hanson	Muir	Reed	Ducros (10), Francis (8)	5
McKenzie	Thackeray	Prindiville	Simpson	Ryder	Angus	Brown	O'Connor	Hanson	Ducros	Reed	Wray (11), Francis (9)	6
McKenzie	Thackeray	Prindiville	Simpson	Ryder	Angus	Brown	Muir	Hanson	Ducros	O'Connor	Francis (11), Blake (9),	7
McKenzie	Thackeray	Prindiville	Brown	Ryder	Angus	Williams B	Muir	Hanson	Ducros	Francis	Blake (11), Wray (9)	8
McKenzie	Thackeray	Prindiville	Brown	Ryder	Angus	Williams B	Muir	Hanson	Ducros	Francis	No subs used	9
McKenzie	Thackeray	Prindiville	Ryder	Brown	Angus	Williams B	Muir	Hanson	Ducros	Francis	O'Connor (11)	10
McKenzie	Thackeray	Prindiville	Simpson	Brown	Angus	Williams B	Muir	Hanson	Ducros	Francis	Blake (9)	11
McKenzie	Thackeray	Ryder	Simpson	Brown	Angus	Williams B	Muir	Hanson	Ducros	Francis	Prindiville (4), Wray (7)	12
McKenzie	Thackeray	Prindiville	Simpson	Ryder	Angus	Brown	Williams B	O'Connor	Ducros	Francis	No subs used	13
McKenzie	Thackeray	Prindiville	Brown	Ryder	Angus	Williams B	Muir	Hanson	Ducros	O'Connor	Francis (11), Simpson (10)	14
McKenzie	Thackeray	Prindiville	Brown	Ryder	Angus	Williams B	Muir	Hanson	Ducros	O'Connor	Simpson (8), Wray (7), Blake (3)	15
McKenzie	Thackeray	Prindiville	Ryder	Brown	Angus	Wray	Williams B	Hanson	Ducros	O'Connor	Muir (7)	16
McKenzie	Thackeray	Prindiville	Ryder	Brown	Angus	Wray	Williams B	Hanson	Ducros	O'Connor	Muir (11), Francis (4), Simpson (9)	17
McKenzie	Thackeray	Prindiville	Simpson	Ryder	Angus	Wray	Williams B	Francis	Ducros	O'Connor	Muir (2)	18
McKenzie	Brown	Prindiville	Simpson	Ryder	Angus	Wray	Williams B	Francis	Ducros	Muir	Reed (11)	19
McKenzie	Brown	Prindiville	Simpson	Ryder	Angus	Wray	Williams B	Hanson	Ducros	Crowley	Francis (9)	20
McKenzie	Brown	Prindiville	Simpson	Ryder	Crowley	Wray	Williams B	Francis	Muir	Murphy	O'Connor (10), Straw (9), Reed (11)	21
McKenzie	Brown	Prindiville	Simpson	Ryder	Angus	Wray	Williams B	Francis	Ducros	Crowley	Reed (6) sub Straw, Carty (5)	22
McKenzie	Williams B	Prindiville	Brown	Ryder	Crowley	Wray	Ware	Hanson	Francis	McDermott	Murphy (10), Muir (8)	23
McKenzie	Thackeray	Crowley	Brown	Ryder	Angus	Carty	Prindiville	Hanson	Francis	McDermott	Ducros (2), Muir (9), Straw (10)	24
McKenzie	Thackeray	McDermott	O'Brien	Brown	Angus	Wray	Williams B	Straw	Ware	Crowley	Francis (9)	25
McKenzie	Thackeray	Brown	Ware	Crowley	Angus	Wray	Williams B	Straw	Ducros	McDermott	Francis (9), Kotylo (8)	26
McKenzie	Thackeray	Prindiville	Ryder	Brown	Williams B	Kotylo	Muir	Francis	Ducros	McDermott	O'Brien (5), Murphy (7), Blake (10)	27
McKenzie	Thackeray	Prindiville	Simpson	Crowley	Angus	Williams B	Blake	Francis	Ducros	McDermott	Murphy (8), Muir (9)	28
McKenzie	Thackeray	Prindiville	Simpson	Murphy	Angus	Wray	Crowley	Broughton	Ducros	McDermott	Prendegast (3), Francis (11)	29
McKenzie	Thackeray	McDermott	Simpson	Murphy	Angus	Wray	Crowley	Broughton	Ducros	Prendegast	Reed (11)	30
McKenzie	Thackeray	McDermott	Simpson	Murphy	Angus	Wray	Crowley	Broughton	Ducros	Prendegast	No subs used	31
McKenzie	Thackeray	McDermott	Simpson	Weaver	Crowley	Wray	Murphy	Broughton	Ducros	Prendegast	Francis (11)	32
McKenzie	Thackeray	Bradshaw	Simpson	Weaver	Crowley	Wray	Murphy	Broughton	Ducros	Prendegast	Francis (10), Williams B (3)	33
McKenzie	Thackeray	Bradshaw	Simpson	Crowley	Williams B	Wray	Murphy	Broughton	Francis	McDermott	Ducros (10), Prendegast (11)	34
McKenzie	Thackeray	Bradshaw	Simpson	Weaver	Brown	Wray	Williams B	Broughton	Ducros	Crowley	Murphy (5), Hanson (10)	35
McKenzie	Thackeray	Bradshaw	Simpson	Brown	Angus	Wray	Williams B	Broughton	Ducros	Crowley	Murphy (8), Hanson (9), Francis (10)	36
McKenzie	Thackeray	Bradshaw	Simpson	Brown	Angus	Wray	Murphy	Hanson	Francis	Crowley	Brennan (2), Ducros (8)	37
McKenzie	Thackeray	Prindiville	Simpson	Weaver	Angus	Wray	Williams B	Broughtin	Ducros	Brown	Kotylo (5), Hanson (9), Prendegast (11)	38
McKenzie	Thackeray	Prindiville	Simpson	Murphy	Angus	Wray	Williams B	Broughtin	Ducros	McDermott	Francis (10), Kotylo (7)	39
McKenzie	Thackeray	Prindiville	Simpson	Murphy	Angus	Wray	Williams B	Hanson	Francis	McDermott	Brennan (7), Reed (11), Weaver (10)	40
McKenzie	Thackeray	Prindiville	Simpson	Murphy	Angus	Wray	Williams B	Hanson	Francis	Reed	Brennan (10)	41
Young	Thackeray	Prindiville	Simpson	Murphy	Brown	Brennan	Williams B	Hanson	Francis	Reed	Prendegast (3) sub McDermott, Weaver (5)	42
McKenzie	Thackeray	Prindiville	Simpson	Brown	Angus	Wray	Williams B	Blake	Ducros	Reed	Crowley (7)	
McKenzie	Thackeray	Prindiville	Simpson	Ryder	Angus	Brown	Williams B	O'Connor	Ducros	Francis	Hanson (11), Muir (10), Wray (5)	
McKenzie	Thackeray	Prindiville	Simpson	Ryder	Angus	Wray	Williams B	O'Connor	Kotylo	Black	Hanson (11)	
McKenzie	Thackeray	Ryder	Brown	Angus	Muir	Murphy	Simpson	B Williams	Hanson	Blake	Prindiville (6), Crowley (9)	
McKenzie	Thackeray	Prindiville	Simpson	Williams B	Angus	Wray	Muir	Ducros	Francis	Hanson (11)	Reed (2), Crowley (8)	

PLAYING SQUAD

NUNEATON BOROUGH

(Bold print indicates an England Semi-Professional International)

Player
Honours

Birthplace

D.O.B.

Previous Clubs

GOALKEEPERS

Chris Mackenzie	Northampton	14.05.72	Corby T, Hereford U, Leyton O
Ryan Young	Birmingham		Plymouth, Chasetown
Kevin Shoemake SLP, FAXI	Chelmsford	28.01.65	Leyton O, Harlow T, Chelmsford C, Welling U, Peterborough, Kettering T, Rushden & D, Kettering T

DEFENDERS

Terry Angus DMP	Coventry	14.01.66	VS Rugby, Northampton, Fulham, Slough T
Mickey Love Ath., Tamworth,	Stockport Northampton, Stevenage B	27.11.73	Bedworth U, Hinckley T, Hinckley Ath., Wigan, Wycombe, Hinckley
Barry Williams ESP, DMP	Birmingham	06.05.73	Alvechurch, Ely C, Redditch U
Andy Thackeray Halifax	Huddersfield	13.02.68	Manchester C, Huddersfield, Newport Co., Wrexham, Rochdale,
Wayne Simpson ESP, DMP	Stoke	19.09.68	Port Vale, Stafford R, Hednesford T
Jon Gittens Portsmouth, Torquay,	Moseley Exeter	22.01.64	Paget R, Southampton, Swindon, Southampton, Middlesbrough,
Steve Prindiville ESP	Harlow	26.12.68	Leicester C, Chesterfield, Mansfield, Doncaster R, Wycombe, Halifax, Dag & Red, Kidderminster H
Simon Weaver	Doncaster	20.12.77	Sheffield Wed., Ilkeston T

MIDFIELDERS

Mark Taylor	Birmingham	22.02.66	Newton Alb., Shrewsbury, Walsall, Sheffield Wed., Hereford U
Alex Sykes British Univ.	Newcastle-u-Lyme	02.04.74	Westfields, Mansfield, Cheltenham, Endsleigh, Forest Green R
Dave Crowley DMP	Coventry	07.09.68	Coventry, Bedworth U, Stafford R
an King IDMP	Rugby	23.12.74	Aston Villa, WBA, VS Rugby, Stoke, Rushden & D, Aylesbury U, Stevenage B
Karl Brennan	Leicester	19.03.81	Leicester

FORWARDS

Shaun Wray	Dudley	14.03.77	Shrewsbury, Stafford R
Lee Charles ESP	Hillingdon	20.08.71	Chertsey T, QPR, Hayes
Delton Francis	Birmingham	12.03.78	Birmingham, Hednesford T, Halesowen T, Kingstonian
Marc McGregor ESP	Southend	30.04.78	Oxford U, Endsleigh, Forest Green R, £35,000 to Nuneaton B
Richard Mitchell	Stoke	14.09.73	Port Vale, Southport, Macclesfield, Droylsden, Stafford R

RUSHDEN & DIAMONDS

Once again, Diamonds began the 1999/2000 season as firm favourites to lift the title and gain promotion to the Nationwide Third Division.

Head Coach Brian Talbot had invested heavily once more, with the club again breaking non-League football's top transfer fee by bringing in Northampton goalkeeper Billy Turley, and the squad looked immensely strong on paper.

Diamonds started impressively and their 5-3 thrashing of Kidderminster Harriers in August saw them top the table and everything looked rosy until, as in previous seasons, Rushden hit a blip in form.

In Diamonds' defence, injuries to key men certainly didn't help their cause, especially the loss of goalscoring midfielder Michael McElhatton, and the tragic death of on-loan striker Martin Aldridge hit the club harder than even they would admit.

In the end Diamonds fell nine points adrift of Kidderminster Harriers but finished six points clear of third-placed Morecambe.

This season Talbot has again broken the non-League transfer record in signing Morecambe striker Justin Jackson and his partnership with another six-figure capture, Duane Darby, could well hold the key to success.

Everything is in place off the field, with Nene Park undergoing even more improvements during the summer. It would be a major surprise if the Northamptonshire club were not to make it this time around.

Steve Whitney

Back Row: Mark Peters, John Hamsher, Duane Darby, Stuart Naylor, Billy Turley, Michael Bertocchi, Michael McElhatton, Darren Bradshaw, Simon Wormull. **Middle:** Jean-Michel Sigere, Gary Butterworth, Gary Setchell, Justin Jackson, Jim Rodwell, Mark Sale, Richard Butcher, Matthew Stowell. **Front:** Simon Parsell (Physio), Paul Underwood, Gary Mills, Jon Brady, Ray Warburton (Captain), Brian Talbot (Manager), Darren Collins, Tarkan Mustafa, Andrew Burgess, David Town, Terry Westley (Coach).

RUSHDEN & DIAMONDS

GROUND DETAILS

Nene Park,
Diamond Way,
Irthlingborough,
Northants

TELEPHONE: 01933 652000
Fax: 01933 650418
Newsline: 09068 44 00 33
Website: www.the diamondsfc.com
email: kieran.farmer@airwair.co.uk

SIMPLE DIRECTIONS:
South from M1 exit 15, A45 bypassing Northampton until A6 -
1st exit North - ground approx 400 yards right.
North & West from A14 exit A6 South (Bedford),follow A6 for
approx 6 miles, ground on left.
East from A14 exit A45 (Northampton) follow A45 for approx 4
miles to A6 - 3rd exit North - ground approx 400 yards on right

CAPACITY: 6,635 - ALL COVERED

SEATED: 4,654

SOCIAL FACILITIES:
Lounge facilities. Open all day, every day.
Full restaurant facilities
CLUB SHOP / DOC SHOP:
Sells programmes, replica shirts, scarves, hats, footwear etc.
Contact Kerry White (01933 652000, extn 22)

Pages: 48   Price: £1.50

Editor: Ted Carrol

Other club publications: None

Local Press: Northants Evening Telegraph;
Chronicle & Echo, Citizen; Herald & Post

Local Radio: Radio Diamonds;
Radio Northampton; KCBC; Northants 96

Founded:	1992
Nickname:	Diamonds
Team Sponsors:	Dr. Martens
Club colours:	White, red & blue trim, shirts, blue shorts, white socks
Change colours:	Yellow and black

Reserve Team's league:
Capital League/Central Conference

Midweek home matchday: Tuesday

CLUB OFFICIALS

President	D Attley
Chairman	W M Griggs CBE
Managing Director	M G Darnell
Directors	A N Gant, S W Griggs, A C Jones, R W Langley, C M Smith

Football Secretary   David Joyce
c/o the club
Tel: 01933 392821 (H) 01933 6520000 (B)

Press Offiicer	David Joyce
Operations Manager	Dean Howells
Business Dev. Manager	Alistair Watley
Corporate Sales Manager	Sue Hughes

FOOTBALL MANAGEMENT TEAM

MANAGER: BRIAN TALBOT

Date of Appointment	April 1997
Date of Birth:	21st July 1953
Place of Birth:	Ipswich

PREVIOUS CLUBS
As manager   West Bromwich Albion, Kettering Town, Hibernians (Malta)
As player   Ipswich T., Arsenal, Watford, Stoke C., Fulham, Aldershot
HONOURS
As manager   R-up Conference 99-00
Maltese Championship.
As player   England - 6 full, 1 `B' & u23 caps
FA Cup winner x 2, Texaco Cup winner

* * *

Assistant Head Coach	Terry Westley
Chief Scout	Cyril Lea
Reserve & Youth Team Coach	Jeff Vetere
Physiotherapist	Simon Parsell
Asst. Physiotherapist	Nigel Gore

Season	League	Div.	Pos.	Home P	W	D	L	F	A	Away W	D	L	F	A	Pts	Manager
99-00	Conference	-	2	42	11	8	2	37	18	10	5	6	34	24	76	Brian Talbot
98-99	Conference	-	4	42	11	4	6	41	22	9	8	4	30	20	72	Brian Talbot
97-98	Conference	-	4	42	12	4	5	44	26	11	1	9	35	31	74	Brian Talbot
96-97	Conference	-	12	42	8	8	5	30	25	6	3	12	31	38	53	Roger Ashby/Brian Talbot

Season	League	Div.	Pos.	P	W	D	L	F	A	Pts	Manager
95-96	Southern	Premier	1	42	29	7	6	99	41	94	Roger Ashby
94-95	Southern	Premier	5	42	19	11	12	99	65	68	Roger Ashby
93-94	Southern	Midland	1	42	29	11	2	109	37	98	Roger Ashby
92-93	Southern	Midland	3	42	25	10	7	85	41	85	Roger Ashby
91-92	Southern	Midland	8	42	16	12	14	66	52	60	Roger Ashby (as Rushden Town)
90-91	Southern	Premier	14*	42	14	11	17	64	66	53	Roger Ashby (as Rushden Town)

Relegated because their ground was deemed unfit for the Premier Division

HONOURS

Conference R-up 1999-2000
Southern League Premier Div 95-96,
Midland Div 94-95,
Northants Senior Cup 94-95 98-99,
Daventry Charity Cup 92-93,
Campri Leisurewear Cup 92-93

*Rushden Town: Southern Lg Midland Div R-up 88-89,
Utd Co's Lg 02-03, 26-27,29-30, 31-32, 34-38, 63-64, 72-73,
R-up 12 times, Lg Cup 33-35, 36-38, 46-47,
Northants Snr Cup 25-28, 29-31, 34-35, 36-37, 57-58, 77-78,
FA Vase QF 89-90.*

*Irthlingborough Diamonds: Utd Co's Lg 70-71, 76-77, 78-79,
82-83, KO Cup 78-79,80-81, Northants Snr Cup 80-81.*

PREVIOUS

Grounds:
*Rushden Town: Hayden Road, Rushden (pre-1992)
IrthlingboroughDiamonds: Manton Road, Irthlingborough*

Leagues: Southern League 92-96
*Rushden Town : Midland 1894-1901; Utd Co's 01-04, 19-56,
61-83; Central Alliance 61-83.*

*Irthlingborough Diamonds : Rushden Yth; Rushden & Dist;
Kettering Amat.; United Counties.*

Names: Rushden Town (1894-1992)
merged with Irthlingborough Diamonds (1946-92)
in 1992 to form Rushden & Diamonds

Past Players who progressed to the Football League

From Rushden Town: Gordon Inwood (WBA 1949),
Robert Peacock (Northampton 1957).

From IrthlingboroughDiamonds: Scott Endersby (Ipswich),
Steve Brown & Dave Johnson (Northampton),

CLUB RECORDS

Attendance: 6,431 v Leeds United
FA Cup 3rd Round, Jan. 1999

Win: 7-0 v Redditch Utd (H),
Southern League Midland Div. 7/5/94

Defeat: 0-5 v Slough Town (A),
GM Vauxhall Conference 96/97

Career goalscorer: Darren Collins 153

Career appearances: Gary Butterworth 290

Transfer fee paid: £150,000
to Morecambe for Darren Jackson June 2000
(undisclosed to Northampton T. for Billy Turley - June 1999)

Transfer fee received: £18,000
from Kingstonian for David Leworthy - June 1997

BEST SEASON

FA Cup: Third Round replay
98-99, 1-3 v Leeds United (A) after 0-0
99-00, 1-1 aet (5-6 after pens) v Sheffield Utd (H) after 1-1

FA Trophy: Semi-Final 94-95

League: 2nd Conference 99-00
(4th 97-98 & 98-99)

LAST SEASON

F.A. Cup: Third round replay (see above)
F.A. Trophy: Quarter Finals
Conference: 2nd
Top Goalscorer: Darren Collins 15
Player of the Year: Jim Rodwell
Captain: Ray Warburton

RUSHDEN & DIAMONDS

	Date	Comp.	H/A	Opponents	Gate	Result & Score		Goalscorers	League Position
1	14.08	N.C.	A	Morecambe	1,797	D	0-0		
2	17.08	N.C.	H	Telford United	2,729	D	1-1	Mison 41	
3	21.08	N.C.	H	Kidderminster Harriers	2,728	W	5-3	Warburton 21,Cooper 36(pen) McIlhatton 41,45, Underwood 88	9
4	28.08	N.C.	A	Sutton United	1,083	W	4-0	Collins 20, 39, West 76, McElhatton 85	5
5	30.08	N.C.	H	Welling United	2,805	W	2-0	McElhatton 76, 81	2
6	04.09	N.C.	A	Northwich Victoria	1,231	L	1-2	Collins 3	7
7	07.09	N.C	H	Hayes	2,434	W	1-0	Peters 18	
8	11.09	N.C.	H	Woking	2,699	L	1-3	Peters 65	5
9	14.09	N.C.	A	Kettering Town	3,744	D	1-1	De Souza 7	5
10	18.09	N.C.	H	Southport	2,619	W	4-2	McElhatton 8, 59, Collins 20 (pen), Peters 52	5
11	25.09	N.C.	A	Hednesford Town	1,608	W	2-1	De Souza 50, Peters 90	4
12	28.09	N.C.	A	Hereford United	1,724	L	0-4		4
13	02.10	N.C.	A	Altrincham	1,114	W	2-1	Town 14, Brady 35	2
14	09.10	N.C.	H	Kingstonian	3,764	W	1-0	Collins 31	1
15	23.10	N.C.	A	Scarborough	1,702	W	1-0	Collins 19	1
16	02.11	N.C.	A	Nuneaton Borough	4,490	D	1-1	De Souza 50	1
17	06.11	N.C.	H	Dover Athletic	3,037	D	1-1	Underwood 87	2
18	13.11	N.C.	A	Yeovil Town	2,180	L	1-5	Underwood 45	3
19	04.12	N.C.	A	Hayes	901	W	5-0	Brady 21, Town 49, 66, Warburton 78, De Souza 90	2
20	18.12	N.C.	A	Telford United	1,414	D	1-1	McElhatton 85	2
21	27.12	N.C.	H	Stevenage Borough	5,721	W	2-1	Collins 16, Brady 79	1
22	03.01	N.C.	A	Stevenage Borough	4,373	D	2-2	Collins 32, Underwood 36	1
23	22.01	N.C.	A	Forest Green Rovers	1,302	L	0-1		4
24	29.01	N.C.	H	Northwich Victoria	3,468	**W**	**6-0**	Simpson 3 (OG), McElhatton 30, 76, Collins 50, Lowe 56, Burgess 67	4
25	12.02	N.C.	A	Dover Athletic	2,904	W	4-0	SeSouza 45, 69, Hamsher 64 (p), Rodwell 73	2
26	15.02	N.C.	H	Forest Green Rovers	3,195	W	3-2	McElhatton 14, Collins 71, 84	2
27	19.02	N.C.	A	Doncaster Rovers	4,187	W	1-0	De Souza 80	1
28	22.02	N.C.	H	Hednesford Town	3,714	D	1-1	Lowe 23	1
29	04.03	N.C.	A	Kingstonian	1,772	W	1-0	OG (Crossley) 29	2
30	07.03	N.C.	H	Yeovil Town	3,611	D	1-1	Burgess 63	2
31	18.03	N.C.	H	Sutton United	2,749	W	4-0	Butterworth 5, Burgess 39, Peters 51, Lowe 83	2
32	25.03	N.C.	H	Hereford United	4,022	D	0-0		2
33	28.03	N.C.	H	Kettering Town	4,752	W	2-0	Lowe 56, Warburton 59	2
34	01.04	N.C.	H	Nuneaton Borough	4,144	D	1-1	Burgess 69	2
35	04.04	N.C.	H	Morecambe	2,533	L	0-2		2
36	08.04	N.C.	A	Kidderminster Harriers	6,250	L	0-2		2
37	11.04	N.C.	A	Woking	1,765	W	3-1	Town 47, Sigere 75, 90	2
38	15.04	N.C.	H	Altrincham	2,731	W	1-0	Town 21	2
39	22.04	N.C.	A	Southport	1,590	L	1-2	Hamsher 48 (p)	2
40	29.04	N.C.	H	Scarborough	2,641	D	0-0		2
41	01.05	N.C.	A	Welling United	1,317	W	3-0	Burgess 66, Sigere 86, 89	2
42	06.05	N.C.	H	Doncaster Rovers	3,177	D	0-0		2

CUP COMPETITIONS

F.A. Cup

	Date		H/A	Opponents	Gate	Result & Score		Goalscorers
	16.10	4Q	H	Sutton United	2,525	W	4-1	McElhatton 11, 45, Brady 14, Collins 74
	29.10	1	H	Scunthorpe Utd.	4,112	W	2-0	Warburton 47, Hamsher 76 (pen)
	20.11	2	A	Ilkeston Town	2,737	D	1-1	De Souza 51
	30.11	2R	H	Ilkeston Town	4,226	W	3-0	Wooding 2, Town 17, Collins 86
	12.12	3	A	Sheffield United	10,104	D	1-1	Brady 45
	21.12	3R	H	Sheffield United	6,010	D	*1-1	Warburton 105 lost 5-6 after penalties

Nationwide McMillan Trophy

	Date		H/A	Opponents	Gate	Result & Score		Goalscorers
	23.11	2	H	Telford United	1,451	L	0-1	

F.A. Trophy

	Date		H/A	Opponents	Gate	Result & Score		Goalscorers
	27.11	2	H	Havant & Waterlooville	1,635	W	1-0	Collins 50
	15.01	3	A	Bath City	2,034	W	2-1	Rodwell 66, Aldridge 72
	05.02	4	A	Billericay Town	2,027	D	0-0	
	08.02	4R	H	Billericay Town	2,132	W	2-1	Lowe 46, De Souza 71
	26.02	5	H	Marine	3,094	W	1-0	Lowe 32
	11.03	6	A	Sutton United	1,586	D	1-1	Rodwell 13
	14.03	6R	H	Sutton United	2,783	L	1-3	Cooper 85

1	2	3	4	5	6	7	8	9	10	11	Substitutes Used	
Turley 1	Wooding	Bradshaw	McElhatton	Peters	Rodwell	Butterworth	Cooper	Mison	Town	Underwood	Sale (8), Collins (9)	1
Turley 2	Wooding	Bradshaw	McElhatton	Peters	Rodwell	Butterworth	Cooper	Mison	Town	Underwood	De Souza (8), Sale (9)	2
Turley 3	Brady	Bradshaw	McElhatton	Peters	Warburton	Butterworth	Cooper	Sale	Town	Underwood	De Souza (9), West (10), Mison (7)	3
Turley 4	Brady	Bradshaw	McElhatton	Peters	Warburton	Butterworth	Cooper	Sale	Collins	Underwood	West (9), Mills (8), Wooding (11)	4
Turley 5	Brady	Bradshaw	McElhatton	Peters	Warburton	Butterworth	Cooper	Sale	Collins	Underwood	West (9), Mills (8)	5
Turley 6	Brady	Bradshaw	McElhatton	Peters	Warburton	Butterworth	Cooper	Sale	Collins	Underwood	Town (9)	6
Turley 7	Brady	Rodwell	McElhatton	Peters	Warburton	Butterworth	Cooper	Sale	Collins	Underwood	Wooding (2)	7
Turley 8	Brady	Rodwell	McElhatton	Peters	Warburton	Butterworth	Cooper	Sale	Collins	Underwood	West (9), De Souza (2), Mills (8)	8
Turley 9	Brady	Rodwell	McElhatton	Peters	Warburton	Butterworth	Cooper	Mison	De Souza	Underwood	No subs used	9
Turley 10	Brady	Rodwell	McElhatton	Peters	Warburton	Butterworth	De Souza	Mison	Collins	Underwood	Town (9)	10
Turley 11	Brady	Rodwell	McElhatton	Peters	Warburton	Butterworth	De Souza	Mison	Collins	Underwood	Wooding (3), Heggs (9)	11
Turley 12	Brady	Wooding	McElhatton	Peters	Warburton	Butterworth	De Souza	Mison	Collins	Underwood	Hamsher (10), Heggs (7), Cooper (4)	12
Turley 13	Brady	Bradshaw	McElhatton	Peters	Warburton	Butterworth	Mills	Town	Collins	Underwood	Rodwell (5), Cooper (8)	13
Turley 14	Brady	Bradshaw	McElhatton	Peters	Warburton	Butterworth	Hamsher	Town	Collins	Underwood	No subs used	14
Turley 15	Brady	Bradshaw	McElhatton	Peters	Warburton	Butterworth	Hamsher	Town	Collins	Underwood	Mills (7), De Souza (9)	15
Turley 16	Brady	Wooding	McElhatton	Peters	Warburton	Butterworth	Hamsher	De Souza	Collins	Underwood	No subs used	16
Turley 17	Brady	Wooding	McElhatton	Peters	Warburton	Butterworth	Hamsher	De Souza	Collins	Underwood	Cramman (3), Town (2)	17
Turley 18	Brady	Rodwell	McElhatton	Peters	Warburton	Butterworth	Hamsher	De Souza	Collins	Underwood	Mills (3), Cramman (8), Mison (10)	18
Turley 19	Wooding	Stowell	McElhatton	Rodwell	Warburton	Butterworth	Brady	Town	Collins	Underwood	Peters (6), Heggs (10), De Souza (9)	19
Turley 20	Wooding	Stowell	McElhatton	Rodwell	Warburton	Mills	Hamsher	Town	Collins	Underwood	Heggs (8)	20
Turley 21	Wooding	Stowell	McElhatton	Rodwell	Warburton	Butterworth	Brady	De Souza	Collins	Underwood	Burgess (3), Heggs (9)	21
Turley 22	Wooding	Stowell	McElhatton	Rodwell	Warburton	Butterworth	Brady	De Souza	Collins	Underwood	Heggs (9)	22
Turley 23	Wooding	Heggs	McElhatton	Rodwell	Warburton	Butterworth	Brady	Aldridge	Collins	Underwood	Burgess (3), De Souza (9)	23
Turley 24	Wooding	Cramman	McElhatton	Rodwell	Warburton	Butterworth	Brady	Lowe	Collins	Burgess	Peters (6), Mills (8), Heggs (9)	24
Turley 25	Wooding	Cramman	McElhatton	Rodwell	Warburton	Butterworth	Hamsher	Lowe	De Souza	Underwood	Mills (4), Burgess (8), Peters (9)	25
Turley 26	Wooding	Cramman	McElhatton	Rodwell	Warburton	Butterworth	Hamsher	Lowe	De Souza	Underwood	Burgess (3), Collins (2)	26
Turley 27	Hamsher	Burgess	McElhatton	Rodwell	Warburton	Butterworth	De Souza	Lowe	Collins	Underwood	Brady (9)	27
Turley 28	Wooding	Burgess	McElhatton	Rodwell	Bradshaw	Butterworth	Hamsher	Lowe	De Souza	Underwood	Heggs (10), Cramman (7), Town (3)	28
Turley 29	Wooding	Cramman	McElhatton	Rodwell	Warburton	Butterworth	Hamsher	Lowe	De Souza	Underwood	Burgess (9)	29
Turley 30	Wooding	Cramman	McElhatton	Rodwell	Warburton	Butterworth	Hamsher	Lowe	De Souza	Underwood	Brady (4), Collins (10)	30
Turley 31	Peters	Burgess	Cooper	Rodwell	Warburton	Butterworth	Wormull	Lowe	De Souza	Underwood	Bradshaw (11), Mills (8), Mison (9)	31
Turley 32	Peters	Burgess	Cooper	Rodwell	Warburton	Butterworth	Wormull	Lowe	De Souza	Underwood		32
Turley 33	Peters	Burgess	Bullock	Rodwell	Warburton	Butterworth	Wormull	Lowe	De Souza	Underwood	Collins (9)	33
Turley 34	Peters	Burgess	Bullock	Rodwell	Warburton	Butterworth	Wormull	Lowe	De Souza	Underwood	Collins (9)	34
Turley 35	Peters	Burgess	Bullock	Rodwell	Warburton	Butterworth	Wormull	Lowe	De Souza	Underwood	Cooper (7), Collins (8)	35
Turley 36	Peters	Burgess	Bullock	Rodwell	Warburton	Butterworth	Brady	Mison	De Souza	Underwood	Wormull (3), Sigere (10), Town (9)	36
Turley 37	Peters	Hamsher	Mills	Rodwell	Warburton	Butterworth	Brady	Town	Sigere	Underwood		37
Turley 38	Peters	Hamsher	Mills	Rodwell	Warburton	Butterworth	Wormull	De Souza	Sigere	Underwood	De Souza (10), Stowell (11)	38
Naylor 39	Peters	Hamsher	Mills	Rodwell	Warburton	Butterworth	Stowell	Town	Sigere	Underwood	Burgess (2), Wormull (3), De Souza (9)	39
Naylor 40	Hamsher	Burgess	Mills	Rodwell	Warburton	Butterworth	Wormull	Town	Sigere	Underwood	Colins (9), Brady (8), Bradshaw (4)	40
Turley 41	Hamsher	Burgess	Mills	Rodwell	Warburton	Butterworth	Wormull	Town	Sigere	Underwood	Collins (9), Peters (8)	41
Turley 42	Hamsher	Burgess	Mills	Rodwell	Warburton	Butterworth	Wormull	Sigere	Collins	Underwood	Bradshaw (2), Brady (8)	42

Turley	Brady	Bradshaw	McElhatton	Peters	Warburton	Butterworth	Hamsher	Town	Collins	Underwood	Bertocchi (1), Mills (7), De Souza (10)	
Turley	Brady	Bradshaw	McElhatton	Peters	Warburton	Butterworth	Hamsher	De Souza	Collins	Underwood	Wooding (3)	
Turley	Wooding	Rodwell	McElhatton	Peters	Warburton	Butterworth	Brady	De Souza	Collins	Underwood	Town (8)	
Turley	Wooding	Burgess	McElhatton	Rodwell	Warburton	Butterworth	Brady	Town	Collins	Underwood	Heggs (9)	
Turley	Wooding	Burgess	McElhatton	Rodwell	Warburton	Butterworth	Brady	Town	Collins	Underwood	De Souza (3), Heggs (9)	
Turley	Wooding	Burgess	McElhatton	Rodwell	Warburton	Butterworth	Brady	Town	Collins	Underwood	De Souza (9), Hamsher (3)	

Turley	Wooding	Cramman	McElhatton	Rodwell	Warburton	Butterworth	Brady	De Souza	Collins	Underwood	Town (10), Burgess (3), Mison (9)	

Turley	Wooding	Stowell	McElhatton	Rodwell	Warburton	Butterworth	Brady	De Souza	Collins	Underwood	Heggs (9),	
Turley	Wooding	Stowell	McElhatton	Rodwell	Warburton	Butterworth	Brady	De Souza	Collins	Underwood	Aldridge (9), Burgess (3)	
Turley	Wooding	Cramman	Cooper	Rodwell	Warburton	Butterworth	Brady	Lowe	Collins	Underwood		
Turley	Wooding	Cramman	Mills	Rodwell	Warburton	Butterworth	Brady	Lowe	Collins	Underwood	Cooper (8)	
Turley	Wooding	Cramman	McElhatton	Rodwell	Warburton	Butterworth	Brady	Lowe	Town	Underwood	Heggs (10), Hamsher (4)	
Turley	Wooding	Cramman	Hamsher	Rodwell	Warburton	Butterworth	Brady	De Souza	Town	Underwood		
Turley	Wooding	Cramman	Hamsher	Rodwell	Warburton	Butterworth	Brady	Lowe	Town	Underwood	De Souza, Cooper, Burgess	

PLAYING SQUAD

RUSHDEN & DIAMONDS

(Bold print indicates an England Semi-Professional International)

Player Honours	Birthplace	D.O.B.	Previous Clubs
GOALKEEPERS			
Billy Turley	Wolverhampton	15.07.73	Evesham U, Northampton, £130,000 to Rushden & D
Michael Bertocchi	Cannes	17.07.81	AS Cannes
Stuart Naylor	Wetherby	06.12.62	Yorkshire Am., Lincoln, WBA, Bristol C, Exeter
DEFENDERS			
Jim Rodwell DMP	Lincoln	20.11.70	Darlington, Sabam, Bury, Boston T, Boston U, Bedworth U, Hednesford T, Nuneaton B, Halesowen T, £40k to Rushden & D
Darren Bradshaw	Sheffield	19.03.67	Matlock T, Chesterfield, York, Newcastle, Peterborough, Blackpool
Tarkan Mustafa FAT	London	28.08.73	Clapton, Wimbledon, Kettering T, Kingstonian
Matty Stowell	Reading	01.03.77	Reading, Slough T, Bristol C
Ray Warburton	Rotherham	07.10.67	York, Northampton, £50,000 to Rushden & D
Paul Underwood ESP	London		Sutton U, Kingstonian, Carshalton Ath., Enfield, £50,000 to Rushden & D
John Hamsher	Lambeth	14.01.78	Fulham
Mark Peters Wales u-21	St.Asaph	06.07.72	Manchester C, Norwich, Peterborough, Mansfield
MIDFIELDERS			
Michael McElhatton	Co.Kerry	16.04.75	Bournemouth, Scarborough
Gary Butterworth ESP, DMP	Peterborough	08.09.69	Peterborough, Dag & Red, £20,000 to Rushden & D
Gary Setchell	King's Lynn		King's Lynn, Wisbech T, King's Lynn, Fakenham T, Kettering T
Simon Wormull ESP	Crawley	01.12.76	Spurs, Brentford, Dover Ath., £50,000 to Rushden & D
Gary Mills	Northampton		Youth team
Jon Brady	Newcastle(Aust)	14.01.75	Adamstown Rosebuds, Swansea, Brentford, Wycombe, Hayes, Mjolner, Hayes, £40,000 to Rushden & D
Shaun Carey	Kettering	13.05.76	Norwich
FORWARDS			
Justin Jackson FAT	Nottingham	26.06.75	Bolton, Ayr U, Penrith, Ilkeston T, Morecambe, Woking, Notts Co., Halifax, Morecambe, £180,000 to Rushden & D
Jean-Michel Sigere	France		Bordeaux
Duane Darby	Birmingham	17.10.73	Torquay, Doncaster R, Hull, Notts Co., £100,000 to Rushden & D
Mark Sale	Burton	27.02.72	Stoke, Camb.U, Birmingham, Torquay, Preston, Mansfield, Colchester, £30,000 to Rushden & D
David Town	Boscombe	09.12.76	Bournemouth, £20,000 to Rushden & D
Darren Collins ESP, DMP	Winchester	24.05.67	Petersfield U, Northampton, Aylesbury U, Enfield, £20,000 to Rushden & D
Andy Burgess	Luton		Luton

SCARBOROUGH

Although Scarborough finished in fourth spot they never really threatened the leaders, which must have been a disappointment to manager Colin Addison and Boro supporters.

The Seadogs were expected to do much better on their return to the Conference, and indeed their opening day performance when they put five passed Yeovil Town suggested they would be a force to be reckoned with. However four defeats in five games soon dispelled any false hopes. Their defence, well marshalled by former England under-21 international Lee Sinnott, played its part by being the meanest in the league - only 35 goals conceded - but, despite possessing players such as Chris Tate, Darren Roberts and Steve Brodie in attack, Boro couldn't score enough to sustain a serious challenge, especially away from home. In fact they failed to score at all on thirteen occasions in the league which does make a real challenge very difficult.

The FA Cup didn't bring any relief, as they were knocked out by Tamworth at home in the 4th Qualifying Round and although for a while it did look as if a Trophy run was on the cards an akward away trip to Bishop Auckland in the Fifth Round put paid to that.

The summer has seen the vastly experienced Addison depart and one-time York boss Neil Thompson take over and, despite rumours of financial problems and doubts as to the club's future, Scarborough remain one of the favourites for the title.

If the club can overcome their mounting financial worries in time and allow Thompson to add to his squad, they will undoubtedly push hard for a return to the League, although it may be too much this season.

While personnel may change the McCain Stadium looks as smart as ever.
Photo: D Nicholson

SCARBOROUGH

GROUND DETAILS

McCain Stadium
Seamer Road
Scarborough
N. Yorkshire YO12 4HF

TELEPHONE Tel: 01723 375094
Fax: 01723 378733
Newsline: 0891 121650

SIMPLE DIRECTIONS The ground is situated on the main Scarborough to York road (A64), about half a mile beyond B&Q on the left as you go into Scarborough. Scarborough central (BR) about 2 miles. Car Parking: Ample in streets around the ground.

CAPACITY 5,900
SEATING 3,500
COVERED TERRACING 1,000

CLUB SHOP: Monday to Friday 09.00-17.00 and matchdays

SOCIAL FACILITIES: Clubhouse - open matchdays only

Founded: 1879
Nickname: The Seadogs
Club Sponsors: Albany Holdings
Colours Red & white shirts, white shorts, red socks
Change colours: White shirts, black shorts, white socks
Midweek Matchday: Tuesday
Reserves' League: Pontin's League
Youth League Youth Aliance

CLUB OFFICIALS

Owner Brookes Mileson
Chairman Trevor Milton
President John R Birley
Vice Chairman Ray Kemp
Chief Executive Keith Agar
Directors Russ Green
Acting Secretary Jade Sprintall
Admin. Manager Karola Powell

THE Seadog
SCARBOROUGH FOOTBALL CLUB
1999-2000 SEASON

MATCHDAY PROGRAMME

McCain

AVEC Sportswear

Scarborough Evening News

Trader and Weekly News

Nationwide

OFFICIAL PROGRAMME PRICE £1.50

BORO vs MORECAMBE

Pages: 44   Price: £1.50
Editor: James Hunter

Other club publications: None

Local Press:
Scarborough Evening News; The Mercury

Local Radio: Radio York; Y.C.R. Radio

FOOTBALL MANAGEMENT TEAM

MANAGER: NEIL THOMPSON

Date of Appointment   August 2000
Date of Birth   19th October 1963
Place of Birth   Beverley

PREVIOUS CLUBS
As manager
As coach
As player   Nottm. Forest , Hull City, Scarborough, Ipswich Town
*   *   *

Assistant Manager   Ray McHale
Player Coach   Lee Sinnott
Physiotherapist   Kevin Sullivan
Community Officer   Mitch Cook
Youth Team Coach   Ian Kerr
Groundsman   Paul Barnett

Season	League	Div.	Pos.	Home						Away					Pts	Manager
				P	W	D	L	F	A	W	D	L	F	A		
99-00	Conference	-	4	42	10	6	5	36	14	9	6	6	24	21	69	Colin Addison
98-99	F. League	3	24	46	8	3	12	30	39	6	3	14	20	38	48	Mike Wadsworth

Season	League	Div.	Pos.	P	W	D	L	F	A	Pts	Manager
97-98	F. League	3	6	46	19	15	12	67	58	72	Mike Wadsworth
96-97	F. League	3	12	46	16	15	15	65	68	63	Mike Wadsworth
95-96	F. League	3	23	46	8	16	22	39	69	40	Ray McHale
94-95	F. League	3	21	42	8	10	24	49	70	34	Philip Chambers
93-94	F. League	3	14	42	15	8	19	55	61	53	Philip Chambers
92-93	F. League	3	13	42	15	9	18	66	71	54	Ray McHale
91-92	F. League	4	12	42	15	12	15	64	68	57	Ray McHale
90-91	F. League	4	9	46	19	12	15	59	56	69	Ray McHale

HONOURS

FA Trophy 72-73 75-76 76-77
Vauxhall Conference 86-87
Bob Lord Trophy 83-84
NPL Lge Cup 76-77
North Eastern Cos Lge 62-63, Lge Cup 62-63
Midland Lge 29-30
Scarborough & Dist. Lge 45-46
E. Riding Cup x 8; N. Riding Sen. Cup x 17

PREVIOUS

Leagues: Northern 1898-1910 14-26
Yorkshire Combination 10-14; Yorkshire 26-27;
Midland 27-40 46-60 63-68
Scarborough & Dist. 45-46
Northern Counties 60-62; North Eastern 62-63;
Northern Premier 68-79
Alliance Premier 79-87 99-
Football League 87-99

Name: None

Past Players who progressed to the Football League

Not yet applicable

CLUB RECORDS

Attendance: 11,162
v Luton Town, FAC 3rd Rd, 1938

Victory: 6-0 v Rhyl Athletic, FA Cup 29.11.30

Defeat: 0-8 v Mansfield Town (H), FA Cup 22.11.52

Career Goalscorer: Unknown

Career Appearances: 196 Steve Richards 87-91

Transfer Fee Paid: £100,000
for Martin Russell to Leicester C., Feb. 87

Transfer Fee Received: £350,000
for Craig Short from Notts Co. (£150K 7/89 + £250K9/92)

BEST SEASON

FA Cup: 3rd Round 30-31 37-38 75-76 77-78

FA Trophy: Winners 72-73 75-76 76-77

Football League: 5th in Division 4, 88-89

League Cup: 4th Round 92-93

LAST SEASON

F.A. Cup: 4th Qualifying Round
F.A. Trophy: Fifth Round
Conference: 4th
Top Goalscorer: Steve Brodie (17)
Player of the Year: Simon Betts
Captain: Lee Sinnott

SCARBOROUGH

	Date	Comp.	H/A	Opponents	Gate	Result & Score		Goalscorers	League Position
1	14.08	N.C.	H	Yeovil Town	2,005	W	5-0	Brodie 6, Roberts 37, 76, McAlindon 37, 76	
2	17.08	N.C.	A	Southport	1,632	D	2-2	Roberts 41 (pen) Brodie 61	
3	21.08	N.C.	A	Forest Green Rovers	863	W	1-0	Betts 40	3
4	24.08	N.C.	H	Hednesford Town	2,198	D	1-1	Brodie 42	
5	28.08	N.C.	H	Stevenage Borough	2,291	L	1-3	OG (Love) 75	6
6	30.08	N.C.	A	Morecambe	2,301	W	1-0	Betts 64	3
7	04.09	N.C.	H	Kingstonian	1,671	L	0-1		8
8	11.09	N.C.	A	Kidderminster Harriers	1,784	L	0-2		11
9	14.09	N.C.	A	Northwich Victoria	1,036	L	0-2		13
10	18.09	N.C.	H	Nuneaton Borough	1,662	D	1-1	Stoker 89	13
11	25.09	N.C.	H	Hayes	1,295	W	4-1	Morris 5, Brodie19, Roberts 44, Quinn 77.	9
12	02.10	N.C.	A	Hereford United	1,886	D	4-4	Morris 17, Harriott 35, Stoker 59, Brodie 87	11
13	09.10	N.C.	A	Dover Athletic	945	D	1-1	Roberts 27 (pen)	13
14	23.10	N.C.	H	Rushden & Diamonds	1,702	L	0-1		14
15	06.11	N.C.	A	Stevenage Borough	1,743	W	1-0	Russell 69	14
16	12.11	N.C.	H	Telford United	1,317	W	2-0	Jones 45, McAlindon 69	9
17	20.11	N.C.	H	Kettering Town	1,462	D	0-0		12
18	04.12	N.C.	A	Welling United	540	L	1-2	Brodie 45	12
19	11.12	N.C.	H	Kidderminster Harriers	1,125	D	0-0		12
20	18.12	N.C.	H	Hereford United	1,242	W	3-0	Stoker 22, Brodie 60, Bass 70	11
21	27.12	N.C.	A	Doncaster Rovers	4,706	W	1-0	Tate 6	10
22	03.01	N.C.	H	Doncaster Rovers	3,510	D	0-0		10
23	08.01	N.C.	A	Hednesford Town	1057	W	3-0	Tate 26, Stoker 28, Brodie 57	8
24	22.01	N.C.	H	Northwich Victoria	1502	W	3-0	Betts 54 (p), Brodie 76, Roberts 87	6
25	29.01	N.C.	A	Telford United	1041	L	0-1		6
26	12.02	N.C.	A	Kettering Town	1,270	D	0-0		8
27	19.02	N.C.	H	Sutton United	1,395	W	3-0	Tate 10, 90, McNiven 42	8
28	22.02	N.C.	A	Altrincham	761	L	1-2	OG (Hodson) 25	
29	29.02	N.C.	H	Southport	1,002	W	3-0	Tate 37, Rennison 60, Morris 65	4
30	04.03	N.C.	H	Dover Athletic	1,376	L	1-2	McNiven 45	6
31	11.03	N.C.	A	Nuneaton Borough	1,351	D	1-1	Tate 4	6
32	18.03	N.C.	H	Woking	1,345	W	3-2	Tate 33, Brodie 38, Betts 88 (p)	5
33	25.03	N.C.	A	Yeovil Town	2,031	W	2-1	Betts 15, Tate 84	4
34	01.04	N.C.	H	Welling United	1,302	D	0-0		4
35	08.04	N.C.	A	Kingstonian	983	L	0-2		6
36	11.04	N.C.	A	Hayes	506	W	1-0	Roberts 64	4
37	15.04	N.C.	H	Forest Green Rovers	1,636	W	5-0	OG (Hedges) 3, Roberts 8, Tate 8, Brodie 65, Thompson 76	3
38	20.04	N.C.	A	Sutton United	463	W	2-1	Rennison 22, Brodie 37	3
39	26.04	N.C.	H	Altrincham	1,273	W	1-0	Morris 83	3
40	29.04	N.C.	A	Rushden & Diamonds	2,641	D	0-0		3
41	01.05	N.C.	H	Morecambe	1,505	L	0-2		4
42	06.05	N.C.	A	Woking	2,214	W	2-0	Brodie 9, McNaughton 90	4

CUP COMPETITIONS

F.A. Cup

	Date		H/A	Opponents	Gate	Result & Score		Goalscorers
	16.10	4Q	H	Tamworth	1,354	L	0-1	

Nationwide McMillan Trophy

	Date		H/A	Opponents	Gate	Result & Score		Goalscorers
	09.11	2	A	Southport	339	W	2-1	Betts 27 (p), Brodie 82
	01.02	4	H	Doncaster Rovers	1,188	L	1-2	Roberts 42

F.A. Trophy

	Date		H/A	Opponents	Gate	Result & Score		Goalscorers
	27.11	2	A	Ilkeston Town	840	W	4-2	Betts 75, Morris 80, Brodie 90, Rogan 90
	15.01	3	A	Stocksbridge P.S.	634	D	0-0	
	18.01	3R	H	Stocksbridge P.S.	960	W	5-0	Betts 3 (4, 29, 65), Brodie 34, 44
	05.02	4	A	Burnham	462	D	1-1	OG (O'Sullivan) 70
	08.02	4R	H	Burnham	877	W	6-0	Tate 5, 9, Russell 31, Roberts 35, Jones 62, Stoker 76
	26.02	5	A	Bishop Auckland	747	L	1-2	Jones 60

Substitutes Used

1	2	3	4	5	6	7	8	9	10	11	Substitutes Used	
Martin	Betts	Tyrrell	Sinnott	Middlemass	Jones	McAlindon	Bass	Brodie	McGinty	Roberts	Milbourne (9), Gildea (11)	1
Martin	Betts	Tyrrell	Sinnott	Middlemass	Jones	McAlindon	Bass	Brodie	McGinty	Roberts	No subs used	2
Martin	Betts	Tyrrell	Sinnott	Middlemass	Jones	McAlindon	Bass	Brodie	McGinty	Roberts	Milbourne (8), Rennison (8)	3
Martin	Betts	Tyrrell	Sinnott	Middlemass	Jones	McAlindon	Bass	Brodie	McGinty	Roberts	Milbourne (7)	4
Martin	Betts	Tyrrell	Sinnott	Middlemass	Jones	McAlindon	Bass	Brodie	McGinty	Roberts	McNaughton (7), Rennison (5), Gildea (11)	5
Martin	Betts	Tyrrell	Sinnott	Rennison	Jones	Milbourne	Bass	Brodie	McGinty	Roberts	S Morris (7), Gildea (9), McNaughton (11)	6
Martin	Betts	Tyrrell	Sinnott	Rennison	Jones	McAlindon	Bass	Milbourne	McGinty	Roberts	S Morris (9), Harriot (2), Carr (10)	7
Woods	Betts	Tyrrell	Sinnott	Rennison	Jones	McAlindon	Bass	Brodie	McGinty	Roberts	Harriot (3), Roberts (7)	8
Woods	Betts	Harriot	Sinnott	Rennison	Jones	McAlindon	Stoker	Brodie	Middlemass	Stoker	No subs used *Roberts*	9
Woods	Betts	Harriot	Sinnott	Middlemass	Jones	Bass	Stoker	Brodie	A Morris	Roberts	Quinn (3), Rennison (6)	10
Woods	Betts	Harriot	Sinnott	Middlemass	Jones	Stoker	Bass	Brodie	A Morris	Roberts	Rennison (5), Walker (8), Quinn (3)	11
Woods	Betts	Harriot	Rennison	Middlemass	Jones	Bass	Stoker	Brodie	A Morris	Roberts	McNaughton (5), McAlindon (11)	12
Martin	Betts	Tyrrell	Rennison	Harriot	Jones	Bass	Stoker	Brodie	A Morris	Roberts	Quinn (11), McAlindon (3)	13
Woods	Betts	Russell	Sinnott	Rennison	Harriot	Quinn	Stoker	Brodie	A Morris	Carr	Tyrrell (6), Roberts (10), McAlindon (4)	14
Woods	Betts	Russell	Sinnott	Harriot	Jones	Rennison	Stoker	Brodie	McAlindon	Roberts	Middlemass (11)	15
Woods	Russell	Betts	Sinnott	Harriot	Jones	Rennison	Stoker	Brodie	McAlindon	Bogan	A Morris (11), Bass (9)	16
Woods	Russell	Betts	Sinnott	Harriot	Jones	Rennison	Stoker	Brodie	McAlindon	Roberts	A Morris (10), Bogan (11)	17
Woods	Russell	Betts	Ellender	Harriot	Jones	Rennison	Stoker	Brodie	Bass	A Morris	Roberts (5), S Morris (3)	18
Woods	Russell	Betts	Harriot	Jones	Gildea	Stoker	Brodie	Bass	Ellender	Williams	S Morris (2), A Morris (11), Rennison (4)	19
Woods	Russell	Betts	Harriot	Ellender	Jones	Bass	Stoker	Tate	Brodie	Williams	Roberts (2), S Morris (10), Gildea (11)	20
Woods	Russell	Williams	Harriot	Ellender	Jones	Bass	Stoker	Tate	Brodie	Roberts	No subs used	21
Woods	Russell	Betts	Harriot	Ellender	Sinnott	Roberts	Stoker	Tate	Brodie	Williams	S Morris (7)	22
Woods	Russell	Betts	Harriot	Ellender	Sinnott	Roberts	Stoker	Tate	Brodie	Williams	Jones (5), Bass (3), S Morris (9)	23
Woods	Betts	Williams	Harriot	Ellender	Sinnott	Jones	Stoker	Tate	Brodie	Roberts	No subs used	24
Woods	Betts	Williams	Harriot	Ellender	Sinnott	Jones	Stoker	Tate	Brodie	Roberts	Akatib (11)	25
Woods	Russelll	Betts	Harriot	Ellender	Sinnott	Jones	Stoker	Tate	McNiven	Williams	Akatib (10)	26
Woods	Russelll	Betts	Harriot	Ellender	Sinnott	Jones	Stoker	Tate	McNiven	S Morris	Roberts (10)	27
Woods	Russelll	Betts	Harriot	Ellender	Sinnott	Jones	Stoker	Tate	McNiven	S Morris	Rennison (4), Alkatib (7)	28
Woods	Betts	Russell	Rennison	Ellender	Bass	Jones	Stoker	Tate	McNiven	S Morris	Tyrrell (6) sub Brunton	29
Woods	Russell	Bettts	Rennison	Ellender	Jones	Williams	Stoker	Tate	McNiven	S Morris	Milbourne (10), McNaughton (6)	30
Woods	Russell	Bettts	Rennison	Ellender	Jones	Williams	Stoker	Tate	Brodie	Roberts	S Morris (11)	31
Woods	Russell	Bettts	Rennison	Ellender	Jones	Williams	Stoker	Tate	Brodie	Ingram	S Morris (11) sub Tyrell	32
Woods	Russell	Bettts	Rennison	Thompson	McNaughton	Morris	Stoker	Tate	Brodie	Ingram	No subs used	33
Woods	Russell	Bettts	Rennison	Ellender	Jones	Morris	Stoker	Tate	Brodie	Ingram	Harriot(2), Alkatib (7), Roberts (5)	34
Woods	Bettts	Williams	Rennison	Ellender	Jones	Ingram	Stoker	Thompson	Brodie	Roberts	Morris (7), Gildea ((11), McNaughton (6)	35
Woods	Bettts	Williams	Rennison	Ellender	Thompson	Ingram	Stoker	Tate	Brodie	Roberts	Morris (9), McNaughton (11)	36
Woods	Bettts	Williams	Rennison	Ellender	Thompson	Ingram	Stoker	Tate	Brodie	Roberts	Gildea (8), Morris (9)	37
Woods	Bettts	Williams	Rennison	Ellender	Thompson	Ingram	Stoker	Tate	Brodie	Roberts	Morris (11)	38
Woods	Ingram	Williams	Rennison	Ellender	Thompson	Jones	Stoker	Tate	Brodie	Roberts	Morris (11)	39
Woods	Ingram	Williams	Rennison	Ellender	Thompson	Jones	Stoker	Tate	Brodie	Roberts	Harriot (11), Gildea (10)	40
Woods	Ingram	Williams	Rennison	Ellender	Thompson	Jones	Stoker	Tate	Brodie	Roberts	Harriot (5), Morris (9), Gildea (11)	41
Woods	Ingram	Williams	Rennison	Betts	Thompson	Jones	Stoker	Tate	Brodie	Roberts	Harriot (7), Morris (9) sub McNaughton	42
Woods	Betts	Tyrrell	Rennison	Harriott	Jones	Bass	Stoker	Brodie	A Morris	Roberts	McAlindon,Newton,SMorris,Quinn,Middlemass	
Woods	Russell	Betts	Sinnott	Harriott	Jones	McNaughton	Stoker	Brodie	McAlindon	Bogan	AMorris,Martin,Gildea,Middlemass,Bass	
Woods	Betts	Williams	Harriott	Ellender	Sinnott	Jones	Stoker	Tate	Brodie	Roberts	Russell, Martin, Bass, Gildea, Alkhatib	
Woods	Russell	Betts	Sinnott	Harriott	Jones	Rennison	Bass	Brodie	McAlindon	A Morris	SMorris, Martin, McNaughton, Roberts, Tyrrell	
Woods	Russell	Betts	Harriott	Ellender	Sinnott	Roberts	Stoker	Tate	Brodie	Williams	Jones, Martin, Bass, Gildea, McAlindon	
Woods	Betts	Williams	Harriott	Ellender	Sinnott	Jones	Stoker	Tate	Brodie	Roberts	Bass, Martin, McAlindon, Gildea, SMorris	
Woods	Betts	Williams	Harriott	Ellender	Sinnott	Jones	Stoker	Tate	Brodie	Russell	Roberts, Martin, Bass, McNaughton, Alkhatib	
Woods	Russell	Betts	Harriott	Ellender	Sinnott	Jones	Stoker	tate	Brodie	Williams	Roberts, Martin, Bass, McNaughton, Alkhatib	
Woods	Russell	Betts	Rennison	Ellender	Sinnott	Jones	Stoker	Tate	Bass	Roberts	McNiven, Martin, McNaughton, Tyrrell, SMorris	

PLAYING SQUAD

SCARBOROUGH

Bold print denotes England semi-professional international.

Player Honours	Birthplace	D.O.B.	Previous Clubs

GOALKEEPERS

Andy Woods	Colchester	15.01.76	Halifax, Doncaster R

Andy Woods
kept 21 clean sheets
in the league last season

DEFENDERS

Lee Sinnott EY, Eu-21	Pelsall	12.07.65	Walsall, Watford, Bradford, Crystal P, Huddersfield, Oldham
Paul Ellender	Yorkshire	21.10.74	Scunthorpe, Gainsborough T, Altrincham, £50,000 Scarborough
Denny Ingram	Sunderland	27.06.76	Hartlepool
Simon Betts	Middlesbrough	03.0373	Colchester
Shaun Rennison	Northallerton	23.11.80	From Trainee
Neil Thompson GMVC	Beverley	02.10.63	Nottingham F, Hull, Scarborough, Ipswich, Barnsley, York
Danny Brunton	Bridlington	13.12.80	From Trainee

MIDFIELDERS

Gareth Stoker	Bishop Auckland	22.02.73	Leeds, Hull, Hereford U, Cardiff, Rochdale
Marcus Jones	Stone	24.06.74	Stoke, Chasetown, Bolehall Swifts, Willenhall T, Hinckley Ath., VS Rugby, Telford U
Steve Brodie	Sunderland	14.01.73	Sunderland
Matthew Russell	Leeds	17.01.78	Scarborough, Halifax, £5,000 to Scarborough
Gareth Williams	Newport IOW	12.03.67	Gosport B, Aston Villa, Barnsley, Bournemouth, Northampton, Scarborough, Hull

FORWARDS

Chris Tate	York	27.12.77	York, Sunderland, Scarborough, Halifax
Ian Milbourne	Bradford	21.01.79	Newcastle
Stewart Morris	Newcastle	21.09.80	From Trainee

SOUTHPORT

What a roller coaster ride Southport gave their supporters last season.

Even as late as Easter, 'Port looked in danger of ending their six-year tenure in the Conference.

Their early season form cost Paul Futcher his job and a few eyebrows were raised when ex-Liverpool and England star Mark Wright was appointed.

With no previous experience of non-League football, it was indeed a gamble on Southport's part but, like Kidderminster Harriers' decision to appoint another former Anfield favourite Jan Molby, it now looks like being a master stroke.

Wright has taken Southport from being relegation candidates to being amongst the pre-season favourites for the title - some change that in six months!

It was clear to see where Wright saw his priorities, and his 500-odd game professional career as as a quality defender obviously rubbed off on his own players, with Phil Bolland seemingly benefitting most, ending the campaign as a double player of the year.

Summer recruitment seems to have put Southport in the frame and it looks as though Sandgrounders' fans will have an enjoyable season.

Steve Whitney

Back Row: Dave Linighan, Simon Parke, Phil Bolland, Robert Pell. Middle: Barry Hedley (Chief Scout), Mark Stuart, Stuart Whittaker, Noureddine Maamria, Shaun Teale, Steve Dickinson, Martin Clark, Mike Marsh, Wes hall (Kit NManager), Neil Grayston, Scott Guyett, Brett Harris (Physio). Front: Lee Furlong, Ian Arnold, Mark Wright (Manager), Andy Gouck (Captain), Ted McMinn (Asst. Manager), Carl Macauley, Lee Elam.

Photo courtesy of Southport Visiter

SOUTHPORT

GROUND DETAILS

Haig Avenue,
Southport,
Merseyside. PR8 6JZ

TELEPHONE: Ground: 01704 533422
Ticket Office: 01704 533422
Fax: 01704 533422

SIMPLE DIRECTIONS:
From M6 - M58 through Ormskirk (A570) to Southport.
Straight on at Tesco/McDonalds roundabout.
Right at the mini roundabout and the ground is on the right

CAPACITY: 6,008
SEATED: 1,660
COVERED TERRACING: 1,100

SOCIAL FACILITIES:
Clubhouse open 6.00-11.00 every night and match days.
Tel: 01704 530182

CLUB SHOP: New shop opened 1999.
Scarves, replica kits and large range of souvenirs for sale.
Contact D Hitchcock, c/o Southport F.C or

e-mail: derek@hitchcock98.freeserve.co.uk

Pages: 40   Price: £1.50

Editor: Derek Hitchcock (0976 555782)

Other club publications: None

Local Press: Southport Visiter; The Champion
Local Radio: Dune F.M.; Radio Merseyside; Red
Rose, Radio City; Radio Lancashire

Founded:	1881
Nickname:	The Sandgrounders
Club Sponsors:	Apollo Leisure
Club colours:	Old Gold & black
Change colours:	tbc
Midweek home matchday:	Tuesday
Reserves' League:	Lancashire League

CLUB OFFICIALS

President Jack Carr

Chairman Charles Clapham
Directors C Clapham, B J Hedley, A Pope, P Abrams,
T Medcroft, J Carr, S Porter, S Shrouder.

Football Secretary Ken Hilton
34 Mill Lane, Burscough, Ormskirk, Lancs. L40 5TS
Tel: 01704 894504 (H) 01704 840775 (B)

**Sales &
Marketing Manager** Derek Hitchcock
Tel: 0976 555782
e-mail: derek@hitchcock98.freeserve.co.uk
Press Officer Derek Hitchcock

FOOTBALL MANAGEMENT TEAM

MANAGER: MARK WRIGHT

Date of Appointment   December 1999
Date of Birth: 1st August 1963
Place of Birth: Dorchester (Ox.)

PREVIOUS CLUBS
As manager   None
As player   Oxford Utd., Southampton, Derby Co.,
Liverpool
HONOURS
As manager   N/A
As player   England: u21: 4; E: 45
FAC '92

*   *   *

Assistant Manager: Ted McMinn
Reserve Team Coach: Mike Vaughan
Physiotherapist: Chris Goodson
Youth development: tbc

Season	League	Div.	Pos.	P	W	D	L	F	A	W	D	L	F	A	Pts	Manager
						Home						Away				
99-00	Conference	-	9	42	10	5	6	31	21	5	8	8	24	35	58	Paul Futcher / Mark Wright
98-99	Conference	-	18	42	6	9	6	29	28	4	6	11	18	31	45	Paul Futcher
97-98	Conference	-	16	42	9	5	7	32	26	4	6	11	24	32	50	Paul Futcher
96-97	Conference	-	11	42	8	5	8	27	28	7	5	9	24	33	55	Steve Joel / Ronnie Moore

Season	League	Div.	Pos.	P	W	D	L	F	A	Pts	Manager
95-96	Conference	-	6	42	18	12	12	77	64	66	Billy Ayre
94-95	Conference	-	3	42	21	9	12	68	50	72	Brian Kettle/Billy Ayre
93-94	Conference	-	4	42	18	12	12	57	51	66	Brian Kettle
92-93	N.P.L.	Premier	1	42	29	9	4	103	31	96	Brian Kettle
91-92	N.P.L.	Premier	7	42	16	17	9	57	48	65	Brian Kettle
90-91	N.P.L.	Premier	5	40	18	14	8	66	48	68	Brian Kettle

HONOURS

FA Trophy R-up 97-98;

Football League Division Four Champions 1972/73
Runners-up 1966/67;

Third Division North Section Cup 1937/38;

Northern Premier League 1992/93
League Cup 1990/91, League Shield 1993/94;

Liverpool Senior Cup 1930/31, 1931/32, 1943/44,
1957/58 (shared), 1963/64 (shared), 1974/75,
1990/91, 1992/93, 1998/99;

Lancashire Senior Cup 1904/05;
Lancashire Junior Cup 1919/20, 1992/93, 1996-97,
1997-98

PREVIOUS

Leagues: Northern Premier League,
Football League,
Lancashire Combination

Grounds: Ash Lane

Names: Southport Central; Southport Vulcan

Past Players who progressed to the Football League

Shaun Teale,
Andy Mutch,
Steve Whitehall,
Tony Rodwell

CLUB RECORDS

Attendance: 20,010 v Newcastle United
FA Cup - 1932

Record win: 8-1 v Nelson - 01.01.31

Record defeat: 0-11 v Oldham - 26.12.62

Career goalscorer: Alan Spence 98

Career appearances: Arthur Peat 401 - 1962-72

Transfer fee paid: £20,000
for Martin McDonald from Macclesfield Town - 1995

Transfer fee received: £25,000
from Rochdale for Steve Whitehall - 1991

BEST SEASON

FA Cup: Quarter Final, 1931-32.
Lost to Newcastle Utd
(The first Division 3 North team to reach the Quarter Finals)

FA Trophy: Runners-up 97-98,
0-1 v Cheltenham Town

League: Football League Div. 3 ??th

LAST SEASON

F.A. Cup: 1st Round
F.A. Trophy: 6th Round replay
Conference: 9th
Top Goalscorer: Ian Arnold 17
Player of the Year: Phill Bolland
Captain: Andy Gouck

SOUTHPORT

	Date	Comp.	H/A	Opponents	Gate	Result & Score		Goalscorers	League Position
1	14.08	N.C.	H	Woking	1,378	W	4-1	Gouck 4, Elam 32, 46, Furlong 80	
2	17.08	N.C.	H	Scarborough	1,632	D	2-2	Arnold 81, Sinnott 88 (o.g.)	
3	21.08	N.C.	A	Kingstonian	1,027	L	2-4	Bolland 28, Woods 37	12
4	24.08	N.C.	A	Doncaster R	4,285	D	1-1	Smart 60	
5	28.08	N.C.	H	Forest Green R	1,241	W	2-1	Arnold 7, 85 (Pen)	7
6	30.08	N.C.	A	Atrincham	1,226	L	0-3		12
7	04.09	N.C.	A	Hayes	637	W	2-0	Arnold 12 (pen), Guyett 85	9
8	11.09	N.C.	H	Hereford United	1,287	L	0-1		12
9	18.09	N.C.	A	Rushden & Ds	2,619	L	2-4	Guyett 17, Arnold 27 (pen).	15
10	25.09	N.C.	H	Sutton United	1,122	D	1-1	Elam 73	15
11	02.10	N.C.	A	Nuneaton Borough	2,519	W	2-0	Arnold 30, Elam 89	12
12	09.10	N.C.	H	Welling United	1,003	W	3-2	Stuart 6, Arnold 50, Woods 82	11
13	23.10	N.C.	A	Yeovil Town	2,217	D	1-1	Elam 54	12
14	06.11	N.C.	A	Kettering Town	1,032	L	0-1		15
15	13.11	N.C.	A	Kidderminster Harriers	1,404	L	0-5		16
16	20.11	N.C.	H	Dover Athletic	1,015	L	1-2	Stuart 83	17
17	04.12	N.C.	A	Hereford United	2,610	L	1-2	Elam 82	18
18	18.12	N.C.	H	Northwich Victoria	1,352	L	0-1		20
19	27.12	N.C.	A	Morecambe	3,583	D	3-3	Morley 5, Clark 10, Gouck 47	21
20	03.01	N.C.	H	Morecambe	2,202	D	1-1	Arnold 59 (pen)	20
21	08.01	N.C.	A	Woking	2026	D	0-0		20
22	22.01	N.C.	H	Hednesford Town	1122	W	2-0	Arnold 39, 41	19
23	25.01	N.C.	A	Telford United	1037	D	0-0		
24	29.01	N.C.	A	Sutton United	850	D	1-1	Pell 47	19
25	12.02	N.C.	H	Yeovil Town	1,343	D	1-1	Elam 70	18
26	19.02	N.C.	A	Forest Green Rovers	903	L	0-1		19
27	29.02	N.C.	A	Scarborough	1,002	L	0-3		19
28	04.03	N.C.	H	Hayes	1,097	W	4-1	Bolland 28, Elam 52, Pell 66, Mike 86	19
29	18.03	N.C.	A	Kettering Town	1,209	W	3-0	Furlong 17, Stuart 32, Guyett 45	19
30	21.03	N.C.	H	Doncaster Rovers	1,156	W	1-0	Guyett 84	16
31	25.03	N.C.	H	Stevenage Borough	1,310	W	2-1	Bolland 16, McNiven 21	16
32	01.04	N.C.	A	Northwich Victoria	1,127	W	1-0	Grayston 45	13
33	04.04	N.C.	H	Nuneaton Borough	1,064	W	2-0	Elam 44, Arnold 70 (p)	12
34	08.04	N.C.	A	Welling United	672	L	1-4	Furlong 54	12
35	11.04	N.C.	H	Telford United	1,010	L	1-3	Arnold 68	12
36	15.04	N.C.	H	Kidderminster Harriers	2,033	L	0-1		12
37	22.04	N.C.	H	Rushden & Diamonds	1,590	W	2-1	Arnold 41 (p), Elam 90	
38	24.04	N.C.	A	Hednesford Town	850	W	2-1	Stuart 13, 69	10
39	29.04	N.C.	A	Dover Athletic	773	D	1-1	Elam 28	
40	01.05	N.C.	H	Altrincham	1,427	W	2-0	Arnold 59, Guyett 83	10
41	04.05	N.C.	H	Kingstonian	1,039	D	0-0		
42	06.05	N.C.	A	Stevenage Borough	1,485	D	1-1	Stuart 45	9

Mark Wright takes over as manager

CUP COMPETITIONS

F.A. Cup

	Date	Round	H/A	Opponents	Gate	Result & Score		Goalscorers	
	16.10	4Q	H	Emley	1,310	D	1-1	Gouck 50	
	18.10	4Q R	A	Emley		W	2-0	Arnold 9p), Ellison	
	30.10	1	A	Darlington	4,313	L	1-2	Bolland 52	

Nationwide McMillan Trophy

	04.10	1	A	Morecambe	468	W	2-1	Ellison 50, Courtney 85	
	09.11	2	H	Scarborough	339	L	1-2	Stuart 84	

F.A. Trophy

	27.11	2	A	Barrow	1,334	W	3-2	Doherty 12, Arnold 65, 67	
	15.01	3	H	Altrincham	1387	D	0-0		
	18.01	3R	A	Altrincham	766	D	1-1*	Pell	Won 4-3 after penalties
	05.02	4	H	Emley	1,272	W	2-0	Pell 39, Elam 46	
	26.02	5	H	Woking	1,560	W	3-0	Arnold 25(p), Grayston 70, Pell 90	
	11.03	6	A	Kingstonian	1,201	D	0-0		
	14.03	6R	H	Kingstonian	1,576	L	0-1		

1	2	3	4	5	6	7	8	9	10	11	Substitutes Used	
Dickinson	Clark	Formby	Morley	Guyett	Ryan	Elam	Gouck	Arnold	Woods	Stuart	Furlong (9), Grayston (4), Ellison (10)	1
Dickinson	Clark	Grayston	Morley	Guyett	Ryan	Elam	Gouck	Arnold	Woods	Stuart	Furlong (11), Ellison (10)	2
Dickinson	Bolland	Formby	Morley	Guyett	Ryan	Elam	Gouck	Arnold	Woods	Stuart	Furlong (9), Ellison (10), Grayston (8)	3
Dickinson	Bolland	Formby	Morley	Guyett	Ryan	Elam	Gouck	Arnold	Woods	Stuart	Furlong (7), Grayston (9)	4
Dickinson	Bolland	Formby	Morley	Guyett	Ryan	Elam	Gouck	Arnold	Ellison	Stuart	Grayston (4), Woods (7), Furlong (10)	5
Dickinson	Clark	Formby	Morley	Guyett	Ryan	Elam	Gouck	Arnold	Woods	Grayston	Stuart (11), Furlong (9)	6
Dickinson	Clark	Formby	Morley	Bolland	Ryan	Elam	Guyett	Arnold	Ellison	Stuart	Grayston (7), Woods (10)	7
Dickinson	Clark	Formby	Morley	Bolland	Ryan	Elam	Guyett	Arnold	Ellison	Stuart	Gouck (4), Furlong (10)	8
Dickinson	Clark	Formby	Guyett	Bolland	Ryan	Elam	Gouck	Arnold	Woods	Stuart	Taylor (5), Ellison (10), Furlong (11)	9
Dickinson	Bolland	Formby	Grayston	Guyett	Ryan	Elam	Gouck	Arnold	Ellison	Stuart	Furlong (10), Clark (4)	10
Dickinson	Clark	Formby	Guyett	Bolland	Ryan	Grayston		Arnold	Ellison	Stuart	Woods (10), Elam (9)	11
Dickinson	Clark	Formby	Guyett	Bolland	Ryan	Elam	Gouck	Arnold	Ellison	Stuart	Grayston (7), Woods (10)	12
Dickinson	Clark	Grayston	Guyett	Bolland	Ryan	Woods	Gouck	Arnold	Ellison	Stuart	Elam (4), Morley (10)	13
Dickinson	Clark	Grayston	Woods	Bolland	Ryan	Elam	Gouck	Arnold	Ellison	Stuart	Morley (10), Furlong (9)	14
Dickinson	Clark	Formby	Morley	Guyett	Ryan	Elam	Grayston	Arnold	Woods	Stuart	Courtney (10), Trundle (7)	15
Dickinson	Guyett	Grayston	Morley	Bolland	Ryan	Elam	Gouck	Arnold	Furlong	Stuart	Trundle (10), Courtney (7)	16
Dickinson	Guyett	Grayston	Morley	Bolland	Ryan	Clark	Gouck	Arnold	Furlong	Stuart	Elam (7), Trundle (10)	17
Dickinson	Guyett	Grayston	Morley	Bolland	Ryan	Clark	Gouck	Arnold	Furlong	Elam	Ellison (9), Trundle (10)	18
Dickinson	Guyett	Grayston	Morley	Bolland	Ryan	Clark	Gouck	Arnold	Mike	Elam	Furlong (11), Formby (3)	19
Dickinson	Guyett	Stuart	Morley	Bolland	Ryan	Clark	Grayston	Arnold	Mike	Elam	Pell (3)	20
Dickinson	Guyett	Grayston	Morley	Bolland	Ryan	Clark	Gouck	Arnold	Mike	Pell	Formby (8), Elam (9), Furlong (11)	21
Dickinson	Guyett	Stuart	Morley	Bolland	Ryan	Clark	Grayston	Arnold	Mike	Elam	Pell (10)	22
Dickinson	Guyett	Stuart	Morley	Bolland	Ryan	Clark	Grayston	Arnold	Mike	Elam	Pell (10), Furlong (11)	23
Dickinson	Guyett	Stuart	Morley	Bolland	Ryan	Clark	Grayston	Arnold	Pell	Elam	Furlong (11)	24
Dickinson	Guyett	Stuart	Morley	Bolland	Ryan	Clark	Grayston	Mike	Pell	Elam	No subs used	25
Dickinson	Guyett	Stuart	Morley	Bolland	Clark	Gouck	Grayston	Pell	Elam	Takano	Mike (9), Arnold (11)	26
Dickinson	Guyett	Stuart	Morley	Bolland	Grayston	Clark	Gouck	Arnold	Pell	Elam	Ellison (11), Formby (6), Mike (10)	27
Dickinson	Grayston	Stuart	Morley	Bolland	Ryan	Clark	Gouck	Arnold	Pell	Elam	Formby (3), Mike (10), Trundle (11)	28
Dickinson	Guyett	Stuart	Morley	Bolland	Ryan	Clark	Grayston	Arnold	Furlong	Elam	Takano (10)	29
Dickinson	Guyett	Stuart	Morley	Bolland	Grayston	Clark	Gouck	Arnold	Furlong	Elam	Deveraux (11), Takano (3), Mike (10)	30
Dickinson	Guyett	Stuart	Morley	Bolland	Ryan	Deveraux	Gouck	Arnold	McNiven	Grayston	Lyons (7), Clark (3), Elam (10)	31
Dickinson	Guyett	Grayston	Morley	Bolland	Ryan	Clark	Gouck	Arnold	McNiven	Elam	Furlong (10), Deveraux (11)	32
Dickinson	Guyett	Grayston	Morley	Bolland	Ryan	Clark	Gouck	Arnold	Furlong	Elam	McNiven (11)	33
Dickinson	Guyett	Grayston	Morley	Bolland	Ryan	Clark	Gouck	Arnold	McNiven	Furlong	Elam (10), Gummer (7)	34
Dickinson	Guyett	Stuart	Morley	Bolland	Ryan	Clark	Gouck	Arnold	McNiven	Furlong	Deveraux (3), Mike (10), Elam (11)	35
Dickinson	Guyett	Stuart	Morley	Bolland	Ryan	Clark	Gouck	Arnold	McNiven	Grayston	Deveraux (7), Furlong (3), Mike (11)	36
Dickinson	Guyett	Stuart	Grayston	Formby	Ryan	Clark	Deveraux	Arnold	Mike	Takano	Furlong (8), Elam (11), McNiven (10)	37
Dickinson	Guyett	Stuart	Grayston	Formby	Ryan	Clark	Gouck	Arnold	Mike	Deveraux	Furlong (5), Elam (11), McNiven (10)	38
Dickinson	Guyett	Stuart	Grayston	Formby	Ryan	Clark	Gouck	Arnold	Furlong	Elam	McNiven (5)	39
Dickinson	Guyett	Stuart	Grayston	Bolland	Ryan	Clark	Gouck	Arnold	McNiven	Mike	Elam (11), Morley (10)	40
Dickinson	Guyett	Stuart	Morley	Bolland	Ryan	Clark	Grayston	Arnold	McNiven	Elam	Formby (2), Furlong (10)	41
Dickinson	Grayston	Stuart	Morley	Bolland	Ryan	Clark	Formby	Arnold	McNiven	Elam	Furlong (9)	42

1	2	3	4	5	6	7	8	9	10	11	Substitutes Used
Dickinson	Clark	Grayston	Guyett	Bolland	Ryan	Woods	Gouck	Arnold	Ellison	Stuart	Elam (5), Furlong (10)
Dickinson	Clark	Grayston	Morley	Guyett	Ryan	Woods	Gouck	Arnold	Ellison	Stuart	no subs used
Dickinson	Clark	Grayston	Guyett	Bolland	Ryan	Woods	Gouck	Arnold	Ellison	Stuart	Elam (4), Furlong (9)

1	2	3	4	5	6	7	8	9	10	11	Substitutes Used
Stuart	Clark	Formby	Woods	Bolland	Cullen	Elam	Gouck	Furlong	Ellison	Grayston	Courtney (9), Stuart (8), Arnold (7)
Dickinson	Clark	Formby	Morley	Guyett	Ryan	Elam	Grayston	Arnold	Woods	Stuart	Furlong (10), Trundle (8)

1	2	3	4	5	6	7	8	9	10	11	Substitutes Used
Dickinson	Guyett	Grayston	Morley	Bolland	Ryan	Elam	Gouck	Arnold	Furlong	Stuart	Trundle (10), Clarke (7)
Dickinson	Guyett	Stuart	Morley	Bolland	Ryan	Clark	Grayston	Pell	Mike	Elam	Furlong (9)
Dickinson	Guyett	Formby	Stuart	Bolland	Ryan	Clark	Grayston	Furlong	Mike	Elam	Pell (9), Ellison (3), Trundle (10)
Dickinson	Guyett	Stuart	Morley	Bolland	Ryan	Clark	Grayston	Arnold	Pell	Elam	Ellison (9), Mike (10)
Dickinson	Guyett	Stuart	Morley	Grayston	Ryan	Clark	Gouck	Arnold	Pell	Elam	no subs used
Dickinson	Guyett	Formby	Morley	Bolland	Grayston	Clark	Gouck	Arnold	Furlong	Elam	Pell (9) sub Mike
Dickinson	Guyett	Stuart	Morley	Bolland	Ryan	Clark	Gouck	Arnold	Mike	Grayston	Elam (3), Furlong (10)

PLAYING SQUAD

(Bold print indicates an England Semi-Professional International)

Player Honours	Birthplace	D.O.B.	Previous Clubs

GOALKEEPERS

Steve Dickinson	Bradford		Bradford C, Guiseley

DEFENDERS

Scott Guyett DMP	Australia		Brisbane C, Gresley R
Shaun Teale ESP	Southport	10.03.64	Southport, Northwich V, Weymouth, Bournemouth, Aston Villa, Tranmere, Happy Valley, Motherwell, Carlisle
Phil Bolland	Manchester		Altrincham, Salford C, Trafford, Knowsley U, Altrincham
Neil Grayston	Keighley	25.11.75	Bradford C, Bradford PA
David Linighan	Hartlepool	09.01.65	Hartlepool, Derby, Shrewsbury, Ipswich, Blackpool, Dunfermline, Mansfield
Carl Macauley	Liverpool		Manchester C, Witton Alb., Vauxhall GM, Prescot Cables, Barrow, Telford U
Martin Clark	Accrington	12..09.70	Preston, Lancaster C, Accrington Stanley, Crewe

MIDFIELDERS

Andy Gouck	Blackpool	08.06.72	Blackpool, Rochdale
Mark Stuart	Chiswick	15.12.66	Charlton, Plymouth, Bradford C, Huddersfield, Rochdale
Mike Marsh NC	Liverpool	21.07.69	Kirkby T, Liverpool, West Ham, Coventry, Galatasaray, Southend, Barrow, Southport, Kidderminster H
John Deary	Ormskirk	18.10.62	Blackpool, Burnley, Rochdale
Lee Elam	Bradford		Guiseley

FORWARDS

Ian Arnold ESP	Durham	04.07.72	Middlesbrough, Carlisle, Kettering T, Stalybridge C, Kidderminster H, £10,000 to Southport
Lee Furlong	Blackpool		Youth team
Noureddine Maamria Tunisia u-21	Tunisia	26.05.71	Ayr U, Doncaster R
Simon Parke	Bradford		Bradford PA, Guiseley
Robert Pell	Leeds	05.02.79	Rotherham

STEVENAGE BOROUGH

The 1999/2000 season was a real mixed bag for Borough.

So stable for years under the managership of Paul Fairclough, Stevenage suddenly found themselves going through three bosses during the season.

Richard Hill, who succeeded Fairclough, was fired midway through and former Boreham Wood manager Bob Makin, who had re-joined chairman Phil Wallace in a general managers' role, took charge temporarily and things picked up on the field.

The club took their time in appointing a successor to Hill and speculation was rife for months. In the end they plumped for erstwhile Colchester boss Steve Wignall, who had done such a marvellous job at Aldershot Town previously.

Sadly for Borough, despite the months it took searching for what they had assumed was the right man, Wignall upped sticks and left for another of his previous clubs Doncaster Rovers just six weeks after settling in at Broadhall Way.

Despair turned to joy for Borough fans, however, when the summer saw the return of the hugely popular Paul Fairclough as manager. He really should never have left in the first place and jumped at the chance to return.

He faces a big task now if the club are to return to their former glories and they will have to do so without top scorer Carl Alford. But I have the feeling they will be okay now that the right man is in place at the helm.

Steve Whitney

Back Row: Paul Armstrong, Robert Miller, Kofi Nyamah, gary Wraight, Darren Hay, Mark Graham, Neill Illman. **Middle:** Terry (Kit Man), Sam McMahon, Christian Metcalfe, Richard Leadbeater, Chris Taylor, Paul Wilkerson, Danny Hockton, Ross Harrison. **Front:** Kevin Hales (Asst. Man.), Ryan Kirby, Nathan Bunce, Paul Fairclough (Manager), Robin Trott, Mark Smith, Keith Allinson (Physio)

STEVENAGE BOROUGH

GROUND DETAILS

**Stevenage Stadium,
Broadhall Way,
Stevenage,
Herts SG2 8RH**

Tel: 01438 223223
Fax: 01438 743666
email: ???????
Web site: http://www.stevenageborofc.com

SIMPLE DIRECTIONS:
Stevenage South exit off A1(M) - ground on right at second roundabout.Spectators are however advised to go straight on at this roundabout and park inthe Showground opposite the stadium. The stadium is one mile from Stevenage BRstation. Buses SB4 and SB5

CAPACITY:	6,546
SEATED:	2,002
COVERED TERRACING:	2,000

Groundsman: Colin Payne

CLUB SHOP: Mon - Sat 9-5.30. Broadhall Way, Stevenage. 01438 218061. Sells a complete range of club merchandise including a customising service. Mail Order, credit cards accepted, contact Emma Doherty (01438 218061)

SOCIAL FACILITIES:
Tel.: 01438 218079. Clubhouse at ground open Monday to Friday 7 - 11pm,Saturday noon - 2.00 & 4.30 - 11pm, Sunday: All day from noon. Contact: PamTerry

For up to the minute news, results, fixtures, plus general facts & figures from the world of non-league football

log on to

www.nlfootball.com

Nickname:	Boro'
Club Sponsors:	Sun Banking Corporation
Club colours:	White & red shirts, black & white trim shorts and white with red trim socks
Change colours:	Blue shirts, blue shorts, blue socks
Midweek home matchday:	Monday
Reserve Team's League:	Capital League
Programme:	Pages: 36 Price: £1.50 Editor: Steve Watkins Tel: 01438 318891
Other club publications:	The Borough Yearbook
Local Press:	Stevenage Gazette; Comet; Stevenage Mercury; Herald
Local Radio:	Chiltern Radio; BBC Three Counties Radio

CLUB OFFICIALS

Chairman	Phillip Wallace
Club Administrator (Including Press work)	Roger Austin 01438 218072
Commercial Manager	Clive Abrey 01438 218073

FOOTBALL MANAGEMENT TEAM

MANAGER: **PAUL FAIRCLOUGH**

Date of Appointment	2000
Date of Birth	31st January 1950
Place of Birth	Liverpool

PREVIOUS CLUBS

As manager	Hertford Town, Stevenage Bor. (90-99)
As coach	Hemel Hempstead, Finchley
As player	Harlow Town, St Albans City, Hertford Town

HONOURS

As manager	GMVC 95-96, Isthmian Prem 93-94, Div. 1 91-92
As player	None

Assistant Manager	Kevin Hales
1st Team Coach	Kevin Hales
Reserve Team Manager	Neil Trebble
Physiotherapist	Keith Allinson
Chief Scout	Robbie Morgan
Scouts	Steve Williams, Keith Blackham, Frank Radcliffe, Peter Lawrence

Season	League	Div.	Pos.	Home						Away					Pts	Manager
				P	W	D	L	F	A	W	D	L	F	A		
99-00	Conference	-	10	42	8	5	8	26	20	8	4	9	34	34	57	Richard Hill / Steve Wignall /
98-99	Conference	-	6	42	9	9	3	37	23	8	8	5	25	22	68	Paul Fairclough / Richard Hill
97-98	Conference	-	15	42	8	8	5	35	27	5	4	12	24	36	51	Paul Fairclough
96-97	Conference	-	3	42	15	4	2	53	23	9	6	6	34	30	82	Paul Fairclough

Season	League	Div.	Pos.	P	W	D	L	F	A	Pts	Manager
95-96	Conference	-	1	42	27	10	5	101	44	91	Paul Fairclough
94-95	Conference	-	5	42	20	7	15	68	49	67	Paul Fairclough
93-94	Isthmian	Prem.	1	42	31	4	7	88	39	97	Paul Fairclough
92-93	Isthmian	Prem.	7	42	18	8	16	62	60	62	Paul Fairclough
91-92	Isthmian	One	1	40	24	10	6	83	34	82	Paul Fairclough
90-91	Isthmian	2 North	1	42	34	5	3	122	29	107	Paul Fairclough

HONOURS

GM Vauxhall Conference 95-96,
Isthmian Lge Prem 93-94,
Div 1 91-92, Div 2 (North) 85-86 90-91;
Utd Counties Lg Div 1 80-81 (Div 1 Cup 80-81),
Herts SnrCup R-up 85-86, 93/94;
Herts Charity Cup R-up 93-94,
Herts Charity Shield R-up83-84,
Televised Sports Snr Floodlit Cup 89-90,
Eastern Professional F'lit Cup Group winner
81-82 85-86 86-87 88-89 90-91 91-92,
South Co's Comb. Cup 91-92;
Essex & Herts Border Comb.(Reserves) 94/95
Essex & Herts (Western Div) 95-96

PREVIOUS

Leagues: Chiltern Youth 76-79;
Wallspan South Combination 79-80;
United Counties 80-84;
Isthmian 84-94

Grounds: King George V Playing Field 1976-80

Past Players who progressed to the Football League

Richard Wilmot & NeilTrebble (Scunthorpe Utd) 1993,
Simon Clark (Peterborough United) 1994,
Leo Fortune West (Gillingham) 1995,
Phil Simpson (Barnet) 1995,
Barry Hayles (Bristol C.) 1997)

CLUB RECORDS

Attendance: 6,489 v Kidderminster H.,
GM Vauxhall Conference 25.1.97

Win: 11-1 v British Timken Athletic (H),
United Counties League Div.1, 1980-81

Defeat: 0-7 v Southwick (H),
Isthmian League Div. 1, 1987-88

Career goalscorer: Barry Hayles

Career appearances: Martin Gittings

Transfer fee paid: £20,000
for Richard Leadbetter to Hereford United 1999

Transfer fee received: £300,000
for Barry Hayles (Bristol R.) July 97

BEST SEASON

FA Cup: Fourth Round replay 97-98.
1-2 v Newcastle Utd. (A) after 1-1
also 3rd Round 1996-97.
0-2 v Birmingham City (A)
League clubs defeated: Leyton Orient 96-97;
Cambridge Utd., Swindon Town 97-98

FA Trophy: Semi Final 96-97.
1-2 v Woking in Replay at Watford

League: Conference Champions 95-96

LAST SEASON

F.A. Cup: 4th Qualifying Round
F.A. Trophy: 3rd Round
Conference: 10th
Top Goalscorer: Carl Alford 26
Player of the Year: Dean Martin
Captain: Mark Smith

STEVENAGE BOROUGH

Match Facts 1999-00

	Date	Comp.	H/A	Opponents	Gate	Result & Score	Goalscorers	League Position
1	14.08	N.C.	A	Altrincham	853	W 1-0	Strouts 30	
2	16.08	N.C.	H	Doncaster Rovers	3,361	W 3-0	Alford 14, Love 24, 90	
3	21.08	N.C.	H	Telford United	2,191	W 2-0	Alford 35,Samuels 38	1
4	24.08	N.C.	A	Sutton United	1,152	W 2-0	Samuels 41, 69	1
5	28.08	N.C.	A	Scarborough	2,291	W 3-1	Alford 15, 86 (pen), Samuels 82	1
6	30-08	N.C.	H	Kettering Town	4,017	W 3-0	Alford 6, McMahon 74, Strouts 82.	1
7	04.09	N.C.	H	Kidderminster Harriers	2,894	L 0-2		1
8	11.09	N.C.	A	Hednesford United	1,525	D 2-2	Howarth 11, Alford 67	1
9	18.09	N.C.	A	Hereford United	2,143	W 2-1	Strouts 52, Alford 67	1
10	25.09	N.C.	H	Kingstonian	2,775	L 0-1		1
11	02.10	N.C.	A	Forest Green Rovers	963	L 2-3	Alford 29, 40	4
12	09.10	N.C.	H	Morecambe	2,039	L 1-2	Alford 27	5
13	23.10	N.C.	A	Northwich Victoria	1,010	D 3-3	Trott 34, Alford 72, 90	5
14	30.10	N.C.	A	Dover Athletic	1,001	L 2-4	Leadbeater 47, Alford 90.	5
15	06.11	N.C.	H	Scarborough	1,743	L 0-1		8
16	14.11	N.C.	A	Hayes	906	W 2-1	Wraight 44, Alford 60	7
17	04.12	N.C.	A	Doncaster Rovers	2,631	W 2-1	Samuels 83, Martin 87	7
18	11.12	N.C.	H	Dover Athletic	1,853	W 3-1	Alford 7, 42, Leadbeater 26	7
19	18.12	N.C.	H	Woking	2,992	L 0-1		7
20	27.12	N.C.	A	Rushden & D.	5,721	L 1-2	Alford 60	9
21	03.01	N.C.	H	Rushden & D.	4,373	D 2-2	Miller 14, Kirby 83	9
22	08.01	N.C.	A	Morecambe	1518	D 3-3	Alford 1, 23, Morrison 10	9
23	22.01	N.C.	A	Welling United	710	L 1-2	Alford 45 (p)	10
24	29.01	N.C.	H	Altrincham	1762	D 1-1	Leadbeater 29	9
25	05.02	N.C.	H	Nuneaton Borough	1,711	W 2-1	Alford 17, Hockton 45	7
26	12.02	N.C.	A	Woking	2,318	W 2-0	Hockton 25, 35	5
27	16.02	N.C.	A	Kingstonian	1,034	L 0-1		6
28	19.02	N.C.	H	Northwich Vics.	1,586	W 3-1	Hockton 9, Alford 27, 66(p)	5
29	28.02	N.C.	H	Hereford United	1,940	L 0-3		6
30	04.03	N.C.	A	Kidderminster H.	2,832	L 1-3	Alford 19	7
31	11.03	N.C.	H	Welling United	1,581	L 0-1		8
32	18.03	N.C.	H	Hednesford Town	1,213	L 0-1		8
33	25.03	N.C.	A	Southport	1,310	L 1-2	Wraight 58	11
34	01.04	N.C.	H	Hayes	1,617	W 3-0	Hockton 7, Kirby 75, Leadbeater 90	9
35	04.04	N.C.	A	Yeovil Town	1,455	D 2-2	Forbes 20, Hockton 88	10
36	08.04	N.C.	H	Forest Green R.	1,479	D 1-1	Leadbeater 90	10
37	17.04	N.C.	H	Yeovil Town	1,452	D 0-0		10
38	22.04	N.C.	A	Telford United	1,828	L 1-2	Kirby 55	
39	24.04	N.C.	H	Sutton United	1,485	W 1-0	Pearson 85	9
40	29.04	N.C.	A	Nuneaton Borough	1,250	W 1-0	Martin 48	
41	01.05	N.C.	A	Kettering Town	1,575	L 0-1		8
42	06.05	N.C.	H	Southport	1,485	D 1-1	Martin 16	10

CUP COMPETITIONS

F.A. Cup

16.10	4Q	H	Bath City	845	D 1-1	Strouts 45
19.10	4Q R	A	Bath City	1,427	L 0-1	

Nationwide McMillan Trophy

09.11	2	A	Woking	791	L 1-3	Alford 33

F.A. Trophy

27.11	2	A	Merthyr Tydfil	583	D 0-0	
15.01	3	A	Yeovil Town	2604	L 1-2	Kirby 71

1	2	3	4	5	6	7	8	9	10	11	Substitutes Used	#
Taylor C	Harvey	Love	Smith	Trott	Howarth	Kirby	McMahon	Alford	Samuels	Strouts	Leadbeater (10), Plummer (9)	1
Taylor C	Harvey	Love	Smith	Trott	Howarth	Kirby	McMahon	Alford	Samuels	Strouts	McGhee (11), Leadbeater (10)	2
Taylor C	Harvey	Love	Smith	Trott	Howarth	Kirby	McMahon	Alford	Samuels	Strouts	McGhee(11)Leadbeater(9)Pearson(10)	3
Taylor C	Harvey	Love	Smith	Trott	Howarth	Kirby	McMahon	Alford	Samuels	Strouts	Leadbeater(10), Plummer (8)	4
Taylor C	Harvey	Love	Smith	Plummer	Howarth	Kirby	McMahon	Alford	Samuels	Strouts	Harrison(5), Naylor(10), Pearson (9)	5
Taylor C	Harvey	Love	Smith	Trott	Howarth	Kirby	McMahon	Alford	Samuels	Strouts	Harrison(30) Leadbeater(10) Naylor(2)	6
Taylor C	Naylor	Love	Smith	Trott	Harrison	Kirby	McMahon	Alford	Samuels	Strouts	Leadbeater (2), Ougham (5)	7
Taylor C	Kirby	Love	Smith	Trott	Howarth	Plummer	McMahon	Alford	Leadbeater	Strouts	Harrison (7), Samuels (10)	8
Taylor C	Harvey	Harrison	Smith	Trott	Howarth	Kirby	McMahon	Alford	Leadbeater	Strouts	Plummer (8), Samuels (10)	9
Taylor C	Kirby	Harrison	Smith	Trott	Howarth	Wraight	Love	Alford	Samuels	Strouts	Plummer (7), Leadbeater (3)	10
Taylor C	Harvey	Love	Smith	Trott	Howarth	Houghton	Kirby	Alford	Samuels	Strouts	Leadbeater (5), Wraight (6)	11
Taylor C	Kirby	Love	Smith	Howarth	Wraight	Houghton	Harrison	Alford	Samuels	Strouts	Leadbeater (8), Barr (6)	12
Taylor C	Harvey	Harrison	Smith	Trott	Kirby	Wraight	Love	Alford	Leadbeater	Strouts	Samuels (2)	13
Taylor C	Wraight	Harrison	Smith	Trott	Kirby	Houghton	Love	Alford	Leadbeater	Strouts	King (11), Samuels (3), Armstrong (7)	14
Taylor C	Futcher	Love	Smith	Howarth	Kirby	Wraight	King	Alford	Samuels	Strouts	Harrison (10)	15
Taylor C	Futcher	Harrison	Smith	Howarth	Kirby	Wraight	King	Alford	Samuels	Strouts	Harvey (2)	16
Taylor C	Harvey	Harrison	Smith	Howarth	Kirby	King	Love	Alford	Samuels	Miller	Martin (3), Armstrong (11), Leadbeater (10)	17
												18
Taylor C	Harvey	Love	Smith	Collins	Kirby	Martin	King	Alford	Leadbeater	Miller	Harrison (10)	19
Taylor C	Harvey	Miller	Smith	Howarth	Kirby	Morrison	King	Alford	Leadbeater	Strouts	Harrison (6), Samuels (7)	20
Taylor C	Harvey	Miller	Smith	Howarth	Kirby	Martin	King	Alford	Leadbeater	Strouts	Love (4)	21
Taylor C	Harvey	Miller	Smith	Howarth	Kirby	Martin	King	Alford	Leadbeater	Wraight	Samuels (10), Morrison (8), Love (3)	22
Taylor C	Harvey	Love	Smith	Howarth	Wraight	Martin	King	Alford	Hockton	Morrison	Miller (2), Kirby (8), Strouts (11)	23
Gallagher	Miller	Love	Smith	Howarth	Harvey	King	Strouts	Alford	Hockton	Martin	Samuels (7)	24
Taylor C	Kirby	Love	Smith	Kersey	Howarth	Martin	Wraight	Hockton	Leadbeater	Harrison	King (11), Samuels (10)	25
Taylor C	Harvey	Love	Smith	Kersey	Howarth	Martin	Wraight	Alford	King	Hockton	Kirby (5), Leadbeater (11), Harrison (9)	26
Taylor C	Harvey	Love	Smith	Ayres	Howarth	Wraight	King	Leadbeater	Kirby	Hockton	Martin (8), Kersey (7), Harrison (11)	27
Taylor C	Harvey	Love	Smith	Ayres	Howarth	Wraight	King	Leadbeater	Kirby	Hockton	Alford (7), Martin (9)	28
Taylor C	Harvey	Love	Smith	Ayres	Howarth	Martin	King	Alford	Kirby	Hockton	Wraight (6), Leadbeater (11)	29
Taylor C	Harvey	Love	Kersey	Ayres	Howarth	Martin	King	Alford	Kirby	Hockton	Wraight (8), Samuels (4)	30
Taylor C	Harvey	Love	Smith	Ayres	Howarth	Martin	Kirby	Alford	Hockton	Wraight	No subs used	31
Taylor C	Harvey	Love	Smith	Ayres	Howarth	Martin	Kirby	Alford	Hockton	King	Wraight (5), Leadbeater (7)	32
Taylor C	Kirby	Love	Smith	Collins	Harvey	Martin	King	Alford	Hockton	Wraight	Howarth (5), Field (9)	33
Taylor C	Harvey	Love	Pluck	Howarth	King	Wraight	Leadbeater	Alford	Hockton	Martin	Collins (4)	34
Taylor C	Harvey	Love	Collins	Trott	Howarth	Martin	Bass	Alford	Hockton	Wraight	Kirby (7), Leadbeater (9), Forbes (8)	35
Taylor C	Harvey	Harrison	Collins	Howarth	Trott	Wraight	Forbes	Alford	Hockton	Bass	Smith (5), Leadbeater ((7)	36
Taylor C	Harvey	Miller	Smith	Trott	Howarth	Bass	Forbes	Alford	Hockton	Wraight	Leadbeater (3), Kirby (8)	37
Taylor C	Harvey	Pluck	Smith	Trott	Kirby	Bass	Forbes	Alford	Hockton	Martin	Wraight (6), Leadbeater (9)	38
Taylor C	Wraight	Pluck	Smith	Trott	Kirby	Bass	Forbes	Leadbeater	Hockton	Martin	Howarth (3), Love (11), Pearson (8)	39
Taylor C	Kirby	Love	Smith	Trott	Howarth	Bass	Martin	Alford	Leadbeater	Wraight	Hockton (10), Pearson (9)	40
Hassell	Trott	Love	Smith	Howarth	Bass	Wraight	Kirby	Alford	Leadbeater	Martin	Hockton (10), Pearson (9)	41
Hassell	Harvey	Love	Smith	Howarth	Trott	Bass	Kirby	Alford	Hockton	Martin	Leadbeater (10), Forbes (11), Pearson (6)	42

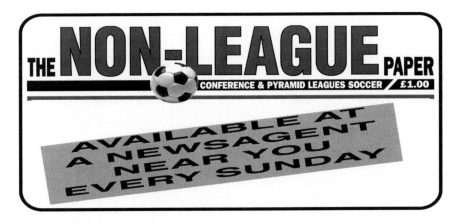

THE NON-LEAGUE PAPER
CONFERENCE & PYRAMID LEAGUES SOCCER / £1.00
AVAILABLE AT A NEWSAGENT NEAR YOU EVERY SUNDAY

PLAYING SQUAD

STEVENAGE BOROUGH

Bold print indicates England Semi-Professional Internationals

Player Honours	*Birthplace*	*D.O.B.*	*Previous Clubs*

GOALKEEPERS

Chris Taylor SC	Bromsgrove		Everton, Bromsgrove R, Halesowen T, Evesham U, Moor Green, Solihull B, Bromsgrove R, Cheltenham T, Kettering T
Paul Wilkerson	Hertford	11.12.74	Watford, Slough T, Welling U

DEFENDERS

Ryan Kirby	Chingford	06.09.74	Arsenal, Doncaster R, Northampton
Mark Smith ESP, GMVC, RP	Luton		Hitchin T, Letchworth GC, Hitchin T, Woking, Hitchin T
Nathan Bunce	Hillingdon	02.05.75	Brentford, Yeading, Woking
Robin Trott	Orpington	17.08.74	Gillingham, Welling U, £8,000 to Stevenage B
Kofi Nyamah	Islington	20.06.75	Camb.U, Kettering T, Stoke, Luton, Exeter
Rob Miller	Bedford	28.03.80	West Ham, Coventry

MIDFIELDERS

Sam McMahon	Newark	10.02.76	Leicester, Camb.U
Christian Metcalfe	London	14.12.74	Chelsea, Harrow B, Hayes
Ross Harrison	Leamington	28.12.79	Reading
Gary Wraight	Epping	05.03.79	Wycombe
Mark Graham	Newry	24.10.74	QPR, Glenavon

FORWARDS

Richard Leadbeater	Dudley	21.10.77	Wolves, Hereford U, £20,000 to Stevenage B
Darren Hay FAT	Hitchin	17.12.69	Biggleswade T, Camb.U, Woking
Chris Pearson	Leicester	05.01.76	Hinckley T, Notts Co., Hinckley T, Kettering T, £14,000 to Stevenage B
Adrian Clarke ES	Cambridge	28.09.74	Arsenal, Southend
Danny Hockton	Barking	07.02.79	Millwall
Paul Armstrong	Herts		From Academy

TELFORD UNITED

Telford were one of a number of Conference clubs to have a change of manager mid-season.

However, in their case it was due more to the fact that Alan Lewer was unable to make the commitment to become full-time rather than for on the field problems, although things were not looking too good on that score.

Jake King returned to the Buck's Head, after a three-year sojourn at Shrewsbury Town, and he immediately brought in a number of very experienced players, such as former Wimbledon defender Brian Gayle.

With their help relegation was comfortably avoided, although to be fair, Telford were in fifteenth position when he took over and they finished the campaign in sixteenth.

They did have a good run in the FA Umbro Trophy where they reached the semi-finals before eventually bowing out to Kettering Town, and in the Nationwide McMillan Trophy they also reached the semi-finals losing out to Doncaster Rovers.

They have now become one of a number of full-time clubs in the Conference and with the rebuilding of the Buck's Head in full flow, Telford have a very bright future ahead.

They may not be realistic title challengers this term but if they can stay on board, who knows for the following campaigns?

Steve Whitney

An end of season photo, however only Charlie Hartfield is no longer at the Buck's Head
Back Row: Brian Gayle, Brian McGorry, Charlie Hartfield, Kevin Dandwith, Jon Ford, Chris Malkin, Jake Edwards, Neil Moore.
Front: Simon Travis, Roger Preece, Gez Murphy, Gary Martindale, Steve Palmer.

TELFORD UNITED

GROUND DETAILS

Bucks Head Ground,
Watling Street,
Wellington,
Telford,
Shropshire TF12NJ

Tel: 01543 278222
Fax: 01543 278333
email: dawnbird@lineone.net
web site: http://www.telfordunited-fc.co.uk

SIMPLE DIRECTIONS:
M54 Junction 6, A518 to B5061 (Watling Street).
Ground is on several bus routes
Nearest railway station - Wellington

Due to contruction of a new stadium on the same site
the following details apply for season 2000-01

	Prior to 12/00	After 12/00
CAPACITY:	2,788	4,268
SEATED:	Nil	Nil
COVERED TERRACING:	1,480	2,960

SOCIAL FACILITIES:
During 2000-01 season - nil

CLUB SHOP:
Telephone 01543 273515 for details

Pages: 32   Price: £1.60

Editor: Dawn Bird (General Manager)

Other club publications: None

Local Press: Shropshire Star; Telford Journal
Local Radio: BBC Radio Shropshire;
Beacon Radio; Telford FM; WABC

Founded:	1876
Nickname:	The Bucks
Club Sponsors:	tba
Club colours:	White shirts, black shorts, white socks
Change colours:	Red shirts, blue shorts and red socks
Midweek home matchday:	Tuesday
Reserves' League:	Central Conference

CLUB OFFICIALS

President	Gerald Smith
Chairman	Andy Shaw
General Manager	Dawn Bird
Football Secretary	Mike Ferriday c/o the club 01543 273516
Commercial Manager	Kevin Reardon 01543 273515
Press Officer	Robert Cave 0771 0227337

FOOTBALL MANAGEMENT TEAM

MANAGER: JAKE KING
Date of appointment: March 2000
Date of Birth: 29th January 1955
Place of Birth: Glasgow

PREVIOUS CLUBS
as manager   Telford Utd (11.96-5.97),
             Shrewsbury Town (97-2000)
as player   Shrewsbury T., Cardiff C., Wrexham

HONOURS
as manager   None
as player   Football League 3rd Div. Championship;
             4th Div. Runners-up

*   *   *

Assistant Manager: Kevin Jobling
Coach: Roger Preece
Chief Scout: Charlie Walker
Physio: Andy Rose
Youth development: Charlie Walker

Season	League	Div.	Pos.	Home						Away					Pts	Manager
				P	W	D	L	F	A	W	D	L	F	A		
99-00	Conference	-	16	42	12	4	5	34	21	2	5	14	22	45	51	Alan Lewer / Jake King
98-99	Conference	-	17	42	7	8	6	24	24	3	8	10	20	36	46	Jimmy Mullen / Alan Lewer
97-98	Conference	-	20	42	6	7	8	25	31	4	5	12	28	45	42	Steve Daly / Jimmy Mullen
96-97	Conference	-	9	42	6	7	8	21	30	10	3	8	25	26	58	Wayne Clarke

Season	League	Div.	Pos.	P	W	D	L	F	A	Pts	Manager
95-96	Conference	-	13	42	15	10	17	51	56	55	Wayne Clarke
94-95	Conference	-	19	42	10	16	16	53	62	46	Gerry Daly / George Foster
93-94	Conference	-	17	42	13	12	17	41	49	51	Gerry Daly
92-93	Conference	-	15	42	14	10	18	55	60	52	Gerry Daly
91-92	Conference	-	6	42	19	7	16	62	66	64	Gerry Daly
90-91	Conference	-	6	42	20	7	15	62	52	67	Gerry Daly

HONOURS

FA Trophy Winners 71-72, 82-83, 88-89.
R-up 69-70, 87-88;
Birmingham League1920-21, 1934-35, 1935-36;
Cheshire League 1945-46, 1946-47, 1951-52;
Edward Case Cup 1952-53, 1954-55;
Welsh Cup 1901-02, 1905-06, 1939-40;
BirminghamSenior Cup 1946-47;
Walsall Senior Cup 1946-47;
Birmingham League Challenge Cup 1946-47;
Shropshire Senior Cup (30);
Southern League Cup 1970-71;
Midland Floodlit Cup 1970-71, 1982-83, 1988-89,
Runners-up 1969-70, 1987-88

CLUB RECORDS

Attendance:	13,000 v Shrewsbury Town
	Birmingham League - 1936
Win:	**Unknown**
Defeat:	**Unknown**
Career appearances:	**Unknown**
Career goalscorer:	Jack Bentley
Transfer fee paid:	£20,000
	to Wrexham for Jake Edwards
Transfer fee received:	£50,000
	from Scarborough for Stephen Norris

PREVIOUS

Leagues:	Southern League,
	Cheshire League,
	Birmingham League
Name:	Wellington Town (prior to 1969)
Grounds:	None

BEST SEASON

FA Cup:		5th Round 84-85,
		0-3 v Everton (A), 47,402.
	Also	4th Rd. 83-84,
		3rd Rd.86-87,
		2nd Rd. 82-83, 85-86, 91-92

League clubs defeated: Wigan, Rochdale, Stockport C., Darlington, Stoke C.,Lincoln C., Bradford C

FA Trophy:	Winners 70-71, 82-83, 88-89.
	R-up 69-70, 87-88
League:	3rd Conference 81-82

Past Players who progressed to the Football League

A.Walker (Lincoln City),G.French (Luton Town),
K.McKenna (Tranmere Rovers), S.Norris (Scarborough),
David Pritchard (Bristol Rovers) 1994,
Sean Parrish (Doncaster Rovers) 1994,
Steve Foster (Bristol R.);
Peter Wilding, Roger Preece, Mark Williams & Martyn Naylor
- all to Shrewsbury 1997

LAST SEASON

F.A. Cup:	4th Qualifying Round
F.A. Trophy:	Semi-Final
Conference:	16th
Top Goalscorer:	Gez Murphy 16
Player of the Year:	Lee Fowler
Club Captain:	Jim Bentley

TELFORD UNITED

Match Facts 1999-00

	Date	Comp.	H/A	Opponents	Gate	Result & Score	Goalscorers	League Position
1	14.08	N.C.	H	Kingstonian	920	W 1-0	Fitzpatrick 44	
2	17.08	N.C.	A	Rushden & Diamonds	2,729	D 1-1	Palmer 51	
3	21.08	N.C.	A	Stevenage Borough	2,191	L 0-2		14
4	24.08	N.C.	H	Forest Green Rovers	830	W 2-0	Bentley 11 Malkin 27	
5	28.08	N.C.	H	Dover Athletic	838	D 1-1	Murphy 45 (pen)	9
6	30.08	N.C.	A	Hereford United	1,910	D 2-2	Murphy 67,76	9
7	04.09	N.C.	A	Morecambe	1,280	L 2-5	Murphy 43 Palmer 52	12
8	11.09	N.C.	H	Hayes	811	L 1-2	Malkin 4	17
9	18.09	N.C.	A	Welling United	627	L 0-2		18
10	25.09	N.C.	H	Yeovil Town	1,002	W 3-1	Murphy 47, 81 (pen), McGorry 66	16
11	02.10	N.C.	A	Sutton United	825	L 1-2	Bentley 52	16
12	09.10	N.C.	H	Altrincham	1,017	L 0-1		18
13	22.10	N.C.	H	Doncaster Rovers	1,157	L 0-2		21
14	30.10	N.C.	H	Nuneaton Borough	1,217	W 1-0	Hartfield 70 (pen)	18
15	06.11	N.C.	H	Kidderminster H.	1,409	W 3-2	Edwards 3, Cooper 33, Hartfield 90(p)	18
16	12.11	N.C.	A	Scarborough	1,317	L 0-2		19
17	20.11	N.C.	A	Nuneaton Borough	2,203	D 1-1	Huckerby 73	18
18	04.12	N.C.	A	Kettering Town	1,267	D 0-0		16
19	11.12	N.C.	H	Welling United	921	W 2-1	Fitzpatrick 6, Edwards 40	15
20	18.12	N.C.	H	Rushden & Diamonds	1,414	D 1-1	Albrighton 70	15
21	27.12	N.C.	A	Hednesford Town	1,550	L 1-2	Bentley 39	17
22	03.01	N.C.	H	Hednesford Town	1,714	W 6-2	Malkin 8, 37, **Edwards 3** (18, 45, 51), Fitzpatrick 60	16
23	08.01	N.C.	A	Kingstonian	1,026	L 2-4	Edwards 14, Hartfield 64 (p)	16
24	18.01	N.C.	H	Morecambe	914	W 3-2	Bentley 59, Edwards 85, Huckerby 89.	
25	22.01	N.C.	A	Yeovil Town	2,174	L 1-2	Naylor 75	15
26	25.01	N.C.	H	Southport	1,037	D 0-0		
27	29.01	N.C.	H	Scarborough	1,041	W 1-0	Malkin 77	12
28	01.02	N.C.	A	Altrincham	720	D 3-3	Ford 45 (p), Macaulay 77, Fitzpatrick 83	
29	12.02	N.C.	A	Forest Green Rovers	851	L 2-5	Ford 29, Edwards 58	13
30	04.03	N.C.	H	Woking	1,019	L 1-2	Malkin 16	17
31	18.03	N.C.	H	Northwich Victoria	1,015	L 0-1		18
32	25.03	N.C.	A	Kidderminster Harriers	3,138	L 0-2		19
33	04.04	N.C.	H	Kettering Town	824	W 3-1	Edwards 34, Sandwith 45, Martindale 63	17
34	08.04	N.C.	H	Sutton United	1,011	W 2-0	Martindale 34(p), 69	17
35	11.04	N.C.	A	Southport	1,010	W 3-1	Martindale 22, Palmer 48, 90	15
36	20.04	N.C.	H	Hereford United	908	D 1-1	Murphy 50	
37	22.04	N.C.	H	Stevenage Borough	1,828	W 2-1	Murphy 11, Ford 45	
38	24.04	N.C.	A	Woking	1,909	L 0-1		15
39	26.04	N.C.	A	Doncaster Rovers	1,871	L 0-2		
40	29.04	N.C.	A	Hayes	591	W 2-1	Murphy 10, 21	
41	03.05	N.C.	A	Northwich Victoria	663	L 1-2	OG (Birch) 15	16
42	06.05	N.C.	A	Dover Athletic	704	L 0-3		16

CUP COMPETITIONS

F.A. Cup

	Date		H/A	Opponents	Gate	Result & Score	Goalscorers
	16.10	4Q	H	Gateshead	611	D 0-0	
	20.10	4Q R	A	Gateshead	318	L 1-2	Murphy 52

Nationwide McMillan Trophy

	Date		H/A	Opponents	Gate	Result & Score	Goalscorers
	06.10	1	A	Forest Green Rov.	424	W 2-1	McGorry 6, Fitzpatrick 46
	23.11	2	A	Rushden & Diamonds	1,451	W 1-0	McGorry 17
	08.02	4	A	Altrincham	319	W 3-1	Hartfield 45(p), Naylor 55, Edwards 90
	28.03	NMT SF2	A	Doncaster Rovers	1,867	L 0-1	

F.A. Trophy

	Date		H/A	Opponents	Gate	Result & Score	Goalscorers
	27.11	2	A	Kidderminster H.	1,618	W 4-2	Murphy 49, 57, Edwards 75, 85
	15.01	3	A	Whitby Town	547	W 3-1	Edwards 28, 42, Travis 75
	05.02	4	H	Farnborough Town	944	W 2-1	Murphy 51, 82
	26.02	5	H	Worcester City	2,085	W 4-1	Ford 15, Palmer 49, Malkin 72, 79
	11.03	6	H	Runcorn	1,557	W 2-0	Palmer 18, Murphy 85
	01.04	FAT SF1	A	Kettering Town	2,915	L 0-1	
	15.04	FAT SF2	H	Kettering Town	2,165	D 0-0	

Jake King takes over as manager

	1	2	3	4	5	6	7	8	9	10	11	Substitutes Used	
1	Williams	Travis	Sandwith	MacAuley	Bentley	Fowler	Doyle	Fitzpatrick	Malkin	McGorry	Murphy	Palmer (9), Huckerby (11)	1
2	Williams	Travis	Sandwith	MacAuley	Bentley	Fowler	Doyle	Fitzpatrick	Malkin	McGorry	Murphy	Palmer (5), Ford (3), Huckerby (9)	2
3	Williams	Travis	Sandwith	MacAuley	Ford	Fowler	Doyle	Fitzpatrick	Malkin	McGorry	Palmer	Naylor (2), Murphy (7), Huckerby (5)	3
4	Bray	Naylor	Ford	MacAuley	Bentley	Fowler	Doyle	Fitzpatrick	Malkin	McGorry	Murphy	Palmer (8), Cornes (4), Huckerby (10)	4
5	Bray	Naylor	Ford	MacAuley	Bentley	Fowler	Doyle	Fitzpatrick	Malkin	McGorry	Murphy	Palmer (9), Cornes (4), Huckerby (3)	5
6	Bray	Huckerby	Ford	MacAuley	Bentley	Fowler	Doyle	Fitzpatrick	Palmer	McGorry	Murphy	Naylor (3), Cornes (2)	6
7	Bray	Naylor	Palmer	MacAuley	Bentley	Fowler	Doyle	Fitzpatrick	Ford	McGorry	Murphy	Cornes (7), Travis 2)	7
8	Williams	Naylor	Palmer	MacAuley	Bentley	Fowler	Doyle	Fitzpatrick	Malkin	McGorry	Murphy	Cornes (9), Ford (6)	8
9	Williams	Naylor	Travis	MacAuley	Bentley	Fowler	Doyle	Fitzpatrick	Palmer	McGorry	Murphy	Ford (6), Huckerby (7), Malkin (2)	9
10	Williams	Travis	Ford	MacAuley	Bentley	Albrighton	Palmer	Fitzpatrick	Malkin	McGorry	Murphy	Cornes (4), Doyle 97), Huckerby (9)	10
11	Williams	Travis	Ford	Fowler	Bentley	Albrighton	Palmer	Fitzpatrick	Malkin	McGorry	Murphy	Naylor (2), Huckerby (3), Bray (9)	11
12	Williams	Naylor	Ford	Fowler	Bentley	Albrighton	Palmer	Fitzpatrick	Malkin	McGorry	Murphy	Doyle (4), Huckerby (2), Travis (3)	12
13	Bray	MacAuley	Ford	Hartfield	Bentley	Albrighton	Doyle	Fitzpatrick	Palmer	McGorry	Murphy	Travis (3), Naylor (8), Mutch (9)	13
14	Williams	MacAuley	Ford	Hartfield	Bentley	Albrighton	Cooper	Fitzpatrick	Palmer	McGorry	Murphy	Fowler (3), Travis (8), Malkin (9)	14
15	Williams	MacAuley	Fowler	Hartfield	Bentley	Albrighton	Cooper	Fitzpatrick	Palmer	Edwards	Murphy	Malkin (10), Travis (9), Naylor (11)	15
16	Williams	MacAuley	Travis	Hartfield	Bentley	Albrighton	Cooper	Fitzpatrick	Edwards	Palmer	Murphy	Malkin (9), Naylor (10)	16
17	Williams	MacAuley	Fowler	Ford	Bentley	Albrighton	Cooper	Fitzpatrick	Edwards	Doyle	Murphy	Travis (3), Malkin (9), Huckerby (10)	17
18	Price	MacAuley	Travis	Hartfield	Bentley	Ford	Cooper	Fitzpatrick	Palmer	McGorry	Edwards	Huckerby (4), Malkin (11), ,Doyle (9)	18
19	Price	MacAuley	Travis	Ford	Bentley	Albrighton	Fitzpatrick	Malkin	McGorry	Palmer	Edwards	Sandwith (7), Doyle (10)	19
20	Price	MacAuley	Travis	Ford	Bentley	Albrighton	Edwards	Fitzpatrick	Malkin	Hartfield	Palmer	Huckerby (9), Sandwith (10)	20
21	Price	Sandwith	Travis	Ford	Bentley	Albrighton	Doyle	Fitzpatrick	Malkin	McGorry	Palmer	Bray (11), Huckerby (7), Edwards (9)	21
22	Price	MacAuley	Travis	Ford	Bentley	Albrighton	Edwards	Fitzpatrick	Malkin	McGorry	Hartfield	Huckerby (9), Sandwith (10)	22
23	Price	MacAuley	Travis	Ford	Bentley	Albrighton	Edwards	Fitzpatrick	Malkin	McGorry	Hartfield	Sandwith (5), Murphy (4), Huckerby (9)	23
24	Bray	MacAuley	Sandwith	Travis	Bentley	Albrighton	Edwards	Fitzpatrick	Murphy	McGorry	Hartfield	Malkin (9), Doyle (7)	24
25	Bray	MacAuley	Sandwith	Travis	Bentley	Albrighton	Edwards	Fitzpatrick	Murphy	McGorry	Hartfield	Malkin (9), Naylor (4)	25
26	Price	MacAuley	Sandwith	Travis	Bentley	Albrighton	Edwards	Fitzpatrick	Malkin	McGorry	Hartfield	Ford (6), Murphy (9), Naylor (5)	26
27	Price	MacAuley	Travis	Sandwith	Ford	Albrighton	Doyle	Fitzpatrick	Edwards	McGorry	Murphy	Naylor (6), Malkin (11)	27
28	Price	MacAuley	Travis	Sandwith	Ford	Albrighton	Doyle	Fitzpatrick	Edwards	McGorry	Murphy	Naylor (4), Malkin (11)	28
29	Price	Naylor	Travis	Fitzpatrick	Ford	Palmer	MacAuley	Fitzpatrick	Edwards	Hartfield	Murphy	Malkin (6)	29
30	Price	Travis	Fitzpatrick	MacAuley	Ford	Fowler	Hartfield	Palmer	Malkin	McGorry	Edwards	Naylor (2), Murphy (8)	30
31	Price	MacAuley	Travis	Preece	Ford	Fowler	Palmer	Fitzpatrick	Malkin	Hartfield	Murphy	Edwards (8)	31
32	Price	Travis	Fowler	Preece	Gayle	Ford	Martindale	Hartfield	Malkin	McGorry	Moore	Edwards (9), Murphy (7)	32
33	Price	Travis	Sandwith	Moore	Gayle	Fowler	Preece	Palmer	Malkin	Edwards	McGorry	Martindale (9), Murphy (10), Hartfield (8)	33
34	Price	Travis	Sandwith	Moore	Gayle	Fowler	Preece	Palmer	Martindale	Edwards	McGorry	MacAuley (2), Murphy (10)	34
35	Price	Travis	Sandwith	Moore	Gayle	Fowler	Preece	Palmer	Martindale	Edwards	McGorry	Murphy (10)	35
36	Price	Travis	Sandwith	Ford	Gayle	Fowler	Hartfield	Palmer	Martindale	Murphy	McGorry	MacAuley (2)	36
37	Price	MacAuley	Sandwith	Ford	Gayle	Fowler	Preece	Palmer	Martindale	Murphy	McGorry	Travis (2), Edwards (10)	37
38	Williams	MacAuley	Sandwith	Ford	Gayle	Fowler	Preece	Doyle	Edwards	Murphy	Hartfield	Fitzpatrick (8), Malkin (10)	38
39	Williams	MacAuley	Sandwith	Ford	Gayle	Fowler	Preece	Palmer	Edwards	Murphy	Fitzpatrick	Travis (2), Hartfield (7), Naylor (8)	39
40	Williams	Travis	Sandwith	Ford	Gayle	Fowler	McGorry	Palmer	Edwards	Murphy	Fitzpatrick	Malkin (9), Doyle (7), Naylor (10)	40
41	Williams	Travis	Sandwith	Doyle	Ford	Fowler	Hartfield	Fitzpatrick	Edwards	Murphy	Palmer	Naylor (11)	41
42	Williams	Travis	Sandwith	Doyle	Ford	Fowler	Preece	Palmer	Edwards	Murphy	Hartfield	Bridgwater (7), MacAulay (6), Fitzpatrick (8)	42

	1	2	3	4	5	6	7	8	9	10	11	Substitutes Used
	Bray	Travis	Ford	Macauley	Bentley	Doyle	Palmer	Fitzpatrick	Malkin	McGorry	Murphy	Sandwith (8), Corns (9), Henshaw(6)
	Bray	Macauley	Ford	Travis	Bentley	Doyle	Palmer	Fitzpatrick	Malkin	Murphy	McGorry	no subs used
	Williams	Naylor	Ford	Fowler	Bentley	Albrighton	Palmer	Fitzpatrick	Malkin	McGorry	Murphy	Doyle (7)
	Price	Macauley	Travis	Ford	Bentley	Albrighton	Cooper	Fitzpatrick	Edwards	McGorry	Huckerby	no subs used
	Price	Macauley	Fowler	Naylor	Ford	Fitzpatrick	Doyle	Palmer	Malkin	McGorry	Hartfield	Edwards (8), Travis (3), Bridgewater (7)
	Price	Macauley	Travis	Fitzpatrick	Ford	Fowler	Doyle	Palmer	Murphy	Hartfield	Edwards	McGorry (4), Naylor (10)
	Bray	Macauley	Travis	Ford	Bentley	Albrighton	Cooper	Fitzpatrick	Palmer	McGorry	Murphy	Edwards (9), Huckerby (11)
	Bray	Macauley	Ford	Travis	Fowler	Albrighton	Edwards	Fitzpatrick	Murphy	McGorry	Hartfield	Sandwith (5)
	Price	Macauley	Travis	Naylor	Ford	Albrighton	Doyel	Palmer	Edwards	McGorry	Murphy	Malkin (8)
	Price	Travis	Fitzpatrick	Macauley	Ford	Fowler	Hartfield	Palmer	Malkin	McGorry	Edwards	Murphy (11), Naylor (7)
	Price	Macauley	Travis	Fitzpatrick	Ford	Fowler	Doyle	Palmer	Malkin	Hartfield	Edwards	Murphy (11)
	Price	Travis	Sandwith	Moore	Ford	Gayle	Preece	McGorry	Malkin	Edwards	Hartfield	Murphy (9), Palmer (11)

PLAYING SQUAD

TELFORD UNITED

(Bold print indicates an England Semi-Professional International)

Player Honours	Birthplace	D.O.B.	Previous Clubs

GOALKEEPERS

Ryan Price ESP, GMVC	Wolverhampton	13.03.70	Bolton, Stafford R, Birmingham, Macclesfield, £10,000 to Telford U
Dean Williams	Lichfield	05.01.72	Tamworth, Brentford, Doncaster R, Gateshead

DEFENDERS

Mark Allbrighton	Coventry		Nuneaton B, Atherstone U, £15,000 to Telford U
Jim Bentley	Liverpool	11.06.76	Manchester CM
Kevin Sandwith	Workington	30.04.78	Carlisle, Barrow
Martin Naylor	Walsall	02.08.77	Hereford U, Telford U, Shrewsbury
Brian Gayle	Kingston	03.06.65	Wimbledon, Manchester C, Ipswich, Sheffield U, Exeter, Rotherham, Bristol R, Shrewsbury
Neil Moore	Liverpool	21.09.72	Everton, Norwich, Burnley, Macclesfield

MIDFIELDERS

Jamie Cartwright	Lichfield	11.10.79	Stoke
Steve Palmer	Birmingham		Wednesfield
Simon Travis British Univ.	Preston	22.03.77	Torquay, Holywell T, Stockport
Gary Fitzpatrick Eire Y	Birmingham	05.08.71	Leicester C, VS Rugby, Moor Green, Hednesford T, £15,000 to Telford U
Kevin Davies	Sheffield	15.11.78	Sheffield U
Kevin Jobling	Sunderland	01.01.68	Leicester, Grimsby, Shrewsbury
Roger Preece	Much Wenlock	09.06.69	Coventry, Wrexham, Chester, Telford U, Shrewsbury
Brian McGorry	Liverpool	16.04.70	Weymouth, Bournemouth, Peterborough, Wycombe, Cardiff, Hereford U, Torquay

FORWARDS

Gez Murphy	Leicester		Leicester, VS Rugby, Solihull B, Atherstone U, Gresley R
Scott Huckerby	Nottingham		Lincoln C, Ilkeston T, £10,000 to Telford U
Gary Martindale	Liverpool	24.06.71	Burscough, Bolton, Peterborough, Notts Co., Rotherham
Jake Edwards	Manchester	11.05.76	Wrexham, £20,000 to Telford U
Chris Malkin	Hoylake	04.06.67	Stork, Overpool, Tranmere, Millwall, Blackpool
Ben Henshaw	Wolverhampton		Oxford U

WOKING

Brian McDermott had impressed everyone in the previous season and hopes were high as "The cardinals" kicked off the season with a strong side on paper.

Three games later, in eighteenth place with two defeats and a draw, doubts started to appear, and from then on a lack of goals prevented Woking from getting away from the danger zone.

An impressive 3-1 victory at Rushden did lift morale but sadly in the next sixteen games only eleven goals were scored with just three victories and the Surrey club were languishing in twentieth position. A Trophy run to the last sixteen partially made up for their FA Cup defeat at Burton Albion but their Conference place was in doubt.

The inevitable result was that the manager had to go, however old favourite, Colin Lippiatt, who had been pleased to get away from the Yeovil pressures and had been assisting Geoff Chapple at Kingstonian was happy to "come home" where he felt secure.

Two wins from the first three games, including a 4-2 success at Hereford, lifted supporters hopes, but then a very poor run of eight games producing just four points found them down in 21st place with only six games left.

Something special must have happened as five straight victories without conceding a goal were reeled off, including a win over Champions elect Kidderminster Harriers and a 3-0 triumph at Yeovil just about added up to Championship form and it did bring a comfortable finish in fourteenth place. It's a funny old game!

T.W

Back Row: Damian Panter, Dante Alighieri, Steve Perkins, Darron Wilkinson, Richard Taylor, Mark Druce. **Middle:** Ian Burns (Reserve & Youth Manager), Steve Jenner (Asst. Res. & Yth Man.), Michael Danzey, Mark Ormerod, Stuart Baverstock, Michael Bullen, Rob Hollingdale, Ron Rawlings (Kit Man), Barry Kimber (Physio). **Front:** Mark Watson, Matthew Hayfield, Scott Steele, Steve West, Colin Lippiatt (Manager), David Vaughan (Asst. Man.), Kevan Brown, Nick Roddis, Jamie Pitman, Joe Martin. Missing: Scott Smith.

WOKING

GROUND DETAILS

Kingfield Stadium,
Kingfield,
Woking,
Surrey. GU22 9AA.

Tel: 01483 772470
Fax: 01483 888423

Web site: http://www.wokingfc.co.uk

Simple Directions:
M25 J10 or 11, signposted from outskirts of Town. Ground 1 mile. Woking B.R. Station & buses from Woking.

Capacity:	6,000
Seated:	2,500
Terracing -	**Covered:** 1,400
	Uncovered: 2,100

SOCIAL FACILITIES:
Clubhouse open on matchdays. Food available.

CLUB SHOP: Phone 01483 772470 for details.

Founded:	1889
Nickname:	The Cards
Club colours:	Red & white halved shirts & black shorts
Change colours:	Yellow and navy
Reserve team's league:	Suburban Football League
Midweek home matchday:	Tuesday 7.45pm.
Club Sponsors:	Tele People.com
Newsline	0930 555070

CLUB OFFICIALS

Chairman	Terry Molloy J.P
Vice Chairman	**John Buchanan**
Football Secretary	Phil J Ledger J.P.

19 Ainsdale Way, Woking, Surrey. GU21 3PP.
Tel: 01483 725295 (H), 0831 271369 (M)

Commercial Director	Peter Jordan
Press Officer	Terry Molloy 01483 767417
Club Administrator	Sue Day
Commercial Manager	Rosemary Hurl

FOOTBALL MANAGEMENT TEAM

MANAGER: **COLIN LIPPIATT**

Date of Appointment	March 2000
Date of Birth:	1st January 1942
Place of Birth:	Hayes
PREVIOUS CLUBS	
As manager	Yeovil Town 2.98-10.99
As asst. man./coach	Windsor & Eton, Farnborough Town, Woking, Kingstonian; Kingstonian
As player	Hayes, Wokingham & Maidenhead
HONOURS	
As asst. man./coach	(Woking) FA Trophy 94, 95, 97, Conf R-up 95, 96; (Windsor & Eton) Athenian Lge (2); FA Vase S-F & Q-F

*   *   *

Assistant Manager:	Dave Vaughan
Reserve Team Manager:	Ian Burns
Youth Team Manager:	Ian Burns
Physio:	Barry Kimber

MATCHDAY PROGRAMME

WOKING -v- YEOVIL TOWN
Nationwide Conference
Tuesday 22nd August 2000 - Kick Off - 7.45pm
Vol 9 No.1

SEASON 2000/01 OFFICIAL PROGRAMME £1.50

Pages: 40   **Price:** £1.30
Editor: Paul Beard 01344 482018

Other club publications:
"Winning isn't Everything" (fanzine)

Local Press: Woking News & Mail; Woking Herald; Surrey Advertiser
Local Radio: BBC Surrey Sussex; County Sound; BBC Southern Counties

Season	League	Div.	Pos.	P	Home W	D	L	F	A	Away W	D	L	F	A	Pts	Manager
99-00	Conference	-	14	42	5	6	10	17	27	8	7	6	28	26	52	Brian McDermott/Colin Lippiatt
98-99	Conference	-	9	42	9	5	7	27	20	9	4	8	24	25	63	John McGovern/Brian McDermott
97-98	Conference	-	3	42	14	3	4	47	22	8	5	8	25	24	74	John McGovern
96-97	Conference	-	5	42	10	5	6	41	29	8	5	8	30	34	64	Geoff Chapple

Season	League	Div.	Pos.	P	W	D	L	F	A	Pts	Manager
95-96	Conference	-	2	42	25	8	9	83	54	83	Geoff Chapple
94-95	Conference	-	2	42	21	12	9	76	54	75	Geoff Chapple
93-94	Conference	-	3	42	18	13	11	58	58	67	Geoff Chapple
92-93	Conference	-	8	42	17	8	17	58	62	59	Geoff Chapple
91-92	Isthmian	Prem.	1	42	30	7	5	96	25	97	Geoff Chapple
90-91	Isthmian	Prem.	4	42	24	10	8	84	39	82	Geoff Chapple

HONOURS

FA Trophy 93-94, 94-95, 96-97
FA Amateur Cup 57-58
GM VauxhallConference R-up 94-95, 95-96
Isthmian League: 91-92, R-up 56-57
Div.2 South 86-87
Isthmian Lge Cup: 90-91, R-up 89-90
Surrey Senior Cup: 12-13, 26-27, 55-56, 56-57,
71-72, 90-91, 93-94, 95-96, 99-00;
London Senior Cup R-up 82-83
Isthmian League Charity Shield 91-92, 92-93
Vauxhall Championship Shield 94-95, R-up 95-96.

PREVIOUS

Leagues: Isthmian 1911-92

Grounds: Wheatsheaf, Ivy Lane (pre 1923)

Past Players who progressed to the Football League

Ray Elliott (M'wall 46), Charlie Mortimore (A'shot 49),
Robert Edwards (Chelsea 51), Ron Newman (Portsmouth 55),
Mervyn Gill (Southampton 56),John Mortimore (Chelsea 51),
Reg Stratton (Fulham 59), George Harris (Newport Co. 61),
Norman Cashmore (A'shot 63), Alan Morton (C. Palace 67),
William Holmes (Millwall 70), Richard Forbes (Exeter 79),
Kevin Rattray (Gillingham 95), Steve Foster (Bristol Rov. 97),
Justin Jackson (Notts Co. 98), Kevin Betsy (Fulham 98).

CLUB RECORDS

Attendance:	6,000
	v Swansea, FA Cup - 1978/79
	v Coventry C., FA Cup - 1996-97
Win:	17-4 v Farnham, 1912-13
Defeat:	0-16 v New Crusaders, 1905-06
Career Goalscorer:	C Mortimore 331, 1953-65
Career Appearances:	B Finn 564, 1962-74
Transfer Fees Paid:	£30,000 for Justin Jackson (Morecambe) - 1996
Received:	£150,000 for Steve Foster (Bristol Rovers) - May 1997
	£125,000 for Kevin Betsy (Fulham)

BEST SEASON

FA Cup:	4th Round 90-91, 0-1 v Everton (H)
League clubs defeated:	West Brom. Alb., Cambridge U., Millwall (96-97)
FA Trophy:	Winners 93-94, 94-95, 96-97.
FA Amateur Cup:	Winners 75-58
League	Conference Runners-up 94-95, 95-96

LAST SEASON

F.A. Cup:	4th Qualifying Round
F.A. Trophy:	5th Round
Conference:	14th
Top Goalscorer:	Nassim Akrour 17
Player of the Year:	Steve West
Captain:	Steve West

WOKING

	Date	Comp.	H/A	Opponents	Gate	Result & Score	Goalscorers	League Position
1	14.08	N.C.	A	Southport	1,378	L 1-4	West 66	
2	17.08	N.C.	H	Kettering Town	2,205	D 1-1	Steele 70 (Pen)	
3	21.08	N.C.	H	Doncaster Rovers	2,358	L 1-3	Bolt 10 (Pen)	18
4	24.08	N.C.	A	Welling United	737	W 2-1	Steele 15 (Pen), Goddard 81	
5	28.08	N.C.	A	Kidderminster Harriers	1,729	L 2-3	Payne 24, Hay 65	17
6	30.08	N.C.	H	Yeovil Town	2,340	W 2-0	Hay 41, West 64	14
7	04.09	N.C.	H	Hednesford Town	1,622	L 0-1		17
8	11.09	N.C.	A	Rushden & Diamonds	2,699	W 3-1	Danzey 63, Akrour 69, Payne 85	15
9	18.09	N.C.	A	Altrincham	1,006	D 1-1	Hay 25	16
10	02.10	N.C.	A	Morecambe	1,218	L 0-1		18
11	09.10	N.C.	H	Hereford United	2,128	L 0-2		20
12	23.10	N.C.	H	Forest Green Rovers	1,505	W 2-1	Payne 16, Hay 49	18
13	30.10	N.C.	H	Northwich Victoria	1,606	D 1-1	Akrour 71	16
14	06.11	N.C.	H	Nuneaton Bor.	1,711	D 1-1	Akrour 5	20
15	13.11	N.C.	A	Doncaster Rovers	1,960	D 0-0		20
16	20.11	N.C.	H	Welling United	1,550	L 2-3	West 59, Akrour 77	20
17	04.12	N.C.	A	Hednesford Town	978	L 0-3		21
18	11.12	N.C.	H	Morecambe	1,517	D 0-0		19
19	18.12	N.C.	A	Stevenage Borough	2,992	W 1-0	West 78	18
20	27.12	N.C.	H	Kingstonian	3,614	D 1-1	Perkins 55	19
21	03.01	N.C.	A	Kingstonian	2,467	W 2-0	Perkins 3, Akrour 81	17
22	08.01	N.C.	H	Southport	2,026	D 0-0		17
23	22.01	N.C.	A	Kettering Town	1282	D 0-0		18
24	12.02	N.C.	H	Stevenage Borough	2,318	L 0-2		20
25	19.02	N.C.	A	Altrincham	1,565	L 0-1		20
26	04.03	N.C.	A	Telford United	1.019	W 2-1	Akrour 15, Bolt 47	20
27	11.03	N.C.	H	Hayes	2,041	L 0-3		21
28	14.03	N.C.	A	Hereford United	2,216	W 4-2	Hay 11, Akrour 21, 90, Steele 28	19
29	18.03	N.C.	A	Scarborough	1,345	L 2-3	West 50, Perkins 80	20
30	25.03	N.C.	H	Sutton United	2,065	L 1-2	Akrour 49	20
31	28.03	N.C.	A	Dover Athletic	780	D 2-2	Hayfield 61, Akrour 80	
32	01.04	N.C.	A	Forest Green Rovers	1,102	D 0-0		19
33	05.04	N.C.	A	Sutton United	935	D 1-1	Steele 83	19
34	08.04	N.C.	A	Hayes	1,067	D 0-0		19
35	11.04	N.C.	H	Rushden & Diamonds	1,765	L 1-3	West 61	21
36	18.04	N.C.	H	Northwich Victoria	831	L 1-3	West 20	21
37	22.04	N.C.	A	Nuneaton Borough	1,355	W 1-0	Hay 5	
38	24.04	N.C.	H	Telford United	1,909	W 1-0	Steele 68 (p)	19
39	29.04	N.C.	H	Kidderminster H.	3,210	W 1-0	Steele 20 (p)	
40	01.05	N.C.	A	Yeovil Town	2,727	W 3-0	Akrour 2, Hay 14, Hayfield 19	17
41	03.05	N.C.	A	Dover Athletic	1,560	W 2-0	Akrour 40, Hay 50	14
42	06.05	N.C.	H	Scarborough	2,214	L 0-2		14

Colin Lippiatt took charge from here

CUP COMPETITIONS

F.A. Cup

16.10	4Q	H	Burton Albion	2,015	D 1-1	Payne 57	
19.10	4Q R	A	Burton Albion	2,081	L *1-3	Hay 43	

Nationwide McMillan Trophy

09.11	2	H	Stevenage Borough	791	W 3-1	Akrour 8, 70, West 32.	
26.01	3	A	Kingstonian	416	L 0-2		

F.A. Trophy

27.11	2	A	Ashford Town	826	W 5-0	**Akrour 3** (1, 30, 65), Hay 9, 57	
15.01	3	H	Whyteleafe	1550	W 4-2	Hay (2), West, Akrour	
05.02	4	H	Aldershot Town	4,973	D 0-0		
15.02	4R	A	Aldershot Town	5,307	W 1-0	Hay 31	
26.02	5	A	Southport	1,560	L 0-3		

1	2	3	4	5	6	7	8	9	10	11	Substitutes Used	
Batty	P Smith	Hollingdale	Saunders	S Smith	Danzey	Perkins	Wilkinson	Akrour	Payne	Steele	West (10), Hay (11), Bolt (3)	1
Batty	P Smith	Hollingdale	Saunders	S Smith	Danzey	Girdler	Wilkinson	Akrour	West	Hay	Steele (11), Bolt (3)	2
Batty	P Smith	Hollingdale	Saunders	S Smith	R Smith	Girdler	Wilkinson	Akrour	West	Bolt	Steele (11), Goddard (6)	3
Batty	P Smith	Hollingdale	Saunders	S Smith	Payne	Perkins	Gridelet	Akrour	West	Steele	Hay (9), Girdler (7)	4
Batty	P Smith	Hollingdale	Saunders	S Smith	Payne	Perkins	Gridelet	Akrour	West	Steele	Hay (9), Girdler (8)	5
Flavahan	P Smith	Hollingdale	West	S Smith	Danzey	Perkins	Gridelet	Payne	Hay	Steele	Akrour (10), Wilkinson (8)	6
Flavahan	Girdler	Hollingdale	West	S Smith	Danzey	Perkins	Gridelet	Payne	Hay	Steele	Akrour (2), Bolt (11)	7
Flavahan	Wilkinson	Hollingdale	West	S Smith	Danzey	Perkins	Gridelet	Akrour	Hay	Steele	Payne (7), Bolt (11)	8
Flavahan	Girdler	Hollingdale	West	S Smith	Danzey	Wilkinson	Gridelet	Akrour	Hay	Steele	Payne (11)	9
Flavahan	Girdler	Hollingdale	West	S Smith	Danzey	Perkins	Wilkinson	Akrour	Hay	Steele	Payne (9), Goddard (3), Bolt (11)	10
Flavahan	Perkins	Hollingdale	West	S Smith	Danzey	Wilkinson	Gridelet	Akrour	Hay	Bolt	Payne (3), Steele (9)	11
Flavahan	P Smith	Hollingdale	West	S Smith	Danzey	Perkins	Gridelet	Payne	Hay	Wilkinson	Steele (8), Akrour (10)	12
Flavahan	P Smith	Hollingdale	West	S Smith	Danzey	Perkins	Gridelet	Payne	Hay	Steele	Akrour (10), Wilkinson (8)	13
Batty	Perkins	Girdler	West	Goddard	Danzey	Akrour	Gridelet	Payne	Hay	Steele	Wilkinson (2)	14
Batty	P Smith	S Smith	Smith R	Goddard	Danzey	Perkins	Gridelet	Akrour	Hay	Steele		15
Batty	P Smith	Goddard	Smith R	S Smith	Danzey	Perkins	Gridelet	West	Akrour	Steele	Bolt (4), Wilkinson (8), Flavahan (1)	16
Flavahan	S Smith	Hollingdale	West	Goddard	Danzey	Perkins	Gridelet	Hay	Akrour	Wilkinson	P Smith (3)	17
Flavahan	P Smith	Hollingdale	West	S Smith	Danzey	Perkins	Wilkinson	Akrour	Hay	Steele		18
Flavahan	P Smith	Hollingdale	West	S Smith	Danzey	Perkins	Wilkinson	Akrour	Hay	Steele		19
Flavahan	P Smith	Hollingdale	West	S Smith	Danzey	Perkins	Wilkinson	Akrour	Hay	Steele	Goddard (5)	20
Flavahan	P Smith	Hollingdale	West	S Smith	Danzey	Perkins	Girdler	Akrour	Hay	Steele	Panter (10)	21
Flavahan	P Smith	Hollingdale	West	S Smith	Danzey	Perkins	Wilkinson	Akrour	Panter	Steele	Girdler (8), Goddard (2)	22
Flavahan	Gridelet	Hollingdale	West	Goddard	Alighieri	Perkins	Wilkinson	Akrour	Hay	Steele		23
Flavahan	Girdler	Hollingdale	West	S Smith	Danzey	Perkins	Wilkinson	Akrour	Hay	Bolt	P Smith (5), Goddard (7)	24
Flavahan	P Smith	Alighieri	West	S Smith	Danzey	Gridelet	Wilkinson	Akrour	Hay	Simpson	Bolt (2), Panter (11), Goddard (7)	25
Flavahan	Miller	Hollingdale	West	S Smith	Goddard	Perkins	Girdler	Akrour	Charles	Bolt		26
Flavahan	Miller	Hollingdale	West	S Smith	Goddard	Perkins	Girdler	Akrour	Charles	Bolt	Wilkinson (10), Alighieri (8)	27
Flavahan	R Smith	Miller	West	Alighieri	S Smith	Wilkinson	Perkins	Steele	Hay	Akrour	Bolt (10)	28
Flavahan	Miller	Alighieri	West	R Smith	S Smith	Perkins	Wilkinson	Akrour	Hay	Steele	Bullen (3), Hayfield (8)	29
Flavahan	Miller	Alighieri	West	R Smith	S Smith	Perkins	Hayfield	Akrour	Hay	Steele	Brown (4), Bolt (3), Charles (5)	30
Flavahan	Panter	Hollingdale	Brown	S Smith	Miller	Wilkinson	Hayfield	Akrour	Charles	Steele	Bolt (2), Hay (9)	31
Batty	Miller	Hollingdale	Brown	S Smith	Perkins	Wilkinson	Hayfield	Akrour	Charles	Steele	Hay (10)	32
Batty	Perkins	Hollingdale	Miller	S Smith	Brown	Wilkinson	Hayfield	Akrour	Hay	Steele	Bolt (2), Stott (7)	33
Batty	Wilkinson	Hollingdale	Miller	S Smith	Brown	Stott	Hayfield	Akrour	Panter	Steele	Hay (10), Bolt (3)	34
Batty	Hayfield	Hollingdale	Miller	S Smith	Brown	Stott	Perkins	Akrour	West	Steele	Bolt (11), Hay (10), Charles (3)	35
Batty	French	Hollingdale	Miller	S Smith	Brown	Hayfield	Alighieri	Akrour	West	Bolt	Wilkinson (2), Hay (3), Charles (9)	36
Batty	Miller	Hollingdale	West	S Smith	Brown	Hayfield	Stott	Akrour	Hay	Steele	Alighieri (8)	37
Batty	Miller	Hollingdale	West	S Smith	Brown	Hayfield	Stott	Akrour	Hay	Steele	Wilkinson (7)	38
Batty	Miller	Hollingdale	West	S Smith	Brown	Hayfield	Stott	Akrour	Hay	Steele	Wilkinson (8), Perkins (7), Charles (9)	39
Batty	Miller	Hollingdale	West	S Smith	Brown	Hayfield	Stott	Akrour	Hay	Steele	Wilkinson (8), Perkins (11), Charles (9)	40
Flavahan	Miller	Hollingdale	West	S Smith	Brown	Hayfield	Stott	Akrour	Hay	Perkins	Charles (10), Wilkinson (7), Bolt (8)	41
Flavahan	Miller	Hollingdale	West	S Smith	Brown	Hayfield	Stott	Akrour	Hay	Steele	Perkins (11), Charles (9)	42

THE NON-LEAGUE PAPER
CONFERENCE & PYRAMID LEAGUES SOCCER / £1.00

AVAILABLE AT A NEWSAGENT NEAR YOU EVERY SUNDAY

PLAYING SQUAD

WOKING

(Bold print indicates an England Semi-Professional International)

Player Honours	Birthplace	D.O.B.	Previous Clubs

GOALKEEPERS

Mark Ormerod	Bournemouth	05.02.76	Brighton

DEFENDERS

Player	Birthplace	D.O.B.	Previous Clubs
Scott Smith New Zealand Int.	Christchurch	06.03.75	Rotherham, Kettering T
Robert Smith	London		Wycombe, Chesham U, Slough T, Yeovil T
Aiden O'Brien ES	London		QPR, Oxford U, Barnet, Leyton O, S.Shields, Morpeth T, Abingdon T, Aylesbury U, Harrow B, Hayes, Slough T, Nuneaton B, Harrow B
Kevan Brown ESP, FAT, Div.3	Andover	25.06.68	Southampton, Brighton, Aldershot, Woking, Yeovil T
Michael Danzey ESP	Widnes	08.02.71	Nottingham F, Peterborough, St.Albans C, Camb.U, Aylesbury U, £15,000 to Woking
Jamie Pitman	Trowbridge	06.01.76	Swindon, Hereford U, Yeovil T

MIDFIELDERS

Player	Birthplace	D.O.B.	Previous Clubs
Scott Steele FAT, SS	Motherwell	19.09.71	Airdrie
Darron Wilkinson	Reading	24.11.69	Wokingham T, Brighton, Kuitan, Hayes
Steve Perkins British Univ.	Southport	05.11.75	Plymouth, Stevenage B, £10,000 to Woking
Nick Roddis British Univ.	Rotherham	18.02.73	Nottingham F, Boston T, Boston U, Yeading, Hayes
Matt Hayfield	Bristol	08.08.75	Bristol R, Yeovil T

FORWARDS

Player	Birthplace	D.O.B.	Previous Clubs
Steve West	Essex	15.11.72	Arsenal, Purfleet, Tilbury, Aveley, E.Thurrock U, Concord R, Enfield, £35,000 to Woking
Mark Watson	Birmingham	28.12.73	Sutton U, West Ham, Bournemouth, Welling U, Sutton U
Jae Martin	London	05.02.76	Southend, Birmingham, Lincoln, Peterborough
Mark Druce NC	Oxford	03.03.74	Oxford, Rotherham, Hereford U, Kidderminster H
Dante Aligheiri	London		From Youth team

YEOVIL TOWN

After a nightmare result (0-5) in their first game away to Scarborough, Yeovil found themselves on top of the Conference in mid-September!

Seven victories including five goals at Welling took them up the table, but strangely the crowds at home never topped 3,000 apart from the New Year fixture against local Forest Green Rovers.

From then on Conference consistency was unobtainable, fourth position after the next seven games. Then three more wins and top again. However, only seven victories from the second half of the season saw crowds sink below the 2,000 mark.

Manager Colin Lippiatt didn't want to go full time, so was not considered suitable and coach Steve Thompson took over early in September. The top spot was obtained again early in December, but still attendances were limited.

Thompson didn't appear comfortable, so David West was introduced to the club amidst much conjecture about the manager's job. Eventually he took over with Thompson reverting to coach and the season drifted to an end with senior players leaving by the week and full time football promised for the staff in the future.

Kingstonian had halted a promising Trophy run - again - and a visit to the Madejski Stadium, Reading was the only bright spot of a disappointing, by Yeovil's standard, F.A. Cup campaign.

Yeovil was never lower than seventh and had hit the top twice, something the club had never before achieved, yet no one really seemed to enjoy the season - very strange!

The new full time youth policy could change all that.   TW

Back Row: David Piper, David Seal, Tony Pennock, Paul Steele, Chris Giles,
Middle: Tony Tonkin, Ben Smith, Jason Matthews, Chris Weale, Terry Skiverton (Captain), Tony Farmer (Physio).
Front: Andy Lindgaard, Glenn Poole, Adrian Foster, David Webb, James Bent, Barrington Belgrave, Steve Thompson
(Manager)   (Player Coach)

YEOVIL TOWN

GROUND DETAILS

Huish Park,
Lufton Way,
Yeovil
Somerset, BA22 8YF

TELEPHONE   01935 423662
                        Fax 01935 473956
            Web site: http://www.ytfc.net

SIMPLE DIRECTIONS:
Leave A303 at Cartgate r'about, take A3088 signed
Yeovil. 1st exit at next r'about, 1st exit at next r'about into
Lufton Way.
Railway station - Yeovil Pen Mill (Bristol/Westbury to
Weymouth) 2.5 miles from ground.
Bus service from station on Saturday

CAPACITY: 8,761
SEATED: 5,253
COVERED TERRACING: 3,508

SOCIAL FACILITIES: Matchdays hot + cold food available.
Meals can be orderedprovided advance notice is given.
All weather astro turf pitch available forbookings 9am-10pm

CLUB SHOP: Open matchdays & 10-4 weekdays, selling a full
range of souvenirs, match programmes,scarves, hats,
replica kits and badges

Pages: 48   Price: £1.50

Editor: Bryan Moore

Other club publications: "100 Huish Heroes" £3; Centenary Book
£14.99 (Both available from the club)

Local Press: Western Gazette; Western Daily Press; Bristol
Evening Post; Sunday Independent; Yeovil Express & Clarion
Local Radio: Radio Bristol; Somerset Sound; Orchard FM

Nickname:	Glovers
Sponsors:	Mostly Media
Club Colours:	Green & white shirts
	white shorts & green socks
Change Colours:	Yellow, green trim shirts
	white shorts & green socks
Midweek matchday:	Tuesday
Reserve League:	Screwfix Direct Western League
	Prem. Div

CLUB OFFICIALS

Chairman	John Fry
President	S N Burfield M.B.E.
Company Secretary	G R Smith
Club Secretary	Jean Cotton
	c/o the club
Commercial Manager	Alan Skirton

FOOTBALL MANAGEMENT TEAM

MANAGER: **DAVID WEBB**
Date of Appointment   August 2000
Date of Birth: 9th April 1946
Place of Birth: Stratford

PREVIOUS CLUBS
As manager   Torquay Utd., Southend, Chelsea,
               Bournemouth, Brentford.
As coach   None
As player   West Ham, Leyton O., Southampton,
               Chelsea, Q.P.R., Leicester C., Derby
               Co., Bournemouth, Torquay (N.C.).

HONOURS
As manager   None
As player   FA Cup '70, Euro CWC '71

*   *   *

Assistant Manager:	Steve Thompson
Reserve team manager:	Maurice O'Donnell
Youth development:	Stuart Housley
Chief Scout:	Frank Leworthy
Physio:	Tony Farmer

Season	League	Div.	Pos.	Home						Away					Pts	Manager
				P	W	D	L	F	A	W	D	L	F	A		
99-00	Conference	-	7	42	11	4	6	37	28	7	6	8	23	35	64	C.Lippiatt/Steve Thompson/Dave Webb
98-99	Conference		5	42	8	4	9	35	32	12	7	2	33	22	71	Colin Lippiatt
97-98	Conference		11	42	14	3	4	45	24	3	5	13	28	39	59	Graham Roberts/Colin Lippiatt
96-97	Isthmian	Prem.	1	42	17	3	1	49	17	14	5	2	34	17	101	Graham Roberts

Season	League	Div.	Pos.	P	W	D	L	F	A	Pts	Manager
95-96	Isthmian	Prem.	4	42	23	11	8	83	51	80	Graham Roberts
94-95	Conference	-	22	42	8	14	20	50	71	*37	Brian Hall/Graham Roberts
93-94	Conference	-	19	42	14	9	19	49	62	51	Steve Rutter/Brian Hall
92-93	Conference	-	4	42	18	12	12	59	49	66	Steve Rutter
91-92	Conference	-	15	42	11	14	17	40	49	47	Steve Rutter
90-91	Conference	-	14	42	13	11	18	58	58	50	Clive Whitehead/Steve Rutter

HONOURS

Southern Lge 54-55, 63-64, 70-71
R-up 23-24, 31-32, 34-35, 69-70, 72-73
Southern Lge Cup 48-49, 54-55, 60-61, 65-66
Vauxhall-Opel Lge (Isthmian) 87-88, R-up 85-86, 86-87
ICIS Prem. (Isthmian) 96-97;
AC Delco Cup 87-88.
Bob Lord Trophy 89-90
R-up 93-94

PREVIOUS

Leagues: Western League, London Combination, Southern League, Alliance Premier79-85, Isthmian85-88, GMV Conference 88-95, Isthmian 95-97

Names: Yeovil & Petters Utd

Ground: Pen Mill ground 1895-1921, Huish 1921-1990

Past Players who progressed to the Football League

Over 40 players & 18 managers including, since 1985,

Nigel Jarvis (Torquay), Ian Davies (Bristol Rovers),
Alan Pardew(Crystal Palace), Paul Miller (Wimbledon)
John McGinlay (Bolton), Guy Whittingham (Portsmouth),
Mark Shail (Bristol City), Malcom McPherson (WestHam),
Howard Forinton & Jerry Gill (Birmingham City)

ACHIEVE BY UNITY

CLUB RECORDS

Attendance:	8,612
	v Arsenal 3rd Rd FA Cup 02/1/93
Career Goalscorer:	Dave Taylor 285 1960-69
Career Appearances:	Len Harris, 691, 1958-72
Win:	10-0
	v Kidderminster Harriers (H), Southern Lge. 27.12.1955
	v Bedford Town (H), Southern Lge. 4.3.61
Defeat:	0-8
	v Manchester Utd., FA Cup 5th Rd.
	12.2.49 at Maine Rd. (81,565)
Transfer Fee Paid:	£17,500
	to Oxford City for Howard Forinton 1.97
Transfer Fee Received:	£75,000
	for Mark Shail from Bristol City

BEST SEASON

FA Cup: 5th Rd 1948-49
League clubs defeated: 16

FA Trophy: Semi-Final
70-71 71-72

League: 4th Conference 92-93

LAST SEASON

F.A. Cup: 1st Round
F.A. Trophy: 5th Round
Conference: 7th
Top Goalscorer: Warren Patmore 17
Captain: Terry Skiverton
Player of the Year:
Supporters' Club — Terry Skiverton
Independent Supporters' Club — Tony Pennock
Western Gazette — Tony Pennock

YEOVIL TOWN Match Facts 1999-00

	Date	Comp.	H/A	Opponents	Gate	Result & Score	Goalscorers	League Position
1	14.08	N.C.	A	Scarborough	2,005	L 0-5		
2	17.08	N.C.	H	Kidderminster Harriers	2,473	W 1-0	Foster 31	
3	21.08	N.C.	H	Altrincham	2,214	W 3-0	Patmore 28, Foster 43 Hayfield 62	7
4	24.08	N.C.	A	Nuneaton Borough	2,216	D 1-1	Norton	
5	28.08	N.C.	H	Kettering Town	2,347	W 2-0	Hayfield 13 Patmore 28	3
6	30.08	N.C.	A	Woking	2,340	L 0-2		7
7	04.09	N.C.	A	Welling United	716	W 5-2	Eaton 4,18, Smith 63, Patmore 74(p),Thompson 90	5
8	07.09	N.C.	H	Hereford United	2,632	W 1-0	Piper 26	2
9	11.09	N.C.	H	Morecambe	2,642	W 2-0	Patmore 63, 78	2
10	14.09	N.C.	A	Hayes	747	W 3-2	Hayfield 33, Foster 45, Patmore 79 (pen)	1
11	18.09	N.C.	H	Welling United	2,839	L 1-2	Hayfield 45	2
§ 12	25.09	N.C.	A	Telford United	1,002	L 1-3	Pitman 48	3
13	02.10	N.C.	H	Dover Athletic	2,420	D 1-1	Foster 90	3
14	09.10	N.C.	A	Kidderminster Harriers	1,769	L 0-4		4
15	13.10	N.C.	A	Kingstonian	1,421	W 1-0	Griffen 60	3
16	23.10	N.C.	H	Southport	2,217	D 1-1	Foster 29	4
17	06.11	N.C.	A	Hednesford Town	972	L 0-1		4
18	13.11	N.C.	H	Rushden & Diamonds	2,180	W 5-1	Skiverton 1, 44, Hayfield 51, 66, Smith B. 68	4
19	20.11	N.C.	A	Sutton United	1,010	W 1-0	Smith 38	3
20	04.12	N.C.	H	Northwich Victoria	2,239	W 3-2	Skiverton 69, Hayfield 79, Patmore 90	1
21	18.12	N.C.	H	Hayes	2,603	L 2-4	Skiverton 7, Patmore 38	3
22	27.12	N.C.	A	Forest Green Rovers	1,837	L 0-3		4
23	03.01	N.C.	H	Forest Green Rovers	3,028	W 1-0	Foster 76	3
24	08.01	N.C.	A	Dover Athletic	1442	L 0-3		5
25	22.01	N.C.	H	Telford United	2174	W 2-1	Patmore 24, 27	3
26	29.01	N.C.	A	Kettering Town	1329	W 2-1	Cousins 2, Skiverton 52	3
27	12.02	N.C.	A	Southport	1,343	D 1-1	Foster 50	3
28	19.02	N.C.	H	Nuneaton Borough	2,629	L 1-3	Pitman 21	3
29	04.03	N.C.	A	Northwich Victoria	1,011	L 0-3		5
30	07.03	N.C.	A	Rushden & Diamonds	3,611	D 1-1	Hayfield 86	4
Σ 31	11.03	N.C.	H	Doncaster Rovers	2,079	L 1-3	Tisdale 1	5
32	18.03	N.C.	A	Doncaster Rovers	2,498	W 3-0	OG (Walling) 35, Patmore 70, Bent 84	4
33	25.03	N.C.	A	Scarborough	2,031	L 1-2	Patmore 76	6
34	04.04	N.C.	H	Stevenage Bor.	1,455	D 2-2	Skiverton 43, Steele 44	6
35	08.04	N.C.	A	Hereford United	1,819	W 1-0	Belgrave 44	5
36	11.04	N.C.	H	Kingstonian	1,593	W 3-2	Steele 5, Smith 41, Hale 45	3
37	15.04	N.C.	H	Welling United	1,812	D 1-1	Patmore 18	5
38	17.04	N.C.	A	Stevenage Bor.	1,452	D 0-0		4
39	22.04	N.C.	H	Hednesford Town	2,012	W 3-0	Foster 42, Lindegaard 68, Hale 81	4
40	29.04	N.C.	A	Altrincham	792	D 2-2	Steele 33, Bent 68	
41	01.05	N.C.	H	Woking	2,727	L 0-3		6
42	06.05	N.C.	A	Morecambe	1,490	D 1-1	Foster 49	7

§ - Steve Thompson takes over as manager   Σ - David Webb takes over as manager

CUP COMPETITIONS

F.A. Cup

16.10	4Q	H	Witney Town	2,092	W	2-1	Alder 70 (og), Foster 78
30.10	1	A	Reading	8.032	L	2-4	Foster 36, Eaton 90

Nationwide McMillan Trophy

09.11	2	H	Hereford United	823	W	3-0	Pole 20, Patmore 31, 36
08.02	3	A	Hayes	364	L	1-2	Eaton 39

F.A. Trophy

28.11	2	A	Weymouth	4,053	D	0-0	
30.11	2R	H	Weymouth	3,196	W	2-1	Patmore 76, Tisdale 85
15.01	3	H	Stevenage Bor.	2,604	W	2-1	Foster 8, 51
05.02	4	A	Bedford Town	2,010	W	4-0	OG (Lovington) 5, Patmore 15, Eaton 56, Cousins 60
26.02	5	H	Kingstonian	3,330	L	0-1	

	1	2	3	4	5	6	7	8	9	10	11	Substitutes Used	
1	Pennock	Piper	Fishlock	Brown	Hayfield	Cousins	Eaton	Patmore	Foster	Smith B	Stott	Chandler (4), Skiverton (6), Norton (10)	1
2	Pennock	Piper	Fishlock	Chandler	Skiverton	Cousins	Hayfield	Stott	Patmore	Foster	Norton	Pounder (3)Brown (4), Eaton (10)	2
3	Pennock	Pitman	Fishlock	Chandler	Skiverton	Cousins	Hayfield	Stott	Patmore	Foster	Norton	Simpson (8), Eaton (9)	3
4	Pennock	Pitman	Fishlock	Chandler	Skiverton	Cousins	Hayfield	Stott	Patmore	Foster	Norton	Piper (3), Brown (4)	4
5	Pennock	Pitman	Fishlock	Chandler	Skiverton	Cousins	Hayfield	Stott	Patmore	Foster	Norton	Smith B. (7), Eaton (9)	5
6	Pennock	Pitman	Fishlock	Brown	Chandler	Cousins	Smith B.	Stott	Patmore	Foster	Norton	Eaton (3), Pounder (4), Simpson (11)	6
7	Pennock	Piper	Pitman	Sparks	Skiverton	Cousins	Eaton	Stott	Patmore	Smith B	Norton	Brown (9), Thompson (11)	7
8	Pennock	Piper	Pitman	Sparks	Skiverton	Cousins	Eaton	Stott	Patmore	Smith B	Norton	Brown (7)	8
9	Pennock	Piper	Pitman	Sparks	Skiverton	Cousins	Eaton	Stott	Patmore	Smith B	Hayfield	Foster (7)	9
10	Pennock	Piper	Pitman	Sparks	Skiverton	Cousins	Hayfield	Stott	Patmore	Smith B	Foster	Browne (11), Pounder (10)	10
11	Pennock	Piper	Pitman	Sparks	Skiverton	Cousins	Hayfield	Stott	Patmore	Smith B	Foster	Eaton (11), Archer (2), Browne (10)	11
12	Pennock	Archer	Pitman	Stowell	Skiverton	Cousins	Hayfield	Stott	Patmore	Smith B	Foster	Tisdale (10), Eaton (11), Brown (2)	12
13	Pennock	Stowell	Archer	Sparks	Skiverton	Cousins	Hayfield	Stott	Patmore	Smith B	Eaton	Foster (9), Tisdale (10), Pounder (3)	13
14	Pennock	Stowell	Archer	Sparks	Brown	Cousins	Hayfield	Stott	Griffin	Pitman	Eaton	Tisdale (6), Smith B (11)	14
15	Pennock	Piper	Pitman	Sparks	Brown	Stowell	Griffin	Stott	Foster	Smith B	Archer	Pounder (11), Eaton (7)	15
16	Pennock	Piper	Pitman	Sparks	Brown	Stowell	Hayfield	Stott	Foster	Griffin	Pounder	Patmore (10), Cousins (11), Smith B (8)	16
17	Pennock	Piper	Pitman	Sparks	Brown	Cousins	Hayfield	Stowell	Patmore	Eaton	Pounder	Skiverton (4), Smith B (11), Thompson	17
18												(10)	18
19	Pennock	Piper	Pitman	Skiverton	Brown	Cousins	Hayfield	Stowell	Patmore	Smith B	Tisdale	Norton (3), Poole (11)	19
20	Pennock	Piper	Pitman	Skiverton	Brown	Cousins	Hayfield	Steele	Patmore	Smith B	Tisdale	Norton (7), Eaton (10)	20
21	Pennock	Piper	Pitman	Skiverton	Brown	Cousins	Eaton	Chandler	Patmore	Smith B	Tisdale	Pounder (2), Hayfield (7)	21
22	Pennock	Piper	Pitman	Skiverton	Chandler	Cousins	Hayfield	Fishlock	Patmore	Smith B	Tisdale	Pounder (2), Thompson (7)	22
23	Pennock	Pounder	Sparks	Chandler	Brown	Cousins	Hayfield	Pitman	Patmore	Thompson	Tisdale	B Smith (10), Eaton (4). Fishlock (7)	23
24	Pennock	Fishlock	Pitman	Sparks	Brown	Cousins	Hayfield	Chandler	Foster	Eaton	Tisdale	Piper (7)	24
25	Pennock	Piper	Fishlock	Sparks	Brown	Cousins	Pitman	Skiverton	Patmore	Foster	Tisdale	Poole ((3), B Smith (4), Pounder (6)	25
26	Pennock	Pounder	Poole	Skiverton	Brown	Cousins	Pitman	Chandler	Patmore	Foster	B Smith	Thompson (3), Eaton (10)	26
27	Pennock	Poole	Piper	Skiverton	Brown	Cousins	Pitman	Chandler	Patmore	B Smith	Eaton	Wilmot (10)	27
28	Pennock	Piper	Poole	Skiverton	Brown	Cousins	Pitman	Chandler	Patmore	Foster	B Smith	Tisdale (11), Pounder (3), Eaton (10)	28
29	Pennock	Piper	Pitman	Skiverton	Brown	Cousins	Tisdale	Chandler	Patmore	B Smith	Eaton	Hayfield (4), Foster (11), Pounder (10)	29
30	Pennock	Pounder	Hale	Skiverton	Tisdale	Cousins	Hayfield	Chandler	Patmore	Foster	Poole	Eaton (9), Piper (3), Wilmot (5)	30
31	Pennock	Tonkin	Piper	Skiverton	Brown	Cousins	Pounder	Tisdale	Patmore	B Smith	Hale	Foster (7), Hayfield (8)	31
32	Pennock	Piper	Hale	Skiverton	Cousins	Pounder	Tonkin	Patmore	B Smith	Tisdale	Brown	Eaton (6), Hayfield (7), Poole (9)	32
33	Pennock	Piper	Hale	Skiverton	Sparks	Cousins	Lindegard	B Smith	Patmore	Foster	Poole	Bent (10)	33
34	Pennock	Piper	Tonkin	Skiverton	Sparks	Cousins	Lindegard	B Smith	Patmore	Foster	Poole	Bent (10), Steele (5), Pitman (6)	34
35	Pennock	Piper	Tonkin	Skiverton	Steele	Pitman	Lindegard	B Smith	Patmore	Belgrave	Hale	No subs used	35
36	Pennock	Piper	Tonkin	Skiverton	Steele	Pitman	Lindegard	B Smith	Patmore	Belgrave	Hale	Cousins (7)	36
37	Pennock	Piper	Tonkin	Skiverton	Steele	Pitman	Lindegard	B Smith	Patmore	Belgrave	Hale	No subs used	37
38	Pennock	Piper	Tonkin	Chandler	Steele	Pitman	Lindegard	B Smith	Patmore	Belgrave	Poole	Bent (11)	38
39	Pennock	Piper	Tonkin	Chandler	Steele	Pitman	Lindegard	B Smith	Patmore	Belgrave	Poole	Cousins (11)	39
40	Pennock	Piper	Tonkin	Skiverton	Steele	Pitman	Lindegard	B Smith	Foster	Belgrave	Hale	Bent (10)	40
41	Pennock	Wilmot	Tonkin	Skiverton	Steele	Pitman	Belgrave	B Smith	Patmore	Bent	Hale	Chandler (2), Piper (7), Foster (10)	41
42	Pennock	Piper	Tonkin	Skiverton	Steele	Pitman	Lindegard	Cousins	Patmore	Bent	Hale	Foster (7)	42

	1	2	3	4	5	6	7	8	9	10	11	Substitutes Used
	Pennock	Pitman	Pitman	Sparks	Brown	Stowell	Pounder	Stott	Patmore	B Smith	Foster	Cousins (8), Hayfield (10), Thompson (11)
	Pennock	Piper	Pitman	Sparks	Brown	Stowell	Hayfield	Stott	Patmore	Foster	Pounder	Cousins (6), Smith B (11), Eaton (10)
	Pennock	Piper	Poole	Skiverton	Brown	Cousins	Hayfield	Chandler	Patmore	B Smith	Tisdale	Pitman (3), Norton (6), Bent (9)
	Pennock	Wilmot	Pounder	Sparks	Steele	Cousins	Tonkin	Thompson	Foster	Tisdale	Eaton	Hapgood (8), Bent (9), Patmore (11)
	Pennock	Piper	Skiverton	Chandler	Brown	Cousins	Hayfield	Pitman	Patmore	B Smith	Tisdale	Thompson (10)
	Pennock	Piper	Pitman	Skiverton	Brown	Cousins	Hayfield	Chandler	Patmore	B Smith	Tisdale	Eaton (7), Norton (10), Pounder (3)
	Pennock	Pounder	Piper	Skiverton	Brown	Cousins	B Smith	Chandler	Patmore	Foster	Tisdale	Wilmot (7)
	Pennock	Piper	Poole	Skiverton	Brown	Cousins	Pitman	Chandler	Patmore	Eaton	B Smith	Pounder (2), Foster (9), Wilmot (6)
	Pennock	Piper	Poole	Skiverton	Brown	Cousins	Pitman	Chandler	Patmore	Foster	B Smith	Tisdale (7), hayfield (8), Eaton (2)

PLAYING SQUAD

YEOVIL TOWN

(Bold print indicates an England Semi-Professional International)

Player Honours	Birthplace	D.O.B.	Previous Clubs

GOALKEEPERS

Tony Pennock ILP	Swansea	10.4.71	Stockport Co, Wigan A, Hereford U
Jason Matthews Nuneaton B, Exeter	Bath		Bath C, Paulton R, Mangotsfield U, Taunton T, Salisbury C,

DEFENDERS

Murray Fishlock ESP	Marlborough	23.09.73	Swindon, Gloucester C, Trowbridge T, Hereford U
Anthony Tonkin British Univ.			Falmouth T., Plymouth Arg.
Dean Chandler	London	05.06.76	Charlton, Torquay, Lincoln
Terry Skivington	Mile End	26.06.75	Chelsea, Wycombe, Welling U
David Piper	Bournemouth	31.10.77	Southampton
Paul Steele			Chippenham Town

MIDFIELDERS

Ben Smith	Chelmsford	23.11.78	Arsenal, Reading
Glenn Poole			Tottenham H. (YTS), Witham Town, Ford United
Nick Crittenden	Ascot	11.11.78	Chelsea
Steve Thompson ESP, FAT, GMVC, RP	Plymouth	12.01.63 £5,000 to Yeovil T	Bristol C, Torquay, Saltash U, Slough T, Wycombe, Woking,
Andy Lindegard	Dorset		Westlands Sports
Roy O'Brien Rep.of Ire S & Y	Cork	27.11.74	Arsenal, Wigan, Bournemouth, Dorchester T

FORWARDS

Warren Patmore ESP, RP	Kingsbury	14.08.71	Northwood, Camb.U, Millwall, Northampton, Ards
James Bent	Yeovil		From Youth team
Adrian Foster	Kidderminster	19.03.71	WBA, Torquay, Gillingham, Hereford U, Rushden & D
Barrington Belgrave	Plymouth		Plymouth

NORTHERN PREMIER LEAGUE

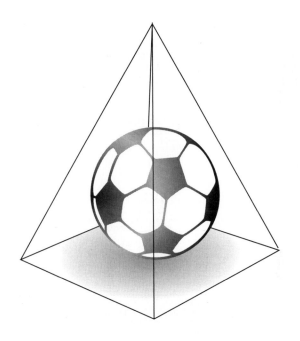

PYRAMID SECTION

UniBond
NORTHERN PREMIER

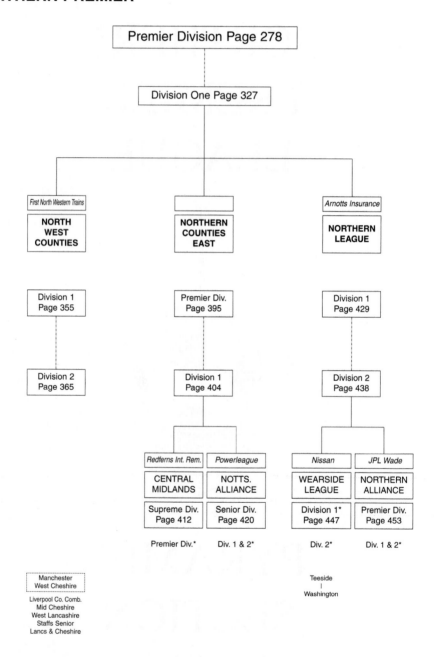

Premier Division Page 278

Division One Page 327

First North Western Trains
NORTH WEST COUNTIES

NORTHERN COUNTIES EAST

Arnotts Insurance
NORTHERN LEAGUE

Division 1 Page 355

Premier Div. Page 395

Division 1 Page 429

Division 2 Page 365

Division 1 Page 404

Division 2 Page 438

Redferns Int. Rem.
CENTRAL MIDLANDS
Supreme Div. Page 412
Premier Div.*

Powerleague
NOTTS. ALLIANCE
Senior Div. Page 420
Div. 1 & 2*

Nissan
WEARSIDE LEAGUE
Division 1* Page 447
Div. 2*

JPL Wade
NORTHERN ALLIANCE
Premier Div. Page 453
Div. 1 & 2*

Manchester
West Cheshire
Liverpool Co. Comb.
Mid Cheshire
West Lancashire
Staffs Senior
Lancs & Cheshire

Teeside
|
Washington

Leagues with clubs in F.A. competitions

* indicates no clubs in F.A. competitions

UniBond League

President: N White F.S.C.A.

Chairman: Ken Marsden

Secretary & Treasurer: R D Bayley
22 Woburn Drive, Hale, Altrincham, Cheshire WA15 8LZ
Tel: 0161 980 7007   Fax: 0161 904 8850

Press Secretary: P Bradley
7 Guest Road, Prestwich Manchester M25 7DJ
Tel: 0161 798 5198   Fax: 0161 773 0930

By the 11th September Emley, Hyde United and Leigh had all topped the Premier Division table but it was the ultra consistency of the latter that eventually saw them win the race for a place in Conference football. Once they returned to the head of affairs in mid-January Steve Waywell's side were never agin headed and took the title by a seven point margin from Hyde who, with not much cash about, probably surprised themselves as well as everybody else by being in the top four virtually throughout the campaign. It was a disappointing campaign by their own standards, however, for Emley who fell away to finish fifth and they also lost out to Hyde in the Unifill Cup Final. Elsewhere Gateshead and Marine both briefly threatened but couldn't quite deliver to finish third and fourth respectively.

At the other end of the table it was a torrid time for Winsford United, who didn't win a game until the end of January when they beat Guiseley 4-2. The Yorkshire side were then in a comfortable sixteenth place, but their collapse thereafter was such that they finished up being relegated with Winsford after the cash strapped Spennymoor United took a point on the final day of the season from Marine to reprieve themselves and condemn Guiseley, League Cup Finalists and third in the table just twelve months earlier, to the drop. None of the four newcomers to the top flight set the world alight but didn't ever look like being in trouble either. Leek Town, relegated from the Conference, finished lowest of the four in nineteenth place but owed much of that final placing to a poor run-in once they sold leading goalscorer Paul Kiely to Stafford Rangers. Accompanying Leek from the Conference, but in much more contentious circumstances, were Barrow who, after being placed in the UniBond League by the Football Association, finished thirteenth with the two promoted clubs Droylsden and Hucknall Town in fifteenth and eighteenth respectively.

The previous campaign had seen Droylsden and Hucknall Town involved in a last day drama when they finished level on both points and goal difference and the First Division title again went right to the wire when Accrington Stanley defeated Farsley Celtic 3-0 in front of a crowd approaching two and a half thousand to land the spoils on goal difference from Burscough and the unlucky third placed outfit Witton Albion with all three clubs finishing on 84 points. Saying goodbye to the UniBond League are Flixton and Whitley Bay, both of whom were in the bottom three virtually all season long and, unlike Gretna who were alongside the two relegated clubs for most of the time, were not able to put together a life saving run. We wish them well and hope to see them back sooner rather than later but their misfortune opens the door to North Ferriby United and Vauxhall GM who will replace them next August.

Lancaster City lifted the UniBond League Challenge Cup with a single goal victory over Worksop Town, whilst there was a major surprise in the President's Cup where lowly First Division Trafford beat top flight Whitby Town in a penalty shoot out after drawing 5-5 on aggregate.

In the FA Cup the UniBond League had six representatives in the First Round Proper with two, Stalybridge Celtic and Bamber Bridge, progressing to the Second Round Proper before failing by the odd goal in each instance to overcome full time opposition in Cambridge United and Chester City respectively. The same fate had befallen Gateshead and brave little First Division side Eastwood Town in the First Round at Cambridge and Exeter City, whilst Runcorn and Guiseley also went out at this stage away at Hayes and Forest Green. UniBond clubs were also at the forefront of the FA Umbro Trophy with the League the only one outside the Football Conference to have representation at the quarter-final stage of the competition. Unfortunately, Runcorn went down at Telford but Bishop Auckland looked all set for a semi-final place when leading 2-0 at Kettering only to see their lead evaporate resulting in a replay which Bishops lost.

Phil Bradley, UniBond League Press Secretary

UNIBOND LEAGUE NEWSLINE
09066 555 800

PREMIER DIVISION
FINAL LEAGUE TABLE 1999-2000

			Home					Away					
		P	W	D	L	F	A	W	D	L	F	A	Pts
1	Leigh	44	15	3	4	42	17	13	5	4	49	28	92
2	Hyde United	44	14	5	3	47	20	10	8	4	30	24	85
3	Gateshead	44	12	6	4	41	17	11	7	4	38	24	82
4	Marine	44	10	9	3	40	25	11	7	4	38	21	79
5	Emley	44	9	7	6	25	18	11	5	6	29	23	72
6	Lancaster City	44	14	4	4	40	18	6	7	9	25	37	71
7	Stalybridge Celtic	44	13	5	4	42	27	5	7	10	22	27	66
8	Bishop Auckland	44	9	8	5	33	23	9	3	10	30	38	65
9	Runcorn	44	11	4	7	36	25	7	6	9	28	30	64
10	Worksop Town	44	10	3	9	44	29	9	3	10	34	36	63
11	Gainsborough Trinity	44	12	6	4	40	22	4	9	9	19	27	63
12	Whitby Town	44	11	7	4	38	24	4	6	12	28	42	58
13	Barrow	44	6	7	9	35	40	8	8	6	30	19	57
14	Blyth Spartans	44	10	2	10	39	34	5	7	10	23	33	54
15	Droylsden	44	9	4	9	26	26	5	8	9	27	34	54
16	Frickley Athletic	44	8	8	6	39	40	7	1	14	25	45	54
17	Bamber Bridge	44	7	7	8	38	32	7	4	11	32	35	53
18	Hucknall Town	44	11	5	6	33	22	3	6	13	22	39	53
19	Leek Town	44	8	5	9	30	34	6	5	11	28	45	52
20	Colwyn Bay	44	5	7	10	20	35	7	5	10	26	50	48
21	Spennymoor United*	44	6	10	6	23	24	4	3	15	18	47	42
22	Guiseley	44	6	10	6	23	24	4	3	15	18	47	42
23	Winsford United	44	2	3	17	24	58	1	4	17	16	58	16

* points deducted

PREMIER DIVISION LEADING GOALSCORERS 1999-2000
(In order of League goals)

Lge	Cup	Total		Lge	Cup	Total	
23	14	37	Simon Yeo Hyde United	20	13	33	Paul Kiely Leek Town - now Stafford R
21	9	30	Simon Parke Guiseley	19	15	34	Andy Hayward Frickley Athletic
21	6	27	Andy Whittaker Bamber Bridge	19	8	27	Nickey Peverill Barrow

PREMIER DIVISION AVERAGE ATTENDANCES

	99-00	98-99		99-00	98-99
Barrow	1191	1624	Hyde United	538	516
Bamber Bridge	328	396	Lancaster City	287	243
Bishop Auckland	233	230	Leek Town	302	607
Blyth Spartans	366	429	Leigh	284	247
Colwyn Bay	226	271	Marine	317	288
Droylsden	266	220	Runcorn	256	300
Emley	289	275	Spennymoor United	227	242
Frickley Athletic	166	222	Stalybridge Celtic	416	523
Gainsborough Trinity	427	462	Whitby Town	423	581
Gateshead	282	303	Winsford United	165	197
Guiselely	274	349	Worksop Town	418	597
Hucknall Town	275	235			

PREMIER DIVISION RESULTS CHART 1999-2000

		1	2	3	4	5	6	7	8	9	10	11	12	13	14	15	16	17	18	19	20	21	22	23
1	Bamber B	X	2-3	4-0	1-1	1-2	1-3	0-1	2-1	0-0	0-3	2-2	1-1	0-0	6-1	5-0	2-2	0-2	2-0	2-0	1-4	2-2	2-1	2-3
		X	631	230	335	282	325	335	311	243	292	245	251	318	525	230	406	327	441	269	459	244	315	196
2	Barrow	4-0	X	1-3	3-2	4-0	0-3	0-2	2-0	1-1	3-5	1-1	4-2	1-2	2-2	1-4	2-2	2-2	0-2	1-0	1-1	0-3	0-0	2-3
		1083	X	944	1006	911	1072	1175	1073	1032	1542	1709	1054	985	784	1220	900	1314	1599	1035	1076	1135	2400	1154
3	Bishop A	0-1	1-3	X	1-1	4-0	1-0	1-1	3-2	0-0	1-1	1-0	3-1	2-2	1-1	1-1	1-1	0-2	2-0	0-3	1-0	4-0	4-1	1-2
		226	333	X	357	195	183	216	173	190	288	220	236	203	233	181	226	193	207	424	191	236	192	214
4	Blyth Sp.	1-2	1-1	0-2	X	4-1	3-0	3-2	4-1	1-1	0-1	1-2	1-0	3-4	0-2	2-3	0-1	3-1	4-2	2-3	1-4	2-0	1-0	2-1
		357	359	448	X	304	304	318	316	347	793	374	275	412	315	346	402	384	312	363	276	392	311	338
5	Colwyn B	0-7	0-0	0-1	0-0	X	1-2	0-1	1-0	0-0	1-3	0-2	2-0	2-3	1-1	1-1	3-5	0-5	1-1	0-2	0-0	2-0	2-0	3-1
		230	195	220	270	X	221	257	195	219	213	243	243	241	186	161	280	239	332	179	258	176	189	224
6	Droylsden	2-0	0-3	1-0	1-0	1-2	X	1-1	1-1	1-0	2-2	3-0	0-0	1-3	3-4	1-2	0-2	0-1	1-0	0-1	1-0	3-2	3-0	0-2
		253	401	221	181	346	X	321	237	248	147	224	262	473	241	370	193	202	322	182	445	215	207	163
7	Emley	3-0	0-0	2-0	2-0	1-2	1-0	X	1-3	0-0	1-1	1-1	1-1	0-1	0-0	0-0	3-1	0-2	1-0	2-0	0-1	2-1	3-2	1-2
		201	486	181	259	163	163	X	528	198	301	498	248	301	289	238	316	278	196	291	353	286	206	371
8	Frickley	2-0	2-5	4-2	1-1	4-1	0-4	0-0	X	0-0	1-4	2-2	3-2	3-1	3-2	1-1	2-4	2-2	1-2	1-1	1-1	2-1	3-1	1-3
		131	257	141	169	154	152	189	X	241	179	150	106	145	136	199	151	137	106	144	152	178	144	283
9	Gainsboro	1-0	1-3	4-1	0-1	2-0	2-1	2-1	1-2	X	1-2	0-0	5-2	1-1	1-0	3-2	4-3	0-0	1-1	4-0	1-1	1-1	3-0	2-0
		284	456	387	394	328	401	438	342	X	376	304	526	408	386	487	341	366	341	394	345	575	290	1231
10	Gateshd	2-1	0-0	0-0	3-0	6-0	1-1	0-1	2-0	0-1	X	3-1	0-0	2-3	4-0	2-1	1-1	2-0	0-3	6-2	2-0	0-0	2-0	3-2
		212	258	387	497	253	235	254	204	312	X	209	204	276	210	236	408	281	268	278	278	404	256	286
11	Guiseley	2-4	0-0	0-3	2-1	2-2	2-0	1-1	0-1	1-3	1-1	X	1-2	0-1	0-1	1-1	0-3	1-3	2-2	3-1	2-2	0-1	2-2	0-1
		266	282	305	383	272	306	270	156	274	207	X	310	204	313	267	274	273	240	267	274	317	278	297
12	Hucknall	2-1	0-3	1-0	0-1	2-2	3-3	2-0	2-1	1-0	1-0	1-1	X	0-1	1-3	2-0	1-2	2-0	1-1	0-0	4-0	3-2	4-0	0-1
		225	258	245	218	168	180	298	229	425	263	328	X	319	206	285	259	273	265	169	275	210	220	690
13	Hyde U	3-1	1-0	1-1	5-2	3-0	2-0	2-3	2-3	4-0	1-1	2-0	4-3	X	4-1	2-0	1-2	1-1	0-0	2-1	1-0	4-1	2-0	0-0
		385	480	367	372	374	752	552	303	403	522	414	553	X	465	392	903	552	535	401	1772	407	424	518
14	Lancaster	1-1	1-0	0-1	3-0	3-0	4-0	2-1	2-0	2-0	1-1	2-0	1-0	1-0	X	1-3	1-3	1-1	3-2	3-0	3-2	1-2	4-1	0-0
		269	826	220	315	261	267	315	213	234	365	277	228	261	X	201	260	238	277	242	345	262	146	292
15	Leek T	0-0	2-1	1-4	1-4	0-2	0-0	1-3	1-2	3-2	1-2	2-2	2-2	2-0	3-1	X	2-0	2-4	0-1	1-0	0-0	2-1	1-2	3-1
		325	494	131	330	346	271	173	300	265	316	340	267	408	267	X	325	274	213	320	274	352	298	368
16	Leigh	3-0	1-0	4-1	2-0	1-2	1-2	1-0	5-0	1-1	3-1	0-1	1-0	0-0	2-1	0-2	X	2-1	2-0	4-0	2-0	2-1	3-2	2-2
		260	331	203	695	211	235	419	241	201	215	247	209	427	401	228	X	266	161	253	304	202	255	275
17	Marine	0-3	1-0	3-1	0-0	1-1	3-2	3-1	1-0	2-2	1-1	2-2	3-0	0-0	0-0	6-1	1-1	X	0-1	3-0	1-3	3-3	3-1	3-2
		279	357	263	314	264	244	382	231	304	459	273	233	279	301	237	663	X	362	358	397	246	223	303
18	Runcorn	2-0	2-2	2-0	3-0	1-2	1-1	1-3	2-1	3-2	2-0	2-2	0-1	0-3	0-1	5-0	0-2	1-2	X	3-2	0-0	3-1	1-0	2-0
		203	202	198	279	312	222	279	203	212	232	307	315	229	170	298	254	443	X	179	225	265	286	310
19	Spennym.	3-1	0-0	0-1	0-0	1-1	1-1	2-3	3-2	0-2	0-2	1-4	1-1	0-0	0-0	3-1	1-3	0-0	3-0	X	1-0	1-1	0-0	2-1
		191	201	457	297	163	135	279	207	171	305	266	171	192	254	155	235	263	176	X	160	319	231	167
20	Staly. C	2-2	3-1	5-0	2-0	3-1	0-0	0-0	2-3	3-2	0-2	0-2	1-4	3-1	1-1	3-2	1-3	0-3	1-1	1-0	X	0-3	4-1	4-3
		138	338	368	461	275	422	418	309	381	420	377	204	1728	383	413	423	440	220	372	X	387	526	428
21	Whitby	1-1	1-1	2-2	1-2	1-1	5-2	0-1	3-0	2-1	0-2	3-1	2-1	1-1	1-0	3-1	2-0	0-3	4-0	1-1	1-0	X	2-2	2-1
		375	481	633	481	366	344	363	306	489	389	494	611	369	468	445	489	311	354	310	399	X	388	447
22	Winsford	1-5	0-2	2-5	0-5	1-2	1-1	1-2	1-2	1-2	1-3	4-2	1-2	1-2	0-2	0-2	0-5	2-2	1-6	3-0	1-2	1-1	X	1-3
		105	371	135	133	210	158	151	160	118	145	143	132	247	133	203	101	250	150	105	201	92	X	178
23	Worksop	0-2	0-2	1-2	2-2	4-2	1-1	0-1	4-0	2-1	1-2	1-2	1-0	1-1	4-1	2-0	0-3	0-1	0-3	5-1	2-1	4-1	9-0	X
		457	383	390	385	317	351	448	505	621	409	406	464	434	462	384	449	530	404	339	337	400	329	X

LEAGUE CHALLENGE CUP 1999-2000

QUARTER FINALS

Accrington Stanley	v	Belper Town	2-1	Frickley Athletic	v	Marine	2-1
Lancaster City	v	Bradford Park Ave	1-0	Worksop Town	v	Runcorn	1-0

SEMI-FINALS

Frickley Athletic	v	Lancaster City	2-3	Accrington Stanley	v	Worksop T	1-1, 1-1, 3p4

FINAL

LANCASTER CITY	v	WORKSOP TOWN	1-0	at Stalybridge Celtic FC

PRESIDENT'S CUP 1999-2000

QUARTER-FINALS

Blyth Spartans	v	Bamber Bridge	2-2	Leigh	v	Eastwood Town	1-0
Trafford	v	Lincoln United	1-1, 3-2	Radcliffe Borough	v	Whitby Town	0-2

SEMI-FINALS

Blyth Spartans	v	Trafford	0-1	Leigh	v	Whitby Town	1-3

FINAL (over 2 legs)

TRAFFORD	v	WHITBY TOWN	2-1	
WHITBY TOWN	v	TRAFFORD	4-3	aet. Trafford won 4-2 on penalties

UNIFILLA CUP 1999-2000

QUARTER-FINALS

Guiseley	v	Emley	1-1, 2-2*	Hyde United	v	Gateshead	2-0
Leek Town	v	Congleton Town	2-0	Workington	v	Colwyn Bay	0-1

* Emley won on penalties after extra time

SEMI-FINALS

Hyde United	v	Leek Town	3-2	Emley	v	Colwyn Bay	6-2

FINAL

HYDE UNITED	v	EMLEY	2-0	at Hyde United FC

UNIBOND CLUB OF THE MONTH AWARDS

PREMIER DIVISION

August	Marine
September	Lancaster City
October	Gateshead
November	Marine
December	Gateshead
January	Barrow
February	Bishop Auckland
March	Whitby Town

SPORTSLINE (EUROPE) PERFORMANCE OF THE MONTH AWARDS

April/May	Hyde United

PREMIER DIVISION

Aug/Sept	Leigh
October	Bamber Bridge
November	Frickley Athletic
December	Whitby Town
January	Winsford United
February	Bishop Auckland
March	Gainsborough Trinity

NORTHERN PREMIER LEAGUE - PREMIER DIVISION - THE LAST TEN YEARS

	90-91	91-92	92-93	93-94	94-95	95-96	96-97	97-98	98-99	99-00
Accrington Stanley	-	8	6	16	15	7	11	20	22r	-
Alfreton Town	-	-	-	-	-	-	21	22r	-	-
Altrincham	-	-	-	-	-	-	-	8	1p	-
Bamber Bridge	-	-	-	-	-	1	20	19	4	17
Bangor City	18	20	-	-	-	-	-	-	-	-
Barrow	-	-	8	8	11	4	5	1p	-	13
Bishop Auckland	7	11	10	4	9	11	2	10	20	8
Blyth Spartans	-	-	-	-	-	6	7	18	14	14
Boston United	-	-	-	3	5	2	6	2	-	-
Bridlington Town	-	-	-	21	-	-	-	-	-	-
Buxton	8	5	14	15	7	20	23	-	-	-
Chorley	14	21	18	10	18	14	13	15	21r	-
Colwyn Bay	-	-	12	6	12	18	16	13	15	20
Droylsden	13	15	20	17	20	21	-	-	-	15
Emley	-	6	16	13	13	8	4	6	13	5
Fleetwood Town	4	10	19	22	-	-	-	-	-	-
Frickley Athletic	10	14	7	5	19	19	18	16	16	16
Gainsborough Trinity	20	18	11	12	8	5	10	5	6	11
Gateshead	-	-	-	-	-	-	-	-	-	3
Goole Town	12	12	22	-	-	-	-	-	-	-
Guiseley	-	-	-	-	3	10	9	9	3	22r
Horwich RMI	16	13	13	20	22	-	-	-	-	-
Hucknall Town	-	-	-	-	-	-	-	-	-	18
Hyde United	11	9	9	9	4	3	3	12	9	2
Knowsley United	-	-	-	18	16	15	15	-	-	-
Lancaster City	-	-	-	-	-	-	17	19	19	6
Leek Town	-	9	4	5	2	17	1p	-	-	19
Leigh RMI	-	-	-	-	-	-	-	3	8	1p
Marine	6	2	4	1	1	12	8	11	17	4
Matlock Town	17	19	15	14	14	22	-	-	-	-
Morecambe	3	3	3	7	2	-	-	-	-	-
Mossley	15	16	21	-	-	-	-	-	-	-
Radcliffe Borough	-	-	-	-	-	-	-	21r	-	-
Runcorn	-	-	-	-	-	-	12	4	12	9
Shepshed Albion	-	22	-	-	-	-	-	-	-	-
Shepshed Charterhouse	21	-	-	-	-	-	-	-	-	-
South Liverpool	9	-	-	-	-	-	-	-	-	-
Southport	5	7	1p	-	-	-	-	-	-	-
Spennymoor United	-	-	-	-	6	9	19	14	18	21
Stalybridge Celtic	2	1p	-	-	-	-	-	-	-	7
Witton Albion	1p	-	-	-	10	13	22	-	-	-
Whitby Town	-	-	-	-	-	-	-	-	7	12
Whitley Bay	-	17	17	11	21	-	-	-	-	-
Winsford United	-	-	2	19	17	16	14	7	11	23r
Worksop Town	-	-	-	-	-	-	-	-	2	10

ACCRINGTON STANLEY

CLUB OFFICIALS

Chairman: **Eric Whalley**
President: **J C Prescott/J Hudson**
Secretary: **Philip Terry**
8 Princess Street, Colne, Lancs BB8 9AN.
Tel: 01286 866768 (H), 01282 864000 (B).
Commercial Director: **John de Maine**

FOOTBALL MANAGEMENT TEAM

Manager: John Coleman
Asst Manager: Jimmy Bell
Osteopath: Martin Dixon D.O.
Physio: Kevin Clarke mscp. acpsm.

FACT FILE

Formed: 1968
Nickname: Reds
Sponsors: Asda.
Newsline: 09068 543 121
Colours: Red/white/red
Change colours: Yellow/Blue/Blue
Midweek home matchday: Tuesday
Youth Lge: Lancs Youth Floodlit League.
1999-00
Player of the Year: Mark shirley
Players Player of the Year: Karl Bell
Young Player of the Year: Jonathan Smith
Captain: Jay Flannery
Top Scorer:Gary Williams

Programme - Pages: 32 Price: £1
Editor: P Terry/D Ellis. (01282 866768)
Local Press: Accrington Observer, Lancashire
Evening Telegraph. Local Radio: Radio
Lancashire, Red Rose Radio.

GROUND

Crown Ground, off Livingstone Road, Accrington. Tel: 01254383235.
Directions: Arriving on A680 from Clayton-le-Moors Livingstone Rd is on left 50 yds past
Crown Hotel. From M62/M66, through town centre on A680 -Livingstone Rd 500 yds on right
after Victoria Hospital. 1 1/2 miles from Accrington(BR).
Capacity: 4,000   Cover: 1,650   Seats: 700
Clubhouse: Open five nights and matchdays. Private functions. Well stocked tea-bar in ground.
Club Shop: Sells replica kits, sweaters, t-shirts, videos, photos etc. Contact: Liz Rackstraw

PREVIOUS   Leagues: Lancs Combination 70-78; Cheshire County 78-82; North West Counties 82-87.
                   Names: None.   Grounds: None.

CLUB RECORDS   Attendance: 2,270 v Gateshead 14/11/92 FA Cup 1st Rd
                   (10,081 v Crewe Alexandra, F.A. Cup Second Round Proper 5/12/92 - played at Ewood Park,Blackburn).
                   Career Goalscorer: David Hargreaves 318.   **Career Appearances**: Chris Grimshaw 352.
                   Win: 10-0 v Lincoln United 99-00, 9-0 v Ashton Town 75-76
                   Fee Paid : £10,000 Liam Watson from Runcorn 99-00 **Fee Received**: £ 60,000 for Gary Williams from Doncaster Rovers

BEST SEASON   **FA Trophy**: 2ndt Rd 99-00   **F.A.Cup**:   2nd Rd 92-93 1-6 v Crewe Alexandra (H)   League clubs defeated: None.

HONOURS   N West Counties Lg R-up 86-87; Cheshire County Lg Div 2 80-81 (R-up 79-80);Lancs Comb 73-74 77-78 (R-up 71-72 75-
                   76), Lg Cup 71-72 72-73 73-74 76-77;George Watson Trophy 71-72 73-74 74-75; John Duckworth Trophy 85-86; Lancs
                   Junior Cup (now ATS Trophy) R-up 85-86 96-97; Lancs U18 Cup 89-90;N.W.All Div Cup 94-95; Anglo-Barbados Cup 95.

Players Progressing: David Hargreaves (Blackburn R. 77), Ian Blackstone (York C.), Gus Wilson (Crewe), Glen Johnstone (Preston),
                       DarrenLyons (Bury), Martin Clark (Crewe 92-93), Mark Wright (Wigan 93-94), Paul Collings (Bury 93-94),
                       Brett Ormerod (Blackpool 96-97), Harvey Cunningham (Doncaster R.).

Back Row: Mark Brennan, Steve Caswell, Gerard Courtney, Karl Bell, Steve Hollis, Liam Watson. **Middle Row:** Russell Payne, Robbie Williams, Paul Tomlinson, Jamie Spence, Jonathon Smith, Mark Ceraolo, Calvin Clarke (Physio). **Front Row:** Brett Baxter, John Bollan, John Coleman (Manager), Jimmy Bell (Asst. Manager), Jay Flannery (captain), Mark Shirley, Steve Carragher.   **Photo** courtesy of Accrington Observer

Match Facts 1999-00

#	Date	Comp.	H/A	Opponents	Att.	Result	Goalscorers	Lge Pos.
1	14.08	UNIB 1	A	Lincoln United	209	L	0-1	
2	17.08	UNIB 1	H	Trafford	334	L	1-2	Diggle	
	21.08	FAC Pre	H	Peterlee	231	W	3-0	Payne, O'Callaghan, Ceraolo	
3	24.08	UNIB 1	A	Burscough	187	D	1-1	Williams	
4	28.08	UNIB 1	A	Matlock Town	234	L	1-2	Shirley	20
5	30.08	UNIB 1	H	Netherfield Kendal	404	W	4-1	Payne, Flannery (p), Coleman, Ceraolo	
	04.09	FAC 1Q	A	Consett	149	W	2-0	Carragher, Williams	
6	07.09	UNIB 1	A	Harrogate Town	262	W	2-0	Ceraolo, Williams	
7	11.09	UNIB 1	H	Eastwood Town	341	D	2-2	Williams, Coleman	13
	14.09	LC 1st Gp	A	Stalybridge Celtic	254	W	3-0	Hollis, Flannery, Williams	
	18.09	FAC 2Q	H	Whitby Town	357	L	0-2	
8	21.09	UNIB 1	A	Netherfield Kendal	197	L	0-1	
9	25.09	UNIB 1	H	Whitley Bay	342	W	3-0	Flannery (p), Coleman, Williams	12
	28.09	LC 1st Gp	D	Droylsden	171	W	3-1	Doolan (p), Carragher, Williams	
10	02.10	UNIB 1	A	Bradford Park Avenue	204	L	0-1		13
	09.10	FAT 1	A	Leek Town	302	D	2-2	Coleman, Smith	
	12.10	FAT 1R	H	Leek Town	221	W	5-4	Coleman, Baxter, Carragher, Hollis, Shirley	
11	16.10	UNIB 1	H	Lincoln Unted	376	W	10-1	Williams 4, Howard, Smith, Shirley, Ceraolo, Payne, Hollis	13
12	19.10	UNIB 1	H	Workington	461	W	4-1	Carragher, Coleman, Williams, Shirley	
13	23.10	UNIB 1	A	Ossett Town	160	D	2-2	Flannery (p), Carragher	12
14	26.10	UNIB 1	A	Farsley Celtic	143	L	1-2	Carragher	
15	30.10	UNIB 1	H	Stocksbridge Park Steels	394	W	4-1	Baxter, Williams 2, Payne	9
16	06.11	UNIB 1	A	Flixton	137	W	5-0	Flannery (p), Brennan, Coleman, Williams, Ceraolo	10
	08.11	LC 2nd Gp	A	Hyde United	305	W	3-1	Ceraolo 3	
17	13.11	UNIB 1	H	Matlock Town	404	D	0-0		9
18	20.11	UNIB 1	A	Gretna	111	W	1-0	Smith	8
	23.11	LC 2nd Gp	H	Bamber Bridge	331	W	3-1	Williams 2, Carragher	
	27.11	FAT 2	H	Spalding United	401	D	2-2	Flannery, Williams	
	30.11	FAT 2 R	A	Spalding United	260	L	0-1	
19	04.12	UNIB 1	A	Belper Town	220	W	2-1	Carragher, Coleman	7
20	11.12	UNIB 1	H	Ossett Town	437	W	2-1	Carragher, Coleman	6
21	14.12	UNIB 1	H	Witton Albion	355	D	0-0		
22	18.12	UNIB 1	A	Workington	549	L	0-1		6
23	27.12	UNIB 1	H	Radcliffe Borough	687	L	1-3	Brennan	
24	03.01	UNIB 1	A	Congleton Town	206	W	3-2	Williams 2, Payne	7
25	08.01	UNIB 1	A	Trafford	262	W	4-2	Shirley, Bell, OG, Williams	5
	11.01	Lancs Tphy 2	H	Ramsbottom United	211	W	4-2	Caswell, Ceraolo, Williams, Flannery	
26	15.01	UNIB 1	A	Chorley	405	W	3-2	Wiliams 2, Ceraolo	5
	22.01	LC QF	H	Belper Town	303	W	2-1	Payne, Ceraolo	
27	29.01	UNIB 1	H	Harrogate Town	504	W	5-0	Ceraolo 2, Baxter, J Bell 2	4
	01.02	Lancs Tphy 3	H	Leigh RMI	303	L	1-2	Ceraolo	
28	05.02	UNIB 1	A	Whitley Bay	156	D	1-1	Payne	4
29	12.02	UNIB 1	H	Flixton	433	W	2-0	Ceraolo, Doolan	4
30	19.02	UNIB 1	A	Eastwood Town	217	W	7-1	Payne 4, Hollis, Ceraolo, Doolan (p)	4
31	26.02	UNIB 1	H	Bradford Park Avenue	738	W	2-1	Ceraolo, Brennan	4
	04.03	LC SF	H	Worksop Town	512	D	1-1	Ceraolo	
32	11.03	UNIB 1	H	Congleton Town	617	W	1-0	Bell	4
	14.03	LC SF R	A	Worksop Town	588	D	*1-1	Brennan	Lost 3-4 after penalties
33	18.03	UNIB 1	A	Ashton United	304	W	2-1	Watson (p), Smith	4
34	21.03	UNIB 1	H	Gretna	505	W	3-2	Watson 2, Brennan	
35	24.03	UNIB 1	A	Witton Albion	659	D	0-0		3
36	01.04	UNIB 1	H	Chorley	758	D	0-0		4
37	08.04	UNIB 1	H	Burscough	912	D	2-2	Smith, Coleman	4
38	15.04	UNIB 1	A	Stocksbridge Park Steels	235	W	3-1	OG, Coleman, Shirley	
39	22.04	UNIB 1	H	Ashton United	702	W	2-1	Watson 2	
40	24.04	UNIB 1	A	Radcliffe Borough	890	W	3-2	Smith, Bell, Carragher	3
41	01.05	UNIB 1	A	Belper Town	1,826	W	4-1	Smith, Watson, Baxter, Coleman	3
42	06.05	UNIB 1	H	Farsley Celtic	2,468	W	3-0	Smith, Coleman, Shirley	1

PLAYING SQUAD

GOALKEEPERS: James Speare (Droylsden)

DEFENDERS: Steve Hollis (Ashton U), Paul Burns (Morecambe), Steve Caswell (Droylsden), Dave Higgins (Stalybridge C), Jay Flannery (Lancaster C), Steve Carragher (Runcorn)

MIDFIELDERS: John Doolan (Ashton U), Mark Shirley (Morecambe), Bobby Harris (Padiham), Brett Baxter (Ashton U), Mark Brennan (Ashton U)

FORWARDS: **Liam Watson** (Runcorn), Mark Ceraolo (Ashton U), Servet Tasdimer (Torbali Spor (Turkey)), **John Coleman** (ASHTON U), John Mohan (Hyde U)

ALTRINCHAM

CLUB OFFICIALS		**FACT FILE**	
Chairman:	Gerry Berman	Formed:	1903
President:	Noel White	Nickname:	The Robins
Deputy Chairman:	Mark Harris		
Vice President:	Bill King	Sponsor:	TBA
Secretary:	Graham Heathcote	Colours:	Red & white striped/black/white
Press Officer:	Mark Harris	Change colours:	Yellow/green/green
Match Secretary:	George Heslop	Midweek matchday:	Tuesday

FOOTBALL MANAGEMENT TEAM
Manager: Mark Ward
Coach/Asst Manager: Graham Heathcote
Assistant Coach: George Shepherd
Physiotherapist: Ian Liversedge
Kit Manager: Vic Green

Reserves' League: None
Youth League: Altrincham Youth

Season 99-00
Leading Scorer: Kevin Ellison 15

For up to the minute news, results, fixtures, plus general facts & figures from the world of non-league football

log on to

www.nlfootball.com

GROUND: Moss Lane, Altrincham, Cheshire WA15 8AP
Tel: 0161 928 1045 Fax: 0161 926 9934
Directions: M6 junction 19; A556/M56 (Manchester Airport) to junction 7; signs Hale and Altrincham; through 1st traffic lights then 3rd right into Westminster Road and continue into Moss Lane. Ground on right.
CAPACITY: 6,085 **COVER:** Yes **SEATS:** 1,154
Clubhouse: Bar under the stand open on match days only. Two snack bars on ground for pies, crisps, soft drinks etc **Club Shop:** Yes

Programme
Pages: 36 Price: £1.20
Editor: Graham Rowley, Tel: 0161 928 1045
Local Press: Sale & Altrincham Messenger;
Sale & Altrincham Express;
Manchester Evening News
Local Radio: GMR (BBC); Signal Radio;
Piccadilly Radio

PREVIOUS **Leagues:** Manchester 03-11, Lancashire Comb. 11-19, Cheshire County 19-68, Northern Premier 68-79, 97-99; Conference 79-97 99-00 **Grounds:** Pollitts Field -1903-1910 **Names:** None

RECORDS **Attendance:**10,275 Altrincham Boys v Sunderland Boys,English Schools Shield 3rd Round 28.02.25
Goalscorer: Jack Swindells 252 - 1965-71 **Appearances:** JohnDavison 677 - 1971-86
Win: 9-2 v Merthyr Tydfil,Vauxhall Conference, Feb 1991 **Defeat:** Unknown
Fee Paid: £15,000 to Blackpool for Keith Russell
Fee Received: From Crewe Alexandra for Paul Edwards - 1988

BEST SEASON **FA Trophy:** Winners 77-78, 85-86 **League:** Conference Champions 1979-80, 80-81
FA Cup: 85-86 4th Round, 0-2 v York City (A) **League clubs defeated:**10

HONOURS FA Trophy 77-78, 85- 86; Alliance Premier League 79-80, 80-81; Bob Lord Trophy 80-81;
Northern Prem. Lge: Champions 98-99; Lge.Cup 69-70 97-98; N.P.L. Shield 79-80;
Cheshire County League: Champions 65-66, 66-67; Lge Cup 50-51, 52-53, 63-64; Cheshire Senior Cup 04-05, 33-34, 66-67,81-82; Manchester League 04-05; Cheshire Amateur Cup 03-04.

Players Progressing: Several, most recent being G Barrow (Wigan Ath. 81), J Rogers(Wigan Ath., 82), P Conning (Rochdale, 86), E Bishop (Tranmere R. 88), P Edwards (Crewe, 88), A Kilner (Stockport C. 90), P Showler (Barnet, 91), S Johnson & A Reid (Bury 92), C Freeman (Doncaster R. 93), T Carke (Shrewsbury T. 93), .

Altrincham's Keith Russell is a study of concentration as he prepares to take on Kiddy's Adie Smith during the match on the 6th May.
Photo: Colin Stevens

Match Facts 1999-00

	Date	Comp.	H/A	Opponents	Att.	Result	Goalscorers	Lge Pos.
1	14.08	N.C.	H	Stevenage Borough	853	L 0-1		
2	17.08	N.C.	H	Hednesford Town	851	L 0-1		
3	21.08	N.C.	A	Yeovil Town	2,214	L 0-3		22
4	28.08	N.C.	A	Kingstonian	984	D 2-2	Ellison 26 Talbot 36	20
5	30.08	N.C.	H	Southport	1,226	W 3-0	Landon 64 Ellison 80,85	
6	04.09	N.C.	H	Dover Athletic	938	W 3-0	Talbot 27 Ellison 32, 54	16
7	06.09	N.C.	A	Doncaster Rovers	2,978	W 1-0	Walling 81 (o.g.)	
8	11.09	N.C.	A	Sutton United	805	L 0-3		14
9	18.09	N.C.	H	Woking	1,006	D 1-1	Landon 4	14
10	25.09	N.C.	A	Nuneaton Borough	2,205	L 1-3	Ellison 38	18
11	02.10	N.C.	H	Rushden & Diamonds	1,114	L 1-2	Power 46	19
12	09.10	N.C.	A	Telford United	1,017	W 1-0	Burke 45 (pen)	16
13	23.10	N.C.	A	Welling United	607	D 2-2	Talbot 52, Ellison 78	15
14	06.11	N.C.	H	Hereford United	1,006	W 2-1	Landon 51, Ellison 85	16
15	14.11	N.C.	A	Kettering Town	1,170	D 0-0		16
16	20.11	N.C.	H	Morecambe	1,159	D 2-2	Russell 25, Ellison 33	15
17	30.11	N.C.	H	Nuneaton Borough	765	D 2-2		15
18	04.12	N.C.	A	Dover Athletic	1,015	D 2-2	Power 15, Kelly 40.	15
19	18.12	N.C.	H	Forest Green Rovers	853	D 1-1	Power 44	17
20	27.12	N.C.	A	Northwich Victoria	1,814	D 1-1	Landon 90	15
21	03.01	N.C.	H	Northwich Victoria	1,713	W 2-0	Ellison 34, Landon 82	15
22	08.01	N.C.	A	Forest Green Rovers	901	D 1-1	Landon 80	15
23	22.01	N.C.	A	Hereford United	1,789	D 2-2	Price 53, Landon 90	16
24	29.01	N.C.	A	Stevenage Borough	1,762	D 1-1	Landon 89	17
25	01.02	N.C.	H	Telford United	720	D 3-3	Price 14, Gallagher 18, Chambers 88	
26	05.02	N.C.	A	Hednesford Town	1,193	L 0-5		15
27	12.02	N.C.	H	Welling United	839	L 0-1		17
28	19.02	N.C.	A	Woking	1,565	W 1-0	Gallagher 47	17
29	22.02	N.C.	H	Scarborough	761	W 2-1	Timmons 5, Lovelock 69	
30	26.02	N.C.	A	Morecambe	1,240	D 3-3	Russell 24, Talbot 37, Landon 86	12
31	04.03	N.C.	H	Sutton United	889	W 3-0	Timons 46, Ellison 49, Russell 83	10
32	11.03	N.C.	A	Kidderminster Harriers	3,054	D 1-1	Morrell 60	11
33	18.03	N.C.	A	Hayes	642	D 1-1	Russell 66	11
34	25.03	N.C.	H	Kettering Town	939	D 1-1	Ellison 47	12
35	15.04	N.C.	A	Rushden & Diamonds	2,731	L 0-1		13
36	18.04	N.C.	H	Hayes	657	L 1-2	Landon 86	17
37	24.04	N.C.	H	Doncaster Rovers	1,066	L 1-2	Ellison 73	18
38	26.04	N.C.	A	Scarborough	1,273	L 0-1		
39	29.04	N.C.	H	Yeovil Town	792	D 2-2	Talbot 28, Landon 53 (p)	19
40	01.05	N.C.	A	Southport	1,427	L 0-2		19
41	03.05	N.C.	H	Kingstonian	779	L 1-3	Landon 4 (p)	19
42	06.05	N.C.	H	Kidderminster H.	1,761	D 0-0		21

CUP COMPETITIONS

F.A. Cup

	Date	Round	H/A	Opponents	Att.	Result	Goalscorers
	16.10	4Q	H	Stalybridge Celtic	1,186	D 0-0	
	30.10	4Q R	A	Stalybridge Celtic		L 2-3	Ellison 26, Ellender 28

Nationwide McMillan Trophy

	Date	Round	H/A	Opponents	Att.	Result	Goalscorers
	05.10	1	H	Kidderminster H.	370	W 1-0	Burke 5 (pen)
	15.12	2	A	Northwich Victoria	402	W 6-1	Power 15, Gallagher 43 89, Kielty 57, Talbot 71, Timons 90
	08.02	4	H	Telford United	319	L 1-3	Price 41 (p)

F.A. Trophy

	Date	Round	H/A	Opponents	Att.	Result	Goalscorers	
	27.11	2	H	Gateshead	578	W 1-0	Power 73	
	15.01	3	A	Southport	1,387	D 0-0		
	18.01	3R	H	Southport	766	D *1-1	Landon 61	Lost 3-4 after penalties

PLAYING SQUAD

GOALKEEPERS Stuart Coburn (Trafford)

DEFENDERS Jason Gallagher (Hyde United), Adam Farley (Everton), Danny Adams (Congleton Town) Eddie Turkington (Leigh RMI), Mark Maddox (Barrow), Gary Talbot (Winsford United) Paul Walsham (Tranmere Rovers)

MIDFIELD **Mark Ward** (Leigh RMI), Barry Crowe (Tranmere R.), Stuar Quinn (Leigh RMI), Steve Hawes (Hull), Scott Wilson (Rochdale), Stuart Scheuber (Stoke C.)

FORWARDS **Phil Power** (Macclesfield T.), Richard Landon (Macclesfield T.), Mark Quayle (Ilkeston T.), Kevin Ellison (Conwy Utd.), Leroy Chambers (Macclesfield T.), Carl Furlong (Kendal T.)

BAMBER BRIDGE

CLUB OFFICIALS

President: **Arthur Jackson**
Chairman: **D Allan**
Vice Chairman: **Dave Spencer**
Secretary : **Russ Rigby**
c/o B.B.F.C.
Commercial Manager: **Keith Brindle**

FOOTBALL MANAGEMENT TEAM

Manager: **Tony Greenwood**
Asst Manager: **Phil Entwistle**
Physio: **Shaun Riley**

FACT FILE

Founded: 1952
Nickname: Brig
Sponsors: Baxi Partnership
Colours: White/black/black
Change Colours: All yellow
Midweek Matches: Tuesday
Reserves' League: Lancashire Legue

UNIBOND PREMIER DIVISION
'versus'
WORKSOP TOWN
TUESDAY 18TH APRIL
Kick Off 7.30pm

Pages: 36   Price: £1

Editor: Dave Rowland (01772 465659)

GROUND

Irongate, Brownedge Road, Bamber Bridge, Preston, Lancs.PR5 6UX
Tel Nos: Club Office 01772-909690; Social Club 01772-909695; Fax No. 01772-909691
Directions: M6 Junct 29, A6 (Bamber Bridge Bypass) towards Walton-le-Dale, to r'bout, A6
London Road to next r'bout, 3rd exit signed Bamber Bridge (Brownedge Road) and first right.
Ground 100 yds at end of road on left. Just over a mile from Bamber Bridge (BR).
Capacity: 2,500   **Seats:** 500   **Cover:** 800
Clubhouse: On ground. Open all day Saturday matchdays, every evening and Sunday lunch.
Refreshment cabin on ground serves hot & cold drinks & snacks etc during matches.
Club Shop: Sells various club souvenirs etc plus large selection of programmes. Contact
Russ Rigby (01772 909690)

PREVIOUS	**Leagues:** Preston & District 52-90; North West Counties 90-93. **Grounds:** King George V Ground, Higher Walton 1952-86. **Names:** None
CLUB RECORDS	**Attendance:** 2,300 v Czech Republic, Pre-Euro 96 Friendly. **Win:** 8-0 v Curzon Ashton N.W.Co. 94-95. **Defeat:** Unknown **Fee Paid:** £10,000 to Horwich R.M.I.for Mark Edwards. **Fee Received:** £15,000 from Wigan Athletic for Tony Back, 1995.
BEST SEASON	**FA Vase:** Semi Final 91-92 (lost 0-2 on agg to Wimborne Tn). **FA Cup:** 2nd Round Proper, 99-00, v Cambridge United (A) Lost 0-1
HONOURS	Nth West Co's Lge R-up 92-93 (Div 2 91-92, F'lit Cup R-up 91-92); Preston &Dist Lge(4) (R-up (3); Guildhall Cup 78-79 80-81 84-85 89-90, R-up 77-78 79-80 87-88; Lancs Amtr Shield 81-82, R-up 80-81 89-90; Lancastrian Brigade Cup 76-77 89-90 90-91; A.T.S.Lancs Trophy 94-95, R-Up 95-96, NPL Chall Cup 94-95; NPL 1st Div R-Up 94-95; NPL Prem Div Champ 95-96.

Back Row: Tony Greenwood (Manager), Simon Woodward, Simon Bridge, Mick Noblett, Craig Dootson, Shaun McHugh, Andy Whittaker, Ian Bryson, Mark Jones, Phil Entwistle (Asst. Man.), Nigel Greenwood. **Front:** Dean Cooper, John Turner, Carwyn Williams, Dave Hayes, Dave Carroll, Darren Brown, Steve Aspinall, Shaun Riley (Physio).

Match Facts 1999-00

	Date	Comp.	H/A	Opponents	Att.	Result	Goalscorers
1	14.08	UNIB P	A	Worksop Town	457	W 2 - 0	Whittaker 46 47
2	17.08	UNIB P	H	DROYLSDEN	325	L 1 - 3	Greenwood 5
3	21.08	UNIB P	H	EMLEY	335	L 0 - 1	
4	24.08	UNIB P	A	Leigh RMI	260	L 0 - 3	
5	28.08	UNIB P	A	Blyth Spartans	357	W 2 - 1	Melrose 60[og], Carroll 73
6	30.08	UNIB P	H	RUNCORN	441	W 2 - 0	Smith 20, Whittaker 80
7	04.09	UNIB P	A	Bishop Auckland	226	W 1 - 0	Lee 60[og]
8	07.09	UNIB P	H	WINSFORD UNITED	315	W 2 - 1	Aspinall 47 90[p]
9	11.09	UNIB P	H	Hucknall Town	225	L 1 - 2	Whittaker 85
	14.09	ULC 1G	A	Barrow	635	W 4 - 3	Whittaker 32, Bryson 65, Greenwood 67, Reynolds 75
	18.09	FAC Q2	A	Trafford	215	D 2 - 2	Smith 50, Greenwood 60
	21.09	FAC Q2 R	H	TRAFFORD	233	W 2 - 1	Vickers 62, Smith 65
10	25.09	UNIB P	H	FRICKLEY ATHLETIC	311	W 2 - 1	Carroll 56, Whittaker 85
	28.09	ULC G2	H	LANCASTER CITY	317	L 1 - 2	Aspinall 4[p]
	02.10	FAC Q3	H	MORPETH TOWN	271	W 3 - 0	Greenwood 20, Maddock 31, Smith 63
11	09.10	UNIB P	A	Whitby Town	375	D 1 - 1	Carroll 24
12	12.10	UNIB P	H	COLWYN BAY	282	L 1 - 2	Vickers 67
	16.10	FAC Q4	A	Lancaster City	645	D 0 - 0	
	19.10	FAC Q4 r	H	LANCASTER CITY	699	W *4 - 3	Vickers 24, Whittaker 96, Aspinall 113[p], Turner 120
13	23.10	UNIB P	A	Spennymoor United	191	L 1 - 3	Maddock 3
14	26.10	UNIB P	H	LEIGH RMI	406	D 2 - 2	Whittaker 39, Turner 43
	30.10	FAC 1	A	St Albans City	1127	W 2 - 0	Whittaker 45, Carroll 89
	02.11	ULC GB	A	HYDE UNITED	237	W 2 - 0	Carroll 12, Vickers 51
15	06.11	UNIB P	A	Leek Town	325	D 0 - 0	
16	09.11	UNIB P	H	BARROW	631	L 2 - 3	Carroll 2 80
17	12.11	UNIB P	A	Gateshead	212	L 1 - 2	Carroll 66
18	16.11	UNIB P	A	Lancaster City	269	D 1 - 1	Greenwood 53
	20.11	FAC 2	A	Cambridge United	3303	L 0 - 1	
	23.11	ULC GB	A	Accrington Stanley	331	L 1 - 3	Spencer 83
	27.11	FAT 2	H	BURTON ALBION	402	L 0 - 2	
19	04.12	UNIB P	A	Runcorn	203	L 0 - 2	
20	27.12	UNIB P	H	LANCASTER CITY	525	W 6 - 1	Grimshaw 8, Aspinall 37p, Greenwood 55, Carroll 56, Smith 61, Whittaker 61
21	08.01	UNIB P	H	STALYBRIDGE CELTIC	459	L 1 - 4	Williams 82
22	15.01	UNIB P	A	Barrow	1083	L 0 - 4	
	22.01	Pres. Cup QF	A	Blyth Spartans	235	D 2 - 2	Aspinall 12, Whittaker 17
23	05.02	UNIB P	H	GAINSBOROUGH TRINITY	243	D 0 - 0	
	08.02	Lancs 2	H	LANCASTER CITY	189	W 2 - 1	Williams 48, Whittaker 79
24	12.02	UNIB P	H	GATESHEAD	292	L 0 - 3	
25	19.02	UNIB P	A	Guiseley	266	W 4 - 2	Greenwood 34, Brown 47, Carroll 67, Whittaker 90
	22.02	Lancs QF	A	Clitheroe	266	W 2 - 0	Aspinall 95[p], Williams 116
26	26.02	UNIB P	A	Droylsden	253	L 0 - 2	
27	29.02	UNIB P	H	HYDE UNITED	318	D 0 - 0	
28	04.03	UNIB P	A	BISHOP AUCKLAND	230	W 4 - 0	Aspinall 11, Whittaker 27 80, Cliff 65
	07.03	Lancs SF	H	BARROW	354	W 2 - 1	Aspinall 45, Whittaker 46
29	11.03	UNIB P	H	BLYTH SPARTANS	335	D 1 - 1	Whittaker 20
30	14.03	UNIB P	A	Marine	279	W 3 - 0	Noblett 21, Brown 54, Cliff 90
31	18.03	UNIB P	H	HUCKNALL TOWN	281	D 1 - 1	Whittaker 55
32	20.03	UNIB P	A	Emley	201	L 0 - 3	
33	25.03	UNIB P	A	Gainsborough Trinity	284	L 0 - 1	
34	01.04	UNIB P	H	SPENNYMOOR UTD	269	W 2 - 0	Whittaker 16, Noblett 38
35	04.04	UNIB P	H	Stalybridge Celtic	138	D 2 - 2	Noblett 43, Whittaker 65
36	08.04	UNIB P	H	LEEK TOWN	280	W 5 - 0	**Trundle** 3 (5, 57, 85), Carroll 87, Maddock 89
	11.04	Lancs Final	A	Marine		L 0 - 5	
37	15.04	UNIB P	A	Frickley Athletic	131	L 0 - 2	
38	18.04	UNIB P	H	WORKSOP TOWN	196	L 2 - 3	Whittaker 29, Turner 33
39	22.04	UNIB P	A	Winsford United	105	W 2 - 1	Carroll 2, 40, Whittaker 7, Noblett 67, Trundle 86
40	24.04	UNIB P	H	MARINE	327	L 0 - 2	
41	29.04	UNIB P	A	Guiseley	245	D 2 - 2	Trundle 21, 66 (p)
42	01.05	UNIB P	A	Colwyn Bay	230	W 7 - 0	**Trundle** 4 (15, 22, 26, 46), **Whittaker** 3 (20, 65, 75)
43	03.05	UNIB P	A	Hyde United	385	L 1 - 3	Whittaker 85
44	06.05	UNIB P	H	WHITBY TOWN	244	D 2 - 2	Trundle 31, Whittaker 90

PLAYING SQUAD

GOALKEEPERS: Billy Stewart (Hednesford T)

DEFENDERS: Mark Jones (Chorley), Paul Lin (Preston), Wayne Maddock (Morecambe), Simon Woodward (Local Football), Steve Aspinall (Chorley), Andy Farley (Southport)

MIDFIELDERS: Dave Carroll (Witton Alb), Peter Smyth (Leigh RMI), Mick Noblett (Local Football), David Mayes (Winsford U), Stuart Cliff (Gt.Harwood T)

FORWARDS: Andy Whittaker (Southport), Colin Potts (Chorley), Nigel Greenwood (Accrington Stanley), Simon Burton (Atherton LR)

BARROW

CLUB OFFICIALS

Match Secretary; Neil McDonald
Birchfield, 6A Salthouse Rd., Barrow-in-Furness, Cumbria Tel: 01229 828227 (H)
0403 499482 (M)

Press Officer: Phil Yelland
83 Camus Drive, Edinburgh EH10 6QY
Tel: 0131 445 1010 (H) & Fax
0131 476 8131 (B)

MANAGER
Kenny Lowe

FACT FILE
Founded: 1901
Nickname: Bluebirds
Sponsors: Chas Kendall - Bookmakers
Club Colours: All white with blue trim
Change Colours: Yellow/blue/blue
Midweek matchday: Tuesday
Barrow Soccer Hotline: 09066 555820
Local Press: North West Evening Mail,
Barrow & West Cumberland Advertiser
Local Radio: BBC Radio Furness, BBC Radio
Cumbria, Red Rose Radio, Bay Radio

GROUND: Holker Street Stadium, Wilkie Road, Barrow-in-Furness, CumbriaLA14 5UW
Tel: 01229 820346
Directions: M6 to junction 36, A590 to Barrow, enter Barrow on Park Road and after about 2 miles turn left into Wilkie Rd - ground on right. B.R.1/4 mile
Capacity: 4,500　　**Seated:** 1000　　**Covered Terracing:** 1,200

Clubhouse: Barrow Sports & Leisure centre next to ground.
Open matchdays and Functions only. Snack bars on ground
Club Shop: Situated on the ground.

Pages: 44　　Price: £1.40
Editorial Team:
Darren Gardner, Phil Yelland, & Russell Dodd

PREVIOUS　　**Leagues:** Lancs Comb 01-21; Football League 21-72; Northern Premier 72-79, 83-84,86-89, 92-98; 99- GM Vauxhall Conference 79-83, 84-86, 89-92, 98-99 **Grounds:** The Strawberry & Little Park, Roose **Names:**None

RECORDS　　**Attendance:** 16,854 v Swansea Town, FA Cup 3rd Rd. 1954
Career Appearances: Colin Cowperthwaite 704　　**Career Goalscorer:** Colin Cowperthwaite 282 (Dec '77-Dec '92).
Defeat: 1-10 v Hartlepool Utd, Football Lge Div 4, 1959　　**Win:** 12-0 v Cleator, FA Cup 1920.
Transfer Fee Paid: £9,000 for Andy Whittaker (Ashton Utd, July 94).
Transfer Fee Received: £40,000 for Kenny Lowe (Barnet, Jan 91)

BEST SEASON　　**FA Trophy:** Winners 1989-90, Semi-Final 87-88
FA Cup: Third Round Proper 9 times including once as a non-League club 90-91, 0-1 v Bolton Wanderers (A)

HONOURS　　F.A. Trophy Winners 89-90, Northern Premier League 97-98, 88-89, 83-84; Lge Cup R-up 87-88, Lge Shield 84-85 R-up 89-90 98-99; Bob Lord Trophy R-up 90-91, Cumbrian Cup 82-8383-84 (R-up 84-85), Lancs Floodlit Cup R-up 86-87, Lancs Sen Cup 54-55 (R-up 51-52 65-66 66-67 69-70), Lancs Challenge Trophy 80-81 (R-up 81-82 84-85), Lancs Comb 20-21, R-up 13-14, Div 2 R-up 04-05 10-11.

Players progressing:　　I McDonald, N McDonald, J Laisby, B Diamond, F Gamble, B Knowles, G Skivington, P Byron, L Edwards, K Lowe, M Dobie, T Rigby, N Doherty.

Good Barrow defensive cover enures that no danger comes from this Whitby attack.

Match Facts 1999-00

	Date	Comp.	H/A	Opponents	Att.	Result	Goalscorers
1	28.08	UNIB P	H	GUISELEY	1,709	D 1 - 1	Challender 25
2	30.08	UNIB P	A	Emley	486	D 0 - 0	
3	07.09	UNIB P	A	Droylsden	401	W 3 - 0	Finney 20, 77, Peverill 64[p]
4	11.09	UNIB P	H	RUNCORN	1,599	L 0 - 2	
	14.09	**ULC 1G**	H	BAMBER BRIDGE	635	L 3 - 4	Peverill 5, 41, Murphy 77
	18.09	**FAC Q2**	H	MARINE	1,218	D 2 - 2	Peverill 4, Whittle 18
	21.09	**FAC Q2 R**	A	Marine	425	L 2 - 3	Doherty 13, Peverill 77
5	25.09	UNIB P	A	Leigh RMI	331	L 0 - 1	
6	02.10	UNIB P	H	WORKSOP TOWN	1154	L 2 - 3	Waller 14, Lowe 65
	09.10	**FAT 1**	H	NETHERFIELD KENDAL	1059	W 4 - 0	Bullimore 11, Peverill 19, O'Keefe 29, 30
	12.10	**ULC G2**	A	Lancaster City	337	D 0 - 0	
7	16.10	UNIB P	A	Gainsborough Trinity	456	W 3 - 1	**Peverill 3** (18, 20, 84)
8	23.10	UNIB P	H	LEEK TOWN	1220	L 1 - 4	Brydon 31
9	25.10	UNIB P	A	Hyde United	480	L 0 - 1	
10	30.10	UNIB P	H	GAINSBOROUGH TRINITY	1032	D 1 - 1	Rush 24
11	02.11	UNIB P	H	BISHOP AUCKLAND	944	L 1 - 3	Peverill 47
12	06.11	UNIB P	H	STALYBRIDGE CELTIC	1076	D 1 - 1	Waller 45
13	09.11	UNIB P	A	Bamber Bridge	631	W 3 - 2	Doherty 31, Waller 40, Peverill 78
	16.11	**Lancs 1**	H	SKELMERSDALE UNITED	302	W 3 - 1	Doherty 35, Peverill 76, Toman 89
14	20.11	UNIB P	H	SPENNYMOOR UNITED	1035	W 1 - 0	Peverill 69
	27.11	**FAT 2**	H	SOUTHPORT	1334	L 2 - 3	Doherty 12, Rush 35
15	30.11	UNIB P	A	Colwyn Bay	195	D 0 - 0	
16	04.12	UNIB P	H	BLYTH SPARTANS	1006	W 3 - 2	Peverill 6[p], Hume 8, Toman 63
17	07.12	UNIB P	A	Gateshead	358	D 0 - 0	
18	11.12	UNIB P	A	Frickley Athletic	257	W 5 - 2	Hume 9, **Peverill 3** (22 31 78), Doherty 45
19	18.12	UNIB P	H	DROYLSDEN	1072	L 0 - 3	
20	27.12	UNIB P	A	Leek Town	494	L 1 - 2	Rush 57
21	30.12	UNIB P	H	WINSFORD UNITED	2400	D 0 - 0	
22	03.01	UNIB P	A	Lancaster City	826	L 0 - 1	
23	08.01	UNIB P	A	Winsford United	370	W 2 - 0	Peverill 85, Doherty 88
24	15.01	UNIB P	H	BAMBER BRIDGE	1083	W 4 - 0	Bullimore 5, Peverill 8, Hume 10, Rush 77
25	22.01	UNIB P	A	Bishop Auckland	333	W 3 - 1	Housham 12, Waller 58, Peel 70
	25.01	**L Mars 2**	A	Morecambe	576	W 2 - 0	McKechnie 18, Peverill 40
26	29.01	UNIB P	H	MARINE	1314	D 2 - 2	Peel 4, Housham 76
27	05.02	UNIB P	H	FRICKLEY ATHLETIC	1073	W 2 - 0	Housham 26, Doherty 53
	15.02	**Lancs QF**	H	ROSSENDALE UNITED	572	W 3 - 2	Peel 36 49, Hume 52
28	19.02	UNIB P	H	EMLEY	1175	L 0 - 2	
29	29.02	UNIB P	H	LEIGH RMI	900	D 2 - 2	Hill 8, Hume 88
30	04.03	UNIB P	A	Spennymoor United	201	D 0 - 0	
	07.03	**Lancs SF**	L	Bamber Bridge	354	L 1 - 2	Peverill 31
31	11.03	UNIB P	H	HUCKNALL TOWN	1054	W 4 - 2	Hill 25, Holt 37, Doherty 63, Peverill 83
32	14.03	UNIB P	A	Runcorn	202	D 2 - 2	Peverill 66, Hume 88
33	21.03	UNIB P	A	Guiseley	282	D 0 - 0	
34	25.03	UNIB P	H	WHITBY TOWN	1135	L 0 - 3	
35	28.03	UNIB P	A	Marine	357	L 0 - 1	
36	01.04	UNIB P	A	Stalybridge Celtic	338	L 1 - 3	Hume 90
37	04.04	UNIB P	H	LANCASTER CITY	784	D 2 - 2	Hume 32, OG (Kilblane) 75
38	08.04	UNIB P	A	Whitby Town	481	D 1 - 1	Peel 55
39	15.04	UNIB P	H	HYDE UNITED	985	L 1 - 2	Waller 29
40	18.04	UNIB P	A	Blyth Spartans	359	D 1 - 1	Peverill 90
41	22.04	UNIB P	H	COLWYN BAY	911	W 4 - 0	Peverill 45, Waller 47, Doherty 54, OG (Donnelly) 89
42	24.04	UNIB P	A	Hucknall Town	258	W 3 - 0	Ellison 9, 70 (p), Hume 55
43	26.04	UNIB P	A	Worksop Town	383	W 2 - 0	Ellison 70, Doherty 79
44	01.05	UNIB P	H	GATESHEAD	1543	L 3 - 5	Peverill 10, 79, Hume 52

PLAYING SQUAD

GOALKEEPERS: Mark Thornley (Lancaster C), Paul Heritage (Carlisle)

DEFENDERS: Lee Warren (Doncaster R), Lee Turnbull (Halifax), Mark Hume (Doncaster R), Chris Whittle (Blackburn), Lee Rogers (Grantham T), Tony Hopper (Carlisle), Lee Taylor (Workington), Darren Roulston (Bishop Auckland)

MIDFIELDERS: Wayne Bullimore (Grantham T), Steve Housham (Scunthorpe), Scott Maxfield (Doncaster R), Nathan Peel (Northwich V)

FORWARDS: **Neil Doherty** (Kidderminster H), Troy Bennett (Gainsborough T), Nicky Peverill (Blyth Spartans), Lee Ellison (Southport)

BISHOP AUCKLAND

CLUB OFFICIALS

Chairman: **Tony Duffy**
Vice-Chairman: T.B.A.
Secretary: **Tony Duffy,**
8 Ennerdale Grove, West Auckland,
Co.Durham. DL14 9LN.(01388 833410)
Press Officer: **Tony Duffy**
Commercial Manager: **Bryan Collinson**

FOOTBALL MANAGEMENT TEAM

Manager: Tony Lee
Asst Mgr: Tony Boylan
Physio: Dave Nesbitt

FACT FILE

Formed: 1886
Nickname: Bishops
Sponsors:
Colours: Sky & Navy blue
Change colours: Red & white.
Midweek home matchday: Wednesday.
Reserve Team: None.

1999-00
Captain: David Bayles
Top scorer: Andrew Shaw

SEASON 1999/2000

THE
OFFICIAL
MATCH PROGRAMME
OF
BISHOP AUCKLAND FC

GROUND

Kingsway, Bishop Auckland, County Durham   Tel. 01388 603686
Directions: A1 to Scotch Corner (Turn off A68 from A1) or M6 Junc A38 (A685 to Brough),
then follow signs to Bishop Auckland. Ground in town centre (rear off Newgate St.). Half mile
from station.
Capacity: 3,500   **Cover:** 2,000   **Seats:** 600
Clubhouse: Open every day noon-4 & 7-11pm, plus Saturday matchdays all day. Large bar,
pool, juke box. Also snack bar within grounds sells hot & cold pies & drinks.
Club Shop: Yes   Metal Badges: £3 . 00.

Pages: 28 Price: £1.
Editor: Bobby Wake (01388 609428)

Local Press: Northern Echo, Evening Gazette,
N'castle Journal. Local Radio: Radio
Cleveland, Radio Metro, Radio Newcastle.

PREVIOUS   Leagues: N East Counties 1889-90/ Northern Alliance 1890-91/ Northern 1893-1988.

CLUB RECORDS **Attendance:** 17,000 v Coventry, FA Cup 2nd Rd 6/12/52.   **Appearances:** Bob Hardisty.
          Win: 12-3 v Kingstonian, Amateur Cup 55.   **Defeat:** 0-7 v Halifax Tn FA Cup 2nd Rd66-67.
          Fee Paid: £2,000.   Fee Received: £9,000 for David Laws from Weymouth.

BEST SEASON **FA Amateur Cup:** Winners 8 times   **FA Trophy:** Quarter Finals 78-79, 88-89, 96-97, 99-00
          FA Cup: 4th Rd 54-55, 1-3 v York City (H).   League clubs defeated: Crystal Palace, Ipswich 54-55, Tranmere 56-57.

HONOURS   FA Amateur Cup 1895-96, 1899-1900 13-14 20-22 34-35 38-39 54-56 57-58 (R-up(8)01-02 05-06 10-11 14-15 45-46 49-51 53-
          54); Northern Lg(19) 1898-99 1900-02 08-10 11-12 20-21 30-31 38-39 46-47 49-52 53-5666-67 84-86, R-up (17) 78-
79 86-87   96-97, Lg Cup(7) 49-51 53-55 59-60 66-67 75-76); D'ham Chall Cup 1891-92 98-99 1930-31 38-39 51-52
55-56 61-62 66-67   84-8585-86 87-88 96-97, 98-99 HFS Loans Lg Div 1 R-up 88-89. Plus tournaments in Isle of
Man, Spain, Portugal etc

Players Progressing: B Paisley (Liverpool), F Richardson & S O'Connell (Chelsea 46 & 54), R Hardisty & K Williamson (Darlimgton 46 & 52), WShergold
(Newport 47), N Smith (Fulham 48), R Steel & K Murray (Darlington 50),A Adey (Doncaster 50), F Palmer & A Stalker (Gateshead 51 & 58), A
Sewell(Bradford City 54), G Barker (Southend 54), J Major (Hull 55), H Sharratt(Oldham 56), F McKenna (Leeds 56), J Barnwell (Arsenal 56), D Lewis
(Accrington Stanley 57), C Cresswell (Carlisle 58), W Bradley (Man Utd), L Brown(Northampton), P Baker (Southampton), M Gooding (Rotherham), K

Two old Northern League foes clash in the Unibond. Bishop Auckland in light shorts attacking the Whitby Town goal from their corner.

Match Facts 1999-00

	Date	Comp.	H/A	Opponents	Att.	Result	Goalscorers
1	14.08	UNIB P	A	Whitby Town	633	D 2 - 2	Hutt 27, Brunskill 44
2	17.08	UNIB P	A	Guiseley	305	W 3 - 0	**Shaw 3** (24 58[p] 90)
3	21.08	UNIB P	A	Stalybridge Celtic	368	L 0 - 5	
4	24.08	UNIB P	A	Blyth Spartans	322	W 2 - 0	Veart 12, Brunskill 56
5	28.08	UNIB P	A	Worksop Town	390	W 2 - 1	Brightwell 27, Irvine 29
6	01.09	UNIB P	H	HUCKNALL TOWN	236	W 3 - 1	Lee 31, Brightwell 44, Veart 90[p]
7	04.09	UNIB P	H	BAMBER BRIDGE	226	L 0 - 1	
8	07.09	UNIB P	A	Gainsborough Trinity	387	L 1 - 4	Veart 63[p]
9	11.09	UNIB P	H	MARINE	193	L 0 - 2	
10	15.09	UNIB P	H	DROYLSDEN	183	W 1 - 0	Veart 63[p]
	18.09	FAC Q2	A	Worksop Town	351	W 3 - 2	Gallagher 59, Holmshaw 81[og], Irvine 90
11	21.09	UNIB P	A	Frickley Athletic	141	L 2 - 4	Lee 58, 79
12	25.09	UNIB P	H	WINSFORD UNITED	192	W 4 - 1	Gallagher 13, 80, Brunskill 30, Shaw 83
	28.09	ULC G13	A	Spennymoor United	287	D 2 - 2	Lee 26, Mellanby 68
	02.10	FAC Q3	H	BEDLINGTON TERRIERS	413	D 1 - 1	Bayles 85
	06.10	FAC Q3 R	A	Bedlington Terriers	430	W 1 - 0	Shaw 10[p]
13	09.10	UNIB P	A	LANCASTER CITY	233	D 1 - 1	Shaw 74[p]
	13.10	ULC G13	H	WHITBY TOWN	147	L 0 - 1	
	16.10	FAC Q4	A	Morecambe	868	L 0 - 1	
14	23.10	UNIB P	A	Hucknall Town	215	L 0 - 1	
	27.10	Durh.CC1		Murton	73	W 7 - 0	**Mellanby 4** (25, 50, 65, 82), Lee 33, Brunskill 41, Salmon 55
15	30.10	UNIB P	H	LEEK TOWN	181	D 1 - 1	Shaw 78
16	02.11	UNIB P	A	Barrow	944	W 3 - 1	Mellanby 26 63, Brunskill 43
17	10.11	UNIB P	H	GATESHEAD	288	D 1 - 1	Bayles 89
	16.11	Durh.CC2	H	DUNSTON FED. BREW.	94	W 3 - 0	Adams 16, Bayles 53, Naylor 57
18	20.11	UNIB P	A	Colwyn Bay	220	W 1 - 0	Shaw 40
	27.11	FAT 2	A	Wisbech Town	420	W 2 - 1	Naylor 40, Shaw 65
19	04.12	UNIB P	H	WORKSOP TOWN	214	L 1 - 2	Shaw 51
20	11.12	UNIB P	H	HYDE UNITED	203	D 2 - 2	Brunskill 55, Salmon 90
21	18.12	UNIB P	A	Marine	263	L 1 - 3	Lee 80
22	27.12	UNIB P	A	SPENNYMOOR UNITED	424	L 0 - 3	
23	03.01	UNIB P	H	Spennymoor United	457	W 1 - 0	Shaw 79
	05.01	D CC QF	A	Darlington	230	L 2 - 3	Mellanby 22, Shaw 38[p]
24	08.01	UNIB P	H	COLWYN BAY	195	W 4 - 0	**Brunskill 4** (13 76 84 89)
	15.01	FAT 3	A	Spalding United	275	D 2 - 2	Appleby 27[og], Mellanby 52
	19.01	FAT 3R	H	SPALDING UNITED	232	W 2 - 0	Brunskill 16 46
25	22.01	UNIB P	H	BARROW	333	L 1 - 3	Shaw 34
26	29.01	UNIB P	A	Runcorn	198	L 0 - 2	
	05.02	FAT 4	A	Spennymoor United	422	W 3 - 0	Brunskill 19, Shaw 29 31
27	12.02	UNIB P	H	LEIGH RMI	226	D 1 - 1	Bayles 87
28	16.02	UNIB P	H	WHITBY TOWN	236	W 4 - 0	Hutt 7, Gallagher 48 56, Brunskill 71
29	19.02	UNIB P	A	Winsford United	135	W 5 - 2	Mellanby 16 49, Shaw 51, Bayles 89, Hutt 90
	26.02	FAT 5	H	SCARBOROUGH	747	W 2 - 1	Shaw 11[p], Mellanby 44
30	04.03	UNIB P	A	Bamber Bridge	230	L 0 - 4	
	11.03	FAT QF	A	Kettering Town	2074	D 2 - 2	Shaw 18, Downey 21
	15.03	FAT QF R	H	KETTERING TOWN	1087	L 0 - 2	
31	18.03	UNIB P	H	RUNCORN	207	W 2 - 0	Lee 52, Shaw 89
32	22.03	UNIB P	H	STALYBRIDGE CELTIC	191	W 1 - 0	Milroy 86
33	25.03	UNIB P	H	Droylsden	221	L 0 - 1	
34	29.03	UNIB P	H	GUISELEY	220	W 1 - 0	Brunskill 17
35	01.04	UNIB P	A	Hyde United	367	D 1 - 1	Bayles 2
36	05.04	UNIB P	A	GAINSBOROUGH TRIN.	190	D 0 - 0	
37	08.04	UNIB P	H	FRICKLEY ATHLETIC	173	W 3 - 2	Brunskill 7, Smith 40, Mellanby 42
38	11.04	UNIB P	A	Leigh RMI	203	L 1 - 4	Brunskill 40
39	15.04	UNIB P	H	EMLEY	216	D 1 - 1	Shaw 8
40	18.04	UNIB P	A	Leek Town	131	W 4 - 1	Shaw 19, 44, Brunskill 27, 81
41	22.04	UNIB P	H	BLYTH SPARTANS	357	D 1 - 1	Shaw 63 (p)
42	24.04	UNIB P	A	Gateshead	387	D 0 - 0	
43	26.04	UNIB P	A	Emley	181	L 0 - 2	
44	01.05	UNIB P	A	Lancaster City	220	W 1 - 0	Shaw 27

PLAYING SQUAD

GOALKEEPERS: Steve Jones (Gateshead)

DEFENDERS: Thomas Dunn (Middlesbrough), Craig Lake (Hartlepool), Glen Downey (Hartlepool), Michael Nelson (Spennymoor U), Mark Foster (Youth), Mark Salmon (Acklam Steel Works), Steve Hutt (Hartlepool)

MIDFIELDERS: Andy Howarth (Spennymoor U), David Gallagher (Guisborough T), Danny Brunskill (North Shields Ath), David Wells (Darlington)

FORWARDS: Andy Shaw (Spennymoor U), Danny Mellanby (West Auckland T), Mike Dunwell (Hartlepool)

BLYTH SPARTANS

CLUB OFFICIALS

Chairman: **Mike Mitchell**
Secretary: **Scott Sawyer**
53 Ninth Avenue, Blyth, Northumberland
NE24 2TE (01670 355669).
Press Officer: **Ken Teasdale**

FOOTBALL MANAGEMENT TEAM

Manager: John Charlton
Assistant Manager: TBA

FACT FILE

Formed: 1899
Nickname: Spartans
Sponsors: Federation Brewery.
Colours: Green & white stripes
Change colours: Orange
Midweek Matches: Tuesday
Reserves' League: Northern Alliance
Local Press: Newcastle Journal
& Evening Chronicle.

Pages: 64 Price: £1
Editor: Brian Grey (0191 2650119)

GROUND

Croft Park, Blyth, Northumberland. (01670) 354818 FAX: 01670 545592
Directions: Through Tyne tunnel heading north on A19, take Cramlington turn A1061, follow signs for Newsham/Blyth. Right fork at railway gates in Newsham,down Plessey Rd, ground can be seen on left. Buses X24, X25, X26, X1 from Newcastle.
Capacity: 6,000   Seats: 300   Cover: 1,000
Clubhouse: Open every night plus Saturday & Sunday lunch & matchdays. Available for wedding functions. Pies & sandwiches available.
Souvenir Shop: Large selection. Contact: Malcom Allen (01670 369209)

PREVIOUS Leagues: Northumberland 01-07; Northern Alliance 07-13, 46-47; North Eastern13-14 19-39 47-58 62-64; Northern Combination 45-46; Midland 58-60; Northern Counties 60-62; Northern 62-94. Names: None   Grounds: None

CLUB RECORDS Fee Received: £30,000 for Les Mutrie (Hull City) 1979.   Fee Paid:

BEST SEASON **FA Trophy:** Quarter-Final replay 79-80 82-83. **FA Amateur Cup:** Semi-Final 71-72.
FA Cup: 5th Rd replay 77-78 (lost to Wrexham). 1st Round on 47 occasions. League Clubs defeated: Ashington, Gillingham 22-23, Crewe Alexandra,Stockport County 71-72, Chesterfield, Stoke City 77-78, Bury 95-96.

HONOURS Nth Lg(10) 72-73 74-76 79-84 86-88 94-95, (R-up 71-72 73-74 77-78 84-85 94-95),Lg Cup(5) 72-73 77-79 81-82 91-92 94-95, Presidents Cup 96-97; Nth Eastern Lg35-36 (R-up 22-23, Lg Cup 49-50 54-55); Northumberland Lg 03-04; Northern All.08-09 12-13 (R-up 46-47); Northumberland Snr Cup (19); Shields Gazette Cup 95-96.

Players Progressing: William McGlen (Manchester Utd 46), Joe Roddom (Chesterfield 48), Henry Mills (Huddersfield 48), John Allison (Reading 49), James Kelly (Watford 49), Robert Millard (Reading 49), Jim Kerr (Lincoln 52), James Milner (Burnley 52), John Hogg (Portsmouth 54), John Allison(Chesterfield 55), John Inglis (Gateshead 57), John Longland (Hartlepool 58),Alan Shoulder (Newcastle 79), Les Mutrie (Hull City 79), Steve Carney(Newcastle 80), Craig Liddle (Middlesbrough 94), Paul O'Connor (Hartlepool 95). Gustavo Di Lella (Hartlepool 98)

Andy Blower Scores Blyth's opening goal in their 4-3 away victory over Hyde United last season.   **Photo: Graham Brown**

Match Facts 1999-00

	Date	Comp.	H/A	Opponents	Att.	Result	Goalscorers
1	14.08	UNIB P	H	LEIGH RMI	401	L 0 - 1	
2	17.08	UNIB P	A	Whitby Town	481	W 2 - 1	Edgcumbe 1, Hutchinson 82
3	21.08	UNIB P	A	Marine	314	D 0 - 0	
4	24.08	UNIB P	H	BISHOP AUCKLAND	322	L 0 - 2	
5	28.08	UNIB P	H	BAMBER BRIDGE	357	L 1 - 2	Edgcumbe 6
6	30.08	UNIB P	A	Gateshead	497	L 0 - 3	
7	04.09	UNIB P	A	Stalybridge Celtic	461	L 0 - 2	
8	07.09	UNIB P	H	EMLEY	318	W 3 - 2	Melrose 12, Edgcumbe 27, Robinson 43
9	11.09	UNIB P	H	LEEK TOWN	346	L 2 - 3	Hutchinson 24, 83
	15.09	ULC 1G	A	Gateshead	215	L 1 - 4	Robson 72[p]
	18.09	FAC Q2	A	Leigh RMI	197	L 3 - 5	**Robson 3** (9[p], 75, 87)
10	20.09	UNIB P	A	Emley	259	L 0 - 2	
11	25.09	UNIB P	A	Lancaster City	315	L 0 - 3	
	28.09	ULC G14	H	WHITLEY BAY	329	W 7 - 0	Robson 36, 55, Hogg 46, Stewart 51, Edgcumbe 75, 78, Burt 79
12	02.10	UNIB P	A	Winsford United	133	W 5 - 0	Pitt 25 74, Blower 37, Edgcumbe 63, Hogg 87
13	05.10	UNIB P	H	SPENNYMOOR UNITED	363	L 2 - 3	Robson 41 44
	09.10	FAT 1	H	STOURBRIDGE	419	W 3 - 0	Stewart 55, Robson 69, O.G. 90
14	12.10	UNIB P	A	Spennymoor United	297	D 0 - 0	
15	16.10	UNIB P	A	Hyde United	372	L 2 - 5	Robson 17 77
16	19.10	UNIB P	H	HUCKNALL TOWN	275	W 1 - 0	Burt 83
17	23.10	UNIB P	A	Runcorn	279	L 0 - 3	
18	26.10	UNIB P	H	FRICKLEY ATHLETIC	316	W 4 - 1	Stewart 9, Edgcumbe 25, Pitt 31 60
19	30.10	UNIB P	H	HYDE UNITED	412	L 3 - 4	Blower 7, Di Lella 9, Stewart 10
	02.11	ULC GE	A	Guiseley	139	L 0 - 2	
20	06.11	UNIB P	A	Droylsden	181	L 0 - 1	
	09.11	ULC GE	A	BRADFORD PARK AVE.	265	W 4 - 0	Hogg 24, Pitt 34 35, Dixon 87
21	20.11	UNIB P	H	GAINSBOROUGH TRIN.	347	D 1 - 1	Edgcumbe 66
	27.11	FAT 2	H	WITTON ALBION	375	W 2 - 0	West 45[og], Edgcumbe 53
22	04.12	UNIB P	A	Barrow	1006	L 2 - 3	Symons 35, Evans 79
	07.12	N.SC QF	H	PONTELAND UNITED	188	D 0 - 0	
23	11.12	UNIB P	H	STALYBRIDGE CELTIC	276	L 1 - 4	Lumsden 44
	18.12	N.SC QF R	A	Ponteland United		L 0 - 1	
24	27.12	UNIB P	H	GATESHEAD	793	L 0 - 1	
25	03.01	UNIB P	H	Guiseley	383	L 1 - 2	Edgcumbe 14
26	08.01	UNIB P	H	WORKSOP TOWN	338	W 2 - 1	Pitt 62, Chandler 75
	15.01	FAT 3	A	Stalybridge Celtic	579	L 0 - 1	
	22.01	Pres.C QF	H	BAMBER BRIDGE	235	D 2 - 2	Symons 57, Hilton 86
27	29.01	UNIB P	A	Worksop Town	385	D 2 - 2	Edgcumbe 74, Jackson 78[p]
28	05.02	UNIB P	H	COLWYN BAY	304	W 4 - 1	Edgcumbe 13 75, Hutchinson 69, Chandler 72
29	12.02	UNIB P	A	Gainsborough Trinity	394	W 1 - 0	Chandler 48
	14.02	PC QF R	A	Bamber Bridge		w/o	Bamber Bridge fielded ineligible player in first match
30	19.02	UNIB P	A	Leek Town	330	W 4 - 1	Chandler 22, Hutchinson 53, Hilton 76, Moat 90
31	26.02	UNIB P	H	GUISELEY	374	L 1 - 2	Hutchinson 90
	04.03	Pres.C. SF	H	TRAFFORD	286	L 0 - 1	
32	11.03	UNIB P	A	Bamber Bridge	335	D 1 - 1	Moat 77
33	18.03	UNIB P	H	DROYLSDEN	304	W 3 - 0	Pitt 27, Chandler 45, Evans 47
34	21.03	UNIB P	H	Hucknall Town	218	W 1 - 0	Evans 10
35	25.03	UNIB P	H	MARINE	384	W 3 - 1	Chandler 2, Moat 19, 42
36	01.04	UNIB P	A	Frickley Athletic	169	D 1 - 1	Lumsden 56
37	08.04	UNIB P	H	WINSFORD UNITED	311	W 1 - 0	Chandler 48
38	15.04	UNIB P	H	Colwyn Bay	270	D 0 - 0	
39	18.04	UNIB P	H	BARROW	359	D 1 - 1	Rowe 69 (p)
40	22.04	UNIB P	A	Bishop Auckland	357	D 1 - 1	Martin 16
41	24.04	UNIB P	H	WHITBY TOWN	392	W 2 - 0	Chandler 80, Hutchinson 85
42	29.04	UNIB P	H	LANCASTER CITY	315	L 0 - 2	
43	01.05	UNIB P	A	Leigh RMI	695	L 0 - 2	
44	06.05	UNIB P	H	RUNCORN	312	W 4 - 2	Chandler 2, Moat 25, Rowe 32(p), 90 (p)

PLAYING SQUAD

GOALKEEPERS: Terry Burke (Whitley Bay)

DEFENDERS: Andy Hay (Hartlepool), Patrick Little (Jarrow Roofing), Mark Dunkerley (Hartlepool), Richard Forster (Hartlepool)

MIDFIELDERS: Steve Stewart (Chester-le-Street), Tony Skedd (Whitby T), Jeff Wrightson (Spennymoor U), Steve Hutchinson (Gateshead), Nick Evans (Hartlepool), Brian Rowe (Spennymoor U)

FORWARDS: Glen Robson (Harrogate T), Ian Chandler (Durham C), Paul Symons (Morpeth T)

BURSCOUGH

CLUB OFFICIALS

Chairman: **Frank Parr**
Vice Chairman: **Stuart Heaps**
President: **Rod Cottam**
Secretary: **Stan Strickland**
109 Redgate, Ormskirk, Lancs L39 3NW
(H 01695574722) (B 01695 574722)
Press Officer: Secretary

FOOTBALL MANAGEMENT TEAM
Manager: John Davison
Asst Manager: Peter King
Physio: Tom Spencer

FACT FILE

Founded: 1946
Nickname: Linnets
Sponsors: Seyfert Ltd.
Colours: Green/white/green
Change colours: Yellow/blue/blue
Midweek Matches: Tuesday
1999-00
Captain: Ged Nolan
Top ScorerRyan Lowe
P.o.Y.:Ryan Lowe

Pages:44 Price £1.00
Editor: Stan Strickland
(01695 574722)
Radio: Radio Lancs,Red Rose.

GROUND Victoria Park, Bobby Langton Way, Mart Lane, Burscough, Ormskirk, Lancs L40 0SD Tel: 01704 893237
Directions: M6 Jct 27, follow signs thru Parbold A5209, right into Junction Lane (signed Burscough & Martin Mere) to lights, right onto A59 to Burscough Village, 2nd left over canal bridge into Mart Lane to ground. 200 yards from Burscough Bridge BR station (Wigan-Southport line). Half mile from Burscough Junction (Ormskirk Preston line)
Capacity: 3,000   Seats: 220   Cover: 1,000
Clubhouse: `Barons Club' (privately owned, access outside grd). Mon-Thurs 7-11pm, Fri 4-11pm, Sat 1-11pm, Sun noon-3 & 7-10.30pm. No food   **Club Shop:** Yes

PREVIOUS   **Leagues:** Liverpool County Comb. 46-53, Lancs Comb. 53-70, Cheshire Co.70-82, North West Counties 82-98
CLUB RECORDS   **Attendance:** 4,798 v Wigan Athletic,F.A.Cup 3rd Qual.Rd.1950-51
        Goalscorer: Johnny Vincent 60 53-54. Most Goals in Game: Louis Bimpson 7. In Career: Wes Bridge 188
        Win: 10-0 v Cromptons Recreation 1947 & v Nelson 1948-49, both Lancs. Comb.
        Defeat: 0-9 v Earlstown,Liverpool County Comb.1948-49 **Fee paid:** Undisclosed for Arthur Green. Burton Alb. 48
        Fee Received: £12,000 for Michael Yates (Dundee) 99-00

BEST SEASON   **FA Cup:** 1st Rd 59-60 77-78 79-80 80-81
        FA Trophy: 1982-83
        FA Vase: 1994-95 (Last 16)

HONOURS   Liverpool Challenge Cup 47-48 50-51,54-55; George Mahon Cup 47-48; Liverpool County Comb Div 1, 49-50 (Div 2 53-54, 67-68); Lancs Comb.Div 2 53-54; Lancs Comb Div 1 55-56 69-70; Lord Wavertree Cup 67-68; Cheshire County Lge R-up 70- 71, League Cup 74-75 (R-up 73-74); Lancs Jnr Cup 47-4849-50 66-67; Liverpool Non-Lg Snr Cup 55/56, 71-72; North West Counties Lge 82-83, Lge Cup 92-93 95-96(R-up 91-92), Challenge Shield 82-83, 95-96; Liverpool Senior Cup R-up 92-93,95-96, 99-00.

Players progressing: L Bimpson, B Parker (Liverpool 53), B Pilson (Stoke 53-54), A Green (Huddersfield), K Waterhouse (Preston),
        K Spencer (Everton), F Gamble (Derby 80), Tony Rigby (Bury), S Teale (Aston Villa), L Watson(Preston),
        K Formby A Russell (Rochdale 94), G Martindale (Bolton 94), S Perkins (Plymouth A. 97), M.Yates (Dundee 99)

Back Row: Mark Wilde, Andy McMullen, Paul Blasbery, Greg Price, Billy Knowles, Ray Birch. **Middle:** Peter King (Asst. Manager), John Lawless, Lee McEvilly, Michael Clandon, Darren Saint, Brian Holmes, Neil Hanson, John Davison (Manager) **Front:** Robbie Talbot, Ryan Lowe (now Shrewsbury Town), Ged Nolan, Bill Ashcroft (Seyfert Ltd), John Newman, Marvin Molyneux.

Match Facts 1999-00

	Date	Comp.	H/A	Opponents	Att.	Result	Goalscorers	Lge Pos.
	07.08	Liv. SC F	A	Southport	736	L	*3-6	Bowen, Knowles, Lowe	
1	14.08	UNIB 1	H	Farsley Celtic	103	W	2-0	Lowe, Wilde	
2	17.08	UNIB 1	A	Gretna	84	W	2-0	Lowe 2	1
	21.08	FAC Pre	A	Workington	751	W	2-1	Birch	
3	21.08	UNIB 1	H	Accrington Stanley	187	D	1-1	Lowe	3
4	28.08	UNIB 1	A	Lincoln United	180	W	1-0	McEvilly	1
	30.08	UNIB 1	H	Flixton	144	W	3-0	Lowe, McEvilly, Wilde	1
	04.09	FAC 1Q	A	Farsley Celtic	96	D	1-1	McMullen	
5	07.09	FAC 1Q R	H	Farsley Celtic	174	L	0-3		
6	11.09	UNIB 1	A	Whitley Bay	162	D	1-0	Lowe	1
7	14.09	UNIB 1	H	Workington	179	D	0-0		2
8	18.09	UNIB 1	A	Matlock Town	183	D	1-1	Morgan	3
9	21.09	UNIB 1	H	Gretna	120	W	4-0	Lowe 3, Wilde	1
10	25.09	UNIB 1	A	Eastwood Town	143	W	2-0	Bowen, Wilde	1
	28.09	LC Group	A	Chorley	187	L	0-1		
11	02.10	UNIB 1	H	Lincoln United	205	D	1-1	Lowe	1
	05.10	Liverpool SC	H	Liverpool	267	D	*2-2	Knowles 2	Lost 2-4 after penalties
	09.10	FAT 1	H	Ilkeston Town	183	L	2-6	Knowles, Wilde	
	12.10	LC Group	H	Marine	176	D	2-2	Wilde, Talbot	
12	16.10	UNIB 1	A	Ossett Town	124	D	1-1	Bowen	2
13	23.10	UNIB 1	H	Bradford Park Avenue	185	L	1-2	Lowe	6
14	26.10	UNIB 1	A	Workington	637	W	3-0	Lowe, Wilde 2	3
15	30.10	UNIB 1	H	Harrogate Town	141	D	2-2	Lowe, Birch	5
16	06.11	UNIB 1	A	Netherfield Kendal	107	W	7-4	Lowe 4, Knowles, Birch, Talbot	2
17	13.11	UNIB 1	H	Stocksbridge Park Steels	150	W	4-1	Lowe, Wilde 2, Birch	2
	16.11	Lancs Trophy	A	Bacup Borough	85	W	4-0	Wilde 3, Morgan	
18	20.11	UNIB 1	A	Farsley Celtic	92	D	0-0		2
19	23.11	UNIB 1	A	Witton Albion	395	D	1-1	Bowen	2
20	27.11	UNIB 1	H	Belper Town	205	W	3-1	Clandon, Lowe, Bowen	2
21	04.12	UNIB 1	H	Osett Town	169	W	3-2	Newman, Lowe, McEvilly	2
22	07.12	UNIB 1	A	Congleton Town	127	D	2-2	Bowen, Talbot	1
23	11.12	UNIB 1	A	Bradford Park Avenue	192	D	1-1	Lowe	1
24	27.12	UNIB 1	A	Netherfield Kendal	202	W	4-3	Clandon, Lowe 2, Wilde	2
25	03.01	UNIB 1	A	Stocksbridge Park Steels	191	W	2-0	Wilde, Talbot	2
26	08.01	UNIB 1	H	Witton Albion	427	D	1-1	Birch	2
	11.01	Lancs T. 2	H	Marine	157	L	1-2	Saint	
27	15.01	UNIB 1	A	Ashton United	202	D	0-0		2
28	22.01	UNIB 1	A	Flixton	104	W	1-0	Birch	2
29	29.01	UNIB 1	H	Radcliffe Borough	249	L	1-2	Howard	2
30	05.02	UNIB 1	H	Chorley	282	W	1-0	Lowe	2
31	12.02	UNIB 1	A	Trafford	152	D	1-1	Howard	2
32	19.02	UNIB 1	H	Matlock Town	186	D	2-2	Knowles, Lowe	2
33	26.02	UNIB 1	A	Radcliffe Borough	342	D	0-0		2
34	04.03	UNIB 1	H	Eastwood Town	161	W	5-0	Howard 2, Lowe, Talbot 2	1
35	11.03	UNIB 1	A	Chorley	317	D	2-2	Knowles, Lowe	1
36	14.03	UNIB 1	H	Trafford	153	W	1-0	Lowe	1
37	18.03	UNIB 1	A	Belper Town	202	W	3-0	Knowles, Wilde, Birch	1
38	25.03	UNIB 1	H	Whitley Bay	163	W	1-0	Lowe	1
39	08.04	UNIB 1	A	Accrington Stanley	912	D	2-2	Wilde, Birch	1
40	15.04	UNIB 1	H	Congleton Town	211	W	5-0	Lowe 3, Wilde 2	1
41	24.04	UNIB 1	H	Ashton United	303	W	1-0	Birch	1
42	01.05	UNIB 1	A	Harrogate Town	325	W	2-1	Knowles, Lowe	1*

* but ended up 2nd on 06.05 when Accrington Stanley won their game in hand

PLAYING SQUAD

GOALKEEPERS:	Paul Blasbery (Hyde U), Greg Price (Prescot Cables)
DEFENDERS:	Neil Hanson (Bootle), Marvin Molyneux (Youth), Matthew Farrell (Southport), Ryan Bowen (Youth), Matthew Innes (Manchester C)
MIDFIELDERS:	Robert Talbot (Marine), Billy Knowles (St.Helens T), Darren Saint (Chorley), John Newman (Runcorn), Kenny Weston (Netherfield K), John Lawless (Youth), Michael Clandon (Youth)
FORWARDS:	Brian Hatton (St.Helens T), Lee McEvilly (Bootle), Stuart Rudd (Skelmersdale U), Mark Wilde (Witton Alb)

COLWYN BAY

CLUB OFFICIALS

Chairman: **Dave Lloyd**
Vice Chairman: **J A Humphreys**
Secretary / Press Officer: **Alan J Banks**
15 Smith Avenue, Old Colwyn, N Wales
LL29 8BE. Tel: 01492 516941 (H)
01492 515133 (B).

FOOTBALL MANAGEMENT TEAM

Manager: Bryn Jones
01244 531974 (H), 01244 812154 (B)
Assistant Manager: Dean Martin
Physio: Colin Edwardsl

FACT FILE

Formed: 1885
Nickname: 'Bay' or 'Seagulls'
Sponsors: Bay View Centre
Colours: Sky Blue.
Change colours: Tangerine
Reserve Team:
Midweek home matchday: Tuesday

99-00 Captain: Colin Caton
P.o.Y.: Colin Caton
Top scorer: James McIlvogue (17)

Pages: 28 Price: £1
Editor: Neil Brampton (01492 533341)
Local Press: North Wales Weekly News, North
Wales Pioneer.

GROUND

Llanelian Road, Old Colwyn, N.Wales.   Tel: 01492 514581
Directions: M55 North Wales Coast - approaching Colwyn Bay take 1st exit signposted Old
Colwyn, left at bottom slip road, straight over r'bout into Llanelian Rd - ground half mile on
right. 2 miles from Colwyn Bar BR station.
Capacity: 2,500   Seats: 250   Cover: 700
Clubhouse: Open matchdays only.
Club Shop: Yes - contact: A Holden 01492 534287 Metal Badges: Yes

PREVIOUS   Leagues: Nth Wales Coast 01-21 33-35; Welsh National 21-30; Nth Wales Comb. 30-31; Welsh Lg (Nth) 45-84; North
West Counties 84-91
Grounds: Eiras Park 1930-82; Llanelian Road 82-92; Northwich Victoria FC 92-93; Ellesmere Port Stadium94-95 (2 years
in exile thro' dispute with FAW re League of Wales).

CLUB RECORDS   **Attendance:** 5,000 (at Eiras Park) v Borough United, 1964.
Goalscorer: Peter Donnelly   **Appearances:** Bryn A Jones

BEST SEASON   **FA Trophy:** Quarter Finals 96-97. **F.A Cup:** Second Round Proper 95-96. League clubs defeated: Wrexham(Welsh Cup)
HONOURS   Northern Premier Lg Div 1 91-92 (Div 1 Cup 91-92); North West Counties Lg R-up90-91 (Div 3 R-up 83-84, Lg Cup 88-89,
Floodlit Cup 90-91; Welsh Cup SF 91-92;Welsh National Lg R-up 27-28 29-30; Nth Wales Comb. 30-31; Welsh Lg Nth 64-
6582-83 83-84 (R-up 35-36 45-46 63-64), Lg Cup 27-28; Alves Cup 63-64; Cookson Cup 73-74 79-80 80-81 81-82 83-84;
Barritt Cup 79-80 81-82 83-84; Nth Wales Coast Chal. Cup 30-31 31-32 81-82 82-83 83-84 95-96 97-98; Nth Wales Coast
Jnr Cup 1898-99. North Wst Coast Cup 99-00.

Players progressing: Peter Suddaby (Blackpool), Gareth Davies (Wrexham).

Back Row
Owain Roberts,
Bevan Humphries,
Richie Roberts,
Paul Jones,
Colin Caton,
Alun Evans,
Stuart Gelling,
Jonathon Cross

Front Row
James McIlvogue,
Deiniol Graham,
Mark Woods,
Frank Gibbons,
Craig Lawton,
Marc Limbert,
Graham Roberts.

Colwyn Bay on the opening day of the 2000-01 season

Match Facts 1999-00

	Date	Comp.	H/A	Opponents	Att.	Result	Goalscorers
1	14.08	UNIB P	H	EMLEY	257	L 0-1	
2	17.08	UNIB P	A	Runcorn	312	W 2-1	Roberts 34, Limbert 56
3	21.08	UNIB P	H	GUISELEY	243	L 0-2	
4	24.08	UNIB P	H	MARINE	239	L 0-5	
5	28.08	UNIB P	A	Droylsden	346	W 2-1	McIlvogue 27 36
6	30.08	UNIB P	H	STALYBRIDGE CELTIC	258	D 0-0	
7	04.09	UNIB P	A	Gateshead	253	L 0-6	
8	07.09	UNIB P	A	Lancaster City	261	L 0-3	
9	11.09	UNIB P	H	WORKSOP TOWN	224	W 3-1	Evans 23, Limbert 24, Lawton 83
	14.09	ULC 1G	A	Runcorn	170	L 1-3	Sharratt 61
	18.09	FAC Q2	A	Stalybridge Celtic	435	L 0-1	
10	21.09	UNIB P	H	LANCASTER CITY	186	D 1-1	Congerton 78
11	25.09	UNIB P	A	Gainsborough Trinity	328	L 0-2	
	28.09	ULC G6	A	WITTON ALBION	188	W 5-2	Donnelly 2 88, Pritchard 20[og], Urquhart 47 66[p]
12	05.10	UNIB P	H	WINSFORD UNITED	189	W 2-0	McIlvogue 53, Evans 72
	09.10	FAT 1	A	Emley	380	L 0-2	
13	12.10	UNIB P	A	Bamber Bridge	282	W 2-1	McIlvogue 35 46
14	16.10	UNIB P	H	SPENNYMOOR UNITED	179	L 0-2	
15	19.10	UNIB P	H	LEEK TOWN	161	D 1-1	Limbert 3
16	23.10	UNIB P	A	Frickley Athletic	154	L 1-4	Limbert 88
17	30.10	UNIB P	H	WHITBY TOWN	176	W 2-0	Congerton 18, Evans 77
	03.11	ULC GC	A	Trafford	107	L 3-4	Evans 14, McIlvogue 15, Sharratt 80[p]
18	13.11	UNIB P	A	Leigh RMI	211	W 2-1	McIlvogue 75 90
19	20.11	UNIB P	H	BISHOP AUCKLAND	220	L 0-1	
	23.11	ULC GC	H	MARINE	157	L 2-5	Donnelly 29, Roberts 49
20	27.11	UNIB P	A	Leek Town	346	W 2-0	McIlvogue 73, Evans 77
21	30.11	UNIB P	H	BARROW	195	D 0-0	
22	04.12	UNIB P	A	Spennymoor United	163	D 1-1	Congerton 63
23	27.12	UNIB P	H	RUNCORN	332	D 1-1	Lawton 55
24	03.01	UNIB P	A	Winsford United	210	W 2-1	Caton 33, Congerton 86
25	08.01	UNIB P	A	Bishop Auckland	195	L 0-4	
26	15.01	UNIB P	H	DROYLSDEN	221	L 1-2	McIlvogue 32
	22.01	Unifilla QF	A	Workington	524	W 1-0	Roberts 85
27	29.01	UNIB P	H	FRICKLEY ATHLETIC	195	W 1-0	McIlvogue 80
28	05.02	UNIB P	A	Blyth Spartans	304	L 1-4	Limbert 15
	12.02	N W.C 5	A	Ruthin Town		W 3-1	McIlvogue 68, Gelling 69, McGoona 87
29	19.02	UNIB P	A	Whitby Town	366	D 1-1	Lawton 19
30	22.02	UNIB P	H	HYDE UNITED	241	L 2-3	Lawton 39, Limbert 89
31	26.02	UNIB P	H	HUCKNALL TOWN	243	W 2-0	Evans 1, Gelling 80
	04.03	UnifillaSF	A	Emley	182	L 2-6	Fairhurst 44, Limbert 77[p]
	07.03	NW Coast QF	A	Porthmadog	98	W *4-1	McIlvogue 34, Lawton 107, Limbert 109, Donnelly 112
32	11.03	UNIB P	A	Guiseley	272	D 2-2	Roberts 13, McIlvogue 29
33	18.03	UNIB P	H	GAINSBOROUGH TRINITY	219	D 0-0	
34	25.03	UNIB P	A	Worksop Town	317	L 2-4	Donnelly 43, McIlvogue 45
35	01.04	UNIB P	H	GATESHEAD	213	L 1-3	McIlvogue 60
36	08.04	UNIB P	A	Emley	163	W 2-1	Norman 34, OG (David) 47
	12.04	NWC FAC SF	A	Glan Conwy		W 4-1	McGoona, Fairhurst, OG, Roberts
37	15.04	UNIB P	H	BLYTH SPARTANS	270	D 0-0	
38	17.04	UNIB P	A	Hyde United	374	L 0-3	
39	22.04	UNIB P	A	Barrow	911	L 0-4	
40	24.04	UNIB P	H	LEIGH RMI	280	L 3-5	Evans 18, Donnelly 50, Caton 65
41	27.04	UNIB P	A	Marine	264	D 1-1	Limbert 66
42	29.04	UNIB P	A	Stalybridge Celtic	275	L 1-3	Limbert 29
43	01.05	UNIB P	H	BAMBER BRIDGE	230	L 0-7	
	03.05	NWC FAC F	N	Glantreath		W 5-0	Congerton 44, Donnelly 47, Caton 49, McIlvogue 57, 84
44	06.05	UNIB P	A	Hucknall Town	168	D 2-2	Donnelly 69, 76

PLAYING SQUAD

GOALKEEPERS: Richie Roberts (Christleton)

DEFENDERS: Colin Caton (Witton Alb), Paul Jones (Connah's Quay Nomads), Jamie Fairhurst (TNS), Mark Price (Connah's Quay Nomads), Dave Norman (Bangor C), Joe Quinn (Conwy U), Paul Lloyd (Conwy U), Lee Dixon (Conwy U), Bevan Humphreys (Conwy U)

MIDFIELDERS: Marc Limbert (Altrincham), Nicky Henderson (Connah's Quay Nomads), Craig Lawton (Port Vale), Stuart Gelling (Lancaster C), Andy Kendrick (Huddersfield), Paul Hawkins (Conwy U), Phil Patel (UWIC), Jon Cross (Chester C), Steve Roberts (Conwy U)

FORWARDS: Graham Roberts (Macclesfield), Frank Givens (Tranmere), Alun Evans (Ebbw Vale), Deniol Graham (Cwmbran T), James McIlvogue (Conwy U), Owain Roberts (Ruthin T)

DROYLSDEN

CLUB OFFICIALS

Chairman: **David Pace**

FACT FILE

Secretary: Alan Slater
83 King Edward Rd.,Hyde,
Cheshire SK14 5JJ
Tel & Fax: 0161 368 3687

Formed: 1892
Nickname: The Bloods
Sponsors:Alpha Court Windows &
Federation Brewery
Alpha Court Windows/ Hastings Taxis

FOOTBALL MANAGEMENT TEAM
Manager: David Pace
Asst Manager: Peter Orr
Physio Alan Cross

Colours: Red /White/Red
Change colours: Green/Black/Black
Midweek matchday: Tuesday

GROUND   The Butchers Arms Ground, Market Street, Droylsden, Manchester M43 7AY
Tel: 0161 370 1426/8341 FAX: 0161 370 8341

Directions: The ground lies 4 miles east of Manchester via the A662 Ashton New Road,
behind Butchers Arms Hotel.From M60 Jct 23 (opening August 2000) Follow A662 to
Doylsden. Right at lights in town centre through mini roundabout and ground on left.
Capacity: 3,500   **Cover:** 2,000   **Seats:** 400

Pages: 24   Price: £1.00
Editor: Martin Crookall
Local Press: Droylsden Reporter, Advertiser
Local Radio: BBC Manchester

Clubhouse: Pub hours except matchdays. Pool and darts   **Shop:** Yes Metal Badges

PREVIOUS   **Leagues:** Manchester; Lancs Com 36-39, 50-68; Cheshire County 39-50, 68-82; NW Counties 82-87

CLUB RECORDS   **Attendance:** 4,250 v Grimsby, FA Cup 1st rd 1976
Scorer: E Gillibrand 78 (1931-32)   **Win:** 13-2 v Lucas Sports Club
Fee Received: £11,000 for Tony Naylor (Crewe)

BEST SEASON   **FA Cup:** 2nd Rd 78-79. League clubs defeated: Rochdale 78-79
FA Vase: **FA Trophy:**

HONOURS   Northern Prem Lge Div 1 R-up 89-90 (Div 1 Cup 87-88); NW Counties Lge Div 2 86-87 ; Cheshire County Lge R-up 39-40
45-46 , Lge Cup 77-78 (R-up 76-77);Lancs Comb Div 2 R-up 55-56 58-59 62-63; Manchester Lge 30-31 32-33 (Lge Cup 23-24
33-34); Manchester Prem Cup 80-81 (R-up 83-84 90-91 93-94); Manchester Sen Cup 72-73 75-76 78-79 (R-up 72-73 75-76
78-79); Manchester Interm Cup 59-6064-65 69-70; Manchester Chall Shield 46-47

Players progressing: Albert Butterworth & F Letchford (Blackpool 1931), William Davies & Maurice Randall (Crewe 1947), William Mellor (Accrington 1950),
Geoff Tonge (Bury 1960), David Campbell (WBA 1962), Kevin Randall (Bury 1965), Peter Litchfield (Preston 1979), Tony Naylor (Crewe 1990)

Match Facts 1999-00

	Date	Comp.	H/A	Opponents	Att.	Result	Goalscorers
1	14.08	UNIB P	H	GAINSBOROUGH TRINITY	248	W 1 - 0	Jones 23
2	17.08	UNIB P	A	Bamber Bridge	325	W 3 - 1	Jones 30, Green 49 84
3	21.08	UNIB P	A	Hucknall Town	180	D 3 - 3	Jones 6, Harold 82, Cooper 87
4	24.08	UNIB P	H	RUNCORN	322	W 1 - 0	Holmes 7[p]
5	28.08	UNIB P	H	COLWYN BAY	346	L 1 - 2	Thomas 72[og]
6	30.08	UNIB P	A	Hyde United	752	L 0 - 2	
7	04.09	UNIB P	H	FRICKLEY ATHLETIC	237	D 1 - 1	Holmes 71[p]
8	07.09	UNIB P	H	BARROW	401	L 0 - 3	
9	11.09	UNIB P	A	Lancaster City	267	L 0 - 4	
10	15.09	UNIB P	A	Bishop Auckland	183	L 0 - 1	
	18.09	FAC Q2	A	Bradford Park Avenue	251	D 2 - 2	Whalley 72, Kinney 82
	21.09	FAC Q2 R	H	BRADFORD PARK AVENUE	261	W 2 - 1	Wright 99, Kinney 120
11	25.09	UNIB P	A	Gateshead	235	D 1 - 1	Stannard 45
	28.09	ULC G15	A	Accrington Stanley	171	L 1 - 3	Cooper 60
	02.10	FAC Q3	H	GAINSBOROUGH TRINITY	289	D 2 - 2	Holmes 63[p], Kinney 69
	05.10	FAC Q3 R	A	Gainsborough Trinity	468	W 2 - 1	Jones 64, Stannard 80
	12.10	ULC G15	H	STALYBRIDGE CELTIC	316	L 0 - 2	
	16.10	FAC Q4	H	EASTWOOD TOWN	524	L 0 - 2	
12	19.10	UNIB P	H	WORKSOP TOWN	163	L 0 - 2	
13	23.10	UNIB P	A	Gainsborough Trinity	400	L 1 - 2	Kinney 61
14	26.10	UNIB P	A	Marine	244	L 2 - 3	Hennigan 55, Thomas 62
15	30.10	UNIB P	H	SPENNYMOOR UNITED	182	L 0 - 1	
16	06.11	UNIB P	H	BLYTH SPARTANS	181	W 1 - 0	Kinney 40
17	09.11	UNIB P	H	LEIGH RMI	193	L 0 - 2	
18	12.11	UNIB P	A	Guiseley	306	L 0 - 2	
19	20.11	UNIB P	H	WINSFORD UNITED	207	W 3 - 0	Holmes 59, Green 82, Kinney 86
	27.11	FAT 2	A	Frickley Athletic	173	L 3 - 4	Carroll 9, Whalley 34, Hennigan 45
20	18.12	UNIB P	A	Barrow	1072	W 3 - 0	Green 5, Holmes 46, Wright 79
21	27.12	UNIB P	A	Frickley Athletic	152	W 4 - 0	Holmes 15[p] 83, Green 67, Carroll 75
22	03.01	UNIB P	H	LEEK TOWN	370	L 1 - 2	Kinney 29
23	08.01	UNIB P	H	EMLEY	321	D 1 - 1	Ashton 25
24	15.01	UNIB P	A	Colwyn Bay	221	W 2 - 1	Green 14, Wright 45
25	22.01	UNIB P	H	HUCKNALL TOWN	262	D 0 - 0	
	25.01	MPC QF	H	ABBEY HEY	249	D 0 - 0	
26	29.01	UNIB P	A	Spennymoor United	135	D 1 - 1	Holmes 27
27	05.02	UNIB P	H	GUISELEY	224	W 3 - 0	Kinney 24 89, Lattie 53
	08.02	MPC QF R	A	Abbey Hey	221	W 2 - 1	Kinney 39, Stannard 92
28	12.02	UNIB P	A	Worksop Town	351	D 1 - 1	Carroll 57
29	15.02	UNIB P	H	MARINE	202	L 0 - 1	
30	19.02	UNIB P	A	Stalybridge Celtic	422	D 0 - 0	
	21.02	MPC SF	A	Ashton United	304	W 2 - 1	Kinney 32, Holmes 65
31	26.02	UNIB P	H	BAMBER BRIDGE	253	W 2 - 0	Holmes 43, Kinney 65
32	29.02	UNIB P	A	Runcorn	222	D 1 - 1	Ashton 74
33	04.03	UNIB P	A	Leek Town	271	D 0 - 0	
34	11.03	UNIB P	A	Winsford United	158	D 1 - 1	Whalley 2
35	14.03	UNIB P	H	STALYBRIDGE CELTIC	445	W 1 - 0	Stannard 90
36	18.03	UNIB P	A	Blyth Spartans	304	L 0 - 3	
37	25.03	UNIB P	H	BISHOP AUCKLAND	221	W 1 - 0	Holmes 43 (p)
38	08.04	UNIB P	A	Leigh RMI	235	W 2 - 1	Holmes 46, 83 (p)
39	11.04	UNIB P	H	GATESHEAD	147	D 2 - 2	Jones 38, Carroll 79
40	15.04	UNIB P	H	LANCASTER CITY	241	L 3 - 4	Corns 3, Jones 68, Carroll 86
41	17.04	UNIB P	A	Emley	163	L 0 - 1	
42	24.04	UNIB P	H	HYDE UNITED	473	L 1 - 3	Green 31
43	26.04	UNIB P	A	Whitby Town	344	L 2 - 5	Jones 31, Holmes 41 (p)
44	29.04	UNIB P	H	WHITBY TOWN		W 3 - 2	Hennigan 31, Stannard 53, Warner 86

PLAYING SQUAD

GOALKEEPERS: Paul Phillips (Curzon Ashton)

DEFENDERS: Dave Ashton (Curzon Ashton), Danny Warner (Curzon Ashton), Aeon Lattie (Flixton), Eddie Johnston (Stalybridge C), Lee Prior (Winsford U), Stuart Corns (Telford U)

MIDFIELDERS: Dominic Morley (Southport), Steve Quinn (Curzon Ashton), Kevin Lampkin (Hednesford T), Dave Collins (Burnley), Mike Wolstenholme (Mossley), Neil Whalley (Runcorn), Carl Holmes (Buxton), Alan Fahy (Doncaster R), Andy Simpson (Curzon Ashton)

FORWARDS: John Stannard (Northwich V), Paul Garvey (Cheadle T), Wes Kinney (Knowsley U)

EMLEY

CLUB OFFICIALS

Chairman: **Peter Matthews.**
President: **Peter Maude**

Secretary/Press Officer: **Richard Poulain**
17, Smithy Lane, Skelmanthorpe,
Huddersfield HD89DF.
Tel:01484 860323 H,07711 620726 M&B

FOOTBALL MANAGEMENT TEAM

Manager: Ronnie Glavin.
Asst Manager: Jimmy Martin
Physio: Daryl Brook.

FACT FILE

Formed: 1903
Nickname: 'The Pewits'

Sponsors: Arrow Self Drive

Colours: Maroon and blue/white/maroon.

Change Colours: White/maroon/white

Midweek matchday: Monday.

Reserve League: Nth Co's (E)

Web: http:// www.emlyyafc.free-online.co.uk

E.Mail: rpemleyfc@talk21.com.

GROUND

Emley Welfare Sports Ground, Emley, Huddersfield   Tel: 01924 848398 . Office: 840087
Directions: Follow Huddersfield signs from M1 junct 38, left onto A636 at r'bout, then right
after about 3/4 mile for Emley. 7 miles from Huddersfield (BR) station - buses to Emley Cross.
Capacity: 3,000   Cover: 1,000   Seats: 300
Clubhouse: (01924 848398). Members' social club open seven nights a week and Saturday
& Sunday. Bingo, discos, occasional cabaret.
Club Shop: Yes Contact Mrs Linda Sykes

Pages: 34 Price: £1
Editor: Alan Blackman (01924 403959)

Local Press: Huddersfield Examiner.
Huddersfield & District Chronicle.
Local Radio: Radio Leeds, Radio Sheffield,
Pulse FM, Huddersfield FM.

HONOURS   FA Vase Runners-up 87-88; Northern Premier Lge Div 1 R-up 90-91; Northern Counties E Lge 87-88, 88-89 (R-up 85-86);
Yorkshire Lg 75-76 77-78 79-80 81-82(R-up(5) 72-74 76-77 78-79 80-81, Lg Cup 69-70 78-79 81-82, Div 2 R-up 69-0;
Sheffield & Hallamshire Senior Cup 75-76 79-80 80-81 83-84 88-89 90-91 91-9297-98; Huddersfield Challenge Cup 82-83
83-84 85-86; Huddersfield Lg(4) 65-69.

PREVIOUS

Leagues: Huddersfield; Yorkshire 69-82;
Northern Counties East 82-89.
Names: None
Grounds: None.

CLUB RECORDS

Attendance:
5,134 v Barking, Amateur Cup 3rd Proper 1/2/69.
    18,629 v West Ham Utd,
    at Upton Pk, 3rd Rd Proper 3/1/99.

Win: 12-0 v Ecclesfield Red Rose9-6-97

Defeat: 7-1 v Altrincham 25-4-98.

Goalscorer: Mick Pamment 305.

Appearances: Ray Dennis 762.

Fee Received: £60,000 for Michael Reynolds (Ayr Utd 98)

BEST SEASON

FA Amateur Cup: Third Round replay 69-70.

FA Vase: Runners-up 87-88 (Semi-Final86-87).

FA Trophy: Quarter Final 98-99

FA Cup: Third Round Proper 97-98 (1-2 v West Ham Utd)

Players progressing:
A Sweeney (Hartlepool Utd 79), G Cooper(Huddersfield Tn 84),
J Francis (Sheffield Utd 88), S Smith (Crewe Alexandra1992),
C Alcide (Lincoln City 95), C Hurst (Huddersfield Tn 97),
G Hurst (Ayr Utd 98), M.Reynolds (Ayr United 1998)

Emley's Paul David seen here out-jumping
Guiseley's Paul Bulgin to head clear.
Photo: Darren C Thomas

Match Facts 1999-00

	Date	Comp.	H/A	Opponents	Att.	Result	Goalscorers
1	14.08	UNIB P	A	Colwyn Bay	257	W 1-0	David 42
2	16.08	UNIB P	H	MARINE	278	L 0-2	
3	21.08	UNIB P	A	Bamber Bridge	335	W 1-0	Fee 40
4	23.08	UNIB P	H	WHITBY TOWN	286	W 2-1	Tonks 5, Robshaw 50
5	28.08	UNIB P	A	Runcorn	279	W 3-1	Day 55, Tonks 77 85
6	30.08	UNIB P	H	BARROW	486	D 0-0	
7	04.09	UNIB P	H	LEIGH RMI	316	W 3-1	Day 63 78, David 71
8	07.09	UNIB P	A	Blyth Spartans	318	L 2-3	Tonks 50, Thorpe 78
9	11.09	UNIB P	A	Winsford United	151	W 2-1	Robshaw 67, Day 90
	13.09	ULC 1G	H	BRADFORD PARK AVENUE	240	D 0-0	
	18.09	FAC Q2	H	LOUTH UNITED	244	W 2-0	Robshaw 50, David 63
10	20.09	UNIB P	H	BLYTH SPARTANS	259	W 2-0	Nicholson 56, Day 69
11	25.09	UNIB P	H	STALYBRIDGE CELTIC	353	L 0-1	
12	28.09	UNIB P	A	Whitby Town	363	W 1-0	Haran 39
	02.10	FAC Q3	A	Ossett Town	590	D 0-0	
	04.10	FAC Q3 r	H	OSSETT TOWN	425	W 4-1	Day 18 39, Robshaw 36, Haran 87
	09.10	FAT 1	H	COLWYN BAY	380	W 2-0	Robshaw 18 31
	12.10	ULC G11	A	Ossett Town	210	W 3-1	Bradshaw 61, Wilson 75, Green 83
	16.10	FAC Q4	A	Southport	1,310	D 1-1	Robshaw 13
	19.10	FAC Q4 r	H	SOUTHPORT	872	L 0-2	
13	23.10	UNIB P	A	Hyde United	552	W 3-2	Thorpe 18 57, Day 75
14	25.10	UNIB P	H	GATESHEAD	300	D 1-1	Day 31
15	30.10	UNIB P	H	LANCASTER CITY	289	D 0-0	
	02.11	ULC GG	A	Worksop Town	312	D 1-1	Wood 90
16	06.11	UNIB P	A	Spennymoor United	279	W 3-2	Nicholson 52[p], Robshaw 61, Day 71
	08.11	ULC GG	H	LINCOLN UNITED	182	L 0-2	
17	12.11	UNIB P	H	WORKSOP TOWN	371	L 1-2	David 39
	13.11	S&H SC1	A	Thorpe Hesley	68	W 6-3	Hamlet 8 87, **Calcutt 3** (27 39 44), Green 43
18	20.11	UNIB P	A	Hucknall Town	298	L 0-2	
	27.11	FAT 2	A	Stafford Rangers	605	W 4-1	Robshaw 60, Calcutt 79, Boughey 89[og], Day 90
	07.12	S&H SC2	H	MALTBY MAIN	100	W *3-1	Haran 26, Calcutt 100, Robshaw 111
19	14.12	UNIB P	A	Frickley Athletic	189	D 0-0	
20	17.12	UNIB P	A	Worksop Town	448	W 1-0	Wilson 47
21	27.12	UNIB P	H	GUISELEY	498	D 1-1	Robshaw 80
22	03.01	UNIB P	A	Leigh RMI	419	L 0-1	
23	08.01	UNIB P	A	Droylsden	321	D 1-1	Fee 57
	15.01	FAT 3	H	FRICKLEY ATHLETIC	416	W 2-1	Robshaw 25, Day 45
	18.01	Unifilla QF	A	Guiseley	195	D 1-1	Hamlet 67
24	22.01	UNIB P	A	Stalybridge Celtic	418	D 0-0	
	24.01	Unifilla QFR	H	GUISELEY	142	D 2-2	Hamlet 20, Fee 68 Won 3-2 after penalties
	05.02	FAT 4	A	Southport	1272	L 0-2	
25	08.02	UNIB P	A	Gainsborough Trinity	438	L 1-2	Robshaw 9
26	12.02	UNIB P	H	WINSFORD UNITED	206	W 3-2	Day 1, Hamlet 86, Nicholson 89
27	14.02	UNIB P	H	GAINSBOROUGH TRINITY	198	D 0-0	
28	19.02	UNIB P	A	Barrow	1175	W 2-0	Wilson 21, Bradshaw 60
29	26.02	UNIB P	H	LEEK TOWN	238	D 0-0	
	04.03	Unifilla SF	H	COLWYN BAY	182	W 6-2	Wood 21, Bradshaw 35 51, Calcutt 76 83, Fee 85
	07.03	S&H SC QF	A	Parkgate	98	W 3-1	Calcutt 64, Bradshaw 69, Bambrook 87
30	11.03	UNIB P	H	HYDE UNITED	301	L 0-1	
31	18.03	UNIB P	H	Marine	382	L 1-3	Nicholson 63[p]
32	20.03	UNIB P	H	BAMBER BRIDGE	201	W 3-0	David 24, Thorpe 34, Day 47
33	25.03	UNIB P	H	FRICKLEY ATHLETIC	528	L 1-3	Bambrook 38
	27.03	Unifilla Final	A	Hyde United	602	L 0-2	
34	01.04	UNIB P	H	RUNCORN	196	W 1-0	Stratford 58
35	06.04	UNIB P	A	Leek Town	173	W 3-1	Robshaw 48, Day 72, Nicholson 75(p)
36	08.04	UNIB P	H	COLWYN BAY	163	L 1-2	Day 78
37	15.04	UNIB P	A	Bishop Auckland	216	D 1-1	Bradshaw 77
38	17.04	UNIB P	H	DROYLSDEN	374	W 1-0	David 33
	20.04	S&H SC SF	A	Worksop Town	324	W 2-1	Bradshaw 6, Tonks 43
39	22.04	UNIB P	H	SPENNYMOOR UTD.	291	W 2-0	Day 9, OG (Stranger) 36
40	24.04	UNIB P	A	Guiseley	270	D 1-1	Day 81
41	26.04	UNIB P	H	BISHOP AUCKLAND	181	W 2-0	David 52, Day 78
42	29.04	UNIB P	A	Gateshead	254	W 1-0	Wilson 9
43	01.05	UNIB P	H	HUCKNALL TOWN	248	D 1-1	Day 3
	03.05	S&H SC Final	A	Frickley Athletic	478	L 0-3	
44	06.05	UNIB P	A	Lancaster City	271	L 1-2	Wilson 19

PLAYING SQUAD

GOALKEEPERS: Paul Cuss (Huddersfield)

DEFENDERS: Nicky Wood (Huddersfield), Simon Jones (Local football), Steve Nicholson (Farsley Celtic), Richard Walker (Youth)

MIDFIELDERS: Miles Thorpe (Frickley Ath), Gary Hatto (Frickley Ath), Simeon Bambrook (Garforth T), Steve Smith (Sheffield FC), Paul David (Bradley R)

FORWARDS: Jamie Robshaw (Denaby U), Charlie Bradshaw (Droylsden), Danny Day (Ossett Alb)

FRICKLEY ATHLETIC

CLUB OFFICIALS

Chairman: **Mike Twiby**
Tel: 01977 648070
Financial Secretary: **D Fisher**
Tel: 01977 643316 B
Secretary / Treasurer: **D Fisher**
31 Vickers Ave., South Elmsall WF9 3LW.
Tel: 01977 643316

FOOTBALL MANAGEMENT TEAM

Manager: Stuart Barraclough
Tel: 01977 609748

FACT FILE

Formed: 1910
Nickname: The Blues
Sponsors: Next Distributions
Colours: All blue
Change colours: Yellow & black.
Midweek home matchday: Tuesday
Reserves' League: None

GROUND

Westfield Lane, South Elmsall, Pontefract   Tel/Fax: 01977 642460
Directions: Follow signs for South Elmsall from A1 and A638. Left at Superdrug warehouse, right at T junction and immediately left up Westfield Lane. Left into Oxford Road (opposite Westfield Hotel) - ground at bottom on right. Two miles from South Elmsall (BR).
Capacity: 6,000   Cover: 2,500   Seats: 800
Clubhouse: On ground open matchdays, food available.
Club Shop: Yes

Pages: 40 Price: £1
Editor: S Pennock Tel: 01302 835956
Local Press: South Yorks Times, Hemsworth & South Elmsall Express. Local Radio: Radio Sheffield, Radio Hallam, Radio Leeds.

PREVIOUS   Leagues: Sheffield; Yorkshire 22-24; Midland Counties 24-33 34-60 70-76;Cheshire County 60-70; Northern Premier 76-80; GMV Conference (Alliance Premier) 80-87.   Name: Frickley Colliery

CLUB RECORDS   **Attendance:** 6,500 v Rotherham United, FA Cup First Round 1971.
Goalscorer: K Whiteley. **Defeat:** 0-4 **Fee Paid:** £1,800.
Fee Received: £12,500 for Paul Shirtliff (Boston Utd) & £12,500 for Russ Wilcox (Northampton)

BEST SEASON   **FA Cup:** 3rd Rd 1985-86 (1-3 v Rotherham H).2nd Rd 84-85 (0-1 at Darlington). 1st Rd 36-37 57-58 63-64 71-72 73-74 83-84 86-87 88-89. League clubs defeated: Hartlepool United 85-86.   **FA Trophy:** Quarter-Finals 84-85.

HONOURS   Alliance Premier Lg R-up 85-86, Midland Counties Lg R-up 72-73 (Lg Cup 75-76),Yorkshire Lg R-up 23-24, Sheffield & Hallamshire Senior Cup 27-28 56-57 60-6162-63 66-67 78-79 85-86 87-88 89-90, Sheffield Assoc. Lg 20-21 (R-up 11-12).
Players Progressing: Dennis Smith & Jack Brownsword (Hull1946), Stan Scrimshaw (Halifax 1947), William Callaghan (Aldershot 1949), Leo Dickens 1950), John Ashley & Graham Caulfield (York 1950 & 67), Ron Barritt(Leeds 1951), John Pickup (Bradford PA 1955), Tom Hymers & Arthur Ashmore &Stewart Gray (Doncaster 1958 & 66 & 78), Colin Roberts (Bradford City 1959),Derek Downing (Middlesbrough 1965), Graham Reed & Russell Wilcox (Northampton1985 & 86), Will Foley (Swansea 1986), Gary Brook (Newport 1987), Wayne Scargill (Bradford City 94-95), Andy Hayward (Rotherham Utd.).

Frickley Atheltic after winning the Sheffield Senior Cup - **Back Row:** Ian Thompson, Paul Haywood, Ian Edge, Derek O'Connor, Scott Collins, Rob Hanby, dave Wilson, Mark Earnshaw, Gary Duffy, Mick Geoghegan, Graham Wrenthorpe.
Front: Mick Thompson, Nicky Cranson, Marc Heckingbottom, Andy Hayward, Gary Hatto, Duane Beckett, Chris Hilton.

Match Facts 1999-00

	Date	Comp.	H/A	Opponents	Att.	Result	Goalscorers
1	14.08	UNIB P	A	Winsford United	160	W 2 - 1	Haywood 18, Edge 70
2	17.08	UNIB P	H	STALYBRIDGE CELTIC	152	D 1 - 1	Gardner 87
3	21.08	UNIB P	H	LEEK TOWN	199	D 1 - 1	Thompson 90
4	24.08	UNIB P	A	Spennymoor United	207	L 2 - 3	Cooper 68[og], Hayward 77
5	28.08	UNIB P	A	Lancaster City	213	L 0 - 2	
6	30.08	UNIB P	H	WORKSOP TOWN	283	L 1 - 3	Duffty 40
7	04.09	UNIB P	A	Droylsden	237	D 1 - 1	Collins 45
8	07.09	UNIB P	H	LEIGH RMI	151	L 2 - 4	Hatto 45, 88[p]
	14.09	ULC 1G	A	Gainsborough Trinity	339	L 0 - 1	
	18.09	FAC Q2	H	BEDLINGTON TERRIERS	206	L 0 - 1	
9	21.09	UNIB P	H	BISHOP AUCKLAND	141	W 4 - 2	Hayward 13 26, Thompson 22, Beckett 63
10	25.09	UNIB P	A	Bamber Bridge	311	L 1 - 2	Collins 82
	28.09	ULC G10	H	LINCOLN UNITED	150	W 4 - 1	Collins 40 74, Thompson 63, Hayward 86
11	02.10	UNIB P	H	HYDE UNITED	145	W 3 - 1	**Hayward 3** (36 61 82)
12	05.10	UNIB P	A	Hucknall Town	229	L 1 - 2	Hatto 43
	09.10	FAT 1	H	ASHTON UNITED	142	D 1 - 1	Beckett 90
	11.10	FAT 1 r	A	Ashton United	142	W 4 - 2	Hatto 75 107[p], Thompson 90, Hayward 115
13	16.10	UNIB P	A	Leek Town	300	W 2 - 1	Hatto 17, Hayward 47
14	23.10	UNIB P	H	COLWYN BAY	154	W 4 - 1	Thompson 25, Brewster 78 80, Duffty 88
15	26.10	UNIB P	A	Blyth Spartans	316	L 1 - 4	Collins 74
16	30.10	UNIB P	A	Marine	231	L 0 - 1	
17	06.11	UNIB P	H	WINSFORD UNITED	144	W 3 - 1	Hayward 10 60, Thompson 58
	09.11	ULC GF	A	Whitby Town	217	W 2 - 0	Hatto 30, Brewater 90
	12.11	Sheff.SC1	H	DAVY	90	W 3 - 1	Brewster 41 45, Duffty 80
18	16.11	UNIB P	H	HUCKNALL TOWN	106	W 3 - 2	Hatto 45[p], Hayward 53, Thompson 64
19	20.11	UNIB P	A	Whitby Town	306	L 0 - 3	
	23.11	ULC GF	H	GATESHEAD	154	W 3 - 1	Hayward 19 74, Thompson 76
	27.11	FAT 2	H	DROYLSDEN	173	W 4 - 3	**Hayward 3** (39 62 84), Thompson 54
20	04.12	UNIB P	A	Hyde United	303	W 3 - 2	Collins 58, Hayward 69, Foster 83[og]
	08.12	Sheff. SC2	H	PHOENIX	46	W 4 - 1	Jones, Beckett(2), Hayward
21	11.12	UNIB P	H	BARROW	257	L 2 - 5	Hayward 20, Hatto 61
22	14.12	UNIB P	H	EMLEY	189	D 0 - 0	
23	18.12	UNIB P	A	Runcorn	203	L 1 - 2	Jones 19
24	27.12	UNIB P	H	DROYLSDEN	152	L 0 - 4	
25	03.01	UNIB P	A	Worksop Town	505	L 0 - 4	
	15.01	FAT 3	A	Emley	416	L 1 - 2	Hayward 33
	22.01	ULC QF	H	MARINE	179	W 2 - 1	Hayward 45, Hatto 67
26	29.01	UNIB P	A	Colwyn Bay	195	L 0 - 1	
27	01.02	UNIB P	H	GAINSBOROUGH TRINITY	241	D 0 - 0	
28	05.02	UNIB P	A	Barrow	1073	L 0 - 2	
29	08.02	UNIB P	A	Guiseley	156	W 1 - 0	Colcano 53[og]
30	12.02	UNIB P	H	WHITBY TOWN	178	W 2 - 1	Hayward 83, Beckett 88
31	15.02	UNIB P	H	SPENNYMOOR UNITED	144	D 1 - 1	Hatto 61
32	19.02	UNIB P	A	Leigh RMI	241	L 0 - 5	
33	26.02	UNIB P	A	Gainsborough Trinity	342	W 2 - 1	Hayward 19, Hanby 84
	04.03	LC SF	H	LANCASTER CITY	230	L 2 - 3	Thompson 47, Duffty 53
	08.03	Sheff. SC QF	H	DONCASTER ROVERS	428	W 2 - 0	Thompson 37, Hayward 78
34	11.03	UNIB P	H	LANCASTER CITY	136	W 3 - 2	Thompson 29 70, Beckett 51
35	15.03	UNIB P	A	Gateshead	204	L 0 - 2	
36	18.03	UNIB P	A	Stalybridge Celtic	309	W 3 - 2	Earnshaw 28, Hatto 57, Hayward 74
37	25.03	UNIB P	A	Emley	528	W 3 - 1	Hayward 38, 42, Hanby 77
38	01.04	UNIB P	H	BLYTH SPARTANS	169	D 1 - 1	Heckingbottom 5
39	04.04	UNIB P	H	GUISELEY	150	D 2 - 2	Hurst 13, 26
40	08.04	UNIB P	A	Bishop Auckland	173	L 2 - 3	Hatto 50, Hanby 75
41	15.04	UNIB P	H	BAMBER BRIDGE	131	W 2 - 0	OG (Noblett) 81, Thompson 86
	20.04	S&H SC SF	A	Hallam	-	W *6 - 3	Duffy 39, Hilton 47, **Hayward 3** (59, 108, 113), Edge 102
42	22.04	UNIB P	H	GATESHEAD	179	L 1 - 4	Beckett 47
43	24.04	UNIB P	H	RUNCORN	106	L 1 - 2	Beckett 65
44	29.04	UNIB P	H	MARINE	137	D 2 - 2	Hayward 60, 86
	03.05	S&H SC F	N	Emley	478	W 3 - 0	Thompson 11, Edge 26, Hayward 44

PLAYING SQUAD

GOALKEEPERS: Matthew Wilkinson (Selby T)

DEFENDERS: Robert Hanby (Gainsborough T), Brendan West (Hallam), Paul haywood (Emley), Martin Fox (Pontefract Coll), Chris Hilton (Rotherham), James Watson (Grimethorpe MW)

MIDFIELDERS: Ian Edge (Sheffield FC), Nicky Cranston (Barrow), Nicky Green (Selby T), Andy Watson (Farsley Celtic), Mark Lafferty (Hull C)

FORWARDS: Andy Hayward (Barrow), Gary Duffty (Matlock T), Chris Hurst (Ilkeston T)

GAINSBOROUGH TRINITY

CLUB OFFICIALS

Chairman: **Pat Lobley**
President: **Ken Marsden.**
Secretary/Press Officer: **Frank Nicholson**
9 North Street, Morton,
Gainsborough, Lincs DN213AS.
Tel. 01427 615239, Fax 01427 615239.
Commercial Director: **Tim Hanson.**

FOOTBALL MANAGEMENT TEAM

Manager: Greg Fee
Asst Manager: Phil Tingay
Physio: Mick Gilbert

FACT FILE

Formed: 1873
Nickname: The Blues
Sponsors: Eastern Generation.
Colours: All Blue
Change colours: Green/black/green
Midweek home matchday: Tuesday
Reserve Team's League:

1999-00
Captain: Neil Allison
P.o.Y.: Steve Curry
Top scorer: Troy Bennett

GAINSBOROUGH TRINITY
versus
BURSCOUGH

2000/01 SEASON
26th August 2000

Main Club Sponsor
T BLAND
WELDING

THE BLUES

OFFICIAL MATCHDAY PROGRAMME Price £1

GROUND

The Northolme, Gainsborough, Lincs DN21 2QW
Tel: 01427 - 613295 (office) 615625 (club) 613295 (Fax)
Directions: The Northolme is situated opposite the Texaco and Fina petrol stations on the
A159 Gainsborough to Scunthorpe road. Two miles from Lea Road (BR)
Capacity: 3,500 Cover: 2,500 Seats: 515
Clubhouse: Executive `Club on the Park' (01427 615625) open Saturday matchday
lunchtimes. Restaurant facilities.
Club Shop: Yes, contact Nigel Tasker on 01522 542014.

Pages: 44 Price: £1
Editor: Basil Godley Tel: 01427 611612
Local Press: Gainsborough News,
Lincolnshire Echo.
Local Radio: BBC Radio Lincs, Lincs FM

PREVIOUS **Leagues:** Midland Counties 1889-96, 12-60, 61-68, Football Lge 1896-1912, Central Alliance 60-61.
Names: None **Grounds:** None

CLUB RECORDS **Attendance:** 9,760 v Scunthorpe Utd. Midland Lge. 1948.
Fee Paid: £3,000 for Stuart Lowe (Buxton 89-90). **Fee Received:** £30,000 for Tony James (Lincoln 1988).
Win: 7-0 v Fleetwood Town and Great Harwood Town. **Defeat:** 2-7 v Hyde Utd.

BEST SEASON **FA Cup:** 3rd Rd 1886-87, 1st Rd on 33 occasions. **FA Trophy:** 2nd Rd, 2nd replay86-87.

HONOURS Northern Premier Lge Cup 81-82 96-97 (R-up 71-72); Midland Co's Lge 1890-91,1927-28, 48-49, 66-67 (R-up 1891-92,
1895-96, 13-14, 28-29); Lincs Senior Cup 1889-90, 92-93, 94-95, 97-98, 1903-05, 06-07, 10-11, 46-49, 50-51, 57-59, 63-64

Players Progressing: Since 1980 - Stewart Evans (Sheffield Utd 80), Tony James, Ian Bowling & John Schofield (Lincoln 88), Dave
Redfern(Stockport 91), Richard Logan (Huddersfield 93), Glenn Humphries (Hull City).

Gainsborough Trinity - 2000-01 **Back Row:** Andy Sharpe, Chris James, Paul Watts, Steve Price, Steve Curry, Neil Allison,
Steve Williams, Alex Allen, Kevin Noteman. **Front:** Nick Limber, Ian Gore, Simon Drayton, Chris Newton, John Reed, Ian
McLean, Colin Hunter. Missing: Steve Circuit

Match Facts 1999-00

	Date	Comp.	H/A	Opponents	Att.	Result	Goalscorers
1	14.08	UNIB P	A	Droylsden	248	L 0 - 1	
2	17.08	UNIB P	H	LEEK TOWN	487	W 3 - 2	Diskin 6[og], Bennett 15, Circuit 39
3	21.08	UNIB P	H	HYDE UNITED	408	D 1 - 1	Bennett 65[p]
4	24.08	UNIB P	A	Stalybridge Celtic	381	L 0 - 2	
5	28.08	UNIB P	H	GATESHEAD	376	L 1 - 2	Charles 38
6	04.09	UNIB P	A	Marine	304	D 2 - 2	Saville 27, Norbury 48
7	07.09	UNIB P	H	BISHOP AUCKLAND	387	W 4 - 1	Circuit 34, Fothergill 44, Saville 51, Bennett 77[p]
8	11.09	UNIB P	H	Spennymoor United	171	W 2 - 0	Limber 17, Drayton 87
	14.09	ULC 1G	H	FRICKLEY ATHLETIC	339	W 1 - 0	Norbury 56
	18.09	FAC Q2	H	ECCLESHILL UNITED	340	W 2 - 0	Lacey 16, Bennett 90
9	21.09	UNIB P	A	Leek Town	265	L 2 - 3	Lacey 38, Bennett 90[p]
10	25.09	UNIB P	A	COLWYN BAY	328	W 2 - 0	Saville 26, Bennett 90
	02.10	FAC Q3	A	Droylsden	289	D 2 - 2	Sharman 14, Saville 83
	05.10	FAC Q3 r	H	DROYLSDEN	468	L 1 - 2	Saville 34
11	09.10	UNIB P	A	Winsford United	118	W 2 - 1	Drayton 13, Fothergill 40
	12.10	ULC G10	A	Lincoln United	262	L 1 - 3	Bennett 16
12	16.10	UNIB P	H	BARROW	456	L 1 - 3	Hume 9
13	19.10	UNIB P	A	Guiseley	274	W 3 - 1	Price 62 75, Housham 86
14	23.10	UNIB P	H	DROYLSDEN	400	W 2 - 1	Housham 72, Riley 88
15	26.10	UNIB P	H	HUCKNALL TOWN		W 5 - 2	Drayton 14, Reed 20, Housham 68, Riley 73, Bennett 83[p]
16	30.10	UNIB P	A	Barrow	1,032	D 1 - 1	Bennett 10
17	06.11	UNIB P	A	Leigh RMI	201	D 1 - 1	Reed 88
18	12.11	UNIB P	H	WHITBY TOWN	575	D 1 - 1	Reed 34
19	20.11	UNIB P	H	Blyth Spartans	347	D 1 - 1	Drayton 13
	27.11	FAT 2	A	Stalybridge Celtic	420	D 1 - 1	Fothergill 33
	30.11	FAT 2R	H	STALYBRIDGE CELTIC	429	L 1 - 3	Saville 76
20	11.12	UNIB P	A	Lancaster City	234	L 0 - 2	
21	27.12	UNIB P	H	WORKSOP TOWN	1231	W 2 - 0	Reed 27, Allen 88
22	03.01	UNIB P	A	Hucknall Town	425	L 0 - 1	
23	08.01	UNIB P	A	Whitby Town	489	L 1 - 2	Reed 28
24	15.01	UNIB P	A	Gateshead	312	W 1 - 0	Reed 38
25	22.01	UNIB P	H	SPENNYMOOR UNITED	394	W 4 - 0	Drayton 6 10, Woods 59, Saville 75
26	29.01	UNIB P	H	LANCASTER CITY	386	W 1 - 0	Drayton 15
27	01.02	UNIB P	A	Frickley Athletic	241	D 0 - 0	
28	05.02	UNIB P	A	Bamber Bridge	243	D 0 - 0	
29	08.02	UNIB P	H	EMLEY	438	W 2 - 1	Riley 59, Bennett 61
30	12.02	UNIB P	H	BLYTH SPARTANS	394	L 0 - 1	
31	14.02	UNIB P	A	Emley	198	D 0 - 0	
32	19.02	UNIB P	A	Hyde United	403	L 0 - 4	
33	26.02	UNIB P	H	FRICKLEY ATHLETIC	342	L 1 - 2	Circuit 87
34	04.03	UNIB P	H	WINSFORD UNITED	290	W 3 - 0	Allen 86, Saville 87, Drayton 89
35	11.03	UNIB P	H	MARINE	366	D 0 - 0	
36	14.03	UNIB P	H	GUISELEY	304	D 0 - 0	
37	18.03	UNIB P	A	Colwyn Bay	219	D 0 - 0	
38	25.03	UNIB P	H	BAMBER BRIDGE	284	W 1 - 0	Woods 82
39	01.04	UNIB P	H	LEIGH RMI	341	W 4 - 3	Williams 27, 55, Price 70, Limber 77
40	05.04	UNIB P	A	Bishop Auckland	190	D 0 - 0	
41	08.04	UNIB P	A	Runcorn	212	L 2 - 3	OG (Bennett) 68, Ruffer 72
42	11.04	UNIB P	H	STALYBRIDGE CELTIC	345	D 1 - 1	Williams 34
43	22.04	UNIB P	H	RUNCORN	341	D 1 - 1	Price 30 (p)
44	24.04	UNIB P	A	Worksop Town	621	L 1 - 2	Woods 64

PLAYING SQUAD

GOALKEEPERS: Steve Curry (Hatfield Main)

DEFENDERS: Steve Price (Leek T), Greg Fee (Emley), Neil Allison (Woodland Wellington (Singapore)), Nicky Limber (Weymouth), Ian McLean (Oldham), Chris James (Leek T), Ian Gore (Boreham Wood)

MIDFIELDERS: Steve Circuit (Leek T), John Reed (Ethnikos (Greece)), Colin Hunter (Hednesford T), Simon Drayton (Limestone R), Kevin Riley (Leek T)

FORWARDS: Alex Allen (Brodsworth Welfare), Kevin Noteman (Ilkeston T), Paul Watts (Boston U), Steve Williams (Kettering T)

GATESHEAD

CLUB OFFICIALS

President: **J C Thomas**
Chairman: **John Gibson**
Vice Chairman: **Mark Donnelly**
General Manager: **Mark Donnelly**
Secretary: **Arthur Waggott**
Press Officer: **Andy Wilson**

FACT FILE
Founded: 1930
Nickname: The Tynesiders
Sponsors: Cameron Hall Developments Ltd
Club colours: White with black
trim/black/white
Change colours: All yellow
Midweek home matchday: Wednesday
Reserves League: Vaux Wearside League

For up to the minute news,
results, fixtures,
plus general facts & figures
from the world of
non-league football

log on to

www.nlfootball.com

FOOTBALL MANAGEMENT TEAM
Manager : Matt Pearson
Physio: Bev Dougherty

GROUND   International Stadium, Neilson Road, Gateshead, NE10 0EF.
Tel: 0191 478 3883   Fax : 0191 477 1315.
Directions: From the South follow A1(M) to Granada services (Birtley),take right hand fork marked A194(M) (Tyne Tunnel, South Shields) follow A194 to first roundabout, turn left onto A184 - then 3 miles to stadium. Turn right at traffic lights into Neilson Road.   BY RAIL to Newcastle Central Station,transfer to the Metro System and then to Gateshead Stadium.
Capacity: 11,795   Seats: 11,795   Cover: 3,300
Clubhouse: Bar inside Tyne & Wear stand open before, during and after matches.The Stadium P.H. adjacent to ground. **Club Shop:** Sells full range of souvenirs, badges, pro- grammes & fanzines.Contact: Mike Coulson (0191 478 3883)

Programme
Pages: 36   Price: £1.20
Editor: Andy Wilson (0191 284 2235)
Local Press: Gateshead Post, Newcastle Chronicle & Echo, Sunderland Echo,Sunday Sun.
Local Radio: BBC Radio Newcastle, Metro FM, Century Radio.

PREVIOUS   **Leagues:** Football League - Div. 3 N. 30-58, Div.4 58-60, Northern Counties League 60-62, North Regional League 1962-1968, Northern Premier 68-70, 73-83,85-86, 87-90; Wearside 70-71; Midland Lge 71-72; Alliance Premier (Conference)83-85, 86-87, 90-98.   **Grounds:** Redheugh Park - 1930-1971

CLUB RECORDS   **Attendance:** 11,750 v Newcastle United (Pre-Season Friendly. 7th August 95)
Win: 8-0 v Netherfield, Northern Premier League.   **Defeat:** 0-9 v Sutton United, 22.09.90, GMVC.
Career goalscorer: Bob Topping   **Career appearances:** Simon Smith, 450, 85-94
Fee paid: £9,000 for Paul Cavell (Dagenham &Redbridge).   **Fee received:** For Kenny Cramman from Rushden & D.

BEST SEASON   **FA Cup:** Quarter Final, 1952-53.   **FA Trophy:** Quarter Final, 0-1 v Wycombe W. (A) 13.3.93

HONOURS   Football League Div. 3 North R-up 31-32, 49-50; Northern Premier - Champions82-83, 85-86; Runners-up 89-90; Northern Premier League Cup R-up 89-90;Multipart Shield 85-86.

Players Progressing: Osher Williams(Southampton, Stockport, Port Vale, Preston), John McGinley (Sunderland,Lincoln), Billy Askew (Hull City, Newcastle United), Lawrie Pearson (Hull City,Port Vale), Ian Johnson (Northampton Town), Ken Davies (Stockport), Kenny Lowe(Birmingham C., Barnet, Darlington, Stoke C.)

Relieved defenders can only watch as Gateshead's 'keeper Adrian Swan makes a fine save in the local clash with Blyth Spartans.   **Photo:** Graham Brown

Match Facts 1999-00

#	Date	Comp.	H/A	Opponents	Att.	Result	Goalscorers
1	14.08	UNIB P	H	HYDE UNITED	276	L 2-3	Fletcher 43 55
2	21.08	UNIB P	A	Leigh RMI	215	L 1-3	Thompson 75
3	24.08	UNIB P	A	Guiseley	207	D 1-1	Fletcher 90
4	28.08	UNIB P	A	Gainsborough Trinity	376	W 2-1	Bowey 12[p], Preen 53
5	30.08	UNIB P	H	BLYTH SPARTANS	497	W 3-0	Preen 50, Alderson 77, Fletcher 89
6	04.09	UNIB P	H	COLWYN BAY	253	W 6-0	Preen 18, Alderson 33 71, Fletcher 34, Bowey 42 90
7	07.09	UNIB P	A	Whitby Town	389	W 2-0	Fletcher 20, Preen 28
8	11.09	UNIB P	A	Stalybridge Celtic	420	L 0-1	
	15.09	ULC 1G	H	BLYTH SPARTANS	215	W 4-1	Bowey 13, Fletcher 57, Alderson 75, Moss 87
	18.09	FAC Q2	H	WINSFORD UNITED	226	W 3-0	Hall 35, Alderson 52, Fletcher 67
9	25.09	UNIB P	H	DROYLSDEN	235	D 1-1	Preen 59
10	28.09	UNIB P	A	Worksop Town	409	W 2-1	Alderson 23, Raitt 87
	02.10	FAC Q3	H	BRIGG TOWN	237	W 4-0	Preen 10, Raitt 68, Thompson 85 89
	05.10	ULC G14	A	Whitley Bay	207	W 1-0	Preen 44
	09.10	FAT 1	H	BRADFORD PARK AVE.	254	W 4-1	Alderson 5, Preen 31, Thompson 82 89
	16.10	FAC Q4	A	Telford United	611	D 0-0	
	20.10	FAC Q4 r	H	TELFORD UNITED	318	W 2-1	Bowey 75, Thompson 78
11	23.10	UNIB P	H	WINSFORD UNITED	256	W 2-0	Alderson 33, Bowey 90[p]
12	25.10	UNIB P	A	Emley	300	D 1-1	Preen 77
	30.10	FAC 1	A	Cambridge United	2,970	L 0-1	
	03.11	ULC GF	H	WHITBY TOWN	180	L 2-3	Fletcher 40, Bowey 89[p]
13	06.11	UNIB P	A	Lancaster City	365	D 1-1	Thompson 85
14	10.11	UNIB P	A	Bishop Auckland	288	D 1-1	Lynch 56
15	12.11	UNIB P	H	BAMBER BRIDGE	212	W 2-1	Preen 22, Alderson 84
16	15.11	UNIB P	H	SPENNYMOOR UNITED	279	W 6-2	Alderson 2, Lynch 16, Thompson 32, Proudlock 40, Bowey 73, Preen 86
17	20.11	UNIB P	A	Runcorn	232	L 0-2	
	23.11	ULC GF	A	Frickley Athletic	154	L 1-3	Fletcher 82
	27.11	FAT 2	A	Altrincham	578	L 0-1	
18	04.12	UNIB P	H	LEEK TOWN	236	W 2-1	Dundas 25[og], Preen 80
19	07.12	UNIB P	H	BARROW	358	D 0-0	
20	18.12	UNIB P	H	LANCASTER CITY	210	W 4-0	Bowey 12, Thompson 19 76, Fletcher 73
21	27.12	UNIB P	A	Blyth Spartans	793	W 1-0	Ainsley 60
22	03.01	UNIB P	H	WHITBY TOWN	404	D 0-0	
23	08.01	UNIB P	A	Leek Town	316	W 2-1	Preen 8, Alderson 76
24	15.01	UNIB P	H	GAINSBOROUGH TRINITY	312	L 0-1	
	22.01	Unifilla QF	A	Hyde United	314	L 0-2	
25	29.01	UNIB P	H	LEIGH RMI	408	D 1-1	Fletcher 9
26	05.02	UNIB P	H	HUCKNALL TOWN	204	D 0-0	
27	12.02	UNIB P	A	Bamber Bridge	292	W 3-0	Bowey 14 25, Fletcher 33
28	16.02	UNIB P	H	GUISELEY	209	W 3-1	Preen 8, Alderson 17, Kitchen 75
29	19.02	UNIB P	A	Marine	459	D 1-1	Preen 57
30	26.02	UNIB P	H	STALYBRIDGE CELTIC	278	W 2-0	Lynch 7, Ainsley 12
31	04.03	UNIB P	H	RUNCORN	268	L 0-3	
32	11.03	UNIB P	A	Spennymoor United	305	W 2-0	Preen 19, Tremble 45
33	15.03	UNIB P	A	FRICKLEY ATHLETIC	204	W 2-0	Thompson 22, Lynch 39
34	18.03	UNIB P	A	Hyde United	522	D 1-1	Thompson 90
35	25.03	UNIB P	A	Hucknall Town	263	L 0-1	
36	01.04	UNIB P	A	Colwyn Bay	213	W 3-1	Proudlock 16, Thompson 71, Fletcher 79
37	08.04	UNIB P	H	WORKSOP TOWN	286	W 3-2	Dalton 30, Hall 61, Fletcher 65
38	11.04	UNIB P	A	Droylsden	147	D 2-2	Fletcher 21, Bowey 44 (p)
39	15.04	UNIB P	H	MARINE	281	W 2-0	Fletcher 20, Bowey 74
40	22.04	UNIB P	A	Frickley Athletic	179	W 4-1	Dalton 14, Hall 70, Preen 75, 86
41	24.04	UNIB P	H	BISHOP AUCKLAND	387	D 0-0	
42	29.04	UNIB P	H	EMLEY	254	L 0-1	
43	01.05	UNIB P	A	Barrow	1542	W 5-3	**Fletcher 3** (15, 65, 89), Proudlock 24, Preen 41
44	06.05	UNIB P	A	Winsford United	145	W 3-1	Bowey 8, Preen 26, 66

PLAYING SQUAD

GOALKEEPERS: Adrian Swan (Spennymoor U)

DEFENDERS: Tony Hall (Kilkenny C), Graham Pepper (Spennymoor U), Sam Kitchen (Doncaster R), Simon Bates (Spennymoor U), Chris Lynch (Bishop Auckland), Richie Watson (Spennymoor U), Phil Ross (Bishop Auckland)

MIDFIELDERS: Steve Bowey (Forest Green R), Don Riatt (Spennymoor U), Nicky Scaife (Dunston Fed), Paul Proudlock (Carlisle), Paul Thompson (Stevenage B)

FORWARDS: Richie Alderson (Blyth Spartans), Gareth McAlinden (Scarborough), Paul Dalton (Huddersfield), Steve Preen (Tow Law T), Wayne Edgcumbe (Blyth Spartans)

HUCKNALL TOWN

CLUB OFFICIALS

Chairman: **JohnBeharall**
Vice-Chairman: **Glen Lathell**
President: **Andy Stewart**
Secretary: **Brian Scothern**
95 Brookfield Ave., Shortwood Estate,
Hucknall, Notts NG15 6FF
Tel: 0115 956 3151

FOOTBALL MANAGEMENT TEAM

Manager: John Ramshaw
Assistant Manager: Billy Millar
Physio: Ken Burton

FACT FILE
Founded: 1987
Nickname: The Town
Sponsors: Doff-Portland
Colours: Yellow/black/black
Change colours: All red
Midweek matches: Tuesday
Reserves' League: Mid Reg Alliance Prem
1999-00 Captain: Dave McCarthy
P.o.Y.: Kieran Pegley
Top Scorers: PaulTomlinson & Simon
Martin(13)

Pages: 92   Price: £1.20
Editor/Press Officer: Simon Matters
Tel: 0115 9525338

Local Press : Hucknall & Bulwell Dispatch;
Nottm Evening Post; Nottm Football Post

GROUND   Watnall Road, Hucknall, Notts NG15 7LP Tel: 0115 956 1253
Directions: M1 jct 27, A608 to lights, right onto A611 to Hucknall, right at r'bout (new
by-pass), over next r'bout, right at next r'bout into Watnall Rd -grd on right.
From M1 jct 26 follow Nottm signs to lights on island, left onto A610, right at
Three Ponds Pub onto B600 towards Watnall, 200 yds past Queens Head turn
right signed Hucknall, follow over m'way and past Rolls Royce -ground on left.
Nearest station Hucknall
Capacity: 5,000   Seats: 270   Cover: 2,200   Floodlights: Yes
Clubhouse: Every night and weekend lunchtimes   **Club Shop:** Yes

PREVIOUS   **Leagues:** Bulwell & Dist. 46-59 60-65; Central All. 59-60; Notts Spartan 65-70; Notts All. 70-89; Central Midlands 89-92
Northern Counties East 92-97, Unibond 97-
Ground: Wigwam Park 46-54 Name: Hucknall Colliery Welfare (until pit closure 1988)

CLUB RECORDS   **Attendance:** 1,305 v Macclesfield, FA Cup 2nd Qual 26/9/92.   **Appearances:** Paul Tomlinson 210(80s -90s)
Goals: Maurice Palethorpe approx 400 (80s & (0s)

BEST SEASON   **FA Cup:** 3rd Q Rd v Stourbridge 98-99 lost 0-3 after 0-0
FA Vase: Quarter Final 85-86   **FA Trophy:** 3rd Rd v Redditch 98-99

HONOURS   Northern Counties (East) Lg Div 1 R-up 92-93 (Lg Cup 93-94 96-97 97-98) Presidents Cup 96-97;
Central Mids Lg x2 89-91 R-up 91-92, Lg Cup x3 89-92; Notts All.Sen (4) 76-78 87-89, Div 1 Div 1 72-73 80-81 86-87
Div 2 70-71; Intermediate Cup 72-73 78-81 84-84; Lge Cup 78-79;
Notts Snr Cup 84-85 90-91 97-98 99-00, R-up 83-84 85-86 87-88 89-90 98-99; Unibond Lg.: Div 1 R-Up 98-99

Midfield action from from Hucknall's 3-2 win in the 1st Round of the FA Umbro Trophy away to Lincoln United   **Photo:** Julie Artiss

Match Facts 1999-00

	Date	Comp.	H/A	Opponents	Att.	Result	Goalscorers
1	14.08	UNIB P	A	Marine	233	L 0 - 3	
2	17.08	UNIB P	H	WORKSOP TOWN	690	L 0 - 1	
3	21.08	UNIB P	H	DROYLSDEN	180	D 3 - 3	Martin 41 56, Maddison 85
4	24.08	UNIB P	A	Leek Town	267	D 2 - 2	Pascoe 45, Maddison 58
5	28.08	UNIB P	H	STALYBRIDGE CELTIC	275	W 4 - 0	White 44, Martin 60 78, Daton 65
6	01.09	UNIB P	A	Bishop Auckland	236	L 1 - 3	White 46
7	04.09	UNIB P	A	Winsford United	132	W 2 - 1	Orton 77 80
8	07.09	UNIB P	H	HYDE UNITED	319	L 0 - 1	
9	11.09	UNIB P	H	BAMBER BRIDGE	225	W 2 - 1	Hoy 42 55
	14.09	ULC 1G	A	Worksop Town	272	L 0 - 1	
	18.09	FAC Q2	A	Nantwich Town	98	L 0 - 1	
10	21.09	UNIB P	H	WHITBY TOWN		W 3 - 2	Martin 32 70, Orton 38
11	25.09	UNIB P	A	Runcorn	315	W 1 - 0	White 66
	28.09	ULC G9	H	EASTWOOD TOWN	250	L 1 - 2	Williams 62
12	02.10	UNIB P	H	LEEK TOWN	285	W 2 - 0	Cooke 69, Martin 80
13	05.10	UNIB P	H	FRICKLEY ATHLETIC	229	W 2 - 1	Williams 25, Cooke 80
	09.10	FAT 1	A	Lincoln United	215	W 3 - 2	Gray 9[og], Roberts 24, Martin 90
14	12.10	UNIB P	H	GUISELEY	328	D 1 - 1	Roberts 69
15	16.10	UNIB P	H	LEIGH RMI	259	L 1 - 2	Orton 39
16	19.10	UNIB P	A	Blyth Spartans	275	L 0 - 1	
17	23.10	UNIB P	H	BISHOP AUCKLAND	215	W 1 - 0	Orton 55
18	26.10	UNIB P	A	Gainsborough Trinity		L 2 - 5	Hoy 28, Cooke 53
19	30.10	UNIB P	A	Leigh RMI	209	L 0 - 1	
20	06.11	UNIB P	A	Worksop Town	464	L 0 - 1	
21	16.11	UNIB P	A	Frickley Athletic	106	L 2 - 3	Rankin 21, White 75
22	20.11	UNIB P	H	EMLEY	298	W 2 - 0	Martin 67, White 88
	27.11	FAT 2	A	Morecambe	736	L 1 - 6	Martin 66
23	04.12	UNIB P	H	LANCASTER CITY	206	L 1 - 3	Martin 12
24	27.12	UNIB P	A	Whitby Town	611	L 1 - 2	Woodcock 65
25	03.01	UNIB P	H	GAINSBOROUGH TRINITY	425	W 1 - 0	Taylor 44
26	08.01	UNIB P	A	Guiseley	310	W 2 - 1	Rankin 65, Tomlinson 68
27	15.01	UNIB P	H	WINSFORD UNITED	220	W 4 - 0	Tomlinson 7 33, Woodcock 86, Brown 88
	18.01	NSC 3	H	GEDLING TOWN	165	W 3 - 0	Rankin 6, Roberts 65[p], Tomlinson 70
28	22.01	UNIB P	A	Droylsden	262	D 0 - 0	
29	05.02	UNIB P	A	Gateshead	204	D 0 - 0	
30	12.02	UNIB P	H	RUNCORN	265	D 1 - 1	Regis 84
	16.02	NSC QF	H	ARNOLD TOWN	303	W 2 - 1	Regis 90, Tomlinson 120
31	19.02	UNIB P	A	Spennymoor United	171	D 1 - 1	Martin 88
32	26.02	UNIB P	A	Colwyn Bay	243	L 0 - 2	
33	04.03	UNIB P	H	MARINE	273	W 2 - 0	Mayman 70, Tomlinson 88
34	11.03	UNIB P	A	Barrow	1054	L 2 - 4	Orton 62, Sear 73
35	18.03	UNIB P	A	Bamber Bridge	281	D 1 - 1	Tomlinson 45
36	21.03	UNIB P	H	BLYTH SPARTANS	218	L 0 - 1	
37	25.03	UNIB P	H	GATESHEAD	263	W 1 - 0	Cooke 39
38	01.04	UNIB P	A	Lancaster City	228	L 0 - 1	
	04.04	NSC SF	A	Dunkirk	184	W 2 - 1	Tomlinson 44, 88
39	08.04	UNIB P	H	SPENNYMOOR UNITED	160	D 0 - 0	
40	18.04	UNIB P	A	Stalybridge Celtic	204	L 1 - 2	Martin 82
41	22.04	UNIB P	A	Hyde United	553	L 3 - 4	Tomlinson 20, 22, Martin 27
42	24.04	UNIB P	H	BARROW	258	L 0 - 3	
43	01.05	UNIB P	A	Emley	248	D 1 - 1	Cooke 17
44	06.05	UNIB P	H	COLWYN BAY	168	D 2 - 2	Wilkinson 39, Roberts 50 (p)

PLAYING SQUAD

GOALKEEPERS: Dave McCarthy (Oakham U), James Mason (Arnold T)

DEFENDERS: Mark Place (Matlock T), Wayne Fairclough (Ilkeston T), Richard Taylor (Matlock T), Kieran Begley (Local football), Brian Horseman (Hinckley U)

MIDFIELDERS: Darryl Rankin (Alfreton T), Dale Wright (Ilkeston T), Jamie Roberts (Eastwood T), Chris White (Hinckley U), Russell Cooke (Notts Co), Jon Flint (Gedling T)

FORWARDS: Rob Orton (Gedling T), Paul Tomlinson (Eastwood T), Andy Morris (Rochdale), Dave Regis (Scunthorpe), Simon Martin (Lincoln U), Ricky Jowett (Rothwell T)

HYDE UNITED

Official Match Programme 1999/2000
Sponsored by tmi metals - the winning combination

CLUB OFFICIALS

Chairman: **S C Hartley**
Secretary / Press Officer: **Ray Stanley**
136 Lumn Road, Hyde, Cheshire SK14
1PR Tel No: 0161 366 5154
Commercial Team:**Rod Buxton & Ray Stanley**

FOOTBALL MANAGEMENT TEAM

Manager: Mike McKenzie
Coach: Osher Williams/I.Lamb
Physio: Dave Garlinge

FACT FILE

Formed: 1919
Nickname: The Tigers
Club Sponsors: T.M.I.Metals
Colours: All Red
Change colours: Yellow,blue,yellow
Midweek home matchday: Monday

Pages: 32 Price: £1.
Editor: M Dring

Local Press: North Cheshire Herald
& Hyde Reporter.
Local Radio: GMR, Picadilly.

GROUND

Tameside Stadium, Ewen Fields, Walker Lane, Hyde SK14 5PL (0161 368 1031).
Directions: On entering Hyde follow signs for Tameside Leisure Park - in Walker Lane take 2nd car park entrance nr Leisure Pool, follow road around to the stadium. Quarter of a mile from Newton (BR).
Capacity: 4,000Cover: 2,000Seats: 530
Clubhouse: (0161 368 1621). Open most nights, full facilities, 150 seats.Stewards: Lil & Doug. **Club Shop:** Replica shirts, scarves, sports shirts, baseball caps, bronx hats,badges.
Contact Ray Stanley (0161 366 5154) e-mail: raystanley@i12.com

PREVIOUS   **Leagues:** Lancs & Cheshire 19-21; Manchester 21-30; Cheshire County 30-68, 70-82; Northern Prem. 68-70
CLUB RECORDS   **Attendance:** 9,500 v Nelson, FA Cup 1952. **Scorer:** P O'Brien 247. **Appearances:** S Johnson 623.
   Defeat: (as Hyde F.C.) 0-26 v Preston North End, F.A. Cup.
   Fee Paid: £8,000 for Jim McCluskie (Mossley, 1989). **Fee Received:** £50.000 for Colin Little (Crewe Alexandra) 1995.

BEST SEASON   **FA Cup:** 1st Rd 54-55 (v Workington), 83-84 (v Burnley),94-95 v Darlington.
   FA Trophy: Semi Final 88-89 94-95 95-96

HONOURS   Prem Inter-Lge Cup R-up(2) 88-90; NPL R-up(2) 87-89, 99-00 (Lg Cup 85-86 88-89 95-96(R-up 83-84 94-95), Chal. Shield 96-97, (R-up 86-87 90-91); Cheshire Co. Lg(3)54-56 81-82 (Lg Cup 33-34 52-53 54-55 72-73 81-82, Lg Chal. Shield(2) 80-82; Manchester Lg(5) 20-23 28-29 29-30 (Lg (Gilgryst) Cup(4) 27-29 49-50 70-71);Cheshire Snr Cup 45-46 62-63 69-70 80-81 89-90 96-97; Manchester Prem. Cup 93-94, 94-95, 95-96, 98-99,Snr Cup 74-75, Int Cup 55-56 56-57(jt), Jnr Cup 21-22 68-69;Lancs & Cheshire F'lit Cup(2) 54-56; Ashton Chal. Cup(6) 30-34 39-40 47-48;Hyde Chal Cup(2) 27-29; Reporter Cup(3) 72-74 75-76; Gavin Nicholson Mem Trophy79-80; Lancs F'lit Trophy(2) 86-88; Edward Case Cup(4), Unifilla Cup Winners: 99-00.
   Players P rogressing: C McClelland & J Webber & P Barry (B'burn 1946 & 47 & 48),L Battrick (Manc. City 1968), J Hilton (Wrexham 1950), D Teece (Hull 1952), R Calderbank & William Bell & Neil Colbourne (R'dale 1953 & 74 & 80), Jeff Johnson (Stockport 1976), David Constantine & Donald Graham (Bury 1979), George Oghani (Bolton 1983), Kevin Glendon (Burnley 1983), Peter Coyne (Swindon 1984),Colin Little. (Crewe Alex. 1995),Lutel James (Bury)

Back Row: Mike McKenzie (manager), Brendan Aspinall, Gavin Salmon, Peter Band, Paul Taylor, Graham Bennett, Karl Marginson, Ally Pickering, Stuart Lamb, Ian Lamb (Coach). **Front:** John Foster, Steve Tobin, Neil Hall, Paul Robertson, Matty Taylor, Lloyd Richardson, Simon Yeo, Gus Wilson (Captain).   **Photo:** Don Goodwin

Match Facts 1999-00

	Date	Comp.	H/A	Opponents	Att.	Result	Goalscorers
1	14.08	UNIB P	A	Gateshead	276	W 3 - 2	Yeo 60, 85, Taylor 89[p]
2	16.08	UNIB P	H	WINSFORD UNITED	424	W 2 - 0	Aspinall 26, Yeo 73
3	21.08	UNIB P	A	Gainsborough Trinity	408	D 1 - 1	Yeo 41
4	24.08	UNIB P	A	Worksop Town	434	D 1 - 1	Aspinall 90
5	28.08	UNIB P	H	SPENNYMOOR UNITED	401	W 2 - 1	Brenchley 40, Yeo 52
6	30.08	UNIB P	H	DROYLSDEN	752	W 2 - 0	Yeo 12, Banim 35
7	04.09	UNIB P	A	Whitby Town	369	D 1 - 1	Banim 70
8	07.09	UNIB P	A	Hucknall Town	319	W 1 - 0	Moncrieffe 55
9	11.09	UNIB P	H	GUISELEY	414	W 2 - 0	Moncrieffe 52, Yeo 64
	13.09	ULC G5	H	TRAFFORD	372	D 2 - 2	Yeo 45, 51
	18.09	FAC Q2	H	CROOK TOWN	411	D 1 - 1	Taylor 4[p]
	22.09	FAC Q2 R	A	Crook Town	240	L 1 - 2	M Taylor 84
10	25.09	UNIB P	H	MARINE	552	D 1 - 1	Yeo 11
	28.09	Ches.SC1	A	Nantwich Town	72	W 4 - 3	Yeo 28, 110, Banim 83 115
11	02.10	UNIB P	A	Frickley Athletic	145	L 1 - 3	Walker 87
	05.10	ULC G5	A	Flixton	96	W 2 - 1	Yeo 49, 63
12	09.10	UNIB P	H	WORKSOP TOWN	518	D 0 - 0	
13	16.10	UNIB P	H	BLYTH SPARTANS	372	W 5 - 2	Yeo 3 (15, 2,2 44), Brenchley 49, Hulse 59
14	23.10	UNIB P	H	EMLEY	552	L 2 - 3	Hulse 40 58
15	25.10	UNIB P	H	BARROW	480	W 1 - 0	Walker 58
16	30.10	UNIB P	A	Blyth Spartans	412	W 4 - 3	Tobin 42, Hulse 3 (57, 70, 80)
	02.11	ULC GB	A	Bamber Bridge	237	L 0 - 2	
	08.11	ULC GB	A	ACCRINGTON STANLEY	305	L 1 - 3	Band 15
17	12.11	UNIB P	H	LANCASTER CITY	465	W 4 - 1	Hulse 51 82, Walker 87, Aspinall 89
	15.11	Ches.SC QF	H	CREWE ALEXANDRA	366	L 1 - 3	Banim 78
18	20.11	UNIB P	A	Leek Town	408	L 0 - 2	
	27.11	FAT 2	A	WHITLEY BAY	398	W 6 - 0	Yeo 5 (22 36 40 42 80), Banim 83
19	29.11	UNIB P	H	Runcorn	535	D 0 - 0	
20	04.12	UNIB P	H	FRICKLEY ATHLETIC	303	L 2 - 3	Banim 60, Yeo 81
21	11.12	UNIB P	A	Bishop Auckland	203	D 2 - 2	Hulse 60, Walker 88
22	27.12	UNIB P	H	STALYBRIDGE CELTIC	1772	W 1 - 0	Hall 13
23	03.01	UNIB P	A	Stalybridge Celtic	1728	L 1 - 3	Banim 52
24	08.01	UNIB P	A	Leigh RMI	427	D 0 - 0	
	15.01	FAT 3	A	Hednesford Town	710	D 1 - 1	Taylor 90
	17.01	FAT 3R	H	HEDNESFORD TOWN	518	W 2 - 0	Walker 20, Banim 81
	22.01	Unifilla QF	A	GATESHEAD	314	W 2 - 0	Yeo 72, Band 89
25	29.01	UNIB P	H	LEEK TOWN	392	W 2 - 0	Yeo 16, Band 69
	05.02	FAT 4	H	RUNCORN	764	D 0 - 0	
	09.02	FAT 4Rr	A	Runcorn	649	L 2 - 3	Aspinall 22, Wilson 96
	12.02	Unifilla SF	H	LEEK TOWN	315	W 3 - 2	Yeo 15, Band 56, Banim 67
26	19.02	UNIB P	H	GAINSBOROUGH TRINITY	403	W 4 - 0	Yeo 3 (13 66[p] 69), Banim 63
27	22.02	UNIB P	A	Colwyn Bay	241	W 3 - 2	Marginson 32, Banim 42, McDonald 82
28	26.02	UNIB P	H	WHITBY TOWN	407	W 4 - 1	Banim 16, Band 42, Robertson 58, Taylor 68[p]
29	29.02	UNIB P	A	Bamber Bridge	318	D 0 - 0	
30	11.03	UNIB P	A	Emley	301	W 1 - 0	Aspinall 71
31	13.03	UNIB P	H	LEIGH RMI	903	L 1 - 2	Yeo 73
32	18.03	UNIB P	H	GATESHEAD	522	D 1 - 1	Band 34
33	21.03	UNIB P	A	Winsford United	247	W 2 - 1	Band 36, Banim 41
34	25.03	UNIB P	A	Spennymoor United	192	D 0 - 0	
	27.03	Unifilla Final	A	Emley	602	W 2 - 0	Yeo 23, Band 44
35	01.04	UNIB P	H	BISHOP AUCKLAND	367	D 1 - 1	Yeo 8
36	04.04	UNIB P	A	Marine	279	D 0 - 0	
37	08.04	UNIB P	A	Lancaster City	261	L 0 - 1	
38	11.04	UNIB P	A	Guiseley	204	W 1 - 0	Richardson 73
39	15.04	UNIB P	A	Barrow	985	W 2 - 1	Hall 50, Band 89
40	17.04	UNIB P	H	COLWYN BAY	374	W 3 - 0	Robertson 51, Richardson 66, Yeo 87
41	22.04	UNIB P	H	HUCKNALL TOWN	553	W 4 - 3	Richardson 4 (18, 21, 45, 89)
42	24.04	UNIB P	A	Droylsden	473	W 3 - 1	Banim 35, Yeo 44, 83
43	29.04	UNIB P	A	Runcorn	229	W 3 - 0	Hall 35, Yeo 69, Foster 85
44	03.05	UNIB P	H	BAMBER BRIDGE	385	W 3 - 1	Yeo 35, Richardson 39, 57

PLAYING SQUAD

GOALKEEPERS: Graham Bennett (Flixton), Jimmy O'Donnell (Trafford)

DEFENDERS: Gus Wilson (Crewe), Paul Taylor (Bamber Bridge), Mark Beeston (Crewe), Ally Pickering (Altrincham), Paul Robertson (Droylsden)

MIDFIELDERS: Martin McDonald (Droylsden), Steve Tobin (Leigh RMI), Jody Banim (Flixton), Neil Hall (Droylsden), Stuart Walker (Altrincham), Scott Brenchley (Witton Alb)

FORWARDS: Dave Hanson (Nuneaton B), Simon Yeo (Coleraine), Karl Marginson (Stalybridge C), Peter Band (Bollingham U), Lee Wilkinson (Mossley)

LANCASTER CITY

CLUB OFFICIALS

Chairman: **Ian Sharp**

President: **M Woodhouse**

Chief Executive: **M.Parkinson**

Secretary: **Mike Sparks**
30 Salisbury Road, Lancaster LA1 5PJ
Tel: 0780 352 5799

Commercial Man./Press Offr: **Dave Byrne**

FACT FILE

Formed: 1902
Nickname: Dolly Blues
Sponsors: Reebok
Colours: Blue/white/blue
Change colours: All white
Midweek matchday: Tuesday
Reserve League: Lancashire League
99-00 Captain:P.Horner
Top Scorer: C.Ward
Joint P.o.Y:J.Graham & P.Horner

**FOOTBALL
MANAGEMENT
TEAM**

ManagerTony Hesketh
Coach: Barry Stimpson
Physio: G.Hardy, D Hughes

GROUND

Giant Axe, West Road, Lancaster LA1 5PE
Tel: 01524 382238 (Office). Directions: M6 junc 33, follow
into city, left at lights immediately after Waterstones bookshop, 2nd right, pass railway station
on right, follow road down hill, ground 1st right. 5 mins walk from both bus & rail stations
Capacity: 3153   Cover: 900   Seats: 313
Clubhouse: "The Dolly Blue Tavern" just outside the ground. Also a new tea bar inside
ground serving food and drinks.   **Club Shop:** Inside ground, selling metal badges,
pennants, programmes and other souvenirs etc. Contact Dave Crawford at club.

Pages: 32 Price: £1
Editor: Bill Byrne

Local Press: Lancaster Guardian, Morecambe
Visitor, Lancashire Evening Post, Lancaster
Citizen. Local Radio: Red Rose , Radio
Lancashire and Bay Radio

PREVIOUS   **Leagues:** Lancs Combination 05-70; Northern Premier 70-82; North West Counties82-87.
Name: Lancaster Town.   **Ground:** Quay Meadow 05-06 (club's 1st 2 games only!)

CLUB RECORDS   **Attendance:** 7,500 v Carlisle, FA Cup 1936.
Goalscorer: David Barnes 130 League & cup.   **Appearances:** Edgar J Parkinson, 591 league & cup.
Win: 8-0 v Leyland Motors (A), 83-84.   **Defeat:** 0-10 v Matlock T, NPL Division One, 73-74

BEST SEASON   **FA Vase:** Second Rd 86-87 90-91.   **FA Cup:** 2nd Rd 46-47 (1-4 v Gateshead) 72-73 (1-2 v Notts County)
FA Trophy: Third Rd 74-75 75-76.   League Clubs defeated: Barrow, Stockport County 21-22

HONOURS   Northern Prem. Lg Cup R-up 79-80 (Div 1 Cup R-up 90-91), Lancs Combination 21-22 29-30 34-35 35-36 (R-up 19-20 22-
23 27-28 51-52, Lg Cup 21-22, Div 2 R-up14-15), Lancs Jun. Cup (ATS Challenge Trophy) 27-28 28-29 30-31 33-34 51-52
74-75 (R-up 06-07 08-09 19-20 26-27), Lancs Yth (u18) Cup 87-88 88-89 (R-up 86-87 89-90), President's Cup 1994-95.
Unibond Div 1 95-96, Div 1 Lge Cup 95-96., Lg.Challenge Cup 99-00

Players Progressing: J McNamee (Workington 75), B O'Callaghan (Stoke C.), I Stevens (Stockport Co. 86), G Johnstone (P.N.E. 93), M Clark & W
Collins (Crewe Alex.), G Wilson (Crewe Alex.). P.Thomson (NAC Breda 99)

Back Row: P Crompton, F Kilbourne, G Taylor, S Abram, M Thornley, C Sharrock, P Horner, J Udall, K Barnes, K Mayers, I Finch.
Middle: A Bent (Physio), C Ward, P Haddow, M Cheal, S Sugden, S Trainor, J Graham, D Martin, S Hartley, G Bryam (Coach)
Front: M Donnelly, J Kennedy, T Hesbeth (Manager), I Sharp (Chairman), B Stimpson (Asst. Man.), C Pollitt, C Sharrott.
Photo: Lancaster & Morecambe Newspapers Ltd.

Match Facts 1999-00

	Date	Comp.	H/A	Opponents	Att.	Result	Goalscorers
1	14.08	UNIB P	A	Stalybridge Celtic	383	D 1 - 1	Taylor 90
2	17.08	UNIB P	H	LEIGH RMI	260	L 1 - 3	Kennedy 32
3	21.08	UNIB P	H	WORKSOP TOWN	292	D 0 - 0	
4	24.08	UNIB P	A	Winsford United	133	W 2 - 0	Cheal 7, Ward 21
5	28.08	UNIB P	H	FRICKLEY ATHLETIC	213	W 2 - 0	Horner 28, Mayers 31
6	30.08	UNIB P	A	Marine	301	D 0 - 0	
7	04.09	UNIB P	A	Guiseley	313	W 1 - 0	Mayers 42
8	07.09	UNIB P	H	COLWYN BAY	261	W 3 - 0	Ward 6, Haddow 67, Barnes 83
9	11.09	UNIB P	H	DROYLSDEN	267	W 4 - 0	Ward 43, **Kennedy 3** (48, 75, 79)
	18.09	FAC Q2	H	FLEETWOOD FREEPORT	w/o		Fleetwood Freeport expelled
10	21.09	UNIB P	A	Colwyn Bay	186	D 1 - 1	Kennedy 90
11	25.09	UNIB P	H	BLYTH SPARTANS	315	W 3 - 0	Sparrow 2, Morton 52, 65
	28.09	ULC G2	A	Bamber Bridge	317	W 2 - 1	Morton 49, Ward 68
	02.10	FAC Q3	H	WHITBY TOWN	295	D 2 - 2	Ward 66, Kilbane 87
	05.10	FAC Q3 r	A	Whitby Town	418	D *2 - 2	Ward 30, 80 Won 4-2 after penalties
12	09.10	UNIB P	A	Bishop Auckland	233	D 1 - 1	Mayers 45
	12.10	ULC G2	H	BARROW	337	D 0 - 0	
	16.10	FAC Q4	H	BAMBER BRIDGE	645	D 0 - 0	
	19.10	FAC Q4 r	A	Bamber Bridge	699	L *3 - 4	Mayers 19, Haddow 99, Barnes 115
13	23.10	UNIB P	A	Worksop Town	462	L 1 - 4	Mayers 81
14	26.10	UNIB P	H	STALYBRIDGE CELTIC	345	W 3 - 2	Morton 18, Martin 41, Ward 81
15	30.10	UNIB P	A	Emley	289	D 0 - 0	
	02.11	ULC GA	A	Leigh RMI	161	D 2 - 2	Ward 75, Barnes 90
16	06.11	UNIB P	H	GATESHEAD	365	D 1 - 1	Martin 22
	09.11	ULC GA	H	WORKINGTON	184	W 1 - 0	Ward 31
17	12.11	UNIB P	A	Hyde United	465	L 1 - 4	Barnes 23
18	16.11	UNIB P	H	BAMBER BRIDGE	269	D 1 - 1	Barnes 11
19	20.11	UNIB P	H	GUISELEY	277	W 2 - 0	Ward 44, Martin 59
	27.11	FAT 2	H	CORBY TOWN	197	W 3 - 0	Ward 32 76, Barnes 72
20	04.12	UNIB P	A	Hucknall Town	206	W 3 - 1	Barnes 46 73, Mayers 53
21	11.12	UNIB P	H	GAINSBOROUGH TRINITY	234	W 2 - 0	Mayers 57 82
22	14.12	UNIB P	H	MARINE	238	D 1 - 1	Martin 9
23	18.12	UNIB P	A	Gateshead	210	L 0 - 4	
24	27.12	UNIB P	A	Bamber Bridge	525	L 1 - 6	Horner 26
25	03.01	UNIB P	H	BARROW	826	W 1 - 0	Ward 29
26	08.01	UNIB P	H	RUNCORN	277	W 3 - 2	Nolan 4[og], Barnes 24, Ward 68
	15.01	FAT 3	A	Worksop Town	440	D 1 - 1	Martin 86
	22.01	LC QF	H	BRADFORD PARK AVENUE	198	W 1 - 0	Mayers 21
	25.01	FAT 3R	H	WORKSOP TOWN	260	L 0 - 3	
27	29.01	UNIB P	A	Gainsborough Trinity	386	L 0 - 1	
28	05.02	UNIB P	A	Whitby Town	468	L 0 - 1	
	08.02	Lancs 2	A	Bamber Bridge	189	L 1 - 2	Haddow 42
29	12.02	UNIB P	H	SPENNYMOOR UNITED	242	W 3 - 0	Jessop 19, Mayers 62, Trainor 85
30	25.02	UNIB P	A	Leigh RMI	401	L 1 - 2	Mayers 65
	04.03	L.C. SF	A	Frickley Athletic	230	W 3 - 2	**Ward 3** (23 45 65)
31	07.03	UNIB P	H	WINSFORD UNITED	146	W 4 - 1	Horner 5, Dickinson 12, Ward 23 48
32	11.03	UNIB P	A	Frickley Athletic	136	L 2 - 3	Kilbane 6, Haddow 88
33	18.03	UNIB P	H	WHITBY TOWN	262	L 1 - 2	Ward 29[p]
34	21.03	UNIB P	A	Runcorn	170	W 1 - 0	Jessop 88
35	25.03	UNIB P	A	Leek Town	267	L 1 - 3	Fowler 3
36	01.04	UNIB P	H	HUCKNALL TOWN	228	W 1 - 0	Ward 44
37	04.04	UNIB P	A	Barrow	784	D 2 - 2	Haddow 49, 71
38	08.04	UNIB P	H	HYDE UNITED	261	W 1 - 0	Barnes 57
	11.04	ULCC F	A	Worksop Town	669	W 1 - 0	Haddow 70
39	15.04	UNIB P	A	Droylsden	241	W 4 - 3	Haddow 32, Kilbane 34, Mayers 82, Fowler 90 (p)
40	22.04	UNIB P	H	LEEK TOWN	201	L 1 - 3	Fowler 90 (p)
41	24.04	UNIB P	A	Spennymoor United	254	D 0 - 0	
42	29.04	UNIB P	A	Blyth Spartans	315	W 2 - 0	OG (Martin) 4, Eatock 37
43	01.05	UNIB P	H	BISHOP AUCKLAND	220	L 0 - 1	
44	06.05	UNIB P	H	EMLEY	271	W 2 - 1	Fowler 17 (p), Martin 90

PLAYING SQUAD

GOALKEEPERS: Steve McIlhargey (Morecambe), Paul Horridge (Bamber Bridge)

DEFENDERS: Farrell Kilbane (Stafford R), Pat Johnston (Kendal T), Paul Sparrow (Rochdale), Jimmy Graham (Guiseley), Stewart Cliheroe (Port Vale), Phil Horner (Southport)

MIDFIELDERS: Brian Butler (Leigh RMI), Kenny Mayers (Morecambe), Dean Martin (Stalybridge C), Paul Haddow (Barrow), John Fowler (Camb.U), Paul Compton (Leigh RMI)

FORWARDS: Neil Morton (Morecambe), Chris Ward (Fulwood Am), Michael Holt (Rochdale), Lee Clitheroe (Oldham), Mark Cheal (Youth), Kevin Barnes (Fleetwood Freeport), Steve Trainor (Bamber Bridge)

LEEK TOWN

CLUB OFFICIALS

President: **Godfrey Heath**
Chairman: **Mike Howson**
Vice Chairman: **Mike Cope**
Directors: **Robin Halton, Carl France,**
Warren France, Tony Pickford

Football Secretary: **Mike Rowley**
62 London Rd., Chesterton, Newcastle,
Staffs. ST5 7DY Tel: 01782 562890
Commercial Manager: **Ken Warburton**
Press Officer: **Mike Cope**

FOOTBALL MANAGEMENT TEAM

Manager:Andy Holmes

Physio: K Birch-Martin

FACT FILE

Founded: 1946

Nickname: The Blues

Club Sponsors: Kerrygold

Club colours: All blue

Change colours: All yellow

Reserve team league: Manchester League

Midweek home matchday: Tuesday

Newsline: 0930 55 54 53

For up to the minute news, results, fixtures, plus general facts & figures from the world of non-league football

log on to

www.nlfootball.com

GROUND	Harrison Park, Macclesfield Road, Leek ST13 8LD
	Tel: 01538 399278 Fax: 01538 399826
Directions:	Opposite Courtaults chemical works on A523 Macclesfield to Buxton road half a mile out of Leek heading towards Macclesfield.
Capacity: 3,600	Seated: 625 Covered Terracing: 2,675

Club Shop: Contact club on 01538 399278.
Clubhouse: `Blues' Bar open nightly & weekend lunchtimes. 01538 383734

Programme
Pages: 40 Price: £1.50
Editor: M.Cope
Local Newspapers: Leek Post & Times,
Evening Sentinel
Local Radio: Radio Stoke, Signal Radio

PREVIOUS   **Leagues:** Staffs County, Manchester 51-54 57-73, West Mids (B'ham) 54-56,Cheshire County 73-82, North West Counties 82-87, Northern Premier 87-94 95-97,Southern League 94-95, Conference 97-99
     Names: Abbey Green Rovers/ Leek Lowe Hamil.   **Grounds:** None
CLUB RECORDS **Attendance:** 5,312 v Macclesfield Town, F.A. Cup Second Qualifying Round 73-74   **Win:** Unknown   **Defeat:** Unknown
     Transfer fee paid: £2,000 for Simon Snow (Sutton Town)   **Transfer fee received:** £30,000 for Tony Bullock (Barnsley)
     Career goalscorer: Dave Suttons 144   **Career appearances:** Gary Pearce 447.
BEST SEASON **FA Cup:** 2nd Rd 90-91, 0-4 v Chester (A) after 1-1   League clubs defeated: Scarborough 90-91.
     FA Trophy: Runners-up 89-90, Q-F 85-86.
HONOURS   FA Trophy R-up 89-90; Northern Premier Lg 96-97, R-up 93-94 (Div 1 89-90, Div 1Cup R-up 88-89, Presidents Cup R-up 93-94, Lg Shield 90-91); North West Co's LgCup 84-85 (Charity Shield 84-85); Cheshire County Lg 74-75 (Challenge Shield74-75); Manchester Lg 51-52 71-72 72-73 (Lg Cup 72-73); Staffs Snr Cup 95-96,R-up 54-55 81-82 95-96, Jnr Cup 51-52 70-71 (R-up 47-48 48-49 49-50)); StaffsCo. Lg 50-51 69-70 70-71 73-74 (R-up 47-48 49-50, Lg Cup 70-71 73-74); LeekPost Charity Shield 46-47; Leek Cup 47-48 52-53 70-71 71-72 (R-up 46-47); MayBank Cup 47-48 50-51 71-72; Hanley Cup 48-49 70-71 (R-up 49-5); Mid Cheshire LgDiv 2 87-88 (Div 2 Cup 87-88); Evans Halshaw Floodlit Cup Winners 93-94 94-95; Southern Lge Cup R-up 94-95; Unibond Lge Chall Cup R-up 95-96
Players progressing: Geoff Crosby (Stockport 52), Bill Summerscales (70), Mark Bright (81) & Martyn Smith (84) allto Port Vale, Paul Edwards (Crewe 89), Tony Bullock (Barnsley 97)

Match Facts 1999-00

	Date	Comp.	H/A	Opponents	Att.	Result	Goalscorers
1	14.08	UNIB P	H	GUISELEY	340	D 2 - 2	Davies 18, Callan 31
2	17.08	UNIB P	A	Gainsborough Trinity	487	L 2 - 3	Callan 24, Kelly 63
3	21.08	UNIB P	A	Frickley Athletic	199	D 1 - 1	Lovatt 12
4	24.08	UNIB P	H	HUCKNALL TOWN	267	D 2 - 2	Lovatt 5, Kiely 27
5	28.08	UNIB P	H	LEIGH RMI	325	W 2 - 0	Sutton 46 85
6	30.08	UNIB P	A	Winsford United	203	W 2 - 0	Wilkes 38, Hobby 56
7	04.09	UNIB P	H	SPENNYMOOR UNITED	320	W 1 - 0	Callan 76
8	07.09	UNIB P	A	Runcorn	298	L 0 - 5	
9	11.09	UNIB P	A	Blyth Spartans	346	W 3 - 2	Callan 22, Kiely 66, Dundas 74
	14.09	ULC 1G	H	WINSFORD UNITED	161	D 3 - 3	Callan 13, Whittaker 28, Wade 73
	18.09	FAC Q2	H	BLAKENALL	306	L 0 - 2	
10	21.09	UNIB P	H	GAINSBOROUGH TRINITY	265	W 3 - 2	Hawtin 25, Sutton 47, Reed 73[og]
11	25.09	UNIB P	H	WHITBY TOWN	352	W 2 - 1	Callan 43, Kiely 73
12	28.09	UNIB P	A	Stalybridge Celtic	413	L 2 - 3	Kiely 70, 80
13	02.10	UNIB P	A	Hucknall Town	285	L 0 - 2	
	05.10	ULC G7	A	Congleton Town	199	W 3 - 1	Kiely 10, Hobby 15, Dundas 90
	09.10	FAT 1	A	ACCRINGTON STANLEY	302	D 2 - 2	Dundas 15, 80
	12.10	FAT 1 r	A	Accrington Stanley	221	L 4 - 5	Hobby 19, 44, Callan 45, Dundas 84
14	16.10	UNIB P	H	FRICKLEY ATHLETIC	300	L 1 - 2	Kiely 79
15	19.10	UNIB P	A	Colwyn Bay	161	D 1 - 1	Kiely 42
16	23.10	UNIB P	A	Barrow	1220	W 4 - 1	Whittaker 36, 43, Hobby 48, Callan 84
17	26.10	UNIB P	H	WORKSOP TOWN	368	W 3 - 1	Kiely 3 (3, 6, 46)
18	30.10	UNIB P	A	Bishop Auckland	181	D 1 - 1	Dundas 38
	02.11	Staffs SC2	H	KIDSGROVE ATHLETIC	189	W 2 - 0	Kiely 31 78
19	06.11	UNIB P	H	BAMBER BRIDGE	325	D 0 - 0	
	09.11	ULC GH	H	BELPER TOWN	197	L 1 - 2	Kiely 67[p]
20	13.11	UNIB P	A	Marine	237	L 1 - 6	Sutton 90
21	20.11	UNIB P	H	HYDE UNITED	408	W 2 - 0	Kiely 22 37
	23.11	ULC GH	A	Eastwood Town	88	L 3 - 5	Kiely 48 63, Sutton 69
22	27.11	UNIB P	H	COLWYN BAY	346	L 0 - 2	
23	04.12	UNIB P	A	Gateshead	236	L 1 - 2	Kiely 74
24	11.12	UNIB P	H	MARINE	274	L 2 - 4	Wade 12, Kiely 26
25	27.12	UNIB P	H	BARROW	494	W 2 - 1	Whittaker 64, Kiely 78
26	03.01	UNIB P	A	Droylsden	370	W 2 - 1	Whittaker 18, Kiely 51
27	08.01	UNIB P	H	GATESHEAD	316	L 1 - 2	Kiely 54[p]
	11.01	S SC QF	A	Stafford Rangers	286	D 2 - 2	Kiely 17 23
28	15.01	UNIB P	A	Leigh RMI	228	W 2 - 0	Lovatt 31, Kiely 65
	22.01	Unifilla QF	H	CONGLETON TOWN	255	W 2 - 0	Kiely 60, Whittaker 78
29	29.01	UNIB P	A	Hyde United	392	L 0 - 2	
	01.02	S SC QF R	H	STAFFORD RANGERS	227	W 2 - 1	Sutton 11, Kiely 60
	12.02	LC SF	A	Hyde United	315	L 2 - 3	Kiely 10 58
30	19.02	UNIB P	H	BLYTH SPARTANS	330	L 1 - 4	Kiely 74[p]
31	22.02	UNIB P	H	WINSFORD UNITED	298	L 1 - 2	Callan 44
32	26.02	UNIB P	A	Emley	238	D 0 - 0	
33	04.03	UNIB P	H	DROYLSDEN	271	D 0 - 0	
34	18.03	UNIB P	H	Guiseley	267	D 1 - 1	Williams 42
	21.03	S SC SF	H	BLAKENALL	162	D 1 - 1	Kiely 57
35	25.03	UNIB P	H	LANCASTER CITY	267	W 3 - 1	Whittaker 1, Mountford 36, Kiely 83
36	01.04	UNIB P	A	Whitby Town	445	L 1 - 3	Batho 75
	04.04	S SC SF R	A	Blakenall	260	L *0 - 2	aet
37	06.04	UNIB P	H	EMLEY	173	L 1 - 3	OG (Haran) 50
38	08.04	UNIB P	A	Bamber Bridge	280	L 0 - 5	
39	11.04	UNIB P	A	Spennymoor United	155	L 1 - 3	Hawtin 45
40	15.04	UNIB P	H	RUNCORN	213	L 0 - 1	
41	18.04	UNIB P	H	BISHOP AUCKLAND	131	L 1 - 4	Whittaker 65
42	22.04	UNIB P	A	Lancaster City	201	W 3 - 1	Lovatt 5, Whittaker 21, Batho 77
43	29.04	UNIB P	A	Worksop Town	384	L 0 - 2	
44	01.05	UNIB P	H	STALYBRIDGE CELTIC	274	D 0 - 0	

PLAYING SQUAD

GOALKEEPERS: Mark Statham (Stalybridge C)

DEFENDERS: John Diskin (Nantwich T), Dale Hawtin (Witton Alb), Dean Stokes (Rochdale), Matthew Beeby (Leek CSOB), Bradley Sandeman (Worcester C), Anthony Tarr (Port Vale)

MIDFIELDERS: Aidan Callan (Stoke C), Richard Carter (Witton Alb), Craig Lovatt (Kidsgrove Ath), Andy Myatt (WBA), Darryl Wilkes (Kidsgrove Ath)

FORWARDS: Danny Hobby (Kidsgrove Ath), Darren Twigg (Newcastle T), Stuart Leicester (Radcliffe B), Dave Whittaker (Crewe), Ian Palin (Knypersley V), Dave Sutton (Newcastle T)

MARINE

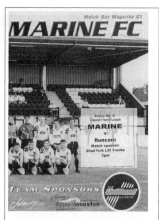

CLUB OFFICIALS

Chairman: **Tom Culshaw**

President: **Dennis Hargreaves**

Secretary: **John Wildman**
4 Ashbourne Avenue, Blundellsands,
Liverpool L23 8TX   Tel: 0151 924 5248

Press Officer: **David Wotherspoon**

FOOTBALL MANAGEMENT TEAM

Manager: Roly Howard
Asst Mgr/Coach: Roger Patience
Physio: John Bradshaw

FACT FILE

Formed: 1894
Nickname: The Mariners
Sponsors: Johnsons the Cleaners
Colours: White/black/black
Change colours: Yellow & Green
Midweek matchday: Tuesday
Reserves' League: Lancs. League Div. One

GROUND Rossett Park, College Road, Crosby, Liverpool(Tel: 0151 924 1743)
Directions: College Road is off main Liverpool-Southport road (A565) in Crosby. Ground ten minutes walk from Crosby & Blundellsands (Mersey Rail). Bus No. 92
Capacity: 2,800   Cover: 1,400   Seats: 400

Clubhouse: Open daily. Concert Hall (250 seats), Members Lounge (100 seats).
Club Shop: Sells replica kit and range of souvenirs.Metal Badges in home and away colours.
Contact Dave Rannard 0151474 9848

Pages: 24 Price: 80p
Editor: David Wotherspoon
Local Press: Crosby Herald, Liverpool Echo,
Daily Post Local Radio: BBC Radio
Merseyside, Radio City

PREVIOUS   **Leagues:** Liverpool Zingari; Liverpool Co. Comb.; Lancs Combination 35-39, 46-69; Cheshire County 69-79.
Name: Waterloo Melville   **Ground:** Waterloo Park1894-1903

CLUB RECORDS   **Attendance:** 4,000 v Nigeria, Friendly 1949
Goalscorer: Paul Meachin 200   **Win:** 14-2 v Rossendale Utd (A), Cheshire County Lge 25/2/78
Appearances: Peter Smith 952   **Defeat:** 2-11 v Shrewsbury Town F.A.Cup 1st Rd 1995
Fee Paid: £6,000 for Jon Penman (Southport Oct. 1995)   **Fee Received:** £20,000 for Richard Norris (Crewe 96)

BEST SEASON   **FA Trophy:** Semi Final 83-84, 91-92   **FA Amateur Cup:** Runners up 31-32 (SF 46-47)
FA Cup: 3rd Rd 92-93, 1-3 v Crewe Alex. (A)   League clubs defeated: Barnsley 75-76, Halifax T. 92-93

HONOURS   FA Amateur Cup R-up 31-32; Northern Prem Lg 94-95, R-up 85-86 91-92, Lg Cup 84-85 91-92 (R-up 80-81 85-86); Presidents Cup R-up 83-84 86-87; Cheshire Co. Lg73-74 75-76 77-78 (R-up 72-73); Lancs Comb. R-up 46-47 (Lg Cup 46-47 63-64 68-69); Liverpool Comb. 27-28 30-31 33-34 34-35 (Lg Cup 30-31); Lancs Tphy 87-88 90-91; Lancs Jnr Cup 78-79; Lancs Amtr Cup (5); Liverpool Snr Cup 78-79 84-8587-88 89-90 94-95 99-00; Liverpool Non-Lge Cup 68-69 75-76 76-77; Liverpool Chal. Cup 42-43 44-45 71-72.

Players Progressing: A Sharrock, S Brooks (Southport 73 &77), A Jones (Leeds 60), G Williams (Preston 72), J Lacy (Fulham), P Beesly (Sheffield Utd), M Kearney (Everton 81), A Finlay (Shrewsbury 81), P Cook (Norwich), P Edwards (Crewe), I Nolan (Tranmere), J McAteer(Bolton W.), R Norris (Crewe 96).

Marine celebrate after winning the Marsden Lancashire Challenge Trophy at Chorley in April.
They also later beat Tranmere Rovers to win the Liverpool Senior Cup.   **Photo:** Michael Morgan

Match Facts 1999-00

	Date	Comp.	H/A	Opponents	Att.	Result	Goalscorers
1	14.08	UNIB P	H	HUCKNALL TOWN	233	W 3-0	Morgan 30, Townsend 58, Schofield 70
2	16.08	UNIB P	H	Emley	278	W 2-0	Morgan 42[p], Randles 90
3	21.08	UNIB P	A	BLYTH SPARTANS	314	D 0-0	
4	24.08	UNIB P	A	Colwyn Bay	239	W 5-0	Scott 7, Gamble 23, Townsend 36, Douglas 45, Randles 90
5	30.08	UNIB P	H	LANCASTER CITY	301	D 0-0	
6	04.09	UNIB P	H	GAINSBOROUGH TRINITY	304	D 2-2	Morgan 43 61
	07.09	L'pool SC1	A	Warrington Town	105	W 4-1	Morgan 46, 76, Townsend 56, Worthington 88
7	11.09	UNIB P	A	Bishop Auckland	193	W 2-0	Townsend 36, 52
	14.09	ULC 1G	H	CHORLEY	197	W 3-0	Griffiths 5, Scott 42, Price 79
	18.09	FAC Q2	A	Barrow	1218	D 2-2	Townsend 44, Price 60
	21.09	FAC Q2 R	H	BARROW	425	W 3-2	Morgan 3 (17, 49, 86 [p])
8	25.09	UNIB P	A	Hyde United	552	D 1-1	Morgan 35
9	28.09	UNIB P	A	Leigh RMI	266	L 1-2	Morgan 36
	02.10	FAC Q3	H	CHORLEY	414	W 2-0	Townsend 61, Price 89
10	09.10	UNIB P	H	STALYBRIDGE CELTIC	397	L 1-3	Douglas 5
	12.10	ULC G3	A	Burscough	176	D 2-2	Townsend 6, Scott 51
	16.10	FAC Q4	H	RUNCORN	665	D 1-1	Townsend 65
	19.10	FAC Q4R	A	Runcorn	603	L 2-3	Morgan 19 37
11	23.10	UNIB P	H	GUISELEY	273	D 2-2	Price 22, Scott 90
12	26.10	UNIB P	H	DROYLSDEN	244	W 3-2	Gamble 52, Whalley 72[og], Bainbridge 83
13	30.10	UNIB P	A	FRICKLEY ATHLETIC	231	W 1-0	Bainbridge 76
	03.11	Liv. SCQF	A	Southport		W 4-2	Gautrey 14, Bainbridge 70 91, Rigoglioso 111
14	06.11	UNIB P	A	Whitby Town	311	W 3-0	Scott 14, Price 49, Bainbridge 89
	09.11	ULC GC	H	TRAFFORD	159	D 1-1	Rigoglioso 54
15	13.11	UNIB P	H	LEEK TOWN	237	W 6-1	Bainbridge 5 53, Gamble 27[p] 39[p], Morgan 68 90
	16.11	Lancs 1	A	Atherton LR	96	W 6-0	Scott 8 25, Gautrey 12, Rigoglioso 55, Morgan 70 80
16	20.11	UNIB P	A	Worksop Town	530	W 1-0	Gautrey 68
	23.11	ULC GC	A	Colwyn Bay	157	W 5-2	Morgan 18, Schofield 28, Gautrey 64 86, Smith 75
	27.11	FAT 2	A	Hinckley United	322	D 1-1	Thompson 21
17	04.12	UNIB P	H	WHITBY TOWN	246	D 3-3	Gamble 45[p], Rigoglioso 47, Bainbridge 53
18	11.12	UNIB P	H	Leek Town	274	W 4-2	Bainbridge 46, Rigoglioso 65, Randles 79, Gamble 89
19	14.12	UNIB P	A	Lancaster City	238	D 1-1	Schofield 22
20	18.12	UNIB P	A	BISHOP AUCKLAND	263	W 3-1	Thompson 12, Rigoglioso 72, Bainbridge 90
21	27.12	UNIB P	H	LEIGH RMI	663	D 1-1	Price 90
22	03.01	UNIB P	A	Runcorn	443	W 2-1	Rigoglioso 55 57
23	08.01	UNIB P	H	SPENNYMOOR UNITED	358	W 3-0	Thompson 18, Scott 37 70
	11.01	L Mars 2	A	Burscough	157	W 2-1	Gamble 42 57[p]
	15.01	FAT 3	H	GUISELEY	397	W 2-1	Gautrey 42, Bainbridge 90
	22.01	ULC QF	A	Frickley Athletic	179	L 1-2	Scott 12
24	29.01	UNIB P	A	Barrow	1314	D 2-2	Morgan 17, Price 81
	05.02	FAT 4	A	Blakenall	407	W 1-0	Fearns 35
	08.02	Lancs QF	A	Darwen	157	W 1-0	Morgan 85
25	12.02	UNIB P	A	Stalybridge Celtic	440	W 3-0	Rigoglioso 25, Robinson 36, Morgan 75
26	15.02	UNIB P	A	Droylsden	202	W 1-0	Rigoglioso 31
27	19.02	UNIB P	H	GATESHEAD	459	D 1-1	Robinson 72
	26.02	FAT 5	A	Rushden & Diamonds	3,094	L 0-1	
28	04.03	UNIB P	A	Hucknall Town	273	L 0-2	
	07.03	Lancs SF	A	Leigh RMI	179	W 4-2	Gamble 18 55, Price 25, Morgan 50
29	11.03	UNIB P	A	Gainsborough Trinity	366	D 0-0	
30	14.03	UNIB P	H	BAMBER BRIDGE	279	L 0-3	
31	18.03	UNIB P	H	EMLEY	382	W 3-1	Nulty 23, Bainbridge 24, David 85[og]
	21.03	Liv. SC SF	H	LIVERPOOL	471	W 2-1	Gautrey 45, Price 78
32	25.03	UNIB P	A	Blyth Spartans	384	L 1-3	Morgan 39
33	28.03	UNIB P	H	BARROW	357	W 1-0	Bainbridge 73
34	01.04	UNIB P	A	Winsford United	250	D 2-2	Bainbridge 76, Gamble 86
35	04.04	UNIB P	H	HYDE UNITED	279	D 0-0	
36	08.04	UNIB P	A	Guiseley	273	W 3-1	Gamble 34, Schofield 44, Rigoglioso 65
	11.04	Lancs Final	A	Bamber Bridge		W 5-0	Morgan 4, Price 9, 29, Gautrey 13, Gamble 70
37	15.04	UNIB P	A	Gateshead	281	L 0-2	
38	18.04	UNIB P	H	WINSFORD UNITED	223	W 3-1	Bainbridge 78, 83
39	22.04	UNIB P	H	WORKSOP TOWN	303	W 3-2	Morgan 4, Rigoglioso 68, Gautrey 90
40	24.04	UNIB P	H	Bamber Bridge	327	W 2-0	Schofield 36, Black 90
41	27.04	UNIB P	H	COLWYN BAY	264	D 1-1	Wilson 10
42	29.04	UNIB P	A	Frickley Athletic	137	D 2-2	Gautrey 68, Wilson 74
43	01.05	UNIB P	H	RUNCORN	362	L 0-1	
	04.05	Liv. SC Final	A	Tranmere Rovers		W *1-0	Gautrey 99
44	06.05	UNIB P	A	Spennymoor United	263	D 0-0	

GOALKEEPERS: Chris Clarke (Chorley), John Gillies (Tranmere)

DEFENDERS: Ian Baines (Southport), Jon Gautrey (Southport), Kevin Formby (Southport), Mark Schofield (Leigh RMI), Mark Nulty (Youth), Neil Black (Tranmere)

MIDFIELDERS: Gary Randles (Runcorn), Simon Wilson (Peterborough), Dave Gamble (Southport), Michael Douglas (Ashville), Ricky Bainbridge (Buxton), Kris McHale (Tranmere), Kieran England (Preston)

FORWARDS: John Morgan (Southport), Karl Robinson (Caernarfon T), Richie Townsend (Cwmbran T), David Thompson (Southport)

PLAYING SQUAD

313

RUNCORN

CLUB OFFICIALS

Chairman: **Dr David Robertson**

Vice Chairman: **Tony Bamber**

Secretary: **Chris Henshall**
58 Minerva Close, Warrington,
Cheshire WA4 2XN.
Tel.01925 650311 or 241975 (H) &Fax
Tel/Fax 01928 560076 (Sec office)

FACT FILE

Formed: 1918
Nickname: The Linnets
Midweek matchday: Tuesday
Colours: Yellow/&green/black
Change colours: All red
Reserve's league: Lancashire
Youth's league: Northwest Alliance
99-00 Captain: Carl Ruffer
P.o.Y.: Richard Acton
Top scorer: Mike Moseley (14)

FOOTBALL MANAGEMENT TEAM

Manager: Mark (Spike) Carter
Assistant Manager: John Imrie

GROUND

Canal Street, Wivern Place, Runcorn, Cheshire WA7 1RZ.
Tel. 01928 560076. Fax01928 560076.

Directions: From South: Leave M56 (junct 11). Follow A56 to Warrington for 1.5miles. Turn left at r'about onto A558 signed Liverpool for 3 miles. Take left hand slipway signed Football Ground. From North: Leave M62 (junct 7).Travel via Widnes and over Runcorn bridge. Follow signs for Northwich for 1mile. Take left hand slipway signed Football Ground.
Capacity: 3,928   **Cover:** 1,327   **Seats:** 499
Clubhouse: Open on matchdays. Light snacks available.
Club Shop: Sells range of club memorabilia. Contact Roy Pickering Tel. 01928568665.

Pages: 36   Price: £1.30
Editor: Alex Keenan Tel. 01928 590425

Local Press: Runcorn Weekly News,
Liverpool Echo, Runcorn World, Manchester
Evening News.
Radio: Radio Merseyside, GMR.Wire F.M

PREVIOUS   **Leagues:** Lancs Combination; Cheshire Co. Lg; Northern Prem. Lge. 68 -81;Alliance Premier (Conference) 81-96.
Names: None.   **Grounds:** None

CLUB RECORDS   **Attendance:** 10,111 v Preston - FA Cup 1938-39.
Goalscorer: Alan Ryan (66 goals in 64 appearances 67-68).
Win: 11-1 v Congleton Town 64-65.   **Defeat:** 0-9 v Wellington 46-47.
Fee Paid: £17,000 for Simon Rudge, Hyde Utd, 1989.   **Fee Received:** £80,000 for Ian Woan, Nottm Forest, 1990.

BEST SEASON   **FA Trophy:** Runners-up 85-86, 92-93, 93-94.   **FA Cup:** Second Round Replay 85-86,0-4 v Wigan Ath. (A), after 1-1.
Second Round also 47-48, 67-68, 77-78, 86-87,87-88, 88-89. League clubs defeated: Scunthorpe Utd., Notts. Co.,
Chester City,Wrexham.

HONOURS   Lancs Jnr Cup 1918-19; Cheshire Lg 1919-20, 36-37, 38-39, 39-40, 62-63;Cheshire Snr Cup 24-25, 35-36, 61-62, 64-65,
67-68, 73-74, 74-75, 84-89 (5times); R-up 93-94; Cheshire Co. Bowl 37-38; Northern Premier Lg 75-76, 80-81(R-up 74-75);
NPL Chall Cup 74-75, 79-80, 80-81; NPL Challenge Shield 80-81,81-82; Alliance Premier Lg 81-82, Gola Lg Championship   Shield 82-
83, 85-86; Bob Lord Trophy 82-83, 84-85, R-up 91-92. FA Trophy R-up 85-86, 92-93, 93-94.NPL Pres.Cup 98-99

Players Progressing: Mark McCarrick, Eddie Bishop, Jim Cumbes, Graham Abel,Barry Knowles, Mark Jones, Don Page, David Pugh, Ian Woan,
Gary Brabin, Paul Robertson, Mike Smith,Mark Carter

Action from
Runcorns's 4th Round
FA Trophy match
against Hyde Utd.
Photo: Colin Stevens

Match Facts 1999-00

	Date	Comp.	H/A	Opponents	Att.	Result	Goalscorers
1	14.08	UNIB P	A	Spennymoor United	176	L 0-3	
2	17.08	UNIB P	H	COLWYN BAY	312	L 1-2	Carter 67
3	21.08	UNIB P	H	WHITBY TOWN	285	W 3-1	Moseley 37, Watson 52, Nolan 67
4	24.08	UNIB P	A	Droylsden	322	L 0-1	
5	28.08	UNIB P	H	EMLEY	279	L 1-3	Wood 5 [og]
6	30.08	UNIB P	A	Bamber Bridge	441	L 0-2	
7	04.09	UNIB P	A	Worksop Town	404	W 3-0	Burke 3, 72, Johnson 79
8	07.09	UNIB P	H	LEEK TOWN	298	**W 5-0**	McNally 35, **McDonald 3**(37 43 56), Moseley 52
9	11.09	UNIB P	A	Barrow	1599	W 2-0	Carter 20[p], Burke 55
	14.09	ULC 1G	H	COLWYN BAY	170	W 3-1	Griffiths 8, Moseley 31, Nolan 71
	18.09	FAC Q2	H	GRETNA	313	W 2-0	Moseley 52, Watson 82
	21.09	Ches.SC1	H	WARRINGTON TOWN	174	L 2-4	Carter 46, 89
10	25.09	UNIB P	H	HUCKNALL TOWN	315	L 0-1	
11	28.09	UNIB P	A	Guiseley	240	D 2-2	Nolan 32, Watson 67
	02.10	FAC Q3	A	Dunston Fed. Brewery	239	W 2-0	Moseley 33, Carter 55
	05.10	ULC G6	A	Witton Albion	276	D 2-2	McNally 83 84
	09.10	FAT 1	A	Solihull Borough	155	W 2-1	McNally 84, Griffiths 89
	16.10	FAC Q4	A	Marine	665	D 1-1	Burke 75
	19.10	FAC Q4 r	H	MARINE	603	W 3-2	McNally 7 53, Watson 120
12	23.10	UNIB P	H	BLYTH SPARTANS	279	W 3-0	Brunskill 36, Carter 60, Watson 61
13	26.10	UNIB P	A	WINSFORD UNITED	286	W 1-0	Rose 82
	30.10	FAC 1	A	Hayes	890	L 1-2	McDonald 45
14	06.11	UNIB P	H	GUISELEY	307	D 2-2	Watson 17, Nolan 64
	16.11	ULC GD	A	Congleton Town	107	D 2-2	Watson 44, Ward 87
15	20.11	UNIB P	H	GATESHEAD	232	W 2-0	Moseley 32 57
	23.11	ULC GD	H	RADCLIFFE BOROUGH	118	W 4-1	**Moseley 3** (3 27 75), McNally 60
	27.11	FAT 2	H	NORTHWICH VICTORIA	875	W 2-0	Moseley 25 41
16	29.11	UNIB P	A	Hyde United	535	D 0-0	
17	04.12	UNIB P	H	BAMBER BRIDGE	203	W 2-0	Watson 47, Carter 87
18	11.12	UNIB P	A	Whitby Town	354	**L 0-4**	
19	14.12	UNIB P	A	Leigh RMI	161	L 0-2	
20	18.12	UNIB P	H	FRICKLEY ATHLETIC	203	W 2-1	McNally 8, Smith 9
21	27.12	UNIB P	A	Colwyn Bay	332	D 1-1	Smith 23
22	03.01	UNIB P	H	MARINE	443	L 1-2	Smith 43
23	08.01	UNIB P	A	Lancaster City	277	L 2-3	Robinson 59, Horner 76[og]
	15.01	FAT 3	A	Tamworth	894	W 1-0	McDonald 48
	22.01	ULC QF	A	Worksop Town	347	L 0-1	
24	29.01	UNIB P	H	BISHOP AUCKLAND	198	W 2-0	Moseley 69, McNally 81
	05.02	FAT 4	A	Hyde United	764	D 0-0	
	09.02	FAT 4 R	H	HYDE UNITED	649	W *3-2	Smith 11 119, Burke 95
25	12.02	UNIB P	H	Hucknall Town	265	D 1-1	Langton 88
26	19.02	UNIB P	H	WORKSOP TOWN	310	W 2-0	Nolan 51, Ruffer 68
	26.02	FAT 5	H	HEYBRIDGE SWIFTS	759	W 2-1	McDonnell 37, Griffiths 76
27	29.02	UNIB P	H	DROYLSDEN	222	D 1-1	Tomlinson 8
28	04.03	UNIB P	A	Gateshead	268	W 3-0	Nolan 20, Burke 25, Griffiths 26
	11.03	FAT QF	A	Telford United	1557	L 0-2	
29	14.03	UNIB P	H	BARROW	202	D 2-2	McNally 52, Smith 74[p]
30	18.03	UNIB P	A	Bishop Auckland	207	L 0-2	
31	21.03	UNIB P	H	LANCASTER CITY	170	L 0-1	
32	25.03	UNIB P	H	STALYBRIDGE CELTIC	225	D 0-0	
33	28.03	UNIB P	A	Stalybridge Celtic	220	D 1-1	Carter77
34	01.04	UNIB P	A	Emley	196	L 0-1	
35	04.04	UNIB P	H	Winsford United	150	W 6-1	McNally 24, Burke 25, 37, Carter 45, OG (Jones) 60, Ruffer 89
36	08.04	UNIB P	H	GAINSBOROUGH TRINITY	212	W 3-2	McAllister 65, OG (Bennett) 68, Ruffer 72
37	15.04	UNIB P	A	Leek Town	213	W 1-0	Moseley 30
38	18.04	UNIB P	H	LEIGH RMI	254	L 0-2	
39	22.04	UNIB P	H	Gainsborough Trinity	341	D 1-1	OG (Allinson) 9
40	24.04	UNIB P	A	Frickley Athletic	106	W 2-1	Carter 80, 90
41	29.04	UNIB P	H	HYDE UNITED	229	L 0-3	
42	01.05	UNIB P	A	Marine	362	W 1-0	Ruffer 10
43	04.05	UNIB P	H	SPENNYMOOR UTD.	179	W 3-2	Nolan 28, Robinson 76, 81
44	06.05	UNIB P	A	Blyth Spartans	312	L 2-4	Smith 44, Nolan 68

PLAYING SQUAD

GOALKEEPERS: Ray Newlands (Leigh RMI), Mark Morris (Wrexham)

DEFENDERS: Tony Ward (Chorley), David Ness (Youth), Wayne McDermott (Nuneaton B),
Iain Brunskill (Hednesford T), Peter Ellis (Knowsley U), David Robinson (Ashton U),
Mike Tomlinson (Warrington T)

MIDFIELDERS: Paul McNally (Marine), John Benson (Marine), Phil Johnson (Real Madrid),
Dave Nolan (Hyde U), James Chantler (South Carolina Shamrocks (USA))

FORWARDS: Mark Carter (Ashton U), Mike Heverin (Northwich V), Mike Moseley (Youth),
Mike Smith (Barrow), John McAllister (Prescot Cables), Lee Griffiths (Marine)

SPENNYMOOR UNITED

CLUB OFFICIALS
Chairman: **Barrie Hindmarch**
Vice Chairman: **P.Fletcher**
Secretary: **Brian Boughen**,141Durham Road,Spennymoor, Co.Durham. DL16 6JU
Tel No: 01388 811874)
Commercial Manager: **Des Beamson**
Press Officer.: Chairman

FOOTBALL MANAGEMENT TEAM

Manager: Peter Mulcaster
Physio: Peter carey
Coach: Managerial team

FACT FILE
Founded: 1904
Nickname: The Moors
Sponsors: Rothmans (Spennymoor).
Club colours: Black & white stripes/black/white.
Change colours: All red
Midweek home matches: Tuesday
Reserve Team: None
99-00 Captain:Andy Howarth
P.o.Y.: David Holloway
Top scorer: Andy Howarth

GROUND Brewery Field, Durham Road, Spennymoor, County Durham DL16 6JN
Tel: 01388 811934 Directions: From South; A1(M), A167, A688, straight on at mini-r'bout, 3rd exit at next large r'bout (St Andrews church opposite), pass Asda on left, straight on at junction, pass Salvin Arms (Durham Rd), ground 200 yds on left. From A167North - leave at Croxdale (N.E.S.S. factory), right at cemetery on left - this is Durham Rd - ground half mile on right. Nearest rail station is Durham -buses from there.
Capacity: 7,500 Seats: 300 Cover: 2,000
Clubhouse: (01388 814100) Open eves. 7-11pm, Sat 12-11pm (matchdays only), Sun12-2 & 7-10.30pm. Bar snacks. Private functions. Tea bar in ground. **Club Shop:** Sells replica kit, memorabilia, programmes etc. Contact Peter Fletcher (01388 814100).

Pages: 44 Price: £1
Editor: Gary Nunn

Local Press: Northern Echo; The Journal

PREVIOUS **Leagues:** Northern 05-08 60-90; North Eastern 08-37 38-58; Wearside 37-38;Midland Counties 58-60; Northern Counties East 90-93. **Ground:** Wood Vue 1901-1904. **Names:** None.
CLUB RECORDS **Attendance:** 7,202 v Bishop Auckland, Durham County Challenge Cup 30/3/57.
Win: 19-0 v Eden Colliery, North Eastern Lge 6/2/37. **Defeat:** 0-16 v Sunderland`A', Durham Snr Cup 4.1.02 (H.T.: 0-10)
Goalscorer: Dougie Humble 200+. **Appearances:** Ken Banks 600+.
Fee Paid: £3,500 for Don Prattie (Gretna) Fee Received: £20,000 for Michael Heathcote (Sunderland, 88).
BEST SEASON **FA Trophy:** Semi Final 77-78
FA Cup: 3rd Rd 36-37, 1-7 v West Bromwich Albion(A). League clubs defeated : Hartlepool 27-28, Southport 75-76.
HONOURS Northern Premier Lg Cup 93-94 (Div 1 R-up 93-94); Northern Lg(6) 67-68 71-7273-74 76-79 (R-up(3) 74-75 79-81), Lg Cup(5) 65-66 67-68 79-81 86-87; Turney Wylde Cup 80-81; J R Cleator Cup 80-81 86-87; Northern Counties (East) Lg 92-93(Lg Cup 92-93); Durham Challenge Cup 29-30 44-45 45-46 53-54 62-63 67-68 72-7373-74 74-75 75-76 78-79 82-83 93-94 94-95 95-96 97-98; Durham Benevolent Bowl26-27 29-30 31-32 47-48 58-59 60-61; North Eastern Lg(4) 09-10 44-46 56-57 (Lg Cup 28-29).
Players Progressing: Over fifty, including: H. Hubbick (Burnley, 3.25), T .Dawson (Charlton, 3.39), T. Flockett (Charlton, 4.49), J. Smallwood(Chesterfield, 12.49), J. Oakes (Aldershot, 5.54), J. Adams (Luton Town, 53),Alan Moore (Chesterfield), Michael Heathcote (Sunderland, 5.87), Jason Ainsley(Hartlepool, 94), Richie Alderson (York City 97), Graeme Paxton (Newcastle Utd 97)

Action from the Moors match against Emley at Wakefield Trinity

Match Facts 1999-00

	Date	Comp.	H/A	Opponents	Att.	Result	Goalscorers
1	14.08	UNIB P	H	RUNCORN	176	W 3 - 0	Powell 9 23, Howarth 54
2	21.08	UNIB P	H	WINSFORD UNITED	231	D 0 - 0	
3	24.08	UNIB P	H	FRICKLEY ATHLETIC	207	W 3 - 2	Howarth 12[p], Powell 24, Moat 31
4	28.08	UNIB P	A	Hyde United	401	L 1 - 2	Powell 10
5	30.08	UNIB P	H	WHITBY TOWN	319	D 1 - 1	Moat 15
6	04.09	UNIB P	A	Leek Town	320	L 0 - 1	
7	07.09	UNIB P	A	Guiseley	267	L 1 - 3	Nelson 3
8	11.09	UNIB P	H	GAINSBOROUGH TRINITY	171	L 0 - 2	
	14.09	ULC 1G	A	Whitby Town	269	L 1 - 3	Vine 23
	18.09	FAC Q2	A	Ossett Town	127	L 1 - 2	Ramsey 78
9	21.09	UNIB P	A	WORKSOP TOWN	167	W 2 - 1	Ramsey 9, Howarth 23
	28.09	ULC 1G	H	BISHOP AUCKLAND	287	D 2 - 2	Vine 6, Fairhurst 85
10	05.10	UNIB P	A	Blyth Spartans	363	W 3 - 2	Howard 16, Fairhurst 65, Burke 90[og]
	09.10	FAT 1	A	Paget Rangers	107	W 1 - 0	Williams 53
11	12.10	UNIB P	H	BLYTH SPARTANS	297	D 0 - 0	
12	16.10	UNIB P	A	Colwyn Bay	179	W 2 - 0	Powell 56, Howarth 90
13	19.10	UNIB P	A	Whitby Town	310	D 1 - 1	Dixon 52[og]
14	23.10	UNIB P	H	BAMBER BRIDGE	191	W 3 - 1	Nelson 10 34, Howarth 18
15	26.10	UNIB P	H	GUISELEY	266	L 1 - 4	Howarth 49
16	30.10	UNIB P	A	Droylsden	182	W 1 - 0	Bowes 85
17	06.11	UNIB P	H	EMLEY	279	L 2 - 3	Bowes 38 77
18	13.11	UNIB P	A	Stalybridge Celtic	372	L 0 - 1	
19	20.11	UNIB P	A	Gateshead	279	L 2 - 6	Howarth 45, Moat 46
20	20.11	UNIB P	A	Barrow	1035	L 0 - 1	
	27.11	FAT 2	H	GRETNA	199	W 2 - 1	Bowes 71, Fairhurst 86
21	04.12	UNIB P	H	COLWYN BAY	163	D 1 - 1	Bowes 22
22	27.12	UNIB P	A	Bishop Auckland	424	W 3 - 0	Bates 33, Moat 79 88
23	03.01	UNIB P	H	BISHOP AUCKLAND	457	L 0 - 1	
24	08.01	UNIB P	A	Marine	358	L 0 - 3	
	15.01	FAT 3	H	HARROGATE TOWN	218	D 1 - 1	Bowes 5
	18.01	FAT 3R	A	Harrogate Town	282	L 2 - 3	Moat 20 58
25	22.01	UNIB P	A	Gainsborough Trinity	394	L 0 - 4	
26	29.01	UNIB P	H	DROYLSDEN	135	D 1 - 1	Howarth 11
	01.02	FAT 3 rematch	A	Harrogate Town	356	W 2 - 0	Moat 45, Bowes 75
	05.02	FAT 4	H	BISHOP AUCKLAND	422	L 0 - 3	
27	12.02	UNIB P	A	Lancaster City	242	L 0 - 3	
28	15.02	UNIB P	A	Frickley Athletic	144	D 1 - 1	Lowe 90
29	19.02	UNIB P	H	HUCKNALL TOWN	171	D 1 - 1	Flanagan 21
30	26.02	UNIB P	A	Worksop Town	339	L 1 - 5	Veart 85
31	04.03	UNIB P	H	BARROW	201	D 0 - 0	
32	11.03	UNIB P	H	GATESHEAD	305	L 0 - 2	
33	18.03	UNIB P	A	Winsford United	105	L 0 - 3	
34	25.03	UNIB P	H	HYDE UNITED	192	D 0 - 0	
35	28.03	UNIB P	A	Leigh RMI	253	L 0 - 4	
36	01.04	UNIB P	A	Bamber Bridge	269	L 0 - 2	
37	08.04	UNIB P	A	Hucknall Town	160	D 0 - 0	
38	11.04	UNIB P	H	LEEK TOWN	155	W 3 - 1	Forster 70, Fletcher 89, Howarth 90 (p)
39	15.04	UNIB P	H	STALYBRIDGE CELTIC	160	W 1 - 0	Howarth 11 (p)
40	22.04	UNIB P	A	Emley	291	L 0 - 2	
41	24.04	UNIB P	H	LANCASTER CITY	254	D 0 - 0	
42	29.04	UNIB P	H	LEIGH RMI	235	L 1 - 3	Zand 64
43	04.05	UNIB P	A	Runcorn	179	L 2 - 3	Bowes 12, 79
44	06.05	UNIB P	H	MARINE	263	D 0 - 0	

PLAYING SQUAD

GOALKEEPERS: John Jackson (Billingham Synthonia)

DEFENDERS: Matthew Sowden (West Auckland T), Robert Jones (Northallerton T), Steve Makin (Whitley Bay), Gary Andison (Bedlington Terriers), Andy Bowes (Shildon), David Bellamy (Crook T)

MIDFIELDERS: Craig Veart (Bishop Auckland), Paul Zand (West Auckland T), Chris Leonard (Macclesfield T), Lee Bennett (Crook T), Martin Mulcaster (Northallerton T)

FORWARDS: Martin Bowes (Middlesbrough), Mark Wheldon (West Auckland T), Ross Foreman (Northallerton T), Andy Swalwell (Ballymena U)

STALYBRIDGE CELTIC

CLUB OFFICIALS
President: Roy Oldham
Chairman: **Peter Dennerley**
Vice Chairman:
Football Secretary: **Martyn Torr**
c/o the club. Tel: 0161 628 3387 (H)
0161 338 2828 (B) 0161 338 8256 (Fax)
Commercial Manager: **Terry Hollis**
Tel: 0161 338 2681 (B)
Press Officer: **Keith Trudgeon**
Tel: 0161205 7631 (B) 0161 304 8934 (H)

FOOTBALL MANAGEMENT TEAM
Manager: Phil Wilson
Asst. Man.: Peter Ward
Physio: Dave Pover

FACT FILE

Sponsors: Manro Ltd.
Formed: 1909
Nickname: Celtic
Club colours: Blue & white/blue/blue
Change colours:Old Goldhoops/green/green
Midweek home matchday: Tuesday
Reserves' League: None

1999-00
Top Scorer: Winfield Steele
P.o.Y.: Steve Pickard

GROUND Bower Fold, Mottram Road, Stalybridge, Cheshire SK15 2RT
Tel: 0161 338 2828 Fax: 0161 338 8256.
Directions: M6 to A556 to M63 to M67; end of Motorway through roundabout to traffic lights, left; left at end into Mottram Road, up hill, down hill into Stalybridge, ground on left next to Hare & Hounds pub.
Capacity: 6,000   Seats: 1,300   Cover: 1,300
Clubhouse: Open matchdays and evenings during the week. Food available on matchdays.
Club Shop: Contact John Hall (H) 01457 869262

Pages: 40 Price: £1.30
Editor: Nick Shaw (0161 633 1117)
Local Press: Manchester Evening News,
Manchester Evening News Pink (Sat.eve.),
Aston Reporter, Ashton Advertiser
Local Radio : G.M.R. (BBC Manchester),
Piccadilly Radio

PREVIOUS   **Leagues:** Lancashire Combination 1911-12, Central Lge 1912-21, Football Lge1921-23, Cheshire Co. Lge 1923-1982, North West Co's 1982-87, Northern Prem.Lge 1987-92.   **Grounds:** None   **Names:** None

CLUB RECORDS   **Attendance:** 9,753 v WBA, FA Cup replay, 22-23
Win: 16-2 twice; v Manchester NE 1.5.26; v Nantwich 22/10/32   **Defeat:** 0-6 vNorthwich Victoria
Career appearances: Kevin Booth 354   **Career goalscorer:** Unknown   **Goalscorer(season):** Chris Camden 45, 91-92
Fee paid: £15,000 to Kettering Town for Ian Arnold 95   **Fee received:** £16,000 for Lee Trundle from Southport

BEST SEASON   **FA Cup:** Second Round 93-94, 1-3 v Carlisle Utd.(A) and Chester City 99-00 , 1-2 League clubs defeated: None
FA Trophy: Third Round 1991-92, 0-1 v Witton Albion (A).

HONOURS   Northern Premier Lg Prem Div 91-92, R-up 90-91 (Div.1 R-up 87-88); Cheshire Cnty Lg 79-80 (R-up 77-78), Lg Cup 21-22 (R-up 46-47,81-82); Challenge Shield77-78 (R-up 79-80), Res Div R-up 81-82; NW Co's Lg 83-84, 86-87 (Lge Cup R-up83-84), Champions v Cup Winners Trophy 83-84; Lancs Comb Div 2 11-12; Cheshire Snr Cup 52-53 (R-up 54-55, 80-81); Manchester Snr Cup 22-23, Intermediate Cup57-58, 68-69 (R-up 56-57, 67-68, 69-70); Challenge Shield 54-55, (Junior Cup62-63); Lancs Floodlit Cup 88-89 (R-up 89-90); Reporter Cup R-up 74-75; Edward Case Cup 77-78.

Players Progressing : Too numerous to list.

Celtic's Tony Sullivan battling it out with former colleague Brendan Burke in the Unibond Challenge Shield match last season.
Photo: Colin Stevens

Match Facts 1999-00

	Date	Comp.	H/A	Opponents	Att.	Result	Goalscorers
1	14.08	UNIB P	H	LANCASTER CITY	383	D 1 - 1	Steele 38
2	17.08	UNIB P	A	Frickley Athletic	152	D 1 - 1	Bauress 68
3	21.08	UNIB P	H	BISHOP AUCKLAND	368	W 5 - 0	Parr 30, Jones 34 36, Ward 68, Steele 90
4	24.08	UNIB P	H	GAINSBOROUGH TRINITY	381	W 2 - 0	Curtis 69[og], Steele 89
5	28.08	UNIB P	A	Hucknall Town	275	L 0 - 4	
6	30.08	UNIB P	A	Colwyn Bay	258	D 0 - 0	
7	04.09	UNIB P	H	BLYTH SPARTANS	461	W 2 - 0	Pickford 8, Steele 43
8	07.09	UNIB P	A	Worksop Town	337	L 1 - 2	Jones 56
9	11.09	UNIB P	H	GATESHEAD	420	W 1 - 0	Filson 76
	14.09	ULC 1G	H	ACCRINGTON STANLEY	254	L 0 - 3	
	18.09	FAC Q2	H	COLWYN BAY	435	W 1 - 0	Sullivan 17
	21.09	Ches.SC 1	A	Woodley Sports	151	W 3 - 0	Sullivan 45, Steele 60, Marginson 88
10	25.09	UNIB P	A	Emley	353	W 1 - 0	McNeil 76
11	28.09	UNIB P	H	LEEK TOWN	413	W 3 - 2	Steele 10 82, Jones 51
	02.10	FAC Q3	H	FARSLEY CELTIC	447	W 4 - 2	Bauress 9[p], Jones 30, Marginson 85, Steele 89
12	09.10	UNIB P	H	Marine	397	W 3 - 1	Parr 42, Steele 59 90
	12.10	ULC G15	A	Droylsden	316	W 2 - 0	McNeil 65, Steele 90
	16.10	FAC Q4	A	Altrincham	1186	D 0 - 0	
	19.10	FAC Q4 r	H	ALTRINCHAM	791	W 2 - 1	Bauress 25, Mason 60
13	23.10	UNIB P	A	Whitby Town	399	L 0 - 1	
14	26.10	UNIB P	A	Lancaster City	345	L 2 - 3	Pickford 40, Parr 75
	30.10	FAC Q4 r*	H	ALTRINCHAM	1051	W 3 - 2	Filson 50 72, Steele 107
	02.11	FAC 1	A	Merthyr Tydfil	871	D 2 - 2	Parr 9, Sullivan 42
15	06.11	UNIB P	A	Barrow	1076	D 1 - 1	Jones 18
	09.11	FAC 1 r	H	MERTHYR TYDFIL	1399	W 3 - 1	Bauress 2[p], Pickford 24, Sullivan 86
16	13.11	UNIB P	H	SPENNYMOOR UNITED	372	W 1 - 0	Mason 36
	16.11	Ches.SC QF	H	WARRINGTON TOWN	175	W 2 - 0	Marginson 14, Mason 87
	20.11	FAC 2	A	CHESTER CITY	3312	L 1 - 2	Scott 8
	27.11	FAT 2	H	GAINSBOROUGH TRIN.	420	D 1 - 1	Sullivan 68
17	04.12	UNIB P	A	Guiseley	274	D 2 - 2	Jones 1, Johnston 26
18	11.12	UNIB P	A	Blyth Spartans	276	W 4 - 1	Jones 16, Sullivan 81, Mason 81, Steele 90
19	27.12	UNIB P	A	Hyde United	1772	L 0 - 1	
20	03.01	UNIB P	H	HYDE UNITED	1728	W 3 - 1	Bauress 70[p], Johnston 89, Steele 90
21	08.01	UNIB P	A	Bamber Bridge	459	W 4 - 1	Mason 5 15 50, Maddock 64[og]
	15.01	FAT 3	H	BLYTH SPARTANS	579	W 1 - 0	Stratford 22
22	18.01	UNIB P	H	LEIGH RMI	423	L 1 - 3	Johnston 45
23	22.01	UNIB P	H	EMLEY	418	D 0 - 0	
	25.01	Ches. SC SF	A	Altrincham	457	L 1 - 2	Sullivan 37
24	29.01	UNIB P	H	WHITBY TOWN	387	L 0 - 3	
25	01.02	UNIB P	A	Winsford United	201	W 2 - 1	Sullivan 5, Mason 86
	05.02	FAT 4	H	WORCESTER CITY	747	L 0 - 1	
26	12.02	UNIB P	H	MARINE	440	L 0 - 3	
27	19.02	UNIB P	H	DROYLSDEN	422	D 0 - 0	
28	26.02	UNIB P	A	Gateshead	278	L 0 - 2	
29	04.03	UNIB P	H	GUISELEY	377	W 2 - 1	Sullivan 4, Jones 43
30	11.03	UNIB P	H	WORKSOP TOWN	428	W 4 - 3	Sullivan 4, Jones 45, Steele 81, Bauress 90[p]
31	14.03	UNIB P	A	Droylsden	445	L 0 - 1	
32	18.03	UNIB P	H	FRICKLEY ATHLETIC	309	L 2 - 3	Parr 52, Filson 77
33	22.03	UNIB P	A	Bishop Auckland	191	L 0 - 1	
34	25.03	UNIB P	A	Runcorn	225	D 0 - 0	
35	28.03	UNIB P	H	RUNCORN	220	D 1 - 1	McNeil 69
36	01.03	UNIB P	H	BARROW	338	W 3 - 1	Steele 59, Sullivan 65, Filson 89
37	04.04	UNIB P	H	BAMBER BRIDGE	138	D 2 - 2	Steele 49, Parr 81
38	11.04	UNIB P	A	Gainsborough Trinity	345	D 1 - 1	McNeil 5
39	15.04	UNIB P	A	Spennymoor United	160	L 0 - 1	
40	18.04	UNIB P	H	HUCKNALL TOWN	204	W 2 - 1	Sullivan 16, Johnston 39
41	22.04	UNIB P	A	Leigh RMI	304	L 0 - 2	
42	24.04	UNIB P	H	WINSFORD UNITED	256	W 4 - 1	Bauress 3 (p), Jones 35, Stanhope 70, McNeill 89
43	29.04	UNIB P	H	COLWYN BAY	275	W 3 - 1	Johnston 10 (p), Sullivan 13, Parr 23
44	01.05	UNIB P	A	Leek Town	274	D 0 - 0	

PLAYING SQUAD

GOALKEEPERS: Gary Ingham (Leek T)

DEFENDERS: Billy McCartney (Trafford), Gary Bauress (Barrow), Matt Williamson (Glossop NE), Dominic Crookes (Northwich V), Stuart Locke (Leigh RMI), Derek Ward (Northwich V), Martin Filson (Bangor C)

MIDFIELDERS: Kevin Parr (Glossop NE), Steve Pickford (Glossop NE), Andrew Scott (Rochdale), Winfield Steele (Chorley), Steve Jones (Leek T), Jon Stanhope (Wrexham)

FORWARDS: Tony Sullivan (Prescot Cables), Steve Heaton (Glossop NE), Matt McNeil (Woodley Sports), Paul Higginbotham (Salford C)

WHITBY TOWN

CLUB OFFICIALS

Chairman: **Graham Manser.**
President: **Brooks Mileson**
Secretary: **Charlie Woodward**
6 Westlands Ave, Whitby,
North Yorks YO21 3DZ Tel: 01947 602312
Press Officer: Secretary

FOOTBALL MANAGEMENT TEAM

Manager: Harry Dunn
Asst Manager: David Logan
Physio: S.Collins

FACT FILE
Formed: 1926
Nickname: Seasiders
Sponsors: Sports Net.
Colours: All Royal Blue
Change Colours: All white.
Midweek matchday: Tuesday
Reserve League: Teeside League

1999-00
Captain: David Logan
P.o.Y.: David Logan
Top scorer: David Goodchild (17)

GROUND

Turnbull Ground, Upgang Lane, Whitby, North Yorks
Fax: 01947 603779   Tel: 01947 604847

Directions: Take the A174 road from town centre.
Ground on offside travelling towards Sandsend.
Capacity: 3,200   Cover: 500   Seats: 300
Clubhouse: Mon-Fri 7-11pm, Sat 12-11pm, Sun 12-2 & 7-10.30.
Club Shop: Yes

The F.A. UMBRO TROPHY 3rd Round
WHITBY TOWN
v
TELFORD UNITED
Saturday 15th January 2000   K.O. 3.00 p.m.

£1.20

Pages: 40 Price: £1
Editor: C Woodward (01947 602312)

Local Press: Whitby Gazette, Northern Echo.
Local Radio: Yorkshire Coast Radio

PREVIOUS   **Leagues:** Northern League 1926-97.   **Name:** Whitby United (pre 1950).   **Grounds:** None

CLUB RECORDS   **Attendance:** 4,000 v Scarborough, N Riding Senior Cup 18.4.65
Career Goalscorer: Paul Pitman (375)   **Career Appearances:** Paul Pitman (468)
Win: 11-2 v Cargo Fleet Works 1950   **Fee Paid:** £2,500 for John Grady (Newcastle Blue Star 90)
Defeat: 3-13 v Willington 24.3.28   **Fee Received:** £5,000for Graham Robinson (Gateshead 97)

BEST SEASON   **FA Vase:** Winners 97.   **FA Amateur Cup:** Runner-up 1964-65
FA Trophy: QuarterFinals 1983-84   **FA Cup:** 2nd Round 83-84

HONOURS   FA Amateur Cup Runners-up 64-65; FA Vase Winners 96-97; NPL Div 1 97-98;Northern Lge 92-93 96-97 (R-up 27-28 63-64 67-68 81-82 82-83), Lg Cup 28-29 63-64 69-70 76-77 84-85 95-96; Rothmans National Cup 75-76 77-78; Nth Riding SnrCup 64-65 67-68 82-83 89-90, 98-99; N Riding Bene Cup 92-93; J R Cleator Cup 84-85 92-93 95-96 96-97; Mickey Skinner Trophy [5], Unibond Presidents Cup Finalists 99-00

Players Progressing: Malcolm Poskett (Hartlepool), Sammy Kemp (Huddersfield), Jimmy Mulvaney (Hartlepool, Barrow, Stockport), Bobby Veart (Hartlepool), Derek Hampton & Trevor Smith & John Linacre & Phil Linacre(Hartlepool), Mark Hine (Grimsby). David Logan (Mansfield)

Left - Right
Back Row:
L Ludlow,
G Messer,
M Donnelly,
S Dawson,
D Goodchild,
C Hudson,
B Dixon.

Front Row:
J Dobbin,
A Skedd,
G Willimas,
mascots,
D Logan
(captain)

Match Facts 1999-00

#	Date	Comp.	H/A	Opponents	Att.	Result	Goalscorers
1	14.08	UNIB P	H	BISHOP AUCKLAND	633	D 2 - 2	Banks 22, Pitman 64
2	17.08	UNIB P	H	BLYTH SPARTANS	481	L 1 - 2	Harris 90
3	21.08	UNIB P	A	Runcorn	285	L 1 - 3	Williams 89
4	23.08	UNIB P	A	Emley	286	L 1 - 2	Logan 45[p]
5	28.08	UNIB P	H	WINSFORD UNITED	388	D 2 - 2	Logan 26 27
6	30.08	UNIB P	A	Spennymoor United	319	D 1 - 1	Ure 62
7	04.09	UNIB P	H	HYDE UNITED	369	D 1 - 1	Logan 64[p]
8	07.09	UNIB P	H	GATESHEAD	389	L 0 - 2	
9	11.09	UNIB P	A	Leigh RMI	202	L 1 - 2	Banks 31
	14.09	ULC 1G	H	SPENNYMOOR UNITED	269	W 3 - 1	Featherstone 28, West 30, Dunwell 44
	18.09	FAC Q2	A	Accrington Stanley	357	W 2 - 0	Featherstone 27, Goodchild 78
10	21.09	UNIB P	A	Hucknall Town		L 2 - 3	Featherstone 44, Perry 90
11	25.09	UNIB P	A	Leek Town	352	L 1 - 2	Pearson 78
12	28.09	UNIB P	H	EMLEY	363	L 0 - 1	
	02.10	FAC Q3	A	Lancaster City	295	D 2 - 2	Goodchild 17, Skedd 71
	05.10	FAC Q3R	H	LANCASTER CITY	418	D 2 - 2	Goodchild 35, Williams 64 Lost 2-4 after penalties
13	09.10	UNIB P	H	BAMBER BRIDGE	375	D 1 - 1	Ure 28
	13.10	ULC G13	A	Bishop Auckland	147	W 1 - 0	Pearson 67
14	16.10	UNIB P	A	Worksop Town	400	L 1 - 4	Robinson 4
15	19.10	UNIB P	H	SPENNYMOOR UNITED	310	D 1 - 1	Robinson 90
16	23.10	UNIB P	H	STALYBRIDGE CELTIC	399	W 1 - 0	Perry 86
17	30.10	UNIB P	A	Colwyn Bay	176	L 0 - 2	
	03.11	ULC GF	A	Gateshead	180	W 3 - 2	Irvine 44, Pearson 55, Robinson 65
18	06.11	UNIB P	A	MARINE	311	L 0 - 3	
	09.11	ULC GF	H	FRICKLEY ATHLETIC	217	L 0 - 2	
19	12.11	UNIB P	A	Gainsborough Trinity	575	D 1 - 1	Messer 27
20	20.11	UNIB P	H	FRICKLEY ATHLETIC	306	W 3 - 0	Ludlow 33, Robinson 68, Dobbin 86
	27.11	FAT 2	H	STAMFORD	391	W 4 - 1	Dixon 45 48, Robinson 80, Ure 87
21	04.12	UNIB P	A	Marine	246	D 3 - 3	Logan 36[p], Dixon 56, Ludlow 89
22	11.12	UNIB P	H	RUNCORN	354	W 4 - 0	Ludlow 52 59, Donnelly 83, Logan 84
23	18.12	UNIB P	A	Winsford United	92	D 1 - 1	Messer 28
24	27.12	UNIB P	H	HUCKNALL TOWN	611	W 2 - 1	Messer 21, Ludlow 69
25	03.01	UNIB P	A	Gateshead	404	D 0 - 0	
26	08.01	UNIB P	H	GAINSBOROUGH TRINITY	489	W 2 - 1	Messer 43, Goodchild 79
	15.01	FAT 3	H	TELFORD UNITED	547	L 1 - 3	Ludlow 76
	22.01	P. C. QF	A	Radcliffe Borough	170	W 2 - 0	Logan 15[p], Ludlow 90
27	29.01	UNIB P	A	Stalybridge Celtic	387	W 3 - 0	Logan 45, Ludlow 49 57
28	05.02	UNIB P	H	LANCASTER CITY	468	W 1 - 0	West 39
29	12.02	UNIB P	A	Frickley Athletic	178	L 1 - 2	Ludlow 48
30	16.02	UNIB P	A	Bishop Auckland	236	L 0 - 4	
31	19.02	UNIB P	H	COLWYN BAY	366	D 1 - 1	Goodchild 10
	22.02	N R SC4	H	MARSKE UNITED	254	L 2 - 3	Logan 2, Ludlow 77
32	26.02	UNIB P	A	Hyde United	407	L 1 - 4	Ludlow 9
	04.03	P.C. SF	A	Leigh RMI	159	W 3 - 1	Burke 2, Dixon 18, Goodchild 84
33	11.03	UNIB P	H	LEIGH RMI	489	W 2 - 0	Logan 44, Goodchild 45
34	18.03	UNIB P	A	Lancaster City	262	W 2 - 1	Ludlow 37, Goodchild 73
35	25.03	UNIB P	A	Barrow	1135	W 3 - 0	Goodchild 8, Key 15, Robinson 48
36	01.04	UNIB P	H	LEEK TOWN	445	W 3 - 1	Carrlawton 31, Goodchild 54, Burke 67(p)
37	08.04	UNIB P	H	BARROW	481	D 1 - 1	Robinson 15
	11.04	P.C. Final 1	A	Trafford	205	L 1 - 2	Goodchild 58
38	15.04	UNIB P	A	Guiseley	317	W 1 - 0	Carrlawton 45
39	22.04	UNIB P	H	GUISELEY	494	W 3 - 1	Robinson 47, Ure 64, Dixon 84
40	24.04	UNIB P	H	Blyth Spartans	392	L 0 - 2	
41	26.04	UNIB P	H	DROYLSDEN	344	W 5 - 2	Ure 5, Goodchild 10, Graham 13, Logan 65 (p), Carr-Lawton 81
42	29.04	UNIB P	A	Droylsden		L 2 - 3	Logan 40, Goodchild 88
43	01.05	UNIB P	H	WORKSOP TOWN	447	W 2 - 1	Dobbin 5, Goodchild 69
	04.05	P.C. Final 2	H	Trafford	561	W *4 - 3	**Goodchild 3** (47, 65, 90), Ure 111 Lost 2-4 after pens
44	06.05	UNIB P	A	Bamber Bridge	244	D 2 - 2	Logan 4, 87 (p)

PLAYING SQUAD

GOALKEEPERS: Stuart Dawson (Tow Law T), David Campbell (Spennymoor U)

DEFENDERS: Ben Dixon (Woodlands Wellington (Sing)), David Goodchild (North Ormesby), Mark Taylor (Spennymoor U), Mark Donnelly (Bury), Graham Rennison (York), Danny Key (Crook T), David Logan (Bishop Auckland), Graeme Williams (Guisborough T)

MIDFIELDERS: Carl Chillingsworth (Coleraine), Mitch Cook (Scarborough), Terry O'Hanlon (Southport), Neil Radigan (Darlington), John Ewart (Brandon U)

FORWARDS: Lee Ludlow (Bedlington Terriers), Lee Ure (Norton), Gary Messer (Bury), Graeme Robinson (Gateshead), Stuart Irvine (Bishop Auckland)

WORKSOP TOWN

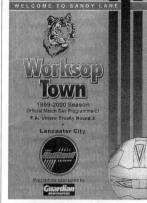

WELCOME TO SANDY LANE

Worksop Town
1999-2000 Season
Official Match Day Programme £1
F.A. Umbro Trophy Round 3
v
Lancaster City

Programme sponsored by
Guardian
NEWSPAPERS

CLUB OFFICIALS
Chairman: **Rick Knowles**
Vice Chairman: **John Shuker**
Club Secretary: **Keith Illett**, 2 Mount Ave.,
Worksop, Notts (01909 487934)
General Manager:**Danny Hague**
Company Secretary: **L.Hood**
Press Officer: **Mel Bradley**
Commercial Manager: **Kevin Barratt**

FOOTBALL MANAGEMENT TEAM
Team Manager: Paul Mitchell
Coach: Peter Rinkcavage
Physio: Graham Bacon

FACT FILE
Formed: 1861   Nickname:The Tigers
Sponsors: D.T.H. Engineers/Eyres of
Worksop/Norwood Fisheries/Erriccsons

Colours: Amber & black/white/white
Change colours: All white/amber/black trim
Midweek home matchday: Tuesday.
Reserves' League: County Sen.B.I.R. U19s:
F.A.Northern Academy
Youth Teams' Lge: U21's Central Mid
U18s Notts Imp.

99-00 Captain: Linden Whitehead
P.o.Y.: Gavin Smith

GROUND
Babbage Way, off Sandy Lane, Worksop, Notts S80 1UJ (01909 501911).
Directions: M1 jct 31 (from north) jct 30 (from south), follow Worksop signs,join A57 and fol-
low signs for Sandy Lane Industrial Estate - ground on left. 5mins walk from station.
Capacity: 3,000   Cover: 1,000   Seats: 900
Clubhouse: Tigers Club. Normal licensing hours. Pool, quiz nights, disco etc.
Club Shop: 'The Tigershop' 30 page catalogue from
Steve Jarvis, 10 Wood End Drive, Ravenshead, Notts NG15 9EJ.

Pages: 28-32   Price: £1
Editor: Mel Bradley (01909 500491/500500)
Local Press: Worksop Guardian, Worksop
Star, Nottingham Football Post.
Local Radio: Radio Sheffield, Radio Hallam,
Radio Lincoln.,Trax FM

PREVIOUS   **Leagues:** Midland (Counties)1896-98 1900-30 49-60 61-68 69-74, Sheffield Assoc. 1898-99 1931-33, Central Comb. 33-
35, Yorkshire 35-39, Central All. 47-49 60-61, Northern Premier 68-69,74-
Grounds: Netherton Road, Bridge Meadow, Central Ave. (pre 1989), The Northolme (Gainsborough Trin. - shared) 89-92.

CLUB RECORDS   **Attendance:** 1,503 v Sheffield Utd, friendly. Central Avenue: 8,171 v Chesterfield, FA Cup 1925 .
Goalscorer: Kenny Clark, 287   **Appearances:** Kenny Clark 347
Win: 20-0 v Staveley, 1/9/1894   **Defeat:** 1-11 v Hull City Res., 55-56.
Fee Received: £47,000 for Jon Kennedy, Sunderland May 2000 **Paid:** £5,000 for Kirk Jackson to Grantham Town, 98-99

BEST SEASON   **FA Cup:** 3rd Rd: 07-08 v Chelsea (A) 1-9, 21-22 v Southend (H) 1-2, 22-23 v Spurs (A) 0-0, 0-9, 55-56 v Swindon (A) 0-1.
2nd Rd: 25-26, 1st Rd: 20-21, 26-27, 61-62, 78-79. **League Clubs defeated:** Rotherham T. 1894-95, Grimsby T. 94-95,
Nelson 1921-22, Chesterfield 22-23, Coventry C. 25-26, Bradford C. 55-56.   **FA Trophy:** 2nd Rd replay 73-74.

HONOURS   N.P.L. Presidents Cup 85-86 95-96, Unibond Div One Runners-up 97-98, Unibond Premier Div. Runners-up 98-99
Sheffield Assoc. Lg 1898-99, Sheffield & Hallamshire Snr Cup 23-24 52-53 54-55 65-66 69-70 72-73 81-82 84-85 96-97,
Mansfield Charity Cup 22-23; Midland Cos Lg 21-22 65-66 72-73 (R-up 62-6366-67 73-74).

Players P rogressing: J Brown (Sheff Wed), G Dale (Chesterfield 48), A Daley(Doncaster 50), K Wood (Grimsby 51), H Jarvis (Notts Co. 51),
B Taylor (Leeds51), S Rhodes 51, D Gratton 52, A Hodgkinson 53, J Harrison 67 (Sheffield Utd),S Lloyd & P Marshall (Scunthorpe 54),
A Rhodes (QPR 54), R Moore (Rotherham55), H Mosby (Crewe 1956), L Moore (Derby 1957), H Bowery (Nottm Forest 75),
T Moore (Rochdale 84), S Adams (Scarborough 87), D Moss (Doncaster 93), Jon Kennedy (Sunderland 00).

Back Row: V Powell, J Gibbins, N Pickering, P Stafford, C Atkinson, G Townsend, J Holmshaw, J Kennedy, L Hobson, K Clark, R
Mason, M Goddard, S Varley. **Front:** G Smith, K Jackson, R Ludlam, R Davis, L Whitehead, S Johnson, C Smith, A Nixon.
Photo © North Notts Newspapers Ltd.

Match Facts 1999-00

	Date	Comp.	H/A	Opponents	Att.	Result	Goalscorers	Lge Pos.
1	14.08	UNIB P	H	BAMBER BRIDGE	457	L 0 - 2		
2	17.08	UNIB P	A	Hucknall Town	690	W 1 - 0	Begley 83[og]	
3	21.08	UNIB P	A	Lancaster City	292	D 0 - 0		
4	24.08	UNIB P	H	HYDE UNITED	434	D 1 - 1	Field 24	
5	28.08	UNIB P	H	BISHOP AUCKLAND	390	L 1 - 2	Goddard 57	
6	30.08	UNIB P	A	Frickley Athletic	283	W 3 - 1	Whitehead 6, Mason 17, Stafford 82	
7	04.09	UNIB P	H	RUNCORN	404	L 0 - 3		
8	07.09	UNIB P	H	STALYBRIDGE CELTIC	337	W 2 - 1	Goddard 5, Stafford 26	
9	11.09	UNIB P	A	Colwyn Bay	224	L 1 - 3	Johnson 45	
	14.09	ULC 1G	H	HUCKNALL TOWN	272	W 1 - 0	Mason 13	
	18.09	FAC Q2	H	BISHOP AUCKLAND	351	L 2 - 3	Clark 52, 67	
10	21.09	UNIB P	A	Spennymoor United	167	L 1 - 2	Womble 58[p]	
11	25.09	UNIB P	H	GUISELEY	406	L 1 - 2	Townsend 70	
12	28.09	UNIB P	H	GATESHEAD	409	L 1 - 2	Clark 67	
13	02.10	UNIB P	A	Barrow	1154	W 3 - 2	Stafford 19, Townsend 39, Johnson 74	
	05.10	ULC G9	A	Eastwood Town	169	D 2 - 2	Townsend 75, Mason 83	
14	09.10	UNIB P	A	Hyde United	518	D 0 - 0		
15	16.10	UNIB P	H	WHITBY TOWN	400	W 4 - 1	Clark 50[p] 81, Ludlam 67, Smith 81	
16	19.10	UNIB P	A	Droylsden	163	W 2 - 0	Clark 45, Townsend 86	
17	23.10	UNIB P	H	LANCASTER CITY	462	W 4 - 1	Johnson 11, Clark 37, Smith 62, Jackson 86	
18	26.10	UNIB P	A	Leek Town	368	L 1 - 3	Johnson 71	
19	30.10	UNIB P	A	Winsford United	178	W 3 - 1	Hughes 64[og], Goddard 66 87	
	02.11	ULC GG	H	EMLEY	312	D 1 - 1	Jackson 26	
20	06.11	UNIB P	H	HUCKNALL TOWN	464	W 1 - 0	Johnson 88	
	09.11	Sheff.SC1	H	STOCKSBRIDGE P. S.		W 4 - 3	Jackson 10, Womble 77[p] 114, Goddard 109	
21	12.11	UNIB P	H	Emley	371	W 2 - 1	Smith 78, Whitehead 81	
22	20.11	UNIB P	H	MARINE	530	L 0 - 1		
	23.11	ULC GG	A	Lincoln United	170	W 3 - 2	Smith 14, Clark 63 86	
	27.11	FAT 2	A	Leigh RMI	232	D 1 - 1	Whitehead 90	
	30.11	FAT 2R	H	LEIGH RMI	335	W 3 - 1	Stafford 2, 35, S Johnson 53	
23	04.12	UNIB P	A	Bishop Auckland	214	W 2 - 1	Hobson 9, Goddard 33	
	08.12	S&H SC2	H	ECCLESFIELD RED ROSE	125	W 5 - 0	Stafford 19 25, Ludlam 52 79, Bark 85[og]	
24	17.12	UNIB P	H	EMLEY	448	L 0 - 1		
25	27.12	UNIB P	A	Gainsborough Trinity	1231	L 0 - 2		
26	03.01	UNIB P	H	FRICKLEY ATHLETIC	505	W 4 - 0	Johnson 28, Clark 45, Smith 49, Townsend 85	
27	08.01	UNIB P	A	Blyth Spartans	338	L 1 - 2	Johnson 9	
	15.01	FAT 3	A	LANCASTER CITY	440	D 1 - 1	Johnson 90	
	22.01	LC QF	H	RUNCORN	347	W 1 - 0	Townsend 30	
	25.01	FAT 3R	A	Lancaster City	260	W 3 - 0	Townsend 38, Johnson 42, Ludlam 66	
28	29.01	UNIB P	H	BLYTH SPARTANS	385	D 2 - 2	Townsend 83, Jackson 86	
	05.02	FAT 4	H	WORKINGTON	657	D 1 - 1	Jackson 64	
29	12.02	UNIB P	H	DROYLSDEN	351	D 1 - 1	Stafford 90	
	15.02	FAT 4 R	A	Workington	1029	L 0 - 1		
30	19.02	UNIB P	A	Runcorn	310	L 0 - 2		
31	26.02	UNIB P	H	SPENNYMOOR UNITED	339	W 5 - 1	Clark 3 (24 56 61), Smith 27, Whitehead 44	
	04.03	L.C. SF	A	Accrington Stanley	512	D 1 - 1	Clark 26[p]	Stafford 84
	07.03	S&H SC QF	H	DENABY UNITED	271	W 7 - 0	Townsend 9, 36, Johnson 27, Mason 64, Whitehead 69, Jackson 78,	
32	11.03	UNIB P	A	Stalybridge Celtic	428	L 3 - 4	Clark 14[p] 69, Goddard 84	
	14.03	L.C.SF R	H	ACCRINGTON STANLEY	588	D 1 - 1	Whitehead 35	Won 4-3 after pens
33	18.03	UNIB P	H	Leigh RMI	275	D 2 - 2	Johnson 20, Clark 25	
34	25.03	UNIB P	H	COLWYN BAY	317	W 4 - 2	Clark 39, 49, Jackson 52, Johnson 63	
35	01.04	UNIB P	A	Guiseley	297	W 1 - 0	Townsend 45	
36	08.04	UNIB P	A	Gateshead	286	L 2 - 3	Clark 41, Hibbins 54	
	11.04	L.C. F	N	Lancaster City	669	L 0 - 1		
37	15.04	UNIB P	A	Winsford United	329	W 9 - 0	Hobson 4, Jackson 3 (15, 37, 42), Whitehead 30, Clark 60 (p), Townsend 61, Atkinson 75, Johnson 89 (p)	
38	18.04	UNIB P	A	Bamber Bridge	196	W 3 - 2	Townsend 44, Frain 76, OG (McHugh) 90	
	20.04	S&H SC SF	H	EMLEY	324	L 1 - 2	Jackson 20	
39	22.04	UNIB P	A	Marine	303	L 2 - 3	Powell 52, 54	
40	24.04	UNIB P	H	GAINSBOROUGH T.	621	W 2 - 1	Townsend 17, Atkinson 88	
41	26.04	UNIB P	H	BARROW	383	L 0 - 2		
42	29.04	UNIB P	H	LEEK TOWN	384	W 2 - 0	Johnson 52, Pickering 75 (p)	
43	01.05	UNIB P	A	Whitby Town	447	L 1 - 2	Atkinson 78	
44	06.05	UNIB P	H	LEIGH RMI	449	L 0 - 3		

PLAYING SQUAD

GOALKEEPERS: Jamie Holmshaw (Gainsborough T), Ian Ironside (Oldham)

DEFENDERS: Adam Nixon (Rotherham), Darren Brookes (Alfreton T), Gavin Smith (Sheffield Wed), Tim Atkinson (Alfreton T), Ryan Ludlam (Sheffield Wed), Richard Mason (Boston U)

MIDFIELDERS: Chris Waddle (Sheffield Wed), Ryan Davis (Luton), Steve Johnson (Buxton), John Hibbins (Sheffield Wed), Linden Whitehead (Alfreton T), Scott Oxley (Hallam)

FORWARDS: Gary Townsend (Youth), Craig Atkinson (Frickley Ath), Kenny Clark (Matlock T), Kirk Jackson (Grantham T). Vill Powell (Derry C)

GUISELEY

Match Facts 1999-00

	Date	Comp.	H/A	Opponents	Att.	Result	Goalscorers
1	14.08	UNIB P	A	Leek Town	340	D 2 - 2	Parke 24, Agana 29
2	17.08	UNIB P	H	BISHOP AUCKLAND	305	L 0 - 3	
3	21.08	UNIB P	A	Colwyn Bay	243	W 2 - 0	Bower 68, Gallagher 80
4	24.08	UNIB P	H	GATESHEAD	207	D 1 - 1	Parke 16
5	28.08	UNIB P	A	Barrow	1,709	D 1 - 1	Parke 66
6	30.08	UNIB P	A	Leigh RMI	247	W 1 - 0	Ireland 8
7	04.09	UNIB P	H	LANCASTER CITY	313	L 0 - 1	
8	07.09	UNIB P	H	SPENNYMOOR UNITED	267	W 3 - 1	**Parke 3** (7 50 63)
9	11.09	UNIB P	A	Hyde United	414	L 0 - 2	
	14.09	ULC 1G	H	HARROGATE TOWN	230	W 1 - 0	Phillips 75
	18.09	FAC Q2	H	PICKERING TOWN	387	W 6 - 0	Agana 14, Poole 18, Reid 30 [og], Parke 66, 75, Daly 69
10	25.09	UNIB P	A	Worksop Town	406	W 2 - 1	Johnson 73[og], Agana 90
11	28.09	UNIB P	H	RUNCORN	240	D 2 - 2	Agana 51, 65
	02.10	FAC Q3	A	North Ferriby United	429	W 3 - 1	Shuttleworth 34, 40, Williams 35
	05.10	ULC G12	A	Farsley Celtic	180	D 1 - 1	Davison 42
	09.10	FAT 1	H	FLIXTON	306	W 2 - 0	Hazel 38, Parke 49
12	12.10	UNIB P	A	Hucknall Town	328	D 1 - 1	Agana 88
	16.10	FAC Q4	A	Nuneaton Borough	2,175	W 3 - 2	Parke 3, 74, Agana 26
13	19.10	UNIB P	H	GAINSBOROUGH TRINITY	274	L 1 - 3	Parke 8
14	23.10	UNIB P	A	Marine	273	D 2 - 2	Parke 19, 79
15	26.10	UNIB P	A	Spennymoor United	266	W 4 - 1	Poole 12, Agana 28, Zoll 35, Bulgin 68
	30.10	FAC 1	A	Forest Green Rovers	1,047	L 0 - 6	
	02.11	ULC GE	H	BLYTH SPARTANS	139	W 2 - 0	Parke 4 57
16	06.11	UNIB P	A	Runcorn	307	D 2 - 2	Parke 7 37
	09.11	W.Rid SC1	A	Yorkshire Amateur	104	L 1 - 2	Stewart 77
17	12.11	UNIB P	H	DROYLSDEN	306	W 2 - 0	Gallagher 12, Poole 61
18	20.11	UNIB P	A	Lancaster City	277	L 0 - 2	
	27.11	FAT 2	H	NUNEATON BOROUGH	597	W 2 - 0	Poole 27, Parke 29
19	04.12	UNIB P	H	STALYBRIDGE CELTIC	274	D 2 - 2	Parke 45 84
20	27.12	UNIB P	A	Emley	498	D 1 - 1	Parke 83
21	03.01	UNIB P	H	BLYTH SPARTANS	383	W 2 - 1	Shuttleworth 39, Agana 42
22	08.01	UNIB P	H	HUCKNALL TOWN	310	L 1 - 2	Ireland 46
	15.01	FAT 3	A	Marine	397	L 1 - 2	Parke 59
	18.01	Unifilla QF	H	EMLEY	195	D 1 - 1	Gallagher 63[p]
23	22.01	UNIB P	H	WINSFORD UNITED	278	D 2 - 2	Parke 51, Shuttleworth 76
	24.01	Unifilla QFR	A	Emley	142	D 2 - 2	Shuttleworth 41, Gallagher 45 Lost 2-3 after pens
24	29.01	UNIB P	A	Winsford United	143	L 2 - 4	Agana 3, Ireland 6
25	05.02	UNIB P	A	Droylsden	224	L 0 - 3	
26	08.02	UNIB P	H	FRICKLEY ATHLETIC	156	L 0 - 1	
27	16.02	UNIB P	A	Gateshead	209	L 1 - 3	Daly 85
28	19.02	UNIB P	H	BAMBER BRIDGE	266	L 2 - 4	Hazel 49, Parke 87
29	26.02	UNIB P	A	Blyth Spartans	374	W 2 - 1	Parke 4 25
30	04.03	UNIB P	A	Stalybridge Celtic	377	L 1 - 2	Parke 45
31	11.03	UNIB P	H	COLWYN BAY	272	D 2 - 2	Cooke 12 75
32	14.03	UNIB P	A	Gainsborough Trinity	304	D 0 - 0	
33	18.03	UNIB P	H	LEEK TOWN	267	D 1 - 1	Daly 30
34	21.03	UNIB P	H	BARROW	282	D 0 - 0	
35	25.03	UNIB P	H	LEIGH RMI	274	L 0 - 3	
36	29.03	UNIB P	A	Bishop Auckland	220	L 0 - 1	
37	01.04	UNIB P	H	WORKSOP TOWN	297	L 0 - 1	
38	04.04	UNIB P	A	Frickley Athletic	150	D 2 - 2	Parke 6, Davison 50
39	08.04	UNIB P	H	MARINE	273	L 1 - 3	Shuttleworth 79
40	11.04	UNIB P	H	HYDE UNITED	204	L 0 - 1	
41	15.04	UNIB P	H	WHITBY TOWN	317	L 0 - 1	
42	22.04	UNIB P	A	Whitby Town	494	L 1 - 3	Cooke 77
43	24.04	UNIB P	H	EMLEY	270	L 1 - 1	Gallagher 52 (p)
44	29.04	UNIB P	A	Bamber Bridge	245	D 2 - 2	Ireland 7, Parke 36

WINSFORD UNITED

Match Facts 1999-00

	Date	Comp.	H/A	Opponents	Att.	Result	Goalscorers	Lge Pos.
1	14.08	UNIB P	H	FRICKLEY ATHLETIC	160	L 1 - 2	Higginbotham 76	
2	16.08	UNIB P	A	Hyde United	424	L 0 - 2		
3	21.08	UNIB P	A	Spennymoor United	231	D 0 - 0		20
4	24.08	UNIB P	H	LANCASTER CITY	133	L 0 - 2		
5	28.08	UNIB P	A	Whitby Town	388	D 2 - 2	Higginbotham 16, Bailey 62	22
6	30.08	UNIB P	H	LEEK TOWN	203	L 0 - 2		
7	04.09	UNIB P	H	HUCKNALL TOWN	132	L 1 - 2	Bailey 37	23
8	07.09	UNIB P	A	Bamber Bridge	315	L 1 - 2	Bailey 15[p]	23
9	11.09	UNIB P	H	EMLEY	151	L 1 - 2	Jones 84	23
	14.09	ULC G7	A	Leek Town	161	D 3 - 3	Brindley 2 20, Williams 62	-
	18.09	FAC Q2	A	Gateshead	226	L 0 - 3		-
	21.09	Ches.SC1	H	MACCLESFIELD TOWN		L 1 - 3	Williams 45	-
10	25.09	UNIB P	A	Bishop Auckland	192	L 1 - 4	Hayes 2	23
11	02.10	UNIB P	H	BLYTH SPARTANS	133	L 0 - 5		23
12	05.10	UNIB P	A	Colwyn Bay	189	L 0 - 2		23
13	09.10	UNIB P	H	GAINSBOROUGH TRINITY	118	L 1 - 2	Posford 8	23
	19.10	ULC G7	H	CONGLETON TOWN	106	L 1 - 2	Jones 89	-
14	23.10	UNIB P	A	Gateshead	256	L 0 - 2		23
15	26.10	UNIB P	A	Runcorn	286	L 0 - 1		23
16	30.10	UNIB P	H	WORKSOP TOWN	178	L 1 - 3	Harley 14	23
17	06.11	UNIB P	A	Frickley Athletic	144	L 1 - 3	Williams 44	23
18	20.11	UNIB P	A	Droylsden	207	L 0 - 3		23
	27.11	FAT 2	H	VS RUGBY	161	D 1 - 1	Hussin 35	-
19	04.12	UNIB P	H	LEIGH RMI	101	L 0 - 5		23
20	18.12	UNIB P	H	WHITBY TOWN	92	D 1 - 1	Moncrieffe 57	23
21	30.12	UNIB P	A	Barrow	2400	D 0 - 0		23
22	03.01	UNIB P	H	COLWYN BAY	210	L 1 - 2	Hussin 45	23
23	08.01	UNIB P	H	BARROW	370	L 0 - 2		23
24	15.01	UNIB P	A	Hucknall Town	220	L 0 - 4		23
25	22.01	UNIB P	A	Guiseley	278	D 2 - 2	Page 12, Worthington 16	23
26	29.01	UNIB P	H	GUISELEY	143	W 4 - 2	Pates 11, Shaughnessy 15, Richardson 23, Worthington 62	23
27	01.02	UNIB P	H	STALYBRIDGE CELTIC	201	L 1 - 2	Shaughnessy 19	23
28	04.02	UNIB P	A	Leigh RMI	255	L 2 - 3	Richardson 21, Gouldbourne 72	23
29	12.02	UNIB P	A	Emley	206	L 2 - 3	Worthington 25, Hussin 46	23
30	19.02	UNIB P	H	BISHOP AUCKLAND	135	L 2 - 5	Worthington 31, Rendell 55	23
31	22.02	UNIB P	A	Leek Town	298	W 2 - 1	Shaughnessy 49 74	23
32	04.03	UNIB P	A	Gainsborough Trinity	290	L 0 - 3		23
33	07.03	UNIB P	A	Lancaster City	146	L 1 - 4	Shaughnessy 54	23
34	11.03	UNIB P	H	DROYLSDEN	158	D 1 - 1	Rendell 86[p]	23
35	18.03	UNIB P	H	SPENNYMOOR UNITED	105	W 3 - 0	Harley 35, Worthington 44 63	23
36	21.03	UNIB P	H	HYDE UNITED	247	L 1 - 2	Worthington 55	23
37	01.04	UNIB P	H	MARINE	250	D 2 - 2	Hibbert 75, Rendell 90	23
38	04.04	UNIB P	H	RUNCORN	150	L 1 - 6	Hayder 27	23
39	08.04	UNIB P	A	Blyth Spartans	311	L 0 - 1		23
40	15.04	UNIB P	A	Worksop Town	329	L 0 - 9		23
41	18.04	UNIB P	A	Marine	223	L 1 - 3	Jones 45	23
42	22.04	UNIB P	H	BAMBER BRIDGE	105	L 1 - 5	Page 43	23
43	24.04	UNIB P	A	Stalybridge Celtic	256	L 1 - 4	Shaughnessy 71	23
44	06.05	UNIB P	H	GATESHEAD	145	L 1 - 3	Hayder 20	23

DIVISION ONE FINAL LEAGUE TABLE 1999-2000

			Home					Away					
		P	W	D	L	F	A	W	D	L	F	A	Pts
1	Accrington Stanley	42	14	5	2	55	19	11	4	6	41	24	84
2	Burscough	42	13	6	2	46	18	9	12	0	35	17	84
3	Witton Albion	42	13	6	2	49	24	10	9	2	39	22	84
4	Bradford P A	42	15	5	1	48	19	8	4	9	29	29	78
5	Radcliffe Borough	42	11	7	3	36	21	11	5	5	35	27	78
6	Farsley Celtic	42	12	5	4	34	20	7	6	8	32	32	68
7	Matlock Town	42	10	7	4	44	30	7	9	5	28	25	67
8	Ossett Town	42	10	5	6	39	24	7	3	11	38	31	59
9	Stocksbridge P S	42	11	2	8	30	30	5	6	10	25	40	56
10	Eastwood Town*	42	8	5	8	35	29	7	6	8	29	36	55
11	Harrogate Town	42	7	8	6	31	26	7	4	10	34	41	54
12	Congleton Town	42	8	5	8	31	30	6	7	8	32	43	54
13	Chorley	42	4	10	7	26	31	9	5	7	27	33	54
14	Ashton United	42	6	9	6	33	31	6	7	8	32	36	52
15	Workington	42	8	4	9	26	27	5	9	7	23	28	52
16	Lincoln United	42	8	5	8	31	37	5	7	9	21	43	51
17	Belper Town	42	8	5	8	31	31	5	6	10	28	41	50
18	Trafford	42	3	8	10	27	29	8	4	9	28	34	45
19	Gretna	42	7	5	9	32	34	4	2	15	16	44	40
20	Netherfield Kendal	42	5	6	10	26	36	3	3	15	20	46	33
21	Flixton	42	6	3	12	28	37	1	6	14	19	48	30
22	Whitley Bay	42	3	6	12	24	45	4	3	14	17	42	30

RESULTS CHART 1999-2000

HOME TEAM		1	2	3	4	5	6	7	8	9	10	11	12	13	14	15	16	17	18	19	20	21	22
1	Accrington S	X	2-1	4-1	2-1	2-2	0-0	1-0	2-2	3-0	2-0	3-2	5-0	10-1	0-0	4-1	2-1	1-3	4-1	1-2	3-0	0-0	4-1
2	Ashton Utd	1-2	X	3-0	2-2	0-0	1-2	1-1	3-1	1-1	2-0	3-1	2-1	2-3	1-1	1-0	2-4	1-4	2-2	0-1	2-2	2-2	1-1
3	Belper T	1-2	4-1	X	0-0	0-3	1-1	1-2	1-1	0-3	5-1	2-1	1-0	0-2	1-0	2-2	2-1	3-2	0-1	3-2	1-2	2-2	1-2
4	Bradford PA	1-0	2-3	2-1	X	1-1	4-1	3-2	1-0	1-1	3-1	6-0	2-2	4-1	4-3	3-0	1-0	1-1	2-0	3-0	1-0	2-2	1-0
5	Burscough	1-1	1-0	3-1	1-2	X	1-0	5-0	5-0	2-0	3-0	4-0	2-2	1-1	2-2	4-3	3-2	1-2	4-1	1-0	1-0	1-1	0-0
6	Chorley	2-3	1-1	0-1	2-1	2-2	X	0-1	0-0	3-0	1-1	0-1	3-1	1-1	2-2	3-0	3-3	1-1	0-3	0-4	0-0	2-5	0-0
7	Congleton T	2-3	1-1	2-2	2-1	2-2	2-1	X	2-2	2-1	1-0	2-1	0-3	1-2	1-2	5-1	1-0	2-0	0-0	1-2	1-3	0-1	1-2
8	Eastwood T	1-7	0-0	2-0	0-1	0-2	0-1	1-2	X	2-5	1-1	2-0	1-2	3-0	1-1	2-1	2-1	4-0	1-1	4-0	6-0	1-3	1-1
9	Farsley Celtic	2-1	2-1	3-1	4-1	0-0	1-2	1-0	1-3	X	3-1	0-1	4-3	0-0	1-1	0-1	2-1	2-1	2-1	4-0	0-0	1-0	1-1
10	Flixton	0-5	1-3	2-1	0-1	0-1	1-2	2-1	2-3	2-1	X	4-0	2-2	1-1	0-1	2-0	1-3	1-2	2-4	3-5	2-0	0-1	0-0
11	Gretna	0-1	1-1	3-4	1-2	0-2	3-2	3-3	1-1	1-1	1-2	X	2-0	4-1	2-5	4-1	2-0	0-1	1-0	1-1	1-0	0-3	1-3
12	Harrogate T	0-2	1-1	2-2	0-3	1-2	1-3	5-0	2-0	0-5	0-0	3-2	X	0-0	1-1	3-0	0-1	1-1	6-1	1-1	1-0	1-1	2-0
13	Lincoln Utd	1-0	2-2	1-1	2-1	0-1	1-2	0-2	2-2	2-2	3-3	1-0	2-1	X	3-2	2-1	1-5	1-2	1-2	0-3	2-1	1-2	3-2
14	Matlock Town	2-1	1-1	3-4	2-2	1-1	1-2	2-2	2-1	3-0	3-2	2-1	3-3	0-0	X	1-2	2-1	0-1	3-1	3-1	5-0	2-2	3-2
15	Netherfield K	1-0	3-4	1-1	1-1	4-7	1-1	1-2	1-3	0-1	3-0	0-2	0-1	2-1	1-0	X	1-1	0-0	0-1	3-3	3-2	0-4	0-1
16	Ossett Town	2-2	4-0	1-1	3-1	1-1	3-0	0-0	1-2	2-0	3-2	2-1	1-2	3-1	1-0	X	2-2	4-1	0-1	1-2	1-2	3-1	
17	Radcliffe B	2-3	2-0	1-1	2-1	0-0	1-1	3-3	3-2	2-1	2-0	0-0	3-1	2-2	1-2	1-1	2-0	X	3-1	0-1	4-1	1-0	1-0
18	Stocksbridge	1-3	2-1	1-0	2-1	0-2	1-2	3-1	0-2	1-1	3-1	1-0	2-1	2-1	0-1	3-2	1-2	2-4	X	1-0	3-2	1-2	1-1
19	Trafford	2-4	0-2	1-2	2-0	1-1	6-0	2-2	1-2	0-1	2-2	0-1	2-3	2-0	0-1	0-0	0-0	0-1	3-3	X	1-2	1-1	1-1
20	Whitley Bay	1-1	1-3	2-1	1-3	1-1	1-3	3-3	0-1	1-3	4-0	0-0	1-2	0-1	0-0	1-3	1-7	1-6	1-0	1-1	X	2-4	1-2
21	Witton Albion	0-0	3-2	2-0	0-2	1-1	2-0	5-3	4-1	2-3	2-2	6-1	3-1	3-1	1-1	2-1	3-2	3-0	1-1	2-0	2-0	X	2-2
22	Workington	1-0	2-4	2-3	0-2	0-3	1-1	1-2	2-0	2-2	1-0	3-1	0-3	4-0	0-1	2-0	0-3	0-1	0-0	2-0	2-0	1-1	X

ASHTON UNITED

CLUB OFFICIALS

Chairman: T N Styring
President: R.Thomasson
Vice Chairman: J Milne
Secretary:Stuart Jones
217 Rose Hill Road,Ashton-under-
Lyne,Lancs. OL6 8HT. H/Fax: 01613441170
Mobile; 07788 613608
Press Officer: S.Howe

FOOTBALL MANAGEMENT TEAM

Manager: Gerry Quinn
Physio: Chris Moseley

FACT FILE
Formed: 1878
Club Sponsors: T.B.A.
Nickname: Robins
Colours: Red & white halves/black/red
Change colours: All yellow
Midweek matchday: Monday

1999-2000
Captain: Jeremy Illingworth
Top Scorer: Jeremy Illingworth
P.o.Y.: Jeremy Illingworth

Ashton United Football Club

SEASON 1999 - 2000
F. W. SINGLETON
THE UNIBOND FOOTBALL LEAGUE DIVISION ONE
Official Matchday Programme £1-

ASHTON UNITED V BRADFORD PARK AVENUE
MON 1ST MAY   KICK OFF 3.00pm
"The Robins Welcome you to Hurst Cross"

Pages: 22 Price: £1
Editor:Ken & Steve Lee
Local Press: Ashton Reporter, Ashton
Advertiser Local Radio: GMR

GROUND Surrey Street, Hurst Cross, Ashton-u-Lyne OL6 8DY.
Tel; 0161339 4158. (office) 01613 301511 (Social Club). Fax 0161 339 4158
Directions: M62 jct 20, A627(M) to Oldham, keep in right hand 2 lanes, leave at Ashton sign after 2 miles passing Belgrade Hotel, take A627 at next island,keep in left lane and take slip road signed Ashton-under-Lyme, at island follow Stalybridge/Park Road sign, go straight ahead for 3 miles to ground at Hurst Cross. BR to Charles Street (Ashton), or Stalybridge. Buses 331, 332, 337, 408(Ashton-Stalybridge) all pass ground
Capacity: 4,500   Seats: 250   Cover: 750
Clubhouse: Open 11am-11pm. Refreshment bar open matchdays
Club Shop: Yes - contact Mr K Lee (0161 330 9800)
PREVIOUS   Leagues: Manchester; Lancs Comb 12-23, 48-64, 66-68; Midland 64-66; Cheshire Co. 23-48, 68-82; Nth West Count 82-92.
Name: Hurst 1878-1947. Ground: Rose Hill 1878-1912
CLUB RECORDS Attendance: 11,000 v Halifax Town, FA Cup First Round 1952.
Scorer: Mark Edwards, 37   **Appearances:** Micky Boyle, 462.
Win: 11-3 v Staylbridge Manchester Interm Cup 55   **Defeat:** 11-1 v Wellington Town Cheshire Lge 46-47.
Fee Paid: £9,000 for Andy Whittaker (Netherfield, 1994)   **Fee Received:** £15,000 for Karl Marginson (Rotherham, Mar. 1993)
BEST SEASON   FA Trophy: Qtr Final v Dagenham (0-1) (A0 96-97
FA Cup: 1st Rd replay 52-53, 1-2 v Halifax T (A), after 1-1. Also 1st Rd 55-56, 1-6 v Southport (A)
HONOURS Northern Prem Lge Div 1 Cup 94-95; Manchester Sen Cup 1884-85 13-14 75-76 77-78; Manchester Lge 11-12; Lancs Comb. Div 2 60-61 (Lge Cup 62-63);Manchester Prem. Cup 79-80 82-83 92-93; North West Counties Lge 91-92;Challenge Cup 91-92, Div 2 87-88; Floodlit League 90-91; Challenge Shield 92-93; Manchester Chall Shield 35-36 38-39 49-50 53-54 (R-up 34-35 39-40), Manchester Interm Cup 58-59 62-63 65-66, R-up 60-61 64-65; Manchester Jnr Cup 1894-95 10-12 32-33; Unifilla Div 1 Cup 96-97,98-99
Players progressing: A Ball (Blackpool), J Mahoney (Stoke C.), B Daniels(Manchester C.), R Jones (Rotherham U.), A Arrowsmith (Liverpool), N Stiffle(Crystal Palace), K Marginson (Rotherham U) P Wilson (Plymouth Argyle)

Ashton United's Chris Adams seen here in action against Accrington Stanley.
Photo: Colin Stevens

BELPER TOWN

CLUB OFFICIALS

Chairman: **Phil Varney**
President: **Alan Benfield**
Secretary: **Brian Rudkin**
121 Marsh Lane, Belper, Derbys, DE56
1GU. Tel: 01773 827091 Mobile: 07710
444195
Press Officer: **Nigel Oldrini**

FOOTBALL MANAGEMENT TEAM

Manager: Martin Rowe
Asst Manager/ Coach: Graham Reiter

FACT FILE

Formed: 1883
Nickname: Nailers
Colours: Yellow/black/black & yellow
Change colours: All white
Midweek home matchday: Tuesday
Reserves' League: Midlands Reg All

1999-2000

Captain:Mark Wood
P.o.Y.: Carl Cunningham
Top scorer: Carl Cunningham

GROUND

Address: Christchurch Meadow, Bridge Street, Belper DE56 1BA (01773825549).

Directions: From M1 North, Jnct 28 onto A38 towards Derby, turn off at A610 (Ripley/Nottingham), then 4 exit at roundabout towards Ambergate. At junction with A6 (Hurt Arms Hotel) left to Belper. Ground on right past traffic lights. 400 yards from Belper (BR)

Capacity: 2,640   Cover: 1,000   Seats: 200

Clubhouse: Open matchdays and for functions with bar and hot and cold food available.

Pages: 36 Price £1.00
Editor: Andy Darlington (01773 822993)
Local Press: Belper News, Derby Evening
Telegraph, Belper Express
Local Radio: BBC Radio Derby

PREVIOUS	**Leagues:** Central Alliance 57-61; Midland Co's 61-82, Northern Counies East 1982-87
	Grounds: Acorn Ground prior to 1951
	Names: None
CLUB RECORDS	**Attendance:** 3,200 v Ilkeston Town, 1955

CLUB RECORDS   **Goalscorer:** Mick Lakin 231   **Appearances:** Gil Rhodes
Fee **Received:** £700 forBrian Hall (Mansfield Town 59) **Fee Paid:** Nil.
Victory: 15-2 v Nottingham Forest 'A'1956   **Defeat:** 0-12 v Goole Town 1965

BEST SEASON   **FA Vase:** Semi-final 94-95**FA Amateur Cup:** Not entered
FA Trophy: 3rd Qual Rd 97-98
FA Cup: 1st Rd Prop 1887-88 (4th Qual. Rnd 1964-65)

HONOURS   Northern Counties East Lge 84-85, Midland Counties Lg 79-80; Central Alliance Lge 58-59;
Derbys Snr Cup 58-59 60-61 62-63 79-80

Players progressing: None

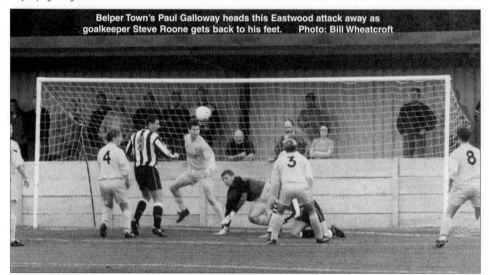

Belper Town's Paul Galloway heads this Eastwood attack away as goalkeeper Steve Roone gets back to his feet.   Photo: Bill Wheatcroft

BRADFORD PARK AVENUE

CLUB OFFICIALS

Chairman: **Frank Thornton**
President: **Charlie Atkinson**
Secretary: **Alan Hirst**
24 Quarryfields, Mirfield, W.Yorks WF14 0NT
Tel.01924 480349 (H)
Press Officer: **Tim Clapham**
Commercial Manager: **Chris Higgins**

FOOTBALL MANAGEMENT TEAM

Manager: Trevor Storton
Asst Manager: Ian Thompson
Physio: Ray Killick

FACT FILE

Formed: 1907
Reformed: 1988
Nickname: Avenue
Club Sponsor: Ham Construction
Colours: Green & white/white/green & white
Change colours W:hite/black/black
Midweek Matches: Wednesday
Reserves' league: N/A

1999-00
Captain: Wayne Benn
Top Scorer:Jason Maxwell
P.o.Y.: Jason Maxwell

For up to the minute news, results, fixtures, plus general facts & figures from the world of non-league football

log on to

www.nlfootball.com

GROUND

Horsfall Stadium, Cemetery Road, Bradford, West Yorks BD6 2NG

Directions: M62 Jct 26. Along M606 to the end. At roundabout takeA6036 (signed Halifax) and pass Odsal Stadium on left hand side. At next roundabout take 3rd exit A6036 (Halifax), in approx. 1 mile turn left into Cemetery Rd (by Kings Head Pub). Ground 150 yards on left
Capacity: 5,000   **Cover:** 2,000   Seats: 1,247
Club Shop: Yes - contact russell Foulds (c/o Ground)   **Clubhouse:** Yes

Programme
Pages: 36 Price: £1.20
Editor: Martin Worthy   01924 384477

Local Press: Telegraph & Argus
Local Radio: Radio Leeds

PREVIOUS   **Leagues:** Southern 07-08; Football League 08-70; Northern Premier 70-74; West Riding County Amtr 88-89; Central Mids 89-90; N. W. Counties 90-95
Grounds: Park Avenue 07-73; Valley Parade 73-74; Manningham Mills 88-89; Bramley R.L.F.C.,McLaren Field 89-93; Batley 93-96

CLUB RECORDS   **Attendance:** 1,007 v Bradford City 97 (Centenary Chall). 32,810 v Blackpool, War Cup 1944
Win: 11-0 v Denby Dale FAC 1908   **Defeat:** 0-7 v Barnsley 1911
Scorer: Len Shackleton 171 1940-46   **Appearances:** Tommy Farr 542 1934-50
Fee Received: £34,000 for K Hector (Derby County 1966)
Fee Paid: £24,500 for L Leuty (Derby County 1950)

BEST SEASON   FA Vase: 2nd Rd Prop 94-95
FA Trophy: 3rd Rd 98-99
FA Cup: Qtr finals 12-13, 19-20, 45-46

HONOURS Football Lge Div 2 R-up 1914; 3rd Div N 28; Yorkshire Lge 21, 23;Midland Lge 32; West Riding Snr Cup 11,13,25,27,32,36,51,53,63, County Cup 29,90-91, N.W.C. Lg Champions 94-95, N.W.C. Carling Challenge Trophy 94-95

Back Row: Paul Marquis, Neil Bagshaw, Phil Denny, Gavi Kelly, Paul Brown, Jason Maxwell, Daniel Verity, Martin James.
Front: Mark Hancock, Michael Thompson, Stephen Ball, Wayne Benn, Dean Calcutt, David Donaldson, Chris Dolby.
Photo: Darren C Thomas

CHORLEY

CLUB OFFICIALS

Chairman: **Jack Kirkland**

Commercial Manager: **T.B.A.**

Secretary / Press Officer: **Mick Wearmouth**
6 Avondale Road, Chorley, Lancs. PR72ED
Tel: 01257 271395

FOOTBALL MANAGEMENT TEAM

Manager: Ken Wright

FACT FILE

Formed: 1883
Founded: The Magpies
Sponsors: Coloroll.
Colours: White & black stripes/black/black &
white
Change colours: All yellow
Midweek matchday: Tuesday
Reserve League: Alliance League.

Pages: 32 Price: £1.
Editor: Mike Neild
Local Press: Lancs Evening Post,
Chorley Guardian.
Local Radio: Radio Lancs, Red Rose.

GROUND
Victory Park, Duke Street, Chorley, Lancs   Tel: 01257 263406
Directions: M61 jct 6, A6 to Chorley, going past Yarrow Bridge Hotel on Bolton Rd turn left at 1st lights into Pilling Lane, 1st right into Ashley St..,ground 2nd left. From M6; jct 27, follow signs to Chorley, left at lights,continue for 2 1/2 miles on A49, right onto B5251, on entering Chorley turn right into Duke Street 200yds after Plough Hotel. 1/4 mile from Chorley (BR).
Capacity: 4,100   Cover: 2,800   Seats: 900
Clubhouse: 01257 275662. Open every evening. Weekend entertainment, Snacks available
Club Shop: Yes.

PREVIOUS   Leagues: Lancs Alliance 1890-94; Lancs 94-1903; Lancs Comb. 03-68, 69-70;Northern Premier 68-69, 70-72, 82-88; Cheshire County 72-82; GMV Conference 88-90.
      Grounds: Dole Lane 1883-1901; Rangletts Park 01-05; St George's Park 05-20. Name: None

CLUB RECORDS   **Attendance:** 9,679 v Darwen, 1931-32. **Goalscorer:** Peter Watson.
      Fee Paid: Undisclosed to Marine for Brian Ross 1995. **Fee Received:** £22,500 for Paul Mariner (Plymouth, 1973).

BEST SEASON   **FA Cup:** 2nd Rd 86-87 (lost in replay at Preston), 90-91 (lost at Shrewsbury). **FA Trophy:** Semi-Final 1995-96.

HONOURS   Northern Premier Lg 87-88, Cheshire Co. Lg 75-76 76-77 81-82, Lancs Comb. 19-2022-23 27-28 28-29 32-33 33-34 45-46 59-60 60-61 63-64 (R-up 21-22 26-27 48-4962-63 64-65 65-66), Lg Cup 24-25 58-59 62-63), Lancs Lg 1896-97 98-99, Lancs Alliance 1892-93 (R-up 94-95), Lancs Jnr Cup 1894-95 1908-09 23-24 39-40 45-4657-58 58-59 60-61 63-64 64-65 75-76 79-80 81-82 82-83.

Players Progressing: Charles Ashcroft (Liverpool 1946),William Healey (Arsenal 49), Stan Howard (Huddersfield 52), Derek Hogg (Leicester 52),
      William Norcross (Southport 59), Micky Walsh (Blackpool 71),Paul Mariner (Plymouth 73), Graham Barrow (Wigan 76),
      Steve Galliers (Wimbledon77), Kevin Tully (Bury 80), Geoff Twentyman (Preston 83), Gary Buckley (Bury84), Chris Hunter (Preston 84).

CONGLETON TOWN

CLUB OFFICIALS

Chairman: **Peter Evans**
Vice Chairman: **Steve Burgess**
Secretary and Press Officer: **David Wilcock**
4,Maxwell Rd., Congleton
Cheshire CW12 3HY.
Tel: 01260 276347 (H) 01260 270275 (B)

FOOTBALL MANAGEMENT TEAM

Manager:Glyn Chamberlain
Assistant Manager: Trevor Brissett
Physio: Paul Kelly

FACT FILE
Formed: 1901
Nickname: Bears
Colours: White & black flashes/black/black & white
Change colours:Red & White
Midweek home matchday: Tuesday
Reserve Team: N/A

1999-00
Captain: Wayne Johnson
P.o.Y.: Rod Thornley
Top Scorer:Rod Thornley

PROGRAMME SPONSORED BY
CREWE COLOUR PRINTERS

Official Matchday Programme £1.00

Pages: 48   Price: £1.00
Editor: Ken Mead c/oClub

Local Press: Congleton Chronicle,
Staffs Evening Sentinel
Local Radio: Radio Stoke, Signal

GROUND   Booth Street Ground, Crescent Road, Congleton, Cheshire Tel: 02602 74460

Directions: On approach to Congleton via Clayton bypass take second right after fire station, into Booth Street. Two miles from Congleton (BR)

Capacity: 5,000   Cover: 1,200   Seats: 250

Clubhouse: Open match days only   **Club Shop:** Yes. Contact:Gerry Brocklehurst

PREVIOUS   **Leagues:** Crewe & Dist; North Staffs; Macclesfield; Cheshire 20-39, 46-65, 78-82; Mid Cheshire 68-78; Nth West Co 82-87
Name: Congleton Hornets (prior to current club's formation in 1901)

CLUB RECORDS   **Attendance:** 7,000 v Macclesfield, League 53-54
Goalscorer: MickBiddle 150+   **Appearances:** Ray Clack 600+ & Graham Harrison 600+
Fee Paid: None.   **Fee Received:** £5,000 for D Frost (Leeds)

BEST SEASON   **FA Trophy:** 3rd Qualifying Rd 89-90 90-91. **FA Vase:** 4th Rd 76-77 80-81
FA Cup: 1st Rd 89-90, 0-2 v Crewe Alex. (A)   League clubs defeated: None

HONOURS   North West Counties League R-up 85-86; Cheshire County League R-up 20-2121-22 (Div 2 81-82); Mid Cheshire League 73-74 75-76 77-78 (R-up 69-70 71-7276-77, League Cup 71-72; Cheshire Senior Cup 20-21 37-38

Players progressing: Ron Broad (Crewe 1955), Jack Mycock (Shrewsbury 1958),Steve Davies (Port Vale 1987), L Hamlet (Leeds), Jimmy Quinn (West Ham, N Ireland), Ian Brightwell (Man City)

Back Row: Glynn Chamberlain (Manager), Darren Chetwyn, Paul Abbey, Wayne Johnson, Graham Dodd, Micky Allison, Andy Park, Steve Callear, Darran Washington, Lyndon Beardmore, Trevor Brissett (Asst. Man.), Paul Kelly (Physio). **Front:** Rod Thornley, John Evans, John Johnston, Spencer Maloney, Adrian Dunn, Lee Ellis, Ben Matthews. Mascot: Debbie Bloor.

EASTWOOD TOWN

CLUB OFFICIALS

Chairman: **George Belshaw**
Vice Chairman: **Roy Cheatle**
President:
Secretary / Press Officer: **Paddy Farrell**
7 Primrose Rise, Newthorpe,
Notts.NG16 2BB Tel/Fax: 01773 786186

FOOTBALL MANAGEMENT TEAM
Manager: Bryan Chambers
Ass.Manager: Jim McGowan Coach: Paul
McFarland Physio: Dave Nicholls

FACT FILE

Formed: 1953
Nickname: The Badgers
Sponsors: Hayley Conference Centres
Colours: Black & white stripes/black/black
Change Colours: Yellow/blue/yellow
Midweek matchday: Tuesday

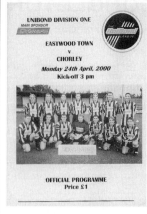

UNIBOND DIVISION ONE
MAIN SPONSOR

EASTWOOD TOWN
v
CHORLEY
Monday 24th April, 2000
Kick-off 3 pm

OFFICIAL PROGRAMME
Price £1

GROUND   Coronation Park, Eastwood, Notts. Tel: 01773 715823

Directions: From North - M1 jct 27, follow Heanor signs via Brinsley to lights in Eastwood.
Turn left then first right after Fire Station - ground entrance on Chewton Street. From South -
M1 jct 26, A610 to Ripley, leave at 1st exit(B6010), follow to Eastwood, left at lights, first left at
`Man in Space' -ground entrance on Chewton Street. Nearest station - Langley Mill. Buses
every10 mins (R11, R12 or R13) from Victoria Centre, Nottingham - approx 40 mins
Capacity: 5,500   **Cover:** 1,150   **Seats:** 200
Clubhouse: Social club open normal licensing hours (Sat 11am-11pm, midweek matches
6.30-11pm). Hot & cold food available. Steward; Richard James (01773715823)
Club Shop: Sells programmes, mugs, scarves, badges etc. Contact R K Storer - 0115 9199596

Pages:50 Price: £1.00
Editor: Jim McVea 01773 717745
Local Press: Eastwood Advertiser
Nottingham Evening Post, Derby Telegraph
Local Radio: Radio Nottingham, Radio Trent

PREVIOUS   **Leagues:** Notts Alliance 53-61; Central Alliance 61-67; East Midlands 67-71; Midland Counties 71-82; N.C.E. 82-87.
      Names: None -predecessors Eastwood Collieries disbanded in 1953
      Ground: Coronation Park 1953-65 - previous pitch now town bowling green
CLUB RECORDS   **Attendance:** 2,723 v Enfield, FA Amateur Cup, February 1965.
      Goalscorer: Martin Wright. Appearances: Arthur Rowley, over 800 1st team games, but not a single booking, 1955-76
      Win: 21-0 v Rufford Colliery 26/10/54 & Ilkeston Town 10/5/69   **Defeat:** 1-8 v Ransome & Marples 2/2/57
      Fee Paid: £500 for Jamie Kay, Gainsborough Trin.90-91   **Fee Received:** £72,500 for Richard Liburd, Middlesbrough 92-93
BEST SEASON   **FA Amateur Cup:** Third Round replay 1967-68.   **FA Trophy:** First Round1978-79
      FA Cup: 1st Round Proper 99-00, v Exeter City (A)
HONOURS   Northern Counties (East) Lg R-up 82-83 84-85; Midland Counties Lg 75-76(R-up 74-75 77-78), Lg Cup 77-78 79-80; Central
Alliance 63-64 (R-up 64-65);Notts Alliance 56-57 (R-up 53-54 54-55 55-56 57-58 58-59 59-60), Lg Cup 55-56;East Midlands Lg R-up 68-69; Notts
Senior Cup (winners 9 and R-up 5);Evans Halshaw Floodlit Cup 94-95R-up 89-90 97-98; Notts Intermediate Cup 86-87;98-99.99-00 Ripley
Hospital Charity Cup(6)76-81.Mid Regional All (Prem) 99-00 R-up 97-8,98-9

Players progressing: J Butler (Notts Co 57), A Woodcock A Buckley Andrew Todd (Nottm F), P Richardson (Derby), S Buckley (Luton), R Liburd
(Middlesbrough 92-93), Martin Bullock (Barnsley 94-95), Neil Illman (Plymouth 95-96), Lee Marshall (Scunthorpe 97), Glenn Kirkwood(Donc"ter

LEFT - RIGHT - Back Row: Richard Williams, Jamie Eaton, 'Freddy' Morgan, Scott Bonsall, Andy Todd, Gavin Worboys, Gary Breach.
Front Row: Gary Castledine, Paul Gould, Paul Tomlinson (Capt.), Richard Parkin, Gary Bonser, Richard Smith, Martyn Chadbourne.
Photo: Bill Wheatcroft

FARSLEY CELTIC

CLUB OFFICIALS

Chairman: **John E Palmer**
Vice Chairman:
Secretary: **Mrs Margaret Lobley**
29 Spring Bank Road, Farsley, Leeds, West
Yorks LS28 5LS
Tel: 01132 575675

FOOTBALL MANAGEMENT TEAM

Manager: Martin Haresign
Assistant Manager: S.Learoyd
Coach: J.Deacy

FACT FILE
Formed: 1908
Nickname: Villagers
Colours: Sky & navy/navy/navy
Change colours: All white
Midweek home matchday: Wednesday
Reserves' League: N.C.E.Res. Div

1999-2000
Captain: S.Learoyd
Top scorer: I.Blackstone

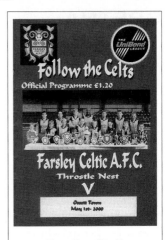

GROUND Throstle Nest, Newlands, Farsley, Pudsey, Leeds LS28 5BE Tel: 01532 561517
Directions: From North East: A1 south to Wetherby, A58 to Leeds, at1st island (approx 8 miles) take 3rd exit (A6120 ring-rd), follow Bradford signs to 12th r'bout (approx 12 miles) - 1st exit (B6157 Stanningley). From M62jct 26, M606 (Bradford) to r'bout, 4th exit (A6177) passing McDonalds on left,continue on Rooley Lane - Sticker Lane passing Morrisons store on left to lights (approx 3 miles) - right onto A647 (Leeds) to 2nd r'bout, 2nd exit(B6157 Stanningley). Continue 800yds passing Police & Fire Stations on left.Turn left down New Street at Tradex warehouse before turning right into Newlands. Ground at bottom of road. 1 mile from New Pudsey (BR)
Capacity: 4,000 Cover: 1,000 Seats: 430
Clubhouse: Lounge, games room and committee room open every evening and Friday and weekend lunchtimes. New multi-purpose Leisure Centre available evenings and afternoons
Club Shop: League & non-League progs & magazines. Club badges, scarves,ties, sweaters, training suits, polo & T-shirts. Various souvenirs & photos.Contact Brian Falkingham, 27 Rycroft Ct., Leeds LS13 4PE. 0113 255 0749 e-mail: clubshop@breathemail.net

Pages: 32   Price £1

Editor: Howard Stevenson

Local Press: Yorkshire Evening Post,
Telegraph & Argus, Pudsey Times
Local Radio: Radio Leeds, Radio Aire,
Radio Pennine

PREVIOUS   **Leagues:** West Riding County Amateur; Leeds Red Triangle; Yorkshire 49-82; Northern Counties East 82-87
Grounds: Red Lane, Farsley; Calverley Lane,Farsley (prior to 1948)
CLUB RECORDS   **Attendance:** 11,000 (at Elland Road) v Tranmere Rovers, FA Cup 1st Rd 1974
BEST SEASON   **FA Amateur Cup:** Third Round, 34-35
FA Cup: 1st Rd 74-75 (see above). Lost 0-2. **FA Vase:** Quarter Final 87-88
HONOURS   West Riding County Cup 57-58 59-60 66-67 70-71 83-84 87-88 95-96 96-97; Yorkshire League 59-60 68-69 (R-up 57-58 58-59 70-71 71-72); Div 2 51-52;League Cup 62-63 63-64 66-67 96-97
Players progressing: Barry Smith (Leeds 1951), Paul Madeley (Leeds 1962),William Roberts (Rochdale 1988), Stuart McCall (Bradford City)

Back: Simon Woodhead, Ian Blackstone, Matthew Surtees, Paul Allen, Mark Stimpson, Andy Watson, Wayne Metcalf, Alastair Long.
Front: Pav Singh, Phil Turner, Robbie Whellans, Matthew Flanagan, Nigel Smith, Ben Thackeray.   Photo: Bill Wheatcroft

GRETNA

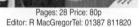

CLUB OFFICIALS

Chairman: **Brian Fulton**
President: **Thomas Kerr**
Secretary: **Ron MacGregor**
Brackenhurst, Lochmaben, Lockerbie,
Scotland DG111QA (01387 811820)

FACT FILE
Formed: 1946
Nickname: Black & whites
Club colours:
Black & white hoops/black/black & white
Change colours: All maroon (b & w trim)
Midweek matchday: Tuesday
Reserves' league: Carlisle & District

FOOTBALL MANAGEMENT TEAM

Manager: Paddy Lowery
Physio: William Bentley

1999-2000
Captain: Paul O'Hagan
Top Scorer:Ross Milligan
Supporters P.o.Y.: Paul O'Hagan
Players P.o.Y.: Lee Armstrong

GROUND
Raydale Park, Dominion Rd., Gretna, Dumfriesshire
Tel: 01461 337602

Directions: 8 miles north of Carlisle on A74. Take slip road to Gretna over border bridge, left at Crossways Inn for Township along Annan Rd for quarter of a mile, left into Dominion Rd, ground on right. Buses leave Carlisle on the half hour. Also trains from Carlisle
Capacity: 2,200   Cover: 800   Seats: 385
Clubhouse: Bar in ground-visitors most welcome.
Club Shop: Yes, contact Alan Watson 01387 251550, matchdays & postal sales

Pages: 28 Price: 80p
Editor: R MacGregorTel: 01387 811820

Local Press : Cumberland News
Evening News & Star ,Dumfries & Galloway
Standard Local Radio: C.F.M.; Radio
Cumbria,West Sound Radio,BBC Solway

PREVIOUS   **Leagues:** Dumfriesshire Amateur 46-47; Carlisle & District 47-51;Cumberland 51-52; Northern 83-92

CLUB RECORDS   **Attendance:** 2,307 v Rochdale, F.A. Cup First Round Proper,16/11/91.
Scorer: Denis Smith   **Appearances:** William Cross
Win: 20-0 v Silloth 62-63   **Defeat:** 0-6 v Worksop Town 94-95 and v Bradford P.A. 99-00
Fee Received: £10,000 from Queen of the South for Derek Townsley 96

BEST SEASON   **FA Trophy:** 2nd Rd 84-85 88-89 90-91 93-94
FA Cup: 1st Rd Prop 91-92 (lost 1-3 in replay at Rochdale) & 93-94 (lost 2-3 to Bolton Wanderers)
FA Vase: 2nd Rd 80-81 83-84

HONOURS   Northern Lg 90-91 91-92 (Lg Cup 90-91); Cumberland Senior Cup (9); JR Cleator Cup 89-90 90-91 91-92; Craven Cup 91-92; Carlisle & Dist. Lg (28)(Charity Shield (25), Lg Cup (20); Benevolent Cup (15)
Players progressing: John Hamilton (Hartlepool Utd) 1982, Russell Black &Don Peattie (Sheffield Utd) 1984, Mark Dobie (Cambridge Utd) derek Townsley (Queen of South,Motherwell),Craig Potts (Queen of South)

Back Row: Adam Kerr, Jim Brown, Paul O'Hagan, Nicky Hill, Ross Milligan, Mark Dobie
Front Row: Jonny Hall, Steve Kendall, Craig Potts, Lee Armstrong, Graham Emerson   **Photo:** Alan Watson

GUISELEY

CLUB OFFICIALS

Chairman: **Philip Rogerson**
Secretary: **Bruce Speller**
71 Oxford Avenue, Guiseley,
Leeds LS20 9BY
Tel: 01943 874534

Press Officer: **John Martin**
Tel: 01943 879473

Directors: P.Rogerson, S.Allen, N.Jukes.
Mrs S.Jukes, D.Pattison

FACT FILE

Formed: 1909
Sponsors: OHS Ltd.
Colours: White/blue/white.
Change colours: Yellow/Navy
Midweek home matchday: Tuesday.
Reserves' League: Lancashire League

FOOTBALL MANAGEMENT TEAM

Manager: Bobby Davison
Asst Manager: Neil Parsley
Physio: John Rhodes

For up to the minute news, results, fixtures, plus general facts & figures from the world of non-league football

log on to

www.nlfootball.com

GROUND: Nethermoor, Otley Road, Guiseley, Leeds LS20 8BTTel: 0943 873223
Directions: Via M1 to M62 jct 28, follow Airport signs to junction of A65 at Horsforth. R-about turn left onto A65 through Rawdon to Guiseley centre. Ground 1/4 mile past traffic lights, on the right,entrance on A65 opposite Silver Cross factory. Further car parking available,frst right after ground, off Ings Crescent. 5 mins walk from Guiseley (BR/Metro) station.
Capacity: 3,000   Cover: 1,040   Seats: 427
Clubhouse: (01943 872872) Open before and after all games (closes 11pm). Snack bar within ground open before and during matches.
Club Shop: Sells programmes, various items of clothing, key rings, badges, mugs etc. Phone Jennifer Rogerson 01943 879236

Programme	
Pages: 40	Price: £1
Editor: T.B.A.	

Local Press: Yorkshire Evening Post, Bradford Telegraph & Argus, Airedale &Wharfedale Observer, Wharfe Valley Times.

PREVIOUS   **Leagues:** West Riding Co. Amtr; West Yorks; Yorkshire 68-82; Northern Co's East82-91.

CLUB RECORDS   **Attendance:** 2,486 v Bridlington Town, FA Vase Semi Final 1st Leg 89-90.

BEST SEASON   **FA Cup:** First Round Proper 1994-95, 1-4 v Carlisle Utd. (at Valley Parade); 99-00, v Forest Green Rov. (A)
                                FA Vase: Winners 1990-91 (R-up 91-92, S.F. 94-95).
                                FA Trophy: Semi-Final 1994-95.

HONOURS   FA Vase 90-91 (R-up 91-92), Northern Premier Lg Div 1 94-95 (Presidents Cup 94-95, Div 1 Cup 92-93), Northern
Counties   (East) Lg 90-91 (Lg Cup 90-91), West Riding County Cup(5 inc 94-95), Yorkshire Lg R-up 79-80 81-82 (Lg Cup 79-80).

Players Progressing: Keith Walwyn (York City), Frank Harrison (Halifax Town),Dean Walling (Carlisle United), Richard Annan (Crewe Alexandra).
Dave Hanson (Halifax Town)

Back Row: Tony Agana, Danny Brown, Matt Daly, James Shutt, Andrew Shuttleworth, Simon Trevitt, Julian Wilkes, Simon Ireland. **Front:** James Nettleton, Colin Hogarth, Des Hazel, Rhys Stead, David Cooke, Kim Evangelatos.
Photo: Darren C Thomas

HARROGATE TOWN

CLUB OFFICIALS

Chairman: **Bill Fotherby**
President: **Leslie Silver**
Director of Football:**GrahamShepherd**
General Secretary: **Roy Dalby**
123a Dene Park, Harrogate
N. Yorkshire HG14JX Tel: 01423 567973
Commercial Director: **Les Wood**

FOOTBALL MANAGEMENT TEAM
Team Manager: **Dave Fell**
Coach: **Peter Gunby**

FACT FILE
Formed: 1919
Nickname: Town
Club Sponsors: Black Horse Vehicle
Management
Colours: all Yellow
Change colours:Allwhite
Midweek home matchday: Tuesday
Youths: Northern Youth Aacademy Lg.

GROUND: Wetherby Road, Harrogate.Tel: 01423 883671(01423 880675-Press +Commercial)
Secretary and Administration Tel.& FAX: 012423 525341

Directions: From Leeds turn right at traffic lights (Appleyard's) into Hookstone Road, continue to Woodlands Hotel (traffic lights) turn left into Wetherby Road, ground on the right. From Harrogate (BR), turn left and left again, cross road (Odeon Cinema), proceed for about 400yds to main road, crossover to The Stray (open land) using footpath which leads to Wetherby Rd, ground200yds on left.
From the West on A59 srtaight on to Wetherby Rd from Empress roundabout. ground on left.
From North: A59 exit from M1 then southern bypass to Wetherby Rd
Capacity: 3,800   Cover: 900   Seats: 450
Clubhouse: On ground, open every match day and for functions & special events.
Club Shop: Variety of souvenirs (Phil Harrison- 01423 525211)

Pages: 32   Price: £1.20
Editor: Bob Head

Local Press: Yorkshire Post Group
Harrogate Advertiser Series
Local Radio: Radio Leeds, Radio York
Stray FM.

PREVIOUS	**Names:** Harrogate FC1919-32, Harrogate Hotspurs 35-48 **Ground:** Starbeck Lane 1919-20
	Leagues: West Riding 1919-20 Yorkshire 20-21, 22-31, 57-82; Midland 21-22; Northern 31-32; Harrogate & District 35-37 West Yorkshire 46-57; Northern Counties East 82-87
CLUB RECORDS	**Attendance:** 3,280 v Railway Athletic, Whitworth Cup final 1948.
	Win: 13-0 v Macklefield **Defeat:** 0-7 v Hyde Utd & v Lancaster City
BEST SEASON	**FA Vase:** 4th Round 89-90 **FA Cup:** 3rd Qual. Rd Replay 87-88 (at Bishop Auckland)
	F.A.Trophy: 3rd Rd Replay v Spennymoor United 99-00
HONOURS	Northern Premier Lge Div 1 Cup 89-90; Northern Counties (East) Div 1(Nth) R-up 84-85 (Reserve Div 85-86, Reserve Div Cup 86-87); Yorkshire League Div 1 26-27 (Div 2 81-82, Div 3 R-up 71-72 80-81); West Riding County Cup 62-6372-73 85-86; West Riding Challenge Cup 24-25 26-27

Players progressing: Tony Ingham (Leeds 47), Stewart Ferebee (York C. 79),Tim Hotte (Halifax T. 85), Andy Watson (Halifax T. 88),
Ian Blackstone(York C. 95) , Eric Stephenson (Leeds United1932)

KENDAL TOWN

CLUB OFFICIALS

Chairman: **David Willan**
President: **M Macklin**
Secretary: **Dale Brotherton**
Lime House, Holme Hill, Dalston, Carlisle.
CA5 7DH (Mobile 07977 759903)
Match Secretary: **Craig Campbell**
34 High Sparrowmire, Kendal Cumbria LA9 5PD
01539 725557 (H)
Press Officer: **Peter Savage** (01539 726488)

FACT FILE

F ormed: 1920
Nickname: The Field
Colours:
Black & white stripes/black/black & white
Change colours:
Yellow/blue/yellow
Midweek home matchday: Tuesday

For up to the minute news,
results, fixtures,
plus general facts & figures
from the world of
non-league football

log on to

www.nlfootball.com

FOOTBALL MANAGEMENT TEAM
Manager:Alan Cook
Asst Manager: Keith Galley
Physio: Stan Casey

GROUND Parkside Road, Kendal, Cumbria Tel: 01539 727472

Directions: M6 junction 36, follow signs for Kendal (South), right at lights,left at r-bout to `K' Village - Parkside Rd on right opposite factory main offices - ground 400 yds. A mile & a half from Oxenholme (BR) station - bus service to `K' village, No 41 or 41A
Capacity: 2,490   Cover: 1,000   Seats: 250
Clubhouse: The Park, open all matchdays. Pies & pasties available   **Club Shop:** No

Programme
Pages: 32   Price: £1.00
Editor: Peter Savage Tel: 01539 726488

Local Press: Westmorland Gazette
Lancaster Evening Post
Local Radio: Radio Cumbria, The Bay.

PREVIOUS   **Leagues:** Westmorland; North Lancs; Lancs Combination 45-68; Northern Premier 68-83; North West Counties 83-87

CLUB RECORDS   **Attendance:** 5,184 v Grimsby Town, FA Cup 1st Rd 1955
Goalscorer: Tom Brownlee. **Win:** 11-0 v Great Harwood 22/3/47. **Defeat:** 0-10 v Stalybridge Celtic 1/9/84
Fee Paid: Undisclosed for Tom Brownlee (Bradford C., 66). **Fee Received:** £10,250 for Andy Milner (Man. City 95)

BEST SEASON   **FA Vase:** 3rd Rd 89-90   **FA Trophy:** 2nd Rd 80-81.
FA Cup: 2nd Rd replay 63-64, 1-4 v Chesterfield(A) after 1-1. 2nd Rd 49-50, 1st Rd 45-4648-49 52-53 54-55 55-56 64-65

HONOURS   Lancs Comb. 48-49 64-65 (R-up 45-46 53-54 61-62 63-64, Lg Cup 55-56 60-61), Westmorland Snr Cup(12) 24-25 31-33 35-36 46-48 63-64 65-66 71-72 86-8789-89 90-91

Players progressing: John Laidlaw (Carlisle 1946), Louis Cardwell (Crewe 1947),Herbert Keen (Barrow 1953), Alec Aston (Preston 1955), Horace Langstreth(Torquay 1956), John Simpson (Lincoln 1957), Dennis Rogers (Accrington 1959),Tom Brownlee (Bradford City 1965), Peter McDonnell (Bury 1973), Keith Silken(Workington 1973), Roger Wicks (Darlington 1981), Andy Milner (Man City)

Kendal's **Neil Reynolds** about to dispossess Gretna's Shane Bird.
Photo: Alan Watson

LINCOLN UNITED

CLUB OFFICIALS

Chairman: **M.Wilson**
President: **A Simpson**
Vice Chairman: **W.White**
Commercial Manager: **S Eastmead**

Secretary/Press Officer: **Tom Hill,**
4,Westwood Drive, Swanpool, Lincoln LN6
0HJTel Nos: 01522 690555 (H) 07771
863048 (W)

FOOTBALL MANAGEMENT TEAM

Managers: John Wilkinson & Tony Simmons
Physio: Anthony Adams

FACT FILE

Formed: 1938
Nickname: United
Colours: White/red/white
Change Colours: Tangerine
Midweek home matchday: Tuesday
Reserves ' League: Lincolnshire

For up to the minute news, results, fixtures, plus general facts & figures from the world of non-league football

log on to

www.nlfootball.com

GROUND   Ashby Avenue, Hartsholme, Lincoln Tel: 01522 690674
Directions: From Newark A46 onto Lincoln relief road (A446), right at 2nd r'bout for
Birchwood (Skellingthorpe Rd), go for 1 mile passing lake and Country Park, 1st right 10yds
after 30mph sign into Ashby Ave., ground entrance200 yds, opposite Old Peoples home. From
north follow A57 via Saxilby until reaching A46 Lincoln Relief Road - continue on this and turn
left at r'bout signed Birchwood then as above. 3 miles from Loncoln Central (BR)
Capacity: 2,714   Seats: 400   Covered: 1,084
Clubhouse: Open daily normal licensing hours. Matchday snack bar -hot &cold food & drinks
Club Shop: Yes. Contact: Julie Portas (01522 885484)

Programme
Pages: 40   Price: 50p
Editor: John Wilkinson Tel: 01522 690674

Local Press: Lincolnshire Echo
Lincoln Standard

PREVIOUS   **Leagues:** Lincs 45-48 60-67; Lincoln 48-60; Yorks 67-82; Northern Co'sEast 82-86, 92-95; Central Mids 82-92
               Grounds: Skew Bridge (40s); Co-op Sports Ground (to mid 60s); Hartsholme Cricket Ground (to 82)
               Name: Lincoln Amateurs (until an ex-pro signed in 1954)

CLUB RECORDS   **Attendance:** 2,000 v Crook Town, FA Amateur Cup 1st Rd Proper, 1968
               Scorer: Tony Simmons 215   **Appearances:** Steve Carter 447
               Win: 12-0 v Pontefract Colls 95.   **Defeat:** 0-7 v Huddersfield Town FA Cup 1st Round Proper16-11-91
               Fee Paid: £250 for Dean Dye (Sutton Town, 7.90) - only player ever bought.
               Fee Received: £3,000 for Dean Dye (Charlton Ath., 7.91)

BEST SEASON   **FA Cup:** First Round Proper 91-92 (0-7 at Huddersfield Town), 97-98 v Walsall (0-2 Away)
               FA Trophy: 3rd 3Rd   **F.A.Vase:**

HONOURS   Northern Counties East - Prem Div. 94-95, Div 1 92-93, Div 1 Sth 82-83,Div 2 85-86, Presidents Cup 94-95; Yorks Lg 70-71
               73-74 (Lg Cup 70-71); Lincs Lg 63-64; Lincs Snr `A' Cup 72-73 85-86 95-96, R-up 91-92 94-95, `B' Cup 63-6470-71;
               Central Mids Lg 91-92 (Wakefield Cup 90-91); Evans Halshaw Floodlit Cup R-up 92-93; Lincs I'mediate Cup(7) 67-73 80-
               81; Blankney Hunt Inter Lge 95-96,Cup 95-96 Lincs Sen Cup: R-up 97-98 Unifila Div 1 Cup R-up 97-98

Lincoln United's
Nigel Baily
holding off Gretna's
George Corrie
Photo: Alan Watson

MATLOCK TOWN

CLUB OFFICIALS

Chairman: **Donald T Carr**
Vice Chairman: **G Michael Tomlinson**
Secretary: **Keith F Brown**
'Barncroft', 1 Malvern Gardens
Matlock, Derbyshire DE4 3JH
01629 584231 (H) 01335 390301 (B)
Press Officer: **Ian Richardson**
Commercial Manager: **Tom Wright**

FOOTBALL MANAGEMENT TEAM

Manager: Tommy Spencer
Physio: Michael Cunningham

GROUND

Directions: On A615, 500 yds from town centre and Matlock (BR)
Capacity: 7,500   Cover: 2,000   Seats: 240
Clubhouse: Gladiators Social Club, on ground, open matchdays only
Club Shop: Yes. Contact: Sue Tomlinson (01629 583866)

FACT FILE

Formed: 1885
Nickname: The Gladiators
Sponsors: Westons of Wirksworth/
Panasonic/ Tarmac & Peak 107 F.M.
Colours: Royal/white
Change colours: All yellow
Midweek home matchday: Tuesday
Reserves' League: Beauvale Mid All
Local Press: Matlock Mercury
Derbyshire Times, Derby Evening Telegraph,
Chesterfield Express
Local Radio: Radio Derby, Peak 107 F.M.

Causeway Lane, Matlock, Derbyshire
Tel: 01629 583866 (& Fax)

Pages 40   Price £1.00
Editor: Contact shop

PREVIOUS   **Ground:** Hall Leys (last century).   **Leagues:** Midland Counties 1894-96; Matlock & District; Derbys Senior;
Central Alliance 24-25 47-61; Central Combination 34-35; Chesterfield & District 46-47; Midland Counties 1961-69

CLUB RECORDS   **Attendance:** 5,123 v Burton Albion, FA Trophy 1975
Win: 10 v 0 Lancaster (A) **74**   **Defeat:** 1-8 v Chorley (A) 71
Career **Goalscorer:** Peter Scott. **Career**   **Appearances:** Mick Fenoughty
Fee Paid: £2,000 for Kenny Clarke1996   **Fee Received:** £10,000 for Ian Helliwell (York)

BEST SEASON   **FA Trophy:** 74-74
FA Cup: 3rd Rd 76-77. 1st Rd 1885-86 86-87 86-8787-88 1959-60 74-75 75-76 89-90
League clubs defeated: Mansfield Town 76-77

HONOURS   Northern Prem Lge R-up 83-84, Lge Cup 77-78, Shield 78-79; Midland Counties Lge 61-62 68-69; Central All (North) 59-60
60-61, R-up 61-62 62-63,Div 1 Cup R-up 61-62, Div 2 59-60, Div 2 Cup 59-60 60-61; Derbyshire Sen Cup74-75 76-
77 77-   78 80-81 83-84 84-85 91-92, R-up 60-61 72-73 73-74 75-76 80-8181-82 82-83 89-90 93-94 97-98;
Derbyshire Div Cup   (North) 61-62 R-up 62-63;Evans Halshaw Floodlit Cup 88-89 91-92; Anglo-Italian Non-League Cup 79

Players progressing: Keith Haines (Leeds 1959), Wayne Biggins (Burnley 1984),Darren Bradshaw (Chesterfield 1987), Les McJannet
(Scarborough 1987), Ian Helliwell (York 1987)

LEFT - RIGHT - **Back Row:** Jimmy Flynn (player/asst. man.), Mark Rookyard, James Lukic, Andy Simpson, Mike Heath, Will Davies, Billy
Heath (capt.), Danny Anson 9now Alfreton Town), Paul Farley. **Front Row:** Lee Mandbury, Simon Bochenski, Mick Cunningham (physio),
Gary Marrow (manager), Danny Campbell, Steve Orr.   **Photo: Bill Wheatcroft**

NORTH FERRIBY UNITED

CLUB OFFICIALS
President: Jeff Frank
Chairman: Les Hare
Vice Chairman: Roy Wallis
Press Officer: Les Hare
Secretary: Stephen Tather
16 Peasholme, Heads Lane, Hessle,
E Yorks HU13 0NY
Tel: 01482 642046 (H) Fax 01482 647244;
01482 351903 (B)

FOOTBALL MANAGEMENT TEAM

Manager: Brian France
Asst Mgr: John Deacey
Coach/Physio: Martin Woodmansey

FACT FILE

Founded: 1934
Nickname: United
Sponsors: Dransfield Developments
Colours: All white
Change colours: All yellow
Midweek matches: Tuesday
Reserves League: N.C.E. Res Div
1999-2000
Captain: Michael Trotter
P.o.Y.: Mickey Trotter
Top Scorer: Andy Flounders 36

For up to the minute news,
results, fixtures,
plus general facts & figures
from the world of
non-league football

log on to

www.nlfootball.com

GROUND   Grange Lane, Church Road, North Ferriby HU14 3AA
Tel: 01482 634601

Directions: Main Leeds-Hull road A63 or M62, North Ferriby is 8 miles west of Hull. Into North Ferriby, thru village past the Duke of Cumberland Hotel, right down Church Rd, ground half mile on left. One mile from North Ferriby (BR)
Capacity: 3,000   Seats: 250   Cover: 1,000   Floodlights: Yes
Clubhouse: Bar, lounge, TV, pool õ open every night   **Club Shop:** Yes

Programme
Pages: 40   Price: 75p
Editor: Jeff Frank Tel: 01482 633387
Local Press: Hull Daily Mail

HONOURS   FA Vase Finalist 96-97; Yorkshire Lg R-up 75-76, Lg Cup 74-75, Div 2 70-71;
N.C.E. Prem Div : Champions 99-00 R-up 97-98, Div 1 85-86 (Lg Cup R-up) 90-91 97-98,
Presidents Cup 90-91, 98-99, 99-00 Div 1 (North), R-up 82-83, Res. Div R-up 90-91;
E. Riding Snr Cup (9), E. Riding Church Lg 37-38

PREVIOUS   Leagues: East Riding Church; East Riding Amateur; Yorks 69-82

BEST SEASON   FA Cup: 3rd Q 97-98,98-99   FA Vase: R-up 96-97, SF 88-89, QF 89-90

RECORDS   Attendance: 1,800 v Tamworth, FA Vase Semi-Final, 1989
Goalscorer: Andy Flounders 50,98-99   Appearances: Richard Womble, 74-94
Win: 9-0 v Hatfield Main, N.C.E. Lge Prem 97-98.   Defeat: 1-7 v North Shields, N.C.E. Lge Prem 91.
Fee received: £6,000 for Dean Windass (Hull City, 1988)

Players progressing: T Hotte (Hull) 88, I Ironside (Halifax) 88, D France, D Windass & M Matthews (Hull) 91.

The Millenium Treble winning squad

OSSETT TOWN

CLUB OFFICIALS

President: **Paul Jervis**

Chairman: **Graham Firth**

Football Chairman: **Peter Wilkinson**

Commercial Manager:**Graham Willis**

Secretary: **Frank Lloyd**,
27 Park Close, Mapplewell,
Barnsley S75 6BY
Tel: 01226 382415

FACT FILE

Founded: 1936
Sponsors: Action Stations
Colours: All red
Change colours: All sky
Midweek matches: Tuesday
Reserves' League: N.C.E. Res Div
Programme: 12 pages, 50p
Editor/Press Off.: Bruce Saul
Tel: 01924 277652
Local Press: Dewsbury Reporter,
Wakefield Express

For up to the minute news, results, fixtures, plus general facts & figures from the world of non-league football

log on to

www.nlfootball.com

GROUND: Ingfield, Prospect Road, Ossett, Wakefield WF5 8AN Tel: 01924 272960
Directions: M1 jct 40, B6129 to Ossett, left into Dale Street, left again at lights opposite bus station on ring road, ground on left. Nearest stations Dewsbury or Wakefield Westgate - both three miles from. Buses 116, 117, 126 and127 from Wakefield, buses 116, 126 and 127 from Dewsbury, buses 117, 118 or 216 from Leeds
Capacity: 4,000   Seats: 360   Cover: 650   Floodlights: Yes
Clubhouse: Open Fri & Sun lunchtimes, all day Sat and every evening. Pie & peas, chips, soup from tea bar   **Club Shop:**

FOOTBALL MANAGEMENT TEAM
Manager: Gary Brook
Asst Manager:B. Crawther
Coach: Mick Polli

PREVIOUS   **Leagues:** Leeds 36-39; Yorkshire 45-82; N.C.E. 83-99   **Ground:** Fern House (pre-1958)

RECORDS   **Attendance:** 2,600 v Manchester Utd, friendly 1988
Win: 10-1 v Harrogate RA (H), N.C.E. Lge Prem. Div. 27/4/93
Defeat: 0-7 v Easington Colliery, FA Vase 8/10/83
Fee received: £1,350 for Derek Blackburn (Swansea 1957)
Appearances: Steve Worsfold   **Goalscorer:** Dave Leadbeater

HONOURS   Northern Counties East - Lg Cup 89-90, Div 2 88-89, Res. Div 88-89, Res.Cup 87-88 88-89;
West Riding County Cup 58-59 81-82.

Players progressing: Arnold Kendall (Bradford C.) 1949, Ron Liversidge(Bradford C.) 56, Derek Blackburn (Swansea) 57, Simon Lowe (Barnsley) 83, Gary Chapman (Bradford C.) 88, Mick Norbury (Scarborough) 1989, Mike Williams(Sheffield W.) 90, Dean Trott (Northampton) 98, Paul Cuss (Huddersfield Town) 98.

Ossett Town on the attack again during their 4-2 away league win against Ashton United.

Photo: Colin Stevens

RADCLIFFE BOROUGH

CLUB OFFICIALS

Chairman: Bernard Manning (Junior)

President: Bernard Manning (Senior)

Vice Chairman: R Doyle

Company/Club Secretary:
Graham E Fielding, c/o Radcliffe Borough

FOOTBALL MANAGEMENT TEAM

Manager: Kevin Glendon
Coach:Mike Farrelly
Physio: Roy Davies

FACT FILE
Formed: 1949
Sponsors: Martin Darlington Transport
Nickname: Boro'
Colours: Blue& white halves
Change colours: All orange
Midweek home matchday: Monday
Reserve Team:No
1999-2000
Captain: Mark Dempsey
P.o.Y.: Simon Kelly
Top scorer: Paul Mullen

GROUND Stainton Park, Pilkington Road, Radcliffe, Lancs M26 3PE
Tel: 0161 724 5937 (club) 0161 724 8346 (Office)   0161 723 3178(Fax)
Directions: M62 junction 17 - follow signs for Whitefield and Bury . Take A665to Radcliffe.
Thro' town centre, turn right into Unsworth St. (opposite Turf Hotel). Ground on left half mile
Colshaw Close East. 1/2 mile from Radcliffe(BR)
Capacity: 3,000   Cover: 1,000   Seats: 350
Clubhouse: (0161 724 5937) `The Boro'- public house on ground. Food available
Club Shop: No

Pages: 28   Price: 80p

Editor: John Stringer

Local Press: Radcliffe Times, Bolton Evening
News, Manchester Evening News
Local Radio: GMR, Piccadilly

PREVIOUS   **Leagues:** South East Lancs; Manchester53-63; Lancs Comb. 63-71; Cheshire County 71-82; North West Counties 82-87
Ground: Bright Street 1949-70.

CLUB RECORDS   **Attendance:** 1,468 v Caernarfon Town, N.W.C. Lge 83
Goalscorer:Ian Lunt   **Appearances:** Chris Lilley.
Fee Paid: £5,000 for Gary Walker(Buxton, 1991). **Fee Received:** £5,000 for Kevin Hulme (Bury, 1989)

BEST SEASON   **FA Trophy:** 3rd Rd v Gateshead 1995-96
FA Cup: 2nd Qual. Rd replay75-76 (1-4 at Rossendale Utd after 2-2 draw). FA Vase: 4th Rd v Boston Town 93-94

HONOURS   Unibond Lge Div One Champ 96-97; North West Counties Lge 84-85 (Div 2 82-83); Lancs Combination Lg Cup 69-70;
Manchester Lg R-up 55-56 (Lg Cup 58-59joint); Manchester Prem Cup R-up 97-98

Players progressing: Jim Hayman (Bury 50), Ian Wood (Oldham Athletic 65), Robert Hutchinson (Rochdale 74),
Gary Haworth (Rochdale 84),Kevin Hulme (Bury 89)

Back Row: James Price, Tony Cullen, Loz Greenhalgh, Simon Carden, Darren Washington (Now Congleton T.), Steve Berryman,
Jeff Parker, David Bean, Simon Kelly, Paul Mullin, Levi Edwards. **Front:** Mike Farrelly (Asst. Man.), Tony Carroll (now Droylsden),
Tony Whealing, Kevin Glendon (Manager), Mark Dempsey (Captain), Ian Lunt, Jason Astley, Roy Davies (Physio).

STOCKSBRIDGE PARK STEELS

CLUB OFFICIALS

President: **J.Newton**
Chairman: **A Bethel**
Vice-Chairman: **M Grimmer**
Secretary: **Michael Grimmer**
48 Hole House Lane, Stocksbridge
Sheffield S36 1BT Tel: 0114 288 6470
Press Officer: **Edwin O'Sullivan**
Commercial Manager: Andrew Horsley
Tel: 0114 288 3867

FOOTBALL MANAGEMENT TEAM

Manager: Mick Horne
Asst Manager: Trevor Gough
Physio: Sean Hird

FACT FILE

Formed: 1986
Nickname: Steels
Sponsors:Weatherglaze
Colours: Yellow/blue/yellow
Change colours: All blue
Midweek matches: Tuesday
Reserves' League: Beefeater County Senior

1999-2000

Captain: Wayne Biggins
P.o.Y.: Lee Wainwright
Top Scorer: Gary Hurlestone (17)

STEELS REVIEW

Club Sponsors
WEATHERGLAZE
WINDOWS LTD

UNIBOND LEAGUE - DIVISION 1 - Season 1999/2000
STOCKSBRIDGE PARK STEELS
v
LINCOLN UNITED
Tuesday 2nd November 1999 - K.O. 7.30pm

Official Matchday Programme   50p

GROUND

Bracken Moor Lane, Stocksbridge, Sheffield
Tel: 0114 288 2045 Fax: 0114 288 8305

Directions: M1 jct 35a (from S), 36 (from N), A616 to Stocksbridge.
On arrival in Stocksbridge turn left into Nanny Hill under the Clock Tower
and continue up the hill for about 500 yds - ground on left

Capacity: 3,500   Cover: 700   Seats: 450
Clubhouse: Open 7 days (lunchtime & evenings). No food. Separate foodbar for matches
Club Shop:(H.O'Sullivan 0114 2884218) badges, mugs, shirts, progs,watches and scarves .

Pages: 28   Price:80p
Editor: Edwin O'Sullivan
Tel: 0114 288 4218

Local Press:
Sheffield Trader, Green'un, The Star

PREVIOUS   **Ground:** Stonemoor 49-51 52-53   **Names:** Stocksbridge Works, Oxley Park;clubs merged in 1986
Leagues: Sheffield Amateur/ Sheffield Association/Yorkshire 49-82

CLUB RECORDS   **Attendance:** 2,000 v Sheffield Wed., Floodlight opening Oct '91
Fee Received: £15,000 for Lee Mills (Wolves, 1992)   **Fee Paid:** Nil
Win: 5-0 v Warrington Town NPL 96-97   **Defeat:** 1-6 v Harrogate NPL 99-00
Scorer: Trevor Jones (145)   **Appearances:** Not known

BEST SEASON   **FA Cup:** 4th Q 50-1, 56-7   **FA Trophy:** 3rd Q 96-97 **FA Vase:** 4th Rd 95-96.

HONOURS   Northern Co's East Prem Div 93-94, R-up 95-96, Div 1 91-92, Lg Cup 94-95; Sheffield Snr Cup 92-93 95-96,98-99.
Oxley Park F C: County Sen Div 1 85-86:Stocksbridge Works FC: Yorkshire Lge Div 1 51-52 54-55 55-56 56-57 57-58
61-62 62-63, Div 2 50-51 64-65, Div 3 70-71 74-75, Lge Cup 61-62 Sheffield Snr Cup 51-52
Players progressing: Peter Eustace (Sheffield Wednesday) 1960 (from Stocksbridge Works) , Lee Mills (Wolverhampton W.) 1992

TRAFFORD

CLUB OFFICIALS

Chairman: **David Brown**

President: **David Roberts**

Secretary: **Graham Foxall**
62 Grosvenor Road, Urmston M41 5AQ
Tel: 0161 746 9726

FOOTBALL MANAGEMENT TEAM

Manager: Mark Molyneaux
Asst Manager: Wayne Goodison
Coach: T.B.A.

FACT FILE

Formed: 1990
Nickname: The North
Sponsors: Caffro Construction Ltd
Colours: All White
Change colours: Azure & black,black,black
Midweek Matchday: Tuesday
Reserve League: Mid Cheshire Div 1
1999-2000
Captain: Garry Vaughan
P.o.Y.: Lee Southwood
Top Scorer: Garry Vaughan (18)

TRAFFORD F.C. 75p
10TH ANNIVERSARY SEASON
REVIEW
Official Matchday Programme

Trafford v Eastwood Town
Shawe View Pennybridge Lane Flixton.

Pages: 44   Price: 75p
Editor: David Murray (0161 775 7509)
Local Press: Stretford & Urmston Messenger,
Manchester Evening News
Local Radio: GMR Talk,
Piccadilly Radio, Century 105

GROUND
Shawe View, Pennybridge Lane, Flixton, Urmston, Manchester M415DL Tel: 0161 747 1727

Directions: M60 jct 9, B5158 towards Urmston, at 1str/about take 1st exit, 1st lights turn right into Moorside Road, at nextr/about 2nd exit into Bowfell Rd, at next lights turn sharp left, thenimmediately right into Pennybridge Lane next to Bird-in-Hand Pub, parking onleft 100 yds
Capacity: 2,500   Cover: 740   Seats: 292
Clubhouse: Yes   **Club Shop:** Yes

PREVIOUS   Leagues: Mid Cheshire 90-92; North West Counties 92-97.   Name: NorthTrafford 90-94.

CLUB RECORDS   **Attendance:** 803 v Flixton (NPL Div 1 27/12/97)
Goalscorer: Garry Vaughan 88   **Appearances:** Garry Vaughan293
Win: 10-0 v Haslingden St Mary's (LancsAmt Shield 91)   **Defeat:** 0-6 v Oldham Town (NWCL Div 2 93)
Fee Paid: Undisclosed for Jock Russell (Radcliffe Borough)   **Fee Received:** Undisclosed for Mike Turner (Witton A.)

BEST SEASON   **FA Vase:** 5th Rd 95-96   **FA Trophy:** 2nd Rd 98-99
FACup: 2nd Rd Qual 95-96,99-00

HONOURS   Lamont Pils Trophy 93-94; NWCL Div 1 96-97, Div 2 R-up 93-94, Lge ChallCup R-up 96-97; Res Div 93-94; Carling Chall Cup R-up 94-95; Manchester PremCup R-up 94-95, R-up 96-97, Res Div Champ 96-97, Cup 96-97; Manchester Amt Cup96-97. Unifilla 1st Div Cup 97-98 Unibond Presidants Cup 99-00 Mid Cheshire Div2 99-00

Players progressing: Anthony Vaughan (Ipswich & Manchester City)

Trafford celebrate winning last season's Unibond President's Cup by defeating Whitby Town after penalties in an enthralling two-legged final. **Back Row:** Billy McCartney, Gary Stones, Marc Clancy, Lee Southwood, Peter Weston, Peter Mellor, Mike Garside, Chris Simms, David Lowe, Mark Molyneaux (Manager), Darren Emmett.
Front Row: Tony Briffa, Garry Vaughan (Captain), Steve Burns, Neil Rigby, Joe Murray.   **Photo:** Dave Murray

VAUXHALL MOTORS F.C.

CLUB OFFICIALS

President: F G Ward

Chairman: Tony Woodley

Vice Chairman: Len Jones

Treasurer: Steven McInerney

Secretary: Mrs Carole Paisey
26 South Rd., West Kirby, Wirral CH48 3HQ
Tel:0151 625 6936

FACT FILE

Formed: 1987
Re-formed 1995
Nickname: Motormen
Club Sponsors: James Edwards
Colours: White/royal blue/white
Midweek Matchday: Tuesday
Reserves' Lge: Wset Cheshire Lge.

FOOTBALL MANAGEMENT TEAM

Manager: Alvin McDonald
Asst. Manager: Peter carroll

For up to the minute news,
results, fixtures,
plus general facts & figures
from the world of
non-league football

log on to

www.nlfootball.com

GROUND Vauxhall Sports Ground, Rivacre Road, Hooton, Ellesmere Port, South Wirrall.
Tel: 0151 328 1114 (Ground) 0151 327 2294 (Club)

Directions: M 53 junction 5, take the A41 to Chester. At the first set of lights (at Chimneys pub) turn left into Hooton Green. Follow to end and turn left at T-junction, to the end & right at the T-junction into Rivacre Rd, ground is 250 yards on right.
Floodlights: Yes
Clubhouse: **Club Shop:**

HONOURS   West Cheshire Lge 86, 95, R-up 84, W. Ches. Lge Bowl 68, Pyke Cup 2000, R-up 73,
N.W.C. Lge. 2nd Div 88-89 95-96; Raab Karcher Chall Cup 90-91;.NWC Challenge Cup 98-99, Division 1 99-00,
Floodlit Trophy Winners 99-00.   Cheshire Amateur Cup R-up 87 94
Wirral Senior Cup 87, R-up 83, 84, 95, 00; Wirrall Amateur Cup 86 R-up 87; Wirral Junior Cup 83

PREVIOUS   **Leagues:** Ellesmer Port Lge., Wirral Combination, West Cheshire League 66-87, 92-95; North West Counties Lg 87-92, 95-00;
Names: Vauxhall Motors 63- 87, Vauxhall GM 88-92, 95-99

BEST SEASON **FA Vase:** S-Final 99-00 v ChippenhamTown 0-1 aet (2 legs)   **FA Cup:**

RECORDS   **Attendance:** 1,500 v English F.A. XI, 1987

WINSFORD UNITED

CLUB OFFICIALS

Chairman: **M Morgan**
President: **A Bayliss**
Vice Chairman: **D Cotterill**
Secretary: **Peter Warburton**
3 Massey Avenue, Winsford,
Cheshire CW7 3DU (01606554295)

FOOTBALL MANAGEMENT TEAM

Manager: K.Tully
Asst Manager: John Imrie

FACT FILE

Founded: 1883
Nickname: Blues
Colours: Royal blue & White/white/blue
Change colours: Maroon/white/white.
Midweek home matchday: Tuesday

For up to the minute news,
results, fixtures,
plus general facts & figures
from the world of
non-league football

log on to

www.nlfootball.com

GROUND

Barton Stadium, Wharton, Winsford, Cheshire CW7 3EU (01606 593021).
Directions: From north; M6 junction 19, A556 towards Northwich to Davenham,then A5018 to Winsford. From south; M6 junction 18, A54 through Middlewich to Winsford. Ground quarter mile off main road in Wharton area of town. 1 mile from Winsford (BR).
Capacity: 6,000   **Cover:** 5,000   **Seats:** 250
Clubhouse: Mon-Sat 8-11pm, Sun 8-10.30pm
Club Shop: Yes, contact Kay Lomas

Programme
Pages: 24 Price: 80p
Editor: R.Astles Tel: 01270 661623

Local Press:
Winsford Chronicle, Winsford Guardian.
Local Radio: Signal, Piccadilly.

PREVIOUS   **Leagues:** The Combination 02-04; Cheshire County 19-40, 47-82; North West Counties 82-87.
Name: Over Wanderers (prior to 1914).

CLUB RECORDS   **Attendance:** 7,000 v Witton Albion 1947.
Goalscorer: Graham Smith 66. **Appearances:** Edward Harrop 400.
Fee Paid: Nil. **Fee Received:** £6,000 for Neville Southall from Bury.

BEST SEASON   **F.A. Cup:** 2nd Rd 1887-88. 1st Rd 1975-76 1991-92.   **F.A. Trophy:** Qtr Finals 77-78.
League clubs defeated: None.

HONOURS   Northern Premier Lg R-up 92-93, Div 1 R-up 91-92, Lg Cup 92-93, Presidents Cup92-93, Div 1 Cup SF 89-90; Cheshire County Lg 20-21 76-77 (R-up 74-75 79-80),Lg Cup 49-50 55-56 59-60 76-77 78-79 79-80 80-81 (R-up 36-37 68-69 77-78); Cheshire Snr Cup 58-59 79-80 92-93; Mid-Cheshire Snr Cup 90-91 92-93 (R-up 88-89); Cheshire Amateur Cup 00-01 02-03; Lancs Comb/Cheshire County Inter-Lg Cup 62-63.

Players P rogressing: W Foulkes (Chester 48), C Marsh (Leeds U. 48), B Nicol(Rochdale 49), E Johnson (Coventry 52), W Hughes (Liverpool 54), R Lewis (Luton54), W Heggie (Accrington 55), J Richardson (Birmingham C. 59), J Abbott (CreweAlex. 61), R Walters (Shrewsbury 62), P Mullington (Rochdale 78), Neville Southall (Bury 80), Mark Came (Bolton Wanderers 84), Dave Bamber (Blackpool),Bob Sutton (West Ham U.), J Richardson (Sheffield U.), Stanley Wood (W.B.A.), R Pearce (Luton T.).

A rare event from last season - Don Page being congratulated by Winsford United colleagues after scoring at Guiseley.
Photo: Darren C Thomas

WITTON ALBION

CLUB OFFICIALS

President: **T Stelfox**

Chairman: **M Worthington**

Secretary: **Phil Chadwick**
29 Jack Lane, Davenham, Northwich,
Cheshire CW9 8LF Tel: 01606 44845

FOOTBALL MANAGEMENT TEAM

Manager: Nigel Gleghorn
Coach: Eddie Bishop
Physio: Steve Crompton

FACT FILE

Formed: 1887
Nickname: The Albion
Colours: Red & white stripes
Change colours: All yellow
Midweek matchday: Tuesday
Reserve League: None

Accrington Stanley
United League First Division, Friday 24th March 2000
Match Sponsor: B2R McDonald's, Northwich
Matchday Magazine Priced £1.20

Pages: 32   Price: £1
Editor: Brian Pritchard (01606 43008)

Local Press: Northwich Guardian,
Northwich Chronicle
Local Radio: BBC GMR, BBC Radio Stoke

GROUND   Wincham Park, Chapel St, Wincham, Northwich. Tel/Fax: 01606 43008

Directions: M6 junc 19. A556 towards Northwich, after 3 miles turn onto A559 at beginning of dual carriageway, after 3/4 mile turn left opposite Black Greyhound Inn, grd 1/2 mile on left immediately after crossing Canal Bridge
Capacity: 4,500   Seated: 650   Cover: 2,300
Clubhouse: Concert room and Vice-Presidents room open matchdays, Tuesday,Thursday, Friday evenings. Food available for private functions   **Club Shop:** Yes

PREVIOUS   **Leagues:** Lancs Comb.; Cheshire County -79; Northern Premier 79-91, GMV Conference 91-94
                         Grounds: Central Ground, Witton Street, Northwich

CLUB RECORDS   **Attendance:** 3,940 v Kidderminster Harriers - FA Trophy Semi-Final 13.4.91 (Wincham Road)
                         11,290 v Northwich Victoria - Cheshire League 15.4.49. (Cenral Ground)
                         Win: 6-0 v Stafford Rangers - 1992/93   **Defeat:** 0-5 v Welling United (H), GMVC12/3/94
                         Fee Paid: £12,500 to Hyde Utd for Jim McCluskie 91   **Fee Received:** £11,500 for Peter Henderson from Chester City.
                         Goalscorer: Frank Fidler 175 (1947-1950)   **Appearances:** Alf Ashley 556 (1946-1958)

BEST SEASON   **FA Trophy:** Runners-up 91-92, Semi-Finals 90-91, 92-93
                         FA Cup: 91-92 Second Round 91-92, 1-5 v Preston North End (A). League clubs defeated: Halifax Town91-92

HONOURS   Northern Prem Lge 90-91; Cheshire County Lge 48-49 49-50 53-54 (R-up 50-51),Lge Cup 53-54 75-76; Cheshire County
                         Sen Cup (7); FA Trophy R-up 91-92 (SF 90-91 92-93)

Players progressing: P Henderson (Chester C.), Chris Nicholl (Burnley - ex-Southampton manager), Phil Power (Crewe), Neil Parsley &
                         Mike Whitlow (Leeds), Geoff Horsfield (Halifax Town ,Fulham), Robert Trees (Bristol Rovers).

Back Row: Peter Billing, Richie Bell, Danny Graystone, Gary Cooley, Alan Minshall, Phil McGing, Lee Cox, Paul Hennin, Lee Murphy, Steve Whitehead. **Front Row:** Mark Cartner, Dave Anane, Lee Anderson, Eddie Bishop, Nigel Gleghorn, Steve Crompton, Brian Pritchard, Ritchie Carter, Charlie Boyd, Martin Faulkner. **Missing:** Steve Haw, Ronnie Sinclair, Gareth Wst, Dave Heywood, Danny Gee.

WORKINGTON

CLUB OFFICIALS

Acting Chairman: Colin Doorbar
President: Eric Fisher
Vice Chairmen:
Dale Brotherton& Humphrey Dobie
Match Sec.: Steve Durham (01946 61380)
Secretary: Dale Brotherton
Lime House, Holm Hill,
Dalston, Carlisle CA5 7BX
Tel: 07977 759903

FOOTBALL MANAGEMENT TEAM
Manager: Peter Hampton
Ass.Man : Keith Hunton
Physios: K Hunton & Tony Elliott

GROUND

FACT FILE

Formed: 1884 (reformed 1921)
Nickname: Reds
Sponsors: AXA Homesearch Direct
Colours: All red
Change colours: yellow & black/black/yellow
Midweek matchday: Tuesday
Reserves' League: West Cumberland

1999-00
Captain Graeme Carr
P.o.Y.: Alan Gray
Top Scorer: Darren Wilson

Borough Park, Workington, Cumbria CA14 2DT

Tel: 01900 602871
Directions: A66 into town, right at 'T' junction, follow A596 for 3/4 mile - ground is then visible and signposted. Ground is north of town centre 1/4 mile from Workington (BR) station &1/2 mile from bus station

Pages: 36   Price: £1
Press Off/ Ed: Steve Durham (01946 61380)

Capacity: 2,500   **Cover:** 800   **Seats:** 300   **Floodlights:** Yes
Clubhouse: Open matchdays and for private functions. Food on matchdays restricted menu
Club Shop: Sells programmes, badges, magazines, pennants, photographs, replica kit,

Local Press: Evening News & Star, Times & Star
Local Radio: BBC Radio Cumbria, C.F.M

HONOURS   Football League: 5th in Div 3 65-66, 3rd Div 4 63-64, Cumberland County Cup 1886-91(x5) 95-99(x4) 1906-08(x2) 09-10 24-25 34-35 36-38(x2) 49-50 53-54 67-68 85-86 95-96 (R-up 1885-86 91-92 1899-1901(x2) 02-03 08-09 11-12 23-24 26-27 29-30 46-47 68-69 78-79) Football League Cup QF 63-64 64-65; N.P.L. Presidents Cup 83-84; North Eastern Lge R-up 38-39, Lge Cup 34-35 36-37 R-up 37-38; N.W. Trains Lg Div 1 98-99

PREVIOUS   **Leagues:** Cumberland Assoc. 1890-94; Cumberland Sen. Lge 94-1901, 03-04; Lancashire Lge 1901-03; Lancashire Comb. 04-10; North Eastern 10-11, 21-51; Football League 51-77
Grounds: Various 1884-1921, Lonsdale Park 21-37

BEST SEASON   **FA Cup:** 4th Rd 33-34. 1st Rd - 53 occasions.
FA Trophy: 1st Round replay 77-78   **FA Vase:** 6th Rd, 98-99 (1st season)

RECORDS   **Attendance:** 21,000 v Manchester Utd, FA Cup 3rd Rd 4/1/58
Goalscorer: Billy Charlton 193
Appearances: Bobby Brown 419
Fee Paid: £6,000 for Ken Chisholm (Sunderland,'56)
Win: 17-1 v Cockermouth Crusaders, Cumb-erland Sen. Lge 19/1/01
Defeat: 0-9 v Chorley (A), NPL Prem. Div., 10/11/87
Fee Received: £33,000 for Ian McDonald (Liverpool, '74)

Players progressing: Numerous, the best known being John Burridge.

Back Row: Wayne Johnson, Gary Messer, Matthew Henney, Stuart Williamson, Barry Irving, Mark Donnelly, Graeme Carr, Gary Hoggeth, Andrew Jones. **Front Row:** Andrew Douglas, Graham Goulding, Marc Green, Brian Dawson, Alan Gray.

NORTHERN PREMIER LEAGUE - DIVISION ONE - THE LAST TEN YEARS

	90-91	91-92	92-93	93-94	94-95	95-96	96-97	97-98	98-99	99-00
Accrington Stanley	4	-	-	-	-	-	-	-	-	1
Alfreton Town	22	20	9	6	4	2	-	-	22	-
Ashton United	-	-	3	3	8	9	8	3	3	14
Atherton L.R.	-	-	-	-	12	10	22	-	-	-
Bamber Bridge	-	-	-	13	2	-	-	-	-	-
Belper Town	-	-	-	-	-	-	-	10	13	17
Blyth Spartans	-	-	-	-	1	-	-	-	-	-
Bradford Park Avenue	-	-	-	-	-	17	7	9	9	4
Bridlington Town	9	6	1	-	-	-	-	-	-	-
Burscough	-	-	-	-	-	-	-	-	7	2
Buxton	-	-	-	-	-	-	-	22	-	-
Caernarfon Town	14	5	16	18	14	-	-	-	-	-
Chorley	-	-	-	-	-	-	-	-	-	13
Colwyn Bay	-	1	-	-	-	-	-	-	-	-
Congleton Town	11	17	20	15	17	18	18	18	20	12
Curzon Ashton	10	11	7	14	15	4	20	-	-	-
Droylsden	-	-	-	-	-	-	10	4	1	-
Eastwood Town	6	15	14	21	10	7	15	8	5	10
Emley	2	-	-	-	-	-	-	-	-	-
Farsley Celtic	21	12	17	19	19	5	4	6	18	6
Fleetwood Town	-	-	-	-	18	20	-	-	-	-
Flixton	-	-	-	-	-	-	13	17	16	21
Guiseley	-	4	4	1	-	-	-	-	-	-
Goole Town	-	-	-	8	21	-	-	-	-	-
Great Harwood Town	-	-	8	9	16	19	9	20	21	-
Gretna	-	-	6	10	11	12	16	15	12	19
Harrogate Town	19	10	10	20	13	21	17	19	11	11
Hucknall Town	-	-	-	-	-	-	-	-	2	-
Irlam Town	17	21	-	-	-	-	-	-	-	-
Knowsley United	-	8	2	-	-	-	-	-	-	-
Lancaster City	8	16	18	4	5	1	-	-	-	-
Leigh R.M.I.	-	-	-	-	-	14	2	-	-	-
Lincoln United	-	-	-	-	-	3	3	5	4	16
Matlock Town	-	-	-	-	-	-	11	14	17	7
Mossley	-	-	-	17	22	-	-	-	-	-
Netherfield Kendal	12	9	15	5	9	15	14	16	15	20
Newtown	13	14	-	-	-	-	-	-	-	-
Ossett Town	-	-	-	-	-	-	-	-	-	8
Penrith	-	-	-	-	-	-	-	-	-	-
Radcliffe Borough	16	13	12	16	7	6	1	-	6	5
Rhyl	5	18	-	-	-	-	-	-	-	-
Rossendale United	15	19	21	-	-	-	-	-	-	-
Shepshed Albion	-	-	19	-	-	-	-	-	-	-
Stocksbridge Park Steels	-	-	-	-	-	-	6	11	10	9
Spennymoor United	-	-	-	2	-	-	-	-	-	-
Trafford	-	-	-	-	-	-	-	12	14	18
Warrington Town	7	7	5	7	3	13	21	-	-	-
Whitby Town	-	-	-	-	-	-	-	1	-	-
Whitley Bay	1	-	-	-	-	8	12	13	19	22
Winsford United	18	2	-	-	-	-	-	-	-	-
Witton Albion	-	-	-	-	-	-	-	7	8	3
Workington	20	22	13	11	20	16	19	21	-	15
Worksop Town	3	3	11	12	6	11	5	2	-	-

An irresistable strike force

Every month

INSIDE! MORE ACTION ✱ MORE PHOTOS ✱ EVERY MONTH!

NO. 1 NON-LEAGUE MAGAZINE

Team Talk

OFFICIAL F.A. MAGAZINE

Every week

THE NON-LEAGUE PAPER

CONFERENCE & PYRAMID LEAGUES SOCCER / £1.00

Every day

For up to the minute news, results, fixtures,
and general facts and figures
from the world of non-league football
log on to

www.nlfootball.com

Brought to you by Non-League Media in conjunction with e-comsport

THE NORTH WEST COUNTIES FOOTBALL LEAGUE

President: W J King   **Chairman:** D Tomlinson

Secretary: Geoff Wilkinson
46 Oaklands Drive, Penwortham, Preston PR1 0YY   Tel: 01772 746312

The last season of the twentieth century started, like so many, with high hopes for many of our teams, and what promised to be an open footrace for both divisional Championships.

In the First Division, Great Harwood's Graeme Lightbown was the first out of the traps, netting the debut goal of the 1999-2000 season after just 20 seconds as the Robins looked to emulate Workington's success of the previous season. It was to be two other newcomers to the Division who would set the early pace as Fleetwood Freeport and Abbey Hey led the table for most of August and September.

From the end of October, though, Vauxhall Motors assumed pole position, and, but for a few occasions, were to remain there in what was to become a fantastic season for the club. It was far from being one way traffic though, and credit must go to those clubs who worked very hard to stay in touch and made the battle so exciting.

Clitheroe, Mossley and Rossendale United were Lancashire's long standing contenders, with the men from Dark Lane emerging as a very potent force during a landmark season for the club. For the Blues, it was a tale of what might have been, whilst Mossley's cup exploits weighed them down as their fellow title chasers made good use of their extra games played to put daylight between them and the Liliwhites.

For Ramsbottom United, St Helens Town and Skelmersdale United, enough quality was on show to indicate a stronger push next term, Rammy being particularly impressive in recovering from a poor start and remaining unbeaten at home in the league all season, eventually finishing third.

Newcastle Town were the Potteries' chief threat, but too many dropped points, plus an excellent Vase run, played a part as they fell away in the New Year, but recovered to finish runners-up. Fleetwood Freeport had a disjointed campaign, changing managers midway through the season but still finished in a creditable top eight position.

For many sides in mid-table, there were highs and lows, through Prescot Cables and Salford City were two sides who impressed after new management took over, as did two of our midlands clubs, Kidsgrove Athletic and Nantwich Town, who also found form after shaky starts.

Abbey Hey fell away after a very good start, but will have learnt enough lessons to set them up again for next season, and Alan Lord's Atherton Collieries became the Division's wild-card club, capable of beating anyone in a momentous second half to the season. Newly relegated Great Harwood Town began well, but faded to finish below half way.

For the clutch of clubs towards the bottom, a nervous season ended with Glossop North End, Cheadle Town, Maine Road and Leek CSOB all finishing safely. It was a particularly sad year for Maine Road as they lost Keith Hunter during the course of the season, who will be missed by all who knew him.

The First Division loses Bootle, who endured a spectacular drop in form after a bright start, and Atherton LR, who made a lot of admirers despite finishing bottom as Steve Plant persevered with a young squad which didn't quite gel in time to save them from relegation.

The Second Division race was to prove as exciting as any recent campaign with half a dozen clubs vying for promotion. Curzon Ashton were to make most of the running in the early months, though Darwen and Nelson were hot on their heels with other teams also in close pursuit.

Curzon though were the outstanding side, and apart from a spell in the Autumn when Darwen held top spot, were always in the driving seat. The dogfight between Darwen and Nelson was to prove one of the most interesting aspects of the season with these Lancashire rivals both recording promotion form throughout the end of 1999 and into the new millennium.

Castleton Gabriels, Bacup Borough and Squires Gate were always in touch, but with the leading three rarely slipping up, their chances were limited. Behind these clubs lay Woodley Sports, who had enough games in hand to catch up, but after a slow start looked very much an outside bet.

By March, the Steelmen were only a couple of wins behind the top three after a long unbeaten run stretching back to November, but it still looked a tall order as the sides above them ran out of games. A win at Curzon, followed by defeat for the leaders at Mechanics, allowed them a chance.

With Curzon finishing on 78 points, Woodley needed maximum points from all five remaining games, and they duly collected to pip an unlucky Curzon Ashton for the title at the death. After such a hard campaign, it was also hard on Darwen and Nelson who must now regroup for another push in August.

Gabriels, Bacup and Squires Gate emerged with much credit, whilst Warrington Town ended on a high and could prove a contender next term. Neighbouring Tetley Walker turned their season around with new management after a bad start. Chadderton also recovered well and Alsager will be happy enough with a solid first season in the League.

Formby were the Division's enigmatic outfit, blowing hot and cold all season, whilst for Colne and Holker Old Boys a patchy season saw both easily clear of the re-election spots.

Blackpool Mechanics, season was turned around by an influx of ex-Freeport personnel, and the club ended in good shape, as did Daisy Hill who were another side to click into gear late on. For Oldham Town and Ashton Town a season of struggle has passed, though interestingly Ashton lead the table in August!

With Padiham, Stand Athletic and Stone Dominoes all recommended for membership, next season looks to be an intriguing prospect in the Second Division.

In the AXA sponsored FA Cup, the League once again performed reasonably well, with Nantwich Town and Fleetwood Freeport making it through the early rounds. It was the Dabbers who made the headlines though, eventually going out to St Albans City by 4-2 in the Third Qualifying Round.

The FA Carlsberg Vase proved a more fertile competition with thirteen clubs in the First Round Proper and five in the Fourth Round. Skem' and Glossop fell to Taunton and Chippenham respectively at this stage, and Mossley also came unstuck at Deal Town in the Sixth Round.

For Vauxhall Motors and Newcastle Town though, Wembley beckoned as both progressed to the Semi-Finals with impressive away victories over Taunton Town and Ramsgate. Alas, this final hurdle saw both go out in unlucky circumstances, but both clubs, and indeed all those who took part, were a credit to themselves and the League making friends wherever they went.

Our domestic cup competitions saw honours shared around. The first silverware up for grabs saw an all-Warrington Second Division Trophy Final between Warrington Town and Tetley Walker at Prescot Cables, and the Yellows claimed the glory with a 2-0 victory in an exciting finale.

Cheadle Town Reserves then collected the Reserve Division Cup with a 3-0 win over Clitheroe Reserves at Salford's Moor Land ground. The Reserve Division South title was collected by Salford City, and Clitheroe edged a tight Reserve Division North campaign.

A near 600 strong crowd saw an excellent Floodlit Trophy Final between Rossendale United and Vauxhall Motors at Dark Lane. It took extra-time to separate the sides with the Wirral club taking the silverware home after a hard fought 3-1 win.

The League's showpiece Final saw Skelmersdale United and Newcastle Town go head to head for the League Challenge Cup at Bury FC's Gigg Lane ground. A nervous encounter ended goal-less after 120 minutes, and it looked like neither side would make an error as the penalty count went to 5-5 in the shoot-out. A sixth goal for Skem' followed by the first miss for 'Castle saw the West Lancashire side collect the Cup, a fitting reward following an impressive season for the club.

Gregg Blundell of Vauxhall Motors and Paul Baker of Darwen ended leading goalscorers in the First and Second Divisions respectively, and our congratulations go to both.

Special congratulations go to Vauxhall Motors, Woodley Sports and Curzon Ashton on promotion, and to Skelmersdale United, Vauxhall again, and Warrington Town on claiming cup glory this term, but all our clubs deserve congratulations after what has been another exciting and enthralling season in the First North Western Trains League.

HONOURS LIST 1999-2000

FIRST DIVISION
Champions	Vauxhall Motors FC
Runners up	Newcastle Town FC

SECOND DIVISION
Champions	Woodley Sports FC
Runners up	Curzon Ashton FC

RESERVE DIVISION NORTH
Champions	Clitheroe FC
Runners up	Darwen FC

RESERVE DIVISION SOUTH
Champions	Salford City FC
Runners up	Woodley Sports FC

LEAGUE CHALLENGE CUP
Champions	Skelmersdale United FC
Runners up	Newcastle Town FC

FLOODLIT TROPHY
Champions	Vauxhall Motors FC
Runners up	Rossendale United FC

SECOND DIVISION TROPHY
Champions	Warrington Town
Runners up	Tetley Walker

RESERVE DIVISION CUP
Champions	Cheadle Town
Runners up	Clitheroe

MANCHESTER PREMIER CUP
Runners up	Mossley FC

MANCHESTER AMATEUR CUP
Runners up	Salford City Reserves

FINAL LEAGUE TABLES 1999-2000

DIVISION ONE

	P	W	D	L	F	A	GD	Pts
Vauxhall Motors	42	29	7	6	101	32	69	94
Newcastle Town	42	26	7	9	82	35	47	85
Ramsbottom Utd	42	23	10	9	87	53	34	79
Mossley	42	23	10	9	80	50	30	79
Rossendale Utd	42	23	9	10	77	46	31	78
Skelmersdale Utd	42	22	9	11	91	53	38	75
Fleetwood Freeport	42	21	10	11	75	45	30	73
Prescot Cables	42	21	10	11	83	55	28	73
St Helens Town	42	20	13	9	81	59	22	73
Clitheroe	42	21	7	14	75	49	26	70
Salford City	42	17	7	18	70	69	1	58
Atherton Colls	42	16	6	20	58	68	-10	54
Kidsgrove Ath	42	14	9	19	47	66	-19	51
Abbey Hey	42	14	8	20	50	75	-25	50
Nantwich Town	42	13	9	20	60	73	-13	48
Gt Harwood Tn	42	12	9	21	55	81	-26	45
Glossop North E	42	10	11	21	52	73	-21	41
Cheadle Town	42	8	13	21	49	85	-36	37
Maine Road	42	9	10	23	59	100	-41	37
Leek CSOB	42	8	10	24	49	101	-52	34
Bootle	42	6	8	28	29	90	-61	26
Atherton LR	42	4	12	26	51	103	-52	24

DIVISION TWO

	P	W	D	L	F	A	GD	Pts
Woodley Sports	34	24	6	4	85	29	56	78
Curzon Ashton	34	24	6	4	78	26	52	78
Nelson	34	21	8	5	77	31	46	71
Darwen	34	20	6	8	69	35	34	66
Bacup Borough	34	15	11	8	68	42	26	56
Squires Gate	34	16	7	11	70	49	21	55
Tetley Walker	34	16	4	14	56	70	-14	52
Castleton Gabriels	34	15	6	13	67	67	0	51
Warrington Town	34	14	8	12	66	44	22	50
Chadderton	34	12	12	10	52	57	-5	48
Formby	34	12	8	14	52	68	-16	44
Alsager	34	11	8	15	48	64	-16	41
Colne	34	12	2	20	44	70	-26	38
Holker Old Boys	34	8	11	15	59	73	-14	35
Blackpool Mechs	34	9	6	19	49	74	-25	33
Daisy Hill	34	7	5	22	41	75	-34	26
Oldham Town	34	4	6	24	43	86	-43	18
Ashton Town	34	5	2	27	30	94	-64	17

RESERVE DIVISION NORTH

	P	W	D	L	F	A	GD	Pts
Clitheroe	20	16	0	4	82	21	61	48
Darwen	20	14	2	4	46	25	21	44
Rossendale Utd	20	13	4	3	56	27	29	43
Ramsbottom Utd	20	13	1	6	66	31	35	40
Nelson	20	9	5	6	48	39	9	32
Colne	20	8	1	11	26	41	-15	25
Squires Gate	20	6	3	11	33	44	-11	21
Fleetwood Frpt	20	6	2	12	41	68	-27	20
Bacup Borough	20	6	0	14	28	59	-31	18
Chadderton	20	4	4	12	37	54	-17	16
Oldham Town	20	4	0	16	29	83	-54	12

RESERVE DIVISION SOUTH

	P	W	D	L	F	A	GD	Pts
Salford City	22	20	1	1	70	16	54	61
Woodley Sports	22	13	4	5	58	31	27	43
Abbey Hey	22	12	6	4	51	27	24	42
Atherton LR	22	9	3	10	42	39	3	30
Cheadle Town	22	8	5	9	42	41	1	29
Maine Road	22	7	6	9	35	37	-2	27
Glossop N E	22	7	5	10	37	51	-14	26
Ashton Town	22	7	4	11	35	44	-9	25
Newcastle Town	22	6	7	9	29	43	-14	25
Daisy Hill	22	5	7	10	31	47	-16	22
Curzon Ashton	22	5	6	11	36	44	-8	21
Atherton Coll	22	2	8	12	21	67	-46	14

FIRST DIVISION TOP ATTENDANCES 1999-2000

Abbey Hey	250	v	Mossley	Maine Road	125	v	Mossley
Atherton Collieries	161	v	Atherton LR	Mossley	356	v	Glossop North End
Atherton LR	124	v	Glossop NE	Nantwich Town	121	v	Newcastle Town
Bootle	123	v	Mossley	Newcastle Town	214	v	Kidsgrove Athletic
Clitheroe	505	v	Great Harwood Tn	Prescot Cables	216	v	St Helens Town
Cheadle Town	172	v	Mossley	Ramsbottom United	316	v	Rossendale United
Fleetwood Freeport	241	v	Vauxhall Motors	Rossendale United	267	v	Clitheroe
Glossop North End	302	v	Mossley	St Helens Town	157	v	Vauxhall Motors
Great Harwood Town	246	v	Rossendale Utd	Salford City	152	v	Cheadle Town
Kidsgrove Athletic	374	v	Newcastle Town	Skelmersdale United	182	v	Mossley
Leek CSOB	120	v	Mossley	Vauxhall Motors	170	v	Newcastle Town

FIRST DIVISION RESULTS CHART 1999-2000

	1	2	3	4	5	6	7	8	9	10	11	12	13	14	15	16	17	18	19	20	21	22
1 Abbey Hey	X	1-3	4-1	1-2	0-2	0-3	0-0	1-1	1-2	2-0	3-1	3-1	0-4	1-1	0-3	1-0	0-3	1-5	2-1	1-2	1-3	1-0
2 Atherton C	1-6	X	4-1	0-1	4-1	1-3	1-1	1-4	0-1	3-0	2-2	3-0	0-1	2-1	2-1	1-1	0-2	0-3	2-3	3-0	0-2	0-1
3 Atherton LR	1-1	2-4	X	4-2	1-1	2-4	1-1	0-0	5-1	1-3	1-1	0-3	2-2	0-4	0-4	1-1	1-2	1-3	1-1	0-2	2-4	1-3
4 Bootle	0-1	0-1	0-0	X	0-0	1-4	0-3	1-0	1-0	0-1	1-2	2-3	2-1	1-1	0-5	1-0	0-0	0-3	1-1	0-0	0-3	0-2
5 Cheadle	0-1	3-4	2-0	1-0	X	0-1	0-2	4-2	0-1	3-0	0-0	2-2	0-0	1-0	1-1	1-5	1-1	3-3	1-1	1-2	1-2	1-3
6 Clitheroe	2-0	0-0	5-2	3-0	4-2	X	2-3	1-1	2-1	1-0	1-1	4-0	2-1	0-0	0-1	0-1	1-0	0-1	2-0	2-2	4-4	0-2
7 Fleetwood	3-1	0-2	2-3	2-0	0-0	1-0	X	3-2	2-0	3-0	5-2	0-0	3-0	6-1	1-2	3-1	2-1	2-2	3-0	1-2	2-0	3-3
8 Glossop NE	0-3	1-1	2-1	5-1	1-0	1-0	1-1	X	1-1	0-1	2-2	1-1	1-2	1-1	1-3	1-1	1-0	0-2	3-5	1-3	0-2	1-1
9 Gt Harwood	5-1	1-3	5-2	3-0	2-2	0-3	2-1	2-1	X	2-2	1-2	4-4	0-1	2-3	0-3	1-1	3-0	0-0	1-1	1-0	1-4	1-2
10 Kidsgrove	5-1	1-3	4-1	1-2	6-0	1-3	0-1	0-1	3-1	X	1-1	4-1	0-2	1-1	1-3	0-0	0-4	2-0	0-2	1-1	2-1	0-0
11 Leek CSOB	0-0	1-2	1-4	3-0	4-5	1-0	1-0	0-1	0-1	0-1	X	0-1	0-3	3-2	2-1	1-1	0-1	0-3	0-3	0-2	3-3	0-4
12 Maine Road	2-2	2-2	4-1	2-2	2-0	2-1	1-4	0-2	1-1	2-1	4-7	X	0-4	4-0	0-3	0-3	1-2	2-2	1-1	0-1	2-6	1-3
13 Mossley	0-3	3-1	2-0	2-1	2-2	4-2	2-1	3-2	4-1	1-1	4-0	1-2	X	2-1	1-1	2-0	4-3	0-1	1-1	3-1	1-1	2-0
14 Nantwich	4-2	4-0	1-0	4-1	0-2	1-0	1-2	3-1	2-1	2-2	5-2	1-0	0-2	X	2-1	0-1	2-3	1-0	2-2	0-3	1-1	1-2
15 Newcastle	0-0	0-1	1-0	3-1	4-1	1-2	3-0	3-2	4-0	1-0	1-0	2-1	2-2	3-1	X	1-3	4-1	0-1	0-1	4-1	2-1	0-1
16 Prescot	2-1	2-1	3-3	2-2	3-1	3-1	2-0	1-2	6-2	6-1	2-1	4-1	1-2	2-0	0-1	X	1-1	1-1	2-0	6-0	3-1	1-2
17 Ramsbottom	7-0	2-0	3-0	2-1	4-1	1-1	1-1	4-1	1-0	0-0	4-2	3-0	3-0	4-2	1-1	6-2	X	3-2	1-1	3-1	3-1	2-2
18 Rossendale	0-1	1-0	1-1	3-2	4-2	1-4	1-1	1-0	1-1	3-0	4-1	3-2	1-1	1-0	0-2	2-3	4-0	X	2-1	2-0	2-1	4-3
19 St Helens	5-1	1-0	1-1	5-0	1-0	3-2	3-2	5-2	0-2	3-1	2-2	4-0	3-3	3-1	1-2	2-3	3-1	1-0	X	3-2	1-5	1-0
20 Salford City	0-2	1-2	4-1	7-0	1-1	2-0	0-3	1-2	2-1	0-1	7-0	5-3	3-1	2-2	1-4	1-0	2-2	2-1	2-3	X	2-2	0-1
21 Skelmersdale	0-0	2-0	3-1	3-0	3-0	0-2	0-1	3-0	4-0	5-2	6-0	3-1	1-4	2-0	0-0	5-1	1-0	0-3	1-1	1-0	X	1-1
22 Vauxhall	4-0	4-0	4-1	3-2	8-0	1-3	1-0	2-0	5-0	4-0	7-0	3-0	1-0	4-1	1-1	1-2	3-0	1-0	1-1	4-0	3-0	X

LEADING GOALSCORERS 1999-2000

FIRST DIVISION

Gregg Blundell	Vauxhall Motors	42
Russell Brierley	Ramsbottom United	39
Craig Sargerson	Rossendale United	39
Andy Gayle	Nantwich Town	35
Robbie Cowley	Skelmersdale United	34
Nicky Young	Vauxhall Motors	33
Peter Cumiskey	Prescot Cables	26
Darren Twigg	Newcastle Town	25
Steve O'Neill	St Helens Town	25
Billy O'Callaghan	Prescot Cables	25
Stuart Rudd	Skelmersdale United	24
Lee Wilkinson	Mossley	23
Stuart Diggle	Fleetwood Freeport	20
David Yorke-Robinson	Ramsbottom United	20
Jimmy Flood	Atherton LR	18
	(2 for Atherton Collieries)	
Graeme Lightbown	Great Harwood Town	17
Gary Laird	St Helens Town	17
Tony Scott	Skelmersdale United	17
Rob Myatt	Newcastle Town	16
Ritchie Batho	Kidsgrove Athletic	15
Steve Orrell	Ramsbottom United	15
Pedro Brennan	Mossley	15
Chris Wilcock	Mossley	15

SECOND DIVISION

Paul Baker	Darwen	30
Carl Waters	Holker Old Boys	26
Jonathon Irvine	Nelson	25
Mark Wilson	Formby	22
Mark Robinson	Nelson	20
Steve Gavin	Curzon Ashton	20
Steve Longworth	Squires Gate	20
Gareth Rowe	Alsager	18
Stuart Farnell	Bacup Borough	17
Ged Bushell	Warrington Town	17
Peter Carty	Woodley Sports	16
	(4 for Abbey Hey)	
Denis Walsh	Blackpool Mechanics	16
	(10 for Fleetwood Freeport)	
Andy Seddon	Woodley Sports	16
Nicky Taylor	Bacup Borough	15
Richard Burgess	Squires Gate	15
Barry Edwardson	Tetley Walker	15

354

ABBEY HEY

Secretary: Gordon Lester, 6 Newhaven Avenue, Hr.Openshaw, Manchestewr M11 1HU
Tel Nos: 0161 370 0270 (H) 0161 200 4630 (W)

Ground: Abbey Stadium, Goredale Avenue, Gorton, Manchester 18
Tel: 0161 231 7147 (Club) Fax: 01823 490281

Directions: A57 towards Hyde, right into Woodland Avenue approx one & a half miles
past Belle Vue junction, right again into Ryder Brow Rd, 1st left after bridge
into Goredale Ave.
Capacity: 1000   Seats: 100   Cover: 300   Floodlights: Yes

Honours Manchester Amat. Lge 65-66: S.E. Lancs Lge 66-67, 68-69 R-up 67-68; Div.2
68-69; Lge Shield 65-66: Manc. Co. Amat. Cup 64-65, 67-68, 68-69, R-up 63-
64: Manchester Lge Prem. Div. 81-82, 88-89, 90-91, 93-94, 94-95; Div. 1 70-
71; Div.2 88-89, 92-93, 93-94; Gilcryst Cup 76-77, 88-89, R-up 97-88; Open
Tphy 78-79,79-80, 92-93: Manchester Chall. Tphy 82-83, 95-96, 96-97. N.W.
Trains Div 2 R-up 98-99Previous

Previous **Leagues:** Manchester Amateur; South East Lancs; Manchester Lge.
Record **Attendance:** 400 v Manchester City XI oct 99

FACT FILE

Formed: 1902
Colours:Red& black/black/black
Midweek matchday: Tuesday

CLUB PERSONNEL

Chairman: James Whittaker
0161 445 0036

Emergency Contact; G.Lester
0161 370 0270 or 0161 236 3311 ext 2800

ATHERTON COLLIERIES

Secretary: Paul Gregory, 5 Spa Road, Atherton M46 9WX 0161 288 6216 (W)

Ground: Atherton Colls Football Ground,Alder St., Atherton, Gt ManchesterTel:01942884649.
Directions: M61 Jct 5, follow sign for Westhoughton, left onto A6, right ontoA579 (Newbrook
Rd/Bolton Rd) into Atherton. At first set of lights turn leftinto High Street, 2nd left into Alder St.
to ground. Quarter mile from AthertonCentral (BR).
Seats: 300   Cover: 1,000   Capacity: 2,500   Floodlights: Yes
Clubhouse: Open Mon-Fri 7-11pm, Sat 11am-11pm, Sun noon-3 & 7-10.30pm. Hot &cold
food on matchdays. **Club Shop:** No, but programmes & badges are available

HONOURS: BNWCFL 3rd Div Champ 86/87; Bridge Shield 85/86; Lancs County FA
Shield19/20, 22/23, 41/42, 45/46. 56/57, 64/65; Tennents F/lit Trophy Finalist
94/95; NWCFL Div 2 R/up 95/96
RECORDS **Attendance:** 3,300 in Lancs Combination, 1920's
PREVIOUS **Leagues:** Bolton Combination 20-50, 52-71; Lancs Combination 50-52, 71-78;
Cheshire County 78-82.
Players Progressing: J Parkinson (Wigan), Russell Beardsmore(Manchester Utd).

FACT FILE

Founded: 1916
Nickname: Colls
Club Sponsors: Kensite
Colours: Black & white stripes/black/black.
Change colours: Yellow/blue/yellow
Reserves' Lge: NWTL Res Div
Midweek Matches: Tuesday
Programme: 40 pages, 70p
Editor: Frank Anderson.
Captain 99-00: Liam Boden
P.o.Y.: Luke Hardman
Top Scorer: Luke Hardman
CLUB PERSONNEL

Chairman: Steve Payne
Vice Chairman:
President: J Fielding
Manager: Alan Lord/Chris O'Brien
Physio: Chris Roberts

CHEADLE TOWN

Secretary: Susan Burton, 2 Lavington Ave., Cheadle, Stockport, Cheshire SK8 2HH
Tel: 0161 491 0823

Ground: Park Road Stadium, Park Road, Cheadle, Cheshire SK8 2AN (0161 4282510).
Directions: M60 Jct 2, follow signs towards Cheadle (A560), first left after lights into Park Road,
ground at end. 1 mile from Gatley (BR), buses from Stockport.
Capacity: 2,500Seats: 300Cover: 300Floodlights: Yes

Clubhouse: Open every night. Food available   **Club Shop:** No

HONOURS Manchester Lg Div 1 79-80 (R-up 80-81 81-82); Manchester Amtr Cup 79-
80;Lamot Pils R-up 90-91; NWCFL Div 2 Trophy R-up 95-96:

PREVIOUS **Leagues:** Manchester (pre 1987)

RECORD **Attendance :** 1,700 v Stockport County, August 1994.
Scorer: Peter Tilley   **Appearances:** John McArdle

Players progressing: Ashley Ward (Crewe), Steve Bushell (York), Dean Crowe(Stoke).

FACT FILE

Founded: 1961
Colours: White/black/black
Change colours: All blue.
Midweek Matches: Tuesday
Reserves' Lge: NW Counties Lge
Programme: 24 pages,80p.
Editor: Stuart Crawford
99-00Captain: Tony McCombe
P.o.Y.: Rick Watson
Top Scorer:Tony Coyne

CLUB PERSONNEL

President: Freddie Pye
Chairman: Chris Davies
Vice-Chairman: Clive Williams
Press Officer: Chris Davies (0161 428 2510).
Manager:Graham Wright
Physio: Chris Molloy

CLITHEROE

Secretary: Colin Wilson, 4 Moss Street, Clitheroe, Lancs BB7 1DP(01200 424370).

Ground: Shawbridge, Clitheroe, Lancs (01200 423344).
Directions: M6 jct 31, A59 to Clitheroe (17 miles), at 5th r'bout continue for half a mile and turn left at Pendle Road. Ground one mile, behind Bridge Inn' on the right. 11 miles from Blackburn BR station: Clitheroe
Capacity: 2,000   Seats: 300   Cover: 1200   Floodlights: Yes

Clubhouse: Open during matches. Snacks available   **Club Shop:** Yes.

HONOURS	FA Vase Runners-up 95-96; Lancs Comb. 79-80, Lg Cup 34-35; Lancs Challenge Tphy 84-85; NW C Lge 85-86, Div 2 84-85, Div 3 83-84; East Lancs Floodlit Trophy 94-95.N.W.Trains Floodlit Cup: 98-99
PREVIOUS	Leagues: Blackburn & Dist.; Lancs Comb. 03-04 05-10 25-82.
BEST SEASON	FA Cup: FA Vase: Runners-up 95-96
RECORDS	Attendance: 2,000 v Mangotsfield, FA Vase Semi/F 95-96. Goalscorer: Don Francis Appearances: Lindsey Wallace.
Players progressing	Ray Woods (Leeds 1950), Chris Sims (Blackburn 1960), Lee Rogerson (Wigan Ath), Carlo Nash (Crystal Palace).

FACT FILE

Formed: 1877.
Nickname: The Blues
Colours: Blue & white /blue/blue
Change colours: All yellow
Midweek matchday: Tuesday
Reserves' Lge: N.W.C.L.
Programme: 12 pages, 60p
Editor: Ian Rimmer

CLUB PERSONNEL

Chairman: S Rush
President: Jer Aspinall
Press Officer: Colin Wilson
Manager:Steve Parry.
Assistant Manager: Malcolm Holt
Physio: Keith Lord.

CURZON ASHTON

Secretary: Robert Hurst, 36 Russell Road, Partington, Manchester M31 4DZ
Tel: 0161 775 3883 Fax 0771 775 8787 Mobile 0771 325 2310

Ground: National Park, Katherine Street, Ashton-under-Lyne OL7 6DA (0161 3306033)
Directions: Behind Ashton police station off Manchester Rd (A635),Ashton-under-Lyne, one and a half miles from Ashton-under-Lyne (BR)
Capacity: 5,000   Cover: 450   Seats: 350   Floodlights: Yes
Clubhouse: Every night. Food on matchdays. **Club Shop:** Contact Roy Howe, 0161 220 8345

PREVIOUS	**Leagues:** Manchester Amat.; Manchester (-1978); Cheshire Co. 78-82; N.W.C. 82-87, Northern Prem. Lge. 87-97, N.C.E. 97-98, N.W.C. 98-
BEST SEASON	**FA Cup:** 3rd Qual. Rd replay 89-90, 1-3 v Mossley (A) after 1-1
	FA Vase: Semi-Final 79-80 **FA Trophy:** 2nd Qual. Rd 82-83, 84-85
HONOURS	**NWC Lge Div.2 r-ip 99-00;** Cheshire Co. Lge Div 2 R-up 78-79: Manchester Lge 77-78, R-up 74-75 75-76; Lge Cup 77-78, R-up 74-75 75-76; Murray Shield R-up 75-76: Manchester Amat. Lge 63-64 65-66, R-up 64-65: Manchester Prem. Cup x 5
RECORDS	**Attendance:** 1,826 v Stamford, FA Vase SF 1980
	Goalscorer: Alan Sykes **Appearances:** Alan Sykes 620
	Win: 7-0 v Ashton United **Defeat:** 0-8 v Bamber Bridge

FACT FILE
Formed: 1963
Nickname: The Blues
Colours: Royal Blue/white/white
Change colours: All Red
Midweek matches: Tuesday
Programme: 40pages £1.00
Editor: Robert Hurst (0161 775 3883)

CLUB PERSONNEL
Chairman: Harry Galloway
Vice Chairman: R.Capstick
Chief Executive: Harry Twamley
President: Peter Mayo
Press Officer:Graham Shuttleworth
Treasurer: Sam Shuttleworth
Manager: Joe Murty
Assistant Manager: Martin Farnworth
Physio: Graham Taylor

FLEETWOOD FREEPORT

FACT FILE

Secretary: Kevin Pennington, 1 Carlisle Avenue, Fleetwood, Lancs. FY7 8LP.
Tel: 01253 771602 (H); 01253 861687 (B)

Ground: Highbury Stadium, Park Avenue, Fleetwood, Lancs (01253 770702)

Directions: From M55, junction 3, follow signs (A585) to Fleetwood. At Nautical College campus (onleft) traffic island take first left, at second island take 6th exit. Stadium is 3/4 mile on left.
Floodlights: Yes

PREVIOUS **Leagues:** None   **Names:** Fleetwood Wanderers (97-98)

RECORD **Attendance:** 6,150 v Rochdale F.A.Cup 1st Round 65-66

HONOURS NWCFL v 2 Champions: 98-99 Div 2 trophy Winners: 98-99

Founded: 1997
(amalgamation of Fleetwood F.C. and Fleetwood Town who had disbanded at the end of season 1995-96)
Colours: Red & white/black/red
Midweek Matchday: Tuesday

CLUB PERSONNEL

Chairman: Jim Betmead
31 St. Peters Place, Fleetwood, Lancs. FY7 6EB.
Tel: 01253 771550 (H); 0966 414750 (B)

FLIXTON

Secretary: Peter Rogers, 55 Benbecula Way, Urmston, Manchester M41 7FW (0161 747 4618)
Ground: Valley Road, Flixton, Manchester M41 8RQ   Tel: 0161 748 2903
Directions: M60 Jct10, B5214 (signed Urmston), follow Trafford General Hosp.signs, at 4th r'bout take 3rd exit (Woodbridge Rd), ground at top. 1¼ miles from Flixton BR station (trains from Manchester Oxford Rd) - turn right out of station onto Flixton Rd, left after 1/4 mile into Woodsend Rd,at r'bout after 1/4 mile take 2nd exit into Woodbridge Rd - ground at top.Take any bus from Manchester Picadilly bus station to Flixton and alight at Flixton Red Lion
Capacity: 2,000   Cover: 650   Seats: 250
Clubhouse: Open daily 1.00pm-11pm. Sandwiches available most eves **Club Shop:** No
PREVIOUS   Leagues: South Manchester & Wythenshawe 60-63; Lancs & Cheshire 63-73; Manchester 73-86; North West Counties 86-96; Northern Premier 97-00
CLUB RECORDS   Attendance: 1:1,543 v Brigg Town FA Vase Semi-Final 95-96
                            Goalscorer: John Mitchell   **Appearances:** John Mitchell & Stan Matthews
                            Win: 10-2 Irlam 94-95 **Defeat:** 1-10 v Knowsley Utd 90-91
BEST SEASON   FA Cup: 1st Qual. Rd 91-92, 1-2 v Mossley (A) after 1-1
                            FA Vase: Semi-final 95-96 v Brigg Town
HONOURS   N.W.Co Div I 95-96, Div 2 94-95 Lg.Cup 94-95 95-96 (R-up 87-88), Div 3 R-up 86-87; Manc. Lg R-up 78-79 81-82 85-86, Div 1 77-78, Open Tphy 80-81; Lancs Amtr Cup 79-80 (R-up 80-81); Manc. Chal. Tphy 83-84 (R-up x2 84-86); Manc. Prem. Cup R-up 86-87 91-92; Manc. Amtr Cup R-up 88-89

FACT FILE

Formed: 1960
Nickname: Valley Roaders
Colours: Blue & white stripes/blue/blue
Change Colours: Gold/black/black
Midweek home matchday: Tuesday
Reserves' League: North West Alliance
Programme - Pages: 36 Price: £1.00
Editor: T.B.A.

CLUB PERSONNEL

Chairman: John Mitchell
President: F H Eadie
Manager: Alan McGreevy

GLOSSOP NORTH END

Secretary: Peter Hammond, 15 Longmoor Road, Simmondley, Glossop, Derbys SK139NH
             Tel: 01457 863852(H) 01457 854411(B)

Ground: Surrey Street, Glossop, Derbys (01457 855469).
Directions: A57 to Glossop.Left at traffic lights (near Tresco sign) into Glossopbrook Road then Follow road to top of hill and ground is on right. Buses 236 and 237 from Manchesterpass ground
Capacity: 2,374   Seats: 209   Cover: 509   Floodlights: Yes
Clubhouse: Licensed bar. Hot & cold drinks and pies etc on matchdays.   **Club Shop:** Yes

HONOURS   NWC Lge Lamot Pils Tphy 90-91; Manchester Lg 27-28(Gilgryst Cup 22-23 29-30 34-35 74-75); FA Amateur Cup QF 08-09. Manchester Premier Cup 1997 and 1998.
PREVIOUS   **Leagues:** Midland 1896-98; Football Lge 1898-1915; Manchester Lge 15-56 66-78; Lancs Combination 56-66; Cheshire County 78-82.
                    Names: Glossop North End 1886-1898; Glossop FC 1898-1992.
BEST SEASON   FA Cup: Quarter Final 1909   **FA Vase:**
RECORDS   Attendance: 10,736 v Preston North End, FA Cup 1913/14
                Fee paid: £3,000 for Andy Gorton (Lincoln City, 1989).
                Fee received: £3,000 for Andy Gorton (Oldham Athletic, 1990).
Players progressing: Jimmy Rollands (Rochdale), Ray Redshaw (Wigan Athletic).

FACT FILE

Founded: 1886 Re-formed 1992
Nickname: Hillmen
Sponsor: T.B.A.
Colours: All royal Blue
Change colours: All gold.
Midweek Matches: Tuesday
Reserves' League: N.W.Co Res Lg
Programme: 32 pages, 50p
Editor: John Hamilton (01457 866216)

CLUB PERSONNEL

Chairman: J Dillon
President: C T Boak
Press Officer: Secretary
Manager: Micky Boyle
Asst Manager: Ian Boyle
Physio:Mick Parr

GREAT HARWOOD TOWN

Secretary: Mark Jones, 15 Elm Close, Rishton,Blackburn, BB1 4HN Tel: 01254 876822(H)
Ground: The Showground, Wood Street, Great Harwood, Lancs Tel: 01254 883913
Directions: M66 from Manchester to Haslingden exit, A680 through Baxenden, Accrington to Clayton-le-Moors, left at the Hyndburn Bridge Hotel into Hyndburn Road and right into Wood Street to ground. Or M6 jct 31,Clitheroe/Skipton road to Trafalgar Hotel, A677 to Blackburn, left at Moat House Hotel and follow ring-road to M65 junction, A678 to Rishton, left at lights (B6536) to Gt Harwood, right at Town Gate into Queen Str., follow signs for Lomax Square, left into Park Rd, right into Balfour Street to ground. 3miles from Rishton (BR), 6 miles from Blackburn (BR). Various buses from Heyes Lane & Park Road to Blackburn & Accrington
Capacity: 2,500   Cover: 700   Seats: 200
Clubhouse: The Sportsman just outside ground. Normal licensing hours. Full bar facilities. Squash courts and gym. Hot & cold snacks & drinks on matchdays from tea bar in ground
Club Shop: Sells programmes, badges, key rings, shirts. Contact: J McKay (c/o club)

HONOURS   North West Counties League R-up 91-92 (Div 2 90-91, Lamot Pils Tphy 89-90 (R-up 90-91), Tennents Floodlit Trophy 91-92), Lancs ATS Challenge Trophy 91-92 (R-up 90-91)

PREVIOUS Leagues: West Lancashire; Lancs Comb. 79-82; N.W.C. 82-92; N.P.L. 92-99

CLUB RECORDS   Attendance: 5,397 v Manchester Utd, 1980.
BEST SEASON   FA Cup: 1st Qual. Round replay 92-93, 1-2 v Atherton LR (H), after 1-1
                       FA Vase: Quarter Finals 90-91, 1-2 v Littlehampton Town (A)

FACT FILE

Formed: 1965
Nickname: Robins
Club Sponsors: None
Colours: All red
Change colours: All blue
Midweek Matches: Monday
Reserves' league: West Lancs Lge
Programme: Pages: 20 Price: 20p
Editor: D Bennet

CLUB PERSONNEL

Chairman: William Holden
Press Officer: K Lambert
Commercial Manager: Mark Smith
Manager: M Crabbe
Asst Manager: Dave Sargent

Above: Newcastle Town FC. Back Row (l-r): Richard Morton, Harry Wilshaw (Physio), Martyn Smith (Assistant Manager), Ray Walker (Player/ Manager), Brett Barlow, Dave Talbot, Chris Holmes, Matt Haddrell, Neil Pesteridge, Dean Cunningham, Darren Twigg. Front row (l-r): Mark Hawkes, Rob Myatt, Peter Weston, Dave Woodvine, Michael Bates, John Brown, Antony Buckle (Captain), Ian Banks, Dean Gillick.

Left: Action from Curzon Ashton versus Squires Gate, a game won by Curzon to keep them on top of the league table at the time.
Photo: Colin Stevens

Left: Mossley's Joe Connor has returned to the club after many seasons playing in higher leagues. Here he is seen in action taking on Gretna's Ross Milligan.
Photo: Colin Stevens

KIDSGROVE ATHLETIC

Secretary: Alan Thompson, 7 Sandown Road, Crewe, Cheshire CW1 3TE
Tel: 01270 256588 (H) 07712 956400 (M)

Ground: Clough Hall, Hollinswood Road, Kidsgrove, Stoke-on-Trent, Staffs
Tel: 01782 782412

Directions: M6 Jct 16, A500 towards Stoke, 2nd jctn onto A34 towards Manchester, turn right at 1st lights down hill,rt at lights into Cedar Rd , 2nd right into Lower Ash Rd, 3rd left into Hollinwood Rd to ground.　　BR Kidsgrove (5mins)
Capacity: 4,500　Seats: 400　Cover: 600　　Floodlights: Yes

Clubhouse: Yes

HONOURS　NWC Div. 1 97-97; NWC Chall. Cup 97-98;　Mid Cheshire Lg 70-71 78-79 86-87 87-88, R-up 68-69 85-86; Lg Cup 67-68 69-70 85-86, R-up 84-85 86-87; Staffs County Lge; Burslem & Tunstall Lge. Floodlit Trophy R-up: 1999

PREVIOUS　Leagues: Staffordshire County, Mid Cheshire Lge.

BEST SEASON　FA Cup:　　FA Vase: Semi-Final 1997-98

RECORDS　**Attendance:** 1,903 v Tiverton Town, FA Vase S-F 1998.

FACT FILE

Formed: 1952
Colours: Royal blue & white/royal blue & white/blue
Change Colours: All white
Midweek Matches: Tuesday

CLUB PERSONNEL

Chairman: Terry Hillman
Vice Chairmen: Arthur Duckworth & Alan Hall
President: Ernie Langford
Manager:Chris Hagan
Coach: Kevin williams
Physio: Graham Plant

LEEK C.S.O.B.

Secretary: Stan Lockett, 5 Fitzherbert Close, Swynnerton, Stone, Staffs ST150PQ,
Tel: 01782 796062 (H)　0944 493106 (M)
Ground: Harrison Park, Macclesfield Road, Leek, Staffs, (01538 383734)
Directions: M6 south Junc 17, A534 to Congleton - follow signs for Leek (A54),carry on until junction with A523, turn right on to A523, this road is direct to Leek, ground is 8 miles, on right just into Leek.
Capacity: 3,600　　　Seating: 625　　Covered Terracing: 2,675　Floodlights: Yes

HONOURS　Refuge Midland Lge 95-96. Lge Cup 94-95 95-96; Leek Cup 94-95 95-96; Midland Ref Charity Shield 95-96; Sportsline Chall Cup 95-96.

PREVIOUS　Leagues: Leek & Moorland Lge, Staffs County North, Refuge Midland Lge.

BEST SEASON　FA Cup: 3rd Q 98-99　　　FA Vase:

RECORDS　**Attendance:** 293 v Tamworth F.A.Cup 1998-99

FACT FILE

Founded: 1945
Colours: Red& Black/Black/Black
Change colours: All Yellow
Midweek Matchday:Tuesday
Programme: Yes
Editor: Stan Lockett
99-00 Captain: Lee Bould

CLUB PERSONNEL

Chairman: K J Hill, 11 Springfield Drive, Leek, Staffs ST13 (01538 371859)
Manager: Kenny Birch-Machin & Andrew Walters
Physio: Noel Carroll

MAINE ROAD

Secretary: Derek Barber,Flat 4, Maple Court, 259 Wellington Rd., Heaton moor, Stockp Sk4 5BS (0161 431 8243) **Ground:** Manchester County FA Ground, Brantingham Rd., Chorlton-cum-Hardy, Manchester M21 0TT (0161 861 0344)
Directions: M60 Jct 7, A56 towards City Centre, right onto A5145 Chorlton/Stockport, thro' lights, left at next lights into Wilbraham Rd(A6010) to Chorlton, thro' lights for approx 1 mile. Left into Withington Rd,first left into Brantingham Rd, ground 300 yds on left. 2 miles from Stretford (Metrolink (tram)), 3 miles from Piccadilly & Victoria , Virgin & First North Western trains. Buses16 16A 85 87 87A 168 188 275. **Clubhouse:** Matchdays (Snacks on ground) **Shop:** No.
Capacity: 2,000　　　　Seats: 200　　Cover: 700　　Floodlights: Yes.

HONOURS　　Manc. Prem. Lg(4) 82-86, Cup 82-83 83-84;98-98 Man.Co Prem. Cup 87-8 Chal. Cup(4) 82-83 84-87; NW Co's Lg Div 2 89-90 (R-up 88-89).

PREVIOUS　　Leagues: Rusholme Sunday 55-66; Manchester Amtr Sunday 66-72; Manchester 72-87　　**Name:** City Supporters Rusholme
　　　　　　Grounds: Hough End PF 55-73; Ward Street O.B. 73-75; Tootal Spts Ground 75-79; Leesfield 79-80
BEST SEASON　**FA Cup:** 2nd Qual. 2nd replay 92-93　**FA Vase:** 4th Rd 94-95
RECORDS　　**Attendance:** 875 v Altrincham, FA Cup 2nd Qual. Rd 29/9/90
　　　　　　Goalscorer: John Wright 140　　**Appearances:** Gordon Wood 465
　　　　　　Win: 15-0 v Little Hulton 2/9/86　**Defeat:**0-7 v Newcastle Town

FACT FILE

Founded: 1955
Nickname: Blues
Sponsors:Parry's Jewellers
Colours: Blue/blue/yellow
Change Colours: Yellow, Green,Yellow
Midweek matchday: Tuesday
Reserves ' League: NW Co's Lge Res. Div.
Programme: 48 pages ,50p
Editor: Mr P,Ramsden (0161 448 1659)

CLUB PERSONNEL

Chairman: R Meredith
President: F G Thompson
Press Officer: P Ramsden
Manager: T.B.A.
Asst Manager:Ossie Smith
Physio: E Jenkinson

MOSSLEY

Secretary: David Buckley, 18 Chellow Dene, Mossley,Ashton -under-Lyne, Lancs. OL5 0NB tel No: 01457 835989
Ground: Seel Park, Market Street, Mossley, Lancs. (Grd 01457 832369), (Club01457 836104)
Directions: From north; M62 Junc 20, A627M/A627 to Ashton-U-Lyne, A670 to Mossley- ground behind market place. From south; M6 Junc 19,A556, M56 to Junc 3, A5103 to M'chester, then Mancunian Way (A57M) to A635.Follow Ashton signs 5m, the Mossley signs via A670 to town centre. Rail:Mossley BR. Buses 153 from Manchester, 343 from Oldham, 350 from Ashton
Capacity: 4,500   Cover: 1,500   Seats: 200   Floodlights: Yes

Clubhouse: Open nights and matchdays   **Club Shop:** Yes

HONOURS   FA Trophy Runners-up 79-80; Northern Premier League 78-79 79-80 (R-up 80-81 81-82 82-83, Chall Cup 78-79; NWC Floodlit Trophy R-up 95-96 NWTL Div 1 R-up 98-99

BEST SEASON   FA Cup: 2nd Rd replay 49-50, also 2nd Rd 80-81 & 1st Rd 6 times.
                    FA Trophy: Runners-up 79-80   **FA Vase:** 6th Rd 96-97

PREVIOUS   **Leagues:** Ashton; South East Lancs; Lancs Comb. 18-19; Cheshire County 19-72; Northen Prem.   **Names:** Park Villa 03-04; Mossley Juniors 04-09.

RECORDS   **Attendance:** 7,000 v Stalybridge, 1950   **Fee Paid:** £2,300
                    Fee Received: £25,000 for Eamon O'Keefe (Everton, 1979)

FACT FILE
Formed: 1903
Nickname: Lilywhites
Colours: White/black/black
Change colours: Yellow/green/green
Midweek matchday: Tuesday
Programme: 28 Pages £1.0
Editor: John A Cawthorne
Local Press : Oldham Evening Chronicle,
Saddleworth & Mossley Reporter
Local Radio: Radio Manchester, Piccadilly

CLUB PERSONNEL
Chairman: Sam Rigby
President: J Wharmby
Manager: Benny Phillips

NANTWICH TOWN

Secretary: Bernard Lycett, 'Rivington", Clay lane, Haslington, Crewe CW11 5SE
                Tel: 01270 584066 (H) 0411 362709 (M)

Ground: Jackson Avenue, off London Road, Nantwich, Cheshire.   Tel: 01270 624098
Directions: M6 Jct 16, A500 for Nantwich (about 8 miles), continue on A52 over railway crossing (London Rd), second right after railway crossing into Jackson Ave. From Chester, use the A51.
                Three miles from Crewe (BR).
Capacity: 1,500   Seats: 150   Cover: 555   Floodlights: Yes

Clubhouse: Every night except Sunday 8pm-11pm. Hot pies available   **Club Shop:** Yes

HONOURS   Cheshire Co. Lg 80-81; Ches. Snr Cup 75-76; N.W. Co.Lg.Cup 94-95

PREVIOUS   **Leagues:** Shropshire & Dist.; The Combination 1892-94; Lancs Comb. 12-15; Cheshire Combination 19-38; Manchester; Mid-Cheshire; Cheshire County 68-82.   **Name:** Nantwich FC (pre 1973)

BEST SEASON   FA Cup: FA Vase:
RECORDS   **Attendance:** 2,750 v Altrincham, Cheshire Senior Cup 66-67
                Fee received: £4,000 from Stafford Rangers for D.Dawson
                Record Goalscorer in Season: Gerry Duffy, 42 in 61-62

FACT FILE
Founded: 1884
Nickname: Dabbers
Club Sponsors: Jim Barrie Plant Hire
Colours: Black & white/black/black
Change colours: All green
Midweek matchday: Thursday
Reserves' League:Springbank Midland
Programme: 18 pages, 65
Editor: Che Kerrin (01270 624098)

CLUB PERSONNEL
Chairman: Clive Jackson
6 Spencer Close, Crewe CW2 8DT
01270 664469 (H) 07970 546238 (B)

Manager: Paul Cuddy
Physio: Ivan Robertson

NEWCASTLE TOWN

Secretary: John F Cotton, 293 Weston Rd., Weston Coyney, Stoke-on-Trent, Staffs. St3 6HA
Tel: 01782 333445 e-mail ntfc@ talke21.com.
Ground: Lyme Valley Parkway Stadium, Lilleshall Rd, Clayton, Newcastle-under-Lyne, Staffs (01782 662351) (Club 01782 662350)
Directions: M6 jct 15, A500 for Stoke, left at r'bout A519 for Newcastle, rightat 2nd r'bout into Stafford Ave., 1st left into Tittensor Road to ground. 3miles from Stoke-on-Trent (BR).
Seats: 300   Cover: 1,000   Capacity: 4,000   Floodlights: Yes   **Club Shop:** Yes
Clubhouse: Saturday matchdays 12-7.30pm, midweek 5-11pm. Hot & cold food available.

HONOURS: Nth West Co's Lg Div 1 R-up 95-96 96-97,99-00 Div 2 R-up 91-92, Challenge Cup 96-97, R-up 99-00 F/Lit Trophy R-up 96-97; Lamot Pils Tphy 91-92; Mid Cheshire Lg Div1 85-86, R-up 86-78, Div 2 82-83, 90-91, Lge Cup 84-85; Walsall Snr Cup 93-94 94-95 R-up 95-96; Sentinel Cup 94-95; Tennents Floodlit Trophy 92-93 95-96; Staffs Snr Cup R-up 95-96; Staffs M/W F/Light Lge 94-95 R-up 95-96; Umbro Over 35 Chall Cup 94-95.
RECORDS - Attendance: 3,948 v Notts County FA Cup Nov 96 **Win:** 8-1 v Holker Old Boys
Defeat: 0-5 v Eastwood Hanley (A) **Appearances:** Neil Pesteridge 315 (Lg only) **Goalscorer:** Shaun Wade 105 (NWCL only) **F.A.Vase:** S-Final 99-00
PREVIOUS - Leagues: Hanley & Dist. Sunday; North Staffs Sunday; Potteries & Dist.Sunday; Res Refuge Ass Mid; Newcastle & Dist/ Staffs Co.; Mid Cheshire. **Names:** Parkway Hanley (founded 1964, later Clayton Park, ParkwayClayton); Newcastle Town (founded 1980) - clubs merged in 1986.

FACT FILE
Founded: 1964
Nickname: Castle.
Club Sponsors: Premaster Mechanical
Services Ltd
Colours: All Royal Blue/blue/white
Change colours: All yellow
Midweek Matches: Tuesday
Reserve Team: N.W.T.L. Res Div
Programme: 40 pages, 50p
Editor: Kim Beckett 01782 659449 (H)
01782 65455(W)

CLUB PERSONNEL
Chairman: J W Walker
Vice-Chairman: K G Walshaw
President: K H Walshaw.
Press Officer: Ray Tatton (01782 644916)
Player/Manager: Ray Walker
Asst Manager: Martin Smith
Physio: Lee Arnold

Top: St Helens' Ste O'Neil heads in his fourth of five goals scored against Glossop.
Bottom: St Helens' Paul Kirwan in midfield action against Skelmersdale United.   *Photos: Malcolm Thacker*

PRESCOT CABLES

Secretary: Doug Lace,20 Cable road,Prescott,Merseyside L35 5AW
Ground: Valerie Park, Hope Street, Prescot. L34 6HD (Tel No: 0151 430 0507)
Ground:Directions: M62 Jct 7. A57 to Prescot. Take 3rd exit at roundabout after two and a half miles. Turn right after another 1/2 mile. Right at Hope & Anchor pub, into Hope Street..
Capacity: 4,400   **Seats:** 200   **Cover:** 550   **Floodlights:** Yes

Clubhouse: Refreshment bar, open matchdays/evenings for hot & cold refreshments
Club Shop: No but ties & metal badges available.

HONOURS	Lancs Comb. 56-57 (Lg Cup 47-48); Ches. Lg Div 2 76-77; Mid Ches. Lg 76-77; L'pool Non-League Cup(4) 51-53 58-59 60-61; L'pool Chal. Cup(5) 28-30 48-4961-62 77-78; George Mahon Cup 36-37.
PREVIOUS	**Leagues:** Liverpool Co. Comb.; Lancs Comb. 1897-98 18-20 27-33 36-67; Ches. Co. 33-36 78-82; Mid Cheshire 67-78. **Names:** Prescot Athletic; Prescot Cables 46-65 80-90; Prescot Town 65-80.
BEST SEASON	**FA Cup:** 2nd Rd 57-58 59-60 **FA Vase:** 2nd Rd 1998-99
RECORDS	**Attendance:** 8,122 v Ashton National, 1932

FACT FILE

Founded: 1886
Nickname: Tigers
Colours: Gold/black/gold
Change colours: All blue
Midweek Matches: Tuesday
Programme: 30 pages,70p
Editor: Ken Derbyshire

CLUB PERSONNEL

President: Mr B F Taylor
Chairman: Ted Mercer
Vice Chairman: G.Hayward
Commercial Manager: Arthur McCumiskey
Manager:Tommy Lawson
Asst Manager: Andy Gray

RAMSBOTTOM UNITED

Secretary: John Maher, 75 Ramsbottom Road, Hawkshaw, Bury BL8 4JS. Tel: 01204852742

Ground: Riverside Ground, Acre Bottom, Ramsbottom. Tel: 01706 822799(Cricket Club)
          Answe Phone: 01204 852742 (for match details)
Directions: M66(North) to junction 1, take A56 towards Ramsbottom. After one mile turn left into Bury New Road. Turn left after the Danisco Paper Mill along the road running parallel with the East Lancs Railway. From North: M65- A56 Follow signs ro Ramsbottominto town centre.
Floodlights: Yes

HONOURS:	Bolton Comb. Div. One Champs 72-73; Bolton Comb. Prem Div. 76-77, 86-87; Manchester Lge Div. One Champs 90-91; Manchester Lge Div. 1 Cup Winners 90-91; Gilgryst Cup Winners 94-95; NWCFL Div 2 Champ 96-97, Trophy 95-96
RECORDS	**Attendance:** 829 v Southport F.A.C. 3Q 98-99 NWCFL Div 2 29/3/97
PREVIOUS	**Leagues:** Bury Amateur League, Bolton Combination, Manchester Lge.
BEST SEASON: F.A.Cup: 3rd Q 1998-99 **F.A.Vase:** 2nd Round 98-99,99-00	

FACT FILE

Formed: 1966
Colours: Blue with white trim/blue/white
Midweek Matchday: Tuesday

CLUB PERSONNEL

Chairman: Harry Williams
35 Nuttall Lane, Ramsbottom
Tel: 01706 823029 (H)

ROSSENDALE UNITED

Secretary: Wendy Ennis, 4 Brow Edge, Newchurch, Rossendale, Lancs BB4 7TT(01706 212634)

Ground: Dark Lane, Staghills Rd, Newchurch, Rossendale, Lancs BB4 7UA
          Tel: 01706 215119 (Ground); 01706 213296 (Club)
Directions: M60 Junc 18, M66 north following signs for Burnley, then A682 to Rawstenstall, take 2nd exit sign Burnley A682, at 1st lights turn right into Newchurch Rd, 1.5 miles turn right into Staghills Rd, grd 800 yards right
Capacity: 2,500   **Cover:** Yes   **Seats:** 500   **Floodlights:** Yes
Clubhouse: Evenings & matchdays. Hot snacks. Pool, satellite TV, concert room

HONOURS	NWC Lg Div 1 88-89 (R-up 87-88 93-94), Div 2 R-up 85-86, Chall Cup 93-94
PREVIOUS	**Leagues:** N.E. Lancs Comb.; Lancs Comb. 1898-99 1901-70; Central Lancs 1899-1901; Cheshire County 70-82; NWC 82-89; NPL 89-93.
BEST SEASON	**FA Cup:** 2nd Rd 71-72, 1-4 v Bolton W. at Bury FC. Also 1st Rd 75-76 **FA Trophy :** 2nd Rd 81-82 **FA Vase:** 5th Rd 86-87,88-89
RECORDS	**Attendance:** 12,000 v Bolton Wanderers FA Cup 2nd Rd 71 **Appearances:** Johnny Clarke 770, 1947-65 **Goalscorer:** Bob Scott **Fee Paid:** £3,000 for Jimmy Clarke (Buxton, 1992) **Fee Received:** £1,500 for Dave O'Neill (Huddersfield Town, 1974) **Win:** 17-0v Ashton Town, Lancs Comb.1911-12 **Defeat:** 0-14 v Morecambe, Lancs Comb. 67-68

FACT FILE

Founded: 1898
Nickname: The Stags
Sponsors: Hurstwood Developments
Colours: Blue & white stripes/blue/blue
Change cols: Red&yellow stroipes/red/red
Midweek matchday: Tuesday
Reserves ' League: First N.W.Reserve
Programme: 28 pages-£1.00
Editor: David Hawarth
Local Radio: Red Rose, Radio Lancashire.
Local Press : Lancs Evening Telegraph,
Rossendale Herald &Post, Rossendale Mail.

CLUB PERSONNEL

Chairman: A Connelly V-Chair: Lee Brierley
President: David White
Manager: Mickey Graham
Press Offcer:Kevin Procter
Coach: John HughesPhysio: Billy Howarth
Capt: Simon O'Brien P.o.Y.Mark Andrews Craig
Sargesson(39 goals)

SALFORD CITY

Secretary: Bill Taylor , 23 Westwood Drive, Pendlebury, Salford M27 4JJ

Ground: Moor Lane, Kersal, Salford, Manchester. Tel: 0161 792 6287

Directions: M62 jct 17, A56 Bury New Road to Manchester, continue thro' 4 sets of lights, right into Moor Lane, ground 500 yds left. 4 miles from Manchester Victoria (BR). Buses 96, 139, 94, 95 to Moor Lane

Capacity: 8,000   Seats: 260   Cover: 600   Floodlights: Yes

Clubhouse: Open matchdays only. Hot snacks

HONOURS	Lancashire Amateur Cup 72-73 74-75 76-77; Manchester Senior Cup, Manchester Challenge Cup, Manchester Lg 74-75 75-76 76-77 78-79.
PREVIOUS	**Leagues:** Manchester 63-80; Cheshire Co. 80-82. **Names:** Salford Central 40-63; Salford Amateurs 1963 until merger with Anson Villa; Salford FC. **Ground:** Crescent, Salford
BEST SEASON	FA Cup: FA Vase:
RECORDS	**Attendance:** 3,000 v Whickham FA Vase 1981

FACT FILE

Founded: 1940
Nickname: Ammies
Colours: Tangerine/white/white
Change colours: Blue & white stripes/blue/blue
Midweek Matches: Tuesday
Reserves' League: NWC Res. Div. S.
Programme: 24 pages, 50p
Editor: Scott White

CLUB PERSONNEL

Chairman: DavidTaylor
Managers: Tom Foster & Matt Wardrop
Press Officer: Scott White
Commercial Manager: Stevie Plant

SKELMERSDALE UNITED

Secretary: Bryn Jones, 34 Bromilow Road,Skelmersdale, Lancs.WN8 8TU
Ground: White Moss Park, White Moss Road, Skelmersdale, Lancs   Tel: 01695 722723

Directions: M58 Jct 3, at 2nd r'bout take 3rd exit towards Skelmersdale,continue for approx 1 mile, ground on the right. 4 miles from Ormskirk (BR)
Capacity: 10,000   Seats: 250   Cover: 1,000   Floodlights: Yes
Clubhouse: None. Matchday food bar sells hot drinks, soup, pies & pasties etc
Club Shop: No, but badges available in two colours.

HONOURS	FA Amateur Cup 70-71 R-up 66-67; Ches. Co. Lg 68-69 69-70, Jubilee Cup 69-70; Lancs F'lit Cup 69-70; Lancs Jnr Cup 69-70 70-71; Ashworth Cup 70-71; Barassi Anglo-Italian Cup 70-71; Lancs Non-Lge Cup 73-74 74-75; North West Co's Lg Cup: 99-00 R-up 82-83.N.W.Co Div 2 R-Up: 97-98
PREVIOUS	**Leagues:** Liverpool County Comb., Lancashire Comb. 1891-93, 03-07, 21-24 55-68, 76-78, Cheshire County 68-71 78-82, Northern Premier 71-76.
BEST SEASON	**FA Cup:** 1st Rd 67-68, 0-2 v Scunthorpe(A), 68-69, 0-2 v Chesterfield(A), 71-72, 0-4 v Tranmere R. (A) **FA Amateur Cup:** Winners 70-71
RECORDS	**Attendance:** 7,000 v Slough, FA Amat Cup Q-F '67

FACT FILE

Founded: 1882
Nickname: Skem
Sponsors:Matalan
Colours: Blue & white stripes/blue/blue
Change colours: Red & white stripes/red/red
Midweek Matches: Thursday
Programme: 28 pages, 50p
Editor: M.Ratcliffe

CLUB PERSONNEL
President: D.Tomlinson
Chairman: A,Gore
Vice Chairman: T Garner
Press Officer: Secretary
Manager: Russ Perkins
Asst Manager:Peter McDermott
Coach: Paul Gallagher
Physio: Billy Leigh

ST HELENS TOWN

Secretary: W J Noctor, 95 Sutton Park Drive, Marshalls Cross, St H .WA9 3TR (01744 816182)
          Ground: St Helens R.L.F.C. ,Knowsley Road, St Helens   **Directions: From South:** M62 Jct 7-5th exit(St Helens) 3rd roundabout (Sherdley),follow Town Centre signs. Left at roundabout to L'pool & Prescot.Rt at lights then left at Black Bullt after 1 mile. Ground on right.
From North: M6.Jct 23 take A580 to L'pool.7 mileIleft to A570 and 1st Rt into Bleak Hilll Road.Left at sharp right hand bend after 1 mile into Mill Brow. At T jct left at Black Bull,turn right - ground on left.   **Capacity:** 19,100   **Seats:** 2,362   **Cover:** 12,408   **Floodlights:** Yes

Clubhouse: Weekdays 8-11pm, Saturday matchdays 2-6.30pm.   **Club Shop:** Yes

HONOURS	FA Vase 86-87; George Mahon Cup 49-50; Lancs Comb. 71-72, Div 2 50-51, Lg Cup R-up 70-71;Liverpool Snr Non Lge Cup R-up 76-77; Lancs Jnr Cup R-up 66-67; Bass Charrington Cup 73-74; Carling Chall Cup r-up 93-94; N.W.C. Floodlit Trophy r-up 97-98.
PREVIOUS	**Leagues:** Lancs Comb. 03-14 49-75; Liverpool County Comb. 49-74; Cheshire County 74-82. **Grounds:** Park Road 01-52; City Road 52-53.
BEST SEASON	**FA Cup:** 4th Q Rd 85-86 **FA Vase:** Winners 86-87
RECORDS	**Gate:** 4,000 v Manchester City, Bert Trautmann transfer match,April 1950. **Goalscorer:** S Pennington **W in:** 10-4 v Everton `B' 1952 **Appearances:** Alan Wellens **Defeat :** 1-8 v Liverpool Res., L'pool Snr Cup 1950

FACT FILE

Founded: 1946
Nickname: `Town'
Colours: Red & white/white/red
Change colours: Royal blue & white/white/royal blue
Midweek Matches: Wednesday
Reserve League:
Programme: 24 pages, 50p
Editor: John McKiernan (01744 600612)
Local Press: Reporter, Star, Leader, Echo.
CLUB PERSONNEL
President: J Jones
Chairman/Press Officer: J Barrett
Public Liaison Officer: John McKiernan
01744 635826 (H) 01744 24348 (W)
Manager: James McBride
Asst Manager: G Walker
Coach: John Neary

WOODLEY SPORTS

Secretary: Ian Woodhouse, 4 Firethorn Drive, Godley, Hyde SK14 3SN
Tel: 0161 3511631 (H), 0161 330 6837 (B) 07713624037 (M)

Ground: Lambeth Grove Stadium, Lambeth Grove, Woodley, Stockport. Tel: 0161 494 6429
Directions: M60 Jct 25, follow signs (A560) Bredbury, take left filter atlights which brings you onto A560 Stockport Road for approx 1 mile, turn leftat pub, Lowes Arms into Mill Street which goes into Mill Lane. Over bridge take2nd right into Woodlands Avenue, then 1st leftinto Lambeth Grove. Ground 200 yards ahead.
Floodlights: Yes

HONOURS	NWC Div 2 99-00
RECORD	**Attendance:** 1,500 v Stockport County
PREVIOUS	**Leagues:** Lancashire & Cheshire, Manchester League.
BEST SEASON	**FA Cup:** 99-00 FA Vase: 1st Round 1998-99

FACT FILE

Founded: 1970
Colours: Red & royal blue/royal/white
Midweek Matchday: Wednesday

CLUB PERSONNEL

Chairman: Ian Campbell
14 Gloucester Rd., Gee Cross, Hyde.
Tel: 0161 368 4060(H),

*Top: Vauxhall 'keeper Stephen Hilton punches clear under the challenge of Taunton Town's Ellis Laight with plenty of back up on the goal line. The Cheshire side won 5-1 in the 6th Round of the FA Vase.
Photo: Ken Gregory*

*Bottom: Buckle in action for Newcastle Town against Chasetown in the FA Vase 5th Round.
Photo: Peter Barnes*

ALSAGER

Secretary: Pauline Matthews, 43 Ellgrave Street, Dalehall,Stoke -0n-Trent St6 4DJ
Tel No: 01782 834296

Ground: The Town Ground, Wood park, Alsager. Tel: 01270 872917

Directions: M6, Junction 16, A500 towards Stoke. Leave A500 at 2nd exit (A34 to Congleton), at 2nd set of lights turn left for Alsager. Turn right opposite Caradon/Twyfords   (500 yds), into Moorhouse Ave., Woodlaid Court 1/2 mile on right.
Nearest Railway station: Alsager

Floodlights: No

HONOURS Jt R-up Mid Cheshire div. 2, R-up Springbank Vending Lge.

PREVIOUS **Leagues:** Mid Cheshire Div. 2; Springbank Vending Lge.

RECORD **Attendance:** 110 v Formby Sept 99, League 200 v Port Vale (friendly)

FACT FILE

Founded: 1968
Colours: Black & white/black/black
Change colours: Yellow & sky blue/yellow/yellow
Midweek Matches: Monday

CLUB PERSONNEL

Chairman: Clive Smart
Tel: 01270 872917 (H)
1st Team Sec.: Pauline Matthews
Tel: 01782 834296 (H)

ASHTON TOWN

Secretary: Stephen Barrett, 11 Clement Avenue, Atherton M46 0PT
Tel Nos: 01942 889492 (H)   01942 529312 (W)
Ground: Edge Green Street, Ashton-in-Makerfield, Wigan WN4 8SY (01942 510677)
Directions: M6 Jct 23, A49 to Ashton-in-M. Right at lights onto A58 towards Bolton. After 3/4 mile turn right at `Rams Head' P.H. into Golbourne Rd. After 200 yds right into Edge Green Str. Ground at end.

Floodlights: No

HONOURS Warrington Lg Guardian Cup.

PREVIOUS **Leagues:** Warrington, Lancs Comb. 03-11 71-78, Ches. Co. 78-82.

BEST SEASON **FA Vase:** Prelim. Rd 84-85

RECORD **Gate:** 600 v Accrington Stanley 76-77

FACT FILE

Founded: 1962
Colours: Red with white trim/red/red
Change colours: All sky blue
Midweek Matches: Tuesday

CLUB PERSONNEL

President: W Pomfrett
Chairman: Len Riley
Manager: Norman Hickson

ATHERTON L.R.

Secretary: Steve Hartle, 32 Greensmith Way, Westhoughton,Bolton BL5 3DR (01942840906-H)
Ground: Crilly Park, Spa Road, Atherton, Greater Manchester (01942 883950).
Directions: M61 to Jct 5, follow signs for Westhoughton, left onto A6, right onto A579 (Newbrook Rd/Bolton Rd) over the railway bridge, right into Upton Rd passing Atherton Central Station, left into Springfield Rd and left again into Hillside Rd into Spa Rd and ground.
Capacity: 3,000   Seats: 250   Cover: 3 sections Floodlights: Yes
Clubhouse: Open normal licensing hours.   **Club Shop:** Yes
HONOURS: North West Co Lge 92-93 93-94, Champs Trophy 92-93 93-94,F/Lit Trophy 93-94; N.P.L.Div.1 Cup R-up 95-96,Goldline Try 98-99, Bolton Hosp Cup: 84-85W.Houghton Ch C 81082 Goldline Trophy Winners 98-99 **BEST SEASON FA Cup:** 3rd Qual Rd 96-97, 0-2 v Bamber Bridge **FA Vase:** Semi-Final rep. 94-95, 1-2 v Diss Town **FA Trophy:** 1st Qual Rd 96-97
PREVIOUS **Name:** Laburnum Rovers 54-79 **Leagues:** Bolton Comb.; Cheshire County 80-82; NWCL 82-94; NPL 94-97. **Grounds:** Laburnum Road 54-56; Hagfold 56-66.
RECORDS **Attendance:** 1,856 v Aldershot Town, FA Vase Quarter-Final replay 5/3/94.

FACT FILE
Formed: 1956
Nickname: The Panthers
Sponsors: Bolton Evening News
Colours: Yellow & Navy
Change colours: Green & White
Midweek Matches: Tuesday
Reserves' League: North West Co Res Div
Programme: 48 pages 70p (Best in league)
Editor: Tim Lees & Chris Green
CLUB PERSONNEL
Chairman:Alan Grundy
Financial Director: Terry Poole
Director of Football&Manager: Steve Plant
Assistant Manager: Malcolm Anderton

BACUP BOROUGH

Secretary: Frank Manning, 38 Acre Avenue, Stacksteads, Bacup OL13 0HN
Tel: 01706 877460 (H)
Ground: West View, Cowtoot Lane, Blackthorn, Bacup, Lancashire (01706 878655).
Directions: From M62, M66 onto A681 through Rawtenstall to Bacup centre, leftonto A671 towards Burnley, after approx 300 yds right (immed. before the IrwellInn) climbing Cooper Street, right into Blackthorn Lane then first left intoCowtoot Lane to ground.
Capacity: 3,000   Seats: 500   Cover: 1,000   Floodlights: Yes
Clubhouse: Open matchdays and private functions (for which buffets can beprovided). Pies and sandwiches on matchdays.   **Club Shop:** Not yet
HONOURS Lancs Jnr Cup 10-11 (R-up 22-23 74-75); Lancs Comb. 46-47 (Lg Cup R-up46-47 80-81; NW Co's Lg Div 2 R-up 89-90.
PREVIOUS **League:** Lancs Comb. 03-82Name: Bacup FC.Grounds: None
BEST SEASON **FA Cup: FA Vase:**
RECORD **Gate:** 4,980 v Nelson 1947   **Scorer:** Jimmy Clarke

FACT FILE
Founded: 1875
Nickname: The Boro
Club Sponsors:B&EBoys Ltd
Colours:White with black trim,black,black
Change colours:Yellow,Blue,Blue
Midweek Matches: Tuesday.
Programme: 22Pages 50p
Editor: D Whatmough (0706 875041)
CLUB PERSONNEL
President: W.Shufflebottom
Chairman: Ken Peters
Vice Chairman: D.Whatmough
Manager: Brent Peters
Assistant Manager: Simon Holding

BLACKPOOL MECHANICS

Secretary: William Singleton, c/o Club. Tel: 01253 313444(H) 01253 761721(B)
Ground: Jepson Way, Common Edge Rd, Blackpool, Lancs FY4 5DY (01253 761721).
Directions: M6 to M55, follow Airport signs. Left at r'bout along A583 (Preston New Rd) to lights, right into Whitehill Rd, becomes School Rd, to lights.Straight over main road & follow signs for Blackpool Mechanics F.C. to ground.Rail to Blackpool North - then bus 11c from Talbot Rd bus station (next to rail station) to Shovels Hotel, Common Edge Rd.
Capacity: 2,000   Seats: 250   Cover: 1,700   Floodlights: Yes
Clubhouse: Match days, training nights. Dancehall. Matchday, hot food.
Club Shop: Manager Andrew Sneddon (01253 729962). Ties, sweaters, old programmes, badges.
HONOURS   Lancs Comb Bridge Shield 72-73; NW Co's. Lg Div 3 85-86; W Lancs Lg 60-61 62-63; Lancs County FA Shield 57-58 60-61:
PREVIOUS   **Leagues:** Blackpool & Fylde Comb., West Lancs, Lancs Comb. 62-68.
                                  Grounds: Stanley Pk 47-49
RECORD   **Gate:** 1,200 v Morecambe, Lancs Comb, August 1968

FACT FILE
Founded: 1947   Nickname: Mechs
Sponsors: Yates Wine Lodge, Blackpool.
Club colours: Tangerine/white/tangerine
Change colours: All blue
Midweek matchday: Tuesday
Programme: 10 pages, 50p
Editor: John Barlow

CLUB PERSONNEL
Chairman: Henry Baldwin
Vice Chairman: John Sanderson
President: Gregory Gregorio
Commercial Manager: John Sanderson
Manager: Dave Rump
Asst Man.: Gary Collings
Coach: William Singleton.

BOOTLE

Secretary: William Jones, 36 Rydecroft, Woolton, Liverpool L25 7UT
                          Tel Nos: 0151 428 2203(H)   0793 912893 (W)
Ground: Bucks Park, Northern Perimeter Rd, Netherton, Bootle. L307PT (0151 526 1850)
Directions: End of M57 & M58 follow signs to Bootle and Docks A5063.
                          Turn right at next lights by Police station. Entrance 100 yds on right.
                          Old Roan station 300yds. Bus 55 (150yds from grd), 302 341 345 350 (350yds).
                          Capacity: 5,000   Seats: 400   Cover: 1,400   Floodlights: Yes
Clubhouse: Normal pub hours. Darts & pool   **Club Shop:** Yes
HONOURS N.W.C. Lge Div 2 R-up 92-93 (F'lit Trophy 93-94), Liverpool Chall. Cup 64-65 75-76 78-79, Liverpool Amtr Cup 65-66 67-68 73-74, Lancs Amtr Cup 69-70, Liverpool Co. Comb. (x9) 64--66 67-74, George Mahon Cup (x6) 66--68 68-70 72--74, Lancs Comb. 75-76 76-77, Lge Cup 75-76, Cheshire County Lge Div 2 78-79.
PREVIOUS Leagues: Liverpool Shipping, Liverpool Co Comb., Lancs Comb. 74-78, Cheshire Lge 78-82. **Name:** Langton 1953-73 **Grounds:** Edinburgh Park 1953-73, Orrell Mount Park 73-8

FACT FILE
Founded: 1954
Nickname: Bucks
Sponsors: Taximex
Colours: All royal blue with amber trim
Change colours: Yellow/black/black
Midweek matchday: Tuesday
Reserves' League: Liverpool Co. Combination
Programme: 32 pages, 50p
Editor: Secretary
CLUB PERSONNEL

Chairman: Frank Doran
Manager: T.B.A.

CASTLETON GABRIELS

Secretary: David Lord, 34 Fairway, Castleton, Rochdale OL11 3BU   Tel: 01706 522719
Ground: Butterworth Park, Chadwick Lane, off Heywood Rd., Castleton, Rochdale. Tel: 01706 527103)   **Directions:** M62 Jct 20, A6272M to r'bout. Left towards Castleton (A664Edinburgh Way) to next r'bout, keeping Tesco Superstore to the left, take 1st exit to next r'bout, take 2nd exit into Manchester Rd (A664), after just under mile turn right at `Top House' P.H. into Heywood Rd., to end & ground on right
Capacity: 1,500   Seats: 400   Cover: 650   Floodlights: Yes
Clubhouse: Open seven nights a night and all day Saturday. Pie & peas and sandwiches available matchdays (pie & peas only at Reserve matches)   **Club Shop:** No
HONOURS   Manchester Lge 86-87, Murray Shield 86-87; Res Div Cup 95-96.
PREVIOUS   **Leagues:** Rochdale Alliance 24-84; Manchester 84-89.
                                  Name: St Gabriels (pre-1960s) **Ground:** Park pitches; Springfield Pk 60-81.
RECORDS   **Gate:** 640 v Rochdale, pre-season friendly 1991 **Win:** 8-0 v Squires Gate N.W.Co.Div 2 94   **Defeat:** 1-10 v Blackpool Mechanics N.W.Co.Div 2 95

FACT FILE
Founded: 1924   Nickname: Gabs
Club Sponsors: Kick Off
Colours: Royal blue with red trim/blue/blue
Change colours: All red
Midweek matchday: Tuesday
Reserves ' League: N.W.C. Res. Div.
Programme: 28 pages, 50p
Editor: David Jones (01942 730220 -W)

CLUB PERSONNEL
Chairman: T E Butterworth
Vice Chairman: R Butterworth
Press Officer: Secretary
Manager/Coach:David Jones
Assistant Manager:Roy Grundy
Coach: Neil Mills

CHADDERTON

Secretary: Ronald Manton,77 Denton Lane, Chadderton, Oldham OL9 9AC
Ground: Andrew Street, Chadderton, Oldham, Lancs (0161 624 9733)
Directions: M62 Jct 20, A627(M) to M'chester.. M'way becomes dual carriageway. Left at 1st major traffic lights A669 Middleton Rd, then first left into Butterworth Street. Andrew Street is 2nd right. Oldham Werneth (BR) 1 m or Mills Hill (BR) l m.Buses 24,181 & 182 to Middleton Rd from Manchester (Piccadilly Gardens).
Capacity: 2,500   Seats: 200   Cover: 600   Floodlights: Yes
Clubhouse: Matchdays only. Hot & cold snack during & after games **Club Shop:** No
HONOURS M'chester Am Lg 62-63, North Div 55-56, M. Prem Cup R-up 82-83, Chall Tphy 71-72, R-up 72-73, M. Lg Div 1 66-67, Div 2 64-65, Gilgryst Cup 69-70, Murray Shield 65-66, Lancs Comb. Cup R-up 81-82, Alf Pettit & Hulme Celtic Cup 61-62, NWC F/lit Tphy R-up 92-93
PREVIOUS Leagues: Oldham Amat., Manchester Amat., Manchester 64-80, Lancs Comb. 80-82
RECORD Gate: 1,500 v Guinness Ex'ts 1969 **Appearances:** Billy Elwell 750+ (64-90)
Players progressing: (include) David Platt (Crewe), John Pemberton (Crewe)

FACT FILE
Founded: 1947   Nickname: Chaddy
Sponsors: Royton Metals,
Nationwide Building Society and Asda
Colours: All red
Change colours: All Yellow
Midweek Matches: Tuesday
Reserves' Lge: NWC Res. Div.
Programme: 28-32 pages Editor: David Greaves
99-00 Top Scorer: David Kershaw
Captain: Tony Lucas **P.o.Y:** Richard Ferguson
CLUB PERSONNEL
Chairman: Harry Mayall
President: Derek Glynn
Press Officer: John Fitton
Manager:Martin Farrell & Glynn Mellor

Top: Mossley 'keeper Martin White saves from Alfreton's top scorer Caine Cheetham. Photo: Bill Wheatcroft

Bottom: Darren Twigg (Newcastle) scores with a superb far post header, despite the efforts of Desborough 'keeper Des Elliot. Photo: Keith Clayton

COLNE F C

Secretary: Mrs Adele Cutts, 22 Snellgrove, Colne. BB8 0QS (01282 862947)

Ground: Holt House Stadium, Holt House, Colne. (Tel: 01282 862545)
Directions: Enter Colne from M65 to roundabout, keep left follow signs for Keighley. At next roundabout turn left, continue on Harrison Drive over mini roundabout & follow road to ground. Nearest Railway station - Colne.
Capacity: 1,800   Seats: 100   Cover: 1000   Floodlights: Yes

Clubhouse: Yes,Small Lounge Bar open on matchdays   **Club Shop:** No
HONOURS   BEP Cup Winners 96-97
BEST SEASON   **FA Cup:**   **FA Vase:**
RECORDS   **Attendance:** 240 v Nelson 97-98
                Scorer: Geoff Payton   **Appearances:** Nick Roscoe
PREVIOUS   **Leagues:** East Lancashire League

FACT FILE

Formed: 1996
Colours: All red
Change colours: All yellow
Midweek Matchday: Thursday
Programme: Yes   Editor: Ray Moore

CLUB PERSONNEL

Chairman: D Blacklock (01282 696340)
Press Officer: Ray Moore(01282 868857)
Manager:Denzil Hart

DAISY HILL

Secretary: Bob Naylor, 8 Bailey Fold, Westhoughton, Bolton, Lancs BL5 3HH(01942 813720)
Ground: New Sirs, St James Street, Westhoughton, Bolton, Lancs (01942 818544)
Directions: M61 Jct 5, A58 (Snydale Way/Park Road) for 1.5 miles, left into Leigh Road (B5235) for 1 mile, right into village then left between Church and School into St James Street. Ground 250 yds on the left. Half mile from Daisy Hill (BR)
Capacity: 2,000   Seats: 200   Cover: 250   Floodlights: No   Club Shop: No
Clubhouse: Open normal licensing hours during any football activity. Snacks on matchdays
HONOURS   Bolton Comb Prem Div 62-63 72-73 75-76 77-78, Lg Cup 59-60 61-62 71-
                72 72-73; Lancs Shield 61-62 71-72 86-87:
PREVIOUS   **Leagues:** Westhoughton; Bolton Comb.; Lancs Combination. 78-82.
                Name: Westhoughton Town **Record Goals & Apps:**Alan Roscoe 300-450
BEST SEASON   **FA Cup:**   **FA Vase:**
RECORD   **Attendance:** 2,000 v Horwich RMI,Westhoughton Charity Cup Final 79-80
PLAYERS PROGRESSING: Barry Butler (Chester C) + Phil Priestley(Rochdale)via AthertonLR

FACT FILE
Founded: 1894(first known records)
Reformed: 1952
Colours: All royal blue
Change:All amber
Midweek Matches: Tuesday
Reserves' Lge NWCL Res Div
Programme: 40 pages 50p
Editor: Committee

CLUB PERSONNEL

Chairman: Tony Veitch
Manager:Brian Richardson
Asst Mgr: Brian Smith

DARWEN

Secretary: Lynn Atkinson, 58 Harwood St.., Darwen, Lancs BB3 1PD (01254761755)
Ground: Anchor Ground, Anchor Road, Darwen, Lancs BB3 0BB, (01254 705627)
Directions: A666 Blackburn / Bolton road, 1 mile north of Darwen town centre,turn right at Anchor Hotel, ground 200 yds on left. One and a half miles from Darwen (BR), bus 51 to Anchor Hotel.From M65 Jct 4 signs to Darwen.Left at A666,1/2 mile left at anchor Hotel. ground 200 yds on left Capacity: 4,000   Seats: 250   Cover: 2,000   Floodlights: Yes
Clubhouse: Matchday only   **Club Shop:** No
HONOURS   Lancs Comb 31 32 73 75: Comb Cup 30 31 75; Lancs Jun Cup 73; Geo
Watson Trophy 73; LFA Yth Cup 75; NWC Cup 83; Lancs F/Lit Trophy 90; NWC Res Div Cup 94;
Blackburn & Dist Yth Lge 94 95 97, Cup 94 95 97; NW All Chall Cup 96.
PREVIOUS   **Leagues:**Football Alliance 1889-91, Football Lg 1891-99, Lancs Lg 99-
                03,Lancs Comb. 03-75, Ches. Co. 75-82. **Ground:** Barley Bank
RECORD   **Gate:** (Anchor Ground) 10,000 v Fleetwood Lancs Jun Cup 1920
BEST SEASON   **FA Cup:** Semi Finals 1881

FACT FILE
Founded: 1875
Sponsors: Prince Moran
Colours: Red & white/red/red
Change colours: All blue
Midweek Matches: Tuesday
Reserves' League: NWC Res. Div.
Programme: 20 pages, £1.00 Editor: S.Hart
Local papers:Darwen Advertiser,Lancs Eve.Tel
CLUB PERSONNEL
President: E Devlin
Chairwoman: Mrs K Marah
Manager: S Wilkes
Asst Manager: M Atkinson
Physio: Mick Sharples

FORMBY

Secretary: Dave Dickinson,2 Seafield,Formby,Merseyside L374EL Tel : 01704 870944
Ground: Brows Lane, Formby,Merseyside (01704 8335050) **Directions:** A565 Liverpool - Southport turn left at lights oppositeTesco into Altcar Rd, left at T junction to r'bout (opposite Cross House Inn) take 2nd exit then sharp left into Duke Street, 1st right into Elbow Lane, ground 50yds on left. Formby (BR) 1/2m, buses from Formby &Southport stations
Capacity: 2,000   Seats: 200   Cover: 500   Floodlights: No
Clubhouse: None. Matchday refreshment bar stocks hot food & drinks
Club Shop: Sells programmes, badges & souvenirs. Contact Paul Lawler (01704878409)
HONOURS   Liverpool Co. Comb. 48-49, R-up 64-65; Liverpool Senior Cup 77-78, R-up
84-85; Challenge Cup 52-53 63-64 67-68, R-up 64-65; Amtr Cup 29-30 47-48 48-49;Lamot Pils
Trophy 94-95; George Mahon Cup 64-65, R-up 55-56 56-57; Lancs Co FA Amt Cup 34-35.
PREVIOUS Leagues: Liverpool Co. Comb. 19-68/ Lancs Comb. 68-71, Ches. Co. 71-82.
BEST SEASON   **FA Cup:** 1st Rd 73-74, 0-2 v Oldham Ath. (H)   **FA Trophy:** 1st Rd 73-74,
                lost to Stalybridge Celtic **FA Vase:** 2nd Rd 96-97, lost to Tetley Walker

FACT FILE
Founded: 1919   Nickname: Squirrels
Club Sponsors: DKS Packaging
Colours: Yellow/blue/yellow
Change: White/black/black
Midweek Matches: Tuesday
Programme: 36 pages, 80p
Editor: Paul Lawler, (01704 875242)

CLUB PERSONNEL

Chairman: Chris Welsh
Comm. Man.: Dave Dickinson (01704 870944)
Press Officer: Paul Lawler (01704 878409)
Managers: Peter Hennerty & Mike Scott
Physio: Keith Johnson

HOLKER OLD BOYS

Secretary: Allan Wilson, 56 Fairfield Lane, Barrow-in-Furness, Cumbria. LA13 9HL
Tel: 01229 822751 (W) 01229 822983 (H)

Ground: Rakesmoor Lane, Hawcoat, Barrow-in-Furness, Cumbria (01229 828176)
Directions: M6 Jct 36, A590 to Barrow-in-Furness, on entering Barrow, continue across r'bout, 2nd right (Dalton Lane) to top of road, right into Rakesmoor Lane, ground on right.
Capacity: 2,500   Seats: 220   Cover: 500   Floodlights: Yes
Clubhouse: Mon-Fri 8-11pm, Sat noon-11pm, Sun normal licensing. Pies & peas on matchdays
Club Shop: No
HONOURS   W Lancs Lg 86-87, R-up 85-86; Lancs Junior Shield 88-89 90-91.
PREVIOUS   **Leagues:** North Western; Furness Premier; West Lancs 70-91.
RECORDS   **Attendance:** 1240 v Barrow ATS Trophy 95-96   **Win:** 12-0
                          Defeat: 1-8 v Newcastle T. (H) 91-92   **Scorer:** Dave Conlin

FACT FILE
Founded: 1936   Nickname: Cobs
Club Sponsors: Kitchen Design Studio
Colours: Green & white stripes/green/green
Change colours: Blue/red
Midweek Matches: Tuesday
Programme: 8 pages, 30p
CLUB PERSONNEL
President: R Brady
Chairman: Ron Moffatt
Vice Chairman: Ray Sharp
Press Officer: John Taylor
Manager: Des Johnson
Asst Manager: Jim Capstick
Coach: Jim Ballantyne
Physio: Mark Hetherington

NELSON

Secretary: Cyril King, 1 Grange Ave, Barrowford, Nelson, Lancashire BB9 8AN(01282 695578)

Ground: Victoria Park, Lomeshaye Way, Nelson, Lancs (01282 613820)
Directions: M65 jct 13, 1st left (A6068 Fence), 2nd left (B6249 for Nelson),2nd right sign Lomeshaye Village to grd
Capacity: 1500   Seats:150Cover: 200   Floodlights: Yes
Clubhouse: Bar open matchdays   **Club Shop:** Yes

HONOURS   Lancs Lge 54-55; Lancs Comb. 1949-50 51-52; Lg Cup 49-50 50-51 59-60;
                          Bridge Shield 75-76 81-82; Lancs Jnr Cup 54-55; N.W.C. Div 2 Cup 96-97.

BEST SEASON   **FA Cup:** 2nd Rd Proper 30-31(replay) **FA Vase:**

PREVIOUS   **Leagues:** Lancashire 1889-98 1900-01; Football League 1898-1900;
                          Lancashire Comb. 01-16 46-82; N.W.C. 82-88; West Lancashire 88-92.

FACT FILE

Founded: 1881
Nickname: Blues
Colours: Blue & white stripes/black/blue
Change colours: White/red
Midweek matchday: Wednesday
Reserve League: N.W.C. Res. Div.

CLUB PERSONNEL

Chairman: A.T.Barnes
Vice-Chairman: A Barnes
Manager: John Bailey
Assistant Manager:Andy Wych

OLDHAM TOWN

Secretary: Billy O'Niel,WhitebankStadium, Whitebank Road,Oldham.OL8 3JH (0161 624 2689)
Ground: Whitebank Stadium, Whitebank Rd, Hollins, Oldham, Lancs OL8 3JH(0161 624 2689)
Directions: M62 jct 18, M66 to Heaton Pk, right on to A576, left at 2nd lights on to A6104, follow Victoria Ave. on to Hollinwood Ave. under bridge to roundabout take 2nd exit onto Hollins Road, follow Hollins Rd for one & a half miles to Fire Station, left on through gate leading onto Elm Rd and follow to next left, Whitebank Rd on left.
Capacity: 1,000   Seats: 101   Cover: Yes   Floodlights: Yes
Clubhouse: Open evenings and matchdays
HONOURS   NWC: Div 2 97-98, R-up 94-95; Div 3 R-up 85--86; Lg.Champions 97-98
                          Res Div R-up 94-95, Cup 94/95:

PREVIOUS   **Leagues:** Manchester Amateur; Lancashire Comb. 81-82.

BEST SEASON   **FA Cup:**   **FA Vase:**
RECORD   **Attendance:** 495 v Halifax Town, '96.

FACT FILE

Founded: 1964
Colours: Blue,white,blue
Change Colours:
Midweek Matches: Tuesday
Programme: 16 pages, 50p
Editor: Secretary
98-99Captain: Steve Hughes
Top Scorer: Bradley Coe

CLUB PERSONNEL

Chairman: Ken Hughes
Manager: Len Cantello

PADIHAM

Secretary: Tony Brooks, 10 Newton Street, Burnley BB12 0LG Tel: 01282 709782 (H)
Ground: Arbories Memorial Sports Ground, Well Street, Padiham, Lancs. BB12 8LE
          Tel: 01282 773742   e-mail: brooks@household60.freeserve.co.uk
Directions: M65, J8, then follow A6068 (signed Clitheroe & Padiham). At lights at bottom of hill, turn right into Dean Range/Blackburn Road towards Padiham. At the next junction turn into Holland street opposite church, then into Well Street at the side of the Hare & Hounds pub to the ground.   Nearest rail station: Burnley
          Floodlights: Yes
Honours: Lancs Amateur Cup R-up 66, Lancs Amateur Shield R-up 97, Burnley, Pendle &
Rossendale Hosp. Cup 96, R-up 91; Lancs Comb. Trophy 81, R-up 82; NWC Div. 3 R-up 83-84;
W. Lancs Div.1 99-00, Div.2 71-72 76-77 R-up 96-97, Pres. Cup R-up 79 94 97; E. Lancs Amat
Lge R-up 06-07   **Best Season:** FA Cup: Third Rd., 1883-84
Previous Leagues: Lancashire Comb.; NW Counties; West Lancs.; N.E. Lancs;
                          NE Lancs Combination; East Lancs Amateur Lge.

FACT FILE

Formed: 1964
Colours: Royal blue & white/white/red
Change: Red & black/black/black
Midweek Matchday: Tuesday

Chairman: Mick Muldoon
Brook Foot Farm Barn, Grove Lane,
Padiham, Lancs.
Tel: 01282 778831

SQUIRES GATE

Secretary: Ian Farish, 19 Brocklewood Ave., Poulton-le-Fylde, Lancs. FY6 8BZ.
Tel/Fax:0161 799 0423 Mobile: 07780973962
Ground: School Road, Marton, Blackpool, Lancs.   Tel: 01253 798584
Directions: M6 to M55 jct 4, left onto A583, right at 1st lights (Whitehall Rd) follow signs for airport. Ground approx 1.5 miles on right. Nearest station Blackpool South.
Capacity: 1000   Seats: 2 new stands (100 seats)   Cover: One side
Floodlights: Yes
Clubhouse: Yes

HONOURS	West Lancs Lg: Div 2 80-81, Richardson Cup 86-87
PREVIOUS	**Leagues:** W. Lancs (pre-1991)
BEST SEASON	**FA Cup:** **FA Vase:**
RECORD	**Attendance:** 600 v Everton 95

FACT FILE

Formed: 1948
Colours: Royal/black/royal
Midweek Matches: Tuesday
Programme: 20 pages

CLUB PERSONNEL
Chairman: P Mack (01772 339955)
Vice President: Brian Addison
ManagerGordon Fell
Assistant Manager: John Chippendale
Reserves Manager: Wayne Hughes

STONE DOMINOES

Secretary: Gordon Chadwick, 52 High Lane, Brown Edge, Stoke-on-Trent, Staffs ST6 8RU
Tel: 01782 505342 (H) 01785 815551 (B)
Ground: Springbank Park, Yarnfield Lane, Yarnfield, nr Stone, Staffs. Tel: 01785 761891
Directions: M6 South , J15, take A500 to A34, take south route to Stone (5 miles), through traffic lights to Walton Hotel (still on A34), turn right to Yarnfield Lane, approx. 2 miles over M6, ground on left before entering village
Nearest rail station: Stoke/Stone   Floodlights: Yes
Honours: Midland League Div. 1 99-00, Div. 2 R-up 96-97,
Div.1 Cup 98-99, Div. 2 Cup 96-97, Charity Shield 00
Previous League: Midland League
Record Attendance: 124 v Audley, Staffs. Vase Nov. 99

FACT FILE

Formed: 1987
Colours: Red/black/black
Midweek Matchday: Wednesday

Chairman: Bob Bowers
Springbank House, Station Road,
Barlaston, Staffs.
Tel: 01782 373298 (H) 01785 815551 (B)

TETLEY WALKER

Secretary: Garry Clarke, 183 Liverpool Road, Gt.Sankey, Warrington, Cheshire Wa5 1QU
Ground: Tetley Walker Club, Long Lane, Orford, Warrington, Ches. WA2 9PB (01925 634904)
Directions: M6 Junc 21A to M62 Junc 9, follow signs to Warrington town centre on A49. After 1 1/2 miles turn left at 2nd r'bout ground about 500yds on left. Nearest station Warrington Central
Capacity: 2,000   Seats: 40   Cover: 150   Floodlights: No   Shop: No
Clubhouse: Open noon-midnight. Food includes sandwiches & pies, (01925 634904)

HONOURS	NWC Div 2 Trophy 97-98; Guardian Cup 84-85 85-86 93-94 95-96 96-97; Jubilee Cup 84-85 93-94; Warrington Lge 86-87 93-94:
PREVIOUS	**League:** Warrington & District 1974-94 **Grounds:** None
BEST SEASON	**FA Vase:** 4th Rd 96-97 **FA Cup:**
RECORDS	**Attendance:** 200 v Durham C., FA Vase 96-97
	Appearances: Ray Arnold **Win:** 15-2 v Nelson, NWCL 96-971999-1999-
1999-00	**Captain:** Neil Maher **Top Scorer:** Barry Edwardson

FACT FILE
Founded: 1974   Nickname: Walkers
Sponsor: Adobe Systems/
Colours: Navy blue with yellow trim
Change Cols: White & Red
Midweek matches: Tuesday
Programme: 40 pages 50p
Editor: Garry Clarke
CLUB PERSONNEL
President: T.B.A.
Chairman:Tommy Tandy
Treasurers; John Hackney
Managers:Alan Aspinall
Physio: Harry Peacey
Press Officer: Garry Clarke

WARRINGTON TOWN

Secretary: Harry Boden, 10 Landseer Ave, Warrington Tel: 01925 659796 (H) 0589 512675(M)
Ground: Cantilever Park, Common Lane, Latchford, Warrington WA4 2RS Tel:01925 631932
(Club), 01925-653044 (FAX). **Directions:** M6 junction 20, then A50 towards Warrington. After 2 miles turn left immediately after swing bridge into Station Road, ground 600yds on left. From town centre travel 1 mile south on A49, left at lights into Loushers Lane, ground quarter mile on right. 2miles from Warrington Bank Quay (BR)
Capacity: 2,000   Cover: 650   Seats: 350   Floodlights: Yes   **Club Shop:** Yes
Clubhouse: Weekdays 1-11pm, Sat. 12-11pm, Sun. 12-3pm, 7-10.30pm. Bar food on matchdays
HONOURS: FA Vase R-up 86-87; N.W.C. Lge 89-90 (Lg Cup 85-86 87-88 88-89 (R-up 89-90),
Div 2 R-up86-87, Div 3 R-up 82-83; Mid-Cheshire Lg 60-61 (R-up 57-58, Lg Cup 54-55 55-56)
11-12 72-73, Altrincham Amat. Cup 54-55,
PREVIOUS   Leagues: Warrington & Dist. 49-52; Mid-Cheshire 52-78; Cheshire Co. 78-82;
N.W.C. 82-90; N.P.L 90-97. **Name:** Stockton Heath 1949-62. **BEST SEASON FA Cup:** 4th
Qual. Rd 94-95 **FA Vase:** Runners-up 86-87 **FA Trophy:** Quarter-Finalists 92-93

FACT FILE
Formed: 1948   Nickname: The Town
Colours: Blue & yellow/blue/blue
Change colours:Blue & yellow squares/blue
Midweek matchday: Tuesday
Reserves' League: Mid-Cheshire
Programme 24 Pages £1.00
Editor:Rob Wood (01925 480207)
CLUB PERSONNEL
Chairman: Harry Boden
Vice Chairman:D.J.Hughes
Press Officer: Colin Serjent
Manager: Alan Lord
Asst Manager: Dave Hughes
Coach: Paul Knights Physio: T.B.A.

NORTH WEST COUNTIES FOOTBALL LEAGUE AWARDS

FIRST DIVISION MANAGER OF THE YEAR
Alvin McDonald   Vauxhall Motors

FIRST DIVISION PLAYER OF THE YEAR
Russell Brierley   Ramsbottom United

FIRST DIVISION FAIR PLAY AWARD
Skelmersdale United

SECOND DIVISION MANAGER OF THE YEAR
Gary Lowe   Woodley Sports

SECOND DIVISION PLAYER OF THE YEAR
Nicky Taylor   Bacup Borough

SECOND DIVISION FAIR PLAY AWARD
Warrington Town

PROGRAMME OF THE YEAR AWARD
OVERALL WINNER   St Helens Town

FIRST DIVISION   Leek CSOB

SECOND DIVISION   Curzon Ashton

1999-2000 ROLL OF HONOUR

FIRST DIVISION

	MANAGER OF THE MONTH	PLAYER OF THE MONTH	SAFE HANDS
September	Ray Walker (Newcastle T)	Andy Gayle (Nantwich Town)	Chris Holmes (Newcastle T)
October	Ray Walker (Newcastle T)	Gregg Blundell (Vauxhall M)	Robbie Holcroft (Skem' Utd)
November	Alvin McDonald (Vauxhall M)	Andy Gayle (Nantwich Town)	Gary Stones (Ramsbottom U)
December	Alvin McDonald (Vauxhall M)	Dave Brown (Salford City)	Steve Hilton (Vauxhall Motors)
January	Alan Lord (Atherton Colls)	Peter Cumiskey (Prescot C)	Steve Morris(Atherton Colls)
February	Benny Phillips (Mossley)	Pedro Brennan (Mossley)	Chris Holmes (Newcastle T)
March	Ken Bridge (Ramsbottom U)	Russell Brierley (Ramsbottom)	Mark Andrews (Rossendale)
April	Alvin McDonald (Vauxhall M)	Chris Smith (Atherton Colls)	Damien Grange (Kidsgrove)

SECOND DIVISION

	MANAGER OF THE MONTH	PLAYER OF THE MONTH	SAFE HANDS
September	Joe Murty (Curzon Ashton)	Mark Wilson (Formby)	Tommy Allen (Curzon Ashton)
October	John Bailey (Nelson)	Paul Baker (Darwen)	Simon Burrows (Nelson)
November	Joe Murty (Curzon Ashton)	Michael Charlton (Curzon A)	John Ogden (Castleton G)
December	Gordon Fell (Squires Gate)	Barry Edwardson (Tetley W)	Neil McCormack (Warrington)
January	Alan Aspinall (Tetley Walker)	Andy Tague (Warrington T)	Thomas Baldwin (Blackpool)
February	M Farrell/G Mellor (Chad'ton)	Jonathan Irvine (Nelson)	Graham Rummens (Formby)
March	Brian Richardson (Daisy Hill)	Dominic Shinks (Daisy Hill)	David Fish (Woodley Sports)
April	Gary Lowe (Woodley Sports)	Peter Carty (Woodley Sports)	David Fish (Woodley Sports)

Top left: The North West Trains Division Two top scorer, Steve Gavin finds himself under close attention from a Squires Gate player during his team, Curzon Ashton's League victory. Photo: Colin Stevens

Top right: Chris Brookes of Atherton LR puts a pass through despite being sandwiched by Matt Walker and Paul Cox of Atherton Collieries. Collieries won this Derby 3-1. Photo: Colin Stevens.

Centre: Tetley Walker FC. Back Row (l-r): Stephen Hunt, Jimmy Woodyer, Lee Webster, Lee Medland, Jamie Lowe, Carl Dermott, Dave Aspinall, Andy Flood. Front Row: Lee Trantum, Simon Corns, Jimmy Collins, Neil Maher, Karl Jones, Kevin Lonsdale.

Bottom: Curzon Ashton keeper Tommy Allen makes a safe catch during his side's 3-3 Vase draw at home to Warrington Town. Photo: Colin Stevens

FRANK ARMITT
LIVERPOOL COUNTY FOOTBALL COMBINATION

Secretary: J F Deal
Press Officer: Jim Stanway, 10 Olive Vale, Liverpool L15 4PQ   Tel: 0151 281 5704

In the Frank Armitt Liverpool County Combination's first season as an official feeder league to the North West Counties League, level four of the pyramid of football under the Nationwide Football League, there has been spectacular success on the field; dominating in virtually all competitions in which County Combination clubs entered. So hats off to League Champions Waterloo Dock (for a record tenth time), League Cup winners Lucas Sports, Lancashire Amateur Cup winners Speke (for the first time) and Liverpool County FA Challenge Cup winners, Yorkshire Copper Tube (also for the first time). No club managed to win more than one trophy, an illustration of the overall strength of the competition and Saint Dominics had to be content with the Carlsberg Tetley Trophy!

However, while the playing strength continued to be up to scratch, the County Combination's presence in the pyramid system will inevitably put the spotlight on the league's playing facilities which in many cases leave plenty to be desired. Many of our grounds are in need of substantial upgrade on and off the pitch and when you consider that we are almost as close to the Conference as likes of Southport are to the Premier League, then action is required. The promises made to grass roots football through the changes in funding are there to be fulfiled in the Liverpool County Combination - let's hope that the expectations of our clubs will be met.

The restructuring of the league which resulted in the formation of one division of nineteen clubs, the first time that the County Combination had been without a Second Division since 1960, produced a much more expanded league programme. However, the weather was not quite as wet as the previous season with only one complete wash-out although several clubs continued to have waterlogging problems. Nevertheless, the expanded division effectively split into two halves with very few surprise results between clubs from either half. The County Combination ideally would like to revert to two divisions but until the numbers are there, there's very little choice.

Still, look again at the role of honour and give ourselves a slap on the back. Congratulations to all our clubs in providing such an entertaining season. As one season ends a new one begins and we all prepare for the start of the new 2000-01 season which kicks off on Saturday August 19th.

HONOURS LIST 1999-2000

County Combination League Champions	Waterloo Dock
Liverpool County FA Challenge Cup Winners	Yorkshire Copper Tube
Liverpool County FA Challenge Cup Runners Up	Lucas Sports
Lancashire Amateur Cup Winners	Speke
Lancashire Amateur Cup Runners Up	Saint Dominics
Peter Coyne Cup Winners	Lucas Sports
Carlsberg-Tetley CupWinners	Saint Dominics
League Record Tenth Championship 1974 - 2000	Waterloo Dock
Reg Kirkpatrick Sportsmanship Trophy	Halewood Town
Leading Goalscorer	Brian Burns (Y C T)
Secretary of the Season	Steve Jones (Halewood Town)
Referee of the Season	Paul Ireland

FINAL LEAGUE TABLE 1999-2000

			Home			Away						
		P	W	D	L	W	D	L	F	A	GD	Pts
1	Waterloo Dock	36	15	2	1	15	2	1	130	45	85	94
2	Yorkshire Copper Tube	36	16	1	1	10	5	3	138	37	101	84
3	Saint Aloysius	36	14	2	2	11	4	2	98	34	64	81
4	Crawfords	36	12	3	3	10	3	5	89	42	47	72
5	Saint Dominics	36	10	5	3	11	2	5	89	62	27	70
6	South Liverpool	36	11	2	5	7	7	4	91	61	30	63
7	Royal Seaforth	36	9	5	4	8	5	5	78	54	22	61
8	Halewood Town	36	10	6	2	8	1	9	88	68	20	61
9	Speke	36	7	5	6	8	4	6	91	77	14	54
10	Mossley Hill	36	7	6	5	6	6	6	59	52	7	51
11	Lucas Sports	36	7	5	6	6	5	7	86	61	25	49
12	Ford Motors	36	6	5	7	5	2	11	82	92	-8	40
13	Prescot Leisure	36	5	4	9	4	5	9	54	87	-33	36
14	Dunningsbridge Park	36	6	2	10	3	3	12	72	114	-42	32
15	Cheshire Lines	36	7	2	9	0	8	10	49	91	-52	31
16	Ayone	36	6	2	10	3	0	15	53	114	-61	29
17	Marconi*	36	4	2	12	3	2	13	61	144	-83	22
18	Birchfield	36	3	4	11	2	1	15	43	109	-66	20
19	BRNESC	36	1	3	14	0	1	17	30	138	-108	7

* points deducted

RESULTS CHART 1999-2000

		1	2	3	4	5	6	7	8	9	10	11	12	13	14	15	16	17	18	19
1	Ayone	X	2-3	5-1	1-1	1-0	6-4	2-1	2-4	1-4	2-1	0-2	3-3	4-2	0-1	1-5	1-3	1-2	0-5	0-2
2	Birchfield	4-3	X	3-0	1-1	1-5	0-1	2-3	0-2	0-3	3-0	0-1	2-2	0-6	2-5	1-4	1-1	0-2	1-9	1-1
3	BRNESC	1-3	1-4	X	1-1	0-6	1-1	2-4	1-3	0-3	7-2	0-4	1-2	0-3	0-3	0-7	0-1	2-6	2-8	2-2
4	Cheshire Lines	2-3	3-1	4-0	X	1-2	2-1	2-2	0-3	2-0	2-1	0-3	2-0	0-0	0-1	1-2	1-0	1-6	3-6	1-3
5	Crawfords	2-0	3-1	5-1	4-0	X	2-3	3-1	2-1	2-1	5-0	4-0	4-0	4-1	0-4	2-2	0-0	4-1	1-2	2-2
6	Dunningsbridge	5-3	4-0	5-2	4-4	0-1	X	1-3	1-3	1-3	11-1	4-2	3-1	1-3	1-1	0-6	0-1	0-1	0-5	2-9
7	Ford Motors	2-1	4-0	2-0	5-1	1-4	2-2	X	1-5	4-4	6-1	2-2	1-4	3-1	1-1	2-3	0-1	4-5	2-2	0-5
8	Halewood T	6-1	3-1	2-0	4-1	1-1	4-1	4-1	X	1-1	5-1	1-1	1-1	3-2	2-1	2-2	2-3	0-2	0-0	3-2
9	Lucas Sports	9-0	6-2	5-1	6-1	1-1	1-3	0-3	7-1	X	1-2	1-1	3-1	0-0	1-1	2-0	1-1	1-2	0-2	0-5
10	Marconi	4-2	3-1	5-1	4-2	1-4	2-2	1-3	5-5	1-7	X	1-2	1-2	1-3	1-2	0-3	0-8	1-5	1-5	0-6
11	Mossley Hill	2-1	2-1	1-1	1-1	0-0	7-1	2-1	1-3	2-1	7-1	X	3-0	1-1	1-1	0-0	1-2	0-2	1-3	1-2
12	Prescot L	0-1	3-1	5-0	1-1	0-1	3-2	4-3	0-4	5-5	0-3	1-1	X	0-2	4-3	0-2	2-6	2-2	0-1	0-2
13	Royal Seaforth	7-0	1-1	1-0	4-2	2-1	3-0	0-0	2-1	3-3	4-1	1-1	1-2	X	4-5	1-0	0-1	4-2	3-6	1-1
14	Sth Liverpool	3-1	4-1	7-0	4-1	1-2	6-0	3-2	3-2	4-3	3-3	2-3	7-1	0-0	X	3-1	0-1	2-1	1-2	1-9
15	Speke	3-0	3-2	3-1	2-2	1-3	6-3	4-3	4-3	1-2	3-3	2-2	3-2	2-3	1-1	X	0-3	2-3	4-5	1-1
16	St Aloysius	6-0	4-0	8-0	4-0	2-4	6-2	6-3	4-3	1-1	5-0	2-0	1-1	1-2	1-0	7-2	X	2-0	2-0	1-0
17	St Dominics	2-0	4-0	2-1	4-1	3-2	2-1	5-2	3-1	2-0	2-6	3-0	2-2	3-3	2-2	4-4	1-1	X	3-4	0-2
18	Waterloo Dock	2-0	2-0	5-0	2-2	3-2	7-2	4-3	3-1	1-0	8-1	4-0	5-0	1-3	5-3	3-2	3-2	0-0	X	3-0
19	Yorkshire CT	11-2	8-2	7-0	5-0	3-1	5-0	4-2	7-0	3-0	7-2	2-1	4-0	3-1	2-2	6-1	3-0	4-0	0-4	X

LEADING GOALSCORERS 1999-2000

52	Brian Burns	Yorkshire Copper Tube	25	Anthony Owen	Speke
41	Keith Jones	South Liverpool	24	Gary Edwards	South Liverpool
41	Mick Feeney	Yorkshire Copper Tube	24	Lee Martindale	Lucas Sports
40	Joe Gibiliru Jnr	Lucas Sports	23	Paul Brown	Yorkshire Copper Tube
40	Jeff Dodd	Saint Dominics	22	Kieron McDonald	Waterloo Dock
29	Adam Williams	Waterloo Dock	22	Brendan Helm	Crawfords UB
26	Terry Jones	Saint Aloysius	21	Tony Shiels	Dunningsbridge Park
26	Mischa Showers	Halewood Town	20	Carl Furlong	Waterloo Dock
25	Barry Smith	Saint Aloysius	20	Phil Smith	Speke

LEAGUE CONSTITUTION

Ayone, Birchfield, BRNESC, Cheshire Lines, Crawfords, Dunningsbridge Park, Ford Motors, Halewood Town, Lucas Sports, Marconi, Mossley Hill Athletic, Prescot Leisure, Royal Seaforth, Saint Aloysius, Saint Dominics, South Liverpool, Speke, Waterloo Dock, Yorkshire Copper Tube

CARLSBERG WEST CHESHIRE A.F.L.

Chairman: R Prescott

Hon. Secretary: John Marshall   Tel: 01244 376844

Press Officer: Ray Condliffe   Tel: 0151 327 2288

The focal point of another extremely interesting season was the centenary of the League's major knockout competition, The Pyke Challenge Cup. The 100 year relationship between local jewellers Pykes and the league has continued throughout with Pykes supporting the competition by providing the Final medals for players and match officials. Ironically, neither of the finalists, Ashville and Vauxhalls, had previously lifted the superb trophy which had been donated to the league by the Pyke company founder, William Pyke. Ashville entered the contest boasting Division One's meanest defence while Vauxhalls relied on a free scoring approach. After 46 minutes Vauxhalls held a 4-0 advantage, but in the space of ten minutes their opponents had a penalty saved and netted twice. A fairytale comeback wasn't to be though and The Motormen added a fifth late in the game collecting the trophy from David Pyke, the great great grandson of William Pyke. Later over 200 guests attended a celebration meal at which the Football Association as well as County and District Associations were well represented.

Undoubtedly the team of the season was BICC Helsby of Division Two who won all five competitions they entered. The League's charity competition, The Bill Weight Memorial Trophy, was the first to come their way when they completed an August Bank Holiday win over Ashville, while they retained the Runcorn Senior Cup by defeating Pavilions, and overcame Christleton Reserves by a single goal in the final of the West Cheshire Bowl. Their most sought after prize was the Second Division championship, and with it elevation to the top flight, which arrived just two seasons after they rejoined the league. The battle for the single promotion spot (increased to two for next season) was an exciting three way affair which also involved Aintree Villa and Castrol Social. The icing on Helsby's cake came when they lifted the Cheshire County Amateur Cup with their 3-1 win over Mid Cheshire league champions, Barnton, thereby extending the West Cheshire AFL's proud recent record.

Previous County Cup holders Poulton Victoria underwent pre-season changes at managerial and playing level but still emerged to pip 1998-99 champions, Cammell Laird, for the Division One title. As representatives of the Cheshire FA, Vics also reached the final of the Northern Counties championship only to lose out to a goal at the end of extra time by opponents, East Riding FA. Having just failed twelve months earlier, Pavilions gained promotion from Division Three and, after remaining unbeaten until April, go up as champions. An intense contest for the second promotion spot was won by new boys MANWEB who edged out Mond Rangers Reserves, and another club in their first season in the league, Mallaby, who did however have the consolation of lifting the West Cheshire Shield when defeating Upton AA Reserves after extra time.

Once again our clubs virtually monopolised the District competitions with Cammell Laird gaining a double as their first team tasted Wirral Senior Cup success after a win over Vauxhalls, while their second string were Wirral Amateur Cup winners. Christleton again lifted the Chester Senior Cup and, as already mentioned, the Runcorn Senior went the way of BICC Helsby.

The annual inter league contest with the Mid Cheshire League was drawn thanks to a last gasp leveller by West Cheshire's Kenny Burgess and the player receiving most "Man of the Match" awards was Willaston's Nick Williams.

The constitution for the first full season of the millennium shows little change. Although the West Cheshire has joined five other leagues in a liaison that will act as a feeder to the First North West Trains AFL, none of our clubs has made an application. However, the departure of both Moreton teams from the league resulted in vacancies which have been filled by Birkenhead & Wirral League champions, FC Pensby, and Helsby Reserves (the BICC tag has been dropped) who join us from the South Wirral League.

FINAL LEAGUE TABLES 1999-2000

DIVISION ONE

	P	W	D	L	F	A	Pts
Poulton Victoria	30	23	6	1	84	36	75
Cammell Laird	30	18	9	3	80	36	63
Vauxhall Motors	30	17	9	4	71	38	60
Ashville	30	15	9	6	62	25	54
Heswall	30	14	12	4	64	29	54
Stork	30	14	6	10	63	59	48
Capenhurst	30	13	9	8	47	46	48
Mersey Royal	30	13	8	9	71	55	47
Christleton	30	9	12	9	51	45	39
General Chemicals	30	10	7	13	52	57	37
Maghull	30	10	4	16	40	48	34
Mond Rangers	30	9	4	17	52	75	31
Shell	30	5	5	20	37	84	20
Blacon Youth Club*	30	6	4	20	55	105	19
Newton	30	3	7	20	29	70	16
Merseyside Police	30	4	3	23	35	85	15

DIVISION TWO

	P	W	D	L	F	A	Pts
BICC Helsby	30	24	2	41	9	43	74
Aintree Villa	30	20	7	3	85	27	67
Castrol Social	30	20	5	5	64	20	65
Cammell Laird Res	30	17	4	9	74	59	55
Ashville Reserves	30	14	6	10	72	71	48
Capenhurst Res	30	14	5	11	54	51	47
Upton Athletic Assn	30	12	7	11	69	56	43
Christleton Reserves	30	13	4	13	56	51	43
New Brighton	30	12	6	12	70	58	42
Heswall Reserves	30	9	9	12	51	50	36
Mersey Royal Res	30	10	5	15	50	78	35
West Kirby	30	8	5	17	48	59	29
Poulton Victoria Res	30	8	5	17	47	80	26
Shell Tessuti Res	30	7	5	18	58	94	23
Moreton	30	4	7	19	32	77	19
Stork Reserves	30	5	4	21	36	101	19

DIVISION ONE RESULTS CHART 1999-2000

		1	2	3	4	5	6	7	8	9	10	11	12	13	14	15	16
1	Ashville	X	4-1	0-0	2-2	0-0	3-0	1-0	2-2	0-0	8-0	4-0	3-0	0-1	2-0	0-0	1-2
2	Blacon Youth Club	0-4	X	1-3	3-4	1-1	1-9	0-5	0-3	4-2	5-1	3-2	2-0	1-3	2-4	2-3	4-4
3	Cammell Laird	2-0	6-1	X	5-0	3-2	2-0	1-1	4-2	1-0	5-1	1-1	3-1	2-2	3-1	1-2	1-1
4	Capenhurst	0-4	1-1	2-3	X	1-1	1-0	1-1	1-0	0-1	2-2	2-0	2-0	2-4	3-0	3-2	2-0
5	Christleton	0-3	5-2	1-3	0-0	X	1-1	1-1	1-1	3-2	3-1	3-0	2-0	2-4	3-3	4-1	1-2
6	General Chemicals	1-1	5-2	1-2	1-3	1-0	X	0-4	2-0	2-3	1-0	4-1	4-0	2-2	2-0	1-4	2-7
7	Heswall	1-1	4-0	1-1	1-1	0-2	4-1	X	2-0	0-0	1-0	3-1	3-0	3-3	4-0	1-1	1-1
8	Maghull	0-1	0-1	5-3	0-1	3-0	2-2	0-4	X	0-2	1-0	2-1	2-0	0-2	2-0	1-3	1-4
9	Mersey Royal	3-3	5-3	5-2	3-6	2-2	2-1	1-1	2-3	X	0-1	5-2	2-0	2-2	6-0	3-3	0-2
10	Merseyside Police	1-2	5-1	0-0	2-0	2-2	0-1	1-6	0-4	0-5	X	4-0	2-3	1-3	1-4	0-3	2-4
11	Mond Rangers	0-4	3-1	0-3	0-2	0-3	3-2	1-2	3-1	4-2	4-3	X	2-2	1-2	5-1	1-2	3-2
12	Newton	0-2	8-4	0-3	0-0	2-2	0-0	1-3	0-2	1-1	3-2	0-5	X	3-4	0-2	1-2	1-2
13	Poulton Victoria	2-1	5-2	1-1	6-1	3-0	2-2	3-1	2-1	1-3	2-0	6-0	1-0	X	5-1	2-1	1-0
14	Shell	0-3	0-3	0-10	1-1	1-4	1-2	0-1	1-1	3-4	3-0	4-4	1-1	1-5	X	3-1	0-2
15	Stork	4-1	3-3	3-5	1-2	0-5	5-1	3-2	2-1	3-4	3-2	3-1	2-2	1-3	1-0	X	1-4
16	Vauxhall Motors	3-2	3-1	1-1	2-1	0-0	1-1	3-3	2-0	2-1	6-1	2-2	5-0	1-2	3-2	0-0	X

PYKE CHALLENGE CUP 1999-2000

FIRST ROUND

Ashville	v	Mersey Royal	2-1		Blacon YC	v	Capenhurst	2-2, 1-2
Heswall	v	Maghull	1-0		Mond Rangers	v	Newton	4-1
Christleton	v	Cammell Laird	1-5		Merseyside Police	v	Stork	2-6
Shell	v	Poulton Vics	4-2		General Chemicals	v	Vauxhall Motors	0-4

SECOND ROUND

| Ashville | v | Capenhurst | 1-1, 2-1 | | Heswall | v | Mond Rangers | 1-3 |
| Cammell Laird | v | Stork | 0-1 | | Shell | v | Vauxhall Motors | 1-6 |

SEMI-FINALS

| Ashville | v | Mond Rangers | 2-0 | | Stork | v | Vauxhall Motors | 2-4 |

FINAL

| Ashville | v | Vauxhall Motors | 2-5 |

LEADING GOALSCORERS 1999-2000

	DIVISION ONE			DIVISION TWO			DIVISION THREE	
24	Alan McDonald		31	Mark Vickers		38	Nick Williams	
	Cammell Laird			Aintree Villa			Willaston	
23	Chris McGinn		30	Kevin Leech		25	Stan Dobbs	
	M Royal			BICC Helsby			Mallaby	
18	Chris Moores		22	Simon Andrews		20	Andy Gott	
	Vauxhall Motors			Upton AA			Mond Rangers Res	
17	Gary Reay		18	Richie White		20	Mark Steggles	
	Poulton Victoria			Ashville Reserves			Pavilions	

CARLSBERG MANAGER OF THE MONTH AWARDS

August	Chris Camden	Poulton Victoria
September	Dave Anderson	Ashville
October	Chris Camden/Micky Dunn	Poulton Victoria
November	Peter Kavanagh/Noel Whelan	Capenhurst Reserves
December	Alan Harvey	Aintree Villa
January	Frank Cannon	BICC Helsby
February	John Crompton	Pavilions
March	John Brett	Mallaby
April	Frank Cannon	BICC Helsby

ASHVILLE

Secretary: Dave Walton, 15 Wellesley Road, Wallasey, Wirral,
Merseyside, L445UR Tel: 0151 639 9196
Ground: Villa Park, Cross Lane, Wallasey Village, Wallasey,
Tel: 0151 638 2127
Colours: White & black/black/black   **Formed:** 1949

BLACON YOUTH CLUB

Secretary: Colin Lawson
54 Adelaide Rd., Blacon, Chester CH1 5SZ Tel: 01244 375508 (H)
Ground: Cairns Crescent Playing Fields,
Cairns Crescent, Blacon, Chester.
Colours: Black & white stripes/black/black   **Formed:** 1964

CAMMELL LAIRD

Secretary: Ray Steele
46 Croft Ave, Bromborough, Wirral L62 2BR Tel: 0151 334 8998
Ground: Kirklands, St Peters Road, Rock Ferry, Birkenhead
Tel: 0151 645 5991
Colours: All blue   **Formed:** 1900

CAPENHURST

Secretary: Martin Williams, 157 Hope Farm Road, Great Sutton,
South Wirral L662TJ Tel: 0151 339 8935
Ground: Capenhurst Sports Ground, Capenhurst Lane, Capenhurst
Tel: 0151 339 4101
Colours: All maroon   **Formed:** 1952

CHRISTLETON

Secretary: Ken Price, 35 Canadian Ave, Hoole, Chester CH2 3HQ
Tel: 01244 313513

Ground: Little Heath, Christleton Tel: 01244 332153
Colours: Red/black/red   **Formed:** 1966

GENERAL CHEMICALS

Secretary: Tony Riley
171 Cotton Lane, Runcorn, Cheshire WA7 5JB Tel: 01928 565390

Ground: Picow Farm Road, Runcorn
Colours: Blue & white/blue/blue & white   **Formed:** 1958

HELSBY

Secretary: John Evans, 35 Hill View Ave., Helsby, Ches. WA6 0ES
Tel: 01928 724817 (H)

Ground: Helsby Sports & Social Club Tel: 01928 722267

Colours: Red/black/black   **Formed:** 1895

HESWALL

Secretary: Jake Horan
13 Reedville Road, Bebington, Wirral L63 2HS Tel: 0151 644 0459
Ground: Gayton Park, Brimstage Road, Heswall, Wirral
Tel: 0151 342 8172
Colours: Yellow/royal blue/yellow   **Formed:** 1891

MAGHULL

Secretary: Danny Sherlock, 14 Alexander Drive, Lydiate, Merseyside
L31 2NJ Tel: 0151 526 2306
Ground: Old Hall Field, Hall Lane, Maghull, Merseyside (0151 526
7320) **Directions:** M57 or M58 to end (Switch Island), A59 towards
Preston (Northway)to lights at Hall Lane, turn right following signs for
Maghull Station. Ground 200 yds on the left. Half mile from Maghull
(Merseyrail)   **Colours:** Blue & red stripes/blue/blue

MERSEY ROYAL

Secretary: Dave Lawson
7 Mount Park, Higher Bebington, Wirral L63 5RD Tel: 0151 608 2261
Ground: Bromborough Pool Village, The Green, South View Rd.,
Bromborough Pool. Tel: 0151 645 3476
Colours: Navy & light blue striped shirts   **Formed:** 1946

MOND RANGERS

Secretary: Thomas Hill, 19 Colworth Rd., Speke, Liverpool L24 1YR
Tel: 0151 486 1284
Ground: Pavilions Club, Sandy Lane, Weston Point, Runcorn WA7 5EX
Tel: 01928 590508
Colours: Blue & black stiped shirts   **Formed:** 1967

NEWTON

Secretary: Alan Dabner, 79A Eleanor Road, Bidston, Wirral CH43
7RW. Tel NOs: 0151 653 2151 (H) 0151 993 2151 (B)

Ground: Millcroft, Frankby Road, Greasby, Wirral Tel: 0151 677 8382
Colours: Yellow/green/yellow **Formed:** 1933

POULTON VICTORIA

Secretary: John McGraa, 1 Wernbrook Close, Nocturum, Wirrall
CH43 9HY Tel: 0151 652 8043 (H)

Ground: Victoria Park, Rankin Street, Wallasey Tel: 0151 638 3559
Colours: All Royal Blue   **Formed:** 1935

SHELL F.C.

Secretary: Martin Wood, 23 Whitefields, Elton, Chester CH2 4LS
Tel Nos: 01928 725689 (H)
Ground: Chester Road, Whitby, Ellesmere Port, South Wirral
Tel: 0151 200 7080
Colours: Yellow /navy/navy   **Formed:** 1924

STORK

Secretary: Steve Carter
7 Elm Road, Bebington, Wirral L63 8PF Tel: 0151 645 6697
Ground: Unilever Sports Ground, Bromborough
Colours: All green   **Formed:** 1920

VAUXHALL MOTORS

Secretary: Carole Paisey, 26 South Road, West Kirby, Wirral L48
3HQ (0151 6256 936)
Ground: Vauxhall Sports Ground, Rivacre Road, Hooton, Ellesmere
Port (0151 3281114)
Colours: White/royal blue/white   **Formed:** 1963

AINTREE VILLA   Formed: 1954
Secretary: Alf Shepherd, 154 Altway, Aintree, Liverpool L10 6LG
Tel: 0151 526 9287 (H)
Ground: Aintree racecourse.
Colours: Tangerine/white/white

CASTROL SOCIAL FC   Formed: 1954
Secretary: Mike Caulfield, 2 Weaver Road, Whitby, Ellesmere Port
CH66 2JJ. Tel: 0151 355 5966 (H)
Ground: Castrol Sports & Social Club, Chester Road, Whitby,
Ellesmere Port(0151 355 1730)
Colours: Royal & emerald/royal/white

MANWEB FC   Formed: 1932
John Shimmin, 54 Gonville Rd., Bootle, Merseyside L20 9LR
tel: 0151 933 5763 (H)
Ground: Manweb Sports & Social Club, Thingwall Rd., Liverpool L15
7LB Tel: 0151 281 5364
Colours: White/navy/white

MERSEYSIDE POLICE   Formed: 1885
Secretary: Gary Dinsmore, 3 Chaffinch Close, West Derby, Liverpool
L12 0NX Tel: 0151 220 0285 (H)
Ground: Police Club, Fairfield, Prescot Road, Liverpool L7 0JD
Tel: 0151 228 2352
Colours: All navy b lue with red trim.

NEW BRIGHTON   Formed: 1993
Secretary: Carl Gidman. 64 Ford Road, Upton, Wirral CH49 0TG Tel:
0151 678 1858 (H/B)
Ground: Harrison Drive, Wallasey Village, Wallasey
Colours: Red & white/white/red & white

UPTON ATHLETIC ASSOC. Formed: 1964
Secretary: Barry Gaulton, 24 St Marks Crescent, Whitby, Ellesmere
Port L66 2XD (0151 339 1504)
Ground: Cheshire County Council Sports & Social Club, Plas Newton
Lane, Chester (01244 318367)
Colours: All blue

PAVILIONS   Formed: 1998
Secretary: Beverley Crilly, 26 Perrin Ave., Weston Point, Runcorn WA7
4BJ Tel: 01928 575938 (H)
Ground: Pavilions Complex, Sandy Lane, Weston Point, Runcorn
Tel: 01928 590508
Colours: Blue & white stripes/blue/blue

WEST KIRBY   Formed: 1895
Secretary: Roy Williamson, 85 Wood Lane, Greasby, Wirrall CH49 2PX
Tel: 0151 677 4860 (H)
Ground: Johnston Recreation Ground, Neston Road, Willaston, South
Wirrall.
Colours: White/black/black

plus

Ashville Reserves	Cammell Laird Reserves
Capenhurst Reserves	Christleton Reserves
Heswall Reserves	Mersey Royal Reserves
Poulton Victoria Reserves	Shell Reserves

Team Talk

provides comprehensive coverage of the whole spectrum of non-League football from the Nationwide Conference to County League

including extensive coverage of

the FA Carlsberg Vase

the FA Umbro Trophy

non-League involvement in

the AXA sponsored FA Cup

and the

England Semi-Professional team

(Team Talk is the ONLY magazine to give such

GREEN CONTRACT SERVICES
MID-CHESHIRE LEAGUE

President: R Atherton Esq.

Hon. Secretary: Michael G Quigley
1 Coppice Drive, Northenden, Manchester M22 4DT
Tel: 0161 998 8562 (H)   01925 754058 (B)

The season started with resignations from Astra Zeneca FC, Beeches FC, Ellesmere Port United FC and Walkers Sports and Social FC. With the addition of Cheadle HN Reserves and Flixton Reserves into Division Two, the League comprised of fourteen teams in Division One and sixteen teams in Division Two.

Barnton clinched their fourth League title in a row by a margin of sixteen points, with Middlewich Town FC finishing in second place. Knutsford FC prevented Barnton winning the double by beating them in the Division One Cup and subsequently going on to defeat Rylands FC in the Final at Trafford FC, on a penalty shoot out.

The Division Two Championship was closely contested, with Trafford Reserves FC taking the title by three points from Crewe FC. However Crewe defeated Trafford Reserves in the Division Two Cup Final at Witton Albion FC.

Grove United were also in the honours, defeating Linotype FC in the President's Cup, their first Mid Cheshire Football League success since 1994.

Both Trafford Reserves and Crewe were promoted to Division One for season 2000-01, with no relegation from the Division, in order to increase numbers to sixteen.

Flixton Reserves FC were sadly expelled from the League, due to failing to fulfil a number of fixtures at the end of the season. New to Division Two are Golborne Sports FC, Kidsgrove Reserves FC and Pilkington Reserves FC.

The League will once again host an Inter-League fixture against the West Cheshire League, for the Cooper Smith Challenge Cup.

FINAL LEAGUE TABLES 1999-2000

DIVISION ONE

	P	W	D	L	F	A	Pts
Barnton	26	20	4	2	59	16	64
Middlewich Tn	26	14	6	6	49	38	48
Poynton	26	15	1	10	55	42	46
Linotype	26	13	4	9	39	36	43
Knutsford	26	10	11	5	43	30	41
Chorlton Town	26	11	4	11	45	43	37
Garswood United	26	9	7	10	35	36	34
Padgate St Oswalds	26	9	6	11	27	32	33
Grove United	26	8	7	11	42	44	31
Bollington Athletic	26	7	8	11	32	54	29
Cheadle H N	26	8	4	14	39	49	28
Rylands	26	7	7	12	35	50	28
Whitchurch Alport	26	6	6	14	39	41	24
Pilkington	26	5	5	16	25	53	20

DIVISION TWO

	P	W	D	L	F	A	Pts
Trafford Res	28	22	2	4	90	29	68
Crewe FC	28	20	5	3	77	25	65
Malpas	28	19	4	5	64	33	61
Broadheath Central	28	19	1	8	77	42	58
Lostock Gralam	28	16	4	8	69	45	52
Cheadle H N Res	28	12	4	12	59	70	40
Chester Nomads	28	11	4	13	57	48	37
Warrington Borough	28	11	3	14	62	61	36
Linotype Res	28	10	5	13	39	46	35
Chorlton Town Res	28	7	6	15	37	62	27
Poynton Res	28	7	5	16	46	70	26
Styal	28	7	5	16	51	75	26
Rylands Res	28	6	6	16	44	72	24
Littlemoor	28	7	2	19	35	78	23
Garswood Res	28	5	6	17	42	88	21

* Flixton Res FC expelled from League, all records expunged

HONOURS LIST

DIVISION ONE	Champions	Runners Up	Cup Winners	Cup Runners Up
1999-2000	Barnton	Middlewich T	Knutsford	Rylands
1998-1999	Barnton	Linotype	Barnton	Beeches
1997-1998	Barnton	Knutsford	Barnton	Knutsford
DIVISION TWO				
1999-2000	Trafford Res	Crewe FC	Crewe FC	Trafford Res
1998-1999	Padgate St Oswalds	Grove United	Padgate St Oswalds	Broadheath C
1997-1998	Garswood Utd Res	Pilkington	Padgate St Oswalds	Garswood Utd Res
JUBILEE CUP			**PRESIDENTS CUP**	
1999-2000	Chorlton Town	Cheadle H N	Grove United	Linotype
CLUB OF THE SEASON			**PLAYER OF THE SEASON**	
1999-2000	Bollington Athletic FC		Stephen Nugent (Garswood United FC)	

DIVISION ONE CLUBS 1999-2000

ASTRA ZENECA
Chairman: David Lea **Manager:** Chris Owen
Secretary: David Stubbs, 11 Petunia Grove, Macclesfield, Cheshire SK11 7YY (01625 423160)
Ground: Mulberry Leisure Centre, Alderley Edge
Colours: All Green
Change Colours: Yellow/Black

BARNTON AFC
Chairman: William Perrin **Manager:** Mark Emmerson
Secretary: Michael Webster, 92 Church Road, Barnton CW8 4JE (01606 782960)
Ground: Townfield, Townfield Lane, Barnton
Colours: Black & White Stripes/Black
Change Colours: Amber/Blue

BEECHES FC
Chairman: Gordon Rigby **Manager:** A Hockenhull
Secretary: David Corrigan, 7 Burrows Ave, Haydock, St Helens WA11 0DE (01744 757273)
Ground: Cowley Fields, Wynne Road, St Helens
Colours: Claret & Blue/Claret
Change Colours: Red & Blue Halves/Blue

BOLLINGTON ATHLETIC FC
Chairman: Albert Hall
Secretary: Anthony Holmes, 1 Princess Drive, Bollington, Macclesfield SK10 5ES (01625 574913)
Ground: Recreation Ground, Bollington
Colours: Green & White Stripes/White
Change Colours: Blue & White Hoops/Blue

CHEADLE HEATH NOMADS
Chairman: Roy Welsh **Manager:** Peter Blundell
Secretary: George Gibbons, 3 Hurley Drive, Cheadle Hulme, Stockport SK8 6DH
Ground: The Heath, Norbreck Ave, Cheadle, Stockport
Colours: Maroon & Sky Blue/Maroon
Change Colours: Black & White Stripes/Black

CHORLTON TOWN
Chairman: TBA **Manager:** Graham Wright
Secretary: Jim Calderbank, 21 South Meade, Timperley, Altrincham, Cheshire WA15 6QL
Ground: Parkway Ground, Rylstone Avenue, Chorlton
Colours: Red & Black/White
Change Colours: Yellow or Blue/Blue

GARSWOOD UNITED FC
Chairman: Barry Mavers **Manager:** Alan Aspinall
Secretary: John Anelay, 128 Victoria Road, Garswood, Wigan WN4 0RE (01942 492623)
Ground: The Wooders, Simms Lane End, Garswood
Colours: Blue & White Halves/Blue
Change Colours: All Yellow

GROVE UNITED FC
Chairman: Mark Boothby **Manager:** John Whiteley
Secretary: Bernard Jordan, 25 Bean Leach Road, Hazel Grove, Stockport SK7 4LD (0161 456 2542)
Ground: Half Moon Lane, Offerton, Stockport
Colours: Red/Black
Change Colours: Lt Blue & Claret Stripes/Claret

KNUTSFORD FC
Chairman: TBA **Manager:** Ken Harrison
Secretary: Kevin Deeley, 28 East Street, Guide Bridge, Manchester, M34 5DX (0161 320 9650)
Ground: Manchester Road, Knutsford
Colours: Red & Black Stripes/Black
Change Colours: White/Blue

LINOTYPE FC
Chairman: James Barry **Manager:** Jim Vince
Secretary: Brian McGuiness, 36 Barrington Road, Altrincham, Cheshire (0161 929 0021)
Ground: British Airways Club, Clay Lane, Timperley
Colours: White/Black
Change Colours: Red & Black/White

MIDDLEWICH TOWN FC
Chairman: Steven Morris **Manager:** David Twite
Secretary: Vic Knop, Ashford, 5 Hough Lane, Aderton, Northwich CW9 6AB (01606 76545)
Ground: Seddon Street, Middlewich (01606 835842)
Colours: Red/White
Change Colours: All Blue

PADGATE ST OSWALDS FC
Chairman: Graham Millins **Manager:** Mick Armitage
Secretary: Brian Hughes, 13 Jubilee Ave, Padgate, Warrington WA1 3JY (01925 490924)
Ground: Bennets Rec. Ground, Station Rd, Padgate
Colours: Black & White Stripes/Black
Change Colours: Yellow/Green

PILKINGTON AFC
Chairman: Barry Meadows **Manager:** David Burrows
Secretary: Paul Pinder, 629 Eltonhead Road, Sutton Heath, St Helens WA9 5SX (01744 816158)
Ground: Ruskin Drive, St Helens
Colours: Blue & Black Stripes/Black
Change Colours: Red & Black Stripes/Red

POYNTON FC
Chairman: David Corcoran **Manager:** Paul Cunningham
Secretary: Mark Warburton, 27 Alderley Close, Hazel Grove, Stockport SK7 6BS (01625 873872)
Ground: London Road North, Poynton
Colours: Red & Black/Black
Change Colours: Blue & White/Blue

RYLANDS FC
Chairman: Alan Jackson **Manager:** Terry Selby
Secretary: Ian Finchett, 31 Elizabeth Drive, Padgate, Warrington WA1 4JQ (01925 816911)
Ground: Rylands Rec. Club, Gorsey Lane, Warrington
Colours: Blue & Black/Black
Change Colours: Red & Royal Blue/Blue

WHITCHURCH ALPORT
Chairman: P Wainwright **Manager:** Alan Smith
Secretary: Robert Dutton, 7 Nessina Grove, Crewe, Cheshire CW2 8EL (01270 663015)
Ground: Yockings Park, Blackpark Rd, Whitchurch
Colours: Green & White/Black
Change Colours: Red/Black

DIVISION TWO
CLUBS 1999-2000

LITTLEMOOR FC
Chairman: Arthur McClelan **Manager:** Frank Sanders
Secretary: Stanley McQuarrie, 96 Mottram Towers,
Mottram St, Hillgate, SK1 3NY (0161 2925461)
Ground: Warth Meadow, Welkin Rd, Lower Bredbury
Colours: Black & White Stripes/Black
Change Colours: All Maroon

BROADHEATH CENTRAL FC
Chairman: Ian Beresford **Manager:** Peter Cavanagh
Secretary: Graham Anderson, 1 Foxglove Drive,
Broadheath, Altrincham (0161 718 9093)
Ground: Viaduct Road, Broadheath, Altrincham
Colours: Black & Red Stripes/Black
Change Colours: Blue & White Stripes/White

LOSTOCK GRALAM FC
Chairman: D Washburn **Manager:** Andy Hough
Secretary: Andy Hough, 31 Beechwood Drive, Wincham,
Northwich CW9 6EY (01565 733383)
Ground: Slow & Easy Hotel, Manchester Rd, Lostock G.
Colours: All Blue
Change Colours: Green & Yellow Halves/Black

CHESTER NOMADS FC
Chairman: Phil Darlington **Manager:** Jerry Ireland
Secretary: Ritz Ritzema, 22 Cross Green Upton,
Chester CH2 1QR (01244 379791)
Ground: Garrison Ground, Eaton Rd, Handbridge
Colours: Amber/Black
Change Colours: Grey/Red

MALPAS FC
Chairman: Robert Leslie **Manager:** Martin Holden
Secretary: Bernard Lloyd, 15 Springfield Ave, Malpas,
Cheshire SY14 8QD (01948 860812)
Ground: Malpas & Dt SC, Oxheys, Wrexham Rd, Malpas
Colours: Green & White Hoops/White
Change Colours: Red/Black

CHORLTON TOWN RESERVES
Chairman: TBA **Manager:** Graham Wright
Secretary: Jim Calderbank, 21 South Meade, Timperley,
Altrincham, Cheshire WA15 6QL
Ground: Parkway Ground, Rylstone Avenue, Chorlton
Colours: Red & Black/White
Change Colours: Yellow or Blue/Blue

POYNTON FC RESERVES
Chairman: David Corcoran **Manager:** Mark Warburton
Secretary: Mark Warburton, 27 Alderley Close, Hazel
Grove, Stockport SK7 6BS (01625 873872)
Ground: London Road North, Poynton
Colours: Red & Black/Black
Change Colours: Blue & White/Blue

CREWE FC
Chairman: Patrick Slack **Manager:** Ian O'Reilly
Secretary: Mrs M Vickers, 59 Hall-o-Shaw St, Crewe
(01270 581578)
Ground: Cumberland Sprts Grnd, Thomas St, Crewe
Colours: Blue/Blue
Change Colours: Yellow/Black

RYLANDS FC RESERVES
Chairman: Alan Jackson **Manager:** Alan Blackstone
Secretary: Ian Finchett, 31 Elizabeth Drive, Padgate,
Warrington WA1 4JQ (01925 816911)
Ground: Rylands Rec. Club, Gorsey Lane, Warrington
Colours: Red & Royal Blue/Blue
Change Colours: Blue & Black/Black

ELLESMERE PORT UNITED FC
Chairman: TBA **Manager:** TBA
Secretary: Tony Wallace, 39 Gantby Road, Birkenhead,
Merseyside L41 7DS (083117 9065)
Ground: Ellesmere Port Stadium
Colours: All Blue
Change Colours: All White

STYAL FC
Chairman: Barry Green **Manager:** TBA
Secretary: Alan Jones, 1 Oak Brow Cottages, Altrincham
Rd, Styal, Wilmslow SK9 4JE (01625 530270)
Ground: Altrincham Road, Styal
Colours: Yellow/Blue
Change Colours: Blue/Black

FLIXTON FC RESERVES
Chairman: Peter Dentitch **Manager:** Len Heywood
Secretary: Stuart Nichols, 20 Brompton Rd, Stretford,
Manchester M32 9PR (0161 747 5288)
Ground: Valley Rd, Flixton, M'chester (0161 7477757)
Colours: Blue & White/Blue
Change Colours: Gold/Black

TRAFFORD FC RESERVES
Chairman: David Brown **Manager:** Dave Norman
Secretary: Graham Foxhall, 62 Grosvenor Rd, Urmston,
Manchester M41 5AQ (0161 746 9726)
Ground: Shawe View, Pennybridge Lane, Urmston
Colours: All White
Change Colours: Red/Navy

GARSWOOD UNITED FC RESERVES
Chairman: Barry Mavers **Manager:** Alan Clarke
Secretary: John Anelay, 128 Victoria Road, Garswood,
Wigan WN4 0RE (01942 492623)
Ground: The Wooders, Simms Lane End, Garswood
Colours: Blue & White Halves/Blue
Change Colours: All Yellow

WALKERS SPORTS & SOCIAL FC
Chairman: Tom Tandy **Manager:** John Green
Secretary: Billy Cowell, 55 Fleetwood Close, Gt Sankey,
Warrington WA5 2US (01925 721494)
Ground: Tetley Walkers SC, Long Lane 01925 634904
Colours: White/Red
Change Colours: All Blue

LINOTYPE FC RESERVES
Chairman: James Barry **Manager:** Philip Deadman
Secretary: Brian McGuiness, 36 Barrington Road,
Altrincham, Cheshire (0161 929 0021)
Ground: British Airways Club, Clay Lane, Timperley
Colours: White/Black
Change Colours: Red & Black/White

WARRINGTON BOROUGH FC
Chairman: Harry Buden **Manager:** Derek Holden
Secretary: John Kent, 126 Cumberland ST, Warrington,
WA4 1EX (01925 482970)
Ground: Cantilever Park (01925 724421)
Colours: Blue & Yellow Halves/Blue
Change Colours: All Red

REAL FOOTBALL PEOPLE

from Bamber Bridge . . .

. . . and Stamford

Photo: Peter Barnes

THE ASDA LOGIC
WEST LANCASHIRE LEAGUE

President: D Procter Esq.

Chairman & Secretary: W Carr Esq.
60 Selby Avenue, Blackpool, Lancashire FY4 2LZ
Tel: 01253 348450

The discussions to arrange automatic promotion between the West Lancashire and the North West Counties League, which started in October 1983, have been completed, and, along with the Manchester, Midland, Mid Cheshire, Liverpool County and West Cheshire League, will operate on the National League System level four from next season. Padiham FC are the last club to be accepted on the old method of direct application and we congratulate them on their return to the NWCFL and wish them well.

Our main sponsors, SGL Leyland, have completed their agreement after four successful seasons and we have been fortunate to come to a similar arrangement with ASDA Logic and our title now becomes The ASDA Logic West Lancashire League.

Kirkham & Wesham achieved the rare distinction of a Cup and League double, and also unusual was the fact that they led from the front for most of the season in such a competitive league, whereas Dalton United had to come from behind to claim the second place closely challenged by Freckleton, who beat the champions in the last match of the season, but they had left their exciting run in just too late. Dalton also had to take second place to Kirkham in the Richardson Cup. Garstang won the Lancashire Shield after being runners-up to Fulwood Amateur last year, and Milnthorpe Corinthians won the Westmorland Senior Cup for the third time in the last four years. Garstang's efforts in the prestigious Lancashire Shield and also in the President's Cup, where they were taken to a penalty shoot-out in the final by bottom team Whinney Hill, almost cost them worthy promotion, with four defeats and one draw in their last five games.

The League normally operates a two up two down system of promotion/relegation but due to two clubs resigning during the past season and the promotion of Padiham FC only one team will be relegated from the Premier Division (Feniscowles). No clubs will be relegated from Division One, to maintain sixteen teams in each of the two supply divisions.

Five new clubs, BAE Canberra, Crooklands Casuals, Crosshills, Glaxo Ulverston and Todmorden Borough, have all been accepted into Division Two.

FINAL LEAGUE TABLES 1999-2000

PREMIER DIVISION

	P	W	D	L	F	A	Pts
Kirkham & Wesham	30	24	3	3	98	22	75
Dalton United	30	19	4	7	80	47	61
Freckleton	30	17	5	8	60	40	56
Charnock Richard	30	17	4	9	66	45	55
Blackrod Town	30	17	3	10	58	51	54
Barnoldswick United	30	15	4	11	63	56	49
Vickers SC	30	14	6	10	49	41	48
Springfields	30	13	3	14	57	65	42
Leyland Motors Ath	30	12	2	16	53	64	38
Norcross & Warbreck	30	9	7	14	53	66	34
Wyre Villa	30	10	3	17	40	65	33
Eagley	30	9	5	16	43	57	32
Burnley United	30	10	1	19	52	76	31
Fulwood Amateurs	30	8	6	16	55	55	27
Lansil	30	6	7	17	49	86	25
Feniscowles	30	7	3	20	23	63	24

DIVISION ONE

	P	W	D	L	F	A	Pts
Padiham	28	19	5	4	65	28	62
Garstang	28	15	7	6	60	48	52
Wigan SMR	28	13	9	6	57	35	48
Poulton Town	28	11	9	8	42	39	42
Carnforth Rangers	28	14	2	12	50	39	41
Bac Ee Preston	28	12	3	13	54	63	39
Tempest United	28	10	8	10	59	48	38
Lancashire Contsab	28	10	8	10	54	56	38
Milnthorpe Corinthians	28	10	8	10	41	45	38
Fleetwood Hesketh	28	11	4	13	51	54	37
Haslingden St Mary's	28	11	4	13	46	60	37
Blackpool Wren Rvrs	28	9	6	13	48	51	33
Thornton Cleveleys	28	6	10	12	46	57	28
Hesketh Bank	28	8	4	16	39	69	28
Whinney Hill	28	5	5	18	37	57	20

	Champions	Runners-Up
DIVISION TWO	Burnley Belvedere	Turton
RICHARDSON CUP	Kirkham & Wesham	Dalton United
PRESIDENT'S CUP	Garstang	Whinney Hill
BASS TAVERN CUP	Millom	Turton

Right: Whitehaven AFC
Back Row (l-r): David Merner,
Alan McGuiness, George Dixon,
Karl McGrady, John George,
Tony Wedgewood
Front Row (l-r): Graham Lilley,
Craig Robson, Mally O'Hare,
Ryan Woods, Steven Rose

Centre: Windscale
Back Row (l-r): Paul Barwise,
Stephen Hodgson, Mark
Hodgson, Clive Heaney, Vinny
Jackson, Kevin Law, Steve
Hodgson, Stuart Sanderson
Front Row (l-r): Mike McDonald,
Stephen Rogers, Joe Shepherd,
Paul Jackson, Russell Meighan,
Ronnie Hughes

Above: Pre-season friendly: Fulwood Amateurs v Manchester United Youth XI 0-4. The stand of Preston Grasshoppers RUFC is visible in the background. Photo: Richard Burton

MANCHESTER FOOTBALL LEAGUE

President: P Morris

Secretary: Paul Bishop, 21 Church Walk, Stalybridge, Cheshire SK15 1DL
Tel: 0161 303 1581

FINAL LEAGUE TABLES 1999-2000

PREMIER DIVISION

	P	W	D	L	F	A	Pts
Stand Athletic	30	23	4	3	100	32	73
Dukinfield Town	30	17	8	5	73	43	59
Mitchell Shackleton	30	18	4	8	63	40	58
Failsworth Town	30	17	5	8	75	52	56
Atherton Town	30	16	4	10	62	44	52
Wythenshawe Amat.	30	15	6	9	58	44	51
Pennington	30	13	8	9	73	58	47
East Manchester	30	14	2	14	58	65	44
Springhead	30	13	4	13	60	58	43
Urmston	30	9	8	13	55	71	35
Willows	30	10	5	15	61	81	35
Monton Amateurs	30	9	6	15	53	74	33
Prestwich Heys	30	9	5	16	61	62	32
Elton Fold	30	9	5	16	52	65	32
Stockport Georgians	30	6	5	19	52	81	23
BICC	30	1	3	26	32	118	6

DIVISION ONE

	P	W	D	L	F	A	Pts
Sacred Heart	30	22	8	0	79	28	74
Gamesley	30	20	4	6	86	39	64
Wythenshawe Town	30	17	6	7	87	44	57
Whitworth Valley	30	15	9	6	84	63	54
Avro	30	13	12	5	64	38	51
Tintwistle Villa	30	14	7	9	79	66	49
Wilmslow Albion	30	14	6	10	82	65	48
New Mills	30	13	6	11	75	72	45
Breightmet Utd	30	12	6	12	59	49	42
Milton	30	11	5	14	65	70	38
Manchester Royal	30	8	9	13	39	58	33
Hindsford	30	9	3	18	56	78	30
Ashton Athletic	30	6	7	17	29	56	25
Hollinwood	30	6	4	20	54	102	22
Whalley Range	30	6	3	21	43	111	21
Old Altrinchamians	30	3	7	20	32	74	16

PREMIER DIVISION RESULTS CHART 1999-2000

		1	2	3	4	5	6	7	8	9	10	11	12	13	14	15	16
1	Atherton Town	X	7-1	0-3	1-0	0-1	1-1	2-1	1-1	1-1	2-0	3-2	1-2	3-1	0-1	5-3	1-2
2	BICC	2-4	X	2-2	0-5	0-2	1-5	2-2	0-1	2-7	3-4	0-1	1-2	4-1	2-3	2-3	3-4
3	Dukinfield Town	4-2	3-1	X	4-1	4-1	3-1	4-2	2-2	7-1	2-0	1-0	2-4	4-2	1-1	0-0	1-0
4	East Manchester	3-2	8-0	0-1	X	0-1	0-2	0-4	3-1	2-7	2-1	2-1	2-0	3-1	2-1	1-3	0-0
5	Elton Fold	0-0	7-0	3-1	1-2	X	3-4	0-2	5-0	3-4	2-6	3-2	0-6	2-0	4-2	2-3	0-2
6	Failsworth Town	1-3	W-L	3-1	5-1	3-2	X	1-2	2-2	0-3	6-2	3-3	1-1	4-0	3-3	4-2	4-0
7	Mitchell Shackleton	0-3	4-1	0-1	2-0	2-2	2-1	X	2-1	1-0	2-0	4-1	0-3	2-0	3-2	2-3	2-2
8	Monton Amateurs	0-3	5-3	1-4	2-1	3-0	1-3	2-6	X	1-1	2-7	1-1	2-3	2-1	1-2	4-1	3-3
9	Pennington	1-3	0-0	4-3	1-2	1-1	1-3	1-3	4-0	X	2-2	3-2	1-1	2-1	4-1	5-2	1-4
10	Prestwich Heys	1-2	3-0	2-2	3-0	3-1	2-3	0-3	5-1	2-2	X	3-2	0-2	2-2	5-1	1-2	1-2
11	Springhead	2-3	5-1	1-1	4-2	3-2	2-3	3-1	1-2	1-0	3-1	X	1-4	1-1	2-1	4-2	3-1
12	Stand Athletic	1-0	13-0	2-2	7-1	2-0	3-0	3-0	3-0	2-3	2-0	4-0	X	6-0	3-5	5-2	3-0
13	Stockport Georgians	3-2	5-0	1-3	2-3	0-0	1-0	1-3	2-6	3-7	3-3	0-1	2-4	X	4-1	6-2	1-2
14	Urmston	2-4	5-1	1-3	2-5	2-2	0-4	1-1	0-3	2-1	2-0	3-1	2-2	4-4	X	3-3	1-1
15	Willows	1-2	W-L	3-3	4-4	6-2	2-5	0-3	3-2	3-5	1-0	2-3	2-4	3-1	0-1	X	0-2
16	Wythenshawe Amat	3-1	7-0	2-1	2-3	2-0	5-0	0-2	2-1	0-0	3-2	1-4	2-3	2-3	2-0	0-0	X

GILGRYST CUP 1999-2000

FIRST ROUND

Dukinfield Town	v	East Manchester	6-0
Failsworth Town	v	Wythenshawe Amat	1-2
Pennington	v	Monton Amateurs	5-0
Urmston	v	Stand Athletic	2-5
Elton Fold	v	Atherton Town	3-3
Mitchell Shackleton	v	BICC	7-0
Stockport Georgians	v	Springhead	4-1
Willows	v	Prestwich Heys	1-4

QUARTER-FINALS

Dukinfield Town	v	Springhead	2-3
Prestwich Heys	v	Stand Athletic	1-6
Pennington	v	Mitchell Shackleton	3-1
Wythenshawe Amat.	v	Atherton Town	0-2

SEMI-FINALS

Pennington	v	Springhead	2-1
Stand Athletic	v	Atherton Town	0*1

FINAL

Atherton Town	v	Pennington	0*0, 6p5

at Stockport Georgians FC

MURRAY SHIELD 1999-2000

FIRST ROUND

Ashton Athletic	v	Wythenshawe Town	0-2	Avro	v	Manchester Royal	3*2
Gamesley	v	Wilmslow Albion	6*4	Hindsford	v	Milton	3-5
Hollinwood	v	Breightmet Utd	2*0	New Mills	v	Old Altrinchamians	1-0
Whalley Range	v	Sacred Heart	1-3	Whitworth Valley	v	Tintwhistle Villa	4-2

QUARTER-FINALS

Gamesley	v	Hollinwood	2-1	Manchester Royal	v	Milton	0-2
New Mills	v	Whitworth Valley	1-3	Sacred Heart	v	Wythenshawe Town	1-3

SEMI-FINALS

Gamesley	v	Whitworth Valley	3-2	Wythenshawe Town	v	Milton	2-0

FINAL

Gamesley	v	Wythenshawe Town	1-2	at Springhead FC

MANCHESTER LEAGUE PREMIER DIV.

ATHERTON TOWN

Secretary: G Butler, 43 Hope Fold Ave., Atherton, Lancs M29 0BW Tel: 01942 870326
Ground: Howe Bridge Spts Centre, Howe Bridge, Atherton Tel: 01942 884882
Directions: A579 Atherton to Leigh road - Sports Centre 800 yds on left
Colours: Royal/white/royal

DUKINFIELD TOWN

Secretary: Paul Bishop, 21 Church Walk, Stalybridge, Cheshire Tel: 0161 303 0398
Ground: Blocksages Playing Fields, Birch Lane, Dukinfield.
Directions: From Ashton centre follow Kings St, turn left into Chapel St. thenright turn into Foundry St/Birch Lane. Ground 880 yds on right, behind publicbaths.
Colours: All yellow

EAST MANCHESTER

Secretary: D Wilkinson, 76 Sandy Lane, Dukinfield, Cheshire SK16 5NL Tel: 0161 330 4450
Ground: Gorton League Complex, Kirkmanshulme Lane, Gorto.
Directions: Turn into Kirkmanshulme Lane at Belle Vue (A57) junction, groundapprox 880 yards on left after Pink Bank Lane.
Colours: All royal blue

ELTON FOLD

Secretary: Guy Mallinson, 14 Lonsdale St, Bury BL8 2QD Tel: 0161 797 7090
Ground: Bolton Rd Sports Club, Bolton Rd, Bury
Directions: A58 from Bury to Bolton. 1 mile from Bury pass Wellington Pub onright 200 yards turn left into Connaught St. Halfway down turn right in betweenhouses into car park
Colours: Blue & black/black/black

FAILSWORTH TOWN

Secretary: David Walton, 45 Woodend Street, Oldham, Lancs Tel: 0161 627 5480
Ground: GMT White House, Heaton Park, Manchester
Directions: M66 junc 5 towards Manchester, ground approx 1mile on right behindWhite House GMT Club.
Colours: Black & white/white/white

MITCHELL SHACKLETON

Secretary: Ian Street, 11 Senior Road, Peel Green, Eccles, M30 7PZ Tel: 0161 789 7061
Ground: Salteye Pk, Peel Green, Eccles Tel: 0161 788 8373
Directions: Leave M63 at Peel Green r'bout (jct 2), take A57 Liverpool Roadtowards Irlam, ground entrance half mile on left behind Kara Cafew opposite Barton airport. Or, follow A57 from Manchester via Salford & Eccles, then follow Irlam signs.
Colours: Green & white/black/black

MONTON AMATEURS

Secretary: T Lee, 28 Wheatley Rd, Swinton, Manchester M27 3RW Tel: 0161 793 8033
Ground: Granary Lane, Worsley
Directions: From Eccles Centre turn right into Worsley Rd at Patricroft Bridge.Ground approx 1 mile on left, entrance just before Bridgewater Hotel
Colours: All royal

PENNINGTON

Secretary: Joanne Hindley, 30 Sycamore Road, Atherton, Manchester (01942897273)
Ground: Jubilee Park, Leigh Rd, Atherton (01942 894703).
Directions: The entrance to the pathway to the ground is approx. 1 mile from Leigh Centre on the left hand side of the B5215 Atherton Road, the entrance is directly opposite the GMT depot.
Colours: White/blue/blue

PRESTWICH HEYS

Secretary: Stephen Howard, 28 Brandram Road, Prestwich, Manchester M25 1HJ Tel: 0161 773 4408
Ground: Sandgate Rd, Prestwich Tel: 0161 773 8888
Directions: Follow Old Bury Rd (A665) from Manchester to Prestwich, right intoHeywood Rd, 3rd left into Mount Rd/Sandgate Rd - ground on right.
Colours: Red & white/red/red

SACRED HEART

Secretary: Joe Devlin, 61 Buersil Ave., Rochdale, Lancs. OL16 4TR Tel: 01706 712602
Ground: Fox Park, Belfield Mill Lane, Rochdale
Directions: From Rochdale town centre follow the A640 to Milnrow, at Kingsway junction turn left into Albert Royds Street and turn right again into Bellfield Mill Lane.
Colours: All red

SPRINGHEAD

Secretary: K Gibson, 1 Little Oak Close, Lees, Oldham OL4 3LW   Tel: 0161 627 3760
Ground: St John St, Lees, Oldham (0161 627 0260).
Directions: From Oldham (Mumps r'bout) follow A669 towards Lees for approx onemile, left into St John St, ground 500yds on right.
Colours: Black & red/black/black

STAND ATHLETIC

Secretary: T H Edwards, 3 Burndale Drive, Unsworth, Bury BL9 8EN Tel: 0161 766 3432
Ground: Elms Playing Fields, George Street, Whitefield.
Directions: From Manc. city centre proceed via Bury New Rd (A56) to Whitefield.George St. is on right just before Fire Station. Car park & changing facilitiesare at Whitefield Community Centre in Green Lane, off George Str.
Colours: Yellow/black/yellow

STOCKPORT GEORGIANS

Secretary: Ged Newcombe, 7 Chiltern Close, Hazel Grove, Stockport SK7 5BQ Tel: 0161483 0004
Ground: Cromley Rd, Stockport, Tel: 0161 483 6581
Directions: Follow A6 from Stockport centre, turn right at Cemetery intoBranhall Lane. After 1 mile turn left at r/about into Woodsmoor Lane. Take 1st right Flowery Fields then right into Cromley Road
Colours: Purple/white/black

URMSTON

Secretary: Sean Brett, 3 Shuttleworth Close, Whalley Range, Manchester Tel: 0161 881 1962
Ground: Flixton Park, Flixton Road.
Directions: M63 junc 3 take Barton Rd to r/about. Then 3rd turning intoBayswater Rd. To r/about, take 2nd left Bowfell Rd, joins Flixton Rd, ground onleft.
Colours: Royal & white/royal/royal

WILLOWS

Secretary: Frank Miller, 11 Edmund Street, Salford, Manchester (0161 737 2411)
Ground: Salteye Park, Peel Green, Eccles
Directions: From Eccles town centre take A57 and pass under M63 at Peel Green Roundabout, after approx. 400 yds turn left into a lay-by, the changing rooms are just behind Kara Cafe. For matchday contacts telephone Willows Club 0161 736 1451
Colours: All red

WYTHENSHAWE AMATEURS

Secretary: John Sobierajsh, 5 Wensley Drive, Withington, Manchester Tel: 0161 445 3415
Ground: Longley Lane, Northenden Tel: 0161 998 7268
Directions: Princess Parkway from Manchester to Post House hotel, via PalatineRd & Moor End Rd to Longley Lane - ground entrance opposite Overwood Rd.
Colours: Blue & white stripes/blue/blue

ASHTON ATHLETIC

Secretary: Steve Halliwell, 20 Kings Road, Golborne, Warrington Tel Nos: 01942 517728 (H) 0374 180165 (M)
Ground: Brocstedes Park, Farm Road , N Ashton, Wigan (01942 716360).
Colours: Yellow & Black stripes/ Black/ Black

AVRO

Secretary: Karen Birch, 27 Brooks Drive, Failsworth, Manchester M35 0L5 (0161 682 6731)
Ground: Lancaster Club, Broadway, Failsworth
Colours: Red & Black/red/red

B.I.C.C.

Secretary: L. Stone, 51 Coppleridge Drive, Crumpsall, Manchester M8 4PB   Tel: 0161 740 6621
Ground: B.I.C.C. Works, Blackley New Road, Blackley.
Colours: Blue & white/blue/blue

BREIGHTMET UNITED

Secretary: Raymond Walsh, 94 Hatherleigh Walk, Breightmet, Bolton (01204435197)
Ground: Moss Park, Back Bury Rd, Breightmet, Bolton (01204 33930).
Colours: Black & white stripes/black/red

HINDSFORD

Secretary: Samantha Evans, 17 Belmont Avenue, Atherton M46 9RR RTel Nos: 01942 895869 (H) 07767 492411 (M)
Ground: Squires Lane, Tyldesley
Colours: Red /blue/red & blue

HOLLINWOOD

Secretary: Ken Evans, 20 Meadow Rise, High Crompton, Shaw, Oldham OL2 7QG (01706840987).
Ground: Lime Lane, Hollinwood (0161 681 3385).
Colours: Yellow & Navy/ Navy / Navy

LEIGH ATHLETIC

Secretary: Mark Harrison, 12 penleach Ave., Leigh, Lancs. WN7 2HJ
Ground: Madley Park, Charles St., Leigh
Colours: Yellow/ Blue/ Blue

MANCHESTER ROYAL

Secretary: N Kinvig, 3 Cranleigh Drive, Cheadle (0161 491 0824)
Ground: Barnes Hospital, Cheadle.
Colours: Red & black/black/black

MILTON

Secretary: Andrew Cole, 21 Whittle Drive, Shaw, Oldham OL2 8TJ Tel Nos: 01706 291973 (H) 0771 8331262 (M)
Ground: Athletic Stadium, Springfield Pk, Rochdale.
Colours: Green& Black,Black/Black

NEW MILLS

Secretary: Barry Land, 165 Lowleighton Rd, New Mills, High Peak SK22 4LR
Ground: Church Lane, New Mills (01663 747435).
Colours: Amber/black/black

OLD ALTRINCHAMIANS

Secretary: P Lewis, 10 Woodfield Grv, Sale, M33 6JW (0161 973 7082)
Ground: Crossford Bridge Playing Fields, Meadows Rd, Sale.
Colours: Black & white stripes/black/black

TINTWISTLE VILLA

Secretary: William Higginbottom, 61 West Drive, Tintwistle, Glossop (01457852467)
Ground: West Drive, Tintwistle
Colours: Black & white stripes/black/black

WHALLEY RANGE

Secretary: Ronnie Lapsley, 16 Mosswood Park , Didsbury, Manchester M20 5QW (0161 613 5467).
Ground: Kings Rd, Chorlton (0161 881 2618).
Colours: Red & black stripes/black/black

WHITWORTH VALLEY

Secretary: Alan Riley, 31 John Street, Whitworth, Rochdale OL12 8BT Tel Nos: 01706 852619 (H) 07930 543924 (M)
Ground: Rawstron Str, Whitworth (01706 853030).
Colours: Black & white/black/red

WILMSLOW ALBION

Secretary: Norma Winn, 236 Derbyshire Lane, Stretford, Manchester (0161 2869520)
Ground: Oakwood Farm, Styal Road, Wilmslow
Colours: Green & White/ Green/ Green

WYTHENSHAWE TOWN

Secretary: Ray Pattison, 68 Westgatel Gardens, Royal Oak Est. Baguley M23 1BA (0161 374 3086)
Ground: Ericstan Pk, Timpson Rd, Baguley, Manchester (0161 998 5076)
Colours: All royal Blue

UNOFFICIAL PYRAMID OF NORTH WEST AMATEUR LEAGUES BELOW NORTH WEST COUNTIES LEAGUE
compiled by Alan Wilson

	1	2	3	4	5
A	LIVERPOOL CO COMB	WEST CHESHIRE	MID-CHESHIRE	MANCHESTER	WEST LANCASHIRE
B	I ZINGARI LEAGUE			LANCASHIRE AMATEUR	
C	I ZINGARI COMB	SOUTH WIRRAL	LANCASHIRE & CHESHIRE AMAT		PRESTON & DIST
D	ST HELENS & DIST COMBINATION (and column 3)	BIRKENHEAD & WIRRAL	CREWE & DISTRICT	BOLTON & DISTRICT AMAT. COMB.	
				STOCKPORT	NORTH LANCS & DISTRICT
	WIGAN & DISTRICT AMATEUR (and column 5)	CHESTER & DISTRICT	WARRINGTON & DISTRICT (and column 1)	EAST LANCASHIRE	
E	ACCRINGTON COMBINATION (5) ALTRINCHAM & DISTRICT (3-4) BLACKBURN & DISTRICT COMB (5) BLACKPOOL & FYLDE COMBINATION (5) BURNLEY & DISTRICT (5) BURY & DIST. AMATEUR (4-5) CHORLEY & DISTRICT AMATEUR (5) DARWEN AMATEUR (5) EAST CHESHIRE (3-4) LEIGH & DISTRICT AMATEUR (4) LIVERPOOL C.M.S. (1) LIVERPOOL OLD BOYS AMATEUR(1) MANCHESTER AMATEUR (4) ROCHDALE ALLIANCE (4) SOUTHPORT & DISTRICT AMATEUR (1 & 5) SOUTH EAST LANCASHIRE (4)				

( ) Column position

Notes about the Pyramid:

Level A represents the highest playing standard. most of those listed at Level E are leagues whose quality of play is unknown to me, therefore they may be placed at either Level C, D or E.

Of the 37 leagues listed altogether, just six have provided the following number of clubs, during the North West Counties' 17 seasons:

Manchester	9	Mid-Cheshire	5	West Lancashire	5
Liverpool Combination	1	Preston	1	Warrington	1

Three of these clubs have gained promotion to the Northern Premier League:
Bamber Bridge (P)   Flixton (M)   Trafford (MC)

Sources:
Lancashire FA and Manchester FA Directories
Lancashire Evening Post, Liverpool Echo, Manchester Evening News
Non-League Club Directory (various)

Further Reading
West Cheshire League 100 Years History, Dave Edmunds, 1991
Mid-Cheshire League Golden Jubilee History, Paul Lavell, 1998
I. Zingari League Centenary, Reg Kirkpatrick, 1997
85 Years of the Lancashire Amateur League, Alan Thompson, 1984
A Centenary of Warrington Football, Bob Smith, 1996

NORTH WESTERN FINAL LEAGUE TABLES 1999-2000

CARLISLE & DISTRICT LEAGUE

	P	W	D	L	F	A	Pts
C.M.C.	24	21	1	2	91	27	64
Northbank	24	17	2	5	62	26	53
Wigton	24	17	1	6	82	48	52
Hearts	24	13	3	8	77	41	42
Abbeytown	24	10	9	5	49	33	39
Emp. Palace	24	12	2	10	60	42	38
Gretna	24	11	3	10	67	47	36
Silloth	24	8	4	11	54	59	28
Longtown	24	7	6	11	45	41	27
Carlisle City	24	6	7	11	56	53	25
Cockermouth	24	6	5	13	40	43	23
Portland	24	6	4	14	40	70	22
N Lakeland	24	0	0	24	16	212	0

I ZINGARI LEAGUE

Premier Division

	P	W	D	L	F	A	Pts
Aigburth PH	26	19	4	3	89	32	61
East Villa	26	18	4	4	68	28	58
St Philomena's	26	16	4	6	66	42	52
NELTC	26	12	9	5	43	27	45
Quarry Bank OB	26	11	10	5	60	38	43
Edge Hill BCOB	26	12	6	8	52	43	42
Old Xaverians	26	12	1	13	51	40	37
ROMA	26	9	5	12	46	60	32
Mills	26	9	2	15	39	67	29
REMYCA United	26	7	5	14	35	51	26
Sacre Coeur FP	26	7	5	14	43	69	26
St Mary's COB	26	6	5	15	29	58	23
Warbreck	26	4	6	16	31	62	18
Dista	26	4	6	16	42	74	18

Division One

	P	W	D	L	F	A	Pts
Hill Athletic	22	15	5	2	67	38	50
Stoneycroft*	22	15	3	4	74	31	47
Liverpool NALGO	22	12	2	8	44	35	38
Collegiate OB*	22	9	6	7	44	43	35
Old Holts	22	10	4	8	55	45	34
Focus	22	9	6	7	55	45	33
Maghull Town*	22	10	4	8	60	52	31
Sefton & District*	22	9	3	10	40	55	30
Home Office	22	8	4	10	59	59	28
Kinsela's*	22	5	6	11	48	55	24
Leyfield*	22	3	4	15	35	66	13
De la Salle OB	22	2	3	17	34	91	9

SOUTHPORT & DISTRICT AMATEUR LEAGUE

	P	W	D	L	F	A	Pts
Birchfield Reserves*	20	16	2	2	72	20	41
St Paul's*	20	10	6	4	68	39	39
EL2	20	11	5	4	62	30	38
Formby Dons 'A'	20	12	2	6	53	31	38
The Dales*	20	10	2	8	62	50	35
Formby Dons 'B'*	20	8	6	6	50	44	33
Formby JSCOB 'B'	20	9	3	8	58	46	30
Southport YMCA	20	7	1	12	46	47	22
Gates	20	5	1	14	46	81	16
Formby JSCOB 'A'	20	4	2	14	24	75	14
Redgate Rovers	20	3	0	17	24	102	9

SOUTH WIRRAL LEAGUE

Premier Division

	P	W	D	L	F	A	Pts
Charing Cross	21	19	1	1	98	26	58
Grange Athletic	22	15	2	5	73	25	47
Vancer	22	12	4	6	61	34	40
Pavilions Reserves	22	12	2	8	54	38	35
Avon Athletic	22	9	4	9	48	53	31
Manor Athletic Res	22	8	3	11	45	57	27
Bronze Social	22	8	3	11	49	70	27
Mersey Ferries*	21	8	5	8	45	66	26
Tricorn	22	8	2	12	48	55	26
Rangers Breaks	22	7	3	12	40	61	24
Ashville 'A'	22	6	5	11	40	53	23
Willaston	22	0	4	18	19	83	4

ST HELENS COMBINATION

Premier Division

	P	W	D	L	F	A	Pts
Carr Mill	22	18	2	2	97	24	56
Shoe FC	22	18	2	2	73	23	56
Penlake Juniors	22	15	4	3	66	33	49
Child Reserves	22	14	1	7	86	32	43
Pilkington Reserves	22	12	4	6	65	40	40
Rainford North End	22	11	1	10	53	56	34
Old Congs	22	8	2	12	45	72	26
Gerard Arms	22	7	3	12	48	50	24
Haresfinch Social	22	6	2	14	36	61	20
East Sutton Labour	22	4	1	17	31	74	13
Carborundum	22	4	1	17	23	82	13
Prescot Leisure Res	22	2	3	17	27	99	9

A & M BUILDERS SHROPSHIRE COUNTY LEAGUE

PREMIER DIV

	P	W	D	L	F	A	Pts
Belvidere	26	19	3	4	79	32	60
Wem Town*	26	16	7	3	66	38	52
Weston Rhyn	26	15	6	5	55	35	51
Broseley Town	26	14	6	6	54	41	48
Hanwood United	26	13	4	9	45	39	43
Belle Vue O B*	26	13	6	7	54	43	42
Ironbridge Town	26	11	5	10	50	42	38
Wellington Ams	26	11	3	12	44	41	36
Tibberton United*	26	11	4	11	58	52	34
Star Reserves	26	6	6	14	29	51	24
Morda United Rs	26	6	5	15	35	49	23
Meole Brace	26	5	5	16	38	64	20
Oakengates Tn	26	5	2	19	35	84	17
Shifnal Utd 97	26	4	4	18	36	67	16

DIVISION ONE

	P	W	D	L	F	A	Pts
Broseley Jnrs	22	14	6	2	60	26	48
Haughmond	22	13	3	6	54	27	42
Drayton Town	22	13	2	7	54	47	41
Highley Welfare	22	11	4	7	46	36	37
Craven Arms	22	10	6	6	54	31	36
Ellesmere Rngrs	22	10	3	9	41	42	33
Church Stretton T	22	8	8	6	48	38	32
Telford Juniors	22	10	2	10	53	50	32
Sutton Albion	22	7	2	13	49	54	23
Ironbridge T Rs	22	7	2	13	37	57	23
Snailbeach W S	22	7	2	13	34	62	23
Brown Clee	22	1	2	19	17	77	5

* points deducted

389

NORTH WESTERN FINAL SUNDAY LEAGUE TABLES 1999-2000

ROCHDALE SUNDAY LEAGUE

PREMIER DIV.	P	W	D	L	F	A	Pts
Heywood Casuals	16	13	1	2	61	15	40
Littleborough	16	12	3	1	42	15	39
Dog & Partridge	16	12	1	3	60	22	37
Dicken Green	16	6	3	7	41	36	21
Greyhound	16	6	3	7	41	36	21
New Victoria	16	6	2	8	30	42	20
Birches	16	6	1	9	27	37	19
Inter Cricketers	16	2	1	13	11	61	7
Highfield Hospital	16	1	1	14	22	70	4

PIONEER BOLTON SUNDAY LEAGUE

DIVISION ONE	P	W	D	L	Pts
Astley Miners	20	18	1	1	55
Cross Guns	20	15	2	2	47
King William	20	13	3	4	42
Horwich RMI	20	12	3	5	39
Cattle Market	20	10	2	8	32
Lodge Bank	20	7	5	8	26
Spread Eagle	20	8	1	11	25
Cheetham Arms	20	6	3	11	21
Masons Arms	20	6	1	13	19
Astley Bridge	20	2	1	17	7
Plus Limited	20	1	2	17	5

WYTHENSHAWE & DISTRICT SUNDAY LEAGUE

PREMIER DIV	P	W	D	L	F	A	Pts
Cornishman Temple	18	15	3	0	31	20	48
Irlam Catholics	18	11	2	5	52	30	35
Trafford Hawks	18	12	3	3	56	24	29
Royal Oak Town	18	8	0	10	39	45	24
Kelly's Celtic	18	6	5	7	42	47	23
Black Boy	18	6	2	10	41	49	20
Farmers Arms	18	5	4	9	44	55	19
Wilmslow Albion	18	4	6	8	44	61	18
Wendover	18	5	2	11	43	66	17
Thorn Cross	18	4	1	13	33	70	13

ALTRINCHAM SUNDAY LEAGUE

PREMIER DIV	P	W	D	L	F	A	Pts
Nelson	20	17	1	2	64	25	52
Brookland Tap	20	15	2	3	53	26	47
Stonemasons	20	10	4	6	52	40	34
Portland	20	9	4	7	51	52	31
Lisbon	20	8	2	10	38	42	26
Jacksons	20	7	4	9	41	46	25
Hale Barns	20	6	3	11	41	53	21
Ashton Rangers	20	6	3	11	38	52	21
Davyhulme	20	6	3	11	48	70	21
Navigation	20	4	8	8	34	38	20
Trafford	20	4	2	14	27	49	14

STOCKPORT & DISTRICT SUNDAY LEAGUE

PREMIER DIV	P	W	D	L	F	A	Pts
Norris Albion	20	19	0	1	96	11	38
Offerton United	20	14	4	2	82	22	32
Carnforth	20	14	2	4	70	36	30
Rifle Volunteer	20	10	6	4	51	38	26
Cheadle Lions	20	9	2	9	50	54	20
Mount Villa	20	8	3	9	39	50	19
St/port Lads Club	20	8	1	11	49	60	17
Devonshire	20	5	4	11	49	60	14
Offerton Green	20	6	0	14	41	62	12
Cherry Tree Athletic	20	6	0	14	43	70	12
Medoak	20	0	0	20	18	125	0

DIVISION ONE	P	W	D	L	F	A	Pts
Victoria Park	22	17	3	2	77	38	37
Reddish Vale	22	16	2	4	83	41	34
Millbrow	22	14	5	3	69	38	33
Ashwood United	22	12	5	5	53	35	29
Monarch	22	8	7	7	68	55	25
S/port County SC	22	8	4	10	42	54	20
Dilke Celtic	22	7	6	9	35	51	20
Higher Poynton	22	7	5	10	43	45	19
Hillgate Spartans	22	6	3	13	49	60	17
Great Moor	22	5	2	15	47	70	12
Cheadle	22	2	8	12	32	70	12
Carnforth Reserves	22	2	6	14	26	67	10

LIVERPOOL & DISTRICT SUNDAY LEAGUE

PREMIER DIV	P	W	D	L	F	A	Pts
Sandon	22	21	0	1	88	18	63
Britannia	22	17	1	4	58	32	52
Allerton	22	12	5	5	44	33	41
Seymour	22	11	3	8	54	42	36
Pineapple	22	11	2	9	42	36	35
Rob Roy	22	10	3	9	44	33	33
Almithak	22	10	3	9	49	54	33
Oyster	22	6	6	10	35	39	24
Lobster	22	5	6	11	35	41	21
Fairfield	22	5	4	13	35	68	19
Blue Union	22	3	5	14	31	50	14
Tithebarn	22	0	4	18	32	100	4

BLACKPOOL & FYLDE FOOTBALL ALLIANCE

PREMIER DIV	P	W	D	L	F	A	Pts
Mammas	22	17	2	3	73	26	53
Clifton Co-op	22	16	2	4	68	19	50
The Bull Villa	22	13	2	7	63	40	41
Whitheads TV	22	12	5	5	59	40	41
G Holiday Flats	22	12	4	6	59	43	40
FC Anchorsholme	22	9	4	9	52	43	31
FC Matrix	22	10	4	8	51	55	31
Fleetwood Freeport	22	8	4	10	53	57	28
H & A Club	22	9	0	13	50	54	27
McMillan	22	6	0	16	25	61	18
Lancs D Glazing	22	3	1	18	32	69	7
Christ the King	22	2	2	18	28	106	5

NORTHERN COUNTIES EAST FOOTBALL LEAGUE

FEEDER TO: NORTHERN PREMIER LEAGUE

President: H F Catt   Chairman: C Morris

Secretary/Treasurer: B Wood, 6 Restmore Avenue, Guiseley, Leeds LS20 9DG
Tel/Fax: 01943 874558

My review of the 1998-99 season as usual begins with a look at the playing records of our clubs outlining the successes and failures throughout that time.

The promotion system between the NCE and the Unibond League at the end of the 1998-99 season was definitely geared to the town of Ossett where Albion were very disappointingly denied a move upwards as Premier Division Champions but Ossett Town took advantage of their second place to move to the higher level and have proved, again, that the quality of NCE teams feeding to the Unibond are well able to make an impact in that sphere. After 'free-falling' through the Unibond's two divisions (as Buxton had done previously) the League welcomed former NCE club Alfreton Town to its ranks as the Unibond's relegated club.

After the success of Ossett last season there was considerable interest in how the NCE's remaining club, Ossett Albion, would fare this time and Unibond relegated club, Alfreton Town, indicated their intentions by promising season ticket holders a money-back guarantee if they did not make a quick move back up the 'Pyramid'. Last season's third-placed club, Brigg Town, were also expected to prove formidable opposition to other Premier Division championship contenders and they took the lead back in September surrendering it for a short while at Christmas to Hallam. However, at the turn of the year there were a number of clubs in contention including Liversedge and Glasshoughton Welfare but, dangerously in fourth place and just behind the leading group, were North Ferriby United.

In February, it did seem that if both leading contenders could hold their nerve the Humber Bridge would separate the eventual honours teams with Ferriby now in second position. Brigg suffered a couple of reverses towards the end of March and perhaps the crucial fixture was on the 20th April when United fought out an away 0-0 draw at the Hawthorns. In the end there was just a four point margin between the two clubs with North Ferriby winning the Premier Division Championship and a promotion place in the Unibond League.

As no club is to be demoted from the Unibond League to take Ferriby's place, next-to-bottom Staveley MW escape the drop and bottom club Thackley remain in the Division because Maltby Main have failed to meet the League's grading requirements and the decision reached in October last year will now be implemented to move them down to Division One. Finally, just a word of praise for Brodsworth MW who just two seasons ago were fourth from bottom in Division One and finished this season sixth in the top flight.

In Division One Goole joined from the Central Midlands League following two successive promotions in that competition and gave immediate notice of their intentions to win a further championship - this time at an even higher level. Initial competition came from Hall Road Rangers and Winterton Rangers with Worsbrough Bridge MW and Glapwell along with other newcomers Mickleover Sports all having spells of ascendancy just behind the leaders. As a fitting tribute to the club's Chairman and chief motivator, Mike Norman, who died in January, Goole took the Division One title in early April with Glapwell eventually eleven points behind occupying runners-up spot. Both clubs have achieved enough off the field in improving their grounds and will be promoted to the Premier Division. At this stage it is not known whether there will be any promotion to the Division from the Central Midlands League though Gedling Town's ground grading is satisfactory for a move up and they have been included in the AGM's Agenda.

In the Reserve Division, Farsley Celtic Reserves have enjoyed an excellent season as champions with just two defeats and a ten point lead over runners-up Ossett Town Reserves. With North Ferriby United Reserves to play locally next season it is likely that the Reserves sides of Harrogate Railway and Pickering Town will join the division.

In our own NCE League Cup Competition Premier Division Garforth Town completed a significant season for retiring manager, Dave Parker, by proving too strong for Division One opponents Glapwell, and taking the cup by a 3-1 margin at Ossett Albion's ground.

The President's Cup was won by all-conquering North Ferriby with a 5-1 aggregate victory over Glasshoughton Welfare whilst the Wilkinson Sword Trophy also went to another successful outfit in Goole who defeated Pontefract Collieries 4-2 over two legs. It is intended to alter the format of the President's Cup from next season when it will be competed for on a conventional knock-out basis by the top eight clubs in each Division with an adjustment for the club promoted to the Unibond League.

The Reserve Division Cup was won for the first time by Liversedge Reserves who defeated Thackley Reserves 2-1 in the Final played at Garforth Town.

In the FA's National competitions, our two leading clubs, North Ferriby United and Brigg Town, both reached the Third Qualifying Round of the FA Cup before bowing out to Unibond League opposition. In the FA Vase, Eccleshill United and Alfreton Town both flew the League's flag until the Fifth Round before going out to North West Counties League opposition. The League was represented at the very last Vase Final at the current Wembley Stadium in May, however, when Bridlington Town, Brigg Town and Guiseley (then an NCE club) were part of a march past of former winners.

The League had the following successes in County Cup competitions.:
East Riding Senior Cup Final: North Ferriby United v Hall Road Rangers 2-1
Lincs Senior 'A' Cup Final: Brigg Town v Lincoln Moorlands 2-0
West Riding County Cup Final: Garforth Town v Eccleshill United 2-0.   *B Wood*

HONOURS LIST 1999-2000

Premier Division	Winners	North Ferriby United	Runners Up	Brigg Town
Division One	Winners	Goole	Runners Up	Glapwell
Reserve Division	Winners	Farsley Celtic Reserves	Runners Up	Ossett Town Reserves
League Cup	Winners	Garforth Town	Runners Up	Glapwell
President's Cup	Winners	North Ferriby United	Runners Up	Glasshoughton Welfare
Wilkinson Sword Trophy	Winners	Goole	Runners Up	Pontefract Collieries
Reserve Division Cup	Winners	Liversedge Reserves	Runners Up	Thackley Reserves
East Riding Senior Cup	Winners	North Ferriby United	Runners Up	Hall Road Rangers
Lincs Senior 'A' Cup	Winners	Brigg Town		
West Riding County Cup	Winners	Garforth Town	Runners Up	Eccleshill United

FINAL LEAGUE TABLES 1999-2000

PREMIER DIVISION

	P	W	D	L	F	A	Pts
North Ferriby Utd	38	25	10	3	87	31	85
Brigg Town	38	25	6	7	73	38	81
Glasshoughton Welf.	38	20	6	12	68	57	66
Liversedge	38	20	5	13	76	45	65
Alfreton Town	38	17	11	10	73	49	62
Brodsworth MW	38	15	10	13	66	69	55
Ossett Albion	38	15	9	14	70	60	54
Arnold Town	38	14	11	13	60	47	53
Selby Town	38	13	14	11	53	49	53
Eccleshill United	38	15	8	15	59	65	53
Armthorpe Welf.	38	14	10	14	45	50	52
Hallam	38	14	9	15	72	67	51
Denaby United	38	13	11	14	46	41	50
Sheffield	38	12	13	13	62	55	49
Garforth Town	38	10	11	17	53	65	41
Harrogate Rail. Ath	38	11	6	21	54	95	39
Maltby Main	38	8	12	18	36	58	36
Buxton*	38	11	6	21	35	67	36
Staveley MW	38	9	8	21	53	83	35
Thackley	38	6	10	22	39	89	28

DIVISION ONE

	P	W	D	L	F	A	Pts
Goole	30	22	5	3	66	19	71
Glapwell	30	18	6	6	74	36	60
Borrowash Victoria	30	14	8	8	48	35	50
Mickleover Sports	30	14	7	9	52	44	49
Bridlington Town	30	15	4	11	43	36	49
Winterton Rangers	30	13	9	8	52	31	48
Yorkshire Amateurs	30	14	5	11	55	37	47
Hall Road Rangers	30	14	5	11	58	49	47
Louth United	30	12	4	14	51	62	40
Worsbrough Bridge MW	30	11	6	13	44	46	39
Pickering Town	30	11	5	14	46	36	38
Parkgate	30	11	5	14	58	59	38
Pontefract Collieries	30	8	9	13	34	50	33
Tadcaster Albion	30	7	3	20	33	84	24
Rossington Main	30	5	7	18	27	62	22
Hatfield Main	30	5	4	21	36	91	19

* points deducted

PREMIER DIVISION RESULTS CHART 1999-2000

		1	2	3	4	5	6	7	8	9	10	11	12	13	14	15	16	17	18	19	20
1	Alfreton Town	X	1-2	2-1	2-1	5-0	0-0	1-0	1-1	0-2	1-2	2-1	4-1	0-0	4-0	3-1	1-3	2-2	0-0	6-2	8-0
2	Armthorpe Welf.	1-0	X	1-0	1-2	0-0	2-1	0-0	1-1	2-1	2-2	0-1	3-0	0-2	1-0	2-3	0-0	1-2	1-1	1-5	1-2
3	Arnold Town	1-2	1-0	X	0-1	2-2	3-1	0-0	2-4	1-0	5-0	4-0	0-2	0-1	0-0	1-3	2-1	3-1	2-1	1-3	5-1
4	Brigg Town	2-1	1-0	4-3	X	0-0	0-1	0-0	4-1	2-0	4-2	0-1	5-2	2-1	1-1	0-0	2-4	5-1	4-1	3-0	1-0
5	Brodsworth MW	1-0	1-4	1-1	1-3	X	3-0	1-3	1-2	2-0	3-2	1-1	0-4	3-5	4-1	3-0	3-2	0-0	1-1	4-1	2-2
6	Buxton	0-3	2-4	1-1	1-2	4-1	X	1-0	2-1	3-1	0-0	0-4	1-2	2-0	1-2	0-1	1-0	0-1	2-1	2-1	1-0
7	Denaby Utd	1-2	0-0	0-1	0-1	3-0	4-1	X	0-2	2-3	1-2	2-0	1-1	2-1	4-1	1-0	1-2	1-2	3-0	1-1	1-2
8	Eccleshill Utd	0-5	3-0	0-1	0-3	0-0	3-1	1-1	X	3-1	6-1	1-1	3-1	3-2	2-1	0-3	1-3	3-0	1-1	2-1	3-3
9	Garforth Town	2-2	1-2	3-1	0-0	3-4	5-1	0-1	3-3	X	2-3	3-3	3-1	0-3	0-0	0-4	0-5	0-0	2-2	1-0	2-2
10	Glasshoughton W	0-0	2-1	1-2	1-3	3-1	3-0	1-2	3-0	3-1	X	2-1	3-1	1-2	1-0	1-2	3-2	1-1	3-0	4-0	1-0
11	Hallam	6-1	7-2	1-1	1-0	2-1	2-1	2-2	5-0	2-1	0-2	X	3-2	1-3	3-2	0-1	2-5	2-2	0-3	5-3	6-2
12	Harrogate Rlwy	1-3	2-3	0-5	0-1	2-3	2-2	2-3	2-0	3-1	2-2	3-2	X	0-10	3-2	0-2	1-0	1-1	1-2	0-0	2-1
13	Liversedge	0-1	1-0	1-1	3-1	2-2	1-2	0-0	0-1	2-2	0-1	2-1	6-0	X	5-0	0-3	1-2	1-0	5-2	0-2	1-0
14	Maltby Main	1-1	0-0	1-3	1-2	0-1	1-1	1-0	3-1	0-2	2-1	1-0	2-1	1-2	X	0-3	0-0	0-0	0-1	6-1	3-1
15	North Ferriby Utd	5-2	0-0	2-1	4-1	4-0	4-0	1-1	3-1	1-1	2-2	3-1	5-2	1-0	1-1	X	1-1	3-1	2-1	5-0	1-1
16	Ossett Albion	2-2	0-0	2-2	1-3	2-4	2-0	2-3	2-1	1-4	0-1	3-1	2-2	0-1	1-1	1-1	X	1-3	3-1	3-2	3-1
17	Selby Town	4-0	4-1	1-1	0-2	1-1	3-0	0-1	0-1	0-1	2-1	1-1	5-2	3-2	0-0	0-1	2-1	X	0-3	3-1	1-1
18	Sheffield	1-1	0-1	1-1	2-3	3-2	0-0	3-0	1-1	0-0	1-2	1-1	5-0	2-4	3-0	1-1	5-2	1-1	X	2-4	5-0
19	Staveley MW	1-1	1-3	1-1	0-3	1-3	1-0	1-1	1-2	1-0	4-2	3-1	1-2	1-3	2-0	1-3	0-2	2-2	1-2	X	2-2
20	Thackley	1-3	0-2	1-0	1-1	0-5	3-0	2-0	2-1	0-2	1-3	1-1	0-1	2-3	1-1	0-7	1-4	1-3	0-2	1-1	X

LEAGUE CUP 1999-2000

FIRST ROUND

Borrowash Victoria	v	Bridlington Main	0-1	Glapwell	v	Hatfield Main	8-0
Tadcaster Albion	v	Pontefracts Collieries	3-4	Yorkshire Amateur	v	Parkgate	2-1

SECOND ROUND

Alfreton Town	v	Ossett Albion	3-2	Buxton	v	Louth United	2-1
Denaby United	v	Bridlington Town	3-0	Glapwell	v	Selby Town	4-1
Hall Road Rangers	v	Goole	2-1	Hallam	v	Eccleshill United	1-5
Harrogate Railway	v	Brodsworth MW	4-0	Liversedge	v	Armthorpe Welfare	3-2
Maltby Main	v	Arnold Town	1-2	North Ferriby Utd	v	Brigg Town	2-1
Pickering Town	v	Rossington Main	4-1	Sheffield	v	Glasshoughton W	4-3
Staveley MW	v	Garforth Town	1-2	Thackley	v	Mickleover Sports	3-2
Winterton Rangers	v	Pontefract Collieries	2-3	Worsbrough Br MW	v	Yorkshire Amateur	4-2

THIRD ROUND

Buxton	v	Pickering Town	0-1	Denaby United	v	Glapwell	0-1
Eccleshill United	v	Harrogate Railway	4-2	Garforth Town	v	Thackley	2-0
Hall Road Rangers	v	Pontefract Collieries	3-4	Liversedge	v	Alfreton Town	2-1
North Ferriby Utd	v	Worsbrough Br MW	3-0	Sheffield	v	Arnold Town	3-2

FOURTH ROUND

Eccleshill United	v	Pontefract Collieries	2-1	Glapwell	v	North Ferriby United	3-0
Pickering Town	v	Garforth Town	0-2	Sheffield	v	Liversedge	5-4

SEMI-FINALS

Eccleshill United	v	Glapwell	3-3, 0-4	Sheffield	v	Garforth Town	2-3

FINAL

Garforth Town	v	Glapwell	3-1

PRESIDENT'S CUP 1999-2000

FIRST ROUND

Armthorpe Welfare	v	Brodsworth MW	1-0	Eccleshill United	v	North Ferriby Utd	1-3
Goole	v	Pickering Town	0-1	Hatfield Main	v	Worsbrough Br MW	2-3

SECOND ROUND

Alfreton Town	v	Denaby United	2-0	Borrowash Victoria	v	Rossington Main	3-1
Bridlington Town	v	Ossett Albion	0-5	Buxton	v	Staveley MW	1-2
Garforth Town	v	Pontefract Collieries	3-1	Glapwell	v	Arnold Town	4-2
Glasshoughton Welf	v	Brigg Town	2-0	Hallam	v	Mickleover Spts	1-1, 2-6
Harrogate Railway	v	Yorkshire Amateur	1-4	Liversedge	v	Winterton Rangers	3-1
North Ferriby Utd	v	Pickering Town	3-1	Parkgate	v	Maltby Main	4-1
Sheffield	v	Louth United	2-0	Tadcaster Albion	v	Hall Rd Rngrs	3-3, 3-4
Thackley	v	Selby Town	1-2	Worsbrough Br MW	v	Armthorpe Welfare	2-4

THIRD ROUND

Alfreton Town	v	Liversedge	2-3	Garforth Town	v	Borrowash Victoria	6-0
Glapwell	v	Hall Road Rangers	3-1	Glasshoughton W	v	Staveley MW	4-3
Mickleover Sports	v	Parkgate	5-2	North Ferriby Utd	v	Ossett Albion	1-0
Selby Town	v	Armthorpe Welfare	4-3	Sheffield	v	Yorkshire Amat	1-1, 1-0

FOURTH ROUND

Glapwell	v	Sheffield	3-0	Glasshoughton W	v	Garforth Town	1-0
Liversedge	v	Mickleover Sports	1-1, 0-3	Selby Town	v	N Ferriby U	1-1,2-4,0-1

SEMI-FINALS

Glasshoughton W	v	Mickleover Sports	2-1	North Ferriby Utd	v	Glapwell	1-0

FINAL 1st Leg

North Ferriby Utd	v	Glasshoughton W	4-0

FINAL 2nd Leg

Glasshoughton W	v	North Ferriby Utd	1-1	North Ferriby United won 5-1 on aggregate

WILKINSON SWORD TROPHY 1999-2000

FIRST ROUND

Bridlington Town	v	Yorkshire Amateur	1-2	Hatfield Main	v	Hall Road Rangers	1-2
Louth United	v	Borrowash Victoria	1-2	Mickleover Sports	v	Pickering Town	2-1
Parkgate	v	Rossington Main	2-1	Tadcaster Albion	v	Pontefract Collieries	0-5
Winterton Rangers	v	Glapwell	0-1	Worsbrough Br MW	v	Goole	1-2

SECOND ROUND

Borrowash Victoria	v	Yorkshire Amateur	1-2	Glapwell	v	Hall Road Rangers	1-6
Parkgate	v	Goole	1-3	Pontefract Collieries	v	Mickleover Sports	5-2

SEMI-FINALS

Goole	v	Hall Road Rangers	3-1	Yorkshire Amateur	v	Pontefract Collieries	1-2

FINAL 1st Leg

Goole	v	Pontefract Collieries	2-1

FINAL 2nd Leg

Pontefract Collieries	v	Goole	1-2	Goole won 4-2 on aggregate

LEADING GOALSCORERS 1999-2000

PREMIER DIVISION

Michael Godber	Sheffield	30
Danny Toronczak	Liversedge	29
Andy Flounders	North Ferriby United	28
Caine Cheetham	Alfreton Town	27
Andrew Cygan	Selby Town	21
Graham Poole	Buxton	21
Richard Dyson	Liversedge	19
Allen Ward	Brigg Town	19
Lee Bradley	Ossett Albion	18
Stephen Davey	Harrogate Railway	18
Craig Elliott	Glasshoughton Welfare	18
Darren Holmes	Hallam	17
Jamie Barnwell	North Ferriby United	16
David Dickinson	Glasshoughton Welfare	16
Stuart Taylor	Eccleshill United	16

DIVISION ONE

Jamie Morgan	Glapwell	22
Chris Parkins	Mickleover Sports	20
Lee Howard	Glapwell	19
Scott Needham	Worsbrough Bridge MW	18
Kevin Severn	Goole	18
Robert Clarke	Glapwell	17
Vernol Blair	Pontefract Collieries	16
Ian Dring	Parkgate	16
Bevan Hudson	Mickleover Sports	16
Jamie Richards	Hall Road Rangers	16
Ian Smith	Parkgate	15
James Little	Yorkshire Amateur	14

ALFRETON TOWN

Secretary: Roger Taylor, 9 Priory Rd, Alfreton, Derbys. DE55 7JT Tel: 01773 835121
Ground: Town Ground, North Street, Alfreton, Derbyshire Tel: 01773 830277.
Directions: M1 junction 28 and follow A38 towards Derby for 1 mile,left onto B600, right at main road to town centre and after half a mile turn left down North Street - ground on right. Half mile from Alfreton (BR) station.buses 242 & 243 from both Derby and Mansfield
Capacity: 5,000   Cover: 1,000   Seats: 350   Floodlights: Yes
Clubhouse: H &C food & drinks on ground. Supporters Club bar outside ground open every day.
Club Shop: Programmes & club souvenirs. Contact Brian Thorpe Tel: 01773 836251

HONOURS   N.C.E. Lg 84-85 (Lg Cup 84-85); Midland Co. Lg 69-70 73-74 76-77 (R-up 71-72 80-81 81-82), Lg Cup 71-72 72-73 73-74; Derbyshire Sen Cup 60-61 69-70 72-73 73-74 81-82 94-95 (R-up 62-63 64-65 77-78 79-80 84-85 87-88 92-93) Div Cup (N) 64-65; Evans Halshaw Floodlit Cup 87-88 95-96; Cent All Lg.R-Up 63-64; NPL Div 1 R-Up 95-96
PREVIOUS   Leagues: Central All.(pre-reformation 21-25) 59-61; Midland (Counties) 25-27 61-82; N.C.E. 82-87; Northern Premier 87-99
BEST SEASON   FA Trophy: 1st Rd Proper 94-95.
FA Cup: 1st Rd 3rd replay 69-70. Also 1st Rd 73-74. - League clubs defeated: Lincoln 24-25
RECORDS   Attendance: 5,023 v Matlock Tn, Central All 60.
Scorer: J Harrison 303   **Win:** 15-0 v Loughborough, Midland Lge. 69-70
Appearances: J Harrison 560   **Defeat:** 1-9 v Solihull FAT 97, 0-8 v Bridlington 92.

FACT FILE

Formed: 1959
Nickname: The Reds
Sponsors: Coldseal Windows
Colours: Red & white/white/red
Change colours: Yellow/blue/yellow
Midweek home matchday: Tuesday
Reserve League: None, Under 13s & 12s
Programme: Pages: 32 Price: £1
Editor: Chris Tacey (01302 722415)

CLUB PERSONNEL

Chairman: Wayne Bradley
Vice Chairman: Dave Gregory

Manager: Jason Maybury
Physio: Mick Jenkins

ARMTHORPE WELFARE

Secretary: Maureen Cottam, The Orchards, Whiphill Lane, Armthorpe, Doncaster DN3 3JP.
Tel: 01302 832514 (H)
Ground: Welfare Ground, Church St, Armthorpe, Doncaster DN3 3AG.Tel:(M)07771 853899 (match days only)
Directions: M18 junc 4, A630, left at r'bout then proceed to next r'bout and turn right. Ground 400yds on left behind Plough Inn. Doncaster (BR) 2 1/2 miles. Buses A2, A3 & 181 pass ground
Capacity: 2,500   Seats: 200   Cover: 400   Floodlights: Yes   **Club Shop:** No
Clubhouse: No. Refreshments on ground. Wheatsheaf Hotel used after matches

HONOURS   Northern Co's East Lg R-up 87-88 (Lg Cup R-up 91-92, Div 1 R-up 83-84, East Central Div 1 84-85); Doncaster & Dist. Lg 82-83 (Div 1 81-82, Div 2 79-80, Div 3 78-79; Lg Cup 79-80 80-81 81-82 82-83; Challenge Cup 82-83); West Riding Chall. Cup 81-82 82-83; Goole & Thorne Dist. Cup 82-83
PREVIOUS   League: Doncaster Senior
BEST SEASON   FA Cup: FA Vase:
RECORD   Attendance : 2,000 v Doncaster R., Charity match 85-86
Appearances: Gary Leighton   **Scorer:** Martin Johnson
Win: 7-0   **Defeat:** 1-7

FACT FILE

Founded: 1926
(Disbanded 1974, re-formed 1976)
Nickname: Wellie
Club Sponsors: Houston Transport
Colours: Green & white hoops,white, green.
Change colours: Navy/white/navy
Midweek matches: Tuesday
Programme: 24 pages
Editor: John Morgan, 01302 834475 (H)

CLUB PERSONNEL

Chairman: Alan Bell, Tel: 01302 833882 (H)
Vice Chairman: James Houston
Comm. Manager: Peter Camm
Press Officer: Sharon Morgan
Manager: Carl Leighton
Asst Manager: John McKeown
Coach: Steve Taylor
Physio: Joey Johnson

ARNOLD TOWN

Secretary: Tony Beale, 6 Elms Gardens, Ruddington, Nottm NG11 6DZ (0115 9211451)
Ground: King George V Recreation Ground, Gedling Rd, Arnold, Notts (0115 9263660)
Directions: From M1 jct 26, take A610 to B6004 (Stockhill Lane) 3 miles to A60. Right at A60, immediate left (St Albans Rd), thru lights byWilkinsons, left onto Hallams Lane. ground on right opposite market. From A1(M)/A614/A60 to lights (Harvester on right), left thru lights to, St Albans Rd then as above. Nottingham Midland (BR) 4 miles. Buses 55,57.58, 59 pass ground. From A6514 left onto A60 for 1/4 m then rt onto Nottingham Rd to town centre by Wilkinsons.
Capacity: 3,400   Seats: 150   Cover: 950   Floodlights: Yes
Clubhouse: Licensed bar open matchdays & training night. Also tea-bar on matchdays
Club Shop: Sells prog, scarves, badges, pennants etc, contact Rob Hornby (0115 974 6769)

HONOURS (Arnold & Arnold Town): Central Mids Lg 92-93 (R-up 88-89, Lg Cup 87-88 (R-up 90-91), F/lit Cup 89-90); NCE Lg 85-86, R-up 83-84, 94-95; Div 1 94-95; Presidents Cup 94-95; Central All 62-63; Notts Snr Cup x10, r-up x 5; Midland Co's Lg R-up 70-71 75-76, Lg Cup 74-75 (R-up 68-69 70-71 80-81). **PREVIOUS Leagues:** Central Mids 89-93. Arnold FC: Bulwell & Dist, Notts Spartan, Notts Comb (pre 55), Central All. 55-63/ Midland 63-82/ NCE 82-86/ Central Mids 86-89. Kingswell: Notts Yth/ Notts Amat./Notts Spartan/ E. Mids Reg.(pre'76)/Midland 76-82/ NCE 82-86/ Central Mids 86-89. **Names:** Arnold FC (founded 1928 as Arnold St Marys) merged with Arnold Kingswell(founded 1962) 1989
BEST SEASON FA Cup:1st Rd replay 77-78 **FA Vase.:** 3rd Rd(3) **FA Trophy:** 2nd Replay 71-2

FACT FILE
Founded: 1989   Nickname: Eagles
Sponsors: Mapperley Sports/Neartone Printers
Colours: Yellow (blue trim)/blue/yellow
Change Colours:All red
Midweek matches: Tuesday
Reserves' Lge: Midland Reg. All
Programme: 48-52 pages 80p
Editor: Rob Hornby (0115 974 6769)
99-00 Captain: Bryn Gunn
Top Scorer : Tristram Whitman (22)
Sup.porters P.O.Y : Peter Davey
Players P.O.Y :. Paul Mitchell

CLUB PERSONNEL
President: Alan Croome
Chairman: David Law
Vice-Chairman: Roy Francis
General Manager: Ray O'Brien
Comm. Manager: Len Robinson
Team Man: Iain McCulloch
Asst Man: Bill Brindley Physio: T.B.A.
Press Officer: Brian Howes (0115 920 7743)

BRIGG TOWN

Secretary: Robert B Taylor, `Highfield House', Barton Rd, Wrawby, Brigg, Lincs DN20 8SH
Tel: 01652 652284 (H) 01724 402749 (W)

Ground: The Hawthorns, Hawthorn Avenue, Brigg (01652 652767) Office: 01652 651605

Directions: From M180 Junc 4 Scunthorpe East, A18 through Brigg leaving on Wrawby Rd, left into East Parade/Woodbine Ave, follow houses on right into Hawthorn Ave. Brigg (BR) 1 mile.
Capacity: 4,000   **Seats:** 250   **Cover:** 2 Stands   **Floodlights:** Yes

Clubhouse: Licensed club open matchdays

HONOURS   F.A. Challenge Vase 95-96; Northern Co's East Lg Presidents Cup R-up 91-92 92-93, R-up 95-96; Lincs Lg 49-50 53-54 73-74 75-76 (Div 1 68-69 69-70 70-71 71-72, Lg Cup 49-50 65-66 68-69 69-70 72-73); Mids Co's Lg 77-78 (Lg Cup 77-78); Lincs `A' Snr Cup 75-76 76-77 94-95; Lincs `B' Snr Cup 54-55 56-57 66-6768-69 84-85

PREVIOUS   **Leagues:** Lindsey; Lincs 48-76; Midland Counties 76-82
Grounds: Manor House Convent, Station Rd (pre 1939); Brocklesby Ox 1939-59

BEST SEASON   FA Vase: Winners 95-96   **FA Cup:**

RECORD   **Attendance:** 2,000 v Boston U. 1953 (at Brocklesby Ox)

FACT FILE

Formed: 1864
Nickname: Zebras
Colours: Black & white stripes/black/red
Change colours: Orange shirts
Midweek Matchday: Wednesday
Programme: 16 pages
Editor: Match Secretary

CLUB PERSONNEL

President: B Robins
Chairman: David Crowder, Tel: 01724 864742 (H)
Match Sec: John Martin. Tel: 01652 654526 (H)
Manager: Ralph Clayton
Coach: John Kaye

BRODSWORTH WELFARE

Secretary: Robert Beswick, 75 Coniston Drive, Bolton-on-Dearne, Rotherham S63 8NE
Tel: 01709 890913

Ground: Welfare Ground, Woodlands, Nr. Doncaster (01302 728380).

Directions: From A1 take A638 to Doncaster, take left after Woodlands Pub into Welfare Road, ground 50yds on left.
Regular bus service from North Bridge Bus Station, Doncaster.
Capacity: 3,000   **Seats:** 228   **Cover:** 400   **Floodlights:** Yes

Clubhouse: Yes, Matchday drinks and snacks   **Club Shop:** No

HONOURS   Yorks Lg 24-25, Donc. & Dist. Lg 84-85 (Lg Cup 85-86, Div 2 78-79, Div 2Cup 78-79), Sheffield Jnr Cup 83-84, Mexborough Montagu Cup 91-92 92-93.R-up N.C.E. Div 1 98-99

PREVIOUS   **Leagues:** Doncaster Snr; Sheffield; Yorkshire.
Name: Brodsworth Main

BEST SEASON FA Cup: **FA Vase:** 3rd Rd 97-98

RECORD   **Fee received:** £2,550 (+ Payments for apps) forDanny Schofield
fromHuddersfield Town, Jan 99

FACT FILE

Founded: 1912
Nickname: Broddy
Colours:Navy & Light Blue/Navy /Navy
Change colours: Purple & White
Midweek home matchday: Wednesday
Programme: 50 pages
Editor: John L. Muldowney

CLUB PERSONNEL

Chairman: Gordon Jennings Tel: 01302 781121
Press Officer & Match Secretary
John Muldowney
Tel: 01302 817173 (H)   07720 832147 (M)
Manager: Neil Brandon
Physio: Eric Beaumont

BUXTON

Secretary / Press Officer: Julie Miszke, 21 Errwood avenue, Buxton. Sk17 9BD
Tel No & Fax : 01335 346211 (office hours)   (H) 01298 70545

Ground : The Silverlands, Buxton, Derbyshire (01298 24733)

Directions: 200 yards of Buxton Market Place, opp. County Police HQ. Buxton (BR) 1/2 mile.
Capacity: 4,000   **Cover:** 2,500   **Seats:** 490   **Floodlights:** Yes
Club Shop: Yes, Pete Scott (01298 79582)
Clubhouse: (01298 23197). Open nightly + Sunday lunchtimes. licensed, no hot food

HONOURS   N.P.L Lg Cup 90-91, Presidents Cup 81-82; Cheshire County 72-73(R-up 46-47 62-63, Lg Cup 56-57 57-58 68-69); Manchester Lg 31-32 (R-up 04-05 28-29 29-30 30-31, Lg Cup 25-26 26-27); Derbys. Sen. Cup 38-39 44-45 45-46 56-57 59-60 71-72 80-81 85-86 86-87.

PREVIOUS   **Leagues:** The Combination 1891-99; North Derbyshire; E Cheshire; Manchester 07-32; Cheshire County 32-73; NLP 73-98.]

BEST SEASON   FA Trophy: Qtr Finals 70-71 71-72.   **FA Vase:** 98-99
FA Cup: 3rd Rd 51-52. 2nd Rd 58-59, 1st Rd 62-63League clubs defeated: Aldershot 51-52

RECORDS   **Attendance:** 6,000 v Barrow, FA Cup 1st rd 51-52
Goalscorer: Dave Herbert   **Fee Paid:** £5,000 for Gary Walker (Hyde Utd)
Appearances: Mick Davis   **Fee Received:** £23,500 for Ally Pickering (Rotherham 89)

FACT FILE

Formed: 1877
Nickname: The Bucks
Sponsors: Triangles, Snooker Hall
Colours: Royal & white halves/royal/royal
Change colours: All yellow with blue trim
Midweek matchday: Tuesday
Programme: 36 pages £1.00
Editor: Tony Tomlinson
99-00 Captain:D.Bainbridge
P.O.Y.: D.Bainbridge
Top scorer: G.Poole

CLUB PERSONNEL

Chairman: B.Goodwin
Manager: Tony Hodkinson
Asst Manager/Coach: David Bainbridge
Reserve Team Manager: Mike Dodd

Top: Alfreton Town
Back Row (l-r): Karl Hammond (coach), Jason Maybury (Player / Manager), Nicky Phelan, Chad Colley, Mark Hopkinson, Richard Harrison, Neil Pickering, Bob Moorwood, Mick Jenkins (Physio), Russ Eagle (Assistant Manager)
Front Row (l-r): Marcus Wood, Darren Schofield, Simon Hennessy, Ryan France, Darren Gradey, Caine Cheetham, Mark Shaw, Nathan Kerry. Photo: Bill Wheatcroft.

Centre: Arnold Town
Back Row (l-r): Danny Heverin, Mark Powell, Stuart Hammonds, Jon Boulter, Neil Wilkinson, Matt Irons.
Middle Row (l-r): Paul Archer, Peter Davey, Kris Maddison, James Mason, Darren Davis, Lee Holmes, Brett Williams.
Front Row (l-r): Adrian Thorpe, Iain McCulloch (Manager), Lee Walshaw, Bill Brindley (Assistant Manager), Tristram Whitman (now Doncaster Rovers)
Photo: Bill Pickering

Bottom: Denaby United.   Photo: Phil Watkins

397

DENABY UNITED

Secretary: Barrie Dalby, 6 Park Lane court,Thrybergh, Rotherham, S.Yorks. 56S 4ET
Tel: 01709 851283 (H)   01709 860764 (B)
Ground: Tickhill Square, Denaby Main, Doncaster. Tel: 01709 864042   **Directions:** From
Conisbrough take first left in Denaby along Wadworth St. From Mexborough take first right after
Milestone Public House, left on to Bolton St. then left on to Wheatley Street. Rail to Conisbrough
Capacity: 6,000   **Seats:** 250   **Cover:** 350   **Floodlights:** Yes
Clubhouse: None   **Club Shop:** Yes
HONOURS Yorks Lg R-up 67-68, Div 2 R-up 66-67, Div 3 R-up 81-82, Lg Cup 71-72; N.C.E. Prem
Div. 96-97, Cup Winners 98-99Div 1 South R-up 83-84; Midland Lg R-up 07-08; Sheffield &
Hallamshire Snr Cup 1905-06,09-10, 32-33 35-36 86-87; Thorn EMI Floodlight Comp. R-up 83-84;
Sheffield Assoc. Lg 40-41; Mexborough Montague Cup (6)
PREVIOUS   Leagues: Sheffield Ass 1900-02 13-18 19-20 40-45; Midland 02-13 20-40
45-60 61-65; Doncaster & Dist. 18-19; Central Alliance 60-61; Yorks 65-82.
Ground: Denaby Recreation Ground 1895-1912.
BEST SEASON   FA Vase: 4th Rd 83-84   **FA Cup:** 1st Rd x 3   **FA Trophy:** 2nd Rd 71-72
RECORDS Attendance: 5,200 v Southport, FA Cup 1st Rd 1927 **Win:** 20-0 v Shirebrook M.W.
(H), Cen. All. 60-61 **Fee paid:** £300 for Kevin Deakin, Mossley 1984 **Fee received:** £3,000 for
Jonathan Brown (Exeter, 1990)
Players progressing: S Cowan (Doncaster 23), R Attwell (W.H.U. 38), W Ardron (Rotherham 43), J Barker (Derby 28), K
Burkinshaw (Liverpool 53), A Barnsley (Rotherham 85), C Beaumont (Rochdale 88), J Brown (Exeter 90)

FACT FILE
Founded: 1895
Nickname: Reds
Colours: Red & white/white/red
Change colours: Royal blue / yellow/blue
Reserves' League: B.I.R. County Sen. Lg.
Midweek matches: Tuesday
Programme: 64 pages £1.00
Editor: Adrian Gillott (01302 856304)
Local press : South Yorks Times, Doncaster
Free Press, Dearne Valley Weekender

CLUB PERSONNEL
Chairman: Jim Dainty
Vice Chairman: T.B.A.
Match Sec.: Derek Mower (01709 329338 H)
President: Alan Wilson
Manager: Peter Daniel
Physio: Jack Bramhall

ECCLESHILL UNITED

Secretary: Ian Gardiner, 14 Tivoli Place, Little Horton, Bradford BD5 0PQ. Tel:01274 226052 (H)

Ground: Plumpton Park, Kingsway, Wrose, Bradford BD2 1PN (01274 615739)

Directions: M62 jct 26 onto M606, right on Bradford Ring Road A6177, left on to A650 for
Bradford at 2nd r'bout. A650 Bradford Inner Ring Road onto Canal Rd,branch right at Staples
(Dixons Car showrooms on right), fork left after 30mph sign to junction with Wrose Rd, across
junction - continuation of Kings Rd, 1st left onto Kingsway - ground 200 yds on right. 2 miles from
Bradford (BR). Buses 624 or 627 for Wrose
Capacity: 2,225   **Seats:** 225   **Cover:** 415   **Floodlights:** Yes
Clubhouse: Open normal licensing hours. Bar, lounge, games room, hot &cold snacks
Club Shop: Sells range of souvenirs. Contact Roy Maule Snr, 01274662428

HONOURS   N.C.E.Div 1 Winners 96-97Div 2 R-up 86-87, Res Div 86-87 89-90, R-up 87-88
94-95)); Bradford Amtr Lg Cup 61-62; Bradford & Dist. Snr Cup 84-85;Bradford & Dist. FA Snr
Cup 85-86; W. Riding County Amat. Lg 76-77 West Riding Cup Finalists 99-00
PREVIOUS   Leagues: Bradford Amat; W Riding Co Amat   **Name:** Eccleshill FC
BEST SEASON   FA Vase: 99-00, 5thRd
RECORDS   Attendance: 715 v Bradford City 96-97
Win: 10-1 v Blackpool Mechs (H), F.A.C /1Q
Defeat: 0-6 v Rossington Main (A), N.C.E. Lge Cup 2nd Rd 92-93, &
v Gt. Harwood T. (A), FA Cup Prel. Rd 91-92

FACT FILE
Founded: 1948
Nickname: Eagles
Colours: Blue & white stripes/blue/blue
Change colours: All yellow
Midweek matches: Tuesday
Reserves' Lge: NCE Res. Div
Programme: 24-28 pages, 50p
Editor: Secretary
Local Press: Bradford Telegraph & Argus,
Bradford Star Free Press
99-00 Goalscorer: Stuart Taylor

CLUB PERSONNEL
Chairman: Keith Firth Tel: 01274 787057 (H)
Press Officer: Bill Rawlings (01274 635753)
Manager: Raymond Price
Physio: Gordon McGlynn

Player to Progress:Terry Dolan (Hudd'sfied U)

GARFORTH TOWN

Secretary: Paul Bracewell, 24 Coupland Rd, Garforth, Leeds LS25 1AD
Tel: 0113 286 3314 (H) 0113 214 1800 (B) 07931 900260 (M)

Ground: Wheatley ParkStadium, Cedar Ridge, Brierlands Lane, Garforth, Leeds LS25 2AA
Tel: 0113 286 4083   Website: www.garforth.town.freeserve.co.uk

Directions: M1 junction 47. Take turning signed 'Garforth' (A642). Approx 200 yards turn left
into housing estate opposite White Ho. (Cedar Ridge). Stadium at end of lane.
Capacity: 3,000   **Seats:** 278   **Cover:** 200   **Floodlights:** Yes
Clubhouse: Full Licensing Hours   **Club Shop:** Yes

HONOURS   N.C.E. Lg Div 1 97-98, R-up 96-97, Div 2 R-up 85-86, Lge Cup 99-00; Yorks Lg
Div 3 R-up 79-80; Barkston Ash Snr Cup 80-81 84-85 85-86 86-87 92-93 94-95;
Wilkinson Sword Trophy 96-97; West Riding County FA Cup 97-98 99-00
PREVIOUS   Leagues: Leeds Sunday Comb 64-72; West Yorks 72-78; Yorks 78-82.
Names: Miners Arms 64-78, Garforth Miners 78-79
BEST SEASON   FA Vase: Q-F 85-86
RECORDS   Attendance: 1,014 Brendan Ormsby Testimonial v Comb. Leeds/A. Villa XI
Goalscorer: Vinnie Archer   **Appearances:** Philip Matthews (82-93)
Record Fee Received: £25k for Andy Watson to Doncaster Rovers 1999
Win: 11-0 v Blidworth Welf, N.C.E.Div. 1 97-98 **Defeat:** 1-7 v Lincoln Utd (A), N.C.E. Div 1 92-93

FACT FILE
Founded: 1964   Nickname: The Miners
Sponsors: Mansfield Breweries
Colours: Yellow/Blue/Yellow
Change colours: Red/black/red
Midweek matches: Wednesday
Reserves' League: NCE Res. Div.
Programme: 32 pages, 50p
Editor: Chris Mather 0113 286 3453 (H)
99-00 Captain: Paul Stevenson
P.o.Y.: Lee Darnbrough
Top Scorer: Duncan Bray (14)

CLUB PERSONNEL
President: Norman Hebbron
Chairman: Stephen Hayle
Press Officer: Ian Coultard 0113 286 8827
Manager/Coach: Dave Harrison
Asst Manager: Phil Hutchinson
Physio: Paul Cavell
Coach: Brendon Ormsby

GLAPWELL

Secretary: Ellen Caton, 111 The Hill, Glapwell, Chesterfield. S44 5LU.
Tel: 01246 854648 (H & Fax) 01623 629123 (B) 0976 838423 (M)

Ground: Hall Corner, Glapwell, Chesterfield, Derbyshire   Tel: 01623 812213

Directions: M1 Junc 29 A617 towards Mansfield, after Young Vanish Inn take filter lane left onto Bolsover Road, ground facing, use rear entrance next to garden centre
Floodlights: Yes

HONOURS Central Midlands Lg 93-94,Floodlit Cup 93-94, NCE Lg Cup Finalists 99-00
Derbyshire Senior Cup Winners 97-98

BEST SEASON   **FA Vase:** 2nd Rd 96-97   **FA Cup:**

FACT FILE

Founded: 1985
Colours: Black & white stripes/white/white
Change colours: All yellow
Midweek matches: Tuesday
Programme: 16 pages,50p
Editor: Jason Harrison
01623 842588 (H)

CLUB PERSONNEL

Chairman: Roger Caton
Manager: Graham Gladwin

Glapwell FC with the Northern Counties East League Division One R U Trophy Photo: Bill Wheatcrof

GLASSHOUGHTON WELFARE

Secretary: Eric Jones, `Marrica', Westfields Ave, Cutsyke, Castleford WF10 5JJ.
Tel: 01977 556257 (H) 01977 514157(B)

Ground: Glasshoughton Welfare, Leeds Rd, Glasshoughton, Castleford (01977518981)

Directions: From M62 use either Junct. 31 or 32 towards Castleford. From Junction 32 the road comes into Glasshoughton. From Junct. 31 turn right at 2nd roundabout at Whitwood Tech. College. The ground is on the left in Leeds Road. Car park on ground. Castleford (BR) 1 mile.
Capacity: 2,000   Seats: None   Covered: 250   Floodlights: Yes

Clubhouse: Bar & refreshment facilities   **Club Shop:** No

HONOURS   West Riding County Cup 93-94

PREVIOUS   **League:** West Yorkshire   **Name:** Anson Sports 1964-76
            Ground: Saville Park 1964-76

BEST SEASON   **FA Vase:**   **FA Cup:**

RECORD   **Attendance:** 300 v Bradford C, 90

FACT FILE

Founded: 1964
Club colours: Blue and white shirts/blue/blue
Change colours: All yellow
Midweek Matchday: Tuesday
Reserves' Lge: N.C.E. Res. Div.
Programme: 20 pages, 20p
Prog. Editor: Nigel Lee (0113 247 6186)-W

CLUB PERSONNEL

President: R Rooker
Chairman: Gordon Day
Tel: 01977 514178 (H)
Match Sec: Barry Bennett
Tel: 01977 682593 (H)
Manager: Wayne Day
Asst Manager/Coach: M Ripley

GOOLE AFC

Secretary:	Malcolm Robinson, 55 Clifton Gardens, Gools, E.Yorks. DN14 6AR Tel: 01405 761078 (H) 07801 092952 (M)
Match Secretary:	Graeme Wilson, 12 Thorntree Close, Goole, E. Yorks DN14 6LN Tel: 01405 763316 (H)
Ground:	Victoria Pleasure Grounds, Marcus St, Goole DN14 6AR Tel: 01405 762794
Directions:	M62 to Junc 36, then follow signs for town centre. Turn right at 2nd lights into Boothferry Rd, then after 300 yards turn right again into Carter St, and the ground is at the end of road.

Capacity: 3000   Seats: 200   Cover: 800   Floodlights: Yes

Club Shop: Yes   **Clubhouse:** Matchdays only

HONOURS   NCE Div. 1 Champions 1999-2000, Div. 1 Trophy 99-00

FACT FILE
Founded: 1997
Colours: Red/ white/ black.
Change Colours: Gold/black/gold & black
Midweek Matchday: Tuesday
Programme Editor: Malcolm Robinson
01405 761078 (H) 07801 092952 (M)

CLUB PERSONNEL
Chairman: Geoffrey Bruines
49A Pinfold Street, Howden, nr Goole,
East Yorks. DN14 7DE
Tel: 01430 430048 (H) 07790 952790 (M)

Manager: John Reed

HALLAM

Secretary:	Richard L Groves, 22 Moorgate Crescent, Dronfield, Sheffield, S181YF. Tel: 01246 413548 (H) 0771 5254323 (M)
Ground:	Sandygate **(The oldest club ground in the world 1860)** Sandygate Road, Crosspool, Sheffield S10 Tel: 0114 230 9484 Two new stands and full access & facilities for wheelchair users.

Directions: A57 Sheffield to Glossop Rd, left at Crosspool shopping area signed`Lodge Moor' on
to Sandygate Rd. Ground half mile on left opposite Plough Inn.   51 bus from Crucible Theatre

Capacity: 1,000   Seats: 250   Cover: 400   Floodlights: Yes   **Club Shop:** Yes
Clubhouse: No, use Plough Inn opposite. Hot & cold snacks on ground for matches
HONOURS   Northern Counties (East) Lg Div 1 R-up 90-91 94-95, Yorkshire Lg Div 2 60-
61 (R-up 56-57), Sheffield & Hallamshire Snr Cup 50-51 61-62 64-65 67-68.
BEST SEASON   FA Vase: 5thRd 80-81**FA Cup:** 3Rd Q Rd 1957 **Previous Lg:** Yorks 52-82
CLUB RECORDS   Attendance: 2,000 v Hendon, FA Amtr Cup 3rd Rd 59
13,855 v Dulwich at Hillsborough, FA Amtr Cup 55)
Goalscorer: A Stainrod 46   **Appearances:** P Ellis 500+
Win: 7-0 v Hatfield Main (H) 92-93, & v Kiveton Park(H) 69-70
Defeat: 0-7 v Hatfield Main (A) 88-89

Players progressing:Sean Connelly (Stockport C), Howard Wilkinson (Sheff. Wed) -The F.A.'s Technical
Director, L Moore (Derby C.)

FACT FILE
Formed: 1860
Nickname: Countrymen
Sponsors: Hallamshire Holdings Ltd.
Colours: Blue/white/blue
Change colours: Red/black/black
Midweek Matches: Wednesday
Programme: Yes 50p
Editor: Mark Radford (Press Off.)
Local Press: Star, Green'Un, Sheffield
Telegraph, Yorkshire Post

CLUB PERSONNEL
Chairman: Tony Scanlan
Tel: 01246 415471 (H)
Vice Chairman: P Fuller
President: A Cooper
Press Officer: Mark Radford
Tel: 0114 249 7287 (H)
Manager: K Johnson
Physio:J.Beachall

HARROGATE RAILWAY ATHLETIC

Secretary:	W Douglas Oldfield, 80 Stonefall Ave., Harrogate, Nth Yorks HG2 7NP Tel: 01423 540786
Ground:	Station View, Starbeck, Harrogate. Tel: 01423 885539
Directions:	A59 Harrogate to Knaresborough road. After approx 1.5 miles turn left just before railway level crossing. Ground is 150 yds up the lane Adjacent to Starbeck (BR). Served by any Harrogate to Knaresborough bus.

Capacity: 3,000   Seats: 300   Cover: 600   Floodlights: Yes

Clubhouse: Games, TV room, lounge. Open normal pub hours. Hot food available.
Club Shop: Yes

HONOURS   Northern Co's (East) Lg Cup 86-87
PREVIOUS   **L eagues:** West Yorkshire; Harrogate District; Yorkshire 55-73 80-82.
RECORD   **Attendance:** 1,400; 1962 FA Amateur Cup

FACT FILE
Founded: 1935   Nickname: The Rail
Sponsors: Calvert Carpets
Colours: Red & green/green/red
Change: All white
Midweek matchday: Monday
Programme Editor: Gordon Ward
Tel: 01423 880423 (H)
Local Press: Yorkshire Post, Harrogate Herald
& Advertiser, York Press

CLUB PERSONNEL
President: J Robinson
Chairman: Dennis Bentley
Comm. Man: T.B.A.
Press Officer/Prog. Editor: Gordon Ward
Tel: 01423 880423 (H)
Manager: P.Marshall
Assistant.Man.: M.Margis
Physio: R.Scarth

LIVERSEDGE

Secretary: Michael Balmforth, 7 Reform St., Gomersal, Cleckheaton BD19 4JX (01274 862123)

Ground: Clayborn Ground, Quaker Lane, Hightown Rd, Cleckheaton, W. Yorks (01274 862108)
Directions: M62 jct 26, A638 into Cleckheaton, right at lights on corner of Memorial Park, through next lights & under railway bridge, 1st left (Hightown Rd) and Quaker Lane is approx 1/4 mile on left and leads to ground. From M1jct 40, A638 thru Dewsbury and Heckmondwike to Cleckheaton, left at Memorial Park lights then as above. Buses 218 & 220 (Leeds-Huddersfield) pass top of Quaker Lane

Capacity: 2,000   **Seats:** 250   **Cover:** 750   **Floodlights:** Yes
Clubhouse: Matchdays, Tues, Thursday. Pool, TV. Snacks **Club Shop:** No

HONOURS   West Riding Co. Chal. Cup 48-49 51-52 69-70; West Riding County Cup 89-90; North Counties East Lg Cup 89-90; West Riding Co.Amtr Lg(6) 23-24 25-27 64-66 68-69 (Lg Cup 57-58 64-65).

PREVIOUS   **Leagues:** Spen Valley; West Riding County Amateur 22-72; Yorkshire 72-82.
Ground: Primrose Lane, Hightown.   **Name:** None

BEST SEASON   **FA Cup:**   **FA Vase:**
Players progressing: Garry Briggs (Oxford), Martin Hirst (Bristol City) Leigh Bromby (Sheffield Wed)

FACT FILE

Nickname: Sedge
Founded: 1910
Colours: All blueAll Red& white
Midweek Matches: Wednesday
Reserves League: NCEL Res. Div.
Programme: 28 pages, 50p
Editor: Secretary
Local Press: Yorkshire Evening Post,
Telegraph & Argus, Spenbrough Guardian

CLUB PERSONNEL

Chairman: Robert Gawthorpe
Press Officer: Secretary
Manager: Eric Gilchrist
Asst Mgr: Tony Passmore

Top: Hallam FC. Back Row (l-r): Guy Glover, Jimmy Pearson, Craig Owen, Mel Sterland, Paul Lodge, Paul Varney, Stuart Lowe, Brendan West, Andrew Sharman, Gary Slack ,John Beachell (Physio). Front Row (l-r): Darren Holmes, Jason Swann, Andy Tibenham, Craig Worsfold, John Oliver, Chris Towey, Mark Smith. Photo: Bill Wheatcroft

Centre: Liversedge FC. Back Row (l-r): Eric Gilchrist (Manager), Andy Yates, Richard Bibby, Dave Thomas, Chris Birkinshaw, Danny Toronczak, Simon O'Hara, Tony Passmore (Assistant Manager). Front Row (l-r): Andy Dodsworth, Paul Sweeney, Richard Dyson, Kevin Blanchard, Michael Carter, James Glover, Paul Slater, Andy Kenton.

Bottom: Ossett Albion. Back Row (l-r): Gerry Quinn (Manager), James Riordan, Gavin Dooley, Mark Whiteley, Dean Johnson, John Hood, Paul Gilbertson, Asa Hatfield, George Grouse (Assistant Manager). Front Row (l-r): Carl Wilcock, Lee Bradley, Malcolm Bolland, Mark Hemingway, Shaun Joyce (Captain), Jon Braime, Chris Cornelly. Photo: Bill Wheatcroft.

OSSETT ALBION

Secretary: David Chambers, 109 South Parade, Ossett, Wakefield, WF5 0BE. Tel:01924 276004 (H)
Ground: Dimple Wells, Ossett (01924 273618-club, 01924 280450-grd)
Directions: M1 jct 40. Take Wakefield road, right at Post House Hotel down Queens Drive. At end right then second left down Southdale Rd. At end right,then first left down Dimple Wells (cars only). Coaches take second left following the road for 200yds bearing left twice. Four miles from both Wakefield and Dewsbury BR stations. Buses 116 and 117
Capacity: 3,000   **Seats:** 200   **Cover:** 500   **Floodlights:** Yes
Clubhouse: 3 bars + function room, open 7 days per week - catering available
Club Shop: Selling various souvenirs & programmes. Contact chairman

HONOURS   Yorks Lg 74-75 (R-up 59-60 61-62, Lg Cup 75-76, 76-77, Div 2 78-79, 80-81 (R-up 58-59)); N.C.E. Div 1 86-87 (Lg Cup 83-84); West Yorks Lg 53-54 55-56 (Div 2 52-53, Lg Cup 52-53); W. Riding County Cup 64-65 65-66 67-68; Wheatley Cup 56-57 58-59
PREVIOUS   **Leagues:** Heavy Woollen Area 44-49; West Riding Co. Amtr 49-50; West Yorks 50-57; Yorks 57-82.   **Ground:** Fearn House
BEST SEASON   FA Cup: FA Vase:
RECORDS   Attendance: 1,200 v Leeds Utd, floodlight opening 1986.   **Win:** 12-0 v British Ropes(H), Yorks. Lge Div. 2 6/5/59   **Defeat:** 2-11 v Swillington (A), W. Yorks. Lge Div. 1 25/4/56   **Goalscorer:** John Balmer   **Appearances:** Peter Eaton, 800+ (22 yrs)

FACT FILE
Founded: 1944
Nickname: Albion
Sponsors: Arco
Colours: Old gold & black/black/gold
Change colours: All white
Midweek matches: Wednesday
Reserves' Lge: NCEL Res Div
Programme: 44 pages, 50p
Editor: N Wigglesworth (01924 275630)
Local Press: Wakefield Express

CLUB PERSONNEL
President: Miss Helen Worth
Chairman: Neville A Wigglesworth
Vice-Chairman: S B Garside
Commercial Man: D Riley 01924 240247
Press Off. Neville Wigglesworth 01924 275630
Manager: Jimmy Martin
Physio: John Hirst
Coach: Peter Eaton

SELBY TOWN

Secretary: T.W.Ardley, 176 Abbots Rd, Selby, N.Yorks.YO8 8AZ Tel: 01757 700356 (H) 07713 413064 (M)
Ground: Flaxley Rd Ground, Richard St, Scott Rd, Selby, N Yorks YO8 0BS.Tel: 01757 210900
Directions: From Leeds, left at main traffic lights in Selby down Scott Rd.then 1st left into Richard St. From Doncaster go straight across main traffic lights into Scott Road then 1st left. From York right at main traffic lights into Scott Rd, and 1st left. 1 mile from Selby (BR)
Capacity: 5,000 **Seats:** 220 **Cover:** 350 **Floodlights:** Yes
Clubhouse: Bar at ground open first and second team matchdays   **Club Shop:** Yes

HONOURS   Yorkshire Lg 32-33 34-35 35-36 52-53 53-54 (R-up 24-25 25-26 27-28 28-29 30-31 31-32 50-51 55-56, Div 3 R-up 74-75, Lg Cup 37-38 53-54 54-55 62-63); N.C.E. Div 1 95-96, Div 2 R-up 89-90; W. Riding Snr Cup 37-38; W. Riding Co Cup 27-28 48-49; W. Riding Chall. Cup 34-35 35-36
PREVIOUS   **League:** Yorkshire (1920-82) Ground: Bowling Green, James St. 1920-51
BEST SEASON   FA Cup: Second Round Proper 54-55   **FA Vase:** Prel Round 89-90
RECORD   Attendance: 7,000 v Bradford Park Avenue (FA Cup 1st Rnd 1953-54)
Players progressing: Numerous

FACT FILE
Founded: 1919
Nickname: The Robins
Sponsors: T.B.A.
Colours: All red
Change colours: Amber/black/amber
Midweek Matches: Tuesday
Reserves' League: N.C.E. Res. Div.
Programme: 30 pages, 50p
Editor: Mark Fairweather, 01757 705376 (H)
Local Newspaper: Selby Times

CLUB PERSONNEL
Chairman: Ralf Pearse, Tel: 0836 336481(M)
President: A Carter
Match Sec: T.B.A.
Manager: B Lyon
Asst Manager:
Coach: P Dooley

SHEFFIELD

Secretary: Stephen Hall, 23 Regent Court, Bradfield Rd, Hillsborough, Sheffield S6 2BT
          Tel: 0114 233 4441 (H), 01246 258918 (B)
Ground: (1) Don Valley Stadium, Worksop Rd, Sheffield S9 3TL (0114 256 0607)
          & **(2)** Coach & Horses Ground, Sheffield Road, Dronfield. (**Check with secretary**)
Directions: (1) M1 Junc 33, dual carriageway sign City centre, take 2nd exit A57. End of slip rd, rt, rt again at lights. Left at lights at rear of Morrison's t.Road passes under bridge, ground on right
(2) C&H - M!, J 29, A617 into Chesterfield. At traffic island turn right onto dual carriageway A61 (Sheffield). Follow over 2 islands & at 3rd follow sign 'Dronfield/Gosforth Valley'. At entrance to Dronfield, C&H ground is at bottom of hill on the right.
Capacity: 25,000   **Seats:** 25,000   **Cover:** 13,000   **Floodlights:** Yes
Clubhouse: Licensed Bar   **Club Shop:** No
HONOURS   FA Amateur Cup 03-04; FA Challenge Vase Runners-up 76-77; Northern Co's East Lg Cup 94-95 (Div 1 88-89 90-91); Yorkshire Lg Div 2 76-77
PREVIOUS   **League:** Yorks 49-82 Grounds: Abbeydale Park, Dore (1956-1989);Sheffield Amateur Sports Club, Hillsborough Park 1989-91; Sheffield International (Don Valley) Stadium 1991-94; Sheffield Sports Stadium 94-97.
BEST SEASON   FA Cup: FA Vase: R-up 76-77
RECORD   Attendance: 2,000 v Barton Rovers, FA Vase SF 76-77
Player progressing: Richard Peacock, Hull 94-95

FACT FILE
Founded: 1857
Nickname: The Club
Sponsors: Bumford Heating
Colours: Red & black halves/black/black
Change: All blue
Midweek matchday: Wednesday
Programme: 16 pages, 50p
Editor: David Dean (0114 232 5901)

CLUB PERSONNEL
Chairman: Richard Tims
Tel: 0114 2728888 (B)
President: Alan Methley

Manager: John Pearson
Asst Manager:

STAVELEY MINERS WELFARE

Secretary: Alec Steels, 42 Ling Road, Walton, Chesterfield, Derbys S40 3HS (01246 208939)

Ground: Inkersall Road, Staveley, Chesterfield, Derbyshire (01246 471441)

Directions: M1 jct 30, follow A619 Chesterfield - Staveley is 3 miles from jct30. Turn left at GK Garage in Staveley town centre into Inkersall Rd - ground200yds on right at side of Speedwell Rooms. Frequent buses (47, 70, 72, 75, 77) from Chesterfield stop in Staveley town centre - 3 mins walk to ground

Capacity: 5,000   Cover: 400   Seats: 220   Floodlights: Yes

Clubhouse: The Staveley Miners Welfare, 500 yds from ground, open before and after games
Club Shop: Yes, contactRod Walker 01246 473655

HONOURS	County Sen Lg Div 2 92-93, Div 3 91-92, Chesterfield & D. Amat Lg R-up89-90 90-91, Byron (Lge) Cup 89-90, R-up 90-91.NCE Div 1 R-up 97-98
PREVIOUS	**Leagues:** Chesterfield & D. Amat 89-91; County Sen 91-93.
BEST SEASON	**FA Cup:** **FA Vase:** 98-99, 3rd Rd at least
RECORDS	**Attendance:** 280 v Stocksbridge, Sheffield Snr Cup 22/1/94
	Goalscorer: Mick Godber
	Appearances: Shane Turner

FACT FILE

Founded: 1989
Nickname: The Welfare
Colours: Blue shirts/white shorts
Change colours: All yellow
Midweek matches: Wednesday
Reserves' League: Beauvale Midlan Regional Alliance: Premier Division
Programme: 32pages, 50p
Editor: Tony Brown(01246 475644)

CLUB PERSONNEL

Chairman: John Edwards
Tel: 01246 475644 (H)

THACKLEY

Secretary: Stewart Willingham, 3 Kirklands Close, Baildon, Shipley, West Yorks BD17 6HN
Tel: 01274 598589
Ground: Dennyfield, Ainsbury Avenue, Thackley, Bradford (01274 615571). **Directions:** On main Leeds/Keighley A657 road, turn off at Thackley corner which is 2 miles from Shipley traffic lights and 1 mile from Greengates lights.Ainsbury Avenue bears to the right 200yds down the hill. Ground is 200yds along Ainsbury Avenue on the right. 3 miles from Bradford Interchange (BR), one and ahalf miles from Shipley (BR). Buses to Thackley corner (400 yds)
Capacity: 3,000   Seats: 300   Cover: 600   Floodlights: Yes
Clubhouse: Tue-Sun evenings, matchdays and w/e lunchtimes. Hot & cold snacks on matchdays
Club Shop: Progs, souvenirs. Metal badges- £2.50 + s.a.eContact Geoff Scott (01274 611520)

HONOURS	N.C.E. Lg R-up 94-95 (Lg Cup R-up 94-95), Yorks Lg Div 273-74, West Yorks Lg 66-67, W. Riding Co. Amtr Lg (x3) 57-60, W. Riding Co. Cup 73-74 74-75, W. Riding Co. Chal. Cup 63-64 66-67,(R-Up 94-95); Bradford & Dist. Snr Cupx 11.
PREVIOUS	**Leagues:** Bradford Amateur, W. Riding County Amateur, W. Yorks, Yorks 67-82.
	Name: Thackley Wesleyians 1930-39
BEST SEASON	**FA Vase:** 5th Rd 80-81 (01-2 v Whickham) **FA Cup:**
RECORD	**Attendance:** 1,500 v Leeds Utd 1983

Players progressing: Tony Brown (Leeds), Ian Ormondroyd (Bradford City).

FACT FILE

Founded: 1930
Sponsors: Diamond International Shipping
Colours: Red & white/white/red
Change colours: All white
Midweek matches: Tuesday
Programme: 20 pages, 50p Editor: Secretary
Local Press: Bradford Telegraph & Argus, BradfordStar, Aire Valley Target.

CLUB PERSONNEL

Chairman: Secretary (acting)
Treasurer: Steven Paley
Secretary: T.B.A.
Manager/Coach: Trevor Best
Asst Manager: David Holmes
Physio: Neil Corker

Staveley Miners Welfare

BORROWASH VICTORIA

Secretary.: Ian Collins, 30 Margreave Road, Chaddesden, Derby DE21 6JDTel: 01332 739437
Ground: Robinson Construction Bowl, Borrowash Road, Spondon, Derby (01332 669688.
Directions: M1 jct 25, A52 towards Derby, 3rd left off by-pass into Borrowash Rd, ground 400 yds on left. 2 miles from Spondon (BR). Nottingham to Derby buses pass nearby.
Capacity: 5,000   Seats: Yes   Covered: 500   Floodlights: Yes
Clubhouse: Normal pub hours. Hot & cold food.   Club Shop: No
HONOURS   N.C.E. Lg Div 1 Sth 83-84 (R-up 84-85, Div 2 Sth R-up 82-83), Derby Comb.
77-78 (R-up(10) 65-66 68-74 75-77 78-79, Lg Cup 68-69 75-76(R-up 63-64 66-67), Midland
Co's Lg Div 80-81 (Div 1 Cup 80-81), Derbys Snr Cup R-up 90-91, Derbys Div. Cup 73-74 (R-up
70-71 72-73), Cen. Midl Lg B E Webbe Cup R-up 88-89 (Res. Cup 94-95),
BEST SEASON   FA Cup 3rd Qual. Rd 91-92.   FA Vase: 4th Rd 90-91
PREVIOUS Leagues: Derby Sun. School & Welf. 52-57; Derby Comb.; Midland 79-82; N.C.E.
Central Midlands League.
RECORDS   Attendance: 2,000 v Nottingham Forest, floodlight opening 22/10/85.

FACT FILE
Founded: 1911 (Reformed 1963)
Nickname: Vics
Club Sponsors: Robinson Construction
Colours: Red & white stripes/black/black
Change Colours: Navy blue/sky/sky
Midweek matches: Tuesday
Programme: 16 pages, 50p
Editor: Ian Collins (01332 739437)
Press Officer: Secretary
CLUB PERSONNEL
Chairman: Ian Anderson
Vice Chairman: Peter Erwin
Manager/Coach:Mick Rodgers
Asst Man:Gary Adul Physio:Geoff.Woolley

BRIDLINGTON TOWN

Secretary:Chris Bemrose, 16 North Back Lane, Bridlington, E. Yorks. YO16 7BA
Tel: 01262 604036 (H & Fax) 01262 676836 (B) e-mail Admin@bridtownafc.freeserve.co.uk
Ground Queensgate Stadium, Queensgate, Bridlington YO16 5LN Tel: 01262 606879
Capacity: 3,000 Seats: 742 Executive Boxes: 2 Shop: Yes ,matchdays Floodlights: Yes
Clubhouse: Open every evening & w/e lunchtimes.
Record Attendance: 432 for an F.A. Sunday Cup Semi-Final 3.3.2000

Directions   From south on A165 - Pass golf course, straight over lights. Turn right at
r'about by B&Q. Turn left at next lights & over rlwy bridge. At r'about bear left and then straight on
up Quay Road. After lights turn right into Queensgate & ground is 800yds on right.
        From south & west via A614 (formerly A166) - Straight on at lights (Hosp. on
right). At r'about straight on to mini-r'about & bear right (2nd exit). Over the first lights, left at next
lights (just after Kwikfit) into Queensgate & ground is 800yds on right.

FACT FILE
Founded: 1994
Sponsors: Barton Engineering
Colours: Red with 1 black stripe/red/red
Midweek Matchday: Tuesday
Programme: 40 pages Price 70p
Prog. Editor: Jonathon Bemrose
CLUB PERSONNEL
Chairman: Gordon Reed
Vice Chairman: Barrie garton
Tel: 01262 673967 (H, B & Fax)
Match Sec.: Jonathon Bemrose
Tel: 01262 604748 (H & Fax)
01262 401487 (B)

GEDLING TOWN

Secretary: Paul Dobson, 26 Chevin Gardens, Top Valley Estate, Nottingham NG5 9ES
        Tel: 0115 927 4790 (H) 0115 986 6541 (B) 07718 269541 (M)
Ground: Riverside Ground, (rear of Ferryboat Inn), Stoke Lane, Stoke Bardolph, Nottingham
        NG14 5HX   Tel: 0115 940 2145 Fax: 0115 967 31310 Office: 0115 967 0047
Directions: A612 Nottingham-Lowdham-Southwell road. Just before Burton Joyce turn right
        into Stoke Lane to Ferryboat P.H. Approx 1.5 miles. Ground at rear of pub.
Capacity: 2,000   Seats: None   Cover: 500   Floodlights: Yes
Clubhouse: Matchdays only. Hot & cold food. Licensed bar.   Club Shop: No
Honours: Central Mids Lg Prem 97-98 R-up 91-92, Div 1 90-91, (Res Prem 96-97 97-98);
        Wakefield Floodlit Trophy 92-93 R-up 95-96; Ken Marsland Cup (Res) 93-94;
        Notts Amtr Lg 89-90 (Snr Cup R-up 89-90).Res Lg & Cp Winners 98-99
Best season FA Vase: 3rd Rd 96-97
RECORDS   Attendance: 250 v Arnold Town.
        Win: 11-0 v Radford 91-92   Defeat: 2-5 v Staveley MW 93-94.
        Goalscorer: Rob Orton 98 in 124   Appearances: Gary Ball 216

FACT FILE
Founded: 1989
Colours: Yellow & navy/navy/yellow
Change colours: All red
Midweek Matchday: Wednesday
Prog 32 pages 50p
Editor: Paul Dobson

Chairman: Roland Ash
0115 952 4790 (H) 0115 967 0047 (B)

Manager: Paul Elrick
Asst. Man: Junior Glave
Physio: Trevor Wells/Pete Tyers

HALL ROAD RANGERS

Secretary: David J Simmons, 24 Gorton Road, Willerby, Hull HU10 6LT.
        Tel: 01482658998 (H), 01482 653203 (B & Fax)
Ground: Dene Park, Dene Close, Beverley Rd, Dunswell, Nr Hull (01482 850101).
Directions: M62 to A63, turn left before Humber Bridge onto A164 to Beverley,after approx 5
miles turn right onto A1079. In 2 miles turn left at large roundabout to ground 20 yards on right.
Capacity: 1,200   Seats: 250   Cover: 750   Floodlights: Yes
Clubhouse: Open all week for drinks and bar snacks. Snooker, pool,darts.   Club Shop: Yes

HONOURS   N.C.E. Lg Div 2 90-91, Yorks Lg Div 3 72-73 79-80, E. Riding Snr Cup 72-73 93-94.

PREVIOUS   Leagues: East Riding; Yorks 68-82   Ground: Hull Co-Op (until 1968)

BEST SEASON   FA Cup: FA Vase:

RECORDS   Attendance:1,200 v Manchester City Aug 93
        Scorer: G James   Appearances: G James
Players progressing: Gerry Ingram (Blackpool, Sheff Wed). Mark Greaves (Hull City)

FACT FILE
Founded: 1959   Nickname: Rangers
Sponsor: Admiral Signs of Hull Ltd.
Colours: Blue & white hoops/ blue/ blue.
Change Colours: Red & Black Stripes,black
Midweek Matches: Wednesday
Reserves' League: East Riding Co.League
Programme: 36 pages, 50p
Editor/Press Officer: Secretary
CLUB PERSONNEL
Chairman: Robert Smailes
Tel: 01482821354 (H)
Player-Manager: Chris Lewis
Asst Mgr: Peter Smurthwaite
Coach: Ian Davis

HATFIELD MAIN

Secretary: Stuart Bagnall,53 Walnut Road, Thorne, Doncaster, S.Yorks. DN8 4HN (01405 740424 (H) 07788 730804(M)
Ground: Dunscroft Welfare Ground, Dunscroft, Doncaster, Sth Yorks   Tel: 01302 841326
Directions: From Doncaster (A18) Scunthorpe Rd to Dunsville, left at Flarepath Hotel down Broadway. Ground half mile on right.
   Stamforth & Hatfield (BR) 1/2 mile. Buses every 15 mins. from Doncaster.
   Capacity: 4,000   Seats: 200   Cover: 600   Floodlights: Yes
Clubhouse: Full licensing hrs. Hot/cold drinks/snacks   **Club Shop:** Yes
HONOURS   Northern Counties East Prem Div 95-96, R-up 88-89, Div One 94-95; Yorks Lge Div 1 R-up 65-66; W Riding Cup 61-62 63-64.
PREVIOUS   **League:** Doncaster Dist, Yorkshire 55-82   **.1998-99 P.o.Y.** Darren Phipps
RECORDS   **Gate:** 1,000 v Leeds, A Jones testimonial. Competitive: 750 v Bishop Auckland,
Appearances: Lal Dutt   **Fee received:** £1,000 for Mark Hall (York City)
Players progressing: Mark Atkins (Scunthorpe), Wayne Hall (York)

FACT FILE
Founded: 1936   Nickname: The Main
Sponsors: Manor Tyres, (Stainforth)
Colours: All red   Change Colours: All blue
Midweek matchday: Tuesday
Reserves' League: None
Programme: 25 pages, 50p
Editor: Tony Ingram (01302 842795)
CLUB PERSONNEL
President: R Wright,Chairman: Peter Wright
Treasurer: Russel Wright
Commercial Manager: Stuart Robinson
Manager: Colin Douglas
Asst Manager:Glenn Hodgit &Stuart Dowing
Physio:Shaun McDonald, MascotRyan Bagnall

LOUTH UNITED

Secretary: Ken Vincent, 64 Frederick St, Grimsby DN31 1XQ: Tel Nos: 01472 344411(H) 0589 874857 (M) and 0797 440 5997 **Match day Secretary:** Albany Jordan(01507 607356)
Albany Jordan Ground: Park Avenue, Louth, Lincs Tel: 01507 607351 FAX: 01507 607351
Directions: A16 To Louth Market Place, exit via Eastgate/Eastfield Rd, to Fire Station turn right into Park Avenue. Ground at bottom of avenue of prefabricated bungalows.
Capacity: 2,500   Seats: None   Cover: 400   Floodlights: Yes   **Club Shop:** No
Clubhouse: Weekdays 6.30-11.45, Sat 12-11.45. Full bar facilities. Snacks available.
HONOURS   Lincs Lg Prem 72-73 85-86 86-87 (Div 1 57-58 66-67 67-68; Lg Challenge Cup 73-74 86-87; Lg Charity Cup 55-56 56-57 67-68; Central Mids Lg Cup R-up 92-93; Wakefield F'lit Cup R-up 91-92; Lincs Snr `A' Cup 77-78. Lincs Sen Cup R-up: 98-99
PREVIOUS   **Leagues:** Lincs 47-75 82-88; Central Midlands 88-93.
   Names: Louth Nats & Louth Town - merged   **Grounds:** None
BEST SEASON   FA Cup: 3Rd Q 0-2 v Emley **F.A Vase:** 4th Rd v Halesowen Town 85-86
RECORDS: Goalscorers: Peter Rawclife 39 **Appearances:** Steve Newby 510 **Att::** 2,500

FACT FILE
Founded: 1947   Nickname: The Lions
Sponsors: 'Brother'
Colours: Blue/black/blue
Change:All Yellow
Midweek matches: Tuesday
Reserves League: Lincolnshire
Prog:50p ED/ PressOff: Albany Jordan
CLUB PERSONNEL
Chairman: George Horton
Vice-Chairman: Jim Walmsley
President: Dave Fairburn
Commercial Manager: Simon Hewson
Manager: Steve Newby
Coaches: Nigel Fanthorpe/D Cole Physio:
Kenny Vincent

MALTBY MAIN

Secretary: Nick Dunhill, 10 Conrad Drive, Maltby, Rotherham, Sth Yorks S66 8RS
   Tel: 01709 815676 01977 669534 (B)
Ground: Muglet Lane, Maltby , Rotherham. Tel: 017941 057883
Directions: Exit M18 at junct 1 with A631. Two miles into Maltby, right at traffic lights at Queens Hotel corner on to B6427 Muglet Lane. Ground 3/4mile on left. Bus 101 from Rotherham stops at ground. Bus 287 from Sheffield to Queens Hotel, then follow as above
Capacity: 2,000   **Seats:** 150   **Cover:** 300   Floodlights: Yes
Clubhouse: No, Miners Welfare Club opposite   **Club Shop:** No
HONOURS Sheffield & Hallamshire Snr Cup 77-78, N.C.E. Lge Presidents Cup 92-93 SF 90-91, Mexborough Montague Cup 76-77 80-81 90-91,Yorks Lg R-up 77-78, Sheffield Wharncliffe Cup 80-81.
CLUB RECORDS   Attendance: 1,500 v Sheffield Wed., June 91-92 (friendly)
PREVIOUS   **Leagues:** Sheffield County Senior; Yorkshire 73-82.
   Name: Maltby Main 1916-65 (disbanded); Maltby Miners Welfare 1970-96

FACT FILE
Founded: 1916   Nickname: Miners
Sponsors: RJB Mining & Morrell Tyres
Colours: Red & white/black/red
Change colours: Red/white/white
Midweek matchday: Tuesday
Programme: 36 pages, 50p Editor: Secretary

CLUB PERSONNEL
Chairman: G McCormick
Vice Chairman: M Richardson
President: H Henson
Match Sec: Dave Morris (01709 814400)
Manager: Glyn Kenny
Asst Manager: Glyn Reeve
Coach: Les Harris

MICKLEOVER SPORTS

Secretary: Tony Shaw, 80 Onslow Road, Mickleover, Derbys. DE3 5JB
   Tel: 01332 512826 (H & Fax)

Ground: Mickleover Sports Ground, Station Rd, Mickleover, Derby (01332 521167).
Directions: Derby ring road A38 to A52, turn off at Markeaton Park Island.Take turn to Ashbourne A52, then 2nd left into Radbourne Lane. Take 3rd left into Station Road, ground on corner.

   Capacity: 1,500   Seats: None   Cover: 200

Clubhouse: Open Thursdays and Fridays (7-11 p.m) Saturdays and Sundays (11am-11pm) Snacks available only on Matchdays
Club Shop: No

FACT FILE
Founded: 1948
Colours: Red & White shirts/black/red
Change Colours: All blue
Midweek Matchday: Tuesday
Programme Editor: Stephen Pritchard
Tel: 01332 516271

CLUB PERSONNEL
Chairman Keith Jenkinson (01332 516 271-H)
Match Sec.: Stephen Brown (01332 516978-H)
Manager: Mark Kelsey

PARKGATE

Secretary: Bruce Bickerdike, 2 Cardew Close, Rawmarsh, Rotherham S62 6LB
Tel: 01709 522305 Fax: 01709 528583.
Ground: Roundwood Sports Complex, Green Lane, Rawmarsh, Rotherham S62 6LA Tel: 01709 826600
Directions: From Rotherham A633 to Rawmarsh. From Doncaster A630 to Conisbrough, then A6023 through Swinton to Rawmarsh. Grd at Green Lane - right from Rotherham, left from Conisbrough at the Crown Inn. Grd 800yds right
Capacity: 1,000   **Seats:** 300   **Cover:** 300   **Floodlights:** Yes   **Club Shop:** No.
Clubhouse: Licensed bar, 2 lounges. Meals available lunchtime Wed-Sat.

HONOURS S&HSC Finalists 0-3 v Emley 97-98, Wilkinson Sword Trophy R-up 98-99

PREVIOUS   Leagues: B.I.R. County Senior Lge; Yorkshire 74-82
Ground: None **Names:** BSC Parkgate (until mid-eighties); RES Parkgate (pre-1994).

RECORD   Attendance: v Worksop 1982

FACT FILE
Founded: 1969
Nickname: The Gate or The Steelmen
Kit Sponsors: JBB Investigations
Colours: All red&White Change: Yellow & Black
Midweek matches: Tuesday
Programme: 20 pages, 50p
Editor: Stuart Bisby (01709 545219)

CLUB PERSONNEL
President: Paul Cristinacce
Chairman: Albert T Dudill Tel: 01709 524533 (H)
Vice Chairman: Les Taylor
Press Officer: Secretary
Manager: Wilfred Race
Asst Manager: Vincent Brady
Physio: David Proctor

PICKERING TOWN

Secretary: Alan Brenkley, 32 The Chase, Norton, Malton, N. Yorks. YO17 9AS
Tel: 01653 692743 (H)
Ground: Recreation Club, Mill Lane (off Malton Rd), Pickering, North Yorkshire (01751 473317)
Directions: A169 from Malton. On entering Pickering take 1st left past Police Station and B.P. garage into Mill Lane, ground 200 yards on right
Capacity: 2,000   **Seats:** 200   **Cover:** 500   **Floodlights:** Yes
Clubhouse: Open 1.30pm for Saturday games, 6pm for midweek games. Food available from Football Club Kitchen at half-time and after games.   **Club Shop:** No

HONOURS Northern Co's East Lg R-up 92-93 (Div 2 1987-88, Div 1 R-up 91-92),Yorks Lg Div 3 73-74, North Riding Snr Cup R-up 93-94 94-95, N. Riding County Cup 90-91.
PREVIOUS   Leagues: Beckett; York & District; Scarborough & District; Yorkshire72-82.
RECORD   Attendance: 1,412 v Notts County, friendly, August 1991
Players progressing: Chris Short (Stoke City), Craig Short (Everton) both via Scarborough

FACT FILE
Founded: 1888   Nickname: Pikes
Club Sponsors: Flamingoland
Colours: Royal/white/royal
Change colours: Amber/black/amber
Midweek matches: Tuesday
Reserves' League: Beckett League
Programme: 32 pages, 80p
Editor: Anthony Dunning (Chairman)

CLUB PER SONNEL
Chairman: Anthony Dunning (01751 473697)
President:J.P.Jennison
Manager:Jimmy Reid
Assistant Manager: Steve Brown
Physio: Clive Reynolds

PONTEFRACT COLLIERIES

Secretary: Frank Maclachlan, 188 Watling Road, Ferry Fryston, Castleford WF102QY
Tel: 01977 512085 (H), 01977 601327 (B), 07710 586447 (M)
Ground: Skinner Lane, Pontefract, West Yorkshire (01977 600818)
Directions: M62 jct 32 towards Pontefract. Left at lights after roundabout for park entrance and retail park. Traffic thro town should follow racecourse signs thro lights to roundabout and back to lights. Monkhill (BR) 1 mile. Bahhill (BR) 300 yds. All Leeds and Castleford buses pass ground.
Capacity: 1,200   **Seats:** 300   **Cover:** 400   **Floodlights:** Yes
Clubhouse: Fully licensed. Hot & cold snacks. Open before and after games   **Club Shop:** No
HONOURS N.C.E. Lg Div 1 83-84 95-96 (Div 2 R-up 82-83); Floodlt Comp 87-88 88-89; Yorks Lg Div 3 81-82; W. Riding Co. Cup R-up 87-88 90-91;Embleton Cup 82-83 86-87 95-96; 99-00 Castleford FA Cup 82-83 86-87,94-95; Wilkinson Sword 95-96
PREVIOUS   Leagues: West Yorkshire 58-79; Yorkshire 79-82
RECORDS   Attendance: 1,000 v Hull City, floodlight opening 1985
Players progressing: David Penney to Derby County, 1985

FACT FILE
Founded: 1958   Nickname: Colls
Sponsors: Kiko's Night Club
Colours: Blue & black stripes/black/black
Change Colours: All green
Midweek Matches: Tuesday
Reserve League: N.C.E. Res. Div.
Programme: 16 pages, 50p
Editor:Trevor Green (01977550922)
Local Press: Pontefract & Castleford Express

CLUB PERSONNEL
Chairman:Steve Lloyd 01977 795581(H)
Manager: Steve Kittrick
Asst Mgr: Alan Billingham
Physio: M.Slater

ROSSINGTON MAIN

Secretary: Gerald Parsons, 15 Seaton Gardens, Rossington, Doncaster DN11 0XA
Tel: 01302 867542 (H)
Ground: Welfare Ground, Oxford Street, Rossington, Doncaster   Tel: 01302 865524
Directions: Enter Rossington and go over the railway crossings. Pass the Welfare Club on right, Oxford Street is next right - ground is at bottom. 8miles from Doncaster (BR).
Capacity: 2,000   **Seats:** 200   **Cover:** 500   **Floodlights:** Yes
Clubhouse: Evenings & matchdays, Sandwiches, rolls, satellite TV, pool.   **Club Shop:** No

HONOURS   Sen Lge 44-45, Cup 44-45, Cen. Mids. Prem Div. 84-85, Cup 83-84 84-85, DDSALShield 90-91 R-up 89-90.

PREVIOUS   Leagues: Doncaster Sen, Yorkshire Lge, Sheffield County Sen, Cent Mids.

BEST SEASON   FA Cup: FA Vase:

RECORDS   Attendance: 864 v Leeds United 8/91.
Goalscorer: Mark Illman   **Appearances:** Darren Phipps

FACT FILE
Founded: 1920   Nickname: The Colliery
Sponsor: RJB Mining
Colours: All blue
Change colours: Blue & black
Midweek matches: Tuesday
Reserves' League: Beefeater County Sen
Programme: 50p
Editor:Chairman

CLUB PERSONNEL
Chairman: Gerald Murden (01302 867542)
Joint Managers: D Ridley & L Ostle
Physio: J White

Garforth Town FC

Selby Town FC. Back Row (l-r): Dominic Moyles, Paul Cygan, Petri Loyttyniemi, Ian Phillips, Simon Acaster, Mike Speight, Paul Dooley (Coach), Bob Lyon (Manager). Front Row: Mark Newstead, Andrew Cygan, Mike Amos, Chris Collier, Andrew Hart, Chris Whalley, Phil Lindley. Photo: Bill Wheatcroft

Sheffield FC. Back Row (l-r): John Pearson (Manager), Liam Cartledge, Matt Dickins, Darren Utley, Neil Booker, David Faulkner, John Harker, Mick Godber (captain), Richard Hawke, Dave McCarthy (Asst Mngr), Mark Wilkinson, Michael Stewart, Steve Naylor (Physio). Front Row: Michael Hoe, Paul Sykes, Paul Wood, Russ Ingram, Martin Beaumont, Steve Spence. Photo: Bill Wheatcroft

TADCASTER ALBION

Secretary: Mrs Angela J Burnett   Tel: 01937 832802 (H/Fax)
6 Beech Grove House, Ouston Lane, Tadcaster N.Yorks. LS24 8DP.

Ground: The Park, Ings Lane, Tadcaster, LS24 9AY.   Tel: 01937 834119

Directions: From West Riding and South Yorks, turn right off A659 at John Smith's Brewery Clock.
From East Riding turn left off A659 after passing over river bridge and pelican crossing (New Street).

Capacity: 1,500   Seats: Planned this season   Cover: 400   Floodlights: Yes
Clubhouse: No   **Club Shop:** No

HONOURS   None
RECORD Attendance:1,200 v Wincanton F.A.Vase 4th Rd 1996-7

FACT FILE
Founded: 1892
Colours: Yellow with Navy & Red trim/yellow
Change colours: Green & Yellow halves
Midweek Matchday: Tuesday
Programme: 20 pages
Programme Editor: Mrs Angela Burnett (Sec.)

CLUB PERSONNEL
Chairman: Michael R Burnett
Tel: 07808 689883 (M)
President: Lord Edward Stourton
Match Sec: 01937 835017 (H/B)
Manager: Wayne Day

WINTERTON RANGERS

Secretary: G Spencer, 2 Dale Park Ave.,Winterton,Scun'pe,N Lincs.DN15 9UY(01724 732039)Players progressing Henry Smith (Leeds), Keith Walwyn (Chesterfield), Rick **Ground:** West Street, Winterton, Scunthorpe, South Humberside (01724 732628).
Directions: From Scunthorpe take A1077 Barton-on-Humber for 5 miles. On entering Winterton take 3rd right (Eastgate), 3rd left (Northlands Rd)and 1st right (West St.). Ground 200yds on left
Capacity: 3,000   Seats: 200   Covered: 200   Floodlights: Yes   **Club Shop:** No.
Clubhouse: Open matchdays & evenings Mon-Sat, hot & cold food available on matchdays
HONOURS   Lincs Jnr Cup 47-48 61-62; Lincs Snr `B' Cup 69-70; Yorks Lg 71-72 76-77 78-79 (Lg Cup 80-81); N.C.E. Div 2 89-90; S'thorpe Lg & Cup many times.
PREVIOUS   Leagues: Scunthorpe & Dist. 45-65; Lincs 65-70; Yorkshire 70-82.
BEST SEASON   FA Vase: QF 76-77 **FA Cup:** 4th Qual Rd replay 76-77, 2-3 after 3-3
RECORD   Attendance: 1,200 v Sheffield Utd, official floodlight opening, Oct. 78
       Fee received: £5,000 for Henry Smith (Leeds United, 1979)
Players Progressing H Smith (Leeds), Keith Walwyn (Chesterfield),Rick Greenhough(Chester)

FACT FILE
Founded: 1930   Nickname: Rangers
Sponsors: Quantum Graphic Studio
Colours: Blue & white/Black/Blue
Change colours: All red
Midweek matches: Monday
Programme: 28-36 pages, 50p
Editor: M Fowler (01724 734570)
Local press: Scunthorpe Evening Telegraph

CLUB PERSONNEL
President: T.B.A.
Chairman: I.Grimshaw
Vice Chairman: A Smith
Press Officer: Secretary
Managers:A.Irvine & M.Newell

WORSBROUGH M.W. & ATHLETIC

Secretary: Garry Wiggan, 9 Pantry Well, Worsbrough Bridge, Barnsley, S. Yorks S70 4SW
       Tel: 01226 247023
Ground: Park Road, Worsbrough Bridge, Barnsley Tel: 01226 284452
Directions: On the A61 Barnsley-Sheffield road two miles south of Barnsley, 2miles from M1 jnt 36 opposite Blackburns Bridge. Two and a half miles from Barnsley (BR). Yorkshire Traction run buses every 10 mins thru Worsbrough Bridge.
Capacity: 2,000   Seats: 175   Cover: 175   Floodlights: Yes
Clubhouse: Yes   **Club Shop:** No

HONOURS   Northern Co's East Div 1 R-up 90-91 (Div 3 R-up 85-86); Sheffield SnrCup R-up 72-73; County Snr Lg 65-66 69-70 (R-up 62-63, Lg Cup 65-66); Barnsley Lg 52-53 58-59 59-60, Lg Cup 56-57 58-59 (R-up 53-54), Beckett Cup 57-58.
PREVIOUS   Leagues: Barnsley 52-61; County Snr 62-70; Yorks 71-82.
BEST SEASON   FA Cup: FA Vase:
RECORD   Attendance: 1,603 v Blyth Spartans, FA Amateur Cup 1971

FACT FILE
Founded: 1923
Reformed: 1947
Colours: All red
Change colours: Yellow/blue
Midweek Matchday: Wednesday
Programme: 60 pages, 50p
Editor: Secretary

CLUB PERSONNEL
Chairman: Mr J Wright
Press Officer: T.B.A.

YORKSHIRE AMATEUR

Secretary: Charles Sharman,44 Roxholme Place, Leeds LS7 4JQ Tel: 0113 293 8894 (H)
Ground: The Bracken Edge, Roxholme Road, Leeds LS8 4DZ Tel: 0113 262 4093
Directions: From South M1 to Leeds, then A58 Wetherby Road to Fforde Green Hotel, left at lights and proceed to Sycamore Ave. (on right). From East A1 to Boot & Shoe Inn then to Shaftesbury Hotel, turn right into Harehills Lane, then to Sycamore Avenue. Two and a half miles from Leeds (BR). Buses 2, 3 & 20 from Briggate to Harehills Ave.
Capacity : 1,550   Seats: 200   Cover: 160   Floodlights: Yes   **Club Shop:** Yes
Clubhouse: Bar, tea bar, games, lounge. Every night 8.30-11, Sat matchdays 12-11, Sun 12-3.

HONOURS   FA Amtr Cup SF 31-32; West Riding Co. Cup(3); Yorks Lg 31-32, Div 2 58-59 (R-up 52-53 71-72), Div 3 77-78, Lg Cup 32-33; Leeds & Dist. Snr Cup.
PREVIOUS   League: Yorks 20-24 30-82.   **Ground:** Elland Road 1919-20
BEST SEASON   FA Cup: FA Vase:
RECORD   Attendance: 4,000 v Wimbledon, FA Amateur Cup QF 1932.

FACT FILE
Founded: 1918   Nickname: Ammers
Sponsors: Screeching Parrot
Colours: White/navy/red
Change colours: All red
Midweek Matches: Tuesday
Programme: 12 pages, 50p
Editor:John Turner (0113 225 2833)

CLUB PERSONNEL
Chairman: Andrew Wilkinson(0113 2650841)
President: Rayner Barker
Manager: Denis Metcalfe
Coach: jim McKay
Physio: Terry Davies

REDFERNS REMOVERS
CENTRAL MIDLANDS LEAGUE

FEEDER TO: NORTHERN COUNTIES LEAGUE

President: Mr R Holmes **Vice President:** Mr D Capenerhurst
Chairman & General Secretary: Frank Harwood
103 Vestry Road, Oakwood, Derby DE21 2BN
Tel: 01332 832372 Fax: 01332 835004 e-mail: frank.harwood@talk21.com

The Cox League Cup final concluded the 1999-2000 season and it was a game that summed up another excellent season for the League - excellent football, exciting, competitive, and a tremendous advertisement for the League.

Gedling Town, playing their final game in the League as they have been promoted to the Northern Counties East League, won the final 3-2 against South Normanton Athletic and the crowd of over 400 was kept entertained right until the final whistle.

The match was held at the Town Ground, Alfreton, and the Alfreton Town club can be justifiably proud of their efforts providing excellent facilities so ensuring the match was a credit to all concerned, and played in excellent weather which added to the occasion.

South Normanton Athletic may have been disappointed with the Cox League Cup result but they were victorious in the Wakefield Floodlit Cup, taking the trophy after a superb display which resulted in a crushing 6-0 victory over Selston at Grange Park, home of Long Eaton United, and again the League was grateful to United for the excellent organisation which must also apply to Stanton Ilkeston Football Club who loaned their ground for the Ready Mixed Concrete Reserves Cup final, which saw Selston Reserves winners with a 3-1 victory over Graham St Prims Reserves.

The Travis Perkins Supreme Division title was taken by Lincoln Moorlands, winners of the Premier Division title in the 1998-99 season. Moorlands completed a notable double but they only secured the title in their last game of the season when a last minute goal ensured the three points they needed to pip Shirebrook Town. Shirebrook had led the table for most of the season and had at one stage headed the Division by eighteen points. However, the last seven games proved a disaster, with one win, and Lincoln Moorlands took advantage with an eight-match unbeaten run, which was rough justice on Shirebrook who had played some superb football throughout the season. Sandiacre Town finished third with Gedling Town fourth. Despite finishing outside the promotion places Gedling were allowed to move up to the Northern Counties East League in view of their record in the League and Cup Competition.

Holbrook took the Premier Division title after a tremendous battle with Graham St Prims, Mickleover Royal British Legion, Shardlow St James, Stanton Ilkeston and Radford. They will be promoted to the Travis Perkins Supreme Division along with Graham St Prims. The other promotion place will be between Mickleover Royal British Legion and Shardlow St James and is subject to facilities.

In their last season in the League Mickleover Sports Reserves were champions of the Reserves Premier Division with Heanor Town Reserves runners up. The Reserve Division One title was taken by Sandiacre Town 'A' with Kimberley Town Reserves runners up.

Frank Harwood completed twenty years as the League Chairman and has also been the League General Secretary for the last six years. Frank, along with Tony Baugh, has been with the League since its inception in 1971.

The League's main sponsor was again Redferns Removers and along with Travis Perkins, Cox Accommodation, Wakefield Trophy World and Ready Mixed Concrete they have contributed vital revenue for which the League is extremely grateful.

Five new clubs join the League for the forthcoming season - Bottersford Town (ex-Lincolnshire League), Ollerton Town (ex-Notts Alliance), Forest Town, North Notts and Dinnington Town, and the last three will be new to Saturday football. Other than Gedling Town and Mickleover Sports Reserves the League will only be losing one other club, Grimethorpe Miners Welfare, who have unfortunately disbanded.

With 67 teams in the League for the 2000-01 season there is confidence that they will be leading the way again for Semi Professional football in the East Midlands area.

Frank Harwood

Lincoln Moorlands FC
Back Row (l-r): Jame Sayce, Mark Bradshaw, Stuart Park, Lee Cooper, Darren Walker, Simon Daniels, Glen Pearson, Rob Kinsela, Darren Chapman, Peter Shelley, Garry Goddard (Manager)
Front Row (l-r): James Parkinson, Stephen Barker, Simon Whittle, James Chesman, David Frecklington, Stuart White.
Photo: Gordon Whittington

FINAL LEAGUE TABLES 1999-2000

TRAVIS PERKINS SUPREME DIVISION

		P	W	D	L	F	A	W	D	L	F	A	Pts
1	Lincoln Moorlands	36	15	2	1	47	11	7	6	5	43	26	74
2	Shirebrook Town	36	13	2	3	41	16	9	5	4	26	17	73
3	Sandiacre Town	36	11	4	3	47	26	10	3	5	43	25	70
4	Gedling Town	36	10	2	6	34	23	12	2	4	43	28	70
5	Heanor Town	36	9	5	4	27	19	10	4	4	34	18	66
6	Dunkirk	36	14	1	3	55	22	7	1	10	26	26	65
7	South Normaton Ath	36	8	4	6	36	27	11	2	5	44	28	63
8	Hucknall Rolls	36	12	3	3	44	27	6	5	7	33	30	62
9	Selston	36	10	6	2	35	24	4	5	9	25	30	53
10	Sneinton	36	8	6	4	30	23	3	7	8	31	46	46
11	Collingham	36	7	2	9	27	36	6	4	8	37	46	45
12	Grimethorpe Miners Welf	36	10	4	4	36	28	2	3	13	18	42	43
13	Kimberley Town	36	8	3	7	41	33	3	6	9	20	27	42
14	Nettleham	36	5	7	6	25	28	5	2	11	24	32	39
15	Clipstone Welfare	36	6	3	9	36	41	4	4	10	24	39	37
16	Welbeck Miners Welf	36	5	4	9	29	42	5	2	11	27	36	36
17	Long Eaton Utd	36	5	2	11	18	34	5	1	12	20	43	33
18	Harworth Colliery Inst	36	4	2	12	27	56	3	1	14	18	64	24
19	Blackwell Miners Welf	36	6	2	10	28	40	0	1	17	20	58	21

PREMIER DIVISION

		P	W	D	L	F	A	W	D	L	F	A	Pts
1	Holbrook	30	12	2	1	54	13	7	4	4	30	21	63
2	Graham St Prims	30	9	4	2	35	18	9	1	5	32	14	59
3	Mickleover RBL	30	9	5	1	38	13	7	5	3	31	15	58
4	Shardlow St James	30	11	1	3	42	18	6	4	5	29	26	56
5	Stanton Ilkeston	30	10	2	3	33	21	7	2	6	20	25	55
6	Radford	30	7	3	5	29	22	8	4	3	29	23	52
7	Askern Welfare	30	6	6	3	22	17	9	1	5	27	21	52
8	Thorne Colliery	30	8	3	4	33	21	6	6	3	22	20	51
9	Greenwood Meadows	30	9	1	5	26	17	4	5	6	30	31	45
10	Yorkshire Main	30	8	4	3	27	20	3	1	11	20	38	38
11	Grantham Rangers	30	6	4	5	22	22	3	2	10	22	37	33
12	Ripley Town	30	7	1	7	28	27	2	2	11	19	44	30
13	Kiveton Park	30	4	1	10	23	34	3	3	9	26	37	25
14	Mexborough Town Athletic	30	3	3	9	14	36	3	2	10	12	29	23
15	Teversal Grange	30	2	3	10	19	36	2	2	11	13	36	17
16	Blidworth Welfare	30	3	3	9	23	45	1	2	12	18	51	17

TRAVIS PERKINS SUPREME DIVISION RESULTS CHART 1999-2000

		1	2	3	4	5	6	7	8	9	10	11	12	13	14	15	16	17	18	19
1	Blackwell Miners Welf.	X	4-2	3-5	2-1	2-3	2-1	2-2	0-1	1-3	1-0	3-5	1-0	0-1	1-5	2-1	0-3	3-3	1-2	0-2
2	Clipstone Welfare	4-2	X	3-2	1-3	2-1	3-1	7-0	0-3	3-3	0-3	0-2	3-1	1-4	1-4	1-1	1-1	2-4	2-3	2-3
3	Collingham	4-1	0-4	X	1-1	1-2	3-2	1-2	0-4	2-1	0-1	0-3	2-1	0-4	2-0	4-1	0-1	5-0	1-6	1-1
4	Dunkirk	4-1	2-1	5-2	X	3-4	6-0	6-0	2-1	3-0	1-0	3-1	4-1	3-1	2-1	4-1	0-1	2-2	1-2	4-3
5	Gedling Town	5-2	4-0	1-1	1-0	X	4-0	1-2	0-2	2-1	3-1	1-0	0-2	2-0	0-3	2-0	1-1	1-3	2-3	4-2
6	Grimethorpe MW	4-2	2-3	3-3	3-2	1-3	X	1-0	0-2	1-1	4-2	1-1	1-0	3-2	3-0	1-1	0-1	3-2	2-1	3-2
7	Harworth C I	2-1	2-1	2-4	0-4	0-2	0-4	X	1-4	1-2	1-1	0-7	3-4	2-3	3-8	1-3	0-1	3-3	4-3	2-1
8	Heanor Town	2-0	1-1	2-1	0-1	1-3	0-0	2-1	X	1-2	1-1	2-0	3-0	1-0	2-1	4-1	0-0	3-2	0-3	2-2
9	Hucknall Rolls	7-2	1-0	5-2	2-1	0-4	3-1	6-0	1-0	X	1-1	0-0	5-2	2-0	2-4	1-0	2-2	2-2	3-2	1-0
10	Kimberley Town	1-0	4-0	1-4	0-6	1-2	1-1	*-0	3-1	2-3	X	2-1	0-1	3-2	2-2	0-3	3-1	1-1	3-4	3-1
11	Lincoln Moorlands	5-0	1-0	1-2	4-0	1-1	3-3	5-1	3-2	1-0	1-0	X	4-0	3-0	2-0	2-1	3-0	4-0	1-0	3-1
12	Long Eaton United	3-1	1-2	0-2	0-1	1-3	1-0	2-1	1-1	1-5	0-2	0-4	X	3-1	0-1	1-0	0-2	1-1	2-5	1-2
13	Nettleham	2-2	4-6	2-2	1-0	0-2	1-0	3-1	2-3	1-1	2-0	1-1	1-3	X	0-0	1-1	2-4	2-1	0-0	0-1
14	Sandiacre Town	2-1	5-0	3-0	4-2	5-2	5-1	1-4	0-2	2-1	2-1	2-2	0-0	3-1	X	1-1	0-3	7-1	2-2	3-2
15	Selston	1-0	3-1	3-3	3-1	1-1	2-0	1-0	1-1	2-2	2-2	2-4	3-0	2-1	2-2	X	2-1	2-1	1-3	2-1
16	Shirebrook Town	2-1	3-1	4-1	2-0	4-3	0-1	2-1	1-1	2-0	2-0	3-2	4-0	3-0	1-3	1-1	X	4-0	3-0	0-1
17	Sneinton FC	4-2	0-0	3-0	0-1	1-0	3-0	2-0	1-3	2-2	2-2	3-3	3-1	2-2	0-3	1-0	1-1	X	0-3	2-0
18	South Normanton Ath	3-0	0-0	4-1	1-2	4-5	2-1	6-0	1-1	2-1	2-1	2-2	3-0	1-2	0-2	1-3	0-3	1-1	X	3-2
19	Welbeck MW	3-2	2-2	1-2	1-0	0-2	3-2	5-3	1-2	1-5	2-2	1-1	3-4	0-0	2-4	2-6	2-0	0-3	0-2	X

COX ACCOMMODATION LEAGUE CUP 1999-2000

THIRD ROUND

Kimberley Town	v	Radford	3-5	Long Eaton United	v	Gedling Town	1-1, 0-4
Lincoln Moorlands	v	Selston	1-1, 3-1	South Normanton A	v	Heanor Town	0-0, 3-1

SEMI FINALS

Gedling Town	v	Lincoln Moorlands	2-1	at South Normanton Athletic FC
Radford	v	South Normanton Ath	1-3	at Dunkirk FC

FINAL

Gedling Town	v	South Normanton Ath	3-2	at Alfreton Town FC

WAKEFIELD FLOODLIT CUP 1999-2000

	P	W	D	L	F	A	Pts
GROUP A							
Heanor Town	4	2	1	1	10	7	7
Selston	4	2	0	2	11	10	6
Kimberley Town	4	1	1	2	5	9	4
Blidworth Welfare withdrew from this group before playing a fixture							
GROUP B							
Dunkirk	6	4	1	1	18	6	13
Sandiacre Town	6	4	0	2	12	13	12
Long Eaton United	6	2	1	3	12	15	7
Stanton Ilkeston	6	0	2	4	5	13	2

	P	W	D	L	F	A	Pts
GROUP C							
South Normanton Ath	6	4	2	0	28	11	14
Shirebrook Town	6	2	2	2	14	13	8
Harworth Colliery Inst	6	1	3	2	11	19	6
Grimethorpe Miners W	6	1	1	4	8	18	4
GROUP D							
Gedling Town	6	4	1	1	12	7	13
Collingham	6	3	0	3	11	8	9
Nettleham	6	3	0	3	7	11	9
Grantham Rangers	6	1	1	4	8	12	4

SECOND ROUND

Dunkirk	v	Shirebrook Town	3-4	Gedling Town	v	Selston	2-4
Heanor Town	v	Collingham	2-0	South Normanton A	v	Sandiacre Town	2-0

SEMI FINALS

Heanor Town	v	Selston	1-3	at Kimberley Town FC
Shirebrook Town	v	South Normanton Ath	0-1	at Blidworth Welfare FC

FINAL

Selston	v	South Normanton Ath	0-6	at Long Eaton United FC

LEADING GOALSCORERS 1999-2000

TRAVIS PERKINS SUPREME DIVISION

M Gadsby	Dunkirk	26
G Smedley	Clipstone Welfare	23
D Thorpe	Welbeck Miners Welfare	20
R Kinsella	Lincoln Moorlands	20
M Timson	Kimberley Town	19
N Booth	Shirebrook Town	18
N Limb	Sandiacre Town	17
G Wright	Hucknall Rolls	17
M Bott	Blackwell Miners Welfare	16
B Yates	Gedling Town	16
M Dickinson	Sneinton	15

PREMIER DIVISION

J Newton	Holbrook	27
M Taplin	Holbrook	24
P Davis	Graham Street Prims	21
L Grant	Shardlow St James	19
P Mighty	Mickleover RBL	17
D Jones	Thorne Colliery	15
M Millward	Shardlow St James	15

BLACKWELL MINERS WELFARE

Colours: Red & white stripes/red/red
Change colours: All Blue
Midweek Matchday: Tuesday

Secretary: Steve Harris, 6 Pennine Close, Newton, Alfreton, Derbys DE55 5UD.
Tel Nos: 01773 779172H) 01246501561(W) 01773 779173 (FAX)
e mail: manor@globalnet.co.uk

Manager:Graham Brentnall

Ground & Directions: Welfare Ground, Primrose Hill, Blackwell, Derbyshire DE55 5JE. (01773
811295). M1 Junc 26, A38 towards Mansfield, left onto B6406, left again at Hilcote Arms, ground
1 mile on left just past Miners Welfare.

CLIPSTONE WELFARE

Founded 1927

Secretary: Barry Clarke, 40 Church Road, Clipstone, Mansfield, NG21 9DG
.Tel: 01623 475106 (H)
Ground & Directions: Clipstone Lido Ground Clipstone Road West, Mansfield,Notts (01632
655674). B6030 from Mansfield, between Forest Town & Clipstone, on left entering Clipstone.
Capacity: 3000   Seats: 90   Cover: 200   Floodlights: No   Club Shop: No
Honours: Notts Snr Cup 85-86 94-95, Notts Alliance 72-73 73-74 74-75 92-93 94-95 (Lg Cup
72-73 73-74 74-75 94-95 (R-up 92-93)), Notts I'mediate Cup 55-56. Central Midlands Premier
Championship 94-95 96-97

Colours: Black & white,black,black
Change Colours: All whiter
Midweek Matchday: Tuesday or Wednesday
Programme: Yes

Chairman: Gordon Costall
Manager: Martin Betts

COLLINGHAM

Colours:All black & amber
Change Colours: All white
Midweek Matchday: Tuesday

Secretary: Johnny Stainton, 41 Rochester Drive, Lincoln LN6 0XL
Tel: 01522 878610 (H) 0585 057179 (B)
Ground: Collingham FC, Station Road, Collingham, Newark, Notts. (01636 892303)
Directions: Take A46 Newark to Lincoln road (Newark bypass).
Turn left into Collingham on the A1133 road. In village turn right at traffic lights.
Ground 100 yards on left.

Manager: Paul Hyde

DUNKIRK

Founded: 1946
Colours: Red/black/black
Change Colours: All blue
Midweek Matchday: Tuesday
Programme : Yes
Chairman: Dave Howes
Manager: Andy Freeman

Secretary: Steve Throssell, 24 Kingfisher Wharf, Castle Marina, Nottingham NG71GA
Tel: 0115 947 3903 (H) 07930 806891 (M)
Ground: The Ron Steel Sports Ground, Trentside Farm, Clifton Bridge, Nottingham
Tel: 0115 985 0803
Directions: Ring Road - Clifton Bridge (North End),Ind Estate, Lenton Lane.
Honours: FA Vase 5th Rd 93-94; Cen Mid Sup Div R-up 96-97, Prem Div R-up 95-96,KO Cup
97-98; Notts Alliance Div 1 84-85, Div 2 82-83, Lg Cup R-up 84-85; Notts I'mediate Cup 83-4
Capacity:1,500 Seats: No Cover: 200 Floodlights: Yes Shop: No Clubhouse: Yes
Record Attendance: 821 v Tiverton Town, F.A.Vase 5th Rd 93-94

Players Progressing: Roger Willis and Matthew
McKemzie (Grimsby T)

GRAHAM STREET PRIMS

Secretary: Mrs E Wright, 6 Athol Close, Sinfin Moor, Derby DE24 9LZ
Tel: 01332 606837 (H) 01332 340131 x6855 (B)

Formed: 1904
Colours: Red & white stripes/black/black
Change Colours: White/navy/navy
Midweek Matchday: Tuesday
Programme: Yes

Ground: Asterdale Sports Centre, Borrowash Road, Spondon, nr Derby. Tel: 01332 668656
Directions: M1 Junc 25, take A52 to Derby. 3rd left Borrowash Road - golf driving range on left,
approx 400m further turn left into Asterdale Sports Centre. Ground at rear.
Capacity: 1,000 Seats: No Cover: Yes Floodlights: No Club shop: No Clubhouse: No

Manager: Martin Spoonerr

HARWORTH COLLIERY INSTITUTE

Secretary: Tom Brogan, 30 Lindsey Road, Harworth, Doncaster, Sth Yorks DN11 8QH
Tel: 01302 750132 (H).
Ground & Directions: Recreation Ground, Scrooby Rd, Bircotes, Doncaster (01302 750614).
Off A1(M) at Blyth, head towards Bawtry for approx 2 miles, take third left, ground in village at
top of hill on left. Or, from Doncaster to Bawtrythen head for A1(M) and turn left after caravan
site - ground at top of hill.
Honours: Wharncliffe Charity Cup 62-63 74-75, Central Midlands League 87-88(Runners-up
86-87, Challenge Cup 86-87 87-88, F'lit Cup 91-92 (Runners-up 89-90)), Sheffield Senior
League 64-65 74-75, Sheffield & Hallamshire Senior Cup SF 87-88

Colours: Yellow & navy/navy/white
Change Colours: Red/white/white
Midweek Matchday: Wednesday

Manager: Alan Needham

412

Blackwell Miners Welfare

Clipstone Welfare. Back Row (l-r): Gavin Saxby, Jason Rohun, Pat Keating, Lee Thompson, Wayne Stark, Phil McHugh, John Cheesmond, Craig Flinton, Chris Mercer. Front Row (l-r): Adrian Carter, Gary Smedley, Stephen Dillon, Darren Smyth, Andy Graham. Photo: Gordon Whittington.

Kimberley Town FC

Long Eaton Utd. Back Row (l-r): S Worthington (Physio), B Sykes (Joint Manager), D Morris, R Ward, W Loseby, S Ward, J Godwin, N Sykes, M Hutchins, N Thorpe, I Roscrow (Player/Coach), J Burns (Commercial Mngr). Front Row (l-r): S Guilor, R Crabtree, M Jenkinson, S Bowler, D Parkes, S Powell, B Smith. Photo: Bill Wheatcroft

HEANOR TOWN

Secretary: Keith Costello, 45 Stainsby Avenue, Heanor, Derbys. DE75 7EL (01773 719446).
Ground & Directions: The Town Ground, Mayfield Avenue, Heanor (01773713742/715815). M1 (J26), take A610 onto A608, ground 200yds from Market Square
Capacity: 3,000   Cover: 1,000+   Floodlights: Yes
Club House: On ground, hot food, open daily
Honours: Central Midlands Lge - Supreme Div. 94-5, 96-7, Cup 94-95 R-up 86-87 92-93, B E Webbe Removals Cup 88-89), West Midlands Reg. Lge R-up 72-73; Midland Co's Lge R-up 65-66 67-68; Derbys Sen. Cup (9) 1892-94 1946-47 65-69 70-7178-79; FA Cup 1st Rd 58-59 63-64, Central All.Lg x2 R-up x4

Nickname: The Lions
Colours: Black& white stripes/black/black
Midweek Matchday: Wednesday
Programme: 32pages 50p
Press Officer & Editor: Stan Wilton
(01332 880199)
Chairman: John McCulloch
Manager: Paul Aklam

HOLBROOK

Secretary: Stevan Broadhurst, 35 Laund Hill, Belper, Derbys. DE56 1FH
     Tel: 01773 821483 (H)   01773 717341 (B)

Ground: The Welfare Ground, Shaw Lane, Holbrook, Derbyshire Tel: 01332 880259

Directions: From A38 take B6179 for Kilburn, turn left at lights for Belper. 1 mile on left at Bulls Head for Holbrook. 2 miles on turn right at Venture garage into Shaws Lane.

Colours: All blue
Change: All yellow

Manager: Mark Webster

HUCKNALL ROLLS

Secretary: Adrian Ward, 7 Redwood Court, Hucknall, Nottm. NG15 6NN Tel: 0115 9538491
Fixture Secretary: Peter Williams, 38 Tiverton Close, Hucknall, Nottingham NG15 6JT
     Tel: 0115 956 33691
Ground: Rolls Royce Sports & Social Club, Watnall Road, Hucknall Notts (0115 963 0134).
Directions: M1 Junc 27. Follow sign A611 to Hucknall. Turn right onto by-pass. 2nd r/about turn right on to Watnall Road. Take 2nd left after fire station on R.R. Sports Ground.
Capacity: 1,000   Cover: Yes   Floodlights: No
Clubhouse: Social Club always open with food

Colours: All bue
Change colours: Yeloow/black/yellow
Midweek Matchday: Wednesday
Programme: yes

Chairman: Darryl Claypole
Manager: Roger Dawkins
Reserves: Peter Needham

KIMBERLEY TOWN

Match Secretary: Alan Jennings, 8 Watchwood Grove, Calverton, Nottingham NG146HX
Tel: 0115 965 6100
Ground & Directions: Stag Ground, Nottingham Road, Kimberley (0115 9382788).Through Nuthall from M1 jct 26 to Kimberley, ground entrance 150 yds after Stag Inn.
Capacity: 2,500   Seats: None   Cover: 150   Floodlights: Yes
Clubhouse: Evenings (Except Sun) & matchdays. Hot & cold snacks available
Honours: Notts Amateur Lg Div 1 54-55, Central Alliance Div 2 R-up 57-58.

Nickname: Stags
Colours: White/blue/white
Change colours: Blue/white/blue
Midweek Matchday: Tuesday
Programme: 40 pages 50p
Editor: George Brown
Chairman: George Giddens
Manager: Julian Garmston
Gen Manager: Brian Harrison

LINCOLN MOORLANDS

Secretary: Colin Edwards, 5 Lansdowne Ave, Lincoln LN6 7PU
     Tel: 01522 520857 (H)   01522 522229 (B)

Ground & Directions: Moorland Sports Ground, Newark Rd, Lincoln (01522 520184).
     From Newark enter Lincoln on A1434, go past Forum Shopping Centre 500yds.
     Ground on left sign Moorland Club.

Colours: All Navy Blue with yellow trim
Change colours: Orange/black/black

Manager: Garry Goddard

LONG EATON UNITED

Secretary: Nigel Lockley, 24 Bushy Close, Long Eaton, Nottm. 0115 973 0352 (H)
Ground & Directions: Grange Park, Station Road, Long Eaton, Nottingham (01159735700). M1 Junc 25, take A52 towards Nottingham, to island by `Bardills Garden Centre', left onto B6003 to t/lights. Turn right A453 and take 2nd left into Station Rd. Entrance on left opposite the Speedway Stadium
Capacity: 5,000   Seats: None   Cover: 500   Floodlights: Yes   Shop: No
Clubhouse: Open matchdays, snacks available Record Attendance: 2,000 1973 FA Cup
Honours: Derbys Snr Cup 64-65 75-76, Midland Co's Lg R-up 76-77, Central Alliance Div South 58-59, Northern Co's (East) Div 1 South 84-85.

Founded: 1956   Nickname: Blues
Colours: White,blue & black/blue/blue
Change colours: Yellow & green/blue/blue
Midweek Matchday: Tuesday
Programme: 20 pages 50p
Editor: G Whitehead
Chairman: J C Fairley
Manager: John Bartlett
Physio: John Burns

MICKLEOVER ROYAL BRITISH LEGION

Secretary: Ray Taylor, 15 Inglwood Avenue, Mickleover, Derby DE3 5RT (01332515047)

Ground: Mickleover RBL, Ypres Lodge, Western Road, Mickleover (01332 513548)

Directions: On west side of Derby off A38, 1/2 mile from Mickleover Villagecentre.

Colours: Yellow/black/black
Change Colours: All red
Midweek Matchday: Tuesday

Manager: Ken Thoresen

NETTLEHAM

Secretary: John Wilson, 21 Chancer Drive, Lincoln LN2 4LN (01522 884051).

Ground & Directions: Mulsanne Park, Field Close, Nettleham (01522 750007). A46approx. 3 miles north of Lincoln, right at Brown Cow Pub, proceed past Church2nd turning on right, ground at end

Honours: Central Mids Lg Premier Division Cup R-up 87-88, Village Tphy, Nursing Cup, Kelly Read Cup, Blankney Hunt Cup, Lincoln & Dist. Amtr Cup R-up, Joe Miller Tphy(2).

Colours: Sky blue & navy/navy/sky b lue
Change Colours: Yellow & green/green/yellow
Midweek Matchday: Tuesday

Manager: Andy McLaughlin

SANDIACRE TOWN

Secretary: Mel Williams, 38 Pasture Rd.,Stapleford, Nottingham NG9 8GL(0115 9174079)
Ground & Directions: St Giles Park, Stanton Road, Sandiacre, Nottingham NG105EP (0115 939 2880). M1 jct 25, follow signs to Sandiacre passing Post House Hotel on right, straight over crossroads into Rushy Lane and towards Stanton Rd, 1st right after 1000yds into Stanton Rd, ground at bottom after another1000yds.
Capacity: 2,000   **Seats:** None   **Cover:** 250   **Floodlights:** Yes   **Shop:** No
Clubhouse: Members Club 8-11pm. Sunday lunch, Saturday 3.45-11pm. Snacks available
Honours: Central Mids Lg Premier Div 92-93 (Lg Cup 92-93), Midlands Regional Alliance R-up 91-92, Central Mids Lge Cup R-up 95-96.

Founded: 1978
Nickname : Saints
Colours:Navy with red frontpanel/navy/red
Change colours: Yellow/sky/yellow
Midweek Matchday: Tuesday
Programme: 44 pages 50p
Editor: Mel Williams (0115 917 4079)
Press Officer: Mel Williams
Manager: Andy Freeman

SELSTON

Secretary: Alan Jones, 6 Derwent Drive, Selston, Nott NG16 6QU (01773 780539)

Ground & Directions: The Town Ground,North Street, Alfreton, Derbyshire De55 7FZ
Leave M1 at Jct 28 and take exit A38(W) towards Derby.2nd exit after 2 miles -B600 .Right into Nottingham Road and left into North St., after 1/2 mile.Ground is 200 yds on right.

Capacity: 5,000 **Seating:** 302 **Cover:** 1,000 **Floodlights:** yes **Clubshop:** Yes
Clubhouse: Only open on matchdays. Hot and cold snacks available. Also Social Club next to car park open every day.

Founded: 1968
Colours:
Black & white stripes/black/white
Change Colours: Orange/white/white
Programme: 32-36 pages Price £1.00
Midweek Matches: Wednesday

Chairman: John Olney
Manager: Ronnie Wright

SHIREBROOK TOWN

Secretary: Steve Wall, 26 Carter Lane West, Shirebrook, Mansfield, Notts NG208NA (01623 747638).
Ground & Directions: BRSA Sports Ground, Langwith Rd, Shirebrook, Mansfield(01623 742535). M1 jct 29, A617 to Mansfield, 2.5 miles, onto B6407 to Shirebrook, through town to Langwith Rd. Clubhouse with refreshments at the ground.
Capacity: 2,000 **Seata:** None **Cover:** 400 **Floodlights:** Yes **Club Shop:**No
Honours: Central Midlands Lg Res Prem Div 94-95 95-96. Floodlit Cup winners 97-98
Most Appearances for club: G Quincey 282

Founded 1985
Colours: All Red & black
Change Colours: All blue
Midweek Matchday: Tuesday
Prog Editor: Mr Harworth (01623 748 375)
Website: football.shirebrook_net.co.uk

Chairman: Mr S.T. Brown (01623 743661)
Managers: S Greenwood, G Charlesworth

SNEINTON

Secretary: Albert Graves, 32 Shelford Road, Gedling, Nottingham NG4 4HW (01159878185)

Ground & Directions: Stoke Lane Gedling, Nottingham, A612 Nottingham to Southwell Road. Stoke Lane is situated off A612 between Gedling & Burton Joyce(signed Stoke Bardolph). Ground 200 yards on left over level crossing. BR. Nearest Station is Carlton.
Capacity: 1000 **Seats:** None **Cover:** 100   **Floodlights:** No   **Club Shop:** No
Clubhouse: No but snacks at Tea Bar.

Founded: 1904
Colours: Blue & black stripes/black/black
Change Colours: All Red
Midweek Matchday: Tuesday
Programme: Yes

Chairman: John W Stokeld
Manager: Tom Brookbanks

SOUTH NORMANTON ATHLETIC

Secretary: Andrew Meredith, 1 Erica Drive, South Normanton, Alfreton, Derbys. DE55 2ET
Tel: 01773 812566 (H) 0771 2568086 (B)
Ground & Directions: South Normanton Athletic FC, Lees Lane, South Normanton,Derby
(01773 581491). M1 Junc 28, B6019 towards South Normanton, right after 1mile (in South
Normanton) at BP garage into Market Street, after quarter mile turn left immediately after The
Clock pub into Lees Lane, ground at bottom on right. (Food available on matchdays)
Capacity: 3000   **Seats:** 150   **Cover:** 300   **Floodlights:**Yes
Clubhouse Yes - open on matchdays **Club Shop:** No

Formed: 1875
Colours: Yellow/navy/yellow
Change colours: Black & white/black/black
Programme: Yes - The Shiner
Midweek Matchday: Tuesday

Chairman: Glindon Davison
Manager: Rob Aitkin

WELBECK COLLIERY M.W.

Secretary: Les Graham, 10 Saville Way, Warsop, Mansfield, Notts. NG20 0DZ. Tel: 01623
844299
Ground: Elksley Road, Meden Vale, Mansfield. (01623 842611)
Directions: 1 1/2 miles off A60 between Worksop and Mansfield. Signed Meden vale. (do NOT
follow signs for Welbeck Colliery.) Turn off at Warsop Church.

Colours: White & navy/navy/white
Change: Black & yellow stripes/black/black

Manager: Graham Critchley

Honours: Notts Alliance Div 2 93-94 (Intermediate Cup 93-94), Chesterfield & District Lg 92-93

Top: Ripley Town FC.
Back Row (l-r): Kevin
Jackson (Mngr), Ben
Johnson (Trainer), Piers
Austin, Mark Barker,
Jason Lebosquet, Mark
Weedon, Scott Miles,
Mark Funnell, Dean
Moore, Mick Boam
(Secretary). Front Row (l-
r): Dean Parkin, Steve
Boyd, Stuart Burgin,
Wayne Allsop (cptn), Karl
Charlton, Stuart
Hollingworth. Mascots:
Stefan Jackson (left), Ben
Callanan (right) Photo:
Gordon Whittington

Centre: Heanor Town.
Back Row (l-r): Graham
Smith, Matt Freeman,
Matt Johnson, Darren
Gare, Alan Rigby, Paul
Standring, Richard
Preston, Steve Travis,
Garry Smith. Front Row:
Clive Ingram, Steve
Froggatt (Burton bound),
Glyn Stacey, Chris
Attwood (captain), Ian
Townsend, Lee Aldred.
Photo:
Gordon Whittington

Bottom: Sandiacre Town
FC. Back Row (l-r): Ian
Naylor (Comm Mngr),
Matt Lowe, Brian Howden,
Kevin Marsh, Paul Wilson,
Neil Walker, Norman
Limb, Paul Frizelle, Andy
Freeman (Manager),
Chris Millichip (Physio).
Front Row (l-r): James
Cameron, Ali Stevenitt,
Pete Davis (Cptn), Andy
Mason, Wes Armstrong,
Scott Wood, Gary
Devonport

ASKERN WELFARE

Secretary: Jon Stewart, 43 Sutton Road, Askern, Doncaster S.Yorks. DN6 0AG Tel Nos: 01302 702502 (H) 01302 703035 (W)
Ground & Directions: Askern Welfare Sports Ground, Doncaster Road, Askern,Doncaster (01302 700957). A1/A639 Pontefract. Follow sign for Askern/Campsall.At T-junction right. Left at Anne Arms, right at Supersave, ground on right.
Colours: White (navy trim)/navy/navy & white
Change colours: Orange/white/yellow
Manager: Paul Curtis   Midweek Matchday: Wednesday

BLIDWORTH WELFARE

Secretary: Paul Deakin, 8 Birks Road, Ladybrook Estate, Mansfield, Notts. NG19 6JU (01623 453812)
Ground & Directions: Welfare Ground, Mansfield Rd, Blidworth, Mansfield (01623 793361). On B6020, Rainworth side of Blidworth. From M1 jct 27 take A608 to Kirby and Annesley Woodhouse, at lights follow A611 to Kirby then take B6020through Ravenshead to Blidworth - thru village and ground at top of hill on right. From A1 follow A614 and A617 to Rainworth, left at lights then 1st right on to B6020 to Blidworth - ground on left at top of hill.

BOTTESFORD TOWN

Secretary: Jim Swan, 36 Cliff Drive, Burton-on-Stather, nr Scunthorpe, N. Lincs. DN15 9HW Tel: 01724 720474 (H) 01724 858661 (B)
Ground: Birch Park, Ontario Road, Bottesford, Scunthorpe, N. Lincs.
          Tel: 01724 871833
Directions: Exit M180 via M181 - Scunthorpe. At r'about right into Scotter Road. Over next r'about then 2nd left into South Park Rd., on to Sunningdale Rd. Right into Goodwood Rd, ground at end.
Colours: Blue & yellow/navy/yellow & navy
Manager: Alan Wilson

DINNINGTON TOWN

Secretary: Jon Paul Wilson, Whitewalls Farm, Swinston Hill Road, Dinnington, Sheffield S25 2RY Tel: 01909 - 569977 (H) 500050 (B)
Ground: Laughton Road, Dinnington. Tel: 0771 3460150
Directions: M1 Juncrion 31 onto A57 towards Worksop.
                          At 1st lights turn left to Dinnington. Follow road into
                          town centre and the ground is on the left.
Colours: Yellow/black/black
Manager: Steve Toyne

FOREST TOWN

Secretary: Richard Fell,   Tel: 01623 633480 (H)
                   8 Stanton Place, Mansfield, Notts. NG18 5PW
Ground: Forest Town Welfare Sports Ground, Clipstone Rd West
                   Forest Town, Mansfield, Notts. Tel: 01623 624678
Directions: From Mansfield follow signs for Clipstone/Forest Town.
                   The ground is situated at the Mansfield end of Forest
                   Town on the right.
Colours: Blue & green/blue/blue
Manager: Douglas Letherland

GRANTHAM RANGERS

Secretary: Geoffrey Green, 67 High Road, Barrowby, Grantham, Lincs. NG32 1BJ. Tel: 01476 563186 (H) 0976 977165 (B)
Ground & Directions: S.K.D.C. Stadium, The Meres, Trent Road, Grantham, Lincs.
Directions: A52 to Grantham over A1 to r'about - turn right into Barrowby Gate, go to next junction, turn right and then immediate left on to Trent Road. Stadium on the left.
Colours: Green & yellow/green/yellow
Manager: TBC

GREENWOOD MEADOWS

Secretary: Brain Hall, 34 Sullivan Close, Marmion Estate, St Ann's, NottinghamNG3 2HX (0115 958 2459)
Ground: Greenwood Meadows, Lenton Lane, Clifton, Nottingham.
          Tel: 0115 986 5913
Directions: M1 Junc 24 take A453Nottingham-Clifton Bridge to Lenton Ind Estate. Left into Old Lenton Lane.Ground second on right on lane.
Colours: Green & white/green/green
Managers: Brian Cawthorn & Chris Nicholson

KIVETON PARK

Secretary: David Carswell, 17 Chesnut Ave., Kiveton Park, Sheffield S26 5LN. Tel: 01909 515607 (H) 0797 427074 (B)
Ground: Hard Lane, Kiveton Park, Sheffield. Tel: 0797 4247074.
Directions: M1 Junct. 31. Take A57 Worksop road, first right to Todwick, at T junct. turn right. Follow road to Kiveton crossroads,. Go over and ground on right after approx 100m.
Colours: Blue & black stripe/black/black
Manager: Tony Fowkes

MEXBOROUGH TOWN ATHLETIC

Secretary: Nev Wheeler, 15 Holmshaw Drive, Sheffield, South Yorkshire S13 8UJ(0114 2694142).
Ground & Directions: Mexborough Athletic Club, New Oxford Road, Mexborough(01709 583426). M18 Junc 2, join A1 for 1 junc. Take Sheffield/Rotherham roadto Conisborough, take right beside castle to Denaby. Go through Denaby tor/about at Mexborough, take right turn into Adwick Road, ground on left
Colours: All blue & white Change colours: Red and black/black/black.
Manager: Nev Wheeler   Midweek Matchday: Tuesday

NORTH NOTTS

Secretary: Shaun Breen, 1 Loundhouse Close, Skegby, Sutton-in-Ashfield, Notts. NG17 3LA. Tel: 01623 461166 (H)
Ground: The Hosiery Mills Ground, Kings Mill Island, Mansfield Road, Sutton-in-Ashfield, Notts. Tel: 01623 552376
Directions: M1 Junct. 28 take A38 towards Mansfield. Turn off the A38 at Kings Mill Island, 1st left (Sutton sign), then 1st right into Hosiery Mills ground.
Colours: Royal blue, yellow trim/royal blue, yellow trim/royal blue
Jt. Managers: Les McJannett & Kevin Gee

OLLERTON TOWN

Secretary: Colin Gibson MBE, 10 Manor Close, Boughton, nr Newark, Nottm. NG22 9JS Tel: 01623 860816
Match Secretary: Jack Graham, 77 Petersmith Drive, New Ollerton.
Ground: Walesby Lane, New Ollerton, Notts
Directions: From Ollerton r'about om A614 take A6075 to Ollerton. At r'about first left & after 30m left into Walesby Lane.
Colours: All red
Manager: Alan Owen

RADFORD

Secretary: Karon Scott, 130 Melbourne Road, Aspley, Nottingham. NG8 5HN. Tel No; 0115 913 7868
Ground: Radford FC, Berridge Rd. West, off Radford Road, Radford, Nottm (0115 943250).
Directions: M1 Junc 26,take A610 to Nottingham, at duel carriageway turn right. Move to right lane andgo immediately right into Wilkinson St. At top turn right & right again at 2nd crossing.
Colours: Claret & sky blue/claret/claret
Manager: Colin Coultan   Midweek Matchday: Tuesday

RIPLEY TOWN

Secretary: Michael E Boam, 5 Valley Drive, Newthorpe, Notts. NG16 2DT. Tel: 01773 715277 (H) 0374 876794 (B)
Ground & Directions: Waingroves Brick Works, Peasehill Road, Ripley, Derbys. M1, J 28, A38 south to A610 signed Nottingham. Continue approx. 1 mile. Turn right into Steam Mill Lane, continue to Peasehill Road to brickworks.
Colours: Royal & white halves/royal/royal.
Manager: Jason Lebosquet

SHARDLOW ST JAMES

Secretary: Thomas Wake, 33 West End Drive, Shardlow, Derbys. DE72 2EY Tel: 01332 792636 (H) 01332 852586 (B)
Ground & Directions: The Wharf, Shardlow, Derby. (01332 799135), M1 Junc 24, A6 Derby/Leicester, 6 miles out of Derby at Shardlow take next left after Shardlowchurch (on right), ground 100yds on left.
Colours: Blue & white/blue/blue.
Manager: Trevor Hammond
Midweek Matchday: Wednesday

STANTON ILKESTON

Secretary: Jim Thornhill, 40 Pasture Road, Stapleford, Notts. NG9 8GL Tel: 0115 939 5740
Ground & Directions: Hallam Fields Sports Ground, Stanton Club, Hallam Fields,Nr Ilkeston, Derbys (0115 9323244), M1 (J26), take A52 Nottingham, then A6002for Ilkeston. Follow road through t/lights, turn right at next lights. Followroad to Rutland Windows. Turn left into Thurman St, to top turn left ground 200yds right.
Colours: All blue & white   Midweek Matchday: Mon. or Wed.
Managers: Jeff Smedley & Chris Trueman

TEVERSAL

Secretary: Kevin Newton, 8 Vere Ave., Sutton in Ashfield, Notts NG17 2ES (01623511402).
Ground & Directions: Teversal Grange Country Inn, Carnarvon Street, Teversal, Sutton-in-Ashfield, Notts. (01623 442021) M1, J28, A38 towards Mansfield. At r'about take A6075 Mansfield Woodhouse. Next lights left B6014, Stanton Hill. At r'about take A6014 Tibshelf. 2nd on right Carnarvon St., ground at the top.
Colours: Red & black/black
Managers: John Courtie & Andrew Farby

THORNE COLLIERY

Secretary: Glyn Jones, Top Town Social, Frederick Street, Grimsby DN31 1RG(01472 350554)
Ground & Directions: Miners Welfare, Grange Road, Moorends, Thorne, Doncaster.(01374 996474), M18 Junc 6, in THorne, turnat lights to Moorends, go almostthrough village, Grange Road on right.
Colours: Green & navy/navy/navy
Manager: Graham Jones
Midweek Matchday: Tuesday

YORKSHIRE MAIN

Secretary: Dennis Tymon, 22 Pamela Drive, Warmsworth, Doncaster DN4 9RP (01302852455)
Ground & Directions: Yorkshire Main Welfare, Edlington Lane, Edlington,Doncaster (01709 864075). A1M junc 36. Proceed on A630 towards Rotherham. At1st lights turn on to B6376. Ground on left after Fire Station.
Colours: Yellow/green/yellow
Manager: Derek Wynne
Midweek Matchday:

Selston FC. Back Row (l-r): Wayne Bradley (Manager), Micky Baines, Martin Jones, Dean Short, Darren Wright, Kevin Price, Jermaine Maxwell, Ian Clarke, Chris Morler, Maurice Bettison (Assistant Manager). Front Row (l-r): Lee Widdowson, Craig Johnstone, Matt Surgey, Darren England, Damon Giles, Kevin Jones, Ian Bettison. Photo: Bill Wheatcroft.

Stanton Ilkeston FC. Back Row (l-r): Jason Winfield, Richard Swain, Nick Ghislanzoni, James Wright, Andy Reddish, Kevin Munn, James Thornhill. Front Row: Keith Meek, Jez Tanner, Andy Flindall, Kevin Hilton, Lee Godsall. Photo: Gordon Whittington

NOTTS FOOTBALL ALLIANCE
Founded 1894
Chairman: Alan Wright
10 Farady Road, Mansfield NG18 4ES   Tel: 01623 624379 (H)
General Secretary & Treasurer: Godfrey Stafford
7 The Rushes, Gotham, Nottingham NG11 0HY   Tel: 01509 820737

The season started with a full compliment of teams, Kingswell FC reforming after being out of local football for some years, and Ollerton Town Reserves were the other team to join.

The Senior Division was won by Wollaton FC. They had to win their final match of the season, which they duly did, and runners up were Ollerton Town who unfortunately, after being in the League for the past ten years, have decided to leave for pastures greener!!

The First Division was won by Kimberley MW, who scored 124 goals and just pipped Kingswell by one goal for the highest goalscorers in the Alliance, they had a healthy 15 point lead at the end. Runners up were Abacus FC who came good in the final weeks of the season and overtook both Wollaton Reserves and Beeston Town, Town's last three matches proving to be a disaster.

Kingswell FC in the Second Division broke all existing records for the Notts Alliance, winning every single League match. Runners up were Calverton MW, who held off a strong challenge from Southwell City Reserves.

The Senior Cup was an all First Division affair, Kimberley MW achieving the double. The final was virtually over in the first twenty minutes when Kimberley scored five times, but credit to Chaffoteaux for the way they kept battling, reducing the deficit to 5.2.

The Intermediate Cup was a very close affair. Kingswell and Southwell City Reserves matched each other stride for stride, the first game finishing 3-3 and in the replay Kingswell came from behind to win in extra time, thus emulating Kimberley in doing the double.

Congratulations to Wollaton FC for reaching the semi-final of the Notts FA Senior Cup, thus upholding the Notts Alliance's high standard in this competition. Kimberley MW and Southbank FC both reached the semi-finals of the Notts FA Intermediate Cup, Kimberley losing on a penalty shoot-out to the eventual winners of the Cup, Eastwood Town Reserves.

The Fourth Division has finally been sanctioned, and fourteen teams have joined the League for the coming season.

FINAL LEAGUE TABLES 1999-2000

SENIOR DIVISION

	P	W	D	L	F	A	Pts
Wollaton FC	30	19	4	7	65	32	61
Ollerton Town	30	18	6	6	54	33	60
Keyworth United	30	17	5	8	69	51	56
Boots Athletic	30	16	5	9	75	49	53
IDP Newwark	30	16	5	9	74	49	53
Bilsthorpe CW	30	15	7	8	68	50	52
Attenborough FC	30	15	5	10	58	38	50
Linby CW	30	15	5	10	58	47	50
Southwell City	30	13	7	10	46	42	46
Rainworth MW	30	10	7	13	42	50	37
Notts Police	30	9	8	13	45	46	35
Clifton FC	30	10	4	16	49	66	34
Pelican FC	30	8	5	17	44	74	29
Ruddington United	30	6	6	18	38	76	24
Cotgrave CW	30	5	4	21	56	82	19
Retford United	30	5	3	22	31	85	18

FIRST DIVISION

	P	W	D	L	F	A	Pts
Kimberley MW	30	22	5	3	124	41	71
Abacus FC	30	16	8	6	69	46	56
Wollaton FC Reserves	30	18	2	10	59	56	56
Beeston Town	30	17	3	10	56	52	54
Chaffoteaux FC	30	13	11	6	54	33	50
Bestwood MW	30	15	5	10	56	49	50
Southbank FC	30	14	7	9	77	53	49
Matrixgrade FC	30	14	6	10	73	55	48
Radcliffe Oly	30	13	7	10	64	53	46
Thoresby CW	30	12	10	8	45	39	46
Bottesford St Marys	30	12	5	13	63	66	41
Boots Ath Reserves	30	7	7	16	32	66	28
Magdala Ams	30	7	5	18	36	62	26
Basford United	30	4	5	21	44	81	17
Awsworth Villa*	30	4	7	19	34	92	16
Gedling MW	30	3	4	23	38	80	13

	MANAGER OF THE YEAR	PLAYER OF THE YEAR	SPORTING TEAM OF THE YEAR
Senior Div	Pete Jepson, Wollaton FC	Gareth Rees, Boots Ath.	Southwell City, 12 points
First Div	George Hulley, Kimberley MW	Mark Brooks, Radcliffe Oly	Boots Athletic Res, 2 points
Second Div	Graham Walker, Kingswell FC	Bryn Parkes, City & Sherwood	Ruddington Utd Res, 5 points

419

ABACUS

Secretary: Trevor Lissaman
43 Carlton St., Mansfield, Notts NG18 2BG
Tel Nos: 01623 462993 (H)   0797 0722194 (M)

Ground: Sherwood Colliery Sports Ground,
Debdale Lane, Mansfield Woodhouse, Notts.
Tel: 01623 631747

Colours: Green & white stripes

ATTENBOROUGH

Secretary: Terry Allen, 5 Coningsby Road,Woodthorpe, Nottingham NG54LG Tel: 0115 920 0698
Ground & Directions: The Village Green, The Strand, Attenborough, Beeston,Nottingham. Midway between Beeston & Long Eaton on A6005 - adjacent to NatureReserve (via Attenborough Lane).
Colours: All Royal Blue
Change colours: White/black/black.

BILSTHORPE COLLIERY WELFARE

Secretary: Mick Cresswell, 40 Scarborough Road, Bilsthorpe, Nottingham. (01623 8700320

Ground: Eakring Road, Bilsthorpe, Notts

Colours: All royal blue

BOOTS ATHLETIC

Secretary: Ian Whitehead
21 Rosthwaite Close, West Bridgford, Nottingham NG26RA
Tel: 0115 981 2830 (H) 0115 968 7535 (B)
Ground: Lady Bay, West Bridgford, Nottingham Tel: 0115 981 2392
Colours: Blue&white stripes, bue,blue.

Honours: Notts Alliance Div 1 91-92 (Lg Cup 91-92), Notts Snr Cup R-up 93-94,Notts Inter R-up 91-92.

CLIFTON

Secretary: Pat Brodie, 21 Cerne Close, Clifton, Nottingham.
Tel: 0115 9215113

Ground: Green Lane, Clifton Est., Nottm Tel: 0115 984 4903

Colours: All white(Blue trim)

COTGRAVE COLLIERY WELFARE

Secretary: Kevin Whitehead, 51 Cross Hill, Cotgrave, Nottinham.
NG12 3NB Tel: 0115 989 4043

Ground: Cotgrave Welfare. Scheme Sports Ground

Colours: All red

I.D.P. NEWARK

Secretary: Kevin Presland, Appleby Lodge, Barnby Road, Newark, Nottingham NG24 2NE Tel: 01636 704606, 07771 507065

Ground: Lowfield Works, off hawton Lane, Balderton, Newark, Nottingham. Tel: 01636 702672

Colours: Orange/blue/orange

KEYWORTH UNITED

Secretary: Stuart Douglas
29 Ashley Crescent, Keyworth, Nottm. NG12 5GF
Tel: 0115 937 5358

Ground: Platt Lane, Keyworth (0115 937 5998)

Colours: Green/black/white

KIMBERLEY MINERS WELFARE

Secretary: Mick Walker
33 Maws Lane, Kimberley, Nottm. NG16 2JB.
Tel: 01159138199 (H) 07771 567145 (B)

Ground: Digby Street, Kimberley, Nottingham (0115 938 2124)

Colours: Black & red/black/black & red

LINBY COLLIERY WELFARE

Secretary: Mrs L. Stevenson,3 Chartwell Road, Kirkby in Ashfield, Nottingham NG17 7BH (01623 469975)

Ground: Church Lane, Linby, Nottingham

Colours: Red & white/white/red

NOTTINGHAMSHIRE POLICE

Secretary: John Beeston
17 Alandene Ave, Watnall, Nottingham NG16 1HH
Tel: 0115 938 2110

Ground: Police Training Centre, Epperstone, Notts.

Colours: All Navy Blue.
Honours: Notts Snr R-up 91-92, Notts All. Div 1 & Lge Snr Cup R-up 85-86, PAANNat. K-O Comp 63-64.

PELICAN

Secretary: Dave Eastwood, 42 Chetwin Road, Bilborough, Nottingham. NG8 4HN (0155 913 8345)
Ground: Brian Wakefield Sports Ground, Lenton Lane, Nottingham
Tel: 0115 986 8255
Colours: All Blue
Honours: Notts Alliance Lg Cup 90-91 (R-up 91-92 93-94).

RAINWORTH MINERS WELFARE

Secretary: Alan Wright, 10 Faraday Road, Mansfield NG18 4ES
Tel: 01623 624379 (H) 01623 553237 (B)
Ground: Kirklington Road, Rainworth, Notts
Directions: On A617 Mansfield - Newark Road
Colours: All white
Honours: Notts Alliance 77-78 78-79 79-80 80-81 81-82 82-83 (R-up 93-94, Lg Cup 81-82), Notts Snr Cup 80-81 81-82 (R-up 82-83 92-93), FA Vase R-up 82-82, ThornEMI F'lit Cup R-up 82-83 83-84 84-85

RUDDINGTON

Secretary: John Fisk, 3 Savages Rd., Ruddington, Nottm NG11 6EW
Tel: 0115 9842552
Ground & Directions: The Elms Park Ground, Loughborough Road, Ruddington (0115 984 4976) On A60 Nottm to Loughborough, 5 miles out of Nottingham.
Colours: Yellow & blue/blue/blue
Honours: Notts Comb. Lg 79-80, Lg Cup 70-71 76-77 80-81

SOUTHWELL CITY

Secretary: Pat Johnson 63 The Ropewalk, Southwell, Notts NG25 0AL
Tel: 01636 812594

Ground: War Memorial Recreation G round, Bishops Drive, Southwell, Notts. 01636 814386

Colours: Black& White stripes/black/black.

WOLLATON

Secretary: Jonathon Hunt
17 Chapman Court, Beechdale Mews, Nottingham NG8 3FQ
Tel: 0115 916 0174
Ground: Wollaton Sports Association, Wollaton Village, Nottm
Tel: 0115 9133 134
Colours: Sky Blue
Honours: Notts All. Div 1 R-up 92-93, Div 2 91-92, I'mediate Cup R-up 91-92.

AWSWORTH VILLA

Secretary: Paul Wilkinson
15 Barlow Drive North, Awsworth, Nottingham NG16 2RQ.
Tel: 0115 930 4905 (H) 0115 932 8721 (B)
Ground: Shilo Park, off Attewell Road, Awsworth, Nottm.
Colours: Red & white/red/red.

BASFORD UNITED

Secretary: Ron Walton.26 Redland Drive, Chilwell Nottingham
Tel: 0115 929 2027
Ground: Greenwich Ave., Bagnall Rd, Basford, Nottm (0115 942 3918). **Directions:** M1, J26 follow signs A610 Nottingham then B6004 Arnold into Mill St. **Colours:** Yellow/black/yellow

BEESTON TOWN

Secretary: Andy Meakin, 26 Redland Drive, Chilwell, Nottingham NG9 5LE Tel: 0115 967 7520
Ground: University Ground, Nottingham Tel: 0115 967 5517
Colours: All white

BESTWOOD MINERS WELFARE

Secretary: Alan Fisher,5 Skipton Close, Ilkeston, Derbyshire DE7 9HX (0115 932 7717)
Ground: Bestwood Workshops, Park Rd, Bestwood
Colours: Gold & black/black/black.

BOOTS ATHLETIC RESERVES

Secretary: Ian Whitehead, 21 Rosthwaite Close, West Bridgford, Nottingham NG2 6RA Tel: 0115 981 2830 (H) 0115 968 7535 (B)
Ground: Lady Bay, West Bridgford, Nottingham Tel: 0115 981 2392
Colours: Blue & white stripes/orange/orange

BOTTESFORD ST. MARYS

Secretary: Miss Micci Angeloni   Tel: 01476 593581
129 Stamford St., Grantham, Lincs. NG31 7BF
Ground: Village hall Playing Fields, Belvoir Rd., Bottesford
Colours: Dark red & black stripes/black/black

CALVERTON M.W.

Secretary: Dean Wilkinson, 46 Pepper Road, Calverton, Nottingham.
Tel: 0115 912 1105
Ground: Calverton Recreation Centre, Hollingwood Lane, Calverton, Nottingham Tel: 0115 965 4390 **Colours:** Blue/navy/navy

CHAFFOTEAUX

Secretary: Mark Nicholls, 31 Telford Drive, Newthorpe, Nottm. NG16 3NN 01773 534169 (H) 0115 942 2400(B)
Ground: Basil Russell Playing Fields, Maple Drive, Nuthall, Nottingham 0115 938 4765 **Colours:** Red & black/black/black

KINGSWELL

Secretary: Phil Smith, 1 Mowbray Rise, Arnold, Nottm NG5 5DW Tel: 0115 956 9585 (H) 07977 633051 (M)
Ground: Williams Lee Memorial Ground, Park Road, Calverton, Nottingham Tel: 0115 965 3097
Colours: Blue/white/blue

MAGDALA AMATEURS

Secretary: Alan Gilmour, 9 Adbolton Grove, West Bridgford, Nottingham NG2 5AR Tel: 0115 982 1071

Ground: Civil Service Sports Ground, Wilford Lane, W Bridgford.
Colours: Amber/Black/Black

MATRIXGRADE

Secretary: Barrie Kerry, 132 Common Lane, Hucknall, Nottm. NG15 6TG. Tel: 0115 953 3268
Ground: Carrington Sports Ground, Mansfield Rd., Nottm.
Colours: Yellow & black/black/black

RADCLIFFE OLYMPIC

Secretary: C Johnson, 2 The Firs, Holme Pierrepoint, Nottingham NG12 2LT Tel: 0115 933 3791
Ground: Wharf Lane, Radcliffe-on-Trent, Nottingham
Colours: All Black with Beige & red trim

RETFORD UNITED
Secretary: Jeff Lamb, 18 Northumbria Drive, Retford, Nottingham DN22 7PR Tel: 01777 705833
Ground: Cannon Park, Leverton Road, Retford
Colours: Black & white stripes/black/black

SOUTHBANK
Secretary: Gerry Bishop, 4 Foxearth Ave., Clifton, Nottm. NG11 8JQ Tel: 0115 984 2363
Ground: Haywood Comprehensive School, Edwards lane, Sherwood, Nottingham. **Colours:** Red & White Stripes/White/Red

THORESBY COLLIERY WELFARE
Secretary: Barry Reece,125 Henton Road, Edwinstowe, NottinghamNG219LD (01623 822415)

Ground: Thoresby Colliery, Fourth Avenue, Edwinstowe, Nr Mansfield
Colours: Black & White Stripes/ Black/ Black & White.

WOLLATON RESERVES
Secretary: Jonathon Hunt, 17 Chapman Court, Beechdale Mews, Nottingham NG8 3FQ   Tel: 0115 916 0174
Ground: Wollaton Sports Association, Wollaton Village, Nottm   Tel: 0115 9133 134
Colours: Sky blue/sky blue/blue

ASC DAYNCOURT
Secretary: Adrian Cridge, 3 Regina Close, Radcliffe on Trent, Nottingham NG12 2EL. Tel: 0115 933 4771

EASTLAKE ATHLETIC
Secretary: Andrew Fletcher, 62 Suthers Road, Kegworth, Derby DE74 2DF Tel: 01509 674752

I.D.P. NEWARK Reserves Sec: as IDP Newark - Senior Div.

GEDLING M.W.
Secretary: Norman Hay, 182 Gedling Rd., Arnold, Nottm. NG5 6NY Tel: 0115 926 5598

KEYWORTH UTD Reserves Sec: as Keyworth Utd - Senior Div.

KIRKTON BRICKWORKS
Secretary: Stuart Douglas, 29 Ashley Crescent, Keyworth, Nottingham NG12 5GF Tel: 0115 937 5358

MELTON MOWBRAY
Secretary: Anne Gibbon, 39 Main Street, Kirby Bellars, Melton Mowbray, Leics. LE14 2EA Tel: 0116 481 2675

NEWARK TOWN
Secretary: David Wildes, Forest Cottage, Brough, Newark, Nottingham NG23 7QZ Tel: 01636 676038

PELICAN Reserves   Sec: as Pelican - Senior Division
PINXTON NORTH END
Secretary: Terry Gospel, 16 PeelRoad, Mansfield, Nottingham NG19 6HB Tel: 01623 634915

RUDDINGTON UTD Reserves Sec: as Ruddington Utd. - Senior Div.

SANDHURST
Secretary: Robert Crawford, 4 The Brambles, Walesby, Newark, Nottingham NG22 9PH Tel: 01623 862985

SOUTHWELL CITY Reserves   Sec: as Southwell C. - Senior Div.

Newly Formed
DIVISION THREE (for Reserve sides)

ATTENBOROUGH RESERVES
AWSWORTH VILLA RESERVES
BASFORD UNITED RESERVES
BEESTON TOWN RESERVES
CHAFFOTEAUX RESERVES
CLIFTON RESERVES
COTGRAVE C.W. RESERVES
KIMBERLEY M.W. RESERVES
LINBY C.W. RESERVES
REDCLIFFE OLYMPICS RESERVES
RAINWORTH M.W. RESERVES
RETFORD UNITED RESERVES
SOUTHBANK RESERVES
THORESBY C.W. RESERVES

THE NON-LEAGUE PAPER
CONFERENCE & PYRAMID LEAGUES SOCCER / £1.00
AVAILABLE AT A NEWSAGENT NEAR YOU EVERY SUNDAY

MIDLAND LEAGUE

FINAL LEAGUE TABLE 1999-2000

	P	W	D	L	F	A	Pts		P	W	D	L	F	A	Pts
Stone Dominoes	38	29	4	5	127	36	91	Stallington	38	14	10	14	59	66	52
Eccleshall	38	24	7	7	80	35	79	Abbey Hulton Utd	38	13	11	14	70	64	50
Audley	38	21	13	4	76	41	76	Milton United	38	12	10	16	56	62	46
Redgate Clayton	38	22	8	8	89	42	74	Hanley Town	38	13	7	18	60	67	46
Hanford	38	21	8	9	79	39	71	Nantwich Town Res	38	13	6	19	61	85	45
Brocton	38	16	11	11	85	47	59	Rists United	38	12	8	18	56	70	44
Vale Juniors	38	16	10	12	74	73	58	Ball Haye Green	38	10	13	15	68	68	43
Adderley Green	38	16	9	13	74	77	57	Cheadle Town OB	38	8	6	24	60	115	30
Baddeley G Rgrs	38	14	14	10	65	43	56	Foley	38	5	5	28	46	132	20
Norton United	38	14	10	14	61	56	52	Goldenhill Wdrs	38	1	2	35	35	163	5

RESULTS CHART 1999-2000

		1	2	3	4	5	6	7	8	9	10	11	12	13	14	15	16	17	18	19	20
1	Abbey Hulton Utd	X	1-1	0-1	1-1	3-2	2-0	3-3	1-2	5-1	7-2	1-1	3-1	2-0	1-1	0-1	0-1	0-2	0-0	0-6	5-5
2	Adderley Green	1-0	X	3-1	1-1	0-4	1-0	3-1	2-2	4-1	4-3	1-3	1-2	2-2	1-3	4-2	1-3	0-1	2-2	2-7	4-3
3	Audley	2-4	3-3	X	2-0	1-1	5-2	4-2	1-1	3-1	3-0	4-3	1-0	2-1	5-0	2-2	2-1	2-1	1-1	3-0	4-0
4	Baddeley Grn Rngrs	1-0	0-1	2-2	X	3-1	1-1	10-0	0-2	1-0	6-0	0-0	2-2	1-1	2-2	1-1	0-0	3-1	1-1	1-3	2-1
5	Ball Haye Green	1-4	2-3	3-0	1-2	X	1-1	2-2	1-1	1-1	7-0	0-3	2-1	0-0	5-1	3-1	1-3	0-0	1-2	1-2	3-1
6	Brocton	3-0	1-1	1-1	1-2	1-1	X	4-2	1-0	11-0	3-0	2-1	3-0	4-0	9-1	1-2	1-1	3-0	3-1	2-2	3-0
7	Cheadle Old Boys	0-0	0-2	0-2	0-4	3-1	1-1	X	0-2	1-5	6-2	0-3	2-2	3-1	1-5	1-1	1-4	2-3	1-2	1-4	1-3
8	Eccleshall	2-2	4-0	0-3	1-0	2-1	2-1	7-2	X	7-0	2-1	3-0	2-1	1-1	1-1	3-0	1-0	1-1	0-3	1-2	2-0
9	Foley	2-3	3-1	1-4	1-5	0-5	2-5	1-5	0-7	X	5-1	0-1	1-4	1-3	2-3	1-1	0-4	1-1	6-1	0-6	2-4
10	Goldenhill Wndrs	1-8	0-4	0-2	1-0	3-3	2-6	2-4	0-4	2-3	X	1-5	0-4	1-4	0-4	0-4	1-10	2-4	0-3	0-6	0-3
11	Hanford	1-1	1-2	1-1	2-0	0-0	2-0	2-0	2-1	5-1	3-1	X	6-0	1-1	7-0	3-3	3-0	3-0	3-2	1-2	0-2
12	Hanley Town	2-1	1-2	1-1	0-2	0-0	1-1	4-0	1-3	4-1	2-2	0-3	X	1-0	4-1	0-2	0-3	2-3	1-3	0-2	1-1
13	Milton United	1-1	2-2	0-1	2-0	2-2	0-2	4-3	2-3	5-1	3-0	0-1	2-5	X	2-1	1-1	3-1	3-0	0-2	1-3	2-0
14	Nantwich Town Res	2-3	4-1	2-1	0-3	1-4	0-3	2-2	0-1	1-1	2-0	2-0	1-2	3-2	X	3-1	1-3	1-3	2-3	1-2	0-1
15	Norton United	2-1	3-1	0-0	0-2	3-1	1-0	1-2	1-0	6-0	5-3	1-0	2-1	1-0	3-0	X	0-1	1-3	1-1	1-3	1-2
16	Redgate Clayton	5-0	2-1	1-1	2-2	6-0	2-1	3-1	1-4	0-0	7-0	3-1	3-2	1-1	1-1	1-0	X	2-0	0-1	1-3	4-2
17	Rists United	0-2	1-2	1-2	2-2	2-2	0-0	2-1	1-2	3-1	6-0	1-2	0-2	3-0	0-1	4-2	0-3	X	1-1	0-5	2-3
18	Stallington	2-1	0-4	0-1	3-0	1-3	2-2	1-2	1-2	2-0	3-2	2-4	1-3	0-2	3-1	1-1	1-3	2-2	X	0-1	2-2
19	Stone Dominoes	5-1	4-2	1-1	2-0	6-0	4-0	10-2	0-1	4-0	6-1	0-1	3-1	7-0	0-2	1-1	3-1	4-2	5-0	X	2-2
20	Vale Juniors	0-3	4-4	1-1	2-2	3-2	3-2	3-2	1-0	3-0	2-1	1-1	0-0	0-2	2-5	3-2	2-2	5-0	2-3	2-1	X

LEAGUE CUP 1999-2000

FIRST ROUND

Eccleshall	v	Cheadle Old Boys	5-0	Goldenhill Wndrs	v	Nantwich Town Res	1-3
Hanford	v	Hanley Town	1-2	Rists United	v	Abbey Hulton Utd	0-1

SECOND ROUND

Audley	v	Foley	6-0	Baddeley Grn Rngrs	v	Abbey Hulton Utd	3-1
Brocton	v	Adderley Green	2-3	Eccleshall	v	Vale Juniors	4-1
Hanford	v	Redgate Clayton	3-1	Nantwich Town Res	v	Norton United	2-3
Stallington	v	Ball Haye Green	1-3	Stone Dominoes	v	Milton United	2-3

QUARTER-FINALS

Adderley Green	v	Milton United	3-0	Baddeley Grn Rngrs	v	Hanley Town	3-2
Ball Haye Green	v	Audley	1-2	Eccleshall	v	Norton United	5-3

SEMI-FINALS

Adderley Green	v	Eccleshall	5-2	Baddeley Grn Rngrs	v	Audley	2-4

FINAL

Adderley Green	v	Audley	2-1	at Kidsgrove Athletic FC	

CONSTITUTION FOR 2000-01

Abbey Hulton Utd, Adderley Green, Audley, Baddeley Green Rngrs, Ball Haye Green, Brocton, Cheadle Town Old Boys, Eccleshall, Foley, Hanford, Hanley Town, Milton Utd, Norton Utd, Redgate Clayton, Rists Utd, Stallington, Vale Juniors

LINCOLNSHIRE LEAGUE

FINAL LEAGUE TABLE 1999-2000

		P	W	D	L	F	A	Pts
1	Boston United Reserves	34	27	7	0	145	39	88
2	Limestone Rangers	34	23	8	3	94	48	77
3	Barton Town Old Boys	34	20	9	5	104	53	69
4	Grimsby & Immingham Amat.	34	18	11	5	84	49	65
5	Lincoln United Reserves	34	16	8	10	64	42	56
6	Epworth Town LC	34	14	8	12	48	45	50
7	Bottesford Town	34	14	6	14	67	81	48
8	Lorne Stewart Barrowby	34	13	7	14	69	74	46
9	Skegness Town	34	11	10	13	58	62	43
10	Wyberton	34	12	5	17	53	69	41
11	Appleby Frodingham Athletic	34	12	5	17	47	63	41
12	Sleaford Town	34	10	9	15	56	54	39
13	Alstom Sports	34	9	12	13	52	62	39
14	Horncastle Town	34	9	6	19	46	86	33
15	Louth United Reserves	34	8	8	18	47	72	32
16	Hykeham Town	34	9	4	21	52	82	31
17	Lincoln Moorlands Reserves	34	7	6	21	48	92	27
18	BRSA Retford	34	6	7	21	37	98	25

CONSTITUTION FOR 2000-01

Alstom Sports, Appleby Frodingham Athletic, Barrowby United, BRSA Retford, Epworth Town, Grantham Town Reserves, Grimsby & Immingham Amateurs, Horncastle Town, Hykeham Town, Limestone Rangers, Lincoln Moorlands Reserves, Lincoln United Reserves, Louth United Reserves, Skegness Town, Sleaford Town

NOW IN ITS RECORD 10TH YEAR OF PUBLICATION

BRITAIN'S MOST POPULAR NATIONAL NON-LEAGUE FOOTBALL MONTHLY

TEAM TALK

Team Talk should be available from your local non-League football club or your local newsagent and is available by subscription from the publishers.

Team Talk is published by Non League Media Plc, c/o Helland, North Curry, Taunton, Somerset TA3 6DU
Tel: 01823 490080 Fax: 01823 490281 e-mail: tony.williams12@virgin.net

ALB**A**NY
THE UNINSURED LOSS RECOVERY SERVICE

NORTHERN LEAGUE
Founded 1889

President: George Courtney MBE   **Chairman:** M Amos
Hon. Secretary & Treasurer: A Golightly, 85 Park Road North, Chester-le-Street,
Co Durham DH3 3SA   Tel: 0191 388 2056   Fax: 0191 3891 1385

Whilst others ate, drank and made merry, the Northern League marked the millennium with a sumptuous 530 page history, concluding that there was nothing new under the sun or - since the first floodlit match was played in 1890 - under the moon, either.

The ball, it was reported, could be made out perfectly well except in the centre of the pitch. On the League's opening day, September 7 1889, a match kicked off 45 minutes after time because British Rail (or one of its arthritic predecessors) turned up late with the trippers. As early as 1893 there was a mass players' brawl and a pitch invasion; in 1929-30 no fewer than 341 players were suspended by Durham FA for alleged financial irregularities - shamateurism, in other words - and on several occasions the North-East weather was so cold that matches had to be abandoned to save the remaining players from frostbite.

What's changed, perhaps, are the regular four (and sometimes five) figure crowds, the special trains, the fiercely contested elections for club committees, the derbies that were as much a part of Christmas Day as turkey, stuffing and a homily from Buckingham Palace, the News Chronicle song sheets, the flat caps, the corncrakes and the days when a big mac was a grey gaberdine raincoat, size 44 chest.

The world's second oldest league carries on confidently, nonetheless, conscious of its heritage but forever aware that times change. They even have fast food joints in the North-East these days.

Among the latest innovations was the formation last summer of the Northern League Club, the launch attended by former England manager Bobby Robson and by many members of the public. The Club, which already has over 250 members in Britain and beyond, offers an information service to anyone interested in the League or the region.

Benefits of the £10 initial membership (£7.50 in subsequent years) include an enamel lapel badge, comprehensive monthly newsletter and fixtures and results guide, competitions, regular copy of the League magazine, discounts and special offers to members - a free programme, perhaps, or a free hot drink - at many clubs. The much acclaimed League magazine, incidentally, celebrated its tenth birthday at the end of 1999 and costs just 30p for 24 pages - as it did when, rather more humbly, it was launched. Football offers no better value.

On the field, Bedlington Terriers completed a hat trick of first division championships despite an impressive run by unfancied Seaham Red Star - once 21 points ahead of the Terriers, though having played many games more - who fell away at the end but finished a highly commendable second. However, Bedlington were unable to repeat the previous season's Wembley march - losing to Chippenham in the quarter-final - and for the first time since 1996 a Northern League side failed to make the FA Carlsberg Vase final.

Brandon United, relegated in 1993-94, took the second division title after a splendid season in which they also reached the Durham Challenge Cup final, losing to Darlington Reserves. Newcastle Blue Star, who lost to Newcastle United Reserves in the Northumberland Senior Cup final, were promoted after just one season in the lower division with Hebburn taking the third promotion place.

The first division in 2000-01 will operate with 21 clubs after Whitely Bay - who left the Northern League in 1988, before the League was a partner in the Pyramid - were relegated from the Unibond. No Northern league club sought promotion in the other direction, after Dunston Federation Brewery withdrew their application and sparked further debate about the workings of the Northern Pyramid.

Dunston chiefly cited the greatly increased cost of travel to clubs in the Manchester and Liverpool areas, and beyond, but also admitted that they were very happy where they were. Though a small number of Northern League clubs would still take promotion if in the top two at the end of the season, the interest in advancement is nothing like as great as in the Unibond's two other feeders - whose geographical catchment areas are much more closely aligned to that of the Unibond.

Amid the danger that North-East clubs could become isolated for reasons unconnected with lack of ambition - simply with cost - the feeling grows that the structure of the Northern Pyramid may again need to be re-examined. For the fourth successive year, no one was promoted from either of the Northern League's two feeders.

Dunston, incidentally, won the League Challenge Cup for the third successive season - only the second time the hat-trick has been achieved - with a stylish victory over Durham City. Hebburn took the Craven Cup, for second division clubs, in a 2-1 win against Alnwick Town.

Other awards proliferated. Veteran Consett centre half Jeff Sugden was voted the League's player of the year, free scoring Bedlington striker John Milner won the BBC Radio Newcastle Player of the Year award, and Tow Law and Penrith the good conduct awards. Horden assistant secretary (and much else) Sylvia Wood lifted the Unsung Hero award, Guisborough Town had the best programme, Peterlee the best tea hut, and Murton the warmest welcome. Millennium history author Brian Hunt won the Arthur Clark memorial award and referee Colin Webster - promoted to the Football League middle with 25-year-old colleague Mark Clattenburg - the silver whistle.

Referees had also attended an inaugural pre-season meeting with League officers in an attempt to bring greater consistency to decision making and to provide a vehicle for an informal exchange of views. It worked very well; this season the gathering will also be open to assistant referees.

In an attempt to improve discipline off the field as well as on it, several club officials have also had warnings or final warnings - usually after being reported for verbal abuse. They have been left in no doubt that a suspension from the League would follow a second offence.

Chiefly, however, the League goes along very happily - not least because of the comfort blanket provided by it principal sponsor, Brooks Mileson and his group of companies. The Arnott Insurance Northern League for the past three seasons, now becomes the Albany Northern League - but with the same overwhelmingly generous benefactor and another three year deal. (That was the one written on the inside flap of a Marlboro packet, Brooks' preferred smoke, but worth its weight in gold.)

As a token of the League's gratitude, many clubs have already raised money for the Butterwick Children's Hospice in Stockton, which is also supported by Mr Mileson.

The new seasons begins with Murton forced into a ground sharing arrangement after a huge crater appeared in their pitch, but with all 40 clubs determined successfully to mark the first full season of the new millennium. For the first time there will be "golden goals" in the League and Craven Cups, too. Whatever happens, they say, it'll all be in the next book.

- The profusely illustrated and expertly printed Northern Goalfields Revisited, complied by Brian Hunt and edited by League chairman Mike Amos, costs £8.99 and is available (plus £3 postage) from Joe Burlison, 4 Carrowmore Road, Chester-le-Street, Co Durham. A de luxe edition, leather bound and gold tooled, will be available before Christmas. Details from Joe Burlison.
- Details of Northern League Club membership from Martin Haworth, 17 The Turn, Morpeth, Northumberland NE612 DU
- Northern Ventures Northern Gains, the Northern League magazine, cost £3.30 (including postage) for six seasonal issues from Peter Lax, 21 Carlton Avenue, Billingham, Cleveland.

Mike Amos

FINAL LEAGUE TABLES 1999-2000
DIVISION ONE

		P	W	D	L	F	A	W	D	L	F	A	Pts
				Home						Away			
1	Bedlington Terriers	38	16	1	2	50	10	9	7	3	39	15	83
2	Seaham Red Star	38	9	3	7	28	35	14	2	3	35	14	74
3	Dunston Fed.	38	10	3	6	36	19	10	4	5	36	22	67
4	Marske United	38	13	2	4	39	19	6	6	7	28	25	65
5	West Auckland Town	38	9	7	3	35	18	8	7	4	30	25	65
6	Billingham Synthonia	38	8	5	6	41	32	9	1	9	31	32	57
7	Jarrow Roofing	38	9	5	5	29	26	6	7	6	35	35	57
8	Morpeth Town	38	9	7	3	33	22	5	8	6	22	34	57
9	Consett	38	7	9	3	30	18	5	9	5	27	25	54
10	Tow Law Town	38	8	4	7	37	26	7	4	8	28	29	53
11	Billingham Town	38	10	4	5	35	23	3	9	7	23	24	52
12	Guisborough Town	38	9	4	6	26	24	6	3	10	31	37	52
13	Chester le Street Town	38	6	7	6	27	32	8	2	9	30	35	51
14	Crook Town	38	5	10	4	26	29	8	1	10	29	28	50
15	Durham City	38	4	7	8	19	30	7	6	6	31	31	46
16	Peterlee Newtown	38	7	3	9	31	37	6	4	9	25	39	46
17	Easington Colliery	38	8	5	6	34	33	2	6	11	22	40	41
18	Thornaby on Tees	38	3	6	10	23	36	4	6	9	24	32	33
19	Shotton Comrades	38	2	4	13	18	46	2	5	12	18	42	21
20	South Shields	38	2	4	13	17	45	1	3	15	16	50	16

FA Vase Round Six
Chippenham Town 2
Bedlington Terriers 2
An action packed defence as Bedlington Terriers' Craig Melrose heads onto the crossbar during the first-half of this Vase tie at Hardenhuish Park.
Photo: Martin Wray

FINAL LEAGUE TABLES 1999-2000

DIVISION TWO

		P	Home					Away					Pts
			W	D	L	F	A	W	D	L	F	A	
1	Brandon United	36	11	6	1	37	12	14	3	1	45	12	84
2	Newcastle Blue Star	36	13	1	4	43	18	11	4	3	51	25	77
3	Hebburn	36	12	3	3	37	14	10	1	7	35	21	70
4	Northallerton FC 1994	36	15	2	1	45	12	6	3	9	31	36	68
5	Shildon	36	12	2	4	34	23	8	5	5	28	21	67
6	Willington	36	12	2	4	44	17	9	1	8	37	24	66
7	Washington Ikeda Hoover	36	10	4	4	59	30	9	3	6	36	27	64
8	Norton & Stockton Anc.	36	10	4	4	34	17	8	4	6	36	34	62
9	Ashington	36	8	6	4	47	15	9	4	5	45	21	61
10	Penrith	36	8	6	4	42	24	7	5	6	27	16	56
11	Alnwick Town	36	10	1	7	38	27	6	6	6	40	31	55
12	Horden C W	36	10	3	5	32	26	3	7	8	21	31	49
13	Prudhoe Town	36	6	5	7	34	41	5	4	9	25	33	39
14	EvenwoodTown	36	7	4	7	34	47	4	2	12	23	53	39
15	Esh Winning	36	7	1	10	32	43	4	1	13	27	38	35
16	Kennek Ryhope CA	36	5	4	9	25	31	4	3	11	24	39	34
17	Whickham	36	3	3	12	17	40	3	4	11	10	30	25
18	Murton	36	1	3	14	10	53	0	1	17	11	80	7
19	Eppleton C W	36	0	2	16	14	70	0	1	17	8	86	3

DIVISION ONE RESULTS CHART 1999-2000

		1	2	3	4	5	6	7	8	9	10	11	12	13	14	15	16	17	18	19	20
1	Bedlington Terriers	X	0-1	3-1	5-0	3-0	2-1	3-0	2-0	4-0	3-1	2-2	4-1	6-0	2-1	0-1	2-0	3-1	1-0	3-0	2-0
2	B'ham Synthonia	1-4	X	2-1	1-1	1-1	2-0	2-2	1-4	2-1	2-3	2-2	2-4	2-1	4-0	0-1	3-1	4-0	6-1	1-2	3-3
3	Billingham Town	1-2	2-1	X	2-1	3-1	2-0	2-0	1-3	2-2	1-0	2-1	2-1	1-1	1-2	1-2	1-1	4-0	2-2	1-2	4-1
4	Chester le Street	0-3	1-3	0-0	X	1-3	2-3	1-1	0-0	3-1	4-3	2-2	1-1	1-1	3-3	0-1	3-1	2-1	1-0	1-0	1-5
5	Consett	0-0	2-0	0-0	4-2	X	0-0	1-1	2-1	0-3	2-2	1-2	1-1	3-0	1-2	3-1	2-0	5-0	1-1	0-0	2-2
6	Crook Town	1-5	1-5	0-0	1-1	3-2	X	0-1	1-1	3-0	2-1	3-3	0-0	1-1	3-2	2-2	3-3	1-0	0-1	0-0	1-1
7	Dunston Fed.	2-0	3-0	1-1	0-2	0-2	1-0	X	4-0	0-2	1-1	2-1	2-0	1-1	7-0	0-4	4-1	3-0	4-0	0-2	1-2
8	Durham City	2-1	0-1	3-3	0-5	1-1	1-3	0-1	X	1-1	0-2	0-2	0-0	2-3	1-3	0-0	0-0	3-2	2-0	3-2	0-0
9	Easington Coll	0-0	5-3	3-2	0-3	2-1	0-2	0-1	4-4	X	1-1	2-5	2-1	0-0	2-2	0-1	3-1	3-1	3-2	4-2	0-1
10	Guisborough T	1-0	3-1	1-0	5-3	1-1	0-2	1-0	1-2	2-1	X	2-0	0-5	0-1	2-0	1-2	2-2	0-0	2-0	2-2	0-2
11	Jarrow Roofing	0-3	2-2	3-2	1-2	1-1	1-0	0-4	3-1	2-1	3-1	X	3-1	0-2	0-0	0-3	1-0	2-2	5-0	2-1	0-0
12	Marske Utd	2-2	1-4	3-0	1-0	1-0	4-0	1-2	2-1	1-0	2-0	4-1	X	2-1	0-0	2-1	5-0	5-1	2-1	0-2	1-3
13	Morpeth T	1-4	2-0	0-0	0-1	2-2	2-1	2-2	1-1	0-0	3-0	1-1	2-1	X	3-2	1-3	2-0	2-1	1-1	2-1	6-1
14	Peterlee N	2-2	0-1	2-0	1-1	2-1	2-1	2-3	5-2	2-3	4-3	0-1	1-1	X	0-1	0-4	3-1	0-5	3-1	1-4	
15	Seaham R S	0-4	2-0	1-4	2-0	0-0	2-4	2-0	1-5	2-0	2-5	3-2	1-0	2-1	2-1	X	3-1	1-0	1-1	2-3	1-2
16	Shotton Com.	1-4	0-3	1-1	2-1	2-2	2-4	0-3	1-1	2-2	2-3	0-1	0-3	2-4	0-2	1-3	X	2-4	0-1	0-4	1-0
17	South Shields	1-1	0-3	0-5	1-2	1-3	1-5	0-4	1-1	5-1	0-1	1-1	2-4	0-1	1-2	0-1	1-0	X	1-8	1-2	0-0
18	Thornaby on Tees	0-0	1-0	0-2	3-4	1-2	1-2	0-4	1-2	1-1	4-2	0-1	2-2	2-2	0-3	1-3	2-2	1-1	X	3-1	0-2
19	Tow Law Town	0-3	2-3	1-1	3-0	1-4	1-0	2-4	0-1	3-2	3-1	2-3	0-1	1-1	6-0	2-1	5-0	4-0	0-0	X	1-1
20	West Auckland	1-1	5-0	0-0	3-0	0-0	2-1	3-5	3-0	2-0	2-1	2-2	1-1	7-0	1-0	0-4	0-1	2-1	0-0	1-1	X

FA Vase Round Six
Chippenham Town 2
Bedlington Terriers 2
Dean Gibb gets past Bluebirds skipper
Lee Burns and heads just wide of the
goal during the opening minutes of the
match at Hardenhuish Park.
Photo: Martin Wray

427

ARNOTT INSURANCE LEAGUE CUP 1999-2000

FIRST ROUND

Newcastle Blue Star	v	Peterlee Newtown	0-1		Chester le Street T	v	Durham City	1-3
Marske United	v	West Auckland Town	2-1		Shotton Comrades	v	Billingham Syn	4-4, 3p4
Willington	v	Tow Law Town	0-1					

SECOND ROUND

Bedlington Terriers	v	Consett	3-1		Billingham Town	v	Esh Winning	5-0
Crook Town	v	Shildon	6-3		Easington Colliery	v	Eppleton CW	3-2
Evenwood Town	v	Jarrow Roofing	4-6		Kennek Ryhope	v	South Shields	1-3
Norton & Stockton	v	Northallerton	4-2		Penrith	v	Whickham	2-4
Prudhoe Town	v	Alnwick Town	4-4		Seaham Red Star	v	Thornaby on Tees	2-4
Washington I H	v	Ashington	1-0		Dunston Federation	v	Prudhoe Town	3-0
Guisborough Town	v	Tow Law Town	3-2		Horden CW	v	Durham City	3-5
Brandon United	v	Billingham Synthonia	5-3		Easington Colliery	v	Morpeth Town	1-4
Murton	v	Hebburn	0-2		Peterlee Newtown	v	Marske United	1-2

THIRD ROUND

Dunston Federation	v	Marske United	4-1		Guisborough Town	v	Whickham	3-1
Bedlington Terriers	v	Norton & Stockton A	3-1		Billingham Town	v	Washington IH	1-2
Jarrow Roofing	v	Thornaby on Tees	2-1		Durham City	v	Hebburn	1-0
Morpeth Town	v	South Shields	2-2, 4p6		Brandon United	v	Crook Town	4-0

FOURTH ROUND

Dunston Federation	v	Washington IH	5-2		Durham City	v	South Shields	2-1
Brandon United	v	Guisborough Town	3-0		Jarrow Roofing	v	Bedlington Terriers	0-2

SEMI-FINALS

Durham City	v	Brandon United	2-2, 3p2		Bedlington Terriers	v	Dunston Fed	1-1, 3p0

FINAL

Dunston Federation	v	Durham City	4-0		at Jarrow Roofing FC

CRAVEN CUP 1999-2000

FIRST ROUND

Eppleton CW	v	Brandon United	1-7		Norton & Stockton A	v	Hebburn	1-2
Shildon	v	Whickham	1-0					

SECOND ROUND

Alnwick Town	v	Willington	4-1		Evenwood Town	v	Penrith	2-1
Horden CW	v	Prudhoe Town	5-2		Kennek Ryhope CA	v	Northallerton 1994	0-3
Washington IH	v	Ashington	3-0		Murton	v	Hebburn	2-2, 2p3
Evenwood Town	v	Newcastle Blue Star	0-2		Shildon	v	Esh Winning	3-4

THIRD ROUND

Alnwick Town	v	Northallerton 1994	3-2		Esh Winning	v	Hebburn	1-2
Newcastle Blue Star	v	Horden CW	2-0		Brandon United	v	Washington IH	4-1

SEMI-FINALS

Brandon United	v	Alnwick Town	0-2		Hebburn	v	Newcastle Blue Star	3-2

FINAL

Alnwick Town	v	Hebburn	1-3		at Newcastle Blue Star FC

FA Vase Round Six
Chippenham Town 2
Bedlington Terriers 2
The goal that set up a replay! Ace goalscorer John Milner (Bedlington Terriers) fires in a cracking shot to equalise in the second half at Hardenhuish Park, bringing the score to 2-2.
Photo: Martin Wray

BEDLINGTON TERRIERS

FACT FILE

Secretary:Shaun Campbell,106 Wright St., Blyth. Northumberland NE24 1HG
    Tel: 01670 353823 (H) 0403 529 869 (M)
Ground: Welfare Park, Park Rd., Bedlington, Northumberland. Tel: 01670 825485
Directions: Into Bedlington, turn left at `Northumberland Arms' on Front St.,then 2nd Right,
    ground on right 100 yds
Capacity: 3,000   Seats: 300   Cover:500   Floodlights: Yes
Clubhouse: Open every evening, 7-11pm Sat. & Sun lunch. Pool, darts etc Club Shop: Yes
Record Att: 2,400 v Colchester U   **Record Seasons Scorer:** John Milner 63 , 98-99

HONOURS Northern League Div 197-98 98-9 99-00 R-up: 85-86 9596 Div 2 94-95 (R-up 84-85), Northern Alliance 66-67 (R-up 67-68 69-70 71-72) Lg Cup 57-58 66-67 69-70 81-82, Lge Chall Cup 96-97,Northumberland Sen Cup 96-97. 97-98 Cleator Cup 97-88, 98-99, 99-00

PREVIOUS   **Leagues:** Northern Alliance   **Names:** Bedlington Mechanics 49-53;
    Colliery Welfare 53-56; Mechanics 56- 61; Bedlington United 61-65;
    Bedlington Colliery 65-68; Bedlington Town 68-74.

BEST SEASON   **FA Cup:** 2nd Rd v Scunthorpe(a) 0-1 **FA Vase:** Final 98-9 VTiverton T 0-1

RECORDS   **Attendance:** 1,013 v Blyth Spartans, Northern Lg 85-86
    Win: 11-0 v West Auckland, (H) Lge 96-97   **Scorer:** John Milner 33

Formed: 1949
Colours: Red & white/red&white/white
Change colours: Blue & whitw/blue&white/blue
Midweek Matches: Wednesday
Programme: 50 pages, £1.00
1999-00
Captain: Warren Teasdale
Top Scorer: John Milner (57)

CLUB PERSONNEL

Chairman: David Perry
(0468 195350)
Vice Chairman: John Feary
Press Officer: Jeff King (01670 735824)
Managers: Keith Perry & Tony Lowrey
Assistant Manager: Steven Locker
Coach: Melvyn Harmison
Physio: Dave Robertson

BILLINGHAM SYNTHONIA

FACT FILE

Secretary: Graham Craggs, 2 Ribble Close, Billingham, Cleveland TS22 5NT Tel: 01642 535856

Ground: The Stadium, Central Avenue, Billingham, Cleveland (Press Box 01642 532348)

Directions: Turn off A19 onto A1027 signposted Billingham, Norton (this applies from either
    north or south), continue straight on along Central Avenue, ground on left
    opposite office block. 1 mile from Billingham (BR)
Capacity: 1,970   Seats: 370   Cover: 370   Floodlights: Yes

Clubhouse: Onthe ground. Normal club hours   **Club Shop:** No
HONOURS   Northern Lg 56-57 88-89 89-90 95-96, R-up 49-50 50-51 51-52, Lg Cup 51-
    52 87-88 89-90, Div 2 86-87, Teeside Lg 36-37 (Lg Cup 34-35 38-39),
    Durham Chall. Cup 88-89 90-91, North Riding Snr Cup 66-67 71-72, North
    Riding Amat. Cup 38-39 56-57 62-63 63-64.

PREVIOUS   **League:** Teeside (1923-War)   **Name:** Billingham Synthonia Recreation

BEST SEASON   **FA Amateur Cup** 4th Rd 48-49   **FA Vase:**
    FA Trophy: Q-F replay 93-94, 1-2 v Woking after 1-1 (A)
    FA Cup:1st Rd 48-49 51-52 56-57 57-58 87-88 89-90

RECORDS   **Attendance:** 4,200 v Bishop Auck. 6/9/58
    Scorer: Tony Hetherington   **Appearances:** Andy Harbron

Founded: 1923
Nickname: Synners
Sponsors: Billingham Arms Hotel
Colours: Green & White quarters/white/white
Change colours: Blue & White
Midweek Matches: Tuesdays
Programme: 40 pages (+ads),75p
Editor: Nigel Atkinson (01642 342469)
1999-00
Captain: Glen Corkain
Top Scorer: Charlie Butler

CLUB PERSONNEL

Chairman: Stuart Coleby
President: Frank Cook
Press Officer: Secretary
Manager: Stuart Coleby
Physio: Tommy Cushley
Coach: Lenny Gunn

BILLINGHAM TOWN

FACT FILE

Secretary: Glen Youngman,13 Blackthorne Grove, fairfield, Stockton, Cleveland TS19 7DG
Tel/Fax: 01642 655516 and Tel: 01642 862058

Ground: Bedford Terrace, Billingham, Cleveland. Tel: 01642 560043

Directions: Leave A19 on A1027 (signed Billingham). Turn left at 3rd r/bout,over bridge 1st left,
    1st left again to grd
Capacity: 3,000   Seats: 176   Cover: 600   Floodlights: Yes
Clubhouse: Open matchdays. Hot & cold food   **Club Shop:** No

HONOURS   Durham Amateur Cup 76-77 77-78, Teesside Lg 77-78 81-82, Nth Riding
    Snr Cup R-up 76-77 81-82, Stockton & Dist. Lg(3)
PREVIOUS   **Leagues :** Stockton & Dist. 68-74; Teesside 74-82.
    Name: Billingham Social Club (pre-1982)   **Ground:** Mill Lane (pre-1974)
BEST SEASON   **FA Cup:** 1st Rd Proper 55-56
    FA Vase:
RECORDS   **Attendance:** 1,500 v Manchester City, FA Youth Cup 1985
    Scorer: Paul Rowntree 100
    Appearances: Darren Marsh, 250 in Northern League
Players progressing: Gary Pallister (Middlesbrough), Gerry Forrest (Southampton), Dave Robinson (Halifax),
Tony Barratt (Hartlepool), Mark Hine (Grimsby), Tony Hall(Middlesbrough), Graham Hall (Arsenal).

Founded: 1967
Nickname: The Social
Colours: All Blue
Change colours: Yellow/green/yellow
Midweek Matches: Tuesday
Reserves' Lge: Stockton & Dist Sunday
Programme: 28 pages, 50p
Editor: Alex Matthews (01642 653621)

CLUB PERSONNEL

Chairman: Peter Martin
Hon.President: F Cook M.P.
President: G A Maxwell
Press Officer: Secretary
Manager: Trevor Arnold
Asst Manager/Coach: Neal Granycome

BRANDON UNITED

Secretary: Brian Richardson, Flat 2, 30 Commercial St, Brandon, Durham DH7 8PL
Tel: 0191 378 1373

Ground: Welfare Ground, rear of Commercial St., Brandon, Durham Tel: 0191 378 2957

Directions: A690 - 3 miles west of Durham City. Buses 49 & 49A from Durham

Capacity: 3,000   Seats: 200   Cover: 300   Floodlights: Yes   **Club Shop:** No
Clubhouse: Open every day, lunch & evening. Pool Entertainment at weekends

HONOURS   FA Sunday Cup 75-76, Northern Lg Div 2 84-85 99-00Northern All.(2) 77-79,
Lg Cup 77-78 79-80 Sunderland Shipowners Cup 81-82, Durham Co. Sunday Cup 73-74 75-76
76-77,Durham & Dist Sunday Lg(4) 73-77 (Div 2 69-70, Div 3 68-69), Staffieri Cup 75-76

PREVIOUS   **Leagues:** Durham & Dist. Sunday 68-77; Northern All. 77-80;
Northern Amtr 80-81; Wearside 81-83.
BEST SEASON   **FA Cup:** 1st Rd replay 88-89 (lost to Doncaster). Also 1st Rd 79-80
FA Vase: QF 82-83 83-84   **FA Trophy:** 3rd Qual. Rd 87-88 89-90
RECORD   **Gate:** 2,500, FA Sunday Cup SF
Record Goalscorer: Tommy Holden
Most Appearances: Derek Charlton 1977-86
Players progressing: Bryan Liddle (Hartlepool 1984) Dean Gibb (Hartlepool 1986),
Paul Dalton (Manchester Utd 1988), Neil Richardson (Rotherham).

FACT FILE
Founded: 1968
Nickname: United
Sponsors: Bramble Down Landscapes
Colours: All red   Change colours: All blue
Midweek Matches: Wednesday
Programme: 40 pages, 30p
Editor: Keith Nellis (0191 378 0704)

1999-00
Top Scorer: Graeme McDonald (27)
Club Captain: Andrew Cunningham

CLUB PERSONNEL
Chairman: Neil Scott
Vice Chairman: John Dickinson
President: Brian Hewitt
Press Officer: Secretary

Manager: Ken Lindoe
Physio: Keith Glendenning

CHESTER-LE-STREET TOWN

Secretary: Melvin Atkinson, 1 St Marys Close, Chester-le-Street, Co Durham DH2 3EG
Tel: 0191 288 3664
Ground: Moor Park, Chester Moor, Chester-le Street, County Durham (0191 388 3363)
Directions: Ground lies approx 2 miles south of town on A167 (C.-le-S. to Durham). Regular
buses from C.-le-S. and Durham pass ground. Railway station 2 miles distant in town centre
Capacity: 3,500   Seats: 150   Cover: 1,500   Floodlights: Yes
Open Matchdays- midweek 6.30p.m.- 11.00 p.m. Saturday 12.00p.m.-7.00.Open Monday 7..30-
11.00pm **Club Shop:** No, but old programmes available from editor

HONOURS   Northern Lg Div 2 83-84 97-98; Wearside Lg 80-81 (R-up 82-83);
Monkwearmouth Cup 80-81 81-82; Washington Lg; Durham Minor Cup; Washington AM Cup.
PREVIOUS   **Leagues:** Newcastle City Amtr 72-75; Washington 75; Wearside 77-83
Names: Garden Farm 72-78

BEST SEASON   **FA Cup: 4th Qual. Rd. 86-87, 2-3 v Caernarfon Town (H)**
FA Vase : 5th Rd v Fleetwood Town 84-85 (1-1,2-2,0-3)

RECORD   **Gate:** 893 v Fleetwood FA Vase 18/2/85,
(3000 Sunderland v Newcastle,Bradford appeal match 85)
Appearances: Dean Ferry 219 (+38 subs)
Win: 9-0 v Washington N.L. 28/2/98   **Defeat:** 0-7 v Consett 6/11/96

FACT FILE
Founded: 1972
Nickname: Cestrians
Colours: Blue & white hoops/white/white
Change colours: All yellow
Midweek Matches: Tuesday
Programme: 40 pages, 50p
Editor/Press Officer:J.Thornback

CLUB PERSONNEL
Chairman: John Tomlinson
Vice Chairman: Jack Thornback
President: John Holden
Press Off.: Jack Thornback (0191 3883554)
Manager: Paul Bryson
Asst Mgr/Coach: Stuart Sherwood
Physio: Ray Hartley

CONSETT

Secretary: Ian Hamilton, 29 Grange Street, Delves Lane, Consett, Co. Durham DH87AG
Tel: 01207 509366
Ground: Belle Vue Park, Ashdale Road, Consett, County Durham (01207 503788)
Directions: Quarter of mile north of town centre - along Medomsley Rd, left down Ashdale Rd,
ground 100m yards on left. Follow signs for Sports Centre and Baths
Capacity: 4,000   Seats: 400   Cover: 1,000   Floodlights: Yes
Clubhouse: Matchdays, and evenings on request. Darts & pool   **Club Shop:** No

HONOURS   North Eastern Lg 39-40 (Div 2 26-27, Lg Cup 50-51(jt) 53-54), Durham
Challenge 5, (R-up 2), Northern Lg R-up 76-77 (Div 2 88-89, Lg Cup 78-79 80-81), Northern
Counties Lg 61-62, Sunderland Shipowners Cup 67-68, Monkwearmouth Charity Cup 67-68,
Wearside Lg 68-69 69-70.
PREVIOUS   **Leagues:** Northern Alliance 19-26 35-37; North Eastern 26-35 37-58 62-64;
Midland 58-60; Northern Counties 60-62; Wearside 64-70
Grounds: Vicarage Field (pre-1948); Leadgates Eden Colliery 48-50
BEST SEASON   **FA Cup:** 1st Rd 58-59, 0-5 v Doncaster Rov. (A)
FA Trophy: 2nd Rd 78-79.   **FA Vase:**
RECORD Gate: 7,000 v Sunderland Reserves, first match at Belle Vue, 1950.
Players progressing: Tommy Lumley (Charlton), Alan Ellison (Reading), Laurie Cunningham
(Barnsley), Jimmy Moir (Carlisle), Jackie Boyd (West Bromwich Albion).

FACT FILE
Founded: 1899
Nickname: Steelmen
Colours: Red with black & white trim/black/red
Change colours: Sky blue/dark blue/sky blue
Midweek Matches: Wednesday
Programme: 16 pages, 30p
Programme Editor: Colin French
Local Press: Journal, Northern Echo,
Consett Advertiser.

CLUB PERSONNEL
Chairman: D.Nicholls
Vice Chairman: I Hamilton
President: D McVickers
Press Officer: Andrew Pearson
Tel: 01207 506194
Manager: Colin Carr
Physio: Joe Darroch

CROOK TOWN

Secretary: Alan Stewart, The Wardens Flat, 47 Grasmere Grove, Crook, Co Durham DL15 8NX
Tel: 01388 763425

Ground: Millfield Ground, West Road, Crook, County Durham (01388 762959)
Directions: 400 yds west of town centre on Wolsingham Road (A689). Nearest BR station is Bishop Auckland (5 miles). Buses 1A & 1B from Bishop Auckland or X46& X47 from Durham
Capacity: 3,500   **Seats:** 400   **Cover:** 300   **Floodlights:** Yes
Clubhouse: Lic Bar open matchdays. Hot & Cold Food available from Shop   **Club Shop:** Yes

HONOURS   FA Amateur Cup Winners 00-01 53-54 58-59 61-62 63-64; Northern Lg 5, (R-up 4), Lg Cup 3, (R-up 4); Durham Challenge Cup 26-27 31-32 54-55 59-60; Durham Benevolent Bowl 5; Ernest Armstrong Mem Trophy 97.

PREVIOUS   **Leagues:** Auckland & Dist. 1894-96; Northern 1896-28 29-30; DurhamCentral 28-29; North Eastern 30-36; Wartime Durham & Northumberland 40-41;Durham Cen. 41-45.

BEST SEASON   **FA Cup:** 3rd Rd, v Leicester 31-32. 2nd Rd(4), 1st Rd.(10)
      FA Trophy: 3rd Rd 76-77   **FA Vase:** 4th Rd 99-00
      FA Amateur Cup: Winners 5 times, plus S-F x 3

RECORD Attendance: 17,500 v Walton & Hersham, FA Amateur Cup Q-F, 24/02/52
      Scorer: Ronnie Thompson 1175 52-65   **Appearances:** Jimmy McMillan 505, 51-68
      Win: 12-0 v South Bank twice, (H) 5/4/58 & (A) 12/4/58, Northern Lge.
      Defeat: 0-11 v Bishop Auckland (A), Northern Lge 17/12/38

FACT FILE
Formed: 1889   Nickname: Black & Ambers
Sponsors: Federation Brewery
Colours: Amber/black/black
Change colours: All White
Midweek Matches: Wednesday
Programme: Yes
Editor: Secretary
1999-00
Captain: Michael Vasey
Top Scorer: Paul Harnett (24)
P.o.Y.:Mark Eccles

CLUB PERSONNEL
Chairman: William Penman
Vice-Chairman:Wilf Dobinson
President: Sir Tom Cowie O.B.E.
Press Officer: Secretary
Manager: Dennis Pinkney
Physio: Melanie Stewart

DUNSTON FEDERATION BREWERY

Secretary: Bill Montague, 12 Dundee Close, Chapel House, Newcastle-upon-Tyne NE5 1JJ
      Tel: 0191 267 2250
Ground: Federation Park, Wellington Road, Dunston, Gateshead   Tel: 0191 493 2935
Directions: Dunston/Whickham exit off A1(M), ground 400 yds north along Dunston Rd on left. 1 mile from Dunston or Metrocentre stations. Buses from Gateshead & Metrocentre stop outside ground
Capacity: 2,000   Seats:120   Cover: 400   Floodlights: Yes
Clubhouse: Matchdays only. Hot & cold snacks, darts.   **Club Shop:** No

HONOURS Northern Lg Challenge Cup 97-8,98-9,99-00 Northern Lg Div 2 92-93, Northern Amtr Lg 77-78 (R-up 2), Lg Cup 77-7878-79 (R-up 75-76), Lg Shield 78-79 79-80), Wearside Lg 88-89 89-90) (R-up 90-91, Lg Cup 90-91), Northern Comb. 86-87 (R-up 3), Lg Cup 83-84 86-87 (R-up 3),Sunderland Shipowners Cup 87-88, Durham Co Tphy 81-82 (R-up 2), Minor Cup79-80 (R-up 78-79)), Gateshead Charity Cup 77-78 80-81, Heddon Homes Cup 80-81.
PREVIOUS   **Ground:** Dunston public park 75-86
      Names: Whickham Sports; Dunston Mechanics Sports
BEST SEASON   **FA Vase:** Quarter-Finals 92-93, 0-2 v Gresley Rov. (A)
      FA Cup: 3rd Qual. Rd 92-93, 0-3 v Northallerton T.
RECORDS   **Attendance:** 1,550 - Sunderland Shipowners Cup Final 1/4/88
Win: 11-0 v Willington (A), Northern Lge Div. 2, 92-93   **Scorer:** Paul King
Defeat: 1-6 v Billingham Synthonia (A), Northern Lge Div. 1, 94-95 **Appearances:** Paul Dixon

FACT FILE
Founded: 1975
Nickname: The Fed
Sponsors: Federation Brewery
Colours: All blue (white trim)
Change colours :All red
Midweek matchday: Tuesday
Floodlights: Yes
Reserve s' League : None
Programme: 28 pages,50p
Editor: Ian McPherson (0191 420 5583)

CLUB PERSONNEL
Chairman: Malcolm James
Vice-Chairman: Fred Fowles
President: John Smart
Press Officer: Ian McPherson (0191 420 5583)
Commercial Secretary: Malcolm James
Manager: Bobby Scaife
Asst Manager: Perry Briggs
Physio: Wayne Farrage

DURHAM CITY

Secretary: Kevin Hewitt, 21 Cerrytree Drive, Langley Park,Co Durham DH7 9FX
      Tel: 0191 3733878 (H 7 FAX) 0191 383 4200 (W)
Ground: New Ferens Park, Belmont Durham (0191 386 9616)
Directions
Capacity: **Seats:**   **Cover:** 300   **Floodlights: Yes**

HONOURS   Northern Lg 94-95 (R-up 70-71, Div 2 R-up 30-31 91-92), Durham Benevolent Bowl 55-56, Durham Challenge Cup R-up (2).Northern Div 2 Champions 98-99, Div 2 Champions 98-99 Durham Challenge Cup R-up (3)
PREVIOUS   **Leagues:** Victory 18-19; N Eastern 19-21 28-38; Football Lge 21-28; Wearside 38-39 50-51.   **Grounds:** Garden House Park 18-21; Holliday Park 21-38; Ferens Park 49-94. NB club disbanded in 1938
BEST SEASON   **FA Cup:** 2nd Rd 25-26 57-58 (Also 1st Rd 27-28 55-56)
      FA Vase: QF 87-88   **FA Amateur Cup:** 2nd Rd rep. 57-58
      FA Trophy: 1st Rd 83-84
RECORD   **Appearances:** Joe Raine, 552

Players progressing: Harry Houlahan (Newcastle 51), Derek Clark (Lincoln 51),Leo Dale & David Adamson (Doncaster 54/70), Stan Johnstone (Gateshead 54),Dennis Coughlan (Barnsley 57), John Wile (Sunderland 66), Brian Taylor(Coventry 68), Paul Malcolm (Rochdale 84)

FACT FILE
Reformed: 1949
Nickname: City
Sponsors: Durham City Housing Partnership
Colours: Blue & Gold Halves/Blue/Blue
Change colours:Red & White
Stripes,white/white
Midweek Matches: Tuesday
Programme: 30 pages
Editor: Gordon Wright (0191 3869616)
Local Press: Northern Echo,
Sunderland Echo, Evening Chronicle

CLUB PERSONNEL
Chairman: Stewart Dawson
Vice Chairman: David Asbery
President: Stewart Dawson
Commercial Manager: David Willis
Press Officer: Secretary
Manager: Brian Honour
Asst Manager/Coach: Derek Bell
Physio: Joanne Dowson

Above: Billingham Synthonia. Back Row (l-r): Brendan Lowes, John Jackson, Paul Brown, Chris Rooney, Gary Popple, Dean McGee, Thomas Marron, David Connor, Chris Fawcett, David O'Gorman, Drew Coverdale, Charlie Butler, Lenny Gunn (Coach). Front Row (l-r): Andrew Ripley, David Baker, Kraig Wilkinson, Glenn Corkan, Ian Williams, Tony Wood, Sean O'Brien, Chris McFee. Photo: Bill Wheatcroft.

Left: Brandon United Back Row (l-r): M Cunningham, K Lindoe (Manager), S Hamil, A Cuthbertson, G Carter, B Cole, D Johnson, M Spragg, A Purvis, D Robson, K Glendenning (Physio), G Clarke. Front Row (l-r): D Smith, A Cunningham, C Myers, G Macdonald, M Patterson, S Pigg, J Ewart, Mascot, C Cuthbertson

Left: Dunston Federation Brewery Back Row (l-r): Elliott Milburn, Keith Mills, Billy Irwin, Andy Hutchinson, Neil Shotton, Kenny Goodrick, Nick Scaife Front Row (l-r): Paul Hogg, Cary Forbes, Andy Elliott, Derek Ord Photo: Bill Wheatcroft

EASINGTON COLLIERY

Secretary: Alan Purvis, 12 Wark Crescent, Jarrow, Tyne & Wear, NE32 4SH (0191489 6930)

Ground: Easington Colliery Welfare Ground, CW Park, Easington, Co Durham. (0191527 3047)

Directions: A19 Easington turn-off, B1284 thru Easington till Black Diamond PH(next to zebra crossing), grd right
Capacity: 2,450   Seats: 175   Cover: 475   Floodlights: Yes
Club Shop: No
Clubhouse: Normal licensing hours. Pies, soup and sandwiches available

HONORS	Northern Lg Div 2 R-up 85-86; Wearside Lge 29-30 31-32 32-33 47-48 48-49, R-up 28-29 46-47 73-74, Lg Cup 32-33 45-46 61-62; Monkwearmouth Cup 30-31 47-48 75-76; Sunderland Shipowners Cup 74-75 79-80.
PREVIOUS	**Leagues:** Wearside 13-37 39-64 73-88
BEST SEASON	**FA Cup:** 1st Round Proper 55-56
	FA Trophy: 2nd Qual. Rd replay 88-89 **FA Vase:** 4th Rd replay 82-83
RECORD	**Attendance:** 4,500 v Tranmere Rovers, FA Cup 1st Round 1955
	Scorer: Andrew McKenna **Appearances:** David Howard
Players progressing:	Ron Greener (Newcastle 1951), Frank Wayman (Darlington1957), John Langridge (Hartlepool 1982).

FACT FILE
Founded: 1913
Nickname: The Colliery
Sponsors: T.B.A.
Colours: Green & white stripes/green/green
Change colours: Yellow/green/yellow
Midweek Matches: Tuesday
Reserves' League : None
Programme: Yes   Editor: Charlie Dodds
1999-00
Captain: Chris Pearson & Ben Davies
P.o.Y.:Andrew Allen
Top Scorer: Andrew McKenna

CLUB PERSONNEL
Chairman: Tommy Goodrum
Vice-Chairman: T.B.A.
Press Officer: Alan Purvis
Manager: Wilf Constantine
Asst Mgr/Coach: Tony Metcalfe

GUISBOROUGH TOWN

Secretary: Keith Smeltzer, 55 Thames Ave., Guisborough, Cleveland TS14 8AR(01287 638993)

Ground: King George V Ground, Howlbeck Rd, Guisborough, Cleveland (01287636925)

Directions: From west: bear left at 2nd set of lights, left into Howlbeck Rd after quarter mile, ground at end. Buses from Middlesbrough
Capacity: 3,500   Seats: 150   Cover: 400   Floodlights: Yes   Club Shop: Yes
Clubhouse: Open evenings & weekends. Hot & cold snacks & drinks from kitchen on matchdays

HONORS	FA Vase R-up 79-80; Northern Lg Cup 87-88 (Div 2 R-up 86-87), Northern Alliance 79-80 (R-up 78-79, Lg Cup 78-79); N. Riding Sen. Cup 89-90 90-91 91-92 92-93 94-95.
PREVIOUS	**Leagues:** Middlesbrough & District; South Bank; Northern Alliance 77-80; Midland Counties 80-82; Northern Counties (East) 82-85.
BEST SEASON	**FA Cup:** 1st Round Proper 88-89, 0-1 v Bury **F.A.Vase:** Finalists 79-80
	FA Trophy: 1st Rd Proper 90-91 91-92 92-93
CLUB RECORDS	**Gate:** 3,112 v Hungerford, FA Vase SF, 1980
	(at Middlesbrough FC - 5,990 v Bury, FA Cup 1st Rd 1988)
	Goalscorer: Mark Davis 323 **Appearances:** Mark Davis 551
	Win: 6-0 v Ferryhill & v Easington **Defeat:** 0-4 v Billingham Synthonia

FACT FILE
Founded: 1973   Nickname: Priorymen
Sponsors: K.Home Engineering
Colours: Red & white stripes/Black/Red
Change colours: Yellow
Midweek matchday:Tuesday
Reserves ' League: Teesside Strongarm
Programme: 32 pages,50p
Editor: M Hollinworth (01287 637737)
Local Press: Northern Echo,
Middlesbrough Evening Gazette

CLUB PERSONNEL
Chairman:Dennis Cope
Vce Chairman: Keith Watson
President: Vacant
Press Officer: Mike Hollinworth
Manager: Mark Forster
Asst Manager: Steve Corden
Physio: Steve Carter

HEBBURN TOWN

Secretary: Tom Derrick, 63 Staneway, Felling, Gateshead, NE10 8LS.Tel: 0191 442 1563

Ground: Hebburn Sports & Social Ground, Victoria Road West, Hebburn Tel: 0191 483 5101

Directions: On the main road through the town about 1 mile from railway station. Hebburn lies on the Metroline - excellent bus service from Heworth Metro
Capacity: 2,000   Seats: 153   Cover: 420   Floodlights: Yes   **Club Shop:** No
Clubhouse: Open 7-11pm weekdays, Sat 11am-1pm, Sun noon-2.30pm. Pool, darts etc

PREVIOUS   Leagues: Jarrow & Dist. Jnr 12-14; SShields Comb. 19-22; Tyneside Comb. 22-27; Tyneside 27-39; Northern Comb. 41-44 45-59; North Eastern 44-45 59-60; Wearside 60-89.
Names: Reyrolles; Hebburn Reyrolles (pre-1988), Hebburn 88-00
HONORS Shields Gazette Cup 91-92, Wearside Lg 66-67 (Monkwearmouth Charity Cup 68-69), Durham Challenge Cup 42-43 91-92, Tyneside Lg 38-39, Northern Comb. 43-44, Gateshead Charity Cup 35-36 37-38, Palmer Hospital Cup 27-28, Hebburn Aged Miners Cup 35-36, Heddon Homes Cup 42-43, Hebburn Infirmary Cup 35-36 36-37 37-38 38-39, Craven Cup 99-00.

BEST SEASON FA Vase: 2nd Rd 91-92 **FA Cup:** 2nd Qual. Rd rep. 89-90, 0-3 v South Bank (A)

RECORD Attendance: 503 v Darwen, FA Cup Prel. Rd replay 7/9/91 **Win:** 10-1 **Defeat** 3-10

FACT FILE

Founded: 1912
Nickname: Hornets
Colours: Yellow /navy blue/yellow
Change colours:Blue and White stripes/black
Midweek Matches: Wednesday
Programme: 24 pages, 30p
Editor: Steve Newton

CLUB PERSONNEL

Chairman: Bill Laffey
Vice-Chairman: Brian Errington
Press Officer: Alan Armstrong 0191 483 2086

Manager: Tony Robinson
Coach: Norman Dryden

Penrith FC. Back Row (l-r): Jeff Rayson (Manager), Nigel McCombie, Alan Stewart, Kev Walker, James Holland, Anthony Rayson, Sonny Askins, Gary Greenan, Ross Cowperthwaite, John Wharton, Jane Barrow (Physio). Front Row: James Thompson, Tim Bell, Paul Rigby, Jamie Howard, Jamie Heath, Colin Dalglish, Neil Edmundson, Simon Savage, Alan Scott. Photo: Bill Wheatcroft

Shotton Comrades. Photo: Bill Wheatcroft

West Auckland Town. Back Row (l-r): G Forster (Manager), D Hellanby, D Kemp-Amber, I Fleming, D Jackson, A Sams, G Lowes, L Innes, P Adamson, G Cowell, J Milroy, D Swainston (Assistant Manager). Front Row (l-r): A Sinclair, M Wheldon, D Bainbridge, K Gorman, P Stout, G Hornsby, G Innes, N Johnson. Photo: S Peart

JARROW ROOFING BOLDON C.A.

Secretary/Manager: Richard McLoughlin, 8 Kitchener Terrace, Jarrow NE32 5PU
Tel: 0191 489 9825

Ground: Boldon CA Sports Ground, New Road, Boldon Colliery (0191 519 1391)

Directions: A19 to junction with A184 (Sunderland/Newcastle). Follow signs to Boldon Asda stores, then to North Road Social Club. Ground behind. East Boldon(BR) 800 yds.

Capacity: 3,500   Seats: 150   Cover: 800   Floodlights: Yes   Club Shop: Yes

Clubhouse: Open eves.& w/e lunchtimes. Hotdogs, burgers etc from tea bar on matchdays

HONOURS	Wearside Lg Div 2 R-up 91-92 95-96; Sunderland Shipowners Cup R-up 93-94, 94-95; Tyneside Amtr Lg R-up 90-91, Chal. Shield 90-91 (R-up 89-90); Bill Dixon Cup 90-91; Mid-Tyne Lg 87-88; Fred Giles Cup R-up 87-88; Gateshead Charity Cup SF 90-91; Monkwearmouth Cup 94-95; Craven Cup 96-97, Northern League Div One Cup R-Up 98-98
PREVIOUS	**Leagues:** Mid-Tyne; Tyneside Amtr 88-91; Vaux Wearside
RECORD	**Attendance:** 500 v South Shields
	Appearances: Mick Haley **Goalscorer:** Paul Thompson

FACT FILE
Founded: 1987
Nickname: Roofing
Sponsors: Jarrow Roofing Co
Colours: Yellow with Blue trim/ Royal Blue/Yellow
Change colours: Yellow & Black
Midweek matchday: Wednesday
Programme: 20 pages, free with entry
Editor: Brian Marshall (0191 4217011)

CLUB PERSONNEL
Chairman: Richard McLoughlin
Press Officer/Treasurer: Rose McLoughlin
Manager/ Secretary: Richard McLoughlin
Coach: John Oliver
Physio: Fred Corner/Alan Leslie

MARSKE UNITED

Secretary: Ian Rowe, 19 High Row, Loftus, Saltburn By The Sea, Cleveland. TS134SA
Tel: 01287 643440 (H) 01642 230546 (B) 01642 241273 (Fax)

Ground: Mount Pleasant, Mount Pleasant Ave., Marske, Redcar, Cleveland. Tel: 01642 471091

Directions: From A19 take A174 exit marked Yarm, Teesport, Redcar, Whitby and head east towards Saltburn until Quarry Lane r/about. Take 1st left (A1085) into Marske, 1st right (Meadow Rd) then 1st left (Southfield Rd),then 1st left again Mount Pleasant Ave directly into car park.
By train: Darlington to Saltburn, Marske station 300 yds from ground.

Capacity: 2,500   Seats: 169   Cover: 300   Floodlights: Yes

Clubhouse: Open every night and weekend lunchtimes. Food served after all games

Club Shop: Yes, contact Pat Hodgson (01642 484006)

HONOURS	N Riding Sen Cup 94-95; N Riding County Cup 80-81 85-86; Teesside Lg 80-81 84-85; Wearside Lg 95-96, R-up 93-94 94-95 96-97, Cup 92-93 94-95 95-96;M/mouth Charity Cup 93-94 95-96; Sunderland Ship. Cup 95-96 96-97.
PREVIOUS	**Leagues:** Cleveland, South Bank & Dist, Teesside, Vaux Wearside.
BEST SEASON	**FA Cup:** **FA Vase:**
RECORDS	**Attendance:** 950 v Sunderland (friendly) 1983 **Win:** 16-0 v North Shields
	Defeat: 3-9 **Goalscorer:** Chris Morgan 169 **Appearances:** John Hodgson 476
Players progressing:	Peter Beagrie (Middlesbrough), Tony Butler (Blackpool), Roy Hunter (Northampton), Dave Logan (Mansfield T.)

FACT FILE
Founded: 1956
Nickname: The Seasiders
Colours: Yellow/royalblue/white
Change: Royal/sky/yellow
Midweek matchday: Tuesday
Programme: 32 pages 50p
Editor: John Hodgson (01642 484006)
Local Press: Sunday Sun, Middlesbrough Evening Gazette, Northern Echo

CLUB PERSONNEL
Chairman: John Hodgson
Vice Chairman: John Corner
President: Raymond Jarvis
Comm.Manager: Chris Sharratt/Steve Davies
Manager: Charlie Bell
Asst Manager: Stephen Dowling
Physio: Barry Schollay
Coaches: Charlie Bell & Stephen Dowling

MORPETH TOWN

Secretary: Joe Hobin, 23 Princes Gardens, Malvins Close, Blyth, Northumberland.NE24 5HJ.
Tel: 01670 360820

Ground: Craik Park, Morpeth Common, Morpeth, Northumberland. (01670 513785)
Directions: Morpeth is signed off the A1 onto A197. Take the B6524, right at Mitford sign, then right after about a mile into the ground, next to Morpeth Common
Capacity: 1000   Seated: 150   Cover: 150   Floodlights Yes
Clubhouse: Yes   **Club Shop:** No

HONOURS	Northern Alliance 83-84, 93-94 (R-up 37-38, 65-66, 73-74, 81-82, 84-85); Challenge Cup Winners 38-39, 85-86, 93-94 (R-up 36-37, 62-63, 73-74).
PREVIOUS	**Leagues:** Northern Alliance pre 1994 **Ground:** Storey Park, Morpeth. pre 1992
BEST SEASON	**FA Cup:** 4th Q Rd v Burton Albion 1998-99

FACT FILE
Colours: Yellow & black stripes/black/black
Change colours: Blue,white,blue
Midweek Matchday: Tuesday   Programme: Yes

CLUB PERSONNEL
Chairman: Ken Beattie Tel.: 01670 515271 (H), 01670 520565 (B)
Press Officer: Secretary

For up to the minute news, results, fixtures, plus general facts & figures from the world of non-league football

log on to

www.nlfootball.com

NEWCASTLE BLUE STAR

GROUND: Wheatsheaf Sports Ground, Woolsington, Newcastle-on-Tyne. NE13 8DF
Tel: 0191 286 0425
Directions: From central station follow airport signs for 7 miles - ground next to Wheatsheaf Hotel on left, approx. 800yds before airport. Callerton Parkway metro station is 400yds from ground
Capacity: 2,000   Seats: 300   Cover: 500   Floodlights: Yes   **Club Shop:** Yes
Clubhouse: Matchdays only. Hotdogs, soup, sandwiches available

HONOURS   FA Vase 77-78; Northern Lg R-up 87-88, Lg Cup 85-86, R-up(1), Div 2 85-86;
Wearside Lg 73-74 75-76 82-83 83-84 84-85, R-up 74-75 77-78 79-80, Lg Cup76-77 79-80 80-81
82-83 83-84; Sunderland Shipowners Cup 82-83 84-85; Monkwearmouth Charity Cup 74-75 79-80
82-83 88-89; Northern Comb. 62-63 68-69, Lg Cup 66-67 71-72; Northumberland Snr Cup 76-77
82-83 85-86 87-88, R-up 74-75 78-79 80-81, Minor Cup 64-65; J R Cleator Cup 86-87.
PREVIOUS   **Leagues:** Newcastle Business Houses 32-38; North East Amateur;
Tyneside Amateur; Northern Comb.; Wearside 75-85
BEST SEASON FA Trophy: Qtr-finals 88-89, 1-4 v Telford Utd (H)
     FA Vase: Winners 77-78, SF 81-82   **FA Cup:** 1st Rd 84-85, 0-2 v York C. (A)
RECORD Attendance: 1,800 v Almondsbury Greenway, FA Vase SF 77-78
       Appearances & Goalscorer: Ian Crumplin
Players progressing: Ian Crumplin & Tony Robinson (Hartlepool 1976 & 1986), Barry Dunn
        (Darlington 1979), Ian McInerney (Huddersfield Town 1988)

FACT FILE
Founded: 1930
Nickname: `Star'
Sponsors: T.B.A.
Colours: Blue/white/blue
Change colours: Same
Midweek matchday: Monday
Reserve s' League: None
Programme: 28 pages,50p Editor: M.Galt

CLUB PERSONNEL
Secretary: Jim Anderson
38 Western Ave.,West Denton,
Newcastle-on-Tyne NE5 5BU
Tel: 0191 243 1025

Chairman: Tom Brash
Press Officer: Secretary

Manager/Coach: S.Leeming
Assistant Manager: P.Johnson
Physio: T.B.A.

PETERLEE NEWTOWN

Secretary: Danny Cassidy, 23 Melbury Str, Seaham, Co. Durham SR7 7NF   0191 581 4591

Ground: Eden Lane, Peterlee, County Durham (0191 586 3004)

Directions: From town centre Fire Station, turn left into Edenhill Rd, thenright into Robson Ave.
Left at the next junction and ground is on the right
Capacity: 6,000   Seats: 50   Cover: 200   Floodlights: Yes
Clubhouse: Open normal licensing hours. Sandwiches etc available **Club Shop:** No

HONOURS   Northern Lg Div 2 82-83, North Eastern F'lit League, 4th Qual Rd FA Cup

PREVIOUS   **Leagues:** Northern Alliance 76-79; Wearside 79-82

RECORD   **Attendance:** 2,350 v Northern, Hillsborough Fund match 1989
           Scorer : Keith Fairless   **Appearances** : Keith Bendelow

BEST SEASON   **FA Cup:** 4th Qual. Rd replay 85-86   **FA Vase:**

Players progressing: Keith Fairless (Scarborough) 1986, Brian Honour(Hartlepool) 1988)

FACT FILE
Formed: 1976
Nickame: Newtowners
Sponsors: Artix Ltd
Colours: Sky/navy/sky
Change colours: Yellow/black/yellow
Midweek Matches: Wednesday
Programme: 10 pages, 30p
Editor: Secretary
Local Press: Hartlepool Mail,
Sunderland Echo, Northern Echo

CLUB PERSONNEL
Chairman: Carl Paylor
Vice-Chairman: Bill Burnett
President: David Brown
Press Officer: Ray Matthews (0191 587 0727)
Manager: Tommy Smith
Asst Manager: Eddie Freeman
Physio: Ron Lamdrel

SEAHAM RED STAR

Secretary: John McBeth, 29 Frederick Street, Seaham, Co. Durham SR7 7HX(0191 581 5712)

Ground: Seaham Town Park, Stockton Road, Seaham, Co. Durham (0191 581 1347)

Directions: From Tyne Tunnel: A19 Teeside approx 8 miles; B1404 Seaham slip road, left at top
of slip road. Right at traffic lights & first left past school into ground
Capacity: 4,000   Seats: 60   Cover: 200   Floodlights: Yes   **Club Shop:** No
Clubhouse: Mon-Sat 11am-11pm, Sun 12-2, 7-10.30pm Bars & restaurant, snooke & pool
HONOURS   Northern Lg Cup 92-93, Phillips F'lit Tphy 78-79, Durham Chal. Cup 79-80,
           Wearside Lg 81-82 (Lg Cup 81-82, Div 2 R-up 87-88, Monkwearmouth Charity
           Cup R-up 79-80).
PREVIOUS   **Name:** Seaham Colliery Welfare Red Star 78-87
       Leagues: Sunday f'tball; Houghton & Dist. 73-74; Northern Alliance74-79; Wearside 79-83.
       Grounds: Deneside Recreation Recreation Park 73-75; Vane Tempest Welfare 75-78.
BEST SEASON   **FA Cup:**   **FA Vase:** 5th Rd 78-79   **FA Trophy** 2nd Rd 89-90
RECORDS   **Attendance:** 1,500 v Guisborough, Wearside Lg
                v Sunderland, floodlight opener 1979
       Scorer: Tom Henderson   **Appearances:** Michael Whitfield
Players progressing: Bobby Davison (Huddersfield 1980), Nigel Gleghorn (Ipswich1985), Billy Stubbs
(Nottm Forest 1987), Paul Nixon (Bristol Rovers (1989), Mick Smith (Hartlepool).

FACT FILE
Formed: 1973
Nickname: The Star
Colours: All Red
Change colours: All blue
Midweek matchday: Wednesday
Reserves ' League: Banks Youth League
Programme: 20 pages
Editor: David Copeland (0191 581 8514)
Local Press : Sunderland Echo, Journal,
Northern Echo, Football Echo,
Washington Times

CLUB PERSONNEL
Chairman: Reg Atkinson
President: Michael English
Press Officer: Secretary
Manager: Chris Copeland
Asst Manager: Paul Walker
Physio: Allan Jackson

TOW LAW TOWN

Secretary: Bernard Fairbairn, 3 Coppice Walk, Mowden Park, Darlington, Co. Durham DL3 9DP
Tel: 01325 350743

Ground: Ironworks Road, Tow Law, Bishop Auckland Tel: 01388 731443

Directions: Just of High Street in Tow Law town centre
Capacity: 6,000   Seats: 200   Cover: 300   Floodlights: Yes
Clubhouse: Every evening 8.30 -10.30   **Club Shop:** Yes

HONOURS FA Vase R-up 97-98; Rothmans National Cup 1977,
Northern League Champions 23-24 24-25 94-95, R-up 28-29 88-89, Lg Cup 73-74;
Rothmans Overseas Cup 76-77, Durham Chal. Cup 1895-96, Durham Amtr Cup 1892-93.

PREVIOUS   Leagues: None

BEST SEASON   FA Cup: 2nd Rd rep. 67-68, 2-6 v Shrewsbury T. (A) after 1-1. Also 1st Rd
68-69 84-85 89-90.   League Clubs defeated:Mansfield Town 67-68
FA Amateur Cup: 3rd Rd rep. 70-71   **FA Trophy:** 2nd Rd rep. 82-83
FA Vase: Runners-up 1997-98
RECORD   Gate: 5,500 v Mansfield Town, FA Cup 1967

Players progressing: Reuben Cook & Ralph Guthrie (Arsenal 1951 & 53), Gordon Hughes, Terry Melling
& Chris Waddle (Newcastle 1956 & 65 & 80), EricJohnstone & Kevin Dixon (Carlisle 1963 & 83), Keith
Adamson (Barnsley 1966),Tom Henderson (Bradford PA 1969), Vincent Chapman (Huddersfield 1988)

FACT FILE
Founded: 1890
Nickname: Lawyers
Colours:
Black & white stripes/black/black & white
Change colours: Red & white
Midweek Matches: Tuesday
Programme: Yes
Editor:Chairman
Local Press : Northern Echo

CLUB PERSONNEL
Chairman: John Flynn
Press Officer: John Flynn (01388 730525)
Manager: Peter Quigley
Assistant Manager: Tony Heslop

WEST AUCKLAND TOWN

Secretary: Allen Bayles, 11 Edith Terrace, West Auckland, Co.Durham.DL14 9JT
Tel: 01388 833783 (H) & FAX, 01388 605221 (B) 01388 661366

Ground: Darlington Road, West Auckland, Co.Durham Tel: 01388 834403

Directions: Leaving West Auckland take A68-ground on right before leavingvillage. Bus route via
Bishop Auckland fron Newcastle or Darlington
Capacity: 3,000   Seats: 250   Cover: 250   Floodlights: Yes   **Club Shop:** No
Clubhouse: On Gound. (The Thomas Lipton Trophy is on display at the local Working Mans
Club five minutes away). Tel No: 01388 661366

HONOURS   FA Amateur Cup Finalists 60-61; Northern League Champions 59-60, 60-61
Div 2 90-91,Lg Cup 59-60,62-639r-UP;48-49,61-62,63-64)
Durham Challenge Cup 63-64 Durham Benevolent Bowl 62-63; Sir Thomas
Lipton Tphy`First World Cup'(as featured in `The Captains Tale') 1909, 1911.
PREVIOUS   League: Auckland & District
Names: St Helens Utd (1919 only), West Auckland Town.
BEST SEASON   FA Cup: 1st Rd 58-59, 61-62,98-99   **FA Trophy:** 3rd Rd. 77-78
FA Vase: **FA Amateur Cup:** Runners-up 60-61; Q-F 59-60
RECORD   Gate: 6,000 v Dulwich Hamlet, FA Amateur Cup 58-59
Victory: 11-0 in Durham County Cup

FACT FILE

Founded: 1892
Nickname: West
Sponsors:Rushlift Mechanical Handling and
F.Hudson Transport
Colours: All white
Change Colours: All Yellow
Midweek Matches: Tuesday

CLUB PERSONNEL

Chairman: Jim Polfreyman
Press Officer: Secretary
Manager: Dr. Graeme Forster
Ass.Manager: Dale Swainston
Coach: T.B.A.

WHITLEY BAY

Secretary: Derek Breakwell 27 Kings Rd, Whitley Bay, Tyne & Wear, NE26 3BD 0191 252 7940
GROUND   Hillheads Park, Rink Way off Hillheads Road, Whitley Bay, Tyne& Wear NE25 8HR
Tel: 0191 291 3637 (Club) Fax (& matchday office) 0191 291 3636
Directions: 1 mile walk from bus station - leave St Pauls Church southward, turn right at r-about,
ground 3rd left at rear of ice rink.
Whitley Bay (25mins from Newcastle) or Monkseaton metro stations, both 1 mile
Capacity: 4,500   Cover: 650   Seats: 450
Clubhouse: Open 7-11pm, except Wed. Bar & concert room. Darts, pool
Club Shop: Sells progs, scarves, hats, metal badges etc. Contact Tom Moody (0191 291 1618)
PREVIOUS   Leagues: Tyneside 09-10, Northern All. 50-55, North Eastern Lge 55-58,
Northern Lge 58-88; N.P.L. 88-00   **Name:** Whitley Bay Athletic 1950-58
CLUB RECORDS   Attendance: 7,301 v Hendon, FA Amateur Cup 1965
Win: 12-0 v Shildon 1961 **Defeat:** 1-8 v Bishop Auckland 1979 **Goalscorer:** Billy Wright 307
Appearances: Bill Chater 640 **Fee Paid:** £500 for Paul Walker from Blyth Spartans
Fee Received: £10,000 for Kevin Todd from Berwick Rangers
BEST SEASON   FA Amateur Cup: Semi Final 65-66 68-69   **FA Trophy:** 3rd Rd 86-87
FA Cup: 3rd Rd 89-90 (0-1 v Rochdale [A]). 2nd Rd 90-91 (0-1 v Barrow [H])
HONOURS: Northern Premier Lg Div 1 90-91 (Div 1 Cup 88-89 90-91), Northern Lg 64-65 65-66
(R-up 59-60 66-67 68-69 69-70), Lg Cup 64-65 70-71 (R-up 67-68); Northern Alliance 52-53 53-54
(Lg Cup 52-53 53-54); Northumberland Sen. Cup x10, R-up x7

FACT FILE
Formed: 1897
Nickname: The Bay
Colours: Blue & white stripes/blue/blue
Change colours: Yellow/sky blue
Midweek home matchday: Tuesday
PROGRAMME Pages: 24 Price: £1.00
Editor: Sean Robinson (0191 251 0356)

CLUB PERSONNEL
Chairman: Michael Robinson
Vice Chairman: Peter Siddle
President: J Hedworth
Press Officer: Gavin Miller
Manager: Dave Styles
Asst Manager: Dave Rooney
Coach: Colin Holloway
Physio: Joe Jabs

ALNWICK TOWN

Secretary: Darren Middleton, 1 Fire Station Houses, Alnwick, NE66 2PB
Ground: St James' Park, Alnwick, Northumberland Tel: 01665 603162
Directions: 35 miles north of Newcastle on A1, take the slip road to Alnwick,then first left. At roundabout turn left, ground is then on your left.
Capacity: 2,500   Seats: 100   Cover: 200   Floodlights: Yes
HONOURS   Northern Lg Div 2 R-up 88-89, Northern Alliance 37-38 62-63 63-64 65-66 67-68 68-69 69-70 70-71 71-72 (R-up 59-60 61-62 66-67 72-73, Lg Cup 61-62 65-6667-68 68-69 70-71, Subsidiary Cup 80-81), Durham Central Lg Cup 64-65, Northumberland Benevolent Bowl 86-87, Northumberland SNR Cup R-up 61-62,Northumberland Amtr Cup 71-72.
PREVIOUS   **League:** Northern Alliance 35-39 46-64 64-82
        Names: Alnwick United Services; Alnwick United.
BEST SEASON   **FA Cup:** 3rd Qual. Rd 51-52 (3-4 at Blyth), 57-58 (4-6 at Easington Coll.).
        FA Trophy: 3rd Qual. Rd 90-91.
RECORD   **Attendance:** 600 v Bedlington Terriers, Northern Alliance 1971.

FACT FILE
Founded: 1879
Colours: Black & white stripes/black/black
Change colours: Green and yellow
Midweek Matches: Tuesday

Local Press: Northumberland Gazette

CLUB PERSONNEL
Chairman:Iain Burns
Manager: Malcolm Beusle
Press Officer: Iain Burns

Players progressing: George Turnbull
(Grimsby 1950) and Brian Pringle (1973)

ASHINGTON

Secretary: Brian Robinson, 80 Milburn Road, Ashington, N/thumberland NE63 0PG
Tel: 01670 852832 (H) 01670 521212 (B) FAX: 01670 852832
Ground: Portland Park, Ashington NE63 9XG (01670 811991 Social Club)
Directions: 200 yds north at traffic lights in centre of town
Capacity: 2,000   Seats: 350   Cover: 2,200   Floodlights: Yes
Clubhouse: Open 6-11 evening & from11am on Tuesdays(market days) Not open Weds and Sun, darts, jukebox, snacks etc. **Club Shop** No but jumpers, baseball caps etc. behind bar
HONOURS   Northumberland Snr Cup (9) , Northumberland Chall. Bowl (6) , Midland Lg 58-59, North Eastern Lg Cup 33-34(jt with Sunderland Res.) 39-40; Northern Alliance x 4, R-up x 6; Lg Cup 47-48, Craven Cu p Winners 98-99
PREVIOUS   **Leagues:** Northern Alliance 1892-93 1902-14 69-70; Football League; North Eastern 14-21 29-58 62-64; Midland 58-60; Northern Counties 60-62;Wearside 64-65; N.P.L. 68-69.
BEST SEASON   **FA Cup:** 3rd Rd 26-27   **FA Amateur Cup** SF 73-74
RECORD   **Attendance:** 13,199 v Rochdale, FA Cup 2nd Rd 9/12/50

FACT FILE
Formed: 1883   Nickname: The Colliers
Sponsors: Liteon
Club colours: Black & white stripes/black/white
Change colours: Blue/white
Midweek Matches: Tuesday
Programme: Yes, 50p
Editor: A Marchett (01670 854585)
CLUB PERSONNEL
Chairman: Geoff Walker
Jt Presidents: Sir Bobby Charlton & Jackie Charlton OBE
Press Officer: Brian Bennett (01670 856606)
Manager: John Connelly
Asst.Manager: Iain Scott
Physio: Bob Robinson

EPPPLETON COLLIERY WELFARE

Secretary: John Gibson, Avondene, Houghton Road, Hetton-le-Hole, Tyne & Wear DH5 9PH
Tel: 0191 526 3782 & FAX
Ground: Eppleton Welfare Park, Park View, Hetton-le-Hole, Tyne & Wear (01915261048)
Directions: Situated behind Front Street Post Office & directly behind Hetton swimming baths, Hetton-le-Hole on A182. Buses 194, 535, 231, X5, X94 in Front Street. 8 miles from Durham BR station; buses 154 and 254 from Durham
Capacity: 2,500   Seats: 250   Cover: 500   Floodlights: Yes
Clubhouse: Bar & lounge on ground. Normal opening hours. Whitbread beers
Club Shop: Club sweaters, polo shirts, metal lapel badges available
HONOURS   Northern Lg Div 2 R-up 92-93, Wearside Lg 90-91 91-92 (Lg Cup 74-75 78-79 87-88, Sunderland Shipowners Cup 47-48 85-86 90-91 (R-up 91-92), Monkwearmouth Charity Cup 89-90 90-91 91-92), Durham Challenge Cup 89-90.
PREVIOUS   **Leagues:** Wearside 51-65 74-92; Houghton & District 65-74.
BEST SEASON   **FA Cup:**   **FA Vase:**
RECORD   **Attendance:** 1,250 - Monkwearmouth Charity Cup Final 1987-88

FACT FILE
Founded: 1929
Nickname: Welfare
Club Sponsors: E & N Ritchie
Colours: Black & sky/black/black
Change colours : Yellow/green/green
Midweek matchday: Wednesday
Programme: 16 pages,50p Editor:
CLUB PERSONNEL
Chairman: Ralph Lawson
President: J.Storey
Commercial Mgr: Secretary
Press Officer: Secretary
Manager: Vin Pearson
Asst Manager: John Cullen

ESH WINNING

Secretary: Alan Morton, 20 Durham Road, Esh Winning, Durham Tel: 0191 373 3611
Ground: West Terrace, Waterhouses, Durham Tel: 0191 373 3872
Directions: Durham to Ushaw Moor, to Esh Winning; ground 1 mile further at Waterhouses
Capacity: 3,500   Seats: 160   Cover: 160   Floodlights: Yes
Clubhouse: Open daily. Snacks served   **Club Shop:** No

HONOURS   Durham & Dist. Sunday Lg 78-79 79-80, Durham Co. Sun. Cup R-up 78-79,Staffieri Cup 74-75, Guards Cup 72-73, N. Durham Yth Lg 94-95, Auckland Yth Lge94-95.
PREVIOUS   **Leagues:** Durham & Dist Sunday; Northern Alliance 81-82.
        Grounds: None   **Names:** Esh Winning Pineapple (pre-1982)
BEST SEASON   **FA Cup:** 2nd Qual Rd 90-91   **FA Vase:** 2nd Round 83-84
RECORDS   **Gate:** 900 v Liverpool Fantail, FA Sunday Cup 1982
        Goalscorer: Paul Ward 31   **Appearances:** Paul Hewitson 40
        Win: 9-0 v Langley Park (H)   **Defeat:** 0-10 v Shotton Comrades
        Fee Paid: Nil   **Fee Received:** £500 for Paul Ward (Brandon Un ited)

FACT FILE
Formed: 1967   Nickname: `Esh'
Sponsors:Lumsden & Carroll
Colours: Yellow/green/yellow & green
Change colours: Green & Navy
Midweek Matches: Tuesday
Programme: 20 pages, 50p
Editor:Nigel Quinn
Press Officer: Secretary

CLUB PERSONNEL
Chairman: Charles Ryan
Vice Chairman: R.Hird
President: Jack Lumsden
Manager:Barrie Fleming
Physio: Lee Sullivan

EVENWOOD TOWN

Secretary: Jim Coates, 43 Fairfield, Evenwood, Bishop Auckland, Co Durham DL14 9SE
Tel: 01388 833035 (H) 07930 213071 (M)

Ground: Welfare Ground, Stones End, Evenwood, County Durham Tel: 01388 832281

Directions: In village centre by Sports & Social club in Stones Rd
Capacity: 3,500   Seats: 32 Cover: 200   Floodlights: Yes
Clubhouse: Open lunch & evening every day

HONOURS Northern Lg 48-49 69-70 70-71 (Lg Cup 35-36), Durham Challenge Cup 69-70.
PREVIOUS **Leagues:** Barnard Castle & Dist. 1894-95; Auckland & Dist. 1894-96 1903-04
08-23 28-31; Wear Valley 1896-99 1904-06 24-25; Gauntlett Valley 06-07;
South Durham 27-28.   **Names:** None
BEST SEASON **FA Cup:** 1st Rd 1936   FA Vase:
RECORD   **Gate:** 9,000 v Bishop Auckland, FA Amtr Cup 1931
Players progressing: Too numerous to record

FACT FILE
Founded: 1890
Nickname: The Wood
Sponsors: C A Roofing
Club colours: All blue
Change: Red & white sleeves/white/red
Midweek Matches: Wednesday
Programme: None

CLUB PERSONNEL
Chairman: Matt Robinson
President: N Colegrove
Press Officer: Secretary
Manager: Dr Graeme Forster

HORDEN COLLIERY WELFARE

Secretary: Robert Wood, 29 Morpeth St., Horden, Peterlee, County Durham SR84BE
Tel: 0191 586 8802

Ground: Welfare Park Ground, Park Road, Horden, Peterlee, Co. Durham Tel: 0191 587 3549
Directions: A19 to Peterlee, signposted from there   (Club)
Capacity: 3,000   Seats: 220   Cover: 370   Floodlights: Yes
Clubhouse: Normal licensing hours. Hot & cold snacks, darts, pool

HONOURS Durham Challenge Cup 35-36 63-64 80-81 81-82, Durham Benevolent Cup 33-34,
Wearside Lg 11-12 12-13 13-14 33-34 64-65 67-68 69-70 70-71 71-72 72-73 (Lg Cup 33-34 49-50, Monkwearmouth Charity Cup 12-13 23-24 32-33 69-70 72-73, Sunderland Shipowners Cup
65-66 72-73), North Eastern Lg 37-38 63-64 (`Non-Reserve' Medal 50-51).
PREVIOUS   **Leagues:** Wearside 07-35 63-75; N. Eastern 35-58 62-64; Midland
(Co's)58-60; Northern Co's 60-62.   **Names:** Horden Athletic
BEST SEASON FA Cup: 2nd Rd 38-39, 2-3 v Newport Co. (H)
RECORD Attendance: 8,000 - FA Cup 1937   Player progressing: Paul Dobson (Hartlepool Utd)

FACT FILE
Reformed : 1980
Nickname: Colliers
Colours: Red/black/red
Change colours:Sky,navy,navy
Reserves League: Wearside Div 2
Midweek Matches: Tuesday
Programme: 10 pages, 50p

CLUB PERSONNEL
Chairman: Norman Stephens
Press Officer: M.Burgon (041 089 064417)

KENNEK RYHOPE C.A.

Secretary: Rob Jones,17Aspatria Avenue, Blackhall, Hartlepool TS27 4EG
Tel No: 0191 5870949
Ground: Meadow Park, Stockton Road, Ryhope, Sunderland (0191 523 6555)
Directions: From Sunderland follow signs for A19 South, ground adj to Cherry
Knowle Hopital in Ryhope
Capacity: 2,000   Seats: 150   Cover: 200   Floodlights: Yes

HONOURS Wearside Lg 61-62 62-63 63-64 65-66(Lg Cup 63-64 77-78),
Durham Chal.Cup 77-78, Monkwearmouth Charity Cup 09-10 65-66 66-67,
Sunderland Shipowners Cup 61-62 (S.C.Vaux) 86-87
PREVIOUS **Names:** Ryhope C.W. (est.1898, prev.Ryhope Villa) merged with Sporting Club
Vaux (est.1968 as Monkwearmouth, later Bishopwearmouth, South Hetton) in 1988; Sunderland
Vaux Ryhope C.W. 88-93. **Leagues:** S. C. Vaux: Tyne & Wear; N.Eastern Amat.
BEST SEASON   **FA Cup** 1st Rd Proper 67-68   **FA Vase** 1st Rd 81-82
RECORD   **Gate:** 2,000; Ryhope Colliery Welfare v Workington, FA Cup 1967

FACT FILE
Founded: 1988
Colours: Red & white/black/red Change
colours: All Blue

CLUB PERSONNEL
Chairman: W.Mathieson
Tel: 0191 534 5496 (H)
Press Officer: Secretary

MURTON

Secretary: Tom Turnbull, 15 Dalton Terrace, Murton, Seaham, Co Durham SR7 9BZ
Tel: 0191 526 6488 (H) 0191 581 9874 (B) and Club Mobile 0411 272474
Ground: Recreation Park, Church Lane, Murton, Co. Durham (0191 517 0814)
Directions: Exit A19 onto B1285 heading west into Murton - Church Lane on left opposite
catholic church
Capacity: 3,500   Seats: 100   Cover: 320   Floodlights: Yes   Club Shop: No
Clubhouse: `The International' 300 yards from ground on B1285. Normal pub hours. Restaurant
upstairs. Matchday snacks at ground
HONOURS   Northern Lg Div 2 89-90, Wearside Lg 28-29 36-37 59-60 (Lg Cup 58-59
70-71), Sunderland Shipowners Cup 59-60 69-70 70-71, Monkwearmouth Charity Cup 21-22
28-29 34-35 35-36 63-64 70-71 87-88, Durham Chall. Cup 92-93, Durham Jnr Cup 50-51.
PREVIOUS   **Leagues:** Wearside 13-46 51-88; North East Counties 46-51.
RECORD   **Gate:** 3,500 v Spennymoor Utd, Durham Challenge Cup 1951
Appearances: Robert Welch 500 (1962-78)

FACT FILE
Founded: 1904   Nickname: Gnashers
Club Sponsors: John Hellyns
Colours: All white with red trim
Change colours: Red/black/red
Midweek matchday: Wednesday
Programme: 12 pages, 30p
Programme Editor: Stuart Upperton
CLUB PERSONNEL
Chairman: Tom Torrence
Vice Chairman: J Hudson
President: John Hellens
Press Officer: Secretary
Commercial Mgr: T Carr
Manager: Jeff Cranson
Asst Mgr: Brian Burlinson
Coach: Richie Madden Physio: Vince Symmonds

NORTHALLERTON TOWN

Secretary: Ken Lomer, 28 Aysgarth Grove, Romanby, Northallerton, North Yorks DL7 8HY Tel No: 01609 7786869 (H) 01609 773970 (W)
Ground: Ainderby Rd, Romanby, Northallerton, North Yorks Tel: 01609 772418
Directions: Leave A1 at Leeming Bar (A684) follow signs to Northallerton,approaching town take B1333 signed Romanby - ground 250yds on left. 3/4 a mile from Northallerton BR station - local bus from town centre(1 1/2 miles) passes ground
Capacity: 3,000   Seats: 150   Cover: 500   Floodlights: Yes
Clubhouse: Mon-Fri 7.30-11pm, Sat noon-7.30pm, Sun 12-2 & 7.30-10.30pm
Club Shop: Yes, Contact Nigel Taylor 01748 836017
HONOURS   Northern Lg Cup 93-94 (Div 2 R-up 89-90), Harrogate & Dist. Lg,N.Riding Snr Cup R-up 83-84, Northern Lg.Div 2 champions 96-97 Harrogate Invit; Alverton Tpy.
PREVIOUS   **Leagues:** Allertonshire; Vale of Mowbray; Ripon& Dist.; Teesside; North Yorks; Darlington & Dist.; Harrogate & Dist.
BEST SEASON   **FA Cup:** 4th Qual. Rd 92-93 **FA Trophy:** 3rd Rnd 92-93
RECORD   **Gate:** 671 v Farnborough, FA Tphy 3rd Rd 20/2/93

FACT FILE
Founded: 1994
Nickname: Town
Colours: Black & White stripes,white
Change Colours: All Yellow
Midweek matchday: Wednesday
Reserves ' League: Harrogate& District
Programme: 16 pages, 50p
Programme Editor: Ian Bolland

CLUB PERSONNEL
Chairman: Ralph Alderson
Vice Chairman: Les Hood
Press Officer: Ian Bolland (01609 776900)
Manager: Mike Hodgson
Physio: T.B.A.

NORTON & STOCKTON ANCIENTS

Secretary: Daniel Day,186 Braemar Road, Billingham, TS23 2AR (01642 899506)
Ground: Norton (Teesside) Sports Complex,Station Road, Norton, Stockton-on-Tees, Cleveland (01642 530203) Clubhouse (01642 5540310
Directions: Norton village 2 miles from Stockton centre, turn into Station Road on outskirts of village
Capacity: 2,000   Seats: 200   Cover: Yes   Floodlights: Yes
Clubhouse: Full bar facilities, 150 yds from ground
HONOURS   Northern Lg Cup 81-82
PREVIOUS   **Leagues:** Teesside (pre-1982)
          Name: Norton & Stockton Cricket Club Trust
BEST SEASON   **FA Cup:** 1st Qual Rd(4) 88-89 90-93   **FA Vase:**
RECORD   **Attendance:** 1,430 v Middlesbrough, Friendly 88

FACT FILE
Formed: 1959
Nickname: Ancients
Colours: Amber, white & black/black & amber/black
Change colours: Red with Green Trim/red socks
Midweek Matches: Wednesday
Programme: 12 pages with entry

CLUB PERSONNEL
Chairman: Steve Warnes
President: Barry Lee
Press Officer: Secretary

PENRITH

Secretary: John Balmer, 58 Castle Hill Road, Penrith, Cumbria   Tel: 01768 866736
Ground: Southend Road Ground, Penrith, Cumbria   Tel: 01768 895990
Directions: M6 Jct 40, onto dual carriageway to Appleby & Scotch Corner, first left at next r'bout, approx 1/2 mile into Penrith on A6 into town, take 1st left for ground. 3/4 mile from Penrith (BR)
Capacity: 4,000   Seats: 200   Cover: 1,000   Floodlights: Yes   Club Shop: No
Clubhouse: Open Thurs, Fri & Sat 9.30pm-2am, & Sat 2-6pm, Wed match nights 6.30-10.30pm
HONOURS   Northern Lg R-up 61-62; NW Co's Lg R-up 83-84; NW Co's F/Light Trophy 95-96 96-97; Cumberland Snr Cup [12], 46-48 50-51 60-66 70-71 72-73 74-75
PREVIOUS   **Leagues:** Carlisle & Dist., Northern 48-82, N.W.C. 82-87, 90-97, N.P.L. 87-90.
BEST SEASON   FA Cup: 2nd Rd 81-82   League Clubs beaten: Chester 81-82
RECORDS   **Attendance:** 2,100 v Chester 1981
          Goalscorer: C Short   **Appearances:** Lee Armstrong
          Win: 13-2 v Parton Utd   **Defeat:** 0-13 v Bishop Auckland

FACT FILE
Founded: 1894   Nickname: Blues
Sponsors: British Gypsum
Colours: Blue/white/blue
Change colours: White/red/white
Midweek Matches: Wednesday
Reserve team: None
Programme: 24 pages, 50p
Press Officer: Secretary
Local Press: Cumberland & Westmorland Herald, Cumberland News
CLUB PERSONNEL
Chairman: Walter Brogden
Vice Chairman: M Robson
Manager: Geoff Byers
Physio: Les Cornwell

PRUDHOE TOWN

Secretary: Brian Tulip, 12 Orchard Close, Prudhoe NE42 5LP   Tel: 01661 833169
Ground: Kimberley Park, Broomhouse Road, Prudhoe, Northumberland NE42 5EH   Tel/Fax: 01661 835900
Directions: Approach Prudhoe along A695, turn right at `Falcon' Inn, 200 yds down Eastwood Rd., left into Broomhouse Rd., ground on right
Capacity: 5,000   Seats: 150   Cover: Yes   Floodlights: Yes
Clubhouse: Open every evening plus Sat/Sun lunchtimes

HONOURS   Hexham & Dist. Lg 68-69 (Lg Cup 68-69), Newcastle & Dist. Lg 69-70 70-71, Lg Cup 69-70, Charity Shield 69-70 70-71), Northern Comb. 79-80, Northern AmtrLg 71-72, Clayton Charity Cup 68-69, Northumberland Minor Cup 78-79, Northumberland Benevolent Bowl 79-80, Heddon Homes Charity Cup 81-82
PREVIOUS   **Leagues:** Hexham & Dist 59-69; Newcastle & Dist 69-71; N. Comb.; N.Amtr; Northern All. 84-88   **Names:** Ovington 1969-75; Prudhoe East End 75-84
RECORD   **Attendance:** 2,500 v Blyth, Northumberland Snr Cup 1981

FACT FILE
Founded: 1959
Nickname: Citizens
Sponsors: Swinton Insurance
Colours: Purple & jade halves/purple/purple
Change: White & blue chevrons/navy/sky
Midweek Matches: Wednesday
Programme: 8 pages, 20p
Editor: J Smith

CLUB PERSONNEL
Chairman: Alex Waters
Press Officer:ErnieGoodfellow(01661 836941)
Manager: Terry Hunter
Asst Manager: Kenny Barton
Physio: Ernie Goodfellow

Top left: Willington's Cy Spayne gets in a brave header against Eppleton CW.
Photo: Alan Watson

Top right: Esh Winning's Brian Wray gets the ball away from Brandon United's Graeme McDonald.
Photo: Alan Watson

Centre righr: The gold shirts of Crook Town on the attack during their 1-1 draw in the FA Cup Second Qualifying round against Hyde United.
Photo: Colin Stevens

Bottom: South Shields keeper Michael Norris stands by in the closely fought Derby with Jarrow Roofing.
Photo: Graham Brown.

SHILDON

Secretary: Mike Armitage, 22 Hambleton Ct, Byerley Park, Newton Aycliffe, Co.Durham DL5 7HR
/Press Officer   Tel: 01325 316322
Ground: Dean Street, Shildon, County DurhamTel: 01388 773877   **Directions:** In the town
centre 1 mile from BR station and 300yds from Darlington-Bishop Auckland bus stop
Capacity: 4,000   **Seats:** 400   **Cover:** 500   **Floodlights:** Yes   **Club Shop:** No
Clubhouse: Every eve. 7.30-11pm (earlier match nights), 1-11pm Sat. matchdays. Pool&Darts
HONOURS   Northern Lg 33-34 34-35 35-36 36-37 39-40 (R-up 32-33 38-39, Lg Cup 33-34
                34-35 37-38 38-39 39-40 52-53), Durham Challenge Cup 07-08 25-26 71-72,
                Durham Amateur Cup 01-02 02-03, Durham Benevelopment Bowl 24-25.
PREVIOUS   Leagues: Auckland & District 1892-96; Wearside 96-97; North Eastern 07-32.
BEST SEASON   FA Cup: 2nd Rd 36-37 1st Rd 27-28 29-30 34-35 36-37 55-56 59-60 61-62
FA Trophy: 3rd Qual. Rd 74-75   **FA Amateur Cup:** 4thRd 58-59   **FA Vase:** 1st Rd 86-87
RECORDS   Attendance: 13,000 - Leeholme v Perkinsville, schoolboys game, 1920s.
                (Shildon game); 11,000 Shildon v Ferryhill Ath., Durham Sen. Cup 1922

FACT FILE
Founded: 1890   Nickname: Railwaymen
Sponsors: Atkinsons Stairs
Colours: Red & green halves,red,red & white.
      Change colours: All blue
Midweek Matches: Wednesday
Programme: 48 pages, 50p
Editor: Neil Bennett (01325 332310)

CLUB PERSONNEL
Chairman: Bill Aisbitt Vice Chairman: G. Elliott
President: John Atkinson
Manager:Ray Gowan
Assistant: John Harland Physio: Jimmy Smalls
1999-00 Top Scorer: Charlie Walton
P.o.Y.: Andrew Bowes
Captain: John Harland

SHOTTON COMRADES

Secretary: Billy Banks, 30 Hamilton Court, Shotton Colliery, Durham DH6 2NL (0191 526 7134)

Ground: Shotton Rec. Ground, Station Road, Shotton Colliery, Co. Durham(0191 526 2859)

Directions: A19 to Peterlee to Shotton, right at the War Memorial t-junction,
                follow round 800yds, ground on right
Capacity: 1,700   **Seats:** 80   **Cover:** 400   **Floodlights:** No   **Clubhouse:** No   **Club Shop:** No
HONOURS   Houghton & District Lg 78-79, Lg Cup x 2, Northern Alliance Lg Cup SF,
                Hetton Charity Cup 78-79, Peterlee Sunday Lg 75-76, Div 2 74-75;
                Northern Lg.Div 2 Cup R-up. 94-95.
PREVIOUS   Leagues: Peterlee Sunday 74-76; Houghton & Dist. 76-80; Northern Alliance 80-83
BEST SEASON FA Cup: 2nd Qual. Rd 85-86, 0-2 v Wingate(H)   **FA Vase** 1st Rd 86-87 90-91
RECORDS   Attendance: 1,726 v Dennis Waterman XI
      Goalscorer: Keith Willets 50   **Win:** 8-0 v Bedlington Ter. (H), '92
      Appearances: J Cudlip   **Defeat:** 1-7 v Brandon Utd (A), FA Cup Prel. Rd 91-92
      Transfer Fee received: £500 for G Gudlip (Shildon)

FACT FILE
Formed: 1973   Nickname: Coms
Colours: Black & white stripes/black/black
      Change colours: All orange
Midweek matches: Wednesday
Reserves' Lge: Banks u-19 Yth
Programme: 12 pages, 20p Editor: E A Jones

CLUB PERSONNEL
Chairman: John Maddison
Vice Chairman: T Robinson
President: G Taylor
Press Officer: Secretary

Manager: B Huntingdon
Physio: W Banks

SOUTH SHIELDS F.C.

Secretary: David Fall, 50 Basil Way, South Shields NE34 8UD   Tel: 0191 426 2135

Ground: Mariners Club, Filtrona Park, Shaftesbury Avenue, Jarrow, Tyne & Wear NE34 9PH.
      Tel: 0191 427 9839

Directions: From A1(M) take A194(M) to South Shields, A194 town centre road for 5 miles,
            ignore A1300 (Sunderland & coast) & turn left at next lights beside Co-op store
            into Simonside Ind. Est. (Shaftesbury Ave.), ground at bottom
Capacity: 2,500   **Seats:** 150   **Cover:** 400   **Floodlights:** Yes
Clubhouse: Two function suites, club kitchen   **Club Shop:** Yes
HONOURS   Northern Lge Div 2 R-up 95-96, Northern Alliance 74-75 75-76, Wearside Lg 76-
77 92-93 94-95, Monkwearmouth Charity Cup 86-87 (R-up 94-95), Shipowners Cup 92-93 (R-up
83-84)), Durham Chal. Cup 76-77 R-up 94-95. **BEST SEASON**   **FA Vase** QF 75-76
PREVIOUS   Leagues: Northern Alliance 74-76   **Ground:** Jack Clarke Park 74-92
RECORD   Attendance: 1,500 v Spennymoor, Durham Challenge Cup Final 94-95

FACT FILE
Founded: 1974   Nickname: Mariners
Colours: Claret & blue/white/white
      Change: All white
Midweek matchday: Tuesday
Reserve team: None
Programme: 50p Editor: Steve Leonard

CLUB PERSONNEL
Chairman: John Rundle
Vice Chairman: George Scott
Press Officer: Secretary
Manager: David Clark
Asst Manager:Paul Brown
Physio: Jim Wilkinson

THORNABY

Secretary: Peter Morris, 20 Wheatear Lane, Ingleby Barwick, Stockton-on-Tees,Cleveland TS17
0TB (01642 760779)
Ground: Teesdale Park, Acklam Road, Thornaby, Stockton-on-Tees TS17 8TZ (01642 606803)
Directions: A19 to Thornaby turn off, ground half mile on right. One mile fromThornaby BR sta-
tion. Any Stockton-Middlesbrough bus - stop at Acklam Rd,Thornaby
Capacity: 5,000   **Seats:** 150   **Cover:** 350   **Floodlights:** Yes   **Club Shop:** No
Clubhouse: Open every eve., Sun. lunch & all day Sat. 150+ social club with concert room,
pool/ games room & bar. Only sandwiches avail. in bar.

HONOURS   Northern Lg Div 2 87-88 91-92, Nth Riding Co. Cup 85-86,
            Inaugralwinners of Craven Cup (Northern Div 2 clubs) 94-95.
PREVIOUS   Leagues: Stockton & District 80-81; Wearside 81-85.
            Names: Stockton Cricket Club 65-80; Stockton 80-99; Thornaby-on-Tees 99-00
BEST SEASON   FA Vase: 2nd Rd   **FA Trophy:** 1st Rd
            FA Cup: 4th Qual. Rd replay 92-93,1-2 v Blyth (H) after 1-1

FACT FILE
Formed: 1980
Colours: Red & black stripes/black/red
      Change colours: All sky
Midweek Matches: Wednesday
Reserves' Lge: Wearside & Teesside Lgs
Programme: 24 pages, 50p
Editor: Peter Morris (01642 585625)
Local Press : Northern Echo, Evening Gazette
CLUB PERSONNEL
Chairman: Lol Lyons
Press Officer: Peter Morris
Manager: Michael Watson
Asst Mgr: Peter May
Coach: Paul Sharkey

WASHINGTON IKEDA HOOVER

Secretary: George Abbott, 14 Grosvenor Street, Southwick, Sunderland SR5 2DG
Tel: 0191 549 1384

Ground: Albany Park, Spout Lane, Concord, Washington   Tel: 0191 417 7779

Directions: Ground situated opposite bus station

Capacity: 3,000   **Seats:** 25 **Cover:** Yes   **Floodlights:** Yes   **Club Shop:** No
Clubhouse: Open normal licensing hours, with live entertainment, pool etc

PREVIOUS   **Leagues:** Washington Amateur; Northern Alliance 67-68; Wearside 68-88
               Ground: Usworth Welfare Park
RECORD   **Gate:** 3,800 v Bradford Park Avenue, FA Cup 1970

FACT FILE
Founded: 1949
Nickname: Mechanics
Colours: All red
Change colours: All blue
Midweek Matches: Wednesday
Programme: 8 pages, 10p
Editor: Secretary

CLUB PERSONNEL
Chairman: Derek Armstrong
Press Officer: Ray Lish (0191 415 7071)

WHICKHAM

Secretary: Harry Hodgson, 2, Dockendale Hall, Dockendale Lane, Whickham,
              Newcastle upon Tyne,NE16 4EN   Tel: 0191 488 2493

Ground: Glebe Ground, Rectory Lane, Whickham (0191 420 0186)   **Directions:** A692
(Consett) from A69. Left at r'bout signed Consett/Whickham. Uphill and right at mini-r'bout.
Continue along & turn left into Rectory Lane (by Lloyds Bank) for 500 yds, clubhouse on right
Capacity: 4,000   **Seats:** 100   **Cover:** Yes   **Floodlights:** Due
Clubhouse: Mon-Fri. 12-3 & 7-11, Sat.11-11, Sun. 12-2, 7.30-11   Souvenir Shop: No

HONOURS   FA Vase 80-81, Wearside Lg 77-78 87-88 (R-up 80-81 84-85, Lg Cup 86-87,
               Monkwearmouth Charity Cup 76-77, Sunderland Shipowners Cup 77-78 80-81),
               Northern Comb. 69-70 72-73 73-74 (Lg Cup 60-61 73-74)
PREVIOUS   **Leagues:** Derwent Valley -55; Northern Comb. 55-57 59-74; Tyneside Amtr 57-
               59; Wearside 74-88   **Ground:** Rectory Rec. Field
BEST SEASON   **FA Cup:** 1st Qual. Rd. 89-90   **FA Vase:** Winners 80-81
RECORD   **Gate:** 3,165 v Windsor & Eton, F.A. Vase SF 81

FACT FILE
Founded: 1944
Colours: Black & White stripes/ Black/Black
Change colours: All white
Midweek Matches: Wednesday
Programme: 20p
Local Press : Newcastle Journal, Sunday Sun,
Evening Chronicle

CLUB PERSONNEL
Chairman: Tommy Thompson
Manager: Keith Sheardown
Press Officer: Secretary

WILLINGTON

Secretary: Bob Nichols, 46 Cavendish Ct, Brandon,Durham DH7 8UW Tel/ FAX 0191378 1981
Ground: Hall Lane, Hall Lane Estate, Willington, County Durham (01388 746221)
Directions: Willington is on A690 7 miles west of Durham City & 2 miles east of Crook. Off main
through road at `The Black Horse Tavern' corner turn off Commercial St, then into Hall Lane after
100yds. Northern Bus Co. operates a service through Willington from Crook or Durham City
Capacity: 2,680   **Seats:** 350   **Cover:** 400   **Floodlights:** Yes   Club shop: Occasionally
Clubhouse: Open eves 7-11pm &Sat. matchdays 1-11pm. Bar facilities.Tea shop on matchdays
HONOURS   FA Amateur Cup 49-50, R-up 38-39; Northern League 13-14 25-26 29-30,
               R-up 12-13 57-58 75-76, Lge Cup 24-25 25-26 27-28 30-31 31-32 48-49 56-57 74-75;
               Durham Benevolent Cup 48-49 50-51 57-58.
BEST SEASON FA Cup: 1st Rd rep. 73-74, 1-6 v Blackburn R (A) after 0-0.Also 1st Rd 45-46
     FA Trophy 3rd Rd 75-76   **FA Amat. Cup:** Winners 49-50   & 50-51
PREVIOUS   Leagues: Auckland & Dist. 1906-11   **Names:** Willington Temperance 1906-11
RECORD Attendance: 10,000 v Bromley, FA Amateur Cup 2nd Rd 24/1/53   **Goalscorer:** J
`Boxer' Taylor 55-69 150 approx.**Appearances:** S Rutherford 47-61 & G.Brown both 350+

FACT FILE
Founded: 1906 Nickname: Blue & Whites
Sponsor:Newfit Services
Colours: Blue & white stripes/blue/blue
Change colours: Yellow/green/green
Midweek Matches: Wednesday
Youth League: Auckland & Dist League
Programme: 50p Editor: Christina Jackson

CLUB PERSONNEL
Chairman: Anne Robson
Vice-Chairman: Alistair Melville
President: Hilary Armstrong M.P.
Press Officer: Secretary
Player/Manager: Dave Taylor
Joint Manager: Les Ryder

Top: Andrew Dugdale (Morpeth) and Alan Stewart (Penrith). Photo: Alan Watson
Bottom: Marske United FC. Photo: Alan Watson

NISSAN WEARSIDE LEAGUE

FEEDER TO:
ARNOTT INSURANCE NORTHERN LEAGUE

President: W Robson   **Chairman:** P J Maguire

Secretary: E Hargreaves, 4 South Mews, Shadforth, Durham DH6 1NS
Tel: 0191 372 2844

FINAL LEAGUE TABLES 1999-2000

DIVISION ONE

	P	W	D	L	F	A	Pts
Washington Nissan*	30	24	0	6	86	35	69
New Marske Social C*	30	21	5	4	95	36	65
Windscale	30	18	7	5	75	40	61
North Shields*	30	17	6	7	76	43	54
Sunderland Red House	30	17	3	10	67	31	54
S Shields Horton & W	30	14	4	12	59	63	46
Boldon Comm Assn	30	13	6	11	58	48	45
Wolviston*	30	12	5	13	69	68	38
Birtley Town	30	9	9	12	52	59	36
Ryhope Coll Welfare	30	10	6	14	46	68	36
Workington Reserves	30	10	5	15	51	54	35
Whitehaven Amateurs	30	7	10	13	38	67	31
Annfield Plain	30	8	4	18	65	92	28
South Shields Cleadon	30	6	7	17	45	76	25
Stanley United	30	6	5	19	46	86	23
Jarrow	30	6	2	22	40	82	20

DIVISION TWO

	P	W	D	L	F	A	Pts
Redcar Town	21	14	4	3	80	32	46
Stokesley SC	21	15	1	5	68	41	46
Simonside Social Club*	21	10	4	7	69	51	31
Thornaby	21	7	10	4	50	41	31
Ferryhill Athletic	21	8	5	8	69	45	29
Herrington Colliery W	21	7	4	10	41	63	25
Whitburn	21	5	3	13	52	77	18
Wallsend Town	21	2	1	18	27	106	7

Note - each team played eachother three times

Divisions One and Two have merged

* points deducted

DIVISION ONE RESULTS CHART 1999-2000

		1	2	3	4	5	6	7	8	9	10	11	12	13	14	15	16
1	Annfield Plain	X	5-2	2-2	2-1	1-4	0-2	2-3	2-2	0-2	2-0	5-2	1-2	5-1	0-3	2-3	1-2
2	Birtley Town	7-4	X	1-0	4-1	1-1	4-3	1-1	0-1	0-2	2-2	0-0	1-5	5-0	0-2	3-1	0-0
3	Boldon Comm. Assn	5-2	5-1	X	2-1	1-4	1-2	2-3	3-0	1-2	3-1	4-1	0-3	5-1	1-1	2-1	2-1
4	Jarrow	8-1	1-1	0-1	X	1-5	0-5	5-2	1-0	0-4	0-3	0-5	0-3	3-0	0-4	2-2	1-0
5	New Marske S C	5-2	2-2	0-2	4-1	X	1-1	8-1	3-1	3-2	7-1	7-0	2-1	2-2	0-0	3-1	3-2
6	North Shields	3-2	3-3	4-1	4-0	1-3	X	3-0	1-1	5-0	4-3	2-1	3-1	5-0	1-3	0-1	1-1
7	Ryhope Coll. Welf.	2-6	3-1	2-2	3-2	1-2	2-0	X	3-4	1-3	2-1	0-2	1-0	0-0	0-6	0-1	3-0
8	S Shields Cleadon SC	6-3	1-2	0-2	1-0	0-3	0-1	3-3	X	0-3	2-1	2-3	3-8	2-5	1-1	2-8	1-1
9	S Shields H & Westoe	2-4	3-2	2-2	3-2	1-5	1-6	2-0	2-2	X	4-1	1-3	1-6	3-1	1-2	3-3	1-1
10	Stanley United	0-1	2-2	3-1	2-1	0-6	1-4	3-2	5-7	0-4	X	0-3	1-6	1-1	1-2	4-2	3-2
11	Sunderland Red Hse	4-1	1-2	2-1	3-1	3-2	2-0	2-2	2-0	2-1	4-1	X	1-2	1-1	1-3	6-2	6-1
12	Washington Nissan	3-1	2-0	3-0	2-0	3-2	2-3	3-1	2-0	4-0	2-1	2-1	X	4-0	3-5	1-4	1-0
13	Whitehaven Amateurs	2-2	1-0	2-1	2-3	0-2	3-3	1-1	1-0	2-0	2-2	2-1	1-3	X	2-2	2-2	2-0
14	Windscale	3-3	3-0	1-1	4-2	1-0	3-2	0-1	2-0	4-1	2-2	2-3	0-3	3-0	X	3-2	2-3
15	Wolviston	3-2	0-3	1-4	6-2	3-4	1-1	3-2	2-2	0-3	2-0	0-1	2-3	4-1	5-4	X	3-1
16	Workington Reserves	8-1	4-2	1-1	4-1	0-2	2-3	0-1	3-1	1-2	4-1	4-1	0-3	2-0	1-4	2-1	X

LEAGUE CUP 1999-2000

FIRST ROUND

Annfield Plain	v	Stokesley SC	0-5	Boldon C Assn	v	Birtley Town	0-1
Ferryhill Athletic	v	Whitehaven Amat.	6-1	Jarrow	v	Thornaby	1-3
New Marske SC	v	Redcar Town	1-0	Ryhope Coll. Welf.	v	Herrington Coll. Welf.	3-0
Simonside S C	v	Wallsend Town	7-0	SS Horton & Westoe	v	North Shields	8-0

SECOND ROUND

Ferryhill Athletic	v	New Marske S C	2-3	Simonside S C	v	Stokesley S C	3-4
SS Cleadon SC	v	Workington Reserves	2-0	SS Harton & Westoe	v	Ryhope Coll. Welf.	2-0
Sunderland Red H	v	Whitburn	14-0	Washington Nissan	v	Jarrow	11-2
Windscale	v	Stanley United	5*4	Wolviston	v	Birtley Town	4-1

QUARTER FINALS

New Marske S C	v	Windscale	1*1, 3p2	SS Harton & Westoe	v	SS Cleadon S C	4-0
Stokesley S C	v	Washington Nissan	1-2	Sunderland Red Hse	v	Wolviston	2-0

SEMI FINALS

SS Harton & Westoe	v	Sunderland R H	0*0, 1p3	Washington Nissan	v	New Marske S C	1-2

FINAL

New Marske S C	v	SS Harton & Westoe	3-1	at New Marske FC

MONKWEARMOUTH CHARITY CUP 1999-2000

FIRST ROUND

Ferryhill Athletic	v	Annfield Plain	1-0	SS Cleadon S C	v	New Marske S C	2-7
SS Harton & Westoe	v	Stanley United	1-2	Stokesley SC	v	Birtley Town	2-3
Thornaby	v	Whitehaven Am	2*2, 5p6	Wallsend Town	v	Simonside S C	1-7
Whitburn	v	Redcar Town	1-2	Workington Res.	v	Washington Nissan	2-0

SECOND ROUND

Boldon C A	v	Wolviston	2-1	Herrington C W	v	Binley Town	2-1
Jarrow	v	Redcar Town	1-0	New Marske S C	v	Ferryhill Athletic	6-1
North Shields	v	Workington Res.	2-0	Ryhope C W	v	Whitehaven Amat.	6-1
Stanley United	v	Sunderland Red Hse	0-6	Windscale	v	Simonside S C	3-0

QUARTER FINALS

Boldon C A	v	Herrington C W	4-0	Jarrow	v	New Marske S C	1-2
Ryhope C W	v	Windscale	3-1	Sunderland Red H	v	North Shields	2-5

SEMI FINALS

New Marske S C	v	Ryhope C W	2*1	North Shields	v	Boldon C W	2*1

FINAL

North Shields	v	New Marske S C	1-2	at Harton & Westoe FC

SUNDERLAND SHIPOWNERS CUP 1998-99

FIRST ROUND

Ryhope C W	v	Herrington C W	R W/O	SS Cleadon S C	v	Annfield Plain	1-3
Stanley United	v	Birtley Town	1-3	Thornaby	v	Workington Reserves	4-2
Washington Nissan	v	Simonside S C	5-0	Whitehaven Amat.	v	Stokesley S C	2-4
Windscale	v	Wallsend Town	14-0	Wolviston	v	Ferryhill Athletic	4-2

SECOND ROUND

Annfield Plain	v	Sunderland Red Hse	5-1	Birtley Town	v	Stokesley S C	3*5
Jarrow	v	Whitburn	3-1	North Shields	v	New Marske S C	1-0
Ryhope Coll. Welf.	v	Redcar Town	1*5	SS Harton & Westoe	v	Thornaby	1*2
Washington Nissan	v	Boldon C A	3-2	Wolviston	v	Windscale	3-2

QUARTER FINALS

Annfield Plain	v	Redcar Town	2-4	Stokesley S C	v	Jarrow	4-2
Washington Nissan	v	North Shields	3-1	Wolviston	v	Thornaby	3-2

SEMI FINALS

Washington Nissan	v	Stokesley S C	0-1	Wolviston	v	Redcar Town	0-1

FINAL

Redcar Town	v	Stokesley	3-2	at Wolviston FC

ANNFIELD PLAIN

Secretary: M Lawson, 24 Northgate, Anfield Plain, Stanley, Co. Durham DH9 7UY
Tel: 01207
Ground: Derwent Park, Annfield Plain. **Directions:** On A693 road to Consett, 200yds west of junction with A6067. Ground behind new housing estate. 6 miles fromDurham (BR). Buses from Sunderland, Newcastle & Durham.
Capacity: 6,000   Seats: 20   Cover: 200   Floodlights: No
HONOURS   Wearside Lg 84-85 (Monkwearmouth Charity Cup 92-93),
FA Cup: 1st Rd 26-27 28-29 64-65.

Founded: 1890.
Colours: Claret/white/blue
Change colours: All blue.
Programme: 16 pages, 20p

Chairman: Frank Ross
Treasurer :Marshall Lawson
Manager: D Longstaff
Press Officer: Frank Ross

BIRTLEY TOWN

Secretary: Ray Melling, 86 Queen Street, Bensham, Gatehead NE8 2SU (01207 235879)
Commercial Manager: Ray Stafford.
Ground: Birtley Sports Complex. **Directions:** (From Durham) Off A1(M) signpstedfor Chester-le-Street, take 2nd turn off r-bout signed Birtley, take last turnoff next r-bout (still signed Birtley), after one and a half miles take 1stleft after AEI Cables - ground at rear of sports complex.
Capacity: Unknown   Seats: None   Cover: None   Floodlights: No.
Clubhouse: Matchdays only
HONOURS: Wearside Lg 45-46 (Lg Cup 35-36), Northern Alliance 23-24 (R-up 13-14).

Founded: 1890   Reformed: 1986
Colours: Green&white hoops/white/green
Change colours: Yellow/blue/red.
Midweek matches: Wednesday
Sponsors: C & C Coachworks
Chairman: John Heslington
Vice-Chairman: J Grainger.
Manager: Barry Fleming
Asst Manager: David Smith
Coach: Malcolm Thompson

BOLDON COMMUNITY ASSOCIATION

Secretary: Tom Robson, 16 Hardie Drive, West Boldon ,Tyne & Wear NE36 0JH.
Ground: Boldon Community Association, New Road, Boldon Colliery.
Directions: A19 to junc A184 Sunderland/Newcastle. Follow signs to Boldon Asdastores, then to North Road Social Club (SHACK). Ground behind. 800 yds fromEast Boldon (BR). Buses 533, 531, 319, 528.
Capacity: 3,500   Seats: 100   Cover: 400   Floodlights: No
Clubhouse: Matchdays only. Bar snacks
HONOURS: Wearside Lg 3, (Lg Cup 3), M/mouth Char Cup 2, Shipowners Cup 6.

Founded: 1892.   Nickname: Villa
Colours: Black & Blue Stripes/ Black/Blue
Change: Scarlet & black
Chairman:Kevin Oliver
Vice Chairman: G Smith
President: A Brewster.
Manager: Bill Newham
Asst Manager: P Quinn
Coach: Tommy Frazer.
Press Off. / Comm. Man.: Secretary

FERRYHILL ATHLETIC

Secretary: Norman Bellwood, 49 Rush Park, Bishop Auckland DL14 6NS
Tel: 01388 451065 (H)
Football Secretary: Rob Ridley, 31 Ravensworth Road, Ferryhill Tel: 0780 3803335
Ground: Dean Bank Recreation Ground
Directions: The ground is situated on the old Dean & Chapter Colliery Welfare site west of the old Athletic ground at Darlington Road. From the top of Darlington Road with the Black Bull on your right, pass over the bridge crossing the A167 cutting. Dean Bank school is immediately on your left, turn left at the one way traffic restriction. Follow the signs to Dean Bank Rec.

Colours: Black & amber/amber/black & amber
Change: Red & white/red/red & white

Chairman: Secretary
Press Officer: Jimmy O'Sullivan
Tel: 01740 635524

JARROW

Secretary: Susan Scott,46 Breamish Street, Jarrow. NE32 5SH (0191 4248610)

Ground: Perth Green Community Centre.
Directions: From A19 or A1(M) followdrections to South Shields, right onto John Reid Road. First slip road ontoBrockley Whinns Estate, follow road past Red Hackle pub, third left left ontoInverness Road, then right into Perth Green Community Centre.

HONOURS: Sth Tyne Lg & Lg Cup, Washington Lg R-up 89-90 (Lg Cup 90-91, Aged Peoples Tphy R-up 90-91), Gateshead Charity Cup 90-91, Durham Tphy R-up 90-91.

Founded: 1980.
Colours: Blue & white/blue/blue
Change: Green/black/green

Chairman: B.Tyreman
Treasurer: Jimmy Kane

NEW MARSKE

Secretary: Peter Whitaker, 28 High Street, Marske, Redcar TS11 7BE (Tel: 01642 486770)

Ground: Gurney Street, New Marske, Redcar

Directions: A19 south onto A174 Redcar- Teesport. Follow A174 towards Saltburn turn right at roundabout with footbridge over road. Ground 500 yds on left.

Colours: Yellow & black/navy/navy or white
Change colours: Blue &black/navy/navy

Charmain: Errol Richter
Tel: 01947 600296
Press Officer: Tony Saunders

NORTH SHIELDS

Secretary: Dave Thompson, 38 Barnstable Road, North Shields. Tel: 0191 259 0249
Ground: Ralph Gardner Park, West Percy Rd., N.Shields, Tyne & Wear, NE29 OES
Directions: A19 northbound through Tyne Tunnel. Take 1st slip round to 1str/about & take 3rd exit & over next r/about. Take 3rd exit again at nextr/about into Waterville Rd. Over another r/about and 2nd left into Silkey'sLane. 1st right into West Percy Rd, grd on right.
Clubhouse: None
HONOURS: FA Amateur Cup 68-69, Northern Lge 68-69, N.C.E. Prem. Div. 91-92, R-up 89-90, 90-91, Lge. Cup 90-91, Presidents Cup 91-92.

Founded: 1896
Nickname: New Robins
Sponsors: Wilkinson Stores
Colours: All red
Change colours: Blue & black/black/blac

Chairman: Alan Matthews.
Treasurer:Mike Taylor
Manager: Bob Weir.Coach: Wilf Keilty.

REDCAR

Secretary: Keith Markman, 2 Riccall Court , Redcar, Cleveland TS10 4HL   Tel: 01642 481966
Ground: British Steel Club, South Ave., Dormanstown, Redcar. **Directions:** Take the A19 South, then the A66 to Middlesbrough. Stay on the A66 following Teeside/Redcar. When A66 ends, at A1053 r'about, take right to Redcar. At next r'about, bear left onto A1085 to Redcar. Over next r'about, right at next r'about into Dormanstown. 1st right along the Fleet, 1st left into South Ave., ground 200 yds on right.

Colours: All red
Change colours: All royal blue

Chairman: Fred Blackburn 01642 471773
Press Officer: Allan Monghan
Tel: 01642 470962

SOUTH SHIELDS CLEADON SOCIAL CLUB

Secretary: Tony Quinn, 61 Quarry Lane, South Shields, Tyne & Wear (0191 456002)

Ground: Jack Clarke Park, South Shields.
Directions: Enter South Shields on A194 to r'bout taking you on to A1300 JohnReid Rd. 2nd left at 3rd r'bout into King George Rd then Sunderland Rd, rightat lights into Grosvenor Rd, left into Horsly Hill Rd. Ground on right
Clubhouse: Cleadon Social Club, Fulwell Ave, S Shields. Normal pub hours except Saturday.
HONOURS: Wearside Lg Div 2 90-91, Shields & Dist. Lg, Washington Lg 77-78 84-85

Nickname: The Club
Sponsors: Cleadon & Dist. Soc. Club
Colours: Yellow/black/black
Change: All red
Midweek matches: Wednesday
Chairman: Gordon Ferries
Vice-Chairman/Press Off . /Manager:
David Wood (0191 455 4607).
Asst Man: Steve Duguid
Commercial Manager: Joan Wood

SOUTH SHIELDS HARTON & WESTOE

Secretary: Alan Bell, 31 Meldon avenue, South Shields, Tyne & Wear NE34 0EL
    Tel Nos: 0191 4218233 (H) 0191 4301446 (W)
Groun: Harton Colliery Welfare.

Directions: A1M at Whitemare Pool take A194 to South Shields for 2 1/2 miles.
    At third roundabout turn right onto A1300. At 2nd roundabout turn left onto
    Boldon Lane. Ground 50 yards on right

Colours: All Blue
Change colours: All red

Chairman: Ronald Wightman
Treasurer: Gordon Smith

SOUTH SHIELDS SIMONSIDE S.C.

Secretary: Dave Convery, 118 Durham Drive, Fellgate Estate, Jarrow NE32 4QZ
    Tel: 0191 536 7298
Ground: Monkton Stadium, Jarrow
Directions: Northbound on A19 take turn-off for A194. At roundabout take left turn A194 Newcastle/Gateshead. Take 2nd left, Monkton Stadium signed from there

Colours: Yellow/blue/yellow
Change: Blue & black stripes/black/black

Chairman: John Nelson 0191 454 7333
Press Officer: Secretary

STANLEY UNITED

Secretary: Vince Kirkup, 9 Brookes Rise, Regents Green, Langley, Durham DH7 8XY
    Tel: 0191 378 0921
Ground: High Road, Stanley, near Crook (nicknamed Hill Top Ground). **Directions:** Teeside on A689 to Bishop Auckland and onto Crook, turn left atMarket Place then 1st right for Tow Law to Billy Row and Stanley, right at topof bank then 1st left, grd 250 yards on left.
Clubhouse: Open matchdays.   Club Shop: No
HONOURS: Northern Lg 3, R-up 62-63, Lg Cup 3,
BEST SEASON: FA Cup 1st Rd 53-54.FA Amateur Cup Semi Final 19-20.

Nickname: The Nops
Sponsors: Company Cars Direct
Colours: Red & white stripes/black/red
Change colours: Sky/navy/navy

President: A Westgarth
Chairman: Barry Waiting.
Asst Manager/ Coach: K Finnegan
Physio: J Burn

STOKESLEY SPORTS CLUB

Secretary: Peter Grainge, 77 Darnton Drive, Easterside, Middlesbrough TS4 3RF Tel: 01642 273934
Ground: Stokesley Sports Ground, Broughton Road, Stokesley
Directions: A19 to Middlesbrough, then A174turn to Whitby/Teesport. At 3rd turning up slip road A172 to Stokesley. Over 1st r'about, next r'about turn to Stokesley, 5 miles. At next r'about keep left to next r'about. Ground 100 yards on left.

Colours: Red & black/black/black
Change: White/red/red

Chairman: Eric Taylor 01642 273934
Press Officer: secretary

SUNDERLAND RYHOPE C.W.

Secretary: George McKitterick, 8 Kilburn Close, Ryhope Village, Sunderland. SR2 0QU
Tel: 0191 523 8436)
Ground: Ryhope Recreation Park, Ryhope Street, Ryhope, Sunderland Tel: 0191 521 2843
Directions: Take A19 (3 miles south of Sunderland centre) to Ryhope village, atVillage Green turn into Evelyn Terrace/Ryhope Street and carry on up bank pastPresto's for 600 yds - ground appears on left. 3 miles from Sunderland Central(BR), bus every 10 mins from Sunderland centre.
Capacity: 1,000　**Seats:** No　**Cover:** No　**Floodlights:** Yes
HONOURS: Wearside Lg 4, (Lg Cup 2), Durham Chall Cup 77-78, M/mouth Charity Cup3, S/land Shipowners Cup 2

Founded: 1988.

Colours: Yellow/black/black & red
Change colours: Red/white/red & white

Chairman:: G. Routledge
Press Officer: Peter Grainge

THORNABY ON TEES

Secretary: Peter Livingstone, 5 Guisborough Road, Thornaby on Tees TS17 8BE
Tel: 01642 646428 (H) 01642 606803 (B)
Ground: Teesdale Park, Acklam Road, Thornaby on Tees
Directions: A19 to Thornaby turn off, ground half mile on right. One mile fromThornaby BR station. Any Stockton-Middlesbrough bus - stop at Acklam Rd,Thornaby

Colours: Red & white/red/red & white
Change colours: All blue
Chairman: David Dale 01642 507850
Press Officer: as Chairman

WASHINGTON NISSAN

Secretary:　Harry English, 22 Rushcliffe, Fulwell , Sunderland SR6 9RG
Tel: 0191 548 7194(H) 0191 4152340 (W)
Ground:　Nissan Sports Complex.
Directions: North along A1 (M) use A690 (signed Sunderland) connect withA19, north on A19, after passing the A1231 turn off, plant on the left. Past plant & follow signs 'Nissan Offices'.
Clubhouse: Open Mon-Fri 5-11pm, Sat 11am-11pm, Sun noon-3 & 7-10.30pm
HONOURS:　Wearside Lg Div 1 93-94 (Lg Cup R-up 91-92, Div 2 Cup 92-93 93-94), Nissan European Trophy 3.

Founded: 1988
Colours: Blue & yellow/ blue/blue
Change colours: Red & white/white/white.
Chairman: Alan Hill
Treasurer: J.Taylor
Press Officer: Paul Curry
Manager: Stan Fenwick
Assistant Manager: Keith Robertson.
Coach: Darren Ward

WHITBURN

Secretary: John Allen, 26 Myrtle Ave., Whitburn, Tyne & Wear SR6 7DP
Tel: 0191 529 5919 (H) 0191 529 4202 (B) 0771 4553524 (M)
Ground: Newfield, Whitburn
Directions: From Sunderland follow signs for Coast Road to Whitburn. At 2nd set of lights turn left & follow road for 1 mile. Sunderland training ground on right Newlands on left.

Colours: Maroon & sky/maroon & sky/maroon
Change: Blue & yellow/blue/blue & yellow
Chairman: Chris Meston 0191 529 5852
Press Officer: as Chairman

WHITEHAVEN AMATEURS

Secretary: Richard Stamp, Johnson House, Hillcrest Avenue, Whitehaven, CA28 6SU
Tel No: 01946 61877
Ground: Whitehaven County Ground, Coach Road, Whitehaven
Directions: Barrow on A595, ignore branch to town centre at B.P. garage turnright at t/lights on A5094. 1/2 mile turn left at Esso garage into Coach Rd.Narrow lane ent immed after l/ crossing to grd behind Rugby Lge Stadium.
HONOURS:　Cumberland Cup 90-91, County League 87-88 88-89, Wearside Lg Div 2 Cup R-up 93-94.

Colours: Yellow/blue/yellow
Change colours: White/navy/white

Chairman: Bill Robson.
Press Officer: Secretary
Manager: Ian Green
Assistant Manager: Ian Atkins

WINDSCALE

Secretary:　Craig Heggie, 12 Bookwell, Egremont, Cumbria CA2 2LS
Tel Nos: 01946 823587 (H) 01946 788337 (W)
Ground:　Falcon Field, Egremont.
Directions:　A66 to Bridgefoot. A595 Barrow,bottom of hill approaching Egremont take 3rd turn off island (signed)Smithfield/Gillfoot, ground in housing estate
HONOURS:　Furness Senior Cup 1985-86

Founded: 1950
Colours:White & Navy Blue/ Navy/White
Change: Blue & white/royal/royal

Chairman: R Napier
Press Officer: Secretary
Treasurer: A Barwise

WOLVISTON

Secretary: Keith Simpson, 14 Lodore Grove, Acklam, Middlesbrough TS5 8PB 01642 823734
Ground: Metcalfe Way, Wynyard Road, Wolviston, Billingham, Cleveland TS22 5NE.
Directions: On Wynyard Road between Thorpe Thewles & Wolviston. A19 onto A689 into Wolviston village, take Wynyard Road towards Thorpe Thewles, grd left before Sir John Halls Estate.
Capacity: 2,000　**Seats:** None　**Cover:** 200　**Floodlights:** No　**Club Shop:** No.
Clubhouse: Licensed bar. Hot & cold meals. Open 11am-11pm on matchdays.
HONOURS: Wearside Lg Div 2 89-90, Lg Cup R-up 92-93, Teesside Lg R-up 84-85, Lg Cup 86-87, Durham FA Trophy R-up 89-90, Stockton & Dist. Lg 3, LgCup 3, Lg Charity Cup 79-80.
Record Gate: 500 v Middlesbrough 27/7/93

Founded: 1910　Nickname: Wolves
Sponsors: R.C.I. Industrial Cleaners
Colours: Royal blue/blue/white
Change: Red & white/red/white
Chairman: Eddie Poole　President: Bob Smith
Vice Chairman: Derek Stockton
Press Officer: Andy Anderson
Manager: John Johnson
Asst Manager: Kevin Smith
Coach: Alan Lucas

An irresistable strike force

Every month

Every week

Every day

For up to the minute news, results, fixtures,
and general facts and figures
from the world of non-league football
log on to

www.nlfootball.com

Brought to you by Non-League Media in conjunction with e-comsport

JPL WADE NORTHERN ALLIANCE FOOTBALL LEAGUE

President: Les Todd   **Chairman:** G F Dobbins
Secretary: John McLackland, 92 Appletree Gardens
Walkerville, Newcastle upon Tyne NE6 4SX   Tel: 0191 2621636
Press Officer: Bill Gardner   Tel/Fax: 0191 4883422

West Allotment Celtic claimed what was their sixth Northern Alliance title and their third in successive seasons and are still setting the standards for their Premier Division rivals to follow. Celtic's manager Ken Scott is undoubtedly one of non-League football's most successful team bosses and brought a string of honours to his previous club Seaton Delaval before moving to Hillheads three years ago.

To retain the Premier Division championship West Allotment had to see off the challenge of Shankhouse, a club which is over one hundred years old and is now once again emerging from the shadows. New manager Garry Kirkup has demonstrated that he really has what it takes to build a successful outfit and his strong squad, finishing only three points short of the champions' total, secured the Northumberland FA Senior Bowl in a very encouraging campaign.

Other up-and-coming sides, indicated by their relative performances last season in the league's top flight are Percy Main Amateurs and Northbank Carlisle. And, while the Cumbrians reached the semi-finals of their County Senior Cup, beating Gretna on the way, Percy Main crowned a great campaign by winning the Stan Seymour League Cup.

Both of these sides are packed with promising youngsters and Northbank's 19-year-old striker Simon Tucker attracted a lot of attention from Football League clubs. Tucker was the Premier Division's top marksman with over 30 goals to his credit.

It was a disappointing season for Ryton who up to the half way stage were serious title contenders and had applied for a step up into the Northern League. Their ambitious plans ended in disarray at the season's end and losing the Durham FA Trophy to close neighbours Winlaton Hallgarth was probably the very least of the blows which befell them.

Having erected a spectator stand at their Kingsley Park base, Ryton were also ready to install fencing and floodlights but failed to meet the deadline for a Northern League inspection. This disappointment was followed by the shock resignation of manager Steve Murray, the departure of recently installed chairman Stan Miller and the defeat in the Durham Trophy final. And a poor finish prevented Ryton claiming a place in the top two which they would have needed for a promotion bid.

Ponteland United were once again on the fringes of the title race, but Barrie Wardrobe's side couldn't sustain the challenge. The high point of United's season was in the Northumberland Senior Cup. For the second year running they reached the semi-final stage after knocking out quarter-final opponents Blyth Spartans. But it looks as though Ponteland, yet to claim a major league honour after several near misses, now need an influx of new blood for the next campaign.

Coxlodge Social Club and Newcastle University won promotion as champions and runners-up in Division One and both were busy with ground improvements in the close season. It was second time lucky for Coxlodge who were knocked back a year ago, but manager Mark Gardiner has a very useful squad who lifted the division's Combination Cup as well as the title. The Students finally made it into the top flight and as a sort of sideline also became English Universities champions. There was news at the end of the season that ground improvements were high on the agenda for several Northern Alliance clubs.

After ground-sharing with Seaton Delaval, Shankhouse were due to move to a posh new ground at Dudley which has been prophetically named Action Park - at least they hope so! Meanwhile Walker Central will be moving back to Monkchester Green, the scene of massive upgrading during their short sojourn at the nearby Lightfoot Stadium. And new dressing rooms and an adjoining club house will be at Benfield Saints' disposal. Ian Riley's side have changed their name from Benfield Park in line with last season's amalgamation with the now defunct North Shields St Columbas.

Following the demise of Premier Division outfit Lemington at the end of the 1998-99 campaign their secretary Alan Findlay picked up the pieces and opted to re-start as Cowgate Sports Club in the Alliance's Second Division. And at the first time of asking the Sports won promotion alongside champions Harraby Catholic Club, who stepped into the breach left by their resigning fellow-Cumbrians Gillford Park. Both clubs are expected to continue their climb through the ranks.

Bill Gardner, League Press Officer

HONOURS LIST 1999-2000

Premier Division Champions	West Allotment Celtic	Runners-up	Shankhouse
Division One Champions	Coxlodge Social Club	Runners-up	Newcastle University
Division Two Champions	Harraby Catholic Club	Runners-up	Cowgate Sports Club
League Cup Winners	Percy Main Amateurs		
Challenge Cup Winners	Carlisle City		
Combination Cup Winners	Coxlodge Social Club		
Amateur Cup Winners	Harraby CC		
Northumberland FA Senior Bowl Winners	Shankhouse		
Durham FA Trophy Winners	Winalton Hallgarth		
Northumberland FA Minor Cup Winners	Amble Vikings		

FINAL LEAGUE TABLES 1999-2000

PREMIER DIVISION

	P	W	D	L	F	A	Pts
West Allotment	30	20	8	2	73	34	68
Shankhouse	30	20	5	5	62	22	65
Northbank	30	17	7	6	74	43	58
Ponteland Utd	30	16	7	7	81	37	55
Ryton	30	15	6	9	65	49	51
Carlisle City	30	14	8	8	63	36	50
Percy Main	30	13	9	8	55	46	48
Benfield Park	30	13	5	12	52	44	44
Walker Cent.	30	12	6	12	61	58	42
S. Delaval	30	11	8	11	49	58	41
Winlaton H.	30	8	8	14	48	63	32
Spittal Rovers	30	7	6	17	40	68	27
Heaton Stann.	30	6	4	20	52	100	22
Hebburn SKL	30	6	3	21	40	89	21
Newbiggin CW*	30	5	8	17	43	79	20
Walker L'wood*	30	5	6	19	33	65	18

TOP LEAGUE GOALSCORERS - PREMIER DIVISION

Simon Tucker	Northbank	31
Mark Cowell	Ponteland United	25
Darren Barker	Ponteland United	21
Tony Woodhouse	Shankhouse	21

DIVISION ONE

	P	W	D	L	F	A	Pts
Coxlodge SC	26	23	2	1	80	28	71
N University*	26	20	4	2	77	19	61
Amble Vikings	26	18	4	4	63	28	58
Amble Town	26	12	7	7	59	40	43
Cullercoats	26	12	5	9	62	50	41
Wark	26	11	6	9	52	56	39
Procter & G	26	8	9	9	48	45	33
Chopwell TC*	26	9	5	12	51	59	29
Heddon Inst	26	7	7	12	49	57	28
Morpeth 'A'*	26	8	4	14	37	45	25
Highfields Utd	26	7	3	16	50	84	24
Ashington H	26	4	5	17	28	59	17
Prudhoe S	26	4	5	17	41	90	17
Rutherford	26	4	4	18	24	61	16

TOP LEAGUE GOALSCORERS - DIVISION ONE

Neil Clegg	Highfields United	25

DIVISION TWO

	P	W	D	L	F	A	Pts
Harraby CC*	26	22	1	3	97	29	64
Cowgate SC	26	19	4	3	75	30	61

TOP LEAGUE GOALSCORERS - DIVISION TWO

Kevin Lightfoot	Harrowby CC	23

* points deducted

PREMIER DIVISION RESULTS CHART 1999-2000

		1	2	3	4	5	6	7	8	9	10	11	12	13	14	15	16
1	Carlisle City	X	7-1	4-0	5-0	3-3	1-0	1-1	0-2	1-2	0-2	2-3	2-0	4-1	2-2	0-1	2-0
2	Heaton Stann.	0-2	X	3-3	2-0	0-2	3-3	2-5	4-3	0-4	1-2	0-1	4-3	1-1	2-1	3-4	0-2
3	Hebburn SKL	2-5	2-2	X	5-0	0-6	2-4	2-0	1-5	2-3	2-0	0-3	0-1	1-4	0-3	2-3	3-1
4	Newbiggin CW	3-3	1-0	5-1	X	0-3	3-3	1-1	0-3	4-0	0-5	1-3	2-2	0-3	2-0	1-2	1-1
5	N Benfield Park	0-3	2-3	3-1	3-1	X	0-1	1-2	4-2	1-3	2-3	2-1	2-0	0-2	3-0	0-2	0-0
6	Northbank	3-2	6-2	7-0	5-2	3-0	X	2-3	0-0	1-0	0-0	0-4	3-0	4-2	3-0	1-2	5-1
7	Percy Main Ams	0-3	2-1	1-2	3-2	2-5	1-1	X	1-1	6-1	1-2	2-1	1-2	4-2	1-0	1-1	2-1
8	Ponteland United	1-1	9-2	4-1	5-1	3-0	2-1	1-2	X	1-2	8-0	1-2	6-1	2-2	2-1	0-0	2-3
9	Ryton	1-1	4-3	6-0	3-1	3-3	0-1	2-2	2-1	X	6-0	1-0	4-1	0-1	2-2	2-2	5-0
10	Seaton Delavel	2-2	7-4	0-2	1-1	1-0	0-3	0-2	1-2	5-1	X	0-2	2-2	4-2	1-0	0-2	2-2
11	Shankhouse	0-1	7-23	5-0	3-0	0-0	4-1	0-0	1-3	4-2	0-0	X	3-0	2-0	3-3	0-0	2-1
12	Spittal Rovers	0-0	4-1	2-1	2-2	1-2	0-2	2-1	1-2	0-1	3-3	0-3	X	1-3	3-1	3-4	2-1
13	Walker Central	3-1	3-1	2-2	3-4	0-2	2-3	2-4	0-5	1-1	1-1	0-2	4-1	X	2-1	1-3	5-0
14	Walker Ledwood	0-2	1-2	3-2	2-1	0-1	1-2	2-2	1-3	0-3	0-1	1-1	0-3	X	1-4	3-2
15	West Allotment	3-1	3-1	2-1	5-2	3-1	2-2	0-0	2-2	2-1	3-0	0-1	3-1	2-2	7-0	X	2-3
16	Winlaton	0-2	6-2	2-0	2-2	1-1	4-4	3-2	0-0	3-0	1-3	0-1	4-1	2-4	1-1	1-4	X

PREMIER DIVISION CLUBS 2000-2001

CARLISLE CITY F.C.
CHAIRMAN: Jackie Ewbank   MANAGER/COACH: Willie Armstrong
SECRETARY: Jackie Williamson,   14 Etterby Street, Stanwix, Carlisle (01228 531654)
GROUND: The Sheepmount Sports Complex, Carlisle (01228 625599)
DIRECTIONS: Take B6264 Brampton-Carlisle road. Follow Workington signpost. Continue on dual carriageway past Carlisle Castle on right. Where opposite dual carriageway intersects go over and follow road on right hand carriageway up to roundabout. Come back the way you came towards Castle. Turn left just before Castle. Follow road down keeping left until you reach the Sheepmount Complex.
COLOURS: Blue & Navy Hoops / Black   CHANGE COLOURS: White / Navy

COXLODGE SOCIAL CLUB F.C.
CHAIRMAN: Bob Fenwick   MANAGER/COACH: Mark Gardiner
SECRETARY:Les Ramsay, 7 Brunton Grove, Fawdon, Newcastle upon Tyne NE3 2PR (0191 2850782)
GROUND: Coxlodge Community Centre, Gosforth
DIRECTIONS: From the north or south on the A1 Western Bypass leave on slip-road signed Fawdon. Turn right at church and follow road over Metro lines onto the Meadows. At traffic lights past the Jubilee PH go straight on and turn in at the opening before the Fire Station, signposted Coxlodge Community.
COLOURS: Blue / Blue   CHANGE COLOURS: Purple & Blue Stripes / Blue

HEATON STANNINGTON F.C.
CHAIRMAN: William Pitt   MANAGER/COACH: Colin Atchinson
SECRETARY: Colin Atchinson, 18 Glenhurst Drive, Chapel Park, Newcastle NE7 7QH (0191 2667464)
GROUND: Newton Park, Newton Road, High Heaton, Newcastle upon Tyne NE5 1SP (0191 2642675)
DIRECTIONS: a) Travelling from Newcastle turn left at the Corner House Hotel traffic lights into Newton Road. Continue to the round-about and bear left for 30 yards. The ground is on the right behind the shops.   b) Travelling from South Gosforth go past the Freeman Hospital and turn left at the next roundabout. The ground is on the left approx. 250 yards further on.
COLOURS: Black & White Quarters / Black   CHANGE COLOURS: Blue with Black Sleeves / Blue

HEBBURN REYROLLE F.C.
CHAIRMAN: Alan Graham   MANAGER/COACH: Bill Pattison
SECRETARY: Gordon Taylor, 29 Crawley Avenue, Hebburn, Tyne & Wear NE31 2LT (0191 4834537)
GROUND: Hebburn Sports Ground, Victoria Road West, Hebburn, Tyne & Wear
DIRECTIONS: From Newcastle and Gateshead via Felling Bypass to Heworth Roundabout and take A195 signed Hebburn/Jarrow. Ground just over 2 miles on left. Alternatively, from Tyne Tunnel take Jarrow & Hebburn road A195 Ground is just over 2 miles on right.
COLOURS: Red & Blue / Blue   CHANGE COLOURS: Green & Blue / Navy

NEWCASTLE BENFIELD SAINTS F.C.
CHAIRMAN: Jimmy Rowe   MANAGER/COACH: Ian Riley
SECRETARY: Tony Baird, 23 Balkwell Avenue, North Shields, Tyne & Wear NE29 7JN (0191 2580833)
GROUND: Benfield Park, Benfield Road, Newcastle upon Tyne
DIRECTIONS: Travelling from Newcastle towards the Coast take the second slip road after the Corner House Public House traffic lights and turn right into Benfield Road. The ground is on the left opposite Walkergate Hospital and adjacent to the school.
COLOURS: All White   CHANGE COLOURS: All Red

NEWCASTLE UNIVERSITY F.C.
CHAIRMAN: Rick Sellers   MANAGER/COACH: Rick Sellers
SECRETARY: Simon Kent, 8/10, Myrtle Grove, Jesmond, Newcastle upon Tyne NE2 3HT (0771 3355388)
GROUND: Cochrane Park, Etherstone Avenue, Newcastle upon Tyne
DIRECTIONS: From Newcastle centre via Jesmond onto Coast Road. After Jesmond Dene and immediately after lights at Corner House P.H. take first slip road, turn left again onto A188. Turn right at first r'bout at garage into Etherstone Ave. Ground is 200 m on left.
COLOURS: Blue / Blue   CHANGE COLOURS: White / Blue

NORTHBANK CARLISLE F.C.
CHAIRMAN: Kenny Brown   MANAGER/COACH: Kenny Dixon / Bob Lancaster
SECRETARY: Bob Lancaster, 25 South Street, Carlisle, Cumbria CA1 2EW (01228 539383)
GROUND: Sheepmount Sports Complex, Carlisle (01228 625599)
DIRECTIONS: Take B6264 from Brampton to Carlisle and follow Workington sign. Continue on dual carriageway past Carlisle Castle on right. Where opposite dual carriageway intersects take next turn right and travel back towards Castle. Turn left just before Castle and follow the road (keeping to the left) until you reach the Sheepmount Complex.
COLOURS: Red with White Sleeves / Red   CHANGE COLOURS: Yellow with Navy Sleeves / Navy

PERCY MAIN AMATEURS F.C.
CHAIRMAN: George Mooney   MANAGER/COACH: Bob Rodgerson
SECRETARY: John Humberstone, 5 Sovereign House, Collingwood Court, Tynemouth NE29 8DD (0191 2571967)
GROUND: Purvis Park, St. John's Green, Percy Main, North Shields, Tyne & Wear
DIRECTIONS: From the Tyne Tunnel follow the signs for Royal Quays and after passing the school take the second turning on the left. The ground is first turn on the right adjacent to Percy Main Cricket Club. Alternatively, if approaching from the north and west, head for the Tyne Tunnel and pick up signs for Royal Quays.
COLOURS: Claret & Blue / Claret   CHANGE COLOURS: White / Navy

PONTELAND UNITED F.C.
CHAIRMAN: Alan Birkinshaw MANAGER/COACH: Barrie Wardrobe / Steve Baxter
SECRETARY: Leo McMahon, 1 Wardle Drive, Annitsford, Cramlington, Tyne/Wear NE23 7DB (0191 2500463)
GROUND: Ponteland Leisure Centre, Ponteland (01661 825441)
DIRECTIONS: Enter Ponteland from Newcastle and turn left at the traffic lights. The ground is situated about 100 metres on the left adjacent to Ponteland Leisure Centre.
COLOURS: Black & White Stripes / Black   CHANGE COLOURS: All White

RYTON F.C.
CHAIRMAN: P.Witheycombe MANAGER/COACH: To be appointed
SECRETARY: Les Robson, 31 Park View Gardens, Runhead, Ryton, Tyne/Wear NE40 3JD (0191 4137628)
GROUND: Kingsley Park, Crawcrook, Tyne & Wear
DIRECTIONS: From Newcastle and the east travel through Blaydon and Ryton to Crawcrook. At traffic lights turn right onto Wylam and Clara Vale road. The ground is 400 yards on right. From the west via Prudhoe to Crawcrook turn left at the lights (see above).
COLOURS: Blue & Black Stripes / Black   CHANGE COLOURS: Yellow & Blue / Blue

SEATON DELAVAL AMATEURS F.C.
CHAIRMAN: Tom Ashburn MANAGER/COACH: Alan Smith
SECRETARY: Bill Fellows, 11 Ridley Street, Klondyke, Cramlington NE23 6RH (01670 731833)
GROUND: Wheatridge Park, Seaton Delaval, Northumberland
DIRECTIONS: Take the A189 from Newcastle to Annitsford roundabout and then take the A190 to Seaton Delaval. At the roundabout in Seaton Delaval turn left. The ground is approx 1/4 mile on the right behind the Dale Garage and the Market Garden.
COLOURS: Red & Blue Halves / Blue   CHANGE COLOURS: Yellow / Black

SHANKHOUSE F.C.
CHAIRMAN: George Davison MANAGER/COACH: Garry Kirkup
SECRETARY: Syd Ramsey, 6 Brinkburn Avenue, Cramlington, Northumberland NE23 6TB (01670 715943)
GROUND: Action Park, Dudley
DIRECTIONS: a) From Tyne Tunnel follow A19 to Moor Farm Annitsford roundabout. Take A1 exit to Morpeth and leave at first slip road. Turn left at junction - to Dudley - and on reaching crossroads (Dudley Hotel opposite) turn right to Seaton Burn. Immediately after Dudley & Weetslade Club the ground is signed on the right.   b) From Newcastle on the A1 turn off at the A19 slip road. From the A19 take the first slip road to Dudley and on reaching the crossroads (Dudley Hotel opposite) turn right to Seaton Burn. Continue as above.
COLOURS: Black & Yellow Quarters / Black   CHANGE COLOURS: White / Blue

SPITTAL ROVERS F.C.
CHAIRMAN: Noel Evans MANAGER/COACH: Carl Hudson
SECRETARY: Graeme Burn, 7 Sea Road, Spittal, Berwick upon Tweed TD15 1RN (01289 306049)
GROUND: Newfields, Berwick-upon-Tweed
DIRECTIONS: From the south take the Berwick By-pass to the third roundabout. The Safeway Store is on the right. The pitch is reached by taking the second left on the roundabout. NOTE: Do NOT park in Newfields Estate beside the clubhouse.
COLOURS: Black & White Stripes / Black   CHANGE COLOURS: Red / Red

WALKER CENTRAL F.C.
CHAIRMAN: Robert Morton MANAGER/COACH: Allan Bell
SECRETARY: Bob Mulroy, 116 Lancefield Avenue, Walker, Newcastle upon Tyne NE6 3ER (0191 2873189)
GROUND: Monkchester Green, Walker, Newcastle upon Tyne
DIRECTIONS: From the City, follow Shields Road to Union Road, then turn left onto Welbeck Road. Turn right at Monkchester Road, then turn left between the houses to enter the car park at Monkchester Community Centre.
COLOURS: All Blue   CHANGE COLOURS: Green & White / White

WEST ALLOTMENT CELTIC F.C.
CHAIRMAN: Joe Mather MANAGER/COACH: Dave Walton / Jimmy Moses
SECRETARY: John Jackson, 4 Rosewood Crescent, Seaton Sluice, Whitley Bay NE26 4BL (0191 2370416)
GROUND: Hillheads Park, Whitley Bay (0191 2913637)
DIRECTIONS: From Newcastle take A1058 (Coast Road) to Tynemouth Swimming Baths. Turn left at roundabout onto A192 (Preston Road North) to the Foxhunters P.H. Turn right and follow A191 to Whitley Bay Ice Rink on the right. Ground is beside ice rink.
COLOURS: Green & White Hoops / Green   CHANGE COLOURS: All Blue

WINLATON HALLGARTH F.C.
CHAIRMAN: Robert Young MANAGER/COACH: Stephen Breen / Jeff Wightman
SECRETARY: Sid Batey, 6 Wylam View, Winlaton, Tyne & Wear NE21 4RJ (0191 4147970)
GROUND: Shibdon Park, Shibdon Road, Blaydon-on-Tyne
DIRECTIONS: From the North on the A1: After crossing over the Tyne River Bridge at Scotswood take the first slip road sign-posted Consett. Bear right at the first roundabout and follow the Swalwell/Consett road to the next roundabout at Swalwell. Turn right and travel towards Blaydon and Winlaton. The ground is about quarter of a mile on the right. Turn into Blaydon Baths Car Park.
COLOURS: Green & White / White   CHANGE COLOURS: Blue & White Stripes / Blue

TEESSIDE FOOTBALL LEAGUE

FEEDER TO: NORTHERN LEAGUE

President: K P Moore **Chairman:** L Crossman

Secretary: R D Marsay, 12 Aislaby Court, Wilton Lane, Guisborough, Cleveland TS14 6TG

Tel: 01287 637087

HONOURS LIST 1999-2000

League Champions	Grangetown Boys Club
Runners up	Acklam Steelworks
Macmillan Bowl Champions	Grangetown Boys Club
Runners up	Acklams Steelworks
North Riding County Cup Champions	Acklam Steelworks
Runners up	Nunthorpe Athletic
RT Raine Trophy Champions	Guisborough Town Reserves
Runners up	Nunthorpe Athletic
JV Madden Trophy Champions	Grangetown BC
Runners up	Nunthorpe Athletic

FINAL LEAGUE TABLE 1999-2000

	P	W	D	L	F	A	Pts	GD		P	W	D	L	F	A	Pts	GD
Grangetown BC	32	24	5	3	107	25	77	82	Whitby Town Res	32	11	5	16	70	69	38	1
Acklam SW	32	24	2	6	108	44	74	64	Guisborough T Rs	32	10	6	16	51	80	36	-29
Nunthorpe Ath	32	18	6	8	94	56	60	38	BEADS FC	32	9	7	16	57	93	34	-36
Cargo Fleet	32	19	2	11	101	66	59	35	British Steel*	32	12	2	18	67	75	32	-8
Thornaby on Tees	32	18	4	10	82	58	58	24	Bedale Athletic*	32	10	3	19	67	90	30	-23
Carlin How	32	17	6	9	78	60	57	18	Stokesley SC	32	7	2	23	39	89	23	-50
Thornaby YC	32	15	8	9	62	60	53	2	New Marske SC	32	4	8	20	40	90	20	-50
Fishburn Park	32	14	7	11	53	44	48	9	Mackinlay Park	32	4	8	20	36	100	20	-64
Richmond Town	32	14	4	14	56	69	46	-13	* points deducted								

MACMILLAN BOWL 1999-2000

PRELIMINARY ROUND

Guisborough T Rs	v	Dormans Ath	G W/O	Richmond Town	v	British Steel	1-0

FIRST ROUND

Stokesley SC	v	Grangetown BC	0-6	Fishburn Park	v	Carlin How	0-2
Mackinlay Park	v	Acklam SW	0-3	Guisborough T Rs	v	New Marske SC	0-2
Whitby Town Res	v	BEADS FC	4-5	Richmond Town	v	Thornaby on Tees	0-4
Bedale Athletic	v	Nunthorpe Athletic	4-3	Thornaby YC	v	Cargo Fleet	1-2

SECOND ROUND

BEADS FC	v	Cargo Fleet	0-8	Carlin How	v	Grangetown BC	1-5
Bedale Athletic	v	Acklam SW	1-2	New Marske SC	v	Thornaby on Tees	0-3

SEMI FINALS

Acklam SW	v	Cargo Fleet	2-1	Grangetown BC	v	Thornaby on Tees

FINAL

Grangetown BC	v	Acklam SW	4*2

LEADING GOALSCORERS 1999-2000

33	N Agiadis	Acklam SW		16	I McGowan	Grangetown BC
31	J Draper	Whitby Town Reserves		15	A Oliver	Acklam SW
27	L Doherty	Nunthorpe Athletic		15	P Pinkney	Nunthorpe Athletic
29	R Teasdale	Cargo Fleet		15	M Allen	Thornaby YC
25	G Simpson	Grangetown BC		15	M Steel	Thornaby YC
23	A Bramley	Bedale Athletic		13	A Peacock	British Steel
22	J Smith	BEAD FC		13	M Hall	Fishburn Park
22	D Blake	Cargo Fleet		11	M Say	Carlin How
21	D Hendry	Acklam SW		11	D Fixter	Thornaby on Tees
20	R Shaw	Thornaby on Tees		10	P Burns	Acklam SW
19	R Scott	Carlin How		10	P Blake	Cargo Fleet
19	D Robson	Grangetown BC		10	S Starsmore	Carlin How
18	J Kirk	British Steel		10	S Bowes	Fishburn Park
18	P Jewitt	Cargo Fleet		10	W Gredziak	Richmond Town
17	L Thompson	Guisborough Town Reserves		10	M Moore	Thornaby on Tees
17	G Hyde	Nunthorpe Athletic		10	J Newton	Whitby Town Reserves

CLUBS IN MEMBERSHIP 1999-2000

ACKLAM STEELWORKS
Gary Bell, 101 Avalon Court, Hemlington,
Middlesbrough TS8 9HU   Tel: 01642 276736

B.E.A.D.S.
Dave Kane, 27 Edgeworth Court, Hemlington,
Middlesbrough TS8 9EP   Tel: 01642 280586

BEDALE ATHLETIC
Mike Allen, 1 Sycamore View, Nosterfield, Bedale, North
Yorks DL8 2QR

CARGO FLEET SC
Mick Connerton, 84 Durham Road, Eston,
Middlesbrough TS6 9LZ   Tel: 01642 502728

CARLIN HOW WMC
Simon Whitwell, 10 Harebell Close, North Skelton,
Saltburn TS12 2FE   Tel: 01287 652135

FISHBURN PARK
Richard & Karen Hutton, 14 Abbots Road, Whitby, North
Yorks YO22 4EB   Tel: 602537

GRANGETOWN BOYS CLUB
Kevin Larkin, 19 Braemar Grove, Teesville,
Middlesbrough TS6 0AN   Tel: 01642 452095

GUISBOROUGH TOWN RESERVES
Ian Tyzack, 57 Bexley Drive, Normanby, Middlesbrough
TS6 0ST   Tel: 01642 469754

HOLLYBUSH UNITED
Michael Griffiths, 7 Penryn Close, Skelton, Saltburn
TS12 2ND   Tel: 01287 651381

MACKINLAY PARK
Martin Coats, 221 High Street, Marske, Redcar TS11
7LR   Tel: 01642 475707

NEW MARSKE SC
Errol Richter, 101 St Peters Road, Whitby, North Yorks
YO22 4HX   Tel: 01947 605423

NUNTHORPE ATHLETIC
Kevin Levitt, 131 Burlham Road, Middlesbrough TS5
5AX   Tel: 01642 824332

RICHMOND TOWN
Linda Blackburn, 14 Westfields, Richmond, North Yorks
DL10 4DD   Tel: 01748 824919

STOKESLEY SC
Peter Grainge, 77 Darnton Drive, Easterside,
Middlesbrough TS4 3RF   Tel: 01642 273934

THORNABY FC
Susan & Andrew Gardner, 25 Brotton Road, Thornaby,
Stockton TS17 8EP   Tel: 01642 671765

THORNABY YOUTH CLUB
Geoff Kirk, 9 Tipton Close, Thornaby, Stockton TS17
9QF   Tel: 01642 676516

WHITBY TOWN RESERVES
Peter Newton, 22 Argyle Road, Whitby, North Yorks
YO21 3HS   Tel: 01947 602631

WOLVISTON RESERVES
Keith Simpson, 14 Lodore Grove, Acklam,
Middllesbrough TS5 8PB   Tel: 01642 823734

THE COUNTY SENIOR FOOTBALL LEAGUE

President: M Matthews Esq.   **Chairman:** A Goodison Esq.

Secretary: R Beadsworth Esq., 32 Cockayne Place, Norton Lees, Sheffield S8 9DG
Tel/Fax: 0114 255 1275   E Mail: roy.norton@talk21.com

FINAL LEAGUE TABLES 1999-2000

PREMIER DIVISION

	P	W	D	L	F	A	Pts
Athersley Rec	26	16	7	3	59	23	55
Phoenix	26	14	4	8	49	33	46
Wombwell Town	26	14	4	8	46	38	46
Parkgate	26	14	4	8	53	47	46
Wombwell Main	26	11	7	8	43	24	40
Mexborough Main St	26	10	6	10	40	50	36
Worksop Town	26	8	10	8	43	29	34
Frecheville CA	26	10	4	12	37	49	34
The Wetherby	26	9	5	12	36	42	32
Ecclesfield Red Rose	26	8	7	11	43	55	31
Hare & Hounds	26	8	6	12	34	48	30
Hallam	26	6	8	12	39	50	26
Sheffield Lane Top	26	7	5	14	37	54	26
Denaby United	26	5	7	14	40	57	22

DIVISION ONE

	P	W	D	L	F	A	Pts
Wickersley	26	17	4	5	74	40	55
Thorpe Hesley	26	15	7	4	55	28	52
Parramore Sports	26	16	2	8	54	41	50
High Green Villa	26	14	6	6	55	33	48
Avesta Sheffield	26	12	6	8	53	56	42
Sheffield	26	12	5	9	59	34	41
Stocksbridge PS	26	12	2	12	59	45	38
Penistone Church	26	11	5	10	45	38	38
Oughtibridge WMSC	26	11	4	11	37	46	37
Woodhouse West End	26	10	2	14	46	52	32
Swinton Athletic	26	6	7	13	51	58	25
Treeton	26	7	4	15	50	70	25
Caribbean Sports	26	6	2	18	45	67	20
NCB Maltby MW	26	4	2	20	26	101	14

PREMIER DIVISION RESULTS CHART 1999-2000

		1	2	3	4	5	6	7	8	9	10	11	12	13	14
1	Athersley Recreation	X	1-0	2-0	0-0	5-0	1-0	6-0	6-0	3-1	7-0	0-1	1-1	3-2	0-0
2	Denaby United	1-2	X	2-1	2-3	0-1	7-1	0-0	1-5	0-3	0-0	3-1	2-1	2-6	5-5
3	Ecclesfield Red Rose	2-4	3-2	X	0-1	2-2	5-4	1-1	0-1	2-1	2-5	1-1	1-1	2-3	0-5
4	Frecheville CA	0-1	2-3	2-2	X	1-4	2-1	5-2	1-1	0-2	0-1	2-1	1-0	1-2	2-1
5	Hallam	0-2	2-1	1-1	1-3	X	1-2	1-1	2-2	1-5	3-0	1-1	0-1	3-4	1-2
6	Hare & Hounds	0-0	1-0	1-2	2-2	3-3	X	2-5	0-2	1-1	2-1	1-1	0-1	1-2	1-0
7	Mexborough Main St	1-3	2-2	4-0	2-1	0-3	0-2	X	1-5	2-0	2-0	1-1	2-1	2-0	0-2
8	Parkgate	4-4	2-1	0-1	4-3	2-1	4-1	5-1	X	0-3	3-2	3-2	0-2	3-2	1-4
9	Phoenix	0-0	2-1	5-1	1-0	1-3	2-3	3-2	0-2	X	4-3	3-0	1-1	1-2	1-1
10	Sheffield Lane Top	1-1	1-1	1-5	1-2	2-1	0-2	2-5	2-1	1-2	X	3-1	2-2	3-1	2-4
11	The Wetherby	2-3	3-0	3-2	0-1	3-0	1-1	0-1	3-0	3-4	1-4	X	0-3	2-4	2-1
12	Wombwell Main	2-4	6-1	0-0	8-2	2-0	4-1	4-0	0-1	1-0	1-0	0-1	X	0-1	1-1
13	Wombwell Town	1-0	3-3	3-5	2-0	1-1	1-0	0-2	2-0	0-2	0-0	0-1	2-0	X	1-1
14	Worksop Town	4-0	0-0	0-2	5-0	3-3	0-1	1-1	2-2	0-1	1-0	0-1	0-0	0-1	X

BRITISH INDUSTRIAL RECLAMATION COUNTY SENIOR LEAGUE CUP 1999-2000

FIRST ROUND

Groves Social (Sat)	v	Oughtibridge WMSC	3-1	The Wetherby	v	Old Edwardians	3-0
Swinton Athletic	v	Wombwell Town	1-3	Caribbean Sports	v	Thorpe Hesley	2-1
ABS Kilnhurst	v	Penistone Church	1-2	Hare & Hounds	v	Davy	3-2

SECOND ROUND

Parkgate	v	Sheffield Bankers	2-2, 2p4	Queens Hotel	v	Phoenix	1-2
South Kirkby Colliery	v	Hallam	0-2	Sheffield	v	Grapes Roy Hancock	0-2
Avesta Sheffield	v	Groves Social (Sat)	1-4	Athersley Recreation	v	Parramore Sports	2-0
Mexborough Main St	v	Wombwell Main	2-4	The Wetherby	v	Penistone Church Rs	4-1
Denaby United	v	Wombwell Town	0-3	Sheffield Lane Top	v	Caribbean Sports	4-0
Treeton	v	Woodhouse West End	2-3	Wickersley	v	High Green Villa	4-2
Sheffield Centralians	v	Worksop Town	1-2	Ecclesfield Red Rose	v	Penistone Church	3-1
Frecheville CA	v	Stocksbridge Park S	6-2	Hare & Hounds	v	NCB Maltby MW	1-0

THIRD ROUND

Sheffield Bankers	v	Phoenix	1-2	Hallam	v	Grapes Roy Hancock	4-5
Groves Social (Sat)	v	Athersley Recreation	0-3	Wombwell Main	v	The Wetherby	1-1, 4p2
Wombwell Town	v	Sheffield Lane Top	2-1	Woodhouse W End	v	Wickersley	2-0
Worksop Town	v	Ecclesfield Red Rose	2-0	Frecheville CA	v	Hare & Hounds	3-2

FOURTH ROUND

Phoenix	v	Grapes Roy Hancock	3-1	Athersley Recreation	v	Wombwell Main	4-3
Wombwell Town	v	Woodhouse West End	6-2	Worksop Town	v	Frecheville CA	2-4

SEMI FINALS

Phoenix	v	Athersley Recreation	1-2	Wombwell Town	v	Frecheville CA	1-2

FINAL

Athersley Recreation	v	Frecheville CA	0-2

NOW IN ITS RECORD 10TH YEAR OF PUBLICATION

BRITAIN'S MOST POPULAR NATIONAL NON-LEAGUE FOOTBALL MONTHLY

TEAM TALK

Team Talk should be available from your local non-League football club or your local newsagent and is available by subscription from the publishers.

Team Talk is published by Tony Williams Publications Ltd., Helland, North Curry, Taunton, Somerset TA3 6DU
Tel: 01823 490080 Fax: 01823 490281 e-mail: tony.williams12@virgin.net

WEST YORKSHIRE ASSOCIATION
FOOTBALL LEAGUE

Founded 1928

President: J Hill   **Chairman:** B Chaplin

Secretary: Kevin Parkinson, 9 Lake Lock Drive, Stanley, Wakefield WF3 4HN

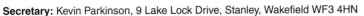

Kirk Deighton Rangers and Ripon City Magnets were new clubs who successfully applied to the League offering excellent on-site facilities and footballing status. many existing clubs have also improved their home venues and, complimented by their team's achievement on the field of play, some have been subsequently rewarded with promotion to the higher division.

The League set up a ground-grading scheme and this has been well received by the clubs, which informs them of their standing and potential to progress through the divisions avoiding surprises or disappointments. this is an excellent example of the club and the League working together to gain mutual benefit.

The challenge for each divisional championship appears to increase in difficulty each season and in most cases, it took till the latter stages of the competition to decide the eventual winners. It was a similar case for those clubs who attempted to gain a promotion opportunity or avoid a relegation/re-election position. The month of April registered the dubious record of the greatest rainfall and this cascaded to extend the conclusion date of the season due to the number of postponements.

With the introduction of a new ruling, each League Cup Competition was to be decided at the first attempt with kicks from the penalty mark if required. To facilitate the playing of the semi-final ties on neutral grounds, without exception, all those clubs that were approached reacted positively. In extending my thanks to enable this positive step to be achieved, I am mindful of may other clubs who readily offered their facilities. This was a shining example indeed of clubs supporting one-another.

Many clubs competing in outside competitions have once again done this with distinction and brought honour to both themselves and the League.

A single goal score-line resulted in victory for the first time in the annual Representative Fixture against the West Riding County Amateur Football League. All players and officials of the team are deserving of the highest praise for the effort and commitment that they displayed.

The League was grateful to Briggsports and the National Grid for the sponsorship they donated with regard to the Premier Division Cup Competition and the Fair Play League/Golden Boot Awards respectively.

In conclusion, I believe the profile of the League has been raised through its season's activities, which is important in keeping our status within the Football Pyramid. With the same determination and careful management at both Club and League level, I am sure that more exciting opportunities and experiences will be there to enjoy in the future.

HONOURS LIST 1999-2000

	League Champions	**League Runners-Up**
PREMIER DIVISION	Nestle Rowntrees	Beeston St Anthony's
DIVISION ONE	Sandy Lane	Mount St Mary's
DIVISION TWO	Rothwell Town	Upper Armley Old Boys
PREMIER RESERVE DIV	Beeston St Anthony's	Carlton Athletic
RESERVE DIVISION	Sandy Lane	Pontefract Labour

	League Cup Winners	**League Cup Runners Up**
PREMIER DIVISION	Beeston St Anthony's	Bardsey
DIVISION ONE	Mount St Mary's	Robin Hood Athletic
DIVISION TWO	Rothwell Town	Methley Rangers
PREMIER RESERVE DIV	Carlton Athletic	Nostell Miners Welfare
RESERVE DIVISION	Robin Hood Athletic	Woodhouse Hill WMC
INVITATION SHIELD	Carlton Athletic Reserves	Rothwell Athletic Reserves

FRED WINTERBURN TROPHY TEAM AWARD   Barwick

GEORGE COPE MEMORIAL TROPHY REFEREE AWARD   Steven Milner

FINAL LEAGUE TABLES 1999-2000

PREMIER DIVISION

	P	W	D	L	F	A	Pts
Nestle Rowntrees	28	24	0	4	100	22	72
Beeston St Anthonys	28	18	4	6	72	38	58
Nostell Miners Welfare	28	15	10	3	64	43	55
Carlton Athletic	28	17	1	10	66	52	52
Horsforth St Margarets	28	17	1	10	56	44	52
Whitkirk Wanderers	28	15	3	10	63	46	48
York R I	28	12	5	11	51	57	41
Knaresborough Town	28	11	5	12	54	56	38
Wakefield	28	9	5	14	51	51	32
Aberford Albion	28	8	6	14	37	58	30
Bardsey	28	7	6	15	43	67	27
Rothwell Athletic*	28	8	5	15	50	61	26
Wetherby Athletic	28	7	4	17	41	72	25
Pudsey	28	6	3	19	35	54	21
Tadcaster Magnet Spts	28	5	4	19	28	90	19

DIVISION ONE

	P	W	D	L	F	A	Pts
Sandy Lane	28	21	5	2	91	33	68
Mount St Mary's	28	18	4	6	88	42	58
Pontefract Labour	28	16	6	6	76	42	54
Armley Athletic	28	16	4	8	73	43	52
Ossett Common Rvrs	28	14	9	5	57	35	51
Woodhouse Hill WMC	28	14	6	8	62	45	51
Robin Hood Athletic	28	13	8	7	54	33	47
Ripon City Magnets	28	12	5	11	65	59	41
Featherstone Colliery	28	11	4	13	39	48	37
Kirk Deighton Rngrs	28	9	6	13	57	67	33
Churwell Lions	28	8	7	13	62	59	31
Sherburn White Rose	28	6	6	16	39	62	24
Garforth WMC	28	5	6	17	47	87	24
Barwick	28	3	2	23	34	113	11
Rothwell Stones*	28	3	4	21	25	101	10
* points deducted							

PREMIER DIVISION RESULTS CHART 1999-2000

		1	2	3	4	5	6	7	8	9	10	11	12	13	14	15
1	Aberford Albion	X	2-1	0-3	2-2	2-4	1-3	0-5	2-3	0-3	3-1	2-1	1-0	3-2	1-2	1-2
2	Bardsey	2-0	X	3-3	1-0	2-1	1-2	0-2	1-1	3-2	2-4	1-4	4-1	3-2	0-4	2-2
3	Beeston St Anthony's	1-4	4-3	X	2-5	1-0	2-4	1-0	1-1	2-0	3-2	8-1	1-1	0-1	0-2	4-0
4	Carlton Athletic	3-1	6-1	2-5	X	1-2	2-1	0-1	2-7			5-0	4-3	5-3	6-3	2-1
5	Horsforth St Margaret's	0-2	3-0	0-2	3-0	X	1-0	1-4	1-0	2-1	1-1	4-0	2-1	4-3	4-1	1-4
6	Knaresborough Town	1-1	4-0	2-5	4-2	1-4	X	1-6	1-1	3-1	0-1	5-2	3-2	2-3	4-0	0-2
7	Nestle Rowntrees	5-0	6-1	1-2	5-1	1-3	6-1	X	3-0	2-1	6-0	7-0	4-1	6-0	3-2	4-0
8	Nostell Miners Welfare	1-1	2-2	2-2	0-3	3-1	2-0	4-2	X		5-4	3-2	1-1	1-0	0-0	5-2
9	Pudsey	1-1	0-2	0-3	1-5	3-1	2-2	1-4	0-3	X	0-2	1-1	6-1	2-0	2-3	1-2
10	Rothwell Athletic	4-1	2-1	0-6	1-3	1-2	3-3	1-3	3-5	4-0	X	6-0	1-1	2-2	1-2	2-2
11	Tadcaster Magnets	0-2	1-1	1-8	2-4	3-2	0-5	0-5	1-2	0-1	1-0	X	0-2	1-0	1-1	1-2
12	Wakefield	3-1	1-0	0-2	2-4	1-2	2-0	0-1	2-2	3-0	3-1	8-0	X	2-2	1-0	6-2
13	Wetherby Athletic	1-1	4-2	0-1	0-2	4-1	1-2	0-4	2-2	2-5	1-3	3-2	1-0	X	0-4	4-1
14	Whitkirk Wanderers	3-3	3-2	4-0	3-1	1-3	3-0	0-1	2-4	2-1	2-0	0-1	2-0	8-0	X	4-3
15	York R I	1-0	1-1	4-1	0-1	1-3	0-0	1-3	2-4	1-0	3-0	2-2	4-3	3-0	3-2	X

FAIR PLAY LEAGUE

PREMIER DIVISION	Wakefield
DIVISION ONE	Kirk Deighton Rangers
DIVISION TWO	Hartshead Senior
PREMIER RES DIV	Knaresborough Town
RESERVE DIVISION	Howden Clough

GOLDEN BOOT AWARD

PREMIER DIVISION	Lee Bond (York RMI)	24
DIVISION ONE	Lee Parker (Mount St Marys)	44
DIVISION TWO	Danny Powell (Harshead Senior)	27
PREM RES DIV	James Wright (Beeston St A)	27
RESERVE DIVISION	David Strathie (Sandy Lane)	47

LEAGUE REPRESENTATIVE FIXTURE
for the McKendrick Trophy

West Riding County Amateur Football League 0 v 1 West Yorkshire Association Football League
Scorer: Jason Wright
at Field AFC

Squad: Lee Williams, Richard Dobson, Nathan Drury, Martin Brook (All Carlton Ath), Nicky Baker (cptn, Beeston St Anthony's), Richard Smith (Horsforth St Margaret's), Darryl Franklin (Carlton Ath), Martin Hewitt (Nostell M W), Jason Wright (Tadcaster Magnet Spts), Andy Lamb (Horsforth St Margaret's), Andy Sharp (Beeston St Anthony's), Lee Bond (York R I), Miles Sutton (Knaresborough T)
Team Manager: John Flynn   **Assistant Manager:** Alan Hunt

WEST RIDING COUNTY AMATEUR FOOTBALL LEAGUE

President: D H Humpleby Esq.

Secretary: S Mitchell, 24 Burnsall Road, Liversedge, West Yorkshire WF15 6QF
Tel: 01924 404684

FINAL LEAGUE TABLES 1999-2000

PREMIER DIVISION

	P	W	D	L	F	A	Pts
Keighley Phoenix	26	18	2	6	85	36	56
Hemsworth MW	26	17	4	5	76	33	55
Campton	26	18	1	7	75	39	55
Brighouse Town	26	14	6	6	62	35	48
Wibsey	26	13	6	7	44	39	45
Ovenden W Riding	26	12	5	9	73	60	41
Storthes Hall	26	11	6	9	43	29	39
Littletown	26	11	6	9	57	56	39
Marsden	26	9	4	13	49	51	31
Golcar United	26	8	5	13	44	60	29
Field	26	7	6	13	50	67	27
Crag Road Utd	26	7	3	16	35	72	24
Altofts	26	6	2	18	39	76	20
Tyersal	26	1	4	21	29	106	7

DIVISION ONE

	P	W	D	L	F	A	Pts
Stump Cross	30	23	2	5	75	36	71
Otley Town	30	20	6	4	75	38	66
Dudley Hill Athletic	30	18	6	6	78	47	60
Halifax Irish Club	30	14	5	11	76	62	47
Pudsey Liberal	30	14	3	13	72	65	45
Eastmoor	30	14	3	13	50	44	45
Lower Hopton	30	12	7	11	59	50	43
Hall Green United	30	12	7	11	62	69	43
Salts Old Boys	30	12	6	12	37	34	42
Ardsley Celtic	30	12	5	13	69	62	41
Bay Athletic	30	9	10	11	58	60	37
Farnley	30	9	3	18	47	72	30
Ventus & Yeadon Celtic	30	8	5	17	46	77	29
Heckmondwike Town	30	7	7	16	61	94	28
Overthorpe SC SV	30	6	7	17	44	68	25
Rawdon Old Boys	30	7	4	19	40	71	25

PREMIER DIVISION RESULTS CHART 1999-2000

		1	2	3	4	5	6	7	8	9	10	11	12	13	14
1	Altofts	X	1-2	2-4	2-0	0-2	2-2	0-2	3-5	0-0	3-1	1-3	2-1	6-1	0-1
2	Brighouse Town	4-1	X	1-3	5-0	7-1	0-1	1-1	3-3	1-0	1-1	2-4	1-1	4-1	4-2
3	Campion	4-0	2-0	X	2-1	8-0	4-0	3-2	0-1	5-6	2-0	4-2	2-1	4-0	2-1
4	Crag Road United	1-0	1-2	1-3	X	0-7	2-2	2-1	3-2	0-2	0-5	3-3	2-0	4-0	2-3
5	Field	2-1	3-5	0-1	10-2	X	2-0	1-2	0-4	3-3	0-4	1-3	0-0	1-1	0-1
6	Golcar United	3-1	2-2	1-2	1-2	5-1	X	1-2	1-3	1-3	0-4	4-4	3-2	4-1	3-0
7	Hemsworth MW	4-1	1-0	0-5	4-1	2-3	5-0	X	2-2	6-4	2-0	2-0	1-0	14-0	4-1
8	Keighley Phoenix	8-2	0-2	5-1	4-1	4-1	4-0	0-3	X	5-2	4-0	4-2	0-2	5-0	5-1
9	Littletown	2-3	2-1	1-0	2-0	4-3	2-3	2-1	1-3	X	6-1	0-5	0-3	4-1	2-2
10	Marsden	6-0	1-1	3-2	2-3	3-2	2-2	2-3	2-4	1-3	X	0-2	2-1	1-2	1-3
11	Ovenden W Riding	7-1	1-6	4-2	3-1	1-1	5-0	1-7	1-4	3-3	1-3	X	1-2	7-3	3-3
12	Storthes Hall	7-1	0-3	2-2	1-0	2-2	2-0	1-1	3-2	0-0	0-1	3-0	X	4-1	2-1
13	Tyersal	2-6	1-2	0-6	3-3	2-4	1-4	2-4	0-3	2-2	2-2	0-3	0-3	X	3-4
14	Wibsey	2-0	1-2	5-2	3-0	0-0	2-1	0-0	2-1	1-1	2-1	0-0	1-0	2-0	X

PREMIER DIVISION CUP

FIRST ROUND

Campion	v	Brighouse Town	3-4		Crag Road United	v	Keighley Phoenix	3-6
Field	v	Hemsworth M W	1-3		Littletown	v	Ovenden W Riding	3-5
Marsden	v	Tyersal	5-1		Wibsey	v	Golcar United	1-2

SECOND ROUND

Altofts	v	Keighley Phoenix	3-5		Brighouse Town	v	Storthes Hall	2-0
Marsden	v	Hemsworth MW	2*2, 0p3		Ovenden W Riding	v	Golcar United	3-1

SEMI-FINALS

Brighouse Town	v	Ovenden W Riding	1-3		Hemsworth M W	v	K'ley Phoenix	0*0, 4p3

FINAL

Ovenden W Rding   v   Hemsworth M W   1-0   at Littletown FC

NORTH EAST SUNDAY LEAGUE TABLES 1999-2000

HEAVY WOOLLEN GATE SUNDAY ALLIANCE

PREMIER DIV.	P	W	D	L	F	A	Pts
Overthorpe	18	13	3	2	61	26	42
Battyeford Wasps	18	13	3	2	50	19	42
Drighlington	18	11	1	6	62	43	34
Scholes Athletic	18	8	5	5	48	33	29
Lowside	18	9	2	7	34	42	29
St John Fisher	18	7	2	9	38	51	21
New Scarborough	18	5	1	12	35	55	18
Wakefield City	18	1	0	17	19	72	3

DIVISION ONE	P	W	D	L	F	A	Pts
Thornhill Lees	22	17	4	1	73	20	55
Bulls Head	22	16	5	1	97	36	53
Mileta	22	12	1	9	88	71	37
Lillebets	22	11	3	8	48	34	36
White Lee	22	12	0	10	69	72	36
Towngate	22	9	7	6	67	39	34
Birkenshaw	22	9	2	11	63	63	29
Pear Tree*	22	9	5	8	60	60	29
Woodman BC	22	7	2	13	56	61	23
Brighton	22	6	3	13	48	83	21
Bulls Head Syke	22	4	3	15	46	63	15
White Horse	22	2	1	19	41	140	7

LEEDS SUNDAY LEAGUE

PREMIER DIV	P	W	D	L	F	A	Pts
Goose 87	22	17	3	2	73	26	54
Diamond Sports	22	15	4	3	79	27	49
Kippax Welfare	22	14	3	5	80	36	45
Whistlestop	22	13	2	7	63	28	41
Manston Hotel	22	12	4	6	76	37	40
Vesper Gate	22	11	3	8	43	41	36
Moorgate	22	9	4	9	38	43	31
Dalesman	22	5	7	10	42	56	22
Adel	22	5	2	15	36	64	17
Seacroft WMC	22	4	1	17	32	72	13
Woodhouse Gun	22	2	2	18	30	127	8

KDM SKIPS SHEFFIELD SUNDAY LEAGUE

PREMIER DIV	P	W	D	L	F	A	Pts
Park 98	18	14	2	2	45	25	41
Rotherham Jags	17	12	1	4	56	27	34
Maltby BL	17	10	4	3	49	24	34
Maltby Prog	17	9	1	7	57	41	31
The Queens	17	8	1	8	37	32	25
Wellington Boot	18	6	4	8	63	57	22
BOC Gasses	17	7	1	9	40	52	22
Whiston	18	6	2	10	33	49	20
New Broom	18	4	0	14	25	51	15
Jockey	17	3	0	14	19	76	9

DIVISION ONE	P	W	D	L	F	A	Pts
Don John Blues	16	15	0	1	63	15	45
Shakespeare Ath	14	10	1	3	40	27	31
Yorks Terrier 'A'	17	10	1	6	45	34	31
Carbrook Hall	16	8	2	6	42	40	26
Reg Vardy RSFC	17	7	2	8	33	39	23
TC Harrisons	17	5	4	8	38	45	19
R'ham Unison 'A'	18	5	1	12	36	66	16
MTE Athletic	19	1	3	15	22	53	6

HULL SUNDAY LEAGUE

PREMIER DIV	P	W	D	L	F	A	Pts
Hessle Rang 'A'	20	18	0	2	73	25	36
Prestige Brighams	20	14	4	2	57	22	32
Orchard Park 'A'	20	11	3	6	50	37	25
Northwood 'A'	20	9	7	4	39	27	25
Chalk Lane 'A'	20	10	4	6	49	32	24
S Eagle Driffield	20	7	7	6	45	29	21
Swanfield 'A'	20	7	4	9	40	39	18
Boothferry Cameo	20	6	1	13	30	65	13
Radphone	20	3	5	12	31	71	11
New Inn	20	3	3	14	29	49	9
Lion	20	3	0	17	25	72	6

DIVISION ONE WEST	P	W	D	L	F	A	Pts
National Tigers	16	12	3	1	81	18	27
Orchard Park 'B'	15	9	4	2	43	24	22
Chalk Lane 'B'	16	9	3	4	56	34	21
Settingdyke YC	16	8	2	6	39	32	18
Cottingham Rang	16	5	5	6	39	33	15
Hessle Rangers 'B'	16	6	2	8	36	53	14
Swanfield 'B'	16	5	3	8	27	35	13
Arctic Rangers	16	4	2	10	36	60	10
B/ferry Cameo 'B'	15	1	0	14	23	91	2

DIVISION ONE EAST	P	W	D	L	F	A	Pts
Prestige Brig 'B'	18	12	5	1	38	18	29
Charlton 'B'	18	13	2	3	70	23	28
Grafton	18	12	2	4	54	21	26
Newbridge	18	10	5	3	30	23	25
Skippers Tavern	18	11	2	5	56	27	24
Keyingham 'A'	18	8	4	6	56	38	20
Van Leer	18	6	1	11	24	58	13
Lambwath Juven	18	3	2	13	25	52	8
Leven MC 1st's	18	1	3	14	11	49	5
Barham United	18	1	0	17	19	74	2

MEXBOROUGH & DISTRICT SUNDAY LEAGUE

PREMIER DIV	P	W	D	L	F	A	Pts
Dearne CMW	20	15	3	2	61	31	48
Queens United	20	14	2	4	71	31	44
Mex Sportsman	20	12	4	4	53	33	40
Groves Social	20	8	6	6	43	42	30
Tom Hill YFC	20	8	3	9	38	35	27
Swinton WMC	20	7	5	8	53	46	26
Darfield Station	20	7	4	9	47	59	25
The Gate	20	6	5	9	49	50	23
New Inn	20	6	3	11	36	50	21
Bolton Social	20	5	4	11	33	69	19
Goldthorpe Coms	20	2	1	17	28	74	7

DIVISION ONE	P	W	D	L	F	A	Pts
Cortonwood	22	19	2	1	82	21	59
Crown Inn	22	17	0	5	90	41	51
Ings Lane	22	13	4	5	86	49	43
Tavern Rangers	22	12	4	6	72	40	40
Edlington WMC	22	13	0	9	71	65	39
The Don 99	22	11	3	8	68	48	36
The Star	22	9	2	11	62	65	29
Wath Saracens	22	6	6	10	41	56	24
Plant	22	6	1	15	51	72	19
Kilnhurst WMC	22	6	0	16	39	82	18
The Cottage	22	4	2	16	42	85	14
Oak Tree Inn	22	2	4	16	33	103	10

CONSETT SUNDAY LEAGUE

PREMIER DIV.	P	W	D	L	F	A	Pts
Consett Rugby C	20	17	2	1	121	26	53
Blackhill Coms	20	16	1	3	100	23	49
Cons Brannigans	20	15	1	4	81	50	46
Craghead	20	13	1	6	64	41	40
Blackhall Mill	20	12	1	7	58	44	37
Consett Fountain	20	9	2	9	48	52	29
Flint Hill Inn	20	5	4	11	44	70	19
B Lintz CC Celtic	20	4	5	11	31	55	17
Cons F/Masons	20	3	4	13	37	79	13
Chopwell Hotel	20	3	2	15	27	87	11
B Pack Horse	20	1	1	18	26	110	4

DIVISION TWO	P	W	D	L	F	A	Pts
Stanley Central	18	14	1	3	65	30	43
C Station Ex-Jun	18	12	2	4	70	51	38
Annfield Plain CC	18	11	2	5	66	43	35
Shotley Bridge VC	18	9	5	4	70	49	32
Annfield Plain D	18	6	6	6	61	50	24
C Horse & Groom	18	7	3	8	55	65	24
Beamish Bird Inn	18	6	2	10	50	66	20
Leadgate CC	18	5	4	9	59	65	19
Burnhope Ivy Leaf	18	5	1	12	47	66	16
M Miners Arms	18	1	2	15	36	94	5

HALLAMSHIRE SUNDAY LEAGUE

DIVISION ONE	P	W	D	L	F	A	Pts
Woodhouse WE	19	14	1	4	55	28	43
AC Ball	19	11	6	2	43	21	39
Railway Hotel	20	11	5	4	69	33	38
Sacred Heart	20	10	4	6	58	49	34
Stannington Village	20	9	4	7	42	38	31
Woodhouse Stag	18	9	1	8	47	45	28
Echo Sports	19	6	5	8	37	40	23
Stann. Village OB	17	4	5	8	28	40	17
Old Harrow	20	4	4	12	40	80	16
Ecclesfield WMC	20	4	3	13	34	52	15
Sherwood	20	4	2	14	26	53	14

HALLAMSHIRE SUNDAY LEAGUE cont.

DIVISION TWO	P	W	D	L	F	A	Pts
H New Crown	21	14	3	4	47	33	45
Royal Hotel	21	13	4	4	68	30	43
Hurlfield	21	10	7	4	68	37	37
Firth Park WMC	21	10	3	8	54	43	33
N'manton Springs	21	7	8	6	45	41	29
SCS Sports	21	7	4	10	53	69	25
Handsworth Social	21	4	2	15	35	74	14
Cock Inn	21	2	3	16	19	63	9

SCUNTHORPE SUNDAY LEAGUE

DIVISION ONE	P	W	D	L	F	A	Pts
Poachers	16	13	2	1	60	17	41
Broughton Town	16	10	4	2	53	24	34
Lincoln Imp	16	8	2	6	36	39	26
Burton Athletic	16	8	1	7	53	42	25
Queen Bess	16	6	4	6	20	27	22
Comet Widers	16	7	0	9	36	42	21
Barge Inn	16	6	1	9	40	48	19
Kirton Inn (Brigg)	16	4	0	12	18	43	12
Beacon	16	3	0	13	23	58	9

DIVISION TWO	P	W	D	L	F	A	Pts
Red Lion	16	12	2	2	55	16	38
Robert Holme Hall	16	11	3	2	69	22	36
George & Dragon	16	9	0	7	29	26	27
Bridge Roofing	16	8	2	6	29	22	26
Poachers Res.	16	8	2	6	31	47	26
Ashby Star	16	7	1	8	32	34	22
Crown Inn	16	5	2	9	26	31	17
Dukes of Haxey	16	3	2	11	24	70	11
Lord Roberts	16	2	0	14	26	53	6

Above: The captain of Mount St Mary's is presented with the West Yorkshire League Division One Knockout Cup after his team had beaten Robin Hood Athletic 1-0 in the Final at Manse Lane, Knaresborough. Photo: Tony Bills

NOW IN ITS RECORD 10TH YEAR OF PUBLICATION

BRITAIN'S MOST POPULAR NATIONAL NON-LEAGUE FOOTBALL MONTHLY

TEAM TALK

Team Talk provides comprehensive coverage of the whole spectrum of non-League football from the Nationwide Conference to County League

including extensive coverage of

the FA Carlsberg Vase

the FA Umbro Trophy

non-League involvement in

the AXA sponsored FA Cup

and the

England Semi-Professional team

(Team Talk is the ONLY magazine to give such support and coverage to this England team)

Team Talk should be available from your local non-League football club or your local newsagent and is available by subscription from the publishers.

Team Talk is published by Non League Media Plc
c/o Helland, North Curry, Taunton, Somerset TA3 6DU
Tel: 01823 490080 Fax: 01823 490281 e-mail: tony.williams12@virgin.net

SOUTHERN
LEAGUE

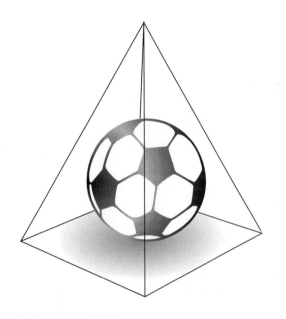

PYRAMID
SECTION

Dr. Martens
SOUTHERN LEAGUE

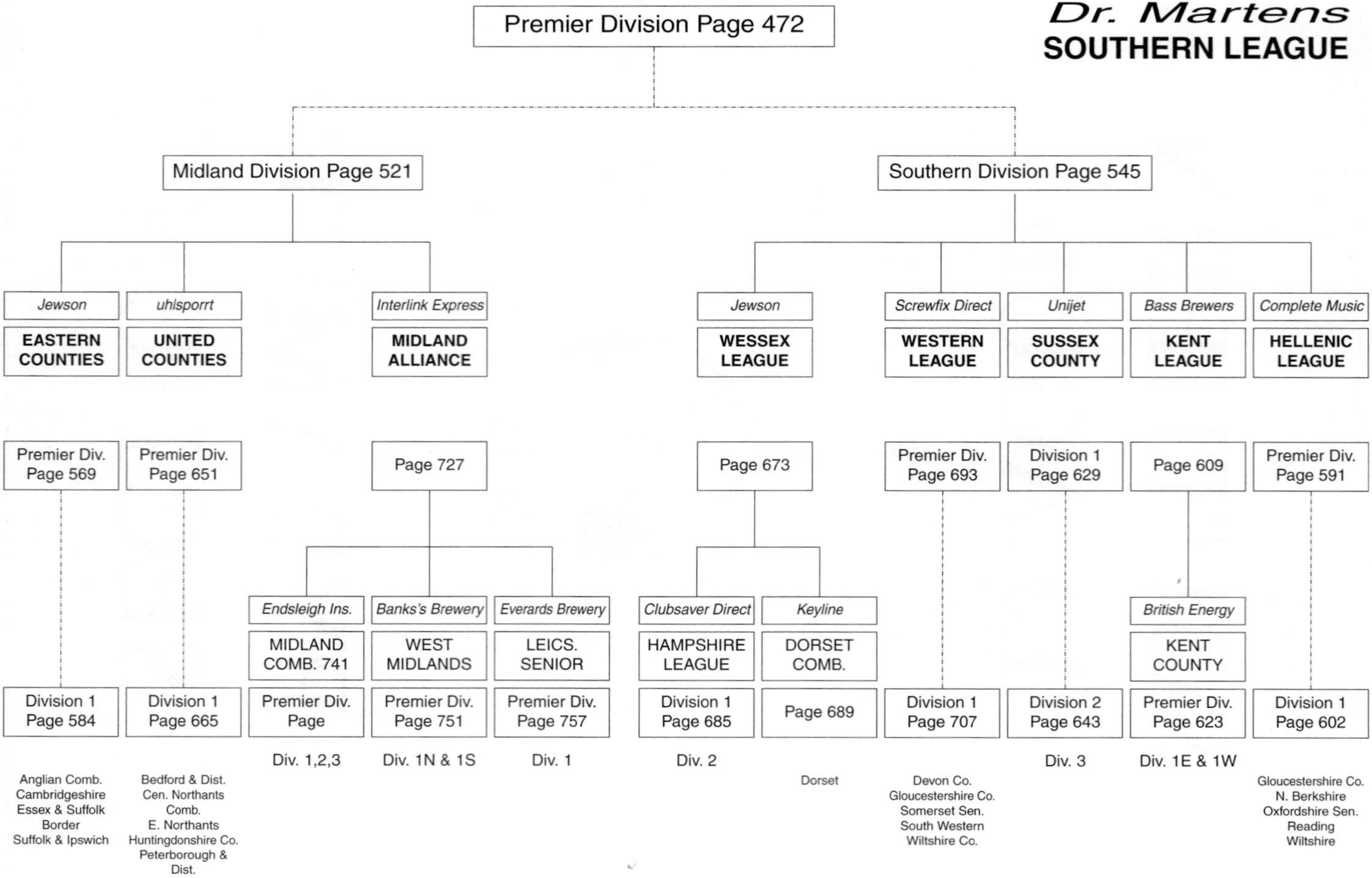

Premier Division Page 472

Midland Division Page 521

Southern Division Page 545

Midland Division

Jewson — EASTERN COUNTIES — Premier Div. Page 569
- Anglian Comb.
- Cambridgeshire
- Essex & Suffolk
- Border
- Suffolk & Ipswich

uhlsporrt — UNITED COUNTIES — Premier Div. Page 651 — Division 1 Page 665
- Bedford & Dist.
- Cen. Northants Comb.
- E. Northants
- Huntingdonshire Co.
- Peterborough & Dist.

Division 1 Page 584

Interlink Express — MIDLAND ALLIANCE — Page 727

Endsleigh Ins. — MIDLAND COMB. 741 — Premier Div. Page — Div. 1,2,3

Banks's Brewery — WEST MIDLANDS — Premier Div. Page 751 — Div. 1N & 1S

Everards Brewery — LEICS. SENIOR — Premier Div. Page 757 — Div. 1

Southern Division

Jewson — WESSEX LEAGUE — Page 673

Clubsaver Direct — HAMPSHIRE LEAGUE — Division 1 Page 685 — Div. 2

Keyline — DORSET COMB. — Page 689 — Dorset

Screwfix Direct — WESTERN LEAGUE — Premier Div. Page 693 — Division 1 Page 707
- Devon Co.
- Gloucestershire Co.
- Somerset Sen.
- South Western Co.
- Wiltshire Co.

Unijet — SUSSEX COUNTY — Division 1 Page 629 — Division 2 Page 643 — Div. 3

Bass Brewers — KENT LEAGUE — Page 609

British Energy — KENT COUNTY — Premier Div. Page 623 — Div. 1E & 1W

Complete Music — HELLENIC LEAGUE — Premier Div. Page 591 — Division 1 Page 602
- Gloucestershire Co.
- N. Berkshire
- Oxfordshire Sen.
- Reading
- Wiltshire

466

Dr MARTENS LEAGUE

President: G E Templeman   Chairman: D S R Gillard
Secretary: D J Strudwick
PO Box 90, Worcester WR3 8RX
Tel: 01905 757509

Boston United are the Flagship of the Dr Marten's League for the 1999-2000 season.

When the Pilgrims left port last August in search of a new world in the Football Conference, they could not have imagined that the flotilla of challengers would be left fourteen points in their wake by May the following year.

Nineteen Dr Marten's Premier Division clubs (more clubs than in any other Football Conference Feeder League) cast off at the start of the season announcing their ambition that promotion was the name of their particular game. That only one club will be successful does not quell ambition in the best supported Competition outside the Nationwide Conference. And given only 22 clubs play in the Premier Division, the Dr Martens League is fortunate to have two Regional First Divisions filled to the gunnells with ambitious and emerging clubs.

Boston United opened their second campaign in the Dr Marten's League with the force of a gale, force six to be precise. Salisbury City visited York Street on the opening day of the season and were sent home feeling the effects of a 6-0 thrashing. Four more straight wins, and only two defeats in their twenty-one matches up to Christmas, set Boston on a course for the Championship. By the turn of the year the Pilgrims were five points clear at the top but had completed significantly more of their fixtures than the armada of clubs in the chasing pack.

Margate, Bath City, Burton Albion and Tamworth led the challengers, and were all in sight of the Premier Division leaders. Bath City, in particular, were a serious threat. Although the Romans were seven points behind at the turn of the Millennium, they had suffered only one defeat in seventeen games and they had five matches in hand. The old argument began to rage. Would Boston's points in the bag be enough, or would Bath City have caught up by the time their fixture backlog had been completed?

Incredibly, it was 21 March before the challenge from Bath was holed again. And the 3-0 defeat by Clevedon Town proved to be devastating. The Romans proceeded to lose the next three games and won only one of their remaining seven fixtures. From being on the crest of a wave (one defeat in 31 games) suddenly the wind was taken from their sails. Burton Albion and Margate proceeded to take full advantage.

Nigel Clough's Brewers fermented second place with eight victories in their final twelve matches. The final win, on the last day of the season against Bath, condemned the Romans to fourth place. Chris Kinnear's Margate won their final four matches of the campaign to finish in berth three.

Although Worcester City, Crawley Town and Havant & Waterlooville all flirted with the relegation zone, Grantham Town, Atherstone United and Rothwell Town were never far away from danger. Indeed, it was ten matches before Grantham secured a single point and thirteen games before their first win. Without suggesting these three clubs were always destined for relegation, the threat was always on the horizon. And by Christmas, Gloucester City were dropping like a depth charge to join them. Dorchester Town also found themselves in grave danger towards the end of the season. Although rarely featuring in the top half of the table, a run of eleven matches without a win between 22 January and 25 March started alarm bells ringing. Grantham meanwhile, were enjoying a run of seven wins in eight games. The Gingerbreads 1-0 victory in Dorset on 8 April was followed seven days later by a 6-0 victory over Dorchester. The result lifted Grantham out of the bottom four for the first time in the season, at the expense of Dorchester. But, despite a final day victory over Crawley Town, Grantham lost the battle against relegation on goal difference. They join Atherstone, Rothwell and Gloucester in the Regional First Division next season. Who would have thought Gloucester would be relegated just three seasons after missing promotion to the Football Conference by a single point - to arch rivals Cheltenham Town?

This year's Regional Divisions were equally well contested. Moor Green took the Western Division by storm, winning their first six matches and dropping only two points out of the first 36 available. Newcomers Tiverton Town quickly found their Dr Martens sea legs. A five match unbeaten run to begin with, however, was followed by a string of injuries and five defeats in fairly quick succession. Twenty wins in the following 28 matches restored Tivi's position towards the top of the table and extended their challenge for a second successive promotion to the final day of the season. Hinckley United were also in the race for honours until the final day. After a consistent performance, during which United lost on only five occasions (avoiding consecutive defeats) manager Dean Thomas will be wondering how promotion slipped through his grasp. Perhaps the twelve draws and the 7-2 hammering at Tiverton on the penultimate Saturday had something to do with it.

Moor Green lost only four matches, but after a superb opening to the campaign a run of two wins from ten matches,

DR MARTENS LEAGUE CLUBCALL
09068 12 11 51
Calls cost 60p per minute

after the turn of the year, lost them their previous vice like grip on the leadership. Like Hinckley, the Moors were also held to draws on twelve occasions and this statistic alone only allowed Stafford Rangers to steam in and take the Championship by three points.

Manager Ian Painter's men won only two of their first seven matches and were lying in fifteenth place at the end of September, fourteen points behind Moor Green. The ship however was quickly steadied, Boro found calmer waters and barged their way to the Championship on a high tide of 25 wins in 31 matches during which only two games were lost.

At the bottom, Yate Town endured the most wretched of seasons. The Bristol side gleaned just three victories throughout the whole campaign. After an open run of six defeats one game was won before sixteen straight defeats followed. Although Bromsgrove Rovers and Shepshed Dynamo were at times moored below Yate, they both battled their way to safety leaving their rivals anchored at the bottom of the table from 2 October. Thereafter, Yate drifted further away until they were 23 points below the plimsole line.

Stourbridge finally met their Waterloo. Nineteen years of continuous membership for the Glassboys was finally broken. Despite a difficult season it was not until 12 February that Stourbridge fell into the bottom two. A titanic battle for safety then ensued with Paget Rangers. A final day defeat at Hinckley condemned the Glassboys to Feeder League football next season. Paget moved to relative safety, thanks to a 2-0 win at Redditch United, leaving Racing Club Warwick one place above the trapdoor.

In the Eastern Division, Fisher Athletic London, Chelmsford City, Stamford, Folkestone Invicta and Raunds Town all shared the leadership during the opening ten weeks of the season. After a sustained spell at the top by Folkestone, Ashford Town took over, before Newport IoW broke clear in December and led the table into the New Year. Folkestone regained the lead by 15 January and were joined by Fisher the following week. These two then shared the lead, unbroken until the end of the season, in spite of the dangers posed by Newport and Chelmsford City.

By the end of the season the Islanders had drifted fifteen points off the pace and Chelmsford were two further points behind. Finishing third was Newport's best performance in the Dr Marten's League. Chelmsford, so often in the top quartile of the table without eventually gaining promotion, will not be consoled by securing the Division's best home win of the season (10-1 against Bashley) and the best away victory (6-0 at Raunds).

With the promotion places secured three weeks before the end of the season, Fisher and Folkestone fought for the Championship. The race was close to the point of being cruel. In a cliff hanger of a finish, Folkestone saw their title aspirations flounder in spite of nine wins in their final twelve games. Fisher netted the Championship thanks to ten victories during the same time, which culminated in a fine 2-0 win at Newport on the last day of the season. After being promoted back to the Southern League, Folkestone can surely be proud of their performance. After suffering relegation from the Football Conference ten years ago, and immediate relegation from the Premier Division, Fisher will surely be satisfied stage one of their recovery is complete. Perhaps it is no coincidence that the League's record marksman, Steve Portway, once again led the Division's scoring chart with 28 goals - for the Fish.

After losing their opening four games by 4 September, Fleet Town found themselves submerged on the Division's seabed. A further four straight defeats were suffered before a 3-2 win over Witney Town was plundered. This success was followed by six more reversals. Although a managerial change in the New Year saw a change of fortunes, a valiant fight for survival ran aground when only two wins were gleaned from their final eleven games.

This year then the Competition must wave farewell to Fleet Town, Stourbridge and Yate Town because of relegation, and Raunds Town who volunteered to resign. A change of mind prompted the Shopmates to seek re-selection but unlike last year there is no vacancy which would allow the Board to accommodate the club's request.

It's goodbye and good luck to Boston United who become the League's flag bearers in the Football Conference next season. Don't forget, the last two clubs to be promoted form the Football Conference to the Football League - Cheltenham Town and Kidderminster Harriers - have deep seated roots in the Southern Football League. Make it a hat trick!

Welcome back Welling United. We hope our Competition will provide you with the vehicle to regain your previous status. The Dr Martens League also greets new recruits from Histon, Langney Sports and Mangotsfield United who are all promoted from the Feeder Leagues. In addition we welcome back Banbury United, who secured promotion from the Hellenic League ten years to the day after losing its Southern League status.

After missing out on the League Championship the League Cup offered some consolation to Burton Albion. Following a fourth round win over Worcester City and a semi-final triumph over King's Lynn, the Brewers reached the Final for the second time in three years. Their opponents, Hastings Town, reached their second final five years after making history repeat itself. On their way to winning the Cup in 1995 Hastings sunk Margate and Havant along the way. The Sussex side had to replicate the feat this season.

Rain had soaked Hastings on the day of the First Leg of the Final Tie. Fortunately the weather relented for much of the match in which Burton Albion recovered after going behind on the hour to win 2-1. A magnificent second leg was staged in even wetter conditions. Despite falling 3-0 behind (5-1 on aggregate) by half-time, the Hastings team stuck to their task in a fashion that poured praise on the club. Their reward was a 74th minute goal. Thereafter wave after wave of attacks were dashed on Burton's rock like defence and eventually the Brewers wrapped up the tie by scoring a further goal five minutes from time.

In the FA Cup seven standard bearers from the Dr Martens League reached the First Round Proper. Sadly, this landmark proved to be the end of the road for Chelmsford City, who lost 4-0 at Oldham Athletic; Bath City (0-2 v Hendon) and Cambridge City (0-2 v Wigan Athletic). Burton Albion held Rochdale but lost the replay 3-0. Merthyr Tydfil drew with Stalybridge Celtic, but lost the replay 3-1. Tamworth equalised twice against Bury to force a draw at the Lamb Ground but were then cruelly beaten in the replay. Warren Haughton scored after fifteen minutes only for Bury to level in the 87th. Bury grabbed the winner in extra time. It wasn't, however, all bad news at this stage of the Competition. Ilkeston Town came from behind to defeat Carlisle United 2-1. Their opponents in the Second Round, Rushden & Diamonds, cancelled an early goal by Paul Eshelby with one from Miguel de Souza. In the replay, the Diamonds proved to be a cut above the Robins and comfortably won 3-0.

Regrettably, this years' entrants into the FA Trophy did not last the pace as well as in previous years. Fourteen clubs reached January's Third Round but only five survived. Blakenall lost at home to Marine; after tying up Scarborough at home, Burnham lost the replay 6-0; Newport IOW fell 1-0 at Heybridge Swifts and Moor Green lost 2-1 on the ground of the eventual winners, Kingstonian. Worcester City, showing an upturn in form following Graham Alner's replacement by John Barton in the Manager's seat, won at Stalybridge Celtic 1-0. As the Dr Martens sole survivor in the last eight of the

Competition, the Faithfuls looked forward to a tie at nearby Telford Untied. Further progress wasn't forthcoming. Sam Bowen was sent off after only fifteen minutes and City capsized 4-1. Steve Lutz scored their only goal two minutes from time.

Once again the League's match officials have enjoyed phenomenal success. Yet another of the Dr Marten's League crew, Brian Curson, has won promotion to the National List of Referees. Six of his shipmates, Steve Dorr, Roger East, Michael McCoy, Keith Stroud, Andre Marriner and Dean Whitestone, have been promoted to the National List of Assistant Referees. Four, Messers. Mark Ives, Andre Marriner, Keith Stroud and Dean Whitestone have been promoted to the Panel List of Referees. No matter how many times we label the 'men in black' "pirates" (or even less complimentary names, from time to time), the League's list of Match Officials has quality as a main ingredient. Six promotions to the National Referees List during the past three years and eighteen to the National List of Assistants are statistics that speak for themselves. And Referee Phil Sharp continues to hoist the Dr Marten's League ensign by travelling the world on the FIFA List of Assistants.

But such success does not happen by coincidence, nor does it occur overnight. Through Jimmy Hill and his hardy band of Assessors, the League's Match Officials receive first class advice. Jim has worked tirelessly to ensure his group have all passed the Football Association's examination which qualifies the information being fed back to the Officials. The scheme is strongly supported by the Southern Football League Match Officials Association. The union with Chairman Mark Ives at the helm, Secretary Steve Tincknell on the tiller and President Laurence Jones in the crows nest is in sound custody. The results of the collective efforts of these two groups are plain to see. Keep up the good work, gentlemen.

Interestingly, success has not been confined to the football field. Following Tony Cuthbert's elevation from Secretary at Ilkeston Town to a similar post in the Football League with Notts County, two more of our able seamen have acquired like moves. In November, former Nuneaton Borough and Atherstone United secretary, Keith Allen secured the post at Wycombe Wanderers. In May, Bath City secretary Jason Turner landed the secretary's position with Cardiff City. Illustrious talents that have long been harboured in the Dr Marten's League are at last being recognised on football's high seas.

None of the above events happen without good management. The League's own 'ship's company', admirably led by its Captain Doug Gillard, provides that management. Doug's ceaseless pursuit for what is best for the League's membership is unrelenting. His drive for excellence is matched by his enthusiasm, scrupulous sense of fairness and his 'Lady Hamilton' at Coppins Corner - Mrs Pat Gillard. Thanks and well done, Doug. Many thanks Pat for your unstinting support of our Captain.

A good Captain always has a good no. 2. During the past ten years Keith Allen has been unfailing in his duty to the League as a whole, and more particularly his encouragement for Doug. But now a change of job, necessitating a relocation, has forced Keith to re-consider his position with the Competition. As mentioned earlier, Keith landed a high profile post with a Football League club during the season. Despite maintaining close ties with, and his Directorship of, Atherstone United FC, Keith's conscience will not allow him to continue an active role with the Dr Marten's League whilst being gainfully employed by a club in another competition. Keith has therefore decided to stand down as the League's Vice-Chairman. Whilst understanding his dilemma, it is a decision the Board regrets. Experience of Keith's calibre is not replaced easily. The new Vice-Chairman will have a huge role to follow. Thanks for your help, Keith, and from me especially, your friendship. I sincerely hop you will accept, and sustain a high profile in your new post as a Vice-President of the Dr Marten's League.

Behind the Captain and his First Mate is the ship's crew. Six Directors who volunteer considerable amounts of their time on behalf of member clubs. The League President (89 years young earlier this year) and Peter Faulkner (a mere 80 last month) are also still as dedicated as the day they signed on. Thanks gentlemen.

It is not an inexpensive exercise to organise, or participate in, a Competition with the profile and quality of the Dr Martens League. On behalf of the member Clubs and the League's Board of Directors, therefore, I extend an unconditional thank you to the League's sponsors.

Without massaging or window dressing any figures, during the past four years R Griggs Group Limited (Dr Martens) has invested nearly £^{1}/$_{2}$ million in the Southern Football League. Approximately £400,000 of that investment has been distributed directly amongst the member clubs. At a time when it seems only the higher echelons of football is awash with money Dr Martens' investment in the Southern Football League is unprecedented. Furthermore, the Company has just agreed a new four year contract announcing a 5 per cent increase on the current sponsorship sum. Thank you Max and Stephen Griggs, and the Board of Directors of R Griggs Group Limited.

Thank you, too, to James Gilbert Limited. Rodney Webb and his colleagues at Rugby have provided 35 Oro match balls to each club during the past fourteen months. A further 25 are on-line for each of the next two seasons. In retail terms I conservatively estimate Gilbert's sponsorship of the Dr Marten's League Match Balls to be worth nearly £60,000 per year. During the full course of the agreement it will be worth an estimated £3,000 to each club.

Vandanel Promotions Limited has kindly sponsored a complete Bench Kit for each club during the past year. Thank you Graham Burke for your assistance during the 1999-2000 campaign. I hope the League will maintain its liaison with your Company in some way.

FIFA's encouragement of 'Fair Play' during the past few years recently prompted the Dr Martens League to introduce an award that would hopefully promote this ideal. Last year's winner, Yate Town, collected a trophy and £500. This year, thanks to a sponsorship provided by Sports.com Limited the club in each Division incurring the fewest disciplinary points will each receive an equivalent cash reward. Congratulations, therefore, to Burton Albion, Spalding United and Yate Town. Thanks, too, to Mike Kelly and his colleagues at Sports.com.

Notwithstanding the League's Management team and a fine array of 'blue chip' sponsors, the Competition still needs to run like a well oiled machine. Teams need to arrive on time (and on the right day!), nets need to be up and the pitch marked out correctly. Match Officials must all arrive at the appropriate time and place. The penultimate slot in my report, therefore, is reserved for the Clubs and their respective Secretaries. I would like to thank every club, especially the much maligned secretary, that has made a constructive and, above all, polite contribution to the League's affairs this season. I am always conscious that, if the clubs are doing well, the League is doing well. But, if you will allow me to contort the words of a famous US President, think not what your League can do for your club, think what your club can do for your League.

Finally, while I am out sailing between meetings, matches or ground grading, my partner Janet usually has to remain in 'dry dock'. Janet steers the good ship 'Dr Martens' on a straight course during my absence. I know it is not easy, but at least you have the consolation of knowing the clubs prefer to speak to you than me! Thanks for your help Rudgie.

So my 18th season, and the Southern Football League's 106th campaign, is completed. Good luck and best wishes to everyone competing in no. 107.

Dennis Strudwick, League Secretary/Treasurer

PREMIER DIVISION FINAL LEAGUE TABLE 1999-2000

		P	W	D	L	F	A	GD	Pts
1	Boston United	42	27	11	4	102	39	63	92
2	Burton Albion	42	23	9	10	73	43	30	78
3	Margate	42	23	8	11	64	43	21	77
4	Bath City	42	19	15	8	70	49	21	72
5	King's Lynn	42	19	14	9	59	43	16	71
6	Tamworth	42	20	10	12	80	51	29	70
7	Newport County	42	16	18	8	67	50	17	66
8	Clevedon Town	42	18	9	15	52	52	0	63
9	Ilkeston Town	42	16	12	14	77	69	8	60
10	Weymouth	42	14	16	12	60	51	9	58
11	Halesowen Town	42	14	14	14	52	54	-2	56
12	Crawley Town	42	15	8	19	68	82	-14	53
13	Havant & Waterlooville	42	13	13	16	63	68	-5	52
14	Cambridge City	42	14	10	18	52	66	-14	52
15	Worcester City	42	13	11	18	60	66	-6	50
16	Salisbury City	42	14	8	20	70	84	-14	50
17	Merthyr Tydfil	42	13	9	20	51	63	-12	48
18	Dorchester Town	42	10	17	15	56	65	-9	47
19	Grantham Town	42	14	5	23	63	76	-13	47
20	Gloucester City	42	8	14	20	40	82	-42	38
21	Rothwell Town	42	5	14	23	48	85	-37	29
22	Atherstone United	42	5	13	24	30	76	-46	28

PREMIER DIVISION LEADING GOALSCORERS 1999-2000

Mark Hallam	Tamworth	35
James Taylor	Havant & Waterlooville	32
Christian Moore	Burton Albion	29
Paul Sales	Salisbury City	27
Philip Collins	Margate	25
Mark Owen	Worcester City	24
Martin Paul	Bath City	20
Mark Rawle	Boston United	20
James Smith	Salisbury City	20
Carl Dale	Newport County	19
Daniel O'Hagan	Dorchester Town	19
Warren Haughton	Tamworth	18
David Laws	Weymouth	18
Ian Cambridge	Cambridge City	14

PREMIER DIVISION RESULTS CHART 1999-2000

plus Attendance/Fixture Chart

Each cell shows the result (top) and attendance (bottom). Rows = home team, columns 1–22 = opponent. "X" marks the team versus itself.

#	Team	1	2	3	4	5	6	7	8	9	10	11	12	13	14	15	16	17	18	19	20	21	22
1	Atherstone U	X	0-0 / 324	1-1 / 435	0-2 / 565	0-1 / 145	1-3 / 155	0-1 / 283	1-1 / 205	1-0 / 363	0-2 / 277	4-5 / 419	0-1 / 147	3-2 / 254	0-2 / 272	0-1 / 241	0-3 / 341	0-1 / 354	3-1 / 286	0-3 / 165	0-5 / 1265	1-1 / 265	2-1 / 371
2	Bath City	2-0 / 643	X	1-1 / 1658	2-1 / 911	2-2 / 722	2-1 / 1512	7-0 / 1124	1-1 / 1365	5-1 / 926	1-1 / 699	0-1 / 674	0-1 / 1056	0-0 / 792	1-1 / 783	1-1 / 735	0-1 / 1138	1-1 / 950	1-0 / 756	4-4 / 1175	4-1 / 842	2-1 / 1133	1-1 / 1287
3	Boston Utd	3-0 / 1210	1-1 / 1731	X	3-1 / 2090	5-0 / 957	5-1 / 1423	1-0 / 2022	3-0 / 1164	6-1 / 2063	3-1 / 4137	4-1 / 1614	4-2 / 1514	3-2 / 1467	1-2 / 3119	3-0 / 1558	4-1 / 1584	1-1 / 2596	2-0 / 1434	6-0 / 1228	1-0 / 1159	3-0 / 1247	2-1 / 1840
4	Burton Albion	5-1 / 891	1-1 / 1202	X / 1920	X	2-2 / 941	2-1 / 815	7-0 / 722	1-1 / 931	2-1 / 948	1-1 / 1175	1-1 / 957	0-1 / 779	1-0 / 2047	1-0 / 1304	1-1 / 1180	0-1 / 834	1-1 / 1426	4-4 / 894	0-3 / 842	1-0 / 1188	2-0 / 876	1-1 / 867
5	Cambridge City	3-2 / 369	0-2 / 480	0-2 / 545	0-1 / 480	X	1-1 / 662	3-2 / 327	0-1 / 410	2-1 / 418	0-2 / 427	1-1 / 328	4-1 / 444	3-2 / 572	2-3 / 534	0-0 / 438	0-0 / 504	0-0 / 718	1-0 / 304	1-3 / 449	1-2 / 382	2-3 / 408	4-2 / 607
6	Clevedon Town	1-0 / 317	3-0 / 1005	0-0 / 407	0-0 / 572	1-0 / 273	X	1-1 / 334	2-1 / 337	3-0 / 481	2-2 / 354	0-0 / 389	0-0 / 402	2-0 / 224	4-2 / 397	1-0 / 249	1-2 / 586	1-0 / 623	1-1 / 245	1-2 / 348	1-0 / 291	1-1 / 556	1-0 / 413
7	Crawley Tn	0-0 / 760	1-6 / 547	1-6 / 1037	1-4 / 464	1-2 / 452	1-3 / 608	X	3-1 / 588	X	3-2 / 692	2-2 / 706	2-2 / 1132	1-1 / 693	1-2 / 620	5-3 / 822	2-0 / 669	2-2 / 542	4-1 / 481	4-1 / 557	2-1 / 706	1-2 / 628	2-2 / 674
8	Dorchester	2-2 / 532	0-0 / 936	3-4 / 904	0-1 / 624	1-2 / 452	2-1 / 502	0-2 / 503	X	2-0 / 554	0-1 / 692	2-2 / 676	4-1 / 519	1-1 / 457	3-4 / 524	1-0 / 405	0-0 / 503	2-2 / 485	0-0 / 626	4-4 / 531	2-1 / 2877	0-1 / 583	3-0 / 657
9	Gloucester	1-1 / 435	1-1 / 695	0-3 / 507	2-1 / 418	1-0 / 446	1-5 / 452	2-2 / 416	0-0 / 340	X	2-0 / 739	2-0 / 562	2-0 / 426	1-0 / 558	0-1 / 429	0-4 / 326	1-0 / 404	0-1 / 889	3-1 / 395	3-3 / 408	0-0 / 509	3-3 / 454	2-1 / 560
10	Grantham T	6-0 / 501	1-3 / 1265	0-3 / 1265	0-1 / 736	2-0 / 476	2-0 / 374	4-2 / 555	0-2 / 242	1-1 / 306	X	2-0 / 292	2-0 / 292	1-0 / 677	1-3 / 544	1-2 / 285	1-1 / 306	0-1 / 365	1-0 / 476	5-1 / 250	0-3 / 375	3-3 / 344	0-2 / 332
11	Halesowen	0-1 / 356	0-3 / 386	1-1 / 465	2-1 / 1084	1-2 / 433	3-0 / 460	1-0 / 425	0-1 / 606	2-1 / 452	2-1 / 422	X	1-0 / 436	3-0 / 443	0-0 / 472	0-3 / 449	0-1 / 578	2-0 / 603	3-3 / 453	3-1 / 353	0-3 / 903	0-0 / 477	2-1 / 708
12	Havant & W	1-1 / 336	1-2 / 430	3-3 / 675	6-0 / 492	3-1 / 378	1-2 / 344	1-0 / 512	1-2 / 490	1-1 / 374	1-0 / 670	X / 402	X	2-3 / 394	2-3 / 304	3-3 / 354	1-2 / 399	2-2 / 372	5-2 / 283	0-1 / 417	0-2 / 522	1-2 / 583	1-0 / 448
13	Ilkeston Town	1-0 / 424	2-2 / 652	1-0 / 1120	4-1 / 1061	2-2 / 521	4-1 / 438	2-0 / 590	3-1 / 532	2-0 / 505	5-4 / 908	0-0 / 715	2-1 / 527	X	2-1 / 718	1-2 / 443	2-1 / 387	2-1 / 697	3-3 / 435	6-0 / 539	4-4 / 562	2-2 / 606	2-2 / 654
14	King's Lynn	1-1 / 829	1-2 / 904	2-1 / 1960	0-1 / 638	0-1 / 820	1-0 / 599	1-0 / 792	4-1 / 631	4-2 / 565	3-3 / 837	3-1 / 518	2-0 / 720	3-2 / 821	X	0-0 / 725	4-2 / 692	2-2 / 1023	0-0 / 1039	5-2 / 552	1-2 / 760	0-1 / 639	0-1 / 627
15	Margate	2-0 / 391	0-2 / 690	2-1 / 953	1-0 / 746	1-2 / —	2-1 / 526	1-0 / 744	1-1 / 503	2-1 / 504	1-2 / 469	3-1 / —	X	3-2 / 681	1-0 / 377	X	0-0 / 407	2-1 / 446	4-1 / 470	0-1 / 356	1-2 / 624	2-0 / 414	0-1 / 404
16	Merthyr Tyd	2-0 / 625	0-2 / 789	1-2 / 594	1-1 / 578	1-0 / 637	2-0 / 602	2-3 / 514	0-0 / 710	5-0 / 687	5-2 / 608	1-0 / 652	0-2 / 655	1-3 / 879	0-0 / 528	3-4 / 567	X	2-5 / 1407	3-1 / 446	1-1 / 617	1-2 / 624	1-2 / 623	0-3 / 635
17	Newport Co	1-1 / 588	2-2 / 1415	1-1 / 907	4-0 / 674	2-2 / 1003	5-0 / 389	4-0 / 607	1-1 / 555	2-1 / 711	2-1 / 620	6-5 / 753	0-2 / 743	2-1 / 604	1-2 / 755	3-1 / 933	2-1 / 1069	X	3-1 / 635	1-1 / 652	4-2 / 721	X	3-4 / 978
18	Rothwell Tn	3-3 / 201	2-3 / 182	0-2 / 345	1-1 / 502	1-4 / 297	3-3 / 203	3-3 / 244	1-4 / 201	2-1 / 557	3-2 / 264	2-2 / 291	1-1 / 237	2-2 / 151	2-1 / 201	0-2 / 167	2-0 / 237	0-3 / 198	X	3-2 / 227	X / 196	1-2 / 201	0-0 / 184
19	Salisbury C	1-0 / 374	1-3 / 721	3-4 / 593	1-2 / 515	4-0 / 371	3-1 / 370	4-1 / 460	1-1 / 557	3-3 / —	5-0 / 535	2-2 / 391	1-2 / 394	1-1 / 352	2-3 / 463	2-0 / 509	2-3 / 405	1-2 / 618	4-2 / 404	X	X / 527	3-1 / 627	1-3 / 381
20	Tamworth	4-0 / 714	3-2 / 716	1-2 / 721	1-2 / 1652	1-2 / 517	4-1 / 545	3-0 / 587	1-1 / 687	3-4 / 493	3-4 / 711	1-2 / 505	5-0 / 480	2-1 / 453	3-0 / 506	2-0 / 556	3-1 / 570	4-2 / 807	2-1 / 326	1-2 / 574	X	3-1 / 723	4-2 / 1309
21	Weymouth	0-0 / 674	3-0 / 914	2-2 / 922	1-2 / 901	0-0 / 446	5-0 / 725	4-0 / 721	2-2 / 2203	0-0 / —	3-2 / 643	0-0 / 647	2-2 / 734	4-1 / 641	1-1 / 676	0-1 / 697	2-1 / 644	4-2 / 745	3-0 / 893	1-0 / 878	X	X	1-1 / 680
22	Worcester	0-0 / 803	0-1 / 1611	1-1 / 1151	2-2 / 1103	3-2 / 827	1-0 / 702	2-5 / 858	4-4 / 802	1-0 / 1609	3-1 / 903	0-0 / 1069	0-3 / 804	2-1 / 717	1-1 / 787	1-3 / 1060	2-1 / 1075	3-4 / 1115	0-0 / 524	2-3 / 720	X / 935	1-1 / 873	X

DR MARTENS LEAGUE CUP 1999-2000

PRELIMINARY ROUND

Tiverton Town	v	Cirencester Town	4*2		Dartford	v	Burnham	2-0

FIRST ROUND

Hastings	v	Ashford	4-1		Chelmsford	v	Erith & Belvedere	0-2
Folkestone Invicta	v	Fisher Athletic	0-2		Salisbury City	v	Newport I.O.W.	1-4
Tonbridge Angels	v	St Leonards	3-1		Dartford	v	Fleet Town	1-1,7p6
Sittingbourne	v	Margate	0-2		Baldock Town	v	Crawley Town	3-0
Tiverton Town	v	Newport County	2-1		Bath City	v	Merthyr Tydfil	2-1
Gloucester City	v	Yate Town	4-1		Shepshed Dynamo	v	Solihull Borough	3*5
Havant & W'Ville	v	Bashley	5-1		Weymouth	v	Dorchester Town	1-2
Clevedon Townv	v	Weston 'S' Mare	1-1,6p5		Witney Town	v	Cinderford Town	2-1
V.S.Rugby	v	Corby Town	2-2,4p3		Boston United	v	Wisbech Town	2-3
Burton Albion	v	Bedworth United	4*3		Evesham United	v	Halesowen Town	1-2
Worcester City	v	Redditch United	6-1		Paget Rangers	v	Moor Green	1-2
Blakenall	v	Rocester	4-1		Stourbridge	v	Bilston United	0-1
Stamford	v	Ilkeston Town	1*2		Spalding United	v	Kings Lynn	0-0,4p3
Rothwell Town	v	Grantham Town	1-2		Raunds Town	v	Cambridge City	0-1
Tamworth	v	Atherstone United	4-0		Gresley Rovers	v	Hinckley United	3-2
R.C. Warwick	v	Sutton Coldfield	0-4		Bromsgrove Rovers	v	Stafford Rangers	0-1

SECOND ROUND

Hastings	v	Erith & Belvedere	2-0		Fisher Athletic	v	Newport I.O.W.	1-5
Tonbridge Angels	v	Fleet Town	1-4		Margate	v	Baldock Town	4-2
Tiverton Town	v	Bath City	1-2		Gloucester City	v	Solihull Borough	3-1
Havant & W' Ville	v	Dorchester Town	4*3		Weston S Mare	v	Witney Town	1-3
V.S. Rugby	v	Wisbech	4-1		Burton Albion	v	Halesowen Town	3-2
Worcester City	v	Moor Green	3-1		Blakenall	v	Bilston Town	3-1
Ilkeston Town	v	Kings Lynn	1-1,4p3		Grantham Town	v	Cambridge	2-1
Tamworth	v	Gresley Rovers	3-1		Sutton Coldfield	v	Stafford Rangers	2-4

THIRD ROUND

Hastings Town	v	Newport I.O.W.	5-2		Fleet Town	v	Margate	2-5
Bath City	v	Gloucester City	3-0		Havant & W'Ville	v	Witney Town	3-1
V.S.Rugby	v	Burton Albion	0-4		Worcester City	v	Blakenall	4-2
Kings Lynn	v	Grantham Town	1*0		Tamworth	v	Stafford Rangers	4-0

FOURTH ROUND

Hastings	v	Margate	3-1		Bath City	v	Havant & W'Ville	0-1
Burton Albion	v	Worcester City	1-0		Kings Lynn	v	Tamworth	1-1,4p3

SEMI-FINALS

Hastings Town	v	Havant & W'Ville	4*2		Burton Albion	v	Kings Lynn	2-0

FINAL

Hastings Town	v	Burton Albion	1-2,1-4

SOUTHERN LEAGUE - PREMIER DIVISION - LAST TEN YEARS

	90-91	91-92	92-93	93-94	94-95	95-96	96-97	97-98	98-99	99-00
Ashford Town	-	-	-	-	-	-	19	21r	-	-
Atherstone United	15	13	15	4	15	17	11	9	16	22r
Baldock Town	-	-	-	-	-	18	20r	-	-	-
Bashley	10	4	9	21r	-	-	-	-	-	-
Bath City	-	-	-	-	-	-	-	6	4	4
Boston United	-	-	-	-	-	-	xfer from NPL		2	1p
Bromsgrove Rovers	5	1p	-	-	-	-	-	19	22r	-
Burton Albion	7	10	8	11	3	16	6	3	13	2
Cambridge City	3	5	14	17	9	19	18	13	20	14
Chelmsford City	18	18	12	6	15	12	22r	-	-	-
Cheltenham Town	-	-	2	2	2	3	2p	-	-	-
Clevedon Town	-	-	-	-	-	-	-	-	-	8
Corby Town	-	14	3	9	22r	-	-	-	-	-
Crawley Town	19	17	=6	5	11	9	17	10	11	12
Dartford	13	6	-	-	-	-	-	-	-	-
Dorchester Town	11	11	18	18	6	13	15	4	18	18
Dover Athletic	4	2	1p	-	-	-	-	-	-	-
Farnborough Town	1p	-	-	1p	-	-	-	-	-	-
Fisher Athletic	-	21r	-	-	-	-	-	-	-	-
Forest Green Rovers	-	-	-	-	-	-	-	-	1p	-
Gloucester City	2	12	13	10	4	4	3	11	6	20r
Gravesend & Northfleet	21	22r	-	-	14	11	14	to Isthmian Lge		
Grantham Town	-	-	-	-	-	-	-	-	17	19r
Gresley Rovers	-	-	-	14	8	5	1	17	21r	-
Halesowen Town	8	8	10	3	13	2	4	5	8	11
Hastings Town	-	-	16	12	12	8	16	14	5r	-
Havant & Waterlooville								**	-	13
Hednesford Town	-	-	4	13	1p	-	-	-	-	-
Ilkeston Town	-	-	-	-	-	20r	-	-	3	9
King's Lynn	-	-	-	-	-	-	5	8	10	5
Leek Town	-	-	-	-	7	-	-	-	-	-
Margate	-	-	-	-	-	-	-	-	-	3
Merthyr Tydfil	-	-	-	-	-	7	9	2	15	17
Moor Green	16	9	19	19r	-	-	-	-	-	-
Newport AFC (County from 99-00)	-	-	-	-	-	14	21r	-	-	7
Nuneaton Borough	-	-	-	22r	-	-	7	12	1p	-
Poole Town	17	20r	-	-	-	-	-	-	-	-
Rothwell Town	-	-	-	-	-	-	-	16	19	21r
Rushden Town	14r	-	-	-	-	-	-	-	-	-
Rushden & Diamonds	-	-	-	-	5	1p	-	-	-	-
St Leonards	-	-	-	-	-	-	-	22r	-	-
Salisbury City	-	-	-	-	-	15	12	18	12	16
Sittingbourne	-	-	-	8	20r	-	8	20r	-	-
Solihull Borough	-	-	=6	6	19r	-	-	-	-	-
Stafford Rangers	-	-	-	-	-	21r	-	-	-	-
Sudbury Town	-	-	-	-	18	10	11	to Eastern Lge.		-
Trowbridge Town	-	7	5	7	21r	-	-	-	-	-
Tamworth	-	-	-	-	-	-	-	15	9	6
V.S. Rugby	9	3	20r	-	17	22r	-	-	-	-
Waterlooville	20	15	11	20r	-	-	-	-	**	-
Wealdstone	12	19	-	-	-	-	-	-	-	-
Weymouth	22r	-	21r	-	-	-	-	-	14	10
Worcester City	6	16	17	15	10	6	10	7	7	15

BATH CITY

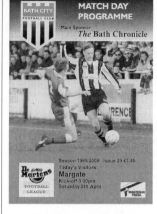

MATCH DAY PROGRAMME

Main Sponsor *The Bath Chronicle*

Season 1999/2000 Issue 29 £1.40
Today's Visitors:
Margate
Kick-off 3.00pm
Saturday 8th April

CLUB OFFICIALS

Chairman: **Stephen Hall**
Directors: J Turner, KLoach,
G.Todd,P.Weaver,M.Hughes.

Secretary: **Quentin Edwards** c/o the club,
01225 423087 (B) & 07785 795532 (M)

Commercial Director: **G.Todd**
Safety Officer: **J Watt**
Press Officer: **P.Weaver**

FOOTBALL MANAGEMENT TEAM

Manager: Paul Bodin
Assistant Manager: Steve White
Physios:Terry Hardwell &Dave Monks

FACT FILE

Founded: 1889
Nickname: Stripes & The City
Midweek home matchday: Tuesday
Colours: Black & white stripes/black/b & w
Change: All yellow
Youth League: South West Counties
Somerset Youth Floodlit
Ladies Team: Yes
1999-00
Captain: Colin Towler
Top scorer:Martin Paul
P.o.Y.: Colin Towler

Pages: 48   Price £1.40

Editor: Chris Stillman
Tel: 01761 433528

GROUND   Twerton Park, Twerton, Bath Avon BA2 1DB.
                                    Tel: 01225 423087/313247 Fax: 01225481391
Directions: Twerton Park is situated on the A4/A36 Lower Bristol Road - on theBristol side of
Bath City Centre (Approx 2.5 miles). The area is serviced byJ18 on the M4. From the centre
of Bath the bus route is No.5 - Twerton HighStreet
Capacity: 8,840   Seated: 1,017   Covered Terracing: 4,800
Clubhouse: Several bars open all week and full service with menu on match-days catering
for up to 250 people   Club Shop: Contact MrM.Brush

PREVIOUS   **Grounds:** The Belvoir Ground, Lambridge 1889-1932
                    Leagues: Southern League, Vauxhall Conference

CLUB RECORDS   **Attendance:** 18,020 v Brighton & Hove Albion, FA Cup.
                    Defeat: 9-0 Yeovil Town 46-47   **Victory:** 8-0 v Boston United 98-99
                    Career goalscorer: Paul Randall.   **Career appearances:** David Mogg (530)
                    Transfer fee paid: £15,000 for Nicky Tanner from Bristol City
                    Transfer fee received: £80,000 for Jason Dodd from Southampton

BEST SEASON   **FA Cup:** Third Round 63-64, 0-3 v Bolton W. (A) after 1-1: 93-94   **FA Trophy:** 4th Round, 89-90
HONOURS   Southern League Champions 59-60, 77-78; R-up 29-33, 61-62, 89-90; Southern League Cup 78-79;
                    Somerset Premier Cup 51-52, 52-53, 57-58, 59-60, 65-66, 69-70, 77-78, 80-81, 81-82, 83-84, 84-85, 85-86, 88-89, 89-90, 93-
                    94, 94-95;Anglo-Italian Cup R-up 76-77, 77-78
Players progressing: Alan Skirton (Arsenal),Tony Book (Plymouth A.), Kenny Allen (Bournemouth), Peter Rogers (Exeter C.), R Bourne (Torquay),
Dave Wiffil (Manchester C.), Stan Mortensen (Blackpool), Brian Wade (Swindon Town), Jeff Meacham (Bristol R.), Martin Hirst (BristolC.), Paul
Bodin (Swindon), Graham Withey (Coventry), Jason Dodd (Southampton), Paul Adcock (Torquay)

Back Row: Scott Walker, Fidell Richards, Stuart James, Tom Gould, Peter Tisdale, Graham Colbourne, Alec Masson, Dave Elsey, Jack Cullis.
Middle: Roy Pitman (Scout), Mike Hughes (Director), Tony Murtagh (Bar Manager), Martin Paul, Jimmy Fraser, Mike Davis, Elliott Jackson, Nick
Brooks, Rob Skidmore, Jon Holloway, Phil Weaver (Director), Jason Turner (Director), Steve Hall (Chairman). **Front:** Frank Entwistle (President),
Lee Vickerman, Colin Towler, Steve White, Paul Bodin, Terry Hardwell, Mark Clode, Mark Harrington, Gilbert Walshaw (President)

Match Facts 1999-00

	Date	Comp.	H/A	Opponents	Att.	Result	Goalscorers
1	14.08	DM P	H	BURTON ALBION	911	W 2-1	Colbourne 16, Walker 45
2	17.08	DM P	A	Dorchester Town	936	D 0-0	
3	21.08	DM P	A	Cambridge City	480	W 2-0	Harrington 32, Colbourne 90
4	24.08	DM P	H	ATHERSTONE UNITED	643	W 2-0	Colbourne 21, Davis 54
5	28.08	DM P	H	GRANTHAM TOWN	699	W 2-1	Paul 37[p], Davis 88
6	30.08	DM P	H	Merthyr Tydfil	789	W 2-0	Colbourne 9, 70
7	04.09	DM P	H	ROTHWELL TOWN	756	W 1-0	Davis 33
8	11.09	DM P	H	TAMWORTH	842	W 4-1	**Paul 3** (10[p] 29 45), Davis 54
	18.09	FAC Q2	H	WESTON-SUPER-MARE	744	W 4-0	Davis 10, Tisdale 46, Paul 50[p], Bird 60[og]
	02.10	FAC Q3	H	FARNBOROUGH TOWN	890	W 3-1	**Paul 3** (6 15 81[p])
	09.10	FAT 1	H	BALDOCK TOWN	547	W 1-0	Paul 35
	16.10	FAC Q4	A	Stevenage Borough	1603	D 1-1	Colbourne 60
	19.10	FAC Q4 R	H	STEVENAGE BOROUGH	1427	W 1-0	Trott 76[og]
9	23.10	DM P	A	Boston United	1731	D 1-1	Davis 50
10	26.10	DM P	H	DORCHESTER TOWN	1365	D 1-1	Lloyd 87
	30.10	FAC 1	H	HENDON	1690	L 0-2	
	02.11	Som. PC2	A	Bridgwater Town	165	W 3-0	Howell 1, Vickerman 61, Allison 82
11	06.11	DM P	H	GLOUCESTER CITY	926	W 5-1	Harrington 2, Paul 14 61, Colbourne 65, Fergusson 79[og]
12	08.11	DM P	A	Atherstone United	324	D 0-0	
13	13.11	DM P	H	ILKESTON TOWN	792	D 0-0	
	16.11	Lg Cup 1	H	MERTHYR TYDFIL	425	W 2-1	Colbourne 12, Walker 45
14	20.11	DM P	A	Tamworth	716	L 2-3	Harrington 67, Paul 72[p]
	27.11	FAT 2	H	ERITH & BELVEDERE	634	W 5-0	Davis 20 63, Harrington 24, Colbourne 47 75
15	04.12	DM P	H	KING'S LYNN	783	D 1-1	Paul 41
	08.12	LC 2	A	Tiverton Town	435	W 2-1	Colbourne 10, Fraser 26
16	18.12	DM P	H	BOSTON UNITED	1658	W 2-0	Colbourne 17 60
17	27.12	DM P	H	CLEVEDON TOWN	1552	W 2-1	Towler 1, Fraser 27
18	03.01	DM P	A	Newport County	1415	W 1-0	Fraser 82
19	08.01	DM P	H	CRAWLEY TOWN	1124	W 7-0	**Paul 3** (15 20 21), Zamora 33, Holloway 41, Towler 60, Harrington 67
	15.01	FAT 3	H	RUSHDEN & DIAMONDS	2034	L 1-2	Paul 24
20	18.01	DM P	H	WEYMOUTH	1133	W 2-0	Zamora 66 79
21	22.01	DM P	A	Ilkeston Town	652	D 2-2	Zamora 32 59
	25.01	LC 3	H	GLOUCESTER CITY	434	W 3-0	Zamora 35, Richards 36, Howell 56
22	29.01	DM P	H	Grantham Town	386	W 3-1	Clode 35, Zamora 45 81
23	05.02	DM P	H	SALISBURY CITY	1175	D 4-4	Harrington 15, Towler 37, Bodin 55, Paul 79
	08.02	SPC QF	H	MANGOTSFIELD UNITED	344	W 4-3	Davis 53, Paul 90 92, Mehew 107
24	12.02	DM P	A	Worcester City	1611	W 1-0	Mehew 29
25	19.02	DM P	A	Gloucester City	695	D 1-1	Davis 16
	22.02	LC QF	H	HAVANT & WATERLOOVILLE	432	L 0-1	
26	26.02	DM P	H	HAVANT & WATERLOOVILLE	1056	D 1-1	Paul 68
27	04.03	DM P	A	Halesowen Town	546	W 3-0	Paul 31 35, Mehew 50
28	07.03	DM P	A	Salisbury City	721	W 3-1	Walker 60, Fraser 84[p], Paul 89
29	11.03	DM P	H	WORCESTER CITY	1287	D 1-1	Paul 55[p]
30	14.03	DM P	H	Rothwell Town	182	W 3-2	Towler 48, Holloway 68, Mehew 79
31	18.03	DM P	A	Margate	690	D 1-1	Mehew 20
32	21.03	DM P	H	Clevedon Town	1005	L 0-3	
33	25.03	DM P	H	MERTHYR TYDFIL	1,138	L 0-1	
34	28.03	DM P	H	HALESOWEN TOWN	674	L 0-1	
35	01.04	DM P	A	King's Lynn	904	L 1-4	Paul 24
36	08.04	DM P	H	MARGATE	735	D 1-1	Paul 4
	11.04	SPC SF	A	Bristol Manor Farm	90	W 4-0	Paul 47, 51(p), Vickerman 78, Fraser 84
37	15.04	DM P	H	Havant & Waterlooville	430	W 2-1	Cox 52, Davis 82
38	18.04	DM P	A	Crawley Town	547	L 1-4	Walker 38
39	22.04	DM P	H	NEWPORT COUNTY	950	D 1-1	Fraser 57
40	24.04	DM P	A	Weymouth	914	L 0-3	
41	29.04	DM P	H	CAMBRIDGE CITY	722	D 2-2	Paul 22, Davis 50
42	06.05	DM P	A	Burton Albion	1202	L 0-3	
	09.05	S PC Final	N	Bristol City		L 2-3	OG (Morrison) 62, Harrington 84

PLAYING SQUAD

GOALKEEPERS: Sal Bibbo (Havant & W)

DEFENDERS: Paul Bodin (Reading), Mark Clode (Swansea), Kevin Lloyd (Cardiff), Phil King (Kidderminster H), Colin Towler (Yate T), Jon Holloway (Gloucester C)

MIDFIELDERS: Jimmy Fraser (Worcester C), Mark Harrington (Paulton R), Scott Walker (Exeter), Lee Vickerman (Swindon)

FORWARDS: Martin Paul (Doncaster R), Steve White (Cardiff), Mike Davis (Bristol R), Peter Tisdale (Welton R), Graham Colbourne (Paulton R)

BURTON ALBION

CLUB OFFICIALS

Chairman: **C B Robinson** 01283 37272(W)
Vice Chairman:
Secretary: **Tony A Kirkland**, 40 Hurst Drive,
Stretton, Burton-on-Trent DE13 0ED
0374 102485 (Mobile)
Commercial Man: **Fleur Robinson**
Press Officer: **David Twigg** (01283 562013**)**

FOOTBALL MANAGEMENT TEAM
Manager: Nigel Clough
Assistant Manager: Gary Crosby
Physio: Matt Brown

FACT FILE

Formed: 1950

Nickname: Brewers

Sponsors: B.I. Industries

Colours: Yellow with black trim

Change colours: White

Midweek matchday: Tuesday

GROUND Eton Park, Princess Way, Burton-on-Trent DE14 2RU Tel: 01283 565938
Directions: From south M42 - A38 (Lichfield), follow signs forBurton, take 2nd turn for Burton
(A5121), right at island - ground on left: From M6 north - jct 15 and follow A50 for Stoke and
Uttoxeter, follow A50 signsto Burton, continue under bypass, left into Shakespeare Rd after
canal bridge (opp. Navigation Inn), ground at end. From M6 North, leave at Jct 15 .Follow A50
Stoke & Uttoxeter. Leave for A38 South to Burton & Lichfield at Toyota Factory.Leave Burton
North A5121 past Pirelli Factory to Island .Turn right ground is on left.
Capacity: 4,500   Cover: 2,500   Seats: 464   Floodlights: Yes
Clubhouse: `The Football Tavern' - open normal pub hours. Full hot & cold menu.
Steward: T.B.A.   Club Shop: Yes

Pages: 48   Price: £1
Editor: David Twigg (01283 562013)

Local Press: Burton Daily Mail (01283 43311)
Local Radio: Radio Derby,Centra F.M.

PREVIOUS   **Leagues:** West Midlands 1950-58; Southern 58-79; Northern Premier 79-8;
               Ground: Wellington Street 50-57
CLUB RECORDS **Attendance:** 5,860 v Weymouth, Southern Lg Cup Final 2nd leg, 1964
                          (22,500 v Leicester City, F.A. Cup 3rd Rd 1984 - played at Derby County F.C.)
               Goalscorer: Ritchie Barker, 157.   **Appearances:** Phil Annable, 567
               Fee Paid: £21,000 to for R Jones and J Pearson (Kidderminster)
               Fee Received: £60,000 for Darren Carr (C Palace 89)
BEST SEASON **FA Trophy:** R-up 86-87 (SF 74-75)   **FA Cup:** 3rd Rd Prop 55-56, 84-85. 1st Rd 9 times
HONOURS   Sth Lg Cup 63-64 96-97, 99-00 (R-up 88-89), Div 1 (Nth) R-up 71-72 73-74; Nth Prem Lg Chall Cup 82-83 (R-up 86-87),
Presidents Cup R-up 85-86 (SF 86-87); BirminghamSnr Cup 53-54 70-71 (R-up 86-87); FA Trophy R-up 86-87; GMAC Cup SF 86-87;
Bass Charity Vase 81-82 85-86, Challenge Cup 84-85; Wt Mids Lg R-up 53-54; Staffs Sen Cup 55-56
Players progressing: L Green & T Parry & S Aston (Hartlepool65/66), G Hunter (Lincoln 65), D Jones (Newport 68), R Barker & J Bourne &
TBailey (Derby 67/69/70), M Pollock & S Buckley (Luton 74), P Ward (Brighton75), Tony Moore (Sheffield Utd 79), C Swan & G Clayton (Doncaster
80 & 86), RJobson (Watford 82), P Haycock (Rotherham 86), A Kamara (Scarborough 87), PGroves (Leicester City 88), S Cotterill & J Gayle
(Wimbledon 89), D Carr(Crystal Pal. 89), D Smith & D Roberts (Wolves 90 & 92)

Back Row: Wayne Sutton, Mark Jones, Andy Garner, Nick Goodwin, Craig Smith. **Middle:** Matt Brown (Physio), Danny George, Anton Thomas, Terry
Henshaw, Mark Blour, Aaron Webster, Allan Davies, Darren Stride, David Holmes, Dale Anderson. **Front:** Neil Glasser, Pat Lyons, Nigel Clough
(Manager), Ben Robinson (Chairman), Gary Crosby (Asst. Manager), Tony Kirkland (Football Sec.), Jamie March, Michael Allsop. Photo © M Bannister

Match Facts 1999-00

	Date	Comp.	H/A	Opponents	Att.	Result	Goalscorers
1	14.08	DM-P	A	Bath City	911	L 1 - 2	Stride 53
2	17.08	DM-P	H	GLOUCESTER CITY	948	W 3 - 0	Anderson 29, Davies 38, Thomas 55
3	21.08	DM-P	H	WEYMOUTH	876	W 1 - 0	George 67
4	23.08	DM-P	A	Worcester City	1,103	D 2 - 2	Anderson 39, Holmes 41
5	28.08	DM-P	A	Dorchester Town	624	W 1 - 0	Glasser 16
6	30.08	DM-P	H	KING'S LYNN	1,304	W 1 - 0	Thomas 29
7	04.09	DM-P	A	Crawley Town	464	W 4 - 1	George 18, Thomas 29, 39, Holmes 86
8	07.09	DMP	H	BOSTON UNITED	1,920	D 1 - 1	George 81
9	11.09	DMP	H	NEWPORT COUNTY	1,426	D 1 - 1	Anderson 12
	18.09	**FAC Q2**		Redditch United	608	W 1 - 0	George 50
10	25.09	DMP	A	Cambridge City	480	W 1 - 0	Stride 4
	02.10	**FAC Q3**	A	Dagenham & Redbridge	919	W 2 - 0	Cole 6[og], Anderson 59
	09.10	**FAT 1**	H	TRAFFORD	795	D 1 - 1	Smith 71
	12.10	**FAT 1 R**	A	Trafford	306	W 3 - 1	Simms 14[og], Stride 25 86
	16.10	**FAC Q4**	A	Woking	2015	D 1 - 1	Stride 67
	19.10	**FAC Q4 R**	H	WOKING	2081	W 3 - 1	Thomas 12, Blount 103, Anderson 113
11	23.10	DM P	H	GRANTHAM TOWN	1175	W 1 - 0	Thomas 53
12	26.10	DM P	A	Gloucester City	418	L 1 - 2	Clough 21
	30.10	**FAC 1**	H	ROCHDALE	3103	D 0 - 0	
13	06.11	DM P	H	ATHERSTONE UNITED	891	W 5 - 1	Thomas 21 46, Blount 24, Stride 45, Anderson 55
	09.11	**FAC 1 R**	A	Rochdale	2633	L 0 - 3	
14	13.11	DM P	A	Havant & Waterlooville	492	L 0 - 6	
	16.11	**Lg Cup 1**	H	BEDWORTH UNITED	296	W 4 - 3	Garner 8, Lyons 14 79, Smith 91
15	20.11	DM P	H	CLEVEDON TOWN	815	W 1 - 0	Lyons 83
	27.11	**FAT 2**	A	Bamber Bridge	402	W 2 - 0	Stride 14, Anderson 56
16	04.12	DM P	A	Boston United	2090	L 1 - 3	Stride 21
	07.12	**LC 2**	H	HALESOWEN TOWN	233	W 3 - 2	Lyons 49, Anderson 50, Thomas 52
17	11.12	DM P	H	MERTHYR TYDFIL	834	W 2 - 0	Lyons 23, Anderson 72
	14.12	**Birm. SC 2**	H	BANBURY UNITED	169	W 2 - 1	Webster 30, Thomas 60
18	18.12	DM P	H	CAMBRIDGE CITY	941	W 3 - 0	Garner 63 68, Thomas 87
19	27.12	DM P	A	Halesowen Town	1084	L 1 - 2	Stride 69
20	03.01	DM P	H	ILKESTON TOWN	2047	W 3 - 1	**Garner 3** (4 53[p] 85)
21	08.01	DM P	A	Rothwell Town	502	D 1 - 1	Garner 13[p]
22	11.01	DM P	H	WORCESTER CITY	867	L 2 - 3	Stride 51, Garner 62
	15.01	**FAT 3**	A	Workington	1041	D 1 - 1	Blount 16
	18.01	**FAT 3R**	H	WORKINGTON	830	D 0 - 0	Lost 2-4 after penalties
23	22.01	DM P	A	Clevedon Town	572	D 0 - 0	
	26.01	**LC 3**	A	VS Rugby	286	W 4 - 0	Glasser 19, Thomas 32, Holmes 41, Webster 88
24	29.01	DM P	A	ROTHWELL TOWN	894	W 2 - 1	Webster 65, Holmes 90
	01.02	**BSC 3**	H	TAMWORTH	701	L 0 - 2	
25	05.02	DM P	A	Merthyr Tydfil	578	D 1 - 1	Holmes 58
26	08.02	DM P	A	King's Lynn	638	W 1 - 0	Blount 37
27	12.02	DM P	H	DORCHESTER TOWN	931	W 5 - 0	Holmes 29, Lyons 55, **Glasser 3** (42 45 60)
	15.02	**LC QF**	H	WORCESTER CITY	609	W 1 - 0	Stride 83
28	19.02	DM P	A	Tamworth	1652	D 1 - 1	Holmes 21
29	22.02	DM P	A	Margate	746	L 0 - 1	
30	26.02	DM P	A	Newport County	674	D 1 - 1	Stride 35
31	04.03	DM P	H	SALISBURY CITY	842	W 4 - 1	Blount 52, Holmes 68, Webster 83, Stride 86
32	11.03	DM P	A	Salisbury City	515	W 3 - 0	Anderson 45 90, Holmes 89
	14.03	**LC SF**	H	KING'S LYNN	1002	W 2 - 0	Stride 15, Lyons 80
33	18.03	DM P	H	Atherstone United	565	W 2 - 0	Blount 52, Moore 65
34	21.03	DM P	H	HAVANT & WATERLOOVILLE	779	W 3 - 0	Moore 1[p] 70, Lyons 90
35	25.03	DM P	H	MARGATE	1180	L 0 - 1	
36	01.04	DM P	H	Grantham Town	736	W 1 - 0	Moore 44 (p)
37	08.04	DM P	H	TAMWORTH	1188	D 1 - 1	Glasser 42
	11.04	**LC Final 1**	A	Hastings Town	557	W 2 - 1	Moore 72, Garner 77
38	15.04	DM P	H	CRAWLEY TOWN	772	W 3 - 0	Moore 39, 74 (p), Stride 79
	18.04	**LC Final 2**	H	HASTINGS TOWN	1529	W 4 - 1	Stride 21, Webster 23, Davies 42, Garner 85
39	22.04	DM P	A	Ilkeston Town	1061	L 1 - 4	Anderson 87
40	24.04	DM P	H	HALESOWEN TOWN	957	W 2 - 4	Holmes 74, Clough 76
41	29.04	DM P	A	Weymouth	901	W 2 - 1	Clough 59, Moore 87
42	06.05	DM P	H	BATH CITY	1202	W 3 - 0	Moore 24 (p), Anderson 22, Lyons 66

GOALKEEPERS: Nick Goodwin (Gresley R)

DEFENDERS: Mark Blount (Gresley R), Pat Lyons (WBA), Jason Kavanagh (Cambridge U), Mike Forsyth (Wycombe), Allan Davies (Manchester C), Darren Wassall (Birmingham)

MIDFIELDERS: Craig Dean (Atherstone U), Darren Stride (Youth), Nigel Clough (Manchester C), Terry Henshaw (Notts Co), Steve Froggatt (Heanor T), Neil Glasser (Grantham T)

FORWARDS: Phil Starbuck (Cambridge C), Christian Moore (Ilkeston T), Anton Thomas (Nuneaton B), Dale Anderson (Bromsgrove R), David Holmes (Gloucester C), Andy Garner (Gresley R), Aaron Webster (Youth)

PLAYING SQUAD

CAMBRIDGE CITY

CLUB OFFICIALS

Chairman: **Dennis Rolph**
President: **Sir Neil Westbrook**, CBE MA FRICS
Secretary: **Stuart Hamilton**
55 Crowhill, Godmanchester,
Huntingdon, Cambs
Tel: 01480 382675
Press Officer: Secretary

FOOTBALL MANAGEMENT TEAM

Manager: Chris Tovey
Asst Manager: Tom Finney
Physios: Joop Tanis and Karen White

FACT FILE

Formed: 1908
Nickname: Lilywhites
Sponsors: Lancer UK
Colours: White /black/ white
Change colours: All Sky Blue
Midweek matchday: Monday
Reserves' League: Eastern Counties

For up to the minute news,
results, fixtures,
plus general facts & figures
from the world of
non-league football

log on to

www.nlfootball.com

GROUND   City Ground, Milton Road, Cambridge CB4 1UY Tel: 01223 357973

Directions: 50 yards on left from start of A1309, Cambridge to Ely Rd.
30 minswalk from Cambridge BR
Capacity: 5,000   Cover: 1,400   Seats:423   Floodlights: Yes
Clubhouse: 11am-11pm Mon-Sat, 12-3 & 7pm-10.30 Sun. Bingo, Dances, Pool, Darts
Club Shop: Sells programmes, club history, badges, scarves, pennants, replica shirts etc.
Contact Neil Harvey (01223 235991)

Programme
Pages: 48   Price: £1.00
Editor: Secretary
Local Press: Cambridge Evening News
Local Radio: BBC Radio Cambridge

PREVIOUS   **Leagues:** Bury & Dist. 08-13 19-20, East Anglian 08-10, Southern Olympian 11-14, Southern Amateur 1913-35, Spartan 35-50, Athenian 50-58   **Name:** Cambridge Town 1908-51

CLUB RECORDS   **Attendance:** 12,058 v Leytonstone, FA Amateur Cup 1st Rd, 1949-50
Scorer: Gary Grogan   **Appearances:** Mal Keenan
Fee Paid: £8,000 for Paul Coe (Rushden & Diamonds)   **Fee Received:**£100,000 from Millwall for Neil Harris 1998

BEST SEASON   **FA Amateur Cup:** Semi Final 27-28   **FA Trophy:** 2nd Rd. 86-87 87-88
FA Cup: 1st Rd; v Ashford 66, v Swindon 46, v Walthamstow Ave. 48, v Hereford 93, v Wigan Ath. 99

HONOURS   Southern Lg 62-63 (R-up 70-71, Southern Div 85-86, Div 1 R-up 69-70, Champ Cup62-63; E Anglian Cup (9); Eastern Prof Floodlit Lg 65-66 72-73, Cambs Prof Cup(6); Cambs Invitation Cup (7); Spartan Lg 47-48 48-49 (R-up 49-50); EasternDiv Champs 45-46); Southern Amat Lg 20-21 27-28 28-29 30-31 31-32; Bury & Dist.Lg (4); E Anglian Lg (6); AFA Snr Cup 30-31 46-47 47-48(shared) 48-49 49-50;AFA Invitation Cup 50-51; Hunts Prem Cup 62-63 64-65; Suffolk Sen Cup 09-10; Addenbrookes Hosp Cup 87-88; The Munns Youth Cup 82-83 83-84 84-85; ChilternYouth Lge Cup R-up 75-76; South Mids Lge Youth Trophy 82-83; Robinson Cup 87-8889-90; Jim Digney 89-90; Essex & Herts Youth Lg 89-90 Southern Lg Cup R-up 98-9

Players progressing: K Wright (West Ham 46), A Gallego(Norwich 47), A Stokes (Watford 61), D Weddle (Middlesbrough 61), D Hicksen(Bury 62), B Harvey (Blackpool 62), R Whitehead (Darlington 62), G Cummins(Hull 62), R Pearce (Peterborough 63), A Banks (Exeter 63), T Carroll (Ipswich66), Dominic Genovese (Peterborough 88), Roy Jones (Swindon), Winston Dubose(Oldham), K Wilkin (Northampton Tn 91), S Flack (Cardiff City 95), D Hedcock(Sheffield Wed 96), Neil Harris (Millwall 1998)

Defending in numbers against Slough Town proved worthwhile for
Cambridge City as they managed an equaliser in injury time and
then won the replay of this 4th Qual. Rd. match in the FA Cup

Match Facts 1999-00

	Date	Comp.	H/A	Opponents	Att.	Result	Goalscorers
1	14.08	DM-P	A	Newport County	1,003	D 2 - 2	l Cambridge 26, 71
2	16.08	DM-P	H	BOSTON UNITED	545	L 0 - 2	
3	21.08	DM-P	H	BATH CITY	480	L 0 - 2	
4	24.08	DM-P	A	Crawley Town	452	W 2 - 1	Taylor 35 80
5	28.08	DM-P	A	Gloucester City	446	L 0 - 1	
6	30.08	DM-P	H	MARGATE	438	D 0 - 0	
7	04.09	DM-P	A	Halesowen Town	433	W 2 - 1	Holden 33, Wylde 73
8	11.09	DMP	A	Merthyr Tydfil	637	L 0 - 1	
	18.09	FAC Q2	H	ARLESEY TOWN	296	W 3 - 1	Cambridge 3 (30 83 87[p])
9	25.09	DMP	H	BURTON ALBION	480	L 0 - 1	
	02.10	FAC Q3	H	KING'S LYNN	812	W 1 - 0	Taylor 25
	09.10	FAT 1	A	Cirencester Town	160	L 2 - 3	Newby 40, Cambridge 53
	12.10	Cambs PC2	A	Wisbech Town	139	L 0 - 1	
	16.10	FAC Q4	A	Slough Town	771	D 1 - 1	McCann 90
	19.10	FAC Q4 R	H	SLOUGH TOWN	650	W 3 - 2	Newby 45[p], McCann 85, Coburn 90
10	23.10	DM P	H	WORCESTER CITY	607	W 4 - 2	Kirkup 25, Wild 34, Cambridge 55 75
11	27.10	DM P	A	Boston United	957	L 0 - 5	
	30.10	FAC 1	A	Wigan Athletic	4024	L 0 - 2	
12	06.11	DM P	A	SALISBURY CITY	449	L 1 - 3	Coburn 60
13	08.11	DM P	H	CRAWLEY TOWN	327	W 3 - 2	Stringfellow 27, Kirkup 41, Cambridge 45[p]
14	13.11	DM P	A	Weymouth	446	D 0 - 0	
	16.11	Lg Cup 1	A	Raunds Town	98	W 1 - 0	Reeder 88
15	20.11	DM P	H	KING'S LYNN	534	L 2 - 3	Randall 76, Coburn 87
	24.11	Cambs IC	A	Histon		W 2 - 1	
16	04.12	DM P	A	Havant & Waterlooville	378	L 1 - 3	S Taylor 44
	07.12	LC 2	A	Grantham Town	187	L 1 - 2	Reeder 37
17	18.12	DM P	A	Burton Albion	941	L 0 - 3	
18	27.12	DM P	A	Rothwell Town	297	W 4 - 1	Stringfellow 8, Wilde 24, Tovey 45, Cambridge 71
19	03.01	DM P	H	ATHERSTONE UNITED	369	W 3 - 2	Cambridge 26 71, Taylor 60
20	08.01	DM P	A	King's Lynn	820	D 0 - 0	
	11.01	C. IC QF	A	Ely City	130	W 4 - 1	Cambridge 12[p], Leete 25, Bartley 52 76
21	15.01	DM P	H	GLOUCESTER CITY	418	W 2 - 1	Holden 61, Wilde 69
22	18.01	DM P	A	Margate	339	W 2 - 1	Collins 55[og], Cambridge 75[p]
23	22.01	DM P	H	TAMWORTH	382	L 1 - 2	Cambridge 59[p]
24	29.01	DM P	H	ILKESTON TOWN	572	W 3 - 2	Taylor 35, Holden 71, Cambridge 80
25	12.02	DM P	H	CLEVEDON TOWN	662	D 1 - 1	Taylor 68
26	19.02	DM P	A	Ilkeston Town	521	D 2 - 2	Holden 17, Cambridge 53
27	26.02	DM P	H	GRANTHAM TOWN	427	L 0 - 2	
28	28.02	DM P	A	Worcester City	827	L 2 - 3	Reader 35, Cambridge 60
29	04.03	DM P	H	MERTHYR TYDFIL	504	D 0 - 0	
30	07.03	DM P	A	Dorchester Town	357	W 2 - 1	Wilkin 9, Holden 19
31	11.03	DM P	A	Tamworth	517	W 2 - 1	Gawthrop 42, Cleaver 51
32	14.03	DM P	A	Grantham Town	476	L 0 - 2	
33	18.03	DM P	H	HAVANT & WATERLOOVILLE	444	W 4 - 1	Holden 10, Wilkin 20, Cleaver 68[p], Cambridge 73
34	25.03	DM P	A	Clevedon Town	273	L 0-1	
35	01.04	DM P	H	NEWPORT COUNTY	718	D 0-0	
	04.04	CIC SF	A	Newmarket Town	160	D *1-1	Reeder 108
36	08.04	DM P	A	Salisbury City	371	L 0-4	
37	10.04	DM P	H	HALESOWEN TOWN	328	D 1-1	Tovey 55
	18.04	CIC SF R	H	NEWMARKET TOWN	197	W *4 - 2	Wilkin 11, Randle 70, Salmons 115, Kirkup 118
38	22.04	DM P	A	Atherstone United	145	W 1 - 0	Salmons 8
39	24.04	DM P	H	ROTHWELL TOWN	304	W 1 - 0	Kirkup 67
40	29.04	DM P	A	Bath City	722	D 2 - 2	Wilkin 56, Wilde 79
41	01.05	DM P	H	DORCHESTER TOWN	410	L 0 - 1	
	04.05	CIC Final	N	Mildenhall Town	450	W 3 - 0	Cambridge 6, 36, Burnham 60
42	06.05	DM P	H	WEYMOUTH	408	L 2 - 3	Wilde 24, Salmons 70

PLAYING SQUAD

GOALKEEPERS: Nicky Rust (Braintree T), Martin Davies (Dover Ath)

DEFENDERS: Jason Burnham (Atherstone U), John Girling (Chelmsford C), **Steve Holden** (Stevenage B), Neil Coburn (Chelmsford C), Steve Wenlock (Leicester C), Des Linton (Peterborough)

MIDFIELDERS: Scott Taylor (Granthat T), Chris Tovey (Chelmsford C), Adam Wilde (Cambridge U), Andy Pincher (Chelmsford C), Dean Randall (Ilkeston T), Adam Salmons (Stockport)

FORWARDS: Peter Leete (Histon), Tesfaye Bramble (Chelmsford C), Ian Cambridge (Chelmsford C), Kevin Wilkin (Nuneaton B), Chrstian McCann (Baldock T), Warren Waugh (Exeter)

479

CLEVEDON TOWN

CLUB OFFICIALS

Chairman: John Croft
Directors: R.J.Ayers,B.W.Bradshaw, S.T.Haasz
Secretary: Mike Williams
34 Robinia Walk, Whitchurch,
Bristol BS14 0SH
Tel: 01275 833835
Commercial Manager: Gary Bradshaw
(M) 0468 270718

FOOTBALL MANAGEMENT TEAM
Manager: Steve Fey
Coach: Wayne Noble
Physio: Ian Weston

FACT FILE
Formed: 1880
Nickname: The Seasiders
Sponsors: Bradshaw Group (Ama na)
Colours: Blue & white stripes/blue/blue
Change colours: All yellow or all green
Midweek Matches: Tuesday
1999-00
Captain:I.Harvey
Players' P.o.Y.: Steve Peters
Supporters' P.o.Y: Steve Lester
manager's P.o.Y.: Lee Jefferies

GROUND
Ha nd Stadium, Davis Lane, Clevedon
Fax: 01275 871601 Tel: 01275 871600(ground)   01275 341913 (office)

Directions: M5 Jct 20 - follow signs for Clevedon Town Sports Complex; first left into Central Way (at island just after motorway), 1st left at mini-r'bout into Kenn Rd, 2nd left Davis Lane; ground half mile on right. Or from Bristol(B3130) left into Court Lane (opposite Clevedon Court), turn right after 1mile, ground on left. Nearest BR station: Nailsea & Backwell. Buses from Bristol
Capacity: 3,650   **Seats:** 300   **Cover:** 1,600   **Floodlights:** Yes
Clubhouse: Open every day and evening. Separate function suite & lounge bar.Hot food available. Matchday refreshment bar within ground sells confectionary, teas & hot food
Club Shop: Sells all types of souvenirs, programmes and replica kit. Exchangeswelcome. Contact J Anderson. **Supporters Club Chairman:** Russell Coneybeare

Pages: 34 Price:£1.20
Editor: Russell Isaac,(01275 343000)
Local Radio: Radio Bristol
Local Press: Clevedon Mercury
Evening Post,Western Daily Press
Web-site: www.clevedontownafc.co.uk

PREVIOUS   **Leagues:** Weston & District, Somerset Senior, Bristol Charity, Bristol &District, Bristol Suburban, Western 74-93
Grounds: Dial Hill ('till early 1890's); Teignmouth Road ('till 1991)
Names: Clevedon FC, Ashtonians (clubs merged in 1974)

CLUB RECORDS **Attendance:** 1,600 v Bristol City, Friendly. 27/7/98
(At Teignmouth Road: 2,300 v Billingham Synthonia, FA Amateur Cup, 52-53)
Win: 18-0 v Dawlish Town (H), Western League Premier Division 24/4/93
Defeat: 13-3 v Yate YMCA (A), Bristol Comb 67-68

BEST SEASON   **FA Cup:** 3rd Qual. Rd 2nd replay 92-93 v Newport AFC, 2-4 after two 1-1
FA Amateur Cup: 3rd Round Proper, 52-53 **FA Vase:** 6th Round 87-88, v Sudbury Town (A) **FA Trophy:** 2nd Round 98-99

HONOURS   Southern League, Midland Division 98-99, Western League 92-93 (R-up 91-92), League Cup (R-up 92-93), Bristol Charity League 37-38,40-41, Somerset Senior Cup 01-02 04-05 28-29 , Somerset Snr League 36-37, Div 1(Res.) 92-93, Bristol & suburbanLeague 25-26,27-28,28-29, Weston & District League: 39-40,43-44,44-45, Somerset Premier Cup;86-87,98-99, Somerset Junior Cup 1897-98,Somerset Medal Competition: 87-88, Clevedon Charity Cup 26-27,30-31.
Players Progressing: Jason Eaton (Bristol City) and Jonathon Gould (Halifax Town)

Back Row: Steve Bobbins (Kit Manager), Lee Jeffries, David Mehew, Jim Rollo, Ray Johnston, Andy Mainwaring, Ian Harvey, Mark Hervin, Steve Peters, Rob Skidmore, Paul Mildom, Ian Weston (Physio). **Front Row:** Marco Micciche, Richard Ford, Mark Badman, Steve Lester, Steve Fey (Manager), Danny Haines, Craig Patch, Andy Llewellyn, Wayne Noble (Asst. Man.)

Match Facts 1999-00

	Date	Comp.	H/A	Opponents	Att.	Result	Goalscorers	
1	14.08	DM-P	A	Crawley Town	608	W 3 - 1	Rawlins 5, Cook 55 71[p]	
2	17.08	DM-P	H	WEYMOUTH	556	D 1 - 1	Cook 85	
3	21.08	DM-P	H	KING'S LYNN	397	W 4 - 2	Rawlins 41, Cook 45[p] 61, Jefferies 85	
4	25.08	DM-P	A	Newport County	869	L 0 - 5		
5	28.08	DM-P	A	Boston United	1,423	L 1 - 5	Rollo 6	
6	30.08	DM-P	H	HAVANT & WATERLOOVILLE	402	D 0 - 0		
7	04.09	DM-P	A	Tamworth	545	L 1 - 4	Birkby 9	
8	07.09	DMP	H	GLOUCESTER CITY	481	W 3 - 0	Lester 31, Rollo 54, Cook 68[p]	
9	11.09	DMP	A	Margate	526	L 1 - 2	Milsom 30	
	14.09	SPC 1	H	ODD DOWN	192	W 3 - 0	Lester 51, Rollo 62, Milsom 88	
	18.09	FAC Q2	H	TIVERTON TOWN	519	W 2 - 1	Rollo 5, Rawlins 30	
10	25.09	DMP	H	GRANTHAM TOWN	354	D 2 - 2	Cook 41[p], Jefferies 65	
	02.10	FAC Q3	A	Lymington & New Milton	313	L 1 - 3	Rollo 85	
	09.10	FAT 1	A	Braintree Town	303	L 2 - 3	Ford 2, Jefferies 75	
11	16.10	DM P	A	Dorchester Town	502	L 1 - 2	Micciche 83	
12	23.10	DM P	H	ATHERSTONE UNITED	317	W 1 - 0	Claridge 47	
13	26.10	DM P	A	Weymouth	725	W 1 - 0	Rawlins 58	
14	30.10	DM P	A	Salisbury City	370	W 2 - 1	Coupe 56, Cook 84	
15	06.11	DM P	A	Halesowen Town	460	L 0 - 3		
	09.11	Som. PC2	H	WESTON-SUPER-MARE	400	L 0 - 1		
16	13.11	DM P	H	MARGATE	249	W 1 - 0	Rawlins 62	
	16.11	Lg Cup 1	H	WESTON-SUPER-MARE	285	D 1 - 1	Cook 90	Lost 5-6 after penalties
17	20.11	DM P	A	Burton Albion	815	L 0 - 1		
18	23.11	DM P	H	NEWPORT COUNTY	623	W 1 - 0	Birkby 80	
19	27.11	DM P	H	BOSTON UNITED	407	D 0 - 0		
20	04.12	DM P	A	Worcester City	702	L 0 - 1		
21	27.12	DM P	A	Bath City	1552	L 1 - 2	Milsom 70	
22	03.01	DM P	A	MERTHYR TYDFIL	586	L 1 - 2	Mainwaring 78	
23	08.01	DM P	A	Gloucester City	452	W 5 - 1	Micciche 18, Mainwaring 3 (38 72 79), Lester 44	
24	18.01	DM P	A	Havant & Waterlooville	344	W 2 - 1	Milsom 15, Haines 44	
25	22.01	DM P	H	BURTON ALBION	572	D 0 - 0		
26	29.01	DM P	H	HALESOWEN TOWN	389	D 0 - 0		
27	05.02	DM P	A	Rothwell Town	203	W 2 - 0	Micciche 63, Milsom 83	
28	12.02	DM P	A	Cambridge City	662	D 1 - 1	Mainwaring 69	
29	19.02	DM P	H	SALISBURY CITY	348	L 1 - 2	Rollo 51	
30	26.02	DM P	A	King's Lynn	599	L 0 - 1		
31	04.03	DM P	H	CRAWLEY TOWN	334	D 1 - 1	Rollo 60	
32	11.03	DM P	A	Grantham Town	374	L 0 - 2		
33	14.03	DM P	H	TAMWORTH	291	W 1 - 0	Mainwaring 68	
34	21.03	DM P	H	BATH CITY	1005	W 3 - 0	Mainwaring 22 86[p], Peters 69	
35	25.03	DM P	H	CAMBRIDGE CITY	273	W 1 - 0	Peters 72	
36	01.04	DM P	A	Ilkeston Town	438	L 1 - 4	Milson 63	
37	08.04	DM P	H	ROTHWELL TOWN	245	D 1 - 1	Lester 14	
38	22.04	DM P	A	Merthyr Tydfil	602	L 0 - 2		
39	24.04	DM P	H	DORCHESTER TOWN	337	W 2 - 1	Lester 4, 34	
40	29.04	DM P	A	Atherstone United	155	W 3 - 1	Mainwaring 3, Lester 40, Badman 87	
41	03.05	DM P	H	ILKESTON TOWN	224	W 2 - 0	Jefferies 29, Mainwaring 47	
42	06.05	DM P	H	WORCESTER CITY	413	W 1 - 0	Rollo 88	

PLAYING SQUAD

GOALKEEPERS: Richard Fey (Youth), Mark Hervin (Gloucester C)

DEFENDERS: Matthew Coupe (Gloucester C), Lee Jefferies (Yate T), Andy Llewellyn (Weston-s-Mare), Danny Haines (Evesham U), Rob Skidmore (Bath C), Steve Peters (Cinderford T)

MIDFIELDERS: Steve Lester (Gloucester C), Mark Badman (Bristol C), Richard Ford (Salisbury C), Jim Rollo (Forest Green R)

FORWARDS: Marco Micciche (Bath C), David Mehew (Bath C), Andy Mainwaring (Newport Co), Paul Milsom (Trowbridge T)

CRAWLEY TOWN

CLUB OFFICIALS
Chairperson: **Ms Jo Gomm**
Vice Chairman: **Dave Brown**
President: **Les Turnbull**
Secretary: **Dave Haining**
20 Irving Walk, Tilgate, Crawley RH10 5BQ
Tel: 01293 535683
Chief Executive: **John Duly**
Managing Director: **Steve Duly**

FOOTBALL MANAGEMENT TEAM
Football TeamManager: Billy Smith
Coaches: Brian Owen & Ron Wilson
Asst Man: J Broughton Physio: R Massimo

FACT FILE
Formed: 1896
Nickname: The Reds
Sponsors: T.B.A.
Colours: All red
Change colours:All white
Midweek matchday: Tuesday
Reserves' League: Suburban

CRAWLEY TOWN FOOTBALL CLUB
SEASON 99/2000

WEYMOUTH F.C

Official Match Programme £1.00

CRUISEWAY
Main Club Sponsors

Pages: 36 Price: £1.50
Editor & Press Off: Jo Fenwick
Tel: 01293 432646
Local Press: Crawley Observer, Crawley
News, The Argus Local Radio: Radio
Mercury, BBC Southern Counties

GROUND　　Broadfield Stadium, Brighton Road, Crawley RH11 9RX Tel: 01293 410000

Directions:　　M23 exit 11, 2nd exit off roundabout, A23, towards Crawley.
　　　　　　Turn left at next r/about into ground

Capacity: 4,996　　　　Cover: 4,200　　　Seats: 1,080　　Floodlights: Yes
Clubhouse: Mon-Fri: Evenings 7-11 Sat: 12-11 Sun 12-8
Club Shop: Sells programmes, metal badges, hats, scarves, mugs, replica kits

PREVIOUS　　**Leagues:** Sussex County 1951-56; Metropolitan 56-63　　**Grounds:** Malthouse Farm 1896-1914 38-40; Victoria Hall + Rectory
　　　　　　　　　Fields 18-38;Yetmans Field 45-49, Town Mead 49-53 54-97, Ilfield Rec Grd 53-54

CLUB RECORDS　**Attendance:** 4,104 v Barnet, FA Cup 2nd Rd 4/12/93
　　　　　　　　Goalscorer: Phil Basey 108 (68-72)　　　　　　**Appearances:** John Maggs 652 (63-73 75-79)
　　　　　　　　Win: 10-0 v Chichester United, Sussex Co. Lge Div. 2 17/12/55
　　　　　　　　Defeat: 0-10 v Arundel (A), Sussex County Lge 9/2/52
　　　　　　　　Fee Paid: £5,000 for David Thompson (Wokingham, May 92)
　　　　　　　　Fee Received: £50,000 for Craig Whitington (Scarborough 93)
BEST SEASON　**FA Trophy:** 3rd Rd 98-99
　　　　　　　　FA Cup: 3rd Rd Proper 91-92, 0-5 v Brighton & HA (A)　　League Clubs defeated: Northampton Town 91-92
HONOURS　　Sussex Snr Cup (2) 89-91 (R-up 58-59 95-96); Sussex I'mediate Cup 26-27; Sussex Prof. Cup 69-70; Southern Lg S Div.R-up
83-84; Merit Cup 70-71;Sussex Floodlit Cup (3) 90-93; Sussex Lg Div 2 R-up 55-56; Gilbert RiceF'lit Cup 79-80 83-84; Southern Co's Comb.
Floodlit Cup 85-86; Met Lg Chal. Cup 58-59; Mid-Sussex Snr 02-03; Montgomery Cup 25-26 Sussex Floodlit Cup 98-99

Players progressing: Ray Keeley, Graham Brown (Mansfield68), Andy Ansah (Brentford 87), Craig Whitington (Scarborough 93),Ben Abbey (Oxford
United 99), John Mackie (Reading 99)

Match Facts 1999-00

	Date	Comp.	H/A	Opponents	Att.	Result	Goalscorers	
1	14.08	DM P	H	CLEVEDON TOWN	608	L 1 - 3	Abbey 84	
2	17.08	DM P	A	Rothwell Town	244	D 3 - 3	Abbey 39 63, McAree 49	
3	21.08	DM P	A	Ilkeston Town	590	L 0 - 2		
4	24.08	DM P	H	CAMBRIDGE CITY	452	L 1 - 2	Webber 82	
5	28.08	DM P	H	NEWPORT COUNTY	542	D 2 - 2	Webber 5, Abbey 51	
6	30.08	DM P	A	Salisbury City	460	L 1 - 4	Webber 3	
7	04.09	DM P	H	BURTON ALBION	464	L 1 - 4	Abbey 10	
8	11.09	DM P	A	Weymouth	721	L 0 - 4		
	18.09	FAC Q2	A	Bromley	334	L 1 - 4	Lovatt 78	
	05.10	Sussex FC2	A	East Preston	142	D 2 - 2	Flint 52, 90	Lost 4-5 after pens.
9	09.10	DM P	A	Tamworth	587	L 0 - 3		
10	23.10	DM P	A	Halesowen Town	425	L 0 - 1		
11	26.10	DM P	H	ROTHWELL TOWN	481	W 4 - 1	Hough 13[og], Vines 45 58, Lovett 54	
12	30.10	DM P	A	King's Lynn	792	L 0 - 1		
13	06.11	DM P	H	WORCESTER CITY	674	D 2 - 2	Ugbah 57 85	
14	08.11	DM P	A	Cambridge City	327	L 2 - 3	Groom 49, Lovett 79	
15	13.11	DM P	H	GRANTHAM TOWN	692	W 3 - 2	Johnson 21, Green 33, Blake 35	
	16.11	Lg Cup 1	A	Baldock Town	106	L 0 - 3		
16	20.11	DM P	A	Atherstone United	283	W 1 - 0	Vines 82	
	23.11	Sussex SC2	H	WICK	230	W 2 - 1	Green 34, Payne 45[p]	
	27.11	FAT 2	H	WEALDSTONE	712	L 0 - 2		
17	04.12	DM P	H	DORCHESTER TOWN	588	W 3 - 1	Vines 59, Boateng 78 89	
18	11.12	DM P	H	WEYMOUTH	628	W 1 - 0	Payne 30[p]	
19	18.12	DM P	A	Gloucester City	416	D 2 - 2	McAree 8, Lovatt 18	
20	27.12	DM P	H	HAVANT & WATERLOOVILLE	1132	L 2 - 3	Payne 7[p], Moore 66	
21	03.01	DM P	A	Margate	744	L 0 - 1		
22	08.01	DM P	A	Bath City	1124	L 0 - 7		
23	18.01	DM P	H	SALISBURY CITY	557	W 4 - 1	Payne 19[p], Lovatt 49, Moore 56 72	
24	22.01	DM P	H	BOSTON UNITED	1037	L 1 - 6	Vines 45	
25	29.01	DM P	A	Newport County	607	W 1 - 0	Pullam 8	
	02.02	SSC 3	H	BRIGHTON & HOVE ALBION	351	L 1 - 2	Wordsworth 80	
26	05.02	DM P	H	KING'S LYNN	620	L 1 - 2	Ugbah 27	
27	12.02	DM P	H	TAMWORTH	706	W 3 - 0	Moore 68, Wordsworth 87, Lovatt 90	
28	19.02	DM P	A	Merthyr Tydfil	514	W 3 - 2	Charman 34, Wordsworth 56, Moore 59	
29	26.02	DM P	H	ATHERSTONE UNITED	760	D 0 - 0		
30	04.03	DM P	A	Clevedon Town	334	D 1 - 1	Sharman 35	
31	11.03	DM P	H	HALESOWEN TOWN	706	D 2 - 2	Wordsworth 20, Ugbah 56	
32	18.03	DM P	A	Dorchester Town	503	W 2 - 0	Hurdle 82, Vines 86	
33	21.03	DM P	H	MERTHYR TYDFIL	669	W 2 - 0	Hurdle 45, Ugbah 66	
34	25.03	DM P	A	Boston United	2002	L 0 - 1		
35	01.04	DM P	H	GLOUCESTER CITY	713	W 2 - 1	Payne 78 (p), 83	
36	08.04	DM P	A	Worcester City	858	W 5 - 2	Wordsworth 21, 80, Taylor 29, Vines 55, 61	
37	15.04	DM P	A	Burton Albion	772	L 0 - 3		
38	18.04	DM P	H	BATH CITY	547	W 4 - 1	Payne 23 (p), Taylor 52, Wordsworth 61, Anderson 75	
39	20.04	DM P	H	MARGATE	822	W 5 - 3	Lovett 6, 45, Wordsworth 64, 90, Anderson 85	
40	24.04	DM P	A	Havant & Waterlooville	512	L 0 - 1		
41	29.04	DM P	H	ILKESTON TOWN	693	D 1 - 1	Wordsworth 58	
42	06.05	DM P	A	Grantham Town	555	L 2 - 4	Hurdle 17, Vines 50	

PLAYING SQUAD

GOALKEEPERS: Andy Little (Banstead Ath)

DEFENDERS: Danny Wackett (Youth), Andy Taylor (Wisbech T), Marc Pullan (Peacehaven), Ian Payne (Vancouver 86ers (Can)), Lee Doherty (Chesham U), John Ugbah (Welling U), Keith Sharman (Ashford T)

MIDFIELDERS: Rod McAree (Chesham U), Danny Carroll (Dulwich Hamlet), Matthew Woolf (Bromley), Dean Wordsworth (Ashford T), Luke Anderson (Gravesend), Nigel Brake (Horsham), Andy Fernley (Camb. Univ)

FORWARDS: Lionel Best (Croydon), Francis Vines (Staines T), Curtis Johnson (Bromley), David Powell (Gravesend), Mark Hynes (Dover Ath), Danny Oatkins (Chipstead)

DORCHESTER TOWN

CLUB OFFICIALS
Chairman: **C E Clark**
President: **A.E.Miller**
Vice Chairman: **K Miller**
Comm Mgr: **Brian Benjafield**
Secretary: **David Martin**
21 Diggory Crescent, Dorchester
01305 262345
General Manager: **Keith Kellaway**

FOOTBALL MANAGEMENT TEAM

Manager: Mark Morris
Physio: Geoff Dine

FACT FILE

Formed: 1880
Nickname: The Magpies
Sponsors:Contract Motoring Services
Colours: Black & white stripes/black/black
Change colours: All red
Midweek games: Tuesdays (7.45)
Newsline (Magpies Hotline): 0839 664412
Reserves' League: Dorset Comb

BOSTON UNITED
Saturday 6th May 2000 K.O. 3.00pm
Match Sponsor : Carlsberg Tetley Brewing Ltd
Matchball Sponsors : The Casterbridge Hotel
& Tony Johns Bodycraft
Premier Division 1999/2000

GROUND Avenue Stadium, Weymouth Avenue, Dorchester DT1 2RY Tel: 01305 262451

Directions: Situated at the junction of the town bypass (A35) and the Weymouth road (A354)
Nearest station: Dorchester South
Capacity: 7,210   Cover: 4,000   Seats: 710   Floodlights: Yes

Clubhouse: Dorchester Lounge Club - access via main entrance to stadium.
Cold food and snacks
Club Shop: Sells replica shirts, badges, mugs, etc

Pages: 32 Price:£1.00
Editor: Melvin Cross(01305 848365)
Local Press: Dorset Evening Echo,
Western Gazette, Western Daily Press
Local Radio: Two Counties Radio, Wessex FM

PREVIOUS **Leagues:** Dorset; Western 1947-72
Grounds: Council Recreation Ground, Weymouth Avenue 1880-1929; The Avenue Ground, Weymouth Avenue 29-90

CLUB RECORDS **Attendance:** 4,000 v Chelsea, official ground opening 1990. Competitive: 4, 159 v Weymouth, Southern Lge Prem Div , 99
Goalscorer: Dennis Cheney 61 (in one season)   **Appearances:** Derek (Dinkie) Curtis 458 50-66
Win: 7-0 v Canterbury (A), Southern Lge Southern Div 86-87
Defeat: 0-13 v Welton Rovers Western Lge 66
Fee Paid: £12,000 for Chris Townsend (Gloucester City, 1990)
Fee Received: £35,000 for Trevor Senior (Portsmouth, 1981)

BEST SEASON **FA Trophy:** 3rd Rd replay 71-72, 96-97
FA Cup: 2nd Rd Replay 81-82, 1-2 v A.F.C. Bournemouth after 1-1. 2nd Rd 54-55 57-58; 1st Rd 7 times

HONOURS Southern Lg 85-85, R-up 79-80 (Div 1 Sth R-up 77-78), Lg Cup 86-87 (R-up 91-92); Western Lg 54-55 (R-up 60-61, Div 2 R-up 49-50), Lge Cup 54-54; Dorset SnrCup 50-51 60-61 67-68 68-69 71-72 93-94 94-95; Dorset Lg 37-38

Players progressing: Len Drake (Bristol Rovers 57), David Noake (Luton 59), Mike Turner (Swindon 61), Trevor Senior (Portsmouth 81), David West (Liverpool 83), Mike Squire (Torquay 84), Jeremy Judd (Torquay 84),Tony White(Bournem'th 85), Graham Roberts (Spurs, Chelsea, Rangers, England) whoprogressed via Weymouth. Darren Garner (Rotherham U, 95), Craig Taylor(Swindon),Syfyan Ghazghazi(Club African De Tunis 98)

Back Row: Danny O'Hagan, Dean May, Rob Murray. **Middle Row:** Peter Peavoy (Kit Manager), Matt Lonnon, Mark Kenway, Simon Baines, Geoff Dine (Physio). **Front Row:** Andy Harris, Matt Holmes, Simon Radcliffe, Mark Morris (Player-Manager), Brian Benjafield (Asst. Manager), Marcus Oldbury, Matt Groves, Mike White.

Match Facts 1999-00

	Date	Comp.	H/A	Opponents	Att.	Result	Goalscorers	
1	14.08	DM P	A	Halesowen Town	606	W 1 - 0	O'Hagan 57[p]	
2	17.08	DM P	H	BATH CITY	936	D 0 - 0		
3	21.08	DM P	H	WORCESTER CITY	657	W 3 - 0	Coates 71, O'Hagan 85, Lovell 87	
4	24.08	DM P	A	Merthyr Tydfil	710	D 0 - 0		
5	28.08	DM P	H	BURTON ALBION	624	L 0 - 1		
6	30.08	DM P	A	Weymouth	2,203	D 2 - 2	Groves 46, O'Hagan 49	
7	04.09	DM P	A	Gloucester City	340	D 0 - 0		
8	11.09	DM P	A	Ilkeston Town	532	L 1 - 3	Groves 61	
	18.09	FAC Q2	A	Taunton Town	663	L 0 - 3		
9	25.09	DM P	H	ATHERSTONE UNITED	532	D 2 - 2	Sullivan 16, Murray 44	
10	02.10	DM P	H	HALESOWEN TOWN	506	D 2 - 2	O'Hagan 11, Groves 37	
	09.10	FAT 1	A	Tiverton Town	773	D 1 - 1	O'Hagan 49[p]	
	12.10	FAT 1 R	H	TIVERTON TOWN	490	D 2 - 2	Groves 28, Sullivan 79	Lost 3-5 after pens
11	16.10	DM P	H	CLEVEDON TOWN	502	W 2 - 1	Pickard 39, O'Hagan 82	
12	23.10	DM P	A	Tamworth	687	D 1 - 1	Coates 90	
13	26.10	DM P	A	Bath City	1365	D 1 - 1	Pickard 1	
14	06.11	DM P	A	Boston United	1164	L 0 - 3		
	16.11	Lg Cup 1	A	Weymouth	842	W 2 - 1	O'Hagan 1, Sullivan 25	
15	20.11	DM P	H	SALISBURY CITY	626	D 4 - 4	O'Hagan 11 77, Harris 68, Sullivan 69	
16	27.11	DM P	A	King's Lynn	631	L 1 - 4	Harris 1	
17	04.12	DM P	A	Crawley Town	588	L 1 - 3	Pickard 68	
	07.12	LC 2	A	Havant & Waterlooville	150	L 3 - 4	McDonald 5[og], Harris 20, Sullivan 150	
18	18.12	DM P	A	Grantham Town	242	W 2 - 0	O'Hagan 23, Sullivan 56	
19	27.12	DM P	H	WEYMOUTH	2877	L 0 - 1		
20	03.01	DM P	A	Havant & Waterlooville	490	W 2 - 1	Wakefield 25[og], Alsford 88	
21	08.01	DM P	H	MARGATE	524	W 1 - 0	O'Hagan 27	
22	15.01	DM P	A	Salisbury City	557	L 1 - 1	McClean 90	
23	22.01	DM P	A	Rothwell Town	201	W 4 - 1	O'Hagan 16 49, Smeathers 80[og], Sigher 88	
24	29.01	DM P	H	GLOUCESTER CITY	574	L 1 - 2	O'Hagan 12	
25	05.02	DM P	H	ILKESTON TOWN	519	D 1 - 1	Sullivan 39	
26	12.02	DM P	A	Burton Albion	931	L 0 - 5		
27	19.02	DM P	H	KING'S LYNN	457	L 3 - 4	Pickard 55, Dean 64, Groves 78	
28	23.02	DM P	A	Newport County	555	L 1 - 1	McLean 49	
29	26.02	DM P	H	ROTHWELL TOWN	485	D 0 - 0		
30	04.03	DM P	H	NEWPORT COUNTY	503	L 1 - 2	O'Hagan 26	
31	07.03	DM P	H	CAMBRIDGE CITY	357	L 1 - 2	Dean 51	
32	11.03	DM P	A	Atherstone United	205	D 1 - 1	Groves 45	
33	14.03	DM P	H	MERTHYR TYDFIL	405	D 0 - 0		
34	18.03	DM P	H	CRAWLEY TOWN	503	L 0 - 2		
35	25.03	DM P	H	TAMWORTH	531	W 2 - 1	Waugh 34, Pickard 35	
36	01.04	DM P	A	Margate	503	D 1 - 1	Ghazaghi 85	
37	08.04	DM P	H	GRANTHAM TOWN	554	L 0 - 1		
38	22.04	DM P	H	HAVANT & WATRELOOVILLE	676	W 4 - 1	O'Hagan 21, Coates 22, Pickard 85, Sullivan 89	
39	24.04	DM P	A	Clevedon Town	337	L 1 - 2	O'Hagan 44	
40	29.04	DM P	A	Worcester City	802	D 4 - 4	Pickard 21, 44, Waugh 35, Sullivan 75 (p)	
41	01.05	DM P	A	Cambridge City	410	W 1 - 0	Dean 42	
42	06.05	DM P	H	BOSTON UNITED	904	L 3 - 4	Pickard 7, Sullivan 79, O'Hagan 86	

PLAYING SQUAD

GOALKEEPERS: Dean May (Weymouth), David Wells (Barry T)

DEFENDERS: Marcus Oldbury (AFC Lymington & NW), Mark Morrris (Hastings T), Chris Ferrett (Salisbury C), Simon Radcliffe (Bridport), Michael White (Wimborne T), Jon Nicholls (Torquay), Mark Jermyn (Torquay), Jason McIvor (Portland U)

MIDFIELDERS: Matty Holmes (Charlton), Matt Lonnen (Youth), Jamie Patterson (Weymouth), Rob Murray (Richmond Kickers (USA))

FORWARDS: **Owen Pickard** (Yeovil T), Danny O'Hagan (Weston-S-Mare), Andy Harris (Weymouth), Peter Knox (Bridport), Matthew Groves (Bournemouth)

FISHER ATHLETIC (LONDON)

CLUB OFFICIALS

Chairman: **Chris Georgiou**
Vice Chairman: **Dave Wilding**
Secretary: **John Leyden** c/o Club
General Manager: **Cheryl Stepton**

FOOTBALL MANAGEMENT TEAM
Manager: Alan Walker
Coach: Chris Hiscock
Physio: Joe Miller

FACT FILE

Formed: 1908
Nickname: The Fish
Sponsors:
Colours: Black & white stripes/white/white
Change colours: Blue/white/white
Midweek matchday: Tuesday
Reserves' League: Suburban Premier
99-00- Captain: Lloyd Hume
P.o.Y.: Sam Tydeman
Top scorer: Steve Portway

Fisher Athletic
(LONDON) FOOTBALL CLUB

OFFICIAL PROGRAMME

SEASON 1999/2000

FOOTBALL LEAGUE
— EASTERN DIVISION —
FLEET TOWN FC
Saturday 6th November 1999 · Kick Off 3.00pm

Pages: 40   Price: £1.50
Editor: Cheryl Stepton
Local Press: Southwark News,
South London Press
Local Radio: Capital & Capital Gold

| **GROUND** | The Surrey Docks Stadium, Salter Road, London SE16 1LQ |
| | 15 mins from Canada Water (tube)Tel: 0207 231 5144 Fax:0207 2520060 |

Directions: 8 minutes walk from Rotherhithe (tube).
2 miles from London Bridge (main line). Buses 381,225

Capacity: 5,300   Cover: 4,283   Seats: 400   Floodlights: Yes
Clubhouse: None   Club Shop: None

PREVIOUS   **Leagues:** Parthenon, West Kent, Kent Amateur, London Spartan 76-82, Southern 82-87, GMV Conference 87-91
Names: Fisher Athletic 08-93, Fisher`93 93-96   **Ground:** London Road, Mitcham

CLUB RECORDS **Attendance:** 4,283 v Barnet, GMV Conference 4/5/91
Win: 7-0 v Lewes Sept 95, FA Cup   **Defeat:** 0-6 v Salisbury, 21/8/93
Career Goalscorer: Paul Shinners 205   **Career Appearances:** Dennis Sharp 720
Transfer fee paid: £2,500 for Ben Taylor (Sittingbourne)
Transfer fee received: £45,000 for Paul Gorman (Charlton 1991)

BEST SEASON **FA Cup:** 1st Rd 84-85 (0-1 at home to Bristol City), 88-89 (0-4 at BristolRovers)
FA Trophy: Third Round replay 87-88 **FA Vase:** Second Round replay 82-83   **FA Amateur Cup:**

HONOURS   Southern Lg 86-87 (R-up 83-84, Southern Div 82-83, Lg Cp 84-85, Championship Cup 87-88, Merit Cup), London Spartan Lg
80-81 81-82 (R-up 78-79, Senior Div77-78, Div 2 R-up 76-77), Parthenon Lg 61-62 (Lg Cup 63-64 65-66), Kent AmateurLg 73-
74 74-75 (R-up 72-73),Kent Intermediate 97-98.98-99 London Senior Cup 84-85 87-88 88-89, LondonIntermediate Cup 59-60
(R-up 75-76), Kent Senior Cp 83-84, Kent Senior Trophy 81-82 82-83, Surrey Inter Cup 61-62,Southern Lg. Eastern Div 99-00

Players progressing: John Bumstead (Chelsea), Trevor Aylott (Bournemouth), Paul Shinners (Orient 84), Dave Regis (Notts Co. - via Barnet),
Paul Gorman(Charlton 91), Sean Devine (Barnet via Okonia Nicossia), George Barry (LeytonOrient),
Dean Martin (West Ham Utd), Jason Lee (Charlton), Ken Charlery (Barnet), Steve Watts (Leyton Orient)

Back Row: Peter Overton, Sam Tydeman, Bryn Charles, Mo Munden, Karl Shuttlewood, Hamid Barr.
Front: Leroy Huggins, Ray Powell, Mark Newson, Lloyd Hume, Jamie Beer, Ryan Robinson.   Photo: Mark Sandom

Match Facts 1999-00

	Date	Comp.	H/A	Opponents	Result		Goalscorers
1	14.08	DM E	H	Dartford	W	4-0	Charles 2, Portway, McEntegart
2	18.08	DM E	A	St. Leonards	D	1-1	McEntegart
	21.08	FAC Pre	A	Raynes Park Vale	W	*2-1	OG, Aris
3	28.08	DM E	A	V S Rugby	D	1-1	McEntegart
4	30.08	DM E	H	Burnham	W	3-0	Saunders, Gamble, Walker
	04.09	FAC 1Q	A	Ashford Town	W	2-0	Gamble, Charles
5	11.09	DM E	H	Newport I.o.W.	L	0-1	
6	14.09	DM E	A	Folkestone Invicta	L	0-1	
	18.09	FAC 2Q	A	Gravesend & Northfleet	D	1-1	Newson
	21.09	FAC 2Q R	H	Gravesend & Northfleet	W	2-1	Gamble, Gordon
7	25.09	DM E	A	Bashley	W	5-2	Charles 2, Gamble, Boniface, Walker
8	28.09	DM E	H	Chelmsford City	D	1-1	Charles
	02.10	FAC 3Q	H	Aldershot Town	L	1-2	McEntegart
	05.10	London Chal. C	A	Uxbridge	L	0-3	
	09.10	FAT 1	H	Burnham	L	1-3	Charles
9	16.10	DM E	A	Spalding United	W	2-1	Charles, Newson
10	23.10	DM E	H	Stamford	W	6-0	Barr 3, Turner, Portway, Gamble
11	26.10	DM E	H	St Leonards	W	3-1	Charles, Portway, Tydeman
12	30.10	DM E	A	Witney Town	W	5-2	Portway 2, Dolby, Newson, McEntegart
	02.11	Kent SC 1	A	Bromley	W	1-0	Barr
13	06.11	DM E	H	Fleet Town	W	3-0	McEntegart, Newson, Barr
14	09.11	DM E	A	Burnham	L	1-2	Charles
15	13.11	DM E	A	Baldock Town	W	4-3	Portway 4
	16.11	LC 1	A	Folkestone Invicta	W	2-0	Dolby, Barr
16	20.11	DM E	H	Bashley	W	2-1	Dolby, Charles
17	30.11	DM E	A	Sittingbourne	W	1-0	Charles
18	04.12	DM E	A	Raunds Town	W	1-0	Barr
19	11.12	DM E	H	Spalding United	D	0-0	
20	18.12	DM E	A	Hastings Town	L	2-3	Newson, Barr
21	27.12	DM E	A	Erith & Belvedere	W	2-0	Overton, Charles
22	03.01	DM E	H	Witney Town	W	5-0	Charles 2, Portway, Dolby, Powell
23	08.01	DM E	A	Ashford Town	W	3-1	Portway 2, Barr
	11.01	LC 2	H	Newport I.o.W.	L	1-5	Portway
24	15.01	DM E	H	Corby Town	W	2-0	Portway 2
25	22.01	DM E	H	Baldock Town	W	4-1	Charles 2, Portway 2
26	29.01	DM E	A	Tonbridge Angels	W	1-0	Barr
	01.02	Kent SC 2	A	Gravesend & Northfleet	L	0-4	
27	05.02	DM E	A	Corby Town	W	2-1	Newson, Barr
28	19.02	DM E	H	Erith & Belvedere	W	4-2	Pearson, Newson, Charles, Portway
29	22.02	DM E	H	Folkestone Invicta	D	2-2	Portway, Barr
30	26.02	DM E	A	Dartford	W	3-0	Portway 2, Barr
31	04.03	DM E	H	Tonbridge Angels	L	0-2	
32	11.03	DM E	H	V S Rugby	W	3-2	Dolby, Portway, Turner
33	18.03	DM E	H	Ashford Town	W	3-0	Barr 3
34	25.03	DM E	A	Wisbech Town	L	2-4	Portway, Barr
35	01.04	DM E	A	Fleet Town	W	5-0	Powell 4, OG
36	08.04	DM E	H	Hastings Town	W	4-2	Beer, Charles, Portway, Barr
37	15.04	DM E	A	Stamford	W	4-1	Portway 2, Tydeman 2
38	19.04	DM E	H	Raunds Town	W	3-0	Dolby, Hume, Gamble
39	22.04	DM E	H	Sittingbourne	W	3-0	Charles 2, Hume
40	24.04	DM E	A	Chelmsford City	W	2-1	Powell, Barr
41	29.04	DM E	H	Wisbech Town	W	3-1	Portway 2, Hume (p)
42	06.05	DM E	A	Newport I.o.W.	W	2-0	Overton 2

PLAYING SQUAD

GOALKEEPERS: Maurice Munden (Deal T)

DEFENDERS: **Mark Newson** (Gravesend), Steve Aris (Millwall), Ben Taylor (Sittingbourne), Karl Shuttlewood (Bishop's Stortford), Lloyd Hume (Sittingbourne), Terry Cohen (Youth), Tony Dolby (Gravesend), Scott Saunders (Sittingbourne), Ricky Pearson (Sittingbourne), Matthew Ball (Hastings T)

MIDFIELDERS: Sam Tydeman (Sittingbourne), Jamie Beer (Hayes), Hamid Barr (Crockenhill), Bradley Gamble (Welling U), Adam Young (Youth), Sean McEntaggart (Crawley T), Peter Overton (Sheppey U), Paul Manning (Havant & W)

FORWARDS: Bryn Charles (Fleet T), Darren Adams (Hampton & R), Ray Powell (Welling U), Stewart Boniface (Sittingbourne)

487

FOLKESTONE INVICTA

CLUB OFFICIALS

Chairman: **Bob Dix**

President: **Bill Hewson**

Secretary: **Frank Clarke**
c/o Football club

FOOTBALL MANAGEMENT TEAM

Manager: Neil Cugley
Asst Manager: Dave Williams
Physio: Frank Clarke

FACT FILE

Founded: 1936

Sponsors: Eurotunnel(Le Shuttle)
Colours: Amber & black stripes/black/amber
Change Colours:white/blue/white
Midweek matchday: Tuesday
Reserve's League: Winstonlead Kent Div 1

WITNEY TOWN
Dr. Martens League Eastern Division
Saturday April 29th 2000 – Kick Off 3.00pm
Today's Match Sponsored by:
JOHN COLBERT
Match Ball Sponsored by:
BARKAWAY, SLEE & ASSOCIATES   No. 32

EURO TUNNEL   SILVER SPRING

GROUND   The New Pavilion, Cheriton Road, Folkestine, Kent CT20 5JU
Tel: 01303 257461

Pages: 60 Price: £1
Editor: Richard Morrell (01303 276517)

Directions: On the A20 behind Safeway foodstore, midway between Folkestone Central & West BR stations

Capacity: 6,500   Seats: 900   Cover: 3,500   Floodlights: Yes

Local Press: Folkstone Herald
Local Radio: Neptune Radio, Radio Light

Clubhouse: Yes, Stripes Club & Invicta Club
Club Shop: Yes

PREVIOUS   **Ground:** South Rd, Hythe (pre-1991). Kent County Lg matches were played on council pitches
Leagues: Kent County (pre-1991-98)   **Name:**

CLUB RECORDS **Attendance:** 2,332 v West Ham Utd Friendly Nov 96
Ground Record: 7,881 Folkestone Town v Margate, Kent Snr.Cup 1958
Win: 9-0 v Crockenhill WHL Div 1   **Defeat:** 0-7 v Crockenhill WHL Div 1

BEST SEASON   **FA Vase:** Last sixteen 97-98
FA Cup: 2nd Qual Rd 95-96   Leagues Clubs Defeated: None

HONOURS   (since joining Winstonlead Kent League) Kent Lge R-up 97-98, Kent Senior Trophy R-Up 93-94, 94-95,98-99,99-00
Dr.Martens League ,Eastern Division Runners-up: 99-00

Back Row: Paul Fisk (Res. Manager), Brian Pearce (Co. Secretary)), Tom Brazier, Tom Parkes, Andy Morris, Dick Curner (Dir.), Frank Clarke (Physio). **Middle:** Bill Hewson (President), Roy Guiver, Lee Palmer, Nicky Dent, Dave Wietecha, Steve Lawrence, John Ayling, Andy Larkin, Brian Merryman (Dir.). **Front:** Ian Hayes, Paul Chamber, Billy Manual, Neil Cugley (Manager), Brett Smith, Richard Pousford, Jeff Ross. Mascot

Match Facts 1999-00

	Date	Comp.	H/A	Opponents	Att.	Result		Goalscorers
1	14.08	DM E	H	Wisbech Town	405	W	3-1	Dent 3
	21.08	FAC Pre	H	Croydon Athletic	277	W	4-2	Manuel, Dent, Ayling 2
2	28.08	DM E	H	Bashley	374	W	4-0	Ayling, Lawrence, Ross, Everitt
3	30.08	DM E	A	St Leonards	374	W	2-1	Ponsford, Ayling
	04.09	FAC 1Q	H	Ramsgate	335	L	1-3	Dent
4	11.09	DM E	A	Baldock Town	126	W	6-1	Ayling 3, A Morris 2, Ponsford
5	14.09	DM E	H	Fisher Athletic London	324	W	1-0	Ross
6	25.09	DM E	A	Chelmsford City	628	L	1-5	Ayling
7	28.09	DM E	H	Ashford Town	715	D	1-1	Ponsford
8	02.10	DM E	A	Erith & Belvedere	145	W	2-1	Lawrence, Ponsford
9	04.10	DM E	A	Dartford	219	W	3-1	Manning, Dent, OG
10	09.10	DM E	A	V S Rugby	300	L	1-2	Ponsford
11	16.10	DM E	H	Raunds Town	387	W	3-0	Dent 2, Ponsford
12	23.10	DM E	A	Witney Town	150	W	3-0	Ponsford, Lawrence, Summers
13	30.10	DM E	H	Spalding United	387	W	5-0	Ponsford, Lawrence, Ayling, Godden, OG
14	06.11	DM E	A	Tonbridge Angels	482	W	4-1	Dent 2, Smith, Ayling
15	09.11	DM E	H	St. Leonards	392	W	4-1	Dent 3, Smith
16	14.11	DM E	A	Newport I.o.W.	470	L	0-3	
	16.11	LC 1	H	Fisher Athletic London	197	L	0-2	
17	20.11	DM E	H	Corby Town	374	D	0-0	
	27.11	FAT 1	H	Kingstonian	727	L	0-1	
18	04.12	DM E	A	Burnham	121	W	2-1	White, Dryden
19	18.12	DM E	H	Fleet Town	335	W	2-0	Lawrence, Dryden
20	27.12	DM E	A	Ashford Town	1235	W	3-1	Dent 2, Chambers
21	03.01	DM E	H	Sittingbourne	545	W	3-2	Dent 2, Chambers
22	08.01	DM E	A	Corby Town	120	W	1-0	Lawrence
23	22.01	DM E	H	Tonbridge Angels	445	W	3-0	Dent 2, OG
	25.01	Kent SC 3	A	Margate	307	W	3-2	Dent 2, Dryden
24	29.01	DM E	H	Chelmsford City	487	D	1-1	Dent
25	05.02	DM E	A	Stamford	151	D	1-1	Dent
26	12.02	DM E	A	Hastings Town	710	W	1-0	Lawrence
27	19.02	DM E	H	Burnham	374	W	4-1	A Morris, Ayling, Lawrence, Ross
28	22.02	DM E	A	Fisher Athletic London	349	D	2-2	Ayling, A Morris
29	26.02	DM E	H	Fleet Town	85	W	5-0	Dent, Ayling, Ross 2, Ponsford
	29.02	K SC SF	A	Dover Athletic	458	W	4-1	Dent 2, Dryden 2
30	04.03	DM E	H	Stamford	427	L	2-4	Dryden 2
31	11.03	DM E	H	Newport I.o.W.	621	W	2-1	Dryden, Ayling
32	18.03	DM E	H	Raunds Town	121	D	0-0	
33	21.03	DM E	H	Dartford	467	W	4-1	Manuel, Lawrence, Ayling, OG
34	25.03	DM E	A	Bashley	132	W	3-0	Dent 2, Ross
35	28.03	DM E	H	Hastings Town	529	W	3-0	White, Chambers, Ayling
36	01.04	DM E	H	Baldock Town	527	D	1-1	Dent
37	08.04	DM E	A	Spalding United	260	W	1-0	Dent
38	15.04	DM E	H	V S Rugby	491	W	6-1	Wynter, Chambers, Lawrence 2, Dryden
39	22.04	DM E	H	Erith & belvedere	672	L	1-2	Chambers
40	24.04	DM E	A	Sittingbourne	445	W	2-1	Hayes, Ayling
41	29.04	DM E	H	Witney Town	452	W	2-0	Palmer, Lawrence
	01.05	K SC Final	A	Gravesend & Northfleet	880	L	0-3	
42	06.05	DM E	A	Wisbech Town	334	W	3-1	Chambers, Dryden, White

PLAYING SQUAD

GOALKEEPERS: Dave Wietecha (Tonbridge)

DEFENDERS: Richard Ponsford (Margate), Ian Hayes (Hythe U), Scott Daniels (Dover Ath), Lee Palmer (Dover Ath), Andy Morris (Ashford T), Andy Larkin (Hastings T)

MIDFIELDERS: Billy Manuel (Barnet), Stuart White (Ashford T), Mike Everitt (Youth), Paul Chambers (Ashford T), James Dryden (Youth), Brett Smith (Hastings T)

FORWARDS: Steve Lawrence (Dover Ath), Jeff Ross (Ashford T), Nicky Dent (Hastings T), Jon Ayling (Youth), Roy Guiver (Youth)

HALESOWEN TOWN

CLUB OFFICIALS
Chairman: **Ron Moseley**
President: **Laurence Wood**
Vice Chairman: **Nigel Pitt**
Secretary: **Stewart Tildesley**
83 Bloomfield Street, Halesowen B63 3RF
Tel: 0121 5508443(H) 07710 434708(M)
Commercial Manager: **Nigel Pitt**
Press Officer: **Paul Floud** (0121 550 8999)

FOOTBALL MANAGEMENT TEAM
Manager: John Chambers
A sst Manager: Alan Moore
Physio: Jeff Jones

FACT FILE
Formed: 1873 Nickname: Yeltz
Sponsors: Hamer Ford
Newsline: 0930 555818
Colours: Yellow and Black
Change colours: All Blue & White trim
Midweek home matchday:Tuesday
Reserve's League: None
99-00- Captain: Phillip Wood
P.o.Y.:Daniel McDonnell
Top Scorers:Richard Crisp,Clinton
Thomas(10)

GROUND   The Grove, Old Hawne Lane, Halesowen, West Midlands B63 3TB
FAX No: 0121 602 0123 Tel No: 0121 550 2179

Directions: M5 jct 3, A456 (signed Kidderminster) to 1st island turn right (signed A459 Dudley), left at next island (signed A458 Stourbridge), at next island take 3rd left into Grammar School Lane, then Old Hawne Lane - ground 400 yds on left
Capacity: 5,000   Cover: 1,499   Seats: 499   Floodlights: Yes
Clubhouse: (0121 602 2210) 12-2.30 & 7-11 (10.30 Sun) pm daily.Cold snacks served.
Club Shop: Sells replica strips, T-shirts, waterproof tops, coats, scarves, programmes, badges etc

Pages: 44 Price: £1.20p Editor: R Pepper
Local Press: Sports Argus, Express & Star,
Birmingham Mail, Halesowen News,
Stourbridge & Halesowen Chronicle
Local Radio: BBC West Midlands,
B.R.M.B., Beacon

PREVIOUS   **Leagues:** West Mids 1892-1905 06-11 46-86, Birmingham Comb. 11-39

CLUB RECORDS **Attendance:** 5,000 v Hendon F.A. Cup 1st Rd Proper 1954, (18,234 v Southall,1986 FA Vase Final at Wembley)
Goalscorer: Paul Joinson 369   **Appearances:** Paul Joinson 608
Win: 13-1 v Coventry Amateurs, Birmingham Senior Cup, 1956
Defeat: 0-8 v Bilston, West Midlands League, 7/4/62
Fee Paid: £7,250 for Stuart Evans (Gresley 1996)
Fee Received: £40,000 for Jim Rodwell (Rushden & Diamonds 96)

BEST SEASON   **FA Vase:** Winners 84-85, 85-86 R-up 82-83   **FA Trophy:** 3rd Round Proper 94-95
FA Cup: 1st Rd 9 times: 54-55 then each season from 84-85 to 91-92

HONOURS   Southern Lg Premier Div R-up 96, Southern Lg Midland Div 89-90, W Mids Lg(5) 46-47 82-85 85-86 (R-up 64-65, Lg Cup 82-83 84-85),B'ham Snr Cup 83-84,97-98 (R-up 51-52 67-68), Staffs Snr Cup 88-89 (R-up 83-84), FA Vase (2) 84-86 (R-up 82-3)
Worcs Snr Cup 51-52 61-62 (R-up 87-88), Midland Comb. Res Div 89-90

Players progressing: Arthur Proudler (Aston Villa), Cyril Spiers (Aston Villa), Billy Morris (Wolves), Dean Spink (Aston Villa), Stuart Cash (Nottm Forest), Andrew Pearce, Tim Clarke & Sean Flynn (Coventry), Dean Stokes (Port Vale), Frank Bennett (Southampton), Julian Alsop (Bristol Rovers)

Back Row: Jeff Jones (Physio), Matthew Gardiner, Neil Smith, Ross Collins, Wayne Lloyd, Jason Owen, Daniel McDonnell, Phillip Wood, Clinton Thomas, Scott Gennard, Gary Piggott, Alan Moore (Asst. Manager), John Chambers (Manager). **Front:** Ryan Robinson-Little (Kit Boy), Paul Birch, Ashley Brown, Richard Crisp, Neil Cartwright, Adrian Cooper, Ian Aldridge, Darren Wright, Stuart Payne.

Match Facts 1999-00

	Date	Comp.	H/A	Opponents	Att.	Result	Goalscorers
1	14.08	DM P	H	DORCHESTER TOWN	606	L 0 - 1	
2	16.08	DM P	A	Ilkeston Town	715	D 0 - 0	
3	21.08	DM P	A	Salisbury City	391	L 0 - 2	
4	24.08	DM P	H	GRANTHAM TOWN	422	W 2 - 1	Rowland 57, Dennison 90
5	28.08	DM P	H	WEYMOUTH	477	D 0 - 0	
6	30.08	DM P	A	Rothwell Town	291	D 2 - 2	Rowlands 52, Cooper 71
7	04.09	DM P	H	CAMBRIDGE CITY	433	L 1 - 2	Cooper 15
8	06.09	DM P	A	Atherstone United	419	W 5 - 4	Brown 12 17, Cooper 18, Crisp 47 72
9	11.09	DM P	H	BOSTON UNITED	465	D 1 - 1	Crisp 68[p]
	18.09	FAC Q2	A	Oadby Town	259	L 1 - 2	Rowland 20
10	25.09	DM P	H	MARGATE	449	L 0 - 3	
11	02.10	DM P	A	Dorchester Town	506	D 2 - 2	Wright 49, Payne 72
	09.10	FAT 1	A	Bromsgrove Rovers	517	W 5 - 2	Crisp 3, Thomas 13, 89, Rowland 46, Ulfig 81[og]
12	23.10	DM P	H	CRAWLEY TOWN	425	W 1 - 0	Payne 82
13	26.10	DM P	H	ILKESTON TOWN	443	W 3 - 0	Thomas 31 68, D Wright 75
14	30.10	DM P	A	Newport County	753	D 0 - 0	
15	06.11	DM P	H	CLEVEDON TOWN	460	W 3 - 0	Gardiner 12, Wright 36 58
16	09.11	DM P	A	Grantham Town	274	L 0 - 1	
17	13.11	DM P	A	Merthyr Tydfil	652	L 0 - 1	
	16.11	Lg Cup 1	A	Evesham United	123	W 2 - 1	Collins 65 90
18	20.11	DM P	H	WORCESTER CITY	708	W 2 - 1	Crisp 7[p] 70
	27.11	FAT 2	H	SUTTON COLDFIELD TOWN	375	W 3 - 1	Smith 21, Birch 60 72
19	04.12	DM P	A	Weymouth	647	D 0 - 0	
	07.12	LC 2	A	Burton Albion	233	L 2 - 3	Birch 40, Payne 87
20	18.12	DM P	H	KING'S LYNN	472	D 0 - 0	
	21.12	Birm. SC 2	A	Boldmere St Michaels		D 0 - 0	
21	27.12	DM P	H	BURTON ALBION	1084	W 2 - 1	Davies 18[og], Cooper 32
22	03.01	DM P	A	Gloucester City	562	D 2 - 2	Cooper 45, Payne 56
23	08.01	DM P	H	TAMWORTH	903	L 0 - 3	
	11.01	Birm. SC 2R	A	Boldmere St Michaels	152	L 1 - 2	Payne 82
	15.01	FAT 3	A	Doncaster Rovers	2102	D 1 - 1	Olney 54
	18.01	FAT 3R	H	DONCASTER ROVERS	724	L 2 - 3	Wright 69, Crisp 100
24	22.01	DM P	A	Havant & Waterlooville	402	L 1 - 2	Payne 44
25	29.01	DM P	A	Clevedon Town	389	D 0 - 0	
26	05.02	DM P	H	NEWPORT COUNTY	603	W 2 - 0	Crisp 40[p], Payne 47
	09.02	WSC QF	A	Solihull Borough	107	L 0 - 1	
27	12.02	DM P	H	MERTHYR TYDFIL	578	L 0 - 1	
28	19.02	DM P	A	Boston United	1614	L 1 - 4	Cooper 80
29	04.03	DM P	H	BATH CITY	546	L 0 - 3	
30	06.03	DM P	A	Worcester City	1069	D 0 - 0	
31	11.03	DM P	A	Crawley Town	706	D 2 - 2	Thomas 18 66
32	14.03	DM P	H	ATHERSTONE UNITED	356	L 0 - 1	
33	25.03	DM P	H	SALISBURY CITY	353	W 3 - 1	Crisp 55, 76(p), Aldridge 61
34	28.03	DM P	A	Bath City	674	W 1-0	Aldridge 30
35	01.04	DM P	A	Tamworth	505	W 2-1	Crisp 1, Read 34
36	08.04	DM P	H	HAVANT & WATERLOOVILE	436	W 1-0	Aldrdige 8
37	10.04	DM P	A	Cambridge City	328	D 1-1	Thomas 39
38	15.04	DM P	A	King's Lynn	518	L 0-1	
39	22.04	DM P	H	GLOUCESTER CITY	452	W 4-2	Reed 43, OG (Thorne) 50, Thomas 78, Owen 88
40	24.04	DM P	A	Burton Albion	957	W 4-2	Thomas 30, 73, Birch 41, Aldridge 88
41	29.04	DM P	H	ROTHWELL TOWN	453	D 3-3	Cartwright 18, Smith 70, Aldridge 71
42	06.05	DM P	A	Margate	602	L 1-3	Crisp 45

PLAYING SQUAD

GOALKEEPERS: Andy Quy (Hereford U)

DEFENDERS: Phil Wood (Pelsall Villa), Andrew Dodd (Paget R), **Andy Comyn** (Hednesford T), Ross Collins (Youth), Les Hines (Kidderminster H), Jason Owen (Stafford R), Wayne Lloyd (Willenhall T), Jon Ford (Telford U)

MIDFIELDERS: Richard Crisp (Telford U), Craig Mansell (Weymouth), Michael Griffiths (Torquay), Neil Cartwright (Telford U), Stuart Skidmore (Youth), Scott Gennard (Stourbridge), Scitt Darroch (Stratford T)

FORWARDS: Stuart Payne (Kidderminster H), Michael Mason (Macclesfield), Craig Dutton (Sutton Coldfield T), Gary Piggott (Stafford R), Clinton Thomas (Kidderminster H), Andy Hodgetts (Evesham U)

HAVANT & WATERLOOVILLE

HAVANT & WATERLOOVILLE
Football Club

Official Match Day Programme Price £1.20

FOOTBALL LEAGUE
PREMIER DIVISION

CLUB OFFICIALS
Chairman:**Derek Pope**
President: **Arthur Saitch, Maurie Hibberd**
Vice Chairman: **Peter Dermott**
Directors: Trevor Brock, Ray Jones, John Carter,
Peter Faulkner, Sandy Peters,
Secretary: **Trevor Brock**, 2 Betula Close,
Waterlooville, Hampshire. PO7 8EJ
Tel:02392 267276

FACT FILE
Formed: 1998   Nickname: Hawks
Sponsors: Thomas Sanderson
Colours: White & yellow & navy/navy/navy
Change colours: Green
Midweek matchday: Tuesday
Reserves' League:None
99-00- Top Scorer: James Taylor (38)
P. of Y.:Gary McDonald
Captain:Liam Daish

FOOTBALL Joint Managers: Mick Jenkins & Liam Daish
MANAGEMENT TEAM   Physio: Phil Ashwell

GROUND   Westleigh Park, Martin Road, West Leigh, Havant PO9 5TH Tel: 02392 787822
Directions: Take B2149 to Havant off the A27 (B2149 Petersfield Rd if coming out of Havant).
2nd turning off dual carriageway into Bartons Road then 1st right into Martins Road.
1 mile from Havant station
Capacity: 4,000   Cover: 1,500   Seats: 290   Floodlights: Yes
Clubhouse: Open every day, lunchtime and evening. 2 bars, function suites.
Hot & cold food available   Club Shop: Sells various souvenirs & progs

Pages: 32 Price: £1
Editor: Adrian Gardiner
Local Press: News (Portsmouth)
Local Radio: Radio Victory, Radio Solent

PREVIOUS   (Havant) **Leagues:** Portsmouth 58-71; Hants 71-86; Wessex 86-91. **Names:** LeighPark; Havant & Leigh Park; Havant
Grounds: Front Lawn 1958-83   *(Waterlooville) Leagues: Waterlooville & District, Portsmouth 38-53, Hants1953-71.*
Grounds: *Convent Ground 10-30, Rowlands Avenue Recreation Ground 30-63, Jubliee Park 63-98*
CLUB RECORDS   (Havant) **Attendance:** 3,500 v Wisbech Town, FA Vase QF 85-86
Win: 10-0 three times; v Sholing Sports (H), FA Vase 4th Rd 85-86, v PortsmouthRoyal Navy (H), Wessex League 90-91; v
Poole Town, Southern Lge SouthernDiv. 94-95.   **Defeat:** 1-7 v Camberley Town (H), FA Vase 3rd Rd 88-89
Career Goalscorer: Tony Plumbley 348   **Career Appearances:** Tony Plumbley 510
Transfer fee paid: £5,750 for John Wilson (Bashley, 90)   **Received:** £7,000 for Steve Tate (Waterlooville, 1993)
(Waterlooville) Transfer fee paid: £7,000 for Steve Tate (Havant Town, 93)   **Received:** *£6,000 for Dave Boyce (Gravesend & Northfleet, 93)*
BEST SEASON   (Havant) **FA Cup:** 4thd Qual Rd 98-93 (lost on penalties at Hayes)). **FA Vase:** Qtr Final85-86 **F.A.Trophy:** 3rd Rd 98-99
(Waterlooville)   *FA Trophy: 3rd Rd 98-99 (lost 0-1 at Worcester City)*   *FA Amateur Cup: 1st Rd 59-60*
FA Cup: 1st Rd 2nd replay 83-84, 0-2 v Northampton T. (A) after two 1-1 draws
HONOURS   (Havant): FA Sunday Cup 68-69, Wessex Lg 90-91 (R-up 88-89), Hampshire Lg Div 372-73 (Div 4 71-72), Hampshire Senior
Cup Winners 93-94,94-95 R-up 91-92 Hants.Intermediate Cup, Hampshire Junior Cup, Russell Cotes Cup 91-92, PortsmouthSenior Cup 83-84
84-85 91-92, Gosport War Memorial Cup 74-75 91-92 92-93 94-95,Southern Counties Floodlit Cup R-up 91-92, Hampshire Floodlit Cup 85-
86,Portsmouth Lg*(Waterlooville): Southern Lg Div 1 Sth 71-72 (Lg Cup 86-87, R-up 82-83), HantsLg R-up 69-70 (Div 2 59-60 64-65, Div 3 (East)
R-up 53-54), Hants Snr Cup 69-7072-73 84-85 (R-up 75-76 90-91), Russell Cotes Cup 88-89, Portsmouth Lg 49-5050-51 51-52 (Div 2 46-47, Div
3 38-39), Portsmouth Snr Cup 68-69, PortsmouthVictory Cup 59-60 69-70*
Players progressing   (Havant); Bobby Tambling (Chelsea)   *(Waterlooville); Phil Figgins (Portsmouth 73), Paul Hardyman (Portsmouth 83),*
Guy Whittingham (Portsmouth via Yeovil Town 88), Paul Moody (Southampton 91)

Match Facts 1999-00

	Date	Comp.	H/A	Opponents	Att.	Result	Goalscorers
1	14.08	DM-P	H	TAMWORTH	522	L 0 - 2	
2	17.08	DM-P	A	Margate	614	D 0 - 0	
3	21.08	DM-P	A	Rothwell Town	237	D 1 - 1	Hambley 70[p]
4	24.08	DM-P	H	SALISBURY CITY	417	L 0 - 1	
5	28.08	DM-P	H	ATHERSTONE UNITED	336	D 1 - 1	Wakefield 74
6	30.08	DM-P	A	Clevedon Town	402	D 0 - 0	
7	04.09	DM-P	H	ILKESTON TOWN	394	L 2 - 3	Taylor 45, 63
8	11.09	DMP	H	GLOUCESTER CITY	374	D 1 - 1	Taylor 4
	18.09	FAC Q2	H	LANGNEY SPORTS	290	D 2 - 2	Wyatt 20, Taylor 32
	21.09	FAC Q2R	A	Langney Sports	377	L 1 - 2	Elley 39
9	25.09	DMP	A	Worcester City	804	W 3 - 0	Taylor 5, 48, Wood 57
	09.10	FAT 1	H	AYLESBURY UNITED	289	D 0 - 0	
	12.10	FAT 1 R	A	Aylesbury United	250	W 4 - 2	O'Rourke 17 19, Wakefield 44, Wyatt 89
10	16.10	DM P	A	Newport County	743	D 3 - 3	Taylor 28, 59[p], Wood 53
	19.10	Hants SC2	H	COWES SPORTS	159	L 0 - 3	
11	23.10	DM P	H	KING'S LYNN	304	D 2 - 2	Tate 13, Taylor 49
12	26.10	DM P	H	MARGATE	354	D 3 - 3	**Taylor 3** (67 73 84)
13	30.10	DM P	A	Grantham Town	292	L 0 - 2	
14	06.11	DM P	H	ROTHWELL TOWN	283	W 5 - 2	Taylor 23 87, Wood 44, Jones 48 83
15	09.11	DM P	A	Salisbury City	394	W 2 - 1	Taylor 27 42
16	13.11	DM P	A	BURTON ALBION	492	W 6 - 0	Hamble 6, Taylor 15 46, Wyatt 73, Wood 82
	16.11	LC 1	H	BASHLEY	195	W 5 - 1	Wood 28, Wyatt 55, **Taylor 3** (65 78 84)
	27.11	FAT 2	A	Rushden & Diamonds	1,635	L 0 - 1	
17	04.12	DM P	H	CAMBRIDGE CITY	378	W 3 - 1	Hamble 61, Taylor 78[p], Wood 89
	07.12	LC 2	H	DORCHESTER TOWN	150	W 4 - 3	Wood 59, Taylor 69 120, Daish 116
18	11.12	DM P	A	Tamworth	480	L 0 - 5	
19	18.12	DM P	H	NEWPORT COUNTY	372	D 2 - 2	Jones 10, Wood 36
20	27.12	DM P	A	Crawley Town	1132	W 3 - 2	Wakefield 36, Woods 43 80[p]
21	03.01	DM P	H	DORCHESTER TOWN	490	L 1 - 2	Wood 4
22	08.01	DM P	A	Merthyr Tydfil	655	W 2 - 0	Hambley 57, Taylor 88
23	15.01	DM P	A	Ilkeston Town	527	L 1 - 2	Taylor 29
24	18.01	DM P	H	CLEVEDON TOWN	344	L 1 - 2	Taylor 89
25	22.01	DM P	H	HALESOWEN TOWN	402	W 2 - 1	Wakefield 5, Wyatt 32
	25.01	LC 3	H	WITNEY TOWN	144	W 3 - 1	**Taylor 3** (37 43 44)
26	29.01	DM P	A	King's Lynn	720	W 1 - 0	Hambley 7
	01.02	SCCFC 2 (1)	H	FARNHAM TOWN	193	W 2 - 0	Taylor 73, Hambley 77
27	05.02	DM P	H	WEYMOUTH	583	L 1 - 2	Wyatt 5
28	12.02	DM P	A	Boston United	1514	L 2 - 4	Taylor 2, McDonald 45
	15.02	SCCFC 2 (2)	A	Farnham Town	103	D 4 - 4	Wood 1 21, Osborne 71, Wyatt 89
29	19.02	DM P	H	WORCESTER CITY	448	W 1 - 0	Jones 35
	22.02	LC QF	A	Bath City	432	W 1 - 0	Cook 84
30	26.02	DM P	A	Bath City	1056	D 1 - 1	McDonald 9
31	04.03	DM P	A	Weymouth	734	D 2 - 2	Wood 58, Elley 88
	07.03	LC SF	A	Hastings Town	339	L 2 - 4	J O'Rourke 35, Milkins 66
32	11.03	DM P	H	BOSTON UNITED	675	D 3 - 3	Jones 47, Milkins 51, Hambley 79
	14.03	SCCFC SF1	A	Chipstead		L 1 - 2	
33	18.03	DM P	A	Cambridge City	444	L 1 - 4	Jones 31
34	21.03	DM P	A	Burton Albion	779	L 0 - 3	
35	25.03	DM P	A	Gloucester City	426	D 1 - 1	Taylor 22
	28.03	SCCC SF2	H	CHIPSTEAD	158	W 3 - 1	Taylor 13, 29, Wakefield 67
36	01.04	DM P	H	MERTHYR TYDFIL	399	L 1 - 2	Wakefield 85
37	08.04	DM P	A	Halesowen Town	436	L 0 - 1	
38	15.04	DM P	H	BATH CITY	430	L 1 - 2	Wood 45 (p)
39	22.04	DM P	A	Dorchester Town	676	L 1 - 4	Hambley 57
40	24.04	DM P	H	CRAWLEY TOWN	512	W 1 - 0	Wood 49 (p)
41	29.04	DM P	H	GRANTHAM TOWN	670	W 1 - 0	O'Rourke 20
42	06.05	DM P	A	Atherstone United	147	W 1 - 0	Holbrook 6

PLAYING SQUAD

GOALKEEPERS: Paul Nicholls (Chelsea)

DEFENDERS: Liam Daish (Coventry), Alec Masson (Bognor Regis T), Aaron Cook (Swansea), Ben Price (Portsmouth), Shaun Gale (Exeter), Matt Jones (BAT), Gary Connolly (Portsmouth)

MIDFIELDERS: Tim Hambley (Fisher Ath), Neil Champion (Aldershot T), Gary McDonald (Portsmouth), Craig Anstey (Waterlooville), Jamie O'Rourke (Ryde Sports), Deal Blake (Southampton)

FORWARDS: Paul Wood (Happy Valley (HK)), Dave Wakefield (Portsmouth), James Taylor (Bashley), **David Leworthy** (Kingstonian), Nicky Wyatt (Newport IOW)

ILKESTON TOWN

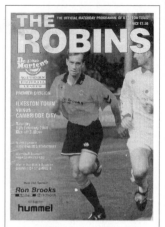

CLUB OFFICIALS
Chairman: **Paul Millership**
President: **Robert Lindsay**
Secretary: **Neil Crofts,**
325 Over Lane, Belp[er,Derbys DE56 0HJ
Tel No: 01773 880611 (H)
0385 307936 (M)
Commercial Management:
J Sports Promotions Ltd

FOOTBALL MANAGEMENT TEAM

Manager / Coach: Keith Alexander
Asst Manager: Gary Simpson

FACT FILE

Re Formed: 1945
Nickname: The Robins
Sponsors: Ron Brooks Ilkeston Toyota
Colours: Red/black/red
Change colours: All purple
Midweek matchday: Monday
Reserves' League: Midland Comb

Pages: 32   Price: £1
Editors: Mic Capill, J Shiels, D Payne

GROUND   New Manor Ground, Awsworth Rd, Ilkeston Tel: 0115 932 4094

Directions: M42 to M1 junc 23A, continue on M1 to junc 26, exit left onto A610 towards Ripley, take 1st exit signed Awsworth and Ilkeston (A6096), follow bypass signed Ilkeston A6096. Turn right after 1/2 mile signed Cotmanhay. Ground 200 yards on left

Capacity: 3,500   Seats: 270   Cover: 1,100   Floodlights: Yes

Clubhouse: Open Wed-Fri 7-11pm, Sat-Sun noon-3 & 7-11pm, and Mon or Tue if there is a match. Snacks behind bar. Large tea bar open matchdays 2-5pm (6.30-9pm for night games)
Club Shop: Sells wide range of souvenirs & programmes + 'Team Talk'.
Contact Manager (0115 9305 622) or club secretary

PREVIOUS   **Leagues:** Midland 1894-1902 25-58 61-71; Notts & Derby Senior 1945-47; CentralAlliance 47-61; Midland Counties 1961-71 73-82; Southern League 1971-73; Northern Co.East 1982-86; Central Midlands 86-90; West Midlands (Regional) 90-94.
Ground: Manor Ground, Manor Rd (1945-92)

CLUB RECORDS   **Attendance:** 2,504 v Boston United FA Cup 1st Rd 15/11/97
Win: 14-2 v Codnor M.W 46-47: 13-0 v Swanwick OB 46-47
Defeat: 1-11 v Grantham T. 47-48: 0-10 v VS Rugby 85-86
Career Goalscorer: Jackie Ward 141. **Career Appearances:** Terry Swincoe 377
Season Goalscorer: Barry Jepson 62, 1952-53
Transfer fee paid: £7,500 Justin O'Reilly (Southport 1998) **Fee received:** £25,000 for Francis Green (Peterborough Utd)
BEST SEASON   **FA Cup:** 2nd Round - 1997-98 1-1, 1-2 v Scunthorpe Utd, 1999-00 0-3 (A) after 1-1 (H) v Rushden & Diamonds
FA Vase: 4th Round 88-89 1-2 v Tamworth
FA Trophy: 3rd Round 82-83 1-5 v Enfield, 94-95 2-2, 1-2 v Kidderminster H
HONOURS   Southern Lge, Midland Div 94-95, (R-up 97-98); West Mids (Regional) Lg 93-94, Lg Cup 93-94, Div 1 91-92, Lg Cup 91-92; Central Mids Lg Cup 87-88; Midland Lg 67-68 (R-up 1898-99); Midland Co Lg 67-68; Central Alliance 51-52 52-53 53-54 54-55(R-up 47-48 55-56)

Match Facts 1999-00

	Date	Comp.	H/A	Opponents	Att.	Result	Goalscorers
1	14.08	DM-P	A	Merthyr Tydfil	879	W 3 - 1	Moore 20, 55, Hurst 80
2	16.08	DM-P	H	HALESOWEN TOWN	715	D 0 - 0	
3	21.08	DM-P	H	CRAWLEY TOWN	590	W 2 - 0	Moore 33, Middleton 37
4	24.08	DM-P	A	King's Lynn	681	D 1 - 1	Moore 21
5	28.08	DM-P	A	Margate	681	L 2 - 3	Moore 65, Helliwell 90
6	30.08	DM-P	H	BOSTON UNITED	1120	W 1 - 0	Noteman 80
7	04.09	DM-P	A	Havant & Waterlooville	394	W 3 - 2	Daish 8[og], White 30, 37
8	06.09	DM-P	H	WORCESTER CITY	654	D 2 - 2	Moore 75, Noteman 82
9	11.09	DM-P	H	DORCHESTER TOWN	532	W 3 - 1	Knapper 30, Moore 37 38
	17.09	FAC Q2	A	Solihull Borough	224	W 4 - 3	White 3, Eshelby 9, Raynor 16, Moore 65
10	25.09	DM-P	A	Gloucester City	558	L 0 - 1	
	02.10	FAC Q3	A	Wingate & Finchley	275	W 5 - 0	Eshelby 16, Hemmings 36 73, Raynor 44, Middleton 62
	09.10	FAT 1	A	Burscough	183	W 6 - 2	Knapper 30[p], Fearon 41, Helliwell 53, 61, Hemmings 77, Manners 82
	16.10	FAC Q4	H	ROMFORD	780	W 3 - 0	Knapper 5[p], Hemmings 55 88
11	23.10	DM-P	H	SALISBURY CITY	539	W 6 - 0	Moore 18, 86, Fearon 43, Hemmings 44, Knapper 63[p], Helliwell 77
12	26.10	DM P	A	Halesowen Town	443	L 0 - 3	
	30.10	FAC 1	H	CARLISLE UNITED	1748	W 2 - 1	Moore 39, Raynor 62
13	06.11	DM P	H	NEWPORT COUNTY	697	W 2 - 1	Knapper 13[p], Helliwell 89
14	08.11	DM P	H	KING'S LYNN	718	W 2 - 1	Hemmings 17 43
15	13.11	DM P	A	Bath City	792	D 0 - 0	
	16.11	Lg Cup 1	A	Stamford	99	W 2 - 1	Jenkinson 85, White 95
	20.11	FAC 2	H	RUSHDEN & DIAMONDS	2737	D 1 - 1	Eshelby 18
	27.11	FAT 2	H	SCARBOROUGH	840	L 2 - 4	Knapper 83[p] 85[p]
	29.11	Derbys.SC 3	H	BORROWASH VICTORIA	240	D *1 - 1	O'Reilly 82 Won 3-0 after penalties
	30.11	FAC 2R	A	Rushden & Diamonds	4,226	L 0 - 3	
16	04.12	DM P	H	TAMWORTH	562	D 4 - 4	Hemmings 39, Moore 44, Hurst 74, Knapper 82[p]
	13.12	LC 2	H	KING'S LYNN	243	D 1 - 1	Hemmings 39 Lost 3-4 after penalties
17	18.12	DM P	A	Worcester City	717	L 1 - 2	Moore 15
18	27.12	DM P	H	GRANTHAM TOWN	908	W 5-4	Moore 3 (13 30 64), Clifford 32, O'Reilly 76
19	03.01	DM P	A	Burton Albion	2047	L 1 - 3	Hemmings 68
20	08.01	DM P	H	WEYMOUTH	606	D 2 - 2	Hurst 47, O'Reilly 82
	11.01	D SC QF	A	Belper Town	236	W 2 - 1	Hurst 45, O'Reilly 65
21	15.01	DM P	H	HAVANT & WATERLOOVILLE	527	W 2 - 1	Hemmings 63[p], Moore 67
22	19.01	DM P	A	Boston United	1467	L 2 - 3	Hemmings 23, White 79
23	22.01	DM P	H	BATH CITY	652	D 2 - 2	White 35, Moore 87
24	29.01	DM P	A	Cambridge City	572	L 2 - 3	Moore 67 90
25	05.02	DM P	A	Dorchester Town	519	D 1 - 1	Moore 8
26	19.02	DM P	H	CAMBRIDGE CITY	521	D 2 - 2	O'Reilly 68 77
	22.02	D SC SF	A	Mickleover Sports	360	W 6 - 0	Quayle 4 (8 50 59[p] 89), O'Reilly 54, Helliwell 84
27	26.02	DM P	A	Weymouth	641	L 1 - 4	Helliwell 90
28	06.03	DM P	A	Atherstone United	254	L 2 - 3	Fearon 19, O'Reilly 68
29	11.03	DM P	H	GLOUCESTER CITY	505	W 1 - 0	Knapper 7[p]
30	18.03	DM P	A	Salisbury City	352	W 2 - 1	Noteman 63, O'Reilly 77
31	20.03	DM P	A	Rothwell Town	435	D 3 - 3	Noteman 4, O'Reilly 24, Fearon 90
32	25.03	DM P	A	Newport County	604	L 1 - 2	Todd 56
33	28.03	D SC F1	A	Gresley Rovers	404	W 1 - 0	Eshelby 58
34	01.04	DM P	H	CLEVEDON TOWN	438	W 4 - 1	Knapper 38, 84 (2p), Eshelby 53, Helliwell 59
35	08.04	DM P	H	ATHERSTONE UNITED	424	W 1 - 0	Eshelby 21
	10.04	D SC F2	H	GRESLEY ROVERS	375	W 3 - 0	Todd 24, Clark 78, OG (Bluck) 89
36	22.04	DM P	H	BURTON ALBION	1061	W 4 - 1	Eshelby 7, Todd 15, 29, Helliwell 77
37	24.04	DM P	A	Grantham Town	677	L 0 - 1	
38	26.04	DM P	A	Rothwell Town	151	D 2 - 2	OG (Bullimore) 3, Helliwell 80
39	29.04	DM P	A	Crawley Town	693	D 1 - 1	Abbott 42
40	01.05	DM P	H	MARGATE	443	L 1 - 2	Wright 17
41	03.05	DM P	A	Clevedon Town	224	L 0 - 2	
42	06.05	DM P	H	MERTHYR TYDFIL	387	W 2 - 1	OG (Walker) 51, Clarke 88

PLAYING SQUAD

GOALKEEPERS: Andy Love (Grimsby)

DEFENDERS: Dean Jones (Frickley Ath), Craig Ludlam (Matlock T), Gary Middleton (Arnold T), Matt McKenzie (Grimsby), Chris Timons (Altrincham), Jamie Eaton (Eastwood T)

MIDFIELDERS: John Knapper (Eastwood T), David Poppleton (Lincoln C), Andy Todd (Eastwood T), Paul Eshelby (Alfreton T), Lee Thompson (Denaby U), Carl Wright (Ipswich)

FORWARDS: Ian Helliwell (Doncaster R), Justin O'Reilly (Southport), Andy Kiwomya (Boston U), Devon White (Shrewsbury), Glenn Kirkwod (Doncaster R)

KING'S LYNN

CLUB OFFICIALS

Chairman:**Mike Brannon**
President: **Jim Chandler**
Secretary: **Martin Davis**
158 Lynn Road, Wisbech,
Cambs PE13 3EB
Tel: 01945 583567 (H & B)
01945 588000 (FAX)

FOOTBALL MANAGEMENT TEAM

Manager:Gary Mills
Asst Man: Darren Gee
Physio: Dave Edgeley

FACT FILE

Formed: 1879
Nickname: The Linnets
Sponsors: Eastern Group
Colours: Royal Blue with gold trim/Blue/Blue
& Gold hoops
Change colours: All red
Midweek home matchday: Tuesday
Reserves League: U.C.L. Res Div 1
99-00 - Captain: D.Robinson
P.o.Y.: G.Fuff
Top scorer: David Puttnam (11)

GROUND   The Walks Stadium, Tennyson Road, King's Lynn PE30 5PB
Tel: 01553 760060
Directions: At mini r-about arriving from A10/A47 take Vancouver Avenue. Ground on left
after a half mile. Quarter mile from King's Lynn (BR), half mile from bus station
Capacity: 8,200   Cover: 5,000   Seats: 1,200   Floodlights: Yes
Clubhouse: Normal licensing hours, with extension on matchdays
Club Shop: Sells metal badges and other merchandise

Pages: 24   Price: £1.20
Editor: Secretary
Local Press: Lynn News & Advertiser,
Eastern Daily Press
Local Radio: KLFM

PREVIOUS   **Leagues:** Norfolk & Suffolk; Eastern Co.s 35-39 48-54; UCL 46-48; Midland Co.s54-58; NPL 80-83
Name: Lynn Town   **Ground:** None
CLUB RECORDS   **Attendance:** 12,937 v Exeter, FA Cup 1st Rd 50-51
Win: 17-0 v Beccles 29/30   **Defeat:** 0-11 v Aston Villa FA Cup 1905/6
Career Appearances: Mick Wright 1,152 (British Record)   **Career Goalscorer:** Malcolm Lindsay 321
Transfer Fee Paid: Shaun Keeble Wisbech 98-99   **Transfer Fee Received:** Mark Paul , Southampton.98-99
BEST SEASON   **FA Cup:** 3rd Rd 61-62 (0-4 at Everton). Competition Proper on 14 occasions; 05-06 37-38 49-50 51-52 58-63 64-65 68-69
71-72 73-74 84-85. Rd 2 97-98   **League clubs defeated:** Aldershot 59-60, Coventry 61-62, Halifax 68-69
FA Trophy: 2nd Rd 78-79   **FA Vase:** 5th Rd 94-95 (0-2 at Diss Town   **FA Amateur Cup:** R-up 1900-01
HONOURS   FA Amateur Cup R-up 1900-01, Southern Lg R-up 84-85 (Div 1 R-up 63-64), NPLPresidents Cup 82-83, Eastern Co's Lg 53-
54 (R-up 49-50 52-53 (Lg Cup 53-54),Norfolk & Suffolk Lg(8)(R-up(6)), E Anglian Lg R-up(2), Norfolk Snr Cup(19)(R-up(20), Norfolk Invitation Cup
94-95, Norfolk Premier Cup 68-69(jt) 73-74, EastAnglian Cup(4)(R-up(3), Eastern Prof Floodlit Lg 68-69, Southern Lg Midland R-up 95-96 ,U.C.L.
Reserve Division, League & Cup 'double', 99-00.

Players progressing: N Rowe (Derby 1949), B Taylor & P Ward (Bradford P. A. 54& 55), T Reynolds (Darlington 54), G Reed (Sunderland 55), P
McCall (Bristol C55), J Neal (Swindon 57), T Dryburgh (Oldham 57), J Hunter (Barrow 59), JStevens (Swindon), G Catleugh (Watford), George
Walters (Chesterfield 64), PMcNamee (Notts County 1966), W Biggins (Burnley), Jackie Gallagher(Peterborough 80), Andy Higgins (Rochdale 83),
Neil Horwood (Grimsby 86),Darren Rolph (Barnsley 87), Mark Howard (Stockport 88), Andy Hunt, MalcolmLindsay

Back Row: Mark Hurst, Shaun Keeble, Lee Wilson, Wayne Halcro, Craig Clark, Tony Marsden, Lee Gibson, Dave Taylor. **Middle:** Richard Simper
(Kit Man), Dave Puttnam, Simon Dakin, Cameron Miles, Chuck Martini, Mark Turner, Glen Fuff, Jon Palmer. **Front:** Richard Butler, Jeremy Goss,
Darren Gee (Asst. Manager), Gary Mills (Manager), Tony Spearing, Dave Robinson, Steve McGinty.   **Photo:** © Anglia Newspapers Ltd.

Match Facts 1999-00

	Date	Comp.	H/A	Opponents	Att.	Result	Goalscorers
1	14.08	DM-P	H	ATHERSTONE UNITED	829	D 1 - 1	Taylor 24
2	17.08	DM-P	A	Grantham Town	544	W 3 - 1	Wilson 8, Turner 37, Puttnam 71
3	21.08	DM-P	A	Clevedon Town	397	L 2 - 4	Wilson 15, Keeble 89
4	24.08	DM-P	H	ILKESTON TOWN	821	D 1 - 1	Robinson 89
5	28.08	DM-P	A	Worcester City	787	D 1 - 1	Puttnam 48
6	30.08	DM-P	A	Burton Albion	1,304	L 0 - 1	
7	04.09	DM-P	H	MERTHYR TYDFIL	692	W 4 - 2	Taylor 10, 75, Puttnam 29, 70
8	07.09	DM-P	H	TAMWORTH	760	W 1 - 0	Taylor 34
9	11.09	DM-P	A	Salisbury City	463	W 3 - 2	Turner 22, 51, Puttnam 48
	18.09	FAC Q2	A	Beaconsfield SYCOB	139	W 3 - 0	Turner 25, Robinson 28, Wilson 50
10	25.09	DM-P	H	NEWPORT COUNTY	1,023	W 2 - 1	Wilson 38, Kemp 61[og]
	02.10	FAC Q3	A	Cambridge City	812	L 0 - 1	
	09.10	FAT 1	A	Leatherhead	177	L 0 - 2	
11	23.10	DM P	A	Havant & Waterlooville	304	D 2 - 2	Dakin 34, Clark 76
12	26.10	DM P	H	GRANTHAM TOWN	837	D 3 - 3	Carmichael 30[og], Wilson 41, Turner 90
13	30.10	DM P	H	CRAWLEY TOWN	792	W 1 - 0	Turner 68
14	06.11	DM P	A	Weymouth	676	D 1 - 1	Rowland 30
15	08.11	DM P	A	Ilkeston Town	718	L 1 - 2	Fuff 45
	16.11	Lg Cup 1	A	Spalding United	208	D 0 - 0	Won 4-3 after penalties
16	20.11	DM P	A	Cambridge City	534	W 3 - 2	Wilson 13 90[p], Dakin 29
17	23.11	DM P	H	MARGATE	725	D 0 - 0	
18	27.11	DM P	H	DORCHESTER TOWN	631	W 4 - 1	Rowland 27 50, Robinson 30, Wilson 70
19	04.12	DM P	A	Bath City	783	D 1 - 1	Wilson 14
	13.12	LC 2	A	Allkeston Town	243	D 1 - 1	Palmer 77 Won 4-3 after penalties
20	18.12	DM P	A	Halesowen Town	472	D 0 - 0	
21	27.12	DM P	A	Boston United	3119	W 2 - 1	Robinson 40, Wilson 42
22	03.01	DM P	H	ROTHWELL TOWN	1039	D 0 - 0	
23	08.01	DM P	H	CAMBRIDGE CITY	820	D 0 - 0	
24	15.01	DM P	A	Atherstone United	272	W 2 - 0	Keeble 25, Palmer 86
25	22.01	DM P	A	Margate	377	L 0 - 1	
	25.01	LC 3	H	GRANTHAM TOWN	549	W 1 - 0	Puttnam 119
26	29.01	DM P	H	HAVANT & WATERLOOVILLE	720	L 0 - 1	
27	05.02	DM P	A	Crawley Town	620	W 2 - 1	Gibson 85, Fuff 90
28	08.02	DM P	H	BURTON ALBION	638	L 0 - 1	
29	12.02	DM P	H	GLOUCESTER CITY	565	W 2 - 0	Spearing 22[p], Puttnam 45
30	19.02	DM P	A	Dorchester Town	457	W 4 - 3	Robinson 13 43, Mills 32, Rowland 34
	22.02	LC QF	H	TAMWORTH	784	D 1 - 1	Rowland 105 Won 4-3 after pens.
31	26.02	DM P	H	CLEVEDON TOWN	599	W 1 - 0	Turner 12
32	04.03	DM P	A	Gloucester City	429	W 1 - 0	Rowland 35
33	11.03	DM P	H	WEYMOUTH	639	W 1 - 0	Puttnam 18
	14.03	L.C. SF	A	Burton Albion	1002	L 0 - 2	
34	18.03	DM P	A	Tamworth	506	L 0 - 3	
35	25.03	DM P	H	WORCESTER CITY	627	L 0 - 1	
36	01.04	DM P	H	BATH CITY	904	W 4 - 1	Puttnam 47, 84, Palmer 50, Mills 79
37	08.04	DM P	A	Merthyr Tydfil	528	D 0 - 0	
38	15.04	DM P	H	HALESOWEN TOWN	518	W 1 - 0	Turner 50
39	24.04	DM P	H	BOSTON UNITED	1960	D 0 - 0	
40	29.04	DM P	H	SALISBURY CITY	552	W 2 - 0	Nwadike 17, 88
41	01.05	DM P	A	Rothwell Town	201	L 1 - 2	Puttnam 33
42	06.05	DM P	A	Newport County	755	W 2 - 1	Nwadike 37, OG (Benton) 83

PLAYING SQUAD

GOALKEEPERS: Chuck Martini (Connecticut Wolves (USA))

DEFENDERS: Gary Mills (Gresley R), Jamie March (Burton Alb), Tony Spearing (Peterborough), Simon Dakin (Grantham T), David Robinson (Grantham T), Andy Bullimore (Rothwell T), Glen Fuff (Rushden & D)

MIDFIELDERS: Lee Gibson (Lincoln C), Emeka Nwadike (Grantham T), Tony Marsden (Gresley R), Darren Bogan (Grantham T)

FORWARDS: Lyndon Rowland (Halesowen T), Tommy Wright (Doncaster R), John Palmer (Boots Ath), Dave Puttnam (Gresley R)

MARGATE

CLUB OFFICIALS
Chairman: **Keith piper**
President: **Gordon Wallace**
Vice Chairman: **Jim Parmenter**
Press Officer: Secretary
Secretary: **K E Tomlinson**
65 Nash Road, Margate , Kent CT9 4BT
Tel & Fax: 01843 291040 (M) 07710033566
Commercial Manager: Dave Jones

FOOTBALL MANAGEMENT TEAM
Manager: Chris Kinnear
As.Manager: Kevin Raine
Physio: John Griffin

FACT FILE
Formed: 1896
Nickname: The Gate
Sponsors: Abacus Insurance Services Ltd.
Newsline: 0891 800 665
Colours:All Royal Blue
Change colours: All Yellow
Midweek matchday: Tuesday
Reserves' League: Bass Kent Lg. Div 1

99-00 Captain; Tony Dixon
P.o.Y.: Phil Collins
Top Scorer: Phil Collins

GATE UPDATE
OFFICIAL MATCHDAY PROGRAMME OF MARGATE FOOTBALL CLUB

Match sponsor
SPICER McCOLL

Saturday, 6th May 2000
Dr Martens League
Premier Division
Special edition £1.50
HALESOWEN TOWN

Pages: 44 Price: £1.50
Editor: Keith Smith
Local Press: Isle of Thanet Gazette, Thanet Times, Thanet Extra
Local Radio: Radio Kent, Invicta Radio, TLR

GROUND   Hartsdown Park, Hartsdown Road, Margate CT9 5QZ Tel: 01843 221769

Directions: A28 into Margate, turn right opposite Dog & Duck P.H. into Hartsdown Road, proceed over crossroads and ground is on left. Ten mins walkfrom Margate (BR)

Capacity: 6,000   Cover: 3 sides   Seats: 400   Floodlights: Yes
Clubhouse: Flexible hours, private functions, matchday facilities.
Club Shop: Contacts: Dave and Debbie Canham (01843 2217690)

PREVIOUS   **Leagues:** Kent 11-23 24-28 29-33 37-38 46-59; Southern 33-37
                  Grounds: Margate College; Dreamland, Northdown Rd; Garlinge   **Name:** Thanet Utd 1981-89

CLUB RECORDS **Attendance:** 14,500 v Spurs, FA Cup 3rd Rd 73
                  Win: 8-0 v Tunbridge Wells (H) 66-67, & v Chatham Town (H) 87-88 **Career Goalscorer:** Dennis Randall 66 (season 66-67)
                  Defeat: 11-0 v AFC Bournemouth (A), FAC 1st Rd. 20.11.71   **CareerAppearances:** Bob Harrop
                  Transfer fee paid: £5,000 for Steve Cuggy (Dover Ath93)
                  Transfer fee received: Undisclosed for Martin Buglione (St Johnstone 92-93)

BEST SEASON **FA Trophy:** Third Round replay 78-79.   **FA Cup:** 3rd Rd 72-73 (0-6 to Spurs), 36-37 (1-3 at Blackpool)
                  League clubs defeated: Gillingham 29-30, Q. P.R., Crystal Palace 35-36, Bournemouth & Boscombe Ath. 61-62, Swansea 72-73

HONOURS   Southern Lg 35-36 (Lg Cp 67-68,97-98 (R-up 61-62 74-75), Div 1 62-63 (R-up 66-67), Div 1 Sth 77-78, East Div R-up 33-34, Southern Div. R-up: 98-99 Merit Cup 66-67 77-78, Midweek Sect. 36-37, Kent Lg (4), (R-up 5, Div 2 4, Lg Cp 4), Kent Snr Cup (5), Kent Snr Shield(8), Kent F'lit Cp 62-63 66-67 75-76

Players progressing: Over 40 including J Yeomanson (West Ham 47), D Bing/GWright (West Ham 51), T Bing (Spurs 56),
                       S Foster (C Palace 61), J Fraser(Watford 62), R Walker (Bournemouth 65), K Bracewell (Bury 66),
                       T Jenkins/RFlannigan (Reading 69-70), M Blyth (Millwall 76), M Buglione (St Johnstone 92)

Lee Williams just misses with this header, from six yards, in the FA Trophy 1st Round match against Croydon.   Photo: Gordon Whittington

Match Facts 1999-00

	Date	Comp.	H/A	Opponents	Att.	Result	Goalscorers
1	14.08	DM-P	A	Worcester City	1,060	W 3 - 1	Sykes 15 19, Lamb 44
2	17.08	DM-P	H	HAVANT & WATERLOOVILLE	614	D 0 - 0	
3	21.08	DM-P	H	GLOUCESTER CITY	504	W 3 - 0	Collins 24 30, Sykes 44
4	24.08	DM-P	A	Weymouth	697	W 1 - 0	Sykes 8
5	28.08	DM-P	H	ILKESTON TOWN	681	W 3 - 2	Collins 54 66, Sykes 71
6	30.08	DM-P	A	Cambridge City	438	D 0 - 0	
7	04.09	DM-P	A	Newport County	933	L 1 - 3	Munday 90
8	11.09	DMP	H	CLEVEDON TOWN	526	W 2 - 1	Munday 52, Porter 81
	18.09	FAC Q2	A	Ramsgate	1,502	W 3 - 0	O'Brien 10, Sykes 35, Collins 65
9	25.09	DMP	A	Halesowen Town	449	W 3 - 0	Collins 56, Martin 74, Utterson 89
	02.10	FAC Q3	A	Taunton Town	720	W 3 - 0	Munday 29, Porter 35, Dixon 56
	09.10	FAT 1	A	Croydon	150	D 0 - 0	
	12.10	FAT 1 R	H	CROYDON	324	W 5 - 0	Munday 56 62[p], Utterson 71 81, Collins 83
	16.10	FAC Q4	A	Hendon	531	L 0 - 1	
10	23.10	DM P	H	ROTHWELL TOWN	470	W 4 - 1	Williams 8 30, Collins 71 89
11	26.10	DM P	A	Havant & Waterlooville	354	D 3 - 3	Pinnock 64, Munday 79[p], Collins 82
	02.11	Kent SC1	H	TONBRIDGE ANGELS	275	W 3 - 2	Dixon 35, Radford 70[og], Gibbs 110[og]
12	06.11	DM P	A	Tamworth	556	L 0 - 2	
13	09.11	DM P	H	WEYMOUTH	414	W 2 - 0	O'Brien 44, Collins 52
14	13.11	DM P	A	Clevedon Town	249	L 0 - 1	
	16.11	Lg Cup 1	A	Sittingbourne	180	W 2 - 0	Chell 23[og], Collins 53
15	20.11	DM P	H	MERTHYR TYDFIL	407	D 0 - 0	
16	23.11	DM P	A	King's Lynn	725	D 0 - 0	
	27.11	FAT 2	H	DARTFORD	400	D 0 - 0	
17	04.12	DM P	H	NEWPORT COUNTY	446	W 2 - 1	Collins 28 78
18	11.12	DM P	A	Grantham Town	285	W 2 - 1	Collins 29, Greatorex 79
19	18.12	DM P	H	ATHERSTONE UNITED	391	W 2 - 0	Dixon 75, Collins 80
	21.12	LC 2	H	BALDOCK TOWN	200	W 4 - 2	Saunders 36, O'Brien 47, Collins 81 83
20	27.12	DM P	A	Salisbury City	509	L 0 - 2	
21	03.01	DM P	H	CRAWLEY TOWN	744	W 1 - 0	Dixon 65
22	08.01	DM P	A	Dorchester Town	524	L 0 - 1	
23	15.01	DM P	A	Boston United	1558	L 0 - 3	
24	18.01	DM P	H	CAMBRIDGE CITY	339	L 1 - 2	Saunders 15
25	22.01	DM P	H	KING'S LYNN	377	W 1 - 0	Sykes 81[p]
	25.01	KSC QF	H	FOLKESTONE INVICTA	307	L 2 - 3	Sykes 15, Lamb 55
26	29.01	DM P	A	Atherstone United	241	W 1 - 0	Sykes 21
	01.02	LC 3	A	Fleet Town	45	W 5 - 2	Sykes 20 41, Porter 50, Collins 82, Greatorex 90
27	05.02	DM P	H	BOSTON UNITED	953	W 2 - 1	Collins 32, Porter 55
28	22.02	DM P	H	BURTON ALBION	746	W 1 - 0	O'Brien 18
29	26.02	DM P	H	TAMWORTH	624	L 1 - 2	Collins 71
	29.02	LC QF	A	Hastings Town	245	L 1 - 3	Collins 18
30	04.03	DM P	H	GRANTHAM TOWN	469	L 1 - 2	Collins 22
31	11.03	DM P	A	Merthyr Tydfil	567	W 4 - 3	Munday 17, Sykes 30 83, Birkby 70[og]
32	18.03	DM P	H	BATH CITY	690	D 1 - 1	Collins 70
33	25.03	DM P	A	Burton Albion	1180	W 1 - 0	Munday 73(p)
34	01.04	DM P	H	DORCHESTER TOWN	503	D 1 - 1	Munday 43(p)
35	08.04	DM P	A	Bath City	735	D 1 - 1	Takalogabashi 48
36	15.04	DM P	H	WORCESTER CITY	198	L 0 - 1	
37	18.04	DM P	A	Rothwell Town	167	W 2 - 0	Collins 52, Greatorex 70
38	22.04	DM P	A	Crawley Town	822	L 3 - 5	Greatorex 17, 44, Munday 56
39	24.04	DM P	H	SALISBURY CITY	356	W 2 - 0	Collins 32, Porter 61
40	29.04	DM P	A	Gloucester City	326	W 4 - 0	OG (Hunt) 14, Porter 32, O'Connell 74, Collins 83
41	01.05	DM P	A	Ilkeston Town	443	W 2 - 1	Takalogabashi 73, Dixon 78
42	06.05	DM P	A	Halesowen Town	602	W 3 - 1	Greatorex 40, O'Connell 48, Collins 64

PLAYING SQUAD

GOALKEEPERS: Lee Turner (Gravesend)

DEFENDERS: Iain O'Connell (Dover Ath), Paul Lamb (Gravesend), Jay Saunders (Gravesend), Graham Porter (Ashford T), Billy Edwards (Sutton U), Tony Dixon (Dover Ath)

MIDFIELDERS: Eliot Martin (Gillingham), Mark Munday (Gravesend), Denver Birmingham (Harrow B), Lee Williams (Gillingham), Dean Yorath (Youth), Paul O'Brien (Ashford T), Mo Takaloboghasi (Local Football)

FORWARDS: Phil Collins (Dartford), Tom Planck (Sittingbourne), Paul Sykes (Welling U), Leon Braithwaite (Welling U), Mark Greatorex (Tonbridge)

MERTHYR TYDFIL

CLUB OFFICIALS
Joint Presidents:
The Archbishop of Cardiff,
His Grace John Aloysious Ward,
The Lord Bishop of Llandaff,
The Right Rev. Roy Davies
Chairman: **Lyn Mittell**
Managing Director: **Owen Edwards**
Football Se/Press Off.**Anthony Hughes**
Commercial Manager: **Owen Edwards**

FOOTBALL MANAGEMENT TEAM

Manager: **Keith Walker**
As.Man/ Physio: **Paul Giles**

FACT FILE
Formed: 19445
Nickname: The Martyrs
Sponsors :Hoover PLC
Colours: White & black/black/black
Change colours: All amber
Midweek home matchday: Tuesday
Reserves' League: None

99-00 - Top scorer: Ian Mitchell
Captain: Gareth Abrahams
P.o.Y.: Danny Carter

Welcome to Penydarren Park home of ... Issue 36

THE MARTYR

PETERS

Merthyr Tydfil
V
Tamworth
Saturday 29th April 2000 Kick Off 3.00pm Price £1.20

GROUND Penndarren Park, Merthyr Tydfil, Mid Glamorgan Tel: 01685 384102
Directions: (South) A470 Express Way to Merthyr through Town Centre to Pontmorlais (traffic lights) turn left then first right, first right at Catholic Church and right again into Park Terrace to ground. (North) Heads of theValley road to Town Centre, to Pontmorlais (traffic lights) turn right, then as above
Capacity: 10,000   Seats: 1,500   Cover: 5,000   Floodlights: Yes
Clubhouse: Open Mon. to Sun. 6.30 - 11.00pm. 2 club cafes open on matchdays for hot food
Club Shop: Sells replica kits, club souvenirs & programmes.
       Contact Mel Jenkins01443 692336

Pages: 36   Price: £1.20
Editor: Anthony Hughes,Tel: 01685 359921
Robert Davies and Mike Donovan
Local Press: Merthyr Express
Local Radio: Capitol Gold

PREVIOUS   **Leagues:** Southern League 46 -89 (Southern League 46-59, 1st Division 59-61, 64-71, !st Div. North 72-79, Premier Div. 61-64, 71-72, 88-89, Midland Div. 79-88), G M Conference 89-95.
       Names: None   **Grounds:** None

CLUB RECORDS **Attendance:** 21,000 v Reading FA Cup 2nd Rnd 1949/50
       Win: 11-0 v Rushden 1987   **Defeat:** 9-2 v Altrincham 1993
       Transfer fee paid: £10,000 to Cardiff City for Robbie James 1992
       Transfer fee received: £12,000 for Ray Pratt from Exeter City 1981

BEST SEASON **Welsh FA Cup:** Winners 48-49 50-51 86-87
       FA Trophy: 3rd Rd v Northwich Vic 95-96   **FA Cup:** 2nd Round on six occasions. League clubs defeated: Bristol Rovers

HONOURS   Welsh FA Cup 48-49, 50-51, 86-87; Southern League 47-48, 49-50, 50-51, 51-52, 53-54; Southern League (Midland) 87-88; Southern League (Premier) 88-89;Southern League Cup 47-48, 50-51

Players Progressing : Syd Howarth (Aston Villa), Cyril Beech, Gilbert Beech,Bill Hullet, Ken Tucker (Cardiff City), Nick Deacy (Hereford United), Gordon Davies (Fulham), Ray Pratt (Exeter City), Peter Jones, Paul Giles (Newport County)

Back Row: Haydn Fleming, Antony Wright, Paul Richards, Eston Chiverton, Lee Price, Neil Thomas, Colin Loss, Craig Evans, Tom Ramasut, Ian Mitchell, Cohen Griffith.
Front: Mike Regan, Danny Carter, Garry Shephard, Adrian Needs, Gareth Abraham, Mark Williams, Andy Power.

Match Facts 1999-00

#	Date	Comp.	H/A	Opponents	Att.	Result	Goalscorers
1	14.08	DM-P	H	ILKESTON TOWN	879	L 1 - 3	Evans 23
2	17.08	DM-P	A	Salisbury City	405	W 3 - 2	Power 43, Mitchell 66 87
3	21.08	DM-P	A	Atherstone United	341	W 3 - 0	Power 43, Carter 57, Evans 86[p]
4	24.08	DM-P	H	DORCHESTER TOWN	710	D 0 - 0	
5	28.08	DM-P	A	Tamworth	570	L 1 - 3	Mitchell 65[p]
6	30.08	DM-P	H	BATH CITY	789	L 0 - 2	
7	04.09	DM-P	A	King's Lynn	692	L 2 - 4	Ramasut 40, Mitchell 85
8	07.09	DMP	H	WEYMOUTH	623	L 1 - 2	Mitchell 29
9	11.09	DMP	H	CAMBRIDGE CITY	637	W 1 - 0	Abraham 83
	14.09	FAW P.B	A	Newtown		D 0 - 0	
	18.09	FAC Q2	A	Basingstoke Town	540	D 0 - 0	
	21.09	FAC Q2R	H	BASINGSTOKE TOWN	523	W 2 - 1	Ramasut 39[p], Griffith 86
	21.09	FAW P.B	H	CARDIFF CITY		D 0 - 0	
10	25.09	DMP	A	Rothwell Town	237	L 0 - 2	
	28.09	FAW P.B	H	BARRY TOWN		D 0 - 0	
	02.10	FAC Q3	A	Gloucester City	729	W 3 - 2	Gannaway 27[og], Ramasut 54, Lima 70
	09.10	FAT 1	A	Cinderford Town	225	W 2 - 1	Griffith 22, Sloan 66
	16.10	FAC Q4	H	HITCHIN TOWN	726	W 2 - 0	Sloan 45, Salton 58[og]
11	23.10	DM P	H	GLOUCESTER CITY	528	W 5 - 0	Ramasut 45, Power 65, **Griffith 3** (48 53 59)
12	26.10	DM P	A	SALISBURY CITY	652	D 1 - 1	Meads 18
	02.11	FAC 1	H	STALYBRIDGE CELTIC	871	D 2 - 2	Mitchell 50 84
13	06.11	DM P	H	GRANTHAM TOWN	608	W 5 - 2	**Mitchell 4** (27 65 70 75), Ryan 80
	09.11	FAC 1 R	A	Stalybridge Celtic	1399	L 1 - 3	Lima 3
14	13.11	DM P	H	HALESOWEN TOWN	652	W 1 - 0	Shepherd 73
	16.11	Lg Cup 1	A	Bath City	425	L 1 - 2	Shepherd 14
15	20.11	DM P	A	Margate	407	D 0 - 0	
	27.11	FAT 2	H	STEVENAGE BOROUGH	583	D 0 - 0	
16	04.12	DM P	H	ATHERSTONE UNITED	625	W 2 - 0	Sloan 23, Bird 54
17	11.12	DM P	A	Burton Albion	834	L 0 - 2	
	14.12	FAW P.B.	A	Cardiff City		D 0 - 0	
18	27.12	DM P	H	NEWPORT COUNTY	1407	L 2 - 5	Mitchell 48, Ryan 52
19	03.01	DM P	A	Clevedon Town	586	W 2 - 1	Loss 35, Carter 39
20	08.01	DM P	H	HAVANT & WATERLOOVILLE	655	L 0 - 2	
21	15.01	DM P	A	Grantham Town	306	D 1 - 1	Abraham 89
22	18.01	DM P	A	Gloucester City	404	L 0 - 1	
23	22.01	DM P	H	WORCESTER CITY	633	L 0 - 3	
	25.01	FAW P B	H	NEWTOWN	422	W 2 - 0	Griffith 12, Shepherd 70
24	29.01	DM P	A	Boston United	1584	L 1 - 4	Jarman 5
25	05.02	DM P	H	BURTON ALBION	578	D 1 - 1	Ramasut 6
26	12.02	DM P	A	Halesowen Town	578	W 1 - 0	McDonnell 15[og]
	16.02	FAWPQF	A	Wrexham	390	L 0 - 8	
27	19.02	DM P	H	CRAWLEY TOWN	514	L 2 - 3	Lima 15, Birkby 88
28	21.02	DM P	A	Worcester City	1075	L 1 - 2	Birkby 22
29	26.02	DM P	H	BOSTON UNITED	594	L 0 - 2	
30	04.03	DM P	A	Cambridge City	504	D 0 - 0	
31	11.03	DM P	H	MARGATE	567	L 3 - 4	Walker 38, Griffith 69, Birkby 80[p]
32	14.03	DM P	A	Dorchester Town	405	D 0 - 0	
33	18.03	DM P	H	ROTHWELL TOWN	446	W 3 - 1	Lima 54, Birkby 66, Evans 68
34	21.03	DM P	A	Crawley Town	669	L 0 - 2	
35	25.03	DM P	A	Bath City	1138	W 1 - 0	Evans 12
36	01.04	DM P	A	Havant & Waterlooville	399	W 2 - 1	Birkby 65, Carter 88
37	08.04	DM P	H	KING'S LYNN	528	D 0 - 0	
38	15.04	DM P	A	Weymouth	644	L 1 - 2	Ryan 45
39	22.04	DM P	H	CLEVEDON TOWN	602	W 2 - 0	Mitchell 15, Ryan 86
40	24.04	DM P	A	Newport County	1069	L 0 - 2	
41	29.04	DM P	H	TAMWORTH	617	D 1 - 1	Ryan 25 (p)
42	06.05	DM P	A	Ilkeston Town	387	L 1 - 2	Mitchell 58

PLAYING SQUAD

GOALKEEPERS: Neil Thomas (Ton Pentre), Mark Jones (Hereford U)

DEFENDERS: Mark Williams (Newport Co), Andy Power (Weston-s-Mare), Lee Price (Ebbw Vale), Paul Richards (Inter Cardiff), Michael Regan (Maesteg Park), Gareth Abraham (Hereford U), Lee Baddeley (Cardiff)

MIDFIELDERS: Dean Clarke (Newport Co), Craig Lima (Newport Co), Danny Carter (Barry T), Adrian Needs (Ebbw Vale), Colin Loss (Ebbw Vale)

FORWARDS: Cohen Griffiths (Weston-S-Mare), Chris Summers (Cwmbran T), Dean Birkby (Clevedon T), Adrian Harris (Cardiff C), Craig Evans (Ebbw Vale), Ian Mitchell (Cwmbran T), Dai Thomas (Cardiff), Darren Ryan (Newport Co)

MOOR GREEN

CLUB OFFICIALS

Chairman: **Ian Childs**
Vice-Chairman: **John Bassford**

Secretary: **Nigel Collins**
7 The Morelands, West Heath,
Birmingham B31 3HA
Tel: 0121243 3661 (H), 0121 475 0240 (B)

Press Officer: **Peter Clynes**
(0121 745 3262)

Commercial Man.: Commercial Dept.
Tel: 0121 777 8961

FOOTBALL MANAGEMENT TEAM

Manager: Bob Faulkner
Coaches:
Doug Griffiths & Kim Casey
Physio: Steve Shipway

FACT FILE

Formed: 1901
Nickname: The Moors
Sponsors: Bradstocks Insurance
Colours: Light/dark blue halves/navy/light blue
Change colours: Jade & lime/jade
Midweek matchday: Tuesday
Reserve League: No reserve team

1999-00
P.o.Y.: Matthew Smith
Top Scorer: Derek Hall(37)

Programme: Pages: 52 Price: £1
Editor: Michael Mulryan (0121 608 7078)
Local Press: Solihull News, Solihull Times,
Birmingham Post & Mail, Express &Star
Local Radio: Radio WM, BRMB

GROUND `The Moorlands', Sherwood Rd., Hall Green. B28 OEX. Tel: 0121 624 2727

Directions: Off Highfield Rd, which is off A34 (B'ham to Stratford)
Hall Green & Yardley (BR) half mile
Capacity: 3,250 Cover: 1,200 Seats: 250 Floodlights: Yes
Clubhouse: Two bars, dance floor. Open nightly & weekend lunch
Club Shop: Selling scarves, mugs, stickers, programmes etc

PREVIOUS Leagues: (friendlies only 1901-21) Birmingham & Dist. A.F.A. 1908-36; Central Amateur 36-39; Birmingham Comb 45-54;
West Mids 54-65; Midland Comb 65-83
Grounds: Moor Green Lane 1901-02; numerous 02-22; Windermere Road 1910-30

CLUB RECORDS Attendance: 5,000 v Romford, FA Amtr Cup 51
Career Goalscorer: Phil Davies 221 Career Appearances: Michael Hawkins 800
Transfer fee paid: £1,000 for Adrian O'Dowd (Alvechurch)
Transfer fee received: £90,000 for Ian Taylor (Port Vale)

BEST SEASON FA Cup: 1st Rd Proper 79-80 (lost 2-3 Stafford Rgs)
FA Trophy: 1st Rd Prop 90-91, 0-3 v Burton Albion; 96-97, 3-5 v AshtonUnited

HONOURS Southern Lg Mid Div R-up 87-88, Mids Comb 80-81 (R-up(4) 74-76 79-80 82-83, Div 185-86, Presidents Cup(2) 66-68 78-79),
Mids Comb Chall Cup 80-81 (R-up 69-7082-83), Lord Mayor of B'ham Charity Cup 90-91, Mids F'lit Cup(2) 90-92, Tony Allden Tphy 81-
82, B'ham Snr Cup 57-58, Worcs Snr Cup R-up 86-87, B'ham Jnr Cup66-67, Worcs Jnr Cup 85-86, Solihull Charity Cup 85-86, Smedley
Crook Mem.Cup 87-88, Cent Amat Lg 36-37 37-38 38-39, Verviers (Belg) Tphy 32-33 36-37,AFA Chall Cup 38-39, AFA Snr Cup 26-27
35-36, Mids F'lit Yth Lg Cup R-up 87-88,B'ham County Yth Lg Cup R-up 83-84

Players progressing: H Smith/R Jefferies (Aston Villa 47/50), F Pidcock(Walsall 53), P Woodward/B Mack (W B Abion 54), S Cooper (Birmingham
City 83),K Barnes (Manchester City), P Brogan (Mansfield Town), I Taylor (Pt Vale 92), S Talbot (Pt Vale 94), D Busst (Coventry 92)

Moor Green 2000-01 Squad **Photo: Keith Clayton**

Match Facts 1999-00

	Date	Comp.	H/A	Opponents	Att.	Result		Goalscorers
1	14.08	DM W	H	Rocester	151	W	2-1	Shepherd 14, Round 36
2	17.08	DM W	A	Shepshed Dynamo	141	W	3-0	Mulholland 43 (p). Hall 45, 56
	21.08	FAC Pre	H	Paget Rangers	197	W	3-0	Hall 31, 37, Casey 89
3	28.08	DM W	H	Bedworth United	197	W	3-1	Pountney 17, Mulholland 43 (p), Hall 60
4	30.08	DM W	A	Stafford Rangers	758	W	1-0	Hall 58
	04.09	FAC 1Q	H	Mickleover Sports	170	W	3-2	Hall 17, 56, Pountney 77
5	11.09	DM W	A	Bromsgrove Rovers	369	W	2-1	Shepherd 76, Hall 90
6	14.09	DM W	H	Paget Rangers	202	W	2-0	Hall 19, Shepherd 35
	18.09	FAC 2Q	H	Atherstone United	298	W	2-1	Softley 15, Shepherd 72
7	21.09	DM W	A	Evesham United	143	D	1-1	Mulholland 52 (p)
8	25.09	DM W	H	Cinderord Town	178	W	2-1	Hall 67, Brighton 75
9	28.09	DM W	A	Blakenall	165	W	2-1	Mulholland 76, Hall 88
	09.10	FAT 1	A	Chorley	219	W	1-0	Hall 32
10	16.10	DM W	A	Cirencester Town	250	W	5-1	Softley 43, Shepherd 50,60, Hall 62, 69
	19.10	Worcs. SC 1	H	Solihull Borough	141	L	0-3	
	21.10	FAC 3Q	A	Chelmsford City	858	L	0-1	
11	23.10	DM W	H	Yate Town	204	W	6-0	**Shepherd 5** (12, 17, 27, 66, 74), Poutney 75
12	26.10	DM W	H	Shepshed Dynamo	253	W	3-0	Petty 18, Shepherd 75, Mulholland 90 (p)
13	30.10	DM W	A	Sutoon Coldfield Town	263	L	0-1	
14	06.11	DM W	H	Redditch United	292	D	1-1	Petty 39
15	09.11	DM W	H	Stafford Rangers	292	L	2-3	Shepherd 54, Mulholland 87
16	12.11	DM W	A	Bilston Town	214	D	2-2	Hall 7, Shepherd 34
	16.11	LC 1	A	Paget Rangers	135	W	2-1	Crisp 2, Casey 65
17	20.11	DM W	H	Gresley Rovers	214	W	1-0	Hall 29
	22.11	Birm. SC 2	A	Atherstone United	141	L	1-3	Casey 30
	27.11	FAT 2	A	Radcliffe Borough	190	W	6-1	Hall 28, 66, Softley 46, 71, Casey 83, Shepherd 89
18	04.12	DM W	A	Weston-super-Mare	215	W	2-1	Brighton 42, Round 70
	06.12	LC 2	A	Worcester City	336	L	1-3	Hall 7
19	18.12	DM W	A	Redditch United	304	W	3-0	Hall 8, Shepherd 45, 58
20	27.12	DM W	H	Racing Club Warwick	388	D	2-2	Shepherd 13, 40
21	03.01	DM W	A	Stourbridge	240	W	3-1	Hall 46, 89, Crisp 79
22	18.01	DM W	A	Paget Rangers	203	W	2-0	Hall 21, 75
23	22.01	DM W	H	Sutton Coldfield Town	289	D	1-1	Hall 90
	25.01	FAT 3	A	V. S. Rugby	452	W	4-1	Shepherd 3, Softley 66, Hayde 75, Round 86
24	29.01	DM W	A	Hinckley United	422	D	1-1	Hall 10
25	05.02	FAT 4	A	Kingstonian	747	L	1-2	Shepherd 33
	12.02	DM W	A	Solihull Borough	257	D	1-1	Shepherd 4
26	15.02	DM W	H	Tiverton Town	248	D	1-1	Shepherd 39
27	19.02	DM W	H	Cirencester Town	276	D	0-0	
28	26.02	DM W	A	Gresley Rovers	435	W	1-0	Shepherd 47
29	04.03	DM W	H	Evesham United	272	W	2-0	Hall 38, 89
30	11.04	DM W	H	Solihull Borough	452	D	0-0	
31	14.03	DM W	A	Cinderford Town	136	D	0-0	
32	18.03	DM W	A	Blakenall	282	L	0-5	
33	25.03	DM W	A	Yate Town	104	W	3-1	Woodley 38, Hall 59, Crisp 83
34	28.03	DM W	H	Bromsgrove Rovers	360	W	5-0	**Hall 3** (10, 47, 66), Softley 42, 45
35	01.04	DM W	A	Rocester	125	W	1-0	Pountney 87
36	04.04	DM W	A	Hinckley United	326	D	1-1	Hall 77
37	08.04	DM W	H	Weston-super-Mare	323	W	2-0	Petty 65, Mulholland 84
38	15.04	DM W	A	Tiverton Town	1,262	L	0-1	
39	22.04	DM W	H	Stourbridge	352	W	7-1	Hall 6, **Pountney 3** (42, 55, 56), Round 43, Baddams 61, Crisp 73
40	24.04	DM W	A	Racing Club Warwick	281	W	4-0	Woodley 36, 85, Petty 86, Hall 90
41	29.04	DM W	A	Bilston Town	413	W	1-0	Hall 19
42	06.05	DM W	A	Bedworth United	444	W	4-1	Hall 23, 34, Woodley 50, Pountney 79

PLAYING SQUAD

GOALKEEPERS: Andy De Bont (Stourbridge)

DEFENDERS: Chris Gillard (Port Vale), **Stewart Brighton** (Redditch U), Denis Mulholland (Bromsgrove R), Matthew Smith (Burton Alb), Tommy Daly (Hinckley U), Jai Stanley (Bedworth U)

MIDFIELDERS: Steve Round (Stafford R), Richard Softley (Bromsgrove R), Jamie Petty (Solihull B), Mick Hayde (Worcester C), Adrian Baddams (Solihull B), Mark Creighton (Kidderminster H), Michael Crawford (Workington)

FORWARDS: **Kim Casey** (Kidderminster H), Derek Hall (Highgate U), Mark Shepherd (Kidderminster H), Mark Crisp (Cheltenham T), Craig Pountney (Shrewsbury T)

NEWPORT COUNTY A.F.C.

CLUB OFFICIALS

Chairman: **John Williams**
President:T.B.A.
Secretary: **Mike Everett**
43 Downing Street, Newport. NP19 0JL
Tel: 01633 669572
Community Director: **Martin Greenham**
Tel: 01633 663110
Commercial & Marketing Executive: **Tim Harris:**

FOOTBALL MANAGEMENT TEAM

Manager: Tim Harris
Asst Manager: Chris Hyde
Physio: John Fitzgerald
Trainer: D Williams, Kit Manager: Tony Gilbert

FACT FILE
Formed: 1989
Nickname: The Exiles
Sponsors: Acorn Recruitment
Colours: Amber shirts and black shorts
Change colours:All white
Midweek matchday: Wednesday
Youth League: South West Counties Youth

99-00 Captain: Gary Kemp
Top scorer: Carl Dale
P.o.Y.: Pat Mountain
Players P.o.Y.:Pat Mountain

GROUND Club Headquarters: Newport Stadium, Spytty Park,Langland Way, Newport, Gwent.
FAX 01633 669572   Tel: 01633 662262
Directions: From Severn Bridge on M4 take 1st exit signed Newport (jct 24), 1st left at r'bout
follow signs for industrial area, left at r'bout after 2 1/2miles, over 2 r'bouts, next left
for ground. Ample free parking available at ground
Capacity: 3,300   Cover: 1,236   Seats: 1,236   Floodlights: Yes
Clubhouse: Small bar at ground with hot and cold scacks also available.
Club Shop: Open matchdays, sells a wide selection of souvenirs & programmes

THE EXILE
THE OFFICIAL MATCH MAGAZINE AND VOICE OF
NEWPORT County
AFC THE EXILES
DR. MARTENS LEAGUE PREMIER DIVISION

NEWPORT COUNTY AFC

Sunday 21st May 2000
Kick-off 7.00pm
v
NEWPORT COUNTY
1980
PRICE £1.20

Pages: 36   Price: £1.50
Editor: Wallace Brown (01633 265500)
Local Press: South Wales Argus, South Wales Echo
Local Radio: Red Dragon

PREVIOUS   Leagues: Hellenic 89-90   **Grounds:** London Road, Moreton-in-Marsh 89-90; Somerton Park, Newport 90-92;
Gloucester City FC 92-94 (exile period due to dispute with FAW re League of Wales)
Names: Newport AFC were formed after the demise of Newport County in1988-89, name change 1999.

CLUB RECORDS Attendance: 2,475 v Redditch United, Beazer (Midland) 24.8.94
Win: 9-0 v Pontllottyn Blast Furnace (A), Welsh Cup First Round 1/9/90
Defeat: 1-6 v Stafford Rangers (A) BHL 6/1/96
Career Goalscorer: Chris Lilygreen 93   **Career Appearances:** Mark Price 275 (222 Lg + 53 cup)
Transfer fee paid:£5,000 for Shaun Chapple from Foreswt Green Rovers £1,000 from RedditchU for Paul Burton
Transfer fee received: £5,000 from Merthyr Tydfil for Craig Lines
BEST SEASON   FA Cup: 4th Qualifying Rd 92-93   **FA Trophy:** 3rd Rd 99-00   **FA Vase:** N/A
HONOURS   Hellenic Lge Prem Div 89-90 (Lge Cup 89-90); Glos Sen Cup Winners 93-94;Southern Lg. Mid Div Champions 94-95, R-up
98-99 Merit Cup Jnt Win 94-95, 98-99 Gwent FA Sen.Cup Winners 96-97,97-98,98-99,99-00 Herefordshire Sen,C. 98-99

Back Row: Tony Gilbert (Kit Man), David Hunt, Nathan Davies, Pat Mountain, Ryan Mackerness, Andy Fisher, Jason Donovan, Michael Flynn, David Williams (Trainer). **Middle:** Brian Godfrey (Chief Scout), Roy Jordan, Karl Bayliss, Andy Mainwaring, Danny Hill, Craig Lima, Grantley Dicks (Captain), Leigh Hall, Scott Jackson, Darren Robison, Danny Hunt, Glyn Jones (Youth Dev. Off.). **Front:** Chris Bale, Lee Brown, Bradley Thomas, Gary Smart, John Fitzgerald (Physio), Tim Harris (Manager), Chris Hyde (Asst. Man.), Phil Kelly, Carl Dale, Dean Clarke, Andrew Thomas.

Match Facts 1999-00

	Date	Comp.	H/A	Opponents	Att.	Result	Goalscorers
1	14.08	DM P	H	CAMBRIDGE CITY	1003	D 2 - 2	Dale 47, Smart 90
2	17.08	DM P	A	Tamworth	807	D 2 - 2	Dale 36, Brown 39
3	21.08	DM P	A	Grantham Town	365	W 1 - 0	Dale 29
4	25.08	DM P	H	CLEVEDON TOWN	869	W 5 - 0	Dale 30 49, Smart 34, Robison 51, Jackson 62
5	28.08	DM P	A	Crawley Town	542	D 2 - 2	Dale 8, Brown 66
6	30.08	DM P	H	WORCESTER CITY	978	W 1 - 0	Brown 51
7	04.09	DM P	H	MARGATE	933	W 3 - 1	Dale 47 52[p], Smart 49
8	07.09	DM P	A	Salisbury City	618	W 2 - 1	Chapple 15, Dale 48 [p]
	08.09	Gwent SC1	H	CALDICOT TOWN	104	W 7 - 0	Dale 9 11, Flynn 17, Jordan 79, **Mainwaring 3** (28 40 85)
9	11.09	DM P	A	Burton Albion	1426	D 1 - 1	Mainwaring 44
	18.09	FAC Q2	H	WIMBORNE TOWN	659	D 1 - 1	Hill 42
	21.09	**FAC Q2R**	A	Wimborne Town	364	W 3 - 0	**Dale 3** (11 54 84[p])
10	25.09	DM P	A	King's Lynn	1023	D 2 - 2	Brown 33, 80
	02.10	FAC Q3	H	BURGESS HILL TOWN	723	L 1 - 2	Thomas 10
	09.10	**FAT 1**	A	YEADING	349	W 2 - 1	Smart 54, Brown 86
11	16.10	DM P	H	HAVANT & WATERLOOVILLE	743	D 3 - 3	Kemp 60, Dale 66, Hill 87
12	23.10	DM P	A	Weymouth	745	L 2 - 4	Mainwaring 42[p], Dale 88
13	27.10	DM P	H	TAMWORTH	721	W 2 - 0	Flynn 10, David Hunt 22
14	30.10	DM P	H	HALESOWEN TOWN	753	D 0 - 0	
15	06.11	DM P	A	Ilkeston Town	697	L 1 - 2	Flynn 32
16	12.11	DM P	A	Gloucester City	889	D 1 - 1	Dale 13
	16.11	**Lg Cup 1**	A	Tiverton Town	539	L 1 - 2	Hill 43
17	20.11	DM P	H	BOSTON UNITED	907	D 2 - 2	Hunt 22, Bayliss 88
18	23.11	DM P	A	Clevedon Town	623	L 0 - 1	
	27.11	**FAT 2**	A	Bashley	257	W 2 - 1	Hill 7, Bayliss 85
19	04.12	DM P	A	Margate	446	L 1 - 2	Hill 9
20	11.12	DM P	H	SALISBURY CITY	640	D 0 - 0	
21	18.12	DM P	A	Havant & Waterlooville	372	D 2 - 2	Smart 6, Flynn 82
22	27.12	DM P	A	Merthyr Tydfil	1407	W 5 - 2	Smart 21 31, Bayliss 29, Dale 50, Hill 72
23	03.01	DM P	H	BATH CITY	1415	L 0 - 1	
24	08.01	DM P	A	Worcester City	1115	W 4 - 3	Flynn 20, Kemp 58, Brown 60 78
	15.01	**FAT 3**	A	Bedford Town	944	D 0 - 0	
	19.01	**FAT 3R**	H	BEDFORD TOWN	669	L 0 - 1	
25	22.01	DM P	H	ATHERSTONE UNITED	588	D 1 - 1	Dale 81
26	29.01	DM P	H	CRAWLEY TOWN	607	L 0 - 1	
27	02.02	DM P	H	GLOUCESTER CITY	577	W 2 - 1	Flynn 2, Dale 66[p]
28	05.02	DM P	A	Halesowen Town	603	L 0 - 2	
29	12.02	DM P	H	GRANTHAM TOWN	620	W 2 - 1	Brown 4, Shephard 15
30	19.02	DM P	A	Atherstone United	354	W 1 - 0	Hill 78
31	23.02	DM P	H	DORCHESTER TOWN	555	D 1 - 1	Dale 84
32	26.02	DM P	H	BURTON ALBION	674	D 1 - 1	Dale 10[p]
33	04.03	DM P	A	Dorchester Town	503	W 2 - 1	Ryan 17, Hill 87
34	11.03	DM P	H	ROTHWELL TOWN	635	D 1 - 1	Flynn 12
	22.03	Gwent SC SF	H	CAERLEON	201	W 1 - 0	Donovan 5
35	25.03	DM P	H	ILKESTON TOWN	604	W 2 - 1	Dale 26, Hill 82
36	01.04	DM P	A	Cambridge City	718	D 0 - 0	
37	08.04	DM P	H	WEYMOUTH	676	W 2 - 1	Dale 26, Eaton 75
38	15.04	DM P	A	Rothwell Town	198	W 3 - 0	OG (Lord) 6, Shephard 30, Thomas 34
39	22.04	DM P	A	Bath City	950	D 1 - 1	Fraser 57
40	24.04	DM P	H	MERTHYR TYDFIL	1069	W 2 - 0	Eaton 34, Rose 90
41	29.04	DM P	A	Boston United	2596	D 1 - 1	Robinson 72
42	06.05	DM P	H	KING'S LYNN	755	L 1 - 2	OG (Robinson) 43
	10.05	Gwent SC F	N	Tredegar town	380	W 3 - 0	Brown (2), Shephard

PLAYING SQUAD

GOALKEEPERS:	Pat Mountain (Gloucester C), Andy Fisher (Milford U)
DEFENDERS:	Mike Flynn (Youth), Gary Kemp (Gloucester C), Gay Thorne (Gloucester C), Stuart James (Bath C), Jason Donovan (Ebbw Vale), David Hunt (Cardiff C)
MIDFIELDERS:	Danny Hill (Cinderford T), Shaun Chapple (Forest Green R), Gareth Wesson (Merthyr Tydfil), Nicky Brooks (Bath C)
FORWARDS:	Carl Dale (Yeovil T), Jason Eaton (Yeovil T), Matthew Rose (Gloucester C), Lee Brown (Pontllanfraith), Darren Robison (Trowbridge T), Karl Bayliss (Forest Green R), Gary Shepherd (Merthyr Tydfil)

SALISBURY CITY

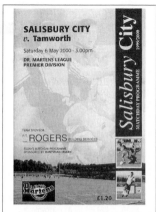

SALISBURY CITY
v. **Tamworth**
Saturday 6 May 2000 · 3.00pm
DR. MARTENS LEAGUE
PREMIER DIVISION

£1.20

CLUB OFFICIALS
Chairman: **P R McEnhill**
Vice-Chairman: **Roger Brocksom**
Secretary: **Sean Gallagher**
1 Tempest Road, Beamont Park, Amesbury,
Wilts SP47UE Tel: 01980 626855 (H & Fax)
Press Off: **David Macey**Tel: 01264 773765
Youth Co-ordinator: **Symon Pickett**
Football in Community Officer:**Andy Cook**
Commercial Manager: **Geoff Butler**

FOOTBALL MANAGEMENT TEAM
Manager: **Geoff Butler**
Reserve Team Manager: **Ian Chalk**
Fitness Therapist: **Dawn Cornforth**
Youth Mans: **Symon Pickett& Terry Hatt**

FACT FILE
Formed: 1947
Nickname: The Whites
Sponsors: Western Daily Press.
Colours: White/black/white
Change colours: yellow/blue/yellow
Midweek matchday: Tuesday
Reserve Team's League: Wessex Comb
Club Line: 'City Line' 0906 555 864
1999-00
Captain: Andy Cook
Top scorer: Paul Sales

GROUND   The Raymond McEnhill Stadium, Partridge Way, Old Sarum, Salisbury SP4 6PU
Tel:01722 326454, Fax 01722 323100
Directions: The Stadium is situated off A345 (Salisbury - Amesbury) road on the northern
edge of the city 2 miles from the City centre. Continue on this road, turn right onto A338
signed Old Sarum Business Park, Partridge Way & ground on left (well signposted)
Capacity: 4,000   Cover: 3,062   Seats: 462   Floodlights: Yes
Clubhouse: On ground, . Hot & cold snacks. Hospitality Boxes available for hire.
Club Shop: Sells replica shirts, memorabilia, programmes, scarves, metal badges, souvenirs.
Contact Commercial Office (01722 326454)

Pages: 48 Price: £1.20
Editor: David Macey
Local Press: Salisbury Journal, Evening Echo
& Sports Echo, Western DailyPress
Local Radio: Wiltshire Sound, Spire F.M

PREVIOUS   **Leagues:** Western 47-68   **Name:** Salisbury FC, 47-92   **Ground:** Hudson Field 47-48, Victoria Park 48-97

CLUB RECORDS Attendance: 8,902 v Weymouth, Western League 48
New Ground: 2,570 v Hull City F.A. Cup 1998.   Win: 9-0 v Westbury United (H), FA Cup 1st Qual. Rd 72   **Defeat:** 0-7 v
Minehead, Southern League 1975
          Career Goalscorer: Royston Watts 180 (59-65)   **Career Appearances:** Barry Fitch 713 (63-75)
          Transfer fee paid: £5,750 for Peter Loveridge (Dorchester Town, 90)
          Transfer fee received: £20,,000 for Adrian Randall (Forest Green Rovers)
BEST SEASON   FA Trophy: 2nd Rd 96-97 (lost to Dorchester Town)
          FA Amateur Cup: 2nd Rd 49-50 (lost to Hendon)   **FA Cup:** 2nd Rd 59-60 (lost to Newport County)
HONOURS   Southern Lg Southern Div Champ 94-95, R-up 85-86 92-93; Western Lg 57-58 60-61,R-up 58-59 59-60 61-62 66-67 67-68;
          Hants Senior Cup 61-62 63-64; Wilts PremierShield 56-57 59-60 61-62 66-67 67-68 70-71 77-78 78-79 95-96 98-99
Players progressing: Eric Fountain (Southampton 48), Cyril Smith (Arsenal 48),Tony Alexander (Fulham 65), John Evans (Stockport County 67), Graham
Moxon (Exeter 75), Eric Welch (Chesterfield 76), Ian Thompson (Bournemouth 83),Trevor Wood (Port Vale 88), Denny Mundee (Bournemouth 88),
Matthew Carmichael (Lincoln 90), Shaun Brookes (Barnet 91), Andrew Dungey (Exeter C. 97), Andrew Sargent (Plymouth A. 97),Jason Matthews
(Exeter C)

Back Row: Geoff Butler (Manager), Darren Curtis, Martin Shepherd, Nick Miles, Roger Emms, Vince Matthews, James Price,
Paul Sales, Andy Cook, Darren Lush, Ian Savage, Ricky Haysom, (Asst. Manager). **Front:** Tyronne Bowers, Ross Anderson,
Scott Bartlett, Danny Rofe, Robbie Harbut, Jimmy Smith, Ian Chalk. Mascot: Rebecca Ray.

Match Facts 1999-00

	Date	Comp.	H/A	Opponents	Att.	Result	Goalscorers
1	14.08	DM-P	A	Boston United	1,228	L 0 - 6	
2	17.08	DM-P	H	MERTHYR TYDFIL	405	L 2 - 3	Powell 41, Harbut 83
3	21.08	DM-P	H	HALESOWEN TOWN	391	W 2 - 0	Sales 62, Shepherd 90
4	24.08	DM-P	A	Havant & Waterlooville	417	W 1 - 0	Shepherd 2
5	28.08	DM-P	A	Rothwell Town	227	L 2 - 3	Shepherd 11, Sales 46
6	30.08	DM-P	H	CRAWLEY TOWN	460	W 4 - 1	Miles 23, Harbut 25 71, Sales 31
7	04.09	DM-P	A	Worcester City	720	W 3 - 2	Emms 50, Chalk 57, Barclay 60
8	07.09	DM-P	H	NEWPORT COUNTY	618	L 1 - 2	Miles 18
9	11.09	DM-P	H	KING'S LYNN	463	L 2 - 3	Sales 55, Miles 82
	18.09	FAC Q2	A	Welton Rovers	254	W 3 - 1	**Shepherd 3** (13 44 90)
10	25.09	DM-P	A	Tamworth	574	W 2 - 1	Shepherd 24, Powell 82
	02.10	FAC Q3	A	Maidenhead United	345	W 1 - 0	Sales 16
	09.10	FAT 1	H	TONBRIDGE ANGELS	471	W 2 - 0	Housley 18, Sales 26
	16.10	FAC Q4	A	Oxford City	461	L 1 - 2	Shepherd 52
11	23.10	DM P	A	Ilkeston Town	539	L 0 - 6	
12	26.10	DM P	A	Merthyr Tydfil	652	D 1 - 1	Sales 45
13	30.10	DM P	H	CLEVEDON TOWN	370	L 1 - 2	Bowers 33
14	06.11	DM P	A	Cambridge City	449	W 3 - 1	Sales 25 80, Chalk 50
15	09.11	DM P	H	HAVANT & WATERLOOVILLE	394	L 1 - 2	Bowers 53
16	12.11	DM P	H	ATHERSTONE UNITED	374	W 1 - 0	Housley 53
	16.11	Lg Cup 1	A	NEWPORT IOW	258	L 1 - 4	Sales 52
17	20.11	DM P	A	Dorchester Town	626	D 4 - 4	McMenemy 6, Shepherd 34 74, Savage 51
	23.11	Wilts P S1	A	Devizes Town	148	L 1 - 2	Shepherd 50
	27.11	FAT 2	H	SUTTON COLDFIELD TOWN	643	L 2 - 5	Shepherd 57, Sales 83
18	04.12	DM P	H	GRANTHAM TOWN	379	W 5 - 0	**Sales 3** (17 59 74), Shepherd 77, Bowers 90
19	11.12	DM P	A	Newport County	640	D 0 - 0	
20	27.12	DM P	H	MARGATE	509	W 2 - 0	Sales 20, Rofe 90
21	03.01	DM P	A	Weymouth	878	L 0 - 1	
22	08.01	DM P	H	BOSTON UNITED	593	L 1 - 2	Sales 39
23	15.01	DM P	H	DORCHESTER TOWN	557	D 1 - 1	Sales 29
24	18.01	DM P	A	Crawley Town	557	L 1 - 4	Bowers 66
25	22.01	DM P	A	Grantham Town	250	L 1 - 5	Shepherd 88
26	29.01	DM P	H	WORCESTER CITY	381	L 1 - 3	Sales 29
27	05.02	DM P	A	Bath City	1175	D 4 - 4	Chalk 16, Bowers 21, Emms 73, Sales 83
28	12.02	DM P	H	ROTHWELL TOWN	404	W 4 - 2	**Sales 3** (19 80 88), Chalk 34
29	19.02	DM P	A	Clevedon Town	348	W 2 - 1	Sales 38, Bowers 43
30	26.02	DM P	H	GLOUCESTER CITY	535	W 2 - 0	Shepherd 19, Chalk 34
31	04.03	DM P	A	Burton Albion	842	L 1 - 4	Sales 1
32	07.03	DM P	H	BATH CITY	721	L 1 - 3	Sales 16
33	11.03	DM P	H	BURTON ALBION	515	L 0 - 3	
34	18.03	DM P	H	ILKESTON TOWN	352	L 1 - 2	Emms 37
35	25.03	DM P	A	Halesowen Town	353	L 1 - 3	Smith 68 (p)
36	01.04	DM P	A	Atherstone United	165	W 3 - 0	Smith 27, 45 (2p), Shepherd 83
37	08.04	DM P	H	CAMBRIDGE CITY	371	W 4 - 0	Sales 60, 70, Shepherd 63, Anderson 86
38	15.04	DM P	A	Gloucester City	408	D 3 - 3	Sales 18, 69, Shepherd 78
39	22.04	DM P	H	WEYMOUTH	627	D 1 - 1	Smith 45
40	24.04	DM P	A	Margate	356	L 0 - 2	
41	29.04	DM P	A	King's Lynn	552	L 0 - 2	
42	06.05	DM P	H	TAMWORTH	527	D 1 - 1	Sales 35

PLAYING SQUAD

GOALKEEPERS: Justin Shuttlewood (Forest Green R), John Simpkins (Red Star Spartans)

DEFENDERS: Roger Emms (Andover), Lee Bradford (Weymouth), Darren Lush (Havant & W), Darren Curtis (Fulham), Danny Flitter (Youth), Scott Bartlett (Cirencester T)

MIDFIELDERS: Andy Cook (Miiwalll), Andy Catley (Forest Green R), Ian Chalk (Warminster T), Neil Housley (Weymouth), Tyrone Bowers (Fareham T)

FORWARDS: Nick Miles (Bournemouth), Kevin Braybrook (Yeovil T), Jimmy Smith (Gloucester C), Adam Rhind-Tutt (Downton), Martin Shepherd (Dorchester T), Paul Sales (Bashley)

STAFFORD RANGERS

CLUB OFFICIALS

Chairman: **D.Parker**
Vice-Chairmam:**T.B.A.**

Secretary: **Peter Wall**
c/o Stafford Rangers F
Tel: 01785 602430
Press Officer: **T.B.A.**

FOOTBALL MANAGEMENT TEAM
Manager: I Painter
Physio: B. Whittaker
Coach: A King

GROUND

Directions: From M6 junction 14, A34 (Stone) to roundabout, straight over into Beaconside, take third right into Common Road, ground one mile ahead. From Town Centre, follow signs for B5066 (Sandon) turn left by new housing estate. Two miles from railway station
Capacity 3,000   Cover 1,500   Seats: 426   Floodlights: Yes
Clubhouse: Yes - Open every evening
Club Shop: Two shops, one old programmes and one souvenirs run by Jim & IreneDalglish

FACT FILE

Formed: 1876
Nickname: The Boro
Colours: Black & White stripes/black/black
Change :Maroon & azure/maroon/maroon
Midweek matchday: Tuesday
Reserves' League: No reserve team

99-00 Captain:L.Everettt
P.o.Y.: R.Mitchell
Top scorer:R.Mitchell

Marston Road Stafford ST16 3BX
Tel: 01785 602430 Fax : 01785 602431

Pages: 40 Price: £1.00
Editor: Peter Wall Tel. 01785 602430
Local Press: Staffordshire Newsletter, Express & Star, Evening Sentinel
Local Radio: Radio Stoke, Beacon Radio, Signal Radio

PREVIOUS   **Leagues:** Shropshire 1891-93, Birm 1893-96, 21-40, N Staffs 1896-1900, Cheshire 00-01, Birm Comb 00-12, 46-52, Cheshire Co. 52-69, N.P.L. 69-79, 83-85, Alliance Prem 79-83, GMVC 85-95
Grounds: Lammascotes, Stone Rd, Newtown, Doxey (until 1896)

CLUB RECORDS **Attendance:** 8,536 v Rotherham Utd FA Cup 3rd Rd 75
Win: 11-0 v Dudley Town FA Cup 6.9.58   **Defeat:** 0-12 v Burton Town Birmingham Lge 13.12.30
Career Goalscorer: M Cullerton 176   **Career Appearances:** Jim Sargent
Transfer fee paid: £13,000 for S Butterworth from VS Rugby 90
Transfer fee received: £100,000 for Stan Collymore from Crystal Palace 1990

BEST SEASON   **FA Trophy:** Winners 1971-72 & 78-79. R-up 75-76
FA Cup: 4th Rd 74-75, 1-2 v Peterborough Utd. (H)   League clubs defeated: Halifax, Stockport, Rotherham

HONOURS   Birm Comb Champ 12-13; Birm Lge Champ 25-26; N.P.L. Champ 71-72, 84-85, Champ Shield 84-85; FA Trophy 71-72, 78-79, R-up 75-76; Bob Lord Trophy 85-86; Wednesday Charity Cup 20-21; Mid F/light Cup 70-71; Jim Thompson Shield 86-87; Staffs Sen Cup 54-55 56-57 62-63 71-72 77-78 86-87 91-92 Dr.Martens Western Division 99-00

Players progressing: M Aleksic (Plymouth), J Arnold (Blackburn), R Williams/MCullerton/T Bailey (Port Vale), K Barnes (Man City), A Lee (Tranmere), ECameron (Exeter), W Blunt (Wolves), G Bullock (Barnsley), K Mottershead(Doncaster), McIlvenny (WBA), S Collymore (C Palace), P Devlin (Notts Co.),R Price (Birmingham C.)

Back Row:
Stuart Ryder,
Gary Price,
Devon White,
Brett Wilcox,
Ronnie Walker,
Darren Boughey.

Front:
Steve Jones,
Scott Dundas,
Leigh Everitt,
David Read,
Richard MItchell,
Jason Smith.

Photo:
Chris Elsey

Match Facts 1999-00

	Date	Comp.	H/A	Opponents	Att.	Result		Goalscorers	
1	14.08	DM W	A	Tiverton Town	922	D	2-2	Walker, Mitchell	
2	17.08	DM W	H	Stourbridge	634	W	7-2	S Jones, Smith, Walker 2, Mitchell 2, Shaw	
	21.08	FAC Pre	H	Glossop North End	493	W	2-0	Shaw, Swain	
3	28.08	DM W	A	Weston-super-Mare	270	D	2-2	Walker, Eccleston	6
4	30.08	DM W	H	Moor Green	758	L	0-1		12
	04.09	FAC 1Q	H	Matlock Town	487	D	2-2	Mitchell, Shaw	
	07.09	FAC 1Q R	A	Matlock Town	485	W	4-0	Smith, Mitchell 2, Shaw	
5	11.09	DM W	H	Cirencester Town	590	L	1-3	Eccleston	14
6	14.09	DM W	A	Rocester	508	W	1-0	Read	12
	18.09	FAC 2Q	H	Eastwood Town	463	L	1-3	Mitchell	
7	25.09	DM W	A	Hinckley United	286	L	1-3	Shaw	15
8	28.09	DM W	H	Gresley Rovers	469	W	3-2	Humphreys, Mitchell, S Jones	11
9	02.10	DM W	A	Solihull Borough	162	L	2-3	Swain, OG	15
10	16.10	DM W	H	Racing Club Warwick	561	W	5-0	**Eccleston 3**, Mitchell, Humphreys	13
11	23.10	DM W	A	Bedworth United	287	L	1-2	Mitchell	14
12	26.10	DM W	A	Stourbridge	236	W	2-0	Eccleston, Mitchell	11
13	30.10	DM W	H	Paget Rangers	531	W	2-0	Boughey, Mitchell	12
14	06.11	DM W	A	Cirencester Town	234	W	2-1	Smith, Mitchell	10
15	09.11	DM W	A	Moor Green	292	W	3-2	Eccleston 2, Bradley	9
16	13.11	DM W	H	Redditch United	500	W	1-0	Mitchell	6
	16.11	LC 1	A	Bromsgrove Rovers	259	W	1-0	Mitchell	
17	20.11	DM W	A	Cinderford Town	190	L	0-2		9
	23.11	Staffs SC 2	A	Rushall Olympic	94	W	3-1	Eccleston, Pau, Shaw	
	27.11	FAT 2	H	Emley	605	L	1-4	Mitchell	
18	04.12	DM W	H	Sutton Coldfield Town	470	W	4-1	Mitchell 2, Smith, Shaw	8
	07.12	LC 2	A	Sutton Coldfield Town	101	W	4-2	Smith, Bradley, Eccleston, Shaw	
19	11.12	DM W	A	Evesham United	171	W	4-1	Eccleston 2, Mitchell 2	3
20	18.12	DM W	H	Bromsgrove Rovers	614	W	3-1	S Jones, Mitchell, Eccleston	2
21	27.12	DM W	A	Bilston Town	675	W	5-1	**Eccleston 3**, Dundas, Mitchell	2
22	03.01	DM W	H	Blakenall	1171	D	2-2	Mitchell, Eccleston	2
23	08.01	DM W	A	Shepshed dynamo	335	W	5-1	Dundas 2, Humphreys, Mitchell, S Jones	2
	11.01	S SC 3	H	Leek Town	286	D	2-2	Humphreys, Mitchell	
24	18.01	DM W	H	Rocester	812	W	2-1	Mitchell, Wilcox	2
25	22.01	DM W	A	Racing Club Warwick	225	D	1-1	Mitchell	2
	25.01	LC 3	A	Tamworth	481	L	1-4	Dundas	
26	29.01	DM W	H	Cinderford Town	646	W	3-1	Mitchell, Dundas, Smith	2
	01.02	S SC 3 R	A	Leek Town	227	L	1-2	Humphreys	
27	05.02	DM W	H	Tiverton Town	995	W	2-1	Everitt, Mitchell	1
28	12.02	DM W	A	Sutton Coldfield Town	457	W	3-1	Walker, Ryder, Smith	1
29	15.02	DM W	A	Shepshed dynamo	720	W	3-0	S Jones, OG, Dundas	1
30	19.02	DM W	H	Redditch United	622	W	3-0	Mitchell, White, OG	1
31	26.02	DM W	H	Hinckley United	1680	D	0-0		1
32	04.03	DM W	H	Bedworth United	914	W	2-1	Mitchell, Humphreys	1
33	11.03	DM W	A	Yate Town	304	W	3-0	White, Mitchell, OG	1
34	18.03	DM W	H	Weston-super-Mare	1002	W	5-2	**White 3**, Dundas, Everitt	1
35	25.03	DM W	A	Paget Rangers	355	W	2-0	Dundas 2	1
36	01.04	DM W	H	Yate Town	1122	W	4-0	Kiely, Mitchell, Dundas, OG	1
37	08.04	DM W	A	Gresley Rovers	712	W	1-0	Mitchell	1
38	15.04	DM W	H	Evesham United	1046	W	5-0	**Mitchell 3**, Kiely 2	1
39	22.04	DM W	A	Blakenall	519	W	4-1	Mitchell 2, Kiely, S Jones	1
40	24.04	DM W	H	Bilston Town	1971	D	1-1	Smith	1
41	29.04	DM W	A	Bromsgrove Rovers	851	L	3-4	Mitchell, Wilcox, S Jones	1
42	06.05	DM W	H	Solihull Borough	1893	W	2-1	Kiely, Mitchell	1

PLAYING SQUAD

GOALKEEPERS: Richard Williams (Nuneaton B), Steve Spittle (Southend)

DEFENDERS: Stuart Ryder (Nuneaton B), Darren Boughey (Macclesfield T), Dave Read (Telford U), Chris Brindley (Hednesford T), Darren Simkin (Blakenall), Leigh Everitt (Nuneaton B), Ged Murphy (Barrow)

MIDFIELDERS: Jason Smith (Bilston T), Darren Middleton (Aston Villa), Neil Smith (HalesowenT), Scott Dundas (Leek T), Steve Jones (Ashton U)

FORWARDS: Tony Eccleston (Hednesford T), Nick Carter (Nottingham Forest), Paul Kiely (Leek T), Richard Swain (North Cave)

509

TAMWORTH

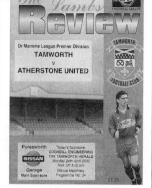

CLUB OFFICIALS

Chairman: **Bob Andrews**
Vice-Chairman:
President: **Len Gendle**
Secretary: **Rod A Hadley**, 38 Godolphin, Riverside, Tamworth B79 7UF
Tel: 01827 66786 & Fax
Press Officer: **Mark Maybury**
Commercial Manager: **Russell Moore**

FOOTBALL MANAGEMENT TEAM

Manager: Paul Hendrie
Asst Man.: Andy Dwyer
Physio: Peter Denham

FACT FILE

Formed: 1933
Sponsors: Nissan - Polesworth Garage
Nickname: Lambs or Town
Colours: Red shirts with white sleeves/black/red
Change colours: White/blue/white or all blue
Midweek home matchday: Tuesday
Reserves' League: Central Conference
99-00 Captain: Darren Crocutt
P.o.Y.: Nick Colley
Top scorer: Mark Hallam (44)

GROUND The Lamb Ground, Kettlebrook, Tamworth, Staffs B77 1AA
Tel: 01827 65798 FAX:0182762236

Directions: Follow the signs for Town Centre/Snowdome, then forKettlebrook.
The entrance to the ground &car parks is in Kettlebrook Road, 50yards
from the traffic island by the railway viaduct (B5000)
Capacity: 3,410   Cover: 1,191 Seats: 438 Floodlights: Yes
Clubhouse: Club on ground - open matchdays, training nights and tote night only
Clubshop: Yes

Pages: 28 Price: £1.20
Editor: Brian & Theresa Whitehouse
Press: Tamworth Herald,Tamworth Times
Radio:Centre FM,Captal Gold/Radio WM

PREVIOUS **Leagues:** Birmingham Combination 33-54, West Midlands (initially Birmingham Lg) 54-72 84-88, Southern 72-79 83-84, Northern Premier 79-83 **Grounds:** Jolly Sailor Ground 33-34

CLUB RECORDS **Attendance:** 4,920 v Atherstone Tn, Birm Comb 48 **Career Goalscorer:** Graham Jessop 195
Win: 14-4 v Holbrook Institute (H), Bass Vase 34 **Season Goalscorer:** Percy Vials 64 (36-37)
Defeat: 0-11 v Solihull (A), Birmingham Comb. 40 **Career Appearances:** Dave Seedhouse 869
Transfer Fee paid: £5,000 for Steve Cartwright (Colchester Utd, 88)
Transfer Fee received: £7,500 for Martin Myers (Telford Utd, 90)

BEST SEASON **FA Cup:** 2nd Rd 69-70 (0-6 at Gillingham) **FA Trophy:** Quarter Final **FA Vase:** Winners 88-89

HONOURS FA Vase 88-89, West Mids Lg 63-64 65-66 71-72 87-88 (R-up(2) 67-69, Div 2 55-56, Lg Cup(5) 64-66 71-72 85-86 87-88 (R-up 70-71)), Birmingham Snr Cup 60-61 65-66 68-69 (R-up 36-37 63-64), Staffs Snr Cup 58-59 63-64 65-66 (R-up 55-56 66-67 70-71), Midland F'lit Cup R-up 71-72 72-73, Camkin Cup 71-72 (R-up 70-71)

Players progressing: P Hilton (WBA 49), A Godridge (Swansea 50), W Ealing (Doncaster), Higgins (Fulham), P Weir (Cardiff), S Fox (Wrexham), S Cartwright (Colchester 88), S Ryder (Walsall), D Williams (Brentford)

Back Row: Buster Belford, Gary Smith, Michael Gray, Darren Acton, Harvey Willetts, Paul Hatton, Mark Wolsey, Rob Mutchell.
Middle: Pete Denham, Wayne Dyer, Warren Haughton, Nick Colley, Darren Grocutt, Jon Howard, Richard Clark, Micky Cotter, Derek Bond. **Front:** Tim Steele, Rob Warner, Andy Dwyer, Paul Hendrie (Manager), David Foy, Mark Hallam. **Photo:** Paul Barber

Match Facts 1999-00

	Date	Comp.	H/A	Opponents	Att.	Result	Goalscorers
1	14.08	DM-P	A	Havant & Waterlooville	522	W 2 - 0	Grocutt 54, Haughton 80
2	17.08	DM-P	H	NEWPORT COUNTY	807	D 2 - 2	Haughton 45, Hallam 82[p]
3	21.08	DM-P	H	BOSTON UNITED	721	L 1 - 2	Hallam 51
4	24.08	DM-P	A	Gloucester City	509	D 0 - 0	
5	28.08	DM-P	H	MERTHYR TYDFIL	570	W 3 - 1	Wolsey 16 59, Hallam 51
6	30.08	DM-P	A	Grantham Town	375	W 3 - 0	Cotter 26, Haughton 77 80
7	04.09	DM-P	H	CLEVEDON TOWN	545	W 4 - 1	**Hallam 3** (23, 48, 55), Batchelor 37
8	07.09	DM-P	A	King's Lynn	*760*	L 0 - 1	
9	11.09	DM-P	A	Bath City	*842*	L 1 - 4	Batchelor 41
	18.09	FAC Q2	H	SPALDING UNITED	527	W 6 - 2	Hallam 33, Batchelor 34, Smith 38 66, Mutchell 62, Haughton 87
10	25.09	DM-P	H	SALISBURY CITY	574	L 1 - 2	Colley 8
	02.10	FAC Q3	A	Belper Town	*641*	W 2 - 1	Hallam 25, Haughton 30
11	09.10	DM P	H	CRAWLEY TOWN	587	W 3 - 0	Hatton 10, Colley 30, Hallam 82
	16.10	FAC Q4	A	Scarborough	*1374*	W 1 - 0	Foy 18
12	23.10	DM P	H	DORCHESTER TOWN	687	D 1 - 1	Hallam 49
13	27.10	DM P	A	Newport County	*721*	L 0 - 2	
	30.10	FAC 1	H	BURY	2743	D 2 - 2	Haughton 8, Hallam 75
14	06.11	DM P	H	MARGATE	556	W 2 - 0	Hallam 1 63
	09.11	FAC 1 R	A	Bury	*2531*	L 1 - 2	Haughton 15
15	13.11	DM P	A	Boston United	*1159*	L 0 - 1	
	16.11	Lg Cup 1	H	ATHERSTONE UNITED	487	W 4 - 0	Hallam 48 66, Foy 73, Colley 82
16	20.11	DM P	H	BATH CITY	716	W 3 - 2	Smith 21, Hallam 68, Haughton 79
	27.11	FAT 2	A	Rocester	*361*	W 2 - 1	Foy 12, Hallam 86
17	04.12	DM P	A	Ilkeston Town	*562*	D 4 - 4	Hallam 14 72, Haughton 43 76
18	11.12	DM P	H	HAVANT & WATERLOOVILLE	480	W 5 - 0	Colley 25, Haughton 27, Haughton 45 81, Hallam 69
	14.12	Birm. SC2	A	VS RUGBY	279	W 5 - 2	Haughton 3, Foy 15, Colley 39, Hallam 45, Howard 48
19	18.12	DM P	A	Weymouth	*564*	W 2 - 1	Hallam 18, Haughton 80
20	27.12	DM P	A	Atherstone United	*1265*	W 5 - 0	Hallam 14 72, Foy 50, M Gray 59, Wolsey 60
21	03.01	DM P	H	WORCESTER CITY	1309	W 4 - 2	Sandeman 22[og], Haughton 80 81, Hallam 87[p]
22	08.01	DM P	A	Halesowen Town	*903*	W 3 - 0	Hallam 20 62, Haughton 52
	11.01	LC 2	H	GRESLEY ROVERS	448	W 3 - 1	Haughton 41, Hatton 66, Hallam 90
	15.01	FAT 3	H	RUNCORN	894	L 0 - 1	
23	22.01	DM P	A	Cambridge City	*382*	W 2 - 1	Hallam 37 45
	25.01	LC 3	H	STAFFORD RANGERS	481	W 4 - 1	Everitt 10[og], Hallam 45, Haughton 59 62
24	29.01	DM P	H	WEYMOUTH	723	W 3 - 1	Foy 7, Wolsey 33, Hallam 75
	01.02	BSC 3	A	Burton Albion	*701*	W 2 - 0	Haughton 15, Hallam 48
25	05.02	DM P	H	GRANTHAM TOWN	711	L 3 - 4	Clark 9, Haughton 34 43
26	12.02	DM P	A	Crawley Town	*706*	L 0 - 3	
	15.02	SSC QF	H	STOKE CITY	320	W 5 - 3	Mutchell 27, Foy 32, Hallam 50, Haughton 74, Cotter 86
27	19.02	DM P	H	BURTON ALBION	1652	D 1 - 1	Gray 44
	22.02	LC QF	A	King's Lynn	*784*	D 1 - 1	Colley 100 Lost 3-4 after pens.
28	26.02	DM P	A	Margate	*624*	W 2 - 1	Grocutt 35, Foy 73[p]
	04.03	BSC QF	A	Studley BKL	*430*	W 5 - 0	Mutchell 8, **Hallam 3** (42 52 56), Guy 68[og]
29	07.03	DM P	H	GLOUCESTER CITY	493	D 1 - 1	Hallam 17
30	11.03	DM P	H	CAMBRIDGE CITY	517	L 1 - 2	Dononwa 46
31	14.03	DM P	A	Clevedon Town	*291*	L 0 - 1	
32	18.03	DM P	H	KING'S LYNN	506	W 3 - 0	B Gray 56, Howard 81, Hallam 85
	21.03	SSC SF	H	BILSTON TOWN	458	W 2 - 1	Lavery 23, Howard 29
33	25.03	DM P	A	Dorchester Town	*531*	L 1 - 2	Hallam 23
34	28.03	DM P	A	Rothwell Town	*196*	D 1 - 1	Hallam 65
35	01.04	DM P	H	HALESOWEN TOWN	505	L 1 - 2	Clark 55
	05.04	BSC SF	H	WALSALL	502	L 1 - 2	Cotter 42
36	08.04	DM P	A	Burton Albion	*1188*	D 1 - 1	Cotter 54
37	11.04	DM P	H	ROTHWELL TOWN	326	W 2 - 1	Colley 31, Hallam 90
38	15.04	DM P	H	ILKESTON TOWN	453	W 2 - 1	Clark 10, B Gray 48
39	18.04	Staffs SC F1	H	BLAKENALL	429	W 2 - 1	Wolsey 30, Colley 77
40	22.04	DM P	A	Worcester City	*935*	W 1 - 0	Hallam 75
41	24.04	DM P	H	ATHERSTONE UNITED	714	W 4 - 0	Hallam 39 75, Colley 70, Gozzard 86
42	29.04	DM P	A	Merthyr Tydfil	*617*	D 1 - 1	Colley 8
	02.05	Staffs SC F2	A	Blakenall	*538*	L *2 - 3	Grocutt 81, Foy 108 - Lost 4-5 after penalties
	06.05	DM P	A	Salisbury City	*527*	D 1 - 1	Wright 75

PLAYING SQUAD

GOALKEEPERS: Darren Acton (Kidderminster H), Harvey Willetts (Bloxwich T)

DEFENDERS: David Foy (Stafford R), Rob Warner (Hereford U), Rob Mutchell (Kettering T), David Haywood (Sutton Coldfield T), Richard Clark (Evesham U), Darren Grocutt (Burton Alb), Paul Hatton (Youth), Jon Howard (Wolves)

MIDFIELDERS: Nick Colley (Telford U), Tim Steele (Exeter), Mark Turner (King's Lynn), Michael Gray (Rushden & D), Paul Gozzard (Walsall)

FORWARDS: Warrem Haughton (Sutton Coldfield T), Christy McKenzie (Stourbridge), Mark Hallam (Forest Green R), Gary Smith (Worcester C), Brian Gray (Worcester C)

WELLING UNITED

CLUB OFFICIALS

President	E Brackstone
Chairman	Paul Websdale
Vice Chairman	Steven Pain
General Manager	Graham Hobbins
Club Secretary	Barrie Hobbins
	c/o the club

Tel: 0181 301 1196 Fax: 0181 301 5676

Press Officer	Paul Carter
	c/o the club

FOOTBALL MANAGEMENT TEAM
Manager: Tony Reynolds
Assistant Manager: Ray Burgess
Res. & Yth Manager: Ken Guiste
Physio: Peter Green

FACT FILE

Founded:	1963
Nickname:	The Wings
Club Sponsors:	E.Coomes,Bookmkers
Club colours:	Red/red/white
Change colours:	Black & White
Midweek home matchday:	Tuesday
Welling Wingsline:	0891 80 06 54

1999-2000

Leading goalscorer:	Ritchie Hanlon 14
Player of the Year:	Mike Rutherford
Captain:	Mike Rutherford

Pages: 32   Price: £1.30
Editor: Barrie Hobbins
Other club publications:
"Winning isn't everything" (Fanzine)

Local Press: Kentish Times;
Bexleyheath & Welling Mercury
Local Radio: Radio Kent;
Radio Invicta; R.T.M.

GROUND   Park View Road Ground, Welling, Kent DA16 1SY
Tel: 0181 301 1196 Fax: 0811 301 5676
DIRECTIONS: M25, then A2 towards London. Take Welling turn-off, ground 1 mile.
By rail to Welling station (BR) - ground 3/4 mile.
CAPACITY: 5,500   **SEATED:** 500   **COVERED TERRACING:** 1,500
CLUBHOUSE: Open on match days
CLUB SHOP: Sells programmes (League & non-League), scarves, mugs, caps, hats, badges, replica kits etc. Manager Peter Mason.

PREVIOUS   **Leagues:** Eltham & Dist. Lge 1963-71, London Spartan Lge 1971-77, Athenian Lge 1977-79, Southern Lge 1979-86, Conference 86-2000   **Grounds:** Butterfly Lane, Eltham - 1963-78
RECORDS   **Attendance:** 4,100 v Gillingham, FA Cup
Win: 7-1 v Dorking 1985-86   **Defeat:** 0-7 v Welwyn garden City 1972-73
Career Goalscorer: John Bartley - 533   **Career Appearances:** Nigel Ransom - 1,066 & Ray Burgess - 1,044
Transfer fee paid: £30,000 for Gary Abbott from Enfield
Transfer fee received: £95,000 from Birmingham City for Steve Finnan.1995

BEST SEASON   **FA Cup:** Third Round 1988-89 0-1 v Blackburn Rovers   League clubs defeated: Gillingham
FA Trophy: Quarter Final 1988-89 0-1 v Macclesfield

HONOURS   London Spartan League 1978; Southern League Premier Division 1985/86; Kent Senior Cup 1985/86 98-99; London Senior Cup 1989/90; London Challenge Cup 1991/92, Runners-up 1993/94.

PLAYERS PROGRESSING: Paul Barron(Plymouth A), Andy Townsend (Southampton), Ian Thompson (AFC Bournemouth), John Bartley (Millwall), Dave Smith (Gillingham), Murray Jones (C. Palace), Kevin Shoemake (Peterborough), Tony Agana (Watford,), Duncan Horton (Barnet), Mark Hone (Southend), Steve Finnan & Steve Barnes (Birmingham City),Dean Standen (Luton Town)

Back Row: Ken Guiste (Coach), Leon Braithwaite, Michael Harle, Mark Hone, Ritchie Hanlon, Andy Harris, Russell Edwards, John Farley, Danny Chapman, Zeke Rowe, Michael Harney, Brian Lloyd (Coach). **Front:** Joe Baker, Darren Adams, Danny Twin, Danny Bailey, Ray Burgess (Asst. Manager), Kevin Hales (Manager), Peter Green (Physio), Mike Rutherford, Charley Side, Anthony Rivere, Kevin Dennis.

Match Facts 1999-00

	Date	Comp.	H/A	Opponents	Att.	Result	Goalscorers	League Position
1	14.08	N.C.	H	Hednesford Town	731	L 1-2	Hanlon 85	
2	17.08	N.C.	A	Hayes	706	L 0-1		
3	21.08	N.C.	A	Northwich Victoria	904	L 2-3	Edwards 36 Rowe 57 (pen)	20
4	24.08	N.C.	H	Woking	737	L 1-2	Hanlon 44 (pen)	
5	28.08	N.C.	H	Hereford United	743	W 3-1	Hanlon 3 (62, 63, 76)	18
6	30.08	N.C.	A	Rushden & D	2,805	L 0-2		20
7	04.09	N.C.	H	Yeovil Town	716	L 2-5	Hanlon 58 64	21
8	11.09	N.C.	A	Nuneaton Boro.	2.007	L 3-4	Braithwaite 24 35 Rowe 41	22
9	18.09	N.C.	H	Telford United	627	W 2-0	Dennis 45, Hanlon 67 (pen)	21
10	21.09	N.C.	A	Sutton United	814	W 3-2	Hanlon 4, Bailey 38, Dennis 70	19
11	25.09	N.C.	H	Forest Green Rovers	765	D 1-1	Hanlon 70 (pen)	19
12	28.09	N.C.	H	Kingstonian	605	L 0-1		19
13	02.10	N.C.	A	Doncaster Rovers	3,497	D 1-1	Bailey 86	20
14	09.10	N.C.	A	Southport	1,003	L 2-3	Rowe 70, Braithwaite 90	21
15	23.10	N.C.	H	Altrincham	607	D 2-2	Rutherford 29, Braithwaite 38	20
16	02.11	N.C.	A	Kettering Town	1,032	L 1-2	Vowden 36 (OG)	21
17	06.11	N.C.	A	Kingstonian	1,023	L 0-1		21
18	12.11	N.C.	H	Sutton United	704	L 2-3	Rowe 45, 66	21
19	20.11	N.C.	A	Woking	1,550	W 3-2	Hanlon 38 (p), 55, Braithwaite 67	21
20	04.12	N.C.	H	Scarborough	540	W 2-1	Watts 13, Dennis 24	19
21	11.12	N.C.	A	Telford United	921	L 1-2	Watts 33	20
22	18.12	N.C.	H	Doncaster Rovers	789	L 0-1		21
23	27.12	N.C.	A	Dover Athletic	1,658	L 1-2	Budden 62 (pen)	22
24	03.01	N.C.	A	Dover Athletic	1,054	D 1-1	Riviere 70	22
25	08.01	N.C.	H	Northwich Vic.	502	L 1-3	Rowe 51	22
26	22.01	N.C.	A	Kettering Town	1282	D 0-0		22
27	29.01	N.C.	H	Nuneaton Borough	708	D 0-0		22
28	12.02	N.C.	A	Altrincham	839	W 1-0	Hone 24	21
29	19.02	N.C.	H	Morecambe	626	D 0-0		21
30	26.02	N.C.	A	Kidderminster Harriers	2,673	L 1-4	Martin 22	21
31	04.03	N.C.	H	Kettering Town	648	W 1-0	Rowe 25	21
32	11.03	N.C.	A	Stevenage Borough	1,581	W 1-0	Martin 6	19
33	18.03	N.C.	H	Kidderminster Harriers	867	L 1-2	Hone 53	20
34	25.03	N.C.	A	Morecambe	1,045	L 1-2	Rutherford 43	21
35	01.04	N.C.	A	Scarborough	1,302	D 0-0		21
36	08.04	N.C.	H	Southport	672	W 4-1	Rowe 45(p), 87(p), Braithwaite 57, Martin 80	21
37	15.04	N.C.	A	Yeovil Town	1,812	D 1-1	Martin 2	19
38	22.04	N.C.	H	Hayes	815	L 1-2	Riviere 45	21
39	24.04	N.C.	A	Forest Green Rovers	1,107	W 2-1	Riviere 15 Barnes 73	20
40	29.04	N.C.	A	Hereford United	1,390	W 2-1	Rutherford 8, OG (Cooksey) 31	20
41	01.05	N.C.	H	Rushden & Diamonds	1,317	L 0-3		21
42	06.05	N.C.	A	Hednesford Town	834	W 1-0	Barnes 43	20

CUP COMPETITIONS

F.A. Cup

	Date		H/A	Opponents	Att.	Result	Goalscorers	
	16.10	4Q	H	Kidderminster Harriers	760	W 2-0	Braithwaite 44, Rutherford 70	
	30.10	1	A	Lincoln City	2,766	L 0-1		

Nationwide McMillan Trophy

	05.10	1	H	Dover Athletic	361	W 3-0	Hanlon 4, Dennis 22, Rutherford 45	

F.A. Trophy

	27.11	2	H	Gloucester City	423	W 2-1	Hanlon 14, Braithwaite 90	
	15.01	3	A	Kettering Town	1031	L 0-2		

PLAYING SQUAD

GOALKEEPERS: Glen Knight (Boreham Wood)

DEFENDERS: Lew Watts (Gravesend), Steve Taylor (Youth), Anthony Riviere (Faversham T), Russell Edwards (Dulwich Hamlet), **Mark Hone** (Kettering T), John Farley (Lewisham Elms), John Budden (Brighton), Michael Harney (Bromley)

MIDFIELDERS: Danny Chapman (Hastings T), Mike Rutherford (QPR), Sam Saunders (Youth), Lee Lough (Crawley T), Tony Dolby (Millwall)

FORWARDS: Paul Whitmarsh (Hendon), Martin Buglione (Boreham Wood), Zeke Rowe (Peterborough), Charlie Side (Youth), Simon Glover (Ashford T), Gareth Gwillim (Youth), Dean Canoville (Chesham U)

WEYMOUTH

CLUB OFFICIALS

Chairman: **Peter Shaw**
Vice Chairman: **Mike Archer**

Secretary: **Terry Northover**
2 Stoke Rd, Weymouth, Dorset DT4 9JF
Tel: 01305 771480

FOOTBALL MANAGEMENT TEAM
Manager: Andy Mason
Coach: Richie Carter
Physio: Bob Lucas

FACT FILE

Formed: 1890
Nickname: The Terras
Sponsors: Park Engineering
Colours: Claret & sky/claret & sky
Change colours: White with terra cotta trim
Midweek matchday: Tuesday
Reserves' League: Wessex Comb
99-00- Captain: Alex Browne
P.o.Y: Alex Browne
Top scorer: David Laws (25)

£1.50

GROUND Wessex Stadium, Radipole Lane, Weymouth, Dorset DT4 9XJ Tel: 01305 785558

Directions: Arriving from Dorchester on A354, turn right following signs to Granby Industrial Estate at Safeway r'bout - ground on right as you enter estate
Capacity: 6,600   Cover: all sides   Seats : 800   Floodlights : Yes
Clubhouse: Matchdays & functions. Hot & cold food available
Club Shop: Matchdays only. Progs & souvenirs.
During week contact Amanda (01305 815752)

Pages: 36 Price: £1
Editor:James Murphy 01305 815656 Tel & Fax

Lcal Press: Dorset Evening Echo
Local Radio: Wessex FM

PREVIOUS   **Leagues:** Dorset Lge, Western 1907-23 28-49, Southern 23-28 49-79, Alliance Premier 79-89
Ground: Recreation Ground (until 1987)

CLUB RECORDS   **Attendance:** 4,995 v Manchester Utd, ground opening, 21/10/87
Career Goalscorer: W Farmer, Haynes. 275   **Career Appearances:** Tony Hobson 1,076
Transfer fee paid: £15,000 for Shaun Teale (Northwich)   **Transfer fee received:** £100,000 for Peter Guthrie (Spurs, 1988)

BEST SEASON   **FA Cup:** Fourth Round 61-62, 0-2 v Preston N.E. (A). 1st rd on 29 occasions
League clubs defeated: Merthyr Town 24-25, Aldershot 49-50, Shrewsbury T. 56-57,Newport County 61-62, Cardiff C. 82-83
FA Amateur Cup: First Round 1900   **FA Trophy:** Fourth Round replay 1976-77

HONOURS   All Prem Lg R-up 79-80 (Lg Cup 81-82); Prem Inter Lg Cup R-up 87-88 (QF 90-91);Sth Lg 64-65 65-66 (R-up 54-55 77-78), Lg
Cup 72-73 (R-up 5), Sthn Div R-up 91-92; Wstn Lg 22-23, Div 2 33-34 36-37, (R-up 35-36 47-48); Dorset Sen. Cup (27);Mark Frowde Cup (13)

Players progressing: A Smith (Accrington 61), G Bond/T Spratt/A Donnelly/M Cave(Torquay 61/65/67/68), P Leggett (Swindon 62), R Fogg (Aldershot
63), B Hutchinson (Lincoln 65), A Wool (Reading 71), A Beer (Exeter 74), B Iles(Chelsea 78), G Roberts (Spurs 80), T Gulliver/R Hill/N Townsend/P
Morrell/JSmeulders (Bournemouth 66/67/79/83/84), T Agana (Watford), A Townsend/D Hughes(Southampton), S Claridge (C Palace), B McGorry/S
Teale (Bournemouth), T Pounder/R Evans (Bristol Rvrs), R Pethick (Portsmouth 93)

Back Row: Peter Dennis (Kit Manager), Carl Turner, Anthony Tilley, Ryan Cross, Danny Potter, Gavin Bates, Matthew Hare,
Mark Gammon, Simon Browne, Gary Funnell, Bob Lucas (Physio). **Front Row:** David Laws (Asst. Manager), Richard Spiller,
Michael cameron, John Waldock, Mark Robinson, Ian Hutchinson, Jamie Vittles, Michael Dean.

Match Facts 1999-00

	Date	Comp.	H/A	Opponents	Att.	Result	Goalscorers	
1	14.08	DM P	H	ROTHWELL TOWN	893	W 3 - 0	Hutchinson 33, 89, Laws 39	
2	17.08	DM P	A	Clevedon Town	556	D 1 - 1	Laws 50	
3	21.08	DM P	A	Burton Albion	876	L 0 - 1		
4	24.08	DM P	H	MARGATE	697	L 0 - 1		
5	28.08	DM P	A	Halesowen Town	477	D 0 - 0		
6	30.08	DM P	H	DORCHESTER TOWN	2,203	D 2 - 2	Laws 2 13	
7	04.09	DM P	H	GRANTHAM TOWN	533	W 3 - 2	Hutchinson 6, Robinson 15, Gammon 34	
8	07.09	DM P	A	Merthyr Tydfil	623	W 2 - 1	Gammon 40, Laws 70	
9	11.09	DM P	H	CRAWLEY TOWN	721	W 4 - 0	Laws 21, Heath 81, Gammon 88, A Hutchinson 89	
	18.09	FAC Q2	H	GLOUCESTER CITY	642	D 0 - 0		
	21.09	FAC Q2R	A	Gloucester City	491	L 1 - 2	Laws 90	
10	25.09	DM P	A	Boston United	1,247	L 0 - 3		
11	09.10	DM P	H	WORCESTER CITY	680	D 1 - 1	Knox 55	
12	16.10	DM P	A	Gloucester City	454	D 1 - 1	Gammon 35	
13	23.10	DM P	H	NEWPORT COUNTY	745	W 4 - 2	Gammon 16, Mason 27, Browne 45, Adcock 90	
14	26.10	DM P	H	CLEVEDON TOWN	725	L 0 - 1		
15	30.10	DM P	A	Atherstone United	265	D 1 - 1	A Browne 52	
16	06.11	DM P	H	KING'S LYNN	676	D 1 - 1	Heath 45	
17	09.11	DM P	A	Margate	414	L 0 - 2		
18	13.11	DM P	H	CAMBRIDGE CITY	446	D 0 - 0		
	16.11	Lg Cup 1	H	DORCHESTER TOWN	842	L 1 - 2	Knox 47	
19	20.11	DM P	A	Rothwell Town	201	W 2 - 1	Knox 57, Tovey 72	
	28.11	FAT 2	H	YEOVIL TOWN	4,053	D 0 - 0		
	30.11	FAT 2R	A	Yeovil Town	3,196	L 1 - 2	Laws 86 (p)	
20	04.12	DM P	H	HALESOWEN TOWN	647	D 0 - 0		
	07.12	Dorset SC3	H	POOLE BOROUGH	211	D 1 - 1	Laws 54	
21	11.12	DM P	A	Crawley Town	628	L 0 - 1		
22	18.12	DM P	H	TAMWORTH	564	L 1 - 2	Hale 1	
23	27.12	DM P	A	Dorchester Town	2877	W 1 - 0	Laws 66	
24	03.01	DM P	H	SALISBURY CITY	878	W 1 - 0	Tate 72	
	05.01	DSC 3R	H	POOLE BOROUGH	251	W 3 - 1	Robinson 41, Laws 58, Adcock 70	
25	08.01	DM P	A	Ilkeston Town	606	D 2 - 2	Laws 48, Gammon 64	
	13.01	DSC QF	H	BRIDPORT	304	W 1 - 0	Adcock 44	
26	18.01	DM P	A	Bath City	1133	L 0 - 2		
27	22.01	DM P	H	GLOUCESTER CITY	643	W 4 - 1	Tate 25, Laws 35, Robinson 61, Tilley 90	
28	29.01	DM P	H	Tamworth	723	L 1 - 3	Hutchinson 58	
29	05.02	DM P	A	Havant & Waterlooville	583	W 2 - 1	Robinson 83, Tate 88	
30	12.02	DM P	H	ATHERSTONE UNITED	674	D 0 - 0		
31	19.02	DM P	A	Grantham Town	344	D 3 - 3	Robinson 64, Laws 65 67	
32	26.02	DM P	H	ILKESTON TOWN	641	W 4 - 1	Laws 3 (2 44 77), Browne 41	
33	04.03	DM P	H	HAVANT & WATERLOOVILLE	734	D 2 - 2	Tate 17 24	
	07.03	DSC SF	N	Poole Town	247	D 0 - 0	Laws 62 72[p], Tate 79	at Bridport
34	11.03	DM P	A	King's Lynn	639	L 0 - 1		
35	18.03	DM P	A	Worcester City	873	D 1 - 1	Bradford 70	
	22.03	DSC SF R	N	Poole Town	323	W 1 - 0	Gammon 62	at Dorchester Town
36	01.04	DM P	H	BOSTON UNITED	922	D 2 - 2	Laws 15, 73	
37	08.04	DM P	A	Newport County	676	L 1 - 2	Tate 2	
38	15.04	DM P	H	MERTHYR TYDFIL	644	W 2 - 1	S Browne 26, A Browne 67	
39	22.04	DM P	A	Salisbury City	627	D 1 - 1	Tate 89	
40	24.04	DM P	H	BATH CITY	914	W 3 - 0	Laws 1, 61, Bradford 28	
	26.04	D SC Final	N	Wimborne	562	W 2 - 1	Laws 43, Nicholson 90	at Dorchester Town
41	29.04	DM P	H	BURTON ALBION	901	L 1 - 2	Laws 35	
42	06.05	DM P	A	Cambridge City	408	W 3 - 2	Hutchinson 72, 86, Hale 90	

PLAYING SQUAD

GOALKEEPERS: Danny Potter (Exeter), Dan Claxton (Dorchester U)

DEFENDERS: Mark Gammon (Truro C), Alex Browne (Youth), Ryan Cross (Dorchester T), Jamie Vittles (Gloucester C), John Waldock (Sunderland), Matthew Hare (Sligo R), Simon Browne (Salisbury C)

MIDFIELDERS: Ian Hutchinson (Halifax T), Michael Dean (Bournemouth), Mark Nicholson (Youth), Andy Mason (Thame U), Matthew Hale (Yeovil T)

FORWARDS: David Laws (Bishop Auckland), Mark Robinson (Gravesend), Martin Underhay (Wimborne T), Darren Rowbotham (Exeter)

WORCESTER CITY

CLUB OFFICIALS

Chairman: **Dr Michael Sorensen**
Vice Chairman: **Laurie Brown**

Secretary: **Steve Bond**
4 Ferry Close, Worcester, Worcs WR2 5PQ
Tel: 01905 423120/23003

FOOTBALL MANAGEMENT TEAM

Manager: John Barton
Assistant Manager: Mick Tuohy
Physio: Archie Richards

FACT FILE
Formed: 1902
Nickname: The City
Sponsors: Banks's
Newsline: 0930 555 810
Colours: Blue & white/white/white
Change colours: All yellow
Midweek matchday: Monday
Reserve Lge: Central Conference
1999-00
Captain: Mark Tucker
P.o.Y: Martin Weir
Top Scorer: Mark Owen

GROUND St George's Lane, Barbourne, Worcester WR1 1QT Tel: 01905 23003 Fax: 26668

Directions: M5 jct 6 (Worcester North), follow signs to Worcester, right at first lights, St Georges Lane is 3rd left. 1 mile from Foregate Street (BR)station

Capacity: 3,443   Cover: 2,000   Seats: 1,223   Floodlights: Yes

Clubhouse: Open every evening and Saturday and Sunday daytime. Cold snacks available

Two shops: Outside ground (souvenirs). Inside ground (programmes) Contact club for details.

Pages: 32   Price: £1.50
Editor: Julian Pugh (01905 723234)
Local Press: Berrows Journal,
Worcester Evening News
Local Radio: Radio Wyvern,
BBC Hereford & Worcester

PREVIOUS   **Leagues:** West Mids (Birmingham) 1902-38, Southern 38-79, Alliance Premier 79-85
Names: Berwick Rangers   **Grounds:** Severn Terrace, Thorneloe, Flagge Meadow

CLUB RECORDS   **Attendance:** 17,042 v Sheff Utd (lost 0-2), FA Cup 4th Rd 24/1/59
Win: 18-1 v Bilston, Birmingham League 21/11/31   **Defeat:** 0-10 v Wellington, Birmingham League 29/8/20
Career Goalscorer: John Inglis 189 (1970-77)   **Career Appearances:** Bobby McEwan 596 (1959-75)
Transfer fee paid: £8,500 for Jim Williams (Telford United, 1981)
Transfer fee received: £27,000 for John Barton (Everton, 1979)

BEST SEASON   **FA Cup:** 4th Rd 58-59. 1st Rd (12)
FA Trophy: QF 69-70 73-74 80-81 81-82   **Welsh Cup:** Semi-Final 78-79

HONOURS   Southern Lg 78-79, Div 1 67-68, Div 1 Nth 76-77, Lg Cup R-up 45-46 59-60, Chal.Cup 39-40, Champs Cup 78-79; West Mids (B'ham) Lg(4) 13-14 24-25 28-30 (R-up (3) 31-34); Worcs Snr Cup (26) 07-14 28-30 32-33 45-46(jt) 48-49 55-59 60-61 62-63 64-65 69-70 77-78 79-80 81-82 83-84 87-88 96-97; B'ham Snr Cup 75-76; Staffs Snr Cup 76-77; Inter Lg Champs Cup 78-79

Players progressing: A Awford (Portsmouth 91), P King/K Ball (Cardiff C.60/65), JWilliams/M Gayle (Walsall 79/91), J Fairbrother (Peterborough 65), DTennant (Lincoln 66), R Davies (Derby 71), N Merrick (Bournemouth 74), J Barton(Everton 79), A Preece (Wrexham 90), D Lyttle (Swansea 92) M.Griffiths (Torquay United 99)

Back Row: Geoff Ashby (Football Dev. Man.), Jon Narbett *, Steve Lutz, Kevin Willetts, Keith Knight, Nathan Jukes, Bradley Sandeman, Martin Obrey (Asst. Physio). **Middle:** Paul Davies (Asst. Man.)*, Graham Brown *, Dave Richards *, Darren Steadman *, Danny Watson, Carl Heeley, John McGrath *, Archie Richards (Physio). **Front:** Ian Cottrill, Sam Bowen, Chris Greenman, Graham Allner (Manager)*, Andy Ellis, Mark Owen, Jon Purdie.   * Left club during 1999-00 season.

Match Facts 1999-00

	Date	Comp.	H/A	Opponents	Att.	Result	Goalscorers
1	14.08	DM P	H	MARGATE	1,060	L 1 - 3	Ellis 82
2	16.08	DM P	A	Atherstone United	371	L 1 - 2	Owen 61
3	21.08	DM P	A	Dorchester Town	657	L 0 - 3	
4	23.08	DM P	H	BURTON ALBION	1,103	D 2 - 2	George 36 [og], Richards 82
5	28.08	DM P	H	KING'S LYNN	787	D 1 - 1	Gray 67
6	30.08	DM P	A	Newport County	978	L 0 - 1	
7	04.09	DM P	H	SALISBURY CITY	720	L 2 - 3	Owen 4, 88
8	06.09	DM P	A	Ilkeston Town	654	D 2 - 2	Purdie 7, 21
9	11.09	DM P	A	Grantham Town	332	W 2 - 0	Bowen 39, 65[p]
	18.09	FAC Q2	A	Christchurch	296	W 3 - 2	Davis 19, Bowen 24, 81[p]
10	25.09	DM P	H	HAVANT & WATERLOOVILLE	804	L 0 - 3	
	02.10	FAC Q3	H	HARROW BOROUGH	767	W 3 - 2	**Bowen 3** (26 42 58)
11	09.10	DM P	A	Weymouth	680	D 1 - 1	Owen 29
	16.10	FAC Q4	H	FOREST GREEN ROV.	1301	L 2 - 5	Bowen 5, Owen 20
12	23.10	DM P	A	Cambridge City	607	L 2 - 4	Davis 63, Owen 66[p]
13	25.10	DM P	H	ATHERSTONE UNITED	803	D 0 - 0	
14	06.11	DM P	A	Crawley Town	674	D 2 - 2	Owen 13, Deakin 31
15	13.11	DM P	H	ROTHWELL TOWN	524	D 0 - 0	
	15.11	Lg Cup 1	H	REDDITCH UNITED	367	W 6 - 1	**Owen 3** (14 60 72[p]), Ellis 57, Knight 69, Lutz 85[p]
16	20.11	DM P	A	Halesowen Town	708	L 1 - 2	Owen 45
	27.11	FAT 2	A	Hayes	671	W 2 - 0	Owen 22 34
17	04.12	DM P	H	CLEVEDON TOWN	702	W 1 - 0	Deakin 38
	06.12	LC 2	H	MOOR GREEN	336	W 3 - 1	Weir 44, Purdie 85, Deakin 87
18	18.12	DM P	H	ILKESTON TOWN	717	W 2 - 1	Ellis 20, Lutz 27
19	27.12	DM P	H	GLOUCESTER CITY	1609	W 4 - 0	Cotterill 10, Owen 44 59, Lutz 52
20	03.01	DM P	A	Tamworth	1309	L 2 - 4	Tucker 32, Lutz 40
21	08.01	DM P	H	NEWPORT COUNTY	1115	L 3 - 4	Lutz 19, Carty 55, Dukes 85
22	11.01	DM P	A	Burton Albion	867	W 3 - 2	Owen 39, Jukes 44, Carty 85
	15.01	FAT 3	H	BROMLEY	783	W 2 - 1	Carty 50, Owen 84
23	17.01	DM P	H	GRANTHAM TOWN	903	W 3 - 1	Knight 3, Owen 26 53
24	22.01	DM P	A	Merthyr Tydfil	633	W 3 - 0	Carty 33, Owen 59 79
	24.01	LC 3	H	BLAKENALL	355	W 4 - 2	**Bowen 3** (47 58 80), Owen 48[p]
25	29.01	DM P	A	Salisbury City	381	W 3 - 1	Bowen 70 71, Owen 79
	05.02	FAT 4	A	Stalybridge Celtic	747	W 1 - 0	Bowen 25
	08.02	Worcs SC 2	A	Evsham United	180	W 2 - 1	Lutz 25, Bowen 60
26	12.02	DM P	H	BATH CITY	1,611	L 0 - 1	
	15.02	LC QF	A	Burton Albion	609	L 0 - 1	
27	19.02	DM P	A	Havant & Waterlooville	448	L 0 - 1	
28	21.02	DM P	H	MERTHYR TYDFIL	1075	W 2 - 1	Purdie 51, Lutz 87
	26.02	FAT 5	A	Telford United	2085	L 1 - 4	Lutz 88
29	28.02	DM P	H	CAMBRIDGE CITY	827	W 3 - 2	Owen 18, Wheeler 46 82
30	04.03	DM P	A	Boston United	1840	L 1 - 2	Owen 37
31	06.03	DM P	H	HALESOWEN TOWN	1069	D 0 - 0	
32	11.03	DM P	A	Bath City	1287	D 1 - 1	Owen 65[p]
33	18.03	DM P	A	WEYMOUTH	873	D 1 - 1	Owen 78[p]
	22.03	WSC SF	A	Solihull Borough	143	L 0 - 3	
34	25.03	DM P	A	King's Lynn	627	W 1 - 0	Deakin 90
35	27.03	DM P	H	BOSTON UNITED	1151	L 1 - 2	Cottrill 60
36	01.04	DM P	A	Rothwell Town	184	W 1 - 0	Knight 45
37	08.04	DM P	A	CRAWLEY TOWN	858	L 2 - 5	Thomas 17, Hyde 67
38	15.04	DM P	A	Margate	198	W 1 - 0	Carty 58
39	22.04	DM P	H	TAMWORTH	935	L 0 - 1	
40	24.04	DM P	A	Gloucester City	560	L 1 - 2	Thomas 16
41	29.04	DM P	H	DORCHESTER TOWN	802	D 4 - 4	Owen 13, Carty 16, Thomas 27, 71
42	06.05	DM P	A	Clevedon Town	413	L 0 - 1	

PLAYING SQUAD

GOALKEEPERS:	Danny McDonnell (Halesowen T)
DEFENDERS:	Carl Heeley (Sutton Coldfield T), Chris Greenman (Bromsgrove R), Andy Bradley (Stafford R), **Mark Tucker** (Kettering T), Martin Weir (Kidderminster H)
MIDFIELDERS:	Ian Cottrill (Nuneaton B), John Deakin (Kidderminster H), Ian Reed (Nuneaton B), Nathan Jukes (Dorchester T), Paul Carty (Hednesford T), Andy Ellis (Woking)
FORWARDS:	Mark Owen (Willenhall T), Steve Lutz (Pershore T), Neil Ross (Leeds), Micky Cotter (Tamworth), Mike Wyatt (Gloucester C)

ATHERSTONE UNITED

Match Facts 1999-00

	Date	Comp.	H/A	Opponents	Att.	Result	Goalscorers	Lge Pos.
1	14.08	DM-P	A	King's Lynn	829	D 1 - 1	White 55	
2	16.08	DM-P	H	WORCESTER CITY	371	W 2 - 1	White 75, Albrighton 77	
3	21.08	DM-P	H	MERTHYR TYDFIL	341	L 0 - 3		
4	24.08	DM-P	A	Bath City	643	L 0 - 2		
5	28.08	DM-P	A	Havant & Waterlooville	336	D 1 - 1	Storer 42	
6	30.08	DM-P	H	GLOUCESTER CITY	363	W 1 - 0	Middleton 61	10
7	04.09	DM-P	A	Boston United	1,210	L 0 - 3		14
8	06.09	DMP	H	HALESOWEN TOWN	419	L 4 - 5	Albrighton 8 26, Storer 62[p], Purvey 84	
9	11.09	DMP	H	ROTHWELL TOWN	286	W 3 - 1	Albrighton 32, Kelly 34, Storer 66[p]	
	18.09	FAC Q2	A	Moor Green	298	L 1 - 2	Storer 9	-
10	25.09	DMP	A	Dorchester Town	532	D 2 - 2	Orton 6, White 73	12
	09.10	FAT 1	H	OSSETT TOWN	208	L 0 - 3		-
11	23.10	DM P	A	Clevedon Town	317	L 0 - 1		
12	25.10	DM P	A	Worcester City	803	D 0 - 0		
13	30.10	DM P	H	WEYMOUTH	265	D 1 - 1	Kelly 10	
14	06.11	DM P	A	Burton Albion	891	L 1 - 5	Vincent 18	
15	08.11	DM P	H	BATH CITY	324	D 0 - 0		
16	12.11	DM P	A	Salisbury City	374	L 0 - 1		
	16.11	Lg Cup 1	A	Tamworth	487	L 0 - 4		-
17	20.11	DM P	H	CRAWLEY TOWN	283	L 0 - 1		
	22.11	Birm SC2	H	MOOR GREEN	141	W 3 - 1	Robinson 45[og], Orton 70, Kelly 80	-
18	04.12	DM P	A	Merthyr Tydfil	625	L 0 - 2		
19	11.12	DM P	H	BOSTON UNITED	435	D 1 - 1	Blake 31	
20	18.12	DM P	A	Margate	391	L 0 - 2		19
21	27.12	DM P	H	TAMWORTH	1265	L 0 - 5		20
22	03.01	DM P	A	Cambridge City	369	L 2 - 3	Pitt 58 70	20
23	08.01	DM P	H	GRANTHAM TOWN	277	L 0 - 2		20
	10.01	Birm. SC 3	H	BIRMINGHAM CITY	202	L 0 - 2		-
24	15.01	DM P	H	KING'S LYNN	272	L 0 - 2		20
25	22.01	DM P	A	Newport County	588	D 1 - 1	Barrett 85[p]	20
26	29.01	DM P	H	MARGATE	241	L 0 - 1		20
27	05.02	DM P	A	Gloucester City	435	D 1 - 1	Lavery 56	21
28	12.02	DM P	A	Weymouth	674	D 0 - 0		21
29	19.02	DM P	H	NEWPORT COUNTY	354	L 0 - 1		21
30	26.02	DM P	A	Crawley Town	760	D 0 - 0		21
31	04.03	DM P	A	Rothwell Town	201	D 3 - 3	Hart 29, Pitt 39, White 42	21
32	06.03	DM P	H	ILKESTON TOWN	254	W 3 - 2	White 12, Pitt 25, Barratt 34[p]	21
33	11.03	DM P	H	DORCHESTER TOWN	205	D 1 - 1	Pitt 49	21
34	14.03	DM P	A	Halesowen Town	356	W 1 - 0	Cooper 81[og]	21
35	18.03	DM P	H	BURTON ALBION	565	L 0 - 2		21
36	01.04	DM P	H	SALISBURY CITY	165	L 0 - 3		21
37	08.04	DM P	A	Ilkeston Town	424	L 0 - 1		21
38	15.04	DM P	A	Grantham Town	501	L 0 - 6		21
39	19.04	DM P	H	CAMBRIDGE CITY	145	L 0 - 1		21
40	24.04	DM P	A	Tamworth	714	L 0 - 4		21
41	29.04	DM P	H	CLEVEDON TOWN	155	L 1 - 3	White 37	21
42	06.05	DM P	H	HAVANT & WATERLOOVILLE	147	L 0 - 1		22

GLOUCESTER CITY

Match Facts 1999-00

	Date	Comp.	H/A	Opponents	Att.	Result	Goalscorers
1	14.08	DM-P	H	GRANTHAM TOWN	739	W 2 - 0	Niblett 65, Smith 80
2	17.08	DM-P	A	Burton Albion	948	L 0 - 3	
3	21.08	DM-P	A	Margate	504	L 0 - 3	
4	24.08	DM-P	H	TAMWORTH	509	D 0 - 0	
5	28.08	DM-P	H	CAMBRIDGE CITY	446	W 1 - 0	Callinan 80
6	30.08	DM-P	A	Atherstone United	363	L 0 - 1	
7	04.09	DM-P	H	DORCHESTER TOWN	340	D 0 - 0	
8	07.09	DM-P	A	Clevedon Town	481	L 0 - 3	
9	11.09	DM-P	A	Havant & Waterlooville	374	D 1 - 1	Smith 75[p]
	18.09	FAC Q2	A	Weymouth	642	D 0 - 0	
	21.09	FAC Q2R	H	WEYMOUTH	491	W 2 - 1	J Smith 66[p], Fergusson 87
10	25.09	DM-P	H	ILKESTON TOWN	558	W 1 - 0	Chenoweth 86
	02.10	FAC Q3	H	MERTHYR TYDFIL	729	L 2 - 3	Wyatt 7, Smith 89
	09.10	FAT 1	H	CHESHAM UNITED	513	W 4 - 2	Chenoweth 20, Cox 31, 50, Smith 78
	13.10	Glos SC1	A	Forest Green Rovers	365	L 0 - 5	
11	16.10	DM P	H	WEYMOUTH	454	D 1 - 1	Thorne 50
12	23.10	DM P	A	Merthyr Tydfil	528	L 0 - 5	
13	26.10	DM P	H	BURTON ALBION	418	W 2 - 1	Cox 10, 76
14	30.10	DM P	H	BOSTON UNITED	507	D 2 - 2	Cox 52, Smith 68
15	06.11	DM P	A	Bath City	926	L 1 - 5	Rose 50
16	12.11	DM P	H	NEWPORT COUNTY	889	D 1 - 1	Rose 82
	16.11	Lg Cup 1	H	YATE TOWN	140	W 4 - 1	Smith 3 (36 47 57), Cairns 56
17	20.11	DM P	A	Grantham Town	306	D 1 - 1	Cox 81
	27.11	FAT 2	A	Welling United	423	L 1 - 2	Smith 38[p]
18	04.12	DM P	H	ROTHWELL TOWN	395	W 3 - 1	Cox 4, Rose 11, Smith 67
	07.12	LC 2	H	SOLIHULL BOROUGH	208	W 3 - 1	Callinan 7, Smith 23 35
19	18.12	DM P	H	CRAWLEY TOWN	416	D 2 - 2	Rose 30, Fergusson 43
20	27.12	DM P	A	Worcester City	1609	L 0 - 4	
21	03.01	DM P	H	HALESOWEN TOWN	562	D 2 - 2	Callinan 45, Thorne 85
22	08.01	DM P	H	CLEVEDON TOWN	452	L 1 - 5	Smith 63
23	15.01	DM P	A	Cambridge City	418	L 1 - 2	Smith 75
24	18.01	DM P	H	MERTHYR TYDFIL	404	W 1 - 0	Smith 9
25	22.01	DM P	A	Weymouth	643	L 1 - 4	Cox 89
	25.01	LC 3	A	Bath City	434	L 0 - 3	
26	29.01	DM P	A	Dorchester Town	574	W 2 - 1	Thorne 43, Abbott 45
27	02.02	DM P	A	Newport County	577	L 1 - 2	Smith 49
28	05.02	DM P	H	ATHERSTONE UNITED	435	D 1 - 1	Smith 26
29	12.02	DM P	A	King's Lynn	565	L 0 - 2	
30	19.02	DM P	H	BATH CITY	695	D 1 - 1	Smith 29
31	26.02	DM P	A	Salisbury City	535	L 0 - 2	
32	04.03	DM P	H	KING'S LYNN	429	L 0 - 1	
33	07.03	DM P	A	Tamworth	493	D 1 - 1	Cox 30
34	11.03	DM P	A	Ilkeston Town	505	L 0 - 1	
35	25.03	DM P	H	HAVANT & WATERLOOVILLE	426	D 1 - 1	Cook 51
36	01.04	DM P	A	Crawley Town	713	L 1 - 2	Cook 49
37	08.04	DM P	A	Boston United	2063	L 1 - 6	Wyatt 86
38	15.04	DM P	H	SALISBURY CITY	408	D 3 - 3	Niblett 57, Bayliss 79, 85
39	22.04	DM P	A	Halesowen Town	452	L 2 - 4	Bayliss 83, Devlin 90
40	24.04	DM P	H	WORCESTER CITY	560	W 2 - 1	Wyatt 18, Bayliss 21
41	29.04	DM P	H	MARGATE	326	L 0 - 4	
42	06.05	DM P	A	Rothwell Town	191	L 0 - 2	

GRANTHAM TOWN

Match Facts 1999-00

	Date	Comp.	H/A	Opponents	Att.	Result	Goalscorers	Lge Pos.
1	14.08	DM-P	A	Gloucester City	739	L 0 - 2		
2	17.08	DM-P	H	KING'S LYNN	544	L 1 - 3	Bogan 88	
3	21.08	DM-P	H	NEWPORT COUNTY	365	L 0 - 1		22
4	24.08	DM-P	A	Halesowen Town	422	L 1 - 2	Featherstone 4	22
5	28.08	DM-P	A	Bath City	699	L 1 - 2	Featherstone 67	22
6	30.08	DM-P	H	TAMWORTH	375	L 0 - 3		22
7	04.09	DM-P	A	Weymouth	533	L 2 - 3	Carvell 43, Bogan 71	22
8	07.09	DM-P	A	Rothwell Town	264	L 0 - 2		22
9	11.09	DM-P	H	WORCESTER CITY	332	L 0 - 2		22
	18.09	FAC Q2	H	NORTHAMPTON SPENCER	298	W 6 - 0	Gilbert 8[p], Bogan 23, Featherstone 46, Wilkes 49 65, Rogers 77	-
10	25.09	DM-P	A	Clevedon Town	354	D 2 - 2	Brogan 39, Wilkes 90	22
	02.10	FAC Q3	A	Hitchin Town	430	L 1 - 2	Wilkes 2	-
	09.10	FAT 1	H	MATLOCK TOWN	298	L 1 - 3	Ranshaw 2	-
11	23.10	DM P	A	Burton Albion	1175	L 0 - 1		22
12	26.10	DM P	A	King's Lynn	837	D 3 - 3	Wilkes 42, Gwyther 72, Bogan 76	22
13	30.10	DM P	H	HAVANT & WATERLOOVILLE	292	W 2 - 0	Neil 27, Gwyther 58	21
14	06.11	DM P	A	Merthyr Tydfil	608	L 2 - 5	Ranshaw 17, Neil 43	22
15	09.11	DM P	H	HALESOWEN TOWN	274	W 1 - 0	Neil 53	
16	13.11	DM P	A	Crawley Town	692	L 2 - 3	Rookes 40, Ranshaw 87	22
	16.11	Lg Cup 1	A	Rothwell Town	143	W 2 - 1	Logan 55, Ranshaw 70	-
17	20.11	DM P	H	GLOUCESTER CITY	306	D 1 - 1	Ranshaw 69	22
18	04.12	DM P	A	Salisbury City	379	L 0 - 5		22
	07.12	LC 2	H	CAMBRIDGE CITY	187	W 2 - 1	Neil 83[p], Ball 90	-
19	11.12	DM P	H	MARGATE	285	L 1 - 2	Logan 51	22
20	18.12	DM P	H	DORCHESTER TOWN	242	L 0 - 2		22
21	27.12	DM P	A	Ilkeston Town	908	L 4 - 5	Neil 43, Gwyther 59, Ranshaw 65, Carvill 74	22
22	03.01	DM P	H	BOSTON UNITED	1265	L 0 - 3		22
23	08.01	DM P	A	Atherstone United	277	W 2 - 0	Wilkes 32, Simmons 44	22
24	15.01	DM P	H	MERTHYR TYDFIL	306	D 1 - 1	Wilkes 64	22
25	17.01	DM P	A	Worcester City	903	L 1 - 3	Ranshaw 61	22
26	22.01	DM P	H	SALISBURY CITY	250	W 5 - 1	Gray 25 48, Ranshaw 29, White 44, McDaid 47	21
	25.01	LC 3	A	King's Lynn	549	L 0 - 1		-
27	29.01	DM P	H	BATH CITY	386	L 1 - 3	Gray 73	21
28	05.02	DM P	A	Tamworth	711	W 4 - 3	McDaid 26 90, Ranshaw 47 81	20
29	12.02	DM P	A	Newport County	620	L 1 - 2	Ranshaw 70	20
30	19.02	DM P	H	WEYMOUTH	344	D 3 - 3	Wilkes 8, Harbottle 31, Gray 86	20
31	26.02	DM P	A	Cambridge City	427	W 2 - 0	Harbottle 35 90	20
32	04.03	DM P	A	Margate	469	W 2 - 1	Speed 4, Ranshaw 75	20
33	11.03	DM P	H	CLEVEDON TOWN	374	W 2 - 0	Speed 45, Gray 66	
34	14.03	DM P	H	CAMBRIDGE CITY	476	W 2 - 0	Speed 24, Neil 61	
35	25.03	DM P	H	ROTHWELL TOWN	476	W 1 - 0	Taylor 45	19
36	01.04	DM P	H	BURTON ALBION	736	L 0 - 1		19
37	08.04	DM P	A	Dorchester Town	554	W 1 - 0	Bradshaw 22	19
38	15.04	DM P	H	ATHERSTONE UNITED	501	W 6 - 0	Speed 6, Gray 22, Taylor 50, McDaid 56, Hawley 79, Stones 83	19
39	22.04	DM P	A	Boston United	4137	L 1 - 3	Neil 1	18
40	24.04	DM P	H	ILKESTON TOWN	677	W 1 - 0	McDaid 58	18
41	29.04	DM P	A	Havant & Waterlooville	670	L 0 - 1		19
42	06.05	DM P	H	CRAWLEY TOWN	555	W 4 - 2	Taylor 9, McDaid 28, Hallcro 66, Wilkes 89	19

ROTHWELL TOWN

Match Facts 1999-00

	Date	Comp.	H/A	Opponents	Att.	Result	Goalscorers	Lge Pos.
1	14.08	DM-P	A	Weymouth	893	L 0 - 3		
2	17.08	DM-P	H	CRAWLEY TOWN	244	D 3 - 3	Lord 56, Moore 75, Machin 90	
3	21.08	DM-P	H	HAVANT & WATERLOOVILLE	237	D 1 - 1	Moore 54	
4	25.08	DM-P	A	Boston United	1,434	L 0 - 2		
5	28.08	DM-P	H	SALISBURY CITY	227	W 3 - 2	Dunlop 1, 55, Keast 58	
6	30.08	DM-P	H	HALESOWEN TOWN	291	D 2 - 2	Machin 39, Bullimore 55	17
7	04.09	DM-P	A	Bath City	756	L 0 - 1		18
8	07.09	DM-P	H	GRANTHAM TOWN	264	W 2 - 0	Keast 11, Moore 72	
9	11.09	DM-P	A	Atherstone United	286	L 1 - 3	Moore 83	
	18.09	FAC Q2	A	Northwood	178	D 3 - 3	Machin 45, Moore 55, Vallence 90	-
	21.09	FAC Q2R	H	NORTHWOOD	216	W 2 - 0	Moore 15, Jowett 59	
10	25.09	DM-P	H	MERTHYR TYDFIL	237	W 2 - 0	Machin 31, Moore 78	11
	02.10	FAC Q3	A	Wealdstone	397	D 1 - 1	Machin 83	-
	05.10	FAC Q3 R	H	WEALDSTONE	425	W 2 - 0	Dunlop 55, Keast 59	-
	09.10	FAT 1	H	BOREHAM WOOD	217	D 0 - 0		-
	12.10	FAT 1 R	A	Boreham Wood	63	W 5 - 3	Gould 14, Grime 29[og], Machin 70, Foley 108, Hough 117	-
	16.10	FAC Q4	H	KETTERING TOWN	1437	D 1 - 1	Vallance 47	-
	19.10	FAC Q4 R	A	Kettering Town	1611	L 1 - 2	Machin 84	-
11	23.10	DM P	A	Margate	470	L 1 - 4	Moore 60	
12	26.10	DM P	A	Crawley Town	481	L 1 - 4	Moore 77	
	02.11	N'hants SC1	H	LONG BUCKBY	101	W 3 - 1	Bullimore 23[p], Machin 38 62	
13	06.11	DM P	A	Havant & Waterlooville	283	L 2 - 5	Howey 17, Jowett 32	
14	09.11	DM P	H	BOSTON UNITED	345	L 0 - 2		
15	13.11	DM P	A	Worcester City	524	D 0 - 0		
	16.11	Lg Cup 1	H	GRANTHAM TOWN	143	L 1 - 2	Jowett 87	-
16	20.11	DM P	H	WEYMOUTH	201	L 1 - 2	Huff 87	19
	27.11	FAT 2	H	EVESHAM UNITED	248	W 4 - 1	West 9[og], Bullimore 35[p], Preston 52, Machin 63	-
17	04.12	DM P	A	Gloucester City	395	L 1 - 3	Dunlop 37	21
18	27.12	DM P	H	CAMBRIDGE CITY	297	L 1 - 4	Bullimore 70	21
19	03.01	DM P	A	King's Lynn	1039	D 0 - 0		21
20	08.01	DM P	H	BURTON ALBION	502	D 1 - 1	Hough 8	21
	15.01	FAT 3	H	WALTON & HERSHAM	207	D 1 - 1	Preston 44	-
	18.01	FAT 3R	A	Walton & Hersham	208	L 0 - 1		-
21	22.01	DM P	H	DORCHESTER TOWN	201	L 1 - 4	Tidey 25	22
	25.01	NSC QF	A	Northampton Spencer	157	D 2 - 2	Spencer 27, Crick 32[og]	-
22	29.01	DM P	A	Burton Albion	894	L 1 - 2	Machin 24	22
23	05.02	DM P	H	CLEVEDON TOWN	203	L 0 - 2		22
24	12.02	DM P	A	Salisbury City	404	L 2 - 4	Wagstaff 45, Cook 87	22
25	26.02	DM P	A	Dorchester Town	485	D 0 - 0		22
	29.02	NSC SF	H	KETTERING TOWN	530	L 0 - 1		-
26	04.03	DM P	H	ATHERSTONE UNITED	201	D 3 - 3	Gould 45, Foley 59, Barratt 65[og]	
27	11.03	DM P	A	Newport County	635	D 1 - 1	Gould 30	
28	14.03	DM P	H	BATH CITY	182	L 2 - 3	Keast 12, Gould 62	
29	18.03	DM P	A	Merthyr Tydfil	446	L 1 - 3	Machin 60	
30	20.03	DM P	H	ILKESTON TOWN	435	D 3 - 3	Preston 5 58, Cook 23	
31	25.03	DM P	A	Grantham Town	476	L 0 - 1		
32	28.03	DM P	H	TAMWORTH	196	D 1 - 1	Preston 17	
33	01.04	DM P	H	WORCESTER CITY	184	L 0 - 1		
34	08.04	DM P	A	Clevedon Town	245	D 1 - 1	Spencer 38	
35	11.04	DM P	A	Tamworth	326	L 1 - 2	Jowett 34	
36	15.04	DM P	H	NEWPORT COUNTY	198	L 0 - 3		
37	18.04	DM P	H	MARGATE	167	L 0 - 2		
38	24.04	DM P	A	Cambridge City	304	L 0 - 1		
39	26.04	DM P	H	ILKESTON TOWN	151	D 2 - 2	Spencer 16, Foley 23	
40	29.04	DM P	A	Halesowen Town	453	D 3 - 3	Turner 10, Bullimore 54 (p), Preston 90	
41	01.05	DM P	H	KING'S LYNN	201	W 2 - 1	Foley 12, Hough 69	
42	06.05	DM P	H	GLOUCESTER CITY	191	W 2 - 0	Hough 59, Gould 86	

WESTERN DIVISION FINAL LEAGUE TABLE 1999-2000

		P	W	D	L	F	A	GD	Pts
1	Stafford Rangers	42	29	6	7	107	47	60	93
2	Moor Green	42	26	12	4	85	33	52	90
3	Hinckley United	42	25	12	5	89	47	42	87
4	Tiverton Town	42	26	7	9	91	44	47	85
5	Solihull Borough	42	20	11	11	85	66	19	71
6	Blakenall	42	19	12	11	70	46	24	69
7	Cirencester Town	42	20	8	14	72	64	8	68
8	Bilston Town	42	16	18	8	66	52	14	66
9	Cinderford Town	42	17	11	14	62	64	-2	62
10	Redditch United	42	17	10	15	73	65	8	61
11	Gresley Rovers	42	14	15	13	54	49	5	57
12	Weston - S - Mare	42	16	9	17	55	55	0	57
13	Sutton Coldfield T	42	13	17	12	49	52	-3	56
14	Evesham United	42	13	12	17	69	61	8	51
15	Bedworth United	42	13	10	19	52	71	-19	49
16	Rocester	42	12	12	18	63	78	-15	48
17	Bromsgrove Rovers	42	13	7	22	59	72	-13	46
18	Shepshed Dynamo	42	12	7	23	46	66	-20	43
19	Paget Rangers	42	11	4	27	44	82	-38	37
20	Racing Club Warwick	42	7	14	21	41	82	-41	35
21	Stourbridge	42	10	3	29	45	101	-56	33
22	Yate Town	42	3	3	36	28	108	-80	12

WESTERN DIVISION LEADING GOALSCORERS 1999-2000

Richard Mitchell	Stafford Rangers	36
Derek Hall	Moor Green	32
Scott Voice	Bilston Town	27
Kevin Nancekivell	Tiverton Town	25
David Sadler	Hinckley United	22
Simon Windsor	Racing Club Warwick	21
Jody Bevan	Cinderford Town	20
Joseph Dowling	Solihull Borough	20
Mark Shepherd	Moor Green	19
Scott Griffin	Cirencester Town	17

Christie McKenzie	Stourbridge	17
David Toomey	Cinderford Town	17
Ian Drewitt	Bedford United	16
Anthony Eccleston	Stafford Rangers	16
Jamie Lenton	Hinckley United	16
John Muir	Blakenall	16
Paul Corcoran	Cirencester Town	15
Philip Everett	Tiverton Town	15
Pater Varley	Tiverton Town	15

WESTERN DIVISION RESULTS CHART 1999-2000

		1	2	3	4	5	6	7	8	9	10	11	12	13	14	15	16	17	18	19	20	21	22
1	Bedworth U	X	1-1	0-1	3-0	0-0	0-2	0-5	1-1	0-1	1-4	3-1	2-0	2-0	3-2	1-2	2-2	2-1	3-0	0-0	0-0	0-0	2-0
2	Bilston T	3-0	X	1-1	1-1	2-2	0-4	1-1	3-1	1-1	2-2	1-1	4-0	1-0	2-2	3-1	3-1	1-5	1-0	1-1	1-0	2-0	3-1
3	Blakenall	6-0	1-1	X	1-0	3-1	2-3	3-3	1-0	3-3	1-2	0-1	3-0	0-0	5-3	4-0	1-1	1-4	2-3	0-1	1-0	2-0	1-0
4	Bromsgrove	0-1	1-2	1-1	X	0-1	1-2	1-0	3-4	1-2	1-2	4-1	1-1	1-3	5-1	0-2	3-0	4-3	4-1	0-2	1-2	2-2	3-0
5	Cinderford	2-1	1-0	1-1	0-4	X	1-2	0-0	1-1	0-2	0-0	4-1	1-0	1-0	1-2	1-0	1-3	2-0	1-0	0-3	1-0	2-1	6-0
6	Cirencester	2-2	2-2	1-1	1-0	0-1	X	2-3	1-1	2-1	1-5	6-2	1-0	2-3	3-2	0-0	2-3	1-2	4-2	1-3	0-3	2-1	3-0
7	Evesham U	2-1	1-3	0-1	0-2	1-1	1-2	X	1-1	2-3	1-1	3-1	3-1	0-3	1-2	2-0	4-3	1-4	4-0	0-0	0-0	0-1	1-1
8	Gresley R	2-1	3-1	0-1	0-0	1-1	0-0	1-1	X	2-2	0-1	2-1	1-1	2-1	0-0	2-0	4-2	0-1	3-0	3-1	1-3	0-0	5-2
9	Hinckley U	1-0	3-1	1-0	5-0	3-0	5-2	1-3	2-0	X	1-1	4-1	4-0	1-1	1-1	1-0	2-1	3-1	3-0	1-0	1-1	4-1	3-2
10	Moor Green	3-1	1-0	0-5	5-0	2-1	0-0	2-0	1-0	1-1	X	2-0	2-2	1-1	2-1	3-0	0-0	2-3	7-1	1-1	1-1	2-0	6-0
11	Paget R	2-4	0-2	2-1	0-1	1-5	1-0	2-1	1-0	0-1	1-2	X	1-2	0-1	2-4	0-0	0-1	0-2	0-0	0-0	1-2	0-2	3-0
12	RC Warwick	1-2	0-0	1-1	3-3	2-2	0-1	1-6	0-2	2-2	0-4	2-3	X	1-1	0-1	1-5	1-1	1-0	0-4	1-4	0-3	1-0	3-1
13	Redditch U	3-0	1-1	2-4	3-1	5-2	3-0	1-0	0-2	2-0	0-3	0-2	3-0	X	3-1	2-2	4-2	0-3	1-2	3-3	1-2	1-0	4-0
14	Rocester	1-1	1-1	0-0	4-0	3-3	3-4	0-7	1-1	1-3	0-1	2-0	2-2	2-3	X	1-5	1-4	0-1	4-2	4-1	1-1	3-0	1-0
15	Shepshed	3-3	0-1	0-1	0-0	2-5	1-0	0-0	0-1	2-3	0-3	1-2	1-3	4-0	2-1	X	1-3	1-5	1-0	3-0	0-2	1-0	5-0
16	Solihull	3-0	1-1	2-1	3-0	0-1	3-4	4-3	3-1	0-0	1-1	4-3	2-2	4-1	4-2	X	3-2	3-1	1-1	2-1	0-0	0-1	0-1
17	Stafford R	2-1	1-1	2-2	3-1	3-1	1-3	5-0	3-2	0-0	0-1	2-0	5-0	1-0	2-1	3-0	2-1	X	7-2	4-1	2-1	5-2	4-0
18	Stourbridge	3-1	1-4	1-2	0-3	2-3	1-3	1-0	2-2	2-1	1-3	0-2	0-4	5-3	0-1	3-1	0-3	0-2	X	1-1	1-5	0-2	3-1
19	Sutton C T	4-1	1-1	0-2	0-3	1-1	2-1	1-0	3-1	2-0	1-0	3-2	0-0	1-1	0-0	0-0	2-2	1-3	0-1	X	0-2	0-1	0-0
20	Tiverton T	3-1	5-2	2-1	2-0	6-1	2-0	1-4	3-0	7-2	1-0	2-1	1-0	3-5	1-1	0-2	6-1	2-2	2-0	0-1	X	5-1	4-0
21	Weston S M	1-3	2-0	3-0	5-2	3-2	1-2	2-2	0-0	1-2	1-2	5-1	0-1	2-1	1-0	1-0	1-0	2-2	3-2	2-2	0-1	X	4-1
22	Yate Town	1-2	0-4	0-2	0-1	1-2	1-1	1-2	0-1	0-7	1-3	1-2	1-2	1-2	0-1	2-0	0-2	0-3	0-3	5-1	1-2	0-1	X

ATHERSTONE UNITED

CLUB OFFICIALS

Chairman: **Ku Akeredolu**
President: **C Culwick**
Secretary: **Neil Dykes**
18 Greendale Close, Atherstone,
Warwickshire CV9 1PR Tel: 01827 714326

Commercial Manager: **T Jago**

FOOTBALL MANAGEMENT TEAM

Manager: Stephen Mackenzie
Asst Manager: R Stockley
Physio: S Welch

FACT FILE

Formed: 1979
Nickname: The Adders
Club Sponsors: T.B.A.
Colours: Red & white stripes/red/red
Change colours: Yellow & blue/blue/blue
Midweek home matchday: Monday 7.30pm
Reserve's Lge: Midland Comb. Reserve Div.
Programme: Pages: 28 Price: £1
Editor: Brian Stephenson 01827 715067
Local Press: Tamworth Herald,
Evening News, Atherstone Herald,
Coventry Telegraph.
Local Radio: Mercia Sound, CWR

For up to the minute news,
results, fixtures,
plus general facts & figures
from the world of
non-league football

log on to

www.nlfootball.com

GROUND Sheepy Road, Atherstone, Warwickshire. CV9 1HG
Tel: 01827 717829

Directions: Half mile north of town centre on B4116 Twycross/Ashby road.

Capacity: 3,500 Cover: 1,000 Seats: 373 Floodlights: Yes

Clubhouse: Open during normal licensing hours, all usual facilities.
Club Shop: Programmes, magazines, souvenirs etc. Contact: Sreve Clark 01827 712812

PREVIOUS **Leagues:** West Midlands 1979-87

CLUB RECORDS Attendance: 2,873 v V.S. Rugby, F.A. Cup 1st Round Proper 1987-88
Win: 12-2 vTipton Town (H), West Midlands (Regional) League Premier Division 86-87
Defeat: 1-7 v Rushden & Diamonds, Beazer League Premier Division 94-95
Goalscorer: Alan Bourton **Appearances:** Lee Spencer
Fee Paid: £4,500 toGloucester City for Gary Bradder, 1989
Fee Received: £40,000 for Andy Rammellfrom Manchester United, September 1989

HONOURS Southern Lge Midland Div 88-89; West Midlands Lge 81-82 86-87 (Lge Cup 81-82,Premier Div Cup 86-87, Div 2 Cup (Res.)
86-87); Walsall Senior Cup 83-84; Midland Combination Reserve Division 87-88; Birmingham Senior Cup R-up 89-90

BEST SEASON FA Cup: 2nd Rd Proper 1990-91, 0-1 v Crewe Alexandra (A)
FA Trophy: 1st Round 88-89 91-92.

Players progressing: Andy Rammell (Manchester United)

THE NON-LEAGUE PAPER

CONFERENCE & PYRAMID LEAGUES SOCCER / £1.00

AVAILABLE AT A NEWSAGENT NEAR YOU EVERY SUNDAY

BEDWORTH UNITED

CLUB OFFICIALS

Chairman: **Peter Randle**
Vice Chairman: **Wayne Harris**

Secretary: **Graham J Bloxham**
43 Mount Pleasant Road,Bedworth,
Warwicks CV12 8EX

Press Officer: **Jamie Home**

FOOTBALL MANAGEMENT TEAM

Managers: Gary Bradder & Dave Grundy.
Club Doctor: Philip Earl
Physio: John Roberts

FACT FILE

Formed: 1896
Nickname: Greenbacks
Sponsors:Bedworth Telegraph
Colours: Green & white/Green/Green.
Change colours: Yellow & green
Midweek matchday: Tuesday
Reserves: Midland Comb Res Lg.
Youth League: Midland Floodlit Youth

GROUND   The Oval, Miners Welfare Park, Coventry Road, Bedworth CV12 8NN
             Tel: 02476 314302
Directions: M6 jct 3, into Bedworth on B4113 Coventry to Bedworth road, ground200yds past
past Bedworth Leisure Centre on this road. Coaches should park atthis Leisure Centre. Buses
from Coventry and Nuneaton pass ground
Capacity: 7,000   Cover: 300   Seats: 300   Floodlights: Yes
Clubhouse: Social club open every day 7.30-11pm & w/e noon-3pm. Hot and cold bar food
Club Shop: Selling a wide range of souvenirs & programmes.
        Contact : Ron Kemp   01203 318014

Pages: 18   Price: £1
Editor: Ron Kemp:(02476 318014)
Local Press: Heartland Evening News, Weekly
Tribune, Bedworth Echo,
Coventry Evening Telegraph
Local Radio: Mercia Sound, BBC CWR

PREVIOUS   **Leagues:** Birmingham Comb. 47-54; West Mids (at first Birmingham) Lg 54-72
            Name: Bedworth Town 47-68   **Ground:** British Queen Ground 11-39

CLUB RECORDS   **Attendance:** 5,127 v Nuneaton Borough, Southern Lg Midland Division 23/2/82
            Win: 11-0   **Defeat:** 1-10
            Career Goalscorer: Peter Spacey (1949-69)   **Career Appearances:** Peter Spacey
            Transfer fee paid: £1,750 for Colin Taylor (Hinckley Town, 1991-92)
            Transfer fee received: £30,000 for Richard Landon (Plymouth Argyle, January 1994)

BEST SEASON   **FA Trophy:** Second Round 80-81
            FA Cup: 4th Qualifying Rd 1983/89/90

HONOURS   Birmingham Comb.(2) 48-50, Birmingham Snr Cup(3) 78-79 80-82, Midland Floodlit Cup 81-82 92-93

Players progressing: Phil Huffer (Derby County 1953), Geoff Coleman(Northampton Town 1955), Ian Hathaway (Mansfield Town 1989), Richard Landon(Plymouth Argyle 1994)

Guy Sanders trying to set up an attack
in Bedworth's match against
Cinderford Town last season.
Photo: Keith Clayton

BILSTON TOWN

CLUB OFFICIALS
Chairman: **Morris Baker**
Vice-Chairman: **A K Hickman**
President: **Dennis Turner MP**
Press Officer: **A Owen**
Secretary: **Jeff Calloway**
4 Mervyn Rd, Bradley, Bilston,
West Midlands WV14 8DF
Tel: 01902 681660

FOOTBALL MANAGEMENT TEAM
Manager: Joe Jackson
Asst Manager: Tom Stokes
Physio: Jon King

FACT FILE

Formed: 1895
Nickname: Steelmen or Boro
Sponsors: Stowlawn Ltd and Second City
Colours: Orange/white/white
Change colours: White/black/orange
Midweek matchday: Tuesday
Reserves' League: No reserve team
Youth Team:West Midland (Regional)
League Youth Division

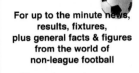

For up to the minute news,
results, fixtures,
plus general facts & figures
from the world of
non-league football

log on to

www.nlfootball.com

GROUND   Queen Street, Bilston WV14 7EX Tel: 01902 491498
Directions: M6 junction 10, A454 towards Wolverhampton then pick up A563 towards Bilston and turn left into Beckett Street after a little over a mile,ground at bottom. 3 miles from Wolverhampton (BR), bus 45 from bus station passes ground. Buses 78 and 79 from Birmingham stop within quarter of a mile of ground
Capacity: 4,000   Cover: 350   Seats: 350   Floodlights: Yes
Clubhouse: Open evenings & weekend lunchtimes (normal pub hours). Usual club activities
Club Shop: Sells a range of souvenirs and programmes.
          Contact Paul Calloway, 4 Mervyn Rd, Bradley, Bilston, West Mids WV14 8DF

PROGRAMME
Pages: 24   Price: 70p
Editor: Secretary (01902 491799)

Local Press:
Expess & Star, Evening Mail
Local Radio:
Radio West Mids, WABC, Beacon, BRMB

PREVIOUS   **Leagues:** Birmingham Comb. 07-21 48-54, (Birmingham) West Mids 21-32 54-85
               Names: Bilston Utd 1895-1932, Bilston   **Ground:** Prouds Lane 1895-1921

CLUB RECORDS **Attendance:** 7,500 v Wolverhampton Wanderers, floodlight opening 1953
                 Competitive: 7,000 v Halifax Town, F.A. Cup First Round 1968
                 Win: 12-2 v Tipton Town   **Defeat:** 0-8 v Merthyr Tydfil
                 Career Goalscorer: Ron McDermott 78   **Career Appearances:** Unknown
                 Transfer fee paid: Transfer fee received: From Southend United for Ron Poutney, 1975

BEST SEASON   **FA Trophy:** 2nd Round 70-71, 74-75   **FA Vase:** Quarter Finals 92-93
                 FA Cup: 2nd Rd replay 72-73 (0-1 at Barnet after 1-1 draw). Also 1st Rd 68-69. League clubs defeated: None

HONOURS   West Mids Lg 60-61 72-73 (R-up 22-23 70-71 73-74 74-75 75-76 84-85, Lg Cup 72-73 (R-up 65-66) Div 2 56-57),
                 Birmingham Senior Cup 1895-96 Wednesbury Charity Cup 1981-81 81-82 82-83 84-85 (R-up 83-84)

Players progressing: R Ellows (Birmingham), James Fletcher (Birmingham 1950),Stan Crowther (A Villa 1955), Ron Pountney (Southend 1975),
          K Price(Gillingham), Campbell Chapman (Wolves 1984) Joe Jackson (Wolves), Mike Turner (Barnsley 1999)

Goalmouth action from Bilston's
Easter Monday clash with
Stafford Rangers.
Photo: Chris Elsey

BLAKENALL

CLUB OFFICIALS
Chairman: **P Langston**
Vice Chairman: **D Cotterill**
President: **J Bridgett**
Secretary: **David Birch**, 64 Wimperis Way,
Great Barr, Birmingham B43 7DF
Tel: 0121 360 3574
Commercial Manager:**Sreve Tittley**
(01922 400600)
Press Officer: **Russell Brown**
(0836 383874 Mobile)

FOOTBALL MANAGEMENT TEAM
Managers : Mick Folland & Paul Knox
Coach: JimSkidmore

FACT FILE

Founded: 1946
Nickname: Nall
Sponsor: T.B.A.
Colours: Blue white trim/blue/blue white trim
Change: Red & Black/black/black & white
Midweek Matchday: Tuesday

1999-00
Captain: Darren Simkin
P.o.Y.: Matthew Lowe
Top scorer: John Muir (19)

Pages: 52 Price: 80p
Editor: Russell Brown Tel: 0836 383874
Local Press: Express & Star, Walsall
Chronicle, Walsall Advertiser, Walsall
Observer, Sunday Mercury, Sports Argus
Local Radio: BBC West Midlands,
BRMB, Beacon Radio

GROUND Red Lion Ground, Somerfield Rd, Leamore, Walsall, West Mids Tel: 01922 405835

Directions: M6 jct 10, follow signs for Walsall centre. At 1st lights turn left (about 200yds from Motorway junction) into Bloxwich Lane.At new traffic island turn left and continue to`T' junction. Then turn right into Leamore Lane, at traffic island (Four C rosses pub) turn left into Somerfield Road. Ground approx. 400yds on right
Nearest Railway Station: Bloxwich North, (5 minutes walk from ground)
Capacity: 2,500   Seats: 250   Cover: 250   Floodlights: Yes
Clubhouse: Open 7-11 (Mon-Sun), 1-11 (Sat). Food available matchdays   Club Shop: No

PREVIOUS   **Leagues:** Bloxwich Comb.; Staffs County; Midland Comb. 60-79; W Midlands Reg Lge79-95; Midland All 95-97
Names: None

CLUB RECORDS **Attendance:** 1,550 v Halesowen Town 85-86
Win: 11-0 v Bilston United 26/4/95
Defeat: 0-7 v Macclesfield Town (Staffs Sen Cup) 31/1/95
Fee Received: £10,000 for Darren Simkin (Wolverhampton Wanderers, 1992)

BEST SEASON   **FA Trophy:** 2nd Rd 98-99   **FA Vase:** 2nd Rd Proper 91-92

HONOURS   Midland Football Alliance 96-97, R-up 95-96; Industrial Rewinds Lge Cup 95-96; Midland Invitation Triangular Cup 94-95, R-up 97-98; West Midlands Reg Prem Div88-89, R-up 94-95, Prem Div Lge Cup 94-95; Walsall Sen Cup 63-64 74-75 75-76 76-77 80-81 88-89 95-96 97-98 98-99; Midland Comb 76-77 Staffordshire Senioe Cup wqinners: 1999-2000

Players progressing: Darren Simkin (Wolverhampton Wanderers)

Back Row: Paul Knox (Jt. Manager), Steve Hillman, Lee Knight, Andy Dodd, Matt Lowe, John Muir, Leon Jackson, Neil Olden, Jim Skidmore (Coach), Mick Folland (Jt. Manager). **Front:** Lee Harper, Chris Smith, Darren Simin (Captain), Ian Cooper, Kevin Thompson, Jack Skidmore (mascot).   **Photo:** © Marshall's Sports Service.

BROMSGROVE ROVERS

CLUB OFFICIALS

Chairman: **Keith McMaster**

President: **Charles W Poole**

Secretary: **Eddie Million**
c/o Bromsgrove Rovers FC

Commercial Manager: **Rebecca O'Neill**

FOOTBALL MANAGEMENT TEAM

Manager:George Rooney
Trainer: Stewart Pinfold
Physio: Paul Sunners

FACT FILE

Formed: 1885
Sponsors: All Saints Masterfit (Bromsgrove).
Nickname: Rovers or Greens
Colours: White with gren trim/white/white
Change colours:red withGreen trim
Midweek matchday: Tuesday
Reserves' league: Central Conference.
Newsline: 0891 88 44 96
Programme: Pages: 40   Price: £1.20
Editors: Brian Perry 0121 628 6009
             Alan Saunders 01527 833838

For up to the minute news,
results, fixtures,
plus general facts & figures
from the world of
non-league football

log on to

www.nlfootball.com

GROUND   Victoria Ground, Birmingham Road, Bromsgrove, Worcs, B61 0DR
                    Tel: 01527 876949

Directions: Ground is situated on the north side of Bromsgrove on the Birmingham Road, off the A38 Bromsgrove by pass. The M5 and M42 join theA38 to the north of the town making it easy to get to the ground without havingto go into town. The 144 Midland Red bus runs from New Street StationBirmingham and passes the ground.

Capacity: 4,893   Seated: 394   Covered Terracing: 1,344

Clubhouse: Victoria Club (01527 878260) - Serves hot & cold food. Big screenTV, pool table & darts. Open matchdays and week-day evenings.

Club Shop: Selling replica clothing & souvenirs. Contact Doug Bratt (01527 874997).

PREVIOUS   **Leagues:** Birmingham Lge 1898-08, Birmingham Combination 1908-53, Birmingham 53-65, West Midlands 65-72, Southern League - Northern Div. 73-79, Midland Div.79-1986, Premier Div. 86-92, GMVC 92-97
                    Grounds: Old Station Road 1885-87, Recreation Ground 87-88, Churchfields 88-97,Well Lane 1897-1910.

CLUB RECORDS   **Attendance:** 7,389 v Worcester City - 1957
                    Win: 11-0 - v Hinckley Ath. 1970, v Halesowen Town `A' 1939     **Defeat:** 0-12 v Aston Villa `A' 1939
                    Career goalscorer: Chris Hanks 238, 1983-84   **Career appearances:** Shaun O'Meara 763, 1975-94
                    Fee paid: £3,000 for Recky Carter (Solihull B.) 93-94   **Fee received:** Undisclosed for Scott Cooksey (Peterborough) Dec. 93

HONOURS   Vauxhall Conference R-up 92-93, Lge Cup 94-95 95-96; Bob Lord Trophy 94-95; Spalding Cup 95/96; Southern Lge Prem 91-92, R-up 86-87, Cup 92-93, R-up 86-87,Midland Div 85-86, Merit Cup 85-86, Cup 85-86, R-up 73-74 87-88; Bill Dellow Cup 85-86; Worcester Sen Cup (8), R-up (10); Birmingham Sen Cup 46-47, R-up 47-48 88-89; W Mid Lge R-up 67-70, Cup 67-68 70-71; Birminham Lge 59-60, R-up 04-05 56-57 60-61; Birmingham Comb 46-47, R-up 49-50 50-51; Hereford Charity ChallCup 46-47, R-up 47-48.

Players progressing: M McKenna (Northampton 46),R Hartle (Bolton 52), A McLean (Bury 53), A Smith (A.Villa 54), M Deakin (CPalace 54), B Puster (Leicester 58), Tom Smith (Sheff Utd 1978), MalcolmGoodman (Halifax 1979), Steve Smith (Walsall 1980), Gary Hackett (Shrewsbury 1983), Bill McGarry, Martyn O'Connor (C Palace 1992), Scott Cooksey (Peterborough 1993), Steve Taylor (Crystal Palace 1995).

CINDERFORD TOWN

CLUB OFFICIALS

Chairman: **Ashley Saunders**
President: **S Watkins**
Vice Chairman: **Ray Reed**
Secretary: **Chris Warren**
9c Tusculum Way, Mitcheldean,
Glos GL17 0HZ
01594543065 (H) 01594 542421 x 2360 (B)
Press Officer: **Keith Aston**

FOOTBALL MANAGEMENT TEAM

Manager: John Murphy (01242 574882)
Asst. Manager:John Freegard
Physio: Dave Baldwin

FACT FILE

Formed: 1922
Nickname: Town
Sponsors: T.B.A.
Club colours: White & Black
Change colours: All Red
Midweek matchday: Tuesday
Reserves' League: No reserve team
99-00Captain:Lyndon Tomkins
Top Scorer: Jody Bevan
P.o.Y.: Dave Toomey & Lyndon Tomkins

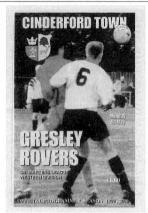

Pages: 50   Price: £1,00
Editor: Mike Bradley
Tel: 01594 824566

GROUND   The Causeway, Hilldene, Cinderford, Glos. Tel: 01594 827147 or 822039

Directions: From Gloucester take A40 to Ross-on-Wye, then A48 - Chepstow. In 8miles turn right at Elton garage onto A4151 signed Cinderford, thru Littledean, up steep hill, right at crossroads, second left into Latimer Rd. Ground 5 minswalk from town centre

Capacity: 2,500   Cover: 1,000   Seats: 250   Floodlights: Yes

Clubhouse: Open every day. 2 bars, kitchen, 2 skittle alleys, darts, dancehall,committee room Club Shop: Souvenirs, club badges (£¨3.00), ties, mugs , scarves and pennants . Contact secretary for shop and programmes.

PREVIOUS   **Leagues:** Glos Northern Snr 22-39 60-62, Western 46-59, Warwickshire Comb 63-64,West Midlands 65-69, Gloucestershire County 70-73 85-89, Midland Comb. 74-84,Hellenic 90-95
Names: None   **Grounds:** Mousel Lane, Royal Oak

CLUB RECORDS   **Attendance:** 4,850 v Minehead, Western League, 1955-56
Win: 13-0 v Cam Mills 38-39
Career Appearances: Russell Bowles 528   **Defeat:** 0-10 v Sutton Coldfield 78-79
Career Goalscorer: Unknown

BEST SEASON   **FA Cup:** 2nd Rd v Gravesend 95-96   **FA Trophy:** 2nd Qual Rd
FA Vase: 2nd Rd 91-92   **FA Amateur Cup:** 3rd Qual Rd 52

HONOURS   Hellenic Lg Premier Champions 94-95, Premier Lg.Cup 94-95, Floodlit Cup 93-94,Div 1 90-91; Glos Northern Snr Lg Div 1 38-39 60-61, R-up (6); Nth Glos Lg Div1 38-39 60-61; Glos Snr Amtr Cup (Nth) (6), R-up (3); Western Lg Div 2 56-57; Warwickshire Comb. 63-64; W Mids Lg Prem Div Cup 68-69; Glos Jnr Cup (Nth) 80-81; Midland Comb. 81-82; Glos Co. Lg R-up 69-70 71-72 73-74; Glos FA Trophy R-up 92-93; Hungerford Cup 94-95

Back Row:
James French,
Lyndon Tomkins,
Will Steadman,
Paul Donnelly,
Paul Weeks,
Nick Beaverstock.
Middle:
Darren McCluskey,
Kris Lewis,
Martin Thompson,
Jody Bevan,
Brian Kyall,
Scott Medcroft.
Front:
Dave Baldwin
(physio),
Adie Harris,
John Freegard
(asst. man.),
James Shore-Nye,
Dave Toomey,
Bob Saunders
(kit man.)
Photo:
Keith Clayton

CIRENCESTER TOWN

CLUB OFFICIALS

Chairman: **Stephen Abbley**
17 Dianmer Close, Hook, Swindon. SN4 8ER.
Tel: 01743853293 (H) 01793 884900 (B)
Secretary: **Jim Saunders**
35 Chesterton Park, Cirencester, Glos. GL7 1XS
Tel: 01258 659002 (H)
Commercial Manager: **Margaret Marsh**
Press Officer: **Jim Saunders**

FOOTBALL MANAGEMENT TEAM

Manager: Ray Baverstock(01242 260619)
Coach: Mark Boyland
Physio: Steve Slaughter

FACT FILE

Founded: 1889
Nickname: Ciren
Sponsors: P.H.H./Cheltenham Windows
Colours: Red & black/ black/ red
Change colours: All Blue
Midweek Matchday: Tuesday
Reserves' League: Cirencester & District

For up to the minute news,
results, fixtures,
plus general facts & figures
from the world of
non-league football

log on to

www.nlfootball.com

GROUND   The Stadium, Smithsfield, Chesterton Lane, Cirencester Tel: 01285 645783

Directions: Follow signs on by-pass to Bristol & West. At the roundabout where the Sports Centre is situated, follow the road `up the hill' and take the first left and then immediately right. Situated 3 miles from Kemble (BR)

Capacity: 3,000   Seats: 236   Cover: 500   Floodlights: Yes

Clubhouse: Open Tuesday - Friday evenings & Saturday. Snacks are available onmatchdays.
Club Shop: None

PREVIOUS   **Leagues:** Hellenic League **Names:** None. **Grounds:** None

CLUB RECORDS **Attendance:** 2,600 v Fareham 1969
Win: Unknown **Defeat:** Unknown
Career Goalscorer: Unknown **Career Appearances:** Unknown
Transfer fee paid: None **Transfer fee received:** None

BEST SEASON **FA Trophy:** 1st Qual. Round 1996-97 (1st season in comp.)
FA Vase: Never past the 1st Round   **FA Cup:** 3rd Preliminary Round, 1996-97

HONOURS   Gloucestershire Senior Amateur Cup 89-90; Hellenic League Div One Challenge Cup 90-91; Hellenic League Prem Div 95-96, League Cup 95-96; Gloucestershire County Cup 95-96

Players progressing: None

PROGRAMME
Pages: Yes   Price: £1
Editor: Margaret Marsh Tel. 01258 645783

Local Press:
Standard, Western Daily Press
Local Radio:
BBC Radio Gloucester, Severn Sound

Cirecester Town's highly rated 'keeper, Kevin Sawyer, gets up well to collect this cross.
Photo: Chris Elsey

EVESHAM UNITED

CLUB OFFICIALS
Chairman: **Jim Cockerton**
Vice Chairman: **Steve Lane**
President: **M E H Davis**
Treasurer: **Dave Wright**
Secretary/Press Officer: **Mike J Peplow**
68 Woodstock Rd, St Johns,
Worcester WR2 5NF
Tel: 01905 425993

FACT FILE

Nickname: The Robins
Sponsors; B anks's
Colours: Red & white/black/black
Change Colours: All blue
Formed: 1945
Midweek matches: Tuesday
Reserves' League: No reserve team
99-00 - Captain:Steve McCarten
P.o.Y: Andy smith
Top Scorer: Andy Hodgetts & Matt Cobbin

FOOTBALL MANAGEMENT TEAM

Manager: Phil Mullen
Asst Manager: Paul Davies
Physio: Lee O'Neill

GROUND   Common Road, Evesham, Worcestershire WR11 4PU Tel: 01386 442303

Directions: From Evesham High Street turn into Oat St, and join one-way system,turn right between Willmotts factory called Conduit Hill into Common Rd, ground 200yds down on right just before railway bridge. 5 minutes walk from Evesham BR station
Capacity: 2,000   Seats: 350   Cover: 600   Floodlights: Yes
Clubhouse: Open matchdays and training nights.
          Cold food available in club, and hot food from tea hut on matchdays
Club Shop: Contact John Hawkins c/o the club

PREVIOUS   **Leagues:** Worcester, Birmingham Combination, Midland Combination 51-55 65-92, West Midlands Regional 55-62
          Name: Evesham Town   **Ground:** The Crown Meadow (pre-1968)

CLUB RECORDS   **Attendance:** 2,338 v West Bromwich A., friendly 18/7/92
          Win: 11-3 v West Heath United   **Defeat:**1-8 v Ilkeston Town
          Career Goalscorer: Sid Brain   **Career Appearances:** Rob Candy
          Transfer fee paid: £1,500; to Hayes for Colin Day, 1992
          Transfer fee received: £5,000 for Simon Brain (to Cheltenham Town)

BEST SEASON   **FA Vase:** Quarter Finals 1991-92   **FA Amateur Cup:** Runners-up 1923-24
          FA Trophy: 3rd Qual Rd 96-97   **FA Cup:** 2nd Qual Rd 96-97

HONOURS   FA Amateur Cup R-up 23-24, Worcestershire Snr Urn(2) 76-78 (R-up 90-91), Midland Comb.(6) 52-53 54-55 65-66 67-69 91-92 (Chal. Cup 53-54 87-88 91-92 (R-up(5) 54-55 71-72 83-84 88-90)), Worcestershire Comb. 52-53 54-55; B'gham Combination R-up 30-31, Evesham Hosp. Cup 89-90, Tony Allden Mem. Cup 1973 19881992

Players progressing: Billy Tucker, Gary Stevens (Cardiff 77), Kevin Rose(Lincoln 78), Andy Preece (Northampton 86),
          Simon Brain (Hereford, viaCheltenham Town), Billy Turley (Northampton Tn)

Evesham United's Steve Shaw holding off the challenge of Stafford Ranger's Jason Smith
Photo: Chris Elsey

GLOUCESTER CITY

CLUB OFFICIALS

Chairperson: Tracy Newport
President: R F Etheridge
Vice-Chairman: Rob Wallace

Secretary: Jason Mills
25 Hewlett Road, Cheltenham,
Gloucestershire GL52 6AD
Tel/Fax: 01242 700496   Mob: 0468 750590

Press Officer: c/o Secretary
General Manager: Mike Bullingham
01452 421400

FACT FILE

Formed: 1889
Nickname: The Tigers
Sponsors: T.B.A.
Colours: Yellow & black/black/black
Change colours: All Red
Midweek games: Tuesday
99-00 Captain: Neil Griffiths
Top scorer: Karl Bayliss (on loan)

FOOTBALL MANAGEMENT TEAM
Manager: Tommy Callinan
Assistant Manager: Brian Godfrey
Player/Coach: Paul Chenoweth
Physio: Adrian Tandy

GROUND Meadow Park, Sudmeadow Road, Hempsted, Gloucester GL2 6HS
Tel: 01452 421400
Directions: From North: A40 then then A4301 towards City Centre & Historic Docks, right into Severn Road over swingbridge, right into Llanthony Road/Hempsted Lane, 2nd right into Sudmeadow Road, ground 50yds on left
Capacity: 3,500   Cover:2,500   Seats: 560   Floodlights: Yes
Clubhouse: Meadow Park Sports & Social Club at entrance to ground. Normal licensing hours. H & C food available. **Club Shop:** Yes

Pages: 44 Price: £1.30
Editor: Mike Dunstan Tel: 01242 250087
Local Press: Gloucester Citizen, Western Daily Press
Local Radio: Severn Sound, BBC Radio Gloucestershire

PREVIOUS **Leagues:** Bristol & Dist. (now Western) 1893-96, Gloucester & Dist. 97-1907, NorthGlos. 07-10, Glos. North Senior 20-34, Birmingham Comb. 1935-39
Grounds: Longlevens 1935-65, Horton Road 65-86   **Name:** Gloucester Y.M.C.A

CLUB RECORDS **Attendance:** 4,000 v Dagenham & Redbridge, FA Trophy S-F 2nd Leg, 12.4.97
Win: 10-0 v Sudbury Town (H), FA Cup 3rd Rd Q., 17.10.98   **Defeat:** 1-12 v Gillingham 9.11.46
Goalscorer: Reg Weaver, 250   **Appearances:** Stan Myers & Frank Tredgett in 1950s
Fee Paid: £25,000 for S Fergusson (Worcester City), and D Holmes (Gresley R.)
Fee Received: £25,000 Ian Hedges (AFC Bournemouth, 1990)

BEST SEASON FA Cup: 2nd Rd 89-90   FA Trophy: Semi-Final 1996-97

HONOURS Southern Lg R-up 90-91 (Lg Cup 55-56 (R-up 81-82), Midland Div 88-89), Glos NthSen Lg 33-34, Glos Sen. Cup 37-38 49-58 65-66 68-69 70-71 74-75 78-79 79-80 81-82 82-83 83-84 90-91 92-93, Sen Amat Cup (Nth) 31-32)

Players progressing: Numerous including William Teague (61) & Rod Thomas (64)to Swindon, John Layton (Hereford 74), Ian Main (Exeter 78), Mike Bruton(Newport 79), Mel Gwinnett (Bradford C. 84), Steve Talboys (Wimbledon 91)

GRESLEY ROVERS

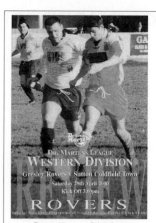

CLUB OFFICIALS
Chairman: Mark Evans
President: Gordon Duggins
Vice Chairman: George Sutton
Secretary / Press Officer: Neil Betteridge,
34 Thorpe Downs Road, Church Gresley,
Swadlincote, Derbys DE11 9FB
Tel: 01283 226229
Commercial Director: Barrie Morton

FOOTBALL MANAGEMENT TEAM
Manager/Coach:Brian Kenning
Asst Manager: Steve Devine
Physio: Mel Mole

GROUND

FACT FILE
Formed: 1882
Nickname: The Moatmen
Sponsors: Dunn Systems
Colours: Red & white/white/red
Change colours: Sky blue & navy/navy/sky
Midweek matchday: Tuesday
Reserves' League: Midland Comb (Res. Div.)

99-00 Captain:Richard Wardle
P.o.Y.: Matt Warren
Top scorer: Neil Kitching

Moat Ground, Moat Street, Church Gresley, Swadlincote, Derbys DE11 9RE
Tel: 01283 216315

Directions: To A444 via either the A5, A38, A5121 or M42 , Junction 11. On reaching A444 head for Castle Gresley. Take exit at large island to Church Gresley,at next island 2nd exit (Church St), then 2nd left (School St) then 1st left into Moat St. 5 miles Burton-on-Trent (BR). Buses from Swadlincote and Burton

Capacity: 2,000   Cover: 1,200   Seats: 400   Floodlights: Yes
Clubhouse: Inside ground, open Mon, Tues & Thurs eves & matchdays
Club Shop: Sells merchandise, programmes, metal badges etc.

Pages: 36   Price: £1.50

Local Press: Derby Evening Telegraph, Burton Mail, Burton Trader, SwadlincoteTimes
Local Radio: BBC Radio Derby & Centre F.M.

PREVIOUS   **Leagues:** Burton Lge 1892-95 97-01 09-10 43-45, Derbyshire Sen 1895-97 02-03,Leics Sen 1890-91 98-99 08-09 10-12 15-16 35-42 45-49, Notts 01-02, Midland 03-06, Central All 11-15 19-25 49-53 59-67, Birmingham Comb 25-33 53-54, Birmingham (now West Mids) 54-59 75-92, Central Comb 33-35, East Mids 67-75
Grounds: Mushroom Lane, Albert Village 1882-95, Church Str., Church, Gresley.1895-1909

CLUB RECORDS   **Attendance:** 3,950 v Burton Albion, Birmingham (now West Mids) Lg Division One,57-58
Win: 23-0 v Holy Cross Priory, Leics Jun Cup 1889-90   **Defeat:** 1-15 v Burton Crusaders, 1886-87
Career Goalscorer: Gordon Duggins 306   **Career Appearances:** Dennis King 579
Transfer fee received: £30,000 for Justin O'Reilly (Port Vale 1996)
Transfer fee paid: £2,500 for David Robinson (Ilkeston Town 97)

BEST SEASON   **FA Vase:** Runners-up 90-91, (SF 92-93)   **FA Trophy:** Qtr Finals 95-96
FA Cup: 1st Rd Proper: 30-31 (1-3 at York City), 94-95 (1-7 at Crewe Alex.)   League clubs defeated: None

HONOURS   Southern Lge Champ 96-97; FA Vase R-up 90-91; West Mids Lg 90-91 91-92 (R-up 85-86 88-89); Lg Cup 88-89 R-Up. 86-87 91-92; Southern Lg Mid Div R-up 92-93; Derbys Snr Cup (7), (R-Up (3); Leics Snr Cup 1898-99 46-47 (R-Up 1899-90 45-46); Leics Sen Lg 00-01 46-47 47-48 R-Up (7); Coalville Charity Cup 46-47; Derby Senior Cup (S) (2) R-up 00-01; Bass Vase (6); Cent All 64-65 66-67 R-Up(3) (Lg Cup 52-53); East Mids Reg Lg (2) R-Up (2); Dr.Martens (S Lge) Cup Fin 93-94

Players progressing: Phil Gee (Derby County 85), Mark Blount (Sheffield Utd 94), Colin Loss (Bristol City 94), Justin O'Reilly (Port Vale 96)

Back Row:
David King
Wayne Thornhill
Richard Selby
Simon Baldwin
Neil Broadhurst
Ian Bluck

Middle:
Steve Devine
(Asst. Man.)
Adrian Doughty
Karl Reynolds
Steve Coates
Kevin Allsop
Carl Middleton
Matt Warren
Mel Mole *(Physio)*

Front:
Matt Boyles
Richard Wardle
Brian Kenning
(Manager)
Mark Peters
Mick Sandar

HINCKLEY UNITED

CLUB OFFICIALS

Chairman: **Kevin Downes**
Vice Chairman: **Rob Mayne**
Secretary: **Ray Baggott**
37 Laneside Drive, Hinckley,Leics
LE10 1TG (01455 447278)
Press Officer: **Andy Gibbs** (01455 233483)

FACT FILE
Formed: 1997
Colours: Red & blue stripes/blue/red
Change colours: Amber & black
stripes/black/amber
Midweek matchday: Tuesday
Reserves' League: Mid Comb Res Div

FOOTBALL MANAGEMENT TEAM
Manager:Dean Thomas Ass Man: Mark
O'Kane, Coach:Charlie Palmer
Physio: Julie Hayton

99-00- Top scorer: Dave Sdaler
P.o.Y.: Dave Sadler
Captain: Morton Titterton

GROUND Middlefield Lane, Hinckley, Leics. LE10 0RB 01455 613553/615012
Directions: From M69 junction 1 take A5 north to Dodwells Island, then A47(sign Leicester).
At 3rd r/about turn right (Stoke Road) then first right(Tudor Road), until crossroads. Turn left
(Middlefield Lane), ground at end oflane on left
Capacity: 5,000 Cover: 1,300 Seats: 320 Floodlights: Yes
Clubhouse: Social club with lounge, games room and concert hall
Club Shop: Sells programmes, books, vidoes, badges, mugs Hinckley Town Records &
Hinckley Athletic Records

Pages: 60 Price: £1
Editor: Alan Mason
Local Radio: Fosse Radio
Local Press: Heartland Evening Echo,
Hinckley Times, Leicester Mercury,Hinckley
Independant,Coventry Evening Telegraph

PREVIOUS **Names:** Hinckley Athletic (1889) & Hinckley Town (prev. Westfield Rovers 58-66) merged in 1997
Grounds: Westfield Playing Field 58-60; Coventry Rd Rec Grd 60-68; Leicester Rd68-97
Leagues: Town: S Leicester & Nuneaton Amat, Leics Snr 72-86, Central Mids 86-88, West Mids 88-90
Athletic: Leics. & Northants; Leics. Sen.; Birmingham Comb. 14-39 47-54; West Midlands (Regional) 54-59 64-94; Southern 63-64
CLUB RECORDS **Attendance: Town:** 2,000 v Real Sociedad 86. *Athletic:* 5,410 v Nuneaton Boro 49 **United:** 939 v Colwyn Bay FAC 4Q 97-98
Win: 7-0 v Yate Town (a) 8.4.2000.
Defeat: 0-6 v Redditch United (a) 7.11.1998
Career Goalscorer: Morton Titterton 35 **Career Appearances:** *Morton Titterton 130*
Fee paid: Town: £1,600 for John Lane (V.S. Rugby) **Fee received:** Town: £1,750 for Colin Taylor (Bedworth Utd)
BEST SEASON **FA Vase:** Town: 3rd Rd 85-86. Athletic: 5th Rd 89-90 93-94 **FA Trophy:** United: 4th Rd 2-3 v Yeovil Town 98-99
FA Cup: 4 th Q Round lost 1-2 v Colwyn Bay 97-98
HONOURS Town: West Midlands (Regional) Lg 89-90, Central Midlands Lg 86-87 (R-up 87-88, B E Webbe Cup R-up 86-87 87-88, Gerry
Mills Cup R-up 87-88), Leics Senior Lg R-up 83-84 (Div 2 72-73, Div 2 Cup 72-73), Leics.Chall. Cup 89-90 (R-up 90-91 93-94), Leics Senior Cup
(Jelson Holmes) R-up 87-88, Leics Senior Cup 88-89, Midland Floodlit Cup 88-89 (R-up 91-92 93-94). *Athletic: Leics Snr Cup 1899-1900 00-01
09-10 82-83, Leics Snr Lg 1896-97 97-98 99-1900 08-09 09-10 13-14, Birmingham Comb. 23-24 26-27 (R-up 22-23), West Mids (Reg.) Lg R-up
82-83,Birmingham Snr Cup 54-55 (jt with Brush Sports), Leics Challenge Cup 57-58 58-5959-60 60-61 61-62 67-68 Rolleston Ch.Cup 98-99,99-00*
Players progressing: *Athletic: John Allen (Port Vale), Keith Scott (Swindon via Wycombe W.), Gary Pick (Hereford), Mike Love (Wigan)*

Hinckley United's John Allcock just has
the edge on Stafford Ranger's on loan
striker Devon White. Photo: Chris Elsey

MANGOTSFIELD UNITED

CLUB OFFICIALS
President: A J Hill
Chairman: Richard Davis
Vice Chairman: P Selway
Secretary & Press Off: Roger Gray
105 Chiltern Close, Warmley, Bristol
BS15 5UW Tel: 0117 961 6523
(Mobile) 0468 467851

FOOTBALL MANAGEMENT TEAM

Manager: Andy Black
Physio:Tammy Mullin

FACT FILE

Founded: 1950
Nickname: The Field
Sponsors: Flocas ?
Colours: Sky & maroon/maroon/sky
Change colours: Yellow/navy/yellow
Midweek matchday: Tuesday
Reserve League: Somerset Senior

Pages: 32   Price: 50p
Editor: Bob Smale (0117 9401926)
Local Press

GROUND   Cossham Street, Mangotsfield, Bristol BS17 3EW Tel: 0117 956 0119

Directions: M4 jct 19, M32 jct 1; A4174 marked Downend, through lights, over double mini-r'bout to Mangotsfield, left by village church onto B4465 signposted Pucklechurch, ground quarter mile on right. From central Bristol take A432 thru Fishponds, Staple Hill, to Mangotsfield and turn right by village church onto B4465. From Bath/Keynsham follow A4175, right at island at Willsbridge onto A431, then rejoin A4175 at next island (Cherry Garden Hill) to Bridge Yate, straight over double mini-r'bout and take 1st left, right into Carsons Rd after 1 mile and follow to Mangotsfield village & turn right by church onto B4465

Capacity: 2,500   Seats: 300   Cover: 800   Floodlights: Yes   Club Shop: Yes

Clubhouse: Open 11-11. Snacks - hot food on matchdays. Lounge bar for functions etc

PREVIOUS   **Leagues:** Bristol & District 50-67; Avon Premier Combination 67-72; Western League 72-00
RECORD   **Attendance:** 2,386 v Bath City, FA Cup 77-78
Goalscorer: John Hill   **Appearances:** John Hill 600+
Win: 14-0 v Dawlish (a) 1993 Western League   **Defeat:** 3-13 v Bristol City United (Bristol & District Div 1)
& 17-0 v Hanham Sports (Bristol & District League `Div 6)

HONOURS   Western Lg 90-91r-up 99-00, Lg Cup 73-74 r-up 86-87, Div 1 r-up 82-83; Somerset Prem. Cup 87-88, r-up 88-89 95-96; Glos Snr Cup 68-69 75-76; Glos FA Trophy 84-85 86-87 90-91 94-95 96-97; Hungerford Invit. Cup 74-75; Rothmans Nat. Cup r-up 77-78; Hanham Invit. Charity Cup 84-85 85-86;
Youth honours: Glos Yth Shield 81-82 84-85 (R-up 82-83); Somerset Floodlit Yth Lg 81-82 82-83 83-84 84-85 87-88 98-99; Somerset Yth Shield 76-77
Reserve honours Somerset Snr Lg (Res.) Div 1 98-99 Div 2 97-98 75-76, Div 3 74-75; Somerset Comb. Cup 74-75
BEST SEASON   **FA Vase:** Semi Final 95-96   **FA Cup:** 3rd Qualifying Rd (4)
Players progress ing: G Megson, S White, G Penrice, P Purnell, N Tanner, M Hooper

Back Row: Mark Lippiatt, Danny Thorpe, Darren Edwards, Stephen Weaver, Lee Barlasi, Rob Claridge, Arthur Appleton.
Front Row: Chris Churchill, Gareth Loydon, Danny Hallett, Andy Black (Manager), Shaun Perry, Noel O'Sullivan, Adam Sims.

PAGET RANGERS

CLUB OFFICIALS

Chairman:
Derek Culling
Secretary: **Roy Smith,**Flat 6, 4 Pixall Walk,
Castle Vale, Birmingham B35 7NJ
Tel: 0121 7491656
Press Officer: **Chris Inman**
Commercial Manager: Chairman

FOOTBALL MANAGEMENT TEAM
Manager: Chris Sharp
Asst Manager: Paul Edwards
Coach: Chris Sharpe
Physio: D J Culling

FACT FILE
Formed: 1938
Nickname: The 'Bears'
Sponsors:INA Bearing Co. Ltd.
Colours: Gold/black/gold
Change colours: All red
Midweek matchday: Tuesday
Reserves' League: No reserve team

For up to the minute news,
results, fixtures,
plus general facts & figures
from the world of
non-league football

log on to

www.nlfootball.com

GROUND Vale Stadium, Farnborough Rd., Castle Vale, Birmingham B35 7BE
Tel: 0121 747 6969 Fax: 0121 747 6862 Press/Matchdays: 0121 749 7707

Directions: M6 North to Junct. 5. Turn right onto A452. Turn right at 1st r'about into Tangmere
Drive. Fork right into Farnborough Rd. 800 yds turn right signed Fort centre.
M6 South to Spaghetti junction. Take signs for Tyburn Rd (A38) Turn right onto
A452. Turn left opposite Jaguar factory then as above (Tangmere Drive)

Capacity: 5000   Cover: 200   Seats: 280   Floodlights: Yes 257 Lux
Clubhouse: 'Spitfire Club'. Open daily. Capacity 150. Servery from kitchen to ground.
No club shop - metal badges, ties etc avail. from committee.

PROGRAMME
Pages: 24   Price: £1
Editor: R R Ruddick 0121 747 6969
Local Press:
Sutton Coldfield News, Sutton Observer
Local Radio:
Radio WM, BRMB Vale FM 106.2

PREVIOUS   **Leagues:** Birmingham Suburban; Central Amateur; Midland Combination 50-81;Southern 87-88; West Midlands (Regional) 88-
94; Interlink Midland Alliance 94-95, Southern League 95-
Grounds: Pype Hayes Park 38-46; Springfield Road, Walmley 46-93, Ground Share Sutton Coldfield Town >98.

CLUB RECORDS   **Attendance:** 2,000 v Aston Villa, F'light opening 1971
Win: 24-1 v Evesham Town 1949   **Defeat:** 1-6 v Gloucester 87/Halesowen Town 87/Moor Green 88
Career Appearances: Gary Williams 618   **Career Goalscorer:** Albert Broadhead
Transfer fee paid: No transfer fee paid for any player   **Transfer fee received:** John Gittens (Southampton) £15,000

BEST SEASON   FA Cup: Third Qual Round 94-95
FA Vase: Fourth Rd 88-89, 0-1 v Wisbech   **FA Trophy:** 2nd Round 98-99, 0-2 v Accrington Stanley
HONOURS   West Mids Lg R-up 91-92 (Lg Cup 91-92); Midland Comb.(6) 59-61 69-71 82-83 85-86 (R-up 77-78, Lg Cup 59-60 66-67, Div 1
Cup 70-71, Div 3 82-83(res)); B'hamJnr Cup 51-52; Walsall Snr Cup 85-86; Midland Alliance 94-95; Lord Mayor of Birmingham
Charity Cup 94-95; Staffs Sen Cup R-up 94-95

Players progressing: John Gittens (Southampton), Gary Bull (Southampton), Lloyd Harrison (Torquay)

Desperate measures by the Paget Rangers' 'keeper to
keep out this Stafford Rangers attack. Photo: Chris Elsey.

RACING CLUB WARWICK

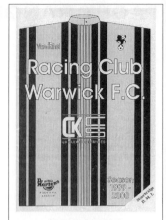

CLUB OFFICIALS

Chairman: **Jim Wright**

Secretary: **Pat Murphy**
Tel: 01926 612675

FOOTBALL MANAGEMENT

Manager:Billy Hollywood

FACT FILE

Formed: 1919
Nickname: Racers
Colours: Gold & black/black/black
Change colours: Red&white/red/red
Midweek matchday: Wednesday
Youth's League: Mid F/Lit Yth Lge

99-00- Captain: B.Agar
P.o.Y.: S.Hepburn
Top scorer: Simon Windsor

Pages: 20 Price: £1.00
Editor: Secretary
Local Press: Warwick Advertiser, Leamington Courier, Coventry EveningTelegraph
Local Radio: BBC Radio Coventry, Bear Radio

GROUND   Townsend Meadow, Hampton Road, Warwick CV34 6JP
Tel: 01926 495786
Directions: On the B4095 Warwick to Redditch road (via Henley in Arden) next to owners' & trainers' car park of Warwick Racecourse. From M40 jct 15 (1 1/2 miles) take A429 into Warwick, left into Shakespeare Ave., straight over island, right at T-junction into Hampton Rd, ground 300yds on left. 2 milesfrom Warwick BR station
Capacity: 1,000   Cover: 200   Seats: 250   Floodlights: Yes
Clubhouse: 01926 495786 Open every evening & Sat &Sun lunchtimes
Club Shop: Scarves, mugs, badges, programmes - contact Secretary

PREVIOUS   **Leagues:** Birmingham & West Mids All., Warwickshire Comb., West Midlands (Regional) 67-72, Midland Comb. 72-89
Names: Saltisford Rovers 1919-68   **Grounds:** Coventry Road

CLUB RECORDS **Attendance:** 1,000 v Halesowen Town, FA Cup 1987
Transfer fee paid: £1,000 for Dave Whetton (Bedworth United)   **Win:** 9-1 v Knowle
Transfer fee received: £2,000 for Ian Gorrie (Atherstone Utd)   **Defeat:** 0-6 v Tamworth
Career Goalscorer: Steve Edgington 200   **Career Appearances:** Steve Cooper 600

BEST SEASON   FA Vase: 4th Round 77-78   **FA Cup:** 3rd Qual Rd 92-93   **FA Trophy:**

HONOURS   Midland Combination 87-88 (R-up 88-89); Warwick Lg 33-34 34-35 35-36; Birmingham & West Mids Alliance 48-49; Birmingham & Dist Alliance Senior Cup 49-50; Leamington & Dist Lg 37-38 45-46 46-47 47-48; Leamington Hospital Cup 37-38 46-47; Warwick Cinderella Cup 35-36 36-37 37-38 38-39 46-47; T G John Cup 36-37; Leamington Junior Cup 38-39 46-47

Players progressing: None

Warren Ayers, the R.C. Warwick 'keeper, has to come out to the edge of the box to make this save with his feet.
Photo: Keith Clayton

REDDITCH UNITED

CLUB OFFICIALS	FACT FILE

Chairman: **Rod Laight**
President: **Major Jim Gillespie MBE**
Secretary: **M A Langfield**
298 Birchfield Rd., Redditch, Worcs
Tel: 01527 67945 (H) 01527 595882 (W)
Commercial Manager: **Pat Cremin**
Press Off:**Gordon Wilkie** Tel:01527 543999

FOOTBALL MANAGEMENT TEAM
Manager: Rob Smith
Asst. Managers:
Larry Chambers & Paul Malloy
Physio: John Kane

Formed: 1900
Nickname: The Reds
Colours: Red & Black
Change colours: All royal blue
Midweek matchday: Tuesday
Reserves' League: Midland Comb. Res Div
Programme: Pages: 50 Price: £1.50
Editor: Gordon Wilkie
Local Press: Redditch Indicator, Redditch
Advertiser, Birmingham Evening Mail,
Redditch Standard
Local Radio: BBC Hereford & Worcester
The Bear Radio FM102

For up to the minute news, results, fixtures, plus general facts & figures from the world of non-league football

log on to

www.nlfootball.com

GROUND Valley Stadium, Bromsgrove Road, Redditch B97 4RN Tel: 01527 67450
Directions: Access 7 on town centre ring-road takes you into Bromsgrove Road (via Unicorn Hill) - ground entrance 400yds past traffic lights on right.Arriving from Bromsgrove take first exit off dual carriageway. Ground 400 ydsfrom Redditch BR station and town centre
Capacity: 5,000   Cover: 2,000   Seats: 400   Floodlights: Yes
Clubhouse: Large clubroom and lounge boardroom. Open matchdays and for private hire.
Food available on matchdays; steaks hot dogs, burgers, chips, bovril etc
Club Shop: Yes

PREVIOUS   **Leagues:** Birmingham Comb. 05-21 29-39 46-53, West Midlands 21-29 53-72, Southern 72-79, Alliance Premier (Conf) 79-80
Name: Redditch Town   **Ground:** HDA Spts Ground, Millsborough Rd

CLUB RECORDS **Attendance:** 5,500 v Bromsgrove, league match 54-55
Transfer fee paid: £3,000 for Paul Joinson from Halesowen Town
Transfer fee received: £42,000 for David Farrell (Aston Villa, 1991)
Career Appearances:

BEST SEASON **FA Cup:** 1st Rd replay 71-72, 0-4 v Peterborough U (A) after 1-1 draw. Also 1st Rd 71-72
FA Trophy: 4th Round 1998-99 0-2 v Boston Umited

HONOURS Southern Lg Div 1 Nth 75-76 (Midland Div R-up 85-86) S.Lg Cup R-up 97-98 West Mids (B'ham) Lg Southern Sect. 54-55, Birmingham Comb. 13-14 32-33 52-53 (R-up 06-07 14-15 51-52), Staffs Snr Cup 90-91, Birmingham Snr Cup 24-25 31-32 38-39 76-77, Worcs Snr Cup 894-95 1930-31 74-75 76-77 (R-up 1888-89 1929-30 52-53 73-74), Worcs Jnr Cup 90-91

Players progressing: Hugh Evans (Birmingham 1947), Trevor Lewes (Coventry1957), David Gilbert (Chesterfield 1960), Mike Tuohy (Southend Utd 1979), Neil Smith (Liverpool), David Farrell (Aston Villa 1992), Neil Davis (Aston Villa 1991)

Redditch United defenders, Mark Dearlove and Neil Manton combine to keep Stafford Rangers' striker Tony Eccleston away from the ball.   **Photo:** Chris Elsey

ROCESTER

CLUB OFFICIALS

Chairman: **A.Hawksworth**

Secretary: **Gilbert Egerton**
23 Eaton Rd, Rocester, Uttoxeter,
Staffs ST145LL.
Tel: 01889 590101

FOOTBALL MANAGEMENT TEAM

Joint Managers: Karl Wilcox & Mark Bromley
Reserves' Manager: Alf Hawksworth

FACT FILE

Founded: 1876
Nickname: Romans
Sponsors:
Colours: Amber/black/black
Change colours: All blue
Reserves' Lge: North Staffs (North)
Midweek matchday: Tuesday

ROCESTER F.C.

MATCHDAY PROGRAMME

DR. MARTENS LEAGUE WESTERN DIVISION
Saturday 6th May 2000
ROCESTER v Tiverton Town
K.O. 3.00 p.m.
League

SEASON 1999/2000

32 pages   £1.00
Editor: Barry Brosnan
Tel: 01889 567795

GROUND   The Rivers Field, Mill Street, Rocester, Uttoxeter, Staffs Tel: 01889 590463

Directions: From A50 r'bout adjoining Little Chef at Uttoxeter take B5030 to Rocester & Alton Towers, right into Rocester village after 3miles over narrow bridge, in village centre bear right at sharp left-hand bend into Mill St., ground 500yds on left just past former cotton mill.

Capacity: 4,000   Seats: 230   Cover: 500   Floodlights: Yes

Clubhouse: On matchdays (normal licensing hours). Hot drinks & snacks.
Club Shop: Yes

PREVIOUS   **Leagues:** Ashbourne; Leek & Moorland; Cheadle & Dist; Uttoxeter Amateur; Stafford 53-57; Staffordshire County North 57-84; Staffordshire Senior 84-87; West Midlands 87-94; Midland alliance 94-99.
Ground: Mill Street, Rocester (early 1900s-1987)

BEST SEASON   **FA Cup:** 3rd Qual. Round 97-98, 1-2 v Bromsgrove Rovers (A)   **FA Vase:** 5th Round 86-87, 1-3 v Garforth Town (H) aet.

RECORDS   **Attendance:** 1,026 v Halesowen T., FA Vase 4th Rd Jan.'87 (at Leek Town)
Goalscorer: Mick Collins   **Appearances:** Peter Swanwick.
Fee Paid: £1,000 for Paul Ede from Burton Albion, Sept.1989.
Fee Received: £12,000 for Mark Sale from Birmingham City 1994
Win: 14-0 (twice)   **Defeat:** 0-9

HONOURS   West Mids Lg R-up 89-90 (Div 1 87-88, Div 1 Cup 87-88), Staffs Senior Lg (2) 85-87, Staffordshire FA Vase 85-86 87-88; Midland Alliance 98-99

Players progressing: Bert Carpenter (Manchester Utd), Joe Carpenter (Brighton), George Shepherd (Derby),
Mark Sale (Birmingham, Torquay),Tony Hemmings (Wycombe via Northwich)

RUGBY UNITED

CLUB OFFICIALS
Chairman: **Brian Melvinlvi**
Secretary: **Doug Wilkins**,
298 Rocky Lane, Great Barr,
Birmingham B42 1NQ
Tel: 0121 681 1544 (H 0121 686 4068 (F)
Press Officer: **Alun Turner**
Tel: 01788 567181
Commercial Manager:**Lisa Melvin**

FOOTBALL MANAGEMENT TEAM
Manager:Martin Sockett
Asst Manager: Martin Smith
Physio: Bob Gardner

FACT FILE
Formed: 1956   Nickname: The Valley
Sponsors: Rugby Telegraph & Melbros Ltd
Colours: Navy & sky/navy/sky
Change colours: All White
Midweek matchday: Tuesday
Club Newsline: 0930 555971
Reserves' League: No reserve team

1999-00
Top scorer: Paul John
P. o Y. & Captain: Jason Woodley

Pages: 36   Price: £1
Editor: Terry Coley Tel: 0121 240 4521
Local Press: Rugby Advertiser, Coventry
Evening Telegraph, Rugby Observer
Local Radio: Mercia Sound, CWR

GROUND   Butlin Road, Rugby, Warks CV21 3ST Tel: 01788 844806
Directions: The ground is situated off Clifton (B5414) on the north side ofRugby. 1 mile walk
from the station
Capacity: 6,000   Cover: 1,000   Seats: 240   Floodlights: Yes
Clubhouse: Open every night and weekend lunchtimes. Entertainment Saturday nights.
Excellent facilities include Long Alley Skittles, darts and pool
Club Shop: Yes

PREVIOUS   Name: Valley Sports, Valley Sports Rugby
Leagues: Rugby & District 1956-63, Coventry & Partnership, North Warks 63-69, United Counties 69-75, West Midlands 75-83

CLUB RECORDS Attendance: 3,961 v Northampton FA Cup 1984
Win: 10-0 v Ilkeston Tn FA Trophy 4/9/85   **Defeat:** 1-11 v Ilkeston Town (A) 18.4.98
Career Goalscorer: Danny Conway, 124   Career Appearances: Danny Conway, 374
Transfer fee paid: £3,500 R Smith, I Crawley, G Bradder   **Transfer fee received:** £15,000 T Angus (Northampton)

BEST SEASON   FA Cup: 2nd round 87-88, plus 1st Rd 84-85 85-86 86-87 94-95 League clubs defeated: None
FA Trophy: FA Vase: Winners 82-83

HONOURS   Southern Lg Midland Div 86-87 (R-up 94-95, Lg Cup 89-90), FA Vase 82-83,Mid Floodlit Cup 84-85 89-90 98 -00(R-up 86-87),
Birmingham Snr Cup 88-89 91-92, Utd Co's Lg Div 3 Cup 69-70.
All-time record FA Trophy win: 10-0 away to IlkestonTown, Preliminary Rd 85-86

Players progressing: S Storer (Birmingham 1985), S Bicknell (Leicester), S Norris (Scarborough), T Angus (Northampton Town),
Ashley Walker (Peterborough), Ian King (Stoke City)

Back Row: Dave Watson, Peter Spacey, Jason Woodley, Steve O'Shea, Paul Berrisford, Jermaine Rainford (now Corby), John Halford.
Front: Richard Wade, Phil Murphy, Boyd Young, Keiran Sullivan, Dave Stringer, Matt Dyer, Jason Wiseman.   **Photo:** Mark Sandom

SHEPSHED DYNAMO

CLUB OFFICIALS
Chairman: **Michael Voce**
President / Vice Chairman: TBA
Secretary: **Peter Bull**
17 Welland Rd, Barrow-on-Soar,
Leicestershire LE12 8NA
Tel: 01509 413338
Press Officer: **Maurice Brindley**
Tel: 01509 267922
Commercial Manager: **T.B.A.**

FOOTBALL MANAGEMENT TEAM
Manager: Dave Williams
Coach: Frank Benjamin
Physio: Alan Cook

FACT FILE

Re-formed: 1994
Nickname: Dynamo
Sponsors: T.B.A.
Colours: Black & white/black/black
Change colours: All Green
Midweek matchday: Tuesday
Reserves' League: Midland Comb.

1999-00
Top scorer:Dave Pearson
P. o Y. & Captain: Jez Carr

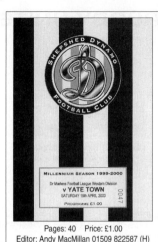

MILLENNIUM SEASON 1999-2000
Dr Martens Football League Western Division
v YATE TOWN
SATURDAY 15th APRIL 2000
PROGRAMME £1.00

GROUND   The Dovecote, Butthole Lane, Shepshed, Leicestershire
                                                              Tel: 01509 650992
Directions: M1 junction 23, A512 towards Ashby, right at first lights, right at garage in Forest Street, right into Butthole Lane opposite Black Swan. Five miles from Loughborough (BR)

Capacity: 5,000   Cover: 1,500   Seats: 209   Floodlights: Yes
Clubhouse: Takes 120 in main room, 50 in others
Club Shop: Yes (Steve Straw & Alan Gibson)

Pages: 40   Price: £1.00
Editor: Andy MacMillan 01509 822587 (H)
email: andy.macmillan@ntlworld.com

Local Press: Loughborough Echo,
Leicester Mercury, Coalville Times
Local Radio: Radio Leicester, Oak FM

PREVIOUS   **Leagues:** Leicestershire Senior 07-16 19-27 46-50 51-81, Midland Counties 81-82, Northern Counties (East) 82-83, Southern 83-88, Northern Premier 88-93, Midland Combination 93-94, Midland Alliance 94-96
                 Names: Shepshed Albion 1890-1975 91-94, Shepshed Charterhouse 75-91
                 Grounds: Ashby Road (pre-1897), Little Haw Farm
CLUB RECORDS **Attendance:** 2,500 v Leicester C. (friendly) 96-97
                 Win: 10-0 v Bloxwixh T. (H), Mid. Comb. 93-94   **Defeat:** 0-7 v Hyde Utd. (A) NPL 90-91
                 Career Goalscorer: Jeff Lissaman 104 (81-86)   **Career Appearances:** Austin Straker 300
                 Transfer fee paid: £2,000 for Doug Newton (Charterhouse)
                 Transfer fee received: £10,000 for John Deakin from Birmingham City (Charterhouse)
BEST SEASON **FA Vase:** Semi-Finalists 78-79   **FA Trophy:** 3rd Rd Replay v Emley 98-99
                 FA Cup: 1st Rd 82-83, 1-5 v Preston North End (A), 96-97 v Carlisle United (a) 0-6
HONOURS   Southern Lge Midland Div. R-up 83-84, N.C.E. Lge 82-83 (League Cup 82-83), Midland Counties Lge 81-82 (League Cup 81-82), Leicestershire Senior Lge 10-11 20-21 78-79 79-80 80-81 (R-up 21-22, Div 2 53-54 65-66 77-78, Div 2 Cup 77-78), Leicestershire Senior Cup (7), Loughborough Charity Cup 92-93 Interlink Midland Alliance Winners 95-96

Players progressing: Neil Grewcock (Burnley 84), Gordon Tucker (Huddersfield 87), Devon White (Bristol R. 87), John Deakin (Birmingham City)

THE **NON-LEAGUE** PAPER
CONFERENCE & PYRAMID LEAGUES SOCCER / £1.00

AVAILABLE AT A NEWSAGENT NEAR YOU EVERY SUNDAY

SOLIHULL BOROUGH

BORO IN THE VALLEY
THE OFFICIAL MATCH PROGRAMME
Season 1999/2000

CLUB OFFICIALS
Chairman: **John Hewitson**
President: **Joe McGorian**
Vice Chairman: **Trevor Stevens**
Commercial Man.:**Ernie Adkins**
Secretary: **John A France**, 22 Swallows Meadow, Shirley, Solihull B90 4QB
Tel: 0121733 6584Club Fax: 0121 711 4045
Press Officer: **Richard Crawshaw**
Tel: 01564 702746

FOOTBALL MANAGEMENT TEAM
Manager: Dave Busst
Coach: Paul Holleran
Physio: Graham Jones F.A.Dep.Ist
Match Sec: Joe Murphy (0121 709 0545)

FACT FILE
Formed: 1953
Nickname: Boro
Sponsors: Carling Black Label
Colours: Red/white/red
Change colours: Yellow/blue
Midweek matchday: Tuesday
Reserve's League: None

1999-00
Captain: Ian Mitchell
P.o.Y.: Gary Knight
Top scorer:Joe Dowling

Pages: 52 Price: £1
Editors: Donna Matthews
0121 682 5783
Local Press: Solihull Times, Solihull News, Sunday Mercury, Sports Argus
Local Radio: Radio WM, BRMB

Ground: Damson Park, Damson Parkway,Solihull,W.Mids B91 2PP(0121 705 6770)
Directions: Leave M42 at Jnct 6. A45 for 2 miles towards B'ham.Past Honda Garage and opp Forte Posthouse Hotel, left at filter to traffic lights into Damson Parkway.I mile to roundabout by Rover works.Go round, down other side of dual crriageway for 100 jds .Ground on left.Coventry use A45 to Posthouse. Solihull,A41 into Hampton Lane and Yew Tree LaneLane.
Capacity: 9,500   Cover: 2,000   Seats: 400   Floodlights: Yes
Clubhouse: Country Club facilities and all type offunctions can be booked.(0121 705 6770)

PREVIOUS   **Leagues:** Mercian; Midland Combination 69-91
   Name: Lincoln FC   **Grounds:** Widney Stadium, Solihull 65-88,Moor Green 88-98,Redditch 98-00

CLUB RECORDS **Attendance:** 2,135 v Darlington FA Cup 1st Rd replay. At previous ground: 400 vMoor Green, Midland Comb . Div . 2 , 1971
   Win: 9-1 v Alfreton Town FA Trophy 1st Rd 97-98
   Defeat: 1-6 v Tiverton Town (A) Southern League (Western) 99-00
   Career Goalscorer: Joe Dowling   **Career Appearances:** Darrel Houghton
   Transfer fee paid: £15,000 for Recky Carter, from Kettering Town
   Transfer fee received: £30,000 for Andy Williams (to Coventry)

BEST SEASON **FA Cup:** 1st Rd 97-98; 1-1,3-3 (2-4pen) v Darlington and 92-93, 2-2,2-3 v V.S.Rugby
   FA Vase: 5th Rd 74-75   **FA Trophy:** 1st Rd Prop 97-98

HONOURS Southern Lg Midland Div 91-92; Midland Comb. R-up 90-91, Chall Cup R-up 73-74 90-91, Presidents Cup R-up 69-70;
   Lord Mayor of Birmingham Charity Cup 91-92 92-93 94-95 96-97; Worcs Sen. Cup R-up 92-93 96-97 97-98; 99-00Birmingham Sen. Cup 94-95

Players Progressing: Kevin Ashley (Birmingham C.), Andy Williams (Coventry C.), Geoff Scott (Leicester C.), Danny Conway (Leicester C.),
   Alan Smith (LeicesterC.), Dean Spink (Aston Villa), John Frain (Northampton T.)

Back Row: Paul Holleran (Asst. Manager), Graham Jones (Physio), Nigel Brown, Chris Pearce, Richard Anstiss, Gary Knight, Russell Dodd, Robin Judd, Ricky Marshall, David Busst (Manager). **Front:** Joe Dowling, Andy Penny, Simon Hollis, Paul Pippard, Ian Mitchell (Captain), Richard Beale.   **Photo:** © Staffordshire Newsletter

SUTTON COLDFIELD TOWN

CLUB OFFICIALS
Chairman: Kevin Holt

Secretary: Alan Fleming, 28 Manor Road,Streetly, West Midlands B75 5PY
Tel : 0121 308 9260 (H) 0121 354 2997 (W)

Press Officer: Brian Turner
Commercial Manager: Peter Young

FOOTBALL MANAGEMENT TEAM
Manager: Chris Keogh
Asst Man: Alan Hampton
Physio: Reg Brassington

FACT FILE
Formed: 1897
Nickname: Royals
Colours: Blue & White/Blue/Blue
Change colours: White/ Red/White
Midweek matchday: Tuesday
Reserves' League: No reserve team

For up to the minute news, results, fixtures, plus general facts & figures from the world of non-league football

log on to

www.nlfootball.com

GROUND   Central Ground, Coles Lane, Sutton Coldfield B72 1NL
Tel: 0121 354 2997 or 0121 355 5475
Directions: A5127 into Sutton, right at Odeon cinema (Holland Rd), then first right into Coles Lane - ground 150 yds on left. 10 mins walk from SuttonColdfield (BR), bus 104 from Birmingham
Capacity: 4,500   Cover: 500   Seats: 200   Floodlights: Yes
Clubhouse: Brick built lounge & concert room, fully carpeted and extensively decorated Open daily, food available
Club Shop: Selling metal badges, scarves, hats, pens, rosettes, progs
Contact Paul Vanes (0121 770 9835)

PROGRAMME
Pages: 20   Price: 80p
Editor: Peter Young

Local Press:
Sutton Coldfield News,
Sutton Observer
Local Radio: BRMB, Radio WM

PREVIOUS   **Leagues:** Central Birmingham, Walsall Sen., Staffs Co., BirminghamComb. 50-54, West Mids (Regional) 54-65 79-82, Midlands Comb. 65-79   **Name:** Sutton Coldfield FC 1879-1921
Grounds: Meadow Plat 1879-89/ Coles Lane (site of current ambulance station) 90-1919

CLUB RECORDS   **Attendance:** 2,029 v Doncaster Rovers, F.A. Cup 80-81 (Receipts £2,727)
Career Goalscorer: Eddie Hewitt 288   **Career Appearances:** Eddie Hewitt 465
Fee paid: £1,500 twice in 1991, for Lance Morrison (Gloucester) & Micky Clarke(Burton A.)
Fee received: £25,000 for Barry Cowdrill (WBA 1979)

BEST SEASON   **FA Cup:** 1st Rd 80-81, 0-1 v Doncaster R (H), 92-93, 1-2 v BoltonWanderers (A)
FA Trophy: 1st Round replay 1989-90   **FA Amateur Cup:** 2nd Round 1970-71

HONOURS   Southern Lg Midland Div R-up 82-83, West Mids Lg 79-80 (Lg Cup 80-81 81-82), Midland Comb.(2) 77-79 (R-up(2) 69-71, Lg Cup 69-70), Walsall Senior Lg 46-47, Walsall Sen. Cup(3) 77-80 (R-up 80-81), Staffs Sen. Cup R-up 89-90, Lord Mayor of Birmingham Charity Cup 95-96, R-up 93-94, Worcs Sen. Cup SF 88-89, Walsall Challenge Cup R-up 46-47 47-48, Sutton Charity Cup 46-47 65-66 71-72 86-87 89-90 90-91, Express & Star Cup 44-45

Players progressing: Arthur Corbett (Walsall 49), Paul Cooper (Manchester C.), Noel Blake (Leeds), Steve Cooper (Barnsley), Peter Latchford (WBA), Mark Smith (Wolves), John Barton (Everton), Barry Cowdrill (WBA 79),Colin Dryhurst (Halifax 79), Dale Belford (Notts Co. 87), Ellis Laight (Torquay 92)

Action from Sutton Coldfield's home game against Stafford Rangers   Photo: Chris Elsey

TIVERTON TOWN

CLUB OFFICIALS

President: **Dan McCauley**
Chairman: **Dave Wright**
Vice-Chairman: **Pete Buxton**

Secretary: **Ramsay Findlay**
35 Park Road, Tiverton, Devon EX16 6AY
Tel: 01884 256341

FOOTBALL MANAGEMENT TEAM

Manager: Martyn Rogers
Asst Manager: Martin Grimshaw
Physio: Alan Morgan

FACT FILE

Formed: 1920
Nickname: Tivvy
Colours: All Yellow
Change colours: All white
Midweek matches: Wednesday
Reserves' League: None
1999-00
Top Goalscorer: Kevin Nancekivell (27)
P.o.Y.: Kevin Nancekivell

Season 1999/2000
Programme No 23

£1

MIDLANDS WEST LEAGUE

F.A. Carlsberg VASE
WINNERS 1999

TIVERTON TOWN
v
PAGET RANGERS
Saturday 18th December
Kick Off 3 pm

MAIN SPONSOR
MARKET CARPETS of Devon

MATCH SPONSOR
FOXFORDS

GROUND Ladysmead, Bolham Road, Tiverton, Devon EX16 8SG
Tel: 01884 252397

Directions: M5 Jct 27, west towards Tiverton on A361, continue to end of dual carriageway
and turn left at r'about; ground entrance 300yds on right alongside BP petrol station
Capacity: 3,500   Seats: 300   Cover: 2,000   Floodlights: Yes

Pages: 56   Price: £1.00 (with colour)
Editor/ Press Officer: John Fournier
Tel No: 01884 32904

Clubhouse: Lunctimes, evenings. All day Sat during season. 3 bars. Food(burgers, chips etc)
Club Shop: Yes

HONOURS FA Vase 97-98 98-99; Western Lg 93-94 94-95 96-97 97-98 (R-up 92-93 95-96 98-99);
Les Phillips Cup 92-93 94-95 95-96 96-97 97-98; Amateur Trophy 77-78 78-79, Div 1 R-up 88-89;
Devon St Lukes Cup 90-91 91-92 92-93 94-95 96-97 (R-up 89-90); Devon & Exeter Lg 51-52 66-67 70-71 84-85;
Devon Snr Cup 55-56 65-66; East Devon Snr Cup 35-36 37-38 52-53 55-56 60-61 62-63 66-67;
North Devon Charity Cup 72-73 86-87. Devon St Luke's Bowl 99-00.

PREVIOUS   **League:** Devon & Exeter; Western League   **Ground:** The Elms, Blundell Road 1920-39

BEST SEASON   **FA Vase:** Winners 97-98 98-99, R-up 92-93
FA Cup: 1st Rnd 90-91 91-92 94-95 97-98

RECORD   **Attendance:** 3,000 v Leyton Orient, FA Cup First Round Proper 1994-95
Career Goalscorer: Phil Everett at start of 01-02 season has 339 (Kevin Smith 303 previous record holder)

Players progressing: Jason Smith (Coventry City 93 & Swansea City 98), Mark Saunders (Plymouth Argyle 95), Kevin Nancekivell (00)

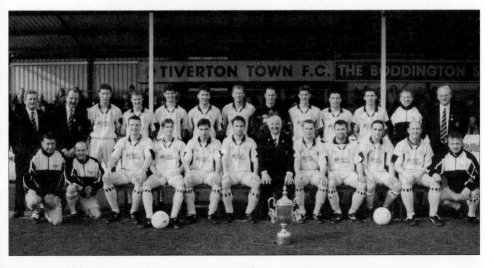

WESTON-super-MARE

CLUB OFFICIALS

President: **D A Usher**

Chairman: **Paul T Bliss**

Secretary/Press Officer: **Keith Refault**
c/o Weston Super Mare FC
Tel: 01934 635665

FOOTBALL MANAGEMENT TEAM

Coach: John Relish
Assistant Coach: Graham Withey
Physio: Dave Lukins

FACT FILE

Formed: 1899
Nickname: Seagulls
Sponsors: Firstgroup
Colours: White/blue/blue
Change colours: All yellow
Midweek matches: Tuesday
Reserves' League: Somerset Senior

For up to the minute news, results, fixtures, plus general facts & figures from the world of non-league football

 log on to

www.nlfootball.com

GROUND   Woodspring Park, Winterstoke Road, Weston-super-Mare BS23 2YG
Tel: 01934 6355665 or 621618

Directions: M5 Jct 21. A370 along dual carriageway to 4th roundabout. First left and immediately right at small roundabout, club on right. FromSouth: M5 Jct 22, follow Weston signs for approx 7 miles, right at first r'bout(by Hospital), left at next r'bout, ground 1 mile on left. Twenty minsutes walk fromWeston-super-Mare (BR)

Capacity: 2,000   Seats: 250   Cover: 1,000   Floodlights: Yes
Clubhouse: Mon-Fri 7-11pm, Sat 12-11pm, Sun 12-3 & 7-11pm.
2 skittle alleys, 2bars. Bar meals and hot meals everyday
Club Shop: Selling a wide range of souvenirs & programmes.Contact Alan White at the club.9

PROGRAMME

Pages: 32   Price: £1
Editor: Secretary   Tel. 01934 635665

Local Press:
Bristol Evening Post, Western Daily Press
Local Radio: Somerset Sound, Radio Bristol

PREVIOUS   **League:** Western 1900-92 (Not continuous)   **Name:** Borough of Weston-super-Mare
Grounds: The Great Ground, Locking Road 48-55, Langford Road 55-83

CLUB RECORDS **Attendance:** 2,623 v Woking, FA Cup First Round Proper replay 23/11/93
At Langford Road: 2,500 v Bridgwater Town, FA Cup First Round Proper replay 1961-62
Win: 11-0 v Paulton Rovers   **Defeat:** 1-12 v Yeovil Town Reserves
Career Goalscorer: Matthew Lazenby, 180   **Career Appearances:** Harry Thomas, 740
Transfer fee received: £20,000 Stuart Jones fromSheffield Wednesday 98   **Transfer fee paid:** None

BEST SEASON   **FA Cup:** 1st Rd Proper replay 61-62, 0-1 v Bridgwater Town after 0-0; 94-95, 0-1 v Woking (A) after 2-2
FA Trophy: 14th Round 98-99   **FA Vase:** Have not entered

HONOURS   Somerset Snr Cup 23-24 26-27; Western Lg Champions 91-92 (R-up 76-77), Merit Cup 76-77 77-78; Somerset Snr Lg (Reserves) Div 1 87-88 (R-up 90-91), Div 2 R-up 85-86, Div 3 84-85
Players progressing: Shaun Rouse (Carlisle United 94), Ian Maine, John Palmer(Bristol City),Wayne Brown(Chester City 97), Stuart Jones (Sheffield Wed 98), Ryan Souter (Bury 99)

Back Row: Dave Williams, John Relish (manager), Micky Copeman, Mike Cook, Jason Price, Justin Pritchard, Jody Bevan, Michael Kearns, Dave Lukins (physio). **Front:** Dave Bell, Lee White, Ben Jones, Andrew Smith, Dave Watts, James Drinkwater.

544

EASTERN DIVISION FINAL LEAGUE TABLE 1999-2000

		P	W	D	L	F	A	GD	Pts
1	Fisher Athletic Lond	42	31	5	6	107	42	65	98
2	Folkestone Invicta	42	30	7	5	101	39	62	97
3	Newport IOW	42	25	7	10	74	40	34	82
4	Chelmsford City	42	24	8	10	74	38	36	80
5	Hastings Town	42	22	9	11	76	56	20	75
6	Ashford Town	42	21	9	12	70	49	21	72
7	Tonbridge Angels	42	20	10	12	82	60	22	70
8	Dartford	42	17	6	19	52	58	-6	57
9	Burnham	42	15	9	18	55	64	-9	54
10	Baldock Town	42	14	10	18	57	69	-12	52
11	Erith & Belvedere	42	14	9	19	62	68	-6	51
12	Witney Town	42	13	11	18	48	60	-12	50
13	V.S. Rugby	42	13	11	18	58	79	-21	50
14	Wisbech Town	42	14	7	21	58	66	-8	49
15	Spalding United	42	14	6	22	52	71	-19	48
16	Sittingbourne	42	13	7	22	48	75	-27	46
17	Stamford	42	9	18	15	50	62	-12	45
18	St. Leonards	42	11	12	19	67	81	-14	45
19	Raunds Town	42	11	12	19	44	63	-19	45
20	Bashley	42	12	7	23	56	95	-39	43
21	Corby Town *	42	11	12	19	56	62	-6	42
22	Fleet Town	42	8	8	26	54	104	-50	32

points deducted

EASTERN DIVISION LEADING GOALSCORERS 1999-2000

Stephen Portway	Fisher Athletic	28
David Arter	Tonbridge Angels	25
Terry White	Hastings Town	25
Oliver Berquez	Chelmsford City	23
Nicholas Dent	Folkestone Invicta	23
Gary Walker	Baldock Town	22
Bryn Charles	Fisher Athletic London	19
Hamid Barr	Fisher Athletic London	18
Andrew Furnell	Wisbech Town	18
Carl Henry	Witney Town	18
Lee McRobert	Ashford Town	18
Mark Frampton	Fleet Town	16
Lee Guiver	Dartford	15
Stephen Lawrence	Folkestone Invicta	15
Philip Andrews	Bashley	14
Stephen Leigh	Newport IOW	14
Stuart Myall	Hastings Town	14
Gavin Smith	Fleet Town	14
Stephen White	Erith & Belvedere	14

EASTERN DIVISION RESULTS CHART 1999-2000

		1	2	3	4	5	6	7	8	9	10	11	12	13	14	15	16	17	18	19	20	21	22
1	Ashford T	X	2-0	3-3	3-0	1-0	1-2	3-1	2-2	1-3	4-0	1-3	2-1	1-1	2-1	7-0	2-0	1-0	1-2	0-0	0-1	3-1	0-0
2	Baldock T	0-2	X	0-2	4-1	0-0	0-1	1-0	0-1	3-4	2-0	1-6	0-1	1-2	1-1	1-1	3-0	3-2	2-2	0-2	5-1	4-3	1-0
3	Bashley	2-4	1-1	X	1-1	0-1	1-2	3-1	0-0	2-5	4-2	0-3	1-3	1-2	2-1	2-1	1-3	0-2	1-0	0-3	2-2	5-0	2-5
4	Burnham	0-2	1+3	1-1	X	3-1	3-0	0-1	1-0	2-1	4-1	1-2	0-5	3-4	1-0	2-0	2-0	2-2	4-3	3-3	2-0	0-0	2-0
5	Chelmsford	2-1	0-0	10-1	1-0	X	1-2	1-0	2-1	4-1	1-2	0-5	3-4	1-0	2-0	2-0	2-2	4-3	3-3	2-0	5-1	1-0	1-1
6	Corby T	0-2	0-1	1-1	0-0	0-2	X	0-1	5-1	1-2	5-0	0-1	1-2	1-1	2-2	1-3	0-2	6-2	3-3	2-2	4-2	2-1	1-1
7	Dartford	1-2	0-3	0-1	3-2	3-0	1-2	X	0-0	0-3	2-1	1-3	4-2	1-2	2-0	1-2	2-1	0-0	2-0	3-0	2-0	0-0	0-1
8	Erith & B	1-2	2-2	1-2	0-1	2-2	3-0	X	0-2	4-3	1-2	2-3	0-2	1-1	2-3	2-0	1-0	1-1	0-2	5-3	1-2	3-1	
9	Fisher A L	3-0	4-1	2-1	3-0	1-1	2-0	4-0	4-2	X	3-2	2-2	4-2	0-1	3-0	3-0	0-0	3-1	6-0	0-2	3-2	3-1	5-0
10	Fleet T	0-1	3-2	2-4	1-1	0-3	2-1	1-0	0-1	0-5	X	0-5	2-3	3-2	1-4	0-1	1-1	2-2	1-1	2-3	3-3	2-3	3-2
11	Folkestone	1-1	1-1	4-0	4-1	1-1	0-0	4-1	1-2	1-0	2-0	X	3-0	2-1	3-2	5-0	4-1	2-4	3-0	6-1	3-1	2-0	
12	Hastings T	2-0	0-1	3-1	1-0	3-1	1-1	2-2	3-2	1-1	0-1	X	2-2	2-1	3-3	2-3	5-2	3-0	1-0	2-0	1-2	2-0	
13	Newport	2-1	2-0	6-1	3-0	1-0	2-0	0-0	5-1	0-2	3-1	3-0	2-1	X	3-0	2-0	1-0	1-1	0-3	1-0	2-1	3-0	
14	Raunds T	0-0	3-0	0-1	1-0	0-6	1-1	2-2	3-2	0-1	1-2	0-0	4-3	1-0	X	0-0	2-1	0-4	1-1	2-2	0-1	1-0	2-3
15	Sittingb'ne	1-3	2-2	2-0	0-1	1-0	0-2	1-0	0-3	0-1	0-2	1-2	0-0	1-4	2-0	X	1-0	2-2	3-1	1-4	3-5	3-1	2-0
16	Spalding U	3-1	2-2	3-2	2-1	2-3	0-0	1-2	1-4	1-2	1-1	0-1	0-3	0-2	X	4-1	1-0	4-2	1-1	2-1	0-3		
17	St Leonards	2-0	1-2	1-2	1-2	2-4	1-0	4-3	1-2	1-1	6-3	1-2	4-1	1-1	1-3	2-2	3-2	X	1-1	2-1	1-2	4-3	1-0
18	Stamford	0-1	3-1	1-0	1-1	0-0	0-0	1-2	1-1	1-4	3-1	1-1	1-1	0-1	1-0	4-0	2-1	0-0	X	2-2	0-2	4-0	1-1
19	Tonbridge	2-2	5-1	5-0	2-1	1-2	2-3	2-4	1-0	0-1	2-0	1-4	3-0	3-3	1-0	3-2	3-1	3-3	4-0	X	2-0	1-0	1-1
20	VS Rugby	2-3	1-0	4-1	1-3	2-1	3-2	1-2	2-1	1-1	2-2	2-1	0-1	1-1	0-1	2-1	1-1	0-0	1-1	X	2-2	1-1	
21	Wisbech T	4-2	4-1	2-0	1-0	0-1	2-0	0-2	1-2	4-2	4-0	1-3	0-0	2-1	0-0	2-0	0-0	3-0	2-1	2-3	3-1	X	0-1
22	Witney T	0-0	0-1	2-1	2-2	1-2	3-1	0-1	2-1	2-5	2-1	0-3	0-2	2-1	0-1	2-0	1-2	1-1	1-1	1-0	3-0	1-1	X

An irresistable strike force

Every month

Every week

Every day

For up to the minute news, results, fixtures,
and general facts and figures
from the world of non-league football
log on to

www.nlfootball.com

Brought to you by Non-League Media in conjunction with e-comsport

ASHFORD TOWN

CLUB OFFICIALS

A,Cooper **Ernie Warren**
President: **Ashley M Batt**
Secretary/Press Officer: **A Lancaster**
128 Kingsnorth Rd, Ashford, Kent TN23
2HY Tel: 01233 621325
Vice Chairman: **Peter Barton**
Commercial Director:
Ernie Warron Tel: 01233 634125

FOOTBALL MANAGEMENT TEAM
Manager: Tony Reynolds
Asst Manager: None
Coach: Nicky Sparks
Physio: George Sargeant

FACT FILE

Formed: 1930
Nickname: Nuts & Bolts
Colours: White/Green/White & Green
Change colours: All Green
Midweek home matchday: Tuesday
Reserves ' League: No Reserve team

GROUND   The Homelands, Ashford Road, Kingsnorth, Ashford, Kent TN26 1NJ
Tel: 01233 611838
Directions: M20 jct 10, follow A2070 signs towards Brenzett & Lydd airport, dual carriageway
to junction of old A2070, ground 1 mile on left thro' village of Kingsnorth. 4 miles south of Ashford
Capacity: 3,200   Cover: 1,250   Seats: 500   Floodlights: Yes
Clubhouse: Open matchdays and for special functions. Licensed bar, function room. Limited
food - sandwiches & simple snacks.
Club Shop: Sells old progs, pennants, scarves, badges etc. Contact Alan Bird(01233 662680)

Pages: 32 Price: £1.00
Editor: Tim Warren

Local Press: Kentish Express
Local Radio: Radio Kent, Invicta Radio

PREVIOUS   **Names:** Ashford United, Ashford Railway, Ashford F.C.
Leagues: Kent 30-59. **Ground:** Essella Park, Essella Rd 30-87

CLUB RECORDS **Attendance:** 6,525 (at Essella Park, previous ground), v Crystal Palace, FA Cup 1st Rd 1959.
3,363 (at current ground), v Fulham FA Cup 1st Round 1994.
Goalscorer: Dave Arter 197. **Appearances:** Peter McRobert 765
Win: 10-1 v Bury Town, February 1964. **Defeat:** 0-8 v Crawley Town, November1964
Fee Paid: £7,000 for J Ross & D Arter (Sittingbourne, March 94)
Fee Received: £25,000 for Jeff Ross & Dave Arter (Hythe Tn, 90). Individually: £20,000 for Lee McRobert (Sittingbourne, 93)

BEST SEASON **FA Trophy:** Semi Final 72-73, 96-97 2nd Rd
FA Cup: 2nd Rd 61-62, 0-3 v QPR (H), 66-67, 0-5 v Swindon (A). 1st Rd 7 times.   League clubs defeated: None.
HONOURS   FA Trophy SF 72-73; Southern Lg Southern Div R-up 86-87 95-96; Kent Lg 48-49(R-up 31-32), Lg Cup 38-39; Kent Senior Cup
58-59 62-63 92-93 95-96
Players progressing: Ollie Norris (Rochdale 61), HowardMoore (Coventry 66), Tony Godden (WBA 75), Lee McRobert (Millwall 94)

Back Row: Paul Giles (Coach), George Sergeant (Physio), Simon Glover, Paul Tuppenny, Ryan Hackett, Steve Robinson, Dave
Root, Matt Bower, Ian Ross, Duncan Horton, Tony Reynolds (Manager), Peter McRobert (Asst. Manager). **Front:** Adrian
Webster, Lee McRobert, Lennie Griffiths, Tony Eeles, Steve Smith, Mike Heather.

BALDOCK TOWN

CLUB OFFICIALS
Joint Chairman: **Ray Childerstone**
Secretary: **Cyril T Hammond**
2 Elmwood Court, High Street.,
Baldock, Herts SG7 6AY
01462 894253(H) 01462 895449(B)
General Manager: **B Williams**
Press Officer: **David Hammond**
Tel: 01462 892797

FOOTBALL MANAGEMENT TEAM

Team Managers:Steve Cook & Gary Roberts
Physio: Fred Day

FACT FILE

Formed: 1889
Nickname: Reds
Colours: All red
Change colours: All white
Midweek home matchday: Tuesday
Reserve Team's League: No reserve team

For up to the minute news,
results, fixtures,
plus general facts & figures
from the world of
non-league football

log on to

www.nlfootball.com

GROUND Norton Road, Baldock, Herts SG7 5AU Tel: 01462 895449
Directions: Off A1(M) at Letchworth/Baldock sign, left to 3rd island, A505 toBaldock, Norton
Road is left off A505, left past Orange Tree pub, ground on right after railway bridge. From North
or East turn left into town, Hitchin Street, right into Norton then proceed as above. From Baldock
station (KingsCross to Royston line) - left down Ickneild Way and right into Norton Road
Capacity: 3,000   Cover: 1,250   Seats: 250
Clubhouse: Members' bar and separate function room. Food available
Club Shop: No. Metal Badges: Yes   Supporters Club: Phil Rosendale (01462 223135)

PROGRAMME	
Pages: 48	Price: £1
Editor: Secretary	
Local Press: Comet, Gazette	
Local Radio: Radio Bedfordshire, Chiltern	

PREVIOUS   **Ground:** Bakers Close (until 1982)
                Leagues: South Midlands 25-39 47-54 63-83, Parthenon 54-59, London 59-63,United Counties 83-87

CLUB RECORDS **Attendance:** 1,588 v Stevenage Boro. FA Cup 2nd Prelim 96-97
                Goalscorer: Unknown. Appearances: Keith (Paddy) Stanton 550
                Fee Paid: £2,000: for Colin Hull (Bishop's Stortford) & for Glen Russell(Braintree 1993)
                Fee Received: £30,000 for Kevin Phillips (Watford F.C.)

BEST SEASON **FA Vase:** 5th Round 83-84   **FA Trophy:** 2nd Qual. Round 90-91
                FA Cup: 4th Qual. Round replay 91-92, 0-1 v Halesowen Town (A) after 1-1

HONOURS   United Counties Lg R-up 83-84 86-87, South Mids Lg 27-28 65-66 67-68 69-70 (R-up 53-54 82-83, Lg Cup 65-66 69-70, Div 1
                49-50, Reserve Div 1 66-67), HertsCharity Cup 91-92 94-95, Herts Charity Shield 57-58 69-70, Wallspan Floodlit Cup 85-86,
                Hinchingbrooke Cup 86-87, TSI Floodlit Cup 88-89, Woolwich E.B.S.Cup 83-84, Herts Intermediate Cup 86-87. Southern Lge
                R-up 94-95. Southern LgeCup Dr Martens 95-96

Players progressing: Ian Dowie (Luton), Alan Stewart (Portsmouth), Kevan Phillips (Watford)

Back Row: Gary Roberts (Asst. Manager), Glen Russell, John Shanks, Gary Simpson, Adam Wheeler, Simon Catmur, Tomas
Johansen, Paul de Luca, Mark Goddard (Physio). **Front:** Steve Cook (Asst. Manager), Dak Lee, Barry Dellar, Danny Flower,
Ricky Dear, Ray Kilby, Gary Walker.   **Photo:** Gordon Whittington

BANBURY UNITED

CLUB OFFICIALS
Chairman: Paul Saunders
Vice Chairman: Brian Kay
President: David Jesson
Commercial Mgr: Nigel Porter
Press Officer: Barry Worsley
General Manager: Phil Lines
Secretary: B Worsley, c/o Sol Systems, Unit 4 Mallorie Hse, Beaumont Rd,Banbury, OX16 7RH
Tel: 01295 265638 (H), 01295 255536 (B)

FOOTBALL MANAGEMENT TEAM

Manager: Kevin Brock
Coach: Brian Robinson
Physio: John Source

FACT FILE
Founded: 1933
Reformed: 1965
Nickname: Puritans
Club Sponsors: T.B.A.
Colours: Red & gold/red/red
Change colours: White & blue/white/white
Midweek matches: Tuesday
Reserves' Lge: Hellenic Res. section
Programme: 24 pages   60p
Editor: Kevin Hicklin

For up to the minute news, results, fixtures, plus general facts & figures from the world of non-league football

log on to

www.nlfootball.com

GROUND The Stadium, off Station Rd, Banbury, Oxon
Tel: 01295 263354

Directions: M40 jct 11, follow signs for Banbury then BR station, turn right down narrow lane before entering station forecourt; eastern end of town
Capacity: 6,500   Seats: 50   Cover: 500   Floodlights: Yes

Clubhouse: Open match days & week-ends. Mid-week on hire.
Hot food available during after matches   **Club Shop:** Yes

HONOURS Oxon Snr Cup 78-79 87-88 (R-up 6); Birmingham Comb. R-up 47-48; Oxon Prof. Cup 52-53(jt) 70-71(jt) 72-73 77-78 79-80(jt); Hellenic Lg.Cup R-Up 91-92; Birmingham Snr Cup R-Up 48-49 59-60 (S.F.46-47); Oxon Snr Lg. 34-35 39-4047-48 (res); Oxon Hosp. Cup 46-47 (R-up 45-46); Oxon Benev. Cup R-up 77-78 80-8182-83; Daventry Charity Cup 88-90; Smiths Mem. Cup 68-70 (R-up 66-68); Hitchin Centenary Cup 68-69 (R-up 67-68); Leamington Charity Cup 51-52; Warks Comb. R-up 57-58 60-61, Presidents Cup R-up 60-61; Midland Floodlit Cup 67-68; Wallspan Comb. 85-86

PREVIOUS **Leagues:** Banbury Jnr 33-34; Oxon Snr 34-35; Birmingham Comb. 35-54; W.Mids 54-66; Southern 66-90
Name: Banbury Spencer

BEST SEASON **FA Cup:** 1st Rd replay 73-74 (Also 1st Rd 47-48 61-62 72-73)
FA Trophy: 3rd Rd 70-71 73-74

RECORDS **Attendance:** 7,160 v Oxford City, FA Cup 3rd Qual.Rd, 30/10/48
Goalscorer: Dick Pike (1935-48), Tony Jacques (65-76) - both 222
Appearances: Ian Bowyer (531)Fee Paid : £2,000 for Phil Emsden (Oxford Utd, Jan 1980)
Fee Received: £20,000 Kevin Wilson (Derby, December 1979)
Win: 12-0 v RNAS Culham, Oxon Snr Cup 45-46
Defeat: 2-11 v West Bromwich Albion `A', Birmingham Comb. 38-39

Players progressing: Ollie Kearns (Reading), Kevin Wilson & Richard Pratley(Derby), Mick Kearns & Terry Muckleberg (Oxford), Martin Singleton (Coventry)

Back Row: John Cramond, Brian Robinson, Carl Standen, Mike Preedy, Jody McKay, Alan Judge, Steve Jenkins, Neil Sole, Andy Wallbridge, Mark Sherlock, Kevin Brock, John Source (Physio). **Front:** Adrian Fuller, Jamie Cramond, Jonathon Corbett, Les Phillips, John Blencowe, Matthew Gooderick, Stuart Fox, Simon Pearce (Mascot). **Photo:** Keith Clayton

BASHLEY

CLUB OFFICIALS
Chairman: **Ray Pinney**
President: **K.D.Taylorl**
Vice Chairman: **Fred Pingram**
Secretary: **Pul Christopher,** 31 Brookside
Road, Bransgrove,Christchurch, Dorset
BH23 8NA (01425 674084)
Commercial Manager: **Mary Whitman**
Press Officer: **Terry Collett**

FOOTBALL MANAGEMENT TEAM

Manager: Barry Blankley
Asst Manager: Trevor Senior
Physio: Chris Lovegrove

FACT FILE

Formed: 1947

Nickname: The Bash

Sponsors: T.B.A.

Colours: Yellow & black

Change colours: Blue & white

Midweek matchday: Wednesday

Reserves' League: Wessex Comb

BASHLEY FOOTBALL CLUB

MATCHDAY PROGRAMME
1999-2000

£1

Pages: 36 Price: £1

Local Press: Bournemouth Echo,
Southern Pink, New Milton Advertiser
Local Radio: 2CR,Solent, Ocean Sound

GROUND Recreation Ground, Bashley, Hampshire BH25 5RY. Tel: 01425 620280

Directions: A35 Lyndhurst towards Christchurch, turn left down B3058 towardsNew Milton, ground on left in Bashley village. Half hour walk from New Milton(BR) station

Capacity: 4,250 Cover: 1,200 Seats: 200 Floodlights: Yes
Clubhouse: Usual licensing hours. Snacks available
Club Shop: Open matchdays

PREVIOUS **Leagues:** Bournemouth 50-83; Hants 83-86; Wessex 86-89

CLUB RECORDS **Attendance:** 3,500 v Emley, F.A. Vase S.F. 1st Leg 87-88
Win: 21-1 v Co-operative (A), Bournemouth Lge, 64 **Defeat:** 2-20 v Air Speed(A), Bournemouth Lge, 57
Career Goalscorer: Colin Cummings **Career Appearances:** John Bone
Transfer fee paid: £7,500 for J Stagg from Andover **Transfer fee received:** £7,500 for Darren Powell from Weymouth 95

BEST SEASON **FA Cup:** 2nd Rd Proper 1994-95, 0-1 v Swansea City
FA Vase: Semi Final 87-88, Qtr Final 88-89 **FA Trophy:** 2nd Round 91-92

HONOURS Southern Lg Southern Division 89-90 (Lg Cup SF 89-90), Wessex Lg 86-87 87-88 88-89, Hants Lg Div 3 84-85,
Hants Lg Combination 88-89, Russell Cotes Cup 88-89 90-91 92-93

Players Progressing : Wayne Brown (Bristol C 1994), David Billington Peterborough 1996), Ryan Young (Plymouth 1997), Dean Higgins (Torquay 1998), Danny Smith (Bournemouith 1998), Craig Davies (Cardiff City 1998), Tony Wallis (Cardiff C 1999), Wade Elliott (AFC Bouremoth 2000)

Bashley's Andy Darton considers his
options with St. Leonards' Chris Stonham
in close attendance.
Photo: Roger Turner

BURNHAM

CLUB OFFICIALS

Chairman: **Malcolm Higton**
Vice Chairman: **Mark Green**
Press Officer: **Secretary**
Secretary: **Alan King**
41 Underwood Road, High Wycombe,
Bucks HP13 6YD (01494523920 (H)
078999 41414(M)

FACT FILE

Founded: 1878
Sponsors: Laing Homes & PKGraphics
Colours: Blue & white/blue/white
Change colours: Yellow/yellow/black
Midweek matchday: Tuesday 7.30
Reserve Team's Lge: Suburban

FOOTBALL MANAGEMENT TEAM

Manager: John Griffith
Coach: Neal McLoughlin
Physio: Melanie Garrett

99-00 Captain: Paul Brett
P.o.Y.: Mark O'Sullivan
Top Scorer: Steve Lockhart (11)

Ground: The Gore, Wymers Wood Road, Burnham, Slough SL1 8JG
Tel: 01628 602467/602697
Directions: North west of village centre, 2 miles from Burnham BR station, 2miles from M4 junction 7, 5 miles from M40 junction 2, 100yds north of Gorecrossroads - fork right into Wymers Wood Rd and ground is immediately on right
Capacity: 2,500   Cover: 250   Seats: 250   Floodlights: Yes   Club Shop: Yes
Clubhouse: Open every evening and w/e lunch. Darts and pool, two bars, usual matchday food

Progrtamme Sponsor: PK Graphics
32 pages   Editor: Cliff Sparkes
Local Press: Slough Observer, South Bucks
Express, Maidenhead Advertiser,
Buckingham Advertiser
Local Radio: Star FM,
BBC Thames Valley

HONOURS   Athenian Lg R-up(2) 78-80, Hellenic Lg 75-76 98-99 (Div 1 R-up 72-73, Lg Cup 75-76 98-99, Div 1 Cup 71-72), London Spartan Lg 84-85 (Lg Cup 84-85), Reading Comb. Lg Cup 70-71 (All Champions Cup 70-71), Wycombe Comb. R-up (4) 65-67 68-70

PREVIOUS   **Leagues:** Sth Bucks & East Berks; Maidenhead Intermediate; Windsor,Slough & Dist; Gt Western Comb. 48-64; Wycombe Comb. 64-70; Reading Comb. 70-71; Hellenic 71-77; Athenian 77-84; London Spartan 84-85; Southern 85-95; Hellenic 95-99
Name: Burnham & Hillingdon 1985-87   **Ground:** Baldwin Meadow (until 20's)

BEST SEASON   **FA Cup:** 3rd Qualifying Rd   **FA Vase:** Semi-Final 82-83, Q-F 77-78.
FA Trophy: 4th Round Replay 99-00

RECORD   **Attendance:** 2,380 v Halesowen Town, FA Vase 2/4/83
Scorer: Fraser Hughes 65, 69-70   **Win:** 18-0 v High Duty Alloys, 70-71
Defeat: 1-10 v Ernest Turners Sports, 63-64

Players progressing: D Hancock (Reading), R Rafferty (Grimsby Town), D Payne(Barnet)

Back Row: Alan King (Secretary), Rod Saunders (Treasurer), Cliff Sparkes (Prog. Editor), Mark O'Sullivan, Adrian Nesbeth, Jamie Jarvis, Daniel Tillson, Paul Sampdon, Steve Lockhart, Matty Clarke, Mike Tomlinson, John Griffith (Coach), Mark Green (Vice Chairman), Michael Broadley (Committee). **Front:** Simon Pentland, Spencer Walsh, Alan Murphy, Jamie Furmage, Malcolm Higton (Chairman), Paul Brett (Captain), Shane Chandler (Manager), Matty Potter, Steve Bunce, Reuben Howell.

CHELMSFORD CITY

CLUB OFFICIALS

Chairman: **Peter Stroud**
Tel: 01245 471917(H) 0385 990233(M)

Secretary: **David Selby**
34 Paddock Drive,Chelmsford CM1 6SS
Tel 01245 464922

FOOTBALL MANAGEMENT TEAM

Manager: Gary Bellamy
Asst Manager: Paul Parker

FACT FILE

Formed: 1938
Nickname: City
Sponsors:Countryside Properties Plc
Colours: Claret, white trim/claret/claret
Change colours: Sky blue/navy/sky blue
Midweek matches : Monday
Reserves' League:
1999-00
Captain: Brett Girling
Top Scorer:Oliver Berquez
P.O.Y: John Girling

GROUND

Ground Share with Billericay Town
New Lodge, Blunts Wall Road, Billericay CM12 9SA Tel: 01277 652188
Directions: From Shenfield (A129) right at 1st lights then 2nd right. FromBasildon (A129) over
1st lights in town, then left at next lights and 2nd right. Half mile from Billericay (GER) station
(London Liverpool St. - Southend line). Ground 5 mins walk from buses 222, 251, 357, 255, 551
Capacity: 3,500   **Seats:** 424   **Cover:** 600   **Floodlights:** Yes
Clubhouse: Open eves 8-11pm (except Mon),1pm-11pm Sat & w/e lunch noon-2.30pm.
Club Shop: Sells progs, badges, scarves, mugs etc. Contact Helen Williams via club

Pages: 52   Price: £1.40
Editor: Trevor Smith (01245 353052)
Local Press: Essex Chronicle,
Chelmsford Weekly News,
East Anglian Daily Times, Evening Gazette
Local Radio: Essex Radio/Breeze AM,
BBC Essex, Chelner FM

PREVIOUS   **Leagues:** None   **Grounds:** New Whittle Street 38-97, Maldon Town 97-98
Name: None (Brentwood Town were incorporated in 1970)
CLUB RECORDS Attendance: 16,807 v Colchester, Southern League 10/9/49
Goalscorer: Tony Butcher, 287 (1957-71)   **Appearances:** Derek Tiffin, 550 (1950-63)
Win: 10-1 v Bashley (H) Dr Martens Leagu 26/4/2000
Defeat: 2-10 v Barking (A), FA Trophy, 11/11/78
Fee Paid: £10,000 for Tony Rogers (Dover Athletic, 1992)   **Fee Received:** £50,000 for David Morrison (Peterborough 94)
BEST SEASON FA Cup: 4th Rd, 1938-39 (v Birmingham City). 1st Rd 26 times
FA Trophy: Semi-final 69-70 v Telford Utd
HONOURS   Southern Lg 45-46 67-68 71-72 (R-up 48-49 60-61 63-64 65-66); Southern Div 88-89, R-up 97-98, Lg Cup 45-46 59-60 (R-up
60-61); Merit Cup 71-72; Southern Lg War-Time (East) 39-40); Essex Prof Cup 5; Essex Snr Cup 85-86 88-89 92-93;
Non-League Champs Chall Cup 71-72; E Anglian Cup 48-49; Eastern Co's Lg(3) 46-49(Lg Cup 59-60); Eastern F'lit Comp 6,
(Cup 72-73 74-75); Metropolitan Lg 67-68, Lg Prof Cup 67-68, Autumn Shield 70-71; Essex Snr Lg Cup 84-85; Harry Fisher Mem. Tphy 88-89
Players progressing: G Merton (Watford 48), G Adams (Orient 49), W O'Neill(Burnley 49), B Farley/S McClellan/L Dicker/P Collins (Spurs 49/49/51/68), O
Hold (Everton 50), R Marden (Arsenal 50), C McCormack (Barnsley 50), D Sexton(Luton 51), W Bellet & R Mason & A Nicholas (Orient 61 & 63 & 65), R
Gladwin(Norwich 66), B King (Millwall 67), J O'Mara (Bradford City 74), N Spink (Aston77), M Dziadulewicz (Wimbledon 79), M Cawston (Southend 84), P
Coleman (Exeter84), J Keeley & A Owers (Brighton 86 & 87), I Brown (Bristol C 93), D Morrison (Peterborough 94)

Chelmsford 'keeper Paul Catley and John
Girling defending this shot from Moor Green's
Craig Woodley.   Photo: Alan Coomes

CORBY TOWN

CLUB OFFICIALS
Chairman: **James Kane**
President: **H Hatterley**
Secretary: **Ian Lochead,**164 Kingsthorpe
Avenue,Corby, Northants NN17 2QATel Nos:
01536 403806(H) 0411 563731 (M)

FOOTBALL MANAGEMENT TEAM

Manager:Lee Adam
Physio: Ian Lochhead

FACT FILE

Formed: 1948
Nickname: The Steelmen
Sponsor: British Steel
Colours: Black& white stripes.black,black
Change colours: White& Red,white,white
Midweek matchday: Wednesday
Reserves' League: United Counties Res Div

For up to the minute news,
results, fixtures,
plus general facts & figures
from the world of
non-league football

log on to

www.nlfootball.com

GROUND   Rockingham Triangle Stadium, Rockingham Road, Corby NN17 2AE
Tel: 01536 406640
Directions: On northern outskirts of town at junction of A6003 and A6116,opposite entrance
to Rockingham Castle grounds. One and a half miles from Corby (BR)
Capacity: 3,000   Cover: 1,150   Seats: 960   Floodlights: Yes
Clubhouse: VP Lounge open matchdays and during the week
Club Shop: Sells badges, programmes etc. Contact C Woolmer Tel: 01536 260900

PROGRAMME
Pages: 32   Price: £1
Editor: David.Tilley

Local Press: Northampton Evening Telegraph
Local Radio: BBC Radio Northampton,
Hereward, KCBC

PREVIOUS   **Leagues:** United Counties 35-52, Midland 52-58

CLUB RECORDS **Attendance:** 2,240 v Watford, pre-season friendly 86-87
At Old Ground; 10,239 v Peterborough Utd, FA Cup 3rd Qual. Rd 52-53
Win: 14-0 v Gainsborough Trinity, 56-57   **Defeat:** 0-10 v Paget Rangers, 95-96
Career Goalscorer: David Hofbauer 141 (84-95)   **Career Appearances:** Derek Walker600 (78-92)
Transfer fee paid: £2,700 for Elwyn Roberts (Barnet, 81) **Transfer fee received:** £20,000 for Matt Murphy (Oxford U. 93)

BEST SEASON   **FA Cup:** 3rd Rd 65-66 (lost to Plymouth). 1st Rd on five occasions; 54-55 63-6667-68
League clubs defeated: Luton Town 65-66   **FA Trophy:** 3rd Rd, 1986-87

HONOURS   UCL 50-51 51-52 (R-up 37-38), Midland Lg R-up 52-53, Southern Lg Midland Div R-up 90-91 (Merit Cup 63-64 90-91),
Northants Snr Cup 6; Maunsell Cup 83-84, Daventry Charity Cup 94-95, Midland Floodlit Cup 74-75, Evans Halshaw F'lit Cup
91-92, Anglia Floodlit Trophy 68-69 72-73, Chelmsford Invitation Cup 63-64 64-65 65-66 (joint), Kettering & Dist Samaritan Cup
60-61(joint) 68-69, Wellingborough Charity Cup 50-51, Desborough Nursing Cup 48-49 50-51 (joint), Bob Cumning Cup 6

Players progressing: A McCabe (Chesterfield 55), L Chalmers (Leicester C. 56), K Brown (Nottm Forest 56), P Kearns (Aldershot 62),
N Dean (Southampton 63), H Curran (Millwall 64), D McNeil/A McGowan/G Reilly (Northampton69/75/76), P Chard (Peterborough 79), T Morley
(West Ham), J Flower (SheffieldUtd), M Murphy (Oxford Utd 93), C McKenzie (Hereford 94)

Back Row: Scott Munton, David Hollis, Dean Tallentire, Tyrone Mintus, Richard Tanner, Kevin Fox, Glyn Davies, Ian
Lochhead (Physio). **Front:** Danum Russell, James Miller, Gavin Cox, Dougie Keast (Captain), Leon Doughty,
Robbie Maddox, Andy Evans.   **Photo:** David Tilley

DARTFORD

CLUB OFFICIALS

Chairman: **David Skinner**

Vice-Chairman: **Norman Grimes**

Secretary: **Andy Clark**

57 Shenley Road, Dartford, Kent DA1 1YF

Tel.01322 221582

Commercial Man.: TBA

Press Officer: Secretary

FOOTBALL MANAGEMENT TEAM

Manager: Gary Julians

Coach:Asst-Manager: Micky Crowe

Physio:Dave Phillips

FACT FILE

Formed: 1888

Nickname: The Darts

Colours: White & black/black/black

Change colours: All Red

Midweek home matchday: Monday

Reserves' League: Winstonlead Kent Div 1

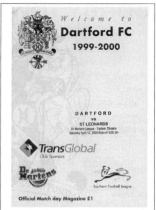

Welcome to

Dartford FC

1999-2000

DARTFORD
vs
ST LEONARDS
Dr Martens League - Eastern Division
Saturday April 10, 2000 Kick-off 3:00 pm

TransGlobal
Club Sponsors

Dr Martens

Southern Football League

Official Match day Magazine £1

Pages: 40 Price: £1

Editor: Mike Brett-Smith Tel: 01322 277243

Press: Dartford Times, Dartford Messenger

Local Radio: Radio Kent, Millennium Radio

GROUND   Purfleet FC, Thurrock Hotel, Ship Lane, Grays, Essex Tel: 01708 868901

Directions: M25 North; through Dartford Tunnel 1st exit, at roundabout take Ship Lane exit (sign Purfleet FC), ground 100 yards on right beside Thurrock Hotel

Capacity: 4,500   Cover: 1,000   Seats: 300   Floodlights: Yes

Clubhouse:

Club Shop: Open matchdays. Mail Order: Norman Grimes 01474 815236

PREVIOUS

Leagues: Kent 1894-96, 97-98, 99-1902, 09-14, 21-26, 93-96; Southern Lg 1896-98, 99-1900, 26-81, 82-84, 86-92; GMVC 81-82, 84-86

Grounds: The Brent/Westgate House, Potters Meadow, Engleys Meadow, Summers Meadow, Watling St, Cray Wanderers, Erith & Belverdere

CLUB RECORDS   **Attendance:** 11,004 v Leyton Orient FA Cup 48

Career Appearances: Steve Robinson 653

Win: 11-1 v Faversham Tn Kent Snr Cup 65   **Defeat:** 0-10 v Guildford City SouthernLge 46

Transfer fee paid: £6,000 for John Bartley (Chelmsford 88) **Received:** £25,000 forAndy Hessenthaler (Redbridge Forest)

BEST SEASON   **FA Trophy:** Runners-up 74   **FA Vase:** 2nd Qual Rd 95/96

FA Cup: 3rd Rd Prop 35-36 & 36-37   League clubs defeated: Cardiff (1935), Exeter(1961), Aldershot (1968)

HONOURS   Southern Lg 1930-31, 31-32, 73-74, 83-84, R-up 87-88, 88-89, Eastern Div 30-31,31-32, Southern Div 80-81, Southern Lg Div 2 1896-97, Lg Cup 76-77, 87-88, 88-89, Championship Shield 83-84, 87-88, 88-89; Kent Lg 1995-96, Lg Cup 24-25,Kent Snr Cup 29-30, 34-35, 38-39, 69-70, Snr Trophy 95-96, Inter Lg Chall 1974;FA Trophy R-up 1974

Players progressing: Idris Hopkins (Brentford 32), Fred Dall(West Ham 36), Riley Cullum/Fred Alexander/Ted Croker (Charlton 47/48/48), Frank Coombs (Bristol C 49), James Kelly (Gillingham 51), Tom Ritchie (Grimsby 58), Dave Underwood (Watford 60), Derek Hales (Luton 72), Andy Hessenthaler (Watfordvia Redbridge F)

Back Row: Dave Phillips (Physio), Danny Evans, Kevin Spriggs, Simon Roberts, Paul Sawyer, Luke Morrish, Colin Lewington, Marc Brown, Paul McCarthy, Scott Appleton, Gary Julians (Manager).
Front: Trevor Hand, Andy Mills, Lee Guiler, Chris Arnold, Tom Adlington, Paul Hennessy.

ERITH & BELVEDERE

CLUB OFFICIALS
Chairman: **John McFadden**
President: **L O'Connell**
Vice Chairman: **Peter Bird**
Secretary: Miss **Kellie Discipline**
108 Chastilion Road, Dartford, Kent DA1
3LG Tel: -01322 275766
Press Off./Commecial Man.: Martin Tarrant
Tel: 01322 275766

FOOTBALL MANAGEMENT TEAM
Manager: Mike Acland 01322 225594
Asst Man ager: Dave Hough
Coach: Steve Rutter
Physio: Rob Couldwell

FACT FILE
Formed: 1922
Nickname: Deres
Colours: Blue & white/blue/blue
Change colours: All red
Midweek home matchday:Tuesday
Reserves' League: None

1999-00
Captain: Danny Francis/Karl Emmerick
P.o.Y.: Dean Lee
Top scorer: Steve White

THE DERES
FOUNDED 1922

**ERITH &
BELVEDERE FC**

Versus

**TONBRIDGE
ANGELS**

Saturday
6 May 2000
kick-off 3.00pm

MAIN SPONSOR
NUFARM UK LIMITED

Dr MARTENS FOOTBALL LEAGUE • EASTERN DIVISION

OFFICIAL PROGRAMME £1

GROUN D Park View Rd Ground, Welling, Kent DA16 1SY Tel: 0181 301 1196
Directions: As for Welling United F.C.:M25,then A2 towards London.Take Welling turn-off,
ground one mile. By rail to Welling stationBR (BR) ground 3/4 mile.
Capacity: 1,500   Cover: 1,000   Seats: 500   Floodlights: Yes
Club Shop: Sells programmes, badges and pens
Clubhouse: Licensed social club open matchdays and weekends. Cold snacks available.
Separate canteen provides hot food on matchdays

Pages: 30 Price: £1.00p
Editor: Mike Tarrant Tel: 01322 275766

Local Press:
Kentish Times, Kentish Independent
Local Radio: Radio Kent, Radio Mellenium

PREVIOUS   **Leagues:** Kent 22-29 31-39 78-82, London 29-31, Corinthian 45-63, Athenian 63-78
Names: Belvedere & District FC (Formed 1918, restructured 1922)

CLUB RECORDS Attendance: 5,573 v Crook Colliery Welfare Amt Cup 3rd Rd 1949
Win: 14-2 v Royal Marines, Kent Lge 18/11/33. (16-2 v RAF Friendly 4/9/41) **Defeat:** 0-15 v Ashford, Kent Lge 28/4/37
Career Appearances: Dennis Crawford 504, 56-71   **Career Goalscorer:** Colin Johnson284, 61-71

BEST SEASON   FA Amateur Cup: Runners-up 1923-24, 37-38 **FA Trophy:** Third Qualifying Round second replay 89-90
FA Vase: Third Round 76-77   **FA Cup:** 4th Qual Rd 1924-25 (Equiv to 1st Rd Prop). League clubs defeated: None

HONOURS   FA Amat Cup R-up 23-24 37-38; Athenian Lge Div 1 R-up 70-71 (Lge Cup 73-74), Memorial Shield 67-68; Corinthian Lge R-up
62-63, (Lge Cup 47-48 48-49 49-50); Kent Lge 81-82, (Lge Cup R-up 81-82); London Sen Cup 44-45 (R-up 38-39); KentAmat
Cup 6, (R-up 4); Kent F/lit Lge R-up 67-68; Kent Interm Cup R-up 90-91; Kent Jun Cup 67-68; Kent County Yth Lge 90-91;
Kent Yth Cup 87-88. Bromley Hosp Cup 38-39; Essex & Herts Border Comb Cup 73-74.

Players progressing: John Coshall (West Ham 28), Fred Ford 36/ Cyril Hammond 46/ KeithPeacock 62 (Charlton),
Tommy Ord (Chelsea 72), Sean Devine (Barnet 95)

Erith's Stuart Abbott
slides this shot into the
net to score their 2nd
goal against Dartford.

Photo: Keith Gillard

GRANTHAM TOWN

CLUB OFFICIALS

Chairman: **Gordon Hotson**
President: **Michael Bird**

Secretary: **Pat Nixon**
72 Huntingtower Road, Grantham,
Lincs NG31 7AU
Tel: 01476 419391 FAX: 01476 419392

FOOTBALL MANAGEMENT TEAM
Manager:John Wilkinson
Asst Mgr:Tony Simmons
Physio: Nigel Marshall

FACT FILE
Formed: 1874
Nickname: Gingerbreads
Sponsors: Crystal Motors
Colours: Black & white stripes/black/black
Change: All Sky Blue
Midweek matchday: Tuesday
Reserves' League: Lincolnshire
Club Website:
www.cheiroa.domon.co.uk/gtfc
1999-00
Captain: Adrian Sped
P.o.Y.: Matt Carvell
Top scorer: Rick Ranshaw

GROUND   South Kesteven Sports Stadium, Trent Road, Grantham, Lincs Tel: 01476 562011

Directions: Midway between A1 and A52 on edge of Earlesfield Industrial Estate; from A1 take A607 to Earlsfield Ind. Est and continue into Trent Rd

Capacity: 7,500   Cover: 1,950   Seats: 750   Floodlights: Yes

Clubhouse: (01476 593506) Open evenings and weekends. Bar, darts, pool etc.Frequent live entertainment. Available for functions (Ground FAX: 01476 590918)

Club Shop: Programmes and a wide range of souvenirs. Contact club number.

DR MARTEN'S LEAGUE – Premier Division

GRANTHAM TOWN FOOTBALL CLUB

1999-2000 Official Matchday Programme – £1.20

Programme: 38 pages £1.50

Local Press: Grantham Journal, Nottingham Evening Post, Melton & GranthamTrader, Grantham Citizen, Lincolnshire Echo
Local Radio: Radio Lincolnshire, Lincs FM

PREVIOUS   **Leagues:** Mid Amat All, Central All. 11-25 59-61, Midland Co's 25-59 61-72,Southern Lge 72-79, Northern Prem. 79-85
Names: Grantham FC, pre-80. Grounds: London Rd up to 90

CLUB RECORDS **Attendance:** 3,695 v Southport. F.A.Trophy Quarter Final 97-98
Win: 13-0 vRufford Colliery (H), FA Cup Preliminary Rd 15/9/34   **Career Goalscorer:** Jack McCartney 416
Defeat: 0-16 v Notts County Rovers (A), Midland Amateur All. 22/10/1892   **Career Appearances:** Chris Gardiner 664
Transfer fee paid:undisclosed for Mario Ziccari   **Transfer fee received:** £20,000 for Gary Crosby (Notts Forest 87)

BEST SEASON   **FA Cup:** 3rd Rd 1883-84 86-87 1973-74. Comp Proper on 23 occasions
FA Trophy: Quarter Final 1971-72, 97-98

HONOURS   Southern Lg R-up 73-74 (Div 1 Nth 72-73 78-79), Merit Cup 72-73), Southern Lg Mid Div Champions 97-98. Midland Co's Lg(3) 63-64 70-72 (R-up 37-38 64-65 69-70, Lg Cup 68-69 70-71), Midland Amtr Lg10-11 (Lg Cup R-up 10-11), Central All. 24-25 (Southern Div R-up 59-60), LincsSnr Cup 1884-851936-37 (R-up(5) 34-36 39-40 45-47), Lincs Co. `A' Cup(3) 53-54 60-62 (R-up 49-50 52-53 57-58), Lincs Co. Snr Cup 71-72 82-83 (R-up 80-81)

Players progressing: E Morris (Halifax 50), P Thompson/R Cooke (Peterborough 64/80), J Rayner (Notts County 64), D Dall (Scunthorpe 79), N Jarvis/H Wood (Scunthorpe 80), D White (Bristol Rvrs 86), T Curran (Grimsby 87), G Crosby (Nottm Forest 87), A Kennedy (Wrexham 87), R Wilson (Lincoln 87)

Grantham Town's Tom Wilkes (10) and Neil Featherstone (9) are just thwarted by the Hitchin Town defence in this FA Cup 3rd Qual. Round match.   **Photo:** Peter Barnes

HASTINGS TOWN

CLUB OFFICIALS

Chairman: Peter Huggins
President: Mick Maplesden
Vice Chairman: T.B.A.
Secretary / Press Officer: R A Cosens
22 Baldslow Road, Hastings TN34 2EZ
01424 427867 (H) 01424 444635 (B)
0771 2634288 (M)

FOOTBALL MANAGEMENT TEAM
Team Managers: Dean White
Asst Manager: Jack Dalton
Physio: Bob Lewis

FACT FILE
Formed: 1894
Nickname: The Town
Sponsors: Alsford Timber
Colours: All white
Change colours:Blue/Yellow
Midweek matchday: Tuesday
Reserves' League: Bass Kent Div 2
Newsline: 0930 555 879
99-00 - Captain: Mat Ball
P.o.Y.: Mat Ball
Top scorer: T.White (33)

GROUND The Pilot Field, Elphinstone Road, Hastings TN34 2AX Tel: 01424 444635

Directions: From A21 turn left at 1st mini-r'bout into St Helens Rd, left after 1 mile into St Helens Park Rd, this leads into Downs Rd, at end of Downs Rd (T-junction) turn left, ground 200yds on right. From town centre take Queens Road (A2101). Right at roundabout into Elphinstone Road - ground 1 mile on right.
1 1/2 miles from Hastings BR station - infrequent bus service fromtown centre to ground

Capacity: 4,050   Cover: 1,750   Seats: 800   Floodlights: Yes

Clubhouse: Open matchdays, Tues, Thurs & Fri eves from 7pm.
Club Shop: Sells replica kits, scarves, programmes, pens, key-rings, badges etc

Pages: 64   Price: £1
Editor: David Bealey Tel: (01797 253310)

Local Press:Hastings Observer,Evening Argus
Local Radio: Radio Sussex,
Southern Sound, Arrow FM

PREVIOUS **Leagues:** South Eastern 04-05, Southern 05-10, Sussex County 21-27 52-85,Southern Amateur 27-46, Corinthian 46-48
Name: Hastings & St Leonards Amateurs   **Ground:** Bulverhythe Rec Gd (pre 76)

CLUB RECORDS **Attendance:** 4,888 v Notts Forest, friendly 23/6/96. Competitive: 1,774 v DoverAthletic, Southern Lge Prem. Div. 12/4/93
Goalscorer: (Season) Terry White (33) 99-00
Transfer Fee Paid: £8,000 for Nicky Dent from Ashford   **Received:** £50,000 for Paul Smith from Notts Forest

BEST SEASON **FA Cup:** 4th Qual. Rd 85-86, 2-3 v Farnborough Town (A)   **FA Trophy: 3rd Rd 1998-99**
FA Amateur Cup: 3rd Rd. 38-39   **FA Vase:** 5th Rd. rep. 90-91

HONOURS Southern Lg Cup 94-95, Southern Div 91-92, Div 2 R-up 08-09, Div 2(B) 09-10; Sussex Co Lg R-up 21-22 25-26,
Lg Cup 80-81, Div 2 79-80 (R-up 59-60), Div 2Cup 79-80; Sussex Sen Cup 35-36 37-38 95-96 97-98; AFA Snr Cup 37-38;
Gilbert Rice F/lit Cup 89-90

Players progressing: Peter Heritage (Gillingham), Paul Smith (Nottm Forest)

Hastings' 'keeper Tony Kessell about to stop a shot from St. Leonards' Simon Fox during their Boxing Day fixture. **Photo:** Roger Turner

HISTON

CLUB OFFICIALS

Chairman: Gareth Baldwin
President: G P Muncey

Secretary: Gareth Baldwin,
5 Caxton Lane, Foxton,
Cambridge CB2 6SR
Tel: 01223 872246

FOOTBALL MANAGEMENT TEAM

Manager: Steve Fallon
Coach: Bobby Broom
Physio; Lee Petrucci

FACT FILE
Founded: 1904
Sponsors:Webster Building & Civil Engineers
Colours: Red and blackstripes/black/black
Change colours: Sky & Navy/navy/sky ?
Midweek Matches: Wednesday
Reserves League: Kershaw Premier
1999-00
Captain: Andrew Jeffrey
P.o.Y.: Paul Barber
Top Scorer: Neil Kennedy (31)

Welcome To The Bridge

HISTON F.C
2000/2001 Season

WEBSTER

GROUND

Bridge Road, Impington, Cambridge
Tel: 01223 232301 Fax: 01223 237373

Directions: Leave A14 northern Cambridge bypass on B1049 (signposted Histon and Cottenham). Ground half a mile on right.
5 miles from Cambridge (BR). Bus No.104

Capacity: 3,250 Seats: 250 Cover: 250 Floodlights: Yes

Clubhouse: Bar/lounge open Tues-Sun eves, Sun lunch and matchdays.Snacks available

48 pages   £1.00
Editor: Lisa Baldwin

Local Press : Cambridge Evening News
Local Radio: Q103
BBC Radio Cambridgeshire

HONOURS Eastern Co's Lg - Prem. Div. 99-00, Div 1 R-up 96-97, Cup 90-91;
Cambridge Invitation Cup 77-78 79-80 96-97 (R-up 50-51 52-53 53-54);
Spartan Lg Div 1 (East) 50-51; Cambs Chall Cup; Cambs Lg Section;
Kershaw Prem Lge R-up 97-98, Sen Lge A 96-97, Cup 96-97;
Auto Trader Lge & Cup (U18) 96-97 Kershaw Champions Co Cup (U18) 98-99, Colts League (U17) Champions 98-99

PREVIOUS **Leagues:** Cambridgeshire 04-48; Spartan 48-60; Delphian 60-63; Athenian 63-65; Eastern Counties 66-00
Name: Histon Institute 04-51

BEST SEASON **FA Cup:** 4th Qual. Rd. 89-90 **FA Vase:** 4th Rd 96-97, 97-98

RECORD **Attendance:** 6,400 v King's Lynn, FA Cup 1956

Back Row: Steve Fallon (Manager), Roscoe Hipperson, Zachary Nedimovic, Andy Mee, Paul Barber, James Saddington, Neil Kennedy, Benjamin Mhishi, Daniel Potter, Michael Lindsey, Sean Audley. Andrew Jeffrey. **Front:** Neil Andrews, jamie barker, Adrian Cambridge, Wayne Goddard, Mark Reeder, Dave Toombs, Mark Abbs, Andy Ross (Youth Team Man.)

LANGNEY SPORTS

CLUB OFFICIALS

Chairman: Len Smith

President: J Stonestreet

Secretary: Mrs Myra Stephens,
7b Erica Close, Langney, Eastbourne,
East Sussex BN23 6HY
Tel/Fax: 01323 766050 0771 8027981 (M)

FOOTBALL MANAGEMENT TEAM

Manager: Garry Wilson

Coach: Nick Greenwood

Physio: Ray Tuppen

FACT FILE

Founded: 1966

Nickname: Sports

Sponsors: T.B.A.

Colours: All red

Change: White & Red/ navy/navy

Midweek Matchday: Tuesday

Reserve League:Sussex Co.Prem Res.

For up to the minute news,
results, fixtures,
plus general facts & figures
from the world of
non-league football

log on to

www.nlfootball.com

GROUND   Langney Sports Club, Priory Lane, Eastbourne, East Sussex
Tel: 01323 766265

Capacity: 2,500   Seats: 300   Cover: 2,500   Floodlights: Yes

Directions: A22 to Polegate, A27 to Stone Cross, right onto B32104 to Langney Shopping
Centre, then left and first right past crematorium.
One mile from Pevensey & Westham(BR). Buses from Eastbourne

Clubhouse: Open every evening & lunchtime with adjoining sports hall, boardroom and
matchday tea bar   **Club Shop:** Yes

PROGRAMME
Editor: Mike Spooner
Tel./Fax: 01323 461003
Local Press: Eastbourne Gazette & Herald

HONOURS   Unijet Sussex County League Champions 99-00, Sussex Co. Lg R-up 91-92, Div 2 87-88, Lg Cup 89-90, Div 3 86-87,
Div 3 Cup 86-87, 5-aside 1990; Sussex I'mediate Cup 85-86, Eastbourne Chall. Cup 85-86 86-87.

PREVIOUS   **League:** Eastbourne & Hastings, Unijet Sussex Oo League.
Grounds: Princes Park, Wartling Rd, Eastbourne/ Adjacent pitch

RECORDS   **Attendance:** 1400Sussex Senior Cup Final May 2000(Brighton & H v Hastings T)
Goalscorer: Nigel Hole 146 **Appearances:** Steve Dell 386
Win: 10-1 v Haywards Heath Town, Sussex County Lg Div. 1 11/4/92
Defeat: 0-8, v Sheppey United (A), FA Vase Prel. Rd 9/10/93
v Peacehaven & Telscombe (A), Sussex County Lg Div. 1 9/11/93

LANGNEY SPORTS - Sussex County League Premier Division Champions

NEWPORT I.W.

CLUB OFFICIALS
Chairman: **Bill Manuel**
Vice Chairman: TBA
President: **W H J Bunday**
Commercial Manager: **Ian Buckman**
Secretary/Press Off.: Chris Cheverton
40 Whitehead Creacent, Wootton
Bridge.I.o.W. PO33 4JF
Tel: 01983883879

FOOTBALL MANAGEMENT TEAM
Manager: Tony Mount
Assistant Manager: Joe Roach
Physio: Chris Cheverton

FACT FILE
Formed: 1888
Nickname: The Port
Colours: Gold & royal blue trim/gold/gold &
royal trim
Change colours: White with purple trim
Midweek matchday: Tuesday
Reserves' League: Wesex League
1999-00
Captain: John Price
P.o.Y.: John Price

NEWPORT I.W. FOOTBALL CLUB

Newport (I.W.) FC v Fisher Athletic
Saturday, May 6 th, 2000.
£1
Match Mascot: Zac Blow
Photograph courtesy of County Press

Pages: 28 Price: £1
Editor:Sheryl Penney (023 9221 0015)
Local Press: Portsmouth Evening News,
I.O.W. County Press,
Southampton Evening Echo
Local Radio: Solent, Isle of Wight Radio,
Power FM

GROUNDSt   George's Park, St George's Way, Newport, Isle of Wight PO30 2QH
Tel: 01983 525027
Directions: Roads from all ferry ports lead to Coppins Bridge R-about at eastern extremity of
town. Take Sandown/Ventnor exit, proceed to small r-about, St George's way is first exit
(straight on), ground immediately visible on left. Five minute walk from Newport bus station;
along Church Litten (past old ground), turn left then right at r-about
Capacity: 5,000   Cover: 1,000   Seats: 300   Floodlights: Yes
Club Shop: Sells souvenirs & programmes. Contact Roger Sanders at ground
Clubhouse: Open normal licensing hours. 2 bars, full range of hot and cold bar snacks. Buffet
inside ground

PREVIOUS   **Leagues:** Isle of Wight 1896-1928; Hants 28-86; Wessex 86-90
Ground: Church Litten (previously Well's Field) 1888-1988

CLUB RECORDS   **Attendance:** 2,217 FA Cup 1st Rd Nov 1994 v Aylesbury U., (6,000 v Watford, FACup 1st Rd 56-57, at Church Litten)
Win: 14-1, v Thornycroft Athletic (H),Hampshire Lge Div. One, 22.12.45
Defeat: 2-10, v Basingstoke Town (H),Hampshire Lge Div. One, 12.10.68
Career Goalscorer: Eddie Walder   **CareerAppearances:** Jeff Austin 540 (69-87)
Fee paid: £4,000 for Danny Gibbons from Weson-super-Mare Nov 99 **Fee received:** £2,250 for Mick Jenkins (Havant) 92-3
BEST SEASON   **FA Trophy:** 4th Rd 99-00   **FA Vase:** Fifth Round 91-92, 93-94
FA Cup: 2nd Rd 35-36 45-46. 1st Rd another 8 times- 45-46 52-55 56-59 94-95 95-96
League clubs defeated: Clapton Orient 45-46

HONOURS   Wessex Lg R-up 89-90, Comb. 91-92 (res.); Hants Lg (11), R-up (7), Div 2 R-up 70-71, Hants Snr Cup (8); Russell Cotes Cup
(3); Pickford Cup (4); Isle of Wight Snr (Gold) Cup (34); Hants F'lit Cup 76-77 77-78; Isle of Wight Lg (4) 07-10 23-24; Hants
I'mediate Cup 31-32 96-97; Hants Comb. Cup 38-39

Players progressing: Gary Rowatt (Cambridge City, Everton)

Back Row:
Danny Husbands,
Tony White,
Ian Lloyd,
Leigh Cole,
Gary Sperry,
Steve Leigh,
Danny Gibbons.

Front Row:
Kevin Gillett,
Jamie Newnham,
Ian Buckman,
John Price (Capt.),
Tom Betteridge,
Dave Wilson.

Photo:
Jim Baldwin.

560

ROTHWELL TOWN

CLUB OFFICIALS
Chairman: **Keith Johnson**
Vice-Chairman: **Keith Johnson**
President: **Ken Cheney**
Secretary: **Roger Barratt**
18 Norton St., Rothwell, Northants NN14 2DE
Tel: 01536 507744
Press Officer/Comm Mgr: **Peter Bradley**
Tel: 01536 710925

FOOTBALL MANAGEMENT TEAM
Manager: T.B.A.
Physio: Graham Simmonds

FACT FILE

Founded: 1895
Nickname: The Bones
Sponsors: Forester Health
Colours: Blue with white trim/blue/blue
Change Colours: Red, black & white trim, black/red
Midweek matchday: Tuesday
Newsline: 0930 555 829
Reserves' League: Utd Counties Res Div

For up to the minute news, results, fixtures, plus general facts & figures from the world of non-league football

log on to

www.nlfootball.com

GROUND   Cecil Street, Rothwell, Northants NN14 2EZ Tel: 01536 710694
Directions: A14/A6 to Rothwell. At town centre r'about turn into BridgeStreet (right if north-bound, left if southbound), take 3rd left into TreshamStreet, ground is at top on left.
3 miles from Kettering (BR); Rothwell is served by Kettering to Market Harborough buses
Capacity: 3,500   Seats: 264   Cover: 1,264   Floodlights: Yes
Clubhouse: Rowellian Social Club, open every evening and weekend lunchtimes.Crisps and rolls available on matchdays (hot food and drinks available in ground). `Top of the Town Ballroom', lounge seats 200
Club Shop: Sells various souvenirs incl. metal badges.

PROGRAMME

Pages: 48 Price: 90p Editor & Media Relations Officer: Mark Southon
Tel: 01162 774877

Local Press: Northants Evening Telegraph, Chronicle & Echo, Herald & Post
Local Radio: BBC Radio Northants, KCBC

PREVIOUS   **Leagues:** Northants 1896-1911 21-33, Kettering Amateur 11-21 33-48, Leics.Senior 48-50, United Counties 50-56 61-94, Central Alliance 56-61   **Grounds:** Harrington Rd, Castle Hill   **Name:** Rothwell Town Swifts

CLUB RECORDS   **Attendance:** 2,508 v Irthlingborough Diamonds, United Counties League 1971
Win: 17-0 v Stamford, FA Cup Preliminary Round replay 1927
Defeat: 1-10 v Coalville Town, Leicestershire Sen Lge 1949
Transfer fee paid: Undisclosed for Andy Wright (Aylesbury 1992)
Transfer fee received: Undisclosed for Matty Watts (Charlton 1990)

BEST SEASON   **FA Cup:** Third Qualifying Round 98-99
FA Trophy: Second Round Proper 94-95   **FA Vase:** Fifth Round 92-93 (1-2 v Bridlington Town)

HONOURS   Northants Lg1899-1900 (R-up 1895-96 96-97 97-98), Northants Snr Cup 1899-1900 23-24 59-60 88-89 95-96 (R-up 24-25 71-72 87-88), United Counties Lg 92-93 94-95 (R-up 69-70 70-71 87-88 89-90 90-91), KO Cup 55-56 70-71 71-72 91-92 92-93 (R-up 77-78 79-80 82-83), Div 2 52-53 53-54, Div 2Cup 52-53 53-54, Benevolent Cup 92-93 94-95 (R-up 89-90 90-91), Southern League Mid Div R-up 96-97

Players progressing: Lee Glover (Nottingham Forest) 1987, Matty Watts (CharltonAth.) 1990

ROTHWELL TOWN celebrate their 2-0 victory over Wealdstone in the FA Cup 3rd Qualifying Round replay.

SITTINGBOURNE

CLUB OFFICIALS

Chairman: **Andy Spice**

President: **E H Bennett**

Secretary:**David Roche**
c/o Sittingbourne F.C.

Commercial Manager:Brian Woodhouse

FOOTBALL MANAGEMENT TEAM

Manager:Hughie Stinson

Coach: Bob Baker

Physio: Gary Wisdom

FACT FILE

Formed: 1881

Nickname: Brickies

Sponsors: Medway Galvanising.

Colours: Red & black stripes/black/red

Change colours: All yellow

Midweek matchday: Wednesday

Newsline: 0891 333 027

Reserves' league: Winstonlead Kent

Pages: 28 Price: £1
Editor: William Rickson c/o the club
Local Press: East Kent Gazette, Kent Today,
Kent Messenger Extra, Sittingbourne &
Sheppy Adscene.
Local Radio: Invicta Supergold, BBC Radio
Kent, Invicta FM

GROUND
Central Park, Eurolink, Sittingbourne, Kent ME10 3SB
Tel: 01795 435077 Fax: 01474 814501
Directions: Through Sittingbourne on main A2, club signposted clearly and regularly from both east and west. 1 mile from Sittingbourne BR station.
Capacity: 8,000   Cover: 3,300   Seats: 2,000   Floodlights: 420 lux
Clubhouse: The Cabin (01795 435077)
Club Shop: Sells a wide selection of souvenirs etc. Open matchdays or contact Ann Morrison (01795 664436)

PREVIOUS   **Leagues:** Kent 1894-1905 09-27 30-39 46-59 68-91, South Eastern 05-09, Southern 27-30 59-67
Grounds: SittingbourneRec. Ground 1881-90, Gore Court Cricket Ground 90-92, The Bull Ground1892-1990
Names: Sittingbourne United 1881-86

CLUB RECORDS   **Attendance:** 5,951 v Tottenham Hotspur, friendly 26/1/93
Transfer fee paid: £20,000 to Ashford Town for Lee McRobert, 1993.
Transfer fee received: £210,000 from Millwall for Neil Emblen and Michael Harle, 1993

BEST SEASON   **FA Cup:** 2nd Rd 25-26 (0-7 at Swindon Town), 28-29 (1-2 at Walsall), plus 1st Rd26-27 30-31 62-63
FA Trophy: **FA Vase:**
HONOURS   Southern Lg Southern Div 92-93 95-96; Kent Lg 1897-98 1902-03 57-58 58-59 75-76 83-84 90-91 (Lg Cup 25-26 58-59 73-74 80-81, Div 2 Cup 54-55 57-58 83-84 86-8787-88); Kent Senior Cup 01-02 28-29 29-30 57-58; Kent Senior Shield 25-26 27-28 53-54; Kent Senior Trophy 89-90; Thames & Medway Cup 55-56 58-59; Thames & Medway Comb 02-03 07-08 11-12 24-25 25-26; Chatham Charity Cup 03-04 19-20;" Kent Midweek Lg(res) 91-92 (Lg Cup 90-91).
Players progressing: Jason Lillis (Walsall 93), Neil Emblen & Michael Harle 93, Steve Forbes 94, Lee McRobert 95 (Millwall) Jimmy Case (Brighton 93), Lee Harper (Arsenal 94)

Back: Dave Jordan, Steve Wren (Asst. Manager), Michaelo Cassar, Gene Clout, Damien Hodge, James Creed, Robert Owen, Mark Miller, Tyrone King, Paul Carlton, Mark Brooks.
Front: Tom Berry, Tom Binks (Captain), Mascot, Neil Miller, Ben Taylor, Stuart Harrison, Shane Davies.

SPALDING UNITED

CLUB OFFICIALS

Chairman: **Alan mitchell**
President: **John Chappell**
Press Officer: **Ray Tucker**
Secretary: **John Franks,2 Samworths Close, Peterborough PE5 7BQ Tel: 01733 380794**

FOOTBALL MANAGEMENT TEAM

Manager: Alan Day
Asst Manager: Glenn Beech
Physio: Sam Seal

FACT FILE

Founded: 1921
Nickname: Tulips
Sponsors: Geest
Colours: Tangerine & black/black/tangerine
Change: Light Blue
Midweek matchday: Tuesday
Reserve League: Utd Counties Res Div 1999-00
Top Goalscore:Craig Wilson (12)
P.o.Y.: Nick Keeble

For up to the minute news, results, fixtures, plus general facts & figures from the world of non-league football

log on to

www.nlfootball.com

GROUND Sir Halley Stewart Playing Field, Winfrey Avenue, Spalding Tel: 01775 713328

Directions: Town centre off A16, adjacent to bus station. 250 yds from Spalding(BR) station

Capacity: 7,000   Seats: 350   Cover: 2,500   Floodlights: Yes

Clubhouse: Open matchdays, and events   Club Shop: Yes

PROGRAMME
36 pages, 50p
Editor: Bernard Holmes

Local Press : Lincs Free Press, Spalding Guardian, Peterborough EveningTelegraph

---

HONOURS   Utd Counties Lg 54-55 74-75 87-88 98-99 R-up 50-51 51-52 52-53 72-73 75-76 96-97; KO Cup 54-55 94-95; Northern Co's East Lg 83-84; Lincs Snr Cup 52-53; Hinchingbroke Cup: 98-99 Lincs Snr `A' Cup 87-88, 98-99 R-up 97-98; Snr `B' Cup 50-51; Evans Halshaw F'lit Cup 89-90

PREVIOUS   **Leagues:** Peterborough; Utd Co's 31-55 68-78 86-88 91-99; Eastern Co's 55-60; Central Alliance 60-61; Midland Co's 61-68; Northern Co's East 82-86; Southern 88-91

BEST SEASON   **FA Cup:** 1st Round 57-58, 1-3 v Durham City (A), 64-65, 3-5 v Newport Co. (A)
FA Trophy: 3rd Rd 99-00
FA Vase: Quarter-Finals 89-90, 1-3 v Guiseley

RECORD   **Attendance:** 6,972 v Peterborough, FA Cup 1952

Players progressing: Carl Shutt (Sheffield Wed.)

Back Row:
Darren Gwyther, Dominic Revill, Ady Barkess, Kevin Cross, Nick Keeble, Darren Cundy, Craig Wilson.
Front:
Nigel Vince, Steve Appleby, Paul Langford, James Campbell.
Missing:
Dave Hercock (capt.), Dave Gilbert, Neil Featherstone & Tommy Henderson.

Photo courtesy of Lincolnshire Free Press

ST. LEONARDS

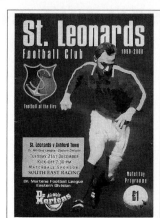

CLUB OFFICIALS
Chairman: **John Cornelius**
Patron: **Leon Shepherdson**
President: **Mrs K Shepperdson**
Vice-Chairman: **Michael James**
Secretary: **Peter High**
8 Oaklea Close, St Leonards -on-Sea,East sussex TN37 7HB (01424 752864)
Commercial Manager: **John Huggett**
Tel: 01424 434755 or 0802 920416

FOOTBALL MANAGEMENT TEAM
Manager: Andy Thomson
Coach:Lloyd Bigg

FACT FILE
Formed: 1971
Nickname: Saints or Blues
Sponsors:Stamco Timber
Clubcall Line: T.B.A.
Colours: Blue/white/blue
Change colours: White/navy/white
Midweek Matchday: Wednesday
Reserves' League: Kent Midweek
99-00 Captain: Keith Miles
Top Scorer: Simon Fox
P.o.Y.: Adam Flanagan

GROUND The Firs, Elphinstone Rd, Hastings, East Sussex Tel: 01424 434755 Matchday Office 01424 716362 Clubcall Line: 09068 800 680

Directions: From M25 & London approach Hastings on the A21. immediately afterthe junct with the A28 on the northern borough boundary, turn right into Junction Rd. At T junct with B2093 turn right onto The Ridge. After 2 miles turn right, opposite the cemetary, into Elphinstone Rd, grd 600yards down hill on left. Nearest station; Ore (Connex South East), 1 mile uphill (no bus or taxi). Hastings (Connex South East) 1.5 miles. Bus service from town centre to ground

Capacity: 3,768 (Day), 3,015 (Even)   Seats: 251   Cover: 1,000   Floodlights: Yes

Pages: 60 Price: £1
Editor: Peter High (01424 752864)
Local Press: Hastings Observer, Evening Argus
Local Radio: Arrow FM, BBC Southern Counties Radio, Southern FM

Clubhouse: Licensed bar open normal pubhours. Hot food matchdays. Hot food from tea bar
Club Shop: Yes, selling leisure & sports wear, souvenirs & publications, open matchdays

PREVIOUS   **Leagues:** Eastbourne & Hastings 71-82, Southern Counties Comb 82-88, Sussex County 88-96
         Grounds: Council pitches 71-73, Pannel Lane, Pett 73-93   **Names:** Stamco (71-96), St Leonards Stamcroft 96-98

CLUB RECORDS **Attendance:** 1,798 v Tiverton Town, FA Vase 4th Rd. 15/1/95
            At old ground: 527v Hastings Town, Sussex Senior Cup 2nd Rd 5/12/92
            Win: 10-1 v Portfield(H), Sussex County League Div One 4/12/93   **Defeat:** 1-6 v Hailsham Town(A) League Cup 23/9/92.
            Career appearances: Wayne Farrier (290 92-97)   **Career Goalscorer:** Keith Miles (132 1995-2000)
            Transfer fee paid: None   **Transfer fee received:** £8,000 for Jon Magee (Margate)

BEST SEASON: **FA Cup:** 3rd Qual Rd 96-97 97-98   **FA Vase:** 5th Rd 94-95   **FA Trophy:** 3rd Rd 96-97

HONOURS   Sussex Sen Cup 96-97; Sussex RUR Charity Cup R-up 94-95; Hastings Snr Cup 89-90 95-96 96-97, R-up 92-93 97-98; Dr Martens Lge Southern Div R-up 96-97, Merit Cup 96-97; Sussex County Div 1 R-up 94-95 95-96, Div 2 R-up 92-93, Cup R-up 89-90 90-91, Div Three R-up 88-89, Cup R-up 88-89 Kent Midweek Lg.Cup Winners 98-99

Player progressing: Sasha Ilic (Charlton Ath 97)

Back Row: Lloyd Brigg (Coach), Andy Thompson (Manager), Tony Sweet, Simon Fox, Tony Hogg, Adam Flanagan, Carelton Chatelier, Graham Bannatyne, Neil Pheasant, Chris Fitkin, Rob Greig (Team Attendant), Wes Tate.
Front: Jason Bourne, Keith Miles, Peter Baker, Paul Ruddy, Danny Fletcher, John Rattray.

STAMFORD

CLUB OFFICIALS
Chairman: **Ken Joinson**
Vice-Chairman:T.B.A.
President: **Mrs C Sturgess**
Secretary: **Andrew Eason**
36 Queens Walk, Stamford, Lincs. PE9 2QE
Tel: 01780 754510
Press Officer: **Jeremy Biggs**
(Tel No: 01780 763048)

FOOTBALL MANAGEMENT TEAM

Manager:Billy Jeffrey
Physio: Pete Foskett

FACT FILE
Founded: 1896
Nickname: Daniels
Sponsors: SilverLink Restaurant
Colours: Red & white
Change Colours: Blue & white
Midweek matchday: Tuesday
Reserves League: UCL Res Div 2
99-00- Captain: Darren Clyde
P.o.Y.: Hamish Curtis
Top Scorer: Richard Bailey

Pages :56   Price:£1,00
Editor: Andrew Eason
Local Newspapers: Stamford Mercury,
Peterborough Evening Telegraph,
Herald &Post
Local Radio:Rutland Radio,LincsFM
Radio Lincolnshire & Radio Cambridgeshire

GROUND   New Flame Stadium, Kettering Road,, Stamford, Lincs
Tel: 01780 763079 (Clubhouse) 01780 766027 (Pressbox)

Directions: Off A43 Kettering Rd, 1 mile east of A1. 200 yds from station
Capacity: 5,000   Seats: 250   Cover: 1,250   Floodlights: Yes
Clubhouse: Open matchdays, Sunday lunchtimes & evenings (bingo).
Food available matchdays - hot and cold
Club Shop: Wide range of Lge + non-Lge progs & club souvenirs.

PREVIOUS   **Leagues:** Peterborough; Northants (UCL) 08-55; Central Alliance 55-61; Midland Co's 61-72; UCL 72-98
Grounds: None   **Names:** None

CLUB RECORDS **Attendance:** 4,200 v Kettering, FA Cup 3rd Qual Rd 53
Win: 13-0 v Peterborough Reserves, Utd Co's Lge 29-30   **Defeat:** 0-17 v Rothwell,FA Cup 27-28
Appearances: Dick Kwiatkowski   **Goalscorer:** Bert Knighten

BEST SEASON   **FA Cup:** 73-74 4th qual. Round
FA Vase: Winners 79-80, R-up 75-76 83-84   **FA Trophy:** 98-99 (1st season) 1st Round

HONOURS   FA Vase 79-80 (R-up 75-76 83-84); Utd Co's Lg 75-76 77-78 79-80 80-81 81-82 96-97 97-98 (KO Cup 51-52 75-76 79-80 81-82 85-86); Northants Lg 11-12; Lincs Snr`A' Cup 78-79 82-83 97-98; Lincs Snr `B' Cup 51-52 53-54; William Scarber Mem. Cup 70-71 82-83 85-86 88-89 93-94 94-95; Stamford Chal. Cup 89-90; Lincs Jnr Cup 48-49 Hinchbrooke Cup 1906-07, 07-08, 97-98

Players progressing: A Birchenall (Chelsea), R Chester(Aston Villa), T Tye (Chelsea), G Fell (Brighton), C Chapman (Wolves), S Collins (Peterborough), K Alexander (Grimsby), A Tillson (Grimsby), B Stubbs (Notts Co.), D Genovese (Peterborough)

Back Row: Matthew Green, Christopher Palmer (mascot), Lee Bradley, Malcolm Ndekwe, Martin Hardy (Asst. Manager), Den Nower, Darron Clyde, Matt Carmichael, Dave Robertson, Hamish Curtis. **Front:** Trish (Asst. Physio), Carl Tallents, Craig Donaldson, Richard Bailey, David Staff, Ronnie Fortune, Pete Foskett (Physio).   **Photo:** Gavin Tutcher

TONBRIDGE ANGELS

CLUB OFFICIALS

Chairman: **Colin Fry**
Vice Chairman: **Maurice Brown**
Secretary: **Ken Jarrett**
8 Faraday Ride, Tonbridge, Kent TN10 4RL
Tel: 01732 351856
Press Officer:T.B.A.
Commercial Manager:Phil Emblen

FOOTBALL MANAGEMENT TEAM

Manager:Colin Blewden
Physio: Chris Dunk

FACT FILE

Founded: 1948
Nickname: The Angels
Sponsors: Tonbridge Coachworks
Colours: Royal Blue with white trim
Change Colours: All yellow
Midweek matchday: Tuesday
Reserves League: Suburban

1999-00
P.o.Y. Nicky Humphrey
Captain: Alan Tutton

TONBRIDGE ANGELS FOOTBALL CLUB
MEMBERS OF
Dr. MARTENS SOUTHERN LEAGUE EASTERN DIVISION
SUBURBAN FOOTBALL LEAGUE
AFFILIATED TO THE KENT COUNTY FOOTBALL ASSOCIATION

MAIN SPONSORS OF TONBRIDGE ANGELS FOOTBALL CLUB

TONBRIDGE COACHWORKS

GROUND	Longmead Stadium, Darenth Avenue, Tonbridge, Kent TN10 3JW
	Tel: 01732 352417
Directions:	From Tonbridge BR station, through High Street, north up Shipbourne Rd (A227 Gravesend road) to 2nd mini-r'bout ('The Pinnacles' pub), left into Darenth Avenue, ground at bottom of Avenue, far side of car park
Capacity:	5,000 Seats: 202 Cover: 400 Floodlights: Yes
Clubhouse:	Open Mon-Sat evenings and Sunday lunchtimes. Hot food on matchdays from burger bar
Club Shop:	Yes, progs, replica kits etc, contact Lorraine Parks (01732 350865)

Pages: 38 Price: £1
Editor:Mayrice Brown c/o Club

Local Press: Kent Messenger, Courier, Sevenoaks Leader
Local Radio: Mercury, Radio Kent, K,F.M.

PREVIOUS   **Leagues:** Southern 48-89, Kent 89-93
Ground: The Angel 48-80   **Names:** TonbridgeAngels, Tonbridge F.C., Tonbridge A.F.C

CLUB RECORDS **Attendance:** 1,463 v Yeovil Town, FA Cup 4th Qualifying Round 26/10/91.
At theAngel Ground: 8,236 v Aldershot, FA Cup 1st Round 1951
Win: 11-1 v WorthingFA Cup 1951   **Defeat:** 2-11 v Folkstone, Kent Sen Cup 1949
Career Goalscorer: Unknown   **Career Appearances:** Mark Gillham, 520 to date
Transfer fee paid: **Transfer fee received:** £7,500 for Paul Emblen (Charlton Ath 97)

BEST SEASON   **FA Cup:** First Round (proper) 50-51 51-52 52-53 67-68 72-73
FA Trophy: **FA Vase:**

HONOURS   Kent League 94-95 (League Cup (2)), Southern League Cup Runners-up (2) (SF(1)), Kent Senior Cup 64-65 74-75 (Runners-up (2)), Kent Senior Shield 51-5255-56 57-58 58-59 63-64

Players progressing: R Saunders, M McMcDonald, T Burns, I Seymour, G Moseley, TMorgan, Neil Emblen, Paul Emblen.

Back: Dave Arter, Colin Blewden, Peter Mortley, Joe Radford, Alan Tutton, Roy Godden, Nick Humphrey, Ian Gibbs, Jon Mayall.
Front: Danny Tingley, Clint Gooding, Andy Kearns, Simon Elliott, Paul Bates, Gene Clout.

WISBECH TOWN

CLUB OFFICIALS

Chairman: **Steve Crown**
Vice Chairman: **Merlin Saddleton**
President: **J W A Chilvers**
Secretary: **John Petch**
34 Walton Rd, Wisbech, Cambs PE13 3EN
Tel: 01945 584333 &Fax)
Press Officer: **John Petch**

FOOTBALL MANAGEMENT TEAM

Player/Manager: Ian Stringfellow
Ass.Manager: Jim Blandford
Physio: P Ward

FACT FILE

Founded: 1920
Nickname: Fenmen
Newsline: 0930 555 865
Colours: Red with black side panel/red/red
Change colours: Blue& white,blue,blue
Midweek Matchday: Tuesday

1999-00
Captain: Paul Hill
P.O.Y.: Paul Hill
Top scorer: Andy Furnell

GROUND Fenland Park, Lerowe Road, Wisbech, Cambs Tel: 01945 584176

Directions: Follow A47 bypass to the West Walton turn off roundabout where there is a Little Chef, turn left for Wisbech, Lerowe Road is first left after 30mph sign. Entering town from north along A1101 cross Freedom Bridge, atroundabout go straight over sign Walsoken/West Walton

Capacity: 3,800   Seats: 284   Cover: 1,000   Floodlights: Yes

Clubhouse: Open every day. Matchday food & drink - Tea, coffee, cold drinks, confectionary, burgers, hotdogs, soup, sandwiches, rolls

Club Shop: Sells replica shirts, caps, pennants, pens, scarves etc. Contact Club Secretary

Pages: 40 Price: £1
Editor: Gordon Smith Tel: 01945 581767

Local Press: Fenland Citizen,
Wisbech Standard, Eastern Daily press
Local Radio: Radio Cambridgeshire

PREVIOUS   **Leagues:** Peterborough; Utd Co's 35-50; Eastern Co's 50-52 70-97; Midland 52-58;Southern 58-70
Grounds: Wisbech Park 20-21; Waisoken Rectory 21-22; Harecroft Rd 22-47

CLUB RECORDS **Attendance:** 8,004 v Peterborough United, Midland League 25/8/57
Goalscorer: Bert Titmarsh 246 (31-37)   **Appearances:** Jamie Brighty (731)
Win: 18-1 v Rushden 45-46   **Defeat:** 1-10 v Brighton FA Cup 65-66
Fee Paid: £500   **Fee Received:** £4,000

BEST SEASON **FA Cup:** 2nd Rd 57-58, 97-98   League clubs defeated: Colchester
FA Trophy: 3rd Qual Rd   **FA Vase:** Semi-Finals 84-85, 85-86

HONOURS Southern Lg Div 1 61-62; Utd Co's Lg (4) 46-48 49-50 61-62 (res) (R-up 48-49, Lg Cup 35-36 (R-up 46-47); Midland Lg R-up 57-58; Eastern Co's Lg 71-72 76-7790-91 (R-up 70-71 73-74 83-84 92-93 96-97), Lg Cup 50-51 70-71 71-72 (R-up 73-74 76-77 86-87); Cambs Invit Cup(8) 52-53 55-56 57-58 74-76 81-83 91-92; E Anglian Cup 87-88 (R-up 40-41 48-49); Peterborough Lg 24-25 27-28 28-29 31-3232-33; Peterborough Snr Cup 32-33 76-77 89-90 97-98

Players progressing: BryanHarvey/Terry Marshall (Newcastle), Jackie Callagher (Peterboro), Paul Scott (Blackpool), Peter Dobson (Ipswich)

WITNEY TOWN

CLUB OFFICIALS

Chairman: **Brian Constable**
President: **Sir Peter Parker**
Vice-Chairman: Vacant
Press Officer: **Kieran Bushnell**
Tel: 01993 703622
Secretary: **Adrian Bircher**
13 Colwell Drive, Witney, Oxon. OX8 7NJ
Tel: 01993 200913 Mobile: 041 007 3207
Commercial Man/ PRO: **T.B.A.**

FOOTBALL MANAGEMENT TEAM

Manager: Brian Hughes
Asst Manager/Coach :Kevin Willetts
Physio: Roger Alder

FACT FILE

Formed: 1885
Nickname: The Blanketmen
Colours: All Yellow
Change colours: White/Green/Green
Midweek matchday: Tuesday
Reserves' League: None
Newsline: 0930 555 901

GROUND	Marriott Stadium, Downs Rd, Witney, Oxon OX8 7LY. Tel: 01993 702549
Directions:	From West on A40; take B4047 at island past Burford, follow signs for Witney West & N.W. Industrial Est., thru Minster Lovell to West Witney, right into Downs Rd, ground on right.
	From the East on A40, 2nd turn off to Witney and follow signs for South & S.W. Industrial Est., right at r'bout to traffic lights, left and proceed to r'bout, straight over, signs to West Witney Industrial Est., left at lights onto B4047, left into Downs Rd, ground on right. Nearest BR station is Oxford 12 miles away
Capacity:	3,500 Cover: 2,000 Seats: 280 Floodlights: Yes
Club Shop:	Selling programmes and souvenirs. Contact secretary
Clubhouse:	Members bar open seven days a week 6.30-11pm. Open all day Saturday. Hot food on matchdays

Pages: 40 Price: £1
Editor s : K Bushnell
Tel: 01993 703622 or 04680 71102

Local Press: Witney Gazette, West Oxon
Standard, Oxford Mail & Oxford Times
Local Radio: Thames Valley FM, Fox (FM)

PREVIOUS	**Leagues:** Reading & Dist., Oxfordshire Senior, Hellenic 53-73
	Name: Witney F.C. **Ground:** Marriotts Close, Welch Way (pre-1992)
CLUB RECORDS	**Attendance:** 3,167 v Chelsea 16/11/98 Stand Opening. Competitive: 734 vWealdstone 8/10/92
	Career Goalscorer: Kenny Clarke 145 **Career Appearances:** Kevin Alder543 +6 sub
	Transfer fee paid: £3,000 for Steve Jenkins(Cheltenham Town)
	Transfer fee received: £5,000 for John Bailey (WorcesterCity)
BEST SEASON	**FA Trophy:** Second Rd 78-79 **FA Amateur Cup:** Second Rd replay - 3 times, 66-67,71-72, 72-73
	FA Cup: 1st Rd 71-72, 0-3 v Romford (H)
HONOURS	Southern Lg Div 1 Nth 77-78; Hellenic Lg (8) 54-55 57-58 64-67 70-73 (R-up 53-54 67-68 69-70), Lg Cup (6), Prem Div Benevolent Cup 59-60 63-64; Oxon Snr Lg(5); Oxon Snr Cup (12)

Players progressing: Herbert Smith, Frank Clack (Birmingham City), Arthur Hall(Bristol Rovers 1959), David Moss (Swindon 1969), Jack Newman

JEWSON EASTERN COUNTIES LEAGUE

Feeder to: Dr Martens League
Founded 1935

Hon. Patron: Derek Needham   **President:** Roger Pauley

Secretary: Colin Lamb, 3 Land Close, Clacton-on-Sea, Essex CO16 8UJ
Tel: 01255 436398

PREMIER DIVISION FINAL LEAGUE TABLE 1999-2000

		P	W	D	L	F	A	Pts	GD
1	Histon	40	29	6	5	95	42	93	53
2	Wroxham	40	28	8	4	86	39	92	47
3	Sudbury	40	28	6	6	106	48	90	58
4	Clacton Town	40	22	9	9	92	59	75	33
5	Lowestoft Town	40	20	10	10	58	36	70	22
6	Mildenhall Town	40	18	9	13	62	52	63	10
7	Woodbridge Town	40	17	9	14	63	51	60	12
8	Diss Town	40	17	9	14	69	62	60	7
9	Maldon Town	40	18	6	16	61	63	60	-2
10	Ipswich Wanderers	40	16	8	16	59	60	56	-1
11	Fakenham Town	40	14	12	14	55	55	54	0
12	Great Yarmouth Town	40	14	10	16	50	52	52	-2
13	Gorleston	40	14	9	17	76	69	51	7
14	Newmarket Town	40	14	8	18	60	69	50	-9
15	Warboys Town	40	13	9	18	55	65	48	-10
16	Soham Town Rangers	40	12	5	23	52	76	41	-24
17	Bury Town	40	8	12	20	38	65	36	-27
18	Halstead Town	40	8	8	24	52	89	32	-37
19	Stowmarket Town	40	8	8	24	40	83	32	-43
20	Harwich & Parkestone	40	7	8	25	42	84	29	-42
21	Felixstowe Port & Town	40	7	7	26	32	84	28	-52

DIVISION ONE FINAL LEAGUE TABLE 1999-2000

		P	W	D	L	F	A	Pts	GD
1	Tiptree United	34	23	9	2	89	19	78	70
2	Ely City	34	23	4	7	89	33	73	56
3	Stanway Rovers	34	21	8	5	68	31	71	37
4	Downham Town	34	22	4	8	77	36	70	41
5	Needham Market*	34	20	5	9	76	46	64	30
6	Cambridge C Res	34	18	6	10	70	44	60	26
7	Dereham Town	34	16	5	13	53	36	53	17
8	Hadleigh United	34	15	7	12	52	44	52	8
9	Swaffham Town	34	16	4	14	47	42	52	5
10	Gornard United	34	14	10	10	42	44	52	-2
11	Whitton United	34	14	6	14	65	58	48	7
12	Somersham Tn	34	14	6	14	55	58	48	-3
13	March Town Utd	34	10	7	17	48	78	37	-30
14	Haverhill Rovers	34	9	7	18	40	71	34	-31
15	Norwich United	34	6	3	25	44	99	21	-55
16	Chatteris Town	34	4	7	23	30	75	19	-45
17	Brightlingsea Utd	34	5	4	25	31	84	19	-53
18	Thetford Town	34	3	4	27	27	105	13	-78

PREMIER DIVISION RESULTS CHART 1999-2000

		1	2	3	4	5	6	7	8	9	10	11	12	13	14	15	16	17	18	19	20	21
1	Bury Town	X	2-5	1-0	1-0	4-0	1-5	1-0	2-2	2-2	1-2	1-2	1-3	0-1	1-2	1-1	0-2	1-1	0-2	0-0	0-0	1-1
2	Clacton Town	5-1	X	2-3	3-0	6-1	2-2	3-2	2-1	5-0	1-3	1-3	3-1	2-1	0-1	0-1	4-0	1-0	1-6	4-2	3-3	1-2
3	Diss Town	1-1	2-0	X	4-1	0-0	4-4	3-2	4-1	2-0	0-3	4-2	0-2	3-1	0-1	3-0	2-0	3-1	0-2	1-2	1-2	2-4
4	Fakenham Town	3-0	2-2	1-0	X	4-1	1-0	3-3	2-0	3-1	1-2	1-1	2-0	1-1	3-1	2-2	1-2	1-1	0-3	0-0	2-3	0-0
5	Felixstowe P & T	0-1	1-1	0-2	0-2	X	3-1	0-1	1-1	1-0	2-2	1-0	1-3	2-4	1-4	1-1	1-4	2-0	0-3	2-1	0-2	1-2
6	Gorleston	1-4	2-3	2-2	1-4	5-0	X	1-1	6-0	1-0	1-2	1-2	1-2	1-3	3-1	5-1	4-2	4-2	1-0	6-3	2-0	1-1
7	Gt Yarmouth T	3-1	1-3	1-1	3-0	0-1	0-1	X	0-1	1-0	2-1	0-0	1-1	2-0	0-2	1-0	0-3	2-0	3-0	1-1	1-0	1-2
8	Halstead Town	1-1	3-5	2-2	1-2	2-1	0-0	3-1	X	4-2	1-4	3-0	1-2	1-2	1-1	2-2	0-2	2-1	0-4	1-2	1-4	2-3
9	Harwick & P	1-1	3-2	0-2	1-1	0-0	5-1	1-3	1-0	X	1-3	1-5	0-3	1-1	2-3	2-0	1-4	1-2	1-2	1-2	0-5	1-1
10	Histon	2-0	1-1	4-0	3-1	4-1	3-0	5-0	4-1	3-1	X	1-1	0-0	1-0	2-1	2-1	2-1	1-0	5-1	3-0	3-3	0-2
11	Ipswich Wndrs	0-1	1-2	0-2	1-4	0-1	1-0	1-2	3-2	2-0	2-2	X	2-1	2-3	4-0	1-0	3-3	3-0	0-0	1-0	1-2	3-2
12	Lowestoft T	1-0	1-1	3-0	1-3	1-1	2-1	1-0	2-1	5-0	0-1	0-0	X	1-0	2-1	3-0	2-0	4-1	2-2	1-1	0-0	2-1
13	Maldon Town	2-1	0-2	1-1	1-0	5-0	0-2	1-3	3-2	1-0	2-0	1-5	1-1	X	3-1	3-4	1-0	1-3	4-5	2-0	4-2	0-2
14	Mildenhall T	3-0	1-1	1-1	1-1	3-1	2-3	1-1	0-1	1-1	1-1	0-1	2-0	3-1	X	3-0	2-0	3-1	0-1	1-1	2-1	1-0
15	Newmarket T	2-1	1-1	7-2	0-0	2-1	3-2	1-1	3-0	1-3	2-3	2-3	1-0	1-2	4-1	X	2-1	1-0	1-2	1-2	1-2	1-4
16	Soham T Rngrs	4-1	2-3	0-2	0-1	3-2	0-0	1-3	2-1	1-2	3-5	2-0	0-0	0-1	0-2	0-3	X	2-2	2-3	2-1	0-0	1-3
17	Stowmarket T	1-2	1-1	1-3	3-0	1-0	1-1	1-1	4-3	1-4	2-4	0-0	1-0	3-1	0-5	0-1	1-3	X	0-3	0-2	1-1	0-4
18	Sudbury	0-0	0-1	3-2	1-0	3-1	2-1	3-2	2-3	2-1	2-4	6-1	2-0	3-0	1-1	2-1	5-0	8-0	X	8-2	2-1	2-2
19	Warboys Town	1-1	0-3	0-3	4-1	4-0	2-0	1-1	1-1	2-0	2-1	3-1	1-2	1-1	1-2	1-2	2-0	0-1	2-3	X	1-2	0-1
20	Woodbridge T	1-0	1-3	2-0	1-1	1-0	1-1	2-0	4-0	1-1	1-2	3-1	0-2	0-1	4-1	2-1	3-0	2-1	0-4	2-3	X	2-3
21	Wroxham	2-0	1-3	2-2	2-0	1-0	3-2	1-0	2-0	4-0	2-1	2-0	2-1	1-1	3-0	5-2	5-0	2-1	3-3	2-1	1-0	X

DIVISION ONE RESULTS CHART 1999-2000

		1	2	3	4	5	6	7	8	9	10	11	12	13	14	15	16	17	18
1	Brightlingsea United	X	1-2	4-1	0-1	0-1	1-3	0-4	2-3	0-0	1-2	0-1	4-0	0-3	0-1	0-2	5-1	0-4	0-1
2	Cambridge City Reserves	0-0	X	3-2	1-2	3-2	3-1	2-3	4-3	2-0	4-0	3-1	4-0	4-1	2-2	1-3	3-1	1-2	3-1
3	Chatteris Town	2-1	1-5	X	2-2	1-1	2-2	0-5	0-1	1-0	4-1	1-4	1-2	1-2	0-3	0-2	1-2	1-1	0-2
4	Cornard United	2-1	1-3	0-0	X	1-0	0-2	1-1	1-4	3-0	0-1	3-2	0-0	3-1	1-4	0-0	2-1	0-1	1-1
5	Dereham Town	1-3	3-0	3-0	1-1	X	0-1	0-2	1-2	5-0	2-0	1-1	6-1	2-1	0-1	4-0	3-1	1-1	2-3
6	Downham Town	3-0	1-0	2-1	0-2	1-0	X	1-2	3-2	6-1	1-2	3-0	6-0	1-2	5-0	2-1	4-2	1-0	1-5
7	Ely City	7-0	1-1	3-1	2-2	1-0	2-1	X	1-0	4-0	2-0	1-2	8-2	0-2	2-1	2-1	9-1	2-2	5-1
8	Hadleigh United	5-0	1-0	1-1	0-0	2-0	0-1	0-1	X	1-1	2-2	3-0	3-1	1-1	2-1	4-1	1-1	0-2	1-0
9	Haverhill Rovers	4-1	2-2	1-1	0-1	1-2	0-1	0-2	4-2	X	0-1	3-1	2-0	1-1	0-5	1-0	3-1	0-3	1-5
10	March Town United	1-0	0-2	5-1	1-1	1-2	2-2	0-5	0-0	3-4	X	1-2	5-1	2-3	0-4	4-2	1-0	1-1	0-0
11	Needham Market	7-0	3-1	4-0	0-3	3-0	2-2	1-4	2-0	3-0	3-0	X	1-0	4-2	2-2	1-0	2-0	0-0	3-2
12	Norwich United	4-1	0-7	2-0	5-1	0-3	0-5	0-1	1-2	1-2	7-1	0-3	X	3-1	1-2	3-4	1-1	0-3	2-2
13	Somersham Town	2-0	1-1	1-0	4-1	1-2	0-4	2-1	1-0	3-3	4-3	1-3	4-2	X	0-2	0-1	2-2	1-2	3-1
14	Stanway Rovers	2-0	0-0	4-0	3-0	2-1	0-2	2-1	3-2	1-0	7-1	2-2	1-0	2-0	X	2-1	4-1	0-0	2-1
15	Swaffham Town	2-0	1-2	1-0	0-1	0-1	1-1	3-1	0-1	4-2	2-1	2-1	3-2	2-1	0-0	X	3-0	0-0	2-1
16	Thetford Town	1-1	2-0	1-3	1-2	0-1	1-4	0-4	0-3	0-3	0-2	0-6	3-2	1-2	0-2	1-3	X	0-5	0-7
17	Tiptree United	0-1	2-0	3-0	2-0	0-0	2-0	2-0	4-0	4-0	5-1	4-2	7-0	2-1	1-1	1-0	7-0	X	2-3
18	Whitton United	1-3	0-1	2-1	0-3	1-2	0-4	2-0	4-0	1-1	4-4	2-4	2-1	1-1	2-0	1-0	4-1	2-4	X

JEWSON EASTERN COUNTIES LEAGUE CUP 1999-2000

FIRST ROUND

Cambridge City Res	v	Ely City	5-2		Diss Town	v	Halstead Town	3*1
Hadleigh United	v	Somersham Town	4*3		Lowestoft Town	v	Gt Yarmouth Town	0-3
Mildenhall Town	v	Chatteris Town	6-1		Newmarket Town	v	Clacton T	3*3, 1*1, 6p5
Norwich United	v	Thetford Town	6*3		Swaffham Town	v	Sudbury	1-6

SECOND ROUND

Bury Town	v	Felixstowe P & T	2-1		Cambridge City Res	v	Walton United	1-4
Fakenham Town	v	Warboys Town	1-0		Gorleston	v	Diss Town	0-1
Gt Yarmouth Town	v	Sudbury	1-0		Hadleigh United	v	Dereham Town	1-2
Harwich & Parkeston	v	Wroxham	1-2		Histon	v	Soham Town Rngrs	0-1
Ipswich Wndrs	v	Haverhill Rovers	3-0		Maldon Town	v	Brightlingsea United	4-2
Mildenhall Town	v	March Town Utd	1*1, 9-2		Needham Market	v	Downham Town	0-1
Newmarket Town	v	Tiptree United	5*2		Norwich United	v	Stowmarket Town	1-3
Stanway Rovers	v	Whitton United	1-0		Woodbridge Town	v	Cornard Utd	3*3, 2*2, 4p3

THIRD ROUND

Bury Town	v	Maldon Town	3-2		Downham Town	v	Dereham Town	1-2
Fakenham Town	v	Watton United	3-2		Gt Yarmouth Town	v	Stowmarket	4-1
Ipswich Wanderers	v	Woodbridge	2*2,2*2,3p5		Newmarket Town	v	Soham Town Rngrs	3-2
Stanway Rovers	v	Diss Town	1-3		Wroxham	v	Mildenhall Town	5-0

QUARTER FINALS

Diss Town	v	Gt Yarmouth Town	3-1		Newmarket Town	v	Dereham Town	2-0
Woodbridge Town	v	Bury Town	1-0		Wroxham	v	Fakenham Town	2-0

SEMI FINALS

Diss Town	v	Newmarket Town	3*2		Woodbridge Town	v	Wroxham	3*4

FINAL

Wroxham	v	Diss Town	3-0		at Dereham Town FC

Diss Town. Back Row (l-r): Matthew Wright, Andy Key, Bob Mayes, Danny Kelly, Sean Trail (captain), Glyn Roberts Front row (l-r): Darren Scoulding, Chris Howlett, Adrian Hayes, Justin Fox, Coren Hardy. Photo: Roger Turner

BURY TOWN

Secretary: Mrs Wendy Turner, 64 Winthrop Rd., Bury-St-Edmunds, Suffolk. IP333UF
Tel Nos: 01284 753688 (H) 01284 762291 (W) Club Website: www.burytownfc.com
Ground: Ram Meadow, Cotton Lane, Bury St Edmunds, Suffolk IP33 1XP Tel: 01284 754721
Directions: Leave A14 at sign to Central Bury St Edmunds, follow signs to town centre at exit r'bout, at next r'bout 1st exit into Northgate St, left at `T' junct (lights) into Mustow St, left immediately into Cotton Lane - grd 350 yds on right, through `Pay & Display' car park. 10 mins from station
Capacity: 3,500   **Cover:** 1,500   **Seats:** 300   **Floodlights:** Yes
Clubhouse: Members'/Public Bars open at matchdays   **Club Shop:** Yes

HONOURS   Eastern Counties Lg 63-64, R-up 37-38, Lg Cup 61-62 63-64; MetropolitanLg 65-66, R-up 67-68 70-71, Lg Cup 67-68, Professional Cup 65-66; Suffolk Premier Cup (9); Suffolk Senior Cup 36-37 37-38 38-39 44-45 84-85
PREVIOUS   **Leagues:** Norfolk & Suffolk; Essex & Suffolk Border; Eastern Co's 35-64 76-87; Metropolitan 64-71   **Names:** Bury St Edmunds 1895-1902; Bury Utd 02-06
BEST SEASON   **FA Cup:** 1st Rd replay 68-69, 0-3 v AFC Bournemouth (A) after 0-0
    FA Vase: Qtr Finals 88-89   **FA Trophy:** 2nd Rd 70-71
CLUB RECORDS Attendance: 2,500 v Enfield, FA Cup 3rd Qual. Rd 1986
    Goalscorer: Doug Tooley 58   **Appearances:** Doug Tooley
    Fee Paid: £1,500 for Mel Springett (Chelmsford 1990)
    Fee Received: £5,500 forSimon Milton (Ipswich)

FACT FILE
Formed: 1872
Nickname: The Blues
Sponsors: Advanced Air
Colours: All blue
Change colours:Red/black/yellow
Midweek matchday: Tuesday
Programme: 40 pages 80p
Editor: Mrs Wendy Turner
1999-00
Captain: R.Cornish
P.o.Y.: Gary Jay
Top scorer: Shane Foreman
CLUB PERSONNEL
Chairman: Colin Hurley
Vice Chairman: Russel Ward
President: Cyril Elsey
Manager: T.B.A.
Asst Manager: Keith Vince
Physio: Darren Gibbs

CLACTON TOWN

Secretary: Mrs Sandra Harris, 57 Coopers Lane, Clacton-on-Sea, Essex CO15 2BY
    Tel: 01255 476133 email: secretary@clacton-town.com
Ground: The Rush Green Bowl, Rushgreen Road, Clacton-on-Sea, Essex CO16 7BQ
    Tel/Fax: 01255 432590 email: supporters@clacton-town.com
Directions: A133 to Clacton, at r'bout right into St Johns Rd, 4th left CloesLane, 3rd right Rushgreen Rd, ground approximately half mile on right. From B1027 take main Jaywick turn off (Jaywick Lane), then 2nd left after about half a mile into Rushgreen Rd. Ground 400 yds. 2 miles from Clacton (BR), buses 3, 5or 5a to Coopers Lane/Rushgreen Rd
Capacity: 3,000   **Seats:** 200   **Cover:** Yes   **Floodlights:** Yes   **Club Shop:** Yes
Clubhouse: Licensed club. Open 7-11pm Mon-Fri, Wed-Fri lunchtimes & all day Sat & Sun.
    Hot & cold food available at all times.

HONOURS   Southern Lg Div 1 59-60; Eastern Co's Lg R-up 36-37 53-54 64-65 74-75 (Lg Cup 73-74), Div 1 98-99 (Lg Cup 98-99); Eastern F/lit Cup 95-96; East Anglian Cup 53-54,99-00; WorthingtonEvans Cup 56-57 67-68 74-75.
PREVIOUS   **Leagues:** Eastern Co's 35-37 38-58; Southern 58-64
    Grounds: Clacton Stadium, Old Road 06-87; Gainsford Av (temp)
RECORD   **Attendance:** 3,505 v Romford, FA Cup 1st Qual. Rd 1952 (at Old Road)
BEST SEASON   **FA Vase:** 4th Rd 74-75,99-00 ,**FA Cup:** 1st Rd,1-3 v Southend U. (H) 60-61
Players progressing: Vivian Woodward (Spurs), Mick Everitt (Arsenal), Christian McLean (Bristol R.)

FACT FILE
Founded: 1892
Nickname: Seasiders
Colours: White/royal blue/royal blue
Change colours: yellow/yellow/royal blue
Midweek Matches: Tuesday
Programme: 40 pages, £1
Editor: Larry Warren (01255 475182)
Local P ress: Clacton Gazette
web Site: http://www.clacton-town.com
CLUB PERSONNEL
Owner: Jeff Dewing
Chairman: Stewart Nicholson
General Manager: Colin Harris
Commercial Manager: Michelle Stanley
Tel:01255822169
Team Manager: Steve Dowman

DISS TOWN

Secretary: Richard Upson, Bamburgh House, Brewers Green Lane, Diss, NorfolkIP22 3QP
    Tel: 01379 642923 (H) 01603 427231 (B) 0836 718729 (M)

Ground: Brewers Green Lane, Diss Tel: 01379 651223

Directions: Just off B1066 Diss-Thetford road, near Roydon School. 1 1/2 miles from Diss (BR)
Capacity: 2,500   **Seats:** 280   **Cover:** Yes   **Floodlights:** Yes
Club Shop: Yes, incl. pennants
Clubhouse: Open evenings (except Sunday), Sat/Sun lunchtimes, and matchdays

HONOURS   FA Vase 94-95; Eastern Co's Lg Div 1 91-92, Anglian Comb. 76-77 78-79(R-up 74-75, Div 1 67-68 73-74, Lg Cup 67-68 79-80 81-82), Norfolk & Suffolk Lg R-up 55-56 (Applegate Cup 56-57 57-58(joint)(R-up 55-56)), Norfolk Snr Cup 74-75 95-96, Norfolk Jnr Cup 1891-92, Jewson Prem Lge R-up 95-96
PREVIOUS   **Leagues:** Norwich & District; Norfolk & Suffolk 35-64; AnglianComb. 64-82
    Ground: Roydon Road 1886-1982
BEST SEASON   **FA Vase:** Winners 94-95, QF 91-92
RECORDS   **Attendance:** 1,731 v Atherton LR, FA Vase SF 1st leg 19/3/94
Players progressing A Thurlow (Man City), M Cawston (Norwich), T Whymark(Ipswich), C Stafford, P Gibbs (Colchester)

FACT FILE
Founded: 1888
Nickname: Tangerines
Sponsors: Apple Garages
Colours: Tangerine/navy/tangerine
Change colours: Sky blue/navy/navy
Midweek Matches: Tuesday
Reserve's League: Anglian Combination
Programme: 16 pages, 50p
Editor: Gary Enderby (01379 608767)
1999-00
Captain: Sean Trail
Top Scorer: Coren Hardy
Player of the Year: Coren Hardy
CLUB PERSONNEL
Chairman: Des Tebble
President: John Bell
Treasurer: Noel Mullenger
Manager: Paul Chick
Coach/Asst Manager: Alan Biley
Physio: Peter Etheridge

ELY CITY

Secretary: Derek Oakey, 11 Frederick Talbot Close, Soham, Nr. Ely Cambs, CB7 5EY
Tel Nos: 01353 722141 (H)   01353 722179 (W)

Ground: Unwin Sports Ground, Downham Road (01353 662035)

Directions: A10 Ely by-pass turn off for Downham. 3 miles (approx) from Ely(BR)

Capacity: 1,500   **Seats:** 150   **Cover:** 350   **Floodlights:** Yes   **Shop:** No

Clubhouse: Open matchdays, refreshments available

Club Shop: Metal Badges: Yes

HONOURS   Cambs Snr Cup 47-48, Eastern Co's Lg R-up 69-70 (Lg Cup 79-80)

PREVIOUS   **Leagues:** Peterborough; Central Alliance 58-60
   Grounds: Paradise Ground (1890 1986)

BEST SEASON   **FA Cup:** 1st Rd 56-56 (2-6 v Torquay)

RECORD   **Gate:** 260 v Soham, Eastern Co's Lg Div 1, 12/4/93
   At old ground: 4,260 v Torquay, FA Cup 56-57

FACT FILE
Founded: 1885
Nickname: Robins
Colours: All red with white trim
Change colours: Jade/black/jade
Midweek Matches: Tuesday
Programme: 24 pages- 50p
Editor: Derek Oakley
Local Press: Ely Standard (01353 667831)

CLUB PERSONNEL
Chairman: Brian Jordan
Manager: Steven Taylor

FAKENHAM TOWN

Secretary: Edric Linnell, 40 Warren Avenue, Fakenham, Norfolk NR21 8NP Tel: 01328 855445

Ground: Clipbush Lane, Fakenham NR21 8SW   Tel/Fax: 01328 855859

Directions: Corner of A148 & Clipbush Lane
Capacity: 3,000   **Seats:** 264   **Cover:** 500   **Floodlights:** Yes
Clubhouse: Bar, TV. Refreshments available Tel: 01328 855859
Club Shop: Yes

HONOURS   Norfolk Snr Cup 70-71 72-73 73-74 91-92 93-94 94-95;,98-99 Eastern Co's
Premier Division R-up: 98-99, Lg Div1, R-up 91-92; Anglian Comb. Cup 78-79

PREVIOUS   **Leagues:** N Norfolk 1884-1910; Norwich & Dist 10-35; Norfolk & Suffolk 35-
   64; Anglian Comb 64-87
   Grounds: Hempton Green 1884-89; Star Meadow 89-1907;
      Barons Hall Lawn 1907-96

BEST SEASON   **FA Vase:** 98-99 3rd Rd   **FA Cup:**

RECORD   **Gate:** 1100 v Watford-official opening of new ground
Players progressing Nolan Keeley (Scunthorpe)

FACT FILE
Founded: 1884
Nickname: Ghosts
Sponsors:English Garages
Colours: Amber & black/black/amber
Change colours: Red & Black,red,red
Midweek Matchday: Tuesday
Reserves' League: Anglian Comb
Programme: 32 pages, 50p
Editor: John Cushion
Tel: 01328 862548
Local Press : Dereham & Fakenham Times

CLUB PERSONNEL
Chairman: Tony Fisher
President: G Middleditch
Press Officer: J Cushion
Commercial Manager: T.Vertigan
Manager: Neil Jarvis

FELIXSTOWE & WALTON UNITED

Secretary: Michael Gosling, 23 Vicarage Road, Felixstowe, Suffolk IP11 2LR
Tel No: 01394 279758

Ground: Dellwood Avenue, Felixstowe IP11 9HT Tel: 01394 282917

Directions: A45 to Felixstowe. Turn right at 3rd r'bout then 1st left - ground100 yds on
left. 5 mins from Felixstowe (BR) and town centre
Capacity: 2,000   **Seats:** 200   **Cover:** 200   **Floodlights:** Yes
Clubhouse: Bar, snack bar, TV, darts, pool table. Snacks available
Club Shop: Yes including enamel badges & pennants.

HONOURS   Suffolk Senior Cup 66-67 74-75
PREVIOUS   **Leagues:** Essex & Suffolk Border; Ipswich & District
   Names: Felixstowe Port & Town, Felixstowe Town, Felixstowe United
   Grounds: Tennis Club,Ferry Road.
RECORD   **Attendance:** 1,500 v Ipswich Town, floodlight inauguration 25/1/91

FACT FILE
Founded: 1890
Nickname: Seasiders
Colours: Red & white stripes/white/red
Change: Navy blue/navy blue/white
Midweek Matches: Wednesday
Programme: 36pages, 30p
Editor: Phil Griffiths
Tel: 01394 277156
Local Press: East Anglia Daily Times

CLUB PERSONNEL
Chairman: Dave Ashford
Fixture Sec: Mike Gosling (01394 279758)
Manager: Scott Clarke
01473 278025 (H)

GORLESTON

Secretary: Mrs Pam Lattermore, 7 Station Road, Pulham St Mary, Diss, Norfolk IP21 4QT
Tel: 01379 608905 (H/Fax) 0411 470858 (M)

Ground: Emerald Park, Woodfarm Lane, Gorleston, Great Yarmouth Tel: 01493 602802

Directions: On Magdalen Estate - follow signs to Crematorium, turn left and follow road to ground.
Five and a half miles from Great Yarmouth Vauxhall (BR)
Capacity: 5,000   Seats:1000   Cover: 4,000   Floodlights: Yes
Clubhouse: Bar, colour TV, pool table, darts, snacks. Matchday Tea, coffee,cold drinks, burgers,
hotdogs, rolls   **Club Shop:** Yes

HONOURS   Eastern Co's Lg 52-53 72-73 79-80 80-81; Lge Cup 55-56; Norfolk Snr
Cup x 13, R-up x 25; Anglian Comb. 68-69, Norfolk & Suffolk Lg x 7;
E Anglian Cup (3);Jewson Lge Div 1 95-96

PREVIOUS   **Leagues:** Gt Yarmouth & Dist; Norfolk & Suffolk; Anglian Comb

BEST SEASON   **FA Cup:** 1st Rd. 51-52, 57-58   **FA Vase:**

RECORD   **Attendance:** 4,473 v Orient, FA Cup 1st Rd 29/11/51

Players progressing: J Joblins (Norwich), M Bailey (Wolves), D Stringer(Norwich), R Carter (Aston
Villa), D Carter (Man City), A Brown (Charlton), S Morgan (Cambridge), P Gibbs (Colchester)

FACT FILE

Founded: 1884
Nickname: Greens
Colours: Green & White
Change colours: All white
Midweek Matchday: Tuesday
Programme: 56/60 pages £1.00
Editor: Secretary

CLUB PERSONNEL

Chairman & President: Jimmy Jones

Managers: Dale Gordon & Robert Fleck

GREAT YARMOUTH TOWN

Secretary: Brian Smith, The Bungalow, Humberstone Farm, Cobholm, Great Yarmouth, Norfolk
NR31 0AZ. Tel & Fax: 01493 656099
Ground: Wellesey Recreation Ground, Wellesey Road (01493 843373)

Directions: Just off Marine Parade, 200yds north of Britannia Pier.1/2 m from Vauxhall BR(BR)
Capacity: 3,600   Seats: 500   Cover: 2,100   Floodlights: Yes   Club Shop: Yes

Clubhouse: (01493 843373). Committee Room, Sky TV, darts, pool. Hot & cold food
HONOURS   Eastern Co's Lg 68-69 (R-up 56-57 67-68 77-78 78-79), Lg Cup 37-38 74-
75 80-81; East Anglian Cup(3); Norfolk Senior Cup x 12, R-up x 22;
Norfolk Premier Cupx 2 jt; Norfolk & Suffolk Lg 13-14 26-27 27-28;
Anglian Comb. Cup 65-66(res); E Anglian Lg 56-57(res)

PREVIOUS   **Leagues:** Norfolk & Suffolk

BEST SEASON   **FA Cup:** 2nd Rd 52-53, 1st Rd 47-48 **FA Vase:** Semi-Final 82-83
RECORD   **Attendance:** 8,944 v Crystal Palace, FA Cup 1st Rd 52-53
Appearances: John `Jilly' Perkins 499 (1897-1923)
Scorer: Gordon South 298 (1927-47)   **Win:** 14-0, 2.2.10

Players progressing: R Hollis (Norwich), M Blyth & N Keeley (Scunthorpe), S Davy (West Ham),
K Ready (Aston Villa), G Butcher (Blackburn)

FACT FILE

Founded: 1897
Nickname: Bloaters
Colours: Amber & black stripes/black/black
Change colours: All red
Midweek Matches: Tuesday
Programme: 40 pages, 80p
Editor: Gerry Brown (014493 663171)

99-00 Captain: Mark Vincent
Top Scorer: Stewart Roach
P.O.Y.: Lee Humphreys

CLUB PERSONNEL

Chairman: Arthur Fiske

Manager: Paul Tong

HALSTEAD TOWN

Secretary: Stephen Webber, 12 Ravens Ave, Halstead, Essex CO9 1NZ
Tel: 01787 476959 (H) 01284 767278 (B)

Ground: Rosemary Lane, Broton Ind Est, Halstead, Essex CO9 2HR
Tel: 01787 472082

Directions: A131 Chelmsford to Braintree - follow signs to Halstead. In Halstead, 1st left
after Police Station, then 1st right, and first left to ground
Capacity: 2,000   Seats: 312   Cover: 400   Floodlights: Yes
Clubhouse: Open evenings and matchdays

HONOURS   Eastern Co's Lg 94-95 95-96, R-up 93-94 (Div 1 R-up 89-90), Cup 95-96;
Essex Senior Trophy 94-95 96-97; Knight Floodlit Cup R-up 90-91; Essex
&Suffolk Border Lg 57-59 77-78 94-95(res), (R-up 49-50 54-55 60-61), Div
1(res)94-95); Essex Snr Lg Cup R-up 79-80; Essex Jnr Cup 01-02 46-47 (R-
up 00-01)

PREVIOUS   **Leagues:** Nth Essex; Halstead & Dist.; Haverhill; Essex & Suffolk Border;
Essex Snr 80-88   **Grounds:** Three Gates 1879-1948, Coggeshall Pieces,
Ravens Meadow, King George Playing Field

RECORD   **Attendance:** 4,000 v Walthamstow Avenue, Essex Senior Cup 1949
Players progressing Steve Allen (Wimbledon Physio)

FACT FILE

Founded: 1879 Nickname 'The Town'
Colours: White & black hoops/black/white
Change colours: All red
Midweek Matches: Tuesday
Page 24 Programme: 50p
Editor: Paul Downes
Tel: 01787 477320 (H)
Local Press : Halstead Gazette

CLUB PERSONNEL

Chairman: Mick Coe
Vice-Chairman:Richard Gugacz
President: Mr E J R McDowell
Fixture sec.: Andy Mizon
Tel: 01787 473898 (H) 01206 894096 (B)
Manager: Terry Benson
Physio: B Dunster

Above: Fakenham Town

Above: Mildenhall Town
Back Row (l-r): Andy Critoph, Mark Winstone, Steve Hencher, Peter Braybrooke, Alex Thorpe, Errol Bailey, Stuart Ogilvie, Craig Osborne
Front Row (l-r): Rhys Nightingale, Steve Tuck, Ben Goddard, Luke Moore, Kevin Sobiechowski, Paul Byatt, Trevor Ball, Gareth Jones.
Photo: Peter Barnes

HARWICH & PARKESTON

Secretary: Andy Schooler, 21 The Vineway, Harwich, Essex CO12 4AX
01255 504590 (H) 01255 509700 (B) 01255 509718 (Bus. Fax)

Ground: Royal Oak, Main Road, Dovercourt, Harwich CO12 4AA   Tel: 01255 503649

Directions: On main road into Dovercourt. 600 yds from Dovercourt (BR)
FLoodlights: Yes Capacity: 5,000   Seats: 350   Cover: 1,000

Clubhouse : Open every day. Dances, bingo, darts, pool, function room   Club Shop: Yes

HONOURS FA Amateur Cup R-up 1898-99 52-53; Eastern Counties Lg 35-36 (jnt) (Lg
Cup 35-36 36-37 96-97); Essex County Lg 37-38; Athenian Lg Div 1R-up 65-
66 (Div 2 64-65, Lg Cup 64-65); Essex Sen. Cup 1898-99 36-37; Essex Sen. Trophy 89-90; AFA
Senior Cup 35-36 36-37; Worthington Evans Cup 80-81

PREVIOUS **Leagues:** Eastern Co's 35-37 38-64; Essex County 37-38; Athenian 64-73
83-84; Isthmian 73-83   **Ground:** Phoenix Field, Seafront

BEST SEASON **FA Vase:** Q-F 90-91   **FA Cup:**
FA Amateur Cup: R-up 1898-99, 52-53

RECORD **Attendance:** 5,649 v Romford, FA Amat Cup 4th Rd 1938

Players progressing: I Gillespie (C Palace), G Waites, K Sanderson, I Brown(Bristol City 91)

FACT FILE

Founded: 1875
Nickname: Shrimpers
Colours: White & black/black/black
Change colours: Mauve & white/white/mauve
Midweek Matches: Tuesday
Reserve Lge: Essex & Suffolk Border Lge
Prem. Div
Programme: 28 pages, 50p
Editor: Carl Allen
01255 552510

CLUB PERSONNEL

Chairman: Graham Firth
President:Terry Rowlands
Press Officer: Carl Allan
Manager: Tony Hall

IPSWICH WANDERERS

Secretary: Martin Head, 246 Sidelate Lane, Ipswich, Suffolk. IP4 3DH Tel: 01473 414390

Ground: Humberdoucey Lane, Ipswich, Suffolk Tel: 01473 728581

Directions: Take Woodbridge Road out of Ipswich,then left fork into Playford Road.Take
first left into Humberdoucy Lane Ground 300yds on right
Capacity: 2,000   Seats: 50   Cover: Yes   Floodlights: Yes

Clubhouse: Bar,Tea, coffee, cold drinks, confectionary, burgers, hotdogs,sandwiches, rolls

HONOURS Eastern Lge Div 1 97-98

BEST SEASON **FA Cup:**   **FA Vase:**

PREVIOUS **Leagues:** Little David SundayNames: Loadwell Ipswich

RECORD **Attendance:** 335 v Woodbridge, ECL Div 1 4/4/94

FACT FILE

Founded: 1983
Nickname: Wanderers
Sponsors:N.T.L.
Colours: Royal & white/blue/blue & white
Change colours: Red & black/black/red & black
Midweek Matches: Tuesday
Programme: Yes
Editor: Alan Haste (01473 711877)
Local Press: East Anglian Daily Times,
Evening Star

CLUB PERSONNEL

Chairman: A.Haste
President: P.Emmerson
Manager:Colwyn Rowe

LOWESTOFT TOWN

Secretary: Terry Lynes, 133 Raglan Street, Lowestoft, Suffolk NR33 2JU
Tel: 01502 564034

Ground: Crown Meadow, Love Rd, Lowestoft Tel: 01502 573818
Directions: Just off A12, 10 mins from Lowestoft (BR)
Capacity: 3,000   Seats: 466   Cover: 500   Floodlights: Yes

Clubhouse: Pub hours, Snacks available   **Club Shop:** Yes (incl metal badges)

HONOURS Eastern Co's Lg(8) 35-36(jnt) 37-38 62-63 64-65 67-68 69-71 77-78, Lg Cup(7)
38-39 54-55 65-67 68-69 75-76 83-84; Norf. & Suffolk Lg(8) 1897-99 1900-04 28-29 30-31; Suffolk
Prem. Cup(6) 66-67 71-72 74-75 78-80; 99-00Suffolk Snr Cup(10) 02-   03 22-24 25-26 31-
32 35-36 46-49 55-56; E Anglian Cup(10); Anglian Comb. (Res.) 77-78 79-80 (Lg Cup 76-77); E
Anglian Lg (Res.) 57-58 63-64

PREVIOUS **League:** Norfolk & Suffolk 1897-1935
BEST SEASON **FA Cup:** 1st Rd 26-27 38-39 66-67, 67-68, 77-78
RECORDS **Attendance:** 5,000 v Watford, FA Cup 1st Rd 67
Goalscorer: M Tooley 383   **Appearances:** C Peck 629
Win: 19-0 v Thetford Town (H), Eastern Counties League

Players progressing: Eddie Spearitt (Ipswich 1965), Nigel Cassidy (Norwich1967), Richard Money
(Scunthorpe 1973), Graham Franklin (Southend 1977)

FACT FILE

Founded: 1885
Nickname: Blues
Sponsors: Office World (Anglia) Ltd
Colours: Royal Blue/white/blue
Change colours: All red
Midweek Matches: Tuesday
Reserves' Lge: Anglian Combination
Programme:44 pages £1.00
Editor: Rachel Harrod

CLUB PERSONNEL

Chairman: Shaun Cole
President: Roy Harper
Manager: Michael Chapman

Top: Lowestoft Town before winning the last game of the season at Maldon Town. Back Row (l-r): Brian Smith (Secretary), Steve Playford (Assistant), Paul Tong (Manager), Arthur Fisk (Chairman), Stewart Roach, Ian George, Mark Vincent (Captain), Daniel Holmes, Dale Cooper, Nick Banham, Bob Pratt (Physio), Simon Scott-Greenard (Assistant), Kevin Cruikshank (Committee). Front Row: Scott Mcintosh, Paul Cushion, Zac Colman, David Lawrence, Neil Prior, Lee Brown, Mark Armes, James Spurgeon, Tom Johnson (Kit). Photo: Gerry Brown

Centre: Halstead Town. Back Row (l-r): John Harding, David Elsbury, Mark Burlong, Ricky Jewitt, Paul Champ, Richard Schultz (capt), Andy Tudor, Peter Emelick, James Keeble, David Schultz, Shaun Bailey (manager). Front Row (l-r): John Reeves, Steve Wareham, Paul Gibbens, Julian Lamb, Lee Fish. Photo: Gordon Whittington

Great Yarmouth Town FC. Back Row (l-r): Paul Tony (Manager), Greg Downes, Dale Cooper, Stewart Roach, Nick Banham, Mark Vincent (Club Captain), Mike Swinnerton, James Spurgeon, Bob Pratt (Physio), Simon Scott-Greenard (Asst Manager). Front Row: Ian George, Robert Egglington, Scott McIntosh, Neil Prior, Paul Cushion, Paul Woodridge, Mark Armes, Gavin Morris, Stephen Bishop. Photo: Neil Thaler

MALDON TOWN

FACT FILE

Secretary: Phil Robinson, 9 Lyndhurst Drive, Bicknacre, Essex CN3 4XL
Tel No: 01245 222633 (H) & 01206 753498 (W)

Ground: Wallace Binder Ground, Park Drive, Maldon CM9 5XX (01621 853762)

Capacity: 2,500   **Seats:** 250   **Cover:** 500   **Floodlights:** Yes

HONOURS Essex Snr Lg 84-85 (Sportsmanship Award 87-88,88-89,94-95, Reserve Shield 93-94), Reserve Cup:94-95, Essex & Suffolk Border Lg 55-56 (Cup 64-65),Essex Intermediate Cup 51-52, Tolleshunt D'Arcy Cup 93-94

PREVIOUS **Leagues:** Mid Essex, N. Essex, Essex & Suffolk Border, Essex Senior **Ground:** Fambridge Road (pre-1994)

BEST SEASON **FA Cup:** **FA Vase:**

RECORDS **Attendance:** 150 v Clacton Town Jewson League 27/12/99

Founded: 1946 Nickname: 'The Town'
Colours: Blue & white hoops/blue/blue
Change colours: Red & black
hoops/black/black
Midweek Matchday: Tuesday
Programme:24 pages £1.00
Editor: Alan Drewer

CLUB PERSONNEL

Chairman: Bob Large
Manager: Ben Embery

MILDENHALL TOWN

FACT FILE

Secretary: Brian Hensby, 14 Sanderling Close, Mildenhall, Suffolk IP28 7LE
Tel: 01638 715772

Ground: Recreation Way, Mildenhall, Suffolk (01638 713449)

Directions: Next to swimming pool/carpark, quarter of a mile from town centre

Capacity: 2,000   **Seats:** 50

Clubhouse: Open matchdays & functions. Light refreshments available

HONOURS Suffolk Junior Cup 1899-1900

PREVIOUS **Leagues:** Bury & District; Cambs Lg 2B, 1B & Premier

RECORD **Attendance:** 350 v Norwich City, friendly 22/7/89

Founded: 1890
Nickname: The Hall
Colours: Amber/black/black
Change colours: All white
Midweek Matchday: Tuesday
Programme: £1.00
Editor: Frank Marshall
Local Press : Bury Free Press,
Newmarket Journal,
Cambridge Evening News,East Anglian Daily
Times,Green 'Un

CLUB PERSONNEL
Chairman: Brian Brigden
Vice Chairman: frank Marshall
Fixture Secretary: Colin Marchant
Tel: 01842 812123
Managers: Steve O'Donoghue& Rob Steele

NEWMARKET TOWN

Fixture Secretary: Elaine Jenkins, 140 New Cheveley Road,Newmarket CB88BY
Tel Nos: 01638 602525 (H) 01638 750201 (W)

Ground: Cricketfield Road, off New Cheveley Road, Newmarket (01638 663637)

Directions: 400 yds Newmarket (BR) - turn right into Green Rd, right at cross roads New Cheveley Rd, ground at top on left

Capacity: 1,750   **Seats:** 144   **Cover:** 150   **Floodlights:** Yes

Clubhouse: Matchdays only. Refreshments available

HONOURS Suffolk Snr Cup 34-35 93-94; Cambs Invitation Cup 58-59; Cambs Chall. Cup 21-22 26-27; Cambs Snr Lg, 19-20; Ipswich Snr Lg 30-31 31-32 32-33 33-34; Peterborough Lg 57-58; Suffolk Premier Cup 93-94 94-95 96-97

PREVIOUS **League:** Bury Snr; Ipswich Snr; Essex & Suffolk Border; Utd Co's 34-37; Eastern Co's 37-52

BEST SEASON **FA Cup:** 4th Qual. Rd 92-93, 0-2 v Hayes (H)
FA Vase: 4th Round 91-92

RECORD **Attendance:** 2,701 v Abbey Utd (now Cambridge Utd), FA Cup 1st Qual.Rd 1/10/49

FACT FILE

Founded: 1877
Nickname: Jockeys
Colours: Yellow & navy/navy/yellow
Change Colours: All Red
Midweek Matches: Tuesday
Programme: 50p
Editor: Tony Pringle (01638 669438)

CLUB PERSONNEL

Acting Chairman: Gill Ouwendijk
President: M J Nicholas

Manager: John Wright

Players progressing: Mick Lambert (Ipswich), M Wright (Northampton), G Tweed(Coventry), R Fuller (Charlton), Colin Vowden (Camb.Utd.)

SOHAM TOWN RANGERS

Secretary: Mrs Wendy Gammon, 32 Broad Piece, Soham, Cambs CB7 5EL
Tel: 01353 722139

Ground: Julius Martins Lane, Soham, Cambs
Tel: 01353 720732

Directions: A142 between Newmarket and Ely
Capacity: 2,000   Seats: 200   Cover: 1,500   Floodlights: Yes

Clubhouse: General bar, Stud Bar, Lounge Bar   **Club Shop:** Yes

HONOURS   Eastern Co's Lg Div 1 R-up 92-93; P'boro. Lg(3)

PREVIOUS   **Leagues:** Peterborough & Dist
Ground: Soham Rangers: Brook Street 1919-47
Names: Soham Town and Soham Rangers merged in 1947

RECORD   **Attendance:** 3,000 v Pegasus, FA Amateur Cup 1963

FACT FILE
Founded: 1947
Nickname: Town or Rangers
Sponsors: C.J.Murfelt
Colours: All Green
Change colours: Blue/black/black
Midweek Matchday: Tuesday
Reserves ' League: Cambs Prem. B
Programme: 50p   Editor : Graham Eley
Local Press : Ely Standard, Newmarket
Journal, Cambridge Evening News

CLUB PERSONNEL
Chairman: C.J.Murffitt
President: A.Turner
Manager: R Goodjohn
Coach: Mick Drury

STOWMARKET TOWN

Secretary: Christine Gillingham,22 Windermere Road, Stowmarket , Suffolk 1P4 1LD
Tel No: 01449 674507
Ground: Green Meadows Stadium, Bury Road, Stowmarket Tel: 01449 612533

Directions: About 800 yds from Stowmarket BR station - turn right at 1st lights and head
out of town over r'bout into Bury Road - ground on right
Capacity: 2,000   Seats: 200   Cover: 450   Floodlights: Yes

Clubhouse: Bar open 6.30pm onwards Mon-Fri, weekends 12.0pm onwards.
Matchday food available   Club Shop: Yes, incl. metal badges.
HONOURS Eastern Co's Lg R-up 91-92, Suffolk Premier Cup(4), Suffolk Snr Cup(10)
Suffolk Jnr Cup., Churchman Cup: 99-00.

PREVIOUS **Leagues:** Ipswich & Dist.; Essex & Suffolk Border 25-52
Grounds: The Cricket Meadow, 1883-1984
Names: Stowupland Corinthians; Stowmarket Corinthians; Stowmarket FC
BEST SEASON   **FA Cup: 2nd Q Rd 1992**   **FA Vase: 4th Rd 1983-84**

RECORD   **Attendance:** 1,200 v Ipswich Town, friendly July 1994
At Cricket Meadow: 3,800 v Romford, FA Amtr Cup 1st Rd 15/12/51

Players progressing: Craig Oldfield (Colchester), Les Tibbott, Ted Phillips & Brian Klug (Ipswich)

FACT FILE
Founded: 1883
Nickname: Stow
Colours: Gold & black/black/black
Change colours: All Red
Midweek Matches: Tuesday
Reserves' Lge: Essex & Suffolk Border
Programme: 20 pages,60p
Ed: John Gillingham (01449 674507&FAX)
Local Press: East Anglian, Bury Free Press
99-00 - Captain: Steve Gayfer
P.o.Y.: Matthew Platt
Top Scorer: Colin Yeomans
CLUB PERSONNEL
Chairman: Derek Barnard
President: John Bultitude
Fixture Sec: Christine Gillingham
Tel: 01449 674507(H) 07880 732416(M)
Manager: Mel Aldis
Coach: Mark Barnard
Physio: John Chandler

AFC SUDBURY

Ground: Kingsmarsh Stadium, Brundon Lane, Sudbury, Suffolk CO10 1WQ (01787 376213)
Directions: From Sudbury centre follow Halstead/Chelmsford signs for about 1mile. 1st right
after railway bridge at foot of steep hill, and 1st right after sharp left hand bend
Capacity: 2,500   Seats: 200   Cover: 150   Floodlights: Yes
Clubhouse: Matchdays/ training nights   Shop: Yes Contact: Darren Witt (M) 0402 159375)

HONOURS WANDERERS - Eastern Co's Lg Div 1 92-93, Ess.& Suff. Border Lg(2) 89-91
(R-up 88-89), Suffolk Snr Cup 90-91

TOWN   Southern Lge - Lge Cup 93-94, R-up 96-97, Championship 93-94, Southern Div
(Post War)   R-up 93-94; Eastern Counties Lg x 7, R-up x 6, Lg Cup x 6, Suffolk Prem.Cup x 13,
R-up x 8, Suffolk Sen. Cup(2); E. Anglian Cup 85-86 91-92, R-up 83-84 95-96; Essex& Suffolk
Border Lg x 5; E.S.B.L. Cup 49-50, R-Up 46-47; Eastern F'lit Group 93-94 94-95

PREVIOUS   **Names:** Sudbury Town (1885) & Sudbury Wanderers (1958) merged 1999
Leagues: Wanderers- Essex & Suffolk Border. Town Suffolk & Ipswich;
Essex & Suffolk Border; Eastern Co 55-90; Southern 91-97 Eastern Co. 98-99

BEST SEASON FA Vase: Quarter Final 97-98, 0-2 v Tow Law Town (A), after 1-1
WANDERERS   FA Cup: 4th Qual Rd., 95-96, 1-4 v Hayes (A),
TOWN   **FA Vase:** Runners-up 88-89   **FA Trophy:** 3rd Rd.Proper 95-96
    FA Cup: 2nd Rd Proper 96-97, 1-3 v Brentford. Played at Colchester Utd. F.C.

FACT FILE
Founded: 1st June,1999
Colours: Yellow/blue/yellow
Change Colours: All Red
Midweek Matchday: Tuesday
Programme: 48 + pages £1
Editor:T.B.A.
Local Press : Suffolk Free Press,
East Anglian Daily Times

CLUB PERSONNEL

Joint Chairmen: Nick F Smith & Phil Turner

Secretary: David Webb
6 Melford Road, Sudbury, Suffolk CO10 1LS
Tel: 01787 372352 (H) 01787 886000 x6223 (B)

Manager: Keith Martin

Top: Cornard United
Back Row (l-r): Mike
Ford (physio), Martin
Freeman, Danny
Chinnery, Trevor Irvine,
Steve Arnold, Darren
Moyes, Matt Chinnery,
Colin Pearce, Jon
Chinnery, Mike Hodson,
Gary Roberts, Jason
Stalker (asst manager)
Front Row (l-r): Lee
Mills, Andy Gooderham,
Keith Featherstone,
Andy McLaughlin, Chris
Symes (manager), Carl
Cook, Tony Ashby, Glen
Birch.
Photo: Suzanne Abbott

Centre: Tiptree United
Back Row (l-r): Tony
French, Phil Battell,
Bradley Green, Steve
Parnell (manager),
Wayne Houghton
Middle Row (l-r): Steve
Quinn, Peter Monk,
Richard Carter, Chris
Powell, Stuart Jarvis
(capt), Craig Lesiak,
Steve Chester, Adam
Flint
Front Row (l-r): Gary
Harvey, Danny
Johnson, Sid Haygreen,
Russell Whittaker (MD,
Milan Europe Teamwear
- Club sponsor), Danny
Saxby, Richard
Wymark, Danny Hill

Bottom:
Stanway Rovers
Back Row (l-r): Paul
Symes, Neil Liffen,
Nathan Munson, James
Todd, David Gray, Neil
Grice, Andy Sapey,
Duncan Jackson
Front Row (l-r): Paul
Brierley, Tom Brannon,
Rob Bate, James
Mackey, Ryan Jones,
Steve Ball (manager)

TIPTREE UNITED

Secretary:	John Wisbey, 103 Peace Road, Stanway, Colchester, Essex
	Tel Nos: 01206 564222 (H) 0403 585814 (M)
Ground:	Chapel Road, Tiptree, Essex Tel: 01621 815213
Directions:	Enter town on B1023 - Chapel Road is left at second crossroads,
	ground 200yds on left. 3 miles from Kelverdon (BR).
	Served by Eastern NationalColchester to Maldon bus

Capacity: 2,500   Seats: 150   Cover: 300   Floodlights: Yes

Clubhouse: Open daily 7-11pm (all day Fri & Sat) & 12-2.30, 7-10.30 Sun.
Large bar, two snooker tables, pool, darts, netball, badminton, pigeon club,
bingo. Dance hall seats 180, small hall seats 60.   **Club Shop:** No

HONOURS   Essex Snr Tphy 80-81, Eastern Co's Lg 81-82 (Lg Cup 81-82 84-85),
Essex Snr Lg R-up 75-76 77-78, Harwich Charity Cup (4),
Jewson Eastern Div 1 Champions 99-00

PREVIOUS   **Leagues:** Essex & Suffolk Border; Essex Snr 78-84

RECORD   **Attendance:** 1,210 v Spurs, floodlight inauguration Dec 1990

FACT FILE
Founded: 1933
Nickname:The Jam -Makers
Sponsors: Tiptree Building Supplies
Colours: Red& blackstripes/black/black
Change colours: Yellow/blue/white
Midweek Matchday: Tuesday
Reserves' League: Essex & Herts Comb
Programme: 32pages*, 50p Editor: Secretary
Local Press : Colchester Evening Gazette,
Essex County Standard'
* Voted Eastern' Programme of the Year'

CLUB PERSONNEL
Chairman: Peter Newman
President: Len Foakes
Manager: Steve Parnell

WARBOYS TOWN

Secretary:	Martin England, 39 High Street, Warboys, Huntingdon, CambsPE28 2TA
	Tel No: 01487 822503
Ground:	Sports Field, Forge Way, off High Street, Warboys, Cambs Tel: 01487 823483
Directions:	Access through Forge Way, half way along south side of High Street
Capacity:	2,000 Seats: 50 Cover: 200 Floodlights: Yes

Clubhouse: Bar, lounge, function hall. Open every evening & Sunday lunchtime
Entertainment, drinks & snacks

HONOURS   Utd Co's Lg Div 2 R-up 54-55, P'boro Lg R-up(2) 59-60 61-62, P'boro SnrCup
63-64, Hunts Snr Cup 26-27 28-29 31-32 32-33,94-95. (R-up 92-93,95-96), Hunts Scott Gatty Cup
30-31. Reserves: Hunts Benevolent Cup 57-58, Hunts Junior   Cup 24-25 27-28 52-53,
Hunts Lower Junior Cup 75-76 77-78.Jewson Eastern Lg.Cup R-up: 97-98, Jewson League Div 1
R-up: 95-96

PREVIOUS   **Leagues:** Peterborough & Dist 46-48 56-88; Utd Co's 50-56; Huntingdonshire 48-50

RECORD   **Attendance:** 500 v Ramsey Town, Hunts Senior Cup Semi Final

Players progressing: Alec Chamberlain (Ipswich and Watford)

FACT FILE
Founded: 1885
Nickname: Witches
Colours: Red & white/black/red
Change colours: White/maroon/maroon
Midweek Matches: Tuesday
Programme: 12 pages,50p
Editor: Martin England
Local Press : Hunts Post (01480 411481)

CLUB PERSONNEL
Chairman: Roger Pauley
Manager: Ian Benjamin

WOODBRIDGE TOWN

Secretary: John Bennett, 67 Cumberland Street,Woodbridge, Suffolk 1P12 4AQ
Tel No: 01394 385973 (H)
Ground: Notcutts Park, Seckford Hall Road, Woodbridge, Suffolk Tel: 01394 385308

Directions: Turning into Woodbridge off last rounda'bout from Lowestoft, or first roundabout from
Ipswich. Take first turning left and first left again. Drive to ground at end of road on left.

Capacity: 3,000   Seats: 50   Cover: 200   Floodlights: Yes

Clubhouse: Visitors bar, lounge bar, function hall.Matchday Tea, coffee, cold drinks, hotdogs,
soup, burgers, sandwiches, rolls. Also cooked meals after match

HONOURS   Suffolk Sen Cup(4), Jun Cup (4); Eastern Co Lg Cup 93-94 97-98, Lge Div 1
R-up 93-94; Ipswich Sen Lge (2)

PREVIOUS   **Leagues:** Suffolk & Ipswich Ground: Kingston PF
BEST SEASON   **FA Cup:**   **FA Vase:** 6thRound 98-99

RECORD   **Attendance:** 3,000 v Arsenal, floodlight opener 2/10/90

FACT FILE
Founded: 1885
Nickname: The Woodpeckers
Sponsors: Brafe Engineering Ltd.
Colours: Black & white stripes/black/black
Change colours: All blue
Midweek Matchday: Tuesday
Reserves' League: Essex & Suffolk Border
Programme: Free with entry
Editor: D Crowley
Local Press : East Anglian Daily Times
99-00 Captain: Carl David
Top Scorer:Paul Smith (16)
P.o.Y.: Jamie Scales

CLUB PERSONNEL
Chairman: Keith Dixon
President:Andrew Dalby
Football Sec: John Bennett, (01394 385973)
Commercial Manager: David Leech
Manager: David Hubbick

WROXHAM

Secretary : Chris Green, 24 Keys Drive, Wroxham, Norfolk NR12 8SS
Tel: 01603 783936 (H) 01603 772303 (B)
Ground: Trafford Park, Skinners Lane, Wroxham, Norfolk Tel: 01603 783538

Directions: Arriving from Norwich turn left at former Castle PH and keep left to ground. One and a half miles from Wroxham + Hoveton (BR). Buses 722, 724 and717
Capacity: 2,500   Seats: 50   Cover: 250   Floodlights: Yes

Clubhouse: Bar, pool, darts etc. Drinks, hot & cold food   Club Shop: No

HONOURS   Eastern Co's Lg 91-92 92-93 93-94 96-97 97-98, 98-99, R-Up 94-95,99-00
Lg.Cup 92-93,99-00R-up 90-91), Div 1 88-89; Norfolk Snr Cup 92-93 96-97 97-98;99-00 Anglian Comb(6) (LgCup(7); Reserves completed the double in 94-95

PREVIOUS   **Leagues:** Norwich City; East Anglian; Norwich & Dist.; Anglian Comb. 64-88
Grounds: Norwich Road; The Avenue; Keys Hill (all pre-1947)
BEST SEASON   **FA Vase:** 5th Round 99-00 v Chippenham Town
RECORDS   **Attendance:** 1,011 v Wisbech Town, E. Counties Lge Prem. Div. 16/3/93
Goalscorer: Matthew Metcalf. **Appearances:** Stu Larter
Win: 15-2 v Thetford Town (H), E. Counties Lge Prem. Div. 17/1/92
Defeat: 1-24 v Blofield (A), Norwich & District League, early 1960s
Players progressing: Matthew Metcalf (Brentford) 93, Paul Warne (Wigan Athletic) 97

FACT FILE
Founded: 1892
Nickname: Yachtsmen
Colours: Royal & white/blue/blue
Change colours: Red & black/black/red & black
Midweek Matchday: Tuesday
Reserves ' League: Anglian Comb Prem Div
Programme: 20 pages
Editor: Matt Carpenter
Local Press : North Norfolk
Eastern Football (Norwich 628311)
Web-site:www.wroxhamfc.demon.co.uk

CLUB PERSONNEL
Chairman: Tom Jarrett
President: L King
Press Officer: Secretary
Joint Managers: Bruce Cunningham
& Marty Hubble
Physio: P.Terrington

Top: Histon's Neil Kennedy heads home his side's third goal in their 4-1 win at Halstead. Photo: Gordon Whittington

Bottom: Clacton Town FC. Back Row (l-r): Mervyn Harry, Colin and Sandra Harris, Glen Hepburn, Simon Gray, Jon Collins, Gary Hudson, Steve Dowman (Manager), Andy Partner, Ian Bennett, Scott Quinlan, Sean Bailey (Coach), Nick Nicolaou. Front Row: Andy McDonald, Terry Clarke, Paul Hillier, Michael Edwards, Steve Howe, Jon Cardy, David Gray, Sean Cambell, Mark Farthing, Gavin Armitage

BRIGHTLINGSEA UNITED

Secretary: John Gwillim, 25 Colne Road, Brightlingsea, Essex CO7 0DL
Tel Nos: 01206 307754 (H) 01206 206630 (W)
Ground: North Road, Brightlingsea, Essex (01206 304199)
Directions: B1027 Colchester - Clacton, B1029 from Thorrington Cross - followChurch Road into town, left into Spring Road, left into Church Road. Neareststation; Colchester then bus 78 to Brighlingsea
Capacity: 2,000   Seats: 50   Cover: 250   Floodlights: Yes   Club Shop: Yes
Clubhouse: Open matchdays & every evening except Sunday. Matchday tea, coffee,& snacks

HONOURS   Essex Snr Lg 88-89 89-90 (Harry Fisher Mem. Tphy 89-90 (R-up 88-89), Lg Cup R-up 78-79), Eastern Co's Lg Div 1 R-up 90-91, Essex & Suffolk Border LgPrem. Div Cup 71-72, Harwich Charity Cup 87-88, Worthington Evans Cup 76-77 77-78 78-79
PREVIOUS   **Leagues:** Tendring Hundred, Essex & Suffolk Border, Essex Senior 1972-90
RECORD   **Gate:** 1,200 v Colchester, friendly 68-69

FACT FILE
Founded: 1887
Nickname: Oystermen
Colours: Red & white,red,red
Change colours: Yellow & Navy, navy,navy
Midweek Matches: Tuesday
Programme: 24 pages, 30p
Editor: Kim Lay (01206 305797)
Local Press: Essex County Standard, Evening Gazette

CLUB PERSONNEL
Chairman: Graham Steady
Manager:Ken Ballard

CAMBRIDGE CITY RESERVES

Secretary: Stuart Hamilton, 55 Crowhill, Godmanchester, Huntingdon, Cambs
    Tel: 01480 382675

Ground: City Ground, Milton Road, Cambridge CB4 1UY Tel: 01223 357973
Directions: 50 yards on left from start of A1309, Cambridge to Ely Rd.
    30 minswalk from Cambridge BR
    Capacity: 5,000   Cover: 1,400   Seats:423   Floodlights: Yes

Clubhouse: 11am-11pm Mon-Sat, 12-3 & 7pm-10.30 Sun. Bingo, Dances, Pool, Darts

Club Shop: Sells programmes, club history, badges, scarves, pennants, replica shirts etc.
    Contact Neil Harvey (01223 235991)

FACT FILE
Colours: White & black halves/black/white & black hoops
Change colours: Green & Yellow halves,green,green& yellow hoops
Midweek matchday: Monday
Programme Editor: Secretary

CLUB PERSONNEL
Chairman: Dennis Rolph
Fixtures Sec.: Andy Dewey
50 Doggett Rd., Cherry Hinton, Cambridge
01223 245694 (H) 01223 555410 (Bus. Fax)
Manager:Jeremy George
Tel; 01954 782484

CHATTERIS TOWN

Secretary: James Gill, 3 West End Close, Chatteris, Cambs. PE16 6HW (01354 693690)

Ground: West Street, Chatteris (01354 692139)
Directions: Entering Chatteris on A141 from Huntingdon turn right into West Street after by-pass roundabout. From A142(Isle of Ely way) turnleft at 2nd roundabout.50yds right to West St.
Capacity: 2,000Seats: 250Cover: 400Floodlights: Yes
Clubhouse: Bar & tea bar. Matchday drinks & snacks available
Club Shop: no but pennants are available

HONOURS   Eastern Counties Lg Cup 67-68, Peterborough Premier Lg(3)
PREVIOUS   **League:** Peterborough   **Ground:** First Drove
RECORD   **Gate:** 2,000 v March Town Utd, League 5/5/88
Players progressing: Andy Rogers (Reading), Dave Gregory (Plymouth)

FACT FILE
Founded: 1920
Nickname: Lillies
Colours: White/blue/white
Change colours: Red & black/black/black
Midweek Matches: Wednesday
Programme: 16 pages, 50p
Chairman: Geoff Allen
President: R.W.Salisbury
Manager: Dennis Lightning

CORNARD UNITED

Secretary: Chris Symes, 22 Greenacres, Mile End, Colchester, Essex CO4 (01206 851489)
Ground: Blackhouse Lane Sportsfield, Great Cornard, Suffolk (01787 376719)
Directions: Left off r'bout on A134 coming from Ipswich/Colchester intoSudbury, follow signs for Country Park - ground is immediately opposite along Blackhouse Lane
Capacity: 2,000   Seats: 250   Cover: 500   Floodlights: Yes   Club Shop: No
Clubhouse: Open matchdays & Sunday lunchtimes. Matchday Tea, coffee, colddrinks, & snacks
HONOURS   Eastern Co's Lg Div 1 89-90 (Lg Cup R-up 92-93), Essex & Suffolk BorderLg 88-89 (Lg Cup 88-89), Suffolk Snr Cup 89-90, Suffolk Jnr Cup R-up 84-85
PREVIOUS   **Leagues:** Sudbury S/day 64-65; Bury St Edmunds & Dist 65-72; Colchester71-78; Essex Suffolk Bord 78-89. Grounds: Cornard Rec 64-71; Great CornardUpper School 71-85
RECORDS   **Appearances:** Malcolm Fisher. Goalscorer : Andy Smiles
    Attendance: 330 v Sudbury Town, Eastern Floodlit League 4/2/92
    Win: 18-2 v St Peters House, Colchester Lge 14/9/72
    Defeat: 4-10 v Finningham, Bury Lge 7/2/68

FACT FILE
Founded: 1964   Nickname: Ards
SponsorsGetech
AColours: Blue & white/white/blue
Change colours: Red
Midweek Matches: Tuesday
Reserve League: Essex & Suffolk Border
Programme: 16 pages   Editor: Secretary
Local Press : Suffolk Free Press

CLUB PERSONNEL
Chairman: Chris Symes
Vice-Chairman: J.Stalker
President: Jim McLaughlin
Manager: Chris Symes
Asst Man.: Jason Stalker   Physio: Mike Ford

DEREHAM TOWN

Secretary: Ian Conway, Aldiss Park, Norwich Road, Dereham, Norfolk NR20 3AL
Tel: 01362 695382 (H) 01362 690460 (B)

Fixtures Sec: David West Tel: 01362 693006 (H) 01362 692433 (B)

Ground: Aldiss Park, Norwich Road, Dereham, Norfolk NR20 3AL
Tel/Fax: 01362 690460
Capacity: 3,000   Seats: 250   Cover: 500   Club Shop: No

HONOURS Anglian Combination 97-98
PREVIOUS **Leagues:** Dereham & Dist., East Anglian, Anglian Combination >98
Names: Dereham, Dereham Hobbies
Grounds: Recreation Ground 1890-1998
RECORD **Defeat:** 0-13, v Gorleston, Norfolk Sen. Cup 9.1.1926

FACT FILE
Formed: 1890
Nickname: The Magpies
Colours: Black & white/black/black
Change colours: White/black/black
Midweek matchday; Tuesday
Programme - 20 pages 50p
Editor: Barnes Print
Tel: 01362 860781 Fax: 01362 860977

CLUB PERSONNEL

Chairman: Tim Warner
Tel: 01362 692419 (H)
Managers: David Seaton & Paul Jarvis

DOWNHAM TOWN

Secretary: F. Thorne, 6 Maple Rd., Downham Market, Norfolk, PE38 9PY. (01366 382563)

Ground: Memorial Field, Lynn Road, Downham Market, Norfolk (01366 388424)

Directions: One and a quarter miles from Downham Market (BR) - continue to townclock, turn left and ground is three quarters of a mile down Lynn Road
Capacity: 1,000   Seats: 60   Cover: Yes   Floodlights: Yes
Clubhouse: Bar open matchdays, refreshments & snacks available

HONOURS P'boro Lg (5) 62-63 73-74 78-79 86-88;
Norfolk Senior Cup 63-64 65-66 (R-up(3) 66-69)
PREVIOUS **Leagues:** Peterborough
RECORD **Attendance:** 325 v Wells Town Norfolk Senior Cup, 1998-99

FACT FILE
Founded: 1881
Nickname: Town
Sponsor: Lynwere Engineering
Colours: Red/white/red
Change colours: Sky/Navy/sky
Midweek Matches: Tuesday
Programme: Yes, with entry
Editor: Chairman

CLUB PERSONNEL
Chairman: John Fysh
President: Louis Barker
Manager: Steve Tyres

HADLEIGH UNITED

Secretary: Peter Hutchings, 3 Mowlands, Capel St Mary, Ipswich. IP9 2XB Tel: 01473 311093

Ground: Millfield, Tinkers Lane, Duke Street, Hadleigh, Suffolk Tel: 01473 822165

Directions: Turn off A12 approx halfway between Ipswich & Colchester. Take B1070 & follow signs to Hadleigh. Duke Street is off the High Street - turn left by Library
Capacity: 3,000   Seats: 250   Cover: 500   Floodlights: Yes
Clubhouse: Open matchdays. **Website:** hadleigh-utd.co.uk

HONOURS Ipswich & Dist./Suffolk & Ipswich Lg 53-54 56-57 73-74 76-77 78-79
(Mick McNeil) Lg Cup 76-77 80-81 81-82 86-87;
Suffolk Senior Cup 68-69 71-72 82-83. Eastern Co.Lg Champions 93-94
PREVIOUS **Leagues:** Suffolk & Ipswich (prev. Ipswich & D.)(pre-1991)
Grounds: Grays Meadow, Ipswich Road
RECORDS **Gate:** 518 v Halstead Town, FA Vase Replay 17.1.95 **Win:** 8-1 v
Chatteris(A) 17/1/95 **Defeat:** 0-7 v Harwich & Parkston (H) 12/10/96, & Wisbech (H) 26/4/97

FACT FILE
Founded: 1892
Nickname: Brettsiders
Sponsors: Lancaster
Colours: White & navy/navy/navy
Change colours: All yellow
Midweek Matches: Tuesday
Reserves' Lge: Essex & Suff. Border
Programme: 12 pages, 50p
Editor: Peter Hutchings (01473 311093)

CLUB PERSONNEL
President: K.Grimsey
Chairman: John Chenery
Manager: Louis Newman

HAVERHILL ROVERS

Secretary: Chris Rice, 23 Ovington Place, Haverhill, Suffolk. CB9 0BA
Tel: 01440 712396 (H) 07880 966423 (M)

Ground: Hamlet Croft, Haverhill, Suffolk Tel: 01440 702137

Directions: Centre of Haverhill

Capacity: 3,000   Seats: 200   Cover: 200   Floodlights: Yes
Clubhouse: Open matchdays and functions. Snacks available
HONOURS Eastern Co's Lg 78-79 Lg Cup 64-65; Essex & Suffolk Border Lg 62-63 63-64;
East Anglian Cup 90-91; Suffolk Sen Cup 96-97
PREVIOUS **League:** Essex & Suffolk Border
RECORD **Attendance:** 1,537 v Warrington Town, FA Vase QF 86-87
Players progressing: R Wilkins (Colchester)

FACT FILE
Founded: 1886   Nickname: Rovers
Colours: All red
Change colours:All yellow
Midweek Matches: Tuesday
Programme: 24 pages,50p
Editor: Ray Esdale (01440 704670)
Local Press : Haverhill Echo,Cambridge
Evening News
CLUB PERSONNEL
Chairman: Terry McGerty
President: N Haylock
Press Officer: Ray Esdale
Managers: John Stephens & Lee Barrett
Physio: Mark Bampton

MARCH TOWN UNITED

Secretary: R S Bennett, 47 Ellingham Ave, March, Cambs PE15 9TE (01354 653271)

Ground: GER Sports Ground, Robin Goodfellows Lane, March (01354 653073)

Directions: 5 mins from town centre, 10 mins from BR station
Capacity: 4,000   **Seats:** 500   **Cover:** 2,000   **Floodlights:** Yes

Clubhouse: On ground, seating 150. Light refreshments available

HONOURS   Eastern Co's Lg 87-88 (Lg Cup 60-61), Utd Co's Lg 53-64, Cambs Invitation Cup 54-55, East Anglian Cup 53-54 (jt withBarking)

PREVIOUS   **Leagues:** Peterborough; Isle of Ely; Utd Co's 48-54
Ground: The Avenue (prior to 1946)

BEST SEASON   FA Cup 1st Rd53-54 77-78,

RECORD   **Gate:** 7,500 v King's Lynn, FA Cup 1956

FACT FILE
Founded: 1885
Nickname: Hares
Club colours: Orange & black/black/black
Change colours: Yellow/blue/blue
Midweek Matches: Tuesday
Programme: 30p
Editor: R Bennett
Local Press : Cambs Times, Fenland Advertiser, Peterborough Evening Telegraph

CLUB PERSONNEL
Chairman: Gary Wesley
President: D Wilkinson

NEEDHAM MARKET

Secretary: D Bloomfield, 33 Quinton Road, Needham Market, Suffolk IP6 8DA
Tel: 01449 720693

Fixture Secrtary: P Collier, Low Street, Badingham, Nr. Woodbridge, Suffolk IP3 8SS
Tel : 01728 638799

Ground: Bloomfields, Quinton Road, Needham Market, Suffolk
Tel: 01449 721000

Directions: Quinton Road is off Barretts Lane which in turn is off Needham Market High Street
Capacity: 1,000   **Seats:** 250   **Cover:** 250   **Floodlights:** Yes   **Club Shop:** No

PREVIOUS   **Leagues:** Ipswich & District; Suffolk & Ipswich >96
Grounds: Youngs Meadow; Crowley Park >96   **Names:** None

HONOURS   Suffolk & Ipswich Lge 95-96

FACT FILE
Founded: 1927
Nickname: N/A
Colours: Green & Black stripes/black/black
Change Coloures: All white
Midweek Matchday: Tuesday
Programme Editor: Ian Verneau
Tel No: 01473 413957

CLUB PERSONNEL
Chairman: A.Sparkes
Managers: Colin Macrow & John Coupe

NORWICH UNITED

Secretary: Nigel Harrowing, 43 Cawston Meadow, Poringland, Norwich NR147SX
Tel No & Fax: 0150-8 494335 (H) 01953600682 (W) Mobile: 07968 442 132
Ground: Plantation Road, Blofield, Norwich, Norfolk NR13 4PL (01603 716963)
Directions: Half a mile from Blofield village - coming from Norwich on Yarmouth Rd turn left in Blofield at Kings Head pub & follow to Plantation Rd (grd on right after bridge over bypass). 1/2 hour Brundall BR (Norwich-Yarmouth line)
Capacity: 3,000   **Seats:** 100   **Cover:** 1,000   **Floodlights:** Yes
Clubhouse: Matchday food & drink: Tea, coffee, cold drinks, hotdogs, burgers, soup, sandwiches, rolls
Club Shop: Yes incl. metal badges & pennants
HONOURS   Eastern Co's Lg Div 1 90-91 (R-up 89-89, Lg Cup 91-92), Anglian Combination 88-89

PREVIOUS   **Ground:** Gothic Club, Heartsease Lane, Norwich (until end of 90-91)

RECORD   **Attendance:** 401 v Wroxham, League match, 2/10/91
Goalscorer: M Money   **Appearances:** Tim Sayer

FACT FILE
Founded: 1903
Nickname: Planters
Colours: Yellow/blue/blue
Change colours: All red.
Midweek Matches: Tuesday
Programme: 24 pages, 50p
Editor:DarrenGoddard
Local Press : Eastern Counties Newspapers

CLUB PERSONNEL
Chairman: John Hilditch,
Vice-Chairman: Peter Powell
President: Michael Miles
Managers: C Carpenter &G.Hewitson
Physio: Martyn Parker

SOMERSHAM TOWN

Secretary: Matthew Dunster, 29 Windsor Gardens,Somersham,Huntingdon, Cambs. PE17 3DY
Tel No: 01487 740786

Ground: West End Ground, St Ives Road, Somersham, Cambs (01487 843384)

Directions: On A604 St Ives to Somersham on right as you enter town
Capacity: 1,500   **Seats:** None   **Cover:** 200   **Floodlights:** Yes
Clubhouse: Open Friday, Sat/Sun lunchtimes

HONOURS   Hunts Snr Cup 72-73 94-95, Peterboro Snr Cup 84-85, Hinchingbrooke Cup 53-54, Cambs Lg Premier B Div 94-95 (reserves)
PREVIOUS   **League:** Peterborough & District
RECORDS   **Attendance:** 538 v Norwich City, floodlights inauguration 91
Goalscorer & Appearances: Terry Butcher

Local Press : Hunts Post, Cambs News, Citizen Express, St Ives Weekly

FACT FILE
Founded: 1893   Nickname: Westenders
Sponsors: Rapidtech (UK) Ltd
Colours: All old gold with black trim
Change colours: red&blue stripes/ blue/ red
Midweek Matchday: Tuesday
Reserve League: Kershaw Senior A
Programme: 76 pages, 50p
Editor: Tim Egan

CLUB PERSONNEL
Chairman: Alan Bailey
Vice-Chairman: Norman Burkett
President: Jack Marjason
Manager: Norman Hudson
Coach: Bob Barnett   Physio: Alan Magnus

STANWAY ROVERS

Secretary: Alan Brierley, 19 Barley Way, Stanway, Colchester CO3 5YD (01206 521606 + Fax)
Ground: `Hawthorns', New Farm Road, Stanway, Colchester, Essex (01206 578187)
Directions: Take turn off marked Stanway off A12. Turn right(from London)or left from Ipsw ch+ go over flyover to Tollgate r'bout, 1st rt into Villa Rd, after 25 yds turn left into Chaple Rd, 200 yds on left into New Farm Rd, ground 400 yds on left.Nearest BR station is Colchester North
Capacity: 1,500   **Seats:** None   **Cover:** 250   **Floodlights:** Yes   **Shop:** No
Clubhouse: 6.45-11pm eves, 12-11pm Sats. Rolls, soup, tea, coffee etc available matchdays
Club Shop: Pennants & ties (Club website:lineone.net/ m alan brierley
HONOURS Esx Intermediate Cup R-up 89-90 90-91, Esx & Suffolk Border Lg R-up 91-2 (Div 1 86-87, Div 2 81-81 85-86), Esx Jnr Cup R-up 74-75
PREVIOUS   **Leagues:** Colchester & E Essex; Essex & Suffolk. Border (pre-1992)
         Ground: Stanway Secondary School, Winstree Road (20 years)
RECORD   **Gate:** 166 v Sudbury Town FA Vase 4/10/97 **Win:** 8-1 v Swaffham Town
    (H), E. Counties Lge Div. 1 26/3/94 **Defeat:** 0-10 v Sudbury Townt (A), E.C.L. Cup

FACT FILE
Founded: 1955   Nickname: Rovers
Sponsors: David Martin Eastate Agents
Colours: Gold& black stripes/black/black
Change : Red & blue halves/ blue/yellow
Midweek matchday: Wednesday
Reserves' Lge: Essex & Suff. Border
Programme: 12 pages, 50p
Editor: Alan Brierleylocal Press:
Essex Co. Standard, Evening Gazette
CLUB PERSONNEL
Chairman: Peter Cracknell
President: Richard Deguille
Manager:Steve Ball
Physio: Stuart Bevis

SWAFFHAM TOWN

Secretary: D.R.Ward, 14 Mount Close, Swaffham. PE37 7BX (01760 722516(H0 01263 540402 (W)
Ground: Shoemakers Lane, Swaffham, Norfolk (01760 722700)
    Capacity: 2,000   **Seats:** None   **Cover:** None   **Floodlights:** Yes
Clubhouse: Open Tuesday, Thursday, Saturday & Sunday lunchtimes & evenings.Drinks, sweets etc

HONOURS   Norfolk Snr Cup (2), Anglian Comb. 89-90 (Div 1 88-89)

PREVIOUS   **Leagues:** Dereham, Anglian Combination

RECORD   **Attendance:** 250 v Downham Town, Eastern Co's League Cup 3/9/91

FACT FILE
Founded: 1892
Nickname: Pedlars
Midweek Matchay: Tuesday
Colours: Black & white stripes/black/black
Change: All yellow
Programme: 36 pages, 30p
Editor: Nigel Claxton

CLUB PERSONNEL
Chairman: Kevin Burton
President: Stewart Collins
Manager: Robin Sainty

THETFORD TOWN

Secretary: John Wordley, 4 Claxton Close, Thetford, Norfolk IP24 1BA
Tel: 01842 762530 (H) 01842 753353 (W)

Ground: Mundford Road, Thetford, Norfolk Tel: 01842 766120

Directions: Turn off bypass (A11) at A143 junction - ground 800yds next tosports ground
Capacity: 2,000   **Seats:** 400   **Cover:** 400   **Floodlights:** Yes
Clubhouse: Bar, teas, refreshments, light meals & snacks   **Club Shop:** No

HONOURS   Eastern Co's Lg R-up 89-90, Norfolk & Suffolk Lg 54-55;
    Norfolk Senior Cup 47-48 90-91
PREVIOUS   **Leagues:** Norfolk & Suffolk   **Grounds:** None
RECORD   **Attendance:** 394 v Diss Town, Norfolk Snr Cup 91
Players progressing: Dick Scott (Norwich C.), Kevin Seggie (Leeds U.),Simon Milton (Ipswich T.)
Local Press: Thetford & Watton Times, Bury Free Press

FACT FILE
Founded: 1884
Sponsors: Anglian Mortgage Advice Services Ltd
Colours: Claret & blue/sky blue/claret
Change: Yellow & black
Midweek Matches: Wednesday
Reserves League: Anglian Comb
Programme: 50p
Editor: Graham Mills (01480 385425)
CLUB PERSONNEL
Chairman: Bob Richards
Vice-Chairman: Mike Bailey
Press Officer: Paul Stephenson
Manager: Peter Jones

WHITTON UNITED

Secretary: David Gould, 7 Karen Close, Ipswich, Suffolk IP1 4LP   Tel: 01473 253838

Ground: King George V Playing Field, Old Norwich Road, Ipswich, Suffolk. Tel: 01473 464030

Directions: Turn off A14, junction A1156 approx 3 miles west of A12/A14junction
Capacity: 600   **Seats:** No   **Cover:** 100   **Floodlights:** Yes
Club Shop: No
Clubhouse: Licensed Bar. Hot & Cold Food available

HONOURS   Suffolk Senior Cup 58-59 62-63 92-93; Suffolk & Ipswich Lge 46-47 47-48
    65-66 67-68 91-92 92-93, Jewson Fairplay Trophy 96-97, 97-98
PREVIOUS   **Leagues:** Suffolk & Ipswich   **Grounds:** Old Norwich Rd, Ipswich
RECORD   **Attendance:** 528 v Ipswich Town 29/11/95
    League 244 v Ipswich Wanderers13/1/96

FACT FILE
Formed: 1926   Nickname: None
Sponsors: Speedyhire
Colours: Green & white/white/green
Change colours: All red
Midweek Matches: Wednesday
Youth's League: U18 Eastern Jun Alliance
Programme: 24pages- 50p
Editor/ Press Officer:Mark Woodward

CLUB PERSONNEL
Chairman: John Watkins
President: Russell Woodward
Fixture Sec: Alan Elliott (01473 461931)
Manager: Paul Smythe

WISBECH TOWN RESERVES

Secretary: John Petch, 34 Walton Rd, Wisbech, Cambs PE13 3EN
Tel: 01945 584333 &Fax)

Ground Fenland Park, Lerowe Road, Wisbech, Cambs Tel: 01945 584176

Directions: Follow A47 bypass to the West Walton turn off roundabout where there is a Little Chef, turn left for Wisbech, Lerowe Road is first left after 30mph sign. Entering town from north along A1101 cross Freedom Bridge, atroundabout go straight over sign Walsoken/West Walton

Capacity: 3,800 **Seats:** 284 **Cover:** 1,000 **Floodlights:** Yes

Clubhouse: Open every day. Matchday food & drink - Tea, coffee, cold drinks, confectionary, burgers, hotdogs, soup, sandwiches, rolls

Club Shop: Sells replica shirts, caps, pennants, pens, scarves etc. Contact Club Secretary

FACT FILE

Nickname: Fenmen

Colours: Red with black side panel/red/red

Change colours: Blue& white,blue,blue

Midweek Matchday: Tuesday

CLUB PERSONNEL

Chairman: Steve Crown

Vice Chairman: Merlin Saddleton

President: J W A Chilvers

Press Officer: John Petch

REGIONAL LEAGUES

ANGLIAN COMBINATION

Premier Division	P	W	D	L	F	A	Pts
Kirkley	30	20	5	5	79	34	65
Attleborough Town	30	20	5	5	67	29	65
Acle United	30	17	5	8	84	44	56
Wells Town	30	14	8	8	48	35	50
Mulbarton United	30	12	9	9	61	54	45
Ashlea	30	11	10	9	49	35	43
Blofield United	30	12	5	13	55	59	41
Wroxham Reserves	30	11	6	13	38	36	39
Cromer United	30	11	6	13	42	49	39
North Walsham Town	30	10	9	11	41	50	39
Scole United	30	8	11	11	39	48	35
Lowestoft Town Reserves	30	9	7	14	41	52	34
Stalham Town	30	9	5	16	36	52	34
Diss Town Reserves	30	8	7	15	38	76	31
Thorpe Village	30	7	6	17	37	65	27
Lakeford Rangers	30	5	8	17	45	82	23

ESSEX & SUFFOLK BORDER LEAGUE

Premier Division	P	W	D	L	F	A	Pts
Sudbury Reserves	30	22	6	2	96	25	*74
Gas Recreation	30	22	6	2	93	33	72
St. Osyth	30	15	5	10	63	43	50
Stowmarket Town Res.	30	15	5	10	49	35	50
Kelvedon Social	30	14	5	11	55	50	47
Rowhedge	30	12	7	11	50	60	43
Little Oakley	31	12	6	12	82	61	42
Earls Colne	30	12	6	12	73	64	42
Sudbury Lucas Athletic	30	11	9	10	46	47	42
Ipswich Wanderers Res.	30	12	5	13	47	56	41
St. Johns Clacton	30	10	4	16	47	64	34
Haverhill Rovers Reserves	30	10	4	16	47	64	34
West Bergholt	30	9	6	15	51	67	33
Harwich & Parkeston Res.	30	9	6	15	53	79	33
Long Melford	30	9	4	17	39	62	31
Royal London	30	3	2	25	22	104	*10

CAMBRIDGESHIRE LEAGUE

Premier Division	P	W	D	L	F	A	Pts
Over Sports	26	17	5	4	69	26	56
Histon Reserves	26	17	3	6	58	35	54
Sawston United	26	14	3	9	57	35	45
Cottenham United	26	11	7	8	69	53	40
Girton United	26	11	6	9	44	38	39
Great Shelford	26	12	3	11	36	36	39
Fordham	26	11	5	10	54	39	38
Debden	26	10	3	13	49	45	33
Waterbeach	26	10	3	13	41	48	33
Bassingbourn	26	8	8	10	45	58	32
Foxton	26	8	4	14	41	70	28
Godmanchester Rovers	26	7	6	13	30	55	27
Newmarket Town Reserves	26	6	6	14	31	52	24
Bluntisham Rangers	26	5	8	13	38	72	23

SUFFOLK & IPSWICH LEAGUE

Grundisburgh	30	24	6	0	92	22	78
Walton United	30	22	4	4	64	27	70
East Bergholt United	30	20	7	3	66	29	67
Walsham-le-Willows	30	18	6	6	75	31	60
Capel Plough	30	15	3	12	55	47	48
Ipswich Athletic	30	13	7	10	65	54	46
Leiston	30	13	6	11	52	56	45
Stonham Aspal	30	10	6	14	57	74	36
Woodbridge Athletic	30	11	2	17	42	53	35
Leiston St. Margarets	30	8	8	14	47	57	32
Framlingham Town	30	9	4	17	39	53	31
Achilles	30	9	4	17	42	58	31
British Sugar	30	9	4	17	46	67	31
Haughley United	30	8	4	18	39	63	28
Westerfield United	30	7	5	18	41	81	26
Brantham Athletic	30	4	4	22	34	84	16

Top: Anglian Combination. Norwich Union FC. A lovely setting for non-league soccer at the leafy Pinebanks Sports Ground in Norwich. Photo: Martin Wray

Centre: Kershaw Cambs League. Cottenham 4   Fordham 3. Cottenham's Gareth Hales (2nd left, turning), scores his side's second goal in this seven goal thriller at Lambs Lane in the opening match of 1999-2000. Photo: Martin Wray

Bottom: Suffolk & Ipswich Lge. Peter Hatcher's header puts Grundiburgh in front despite a valiant efford by the Leiston St Margarets defence. Photo: Gordon Whittington

COMPLETE MUSIC
HELLENIC FOOTBALL LEAGUE

President: Norman Matthews   **Chairman:** Michael Broadley

Secretary: Brian King, 83 Queens Road, Carterton, Oxon OX18 3YF
Tel/Fax: 01993 212738

Banbury United won this season's Premier Division Championship. At the turn of the year Highworth Town were in pole position with a 14-point lead over local rivals Swindon Supermarine with Banbury progressing well in fifth place. With the turn of the year came the change in fortunes of Highworth Town and Banbury United. On 27th December Banbury lost 2-1 at Brackley in front of a crowd of 524 whilst Highworth defeated local rivals Swindon Supermarine by the same score-line in front of a holiday crowd of 476. Banbury United played a further 22 league games winning twenty and drawing two, amassing 62 points to win the title by a clear thirteen points from Highworth Town, whose record for the same period was: p17, W9, D3, L5. Mention must be made of Swindon Supermarine who attained third place having a very hard run-in playing some ten league matches in the last five weeks of the season.

The Division One title this season was won by Cheltenham Saracens FC, who displayed a tremendous level of consistency throughout the season losing only three of their 28 league fixtures and dropping only thirteen points all season, conceding only twenty goals. Cheltenham Saracens secured 64 points, some seventeen points clear of runners up Ardley United, who attained this position for the second season running.

Only one representative football match was played during the season - against the Chiltonian Football League that resulted in another 0-0 draw at Abingdon United in December.

Success in national cup competitions was again somewhat disappointing, but six member clubs did appear in the Second round of the FA Vase. In the FA Cup seven clubs started on the Wembley road back in August, but by the Second Qualifying Round we saw Banbury United visit Purfleet of the Isthmian League, and a 0-0 draw brought Purfleet back to the Stadium for a replay, which resulted in a 1-0 win for Purfleet. Tuffley Rovers visited another Wessex League side, Lymington & New Milton; a draw was the reward and a replay back in Gloucester. However, Tuffley Rovers lost their way and were soundly beaten in the replay 5-0. The reward for Banbury United and Tuffley Rovers was a substantial sum of money towards ground improvements from the FA Cup sponsorship monies.

An excellent entry of eighteen member clubs competed in this season's F.A. Vase. Cirencester Academy and Shortwood United went out in the First Qualifying Round. Twelve clubs competed in the Second Qualifying Round, but, unfortunately, only three clubs, Abingdon United, Banbury United and Didcot Town, managed a win to progress to the First Round Proper. Exempted clubs Carterton Town, Highworth Town and Swindon Supermarine joined these three outfits with only Highworth Town failing to progress in a local derby with Carterton Town. Brackley Town joined the competition in the Second Round on 13th November, but it was a 'black day' for the Hellenic League as Abingdon United lost 1-0 to Paulton Rovers, Banbury United lost to Histon 1-0, Carterton went down 4-0 at home to Porthleven, whilst Swindon Supermarine lost at eventual finalists Chippenham Town 3-0, Didcot Town were overwhelmed by Totton AFC 4-0 and Brackley Town exited 3-1 at Wembley.

Swindon Supermarine where a match for all comers in this season's cup competitions. They contested the 'Complete Music' Norman Matthews Floodlit Cup final with Banbury United on a home and away two-leg basis. The first leg at Banbury United was postponed for a week from the original date, but whether this had an affect on Banbury United we will never know. However, 'Marine' with a packed defence managed to record a 2-0 win at the 'Stadium', and the second leg a week later saw two strong defences overcome all and a 0-0 score-line was the outcome enabling Swindon Supermarine to win the first of the season's silverware.

In the RPM Records Supplementary Cup at last the bridesmaid became the bride with Carterton Town overwhelming a poor Wantage Town team by a 4-0 score-line, following two earlier cup final defeats in previous seasons. In the two-legged semi-finals Carterton Town beat Brackley Town whilst Wantage Town overcame Harrow Hill. The win by Carterton Town was gained in the last season in office of retiring club chairman Gordon Maxwell and is a fitting accolade for all the work that he has put into Carterton Town over many years.

The Cherry Red Records Challenge Cup was a 'David v Goliath' final, and in fact, it is interesting to note that four Division One clubs appeared in the Quarter-Final and two in the Semi-Final. The Semi-Final draw paired the two remaining Division One teams against each other ensuring that both Divisions were represented in the final. Ross Town won three semi against Kidlington with a 2-1 aggregate win over two legs, whilst Swindon Supermarine overcame Abingdon United by a massive 5-1 aggregate victory. The final on a warm sunny day in early May saw an exciting match with Ross Town gaining a late equalizer. With extra time looming 'Marine' gained a very late winner to take their second cup trophy of the season.

Not to be outdone by their seniors Banbury United Reserves won the Anagram Records Reserve Cup in a final against Brackley Town, a single goal in front of a crowd of over 250 being enough to secure the win for Banbury United.

In County Cup Competitions it was a less than satisfactory season for Hellenic League clubs, as Purton were finalists in the Wiltshire Senior Cup losing out to Pewsey Vale in a penalty shoot-out. North Leigh Reserves won through to the final of the Oxfordshire Intermediate Cup again losing in a penalty shoot-out.

Season 1999/2000 saw the third year of sponsorship from 'Complete Music', and I am pleased to report that agreement has been reached for a fourth seasons sponsorship with an enhanced package following the merger of the Hellenic and Chiltonian Leagues. Thanks are extended to Iain McNay and Martin Costello of 'Complete Music' for their company's interest and support of the Hellenic Football League.

Brian King, General Secretary

HONOURS LIST 1999-2000

PREMIER DIVISION
Champions   Banbury United FC
Runners up   Highworth Town FC

DIVISION ONE
Champions   Cheltenham Saracens FC
Runners up   Ardley United FC

RESERVE DIVISION ONE
Champions   North Leigh FC
Runners up   Swindon Supermarine FC

RESERVE DIVISION TWO
Champions   Cheltenham Saracens FC
Runners up   Carterton Town FC

CHERRY RED RECORDS CHALLENGE CUP
Champions   Swindon Supermarine FC
Runners up   Ross Town FC

RPM RECORDS SUPPLEMENTARY CUP
Champions   Carterton Town FC
Runners up   Wantage Town FC

NORMAN MATTHEWS FLOODLIT CUP
Champions   Swindon Supermarine FC
Runners up   Banbury United FC

ANAGRAM RECORDS RESERVE CUP
Champions   Banbury United FC
Runners up   Brackley Town FC

WILTSHIRE SENIOR CUP
Runners up   Purton FC

OXFORDSHIRE INTERMEDIATE CUP
Runners up   North Leigh FC Reserves

CLUB LINESMAN OF THE SEASON
Kevin Dix   Cheltenham Saracens FC

PREMIER DIVISION SPORTSMANSHIP AWARD
Almondsbury Town FC

DIVISION ONE SPORTSMANSHIP AWARD
Ross Town FC

Cheltenham Saracens, Hellenic Football League Division One Champions 1999-2000
Back Row (l-r): Chris Hawkins (Physio), Mark Johnson, Dave Parker, Matthew Stannard, Wayne Vincent, Stuart Parker, John Walton, Matthew Parnell, James Crowest, Matthew Haynes, Gerald Oldham (Assistant Manager).
Front Row: Stephen Nicholas, Ian Ford (Manager), Chris Palmer, Kevin Slack, Chris Nicholas, Stephen Olczak, Simon Powell, Billy Davis

PREMIER DIVISION FINAL LEAGUE TABLE 1999-2000

	P	W	D	L	F	A	Pts		P	W	D	L	F	A	Pts
Banbury United	36	29	5	2	87	22	92	Shortwood United	36	13	10	13	54	55	49
Highworth Town	36	25	4	7	90	54	79	Wantage Town	36	15	4	17	50	64	49
Swindon Supermarine	36	23	4	9	74	27	73	Hallen*	36	13	7	16	55	60	37
Tuffley Rovers	36	22	4	10	76	44	70	Cirencester Academy	36	10	6	20	34	53	36
Brackley Town	36	21	6	9	66	32	69	Bicester Town	36	9	5	22	42	73	32
North Leigh	36	19	7	10	81	53	64	Fairford Town	36	7	8	21	32	69	29
Didcot Town	36	17	10	9	61	50	61	Almondsbury Town	36	7	5	24	42	83	26
Abingdon United	36	17	6	13	58	55	57	Harrow Hill	36	7	1	28	44	96	22
Carterton Town	36	15	6	15	47	50	51	Milton United	36	3	7	26	36	90	16
Pegasus Juniors	36	15	5	16	62	61	50	* points deducted							

PREMIER DIVISION RESULTS & ATTENDANCES CHART 1999-2000

		1	2	3	4	5	6	7	8	9	10	11	12	13	14	15	16	17	18	19
1	Abingdon United	X	1-1	0-7	2-1	1-2	0-1	0-1	1-1	5-1	3-4	3-2	3-1	2-0	0-1	3-0	1-0	1-4	1-0	3-1
		X	95	212	85	77	105	45	145	72	85	45	112	145	128	85	105	75	65	103
2	Almondsbury Town	0-2	X	2-3	4-2	3-4	1-2	0-4	3-1	3-3	0-3	2-1	2-6	1-0	0-0	1-2	3-2	2-3	1-3	0-1
		51	X	90	50	52	66	52	54	40	120	52	55	52	50	52	86	62	66	33
3	Banbury United	2-0	3-0	X	5-1	1-1	3-0	3-1	1-0	3-1	3-1	2-0	1-0	4-0	2-2	3-0	1-0	1-0	2-1	2-0
		189	257	X	234	493	359	189	246	194	194	300	411	159	230	143	170	283	294	142
4	Bicester Town	0-4	1-1	0-1	X	1-1	1-3	1-0	1-3	2-3	2-1	3-2	2-3	1-0	2-0	0-1	1-1	1-4	1-2	1-1
		39	31	191	X	115	57	50	61	26	46	36	63	97	74	38	67	53	31	49
5	Brackley Town	1-0	6-1	2-1	2-0	X	1-2	0-1	1-2	2-0	2-0	5-0	2-3	5-0	0-2	4-0	1-2	0-0	1-2	1-0
		63	106	524	134	X	94	75	58	72	101	82	127	95	125	52	85	70	68	93
6	Carterton Town	0-1	3-1	0-3	0-1	1-2	X	2-1	0-3	1-2	3-0	1-0	1-4	2-2	0-2	4-1	1-2	0-3	3-0	
		46	27	65	25	31	X	12	48	38	14	20	56	25	74	25	24	38	50	15
7	Cirencester Academy	0-4	2-0	0-4	0-1	0-1	0-2	X	1-2	2-0	1-1	2-2	1-3	0-0	0-2	1-1	0-2	0-2	1-3	3-0
		32	43	62	42	54	36	X	42	63	56	47	102	39	65	47	65	35	42	57
8	Didcot Town	3-0	0-0	0-2	3-0	1-1	2-1	2-2	X	1-0	2-2	3-1	2-1	3-2	3-3	1-5	3-1	1-1	4-1	4-2
		141	60	222	80	75	65	75	X	55	78	70	103	158	103	86	90	85	70	180
9	Fairford Town	2-2	1-0	1-4	0-2	0-2	1-1	2-0	1-1	X	0-1	1-0	2-2	1-0	1-3	0-3	1-1	1-0	1-3	1-1
		52	58	125	32	52	37	62	48	X	37	45	65	35	44	35	36	48	75	60
10	Hallen	2-4	2-3	1-1	1-1	1-0	2-0	1-1	1-3	4-1	X	2-0	0-3	3-4	1-2	0-1	0-1	0-1	2-0	2-1
		23	82	80	37	29	18	27	14	27	X	80	40	23	27	18	18	22	23	21
11	Harrow Hill	0-1	5-0	0-2	4-2	0-1	2-4	2-1	0-3	1-0	4-3	X	1-3	2-0	0-4	2-6	2-3	0-4	2-0	0-5
		35	46	130	40	63	55	42	50	50	70	X	50	55	40	53	80	98	45	46
12	Highworth Town	3-1	2-1	2-1	2-1	0-3	0-1	0-2	2-1	3-2	4-4	4-0	X	4-2	3-2	2-1	3-1	2-1	2-3	4-0
		124	187	344	105	115	132	132	92	125	102	80	X	147	103	104	135	476	140	105
13	Milton United	0-0	2-5	1-4	0-3	0-1	1-2	0-2	1-1	1-1	0-3	5-3	2-2	X	6-3	1-7	0-1	0-2	1-1	2-6
		85	30	130	46	61	70	45	180	50	53	42	59	X	102	56	48	50	60	102
14	North Leigh	3-3	3-0	1-1	4-0	2-2	1-2	4-0	4-1	5-0	0-1	7-2	1-3	3-2	X	5-2	2-3	2-1	0-4	0-1
		40	68	162	45	70	88	78	78	72	70	68	71		X	71	64	91	61	78
15	Pegasus Juniors	3-0	2-0	1-5	2-1	0-1	1-0	0-1	0-0	2-0	2-2	2-1	2-3	5-0	1-2	X	2-2	0-1	3-2	0-1
		52	38	115	62	62	39	45	75	52	40	58	115	48	60	X	42	94	55	53
16	Shortwood United	4-0	2-1	1-2	5-1	0-1	1-1	2-0	0-1	1-0	5-1	1-0	3-3	0-0	2-2	1-1	X	1-1	1-5	0-2
		64	95	111	77	60	87	97	100	79	87	81	101	83	78	X	126	61	127	
17	Swindon Supermarine	0-1	4-0	1-1	2-0	3-0	2-1	2-1	3-0	2-0	0-1	5-1	1-3	1-0	1-2	3-0	4-0	X	2-3	3-0
		87	52	132	64	41	75	88	85	70	52	56	252	63	63	97	36	X	72	54
18	Tuffley Rovers	1-1	1-0	1-2	4-2	1-1	1-1	4-1	4-0	1-0	1-2	2-0	0-3	3-2	3-1	6-1	4-0	0-2	X	3-1
		40	44	95	40	42	15	44	48	38	45	65	45	55	48	38	47	45	X	30
19	Wantage Town	2-4	1-0	1-3	2-1	1-6	0-0	0-2	1-0	4-1	1-0	4-2	1-2	3-0	0-1	2-1	4-3	0-6	0-0	X
		70	62	150	50	58	91	74	86	49	57	84	88	81	50	55	76	61	56	X

PREMIER DIVISION LEADING GOALSCORERS 1999-2000

Matty Gooderick	Banbury United	32	Ben Spiero	Wantage Town	20
Mark Davis	Pegasus Juniors	28	Julian Freeman	Tuffley Rovers	19
Steve Jenkins	Banbury United	25	Ryan Lovegrove	Swindon Supermarine	19
Andrew Keveren	Harrow Hill FC	25	David Webb	Highworth Town	17
Richard Hadgkiss	Swindon Supermarine	24	Craig Cole	Shortwood United	16
Alan Tatton	Tuffley Rovers	22	Paul Day	Highworth Town	15
Sean Bott	North Leigh	20	Andy Marriott	Didcot Town	15
Frank Dorrian	Brackley Town	20	Craig Pearman	North Leigh	15

DIVISION ONE FINAL LEAGUE TABLE 1999-2000

	P	W	D	L	F	A	Pts		P	W	D	L	F	A	Pts
Cheltenham Saracens	28	23	2	3	61	20	71	Purton	28	10	4	14	42	56	34
Ardley United	28	16	6	6	63	38	54	Ross Town	28	8	8	12	32	32	32
Wootton Bassett Town	28	15	7	6	54	32	52	Old Woodstock Town	28	8	8	12	43	51	32
Worcester College OB	28	13	6	9	53	46	45	Kidlington	28	9	5	14	36	50	32
Bishops Cleeve	28	12	8	8	44	43	44	Cirencester United	28	10	1	17	38	50	31
Middle Barton	28	12	5	11	49	45	41	Clanfield	28	6	6	16	33	58	24
Letcombe	28	11	5	12	57	45	38	Headington Amateurs	28	6	5	17	29	60	23
Easington Sports	28	10	6	12	50	58	36								

DIVISION ONE RESULTS & ATTENDANCES CHART 1999-2000

		1	2	3	4	5	6	7	8	9	10	11	12	13	14	15
1	Ardley United	X	3-2	1-2	4-1	1-2	1-1	2-0	5-1	8-3	2-0	1-1	3-2	1-2	4-3	0-0
		X	30	47	37	47	31	42	53	64	68	58	54	35	53	36
2	Bishops Cleeve	2-3	X	2-1	1-3	1-1	2-2	2-0	3-0	2-1	1-0	2-2	2-1	1-0	1-4	3-0
		15	X	36	52	27	38	47	20	25	40	25	20	47	67	42
3	Cheltenham Saracens	2-0	2-1	X	1-0	2-0	3-1	3-0	1-0	4-1	1-1	3-0	4-1	1-0	2-1	0-1
		52	85	X	47	31	26	28	31	36	52	61	43	63	25	43
4	Cirencester United	1-0	4-0	1-2	X	3-0	1-0	2-1	1-1	1-3	2-1	1-2	2-0	1-4	0-1	2-3
		35	15	54	X	41	46	31	44	35	60	26	60	62	48	75
5	Clanfield FC	1-3	1-2	0-4	3-2	X	2-3	1-1	0-2	2-0	2-2	2-1	6-2	1-1	0-4	0-7
		82	21	25	27	X	25	23	16	28	40	26	42	34	76	51
6	Easington Sports	1-0	4-3	1-4	6-2	2-1	X	2-3	1-1	0-4	1-2	1-0	5-2	1-2	5-1	1-0
		46	37	45	24	15	X	36	42	39	59	31	40	20	20	15
7	Headington Amateurs	0-4	2-2	1-4	0-3	1-4	1-2	X	0-3	0-3	2-2	2-1	1-0	2-0	3-0	1-1
		63	65	45	59	65	43	X	75	40	44	75	52	38	110	66
8	Kidlington	1-2	0-1	0-3	1-2	1-1	3-0	2-1	X	2-1	3-1	1-1	0-4	1-0	1-3	1-2
		70	30	25	63	45	72	85	X	30	53	85	60	50	50	32
9	Letcombe FC	2-2	1-1	0-1	1-2	4-1	3-3	5-1	2-1	X	0-3	3-0	7-2	1-0	0-1	6-1
		48	26	33	24	37	23	51	30	X	33	24	14	33	17	20
10	Middle Barton	2-3	3-0	3-2	3-1	2-1	2-0	3-2	4-2	1-2	X	2-0	2-3	1-5	0-2	1-3
		104	137	93	79	59	116	48	84	73	X	89	89	79	112	84
11	Old Woodstock	2-2	1-2	2-2	1-0	1-0	2-1	4-1	3-1	1-4	2-2	X	1-2	0-0	0-1	3-4
		37	20	40	31	42	45	35	87	92	85	X	53	64	60	47
12	Purton FC	1-2	2-2	0-1	1-0	0-0	2-2	0-0	3-2	2-0	0-1	2-5	X	1-0	0-2	1-0
		62	78	58	130	64	50	92	88	80	118	28	X	88	88	91
13	Ross Town AFC	1-2	0-1	0-2	1-0	1-0	3-1	4-1	1-1	0-0	0-3	2-3	1-2	X	1-1	0-0
		32	37	39	30	30	40	37	38	20	67	33	40	X	31	45
14	Worcs Coll Old Boys	1-3	1-1	1-2	4-1	1-0	2-2	0-2	4-1	2-1	1-1	3-3	5-3	3-3	X	0-3
		42	20	15	38	25	35	57	35	27	43	25	37	22	X	20
15	Wootton Bassett	1-1	1-1	1-2	3-1	4-1	6-1	1-0	1-2	0-0	2-1	4-1	2-1	0-0	3-1	X
		62	32	48	44	53	42	55	52	37	38	99	24	30	X	

DIVISION ONE LEADING GOALSCORERS 1999-2000

Richard Gardner	Easington Sports	24	Neil Simmons	Ardley United	10
Stephen Ayris	Ardley United	18	Robert Tutton	Worcester Coll OB	10
Kevin Slack	Ch'ham S (4 for B Cleeve)	18	Steve Burry	Letcombe FC	9
Lee Stoddart	Wootton Bassett Town	18	Nick East	Worcester Coll OB	9
Ronnie Williams	Ardley United	14	Tim Fowler	Middle Barton FC	9
Stephen Cleal	Bishops Cleeve	13	David Macey	B Cleeve (6 for Sar's)	9
Ian Gordon	Letcombe	12	Ben Potter	Cirencester United	9
Des O'Connor	Mid Barton (8 for Bic'ter)	12			

ABINGDON UNITED

FACT FILE

Secretary: Terry Hutchinson, 41 Austin Place, Dunmore Farm Estate, Abingdon,Oxon OX14 1LT
Tel: 01235 559019

Ground: Northcourt Road, Abingdon OX14 1PL Tel: 01235 203203
Capacity: 2,000   Seats: 52   Cover: 120   Floodlights: Yes

Directions: From north (Oxford) leave A34 at Abingdon north sign and Northcourt Rd is 1st major turning after r'bout. From South, East or West leave Abingdonon A4183 and turn left into Northcourt Rd after 1 mile. 2 miles from Redley (BR)
Clubhouse: Two bars, food available. Open normal pub hours every day

HONOURS   N Berks Lg 53-54 (Lg Cup R-up 53-54), Charity Shield 52-53;
Hellenic Lge - Prem Div R-up 96-97, Div 1 R-up 76-77 81-82, Res. Div 97-98,
F/Lit Cup 96-97, Lg Cup R-up 89-90, Div 1 Cup 65-66 81-82 R-up 66-67,
Reserve Cup 98-99 R-up 93-94;
Berks & Bucks Senior Cup R-up 83-84, Senior Trophy 97-98 R-up 93-94 96-97

PREVIOUS   **League:** North Berks
Grounds: None

RECORD   **Gate:** 1,500 v Oxford Utd 1994
Appearances: D Webb

Founded: 1946
Nickname: The U's
Colours: All yellow
Change colours: Blue & white
Midweek matchday: Tuesday
Reserves' Lge: Hellenic Res section
Programme: 30p
Editor: W Fletcher, ACJI (01235 20255)
Top Scorer 99-00: Mark Simms 16

CLUB PERSONNEL
Chairman: Pat Evans
General manager: John Blackmore

Manager: Ray Hayward
Coach: Steve Morton
Physio: GrahamCorcoran & Chris Janes
Press Officer: Bill Fletcher (01235 203203)

ALMONDSBURY TOWN

FACT FILE

Secretary: Roger Perry, 61 Brookbridge House, Standfast Road, Henbury, Bristol BS10 7HW
Tel No: 0117 9590309

Ground: Oakland Park, Gloucester Rd., Almondsbury, Bristol BS12 4AGTel: 01454 612220

Directions: Adjacent to M5 junction 16 - follow A38 Thornbury - ground firstleft. 4 miles from Bristol Parkway (BR). County bus services to Thornbury,Stroud and Gloucester
Capacity: 2,000   Seats: None   Cover: No   Floodlights: Yes
Clubhouse: 7 days, all sports, refreshments, function room, entertainment,skittles

HONOURS   Glos Co. Lg(4) 76-78 79-81 (R-up 75-7681-82), GFA Chal. Tphy 78-79 (R-up
80-81), Avon Prem. Comb. 74-75, Glos SnrAmtr Cup 87-88, Hellenic Lg 83-84
(R-up 82-83, Lg Cup(2) 83-85)

PREVIOUS   **Leagues:** Bristol Weslyan; Bristol Suburban; Bristol Premier Comb.; GlosCo
Ground: Almondsbury Rec. (until 1986)

BEST SEASON   **FA Vase:**R-up 78-79, SF 77-78

RECORD   **Gate:** 2,100,Hellenic Cup Final replay 89-90 (Newport AFC v Abingdon U)

Founded: 1897
Nickname: Almonds
Colours: Sky/navy/navy
Change colours: All yellow
Midweek Matchday: Tuesday
Programme: 20 pages 25p
Editor: Roger Perry
Top Scorer 99-00: Ben Walker 12

CLUB PERSONNEL
Chairman: Brian Tufton
President: Peter Howarth
Manager: Simon Panes
Coach: Stuart Evans
Physio: Peter Allen

BICESTER TOWN

FACT FILE

Secretary: Bill Hammond c/o club.

Ground: Sports Ground, Oxford Rd, Bicester
Tel: 01869 246372 & 241036 (office& fax)
Capacity: 2,000   Seats: 250   Cover: 550   Floodlights: Yes

Directions: From Oxford; past Tescos on outskirts of Bicester - ground on right
From Aylesbury; turn left at first island on outskirts of Bicester ontobypass,
right at next island, pass Tescos & ground on right
Clubhouse: One bar

HONOURS   Hellenic Lg 60-1 77-78 (Lg Cup 90-91 (R-up 92-93), Div 1 76-77)

PREVIOUS   **League:** Oxon Senior
Name: Slade Banbury Road (pre-1923)

RECORD   **Attendance:** 955 v Portsmouth, floodlight inauguration 1/2/94

Founded: 1876
Nickname: Foxhunters
Colours: Red & black/black/red or white
Change: Green & yellow/green/green
Midweek Matchday: Tuesday
Reserves' league: Hellenic Lge Res. Div.
Programme: With entry
Editor: Lynn Honour
Top Scorer 99-00 Des O'Conner 8

CLUB PERSONNEL
Chairman: Bill Hammond
Vice Chairman: Ray Honour
President: Michael Kinane
Press Officer: Ray Honour(01689241984)
Manager: Barry Grant
Coach: Kevin Leach
Physio: Ray Huntley

BRACKLEY TOWN

Secretary/Press Officer: Pat Ashby, 9 Riverside, Banbury, Oxon. OX165TU
Tel: 01327 262955 (H) 01295 269056 (Office) 07930 143504(M)
Ground: St James Park, Churchill Way, Brackley, Northants NN13 7EJ   Tel: 01280 704077
Office: 01280 703652

Directions: Churchill Way, east off A43, south end of town
      Capacity: 3,500   Cover: 150   Seats: 300   Floodlights: Yes

Clubhouse: Fully licensed. Lounge & main hall. Food available. Open all week.
Club Shop: Yes, selling club merchandise,programmes and badges etc.
PREVIOUS   **Leagues:** Banbury & District; North Bucks; Hellenic 77-83; United Counties
      83-94; Hellenic 94-97,Southern 97-99   **Names:** None
      Ground: Banbury Road, Manor Road, Buckingham Road (up to 1974)
      CLUB RECORDS Attendance: 720 v Kettering, Northants Senior Cup 1989
      Fee Received: £2,000 for Phil Mason from Oxford City 98
BEST SEASON   FA Trophy: 1st Qual Rd 97-98
      FA Cup: 2nd Qual Rd 97-98   League clubs defeated: **HONOURS**
United Counties R-up 88-89 (Div 1 83-84); Northants Snr Cup R-up 88-89;
Buckingham Charity Cup (3); Hellenic Lg Prem 96-97, Div 1 Cup 82-83. **Players progressing:** Jon
Blencowe (Leicester)   **Transfer Fee Paid:** None

FACT FILE
Formed: 1890
Nickname: Saints
Colours:Red& Black stripes/white/white
Change colours: Sky/Navy Blue
Midweek matchday: Tuesday or Wednesday
Programme: Price: £1
Editor: Brian Martin(01280 706619)
Local Press: Brackley Advertiser,
Banbury Guardian, Herald & Post
Milton Keynes Citizen.
Local Radio: Fox FM
CLUB PERSONNEL
ManagIng Ditrector: Mike Bosher
Chairperson: Kathy Bonner Dunham
Com.Man: Ray Stiles: 0772 0405873
President: Clive Lomax
Press Officer: Brian Martin
Manager: Terry Muckleberg
Coach: Peter Foley

CARTERTON TOWN

Secretary: CathrynTaylor, 105 Glenmore Road, Carterton, Oxon. OX18 1TY (01993 840628)

Ground: Kilkenny Lane, Carterton, Oxfordshire (01993 842410)

Directions: Enter Swinbrook Rd which off the Burford-Carterton road, proceedinto Kilkenny
      Lane (one track road), ground car park 200yds on left beforesharp corner.
      Hourly buses to Carterton from Oxford
Capacity: 1,500   Seats: 50   Cover: 100   Floodlights: Yes
Clubhouse: Lounge & fully licensed bar open every day 7.30-11pm, Sat & Sun noon-2pm,
      Sat 4-6pm. Snacks & meals available

HONOURS   Oxon Junior Shield 85-86; Oxon Snr Cup R-up 90-91 96-97 98-99 Witney &
      Dist.Lg 65-66 (Div 1 84-85 76-77); Hellenic Lg Div 1 89-90 93-94 (Reserve Div
      1989-90 (R-up 93-94)); Oxon Intermediate Cup R-up 93-94(res.)

PREVIOUS   Leagues: Witney & District

RECORD   **Gate:** 600 v Oxford Utd, Oxon Snr Cup 93-94
      Goalscorer: Phil Rodney

FACT FILE
Founded: 1922
Reformed: 1946/1983
Colours: Black & white/black/black
Change colours: Yellow/blue/blue/blue
Midweek matches: Tuesday
Programme: 20 pages with admission
Editor: Jenny Maxwell (01993 212803)

CLUB PERSONNEL
President: G Fox
Chairman: Robert Taylor
Match Secretary: Glyn Yates

Manager: Andrew Slater
Physio: Andy Slater
Coach: Phil Rodney

CHELTENHAM SARACENS

Secretary: Robert Attwood, 179 Arle Road, Cheltenham GL51 8LJ
      Tel: 01242 515855 (H) 01242 241819 (B) 01242 222994 (Fax)

Ground: Harrow Hill FC, Larksfield Road Harrow Hill 01594 543873

Directions: Take A40 west out of Gloucester, follow A40 for 8 miles then takeA4136 to
      Longhope, pass by on the outskirts of Michealdean, up steep hill (Plump Hill),
      then second turn on the right signed Harrow Hill. At phone box on the left turn
      right into Larksfield Road, ground on right at top of hill.

Reserves' Ground: Petersfield Park, Tewkesbury Road, Cheltenham (01242 584134)
Directions: 1 mile from Cheltenham centre on A4019 Tewksbury Road (next to B &Q) - 1st left
over railway bridge, 1st left and follow service road
Clubhouse: 2 mins away at 16-20 Swindon Rd, Cheltenham

HONOURS   Glos Snr Cup 91-92 Glos Primary Cup 71-72, Winners Hellenic div 1 99-00

PREVIOUS   **League:** Cheltenham 1964-86

RECORD   **Attendance:** 120 v Bishops Cleeve, 1.1.95

Players progressing: S Cotterill (Wimbledon) 88, K Knight (Reading) 89

FACT FILE
Founded: 1964
Nickname: Saras
Colours: Blue&yellow/blue/yellow
Change colours: Black, white stripe/black/black
Midweek Matchday: Wednesday
Reserves League: Hellenic Reserve section
Programme : 20 pages, 50p
Editor: Kevin Dix   01242 578479
Email: kdix@fsnet.co.uk
99-00 Top Scorer: Christopher Nicholas (9)

CLUB PERSONNEL
Chairman: Jim Utteridge
Match Secretary: Terry Coates
Press Officer: Terry Coates (01242 692320)
Manager: Ian Ford
Coach:Gerald Oldham
Physio: Chris Hawkins

CIRENCESTER FOOTBALL ACADEMY

FACT FILE

Nickname: Academy
Colours: Green & white/white/white
Change colours: Red & black/black/red
Midweek Matchday: Wednesday

Secretary: Phil Corcoran, 8 Garfield Close, Eldene, Swindon, Wilts. SN3 6BZ.
Tel: 01793 611881 (H) 01793 494941(B) 01285 643938 (F)
Email: Phil.Corcoran@royalmail.co.uk

Ground: Tetbury Road, Cirencester Tel: 01285 654783

CLUB PERSONNEL

Directions: From A419 head towards Cirencester town centre (follow signs for Cirencester Hospital). Turn left at Hospital roundabout, and the ground entrance is on the left at the next roundabout.

Chairman:
Alan Sykes Tel: 01285 654783
Press Officer& Prog Ed:
Kirstine Fraser Tel: 01793 823046

RECORD **Attendance:** 102 v Highworth Town 99-00

Director of Football:
Pat Slattery Tel: 01285 810136

Goalscorer 99-00: Neil Dix (9)

Joint Managers:
John Freeth & David Hawkins
Coach& Physio:
Tony Warrington

DIDCOT TOWN

FACT FILE

Secretary: Chris Thomas, 48 Slade Road, Diudcot, Oxfordshire OX11 7AT (01235 811124)

Founded: 1907
Nickname: Railwaymen
Colours: All red & white
Change colours: Blue & yellow stripes
Midweek Matchday: Tuesday
Programme: 50p
Editor:Steve Clare & Andy Selby

Ground: Loop Meadow Stadium
Capacity: 5,000   Seats: 250   Cover: 500   Floodlights: Yes

Directions: From Town Centre: Take station road (old ground) and turn right under bridge just before station into Cow Lane. Left by Ladygrove Pub into Tamar Way. Then first left at roundabout. From A34: leave at Milton interchange and take Didcot road for approximately one mile. At roundabout take perimeter road Cross three more roundabouts at third into Avon Way

CLUB PERSONNEL

Clubhouse: Every evening and 12 noon to close at weekends and national holidys.

President:
Chairman: John Bailey
Manager: Pete Cox
Ass.Managar: John Heapy
Player-Coach: Andy Cooper
Physio: Mark Roberts

HONOURS Hellenic Lg 53-54,Lg Cup 1965-66 66-67 92-9397-98 Div 1 76-77,Div1 Cup 76-7

PREVIOUS **Leagues:** Hellenic 53-54; Metropolitan League 57-63
RECORD **Attendance:** 550 v Wycombe Wanderers, 1956 (old ground)

FAIRFORD TOWN

FACT FILE

Secretary: William Beach, 33 Park Close, Fairford, GL7 4LF Tel: 01285 712136 (H)

Founded: 1891
Nickname: Town
Colours: Red/white/red
Change colours: All Blue
Midweek matchday: Wednesday
Reserves' League: Hellenic Reserve section
Programme: 20 pages with admission
Editor/Press Officer: Chairman

Ground: Cinder Lane, London Road, Fairford, Cirencester Tel: 01285 712071

Directions: Entering Fairford on A417 from Lechlade turn left down Cinder Lane150yds after 40mph sign. From Cirencester on same road, follow thru village andturn right down Cinder Lane 400yds afterRailway Inn.
Buses from Swindon,Lechlade and Cirencester
Capacity: 2,000   Seats: 100   Cover: 150   Floodlights: Yes
Clubhouse: Open each evening, weekend lunches & before and after all games
Club Shop: No

CLUB PERSONNEL

HONOURS Glos Challenge Trophy 79-80, 98-99 (R-up 82-83); Hellenic Lg R-up 78-79 79-
8090-   91 94-95, (Premier Div Cup 78-79, Div 1 71-72, Div 1 Cup 71-72);
Glos Jnr Cup   62-63; Swindon & Dist Lg 64-65 68-69

Chairman: Michael B Tanner
Tel: 01285 713030
President: B W Wall
Manager: Mark Webb
Physio: T.B.A.

PREVIOUS **Leagues:** Cirencester & District (pre-1946)/ Swindon & District 46-70
Grounds: None

RECORD **Attendance:** 1,500 v Swindon Town, friendly july 93
Goalscorer: Pat Toomey   **Win:** 9-0 v Moreton T   **Defeat:** 0-9 v Sharpness

595

HARROW HILL

FACT FILE

Secretary:	Geoff Tuffley, 10a Bilson, Cinderford GL14 2LJ
	Tel: 01594 825655 (H) 01594 542421 (B) 07803 378317 (M)
Match Sec:	Robert Partridge, 20 Littledean Hill Road, Cinderford GL14 2BE
	Tel: 01594 825360 (H) 01594 542421 (B)
Ground:	Larksfield Road, Harrow Hill Tel: 01594 543873
Directions:	Take A40 west out of Gloucester, follow A40 for 8 miles then takeA4136 to
	Longhope, pass by on the outskirts of Michealdean, up steep hill(Plump Hill),
then second turn on the right signed Harrow Hill. At phone box onthe left
turn right into Larksfield Road, ground on right at top of hill
RECORD	**Attendance:** 350 v Cinderford Town 92
1998-99	Top Goalscorer: Carl Woodroffe (8)

Founded:
Nickname: Harry Hill
Colours: Claret & blue/sky/sky
Change Colours: Purple & green/black/black
Midweek Matchday: Wednesday

CLUB PERSONNEL

Chairman: Reg Taylor
President: Ken Jones

Press Officer: Terry Lark
Tel: 01594 827305 & 827190

Manager: Jake O'Neill
Coach: Nick Cornwall
Physio: Sylvia Durham

HIGHWORTH TOWN

FACT FILE

Secretary: Fraser Haines, 222 Windrush, Highworth, Swindon SN6 7EB (01793861109)

Ground: Elm Recreation Ground, Highworth. (01793 766263)

Directions: Enter on A361 from Swindon, past Simpsons Garage, straight overisland, next sharp left into Green by Vet's Surgery - ground & car park 60ydson left next to Sports Hall

Capacity: 2,000   Seats: 50   Cover: 250   Floodlights: Yes   Club Shop: No

Clubhouse: Sat 12-2.30 & 4.30-11pm. Mon to Fri 7-11pm. Rolls & Hot food

HONOURS   Wilts Snr Cup 63-64 72-73 95-96 97-98(R-up 88-89), Hellenic Div 1 Cup 88-89,Arthur Shipway Cup 88-89 93-94, Swindon & District Lg 63-64 64-65 65-66 68-69 Hellenic Supplementary Cup Winners: 98-99, Hellenic Reserve Division Two Winners 98-99, Hellenic Premier Division R-Up 9-00

PREVIOUS   Leagues: Wilts; Swindon & Dist

RECORD   **Attendance:** 2,000 v QPR opening Floodlights
Scorer: Kevin Higgs   **Appearances:** Rod Haines
Win: 12-0 v Beeches, Arthur Shipway Cup 1992
Defeat: 2-8 v Milton United, Hellenic Lge Div. 1, 1987

Founded: 1894
Nickname: Worthians
Sponsors: One Stop
Colours: Red & black/red
Change colours: Blue/blue/white
Midweek matchday: Wednesday
Reserves Lge: Hellenic Reserve Div
Programme: 16 pages, 60p
Editor: Mike Markham (01793 763462)

CLUB PERSONNEL
President: Alan Vockins
Chairman: Rodney Haines
Match Secretary: Dave Evans (01793 763548)
Press Officer:Chairman
Manager: Gary Goodwin
Coach: Graham Fell
Physio: Kelvin Rutter

MILTON UNITED

FACT FILE

Secretary:	Sue Walker, 122 High Street, Sutton Courtney, Abingdon, OX14 4AX
	Tel: 01235 847158 (H)
Ground:	The Sportsfield,Milton Hill, Potash Lane,Milton Heights,Oxon Tel:01235 832999
Directions:	Exit A34 at Milton, 10 miles south of Oxford & 12 miles north of Jt 13, M4. Take
A4130 towards Wantage, after 100m take 1st left, then 1st right into Milton Hill.
Entrance 200m on left.
Capacity: Seats: 50   Cover:Seats   Floodlights: Yes   Club Shop: No
Clubhouse:	On ground, open matchdays

Founded: 1926
Sponsors: Milton Park
Colours: Sky & claret/claret/sky & claret
Change colours: Orange/white/white
Midweek matchday: Tuesday
Reserves' League: Hellenic Lge Res sect
Programme Editor / Press Officer:
David Taylor (01235 816376)

CLUB PERSONNEL

HONOURS   Hellenic Lg 90-91 (Div 1 89-90 R-Up.94-95)), Nth Berks Lg(4) 85-86 87-89(R-up 84-85 86-87, Lg Cup(3) 84-86 88-89, Div 2 80-81, Charity Shield(4) 84-86 87-89 (R-up 82-83), Nth Berks War Mem. Cup(3) 83-85 87-88, Berks & Bucks I'mediate Cup 90-91

RECORD   **Attendance:** 500 v Almondsbury Picksons, Hellenic Lg 90-91
Goalscorer: Nigel Mott

Chairman: Ken Tull
President: John Cannon
Match Secretary: Sid Tindall (01491 835630)
Manager: Paul Biddle
Coach: Nigel Mott Physio: John Belcher

Abingdon United. Back Row (l-r): Sean Flaherty, Wayne Morton, James Murray, Mathew Hambridge, Simon Tricker, Daniel Riley, Andrew Brown, Neil Edwards. Front Row: Mark Simms, James Blackmore, Ricky Barrett, Anaclet Odhiambo, Karl Brown, Luke Brandon. Photo: Eric Marsh

Banbury United: Back Row (l-r): Brian Robinson (Asst Manager), Steve Jenkins, Ashley McKinness, Ricky Smith, Ian Bowyer, Jon Skeen, Jody McKay, Mark Sherlock, Andy Wallbridge, Kevin Brock (Manager). Front Row: Mike Preedy, Jamie Cramond, Jon Corbett, Kieran Sullivan, Matty Gooderick, Adrian Fuller, Simon Pearce (mascot)

Didcot Town FC. Photo: Andrew Chitty

NORTH LEIGH

Secretary: Peter J Dix, 8 Windmill Close, North Leigh, Nr Witney, Oxon OX8 6RP(01993 881199)

Ground: Eynsham Hall Park Sports Ground, North Leigh, nr Witney, Oxon (0993881427)

Directions: Ground is situated off A4095 Witney to Woodstock road 3 miles eastof Witney. Entrance to ground is 300yds east of Main Park Entrance
Capacity: 2,000   **Seats:** 100   **Cover:** 200   **Floodlights:** Yes
Club Shop: No
Clubhouse: Bar open matches. Snacks available

HONOURS   Hellenic Lg Div 1 R-up 92-93 (Reserves Cup 93-94), Oxon Jnr Shield 56-5783-84, Oxon Charity Cup 84-85 88-89, Witney & Dist. Lg(13) 50-57 84-90 LgCup(10) 47-48 51-52 53-55 56-57 81-82 85-89), Oxon Yth Cup 93-94 94-95,OxonYth u17 Lg & Cup 93-94. Oxford Sen. Cup R-up 94-95. Marriott Cup 95-96Oxon Under 16 Youth Cup Winners 98-99, Allied Counties Under 18 Youth (West Div)Winners

PREVIOUS   **Leagues:** Witney & District 08-89

CLUB RECORDS   **Attendance:** 200 v Oxford United, Friendly August 1998
Scorer: P Coles   **Appearances:** P King

FACT FILE
Founded: 1908
Nickname: None
Sponsors: Various
Colours: Yellow/red/yellow
Change colours: Amber/black/amber
Midweek matches: Wednesday
Programme: 20 pages, £1 with entry
Editor: Janice Carter
CLUB PERSONNEL
President: Mrs Christine Smith
Chairman: Peter King
Vice Chairman: B.Shepperd
Press Officer: Barry Norton (01993 881777)
Match Secretary: Reg Kilfoyle (01993 771852)
Manager: Mark Gee
Asst Manager: David Ebsworth
Physio: Roy Keen

PEGASUS JUNIORS

FACT FILE

Secretary: Brian James, 7 Loder Drive, Hereford HR1 1DS
Tel: 01432 274982 (H) 01568 612367 (B) 077 900 92444(M)

Ground: Leisure Centre, Holmer Road,Hereford
Capacity: 1,000   **Seatrs** 50   **Cover :** Yes **Floodlights:** Yes **Clubhouse:** 48 Stowens Street

Directions: A49 Ross Road over Greyfriars Bridge, Victoria Street to end of Edgar Street, then turn left to next mini roundabout and then right.Leisure Centre 500 yds on left.
HONOURS   Herefordshire Snr Amtr Cup 71-72, Herefordshire Co. Chal. Cup(6) 81-8384-85 87-88 89-90 ,98-99(R-up 93-94), Worcs Snr Urn 85-86, Hellenic Lg Div 1 84-85(R-up) 93-94, Div 1 Winners 98-99, Div 1 Cup R-up 93-94

PREVIOUS   **Leagues:** Leisure Centre

RECORD   **Attendance:** 1,400 v Newport AFC 89-90

Founded: 1955
Colours: All red
Change colours: Blue & white/blue/blue
Midweek Matchday: Tuesday/Wednesday
Programme: 50p
Editor: Kevin Bishop (01432 353805)

CLUB PERSONNEL

President: Mark Ellis
Chairman: Steve Knight
Press Officer: Chris Wells
Manager: Mark Williams
Asst. Mans: Mick Williams& Jarrod Clay
Physio: Dave Smith

SHORTWOOD UNITED

Secretary: Mark Webb, 1 The Bungalow, Shortwood, Nailsworth, Stroud, Glos GL60SD
Tel: 01453 833204 (H) 01453 763611 (B)

Ground: "Meadow Bank", Shortwood, Nailsworth, Gloucestershire (01453 833936)

Directions: In Nailsworth turn into Spring Hill then first left. Continue pastshop and and keep left past "Britannia" (signposted Shortwood) - continue toend for ground. 4 miles from Stroud (BR)
Capacity: 5,000   **Seats:** 50   **Cover:** 150   **Floodlights:** Yes   **Club Shop:** No
Clubhouse: Mon-Sat 7-11pm, Sun 12-2 & 7-10.30pm.. Hot food kitchen on matchdays

HONOURS   Glos.Co.Lg 81-82 (R-up 80-81), Glos Tphy 83-84 91-92,94-95,(R-up 79-80), Hellenic Lg 84-85 91-92 (R-up 85-86 89-90 94-95, Div 1 R-up 83-84, Div 1Cup83-84), Prem Lge Cup R-up 95-96, Hungerford Merit Cup, Glos Snr AmCup 85-86,99-00 R-up 79-80), Stroud Charity Cup 91-92 92-93 94-95 (R-up 95-96), Stroud Lg 27-28 (Div 2 26-27 64-65(res), Div 3 25-26 49-50(res) 62-63(res)), Glos Northern Snr Lg R-up (3)res)(Div 2 62-63 80-81(res) 90-91(res)), Arthur Shipway Cup 78-79 79-80, Supp'tary Cup R-up 98-99, Glos N. Sen 2 R-up 98-99

PREVIOUS   **Leagues:** Stroud; Glos Northern Snr; Glos Co
Ground: Table Land, Wallow Green

RECORD   **Attendance:** 1,000 v Forest Green Rovers, FA Vase 5th Rd 81-82
Goalscorer: Peter Grant   **Appearances:** Peter Grant
Win: 11-0   **Defeat:** 0-9   **Fee Received:** Paul Tester (Cheltenham, 80-81)

FACT FILE
Founded: 1900
Nickname: The Wood
Sponsors: Electricity
Colours: Red & white,red,white
Change: White/blue/white
Midweek matchday: Monday
Reserves' League: Glos Northern Snr 1
Programme: 18 pages, 50p
Editor:Ashley Loveridge
99-00 Captain: Kris Murray
P.o.Y.: Neil Long
Top Scorer: Kevin Pride
CLUB PERSONNEL
Chairman: Peter Webb
Vice C'men: W Stratford, W Lewis
President: R T Tanner
Press Officer: Ashley Loveridge
Tel: 01453 752494
Manager/Coach: John Evans/Roger Smith

SWINDON SUPERMARINE

Secretary: Ellen Lee, 5 Stewart Close, Swindon, Wilts. SN25 4XH Tel: 01793 729176

Ground: Hunts Copse, South Marston, Swindon Tel: 01793 828778

Directions: On A361 Swindon/Highworth road, adjoining South Marston Industrial lEstate. Six miles from Swindon (BR) - buses in direction of Highworth, Fairford &Lechdale. If lost ask for Honda.

Capacity: 1,000   **Seats:** 75   **Cover:** 120   **Floodlights:** Yes   **Clubhouse:** Yes

HONOURS: Hellenic Lge - Premier Div. 97-98, R-up 95-96 98-99; Div. One 85-86 86-87; Reserve Section 96-97; Lge Cup 96-97,99-00; Floodlit Cup 97-98.,99-00 Wiltshire Senior Cup 82-83, 86-87, 89-90. Wiltshire Premier Shield 96-97

PREVIOUS **Leagues:** Wiltshire Lge.
Names: Vickers Armstrong 46-81,Supermarine 82-91 (merged 1992) , Penhill Youth Centre 70-84, Swindon Athletic 84-89 (merged)
Ground: Supermarine: Vickers Airfield (until mid-1960s); Swindon Ath.: Merton 70-84; `Southbrook', Pinehurst Road 84-92

RECORD **Attendance:** 264 v Moreton Town 1986

FACT FILE

Founded: 1992
Nickname: 'Marine'
Colours: Blue & white/blue/blue
Change colours: Yellow/navy/yellow
Midweek Matchday: Tuesday
Programme: Yes

CLUB PERSONNEL

Chairman: Steve Moore
President: Cliff Puffit
Press Officer: Judi Moore(01793 790685)
Manager: Alan Dyton
Coach: Glynn Dubber
Physio: Alan Jennings

TUFFLEY ROVERS

Secretary: Graham Moody, 50 Giles Cox, Quedgeley, Gloucester GL2 4YL Tel: 01452 724083 (H & Fax) 01452 522009 (B)

Ground: Glevum Park, Lower Tuffley Lane, Gloucester Tel: 01452 423402

Directions: Follow Gloucester city ring-rd to traffic lights signed M5 South & Bristol. Turn right signed Hempsted & city centre, after 200yds turn right (McDonalds on corner) into Lower Tuffley Lane, ground 400yds on left
Capacity: Seats: 50   Cover: Yes   Floodlights: Yes

Clubhouse: 800 yds from ground. Open before & after matches, and normal pub hours at other times. Snacks available.   Club Shop: No

HONOURS Hellenic Lg Div 1 92-93 (Div 1 Cup 92-93, F'lit Cup 98-99), Glos Co. Lge 90-91, Glos SnrAmtr Cup 87-88, Stroud Lg 72-73,94-95, Glos Northern Sen. Lg. Div 1 87-88 98-99 (res) Div2 79-80.

PREVIOUS **Leagues:** Stroud; Glos Northern Senior; Glos County (pre-1991)
Grounds: Stroud Rd, Gloucester; Randwick Park, Tuffley

RECORD **Attendance:** 150 v Cinderford Town 94-95

FACT FILE

Founded: 1929
Nickname: Rovers
Club Sponsors: Port security
Colours: Claret & blue/claret/claret
Change colours: White/blue/blue
Midweek Matchday: Tuesday
Reserve League: Glos.Northern Senior Lge
Programme: approx 10 pages with entry
Editor: Mrs Bev Summers (01452 417660)

CLUB PERSONNEL

President: A.W.Purdy
Chairman: Tony Newport
Manager: Chris Gardner
Coach: Geoff Samuels
Physio: Sean Tracey

WANTAGE TOWN

Secretary: Alan Parker, Little Orchard, Manor Road, Wantage, OX12 8DW Tel: 01235 763842 (H & Fax)

Ground: Alfredian Park, Manor Road, Wantage, Oxon Tel: 01235 764781

Directions: Take Hungerford Road from Wantage (A338)
The ground is signposted on right opposite recreation ground
Capacity: 1,500   Seats: 50   Cover: 300   Floodlights: Yes
Clubhouse: Mon-Fri 7.30-11pm, Sat noon-2.30, 4-7pm   Club Shop: No

HONOURS Hellenic Lg R-up 81-82, Div 1 80-81 (R-up 69-70 87-88 91-92 95-96), Div1 Cup R-up 91-92; Oxon Snr Cup 82-83; Berks & Bucks Intermediate Cup 54-55; Swindon & District Lg 07-08 33-34 52-53 55-56

PREVIOUS **Leagues:** Swindon & Dist. 1901-12 30-35 47-56; N Berks 12-22 38-40 46-47; Reading & D. 22-30 35-38
Ground: Challow Park (pre-1922)

RECORD **Attendance:** 500 v Newport AFC 89
Win: 11-1 v Amersham Town (A), Hellenic League 60-61
Defeat: 0-14 v Thame United (A), 20/1/62
Goalscorer: A Rolls

Players progressing: Roy Burton and Colin Duncan (both Oxford United)

FACT FILE

Founded: 1892
Nickname: Alfredians
Sponsors: Broadway Motors
Colours:Green &white/white/green&white
Change Colours: Blue& white/bue/blue&white
Programme: 28 pages, 50p
Editor: Tony Woodward (01367 241328)
Midweek Matchday:Tuesday

CLUB PERSONNEL

Chairman: Tony Woodward
President: Ernie Smart
Match Secretary: Colin Blunsden
Tel: 01235 768605 (H)
1st Team Manager: Stuart Peace
Coach: Terry Delaney
Physio: Ian Howard

WOOTTON BASSETT TOWN

Secretary: Rod Carter, 14 Blackthorn Close, Wootton Bassett, Swindon SN4 7JE
Tel: 01793 851386 (H); 01793 494367 (B); 01793 494355 (F)
Email: rod.carter@woolworths.co.uk

Ground: Gerard Buxton Sports Ground, Rylands Way, Wootton Bassett, Swindon 01793 853880

Directions: M4 jnct 16 to Wootton Bassett (A3102), left at 2nd r'bout (Prince of Wales pub on right), 2nd left into Longleaze (just after Mobil garage) and Rylands Way is 3rd right by shops, ground 100yds on right. From Calne/Devizes direction proceed thru town centre and turn right into Longleaze after Shell petrol station on right - Rylands Ave. is 3rd left. Coming from Malmesbury take last exit off r'bout by Prince of Wales pub and Longleaze is 2nd left

Capacity: 4,000   **Seats:** None   **Cover:** 350   **Floodlights:** Due   **Club Shop:** No
Clubhouse: Open every matchday. Matchday refreshments - teas, coffees, soups & light snacks

HONOURS Hellenic Lg Div 1 Cup 89-90 93-94, Wilts Lg 87-88 (Div 2 84-85,Subsidiary Cup 78-79), Wilts Snr Cup R-up 02-03 03-04 87-88, Ghia Snr 83-84,Ghia Jnr Cup R-up 88-89, FA Amateur Cup QF 26-27
PREVIOUS Leagues: Wilts (pre-1988)   **Grounds:** None
RECORD   Gate: 2,103 v Swindon T., friendly 7/91   **Win:** 11-2   **Defeat:** 0-9
Scorer: Brian (Toby) Ewing   **Appearances:** Steve Thomas

FACT FILE
Founded: 1882
Sponsors: Cathy Moore Recruitment
Colours: Blue & yellow/blue/yellow
Change colours: Red/black/black
Midweek matchday: Wednesday
Reserve's League: Wiltshire
Programme: 12 pages, free

CLUB PERSONNEL
Chairman: Paul Harrison
President: Keith Lodge
Press Officer: Rod Carter (see Sec)

Manager: Barry Giles
Coach: Mal Chivers
Physio: Geoff Hawkins

YATE TOWN

Secretary: Terry Tansley, 1 Tyning Close, Yate, Bristol. BS37 5PN
Tel: 01454 324305
Ground: Lodge Road, Yate, Bristol BS37 7LE Tel: 01454 228103
Directions: M4 jct 18, A46 towards Stroud, then A432 to Yate. Turn right at top of railway bridge into North Road, first left past traffic lights. Five miles from Bristol Parkway BR main line station, half mile from Yate BR station. Buses 329, X68 and 328

Capacity: 2,000   **Cover:** 236   **Seats:** 236   **Floodlights:** Yes

Clubhouse: Open every night & weekend lunchtimes. Skittles, darts, pool, live entertainment
Club Shop: Selling programmes & usual souvenirs. Contact: Secretary
HONOURS Hellenic Lg(2) 87-89 (Div 1 R-up 84-85, Lg Skol Cup R-up 87-88), Glos Chal.Tphy 88-89 (R-up 78-79), Glos Snr Amtr Cup Sth 77-78 91-92(res) 92-93(res),Glos Snr Chal. Cup (Nth) R-up 89-90 92-93 94-95, Stroud Charity Cup R-up 74-75 81-82 84-85 (Sect. A Winners(6) 76-78 79-80 82-83 87-89), Berkeley Hosp. Prem.Cup(3) 73-75 80-81, S.W. Co's Sutton Vase 85-86 Dr.Martens Fairplay award 98-99
BEST SEASON   FA Vase: Fifth Round 1991-92
CLUB RECORDS   Win: 13-3 v Clevedon, Bristol Premier Comb 67-68
CareerGoalscorer: Kevin Thaws   **Career Appearances:** Gary Hewlett
Transfer fee - Paid: None   **Received:** £15,000 for Mike Davis (Bristol Rovers 93)
PREVIOUS   Leagues: Gloucestershire County 68-83, Hellenic 83-89, Southern Lge 89-00

FACT FILE
Formed: 1946
Nickname: The Bluebells
Colours: White/navy/navy
Change colours: All Red
Midweek matchday: Tuesday
Reserve Team's League: Bristol Suburban
Programme - Pages: 40 Price: £1
Editor: Terry Tansley c/o Club

CLUB OFFICIALS

Chairman: Tony Phillips
President: R Hewetson

Press Officer: Secretary
Joint Managers :
Richard Thompson & Gary Hewlett
Physio:Ken Dodd

Yate Town FC
Back Row (l-r):
J Lang, N Barrett, R
Jones, J Aylott, S Cains,
A Stocker, A Taverner
Front Row:
M Winspear, M Madge, D
Iddles, I Howse, A Watts,
M Bokoto

ARDLEY UNITED

Secretary: Alan Mitchell, 24 Orchard Road,Ardley,Bicester,Oxon OX6 9PW
Tel: 01869 346854(H) 01865 846799(W) 01865 846333(FAX)

Ground: The Playing Fields, Ardley Road,Ardley (01869 346429)

Directions: M40 junc 10 take B430 towards Middleton Stoney on the right after1/2 mile.
From Oxford take A430 through Weston-on-the-Green & Middleton Stoney on
the left hand side.
Capacity: Cover: Seats: Floodlights
Clubhouse:

HONOURS Oxon Snr Lg R-up 92-93 (Pres. Cup R-up 90-91 91-92) Hellenic League Div
One 96-97,97-98 Division One Cup 94-5,95-6,96-7,97-98

PREVIOUS   Leagues: Oxon Snr (pre-1993)

RECORD   Attendance: 91 v North Leigh (1999)

FACT FILE
Founded:
Colours: Sky/navy/sky
Change colours: Yellow/black/yellow
Midweek matchday: Tuesday
Programme Yes Ed: Barbara Gow

CLUB PERSONNEL
President: Ben Gow
Chairman: Norman Stacey
Secretary: Alan Mitchell
Tel: 01869 346854 (H)
Manager: Paul Spittle
Coach: Tony Blossom
Physio: Clive Wright

BISHOPS CLEEVE

Secretary: Phil Tustain, 36 Hardy Road, Bishops Cleeve, Cheltenham GL52 4BN
Tel: 01242 697281 (H) 01242 673333 x 2287 (B)

Ground: Kayte Lane, Bishops Cleeve, CheltenhamFloodlights: No

Directions: North of Cheltenham on the A534, pass Racecourse then turn right at traffic
lights and then left into Kayte Lane, ground half a mile on the left.

Clubhouse: Full facilities, bar, dance area

HONOURS   Hellenic Lg Cup R-up 90-91

PREVIOUS   Leagues: Cheltenham, Nth Glos
Grounds: The Skiller (pre-1913), Village Field (pre-1950)

RECORD   Attendance: 1,000 v Newport AFC

FACT FILE
Founded: 1892
Nickname: Skinners
Colours: Green&black/black/black
Change colours: Yellow/blue/green
Midweek Matchday: Wednesday

CLUB PERSONNEL
President: John Davies
Chairman: David Walker
Manager: Paul Collicutt
Press Officer:Will Pember
Tel: 01242 673800
Programme Editor: John Banfield
Coach:John Banfield
Physio: Will Pember

CIRENCESTER UNITED

Secretary/Press Officer: Gordon Varley, 95 Vaisey Rd, Cirencester, Glos GL7 2JW
Tel: 01285 657836 (H) 0973 631650 (M) 01367 718259 (B)
Ground: Four Acres P.F., Chesterton Lane, Cirencester Tel: 01285 885460
Directions: Follow by-pass towards Bristol, under footbridge, first left after Cirencester Town
F.C., ground 200yds on left hand side
Seats: None   Cover: No   Floodlights: No   Club Shop: No
Clubhouse: Training nights & matchdays. Rolls & sundries available
HONOURS   Glos Snr Amtr Cup R-up 86-87 89-90; Cirencester Lg 72-73 74-75 (Div
2(3)71-73 74-75, Lg Cup 74-75, Res. Cup 74-75); Cheltenham Lg 76-77 83-84 (Div 275-76, Lg
Cup 83-84 (R-up 86-87), Snr Charity Cup 86-87); Stroud Charity Cup86-87 (Section A 82-83 83-
84); Arthur Shipway Cup 86-87 (R-up 87-88 92-93);Fairford Hospital Cup R-up(4) 83-85 90-91
92-93; Hellenic Res Div 95-96, Cup96-97
PREVIOUS   Leagues: Cirencester & Dist.(4 yrs); Cheltenham (8 yrs)
RECORDS   Scorer: M Day   **Appearances:** A Smith

FACT FILE
Founded: 1970   Nickname: Herd
Colours: Red & black/black/red
Change colours: All Blue
Midweek Matchday: Wednesday
Programme: 40 pages, 50p
Editor: N Warriner (01285 656187)

CLUB PERSONNEL
President: A Day
Chairman: Paul King
Press Officer: Jason Huxtable (01285 656010)
Manager: Ivor Probert
Coach: P.Messenger
Physio: Brian Muir

CLANFIELD

Secretary: John Osborne, 70 Lancut Road, Witney, Oxon OX8 5AQ   Tel: 01993 771631

Ground: Radcot Road, Clanfield, Oxon   Tel: 01367 810314

Directions: Situated on the A4095, 8 miles west of Witney & 4 miles east of Faringdon, at the
southern end of Clanfield. Buses from Witney - contact Thames Transit for details
Capacity: 2,000   Seats: No   Cover: 300   Floodlights: No
Clubhouse: Every evening & Sat/Sun lunch   Club Shop: No

HONOURS Oxon Jnr Shield 32-33, Oxon I'mediate Cup 67-68, Witney & Dist. Lg 66-67 (Div 1
65-66, Div 2 64-65), Hellenic Lg Div 1 69-70 (Premier Div Cup 72-73, Div1 Cup 69-70 85-86),
Jim Newman Mem. Tphy 83-84 87-88, Faringdon Thursday Memorial Cup 69-70 71-72 96-97

PREVIOUS   Leagues: Nth Berks; Witney & Dist **Player of the Year:** Marcus Townsend

RECORD   Attendance: 65 v Wooton Bassett Town 1997 Top Goalscorer: D.Hamill(9)

FACT FILE
Founded: 1890
Nickname: Robins
Sponsors: Smurfitt
Colours: All red
Change colours: Yellow & Black/black/black
Reserves' League: Hellenic Lge Res. section
Programme: 8 pages, with admission
Editor: Secretary

CLUB PERSONNEL
President: B Wallis
Chairman: J Osborne
Managers: Jason Court & Ray Lock
Press Officer&Physio: Trevor Cuss

EASINGTON SPORTS

Secretary:Steven Paynton, 73 Bloxham Road, Banbury ,Oxon. OX169JS(01295 259480)
Ground: Addison Road, Easington Estate, Banbury, Oxon (01295 257006)

Directions: From Oxford A423. After passing under flyover on the outskirts ofBanbury take first turning left into Grange Road then third right into AddisonRd. Ground at top on left. One and a half miles from Banbury (BR)

Capacity: 1,000   Seats:0   Cover: 30Floodlights: No
Programme: Yes,
Clubhouse: Changing rooms, showers, bar facilities and food

HONOURS   Oxon Snr Cup R-up, Oxon Intermediate League & Cup, Oxon Snr Lg

PREVIOUS   **Leagues:** Banbury Jnr; Oxon Snr; Warkwick Combination
                Ground: Bodicote

RECORD   **Attendance:** 250 v Witney Town 68

FACT FILE
Founded: 1946
Colours: Red & white/red/red & white
Change colours: All white
Midweek Matchday: Wednesday
Reserves' League: Hellenic Res. section

CLUB PERSONNEL
Chairman: Steve Hill
President: Bob Cogbill
Manager/Coach: Andy Maguire
Physio: Bernie Jarvis
Press Officer: Alan Malcolm

GLOUCESTER UNITED

Secretary: Colin Pick, The Grange, Quarry Road, Chipping Sodbury BS37 6AX
               01454 314190 (H); 01454 311848 (B); 01454 311873 (F)

Ground   City Stadium, Meadow Park, Sudmeadow Road, Hempsted
               Tel: 01452 421400

Directions   From junction 11 of M5 take A40 towards City Centre, follow signs for Historic Docks. On approach to docks turn right over narrow bridge into Severn Road (signposted Hempsted). Turn right into Hempsted Lane and then second right into Sudreadow Road. Ground is 50 yards on the left.

Season 1999/2000: New Club   Members of Gloucestershire F.A.

FACT FILE
Colours : All blue
Change colours: Red/red/white
Midweek fixtures: Wednesday

CLUB PERSONNEL
Chairman: Stuart Guy
Press Officer & Program Editor:
Michael Hollyoak 01454 882891

Manager: Douglas Foxwell
01452 538116
Coach: Pat Casey
Physio: Adrian Tandy

HEADINGTON AMATEURS

Secretary: Stephen Giles, 60 Glebelands, Headington, Oxon. OX3 7EN(01865 430133)
Ground: Barton Rec., Barton Village Road, Barton, Oxon Tel: 01865 760489
Directions: From Green Rd r'bout, Headington, (on A40) take Barton/Islip exit(1st exit coming from Witney, last coming from London), turn left into NorthWay, follow road for half mile - ground at bottom of hill on left
Seats: None   Cover: None   Floodlights: No   Club Shop: No
Clubhouse: Tues & Thurs 6-11, Sat matchdays 4.45-11. Rolls, chips,burgers, hot dogs, etc
HONOURS Oxon Snr League(4) 72-74 75-77 (R-up 71-72 74-75 77-78 81-82 84-85, Div1 68-69, Presidents Cup(2) 72-74 (R-up 71-72 77-78 84-85)), Oxon Charity Cup75-76 (Intermediate Cup 88-89), Hellenic League Div 1 R-up 87-88 (Res. Sect.92-93, Res. Cup 91-92)
PREVIOUS Leagues: Oxford City Junr 49-66; Oxford Sen 67-88 **Grounds:**Romanway,Cowley
RECORDS Attendance: 250 v Newport AFC 91 **Scorer:** Tony Penge **Appearances:**Kent
     Drackett **Win:** 6-0 v Carterton (H) 91   **Defeat:** 1-8 v Banbury United (A), Feb. 94
Player Progressing: James Light (Oxford United) 1970s

FACT FILE
Founded : 1949   Nickname: A's
Sponsors: H.B. Services
Colours: All red
Change: Blue/blue/white
Midweek matchday: Tuesday
Reserves' Lge: Hellenic Res. sect
Programme: 8 pages, £1 with entry
Editor: Stan Hawkswood (01865 451869)

CLUB PERSONNEL
President: N Smith
Chairman: Donald Light
Press Officer: Donald Light
Manager: James Light
Coach/Physio: Bruce McCrae

KIDLINGTON

Secretary:Dv id Platt, 57 Cherry Close, Kidlington,Oxon. OX5 1HJ Tel: 01865 370266(evenings and 01865 244161 (daytime)
Ground: Yarnton Rd, Kidlington, Oxford Tel: 01865 375628

Directions: From Kidlington r'bout (junction of A4260 & A34) A423 north toKidlington; after 3rdlights take 2nd left (Yarnton Road), ground is 200yds onthe left
               Floodlights: No
Clubhouse: Two bars open after matches

HONOURS   Oxon Snr Lg 53-54 (R-up 47-48), Hellenic Lg Cup 74-75 (R-up 68-69 73-7474-75, Div 1 R-up 63-64 78-79), Oxon Intermediate Cup 52-53 84-85 (R-up 68-69 73-74 74-75), FA Vase 5th last sixteen 76-77

PREVIOUS   League: Oxon Snr 47-54
RECORD   Attendance: 2500 v Showbiz XI 1973

FACT FILE
Founded: 1909
Colours: Green & white quarters/white/green
Change colours: Red & white stripes/redk/red
Midweek Matchday:Tuesday/ Wednesday
Programme: 32pages £1.00
Editor: M A Canning

CLUB PERSONNEL
President: Gordon Norridge
Chairman: Geoff Tallboys
Manager: Martin Baker
Coach: Paulk Harwood
Physio: Michelle Hopcroft

LETCOMBE

Secretary:	Des Williams, 8 Larkdown, Wantage, Oxon. OX12 8HE
	Tel: 01235 764130 (H) 01235 225714(B)
Ground:	Bassett Road, Letcombe Regis, Wantage, Oxon Tel: 01235 768685
Directions:	B4507 Swindon road from Wantage, left for Letcombe Regis, follow road thru
	Letcombe Regis; ground on right on far side of village
Seats: No	**Cover:** No **Floodlights:** No **Club Shop:** No
Clubhouse:	Open evenings except Monday. Rolls & hot food sold
HONOURS	Chiltonian Lg Div 1 90-91, North Berks Lg 89-90 (Lg Cup 87-88, WarMemorial
	Cup 89-90, A G Kingham Cup 89-90, Faringdon Memorial Cup 98-99
PREVIOUS	**Leagues:** North Berks 60-90; Chiltonian 90-93
RECORDS	**Attendance:** 90 v Courage (Reading) 03.90
	Scorer: R Taylor **Appearances:** P Davies

FACT FILE
Founded: 1960   Nickname: Brooksiders
Sponsors: P.J.Drew & Soro's Pizzas
Colours: Blue& Green/blue/green
Change colours: Red/Green
Midweek Matchday: Wednesday
Reserves' Lge: Hellenic Res. sect
Programme: £1 with entry
Editor: Russell Stock (01235 762387)
CLUB PERSONNEL
President: Maurice Ginniff
Chairman: Dennis Stock
Vice-Chairman: G Delacoze
Manager: Des Williams
Coach: James Simms
Physio: Des Williams

MALMESBURY VICTORIA

Secretary:	Sarah Bush, 16 Bonners Close, Malmesbury, SN16 9UF
	01666 822465(H). E-Mail: sarah@louise-bush.fsnet.co.uk
Ground:	Flying Monk Ground, Gloucester Road, Malmesbury
	Tel: 01666 822141

Directions: From A429 turning signposted Tetbury (by Nurdens Garden Centre), go past school and take next left B4014signposted Sherston. Go down hill to mini roundabout, straight over roundabout. Go past Somerfield's super store, narrow right turning into ground behind super store.

Honours: Wiltshire League Champions 99-00

Season 1999/2000 Wiltshire Football League

FACT FILE
Nickname: The Vic's
Colours: Black & white stripes/black/black
Change colours:
Maroon, blue sleeves/blue/maroon
Midweek fixtures: Tuesday or Wednesday

CLUB PERSONNEL
Chairman: Brian Slade 01666 825705
Press Officer: Elaine Foxall 01666 841227
Program Editor: Sue Neale 01666 823560
Manager: Lester Foxall 01249 783295
Coach: Tom Dryden

MIDDLE BARTON

Secretary:	Julie Reed, 5 Hillside Road, Middle Barton, Oxon OX7 7EY
	Tel: 01869 347388
Match Secretary:	Jeane Beale, 3 Dorne Closer, Middle Barton, Oxon OX7 7HD
	Tel: 01869 340753
Ground:	Worton Road, Middle Barton, Oxon. Tel: 01869 347597
Directions:	Middle Barton village is situated on the B4030, 5 miles east of Enstone. 200
	metres passed the Fox PH turn left at cross roads, ground 200 metres on right.
Clubhouse:	Open every evening
Previous League:	Oxfordshire Senior League
Honours:	Oxfordshire Sen. Lge R-up 98-99

FACT FILE
Founded: 1952
Midweek Matchday: Wednesday
Colours: Blue & white/blue/white
Change colours: Yellow/black/black
Programme: Yes, first season

CLUB PERSONNEL
President: Derrick Jarvis
Chairman: John Hanks
Press Officer: Phil Smith (01869 347471)
Manager/Coach: Tim Fowler
Physio: Lucy Waring

OLD WOODSTOCK TOWN

Secretary:	Ian F.Lenegan c/o Workplace Systems plc.,Precedent Dive, Rooksley,Milton
	Keynes MK13 8PP Tel:08362 42300(H), 01908 251301or 251311 (W) 01908 201287 (Fax)
Ground:	New Road, Woodstock
Directions:	A44 from Oxford into centre of Woodstock, turn right opposite The Crown into
	Hensington Road. After half a mile the road bends to the right, take the first
	turning right into New Road, ground half-way along on the left.
HONOURS	Oxfordshire Sen. Lge 98-99
PREVIOUS	**Leagues:** Oxfordshire Senior League

FACT FILE
Founded:
Midweek Matchday: Tuesday
Colours: Blue & red/blue/ red
Change colours: White/green/blue
Programme : Yes Ed: Mike Harris

CLUB PERSONNEL
President: Ian F Lenagan
Chairman: Ted Saxton
Press Officer: Mick Harris (01865 376018)
Manager: Andrew Townsend
Coach:Trevor Stokes
Physio: Graham Bowerman

PURTON

Secretary:	Alan Eastwood, 12 Hylder Close,Woodhall Park,Swindon,Wilts. SN2 2SL
	Tel: 01793 729844
Ground:	The Red House, Purton, Tel: 01793 770262 (Saturday afternoons only)
Directions:	Purton is on B4041 Wootton Bassett to Cricklade Road. Ground nearvillage hall
	Capacity Seats:None Cover: None Floodlights: No
Clubhouse:	Open after matches

HONOURS Wiltshire Lg Div One 48-49 85-86, Div 2 83-84, Div 3 86-87;
Wilts Senior Cup (6) 38-39 48-49 50-51 54-55 87-89, Wilts Yth Cup 77-78 85-86 88-89, Fairford Hosp. Cup (3) 87-89 93-94 Hellenic League Div One 95-96

RECORD **Attendance:** 508 v Dorcan 5.5.85

FACT FILE
Founded: 1923
Nickname: The Reds
Sponsors: The Care Company
Colours: All red
Change colours: White & blue/blue/blue
Midweek Matchday: Wednesday
Programme: 40 pagesp
Editor: Alan Eastwood (01793 729844)

CLUB PERSONNEL
President: Graham Price
Chairman: Tony Brown
Press Officer: Alan Eastwood
Manager: Keith Skinner

ROSS TOWN

Secretary:	Alan Bridges, Re-adel, Willowbrook,Greytree,Ross-On-Wye HR9 7JS. Tel:01989 564432 (H) 01594 542421 x 1276 (W)
Ground:	Cinderford Town FC, Causeway Ground, Hilldene, Cinderford (01594822039)
Directions:	From Gloucester take A40 to Ross-on-Wye, then A48 - Chepstow. In 10miles turn right at Elton garage onto A4151to Cinderford, thru Littledean, up steep hill, right at crossroads, and left into Latimer Rd.(F.C signposted). Ground 5 mins walkfrom town centre
	Capacity: 3,500 Cover: 1,000 Seats: 250 Floodlights: Yes

HONOURS Hereford Lge 94-95, Charity Shield 95-96; Hereford FA Charity Bowl 94-95;
Worcester & Dist Lge 95-96, Baylis Cup 95-96; Hereford FA County Chall Cup
97-99 R-up 95-96; 98-99 Pershore Hospital Charity Cup R-up 95-96, Hellenic Lg
Cup R-up: 99-00

PREVIOUS **Leagues:** Hereford Lg, Worcester & District League.
RECORD **Attendance:** 147 v Harrow Hill 26/3/97

FACT FILE
Founded:1993
Nickname: Riversiders
Colours: Red /black/black
Change colours:Green/Green/White
Midweek Matchday: Tuesday/Wednesday

CLUB PERSONNEL
Patron: Dave Sexton
Chairman: Geoff Jones
Director of Football and
Press Officer: Chris Parsons (01989 566712)
Manager: Martin Thomas
Coach: Chris Parsons
Physio: Sylvia Durham

WITNEY ACADEMY

Secretary:	Bob Haydon, 25 Wadards Meadow, Witney, Oxon OX8 6YL
	T & F. 01993 771804 (H & B)
Press Officer:	Secretary
Ground:	Marriotts Stadium Down Road Witney 01993 702549
Directions:	From the centre of Witney take A4095 via Tower Hill. At roundabout turn left onto B4047 Burford Road. Turn left at Car Auctions, into Downs Road. Witney Town's ground Marriotts Stadium is on the right had side.
Capacity:	3,500 Cover: 2,000 Seats: 280 Floodlights: Yes

Season 1999/2000 New Club   Members of Oxfordshire F.A.

FACT FILE
Colours: All yellow
Change colours: All red
Midweek fixtures: Wednesday
Program Editor: Gary Walters
01295 270903

CLUB PERSONNEL
President: Dick Lucas
Chairman: David Wesson 01993 779842
General Manager: Steve Warburton
01865 377338
Manager: Paul Lewis 01993 704311
Coach: Kenny Clarke
Physio: Bob Haydon (FA Diploma)

WORCESTER COLLEGE OLD BOYS

Secretary:	Robert Oakes, 112 Leiden Road, Headington, Oxford OX3 8QU
	Tel: 01865 750788 (H & Fax) 01491 652853 (B)
Ground:	Rover Cowley Sports Ground, Cowley, Oxford Tel: 01865 775463
Directions:	Take the ring road to the east of city. Leave at exit sign-posted to Horspath. First right, into Roamn Road, leads to ground entrance on the left..
	Capacity: 2,000 Cover: Yes Seats: Yes Floodlights: No
Clubhouse:	Open luchtimes and evenings every day.

PREVIOUS **League:** Oxfordshire Senior League
HONOURS Oxfordshire Sen Lge 97-98, Oxfordshire Charity Cup 96-97

FACT FILE
Founded: 1974
Midweek Matchday: Tuesday
Colours: Blue & black/black/black
Change colours: All maroon
Programme: Yes Editor: Secretary

CLUB PERSONNEL
Chairman: David Quainton
Tel: 01865 375570
Press Officer: Nick East 01865 842871
Manager: Paul Creed

Above: Middle Barton FC.
Back Row (l-r): Peter Salt (Asst Manager),
John Umney, Paul Eldridge, Chris
Reynolds, Chris Coles, Matt Wiggins,
Chris Fowler, Tim Fowler (Manager). Front
Row: Andy Shepherd, Mike Beale, Keith
Harrison, Andy Robey, Ian Fraser, Gordon
Bedford, Simon Coombes (captain).
Photo: Banbury Guardian

Right: Purton FC. Back Row (l-r): Tony
Clarke, Stuart Cole, Paul Gillett, Ben
Parsons, Richard Watkins, Neil Skinner,
Mark McMeeking, Scott Crumbie, Tim
Goddard. Front Row: Jimmy Griffin, Justin
Frost, Dave Turner, Jeff Roberts, Adam
Smith, Micky Heath.
Photo: Gordon Whittington

HELLENIC LEAGUE DIVISION ONE EAST

ASTON CLINTON

Secretary: Antony Addison, 98 Tring Road Wendover Bucks
Tel: 01296 696952 (H); 01296 633000 (B).

Ground: Aston Clinton Park, London Road Tel 01296 630888
Directions: On the A41 London road opposite the Duck in Pub,
signposted "Aston Clinton Park".

Season 1999/2000   Member of the Chiltonian League

FACT FILE
Colours: Blue & white/blue/blue
Change colours: Red & white/white/red
Midweek fixtures: Tuesday

CLUB PERSONNEL
Chairman: John Roberts 01296 630160
Press Officer & Program Editor
Michael Dedman 01296 631093
Manager: Neil Cozens 01296 630913
Coach: John Roberts

BINFIELD

Secretary: Vernon Bradshaw, 21 Audley Way Ascot Berks SL5 8EE
Tel: 01344 886144 (H); 01344 356651 (B)

Ground: Stubbs Lane Binfield   01344 860822

Directions From A329 Bracknell to Wokingham Road, turn by the Travel Lodge into
St. Marks Road, through the village into Terrace Road South & North,
then at T junction by All Saints' Church turn right & then left into Stubbs Hill.

Record Gate: 150 v Finchampstead 1998

Season 1999/2000   Member of the Chiltonian League

FACT FILE
Colours: All reded.
Change colours: White/blue/blue
Midweek fixtures: Tuesday
Nickname: Moles

CLUB PERSONNEL
Chairman: Bob Alloway
Press Officer: Bob Ellis
Program Editor: Bob Langridge
Manager: Bob Ellis
Coach: Paul Coley

CHALFONT WASPS

Secretary: Denis Higgs, Stevens Mead The Green Chalfont St. Giles Bucks HP8 4QA
01494 875138 (H); (B) T. 01753 655204 & F. 653265
E-mail: denis@interiorplus.fsbusiness.co.uk
Match Sec/Press Off. & Prog. Editor.: Bob Isherwood 01494 871445 (H)

Ground: 01494 875050
Directions On entering Chalfont St. Giles Village from A413 (Aylesbury - Uxbridge Road), turn left into Bolostridge Lane immediately after the shops. After a quarter of a mile turn right into Crossleys by a small green. Ground is directly ahead through the gates

Season 1999/2000: Member of the Chiltonian League

FACT FILE
Colours: Yellow & black striped/black/black.
Change colours: All Green
Midweek fixtures: Tuesday
Nickname: The Stingers
Midweek fixtures: Tuesday
Nickname: The Stingers
CLUB PERSONNEL
Chairman: Steven Waddington
Manager: Steven Simmons
Coach: Paul Massey
Physio: Douglas Whitaker

DRAYTON WANDERERS

Web Site: http://website.lineone.net/~drayton_wanderers

Secretary: Lee Milligan, 66 Cowley Road Uxbridge Middx. UB8 2LU
01895 810971 (H) E-mail: l.milligan@nationalcar.co.uk

Ground: Cowley Hall, Cowley Road Uxbridge 01895 258269

Directions: One and a half miles south of Uxbridge Town Centre, follow signs to Heathrow Airport, entrance to ground opposite the Grand Union Public House.

Season 1999/2000: Member of the Chiltonian League

FACT FILE
Colours: Black & white
Change colours: Red & yellow
Midweek fixtures: Tuesday
Nickname: Wanderers

CLUB PERSONNEL
Chairman: Kevin Kelly
01895 824465
Program Editor: Michael Ash
01753 654413

ENGLEFIELD GREEN ROVERS

Secretary: Terry D Goode, 11 Kingswood Close Englefield Green Surrey TW20 0NQ
T & F. 01784 433251 (H)
Press Officer & Program Editor: Jonathan West 01932 852943

Ground: Coopershill Lane Englefield Green 01784 43566

Directions: Leave M25 at junction 13, A30 by passing Egham, at top of Egham Hill turn right at traffic lights. After passing Village Green on the left take 2nd turning right at the north east of green. Ground on the right after half a mile.

Record Gate: 100 v Eton Wick, 1999

Season 1999/2000: Member of the Chiltonian League

FACT FILE
Colours: All green & white
Change cols.: Red & white halves/white/white
Midweek fixtures: Tuesday
Nickname: The Rovers

CLUB PERSONNEL
Chairman: Paul Solari 01784 477723
Manager: Gerry Kelly
Coach: Paul Solari
Physio: Peter Casey

ETON WICK

Secretary: Barrie Shurville, 21 The Wheat Butts Eton Wick Berks SL4 6JH
Press Officer 01753 862969 (H); 07860262614 (B)
& Program Editor

Ground: 01753 852749
Directions: From M4 junction 7 follow A4 to Maidenhead. At first roundabout (Sainsbury's) take B3026 towards Eton Wick. Ground is on the right after the first road narrowing. From Eton take B3026 and ground is on the left after the 2nd road narrowing.

Record Gate 500 v Andover, 1993 FA Vase

Season 1999/2000: Member of the Chiltonian League

FACT FILE
Nickname: The Wick
Colours: Amber/black/black
Change colours: All white
Midweek fixtures: Tuesday

CLUB PERSONNEL
Chairman: James Hartridge 01753 869860
Manager & Coach: Barry Pitcher
01753 528499
Physio: James Hartridge

FINCHAMPSTEAD

Web Site: www.finchampsteadfc.co.uk
Secretary: John Johnson, 21 Moulsham Lane Yateley Hants. GU46 7QX
T & F. 01252 661039 (H); 0845 6070711 (B) E-mail: john_uk@yahoo.co.uk
Match Sec.: Michael Husk, 16 Sadlers Lane Winnersh Berks RG41 5AJ
01189 785949 (H)
Press Officer: Stephen King E-mail: Stephen@kingsb.fsnet.co.uk
Ground: 01189 732890
Directions: A321 from Wokingham, then fork right onto B3016. At the Greyhound pub turn right onto the B3348. The ground is 200 yards on the right.
Record Gate 425 v Sandhurst, 1958/ 9
Season 1999/2000: Member of the Chiltonian League

FACT FILE
Nickname: Finch
Colours: Sky blue & white/black/black
Change colours: All red
Midweek fixtures: Wednesday

CLUB PERSONNEL
Chairman: Dick West 01344 750400
E-mail: aquaspec@globalnet.co.uk
Manager: Steven McClurg
Coach & Physio: Chris Mather

HARROW HILL ROVERS

Secretary: Stefano Poulos, 7 Fairways Isleworth Middlesex TW7 4NS
0208 560 9763 (H); 0208 232 8959 (B); 0208 560 1295 (F)
07788 155093 (M)   E-mail moscha@lineone.net
Program Editor: Lee-John Tansey   07889 342865   E-mail: l.tansey@talk21.com
Ground: White Lodge Syon Lane Isleworth   0208 560 8829
Directions: From M25 onto M4 at junction 3 then follow signs to Central London. At
Gillett Corner turn left into Syon Lane. Ground 100 metres on the left.
From A40 turn at Target Roundabout and follow A312 Hayes by pass to A4
then follow signs to Central London until Gillett Corner, turn left and ground on the left.
Record Gate 200 v Rayners Lane, 3rd January 2000
Season 1999/2000: Member of the Chiltonian League

FACT FILE
Colours: Blue & white quarters/blue/blue
Change cols.: Red & black quarters/red/red
Midweek fixtures: Tuesday
Nickname: Rovers

CLUB PERSONNEL
Chairman: James Stefanopoulos
0208 667 1269
Manager: Ray Girvan 0411349653
Coach : Gag Sindhu
Physio: Kelly Monk

HENLEY TOWN

Secretary: Tony Kingston, 50 Birdhill Avenue Reading Berks. RG2 7JU
01189 670196 & 07712139502 (H); 01189 844496 (B);
01189 842201 (F); E-mail: kingstonkinp2s@supanet.com
Ground: The Triangle Mill Lane Henley-on-Thames 01491 411083
Directions: From Henley Town Centre take the A4155 Reading Road. Mill Lane is
approx. 1 mile on the left past the Newtown Ind. Est. and immed. before the Garage and
roundabout for Tesco. The ground is on the left, over the railway bridge. Henley-on-Thames
Railway Station ten minutes walk. Buses 328 Reading or 329 Wycombe
Record Gate: 2000+ v Reading, 1922
Season 1999/2000: Member of the Chiltonian League

FACT FILE
Colours: White & black/black/black
Change cols.: Claret or blue/white/white
Midweek fixtures: Tuesday
Nickname: The Lillywhites,
but more recently "The Town"

CLUB PERSONNEL
Chairman: Andrew Bryan
Manager: Bernie Harris 0118 9423545
Coach: Keith Stiles
Physio: Danny Tully

MARTIN BAKER SPORTS

Secretary: Michael Hayselden, 53 Leven Way Hayes Middlesex UB3 2SS
Press Off. & Prog. Editor   0208 5732887 (H); 0208 8406992 (B)

Ground: Martins Field Tilehouse Lane Denham   01895 833077

Directions: A412 from the A40 London / Oxford Road. (Do not confuse the A40 with
the M40 which runs parallel). The entrance to the ground is approximately 150 yards on the
right between the houses.

Season 1999/2000: Member of the Chiltonian League

FACT FILE
Colours: White & blue/blue/blue
Change colours: Green or gold/green or
black/green or black
Midweek fixtures: Tuesday
Nickname: Baker Boys

CLUB PERSONNEL
Chairman: Ken Sibley 01895 824849
Manager: Ray Flegg 0956 980880
Coach & Physio: Guillermo Ganet

PENN & TYLERS GREEN

Secretary: Malcolm James, Woodlands, Forty Green Rd, Forty Green, Beaconsfield HP9 1XS
01494 677311 (H)

Match Secretary: Stanley Laing, 16 Fir View Road Hazlemere High Wycombe Bucks
01494 814312 (H)

Ground: 01494 815346
Directions: Entrance to ground is off the main Hazlemere to Beaconsfield road.
From Beaconsfield follow the road through Penn towards Hazlemere, pass the pond on
green and entrance to ground is on the right had side before going downhill.

Season 1999/2000: Member of the Chiltonian League

FACT FILE
Colours: Blue & white striped/blue/white
Change colours: All yellow
Midweek fixtures: Tuesday

CLUB PERSONNEL
Chairman: Robert Dalling 01494 671424
Press Officer &
Program Editor: Neil Bellamy 01494 812492
Manager: David Raleigh 01494 445533
Coach: David Taylor

PEPPARD

Secretary: Chris Boyles, 14 Redwood Avenue Woodley Reading Berks RG5 4DR
0118 9699488 (H); 0118 9872473 (B); 0118 9628130 (F)
E-mail: peppardfc@dboyles.freeserve.co.uk

Ground: Bishopswood Sports Ground Hurstpond Road Gallowstree Common
0118 9722675
Directions: On the Lane End to Peppard road which runs between the A4074
(Reading to Woodcote & Oxford) and the A481 (Reading to Nettlebed) roads.

Season 1999/2000: Member of Chiltonian League

FACT FILE
Colours: All red
Change colours: Light blue/navy/navy
Midweek fixtures: Tuesday

CLUB PERSONNEL
Chairman: Sean Gillett 0118 9468425

PRESTWOOD

FACT FILE

Colours: Claret & blue/white/white

Change colours: Sky blue/sky blue/claret

Midweek fixtures: Tuesday

Secretary: Guy Stansbury, 31 Colne Road High Wycombe HP13 7XN
H, B & F. 01494 521792 E-mail: gstans@tesco.net

Ground: Prestwood Sports Centre   01494 865946

Directions: From the Chequers Public House in the Centre of Prestwood, take the road signposted to Great Hampden. The ground is approximately half a mile on the left.

Season 1999/2000: Member of the Chiltonian League

CLUB PERSONNEL

Manager: D Yeabsley 01494 783972

Res. Manager: A Henney 01494 712544

QUARRY NOMADS

FACT FILE

Colours: Black & white/black/black

Change colours: All yellow

Midweek fixtures: Wednesday

Web Site;   http://members.tripod.co.uk/Molden/nomads.html

Secretary: Keith Dolton, 58 Pitts Road Headington Oxford OX3 8AZ 01865 450256 (H)

Match Sec.: Linda Dolton, 58 Pitts Road Headington Oxford OX3 8AZ 01865 450256 (H)

Ground: Margaret Road Headington   0860 408769

Directions: Exit M40 at junction 8, then A40 towards Oxford to Green Road Roundabout (McDonalds on the left), then straight over towards Headington.Take third left into Wharton Road, then at T junction turn left into Margaret Road. Ground on left.

Record Gate   267 v Witney Town, 1994

Season 1999/2000: Member of the Chiltonian League

CLUB PERSONNEL

Chairman: Richard Lawrence 01865 873258

Press Officer: Paul Dolton 01865 768970

Prog. Editor: Andrew Molden 01865 433686

E-mail: ac.mold@hotmart.com

Manager: Brian Smith 01865 771414

Physio: Paul Dolton

R.S. BASINGSTOKE

FACT FILE

Colours: Red & black/red & black/black

Change colours: All blue

Midweek fixtures: Wednesday

Secretary: Michael Davis, 451 Abbey Road Popley Abbeys Basingstoke RG24 9EN
& Press Off.   01256 468873 (H); 0468 334672 (B)

Ground: Whiteditch Playingfield Sherborne Road   01256 814618

Directions: From M3 junction 6 cross Black Dam Roundabout A33/A339. At Reading Road Roundabout take second exit into Oakridge Road, after approximately three quarters of a mile you pass school, then turn left into Sherborne Road. Ground approximately 200 metres on left.

Record Gate: 120 v Hartley Witney, 1994

Season 1999/2000: Member of the Chiltonian League

CLUB PERSONNEL

Chairman & Program Editor:

David Brand 01256 357309

Manager: Albert Fox

Coach: Kevin Haystaff

Physio: Chris Townley

RAYNERS LANE

FACT FILE

Colours: Yellow/yellow/green

Change colours: Green/black/black

Midweek fixtures: Tuesday

Nickname: The Lane

Secretary: Tony Pratt, 4 Stirling Close Cowley Uxbridge Middx. UB8 2BAA
01895 233853 (H)

Ground: 51 Rayners Lane South Harrow   0208 8669659

Directions: From A40 Polish War Memorial (First junction after Northolt Aerodrome) turn left into A4180 (West End Road), approx. 500m turn right into Station Approach, at lights turn right into Victoria Road (Sainsbury's on the right). At next roundabout continue straight on to lights at junction with Alexandra Avenue (Farmers House pub on left). Continue straight on over lights and take 2nd turning on left into Rayners Lane. Ground is approx. half a mile on left.

Record Gate   550 v Wealdstone, 1983

Season 1999/2000: Member of the Chiltonian League

CLUB PERSONNEL

Chairman: Richard Mitchell 0208 4726340

Press Off. & Prog.Ed.: Tom Lynn

0208 8684671

Manager/Coach: Richard Hedge

0208 8480843

Physio: Ronald Fairhead

SOUTHALL TOWN

FACT FILE

Colours: Red & white stripes/black/black

Change colours: Yellow & blue/blue/yellow

Midweek fixtures: Wednesday

Nickname: The Wood

Secretary: George Twyman, 119 Dormers Wells Lane Southall Middlesex UB1 3JA
Tel & Fax: 0208 574 5047(H & B)

Match Sec.: Eddie Mee, 11 Charles Hocking Hse, Bollan Bridge Rd, Acton London W3 8DA.
Tel: 0208 993 4477(H) 0956 676516(Bus)

Ground: Yeading FC. The Warren Beconsfield Road Hayes Middx Tel 0208 848 7362

Directions: Leave M4 at junction 3, The Parkway onto Hayes by-pass. Continue to the second filter road and turn right onto A4020 Uxbridge Road, then take first turning on right into Springfield Road. Continue to end of road, turn left into Beconsfield Road, ground on right hand side at end of the road.the left hand side opposite the Church.

Season 1999/2000: Members of Isthmian League Division 3

CLUB PERSONNEL

Chairman & Press Officer: Manjit S Lit

0208 893 5373 Fax: 0208 571 9410

Manager: Dennis Bainborough

Coach: Del Deanus

Physio: Micky Croft

BASS BREWERS
KENT LEAGUE

FEEDER TO: DR MARTENS LEAGUE

President: D D Baker   **Chairman:** P C Wager   **Vice Chairman:** D Richmond
Hon. Secretary & Treasurer: A R Vinter, Bakery House, The Street, Chilham, Nr
Canterbury, Kent CT4 8BX   Tel: 01227 730457   Fax: 01227 738880

The League had new sponsors in Bass Brewers and they could not have timed their entrance better for the 1999-2000 season will, without a doubt, retain a place in the history books with Deal Town winning the Carlsberg FA Vase, overcoming Chippenham Town by 1-0 at Wembley. The League also had Ramsgate in the last eight of the competition and they only lost in extra time. This was the first time that the League had ever had two clubs reach the last sixteen of the Vase and it certainly provoked a lot of interest.

Prior to the domestic season getting under way the League Challenge Shield had been won by Ramsgate who overwhelmed a weakened Deal Town by seven goals to one.

The season was dominated to a large extent by Deal Town and their success in the FA Vase, and whilst there was a lot of publicity and well deserved praise for the club there was also an enormous problem with the fixture backlog, a similar situation had arisen a few years ago with Swanley Furness. In the end Deal lifted the Premier Division title with Thamesmead Town securing the runners-up spot to improve on the previous season. The Premier Division Marion Wager Cup should have been a repeat of the 1998-99 final between VCD Athletic and Deal Town but the latter withdrew from the competition so as not to risk injury to their players only a week before the Wembley date. Faversham Town, who had lost in the semi-final to Deal Town, were re-instated but they were well beaten by VCD 4-0.

In Division One the League Championship went to Thamesmead Town who defeated Deal Town by 1-0 in a playoff after both clubs had won their respective geographical divisions. This was a bitter pill for Deal Town, but for Thamesmead Town, who survive against a lot of clubs chasing a few players, it was yet another success for the hard work of the players and staff. Ashford Town and Swanley Furness had battled through the section stages and the two-legged semi-finals contested the Division One Cup Final. In a match played on Bank Holiday Monday, Ashford emerged as winners.

In County Cup affairs Deal Town won the Kent Senior Trophy beating Chatham Town in the Final and Lordswood were finalists in the Kent Intermediate Cup. There was also some honour for Erith Town, who reached the Final of the London Senior Cup.

ROLL OF HONOUR 1999-2000

	Champions	*Runners Up*	*Third Place*
PREMIER DIVISION	Deal Town	Thamesmead Town	Chatham Town
DIVISION ONE	Thamesmead Town	Deal Town	Dover A / Swanley F

	Winners	*Runners Up*	*Semi Finalists*
PREMIER DIVISION CUP	VCD Athletic	Faversham Town	Ramsgate Deal Town
DIVISION ONE CUP	Ashford Town	Swanley Furness	Thamesmead Town Margate

HIGHEST SCORERS	Premier Division:	Deal Town	87 goals
	Division One:	Deal Town	54 goals
GOLDEN BOOT AWARD	Premier Division:	Steve Jones (Chatham T)	32 goals
		Ian Court (Ramsgate)	26 goals
		Steve Marshall (Deal T)	22 goals
	Division One:	Sam Kodjoe (Swanley F)	24 goals
		Steven Meadows (Deal T)	21 goals
		Darren Waring (Deal T)	17 goals

FINAL LEAGUE TABLE 1999-2000
PREMIER DIVISION

		P	W	D	L	F	A	Pts	GD
1	Deal Town	34	26	5	3	87	28	83	59
2	Thamesmead Town*	34	23	6	5	75	29	72	46
3	Chatham	34	23	3	8	76	40	72	36
4	VCD Athletic	34	18	10	6	53	32	64	21
5	Ramsgate	34	18	9	7	75	41	63	34
6	Greenwich Borough	34	17	5	12	70	44	56	26
7	Erith Town	34	16	8	10	56	54	56	2
8	Hythe United	34	14	6	14	38	50	48	-12
9	Sheppey*	34	12	6	16	45	60	45	-15
10	Beckenham	34	12	8	14	45	51	44	-6
11	Lordswood	34	12	6	16	55	63	42	-8
12	Herne Bay*	34	13	8	13	56	48	41	8
13	Cray Wanderers*	34	10	3	21	42	80	36	-38
14	Tunbridge Wells	34	9	6	19	49	72	33	-23
15	Slade Green	34	8	6	20	41	65	30	-24
16	Whitstable	34	6	9	19	38	56	27	-18
17	Faversham	34	6	6	22	39	70	24	-31
18	Canterbury	34	6	6	22	35	92	24	-57

PREMIER DIVISION RESULTS CHART 1999-2000

		1	2	3	4	5	6	7	8	9	10	11	12	13	14	15	16	17	18
1	Beckenham	X	3-0	1-1	1-0	3-1	0-3	3-1	0-4	1-1	4-1	0-1	2-3	0-1	0-3	2-1	3-1	2-0	3-1
2	Canterbury	0-4	X	1-4	0-3	1-2	0-2	3-1	0-10	1-1	1-1	1-3	0-4	1-1	0-0	3-5	3-2	2-3	2-2
3	Chatham	2-0	5-0	X	2-1	4-1	1-0	4-0	3-0	1-5	2-0	6-1	0-2	2-1	2-0	1-2	2-0	3-2	0-0
4	Cray Wanderers	2-2	2-0	4-3	X	0-1	1-3	3-2	3-4	1-4	3-2	2-2	1-7	2-1	2-0	0-5	2-1	0-2	1-1
5	Deal Town	2-0	5-1	3-1	5-0	X	6-0	3-1	3-1	3-0	6-1	3-0	0-0	1-0	3-3	2-0	3-1	1-0	2-1
6	Erith Town	2-0	1-4	2-1	3-1	2-2	X	1-0	2-0	2-0	0-0	1-0	0-2	1-1	2-3	1-4	1-0	1-1	3-0
7	Faversham	0-2	1-2	0-2	4-0	0-4	1-1	X	1-2	1-4	0-1	1-1	3-1	1-2	4-2	0-1	5-0	1-1	1-0
8	Greenwich Borough	5-0	2-0	1-3	1-2	0-0	0-1	4-1	X	2-0	0-0	6-1	1-1	4-1	1-2	2-2	0-1	0-2	4-2
9	Herne Bay	0-0	2-1	0-1	3-0	2-3	1-3	1-2	1-2	X	1-2	2-1	0-1	0-0	6-1	1-1	3-1	0-1	3-1
10	Hythe United	2-1	1-0	1-0	3-1	1-3	1-3	1-1	0-1	4-1	X	2-0	0-6	2-4	1-2	0-2	2-0	0-0	2-1
11	Lordswood	0-0	5-1	1-3	4-1	1-4	5-3	4-0	1-2	2-2	3-0	X	2-5	0-2	1-1	0-1	2-2	0-3	2-1
12	Ramsgate	6-2	1-0	2-0	3-0	2-1	1-1	3-3	2-0	4-4	0-1	1-0	X	0-0	4-1	2-5	2-2	1-1	1-3
13	Sheppey	2-4	4-4	2-3	1-0	0-4	2-1	2-1	1-3	0-1	1-3	1-5	1-0	X	2-1	2-3	3-0	0-2	2-1
14	Slade Green	0-0	1-2	0-2	1-2	0-2	0-2	5-0	2-4	1-2	0-2	0-1	1-4	2-1	X	0-1	1-3	0-0	2-2
15	Thamesmead	2-0	6-0	4-1	1-0	1-1	4-1	3-0	1-0	1-0	1-0	3-0	1-1	1-2	5-0	X	1-2	1-1	1-0
16	Tunbridge Wells	1-1	1-2	2-4	2-1	1-4	7-2	1-0	2-2	1-4	0-0	1-3	3-1	4-0	1-3	1-3	X	1-3	3-2
17	VCD Athletic	2-1	3-0	1-1	2-1	0-2	1-1	2-2	3-0	1-1	2-0	0-3	1-2	2-1	1-0	2-1	3-0	X	1-0
18	Whitstable	0-0	0-2	1-3	4-0	0-1	4-4	1-0	0-2	1-0	0-1	2-0	1-0	1-1	0-3	1-1	1-1	3-4	X

MANAGER OF THE MONTH AWARDS 1999-2000

September	T Hill	Thamesmead
October	S Waite	Slade Green
November	J Ward	Ramsgate
December	T Sampson	Deal Town
January	N Denly	Herne Bay
February	I Jenkins	Cray Wanderers
March	T Sampson	Deal Town
April	S Hearn	Chatham Town

FINAL LEAGUE TABLES 1999-2000
FIRST DIVISION NORTH

		P	W	D	L	F	A	Pts	GD
1	Thamesmead T Rs	20	13	3	4	44	16	44	28
2	Swanley Furness	20	11	6	3	42	27	38	15
3	Ashford T Res	20	10	4	6	36	23	31	13
4	Hastings Res	20	9	4	7	39	36	31	3
5	VCD Athletic Res	20	8	4	8	36	38	31	-2
6	Greenwich B Res	20	7	7	6	37	33	28	3
7	Chatham Res	20	8	4	8	34	44	28	-10
8	Dartford Res	20	7	6	7	33	36	27	-3
9	Erith Town Res	20	5	6	9	24	32	21	-8
10	Cray Wndrs Res	20	4	5	11	30	42	17	-12
11	Beckenham Res	20	1	5	14	15	42	8	-27

FIRST DIVISION SOUTH

		P	W	D	L	F	A	Pts	GD
1	Deal Town Res	18	14	3	1	54	20	45	34
2	Dover Res	18	12	3	3	37	16	39	21
3	Margate Res	18	10	4	4	35	20	34	15
4	Ramsgate Res	18	9	5	4	27	15	32	12
5	Sittingbourne Res	18	7	3	8	27	34	24	-7
6	Whitstable Res	18	6	4	8	44	36	22	8
7	Lordswood Res	18	6	4	8	21	25	22	-4
8	Folkestone I Res	18	5	4	9	36	34	19	2
9	Herne Bay Res	18	2	3	13	21	47	9	-26
10	Hythe Utd Res	18	2	1	15	17	68	7	-51

* points deducted/awarded

VCD Athletic players celebrating their 4-0 victory over Faversham Town in the Kent League Cup Final

PREMIER DIVISION CUP 1999-2000

FIRST ROUND

Hythe Town	v	Cray Wanderers	0-1		Whitstable Town	v	Greenwich Borough	4-1

SECOND ROUND

Beckenham Town	v	Erith Town	0-1		Canterbury City	v	Slade Green	SG W/O
Faversham Town	v	Herne Bay	2-0		Cray Wanderers	v	Deal Town	0-3
Lordswood	v	VCD Athletic	1*1, 1-5		Ramsgate	v	Tunbridge Wells	5-0
Thamesmead Town	v	Whitstable Town	1-2		Sheppey	v	Chatham Town	1-2

THIRD ROUND

Chatham Town	v	VCD Athletic	0-1		Erith Town	v	Ramsgate	1-2
Slade Green	v	Faversham	0-3		Whitstable Town	v	Deal Town	0-2

SEMI-FINALS (Two legs)

Faversham Town	v	Deal Town	1-2, 1-1		VCD Athletic	v	Ramsgate	1-1, 2-0

FINAL

Faversham Town	v	VCD Athletic	0-4		Note: Deal Town withdrew from the Cup Final

DIVISION ONE CUP 1999-2000

GROUP A

		1	2	3	4	5	6
1	Dartford Res	X	0-2	1-2	1-1	0-1	2-3
2	Greenwich Rs	2-2	X	2-2	1-0	1-2	3-3
3	Hastings Res	2-0	0-1	X	0-0	2-4	2-0
4	Lordswood Rs	1-0	3-3	3-0	X	3-6	6-1
5	Swanley Fnss	1-1	3-0	4-3	4-1	X	1-0
6	Ramsgate Res	1-2	0-1	1-2	2-0	0-1	X

GROUP C

		1	2	3	4	5
1	Cray Wndrs Res	X	2-0	1-2	0-1	1-0
2	Dover Reserves	1-0	X	2-3	0-0	3-1
3	Sittingbourne Res	3-4	4-0	X	2-1	8-0
4	Thamesmead Res	1-2	1-5	2-1	X	4-2
5	Whitstable Res	0-2	1-6	1-3	0-2	X

GROUP B

		1	2	3	4	5
1	Chatham Res	X	2-1	4-3	0-3	1-0
2	Erith Town Res		X		1-2	3-3
3	Herne Bay Res	0-5	0-2	X	0-2	0-2
4	Margate Res	4-0	4-0	2-1	X	1-3
5	VCD Athletic Res	3-4	3-3	5-1	4-2	X

GROUP D

		1	2	3	4	5
1	Ashford Reserves	X	1-0	1-3	7-1	1-1
2	Beckenham Res	0-2	X	2-4	1-3	3-2
3	Deal Town Res	3-4	4-0	X	2-1	8-0
4	Folkestone Inv Rs	1-2	1-5	2-1	X	4-2
5	Hythe Utd Res	0-2	1-6	1-3	0-2	X

SEMI-FINALS (Two legs)

Thamesmead Res	v	Swanley Furness	2-3, 1-1		Margate Reserves	v	Ashford Res	2-2, 0-2

FINAL

Ashford Reserves	v	Swanley Furness	2-1

GOALS OF THE MONTH AWARD 1999-2000

August	Greenwich Borough	Deal Town
September	Deal Town/Thamesmead Town	Folkestone Invicta
October	Deal Town/Greenwich Borough	Deal Town
November	Ramsgate	Deal Town
December	Beckenham Town	Ramsgate
January	Lordswood	Whitstable Town
February	Cray Wanderers	Ashford Town
March	Ramsgate/Whitstable Town	Deal Town
April	Chatham Town	Cray Wanderers

BECKENHAM TOWN

Secretary: Peter Palmer,36 Inglewood,Pixton Way, Selsdon, Surrey CR0 9LP
Tel: 020 86513363 Mobile 0374 728758

Ground: Eden Park Avenue, Beckenham, Kent   Tel: 0181 650 1066

Directions: M25, A21 to Bromley then follow signs to Beckenham. Ground 1 mile west of town off A214, 2 mins walk from Eden Park (BR) station - trains from London Bridge. Bus 264
Capacity: 4,000   **Seats:** 120   **Cover:** 120   **Floodlights:** Yes
Clubhouse: All day opening at weekends. Hot & cold food, teas, etc. Bar & dance area. Pool & fruit machines   **Club Shop:** Yes

HONOURS   London Spartan Lg Cup R-up 77-78 78-79, Kent Snr Tphy R-up 81-82 93-94, Kent Lg Cup R-up 84-85 92-93 (Div 2 Cup R-up 90-91)

PREVIOUS   **Leagues:** S. E. London Amtr 71-73; Metropolitan 73-75; London Spartan 75-82
Ground: Stanhope Grove, Beckenham (60 yrs)

RECORD   **Gate:** 720 v Berkhamsted F.A.Cup 94-95
Scorer: Ricky Bennett   **Appearances:** Lee Fabian

FACT FILE
Reformed: 1971
Nickname: Reds
Colours: Red &White/Red/Red
Change Colours:Blue & White/Blue/Blue
Midweek matchday: Tuesday
Programme: 8 pages, 50p
Editor:Secretary

CLUB PERSONNEL
Chairman: K.Bell
Vice Chairman: B Hollaway
Manager: Kevin Sugrue
Asst Manager: J Moore

CANTERBURY CITY

Secretary: T.B.A.
Ground: T.B.A.   **Directions:** T.B.A.
Capacity: 5,000 **Cover:** 200   **Seats:** 200   **Floodlights:** Yes   **Club Shop:** Yes
Clubhouse: Lounge bar open on matchdays. Snack bar, burgers, hot-dogs, tea, coffee, etc
HONOURS   Kent Lg Div 2 Cup 49-50 89-90, Div 1 Cup 49-50; Kent Sen. Cup 53-54; Kent Sen. Trophy 79-80; Kent I'mediate Cup 73-74; Kent Messenger Trophy 74-75; Frank Norris Mem. Shield 88-89 89-90; Kent Lge Div 2 Champ Res 90-91
PREVIOUS   **Leagues:** Kent 47-59; Metropolitan 59-60; Southern 60-94
Name: Canterbury Waverley   **Grounds:** Wincheap Grove, Bretts Corner 47-58 Kingsmead Stadium 58-99
BEST SEASONFA Cup: 1st Rd 64-65, 0-6 v Torquay; 68-69, 0-1 v Swindon
CLUB RECORDS **Attendance:** 3,542 v Chelsea, Friendly **Win:** 10-0 v Deal Town (H), Southern Lge 30/1/65 **Defeat:** 0-10 v Greenwich B(H) Kent Lg. 14.8.99. **Goalscorer:** Wilf Heathcote 113 (48-51) **Appearances:** John Carragher 627 (60-70) **Fee Paid:** £2,000 for Graham Knight (Maidstone United) **Fee Received:** £2,000 for Dave Wiltshire (Gillingham)
Players progressing: R Gawler (Southend 49), A Hughes (Grimsby 54), A Nugent (Darlington 56), J Richardson (Southport 56), T Horsfall (Cambridge Utd), J Murray (Wolves), K Hill, M Weatherley (Gillingham), T Norton (Brighton), P Hilton (Brighton 73), D Wiltshire (Gillingham 74), G Pugh (Torquay 84)

FACT FILE
Founded: 1947   Nickname: The City
Sponsors: T.B.A.
Colours: Green & white/white/green & white
Change: Red & black/black/red
Midweek matchday: Wednesday
Reserve's League: Kent Lge Div 1
Programme: 32 pages, 50p
Editor: Keith Smith (01227 456116)
99-00 Captain: Lee Jones
Top scorer: lee Jones (11)
P.o.Y.: Lee Jones
Supporters P.o.Y.: Lee Jones

CLUB PERSONNEL
Chairman: T.B.A.
Vice Chairman: TBA
President: V H Heslop
Comm Manager: T.B.A.
Managers: Meirion George/Simon Tutt
Physio: T.B.A.

CHATHAM TOWN

Secretary: Brian Burcombe, 4 Hallwood Close, Parkwood, Rainham, Kent ME8 9NT
Tel: 01634 363419

Ground: Maidstone Road Sports Ground, Maidstone Road, Chatham, Kent Tel: 01634 812194

Directions: M2, A229 Chatham turn-off, follow signs to Chatham, ground one and a half miles on right opposite garage. 1 mile from Chatham (BR)
Capacity: 5,000   **Seats:** 500   **Cover:** 1,000   **Floodlights:** Yes
Clubhouse: Matchdays and functions

HONOURS   Kent Lg(9) 1894-95 03-05 24-25 26-27 71-72 73-74 76-77 79-80 (R-up 02-03 23-24 25-26 70-71 74-75 80-81, Lg Cup 71-72 76-77 (R-up(3)), Thames & Medway Comb.(5) 1896-97 04-06 19-20 23-24, Kent Snr Cup 1888-89 1904-05 10-11 18-19, Kent Snr Shield 19-20

PREVIOUS   **Names:** Chatham FC; Medway FC (1970s) **Leagues:** Southern (several spells); Aetolian 59-64; Metropolitan 64-68;Kent (Sev. spells)
Ground: Great Lines, Chatham 1882-90

BEST SEASON   **FA Cup:** QF 1888-89 (incl 2-0 v Nottm Forest 2-0) **FA Trophy:** 3rd Rd 70-71
RECORD   **Gate:** 5,000 v Gillingham, 1980

FACT FILE
Founded: 1882
Nickname: Chats
Sponsors: Topps Scaffolding
Colours: Red & black/black/black
Change Colours: Yellow & green
Midweek matchday: Tuesday
Programme: 24 pages, 60p
Editor: Tony Smith

CLUB PERSONNEL
Chairman: P Enright
President:
Manager: Steve Hearn
Asst Manager:Peter Coupland

CRAY WANDERERS

Secretary: Mr Greg Mann,25A old Road, london Se13 5SU (0208318 9604)
Ground: Bromley F.C. Hayes Lane, Bromley, Kent BR2 9EF (0181 460 5291 or 0181 313 3992)

Directions: One mile from Bromley South (BR). Buses 316, 146 and 119 passground.
Junction 4 off M25, then A21 towards London

Capacity: 5,000   **Cover:** 2,500   **Seats:** 1,300   **Floodlights:** Yes

Clubhouse: Open pub hours (freehouse). Hot & cold food available   Club Shop: Yes

HONOURS   London Lg(2) 56-58 (Lg Cup 54-55), Aetolian Lg 62-63 (Lg Cup 63-64), GtrLondon
Lg 65-66 (Lg Cup(2) 64-66), Metropolitan Lg Cup 70-71 (Amtr Cup(2) 66-68),
London Spartan Lg(2) 76-78, Kent Lg 01-02 80-81 (R-up 79-80 90-91, Lg Cup 83-
84), Kent Snr Tphy 92-93, Kent Amtr Cup(4) 30-31 62-65

PREVIOUS   Leagues: Kent 1894-1903 6-7 9-14 34-38; W Kent 03-06 07-09; London 20-34 51-
59; Kent Amtr 38-39 46-51; S London All 43-46; Aetolian 59-64; GtrLondon 64-66;
Metropolitan 66-71; London Metropolitan 71-75; London Spartan 75-78
      Grounds: Star Lane; Tothills; Twysden; Fordcroft; Grassmeade, St Mary Cray

CLUB RECORDS Gate: 1,523 v Stamford, F.A. Vase QF 79-80
      Goalscorer: Ken Collishaw, 272   **Appearances:** John Dorey c500, 61-72
      Win: 15-0 v Sevenoaks, 1894-95   **Defeat:** 1-11 v Bromley, 20-21

FACT FILE
Founded: 1860
Nickname: Wands
Sponsors: N.Hillman & Sons
Colours: Amber & black
Change Colours: Blue/white
Midweek matchday: Wednesday
Programme: 32 pages, 50p
Editor/Press Officer: Greg Mann
Tel: 0181 318 9604(H) 0171 500 4496B)

CLUB PERSONNEL
Chairman: Gary Hillman
President: Bill Faulkner
1st Team Manager:Ian jenkins
Asst.Manager: Bobby Pittaway
Reserve Team Manager: T.B.A.

DEAL TOWN

Secretary: Miss Lynne Fox, 32 Manor Road, Deal, Kent CT14 9BX   Tel: 01304 361163

Ground: Charles Sports Ground, St Leonards Road, Deal, Kent   Tel: 01304 375623

Directions: A258 through Walmer, left into Cornwell Road, continue intoHamilton Road, veer left
into Mill Rd, follow round to right into Victoria Road, right into St Leonards Road, ground 100 yards
on right. 1 mile from both Walmerand Deal BR stations. Local buses stop near ground
Capacity: 2,000   **Seats:** 150   **Cover:** 500   **Floodlights:** Yes

Clubhouse: Matchdays & functions. Bar. Tea bar with hot & cold food   Club Shop: No

HONOURS   Kent Lg 53-54 (R-up 88-89, Lg Cup 57-58 81-82 (R-up 94-95), Kent Snr Tphy 94-
95 R-up 82-83 90-91, Gtr London Lg Cup 67-68, Aetolian LgR-up 59-60

PREVIOUS   Leagues: Kent 09-59; Aetolian 59-63; Southern 63-66; Gtr London 66-71

RECORDS   Gate: 4,000 v Billy Wright showbiz XI, Feb '61
      Scorer: Joe Brayne 175
      Appearances: Alan Barrow 544 (recent times)
Player progressing: Danny Wallace (Southampton)

FACT FILE
Founded: 1908
Nickname: Town
Sponsors: Mencare Ltd
Colours: Black & white hoops/white/b & w hoops
Change: Yellow & Blue halves/blue/blue
Midweek matchday: Tuesday
Reserves' Lge: Winstonlead Div 2
Programme: 32 pages, 50p
Editor: Colin Adams (01304 372784)

CLUB PERSONNEL
Chairman: Roy Smith
Vice-Chairman: Graham Jones
Fixture Sec: Colin Adams (01304 372784)

ERITH TOWN
Secretary: Jim Davie, 6 Dashwood Close, Broomfield Road, Bexleyheath, Kent. DA6 7NU
            Tel: 020 8306 7068

Ground: Erith Sports Stadium, Avenue Road, Erith, Kent DA8 3AJ (01322 350 271)
Directions: Off the A206 at Erith, into Victoria Road, then left at T junction into Avenue Road.
First right along driveway which leads to leisure car park, stadium on left.600 yards from Erith BR.
Capacity: 1,450   **Seats:** 1,006   **Cover:** 60Floodlights: Yes (156 lux)
Clubhouse: Use Leisure Facilities   Shop: No

PREVIOUS   Leagues: London Metropolitan Sunday 1959-91, London-Spartan 1991-96
            Names: Woolwich Town 1959-89 and 1990-97 Woolwich Heathway 1998-90

CLUB RECORDS Appearances: Eric Nwaokobia 162 (9)
            Victory: 5-0 v Oakwood ,F.A.Vase **Defeat:** 0-8 v Deal
            Goalscorer: Lee Putnam 23   **Goals in Season:** Ben Hackett 14 in 99-00
            Attendance: 136 v Lewes F.A.Cup 1Q 99-00

HONOURS: Met Sunday Lge: Senior Section 1966, 1971, 1975.
            London Spartan Lge: Intermediate Cup R-up 1994 & 1995. Div 1 R-up: 1995.
            London F.A. Intermediate Cup R-up 1995. London F.A. Senior Cup R-up 2000

FACT FILE
Founded: 1959 Nickname: The Dockers
Colours: White/navy blue/red
Change Colours: Yellow/black/black
Midweek matchday: Monday
Reserve League: Kent League
Programme: 40-52 pages £1.00 (Ian Birrell)
99-00 Captain & P.o.Y.: Paul Reeves
Top Scorer: Ben Hackett
CLUB PERSONNEL
Chairman: Albert Putnam
Vice Chairmen: Phil Legg
President:Cyril Rebak
Manager: Mickey Watts Coach: John Adams
General Manager: Ian Birrell
Press Secretary: David Salmon

Top: Cray Wanderers Back Row (l-r): Bobby Pittaway (assistant manager), Jake Watkins, Matt Smith, Marc Petters, Mark Dudley, Mark Brooks, Sean Cooney, Adam Woods, Andre Vincent (physio) Front Row (l-r): Peter Cirillo, Jamie Wood, Jon Conran, Adam Heaslewood, Ian Jenkins (player/manager), Danny Sweeting. Photo: Jerry Dowlen

Centre: Herne Bay FC. Back Row (players) (l-r): Jamie Allen, Graham Trewinard, Rob Eyres, Gareth Williams, Barry Jefferies, Ray Aboagye, Sean Malyon, Danny Stanton, Dean Henry, Geoff Record (Manager). Front Row: Antony Bathurst, Paul Gurr, Glen Sheather, Andy Thompson, Gary Ware. Photo: Alan Coomes

Bottom: Canterbury City Back Row (l-r): Freddie Doncaster (coach), Chris Wood, Andy Keir, Mark Rees, Rob Appleton, Lee Gardner, Nick Hopkin, Pat Sutcliffe, Lee Bosson (player/manager), Mick Flockhart, Steve Cummings (asst mngr) Front Row (l-r): Dr David Chapman-Jones (club doctor), Garry Elliott, Jimmy Smith, Lee Jones, James Wootton, Carl Otto, Sammy Spence. Photo: Courtesy of Canterbury Times

FAVERSHAM TOWN

Secretary: Reg Parr

Ground: New Stadium, Salters Lane, Faversham, Kent (01795 532738)

Directions: On A2 (Canterbury road) just west of town
Capacity: 2,000   Seats: 350   Cover: 1,500   Floodlights: Yes
Clubhouse: Open matchdays (Sat/Sun/Tues) Wed/Thurs. Snacks sold

HONOURS Kent Lg 69-70 70-71 77-78 89-90, R-up 87-88, Lg Cup 70-71 90-91, R-up 82-83,
Kent Snr Tphy 76-77 77-78 (R-up 87-88 88-89),
Kent Amtr Cup 56-57 58-59 71-72 72-73 73-74

PREVIOUS **Leagues:** Aetolian 59-64; Metropolitan 64-71; Athenian 71-76
Grounds: Ashford Rd 1901-46; Gordon Square 46-58

RECORD **Gate:** 1,400 v Sheppey Utd, 1949
Scorer: Tony Rudd 43   **Appearances:** Bob Mason
Win: 8-0 v Greenwich B., Aug'89   **Defeat:** 0-9 v Sittingbourne, Jan '82

FACT FILE
Founded: 1901
Nickname: Town
Colours: White/blue/red
Change Colours: Red/white/blue
Midweek matchday: Tuesday
Reserves' League: Kent Lg Div 2
Programme: 16 pages, 40p
Editor: Quiram Aisani

CLUB PERSONNEL
Chairman: Sal Aisani
President: Cris Aisani
Commercial Mgr: Terry Whitehead
Manager: John Glover
Coach: Bob Mason

GREENWICH BOROUGH

Secretary: Mehmet Ozkan, 1 Honour Oak Park. Forest Hill, London SE23 1DX 02829 020 Tel
Nos: 020 8291 9933 (H) 020 8291 7479 (W & F) 0961 328889 (M)
Ground: Harrow Meadow, Eltham Green Rd, Eltham, London SE9   Tel: 0181 850 5360

Directions: South Circular (A205) to McDonalds, grd opposite.
1 mile from both Eltham and Kidbrooke BR stations
Capacity: 2,500   Seats: 5o   Cover: 50Floodlights: Yes
Clubhouse: Yes

HONOURS London Spartan Lg 79-80 (Lg Cup 82-83), Kent Lg 86-87 87-88 (Lg Cup 84-85
86-87), Kent Snr Tphy 84-85, FA Vase 5th Rd 89-90

PREVIOUS **Leagues:** South London Alliance; Kent Amateur; London Spartan 77-84
Ground: Erith & Belvedere F.C. 1992-93
Name: London Borough of Greenwich

RECORD **Gate:** 2,000 v Charlton, floodlight opening, 1978
Defeat : 0-8 v Faversham Town, August 1989

FACT FILE
Founded: 1928
Nickname: Boro
Colours: All Red
Change Colours: All white
Midweek matchday: Tuesday
Programme: 16 pages, 50p
Editor: Keith Harmer
Tel: (07930 618911 (M)

CLUB PERSONNEL
President: R Moore
Chairman: P Meagan
Manager: Dave Mehmet
Asst Manager: R Dowling

HERNE BAY

Secretary: L Gladwish, 41 Strangers Lane, Canterbury, Kent CT1 3XJ   Tel: 01227 451529

Ground: Winch's Field, Stanley Gardens, Herne Bay, Kent   Tel: 01227 374156

Directions: Leave new Thanet Way at Herne Bay/Canterbury exit. Follow signs toHerne
Bay via Canterbury Road. After railway bridge (1/2 mile), take first leftinto
SpencerRoad, then first left into Stanley Gardens, Ground on left
Capacity: 4,000   Seats: 200   Cover: 1,500   Floodlights: Yes
Clubhouse: Open matchdays   Club Shop: Yes

HONOURS Kent Lg 91-92 94-95 96-97 97-98, (R-up 92-93), Div 2 62-63 63-64, R-up92-
93(res) 94-95(res), Lg Cup 96-97, R-up 78-79 97-98, Div 2 Cup 53-54; Kent Snr Tphy 78-79, 96-
97; Kent Amtr Cup 57-58 (R-up 58-59 63-64 68-69 72-73); Aetolian LgDiv 2 62-63 63-64 (Lg Cup
R-up 62-63), Div 2 Cup 62-63 63-64; Athenian Lg Div 2 70-71 (Lg Cup 66-67); Kent Amtr Lg Cup
53-54 54-55; Thames & Medway Comb. CupR-up 61-62; FA Cup 4th Qual. Rd 70-71 86-87.

PREVIOUS **Leagues:** East Kent, Faversham & Dist, Canterbury & Dist, Kent Amateur,
Kent 53-59, Aetolian 59-64, Athenian 64-74   **Ground:** Memorial Park 1886-1953

RECORDS **Attendance:** 2,303 v Margate, FA Cup 4th Qual. Rd 70-71
Win: 15-1; v Canterbury Gas & Water, Kent Amateur Lge 1952
Defeat: 0-11 v RAF Manston, Kent Amateur Lge 1935
Fee received: £3,000 for Mark Munday (Gravesend) 1994

FACT FILE
Founded: 1886Nickname: The Bay
Colours: Blue & white halves
Change Colours: Red & black halves
Midweek matchday: Tuesday
Reserves' League: Kent Lge Div One
Programme: 36 pages, 70p
Editor/Press Off.: Doug Smith (01227742182)
99-00Captain: Barry Jeffries
P.o.Y.: Andy Thompson
Top Scorer: Scott Appleton

CLUB PERSONNEL
Chairman: J Bathurst
Vice Chairman: W Dordoy
President: J Hodkinson
Manager: Nick Denly
Asst. Manager:Gerry Allen
Physio: J.Hodkinson

Top: Faversham's Femi Oguoshun heads clear from Chatham's Lou Bovis in the FA Vase First Round.
Photo: Alan Coomes

Above: Sheppey
United FC.
Photo: M Sandom

Right: Tunbridge
Wells FC. Back Row
(l-r): Julian Nye,
Steve Clark
(Player/Mngr), Wayne
Balmer, Luke Hills,
Garry Valli (capt),
Andy Garrett, Andy
Boyle, Steve
Gibbons. Front Row:
Darren Walmsley,
Pete McCleod, Jason
Bourne, Ryan Nicklin,
Grant Styles, Robin
Jenner.

HYTHE UNITED (1992)

Secretary: Martin R Giles, 21 Wych Elm Way, Hythe, Kent. CT21 6QE
Tel: 01303 265962 (H) 01303 267619 (B)

Ground: Reachfields Stadium, Fort Rd, Hythe, Kent. Tel: 01303 264932 or 238256

Directions: On A259 west out of Hythe, turn left after light railway lights (Fort Road), entrance at end
Capacity: 3,000   Seats: 400   Cover: 2,400   Floodlights: Yes

Clubhouse: Bar open weekends/matchdays & training nights
Club Shop: No

HONOURS None as Hythe United

PREVIOUS Leagues: Kent County Lge

RECORD Attendance: 1,655 v Crystal Palace 97-98

FACT FILE
Founded: 1992
Sponsor: T.B.A.
Colours: All Red
Change Colours: All blue
Midweek Matchday: Tuesday
Youth League :East Kent Youth
Programme: 50p
Editor: Martin Wybrow
99-00- Captain: Andy Laker
Top Scorer: Dave Linstrem
P.o.Y.:Steve Chivers

CLUB PERSONNEL
Chairman: David Clapson
President: Rt Hon Michael Howard QC
Press Officer: Richard Giles
Manager: David Linstrem
Physio: Dave Garlinge

LORDSWOOD

Secretary: Steve Lewis, Sunnybrook, Gorsewood Road, Hartley, Longfield, Kent DA3 7DF.
Tel: 01474 708233 (H) 01474 708233 (B) 07775 541573 (M)

Ground: Lordswood Sports & Social Club   Tel: 01634 669138
North Dane Way, Walderslade, Chatham, Kent ME5 9XX
Directions:

Capacity: 600   Seats: 125   Cover: No   Floodlights: Yes

Clubhouse: Yes   **Club Shop:** No

HONOURS None

PREVIOUS **Leagues:** Kent County Lge

RECORD **Attendance:** 386

FACT FILE
Founded: 1968
Nickname: Lords
Colours: Orange/black/black
Change Colours: All green
Midweek Matchday: Tuesday/Thursday
Reserve or Youth League: Both
Programme: Yes
Editor: D Harman

CLUB PERSONNEL
Chairman: J. O'Halloran
Vice Chairman: D Caulfield
Press Officer: D Harman
Manager: B Zillwood

RAMSGATE
Secretary/Press Officer: Steve Lancaster. 66 Park Avenue, Birchington, Kent Tel: 01843 597703

Ground: Southwood Stadium, Prices Avenue, Ramsgate, Kent   Tel: 01843 591662

Directions: From London on A229, A253 into Ramsgate - left into Netherhill atr'bout, right into Ashburnham Rd, right into Southwood Rd. 15 mins walk from Ramsgate BR station; walk thru Warre Recreation Ground, along St Lawrence HighStr., left at `White Horse', follow Southwood Rd and turn right into PricesAvenue

Capacity: 5,000   Seats: 400   Cover: 600   Floodlights: Yes

Clubhouse: Open matchdays & private functions. Two bars, two pool tables,darts. Hot & cold food on matchdays   Club Shop: No

HONOURS Kent Lg 49-50 55-56 56-57 (Lg Cup 48-49 92-93 93-94 94-95) Kent I'mediate Cup 54-55, Kent Snr Cup 63-64, Thames & Medway Cup 60-61, KentSnr Shield 60-61,   Kent Floodlit Tphy 69-70, Kent Snr Tphy(2) 87-89

PREVIOUS **Leagues:** Southern 59-75
Name: Ramsgate Athletic

RECORDS **Gate:** 5,200 v Margate, 56-57
Scorer: Mick Williamson
Win: 9-1 v Crockenhill, Kent League Cup 22/1/94

FACT FILE
Founded: 1946
Nickname: Rams
Sponsors: Hoverspeed
Colours: Red & white
Change Colours: White/blue/blue
Midweek matchday: Tuesday
Reserves' League: Kent Lge Div. Two
Programme: 28 pages
Editor: Steve Redford (01843 596138)

CLUB PERSONNEL
Chairman: R Lawson
Vice Chairman: C Payne
President: Tom Pendry
Commercial Manager: Martin Power
Tel: 01843 597703
Manager/Coach: Lennie Lee
Asst Manager: Dave Bostock
Physio: John Burroughs

Right:
Greenwich
Borough
Photo: Alan
Coomes

Above: Herne Bay FC. Back Row (l-r): Nick Denly (Manager), Andy Thompson, Barry Jeffreys, Ian Hossick, Scott Appleton, Martin Collins, Ray Aboagye, Gareth Williams, Ray Kelly (com), Gavin Wright, Glen Sheather, Steve Sodje, Doug Smith (Press Officer), Gerry Allen (Assistant Manager). Front Row (l-r): Wayne Ball, Antony Bathurst, Andy Bishop, Shane Suter, Gary Pullen, John Bathurst (Chairman), Paul Gladwish (Secretary), Joe Hodkinson (Physio), Harry Roberts (Coach)

Right: Hythe United
Back Row (l-r): Steve
Hobbs, Rhys Taylor-
Ryall (now Dover), Colin
Binder, Mark Towse,
Martin Reene, Steve
Chivers, Andy
Bigginton, Darryl
Haden, Jason Brazier,
Gary Miller, Dave
Linstrem (Manager)
Front Row (l-r): 'Snowy'
Prebble, Paul Stanton,
Ben Bartlett, Andy
Laker (captain), Lloyd
Partner, Steve Ridley,
Dave Gear.
Photo: Martin Wray

SHEPPEY UNITED

Secretary: Barry H Bundock, Dunedin, 104 Southsea Ave., Minster, Sheerness, Kent ME12 2NH
Tel & Fax: 01795 876025 (H) 077127 80322 (Mobile)
Ground: Sittingbourne F.C. - Central Park, Eurolink,Sittingbourne, Kent ME10 3SB
Tel: 01795 435077 Fax: 01474 814501
Directions: Through Sittingbourne on main A2, club signposted clearly and regularly from both east and west. 1 mile from Sittingbourne BR station
Capacity: 8,000   **Cover:** 3,300   **Seats:** 2,000   **Floodlights:** 420 lux
HONOURS   Kent Lg(6) 05-07 27-28 72-73 74-75 78-79 94-95, (R-up 03-04 04-05 77-78 83-84, Lg Cup 75-76 78-79, Div 2(res) 32-33 84-85 (R-up 1894-95 1979-80);Thames & Medway Comb. 08-09 12-13 22-23 25-26 28-29 55-56; Kent Amtr Cup 45-4651-52; Kent Snr Shield 77-78; Kent Snr Cup R-up(3); Gtr London Lg 64-65.
BEST SEASON   **FA Cup:** 6th Qual. Rd 1919-20
FA Trophy: 1st Rd Proper 85-86
PREVIOUS   **Leagues:** Southern 1894-1901 84-91; Kent 01-27 32-59 72-84; Aetolian 59-; Gtr London 64-65; Metropolitan Lg 65-71
Name: Sheppey Athletic/Ites
Ground: Botany Road, St Georges Avenue, Sheerness (pre-1992)
RECORD   **Gate:** 4,000 v Sittingbourne, Kent Senior Trophy 1927 (at Botany Road)
Players progressing: E C Harper (England, Blackburn, Spurs, Preston)

FACT FILE

Founded: 1890
Nickname: Islanders or Ites
Colours: Red & white/white
Change colours: Blue & white stripes
Midweek matchday: Tuesday
Programme: 20 pages, 50p

CLUB PERSONNEL

Chairman:Chris Newman
Manager: Geoff Record

SLADE GREEN

Secretary: Bruce Smith, 15 Gumping Rd, Orpington, Kent BR5 1RX Tel: 01689 858782

Ground: The Small Glen, Moat Lane, Slade Green, Erith, Kent Tel: 01322 351077

Directions: Off A206 between Erith & Dartford.
400 yards from Slade Green BR station. Buses 89 & B13
Capacity: 3,000   **Seats:** 150   **Cover:** 400   **Floodlights:** Yes
Clubhouse: Yes; Hall, Directors Lounge & Canteen   **Club Shop:** No

HONOURS   Kent Snr Tphy 91-92 (R-up 80-81); Kent Lg Cup 82-83; Kent Amtr Lg 52-53 53-54 60-61 (Lg Cup 60-61); Kent Intermediate Cup 61-62; Kent Benevolent Cup46-47; West Kent 60-61 65-66; Dartford Lg R-up 48-49 (Lg Cup 47-48 (R-up 46-47)); Erith Hospitals Cup 46-47 48-49; Gtr London Lg R-up 68-69; Plumstead Challenge Cup 48-49
PREVIOUS   Leagues: Dartford 46-52; Kent Amateur 52-62; Greater London 62-70
Name: Slade Green Athletic 46-86
RECORDS   **Attendance:** 3,000 v Millwall, friendly 25/7/92
Goalscorer: Colin Dwyer   **Appearances:** Colin Dwyer
Win: 14-0 v Island Social, Kent Amtr Lge 1953   **Defeat:** 1-9 v Whitstable Greater London 64-65
Players progressing : Roy Dwight (Nottm Forest), Alan Clark (Charlton) , Fred Lucas (Charlton)Tommy Tute (Millwall Jan. 1999)

FACT FILE
Founded: 1946
Nickname: The Green
Sponsor: T.B.A.
Colours: All white
Change Colours: Yellow /black/blackl
Midweek matchday: Tuesday
Reserve League:
Programme: 44 pages, incl. with admission
Editor: Robert Smith (01322 287982)

CLUB PERSONNEL

Chairman: Brian Smith
President: William Dudley
Press Officer: Robert Smith (01322 287982)
Manager: Srteve Waite
Coach: Micky Orme
Physio: Alan Martin

THAMESMEAD TOWN

Secretary: Peter Andrews,16 Dolphine Close,North Thamesmead, London Se28 (020 8310 7611)
Ground: Bayliss Avenue, Thamesmead, London SE28 8NJ Tel: 0181 311 4211

Directions: By road: From Dartford tunnel A2 to London, exit Danson Interchange and follow signs for Thamesmead and Abbey Wood. From Blackheath tunnel exit on south side and follow signs to Woolwich, to Plumstead and then to Thamesmead

From Abbey Wood (BR) north east along Harrow Manor Way, into Crossway at 3rd r'bout, Bayliss Av. is 3rd right (Bexley bus 272 stops in Crossway near Bayliss Av.

Capacity: 400   **Seats:** 125   **Cover:** 125   **Floodlights:** Yes   **Club Shop:** No

Clubhouse: Mon-Fri 6-11pm, Sat 12-11pm, Sun 12-3 & 7-10.30pm. Double bar,lounge, dance-floor, children's games room, video machines, hot & cold food.New members Bar

HONOURS   Spartan Lg Div 3 79-80 (Lg Cup 84-85 86-87; I'mediate champs 85-86);Kent I'mediate Cup 83-84 94-95; 4 promotions & 9 trophies (inc London & Kent FA Cups) in progress thru Spartan I'mediate Divs, 1980-87; Kent Lge Div 2 94-95, Div 2 Cup 94-95

PREVIOUS   Leagues: London Spartan 80-91
Ground: Meridian Sports Ground, Charlton

RECORDS   **Attendance:** 400 v Wimbledon, ground opening 1988
Appearances: Delroy D'Oyley   **Win :** 9-0 v Kent Police, Kent League 19/4/94

FACT FILE
Founded: 1970
Nickname: The Mead
Sponsors: Courage Brewery
Colours: Green& White/Green/Green
Change Colours: All blue
Midweek matchday: Tuesday
Reserves League: Winstonlead Kent D2
Programmes: Yes. 50p
Editor:

CLUB PERSONNEL
Chairman: Peter Andrews
Vice Chairman: John Kelly
President: Albert Panting
Press Officer: Matthew Panting
Manager: Terry Hill
Coach: Paul Blades
Physio: Allen Martin

Top: Ramsgate's Steve Coatham heads clear from Woodbridge's Paul Smith.
Photo: Alan Coomes

Centre: Enter the Gladiators: Newcastle Town v Deal Town. FA Vase Semi-Final First Leg.
Photo: Keith Clayton

Bottom: The Whitstable goalkeeper with assistance from one of his own defenders going for the ball from a Tunbridge Wells attack.
Photo: Kim Botten

TUNBRIDGE WELLS

Secretary: Mrs J.Rogers, Tappington Farm Cottage, Three oaks Lane, Wadhurst, East Sussex TN5 6PU
Ground: Culverden Stadium, Culverden Down, Tunbridge Wells, Kent TN4 Tel: 01892 520517

Directions: Leaving town on main Tonbridge rd (A26), turn left opposite`The Hooden' pub - grd half mile. 1 mile from Tunbridge Wells Central(BR).
Served by any Tunbridge Wells-Tonbridge bus - to St Johns
Capacity: 3,750   Seats: 350   Cover: 1,000   Floodlights: Yes
Clubhouse: Open matchdays and as required   Club Shop: Yes

HONOURS   Kent Lg 84-85 (R-up 68-69, Lg Cup 74-75 77-78 85-86 87-88)
Kent SnrTphy R-up 85-86 91-92
PREVIOUS   **Names:** None. predecessors: T . Wells FC 1886-1910 47-50 T. Wells Rgrs 03-09 63-67; T. Wells Utd 51-62
Grounds: Down Lane 1906; Combley Park 06-10; Swiss Cottage 06-14;Down Farm 19-39; St Johns 47-50; Eridge Road 50-67
RECORDS   **Attendance:** 967 v Maidstone United, FA Cup 1969
Goalscorer: John Wingate 151   **Appearances:** Tony Atkins 410
Win: 10-0 v Deal (H), May'86
Defeat: 1-11 v Deal Town (H), 20/2/93

FACT FILE
Founded: 1886
Reformed: 1967
Nickname: Wells
Colours: Red/White/Red
Change Colours: Yellow/navy/navy
Midweek Matchday: Tuesday
Reserve League:
Programme: 20 pages, 50p
Editor: Secretary

CLUB PERSONNEL
Chairman: R.Rogers
Vice Chairman:N.Sales
Manager: Steve Clark

VICKERS CRAYFORD, DARTFORD ATHLETIC

Secretary: Brian Norris 47 Oxenden Wood Road, Chelsfield Park, Orpington, KentBR6 6HP
Tel: 01689 854302
Ground: Thamesmead Town FC, Bayliss Avenue, Thamesmead,London SE28 8NJ
Tel: 0181 311 4211 (Temporary Groundshare)
Home Ground (Pending floodlights) Oakwood,Old Road, Crayford, Kent DA1 4DN
Home clubhouse: Lounge Bar every day and evening. Plus snack bar on matchdays.
Directions: From Abbey Wood (BR) north east along Harrow Manor Way, intoCrossway at 3rd r'bout, Bayliss Av. is 3rd right (Bexley bus 272 stops inCrossway near Bayliss Av. By road: From Dartford tunnel A2 to London, exitDanson Interchange and follow signs for Thamesmead and Abbey Wood. From Blackheath tunnel exit on south side and follow signs to Woolwich, to Plumsteadand then to Thamesmead.
Capacity: 400   **Seats:** 125   **Cover:** 125   **Floodlights:** Yes
PREVIOUS   **League:** Kent County. **Grounds:** Flamingo Park, Sidcup (pre 1994);
VCD Sports & Social Club,Old Road, Crayford
RECORD   **Victory:** 8-2 v DealTown 7.2.98   **Defeat:** 1-5 v Ramsgate 25.10.97
HONOURS   Kent County Cup 61-62, 63-64, 94-95, R-Up: 84-85, 89-90. Kent County Lg Div One 96-97 Kent County Premier 96-97. West Kent Cup 87-88.Kent Lge Cup R-up: Winners 99-00 ,Runners up 98-99. Kent Intermediate Shield (2) R-up(1), Erith Hosp Cup x4, R-Up x4

FACT FILE
Founded: 1916
Nickname: The Vickers
Sponsors: MB Fire Protection
Colours: Green & white/green/green
Change Colours: Blue & white/blue/blue
Midweek matchday: Wednesday
Programme: 40 pages 50p

CLUB PERSONNEL
Chairman: Michael Bonello
Manager: Martin Ford
Assistant Manager: Peter Burke
Coach: Roy Passey
Physio: Peter Burke

1999-00
Captain: Terry Barry
Top Scorer:Richard Dimmock
Player of the Year: Steve Roberts

WHITSTABLE TOWN

Secretary: George Corney, 46 Elizabeth Way, Herne Bay, Kent CT6 6ET (01227 363496)
Ground: Belmont Road, Belmont, Whitstable, Kent Tel: 01227 266012

Directions: From Thanet Way (A299), left at Tescos r'bout and down MillstroodRd - ground at bottom of road, 400yds from Whitstable (BR) station. Car park atGrimshall Rd entrance
Capacity: 2,000   Cover: 1,000   Seats: 500   Floodlights: Yes   Club Shop: Yes
Clubhouse: Social & recreation purposes, open all matchdays. Bar. Hot food &drinks at tea-bar

HONOURS   Kent Lg Div 2 27-28 33-34 49-50 (Lg Cup 79-80 (R-up 89-90 91-92)), KentAmtr Lg East 60-61, Kent Amtr Cup 28-29, Kent Snr Tphy R-up 78-79 89-90 92-93,Gtr London Lg Cup R-up 65-66, Kent Amtr Cup 28-29, Kent Midweek Lg Cup 92-93
PREVIOUS   **Leagues:** E. Kent 1897-1909; Kent 09-59; Aetolian 59-60; Kent Amtr 60-62 63-64; S E Anglian 62-63; Gtr London 64-67; Kent Premier 67-68 (also in New Brompton, Thanet & Faversham & Dist. Lges over the years)
Names: Whitstable Utd (pre-1886); Whitstable Swifts 93-95; WhitstableTown 95-1905; Whitstable FC 08-66
RECORDS   **Gate:** 2,500 v Gravesend & Northfleet, FA Cup 3rd Qual. Rd,19/10/87
Goalscorer: Barry Godfrey   **Appearances:** Frank Cox 429 (1950-60)
Win: 18-0 v Greenstreet (H), Faversham & Dist. Lge 20-21
Defeat: 0-10 v Sittingbourne (A), FA Cup 1st Qual. Rd 62-63

FACT FILE
Founded: 1885
Nickname: Oystermen, Reds, Natives
Club Sponsors: D & J Tyres
Shirt Sponsor: McDonalds
Colours: Red & White//White Red & Black
Change Colours: Yellow/blue/yellow
Midweek matchday: Tuesday
Programme: 48 pages, 50p
Editor/Press Off: Bernie Thompson)

CLUB PERSONNEL
Chairman: Joe Brownett
Vice Chairman: Trevor Rapley
President: George Gifford
Manager: Simon Kay/Doug Bosson
Asst Manager: John Crabbe
Physio: Tony Pattenden

BRITISH ENERGY KENT COUNTY FOOTBALL LEAGUE
Founded: 1922

President: W C Manklow   **Chairman:** C T C Windiate

General Secretary: B H Bundock
"Dunedin", Southsea Ave, Minster, Sheerness, Kent ME12 2NH   Tel: 01795 876025

The season commenced with the League Champions, Knatchbull playing Inter-Regional Challenge Cup winners Sevenoaks Town for the "GR Roofing" Champions Trophy. The inaugural match in this Competition proved to be an entertaining curtain raiser to the season. Played at Hatch Park, Mersham on a superb playing surface it took extra time to separate the teams before Knatchbull ran out eventual winners by four goals to one. Not only was soccer the winner as the net proceeds were donated to Cancer Research, this being the sponsor's first nominated beneficiary.

Once again the Premier Division provided an exciting climax to the season with Snodland pipping Bearsted by just one point to land their first ever Premier Division title. Early season form suggested Maidenhead United would be the front-runner as the 'Stones' commenced their first season in the top flight with five consecutive victories. However they can be satisfied with third place and no doubt will be strong title contenders in the next campaign.

Norton Sports won the Division One East title. Having lost two of their first five games they remained unbeaten in the League after that, winning fifteen and drawing four games in a superb run of form. Another nail biting end to the season in Division One West took place as Phoenix Sports ended champions winning the title by just one point from Beauwater. With Premier Division Rye United giving notice of their intention to move into the Sussex County League and Kennington unable to meet the Premier Division ground grading criteria, Beauwater regained their Premier Division place having been relegated in 1995. They will join Norton Sports and Phoenix Sports in the Premier Division.

Smarden lifted the Division Two East title and AFC Blackheath regained their Division One West status after just one season in Division Two West by clinching the championship in their final game of the season. Also promoted from Division Two West were Pembury.

The Division Three West champions were Belvedere who, together with Larkfield and New Hythe Wanderers, were promoted. In the Reserve Divisions Stansfeld Oxford and Bermondsey Club, having been runners-up the previous season, went one better being undefeated in the League and Oakwood won Division Two and were duly promoted. Spare a thought for Division One West Sutton Athletic who won just one of their 22 league matches, still they live to tell the tale.

The League had a record five clubs competing in the 'Plaaya' Kent Senior Trophy with Bearsted reaching the semi-finals and Milton Athletic visiting and defeating Bass Brewers Kent League Slade Green 2-1, in Round Two. In fact, Bearsted proved to be the 'jewel in the crown' for the League following their three victories against Bass Brewers Kent League sides, Herne Bay (2-0), Sheppey United (3-1) and VCD Athletic (1-0). Their dreams of being the first ever County League team to reach the final were ended at Deal Town in the semi-final when they went down by the only goal of the game in a hard fought tie. A crowd of 303, only two fewer then Deal's largest gate of the season at that time witnessed the 'Bears' fight every inch of the way and match their opponents in almost every department. It was to Bearsted's great credit that Deal Town went on to become the first ever Kent side to lift the FA Vase against Chippenham Town at Wembley just a few short weeks later.

Premier Division Snodland completed a memorable double winning the Kent Intermediate Challenge Shield by defeating Division One West Beauwater by two goals to nil.

The first of the League's five cup finals took place in March at Hythe United's ground and in an excellent Eastern Junior final New Romney Reserves defeated Sheerness East Reserves 1-0. Knatchbull retained the Eastern Senior 'Les Leckie' Cup after defeating Milton Athletic 4-1 also on Hythe United's ground, but there was a shock in the Western Reserve Divisions final as Sevenoaks town beat much-fancied Stansfeld O&B Club. In another splendid final the 'Oaks' came back from a two-goal half time deficit to win 3-2 at Erith Stadium, in a thrilling game.

In the West Kent Challenge Shield final staged at Stonebridge Road, Northfleet, home of Ryman League Gravesend & Northfleet, Beauwater lifted the trophy when they beat fellow Division one West Fleetdown united by the only goal of the game.

The last of the League's knockout competitions saw Sevenoaks Town fail in their bid to become the first ever side to win the Inter-Regional Challenge Cup on three consecutive occasions. A new name appeared on the trophy as Sheerness East triumphed with a single goal victory at Dr Martens League Ashford Town's ground.

During the season the League's representative team renewed acquaintances with their Essex Intermediate League counterparts. On a cold January evening they played out an entertaining goalless draw on Tilbury FC's ground and in February they retained the 'Tom Stabler' Trophy when they defeated the Unijet Sussex County League Division Three side by four goals to nil at Gravesend & Northfleet FC.

Saturday 27 May saw the League celebrating the end of another season with a superb Millennium Presentation Dinner and Cabaret at the Jarvis Great Danes Hotel, Hollingbourne. Principle guests were Colin Boswell, Vice Chairman of the Kent County Football Association, Andy Ford of Aford Awards the sponsors of the League's Manager of the Month and Manager of the Year awards, and Andrew Gidley of Kent Sport. Following an excellent meal special guest speaker was the brilliant Bob 'The Cat' Bevan. Also on the bill was comedian Steve Finn and following the presentations, musical trio 'Watch That Space' entertained until very late. During the evening long service Club awards were presented to Robert Hillier, Greenways FC 25 years, Alan Pearson, Phoenix Sports 29 years, John Underdown, St George's (Wrotham) FC 35 years, and Geoff Hunt, Woodnesborough FC 37 years service. What would we do without such stalwarts?

Colin Plummer of Rochester lifted the Referee of the year trophy and the most promising Referee of the Year trophy went to Mark Taylor of Bromley.

At the League's Annual General Meeting on Monday 19 June 2000 six new clubs were elected into the Competition. Holmesdale and Old Roan, formerly of the Surrey County and London Intermediate Leagues respectively, were placed in Division One West. Betteshanger Welfare were placed in Division Two East and Bly Spartans, Danson Athletic and Athletico

Beckenham were placed in Division Three West. In addition the League welcomed six new reserve teams with these being placed as follows: Tenterden Tigers and St Margarets in Division Two East, Snodland in reserve Division One West and Belvedere, Holmesdale and Orpington in Reserve Division Two West.

The highlights of the Annual General Meeting saw University of Kent's Director of Physical Recreation, Mike Wilkins, collect the much-coveted Fair Play award and a cheque for £300 from Dr Andy Spurr, Station Director of British Energy Dungeness 'B' Power Station as the team with the best disciplinary record in the entire League. other cheques for good disciplinary records went to Sevenoaks Town, Kennington, Otford United, Smarden, AFC Blackheath, Belvedere, Stansfeld O & B Club Reserves and Fleetdown United Reserves who each received £100 and Aylesford Paper Mills, Sheerness East Reserves, Pembury, Chipstead, Otford United Reserves and Chipstead Reserves who each received £50.

Brian Wakeman of Fleetdown United received a Long Service Club Award having been unable to attend the dinner.

To cap a superb season Steve McMorrow of Snodland collected the Aford Awards Manager of the Year following his team's excellent County Cup and League double. General Secretary Tony Scott did not seek re-election and Assistant Secretary Barry Bundock was unanimously elected to fill the role. Assistant Referee's Secretary Brian Perryman indicated his intention to resign during the season and Tony Allen joined the Management Committee in his place. All other officers were re-elected unopposed.

The Management Committee announced that they were embarking on a first ever comprehensive publication for the League, which it was felt would be a fitting way to mark the new Millennium. This joint venture called "A Guide to the Kent County Football Association League" is compiled and edited by Kent-based journalist Steve Hemsley and is in partnership with the Kent Messenger. The 48-page book featuring news and information on every Club in the League is priced at £4.00 inclusive of post and packing and is available by forwarding a cheque to League Treasurer John Weller at 52 Rogersmead, Tenterden, Kent TN30 6LF.

The League continues to expand its newsline and Andrew Gidley of Kent Sport will be conducting interviews on the newsline throughout the season. Why not ring 09068 800 664 and keep abreast of all the League News. The line is in operation 24 hours a day seven days a week. *Cyril Windiate, Chairman*

FINAL LEAGUE TABLES 1999-2000
PREMIER DIVISION

	P	W	D	L	F	A	Pts		P	W	D	L	F	A	Pts
Snodland	26	19	5	2	67	21	62	Milton Athletic	26	9	8	9	35	40	35
Bearsted	26	18	7	1	57	17	61	Thames Poly	26	11	1	14	45	48	34
Maidstone United	26	15	4	7	46	28	49	Lydd Town	26	10	4	12	41	55	34
Stansfeld O & B Club	26	12	6	8	39	29	42	Sheerness East	26	8	3	15	31	55	27
Rye United	26	13	3	10	55	47	42	Greenways	26	7	4	15	29	48	25
Knatchbull	26	12	4	10	64	41	40	Crockenhill	26	5	3	18	42	63	18
Sevenoaks Town	26	11	6	9	56	41	39	Aylesford Paper Mills	26	3	0	23	25	99	9

DIVISION ONE WEST

	P	W	D	L	F	A	Pts
Phoenix Sports	22	16	3	3	69	21	51
Beauwater	22	15	5	2	52	20	50
Wickham Park	22	14	2	6	57	26	44
Fleetdown United	22	13	4	5	58	23	43
Westerham	22	12	3	7	42	36	39
Moonshot Athletic	22	9	4	9	46	33	31
Otford United	22	8	5	9	46	31	29
Rusthall	22	8	2	12	58	56	26
St George's (Wrotham)	22	7	4	11	39	48	25
AFC Lewisham*	22	8	2	12	47	58	23
Orpington	22	4	0	18	22	70	12
Sutton Athletic	22	1	0	21	28	142	3

* points awarded/deducted

DIVISION ONE EAST

	P	W	D	L	F	A	Pts
Norton Sports	24	17	5	2	77	27	56
Kennington	24	16	2	6	79	33	50
University of Kent	24	14	3	7	60	31	45
Snowdown Colliery Welf.	24	13	3	8	57	42	42
New Romney	24	9	8	7	58	40	35
Wittersham	24	10	5	8	45	41	35
Broomfield United*	24	9	4	10	52	56	34
Tenterden	24	9	6	9	54	54	33
Bromley Green	24	9	4	11	38	69	31
Iden	24	8	5	11	40	51	29
St Margarets	24	7	6	11	43	53	27
Bishopsbourne	24	4	4	16	36	87	16
Woodnesborough	24	2	1	21	28	83	7

PREMIER DIVISION RESULTS CHART 1999-2000

		1	2	3	4	5	6	7	8	9	10	11	12	13	14
1	Aylesford P Mills	X	0-4	1-4	2-0	2-11	2-1	1-2	0-1	1-4	1-8	1-3	1-3	0-6	1-2
2	Bearsted	6-0	X	2-1	1-0	1-1	1-0	0-0	0-0	3-0	1-0	4-1	1-1	4-1	4-1
3	Crockenhill	2-4	1-3	X	0-1	2-5	1-2	2-0	1-1	0-0	1-1	5-2	0-1	0-1	1-3
4	Greenways	3-0	0-2	3-2	X	3-2	1-2	0-2	0-1	3-4	2-1	1-3	0-3	1-1	0-4
5	Knatchbull	3-0	0-0	7-2	3-0	X	4-2	0-2	3-0	2-3	1-2	5-0	0-5	1-1	3-1
6	Lydd Town	4-2	1-1	3-1	2-0	3-0	X	2-0	0-3	2-3	1-1	3-1	3-2	1-1	0-3
7	Maidstone Utd	7-0	2-3	3-1	1-1	3-0	3-2	X	3-0	3-2	2-1	2-1	0-2	2-0	1-2
8	Milton Athletic	2-1	1-1	2-1	2-1	1-1	1-2	1-1	X	4-2	1-1	4-2	2-2	0-2	0-0
9	Rye United	3-1	2-3	5-2	0-3	2-1	6-1	2-1	4-0	X	0-3	6-1	0-3	0-0	3-0
10	Sevenoaks Town	4-1	1-3	5-3	7-3	0-2	1-1	0-0	1-5	2-1	X	1-0	2-5	2-1	6-0
11	Sheerness East	2-1	1-2	2-6	0-0	1-0	3-1	0-1	2-1	2-1	1-1	X	2-2	0-1	0-1
12	Snodland	5-0	1-0	2-0	0-0	3-1	7-1	3-1	5-0	1-3	1-0	X	2-1	2-0	2-0
13	Stansfeld O & B Club	3-2	0-2	2-0	2-1	1-3	5-1	0-1	3-1	0-0	2-1	0-1	1-1	X	2-1
14	Thames Poly	6-0	1-5	2-3	1-2	1-5	2-0	2-3	3-0	1-2	2-1	4-0	1-2	1-2	X

INTER-REGIONAL CHALLENGE CUP 1999-2000

FIRST ROUND

Snowdown C W	v	University of Kent	5-2		Woodnesborough	v	New Romney	1-4
AFC Lewisham	v	Bearsted	0-5		Snodland	v	Aylesford Paper Mills	3-2
Beauwater	v	Sevenoaks Town	1-7		St Georges (Wroth.)	v	Sutton Athletic	8-2
Phoenix Sports	v	Otford United	1-0					

SECOND ROUND

Kennington	v	St Margarets	4-0		Broomfield United	v	Tenterden	2-1
New Romney	v	Bromley Green	5-2		Iden	v	Sheerness East	0-2
Rye United	v	Knatchbull	1*1, 1-2		Lydd Town	v	Milton Athletic	9-1
Wittersham	v	Bishopsbourne	4-1		Snowdown C W	v	Norton Sports	2*2, 1-3
Thames Poly	v	Snodland	1*1, 0-5		Fleetdown United	v	Westerham	3-2
Sevenoaks Town	v	Stansfeld O & B Club	2-0		Rusthall	v	Greenways	0-3
Crockenhill	v	Moonshot Athletic	2-4		Wickham Park	v	Phoenix Sports	3-2
Bearsted	v	Orpington	4-0		Maidstone	v	St Georges (W'ham)	5*3

THIRD ROUND

Lydd Town	v	Knatchbull	4-2		Wittersham	v	Broomfield United	4-1
Sheerness East	v	Snowdown CW	4-2		Kennington	v	New Romney	2*2, 1p4
Maidstone United	v	Snodland	3-2		Moonshot Athletic	v	Greenways	1-2
Sevenoaks Town	v	Fleetdown United	3-1		Wickham Park	v	Bearsted	1-3

FOURTH ROUND

Wittersham	v	Sevenoaks Town	0-2		Lydd Town	v	New Romney	2-3
Sheerness East	v	Maidstone Utd	2*2, 4p2		Bearsted	v	Greenways	2-1

SEMI FINALS

Sheerness East	v	Bearsted	0*0, 4p2		Sevenoaks Town	v	New Romney	4-0

FINAL

Sheerness East	v	Sevenoaks Town	1-0	at The Homelands, Ashford Town FC

INTER-REGIONAL CHALLENGE CUP RECENT FINALS

SEASON	WINNERS	RUNNERS UP
1990-91	Bearsted	Scott Sports & Social
1991-92	Stansfeld Oxford & Bermondsey	Oakwood
1992-93	Oakwood	Teynham & Lynsted
1993-94	Bearsted	Rye United
1994-95	Vickers Crayford/Dartford Athletic	Teynham & Lynsted
1995-96	Teynham & Lynstead	Lydd Town
1996-97	Bearsted	Milton Athletic
1997-98	Sevenoaks Town	Greenways
1998-99	Sevenoaks Town	Rye United
1999-00	Sheerness East	Sevenoaks Town

Left: Team photograph of Bearsted FC who took on Deal Town in the Semi-final of the 'Plaaya' Kent Senior Trophy just a few weeks before Deal Town's Carlsberg FA Vase victory against Chippenham Town at Wembley Stadium. Right: Jeff Andrews, the New Romney FC manager, receiving his Aford Awards Easter Section Manager of the Month for January 2000 from League Chairman Cyril Windiate. *Photographs courtesy Philip Smith.*

BEARSTED
Secretary: Mrs Liz Owen, 21 Copsewood Way, Bearsted,
Maidstone, Kent ME15 8PL(01622 737709)
Ground: Honey Lane, Otham, Maidstone. (0411 128034)
Founded: 1895
Colours: White/blue/blue
Change Colours: Yellow/blue/blue

BEAUWATER
Founded: 1927
Secretary: Robert Taylor, 24 Sun Lane, Gravesend, Kent DA12
5HG (01474 332208)
Ground: Beauwater Leisure Club, Nelson Road, Northfleet (01474
359222)
Colours: Green& Black Hoops/black & green/black & green.
Change Colours: Yellow & navy stripes/navy/navy

GREENWAYS
Founded: 1965
Secretary: William Miller, 14 Cygnet Gardens, Northfleet, Kent
DA11 7DN (01474 560913)
Ground: Beauwater Leisure Centre, Nelson Road, Northfleet,
(01474 359222)
Colours: Red & Black/ Black /Black
Change Colours: Yellow & Blue/ Blue/ Blue

KNATCHBULL
Founded: 1980
Secretary: Alan Hammon, " Mackay', Bourne Rpad, Aldington,
Ashford, Kent TN25 7AS. (012133 720583)
Ground: Hatch Park, Off A20, Mersham, Nr Ashford, (01233
503549)
Colours: Claret & sky blue/white/sky blue
Change Colours: All White

LYDD TOWN
Founded: 1885
Secretary: Richard Hambley, 62 Roberts Road, Greatstone, Kent.
TN28 8RG (01797 321421)
Ground: The Lindsey Field, Dengemarsh Road, Lydd, Romney
Marsh (01797 321904)
Colours: Red/green/red
ChangeColours:Blue&white/blue/blue.

MAIDSTONE UNITED
Founded: 1966, reformed 1992
Secretary: Richard Yorke, 27 Churchill Way, Faversham, Kent
ME13 7QX (01795 534328)
Ground: Athletic Ground, London Rd, Maidstone(0796 7160053)
Founded: 1992
Colours: Gold/black/black
Change Colours: All white

MILTON ATHLETIC
Founded: 1926
Secretary: Paul Duffin, 18 Hales Road, Tunstall, Sittingbourne,
Kent ME10 1SR (01795 471260)
Ground: UK Paper Sports Ground, Gore Court Road,
Sittingbourne, Kent (01795 564213)
Colours: Royal blue/royal blue/yellow
Change Colours: Red & white stripes/black/black

NORTON SPORTS
Founded: 1927
Secretary: Colin Page, 2 Foxgrove, Milton Regis, Sittingbourne,
Kent ME10 2DW (01795 426675)
Ground: Norton Pk, Provender Lane,Norton,Kent (01795 520088)
Colours: Blue & white stripes/ black/ white
Change Colours: Blue & yellow/ blue/ yellow

PHOENIX SPORTS
Founded: 1935
Secretary: Martyn Cole, 91 Hurst Road, Northumberland Road,
Erith, Kent DA8 3EW (01322 350750)
Ground: Phoenix Spts Club, Mayplace Rd East , Bexleyheath,
Kent DA7 6JT (01322 526159)
Colours: Red & white/ black/black
Change Colours: Yellow/black/black

SEVENOAKS TOWN
Founded: 1883
Secretary: Edwin Diplock, 23 Holly Bush Lane, Sevenoaks, Kent
TN13 3TH (01732 454280)
Ground: Greatness Park, Seal Road, Sevenoaks (01732 741987)
Colours: Azure & black stripes/black/black
Change colours: Navy & scarlet quarters/navy/navy

SHEERNESS EAST
Founded: 1932
Secretary: Jonathan Longhurst, 16 Hilda Road, Halfway,
Sheerness, Kent ME12 3BN (01795 667758)
Ground: Sheerness East Working Mens Club, 47 Queenborough
Rd., Halfway, Sheerness (01795 662049)
Colours: Yellow/royal blue/royal blue
Change colours: All royal blue

SNODLAND
Founded: 1940
Secretary: Terry Reeves, 136 Townsend Road, Snodland, Kent
ME6 5RN (01634 240076)
Ground: Potyn's Field, Paddlesworth Road, Snodland, Kent.
(01634 243961)
Colours: Sky & navy/navy/navy
Change colours: Yellow/red/yellow & red

STANSFELD OXFORD & BERMONDSEY CLUB
Founded: 1897
Secretary: Edward Ellis, 40 Tilbrook Road, Kidbrooke, London
SE3 9QE (0208 319 0903)
Ground: St James Squash & Leisure Club, 35 Marvels Lane,
Grove Park, SE12 (020 8851 3522)
Colours: Blue with grey trim/grey//blue
Change Colours: All white

THAMES POLYTECHNIC
Founded: 1888
Secretary: Mrs Shirley Jarvis, 31 Monkton Road, Welling, Kent
DA16 3JU (0208 854 5509)
Ground: Greenwich University Sports Ground, Kidbrooke Lane,
Eltham, London SE9 (020 8850 0210)
Colours: Yellow /green/yellow
Change Colours: All blue
Previous league: Kent

A.F.C. BLACKHEATH
Secretary: Dave Wilson, 74 Shroffold Road, Bromley ,Kent
Tel: 020 8698 1192
Ground: Huntsman Sports, Manor Way, Blackheath, London SE3
(0181 852 3602)
Founded: 1983
Colours: All Green
Change Colours: White/blue/white

A.F.C. LEWISHAM
Founded: 1998
Secretary: Harry Munday, 18 Thriffwood, Silverdale, Sydenham,
London SE26 4SH (020 8265 6621)
Ground: Ladywell Arena, Doggett Rd., Catford London SE6 (0208
314 1986)
Colours:Yellow/ Sky Blue/ White
Change Colours: Red & White/ Red/Red

AYLESFORD PAPER MILLS
Founded: 1919
Secretary: Brian Reynolds, 98 TEapot Lane, Aylesford, Kent
ME20 7JT (01622 717470)
Ground: Cobdown Sports & Social Club, Ditton Corner, Station
Road, Aylesford (01622 715552)
Colours: White with black trim/black/claret
Change Colours: Claret & Blue/ Blue/ Claret

CROCKENHILL
Secretary: Brian Perfect, 30 Tylers Green Road, Crockenhill,
Swanley, Kent BR8 8LG (01322 663638)
Ground: The Wested Meadow, Wested, Eynsford Road,
Crockenhill, Kent. (01322 662097)
Founded: 1946
Colours: Red & white stripes/ black/ red
Change Colours: White & blue/ red & blue/ black & blue.

FLEETDOWN UNITED
Founded: 1971
Secretary: Brian Wakeman, 670 Princes Road, Dartford, Kent
DA2 6JG (01322 228680)
Ground: Heath Lane, Dartford, Kent (01322 273848)
Colours: Tangerine/black/tangerine
Change colours: Red/white/red

HOLMESDALE
Founded 1956
Secretary: Mark Hayes, 12 Danson Way, Rainham, Kent. ME8
7EW (01634 327954)
Ground: Holmesdale Sports & Social Club, Oakley Road, Bromley
Common (020 8462 4440)
Colours: Yellow & Green/ Green/ Green
Change Colours: White/ Black/Black

MOONSHOT ATHLETIC
Founded: 1970
Secretary: Joseph Collymore, 37 Vaughan Williams Close,
Deptford SE8 4AW (0208 691 2543)
Ground: Ten Em Bee Sports Ground, Bromley Road playing fields,
Old Bromley Road, Downham, Kent (020 8313 9510)
Colours: All Burgandy
Change Colours: T.B.A.

OLD ROAN
Founded: 1905
Secretary: Brian Riley, 33 Buckler Gardens, Mottingham, London
SE9 3BD (020 8857 0401)
Groud: John Roan PLaying Fields, Kidbrooke Park Road,
KIdbrooke, London SE3 (020 8856 1915 or 020 8856 1012)
Colours: Blue/black/black
Change Colours: White/blue/blue.

OTFORD UNITED
Founded: 1900
Secretary: David Dugay, 13 Monckton Road, Borough Green,
Sevenoaks, Kent TN15 8SD (01732 882621)
Ground: Otford Recreation Ground, High Street, Otford, Kent
(01959 524405)
Colours: Amber & black/black/black
Change Colours: Blue/green/blue

PEMBURY
Founded1908
Secretary; Michael Waterman, 26 The Coppice, Pembury,
Tunbridge Wells Kent TN2 4EY 01892 824137)
Ground: Woodside Recreation Ground, Henwoods Mount,
Pembury (07970 026628)
Colours: Black & White stripes/ black/black
Change Colours: All red

RUSTHALL
Founded: 1899
Secretary: Michael Mace, 'The Roos', 28 Allan Close, Rusthall,
Tunbridge Wells, Kent TN4 8PL (01892 540634)
Ground: Jockey Farm, Nellington Lane, Rusthall, Tunbridge Wells
Tel : 01892 517224
Colours: Green & yellow/green/green
Change Colours: Blue/black/black

St GEORGE'S (Wrotham)
Founded: 1965
Secretary: John Underdown, 1 Mountain Close, West St.,
Wrotham, Sevenoaks, Kent TN15 7BD (01732 886106)
Ground: Old Recreation Ground, Old London Road, Wrotham,
Sevenoaks, Kent.
Colours: All royal blue
Change colours: Red & black stripes/black/black

WESTERHAM
Founded: 1888
Secretary: Doug Sayers, 16A The Green, Westerham, Kent TN16
1AX (01959 565520)
Ground: Westerham Sports Assoc., King George V Playing Fields,
Costells Meadow, Westerham. (01959 561106)
Colours: Red/black/black
Change Colours: Green/white/white

WICKHAM PARK
Founded: 1934
Secretary: Brian Greenin, 145 The Avenue, West Wickham, Kent
BR4 0EF (0208 777 2119)
Ground: Wickham Park Sports & Soc. Club, 228-230 Pickhurst
Rise, West Wickham (0208 7772550)
Colours: Red & blacktrim/black/black
Change Colours: White/navy/white

BISHOPSBOURNE
Founded: 1961
Secretary: Nigel Hayes, Robins Grove, 62 The Street, Kingston, Canterrbury ,Kent.CT4 6JC (01227 830360)
Ground: Canteen Meadow, The Street, Bishopsbourne, Nr Canterbury, Kent
Colours: Royal blue
Change Colours: Red & black

BROMLEY GREEN
Founded: 1930
Secretary: David Stanley, 48 Bredgar Close, Stanhope, Ashford, Kent TN23 5SQ (01233 661312)
Ground: The Swan Centre, Newtown Road, South Willesborough, Ashford, Kent
Colours: All Green.
Change Colours: White/green/green

BROOMFIELD UNITED
Founded: 1925
Secretary: Roger Cork, 12 Coulter Road, Herne Bay, Kent CT6 7RH (01227 742480)
Ground: Bridge Recreation Ground, Patrixbourne Road, Bridge, Nr Canterbury
Colours: Scarlet & Navy
Change Colours: Tangerine & Black

IDEN
Founded: 1965
Secretary: Gerard Say, 18 Parkwood, Iden, Rye, East Sussex TN31 7XE (01797 280495)
Ground: Iden Playing Field, Iden, Rye, East Sussex
Colours: Tangerine/black/black
Change Colours: Black & white stripes /black/blackr

KENNINGTON
Founded: 1888
Secretary: Kevin Hayden, 33 Grosvenor Road, Kennington, Ashford, Kent TN24 9PA (01233 627826)
Ground: Kennington Cricket Club Club, Ulley Road, Kennington, Ashford, Kent
Colours: Yellow & sky blue
Change Colours: All red

NEW ROMNEY
Founded: 1895
Secretary: Mr Daryl Masters, 44 Fernbank Cres, Folkestone, Kent CT19 5SF (01303 253961)
Ground: The Maud Pavilion, Station Road, New Romney, Kent (01797 364858)
Colours: Tangerine/ navy/yellow
Change Colours: White & navy stripes/navyblue/navy/navy

SMARDEN
founded: 1984
Secrtary: Tom Carlton, The Barn, New Barn Farm, Bethersden, Ashford, Kent TN26 3EU (01233 820983)
Ground: The Minnis, Smarden, Nr Ashford, Kent
Colours: Blue & White/Blue/Blue.
Change Colours: Green & White/ Black/ Black

SNOWDOWN COLLIERY WELFARE
Founded: 1927
Secretary:Mrs Nicola Tong, 9 Ackholt Road, Aylesham, Canterbury, Kent CT3 3AF (01304 849190))
Ground: Spinney Lane, Aylesham, Canterbury CT3 3AF (01304 840278)
Colours: Black & white stripes/black/black
Change Colours: blue & black/black/black
Previous League: Kent

St MARGARETS
Founded: 1970 Re-formed:1993
Secretary: William Hay, 28 The Freedown, St Margarets at Cliffe, Nr Dover, Kent CT15 6BD (01304 852386)
Ground: The Alexander Field, Kingsdown Road, St Margarets at Cliffe, Nr Dover
Colours: White, red & blue sleeves/blue/red
Change Colours: Dark blue/white/red

TENTERDEN TIGERS
Founded: 1889
Secretary: Colin Feaver, 19 Eastgate Road, Tenterden, Kent TN30 7AH (01580 761311)
Ground: Recreation Ground, Recretaion Ground Rd., Tenterden (01580 762703)
Colours: Yellow/black/black
Change Colours: Blue & white/ blue/blue

UNIVERSITY OF KENT
Founded: 1967
Secretary: Mrs Rene Simmonds, Sports Federation, Sports Centre, University of Kent, Canterbury, Kent CT2 7NL (01227 768027 or 01227 827430)
Ground: The Playing Fields, University of Kent, off Giles Lane, Canterbury
Colours: Black & white stripes/black/black
Change Colours: Blue & yellow stripes/black/black

WITTERSHAM
Founded: 1905
Secretary: Mr Leslie Champion, 4 Woodland View, Wittersham, Tenterden, Kent TN30 7QD (01797 270164)
Ground: Wittersham Sports Club, Poplar Road, Wittersham, Tenterden, Kent.
Colours: White/green/green
Change colours: red & white/black/black

For up to the minute news, results, fixtures, plus general facts & figures from the world of non-league football

log on to

www.nlfootball.com

RICH CITY SUSSEX COUNTY LEAGUE

FEEDER TO: DR MARTENS LEAGUE
FOUNDED 1920

President: P H Strange   **Chairman:** Peter Bentley
Secretary: P Beard, 2 Van Gogh Place, North Bersted, Bognor Regis PO22 9BG
Tel: 01243 822063 (H)   07966 457908 (M)

The Division One Championship was won by Langney Sports, a founder member of Division Three, who carried out tremendous improvements in upgrading their facilities to the standard required by the Southern League. It is a great tribute to Chairman Len Smith and his Committee that their off the field efforts have been rewarded by the players achieving the required results on it. Len was presented with a League award for service as Chairman. At the same time the Club produced a large number of the successful Sussex County F.A. Senior representative side that won the South Western Counties Championship Trophy. Burgess Hill Town, the champions for the previous three seasons finished a creditable runner-up, with Saltdean United in third place. Langney Sports have successfully applied for promotion to the Southern League, we all wish them well and will watch with interest their progress in this venture.

Chichester City and Portfield have decided to merge under the name of Chichester City United. These events create two vacancies in this Division. Wick, Ringmer and Shoreham finished in the relegation positions, with the first two retaining Division One status. Sidlesham, another team who started with us in Division Three, were Champions of Division Two, and, provided their facilities are upgraded, will also enter our top Division for the first time. Runners-up were Arundel, with Lancing third, and they are promoted to Division One. Finishing in the relegation places in Division Two were Shinewater Association and Lingfield, who will both retain their status due to the events in Division One.

Withdean resigned from Division Two, pre-empting the requirement for the League Management Committee to interview them due to their incapability in meeting the requirements of the League Rules, particularly with regard to the postponement of matches, and their inability in the trial period of ground sharing with Brighton & Hove Albion to be able to play any home evening matches except on a Friday. Had their resignation not been submitted, because they had not been able to meet the requirements, the Management Committee would have had no alternative to recommending their expulsion to the Annual General Meeting, when a review of their ground sharing agreement was due to be made to the member Clubs. This creates a further vacancy in Division Two for a promoted Club in accordance with the Rules for maintaining the numbers in our Divisions.

In their first season back in the League, Bosham established an early lead, which they looked unlikely to be overtaken, and this proved the case when they were the first team declared Champions of any Division. They will be promoted to Division Two with Wealden, who finished runners-up by winning their final match on 6th May. Ansty Rangers were unable to fill the third available position, as their facilities do not meet the requirement for senior football, and so Crowborough Athletic have been promoted to fill the vacancy.

By the same effect of the various departures, there will be no relegation from Division Three, and so Newhaven and Royal & Sun Alliance will remain. This leaves three vacancies in Division Three. Two places will be filled by T.S.C. (formerly Thomson), champions of the Crawley League, and Rye United, a former member Club of this League, who will be rejoining from the Kent County League. We have been urged by our pyramid Feeder Leagues with whom we have continued regular meetings, not to lower our standards, and we have confirmed that to them.

In the F.A. Cup, both Burgess Hill Town and Horsham YMCA reached the Fourth Qualifying Round, with the YMCA going down in controversial circumstances by the odd goal in five against Chelmsford City from the Southern League East Division, and Burgess Hill were also unfortunate away to Hereford United from the Conference. Both teams deserve credit for reaching that stage and sharing the special award for it.

Burgess Hill Town, Horsham YMCA and Saltdean United all proceeded to the Fourth Round (last 32) of the F.A. Carlsberg Vase, but were all unfortunately drawn away from home. Burgess Hill lost by the odd goal in five at Metropolitan Police, Horsham YMCA 1-0 at AFC Totton, while Saltdean went down 5-1 away to Mossley, who were then defeated by Deal Town, the eventual competition winners.

FINAL LEAGUE TABLES 1999-2000
DIVISION ONE

	P	W	D	L	F	A	Pts	GD		P	W	D	L	F	A	Pts	GD
Langney Sports	38	31	6	1	101	25	99	76	Whitehawk	38	16	7	15	58	59	55	-1
Burgess Hill Town	38	26	7	5	78	37	85	41	Redhill	38	12	12	14	63	58	48	5
Saltdean United	38	24	7	7	97	45	79	52	Portfield	38	14	3	21	64	105	45	-41
East Preston	38	21	5	12	83	52	68	31	Three Bridges	38	11	9	18	53	76	42	-23
Horsham YMCA	38	18	10	10	78	53	64	25	Eastbourne Utd	38	11	8	19	62	80	41	-18
Sidley United	38	17	10	11	63	54	61	9	Pagham	38	10	9	19	46	68	39	-22
Hassocks	38	18	5	15	56	45	59	11	Chichester City	38	9	7	22	64	77	34	-13
Littlehampton Tn	38	17	6	15	53	55	57	-2	Wick	38	9	4	25	49	102	31	-53
Eastbourne Town	38	14	14	10	73	49	56	24	Ringmer	38	7	5	26	47	95	26	-48
Selsey	38	16	7	15	80	67	55	13	Shoreham	38	7	3	28	43	109	24	-66

DIVISION TWO / DIVISION THREE

	P	W	D	L	F	A	Pts	GD		P	W	D	L	F	A	Pts	GD
Sidlesham	34	25	6	3	85	29	81	56	Bosham	30	24	3	3	109	36	75	73
Arundel	34	23	5	6	89	37	74	52	Wealden	30	22	2	6	78	38	68	40
Lancing	34	18	9	7	64	43	63	21	Ansty Rangers	30	21	3	6	80	33	66	47
Crawley Down	34	18	8	8	54	33	62	21	Crowborough Ath	30	17	7	6	65	44	58	21
Oving	34	15	6	13	59	43	51	16	Haywards Heath T	30	17	6	7	74	38	57	36
East Grinstead T	34	13	8	13	71	57	47	14	Uckfield Town	30	16	3	11	55	48	51	7
Hailsham Town	34	12	11	11	59	48	47	11	Bexhill Town	30	15	4	11	62	60	49	2
Southwick	34	13	8	13	75	76	47	-1	Seaford	30	14	3	13	65	60	45	5
Westfield	34	13	8	13	45	47	47	-2	Forest	30	13	6	11	42	48	45	-6
Storrington	34	12	8	14	52	57	44	-5	St Francis	30	10	6	14	42	50	36	-8
Mile Oak	34	12	7	15	63	61	43	2	Franklands Village	30	9	5	16	39	52	32	-13
Broadbridge Heath	34	11	9	14	62	67	42	-5	Steyning Town	30	9	3	18	55	76	30	-21
Oakwood	34	11	7	16	52	77	40	-25	Ifield	30	5	6	19	43	69	21	-26
Peacehaven & Tels	34	9	10	15	52	70	37	-18	Hurstpierpoint	30	5	5	20	44	81	20	-37
Worthing United	34	10	7	17	46	80	37	-37	Newhaven	30	5	2	23	34	104	17	-70
Withdean	34	8	6	20	40	64	30	-24	Royal & Sun Alnce	30	4	4	22	33	83	16	-50
Shinewater Assn	34	8	6	20	40	77	30	-37									
Lingfield	34	8	5	21	42	84	29	-42									

DIVISION ONE RESULTS CHART 1999-2000

		1	2	3	4	5	6	7	8	9	10	11	12	13	14	15	16	17	18	19	20
1	Burgess Hill Town	X	5-1	1-2	2-1	2-1	1-0	1-0	2-3	1-0	2-2	5-0	1-2	3-2	3-1	2-1	5-1	1-1	4-1	1-0	5-0
2	Chichester City	0-2	X	1-2	0-1	1-1	3-0	1-1	0-2	0-4	0-0	3-5	2-2	1-2	1-9	0-0	2-3	2-2	1-1	3-0	6-1
3	East Preston	0-2	2-1	X	3-3	1-3	2-0	0-4	0-0	0-1	3-0	3-0	4-1	7-1	1-2	2-1	6-0	5-1	5-0	2-0	2-1
4	Eastbourne Town	1-2	3-2	1-2	X	2-2	3-2	3-2	1-1	6-1	5-0	8-0	2-2	1-1	1-1	2-2	3-0	0-0	6-2	0-0	1-0
5	Eastbourne Utd	1-3	3-1	0-5	2-3	X	2-1	2-2	2-3	3-1	3-2	5-4	2-1	0-0	2-2	4-0	0-2	2-2	0-1	4-3	
6	Hassocks	0-1	2-1	0-0	0-1	1-0	X	1-0	0-1	1-2	4-0	5-0	0-0	2-1	0-3	3-4	3-1	0-0	3-2	6-1	2-1
7	Horsham YMCA	1-2	1-0	7-2	1-1	2-2	1-2	X	1-4	3-1	2-2	W/L	2-2	5-2	2-1	2-1	3-3	3-1	2-2	1-1	3-1
8	Langney Sports	1-1	2-0	4-0	0-0	2-0	3-0	4-0	X	1-1	2-0	4-2	2-0	1-0	1-1	1-0	2-1	3-1	7-0	2-1	4-0
9	Littlehampton Tn	0-1	2-1	0-1	1-0	3-1	0-2	0-2	0-2	X	1-0	3-4	2-2	1-0	2-2	1-4	3-1	1-4	3-2	2-0	2-2
10	Pagham	1-4	1-3	2-1	0-0	1-0	0-0	3-0	0-1	0-1	X	0-2	0-0	3-0	4-2	2-2	1-0	3-1	1-2	2-1	0-0
11	Portfield	0-2	2-5	4-2	2-2	3-1	1-2	0-5	0-8	0-1	3-2	X	2-2	1-2	2-3	1-0	3-0	1-2	1-6	2-2	4-0
12	Redhill	1-2	6-0	2-1	4-1	5-2	0-0	0-1	1-5	1-1	2-1	1-2	X	2-1	0-1	1-2	5-2	1-3	0-0	0-1	2-3
13	Ringmer	1-1	0-2	0-4	2-2	1-0	1-4	2-0	0-5	2-2	2-4	0-4	1-5	X	0-2	1-1	5-2	1-2	2-0	2-1	2-4
14	Saltdean United	2-3	3-1	1-0	2-1	6-2	0-2	4-0	1-2	2-1	2-1	4-0	2-2	1-0	X	4-2	5-1	4-1	2-2	3-1	3-1
15	Selsey	2-2	0-7	0-2	2-0	3-1	2-4	1-0	2-4	0-1	6-3	3-0	2-1	6-2	0-1	X	2-1	4-2	3-0	2-3	5-1
16	Shoreham	1-1	0-6	0-3	1-0	2-4	0-1	1-4	0-1	0-3	3-2	4-1	1-2	2-1	0-6	3-2	X	0-3	2-3	2-2	0-2
17	Sidley United	1-1	1-0	2-2	3-1	1-0	2-0	1-1	3-2	2-0	1-2	1-2	2-0	3-0	1-3	1-1	4-2	X	0-0	1-3	2-2
18	Three Bridges	0-1	3-2	1-1	1-0	0-1	1-0	0-2	2-5	0-3	1-2	0-1	0-2	5-2	3-2	3-5	2-0	0-1	X	2-2	0-0
19	Whitehawk	3-0	2-1	4-1	0-2	4-1	0-1	1-2	0-2	2-1	1-1	5-1	1-0	4-3	1-1	1-0	3-1	3-2	0-3	X	2-1
20	Wick	2-0	1-3	1-4	1-5	3-2	4-2	1-7	2-4	0-1	2-1	5-3	1-2	0-3	0-5	0-5	1-2	0-2	0-1	2-1	X

630

JOHN O'HARA LEAGUE CUP 1999-2000

FIRST ROUND

East Grinstead	v	Portfield	1*2	Eastbourne United	v	Arundel	3-2
Sidesham	v	Pagham	1-2	Three Bridges	v	Broadbridge	5-2
Wick	v	Hassocks	2-1	Withdean	v	Langney Sports	0-3

SECOND ROUND

Chichester City	v	Westfield	2-0	Crawley Down	v	Shoreham	1-0
East Preston	v	Mile Oak	3-0	Lancing	v	Horsham YMCA	2-8
Langney Sports	v	Wick	3-1	Lingfield	v	Littlehampton	0-7
Oving	v	Burgess Hill Town	2-3	Pagham	v	Portfield	2-1
Peacehaven & Tels.	v	Selsey	3-6	Shinewater Assn	v	Redhill	1-2
Sidley United	v	Oakwood	3-0	Southwick	v	Ringmer	2-3
Storrington	v	Eastbourne Town	3*2	Three Bridges	v	Eastbourne United	0-2
Whitehawk	v	Hailsham Town	3-0	Worthing United	v	Saltdean United	0-5

THIRD ROUND

Burgess Hill Town	v	Crawley Down	2-1	East Preston	v	Pagham	3-0
Langney Sports	v	Chichester City	0-0, 1-0	Littlehampton Town	v	Sidley United	0-4
Redhill	v	Horsham YMCA	0-2	Ringmer	v	Saltdean United	0-5
Selsey	v	Eastbourne United	4-0	Storrington	v	Whitehawk	2-4

QUARTER-FINALS

Burgess Hill Town	v	Langney Sports	2-0	Saltdean United	v	Horsham YMCA	5-2
Selsey	v	Whitehawk	2-1	Sidley United	v	East Preston	2-1

SEMI-FINALS

Saltdean United	v	East Preston	2-1	Selsey	v	Burgess Hill Town	0-1

FINAL

Saltdean United	v	Burgess Hill Town	3-2	at Three Brides FC

LEADING GOALSCORERS 1999-2000

DIVISION ONE			DIVISION TWO		
Matthew Allen	Langney Sports	42	Miles Scerri	Arundel	30
John Snelgrove	Langney Sports	24	Sam Wincell	Arundel	19
Matthew Russell	Horsham YMCA	22	Justin Turnill	Oving	19
Clinton More	East Preston	21	Steve Banks	East Grinstead	18
Leighton Allen	Saltdean	21	Neil Roberts	Mile Oak	17
Antoni Romasz	Chichester	19	Patrick Massaro	Oakwood	15
James Laing	Hassocks	19	James Hasler	Oving	15
Ian Ford	Selsey	17	Calvin Hore	Sidlesham	14
Dale Seymour	Eastbourne Utd	16	Wayne Whittington	Mile Oak	14
Jonas Templeman	Littlehampton	16	Douglas Cashman	Crawley Down	14
Paul Lee	Selsey	15	Gavin Jones	Worthing United	13
Scott McDonald	Sidley United	15	William Tidey	Broadbridge Heath	13
Stephen Poulton	Portfield	15	Scott Carden	Southwick	13
Gary Brockwell	Eastbourne Town	14	Stuart Hardy	East Grinstead	13
Warren Bagnall	Saltdean	14			
Anthony Holden	Burgess Hill	13	**DIVISION THREE**		
Phillip Churchill	Horsham YMCA	13	Ian Hamlett	Bosham	50
Daren Newman	Burgess Hill	12	Andrew Potter	Uckfield	20
Robert Pearce	East Preston	12	Robert Warner	Bexhill	19
Lee Stevens	Pagham	12	Hugh Howden	Bosham	16
Richard Hudson	Shoreham	12	Richard Lester	Hurstpierpoint	16
Tim Marshall	Shoreham	12	Stephen Lambert	Seaford	15
Gavin Geddes	Wick	11	John Scriven	Haywards Heath	15
Sydney Harman	Whitehawk	11	Paul Franklin	Ansty Rangers	15
Darren Lowery	Selsey	11	Gareth Neathey	Ifield	15
Paul Otway	Redhill	11	Kevin McCutcheon	Bosham	14
Anthony Stephens	Chichester	11	Ian Pendry	Ansty Rangers	13

TEAM OF THE MONTH 1999-2000

	DIVISION ONE	DIVISION TWO	DIVISION THREE
August	Wick FC	Westfield FC	Ansty Rangers FC
September	Langney Sports FC	Withdean FC	Bexhill Town FC
October	Burgess Hill Town FC	Crawley Down FC	Seaford FC
November	Saltdean United FC	Sidlesham FC	Haywards Heath Tn FC
December	Saltdean United FC	Lancing FC	Bosham FC
January	East Preston FC	Mile Oak FC	Crowborough Athletic FC
February	Burgess Hill Town FC	Sidlesham FC	Seaford FC
March	Burgess Hill Town FC	Sidlesham FC	Steyning Town FC
April	Langney Sports FC	Oving FC	Wealden FC

PAST RECORDS

LEAGUE DIVISION ONE

1980-81	Pagham
1981-82	Peacehaven & Tels
1982-83	Peacehaven & Tels
1983-84	Whitehawk
1984-85	Steyning Town
1985-86	Steyning Town
1986-87	Arundel
1987-88	Pagham
1988-89	Pagham
1989-90	Wick
1990-91	Littlehampton Town
1991-92	Peacehaven & Tels
1992-93	Peacehaven & Tels
1993-94	Wick
1994-95	Peacehaven & Tels
1995-96	Peacehaven & Tels
1996-97	Burgess Hill Town
1997-98	Burgess Hill Town
1998-99	Burgess Hill Town
1999-00	Langney Sports

LEAGUE DIVISION TWO

1980-81	Whitehawk
1981-82	Wick
1982-83	Horsham YMCA
1983-84	Portfield
1984-85	Shoreham
1985-86	Wick
1986-87	Pagham
1987-88	Langney Sports
1988-89	Seaford
1989-90	Bexhill Town
1990-91	Newhaven
1991-92	Portfield
1992-93	Crowborough Athletic
1993-94	Shoreham
1994-95	Mile Oak
1995-96	Saltdean United
1996-97	Littlehampton Town
1997-98	East Preston
1998-99	Sidley United
1999-00	Sidlesham

LEAGUE DIVISION THREE

1983-84	East Preston
1984-85	Oakwood
1985-86	Seaford Town
1986-87	Langney Sports
1987-88	Midway
1988-89	Saltdean
1989-90	Worthing United
1990-91	Ifield
1991-92	Hassocks
1992-93	Withdean
1993-94	Bosham
1994-95	Midhurst & Easebourne
1995-96	Ifield
1996-97	Sidlesham
1997-98	Lingfield
1998-99	Oving SC
1999-00	Bosham

LEAGUE CHALLENGE CUP

1980-81	Hastings Town
1981-82	Horsham YMCA
1982-83	Whitehawk
1983-84	Steyning Town
1984-85	Littlehampton Town
1985-86	Steyning Town
1986-87	Arundel
1987-88	Wick
1988-89	Pagham
1989-90	Langney Sports
1990-91	Littlehampton Town
1991-92	Peacehaven & Tels
1992-93	Peacehaven & Tels
1993-94	Whitehawk
1994-95	Hailsham Town
1995-96	Shoreham
1996-97	Wick
1997-98	Burgess Hill Town
1998-99	Burgess Hill Town
1999-00	Saltdean United

DIVISION TWO LEAGUE CUP

1980-81	Whitehawk
1981-82	Lancing
1982-83	Shoreham
1983-84	Haywards Heath
1984-85	Chichester City
1985-86	Pagham
1986-87	Selsey
1987-88	Chichester City
1988-89	Midhurst
1989-90	Oakwood
1990-91	Chichester City
1991-92	Redhill
1992-93	Lancing
1993-94	Shoreham
1994-95	Horsham YMCA
1995-96	Selsey
1996-97	Sidley United
1997-98	Three Bridges
1998-99	Sidley United
1999-00	Sidlesham

MERIT TABLE WINNERS

1980-81	Arundel
1981-82	Wick
1982-83	Peacehaven & Tels
1983-84	Portfield
1984-85	Steyning Town
1985-86	Wick
1986-87	Pagham
1987-88	Three Bridges
1988-89	Wick
1989-90	Wick
1990-91	Littlehampton Town
1991-92	Peacehaven & Tels
1992-93	Pagham
1993-94	Wick
1994-95	Wick
1995-96	Wick
1996-97	Wick
1997-98	Burgess Hill Town
1998-99	Horsham YMCA
1999-00	Arundel

Langney Sports' captain Craig Willard is presented with the Unijet Sussex County League Championship Trophy
Photo: Roger Turner

Horsham YMCA before their FA Cup Fourth Qualifying Round match against Chelmsford City. An historic day for Horsham as it was the first time they had reached this round. The club was founded in 1898.
Photo: Clive Turner

ARUNDEL

Secretary: Doug Feest, 142 Aldsworth Road, Worthing. BN12 4UU Tel: 01903 249276

Ground: Mill Road, Arundel, West Sussex. Tel: 01903 882548

Directions: A27 from Worthing to Arundel over railway bridge to roundabout.
Second exit into Queen Street to town centre, turn right over bridge.
Car park leading to ground 100yards right
Capacity: 2,200   Seats: 100   Cover: 200   Floodlights: 206 lux

Clubhouse: 2 bars, kitchen, toilets, telephone, pool, darts, Sky TV. Normal pub hours. No food

HONOURS Sussex Co. Lg 57-58 58-59 86-87 (Lg Cup 86-87, Div 2 Cup 76-77, Res. Sect.
78-79, Res. Sect. Cup 78-79, Merit Table 80-81,Sussex Fives 1984 1987),
Sussex RUR Charity Cup 68-69 72-73 78-79 79-80, Sussex Jnr Cup 07-08,
West Sussex Lg (Res.) 70-71 (Malcolm Simmonds Cup 70-71)

PREVIOUS **League** : West Sussex 1896-1975 **Grounds:** Castle Park; Station Rd Ground

RECORD **Gate:** 2,200 v Chichester, League 67-68
Scorer: Paul J Bennett **Appearances:** 537, Paul Bennett (goalkeeper)
Win : 13-0 v Horsham YMCA (H), Sussex Co. Lge Div 1 21/12/85

Players progressing: John Templeman (Brighton & Hove Albion 1966)

FACT FILE
Founded: 1889
Nickname: Mulletts
Colours: Red & white halves/white/red
Change colours: Jade & black
Midweek matchday: Tuesday
Reserves' Lge: Sussex Co. Res Div (West)
Programme: 8 pages, free Editor: P Wells
Local Press: Arun Herald

99-00- Captain: Jon Tucker
P.o.Y.:Sam Wincell

CLUB PERSONNEL
Chairman: M.Peters
Vice Chairman: S Brennan
Manager: Mike Rowland

BURGESS HILL TOWN

Secretary: The General Secretary, Burges Hill Town F.C., Leylands Park, Burgess Hill,
W.Sussex RH15 8AW Tel: 0144 242429

Ground: Leylands Park, Burgess Hill, West Sussex RH15 8AW Tel: 01444 242429
Capacity: 2,000   Seats: 100   Cover: Yes   Floodlights: Yes

Directions: Turn east from A273 London Road into Leylands Road, take 4th left (signposted)
Leyland Park. Nearest station Wivelsfield
Clubhouse: Bar & social facilities. Tea bar   **Club Shop:** No. Club badges available

HONOURS Sussex County Lg 75-76 96-97, 97-98,98-99; Lg Cup 73-74 79-80 97-98 98-99 (R-
up 90-91), Div 2 74-75 (Cup 73-73), F/lit Cup 96-97, Res 76-77 77-78 91-92, Res.
Sect. East 77-78 82-83 84-85, Res. Cup 82-83 98-99; Yth Sect. West 91-92 East
95-96 96-97 97-98 98-99 North 96-97 97-98; Sussex Fives 80; Mid-Sussex Lg 00-
01 03-04 39-4046-47 56-57 (Div 2 03-04 (res), Div 3 20-21 36-37, Div 4 (res) 56-57;
Mid Sussex Snr Cup 94-95 96-97; Montgomery Cup 39-40 56-57; Mowatt Cup 45-
46; Sussex RUR Charity Cup 91-92; Sussex I'mediate Cup 76-77; Sussex Yth Lge
96-97 97-98, Cup 91-92 97-98

PREVIOUS **Leagues & Grounds:** None
BEST SEASON **FA Cup:** 4th Qual. Rd. 99-00, 1-4 v Hereford United
RECORD **Gate:** 854 v Clitheroe, FA Vase 4th Rd (H)

FACT FILE
Founded: 1882
Nickname: Hillians
Sponsors: Time 24
Colours: Yellow/white/yellow
Change colours: All red
Midweek matchday: Tuesday
Programme: Yes

1998-99
Captain: Daren Newman
Top Scorer: Gavin Geddes
P.O.Y.: Marc Cable

CLUB PERSONNEL
Chairman: Alan Pook
President: Jack Lake
Manager: Alan Pook

CHICHESTER CITY UNITED

Company Sec: John F Hutter Tel: 01243 785839
28 Stockbrigde Gdns, Donnington, Chichester, W Sussex PO19 2QT
Hon. Secretary: Gary Rustell Tel: 01243 537978 (H)
102 Churchwood Drive, Tangmere, Nr Chichester, West Sussex PO20 6GB

Ground 1: Church Road, Portfield, Chichester, West Sussex PO19 4HN Tel: 01243 779875
Capacity: 2,000   Seats: 20   Cover: 200   Floodlights: Yes
Directions: A27 from Arundel to Chichester, take road to signposted city centre then 1st left
(Church Rd) after supermarket r'bout. 1 mile from Chichester(BR)
Clubhouse:2 bars, pool, snooker, seating for 100, dance floor, darts, Teabar selling h & c food.

(the club will be moving to Oaklands Park, Chichester in 2001)
Ground 2: Oaklands Park, Chichester Tel: 01243 785978
Capacity: 2,500   Seats: 50   Cover: 500   Floodlights: Yes
Directions: Half mile north of city centre adjacent to Festival Theatre. Turn into Northgate car park
from Oaklands Way and entrance is beside Tennis and Squash club.
1 mile from Chichester (BR) - walk north through city centre
Clubhouse: Licensed, open matchdays and some evenings. Tea bar Club Shop: No

PREVIOUS **Names:** Chichester FC (pre-1948), Chichester City 48-00.
Amalgamated with Portfield in 2000

FACT FILE
Formed 2000
Chichester (1873)Portfield (1896)
Sponsors: McDonalds
Nickname: Lilywhites
Colours: White/black/white
Change colours:Blue &Blackstripes,blue,black
Midweek matchday: Tuesday
Programme Editor: T Wallis
Local Press: Chichester Observer

CLUB PERSONNEL
Chairman: Simon Kenny
Match Secretary:Phil Littlejohns
Tel: 01243 528007
Press Officer: T Wallis (01705 464438)
Manager: Adrian Girdler
Chief Coach: Kevin Holston
Physio: NickTaylor
Club Steward: Andy Smith(01243 775455)

EAST PRESTON

FACT FILE

Secretary: Keith Freeman, 41 Ambersham Cres., East Preston, West Sussex BN161AJ
Tel: 01903 771158

Ground: Roundstone Recreation Ground, East Preston, West Sussex Tel: 01903 776026
Capacity: Seats: None   Cover: 40Floodlights: Yes

Directions: Less than a mile from Angmering (BR) station. A259 from Worthing to Roundstone
Hotel (6 miles), turn south over railway crossing, left past Centurion garage, right
into Roundstone Drive

Clubhouse: Licensed bar open Mon-Fri evenings, Sat noon-11pm, Sun noon-11pm. Kitchen
serves light refreshments on matchdays

HONOURS Sussex Co. Lg Div 2 Champions 97-98Div 3 83-84, (R-up 90-91), Div 3 Cup 87-88
(R-up 89-90); West Sussex Lg 77-78 80-81 81-82 82-83 (Malcolm Simmonds Cup
80-81 82-83), Div2 Sth 81-82, Div 3 Sth 79-80, Div 5 Sth 82-83; Chichester Cup 87-
88; BorehamTphy 77-78 90-91 (R-up 93-94); Vernon Wentworth Cup 80-81 89-90;
Worthing Lg 67-68 (Div 2 68-69 (res)); Benev. Tphy 66-67 68-69;
Worthing Charity Cup 68-69

PREVIOUS **Leagues:** Worthing; W Sussex

Reformed: 1966
Nickname: None
Sponsors: Roundstone Garage
Colours: Black & white/white/white
Change: Red/white/red
Reserve's Lge: Sussex Co. Res. Div (Prem)
Programme: Yes
Editor: Andy Mott (01903 726097)
Local Press: Littlehampton Gazette

CLUB PERSONNEL

President: Greg Stanley
Chairman:Mike Barnes
Manager: Jim Quigg
Asst Manager:Jim THompson

EASTBOURNE TOWN

FACT FILE

Secretary: Viv Greenwood, 102 Latimer Rd., Eastbourne BN22 7DR (01323 460695)

Ground: The Saffrons, Compton Place Road, Eastbourne, East Sussex (01323723734)
Capacity: 3,000   Seats: 200   Cover: Yes   Floodlights: Yes

Directions: Turn south west off the A22 into Grove Road (opposite BR station), and the
ground is 1/4 mile on the right

Clubhouse: Fully licensed bar. Board room. Tea bar

HONOURS Sussex County Lg. 76-77; Sussex Sen Cup x12 1889-91, 93-95, 98-1901, 02-03,
21-22, 31-35, 52-53; Sussex RUR Charity Cup 32-33, 47-48, 49-50;
SouthernAmat. Lge. x2; AFA Sen. Cup 21-22, 24-25, R-up 22-23, 23-24;
AFA Invitation Cup69-70, R-up 56-57, 68-69, 70-71

PREVIOUS **Leagues:** Southern Amtr 07-46; Corinthian 60-63; Athenian 63-76

RECORD   **Attendance:** 7,378 v Hastings Utd. 1953

Founded: 1882
Nickname: `Bourne'
Sponsor: Eastbourne Car Auctions
Colours: Yellow & blue/blue/blue
Changes: Blue &white/black/black
Programme Editor: Chris Backhurst
Tel: 01323 505062

CLUB PERSONNEL

Chairman: Roger Addems
Manager: Pete Cherry

EASTBOURNE UNITED

FACT FILE
Founded: 1894

Secretary: Jenny Townsend, 8 Annington Road, Eastbourne BN22 8NG
Tel: 01323 647470 (H) 07909 571285 (M)

Ground: The Oval, Channel View Rd, Eastbourne, East Sussex (011323-726989)
Capacity: 3,000   Seats: 160   Cover: 160   Floodlights: Yes

Directions: From A22 follow signs to eastbourne East/Seafront. Turn left onto seafront.
Turn left into Channel View Rd at Princess Park and ground 1st right.
2 miles from Eastbourne (BR)

Clubhouse: Bar, lounge, dancefloor, stage, tea bar, board room   **Club Shop:** Yes

HONOURS Sussex Co. Lg 54-55, Div 2 R-Up 99-00 Sussex Snr Cup(5) 60-61 62-64 66-67 68-
69(R-up 89-90), Sussex RUR Charity Cup 55-56,Metropolitan Lg Cup 60-61,Athenian Lg Div 2 66-
67 (Div 1 R-up 68-69), Sussex I'mediate Cup 65-66 68-69

PREVIOUS   **Name:** Eastbourne Old Comrades   **Leagues:** Sussex Co. 21-28 35-56;
Metropolitan 56-64; Athenian 64-77;Isthmian 77-92   **Ground:** Lynchmere

RECORD   **Attendance:** 11,000 at Lynchmere

Players progressing: B Salvage, T Funnell, M French, L.Barnard

Nickname: The 'Us'
Colours: White/black/white
Change colours: Blue/white/black
Midweek Matchday: Tuesday
Reserve Lge: Sussex County Res. Premier
Programme: 36 pages
Editor:Kevin Townsend
Local Press: Eastbourne Gazette + Herald,
Evening Argus

CLUB PERSONNEL
Chairman: I Botting
Vice-Chairman: Peter Snaahall
President: T.B.A.
Press Officer: M Stevens
Manager: Mick French
Asst Manager:
Physio: G Bishop

HASSOCKS

Secretary: Bob Preston, 65 Oakhall Park, Burgess Hill, West Sussex RH15 0DA
Tel: 01444 245695

Ground: The Beacon, Brighton Rd, Hassocks Tel: 01273 846040
Capacity: 1,500   Seats: None   Cover: 100   Floodlights: Yes

Directions: Off A273 Pyecombe Road to Burgess Hill, 300yds south of Stonepound cross
roads (B2116) to Hurstpierpoint or Hassocks

Clubhouse: Clubroom, bar, kitchen   Club Shop: No

HONOURS Sussex County Lg Div 3 91-92, Div 2 R-up 94-95, Res. Sect. East R-up 92-93;
Southern Counties Comb. 76-77, Lg Cup R-up 79-80; Brighton Hove & Dist. Lg
71-72; Sussex Intermediate Cup 74-75 (R-up 80-81)

PREVIOUS **Leagues:** Mid Sussex; Brighton Hove & Dist.; Southern Co's Comb
Ground: Adastra Park, Hassocks (pre-1992)

RECORD **Attendance:** 610 v Burgess Hill Town, Sussex County Lge 96-97

FACT FILE
Founded: 1902
Nickname: The Robins
Sponsors: Icon
Colours: Red/white/red
Change colours: Blue/white/blue
Midweek Matchday: Tuesday/Wednesday
Programme: 24 pages, 50p
Editor: Dave Knight
Admission: £1.50
Local Press: Mid Sussex Times,
Evening Argus

CLUB PERSONNEL
President: Maurice Boxall
Chairman: Jim Goodrum
Press Off . : Dave Knight (01273 842023)
Manager: Dave John

HORSHAM YMCA

Secretary: Robin Bishop ,4 Bannister Gdns,Storrington,W.Sussex RH20 3NT
Tel: 01903 746332 (H) 0996 202955 (Mob)

Ground: Gorings Mead, Horsham Tel: 01403 252689
Capacity: 800   Seats: 100   Cover: 200   Floodlights: Yes

Directions: Approaching Horsham fron the East on A281 Brighton Road, the ground is on left &
signposted opposite Gorings Mead

HONOURS Sussex Co Lge Div 2 65-66 82-83 R-up 94-95 (Lg Cup 81-82, Invitation Cup66-67
67-68, Div 2 Invit. Cup 59-60 61-62 94-95)

PREVIOUS **Leagues:** Horsham & Dist/Brighton & Hove/Mid Sussex
Grounds: Lyons Field, Kings Road

RECORD **Attendance:** 600 v Horsham FA Cup

BEST SEASON: **FA Cup:** 4th Qual. Rd. 99-00 2-3 v Chelmsford City

FACT FILE
Founded: 1898
Nickname: YM's
Sponsors: Principal Copiers
Colours: White/black/red
Change colours: All Red
Midweek Matchday: Tuesday
Local Press: West Sussex County Times

CLUB PERSONNEL
Chairman:John Cashman
Match Secretary: Robin Bishop
Tel: 01903 746332
Manager: John Suter
Physio: Robin Bishop

LANCING

Secretary: J Chisnall, 25 Amberley Court, Freshbrook Rd., Lancing, W. Sussex BN15 8DS
Tel: 01903 763048

Ground: Culver Road, Lancing, West Sussex Tel: 01903 764398
Web-site: www.lancingfc.co.uk

Directions: From A27 turn south at Lancing Manor r'about into Grinstead Lane,
3rd turning on right North Farm Rd. Turn left then immed. right into Culver Rd.
From railway station take 3rd turning on left heading north.
Capacity: 2,400   Seats: 350   Cover: 350   Floodlights: Yes

Clubhouse: Open matchdays & training nights. Separate tea bar.
Club Shop: Yes

HONOURS Sussex Co. Lg R-up 49-50 64-65 (Div 2 57-58 69-70 (R-up 82-83),
Div 2 Cup 81-82 92-93, Invitation Cup), Sussex RUR Charity Cup 65-66,
Brighton Lg 46-47 47-48, Sussex Intermediate Cup 46-47,
Brighton Charity Cup 83-84 84-85 86-87.

PREVIOUS **League:** Brighton Hove & District   **Name:** Lancing Athletic
Ground: Croshaw Rec, Sompting.

RECORDS **Attendance:** 2,591 v Tooting, FA Amateur Cup 22/11/47
At Culver Road: 2,340v Worthing 25/10/52
Career Appearances: Dave Menzies 462   **Goals:** Paul Steele 113

FACT FILE
Founded: 1941
Nickname: Yellows
Sponsors: ABS Electrical Supplies
Colours: Yellow/blue/yellow
Change colours: All red
Midweek Matches: Wed   Programme: Yes
Reserves League: Sussex Co Res. Prem.
Editor/Press Off.: Len Ralph (01903 763913)

99-00 Captain: Guy Whitehead
Top Scorers D.Brunton,G.Hall & N.Richardson
P.o.Y.: Guy Whitehead

CLUB PERSONNEL
Chairman: John Brown
President: R G Steele
Match Sec: Don Stevens
Commercial Man.: Brian Hill
Manager: Andy Gander
Physio: Peter Towell

Top: Eastbourne Town FC
Photo: Neil Thaler

Right: Lancing FC
Back Row (l-r): Peter Towell
(trainer), Don Shepherd
(Club Captain), David
Sharman, Dave Schneider,
Richard Whittington, Neil
Richardson, Tony Miles, Des
Guile, Graham Bull, Clive
Towell, Gary Hall, John
Sharman (Coach)
Front Row (l-r): Oliver
Howcroft, Steve Gurney,
Andrew Gander (Manager),
Guy Whitehead, Glen
Souter, Martin Gray, Steve
Fermer (Asst Mngr) Photo:
Worthing & Lancing Herald

Above: Littlehampton Town FC. Back Row (l-r): S Bates, N Freebone, A Stoner, D Chester, J Byatt, B Pidgeon, S Farnell, Andy Taylor (Manager), A Cooper (Coach).   Front Row (l-r): D Fallon, D Akmanblous, J Thornton, J Templeman, T Whitehouse, M Barrett, S Sell, C Lloyd

LITTLEHAMPTON TOWN

Secretary: John Savage, 66 Nelson Road, Worthing. BN12 6EN. (01903 502850)

Ground: The Sportsfield, St Flora's Road, Littlehampton (01903 713944)
Capacity: 4,000   Seats: 260   Cover: 260   Floodlights: Yes

Directions: 10 minutes walk from Littlehampton station (BR) - turn left alongTerminus Rd,
continue through High Street and Church Rd to junction with St Flora's Rd (left)

Club Shop: No, but metal badges available
Clubhouse: Sportsman (Private Club). Separate board room & tea bar

HONOURS Sussex Co. Lg 58-59 (jt with Shoreham) 75-77 84-85 90-91 96-97
Sussex Senior Cup 73-74

RECORD **Gate:** 4,000 v Northampton, FA Cup 1st Rd Proper 90-91

BEST SEASON **FA Vase** Semi-Final 90-91
FA Cup: 1st Round 90-91

FACT FILE
Founded: 1894
Nickname: Marigolds
Colours: Gold/black/black
Change: All white
Midweek Matches: Tuesday
Programme:
Editor:
Local Press: Littlehampton Gazette

CLUB PERSONNEL

President: Ian Cunningham
Chairman:Tony Carter
Manager: Andy Taylor

PAGHAM

Secretary: Ken Randall,1Watson Way,Westergate,Nr Chichester, West Sussex PO20 6WN
Tel: 01243 5459694 (H)
Ground: Nyetimber Lane, Pagham, West Sussex   Tel: 01243 266112
Capacity: 2,000   Seats: 200   Cover: 200   Floodlights: Yes

Directions: Turn off A27 Chichester by-pass (signposted A259 Pagham). Ground invillage of
Nyetimber. Three miles from Bognor (BR). Buses 260 & 240

Clubhouse: Bar open matchdays and some evenings. Hot food, pool, darts,satellite TV. Tea bar
Club Shop: No

HONOURS Sussex Co. Lg R-up 80-81 87-88 88-89 92-93 (Div 2 78-79 86-87, Lg Cup88-89,
Div 2 Cup 71-72 85-86, Res. Sect. West 80-81, Res Section Cup 77-78 80-81 87-
88 88-89 90-91 96-97; Sussex F'lit Cup R-up 88-89; Sussex RUR Charity Cup88-89
(R-up 93-94); West Sussex Lg 65-66 68-69 69-70; Malcolm Simmonds Cup 67-68;
Sussex I'mediate Cup 66-67
PREVIOUS **Leagues:** Chichester 1903-50; West Sussex 50-69   **Grounds:** None

RECORDS **Gate:** 1,200 v Bognor, 1971   **Scorer:** Mark Vickers/ R Deluca
Win: 10-1 v Seaford Town (A), Sussex County League Division Two, 1970
Defeat: 0-7 v Newport IOW (H), FA Amateur Cup, mid-1970s

FACT FILE
Founded: 1903
Nickname: Lions
Sponsors: City Sales Centre
Colours: White/black/red
Change colours: Yellow/green/green
Midweek Matchday: Tuesday
Reserve's League: Sussex Co. Reserve Div
Programme: 12 pages, 50p
Editor: Secretary
Local Press: Bognor Observer

CLUB PERSONNEL
Chairman: Graham Peach
Vice-Chairman: Steve Newdick
President: A Peirce
Press Officer: Ken Randall (01243 545694)
Comm. Manager: Chairman
Manager: Richie Reynolds
Asst Manager: T.B.A.

REDHILL

Secretary: Neil Hoad, 2b Earlswood Rd, Redhill, Surrey RH1 6HE   Tel: 01737 213847

Ground: Kiln Brow, Three Arch Road, Redhill, Surrey   Tel: 01737 762129

Directions: On left hand side of A23, two and a half miles south of Redhill
Capacity: 2,000   Seats: 150   Cover: 150   Floodlights: Yes
Club Shop: Sells usual range of souvenirs. Contact Spencer Mitchell - 01737 780634
Clubhouse: Social club, bar, canteen, board room, club shop, tanoy, toilets

HONOURS Athenian Lg 24-25 83-84 (LgCup 69-70 70-71), East & West Surrey Lg. 1902-03,
Southern Sub Sen West Lg. 1902-03, Surrey Snr Cup 28-29 65-66, Gilbert Rice F'lit
Cup 80-81, Sussex Co. Lg Div 2 Cup 91-92, Southern Co's Comb. Cup 90-91,98-99

PREVIOUS **Leagues:** E & W Surrey; Spartan 09-10; Southern Sub; London 21-23;
Athenian 23-84; Spartan 84-88
Grounds: Memorial Sports Ground, London Road 1894-1986

BEST SEASON **FA Amtr Cup:** Semi-Final 25   **FA Cup:** 1st Round 57-58

RECORDS **Attendance:** 1,200 v Crystal Palace & All Star XI, Brian Medlicott Testimonial 1989
Goalscorer: Steve Turner 119   **Appearances:** Brian Medlicott 766
Win : 10-0 v Saltdean United (H), Sussex Co. Lg Div 1 18/4/98
Defeat : 1-7 v Peacehaven & Telscombe (H), Sussex County Lg Cup 9/2/93

FACT FILE
Founded: 1894
Nickname: Reds/Lobsters
Sponsors: Trident Microsystems Ltd.
Colours: Red & white stripes /red /red
Change colours: White/black
Midweek matchday: Tuesday
Reserve League: Sussex Co.Lg
Programme: 88+ pages, 50p
Editor: Michael Stewart
Local Press : Surrey Mirror & The Independent

CLUB PERSONNEL
Chairman: Nick Creasey
Vice-Chairman: Alan Thurlbeck
President: Malcolm Chatfield
Press Officer: Peter Cox/Michael stewart
Manager: Russell Mason
Coach: Brian Dennis
Physio: Andy Peppercorn

RINGMER

Secretary: Gary Bulle, 13 Browns Parth, Uckfield, East sussex TN22 1LN
Tel Nos: 07769 936272 (M) 01825 769748 (H)

Ground: Caburn Ground, Anchor Field, Ringmer Tel: 01273 812738
Capacity: 1,000   Seats: 100   Cover: Yes   Floodlights: Yes

Directions: From Lewes road turn into Springett Avenue opposite Ringmer village green. Anchor Field first left. Three miles from Lewes (BR)

Clubhouse: 2 bars, function room, boardroom, tea bar **Club Shop:** Club ties & metal badges

HONOURS Sussex Co. Lg 70-71, Div 2 68-69, Invit Cup 66-67; Res. Sect. East 79-80 80-81 (R-up 89-90), Yth Section 87-88, Yth SectionEast 87-88; Sussex Snr Cup 72-73 (R-up 80-81); Sussex Jnr Cup 25-26; Sussex Express Sen Charity Cup 94-95
PREVIOUS **League:** Brighton   **Grounds:** None   **Names:** None
BEST SEASON **FA Cup** 1st Rd Proper 70-71
RECORD **Gate:** 1,200 in FA Cup

FACT FILE
Founded: 1906
Nickname: The Blues
Colours: Sky & navy/navy/navy
Change colours: All yellow
Midweek Matchday: Tuesday
Programme: Yes
Editor: Martin BUrke (01797 230572)
Admission: £2.50
Local Press: Sussex Express

CLUB PERSONNEL
President: Sir G Christie
Chairman: Richard Soan
Manager: Glen Geard
Press Officer: Martin Burke(01797 230572)
Match Sec.: John McWhirter (01323 847743)

SALTDEAN UNITED

Secretary: Iain Fielding, 40 Rowan Way, Rottingdean, Brighton BN2 7FP
Tel: 01273 304995

Ground: Hill Park, Combe Vale, Saltdean, Brighton Tel: 01273 309898
Capacity: 2,000   Seats: 50   Cover: Yes   Floodlights: Yes

Directions: A259 coast road east from Brighton to Saltdean Lido, left into Arundel Drive West, and Saltdean Vale to bridle path at beginning of Combe Vale. Club 200yds along track
Club Shop: Metal badges available
Clubhouse: Licensed bar, lounge, juke box, video games, board room, tea bar.Pool table

HONOURS Sussex Co. Lg Div 3 88-89, Div 2 95-96
PREVIOUS **League:** Brighton Hove & Dist **Ground:** None
RECORD **Attendance:** 676

FACT FILE
Founded: 1966   Nickname: Tigers
Sponsors: FDM
Colours: Red & black/black/black
Change colours: Blue & white
Programme: Yes
Editor:Rod Flavell (01273 888977)
Local Press: Brighton Evening Argus & Sussex Express

CLUB PERSONNEL
Chairman: Greg Hadfield
Vice Chairman:Mike Walker
President: Jim Bower
Press Officer: JIain Fielding
Manager: Glenn Burvill
Asst Manager: Glenn Geard
Physio: Keith Gray

SELSEY

Secretary: Danny Glew, 2 Colt Street, Selsey, Chichester W.Sussex PO20 9EU
Tel: 01243 605027

Ground: High Street Ground, Selsey, Chichester, West SussexTel: 01243 603420
Capacity: 2,250   Seats: 50   Cover: Yes   Floodlights: Yes

Directions: Through Selsey High Street to fire station. Take turning into car park alongside the station. Entrance is in the far corner. Regular buses from Chichester
Clubhouse: Bar, hospitality room, lounge, toilets, kitchen

HONOURS Sussex Co. Lg R-up 89-90 (Div 2 63-64 75-76 (R-up 86-87), Div 2 Cup 86-87 (R-up 84-85), Div 2 Invitation Cup 63-64, Sussex 5-aside 88-89), Sussex SnrCup R-up 63-64, Sussex I'mediate Cup 58-59, Sussex Jnr Cup(Reserves) 76-77,West Sussex Lg 54-55 55-56 57-58 58-59 60-61 (Malcolm Simmonds Cup 55-56 56-57 57-58 58-59)
PREVIOUS **Leagues:** Chichester & Dist.; West Sussex
RECORD **Gate:** 750-800 v Chichester or Portfield, 50's

FACT FILE
Founded: 1903
Nickname: Blues
Sponsors: T.R.P. Glazing
Colours: Blue/white/blue
Change colours:All yellow
Midweek Matchday: Tuesday
Programme Editor: Secretary
Match Secretary: Mandie Glew

CLUB PERSONNEL
President: Roy Glew
Chairman: Mike Hurst
Press Officer: Secretary
Manager:Danny Hinshelwood

SIDLESHAM

Secretary: Gary Tomlin, 5 Shotford, Sidlesham, nr Chichester PO20 7RD
Tel: 01243 641849 (H) 07788 973493 (Mobile)

Ground: Sidlesham Recreation Ground,Sidlesham.   Tel: 01243 641538

Directions: From the Chichester bypass take the B2145, signposted Hunston/Selsey. Head towards Selsey. Upon entering Sidlesham the ground is on the right between houses

FACT FILE
Colours: All green
Change colours: Red & white/white/red

CLUB PERSONNEL
Chairman: Roy Parker
85 Fletchers Estate, Sidlesham PO20 7QG
Tel: 01243 641407 (H)
Manager: Ian Hillman

Top:
Saltdean United.
Back Row (l-r):
Stuart Corlett, Jamie
Bryant, Sean Grice,
Reece Head, John
Essam, Kevin
Townsend, Leighton
Allen, Stewart
Holmes, Max
Hamilton. Front Row
(l-r): Carl Southwell,
Damion Dobbyn,
Terry Cooper,
Darren Longley,
Justin Simmons,
Sean Randell.
Photo: Roger Turner

Bottom:
Sidlesham FC
Back Row (l-r): Dave
Pettican, Jimmy
Brown, Dave Towers,
Mark Stewart, Steve
Parvin, Ben
Johnson, Neil
Parkins
Front Row (l-r):
Steve Warwick,
Duncan Burns,
Calvin Hore, Dave
Barnes, Kevin
Clements.
Photo: Roger Turner

SIDLEY UNITED

Secretary: Brian Martin, 30 Mayo Lane, Bexhill on Sea, East Sussex,TN39 5EA

Ground: Gullivers Sports Ground, Glovers Lane, Sidley, Bexhill-on-Sea
Tel: 01424 217078
Capacity: 1,500   Seats: None   Cover: 150   Floodlights: Yes

Directions: From Brighton on A259 to Bexhill bypass traffic lights, left intoLondon Road,
continue into Sidley, right into Glovers Lane and 1st left into North Road.
One mile from Bexhill (BR)

Clubhouse: Large bar area & function room. Tea bar
Club Shop: No, but metal badges are available.

HONOURS Sussex Co. Lg Div 2 58-59 64-65 98-99, Div. 2 Cup 98-99, Div 2 Invit. Cup
57-58; Sussex Intermediate Cup 47-48, Sussex Jnr Cup 24-25

PREVIOUS **Leagues:** East Sussex; Hastings & District
Grounds: None
RECORD **Attendance:** 1,300 in 1959

FACT FILE

Founded: 1906
Nickname: Blues
Sponsors: C,Campbell & R Cheale
Colours: Navy & sky/navy/navy & sky
Change colours: White
Midweek Matchday: Tues/ Weds
Programme: Yes   Editor: Graham Weston
Local Press: Bexhill Observer, Bexhill News

CLUB PERSONNEL

President: Tom Hyland
Chairman: Ray Cheale
Manager: Dickie Day

THREE BRIDGES

FACT FILE

Secretary:	Martin Clarke, 18 Mannings Close, Pound Hill, Crawley RH10 3TX
	Tel: 01293 883726 (H), 0585 662940 (Mob)
Ground:	Jubilee Field, Three Bridges, Crawley, West Sussex Tel: 01293 442000
	Capacity: 3,500 Seats: None Cover: 400 Floodlights: Yes
Directions:	From West Three Bridges station, turn second right into ThreeBridges Road
	and first left 75 yds down, opposite the Plough Inn
Clubhouse:	Bar, dance floor, pool, darts **Club Shop:** No
HONOURS	Sussex Co. Lg R-up 85-86 87-88 88-89 (Div 2 54-55, Invitation Cup 70-71,
	Div 2 Invitation Cup 62-63), Sussex RUR Charity Cup 82-83
PREVIOUS	**League s:** Mid Sussex; Redhill & District
	Grounds: None
RECORD	**Attendance:** 2,000 v Horsham, 1948

Founded: 1901
Nickname: Bridges
Sponsors: Canon
Colours: Amber & black/black/black
Change colours: Blue & white/blue/white
Midweek Matchday: Tuesday
Programme: Yes
Editor: Andy West (01293 883163)
Local Press: Crawley Observer, Crawley News

CLUB PERSONNEL

President: Jim Steele
Chairman: Alan Bell
Press Officer: Alf Blackler
Managers: John Crumplin & Daren Barker

WHITEHAWK

Secretary:	John Rosenblatt, 25 Arundel Street, Brighton BN2 5TH Tel: 01273 680322
Ground:	The Enclosed Ground, East Brighton Park Tel: 01273 609736
	Capacity: 3,000 Seats: None Cover: 500 Floodlights: Yes
Directions:	Follow Brighton seafront road towards Newhaven, turn inland (Arundel Road) oppo
	site Marina, 3rd right into Roedean Road, 1st left intoWilson Ave. 3 miles from
	Brighton (BR); take Newhaven, Eastbourne or Saltdean bus to Marina
Clubhouse:	Licensed bar, pool, darts. Board room. Tea bar Club Shop: No
Honours:	Sussex Co. Lg 61-62 63-64 83-84 (Div 2 67-68 80-81, Lg Cup 82-83 93-94,
	Invitation Cup 60-61 69-70, Div 2 Cup 80-81), Sussex Snr Cup 50-51 61-
	62,Sussex RUR Charity Cup 54-55 58-59 90-91, Sussex I'mediate Cup 49-50,
	Sussex Jnr Cup 48-49 51-52, Brighton Charity Cup 51-52 59-60 61-62 82-83
	87-88 88-89 89-90 90-91 97-98 98-99 99-00 Worthing Charity Cup 82-83
PREVIOUS	**League:** Brighton Hove & Dist**Grounds:** None
	Name: Whitehawk & Manor Farm Old Boys (until 1958)
BEST SEASON	**FA Vase:** 5th Round 93-94
RECORDS	**Gate:** 2,100 v Bognor Regis Town, FA Cup 4th Qualifying Rd replay 88-89
	Scorer: Billy Ford **Appearances:** Ken Powell 1,103

FACT FILE
Founded: 1945
Nickname: Hawks
Sponsors: Precision Metal Products
Colours: All red
Change colours: All blue
Midweek Matchday: Wednesday
Programme: £3.50 with admission
Editor: Ken Taylor (01273 735154)
Local Press: Evening Argus

CLUB PERSONNEL
President: Ron Wiltshire
Chairman/Comm Mgr: Ken Powell
Match Sec: Fred Moore
Manager: Paul Hubbard
Asst Manager: Alan Head

WICK

Secretary:	Paul Beard, 2 Van Gogh Place, North Bersted, Bognor Regis, W.Sussex PO22 9BG
	Tel: 01243 822063 (H)
Ground:	Crabtree Park, Coomes Way, Wick, Littlehampton, W. SussexTel: 01903 713535
	Capacity: 2,000 Seats: 50 Cover: 200 Floodlights: Yes
Directions:	A27 to Crossbush, left at traffic lights signed Littlehampton, after 1 mile cross
	level crossing, turn left into Coombes Way next to Locomotive PH - ground at
	end. One and a half miles from Littlehampton (BR)
Clubhouse:	First floor. Capacity 120. Tea bar Club Shp: No
HONOURS	Sussex Snr Cup 92-93; Sussex Co. Lg 89-90 93-94, Lg Cup 87-88 96-97 (R-up
	93-94 94-95), Div 2 81-82 85-86, Div 2 Cup R-up 81-82; Norman Wingate Tphy88-
	89 90-91, Res. Sect West 87-88 90-91 94-95; Sussex 5-aside R-up 85-86;Sussex
	RURCharity Cup 89-90 97-98;98-99 Gilbert Rice F'lit Cup R-up 80-81 81-82;
	Sussex Jnr Cup 59-60; Brighton Charity Cup 85-86; Sussex F'lit Cup R-Up 94-95
PREVIOUS	**League:** West Sussex **Grounds:** Southfields Rec
RECORD	**Attendance:** 900

FACT FILE
Founded: 1892
Nickname: Wickers
Sponsors: Swandean
Colours: Red & black/black/black
Change colours: All white
Midweek Matchdays: Tuesday
Reserve League: Sussex Co. Reserve Div
Programme: Yes
Editor:Secretary
Thomas Cairns 01903 501857
Local Press: Littlehampton Gazette

CLUB PERSONNEL
Chairman: Barry Wadsworth
Vice-Chairman: Andy Blackwood
President: Jack Croft
Manager: Carl Stabler
Asst Manager: Ian Cole

Top: Hailsham Town. Photo: Roger Turner

Centre: Portfield FC line up before their last ever match at Church Lane before their merger with Chichester City due for season 2000-01. Back Row (l-r): Musselwhite, Hopkins, Poulton, Horrel, Waterman, Barnes, Chambers, Davies Front Row (l-r): Edwards, Lacy, Savage, Godley, Oliver, Cowie. Photo: Graham Cotterill

Bottom: Bosham FC. Sussex Division 3 Champions 1999-2000. Photo: Graham Cotterill

BOSHAM

FACT FILE

Secretary: Phil Robinson, 3 Rowan Road, Havant Hampshire PO9 2UX
Tel: 02392 345276 (H)   02392 835398 (B) 0793 088 3217 (M)
Email: jennyphil@roft2.freeserve.co.uk

Colours: Red/white/red

CLUB PERSONNEL

Ground: Bosham Recreation Ground, Walton Lane, Bosham, W. Sussex
Tel: 01243 574011

Chairman: Dick Doncaster
Tel: 01243 375184
Manager: Steve Jefkins

Directions: From Chichester take the A259 towards Portsmouth.
On reaching Bosham turn left at the Swan P.H. roundabout.
1/2 mile to T junction, turn left & car park 50 yds on left.

Honours: Sussex County Lge Div. 3 99-00

BROADBRIDGE HEATH

FACT FILE
Founded: 1919
Nickname: Bears
Sponsors: Broadbridge Heath Peugeot
Colours: All royal blue
Change colours: All red
Midweek matches: Tuesday
Programme: Yes
Editor: Andy Crisp (01403 252273)
Admission: £2.50

Secretary: Richard Solman, 13 Monks Court, Monks Walk, Reigate, Surrey RH2 0SR
Tel No: 01403 211311

Ground: Broadbridge Heath Sports Centre, Wickhurst Lane, Horsham   Tel: 01403 211311

Capacity: 1,300   Seats: 300   Cover: 300   Floodlights: Yes

Directions: Alongside A24, Horsham north/south bypass. From the A24 Horsham Bypass, at
thelarge roundabout/underpass take the Broadbridge Heath Bypass towards
Guildford and then at the first roundabout turn left into Wickhurst Lane.

Clubhouse: Bar. Kitchen serving meals,

HONOURS None

CLUB PERSONNEL
Chairman: Keith Soane
President: G W Manketelow
Manager: Sam Chapman

PREVIOUS Leagues: Horsham, West Sussex, Southern Co's Comb

RECORD Attendance: 240

CRAWLEY DOWN VILLAGE

FACT FILE

Secretary: Bob Rashbrook, 3 Collier Row, Southgate, Crawley, West sussex RH10 6ES
Tel 01293 411457 (H) 01273 546714 (W)

Colours: All red
Programme: Yes

Ground: The Haven Sportsfield, Hophurst Lane, Crawley Down.
Tel: 01342 717140

CLUB PERSONNEL

Capacity: 1000   Seats: None   Cover: 50   Floodlights: No

Chairman: Brian Suckling

Directions: From B2028, follow signpost for village to War Memorial, turn left into Hophurst
Lane, ground 100 yards on left. From A22, Felbridge, left into Crawley Down   Road,
ground 2 miles uphill on right.

Vice-Chairman: Michael Martin
President: Tony Clements
Managers: Roger Crouch & Andy Barker
Match Secretary: As Secretary
Physio: Mike Green

HONOURS Sussex County Lge Div 3 R-Up 95-96
Sussex Intermediate Chall. Cup R-up 95-96

PREVIOUS League: Mid Sussex Football League

CROWBOROUGH ATHLETIC

Secretary: David Mackellow, 38 Eridge Drive, Crowborough,TN6 2TJ
Tel: 01892 653122

Ground: Alderbrook Recreation Ground, Fermor Road, Crowborough
Tel: 01892 661893

Directions: Turn east off A26 at Crowborough. Cross traffic lights, through High Street,
right into Croft Rd, continue into Whitehall Rd and Fermor Rd,
Alderbrook is 2nd right after mini-r'bout.

Capacity: 1,000   Seats: None   Cover: 200   Floodlights: Yes.

FACT FILE
Founded: 1894
Nickname: Crows.
Colours: Blue & white/blue/blue
Change colours: All red.
Midweek Matchday: Tuesday
Prog. Editor: James Young: 01892 669021
Local Press: Kent & Sussex Courier,Sussex Express

Clubhouse: Bar facilities & tea bar on matchdays   Club Shop: No, metal badges available

HONOURS Sussex Co. Lg Div 1 92-93, Div 2 Cup 77-78, Div 3 R-up
Sussex Intermediate Cup 86-87

CLUB PERSONNEL
President: Tony Clark
Chairman: Barry J Sykes
Press Officer: Peter Crisp (01892 655470).
Manager: Adrian James

PREVIOUS League: Brighton   **Grounds:** None

RECORD Gate: 439 v Stamco, Sussex County Lge Div. 2 1/5/93

EAST GRINSTEAD TOWN

Secretary: Martin Hill, 2 Balmoral, East Grinstead, W.Sussex RH19 4RJ (01342 325013)
Ground: East Court, East Grinstead   Tel: 01342 325885
Directions: A264 Tunbridge Wells road (Moat Road) until mini-r'bout at bottom of
Blackwell Hollow, turn immediately right by club sign then 1st left, ground
200yds down lane past rifle club on right.
Capacity: 3,000   **Seats:** None   **Cover:** 400   **Floodlights:** Yes   **Club Shop:** No
Clubhouse: Open 1.30-10.30 matchdays, 6-11 midweek matches. Hot food available.

HONOURS   Sussex RUR Charity Cup (R-up 74-75); Sussex Co. Lg Invitation Cup 51-52;
Sussex Jnr Cup (jt) 07-08; Sussex Youth Cup 86-87; Southern Amtr Lg
Snr Div 3 31-32; Mid-Sussex Lg x 6, Lg Cup x 7; Brighton Lg x 3, Lg Cup x 3
PREVIOUS Leagues: Mid-Sussex 00-15 35-37; Sussex Co. 20-32; Southern Amateur 32-35.
RECORD   **Attendance:** 2,006 v Lancing, FA Amateur Cup 8/11/48
Appearances: Guy Hill in 19 seasons - 1977-94

FACT FILE
Founded: 1890   Nickname: Wasps
Sponsors: Rydon Group.
Colours: Gold/black/black
Change colours: All Blue
Midweek Matchday: Tuesday.
Reserves Lge: Sussex Co. Reserve Div East
Programme: 36 pages, 50p (Matt Gardner)
Press Off.: Bruce Talbot 01293 543809
Local Press: East Grinstead Observer/East
Grinstead Courier,SportsArgus
CLUB PERSONNEL
Chairman: Phil Cowland
President: Colin Dixon
Manager: Bobby Smith
Physio: Gary Bullen

HAILSHAM TOWN

Secretary/Press Officer: Derek York, 59 Anglesey Avenue, Horsebridge, Hailsham BN27 3BQ
Tel: 01323 848024 (H)
Ground: The Beaconsfield, Western Road, Hailsham, East Sussex   Tel: 01323 840446
Directions: A22 to Arlington Road, turn east, then left into South Road - left into Diplocks
Way until Daltons. Four miles from Polegate (BR - Brighton-Eastbourne line);
regular bus service from Eastbourne
Capacity: 2,000   **Seats:** None   **Cover:** 300   **Floodlights:** Yes
Clubhouse: Hot and cold snacks. Open every evening, matchdays and Sundays, teabar
HONOURS   Sussex County Lg Div 2 R-up 80-81, Southern Co'sComb. 74-75, Sussex RUR
Charity Cup, Sussex I'mediate Cup, Hastings Snr Cup,Sussex Jnr Cup, E Sussex
Lg Cup, Hailsham Charity Cup, John O'Hara Cup 95-96

PREVIOUS   **League:** E Sussex, Southern Comb   **BEST SEASON**   **FA Vase:** 5th Rd 88-89
RECORD   **Gate:**1,350 v Hungerford, FA Vase Feb '89
Goalscorer: H Stevens 51, 95-96   **Appearances:** P Comber 713

FACT FILE
Founded: 1885   Nickname: None
Colours: Black & yellow/Black/Black
Change colours: All white
Midweek matchday: Tuesday
Programme: Yes
Editor: Secretary
Admission: ¨2.50
99-00 Captain:N.Jones
P.o.Y.: D.Winterton
Top Scorer: S.French 10)
CLUB PERSONNEL
President: J Whippy
Chairman: K.Savage-Brooks
Manager: Mark Leaney

LINGFIELD

Secretary: Ron Devereux, Tanglewood, New Chapel Rd., Lingfield, Surrey RH7 6BJ
Tel No: 01342 835239

Ground: Godstone Road, Lingfield, Surrey.
Tel: 01342 834269

Directions: A22, 4 miles north of East Grinstead, to Mormon Temple roundabout, take
exit Lingfield (B2028) Newchapel Road for 1 1/2 miles. Left at T junction
into Godstone Road (B2029) and ground is 1/2 mile on left.

FACT FILE
Colours: Red & yellow stripes/black/yellow
Change colours:Sky Blue/white/ sky blue

CLUB PERSONNEL
Chairman: Bill Blenkin
Manager: Mark Endsleigh

MILE OAK

Secretary: Colin Brown, 19 The Crescent, Southwick, West Sussex BN42 4LB
Tel: 01273 591346
Ground: Mile Oak Recreation Ground, Graham Avenue, Mile Oak. Tel: 01273 423854

Directions: From A27 take Mile Oak Road or Locks Hill & Valley Road to Chalky Road, ground
500yds on right along Graham Avenue which runs up valley fromcentre of Chalky Road
Capacity: **Seats:** None   **Cover:** Yes   **Floodlights:** Yes
Clubhouse: Mile Oak Pavillion; Hall and tea bar   **Club Shop:** No

HONOURS   Sussex Co.Lg.Div 2 Champions, Div 3 R-up 91-92 (Div 2 Cup R-up 92-93),
Southern Counties Combination 86-87, Brighton Hove & District Lg 80-81,
VernonWentworth Cup 85-86, Sussex Intermediate Cup R-up 88-89
PREVIOUS   **Leagues:** Southern Counties Combination; Brighton Hove & District
Ground: Victoria Rec., Portslade
RECORD   **Attendance:** 186

FACT FILE
Founded: 1960
Nickname: The Oak
Colours: Tangerine/black/tangerine
Change colours: All blue
Midweek Matchday: Tuesday
Programme: Yes
Editor: C Tew (01273 416036)
Admission: £1.50
Local Press: Brighton Evening Argus,
Shoreham Herald
CLUB PERSONNEL
Chairman: L.Hamilton
President: D Bean
Manager: Tony Gratwicke

OAKWOOD

Secretary: Paula West, 12 Woodend Close,Three Bridges,Crawley W.Sussex RH101RS
Tel: 01293 401085
Ground: Tinsley Lane, Three Bridges, Crawley, West Sussex   Tel: 01293 515742

Directions: From A23 to Gatwick, take 1st set of lights into Manor Royal, pass next lights, over r'bout to warehouse marked Canon, turn right signposted Oakwood. Last clubhouse down lane. Two miles north of Three Bridges (BR)
Capacity: 3,000   Seats: 20   Cover: Yes   Floodlights: Yes
Club Shop: Yes, incl. metal badges
Clubhouse: Large bar area, pool tables, multidart boards. Board room & tea bar

HONOURS   Sussex Snr Cup R-up 92-93, Sussex Co. Lg Div 2 R-up 89-90 (Div 2 Cup 89-90, Div 3 84-85), Southern Comb. Cup 83-84
PREVIOUS   Leagues: Crawley & Dist., Southern Co's Comb
Ground: Park pitches
RECORD   Attendance: 367   Appearances: Peter Brackpool

FACT FILE
Founded: 1966   Nickname: Oaks
Sponsors: Linden Plc
Colours: Red & black/black/black
Change colours: Blue/black/black
Midweek Matchday: Tuesday
Reserves' Lge: Sussex Co. Reserve section
Programme: 24 pages
Editor: Scott Packer Local Press: Crawley Observer, Crawley News

CLUB PERSONNEL
Chairman: Stuart Lovegrove
Press Officer & Match Sec: Scott Packer
Manager:Andy Maddox
Physio:MsS Widy ,Ass Physio:Frank Pushman

OVING

Secretary: Peter Hall, St Bruno, Prinsted Lane, Emsworth, Hants PO10 8HR
Tel: 01243 372652
Ground: Highfield Lane, Oving, Nr Chichester, W Sussex. Tel: 01243 778900
Directions: Into Oving past the Gribble Inn, follow road round to housing estate - Highfield Lane (left). Ground sign posted 50 yards on right.
Capacity: 1,000   Cover: 100   Floodlights: No
Clubhouse: Oving Social Club or Gribble Inn Contact 01243 789395 Metal Badges: Yes
HONOURS W. Sussex Lge - Div 5 Cup 81-82, Div 5S 81-82, Div 4 Cup 82-83, Div 4S 82-83, Div 3S84-85. Div 2S 87-88, 91-92, Div 1 94-95, Prem. Div 95-96 96-97; Sussex Jun Cup: 86 91; Chichester char. Cup 90-91; Sussex Co. Inter. Cup R-up 98-99; Sussex Co. Div 3 98-99, Div 3 Cup R-up 98-99
PREVIOUS   Leagues: West Sussex
CLUB RECORDS Attendance: 276 v Westfield, Sussex co. Lge Div. 3 8.5.99
Win: 10-0 v S B Sports (H) Sussex Co.inter. Cup 10.10.98   **Defeat:** 0-5 v Lingfield (A) 13.9.97

FACT FILE
Formed: 1978-79   Nickname: "The Vikings"
Colours: Black & white/white/white
Change colours:Red& Black/Black/Black
Reserves' Lge: Sussex Co. - Res. Sect. West
Programme: 32 pages 50p
Editor: Simon Jasinski (01243 374239)
98-99Captain: John Donogue
Top Scorer: Justin Turnill (20)

CLUB PERSONNEL
Chairman: Dusty Miller
Press off.: Ade Adebayo (01903 856262)
Manager: Paul Gilbert
Asst. Manager: Adie Miles
Coach: Vijay Korgaokar
Physio: Marc Rowbottom

PEACEHAVEN & TELSCOMBE

Secretary: Mrs Margaret Edwards, 2,Tuscan Court, The Esplanade, Telscombe Cliffs, East Sussex BN10 7HF   Tel: 01273 583022 (H) 07803 845329 (M)
Ground: Piddinghoe Avenue, Peacehaven, E. Sussex (01273 582471) **Directions:** Arriving from Brighton on A259, cross r'bout and Piddinghoe Ave. is next left after 2nd set of lights - ground at end. From Newhaven Piddinghoe Ave. is first right after first set of lights. Three miles from Newhaven(BR). Peacehaven is served by Brighton to Newhaven and Eastbourne buses
Capacity: 3,000   Seats: None   Cover: 250   Floodlights: Yes
Clubhouse: Bar open evenings and weekends, pool darts, hot and cold food available. Tea bar
HONOURS   Sussex Co. Lg 78-79 81-82 82-83 91-92 92-93 94-95 95-96 (R-up 77-78 80-81 90-91, Lg Cup 91-92 92-93, Div 2 R-up 75-76, Div 2 Cup 75-76, Norman Wingate Tphy 82-83 91-92 92-93, Hayden Tphy 82-83 92-93, Div 2 Invitation Cup69-70, Sussex Snr Cup R-up 81-82 92-93, Sussex RUR Charity Cup 77-78 81-82 92-93 (R-up 80-81 89-90 90-91 94-95 95-96), Brighton Charity Cup 91-92 92-93 93-94, Vernon Wentworth 91-92 92-93
RECORD Attendance: 1,420 v Littlehampton, Lge 91 **PREVIOUS Leagues:** Lewes; Brighton
BEST SEASON FA Cup: 4th Qual. Rd 90-91   **FA Vase:** 6th Rd (Q-F) 95-96, 5th Rd 92-93

FACT FILE
Founded: 1923
Nickname: The Tye
Sponsors: Anchor Garage
Colours: All white
Change colours: Royal Blue
Midweek Matches: Tuesday
Programme: Yes
Editor: Secretary

CLUB PERSONNEL
Chairman: Jim Edwards
Match Sec: Fred Parris
Press Officer: Secretary
Manager: Peter Edwards

SHINEWATER ASSOCIATION

Secretary: Brian Dowling, 79 Harebeating Drive, Hailsham BN27 1JE
Tel: 01323 442488

Ground: Shinewater Lane, Eastbourne. Tel: 01323 765880
Capacity: 1,000 Seats: None   Cover: 200   Floodlights: No

Directions: A27, take B2104 to Eastbourne. At Stone Cross go under railway bridge, 1st right into Larkspur Drive, 1st left into Milfoil Drive, 3rd left into Shinewater Lane

Clubhouse: Match days (01323 765880)

RECORD   Attendance: 302

FACT FILE
Founded:1990 Club
Sponsors: T.B.A.
Colours: Navy & sky/navy/navy
Change Colours: Claret
Programme: Free with entry
Programme Editor: Brian Dowling
Previous League: East Sussex

CLUB PERSONNEL
Chairman: John Pinyoun
Managers: Peter Coleman

Top: Crawley Down FC. Back Row (l-r): Roy Todman (Kit Manager), Darren Barker, Matt Baker, Bob Chambers, Stuart Hobbs, Dave Conner, Matt Heasman, John Murphy, Andrew Stonley, Mick Green (Physio), Alan Watson. Front Row (l-r): Fred Fleming, Ian Pearce, Adam Alyward, Mark Aldred, Lee Hanson, Tim DeCastro, Doug Cashman.

Shinewater Association FC. Back Row (l-r): Adrian Cowell, Scott Wiseman, Wayne Lawrence, Ross Osborne, Graham Holman, Jason Morley, Ben Hutchinson. Front Row: Jason Cullinane, Glen Mitchell, Michael West, Richard Booth, Ian Nye, Greg Priscott, Clive Connell. Photo: Roger Turner

Withdean FC. Back Row (l-r): Junior Lamont, Mike Reilly, Ryan Pratt, Andy Webb, Adam Simpson, Kevin Bradburn, Mark Sorrell, Dave Wade. Front Row: Mark Bujok, Alex Tasker, Paul Tait, Paul Bunker, Craig O'Dell. Photo: Andrew Chitty

SHOREHAM

Secretary: Mrs Anne Harper, 66 Willow Crescent, Worthing. BN13 2SX   Tel: 01903 267672
Ground: Middle Road, Shoreham-by-Sea, West Sussex   Tel: 01273 454261
Capacity: 1,500   Seats: 20   Cover: 1 stand   Floodlights: Yes
Directions: Half mile from Shoreham-by-Sea (BR) - east across level crossing, up Dolphin
Road, ground 150yds on right. Or, A27 to Shoreham. At Southlands Hospital turn
left down Hammy Lane, left at end, ground opposite

Clubhouse: Seats 70. Bar, pool, darts, tea bar   **Club Shop:** No
HONOURS   Sussex Co. Lg 51-53 77-78 (R-up 34-35, Div 2 61-62 76-77 84-85 93-94,Div 2
Cup 74-75 82-83, Invitation Cup 57-58), Sussex Snr Cup 01-02 05-06,Sussex   F'lit Cup
R-up 89-90, Sussex RUR Charity Cup 02-03 05-06,
VernonWentworth Cup 86-87
PREVIOUS   **League:** West Sussex
Ground: Buckingham Park (pre-1970)
RECORD   **Gate:** 1,342 v Wimbledon (f/lt opening 86)

FACT FILE
Founded: 1892   Nickname: Musselmen
Sponsors: Len German Wholesalers
Colours:All blue
Change colours: All red
Midweek Matchday: Wednesday
Programme: Yes
Editor: Michael Wenham
Local Press: Shoreham Herald
CLUB PERSONNEL
President: Alf Bloom
Chairman: John Bell
Manager: George Parris
Press Officer: Michael Wenham
Tel: 01273 596009

SOUTHWICK

Secretary: Derek Earley,1309 Poplar Ave.,Hangleton, Hove BN3 8PN(01273 328769)
Ground: Old Barn Way, off Manor Hall Way, Southwick, Brighton BN43 4NT Tel: 01273 701010
Directions: Five minutes walk from either Fishergate or Southwick BR stations.By car A27 from
Brighton take 1st left after `Southwick' sign to Leisure Centre. Ground adjacent.
Capacity: 3,500   Seats: 220   Cover: 1,220   Floodlights: Yes
Clubhouse: Weekdays 12-3 & 6-11, all day Sat., normal hrs Sunday. Members bar & board-
room with bar. Matchday snacks from tea bar.
HONOURS Isthmian Lg Div 2 Sth 85-86, Sus. Co. Lg 25-26 27-28 29-30 47-48 68-69 74-75 (R-
up x 9, Lg Cup 77-78 ,Div 1 Invit. Cup 65-66, Div 2 R-up 65-66), Combined Co's Lg R-up 84-85,
Sus.Snr Cup x 10, Sus. RUR Charity Cup (10) 1896-97 08-09 10-11 24-26 27-30 37-38 76-77,
W. Sus. Lg1896-97 97-98 1908-09 10-11, Sus. Jnr Cup 1891-92.
PREVIOUS Leagues: West Sussex 1896-1920; Sussex County 20-52 54-84; Metropolitan52-
54; Combined Co's 84-85; Isthmian 85-92.   **BEST SEASON FA Cup:** 1st Round 74-75, 0-5 v
Bournemouth **FA Amtr Cup:** 3rd Rd. 28-29 **FA Vase:** 3rd Rd. 79-80 85-86
RECORD Attendance: 3,200 v Showbiz side 1971

FACT FILE
Founded: 1882   Nickname: Wickers
Sponsors: Guildcare Nursing Homes
Colours: Red & black stripes/black/red
Change Colours: All white
Midweek matchday: Tuesday
Reserve League: Sussex Co. Res Div
Programme: Yes
Editor/ Press Off.: Paul Symes 01273 594142
CLUB PERSONNEL
Chairman: Peter Keene
Vice-Chairman: Dave Cook
President: Dr D W Gordon.
Manager: Malcolm Saunders
Asst Manager: Dennis Nicholl
Coach: Paul Croft

STORRINGTON

Secretary: Keith Dalmon, 4 End Cottages, Storrington Road, Amberley. BN18 9LX
Tel: 01798 831887

Ground: Recreation Ground, Storrington. Tel: 01903 745860

Directions: Turn west on A283 (off A24).
Ground is opposite the pond to the west of the village.

FACT FILE
Colours: All Blue
Chanbge Colours : All yellow

CLUB PERSONNEL
Manager: Malcolm MacMichael
Managers: Nigel Dyer & Glen Houchen

WEALDEN

Secretary: Peter Byford, Chelwood, Possingworth Park, Cross in Hand, Heathfield TN21 0TN
Tel: 01435 862574 (H)   0410 944364 (M)   Email: pbyford@aol.com

Ground: Wealden Sports Club, Uckfield, East Sussex. Tel: 01825 890905

Directions: Next to the Rajdutt Restaurant on the Old Eastbourne Road,
south of Uckfield town centre.

Honours: Sussex County Lge Div. 3 R-up 99-00

FACT FILE
Colours: All blue
Change colours: All red

CLUB PERSONNEL
Chairman: Brian Smith
Tel: 01273 812329 (H)
Manager: Tom Parker

WESTFIELD

Secretary: Mrs Jenny Drinkwater, 28 Churchfields, Westfield TN35 4SN
Tel: 01424 754032

Ground: Parish Field. Westfield Tel: 01424 751011

Directions: Take A21 towards Hastings, left onto A28. Westfield Lane, towards Ashford
for 2 miles, pitch on left.

FACT FILE
Colours: White & Green/green/green
Change Colours: Yellow & Green/ green/green

CLUB PERSONNEL
Chairman: Brian Over
Westaways, Main Road, Westfield TN35 4QN
Tel: 01424 754844
Manager: Shaun Hardy

WORTHING UNITED

Secretary: Malcolm Gamlen, 1 Westbourne Ave., Worthing, West Sussex BN14 8DE
Tel: 01903 263655

Ground: The Robert Albon Memorial Grd, Lyons Way, Worthing Tel: 01903 234466
Capacity:1,000 Seats: 100 Cover: 500 Floodlights: No

Directions: From west past Hill Barn r'about to 2nd set of lights, turn left into Lyons Way.
From east 1st set of lights at end of Sompting bypass right into Lyons Way

Clubhouse: Bar (capacity 80), refreshment facilities (tea bar) Metal badges: Yes

HONOURS As Wigmore Athletic prior to 1988. Sussex Co. Lg Challenge Cup 74-75
(Invitation Cup 59-60, Div 2 52-53, Div 2 Invitation Cup 59-60, Div 3 89-90,
Reserve Section West 92-93, Sussex Jnr Cup 49-50

PREVIOUS **Names:** Wigmore Athletic (founded 1948) merged with Southdown in 1988
Grounds: Harrison Road, Worthing

RECORD **Attendance:**180 v Northwood, FA Vase 3rd Rd 91-92

FACT FILE
Founded: 1988
Nickname: None
Sponsors: Tinsley Robor
Colours: Sky & white/navy/white
Change colours: All red
Programme: Yes
Editor: D.Treacy (01903 690122)
Local Newspapers: Worthing Herald

CLUB PERSONNEL
President: Bob Albon
Chairman: Len Killpatrick
Press Officer: Secretary
Manager: Geoff Raynsford

*Top: Sidlesham v Withdean Kevin Clements of Sidlesham winds his way through the Withdean defence.
Photo: Graham Cotterill*

*Bottom: Horsham YMCA's Lee Butcher pictured centre (white), slips this ball past East Preston's Terry Withers. Final
score Horsham YMCA 7 East Preston 2. Photo: Clive Turner*

ANSTY RANGERS

Secretary: Mrs Kay Keehan, 71 Sunninghill Avenue,Hove, E Sussex BN3 8JB (01444 454010)
Ground: Deaks Lane, Ansty Tel: 01444 454010) Directions: Take A272 forAnsty/Haywards Heath, to Ansty prior to mini r/about turn left into Deaks Lane
Colours: Red /white/red& white

BEXHILL TOWN

Secretary: Mrs Leigh Quinn, 37 Colebrook Road, Bexhill-on-Sea. TN39 3PX Tel: 01424 214197
Ground: The Polegrove, Brockley Rd, Bexhill-on-Sea, E. Sussex Tel: 01424220732 Directions: At Little Common r'bout take 3rd exit to Cooden Sea Rd, left into Cooden Drive for one and a half miles, Brockley Rd on the right. 3/4 mile from Bexhill Central (BR)
Colours: Green & white/white/white

FOREST

Secretary: Peter Farley,9 Owlbeech Way, Horsham, W.Sussex RH13 6AW. (01403 25256)
Ground: Roffey Sports & Social Club, Spooners Rd., Roffey. Tel: 01403 210221) Directions: Spooners Rd. is off the main Crawley road, 100 yds from the `Star'PH, towards Crawley
Colours: All Dark Blue

FRANKLANDS VILLAGE

Secretary: Mrs Linsey Worsfold, 151a Franklands Village, Haywards Heath. RH163RF. Tel: 01444 416475)
Ground: Hardy Memorial Playing Field, Franklands Village. Tel: 01444 440138) Directions: A272 (Haywards H. to Uckfield). Left at Princess Royal Hosp.r'about. 2nd left & ground at rear of social club
Colours: All Royal blue

HAYWARDS HEATH TOWN

Secretary: Tony Sim, 43 Sunnywood Drive, Haywards Heath RH16 4PE. Tel: 01444 453754
Ground: Hanbury Park Stadium, Haywards Heath Tel: 01444 412837
Directions: A272 to Haywards Heath town centre. At Sussex round-about, north on B2708 (Hazelgrove Road) take first right into New England Road, 4th right (Allen Road) leads to ground.
Colours: Blue & white stripes/white/blue

HURSTPIERPOINT

Secretary: Michelle McDonald, 1 Weald Close, Hurstpierpoint, W,Sussex (01273 835426)
Ground: Fairfield Rec. Ground, Cuckfield Road. (Tel: 01273 834783) Directions: At Hurstpierpoint crossroads, go north into Cuckfield Road (B2117) for 1km. Ground entrance between houses nos.158 & 160
Colours: Blue & white quarters/blue/blue

IFIELD

Secretary: Robert Anderson, 1 Old Orchards, Church Rd, Worth, Crawley. RH107QA. Tel: 01293 886215)
Ground: Ifield Sports Club, Ifield Green, Rusper Road. Tel: 01293 536569) Directions: From A23 Crawley by-pass going north, left at r'about signedCharlwood. Third left into Ifield Green, first right past Royal Oak (PH) intoRusper Rd
Colours: White/black/red

NEWHAVEN

Secretary: Peter Foote, 32 Valley Dene, Newhaven BN9 9NF Tel: 01273 513232
Ground: Fort Road Recreation Ground Tel: 01273 513940
Directions: A259, follow one-way system around town, left at Police Station into South Road, which becomes Fort Road.
Colours: Red & amber/red & amber/red

ROYAL & SUN ALLIANCE

Secretary: JulieJenkins, 59 Drakes Close, Horsham RH12 5UD Tel: 01403 272440
Ground: Sunallon Sports Club, North Heath Lane, Horsham Tel: 01403 253814) Directions: Heading into Horsham on Warnham road, turn left at 1st lights, overmini-r/about to North Heath Lane, grd on left
Colours: Yellow/blue/yellow

RYE UNITED

Founded: 1938
Secretary: Robert Dixon, 32 The Maltings, Peasmarsh, nr Rye, East Sussex TN31 6ST (01797 230430)
Ground: Sydney Allnut Pavilion, Rye Football & Cricket Salts, Fish Market Rd., Rye, East Sussex (01797 223855)
Colours: All white
Change colours: Yellow & green/green/green
Previous league: Sussex Co., Kent Co. >00

ST. FRANCIS

Secretary: Pat Bucknell, 79 Priory Way, Haywards Heath, W.Sussex RH16 3NS (01444 457726)
Ground: St. Francis Hospital, Colwell Lane, Haywards Heath. Tel: 01444 441881) Directions: Enter through main entrance of Princess Royal Hospital on Lewes road, A272 Haywards Heath. Follow signs to Sports Complex
Colours: Green & white/green/green

SEAFORD TOWN

Secretary: Barry Chambers, 47 Bramber Road, Seaford BN25 1AT Tel: 01323 491932
Ground; The Crouch, Seaford. Tel: 01323 892221
Directions; A259 to Seaford. At mini r'about by station, turn LEFT (from Newhaven) RIGHT (from Eastbourne). At end of Church St., across junction, then left at end. After 500 m turn left up Ashurst Rd. Bramber Rd. is at the top.
Colours: Red & blue/blue/red

STEYNING TOWN

Secretary: Gina Barnes, 36 Shooting Fields, Steyning BN44 3RQ Tel: 01903815387)
Ground: The Shooting Field, Steyning Tel: 01903 812228)
Directions: EnteringSteyning from west, take 1st left into High St, follow into Shooting Fieldestate, ground is 4th rurn left
Colours: All Red and white

TSC

Secretary: Mrs Alison Read, 28 Lavington Close, Ifield, Crawley, W.Sussex RH110HX (01293 425607)
Ground: Tinsley lane, Three Bridges, Crawley, West Sussex. Tel: none
Colours: Black & white/black/black
Prev. Lge: Crawley & Dist.>00

UCKFIELD TOWN

Secretary: Jennie Hickman, 10 Wilson Grove, Uckfield, E.Sussex TN22 2BU (01825 762602)
Ground: Victoria Pleasure Grounds, Uckfield. Tel: 01825 769400)
Directions: Take Eastbourne road (old A22) south of Uckfield town centre. Entrance to ground is 1/2 mile on the right (just after the Police station)
Colours: Red/black/black

Amateur Football is a very physical game . . .

Below: Deal Town players take a flyer to congratulate Roly Graham after he scores in the FA Vase Semi Final second leg. Photo: Roger Turner

Above: Redhill goalscorer Zak Newman is mobbed by camera-shy team mates! Photo: D Nicholson

Above: Pitch inspections are becoming more thorough these days. (Eton Manor v Leyton.)   Photo: Francis Short

THE EAGLE BITTER
UNITED COUNTIES LEAGUE
FEEDER TO: DR MARTENS LEAGUE

Chairman: Geoff Paul
Secretary: Roger Gamble, 8 Bostock Avenue, Northampton NN1 4LW   Tel: 01604 637766
Press Officer: Jeremy Biggs   Tel: 01780 763048

FORDS ARE FIRST TIME CHAMPIONS
    An exciting millennium campaign saw a number of first time successes with both Ford Sports and Cottingham emerging as champions of their respective divisions for the first time after captivating title races.
    Ford Sports had underachieved during 1998-99, but the shrewd appointment of ex-Buckingham boss Darren Wood saw them enjoy a triumphant season. The former Robins chief cherrypicked the key men from his former club and blended them in with the best of Fords' existing squad to produce a winning combination which set the pace from late September. Organisation proved the key to the Motormen's success with their goalkeeping duo Pete Bulliman and Graham Bott claiming twenty clean sheets between them. Summer recruits Mark Parsons and Robin Tucker were the lynchpins of the defence while skipper Darren Harmon provided the attacking flair with valuable support from Byron Miller, Justin McClurg and the long serving Martin Jennings. The seeds for Fords' success were sown in a seventeen match unbeaten start - a Premier record - until a Friday night visit to Holbeach saw Motormen colours lowered for the first time on 12 November. Thereafter only Boston - home and away - inflicted defeat on the Daventry side.
    Cogenhoe and Boston ran Fords close at the top, finishing four points behind with the Cooks taking the runners up medals on goal difference. Cogenhoe set the early pace before Fords went to the top, and late on they looked like they might put their name on the Denham-Parker trophy for the first time. Just three wins in their final seven matches proved costly for Steve Forbes's men as a hectic programme of fixtures tested the Cooks' stamina. A record 135 goals - a Premier best since the division kicked off in 1972 - wasn't enough to bring the title to Compton Park and Cogenhoe were left to reflect on a 6-3 defeat at Royal Oak Way in October after leading in the first half. 46 domestic goals out of a season's total of 64 left James Westley one down on ex-Compton Park favourite Kevin Slinn's Premier record while team mate Roy Anderson finished second in the divisional scorechart with a 34 goal haul. Cogenhoe finished unbeaten on home soil - drawing just four times! Third placed Boston were also undefeated at home - just three visitors left with a share of the spoils. Tattershall Road truly became a "bastion of invincibility" between 16 October and 18 March as Poachers' keeper Mick Brown played 897 minutes without conceding a goal on home soil - including nine full matches. Champions-elect Ford Sports eventually ended the sequence but still became Boston victims for the second time!
    Fourth placed Stotfold boasted the top flight's best defensive record - just 24 goals conceded, one fewer than the champions, and 22 clean sheets - while Northampton Spencer's young side had another good season in fifth. Blackstone equalled their best ever top flight finish - sixth - and unearthed a striking sensation in Jamie Graham whose 23 goal haul included seven against Buckingham - equalling a Premier record. Kempston's new look side finished seventh, their best placing since returning to the top flight in 1986, while Premier debutants Bugbrooke recovered from a poor run of results in the winter to finish in the top ten.
    In the lower reaches Eynesbury and Potton both diced with relegation before finding more consistency in the spring and pulling clear of the drop zone. Buckingham and Long Buckby both finished with massive negative goal differences after torrid seasons. The Robins struggled to replace Darren Wood and when Alan Boorn took the reins two weeks before the start of the season he inherited just one player! A hastily assembled squad took some hidings early on before Boorn stepped down to be replaced by ex-youth team boss Adam Sinclair. After some initial success Buckingham had lost eleven consecutive matches when Sinclair too quit in early March. The appointment of a more experienced manager in Morrell Maison saw a new team recruited and seven points from the final five games saw Buckingham end the campaign three points in front of Long Buckby, whose final day success at Wootton followed 26 matches without victory!
    Both strugglers will continue in the top flight for season 2000-01 as neither of the eventual top two in Division One had the necessary facilities to make the step up. Cottingham, Deeping, Harrowby and Thrapston contested the title issue and made this an exciting division with little to separate the top four throughout, Daventry's late challenge adding further spice to the race. Deeping, promoted from the Peterborough League, made a bold bid for a second successive promotion, opening the season with an eleven game unbeaten run until suffering their first defeat against Burton PW on 6 November. Rangers became the division's draw specialists - seven in nine games during mid-winter and four more in their last six games cost them a Premier place. Most costly stalemate was their last when hosts Daventry overturned a three goal half time deficit to equalise six minutes into injury time. That gave Thrapston the chance to go top by beating Vanaid 4-0 in their final outing, but the Chancery Lane club themselves had to settle for a best ever second place as the experienced Cottingham side clinched the crown with a 1-1 draw at Burton Park in

their penultimate match. Berryfield Road chief Rob Dunion assembled an experienced squad comprising players of Premier experience and it paid off as they showed the greatest consistency of the title contenders to finish three points clear. A fifteen match unbeaten run from the end of October until mid-March paved the way for Cottingham's success in which the goals of strike pair Darren Burt and Dave Trimble were key. Harrowby were the division's most improved side and they too had a goal hungry strikeforce in Robbie Williams and Carl Savile - but the loss of player-boss Nicky Andersen with a broken leg in December hit their title chances. Daventry made a late challenge and became everyone's dark horses after recruiting experienced campaigners Jimmy Simpson, Warren Donald, Lee Lavery and Peter Green - but they won just once in their last six outings and had to settle for fifth place.

The big surprise at the other end of the table was perennial title contenders Higham finishing next to bottom. The Lankies lost manager Aidy Mann to ambitious Woodford in September and the side which had finished second the previous May broke up. Lee Howard had to start virtually from scratch after taking charge and Higham needed an Easter Monday win over Irchester to condemn the Romans to bottom place.

There were some spectacular achievements at reserve level. In Reserve Division One Rothwell completed a hat-trick of championships by notching up a points record for the division - an outstanding success for long serving reserve boss Andy Pawluk in his final season in charge. Raunds were running Rothwell close until half their team was called up to the senior side - in the circumstances they did well to pip Cogenhoe for second. At the other end of the table Higham collected a solitary point and suffered relegation. King's Lynn, under the guidance of former Northern Ireland international Paul Ramsey, took Reserve Division Two by storm, setting a league record with 24 successive wins from the start of the season and eventually heading fellow newcomers Deeping by 21 points with Newport Pagnell two points further back in third - all three will be playing higher grade football next term.

On the cup front Cogenhoe found some consolation for their near miss in the league, winning the Knockout Cup for the second time. Kempston, playing in their first final since 1977, led through Steve Pacey's own goal going into the dying seconds only for defender James Fletcher to smash a leveller and extra time goals from old stager Jeff Gilmour and Roy Anderson gave the Cooks a 3-1 victory at St Neots' Rowley Park. In the semis the Cooks had edged out Ford Sports 2-1 in extra time while Kempston were 3-1 winners at Desborough. Both Daventry and Rothwell Corinthians carried the Division One flag into the last eight before suffering heavy defeats - Daventry had seen off top flight pair Buckingham and Bourne en route to the last eight while Corinths had trounced Premier side Eynesbury 6-0 at Hall Road. Round One saw Northampton Spencer create history with an 11-0 win at Higham, a competition record with Scott Coleman's seven goal haul another milestone in the competition's history. Ross McNeil's double gave Kings Lynn a double as they beat Stotfold 2-1 in the Reserve Knockout Cup final at Eynesbury, while the pre-season Benevolent Cup final - a first ever UCL fixture played in July - saw Spalding beat Bugbrooke 3-2 at the Halley Stewart Field, two goals from Craig Wilson and one from Darren Cundy giving the Tulips a winning sign off form UCL football. Lee Isaacs scored both Badger replies.

Best FA Cup performers were Northampton Spencer and Wellingborough who reached the Second Qualifying Round before exiting 6-0 at Grantham and 2-0 at Hinckley respectively. The Millers beat league rivals Desborough and Boston to reach that stage while the Doughboys claimed the scalps of North West Counties pair Kidsgrove and Newcastle Town. Our clubs had a disappointing year in the FA Carlsberg Vase with Stotfold's run to the last 64 the best performance by a member club. The Eagles saw off Cornard, Ware and Cheshunt before surprisingly losing 3-1 at Letchworth.

On the county cup front, Stotfold lifted the Bedfordshire Senior Cup with a 2-1 final win over hosts Arlesey, Dave Drury netting a late winner for Phil Pateman's side, while in Huntingdonshire we had trophies galore to celebrate. Richard Harradine netted the decider in Eynesbury's 2-1 Senior Cup win over Somersham, Peter Saunders scored twice as Kempston demolished Biggleswade Town 6-2 in the Premier Cup final, while St Neots Reserves retained the Benevolent Cup beating their Yaxley counterparts 7-6 on penalties after two hours without a goal. Cottingham became the nineteenth consecutive UCL winners of the Northants Junior Cup; they edged out Eye 3-2 in the final at Raunds with Graham Leech, Dave Trimble and Darren Burt on the mark. In the Northants Senior Cup Desborough were desperately unlucky to miss out in their first final since 1952, holding Conference neighbours Kettering 1-1 at the Waterworks Field and 3-3 at Rockingham Road before a penalty shootout gave the Poppies the trophy.

Other cup action saw Cogenhoe carry off the Buckingham Charity Cup with a 2-1 win over league rivals Wootton, but in the Daventry Charity Cup the Cooks lost 2-1 to lower grade Daventry Town. Desborough thrashed Burton PW 6-2 in the Desborough Charity Cup final, while Kempston won a penalty shootout to claim the North Beds Charity Cup after their third final in five days had ended with a goal apiece against Biggleswade Town. Highlight amongst the other cup competitions was Stotfold's 3-2 Hinchingbrooke Cup defeat of Barton Rovers, two Nathan Buckland goals and a Paul Bloss winner overturning an early two goal deficit.

Rothwell Corinthians joined the floodlit ranks during the season, Deeping following suit at the end of the campaign and Woodford hope to light up next season. From season 2000-01 the third placed club in Division One now will be able to be considered for promotion if either of the top two fail to meet the facility criteria following a summer rule change.

We welcome Raunds Town back into the Premier Division after a four season sojourn in the Dr Martens League; the Stamford second string also return to the fold with Woodford Reserves also checking in. The warmest of welcomes goes to our new sponsors, Charles Wells Brewers of Bedford, who have agreed a three year sponsorship of the league which will now carry the name of the sponsors' flagship brand and will be known as the"Eagle Bitter United Counties League". In view of the name change, who would bet against a title success for Stotfold next May?

Jeremy Biggs, Press Officer

HONOURS LIST 1999-2000

Premier Division
   Champions — Ford Sports Daventry
   Runners Up — Cogenhoe United
Division One
   Champions — Cottingham
   Runners Up — Thrapston Town
Reserve Division One
   Champions — Rothwell Town
   Runners Up — Raunds Town
Reserve Division Two
   Champions — Kings Lynn
   Runners Up — Deeping Rangers
League Knockout Cup
   Winners — Cogenhoe United
   Runners Up — Kempston Rovers
Reserve Knockout Cup
   Winners — Kings Lynn
   Runners Up — Stotfold
Benevolent Cup
   Winners — Spalding United
   Runners Up — Bugbrooke St Michaels
Highest Aggregate of Goals
   Winners — Cogenhoe United
Fair Play Awards
   (First team) — Deeping Rangers
   (Reserves) — Kings Lynn
Hospitality Award
   (Referees) — Rothwell Corinthians
   (Clubs) — Kings Lynn

Referee of the Year
   Winner — Paul Martin
Bedfordshire Senior Cup
   Winners — Stotfold
Huntingdonshire Senior Cup
   Winners — Eynesbury Rovers
Huntingdonshire Premier Cup
   Winners — Kempston Rovers
Huntingdonshire Benevolent Cup
   Winners — St Neots Town Res
Huntingdonshire Benevolent Cup
   Runners Up — Yaxley Reserves
Northants Hillier Senior Cup
   Runners Up — Desborough Town
Northants Junior Cup
   Winners — Cottingham
Buckingham Charity Cup
   Winners — Cogenhoe United
Daventry Charity Cup
   Winners — Daventry Town
Desborough Charity Cup
   Winners — Desborough Town
Hinchingbrooke Cup
   Winners — Stotfold
North Beds Charity Cup
   Winners — Kempston Rovers
Biggleswade Knockout Cup
   Winners — Stotfold Reserves

FINAL LEAGUE TABLE 1999-2000
PREMIER DIVISION

		P	W	D	L	F	A	W	D	L	F	A	Pts
				Home						Away			
1	Ford Sports Daventry	38	15	3	1	45	16	13	4	2	35	9	91
2	Cogenhoe United	38	15	4	0	71	11	12	2	5	64	28	87
3	Boston Town	38	16	3	0	50	8	11	3	5	38	22	87
4	Stotfold	38	14	2	3	38	8	10	5	4	32	16	79
5	Northampton Spencer	38	13	2	4	56	20	10	4	5	40	28	75
6	Blackstone FC	38	12	4	3	46	17	11	1	7	33	36	74
7	Kempston Rovers	38	9	6	4	40	19	11	4	4	30	19	70
8	Desborough Town	38	13	3	3	60	22	8	3	8	35	33	69
9	Stewart & Lloyds Corby	38	9	2	8	46	33	11	1	7	40	37	63
10	Bugbrooke St Michaels	38	8	1	10	27	24	10	2	7	26	26	57
11	Wootton Blue Cross	38	9	4	6	45	29	6	3	10	36	34	52
12	Bourne Town	38	8	3	8	32	23	7	1	11	28	29	49
13	St Neots Town	38	6	3	10	38	32	7	2	10	23	28	44
14	Yaxley	38	7	2	10	25	20	3	5	11	18	40	37
15	Wellingborough Town	38	8	0	11	26	31	3	4	12	23	50	37
16	Holbeach United	38	6	1	12	22	32	4	4	11	26	39	35
17	Eynesbury Rovers	38	4	1	14	19	53	5	1	13	26	67	29
18	Potton United	38	3	5	11	35	45	3	1	15	12	52	24
19	Buckingham Town	38	2	1	16	18	77	3	0	16	9	95	16
20	Long Buckby	38	1	2	16	16	67	2	2	15	13	67	13

FINAL LEAGUE TABLE 1999-2000
DIVISION ONE

			Home					Away					
		P	W	D	L	F	A	W	D	L	F	A	Pts
1	Cottingham	34	11	5	1	55	12	10	3	4	35	21	71
2	Thrapstone Town	34	12	1	4	48	16	9	4	4	35	22	68
3	Deeping Rangers	34	11	5	1	44	15	7	8	2	29	13	67
4	Harrowby United	34	10	5	2	47	16	8	6	3	37	15	65
5	Daventry Town	34	9	4	4	33	19	10	3	4	32	17	64
6	St Ives Town	34	8	5	4	41	21	8	2	7	33	25	55
7	Newport Pagnell Town	34	10	5	2	39	21	5	2	10	30	36	52
8	Blisworth	34	10	4	3	35	21	4	5	8	22	30	51
9	Olney Town	34	9	3	5	29	17	6	2	9	32	40	50
10	Woodford United	34	8	3	6	43	31	7	2	8	28	42	50
11	Northampton Vanaid	34	7	4	6	28	20	6	5	6	29	28	48
12	Burton Park Wanderers	34	5	5	7	24	25	8	4	5	33	25	48
13	Rothwell Corinthians	34	4	5	8	19	29	5	6	6	27	40	38
14	Wellingborough Whits	34	5	3	9	23	35	5	3	9	23	39	36
15	North'pton ON Chenks	34	5	2	10	31	38	3	3	11	16	50	29
16	Sharnbrook	34	4	3	10	21	50	2	3	12	13	46	24
17	Higham Town	34	2	4	11	20	50	2	4	11	15	54	20
18	Irchester United	34	3	1	13	17	42	1	2	14	9	54	15

PREMIER DIVISION RESULTS CHART 1999-2000

		1	2	3	4	5	6	7	8	9	10	11	12	13	14	15	16	17	18	19	20
1	Blackstone FC	X	2-1	2-1	10-0	1-2	4-2	5-1	3-0	1-1	0-0	2-3	2-0	3-0	1-0	2-3	1-1	0-0	3-0	2-1	2-1
2	Boston	4-1	X	1-0	6-0	1-0	1-1	2-0	4-0	2-1	3-1	3-1	3-0	2-1	2-0	2-0	8-2	0-0	0-0	1-0	5-0
3	Bourne	0-1	0-1	X	3-0	3-0	0-2	1-1	5-2	0-2	0-1	0-1	5-1	1-1	4-0	1-0	1-5	1-2	3-0	2-2	2-1
4	Buckingham	0-4	0-6	0-6	X	0-5	0-11	1-5	0-3	0-7	4-4	2-3	0-2	0-6	1-3	1-4	2-3	0-1	4-2	2-0	1-2
5	Bugbrooke	1-2	2-1	2-0	0-1	X	0-3	1-2	6-0	1-2	4-1	0-0	4-0	0-2	1-0	1-0	0-3	0-3	0-1	3-1	1-2
6	Cogenhoe	5-1	5-0	4-0	11-0	2-1	X	1-1	7-2	0-0	5-0	1-0	9-0	3-1	3-0	3-2	4-0	1-1	3-1	3-0	1-1
7	Desborough	6-1	3-3	1-0	6-0	1-2	5-1	X	7-2	1-2	3-2	0-1	4-0	0-0	5-0	2-1	5-1	2-1	3-1	4-4	2-0
8	Eynesbury	2-3	0-6	0-3	0-1	1-2	0-4	1-1	X	0-2	1-0	1-3	1-2	4-2	0-2	0-6	0-4	2-3	0-7	3-1
9	Ford Sports	1-0	1-3	2-1	1-0	0-0	6-3	2-0	3-1	X	3-1	0-0	2-1	5-1	3-0	0-0	4-1	2-1	5-1	1-0	4-2
10	Holbeach	1-2	0-1	0-1	5-2	0-2	1-4	4-2	1-2	2-0	X	1-3	2-0	0-1	0-1	3-2	0-3	0-2	1-0	0-3	1-1
11	Kempston	0-3	0-1	3-0	8-0	0-1	1-1	4-1	0-0	3-2	X	7-0	1-1	2-0	1-1	0-3	3-1	2-2	1-0	1-1
12	Long Buckby	1-2	0-4	1-5	1-2	2-3	0-12	3-7	0-1	0-4	0-5	1-1	X	1-1	5-2	0-2	0-1	1-6	0-5	0-2	0-2
13	N Spencer	8-3	1-0	5-1	7-0	2-0	4-2	3-1	7-0	0-2	1-0	0-1	6-0	X	0-2	3-0	3-1	2-4	1-1	2-1	1-1
14	Potton	0-2	2-2	1-4	10-1	2-2	0-2	0-2	3-4	0-3	0-1	1-3	5-1	1-5	X	0-4	0-1	1-1	4-0	4-4	1-1
15	St Neots	3-2	0-1	1-1	5-0	5-1	0-2	0-2	2-3	0-1	0-0	1-3	2-2	1-2	5-0	X	2-3	0-1	7-3	0-4	4-1
16	Stewart & Lloyds	1-2	5-1	1-2	2-1	4-0	2-3	0-3	3-1	1-2	2-3	0-2	2-2	2-5	10-2	2-0	X	3-1	1-1	3-1	2-1
17	Stotfold	1-0	0-0	1-0	7-0	1-0	0-1	2-0	4-1	1-2	3-0	1-0	3-0	4-1	0-0	0-1	2-0	X	3-1	4-1	1-0
18	Wellingborough	1-2	1-2	2-1	1-0	1-2	0-4	1-2	4-0	0-3	2-1	1-2	1-0	2-5	1-0	4-0	0-3	0-1	X	1-3	3-0
19	Wootton	0-1	0-3	2-1	10-0	0-2	3-2	3-2	3-3	0-0	2-2	3-3	2-3	0-3	3-0	3-0	4-1	0-2	2-1	X	5-0
20	Yaxley	1-1	0-2	0-1	2-1	0-1	1-4	0-2	1-0	0-1	3-0	1-0	5-0	1-2	2-0	0-1	1-2	0-0	6-0	1-2	X

DIVISION ONE RESULTS CHART 1999-2000

		1	2	3	4	5	6	7	8	9	10	11	12	13	14	15	16	17	18
1	Blisworth	X	2-3	0-1	0-0	1-1	1-0	2-0	3-1	3-1	1-2	3-0	5-3	3-3	1-0	2-2	2-1	2-1	4-2
2	Burton PW	3-1	X	1-1	2-0	0-3	0-0	0-0	5-0	3-2	0-3	1-2	1-2	0-3	1-1	3-1	1-1	3-4	0-1
3	Cottingham	4-0	2-0	X	2-0	1-0	2-2	11-1	1-2	4-2	2-2	4-0	3-0	1-1	2-2	4-0	0-0	2-0	10-0
4	Daventry	2-0	0-0	0-1	X	3-3	0-1	5-1	5-1	2-1	2-1	2-2	2-1	4-0	0-2	1-1	2-1	1-0	2-3
5	Deeping	2-0	1-2	1-0	1-1	X	2-2	5-0	5-0	5-0	3-1	3-0	3-2	2-2	3-0	4-2	1-1	2-2	1-0
6	Harrowby	1-1	1-1	4-2	0-4	0-0	X	2-0	7-0	3-2	2-2	7-0	5-0	1-2	2-0	6-0	1-1	4-1	1-0
7	Higham	3-3	2-5	1-1	0-1	1-6	0-5	X	2-1	0-3	1-2	2-2	1-4	3-4	1-5	1-0	0-3	1-1	1-4
8	Irchester	0-3	1-2	0-3	0-2	1-3	1-6	1-1	X	0-4	2-0	0-1	1-4	3-0	1-5	2-1	2-3	1-2	1-2
9	Newport Pagnell	0-0	2-1	2-2	0-2	0-3	3-2	2-1	2-0	X	2-2	5-1	1-1	1-1	2-0	6-2	4-0	4-1	3-2
10	N Vanaid	2-2	2-0	0-1	3-0	0-1	0-1	4-2	3-0	0-3	X	6-1	1-1	3-1	0-2	1-1	0-2	2-2	1-0
11	ON Chenecks	1-0	2-6	2-3	0-3	4-3	0-1	2-0	2-0	3-5	1-5	X	2-0	0-1	3-4	0-2	0-1	6-0	3-3
12	Olney	3-1	3-0	1-0	2-3	0-0	1-3	0-0	2-0	2-0	0-0	3-0	X	1-3	3-2	4-0	2-1	1-2	1-2
13	Rothwell Corinthians	2-0	0-2	0-6	0-2	0-0	1-1	2-3	2-2	0-0	2-1	2-3	0-1	X	2-0	0-1	2-5	2-0	2-2
14	St Ives	3-1	1-1	1-2	1-3	0-1	1-1	4-0	6-0	3-2	0-2	1-0	3-1	3-3	X	3-0	1-3	5-0	5-1
15	Sharnbrook	1-4	1-1	1-3	0-6	0-3	0-5	4-1	2-2	2-2	1-4	2-1	2-1	2-2	1-3	X	1-5	0-5	1-4
16	Thrapston	2-0	5-3	4-2	5-1	1-2	1-1	1-2	1-0	0-1	4-0	4-1	4-0	7-1	1-0	3-0	X	0-2	5-0
17	Whitworths	0-2	0-2	2-3	1-4	1-1	0-5	2-2	3-0	3-1	0-0	2-1	2-6	1-0	1-3	3-0	1-3	X	1-2
18	Woodford	1-3	0-4	1-4	0-0	0-0	2-1	7-1	3-0	3-3	5-2	3-0	4-5	5-0	1-4	3-0	2-4	3-0	X

UHLSPORT UNITED COUNTIES LEAGUE KNOCKOUT CUP 1999-2000

PRELIMINARY ROUND

Northampton Vanaid	v	Newport Pagnell	3-2		Kempston	v	Potton	6-0
Long Buckby	v	Bugbrooke	2*3		Eynesbury	v	Harrowby	2-1
Deeping	v	Bourne	1-2		Thrapston	v	Stotfold	1-4

FIRST ROUND

Higham	v	Northampton Spencer	0-11		Wootton	v	Northampton Vanaid	2-1
Bourne	v	Sharnbrook	2-0		Cogenhoe	v	ON Chenecks	2-1
Holbeach	v	Irchester	2-0		Cottingham	v	Kempston	1-2
Stewarts & Lloyds	v	Ford Sports	2-4		Wellingborough	v	Blisworth	1*0
Stotfold	v	Boston	0-1		Blackstone	v	Woodford	6-1
Bugbrooke	v	St Neots	2-3		Desborough	v	Yaxley	1-0
Eynesbury	v	Rothwell Corinthians	0-6		Olney	v	Whitworths	1-2
Burton PW	v	St Ives	1-4		Buckingham	v	Daventry	1-2

SECOND ROUND

Whitworths	v	Rothwell Corinthians	0-2		Cogenhoe	v	St Neots	4-1
Boston	v	Blackstone	1-3		Wellingborough	v	Hobeach	1*0
Desborough	v	St Ives	2-0		Ford Sports	v	Wootton	3-2
Bourne	v	Daventry	2-4		Kempston	v	Northampton Spncr	2-1

THIRD ROUND

Wellingborough	v	Ford Sports	2-3		Daventry	v	Cogenhoe	0-5
Kempston	v	Blackstone	1-0		Desborough	v	Rothwell Corinthians	6-1

SEMI-FINALS

Desborough	v	Kempston	1-3		Cogenhoe	v	Ford Sports	2*1

FINAL

Cogenhoe	v	Kempston	3-1		at Rowley Park, St Neots

BENEVOLENT CUP FINAL 1999-2000

Spalding	v	Bugbrooke	3-2

UNITED COUNTIES LEAGUE LEADING SCORERS/APPEARANCES 1999-2000
PREMIER DIVISION

	Most Appearances		*Leading Scorers*	
Blackstone	Paul Bryant*	41	Jamie Graham	23
	Ian Flavell*	41		
Boston Town	Lee Rippin	39	Dave Scotney	18
	Andy Warhurst	39		
Bourne Town	Richard Lavin*	41	Willie Straiton	15
Buckingham Town	Darren Ridgway	35	Anton Taylor	7
Bugbrooke St Michaels	Steve Allen	39	Andy Adam	15
Cogenhoe United	Roy Anderson*	43	James Westley	46
	Scott Goodacre*	43		
Desborough Town	Mike McConnell	41	Michael Chong	22
Eynesbury Rovers	Lea Wood *	40	Jason Meeds	13
Ford Sports Daventry	Robin Tucker *	42	Darren Harmon	25
Holbeach United	Phil Barnes	38	Mike Leech	11
Kempston Rovers	Pete Saunders*	44	Pete Saunders	32
Long Buckby	Elliott Grey	35	Martin Musson	9
	Martin Musson	35		
Northampton Spencer	Ian Mann*	40	Scott Coleman	22
	Wayne Richardson*	40		
Potton United	Keeley Thake	38	Martin Westcott	11
St Neots Town	Paul Carey	38	Paul Carey	21
Stewarts & Lloyds Corby	Steve Farr*	39	Dave Torrance	16
Stotfold	Paul Bloss*	40	Roy Boon	12
			Justin Griffiths	12
Wellingborough Town	Adam Sturgess	40	Mark Jameson	13
Wootton Blue Cross	John Hoggett	40*	Steve Kuhne	27
Yaxley	Nicky Conroy*	39	Laurence Clark	10

* denotes ever present

BLACKSTONE

Secretary: Ian McGillivry, 20 New Rd, Ryhall, Stamford, Lincs PE9 4HL
Tel: 01780 762263 (H), 01733 67474 x 2898 (B)

Ground: Lincoln Road, Stamford Tel: 01780 757335

Directions: A6121 Stamford to Bourne road, 2nd left past MB works

Capacity: 1,000   Seats: 100   Cover: Yes   Floodlights: Yes

Clubhouse: Open evenings, lunchtimes & matchdays

HONOURS UCL Div 1 R-up 87-88 (Benevolent Cup R-up), Lincs Snr Cup `A' 92-93

PREVIOUS **Leagues:** Peterborough Works; Peterborough; Stamford & District
Names: Rutland Ironworks; Blackstone (until 1975)

RECORD **Gate:** 700 v Glinton
Win: 11-0 v Brackley, 22/1/94 (A Dunn 6 goals)
Scorer (in one game): A Dunn; 6 v Brackley Town, 22/1/94
Players progressing : Craig Goldsmith (Peterborough), Alan Neilson (Newcastle)

FACT FILE
Founded: 1920
Nickname: Stones
Sponsors: Ideal Shopfitters
Colours: All yellow & royal blue
Change Colours: All red
Midweek matchday: Tuesday
Programme: 32 pages with entry
Editor: Kevin Boor (01780 754584)
Local Press: Stamford Mercury, Herald & Post,
Peterborough Evening Telegraph

CLUB PERSONNEL
President: Darren Laughton
Chairman: Bill Sewell
Manager: Vince Adams
Press Officer: Kevin Boor
Asst Manager: Trevor Smith

BOSTON TOWN

Secretary: A Crick, Daisy Cottage, Shore Rd, Freiston, Boston, Lincs PE22 0LN
Tel: 01205 760162. (H &Fax) 01205 313090 (W)

Ground: Tattershall Road, Boston, Lincs Tel: 01205 365470

Directions: A52 Grantham-Sleaford ,2nd left into Brotherton Rd.,Argyle St.tobridge,immedi
ately over left into Tattersall road,ground 3/4 mile on left

Capacity: 6,000   Seats: 450   Cover: 950   Floodlights: Yes   Club Shop: Yes

Clubhouse: Open evenings (except Sunday), matchdays & functions. Bar & Lounge.Darts & pool

HONOURS Midland Co's Lg 74-75 78-79 80-81 (Lg Cup 76-77); Lincs Snr `A' Cup (5)73-74
79-82 89-90 (Snr `B' Cup 65-66); Central Mids Lg 88-89; Central All 65-66; Lincs
Lg 64-65; Und. Co. Lg.Prem Div 94-95

PREVIOUS **Leagues:** Lincs 63-65; Central Alliance 65-66; Eastern Co's 66-68;Midland 68-82;
Northern Co's East 82-87; Central Midlands 87-91

BEST SEASON **FA Cup:** 1st Rd Proper 76-77, 1-3 v Barnsley (A)
FA Trophy: 2nd Round 79-80, 3-6 v Mossley (A) after 0-0
FA Vase: Semi-Finals 94-95, 0-2 (agg) v Taunton Town)

RECORD **Attendance:** 2,700 v Boston Utd, FA Cup 3rd Qual. Rd 1970
Goalscorer (in a season): Carl Smaller 48, 1994-95
Players progressing: Julian Joachim (Leicester City and Aston Villa) , Neil Mann (Hull City)

FACT FILE
Founded: 1963
Nickname: Poachers
Sponsors: Tempests of Stickney/Keystone
Fabricators
Colours: Sky Blue/ Royal Blue/Sky
Change: Yellow/white/yellow
Midweek Matchday: Tuesday
Reserves League: None 94-95
Programme: 40 pages, 50p
Editor/ Press Officer: Bob Whitaker
Tel: 01205 368445

CLUB PERSONNEL
Chairman: Mick Vines
Vice Chairman: J Rose
Treasurer: J Rose
Manager: Bob Don-Duncan
Ass.Manager: Dave Scotney
Physio: Don Mitchell

BOURNE TOWN

Secretary: Roger Atkins, 4 Orchard Close, Bourne, Lincs PE10 9DF Tel: 01778 424882

Ground: Abbey Lawn, Abbey Road, Bourne, Lincs Tel: 01778 422292

Directions: In market place take A151 Spalding Road, ground 500 yds on right.Public
transport from Peterborough, Stamford and Grantham
Capacity: 3,000   Seats: 300   Cover: 750   Floodlights: Yes
Club Shop: Contact Sec.

Clubhouse: Small, open matchdays and specific events. Food, confectionary available

HONOURS Utd Co's Lg 68-69 69-70 71-72 90-91 (KO Cup 69-70, Benevolent Cup 90-91,
Res Div 2 94-95), Lincs Snr `A' Cup 71-72 (R-up 92-93), Central Alliance
Division 1 South 59-60, Lincs Intermediate Cup 85-86

PREVIOUS **Leagues:** Peterborough; UCL 47-56; Central All. 58-61; MidlandCos 61-63
Ground: Adjacent to cricket field after WW2 until 1947

RECORD **Attendance:** 3,000 v Chelmsford, FA Trophy 1970
Goalscorer: David Scotney
Players progress ing: Peter Grummit (Nottm Forest), Shaun Cunnington (Wrexham),
David Palmer (Wrexham)

FACT FILE
Founded: 1883   Nickname: Wakes
Sponsors: Jaychem
Colours: Maroon & sky/sky/maroon
Change Colours: White & sky/white & sky/sky
Midweek matchday: Tuesday
Reserves' Lge: HSUCL Res Div 1
Programme: 50 pages, 50p
Editor: JimAshton (01778 440065)
Local Press: Stamford Mercury, Lincs Free
Press, Peterborough EveningTelegraph,
Bourne Local

CLUB PERSONNEL
Chairman: Jim Ashton
Vice-Chairman:
President: Jim Ashton
Press Officer: Jeff Hodson
Manager: Dave McNish
Physio: Dick Joy

BUCKINGHAM TOWN

Secretary: Brian Maycock, 31 Westfield, Buckingham, Bucks Tel: 01280 815529

Ground: Ford Meadow, Ford Street, Buckingham Tel: 01280 816257
Capacity: 4,000   Cover: 420   Seats: 420   Floodlights: Yes

Directions: From town centre take Aylesbury (A413) road and turn right at Phillips Garage after 400yds. Public transport: train to Milton Keynes, then bus to Buckingham

Clubhouse: Open evenings 6.30-11 (12-11 Sat & Sun) Rolls etc available on matchdays. Bingo, dominoes, darts & pool. Concert room with stage for hire, capacity 150   **Club Shop:** Yes

HONOURS Southern Lg Southern Div 90-91, Utd Co's Lg 83-84 85-86 (Div 1 R-up 75-76, Div 2 R-up 74-75, Lg Cup 83-84, Div 2 Cup R-up 74-75), Nth Bucks Lg 24-25 28-29 33-34 35-37 38-39 48-50(2) Aylesbury & Dist. Lg 02-03, Berks & Bucks Snr Cup 83-84, Berks & Bucks Jnr Cup 02-03 48-49 (R-up 38-39 72-73), Berks & Bucks Minor Cup 32-33, Buckingham Snr Charity Cup x11, r-up x 5

PREVIOUS **Leagues:** Aylesbury & Dist; Nth Bucks; Hellenic 53-57; Sth Mids 57-77; Utd Co's 74-86; Southern Lge 86-97

BEST SEASON **FA Cup:** 1st Round 1984-85   **FA Vase:** Quarter Finals 1990-91 & 92-93

RECORD **Attendance:** 2,451 v Orient, FA Cup 1st Rd 84-85
Fee paid: £7,000 for Steve Jenkins (Wealdstone, 1992)
Fee received: £1,000 for Terry Shrieves (Kettering)

FACT FILE

Formed: 1883
Nickname: The Robins
Sponsors: Wipac
Colours: All red
Change colours: All white
Midweek Matchday:
Reserves' League: No reserve team
Programme: Yes
Newsline: 0891 884 431
Local Press: Buckingham Advertiser,
MK Citizen, Herald & Post
Local Radio: Chiltern Radio,
Fox FM (102.6 fm), 3 Counties Radio

CLUB PERSONNEL

Chairman: Brian Maycock

BUGBROOKE ST MICHAELS

Secretary: Roger Geary, 31 Kislingbury Rd, Bugbrooke, Northampton NN7 3QG
Tel: 01604 831678

Ground: Birds Close, Gayton Road, Bugbrooke Tel: 01604 830707
Capacity: 2,500   Seats: 120   Cover: Yes   Floodlights: Yes

Directions: M1. Jct 16 Take A45 to Northampton. At 1st roundabout follow signs to Bugrooke. In villagefollow road straight through to club immediately past last house on left.

Clubhouse: Yes - normal licensing hours

HONOURS Northants Junior Cup 89-90, Central Northants Comb. 68-69 69-70 70-71 71-72 76-77 85-86, UCL Res Div 2 R-up 94-95 U.C.L. Div One Champions 98-99

PREVIOUS **League :** Central Northants Combination 1952-87   **Ground:** School Close

RECORD **Attendance:** 1,156   **Scorer:** Vince Thomas   **Appearances:** Jimmy Nord

Players progressing: Kevin Slinn (Watford), Craig Adams (Northampton)

FACT FILE

Founded: 1929
Nickname: Badgers
Sponsors: Unusual Industries
Club colours: Black & white/black/black
Change colours: All Red
Reserves' Lge: UCL Res. Div. 1
Programme: Eight pages
Editor: Teresa Garlick

CLUB PERSONNEL

Chairman: Tom Treacy
President: John Curtis
Manager: Chris Goodchild
Asst Manager: Jon Mundy
Press Officer:Jon Munday

COGENHOE UNITED

Secretary: Sue Wright, 6 Brafield Road, Cogenhoe, Northants NN7 1ND
Tel: 01604 890737 (H), 01604 890277 (B),   Fax: 01604 890641

Ground: Compton Park, Brafield Rd, Cogenhoe, Northants (01604 890521)
Directions: Turn off A428 at Brafield-on-the-Green, first turn right toCogenhoe or A45 to Billing Aquadrome. Carry on, take second Cogenhoe turn on left

Capacity: 5,000   Seats: 100   Cover: 200   Floodlights: Yes   Club Shop: No
Clubhouse: Tues-Fri 7-11, Sat 12-3 & 4-11, Sun 12-3 & 7-10.30 Snacks. Hot food on matchdays

HONOURS UCL Div 1 R-up 86-87 (Res. Div 2 88-89), K.O. Cup 96-97; Daventry Charity Cup 91-92 95-96, (R-up 79-80); Central Northants Comb 80-81 82-83 83-84 (R-up 81-82, Prem Div Cup 82-83 (R-up 78-79), Div 1 Cup R-up 77-78, Charity Shield 82-83 83-84)

PREVIOUS **League:** Central Northants Combination 1967-84
Ground: Cogenhoe Village PF 1967-84

RECORD **Gate:** 1,000 v Eastenders XI, Charity match 8/7/90
Scorer & Appearances: Tony Smith
Win: 22-0 v Ravensthorpe, Cen. Northants Comb. Prem. Div. KO Cup, 79-80
Defeat: 0-6 v Yardley United, Central Northants Comb. Div. 1, 76-77

Players progressing : Darren Bazeley (Watford 89), Darren Harmon (Notts Co. 89),Matt Murphy (Oxford Utd 93), Gary Leonard (Northampton 1978)

FACT FILE

Founded: 1967
Nickname: Cooks
Sponsors: Supertrucking
Colours: All royal
Change: Black & white/white/white
Midweek matchday: Tuesday
Reserves' Lge: UCL Res. Div 1
Programme: 32 pages with Admission
Editor:Sue Wright
Local Press: Chronicle & Echo,
Northants Evening Telegraph

CLUB PERSONNEL

Chairman: Derek Wright
Vice Chairman: Bob Earl
President: Steve Brockwell
Comm. Man.: Robert Jones
Manager: Steve Forbes
Assistant Manager: Dino Cirelli
Physio: Ian Blair

Top: Cogenhoe United celebrate after their United Counties League Cup Final victory over Kempston Rovers.
Photo: Gordon Whittington

Centre: Kemptson Rovers. Back Row (l-r): James McKeaveney, Deep Banghard, Luke Fisher, Matt Hullett, Tony Boatswain, Simon Holroyd, Pete Saunders, Roy Bloxham, Jason Mannion, Carol Collier (Physio). Front Row (l-r): Lee Daly, Bobby Roberts (Coach), Wes Jean, Chris Wells, Keith Snaylam, Asa Smith, Clive Woodland, Ryan O'Neil, Kenny Davidson (Manager)   Photo: Gordon Whittington

Northampton Spencer FC. Back Row (l-r): Nicky Ling, Russell Collyer, Lee West, Barry Thomas, James Twelftree, Nicky Hodges, Mark Duckett, Wayne Hamill, Darren Andrews, Peter Green, John Clare (Physio). Front Row (l-r): Russell Dunkley, Scott Coleman, Mark Pepperell, Tony Calvert, Ian Mann, Paul Tebbutt, Wayne Richardson.
Photo: Peter Barnes

DESBOROUGH TOWN

Secretary: John Lee, 85 Breakleys Road, Desborough, Northants NN14 2PT
Tel: 01536 760002

Ground: Waterworks Field, Braybrooke Rd, Desborough Tel: 01536 761350
Capacity: 8,000   Seats: 250   Cover: 500   Floodlights: Yes

Directions: Half a mile west of A6 following signs for Braybrooke
Clubhouse: Lounge & main hall, 2 bars, games room. Every eve. & w/e lunchtimes
Club Shop: No

HONOURS Utd Co's (Prev. Northants) Lg 00-01 01-02 06-07 20-21 23-24 24-25 27-28 48-49
66-67 (R-up 02-03 10-11 19-20 22-23 79-80, 98-99), Div 2 10-11, 28-9(Res),R-up
09-10 (Res) 26-27(Res) 51-52(Res), KO Cup 77-78 96-97; Northants Snr Cup10-11
13-14 28-29 51-52; Desborough Charity Cup 97-98,98-99

PREVIOUS Leagues: None
RECORD Attendance: 8,000 v Kettering Town
Win: 10-1: v Huntingdon Utd (A) 1957 & v Stewarts & Lloyds (A) 1965, both UCL.
Defeat: 11-0 v Rushden Town (A) 1934
Fee received: £8,000 for Wakeley Gage, from Northampton Town
Players progressing: Wakeley Gage (Northampton), Jon Purdie & Campbell Chapman (Wolves),
Andy Tillson (Grimsby), Matt Murphy (Oxford United)

FACT FILE
Founded: 1896
Nickname: Ar Tarn
Colours: Blue & white/blue/blue
Change Colours: All red
Previous Leagues: None
Midweek matchday: Tuesday
Programme: 40 pages with entry
Editor:John Lee
Local Press: Evening Telegraph,Northants
Post,Chronicle & Echo,& Harborough Mail

99-00 - Captain:Des Elliott
Top Scorer: Michael Chong

CLUB PERSONNEL
Chairman:Alan Panter
President: T.B.A.
Press Officer: John Lee
Manager: Derek Maddox
Asst Manager: Dave McHuchinson
Physio: T.B.A.

EYNESBURY ROVERS

Secretary: Deryck Irons, 12 Hadleigh Close, Bedford MK41 8JW. Tel: 01234 268111

Ground: Hall Road, Eynesbury, St Neots Tel: 01480 477449
Capacity: 3,000   Seats: 270   Cover: 500   Floodlights: Yes

Directions: Approx 2 miles from A1, on South side of St Neots urban area, near Ernulf School

Clubhouse: Large bar, capacity 150, committee room   **Club Shop:** Contact Dave Crisp

HONOURS UCL Div 1 76-77; Hunts Snr Cup 13-14 46-47 48-51 54-55 56-57 69-70 84-85 90-
93 95-96,99-00; Hunts Premier Cup 50-51 90-91 95-96; Hinchingbrooke Cup (7) 46-4748-52 57-
58 66-67; Cambs Invitation Cup 61-62; E Anglian Cup R-up 90-91 91-92;Hunts Scott Gatty Cup
35-36 56-57 84-85 89-90 (R-up 93-94 res); Hunts Jnr Cup 21-22 26-27

PREVIOUS Leagues: Sth Mids 34-39; UCL 46-52; Eastern Co's 52-63

BEST SEASON FA Vase: 2nd Rd 85-86 88-89
FA Cup: 4th Qual. Rd 54-55, 1-3 v Camb. Utd (A)

RECORD Gate: 5,000 v Fulham 1953

Players progressing: Chris Turner (Peterborough), Denis Emery (Peterborough)

FACT FILE
Founded: 1897
Nickname: Rovers
Sponsors: Classic Windows & 'N' Power
Colours: Royal & white/royal/royal
Change Colours: Yellow/black/yellow
Midweek matchday: Tuesday
Reserves' League: Utd Counties Res. Div. 2
Programme: 28 pages, 50p
Editor: Graham Mills
Local Press: Hunts Citizen, Cambridge
Evening News, St Neots Weekly News

CLUB PERSONNEL
Chairman: Brian Abraham
Vice Chairman:John Newland
Manager:Neil King

FORD SPORTS

Secretary: Mick Fryatt, 2 Mayfield Drive, Daventry, Northants NN11 5QB
Tel Nos: 01327 876789 (H) 01327 305407 (W)

Ground: Royal Oak Way South, Daventry, Northants Tel: 01327 709219
Capacity: 1,000   Seats: Yes   Cover: Yes   Floodlights: Yes

Directions: Enter Daventry on A45 or A361 and follow signs for Royal Oak Way

Clubhouse: Yes

HONOURS UCL Div 1 92-93, 95-96, Knockout Cup 97-98, Benevolent Cup R-up 92-93;
Highest Agg. Goalscoring Trophy 92-93; Northants Sen Cup R-up 96-97

PREVIOUS League: Central Northants Comb

Player progressing: Martin Aldridge (Northampton)

FACT FILE
Founded: 1968
Nickname: Motormen
Sponsors: Ford Sports & Social Club
Colours: Blue/black/black
Change : Red & black/black/red & black
Midweek matches:
Reserves' Lge: UCL Res Div 2
Programme: 12 pages
Editor: John Hinton

CLUB PERSONNEL
Chairman: John Bailham
Managers: Darren Wood
Assistant Manager: Shane Geary
Physio: Dave Bull

HOLBEACH UNITED

Secretary: Paul Beeken, 36 West End, Holbeach, Lincs PE12 7HA Tel: 01406 425355 (H)

Ground: Carters Park, Park Road, Holbeach Tel: 01406 424761

Capacity:4,000　　Seats: 200　　Cover: 450　　Floodlights: Yes

Directions: Second left at traffic lights in town centre, 220 yds down road on left. From King's Lynn; sharp right at traffic lights

Clubhouse: Large bar, lounge & kitchen, open every night **Club Shop:** No

HONOURS　Utd Co's Lg 89-90 (KO Cup 64-65 89-90), Benevolent Cup, Evans Halshaw Cup 97-98; Lincs Snr Cup `A' 83-84 84-85 86-87 (Senior Cup `B' 57-58)

PREVIOUS　**Leagues:** Peterborough; Utd Co's 46-55; Eastern Co's 55-62; Midland Co's62-63

BEST SEASON　**FA Cup:** 1st Rd Proper 82-83, 0-4 v Wrexham (at Peterborough)
　　　　　FA Trophy: 2nd Qual. Round 69-70 71-72
　　　　　FA Vase: 5th Round 88-89, 2-4 v Wisbech Town

RECORD　**Gate:** 4,094 v Wisbech 1954

Players progressing: Peter Rawcliffe (Lincoln)

FACT FILE
Founded: 1929
Nickname: Tigers
Sponsors: West End Garage
Colours: Old gold & black/black/black
Change Colours: White/blue/blue
Midweek matchday: Tuesday
Reserves' Lge: Peterborough
Programme: 44 pages, 50p
Editor: David Ingle
Local Press : Lincs Free Press, Spalding Guardian, Peterborough Evening Telegraph

CLUB PERSONNEL
Chairman: Chris Cooper
President: Francis Bissadike
Manager: Jan Czarnecki
Asst Manager/Physio: Howard Shoebridge

KEMPSTON ROVERS

Secretary: Alan Scott, 26 King William Rd, Kempston, Bedford MK42 7AT Tel: 01234 854875

Ground: Hillgrounds Leisure, Hillgrounds Rd, Kempston, Bedford Tel: 01234 852346.
　　Capacity: 2,000　　Seats: 100　　Cover: 250　　Floodlights: Yes

Directions: M1 jct 13, A421 to Kempston, Hillgrounds Rd is off the B531 main Kempston-Bedford road. Entrance to Hillgrounds Road is opposite Sainsburys onthe B531 - ground can be found just over twi miles from Sainsburys entrance.British Rail to Bedford Thameslink/Midland then bus No.103 from Bedford town centre stops outside ground

Club Shop: No, but old programmes available from clubhouse
Clubhouse: Open 7-11pm Tues - Sun. & w/e lunch 12-3pm. Sky TV, pool, hot pies & pasties.

HONOURS　United Counties Lge 73-74 (R-up 56-57 59-60), Div 1 57-58 85-86,
　　　　　Div 2 55-56 (R-up 67-68), KO Cup 55-56 57-58 59-60 74-75 76-77.
　　　　　Beds Senior Cup 08-09 37-38 76-77 91-92 (R-up 92-93)

PREVIOUS　**League:** South Midlands 27-53
　　　　　Grounds: Bedford Rd 1900s-1973; Hillgrounds Road 74-86 (3 grounds in same road!)

BEST SEASON　**FA Cup:**　　　**FA Vase:**

RECORD　**Attendance:** Unknown　　**Scorer:** Doug Jack

Players progressing: Ernie Fenn (WBA), Matthew Woolgar (Luton 1994)

FACT FILE
Founded: 1884
Nickname: Walnut Boys
Club Sponsors: Audi Vindis Bedford
Colours: Red & white stripes/black/red
Change Colours: All yellow
Midweek matchday: Tuesday
Reserves's Lge: Bedford & Dist
Programme: 24 pages, 40p
Editor: Richard Coop (0378 629470)
Local Press: Bedfordshire Times, Herald & Post, Beds on Sunday

CLUB PERSONNEL
President: H Gilbert
Chairman: Mark Salsbury
Vice-Chairman: Russell Shreeves
Press Officer : Secretary
Manager:Ken Davidson
Asst Manager: Bobby Roberts
Coach: Mel Fisher

LONG BUCKBY

Secretary: Dave Austin,8 Pytchley Drive, Long Buckby, Northampton NN6 7PL 01327 842788(H)
Ground: Station Rd, Long Buckby Tel: 01327 842682
　　Capacity: 1,000　　Seats: 200　　Cover: 200　　Floodlights: Yes

Directions: On Daventry - Long Buckby road. 400 yds from station (Northampton -Rugby line)

Clubhouse: Bar & concert room. Open matchdays

HONOURS　UCL KO Cup 84-85, UCL Div 2 70-71 71-72, Div 2 KO Cup 71-72, Div 3 69-70; Northants Snr Cup R-up; Daventry Charity Cup 96-97

PREVIOUS　**Leagues:** Rugby & D.; Central Northants Comb. (pre-1968)
　　　　　Name: Long Buckby Nomads 1936

BEST SEASON　**FA Vase:** 2nd Rd 85-86
　　　　　FA Cup: 1st Qualifying Rd 92-93

RECORD　**Gate:** 750 v Kettering, Northants Snr Cup Final 1984

Players progressing: Gary Mills (Nottm Forest), Vince Overson (Burnley), Des Waldock (Northampton),Steve Norris (Scarborough)

FACT FILE
Nickname: Bucks
Sponsors: Northampton Elec Dist
Colours: All blue
Change colours: All red
Midweek matchday: Tuesday
Reserves' Lge: HSUCL Res Div 1
Programme: 8 pages
Editor: Rod Pryor (01604 845071)
Local Press : Chronicle & Echo, Daventry Weekly News

CLUB PERSONNEL
President: Alister Bruce
Chairman: Ted Thresher
Manager: Kevin Simmonds
Assistant Manager: Martin McNulty
Physio: Robert Stafferton

NORTHAMPTON SPENCER

Secretary: Dave Ling, 26 Pritchard Close, Rectory Farm, Northampton NN3 5BW
Tel: 01604 407124

Ground: Kingsthorpe Mill, Studland Rd., Northampton NN3 1NF Tel: 01604 718898
Capacity: 2000   Seats: 100   Cover: 350   Floodlights: Yes

Directions: Turn off Kingsthorpe Road at traffic lights into Thornton Rd., 1st right into Studland Rd. and ground is at the end.

Clubhouse: Open during normal licensing hours. Lounge and bar.   **Club Shop:** No

HONOURS: UCL 91-92, r-up 92-93, 97-98, Div. 1 84-85, KO Cup 88-89 93-94, r-up 87-88 96-97 97-98, Benevolent Cup 91-92; Northants Sen. Cup r-up 90-91 93-94.

PREVIOUS **League:** Northampton Town Lge 36-68
Name: Spencer School Old Boys
Grounds: Dallington Park 36-70, Duston High School 70-72

BEST SEASON **FA Cup:** 1st Qual. Rd 93-94, 96-97
FA Vase: 4th Round 87-88, 1-2 v Gresley Rovers

RECORDS **Attendance:** 800 v Nottm. Forest, dressing room opener 1993

Players progressing: Paul Stratford (Northampton), Wakeley Gage (Northampton)

FACT FILE
Founded: 1936
Nickname: Millers
Sponsors: Park Lans Windows
Colours: Yellow/green/yellow
Change colours: All red
Midweek matchday: Tuesday
Reserves' League: UCL Res Div 1
Programme: 48 pages 50p
Editor: Andy Goldsmith (01604 412382)

CLUB PERSONNEL
President: J Sampson
Chairman: Graham Wrighting
Press Off.: Andy Goldsmith (01604 412382)
Manager: Gary Sargent
Assistant. Man.: Keith Bowen

POTTON UNITED

Secretary: Derek Inskip, 16 Sheffield Close, Potton, Beds SG19 2NY   Tel: 01767 260355

Ground: The Hollow, Biggleswade Road, Potton Tel: 01767 261100
Capacity: 2,000   Seats: 200   Cover: 250   Floodlights: Yes

Directions: Outskirts of Potton on Biggleswade Road (B1040). 3 1/2 miles from Sandy (BR). United Counties buses from Biggleswade

Clubhouse: Yes

HONOURS   Utd Co's Lg 86-87 88-89, KO Cup 72-73, Benevolent Cup 88-89; Beds Snr Cup(5) 47-49 63-64 75-76 77-78 (R-up 94-95 96-97); Wallspan Floodlit Cup 87-88; Hinchingbrooke Cup 51-52 84-85 89-90 90-91 91-92; Hunts Premier Cup 89-90 91-92 94-95(jt) 96-97; Beds I'mediate Cup 43-44; Southern Comb. Cup 92-93; Nth Beds Charity Cup (12); East Anglian Cup 96-97; Jess Pigott Trophy 96-97

PREVIOUS   **Leagues :** Sth Mids 46-55; Central Alliance 56-61
Ground: Recreation Grnd pre-1947

BEST SEASON   **FA Trophy:** 3rd Qual. Round 71-72 72-73
FA Vase: 5th Round 89-90, 1-2 v Billericay Town
FA Cup: 3rd Qual. Round 74-75, 1-2 v Bedford Town

RECORD   **Attendance:** 470 v Hastings Town, FA Vase 1989

FACT FILE
Founded: 1943
Nickname: Royals
Club Sponsors: T.B.A.
Colours: White/black/black
Change Colours: Red/white/red
Midweek matchday: Tuesday
Reserves' Lge: UCL Res. Div. Two
Programme: 28 pages, 50p
Editor: Bev Strong
Local Press: Biggleswade Chronicle,

CLUB PERSONNEL
President: Peter Hutchinson
Chairman: Nigel Westhorp
Press Officer: Secretary
Manager: Martin Humberstone
Asst Manager: Jeff Wells

RAUNDS TOWN

Secretary   Mrs Carol Warcup, 9 Warwick Close, Raunds, Northants Tel: 01933 626516
Ground: Kiln Park, London Road, Raunds, Northants NN9 6EQ
Tel: 01933 623351, Matchdays 01933 460941
Directions: Take Raunds turning at roundabout on A45 and ground is first left
Nearest station; Wellingborough. Bus services local
Capacity: 3,000   Seats: 250   Cover: 600   Floodlights: Yes
Clubhouse: On ground, open every day
Club Shop: Open matchdays, selling shirts, books programmes, contact Malc York, c/o club
PREVIOUS   **Leagues:** Rushden & Dist., Cen. Northants Comb., U.C.L., Southern Lge 96-00
Grounds: Greenhouse Field (until 1948), The Berristers (1948-91)
BEST SEASON **FA Cup:** 4th Qual Rd, 98-99 (0-2 v Enfield),
FA Vase: Semi-final v Arlesey Tn 94-5
FA Trophy: 3rd Rd v Weston-super-Mare 98-99 (2-2, 0-1)
HONOURS   UCL Prem Champions 95-96, UCL Div 1 82-83 (R-up 91-92), KO Cup 90-91, (R-up 83-84 93-94), Res Div 1 88-89 95-96 (R-up 86-87 87-88 89-90 90-91 91-92), Reserve KO Cup 84-85 88-89 93-94; Northants Snr Cup 90-91; Hunts Premier Cup R-up 92-93; Daventry Charity Cup R-up 83-84; Northants Jnr Cup 82-83 91-92 (res) 92-93 (res)
CLUB RECORDS   Attendance: 1,500 v Crystal Palace, ground opening 23/7/91
Win: 9-0 v Potton 95, 11-2 v Brackley 93   **Defeat:** 0-6 v Baldock 83, vBuckingham 84-85
Career Goalscorer: Shaun Keeble 208   **Career Appearances:** Martin Lewis 355 (+29subs)

FACT FILE
Formed: 1946
Nickname: Shopmates
Colours: Red & black
Change Colours: Yellow
Midweek matchday: Tuesday
Reserves' League: UCL Reserve Div. One
Prog: Pages: Varies Price: £1.00
Editor: Malc York 01933 311586

99-00 - Top Scorer: Garry Harrison (9)
P. of Y.: Steve Jackman

CLUB PERSONNEL
Chairman: George Hagan
President: Mahen Perera
Manager:Adam Sandy
Asst Manager: Adam Sinclair

It's Gordon Whittington country and our ace photographer always gets goals!

Top: United Counties League Cup Final. James Fletcher smashes home Cogenhoe United's injury-time equaliser and they go on to beat Kempston Rovers 3-1 in extra time.

Centre: United Counties League Division One. Thrapston Town 4 Northampton Vanaid 0. Paul Johnson's tenth minute penalty puts Thrapston into the lead as they win handsomely to ensure Runners-up medals.

Bottom: United Counties League Division One. Cottingham 1 Rothwell Corinthians 1. Ian Jaffrey equalises for Cottingham in this Easter Monday Derby.   *Photos: Gordon Whittington*

ST. NEOTS TOWN

Secretary: Graham Izzard, c/o Football club.

Ground: Rowley Park, Cambridge Rd, St Neots, Cambs Tel: 01480 470012
Capacity: 3,000   Seats: No   Cover: 250   Floodlights: Yes

Directions: Through the town centre, under the railway bridge, ground is first on the left
Capacity: 2,500 **Seating:** 160 **Covered Standing:** 300 **Floodlights :** Yes
Clubhouse: Yes with Conference,Banqueting and private functions all bookable

HONOURS Hunts Snr Cup(34), UCL 67-68 (KO Cup 67-68 68-69),
Metropolitan Lg 49-50(Lg Cup 79-80), South Midlands Lg 32-33,
Huntingdonshire Lg 90-91 92-92 92-93 94-95

PREVIOUS Leagues: South Midlands 27-36 46-49; United Counties 36-39 51-56 66-69 73-88; Metropolitan 49-51 60-66; Central Alliance 56-60; Eastern Counties 69-73;
Huntingdonshire 90-94 **Name:** St Neots & District 1879-1957

BEST SEASON FA Cup: 1st Rd 66-67, 0-2 v Walsall (A)
FA Vase: 3rd Rd 78-79   **FA Trophy:** 2nd Qual. Rd 69-70 72-73

RECORD Attendance: 2,000 v Wisbech, 1966
Players progressing: Frank Atkins (Cambridge), John Gregory (Aston Villa)
and Matthew Oakey (Southampton)

FACT FILE
Web site: www.stneotsfc.com
Founded: 1879   Nickname: Saints
Sponsors:Adam Kennedy, Midland Thermal,
and Fleet Car Contracts
Club colours: Sky /navy/sky
Change colours:Yellow/Black/Yellow
Reserves' Lge: UCL Res Div 1
Programme: Yes   Editor: MikeBirch
(Tel: 01480 395505)
'Saintly Text';Revolving Information screen.
Editor: Mike Birch

CLUB PERSONNEL
Chairman: Bob Page
Vice Chairman:Bob Bridges
Commercial Man: Peter Hicks(01733 263656)
Press Officer: Neil Holmes (01480 383382)
Communic'ns Man:Rod Morris(01733 331658)
Team Manager: Chris Howell

STEWARTS & LLOYDS

Secretary: Dave Foster, 29 Tettenhall Close, Corby, Northants NN198 9PJ
Tel: 01536 746004(H) 01536 201234 (W)

Ground: Recreation Ground, Occupation Road, Corby Tel: 01536 401497
Capacity: 1,500   Seats: 100   Cover: 200   Floodlights: Yes

Directions: The ground is situated on Occupation Rd at the rear of Stewart & Lloyds Leisure
Club, next to old Corby Town F.C. ground

Clubhouse: Licensed bar   **Club Shop:** No

HONOURS UCL R-up 85-86, Div 1(2) 73-75; UCL KO Cup, Prem 95-96, Div 1 Cup(2)73-75, Div 2 KO Cup(2) 75-77)

PREVIOUS Leagues: Kettering Amateur

BEST SEASON FA Cup: **FA Vase:**

RECORD Goalscorer: Joey Martin 46 (92-93)

Players progressing : Andy McGowan (Northampton), Willie Graham (Brentford)

FACT FILE
Formed: 1935
Nickname: None
Sponsor: Weldon
Colours: Amber/ navy blue/ navy blue
Change Colours: All red
Midweek matchday: Tuesday
Programme: 12 pages with admission
Editor/Press Officer: Dave Foster

CLUB PERSONNEL
Chairman: Peter Webb
Vice Chairmen: Gordon Hall, Harry Nelson
Manager: Elwyn Roberts
Asst Manager:Stuart Carmichael
Physio: Roger White

STOTFOLD

Secretary: BillClegg, 12 Common Rd, Stotfold, Hitchin, Herts SG5 4BX Tel: 01462 730421

Ground: Roker Park, The Green, Stotfold, Hitchin, Herts Tel: 01462 730765
Capacity: 5,000   Seats: 300   Cover: 300   Floodlights: Yes

Directions: A507 from A1, right at lights, right at T-jct.
A507 from Bedford via Shefford, left at lights, right at T-jct

Clubhouse: Clubroom, bar, refreshment bar, dressing rooms, physio room

HONOURS Utd Co's Lg R-up 93-94, KO Cup Winners 98-99 R-up 91-92, Res Div 1 87-88;
Sth Mids Lg 80-81 (R-up 55-56 57-58 58-59 59-60 63-64 65-66 77-78), Div 1 53-54, Chal. Tphy
81-82; Beds Snr Cup 64-65 93-94; Beds Premier Cup 81-82; 98-99 Beds I'mediate Cup 58-59; Nth
Beds Charity Cup 55-56 56-57 61-62 81-82 87-88 90-91 97-98;Beds Colts Cup 88-89; Southern
Comb Cup 94-95 95-96 96-97; Hinchingbrooke Cup R-up 97-98

PREVIOUS Leagues: Biggleswade & District/ North Herts/ South Midlands 51-84

BEST SEASON: FA Cup: **FA Vase:**

RECORD Attendance: 1,000 v Letchworth Town, FA Amtr Cup
Scorer: Roy Boon   **Appearances:** Roy Boon/Dave Chellew

FACT FILE
Founded: 1904   Reformed: 1945
Nickname: Eagles
Sponsors: Motorola
Colours: Amber/black/black
Change Colours: All Sky blue
Midweek matchday: Tuesday
Reserves' League: UCL Reserve Division One
Programme: 22 pages with entry
Editor: John Talbot (01462 730068)
Local Press: Comet, Biggleswade Chronicle

CLUB PERSONNEL
Chairman: John Talbot
Vice Chairman: Tom Peacock
President: David Chellow
Manager: Phil Pateman
Asst Manager: Dick Newman/Gary Winn
Press Officer: Bill Clegg
Physio: Nobby Kearns

WELLINGBOROUGH TOWN

Secretary : Mick Walden, 5 Fernie Way, Wellingborough, Northants NN8 3LB Tel: 01933 279561

Ground: Dog & Duck, London Road, Wellingborough, Northants Tel: 01933 223536
Capacity: 5,000   Seats: 300   Cover: 500   Floodlights: Yes

Directions: 200yds off A45 by-pass, by Dog & Duck PH. 1 mile from Wellingborough (BR)

Clubhouse: Full facilities. Open evenings & Sat lunchtimes   Club Shop: No

HONOURS   Utd Co's Lg 10-11 62-63 64-65, Metropolitan Lge 69-70, Northants Snr Cup
            1896-97 1901-02 02-03 33-34 47-48 49-50 81-82, Maunsell Cup 20-21 21-22

PREVIOUS   Leagues: Midland 1895-97 98-1901; Southern 01-05 71-89;
            Northants (Utd Co's)19-34 36-56 61-68; Central Alliance 56-61;
            Metropolitan 68-70; West Midlands Regional 70-71

BEST SEASON FA Cup: 1st Round 28-29, v Bristol Rovers; 65-66, 1-2 v Aldershot Town
            FA Trophy: 1st Round 71-72, 0-3 v Dartford after 1-1 & 0-0
            FA Vase: 1sr Rd. 95-96

RECORD   Attendance: 4,013 v Kettering Town
            Goalscorer: S Hill   Appearances: P Hayes 165, 1985-89
Players progressing: Phil Neal (Northampton), Fanny Walden (Spurs)

FACT FILE
Founded: 1867
Nickname: Doughboys
Sponsors: Croyland Motors
Colours: Blue & white hoops/blue/blue.
Change Colours: All red
Midweek matchday: Tuesday
Reserve League: HSUCL Res. Div. Two
Programme: 16 pages 30p
Editor: Secretary

CLUB PERSONNEL
Chairman: Martin Potton
President: T.B.A.
Press Officer: Secretary
Manager: Brian Knight
Coach: Mike Emms
Physio: Tif Felton

WOOTON BLUE CROSS

Secretary: Trevor Templeman, 3 Pollys Yard, Newport Pagnell, Bucks MK16 8YU
             Tel: 0958 718482 (Mobile)
Ground: Weston Park, Bedford Road, Wootton Tel: 01234 767662
             Capacity: 2,000   Seats: 50   Cover: 250   Floodlights: Yes
Directions: Four miles south of Bedford on main road through village at rear of Post Office

Clubhouse: Main hall, bar, darts, pool, bingo. Open every evening and w/e lunchtimes
Club Shop: No

HONOURS   Utd Co's Lg Div 2 67-68 69-70 (KO Cup 82-83, Div 2 Cup 64-65), South
             Midlands Lg 47-48 (R-up 49-50), Beds Sen. Cup 70-71, Hinchinbrooke Cup(5)

PREVIOUS   Leagues: Bedford & District; South Midlands 46-55
             Grounds: Recreation Ground, Fishers Field, Rose & Crown, Cockfield

BEST SEASON FA Vase: 3rd Rd 74-75
             FA Cup: 2nd Qual. Rd 50-51 (3-4 v Hitchin (H))

RECORD   Gate: 838 v Luton, Beds Prem. Cup 1988

Players progressing: Tony Biggs (Arsenal)

FACT FILE
Founded: 1887
Nickname: Blue Cross
Sponsors: Vision Blinds
Colours: Blue & white/blue/blue
Change: All yellow
Reserves' League: United Counties Res. Div 1
Midweek matchday: Tuesday
Programme: 24 pages   Editor: Secretary

Local Press : Bedfordshire Times, Bedford
Herald, Beds Express, Beds on Sunday

CLUB PERSONNEL
President: J Clarke
Chairman: Trevor Templeman
Manager: Steve Kuhne
Assistant Manager: Phil Cavener
Physio: Trevor Templeman
Press Officer: Secretary

YAXLEY

Secretary: Alan Andrews, 3 Farringdon Close, Pterborough. PE1 4RQ 01733 342897(H)
07939 841469(M)
Ground: Holme Road, Yaxley Tel: 01733 244928
             Capacity: 1,000+   Seats: 150   Cover: Yes   Floodlights: Yes

Directions: A1, then A15 at Norman Cross up to traffic lights. Turn right then immediately right
             again. Follow the road for approx. 1 mile, then turn right into Holme Rd..
             The ground is approx. 200 yards on left

HONOURS   UCL Div 1 96-97, Benevolent Cup 97-98; Hunts Senior Cup (5 times Inc 98-99)
             Peterborough League (2); Peterborough Senior Cup (2);
             West Anglia League;Scott-Gatty Cup

PREVIOUS   Leagues: Peterborough & District, Huntingdonshire, West Anglia

FACT FILE
Founded:
Sponsor: Reads Removals
Colours: All blue with white trim
Change colours: All tangerine or yellow
Programme: Yes
Editor: Malcolm Whaley

CLUB PERSONNEL
President: John Dowse
Chairman: Malcolm Whaley
Vice Chairman: Geoff Heathcote
Manager: Paul Humphries
Asst Manager: Jimmy Watson

BLISWORTH

FACT FILE
Founded: 1890

Secretary: Peter Edwards, 31 Windmill Ave, Blisworth, Northants NN7 3EQ
Tel: 01604 858171 (H), 0585 369933 (B)

Sponsors: Target Furniture, JB King Plant Hire
Colours: Yellow/black/yellow
Change colours: All Blue

Ground: Blisworth Playing Field, Courteenhall Road, Blisworth Tel: 01604 858024
Capacity: 1,000   Seats: None   Cover: None   Floodlights: No

Reserves' Lge: UCL Res. Div. 2
Programme: Yes   Editor: Liz Edwards
Tel: 01604 858171

Directions: Courteenhall Road off A43

Clubhouse: Yes

CLUB PERSONNEL
Chairman: Pete Edwards President: L Piggott
Manager: Brian Oldham

HONOURS Northants Junior Cup 88-99

Asst Man:Gary Edwards, Coach:RichardlLarge
Physio: Elaine Johnson

PREVIOUS **League:** Central Northants Combination 1978-87
Player progressing: Dave Johnson (Northampton 83-84)

BURTON PARK WANDERERS

FACT FILE
Founded: 1961   Nickname: The Wanderers

Secretary: David Haynes, 58 Drayton Road, Lowick, Northants NN14 3BG
Tel: 01832 735060 (H), 01933 231961 (W)

Sponsor: Prescott Motors
Colours:Red & Black/Black/Red
Change Colours: Blue & White

Ground: Latimer Park, Polwell Lane, Burton Latimer Tel: 01536 725841
Capacity: 1,000   Seats: 100   Cover: 150   Floodlights: No

Midweek matchday: Tuesday
Prog: 16 pages with entry

Directions: Entering Burton Latimer, turn off A6 Station Rd and right into Powell Lane;
ground on the right

Local Press : Northants Evening Telegraph,
Northants Post

HONOURS UCL Div 1 R-up, Benevolent Cup R-up
PREVIOUS **League:** Kettering Amateur
RECORD **Attendance:** 253 v Rothwell, May 1989
Players progressing : Shaun Wills (Peterborough), Laurie Dudfield (Leicester City)

CLUB PERSONNEL
Chairman: Bernard Lloyd
Vice Chairman: Stuart Coles
Manager: Eddie Lynch
Asst Manager: Kelly Meagan
Physio: Stuart Coles

COTTINGHAM

FACT FILE
Founded:

Secretary: Lindsay Brownlie, 30 Bancroft Rd, Cottingham, Market Harborough LE168XA
Tel: 01536 771009 (H)

Sponsors: B & J Decorators
Colours: Blue/Black/Blue

Ground: Berryfield Rd, Cottingham Tel: 01536 770051
Capacity: 1,000   Seats: None   Cover: Yes   Floodlights: No

Change colours: Yellow/green/yellow
Reserves' Lge: UCL Res. Div. 2
Programme: No

Directions: One and a half miles from Corby on A427 turn right to Cottingham.At junction of
B670 turn left; Berryfield Road 200 yds on right

Clubhouse: Bar & changing rooms

CLUB PERSONNEL
Chairman: Mike Beadsworth
Vice Chairman: Brian Tilley

HONOURS UCL Div 1 R-up 97-98; Northants Junior Cup

Manager: Rob Dunion
Asst Manager: Willie Kelly

PREVIOUS **Leagues:** Market Harborough; Kettering Amateur; East Midlands Alliance

---

DAVENTRY TOWN

FACT FILE
Founded: 1886

Secretary: Miss Joanne Place, 30 The Cherwell, Daventry, Northants NN11 4QJ
Tel: 01327 879878 (H), 01327 300001 (B)

Sponsor: Campbell Estate Agents
Colours:White/black/black

Ground: Elderstubbs Farm, Leamington Way, Daventry, Northants Tel: 01327 706286
Capacity: 2,000   Seats: 250   Cover: 250   Floodlights: Yes

Change colours: All red
Midweek Matchday: Tuesday

Directions Adjacent to A45 by-pass at top of Staverton Road Sports Complex
Clubhouse: Large bar/kitchen

Reserves League: Central Northants Comb
Programme: 4 Pages Editor: Tony Perry

HONOURS UCL Div 1(2) 89-91 (Lg Cup R-up 92-93, Highest Aggregate Cup), Northants
Junior Cup 36-37 60-61 91-92

CLUB PERSONNEL
Chairman: Mel Knowles
Vice Chairman: Grant Hughes

PREVIOUS **Leagues:** Northampton Town (pre-1987)/ Central Northants Combination 87-89
BEST SEASON **FA Cup:** Prel. Rd 94-95

President: Paul Webster
Managers: Kevin Flear/Craig Robson

FA Vase: Preliminary Rd 91-92 94-95

Physio: Tony Jackson

RECORD **Attendance:** 350 v Ford Sports 1991

Asst Man.: Robin Humphries, Moz Elliott

DEEPING RANGERS

Secretary:	Haydon Whitham, 3 Everingham, Orton Brimbles, Peterborough PE2 5XP Tel:01733 238539
Ground:	Deeping Sports Club, Outgang Road, Market Deeping, Lincs. Tel: 01778 344701
	Capacity: 1,000 Seats: 180 Cover: 180 Floodlights: yes
Directions:	From Deeping town centre take the A15 towards Bourne. Turn right at Towngate Tavern following signs to Industrial Estate & club is 1/4 mile on left.
Clubhouse:	Bar and lounge. Changing rooms
HONOURS	Peterborough & Dist. Lge Div 3 67, Div. 2 69, Div. 1 70, Prem. Div. R-up 95-96 98-99; Lincs Junior Cup 83-84 87-88 88-89 Peterborough FA Senior Cup 91-92 96-97 Minor Cup 67,
PREVIOUS	League: Peterborough & District

FACT FILE
Founded: 1966
Nickname; Rangers
Colours: Claret & blue
Change colours: White/claret/sky blue
Programme: Yes

CLUB PERSONNEL
President: Albert Lawrence
Chairman:EdBailey
Match Sec.: Robin Crowson
01778 348287 (H)
Manager: Chris Beckett
Asst. Manager: Dave Simpson

HARROWBY UNITED

Secretary:	Paul Wilson, 3 Ascot Drive, Grantham, Lincs. 01476 402995 (H)
Ground:	Harrowby Playing Fields, Harrowby Lane, Grantham Tel: 01476 590822
	Capacity: 1,500 Seats: 100 Cover: 150 Floodlights: No
Directions:	From A1 take B6403, go past A52 roundabout, past Ancaster turn and take road to Harrowby. Continue into Grantham, ground on right opposite Cherry Tree PH.
Clubhouse:	Large bar open normal licensing hours
HONOURS	Utd Co's Lg Div 1 91-92 (Benev. Cup R-up 91-92), Mids Regional All. 89-90 (Lg Cup 89-90), Lincs Snr 'B' Cup(2) 90-92
PREVIOUS	Leagues: Grantham; Lincs; East Mids Regional Alliance (pre-1990)
BEST SEASON	**FA Vase:** Preliminary Round 91-92

Players progressing: Richard Liburd (Middlesbrough)

FACT FILE
Founded: 1949
Nickname: Arrows
Sponsor: Bailey Trailers
Colours: Blue & white stripes/blue/blue
Change colours: Yellow,blue &red.
Reserves' League: Grantham
Programme: 12 pages Ed: Pete Salvin

CLUB PERSONNEL
Chairman: Paul Daglish
Vice Chairman: Robert Wilson
Manager: Micky Anderson
Asst Mgr: Mick Atter
Coach: Tony Cook
Physio: Simon Shaw

HIGHAM TOWN

Secretary: Chris Ruff, 23 Queensway, Higham Ferrers, Northants. NN10 8BU Tel: 01933 358862
Ground: Recreation Ground, Vine Hill Drive, Higham Ferrers Tel: 01933 353751
         Capacity: 1,000   Seats: Nil   Cover: 100   Floodlights: No
Directions: From Kettering 1st right on A6 after junction to St Neots. From Bedford, 3rd left after entering town on A6 from Rushden. Higham is served by London-Bedford-Corby United Counties Coachlines, and their local services Northampton-Raunds and Bedford-Kettering
Clubhouse: During season 8.30-11pm Tues, Thurs, Fri, Sat after games & 12-1.30pm Sun.
         Light refreshments available after Saturday games
HONOURS   UCL Div 1 97-98, R-up 70-71 71-72 89-90 92-93 93-94 94-95 95-96 98-99;
         Northants Lg 21-22 22-23(R-up 23-24 26-27); Northants Snr Cup 21-22 (R-up 30-31 32-33);
         Maunsell Premier Cup 22-23 33-34
PREVIOUS   Leagues: Wellingborough 20-21; Northants (now UCL) 21-36; Rushden 46-50
RECORD   **Attendance:** 5,700 v Chesterfield, FA Cup final qualifying round replay 22-23
         Scorer: Jon Ogden 157 (Lge)   **Appearances** : Brian Harbour 485

FACT FILE
Founded: 1895 Reformed: 1920 & 1946
Nickname: Lankies
Sponsors: Higham News
Colours: Sky & navy/navy/navy
Change colours: Red& white/red/red
Midweek matchday:: Tuesday
Reserves' Lge: UCL Reserve Div
Programme: 12 pages with admission
Editor: Secretary
CLUB PERSONNEL
President: Vijay Patel
Chairman: Richard Williams
Vice Chairman: Brian Kirk
Manager: Adie Mann Asst Mgr: Matt Carroll
Physio: Keith Bates

IRCHESTER UNITED

Secretary:	Glyn Cotter, 26 Denford Way, Wellingborough, Northants NN8 5UB Tel: 01933 402514
Ground:	Alfred Street, Irchester (01933 312877)
	Capacity: 1,000 Seats: None Cover:Yes Floodlights: No
Directions:	Off Rushden Road to Wollaston Road, next to recreation ground
Clubhouse:	Yes
HONOURS	Northants LgDiv 2 30-31 31-32,Northants Jnr.Cup 29-30,33-34,48-49 75-6, Rushden & Dis.t Lg 28-29 29-30,32-33,33-34 36-3746-47 50-51 51-52 56-57
BEST SEASON	**FA Cup:** Prel. Rd 34-35 **FA Vase:** Preliminary Round 77-78
PREVIOUS	Leagues: Rushden & District 1936-69

FACT FILE
Colours: Blue& Blackstripes,black,black
Change colours:Black&White stripes,black,red
Reserves' Lge: UCL Res. Div. 2
Programme: No

CLUB PERSONNEL
Chairman: Geoff Cotter
Manager: Andy Toon
Physio: Mick Howarth

NEWPORT PAGNELL TOWN

Secretary: John Anderson, 59 Willen Road, Newport Pagnell, Bucks MK16 0DE
Tel: 01908 610440

Ground: Willen Road, Newport Pagnell Tel: 01908 611993
Capacity: 2,000   Seats: 100   Cover: 100   Floodlights: Yes

Directions: Adjacent to A422 Newport Pagnell by-pass

Clubhouse: Open every evening   Club Shop: No

HONOURS UCL Div 1 82-83 (R-up 91-92, Div 1 Cup 77-78), Daventry Charity Cup R-up 93-94

PREVIOUS **Leagues:** North Bucks 63-71; South Midlands 71-73

BEST SEASON **FA Vase:** 2nd Round 84-85

FACT FILE
Founded: 1963
Nickname: Swans
Sponsors: Brian Currie
Colours: White & green/green/green
Change colours: Red/green/green
Midweek Matchday: Tuesday
Reserves League: United Counties
Programme: 56 pages
Editor: Ernie Print (01908 612918)

CLUB PERSONNEL
Chairman: Gerry Ward
Vice Chairman: Ernie Print
President: Ken Inch
Manager: Jim Diggins

NORTHAMPTON O.N. CHENECKS

Secretary: Ashley Clarkson, 11 Tideswell Close, West Hunsbury, Northampton NN4 9XY
Tel Nos:- 01604 708253 (H) 01234 211521 (W) 07775 940992 (M)
Ground: Old Northamptonians Sports Ground, Billing Road, Northampton Tel: 01604 34045

Capacity: 1,350   Seats: Yes   Cover: Yes   Floodlights: No

Directions: South ring road, exit A43 Kettering. Turn left at the lights, to the top of hill and
the ground is 200 yds on right
Clubhouse: Yes

HONOURS UCL Div 1 77-78 79-80, Northants Jnr Cup R-up 93-94

PREVIOUS **Leagues:** N'pton Town (pre-1969)

FACT FILE
Founded: 1946
Colours: Yellow & Blue/Blue/yelow
Change colours: All red
Reserves' League: UCL Res Div 1
Midweek Matchday:
Prog.: 16 pages with entry
Editor: Eddie Slinn

CLUB PERSONNEL
Chairman: John Wilson
Vice Chairman: Eddie Slinn
President: Claude Hasdell
Manager: Neil McAllister
Asst Manager: Claude Hasdell
Physio: John Goodger

NORTHAMPTON SILEBY RANGERS

(formerly Northampton Vanaid)
Secretary: Tony Loveday, 28 Blueberry Rise, Ecton Brook, North'ton NN3 2AX (01604 406606)

Ground: Fernie Fields Sports Ground, Moulton, Northampton Tel: 01604 670366

Capacity: 700   Seats: 100   Cover: Yes   Floodlights: No

Directions: R'bout at Lumbertub pub take turn to Moulton, 1st right signposted

Clubhouse: Large bar. Hot food/bar meals

HONOURS UCL Div 1 93-94, Benevolent Cup R-up 93-94;

Northants Jnr Cup 93-94 96-97 97-98; Northampton Town Lg 88-89 89-90
PREVIOUS **League:** Northampton Town (pre-1993)
Names: Northampton Vanaid >00
RECORD **Attendance:** 78

FACT FILE
Founded: 1968 Nickname: Vans
Sponsors: Personnel Assurance, Barretts Club
Colours: All Blue
Change colours: Black & white/black/black
Reserves' League: UCL Res Div 1
Programme Editors: Tony & June Loveday
CLUB PERSONNEL
Chairman: Rob Clarke
Vice Chairman: Steve Tebbutt
President: A Blundell
Manager: Nick Verity
Asst Manager: Adam May
Physio: Paul Massey

OLNEY TOWN

Secretary: Andrew Baldwin, 49 Midland Road, Olney, Bucks MK46 4BP
Tel: 01234 711071

Ground: East Street, Olney , Bucks. Tel: 01234 712227
Capacity: 2,000   Seats: None   Cover: Yes   Floodlights: No
Clubhouse: Yes

Directions: Enter Olney on A509 from Wellingborough, 100yds on left enter East St,
the ground is 200 yds on left
HONOURS UCL Div 1 72-73, Berks & Bucks I'mediate Cup 92-93

PREVIOUS **Leagues:** Nth Bucks, Rushden & Dist

FACT FILE
Founded: 1910
Sponsors: Cyclo Sports
Colours: Black & white stripes/black/black
Change colours: Green & white
Programme: 32 pages
Editor: Barry Simons

CLUB PERSONNEL
Chairman: Barry Simons
President: Andrew Soul
Manager: John Dower
Asst Manager: Bob Read
Coach: Russell Ward
Physio: Peter Munting

Top: Deeping Rangers. Back Row (l-r): Jim Shilling (Coach), Robbie Greatrex, Jamie Harker, Dean Tarrant, Ian Coupe, Jani Salerno, Andy Preston, Chris Ray, Alex Higgins, John Hickling (Asst Mngr), Jem Wilson. Front Row: Paul Kirk, Martin Bradley, James Anderson, David Jones, Barry Fisher, Steve Paling.
Photo: Gordon Whittington

Centre: Potton United Back Row (l-r): Paul French, Colin Standley, Lee Daly, Keely Thake, Steve Brown, Julian Bennett, Craig Glashin, Richard Piggott, Martin Hammocks Front Row (l-r): Martin Humberstone, Mathew Thorougood, John Frost, Andy Dickenson, Martin Westcott, Ricky Bulzis, Michael Kennedy, Simon Jones, Jeff Wells.

Bottom: Woodford United. Back Row (l-r): A Bodily, J Whiteside, D Taylor, M Clarke, S Haynes, P Linec, A Wyatt, J Grocott. Front Row: G Bodicote, L Parkinson, R Chimes, K Aris, A Powell, M Culcutt.
Photo: Gordon Whittington

ROTHWELL CORINTHIANS

Secretary: Bob Clelland, 5 Drake Close, Rothwell, Northants NN14 6DJ
Tel: 01536 710134

Ground: Seargeant's Lawn, Desborough Road, Rothwell, Northants.
Tel: 01536 418688
Capacity: Unknown   Seats: 50   Cover: 200   Floodlights: Yes

Directions A6 towards Desborough, on right opposite Greening Road
Club House: Yes   **Club Shop:** No

HONOURS East Midlands Alliance (2)
PREVIOUS **League** East Midlands Alliance

FACT FILE
Founded: 1930's
Nickname: Corinthians
Sponsor: Springfir Estates
Colours: Red,black,black
Change colours: All blue
Programme: Yes
Editor: Brian Johnson

CLUB PERSONNEL
Chairman: Brian Johnson
Vice Chairmperson: May Clelland
President: Terry Smith
Manager:Colin Sinclair
Physio:John Dickson

SHARNBROOK A.F.C.

Secretary: Roy Boulton, 10 St Mary's Avenue, Rushden, Northants NN10 9EP
Tel: 01933 315890

Ground: Lodge Rd, Sharnbrook, Northants. Tel: 01234 781080
Capacity: 1,000   Seats: None   Cover: Yes   Floodlights: No

Directions: Second sign to Sharnbrook from Rushden on A6, under railway bridge, right at T-junction, left past church, right into Lodge Road
Clubhouse: Yes

HONOURS Bedfordshire Intermediate Cup 73-74
PREVIOUS **Leagues:** Bedford & Dist (pre-1968)
Player progressing: Matt Jackson (Luton, Everton & Norwich City)

FACT FILE
Sponsor: Lansdown Homes
Colours: Red & Blue Stripes,Blue,Red
Change colours: Yellow,black,yellow
Programme: 12 pages
Editor:Jim Donaldson(01234 852598)

CLUB PERSONNEL
Chairman: Jim Donaldson
President: John Boyles
Manager: Ali Woods
Physio: Jim Donaldson

ST. IVES TOWN

Secretary: Alistair Robinson, 38 High Street,Needingworth,Huntingdon, Cambs.
Tel: 01480 460409 (H) 0585 058733 (M)
Ground: Westwood Road, St. Ives, Cambs.Tel: 01480 463207
Directions: From Huntingdon: A1123 thru Houghton, right at 2nd lighs intoRamsey Rd, after quarter mile turn right opp. Fire Station into Westwood Road
From A604: Follow Huntingdon signs past 5 r'bouts, left into Ramsey Rd at lights then follow as above.
Capacity: 5,000   Seats: 130 Cover: 300   Floodlights: Yes
Clubhouse: Bar and entertainment room. Normal licensing hours.
HONOURS Hunts Snr Cup 00-01 11-12 22-23 25-26 29-30 81-82 86-87 87-88, Cambs League 22-23 23-24 24-25.
PREVIOUS **Leagues:** Cambs; Central Amtr; Hunts; P'boro. & D. (pre-1985).
Ground: Meadow Lane
RECORD **Gate:** 400 v Saffron Walden Town, FA Vase.

FACT FILE
Founded: 1887
Nickname: Saints
Colours: White & black/black/red
Change colours: Blue/black/black
Midweek matchday: Tuesday
Reserves' Lge: UCL Res Div 2
Programme editor: Alastair Robinson
Tel: 01480 460409 (H)

CLUB PERSONNEL
Match Sec.: Alistair Robinson
38 High St., Needingworth, Huntingdon,
Cambs. Tel: 01480 460409 (H)

THRAPSTON TOWN

Secretary: Barry Carter, 23 Fletcher Gardens,Thrapston, Kettering, Northants.nn1 4UJ
Tel No: 01832 735879
Ground: Chancery Lane, Thrapston, Northants Tel: 01832 732470
Capacity: 1,000   Seats: Yes   Cover: Yes   Floodlights: No
Directions: Chancery Lane off A605 in town centre

Clubhouse: Yes
HONOURS Northants Junior Cup 87-88, 98-99 Kettering Am Lg 70-71 72-73 73-74 77-78
UCL Div1 Runners -Up 99-00
PREVIOUS **League:** Kettering Amateur (pre-1978)

FACT FILE
Founded: 1960
Nickname: Venturas
Sponsor: IKEA
Colours: All blue & yellow
Change colours: Yellow/yellow/yellow
Programme: Yes   Editor: Dave Overend

CLUB PERSONNEL
President: Derek Barber
Chairman: Dave Harris
Vice Chairman: Barry Carter
Manager: Gary Petts
Asst Manager: Barry Carter
Physio: Zoe

WELLINGBOROUGH WHITWORTHS

FACT FILE
Sponsor: Whitworth Brothers
Colours: Red & black/yellow/yellow
Change colours: All purple
Reserves' Lge: UCL Res Div 2
Programme: No

Secretary: Mr R Edwards, 15 James Road, Wellingborough, Northants NN8 2LR

Tel: 01933 382376

Ground: London Road, Wellingborough, Northants. Tel: 01933 227324

Capacity: 700   Seats: None   Cover: Yes   Floodlights: No

Directions: Off London Road at Dog & Duck public house

Clubhouse: Yes

PREVIOUS **Leagues:** Rushden & Dist.; E. Mids All. (pre-1985)

HONOURS Rushden & District Lg 76-77; Northants Jun Cup 96

CLUB PERSONNEL
Chairman: Bob Jarvis
Vice Chairman: Dave Woodley
President: Terry Faulkner
Manager: Phil Harvey
Asst Manager: Mick Garrett
Physio: Andrew King

WOODFORD UNITED

FACT FILE
Founded: 1946
Nickname:
Sponsors: Styleglaze
Colours: All red
Change Colours: All blue
Reserves' League: Northants Comb
Programme: 16 pages
Editor: Francis Peacock (01327 263335)

Secretary: Karl Henderson,7 Swan Close, Woodford Close, Daventry, Northants. NN3 6EW
Tel: 01327 262514 (H) 01295 254555 x 220 (W)

Ground: Byfield Road, Woodford Halse, Daventry, Northants. Tel: 01327 263734

Capacity: 3,000   Seats: 25   Cover: 150   Floodlights: No

Directions Off A 361 Daventry to Banbury Rd, on Woodford Road out of Byfield

Clubhouse: Yes

PREVIOUS Leagues: Central Northants Comb pre 70, UCL 70-78, Northants Comb

HONOURS Northants Comb 66 67 90 92 95, KO Cup 66 90 93 95 98;

United Counties Lge Div 2 74, KO Cup 74;

CLUB PERSONNEL
Chairman: Bob Justice
Vice-Chairman: R Adams
Manager: Andy McGuire
Assistant Manager: Justin Cullen

Kempston Rovers v Wootton Blue Cross 1-0
Pete Saunders beats Wootton keeper Steve Fox for the winning goal in this traditional Bank Holiday derby game.
Photo: Gordon Whittington

Top: Rothwell Corinthians. Back Row (l-r): Jimmy Sinclair, Tony Fargnoli, Adam Cann, Greg Smith, Jim Wilson, John Coe, Anthony Povey, Colin Sinclair (Manager). Front Row (l-r): David Briffa, Nathan Jones, Stephen Brydon, David Hanger, David Harding, Steven Keogh, Kevin Fowler.

Centre: Olney Town. Back Row (l-r): Russell Ward (Manager), Mark Lancaster, Guy Stewart, Stuart Keeping, Trevor Stone, Greg Hardie, Paul Simpson, Brian Stonnell, Dave Lancaster, Pete Munting (Physio). Front Row (l-r): Richard Barrass, Paul Adams, Scott Wrighting, Des Cook, Malcolm Thomas, Conrad Proud, Danny Munday.

Bottom: United Counties League Division One Champions Cottingham. Back Row (l-r): Willie Kelly (Asst Mngr), Rob Dunion (Mngr), Andy O'Neill, Adam Bell, Dave Trimble, James Keeney, Duncan McNish, Rob Muir, Graham Leech, Neil Addy. Front Row (l-r): Neil Pask, Lee Addy, Martin McLeod, Ian Jaffrey, Willie Moore, Darren Burt, John Cairns, Rab Armour (Physio).   *Photos: Gordon Whittington*

ISLE OF WIGHT F.A.

Chairman: K R Morris
Secretary: A P Justice, 12 The Mall, Binstead, Ryde, Isle of Wight PO33 3SF
Tel: 01983 565244

Binstead and Oakfield led the pack right from the first week of the season to the last and were neck and neck for a long time. However, Binstead's two victories over Oakfield proved decisive and rightly gave them the title. Strangely enough, in the two cup games that they played Oakfield won both! Both Sandown and Osborne Coburg fought to the end but without success and they failed to beat the drop.

THE SATURDAY LEAGUE FINAL TABLE

	P	W	D	L	F	A	Pts		P	W	D	L	F	A	Pts
Binstead	22	19	2	1	72	20	59	East Cowes Vics Res	22	7	4	11	40	60	25
Oakfield	22	17	3	2	72	22	54	Seaview	22	6	5	11	37	47	23
Cowes Sports Res	22	13	2	7	49	40	41	W & B Sports	22	7	2	13	24	48	23
Shanklin	22	13	1	8	54	37	40	Brading Town Res	22	7	1	14	44	60	22
W Wight Mayflower Rs	22	10	2	10	41	42	32	Sandown	22	5	4	13	36	62	19
Red Star Spartans	22	8	4	10	49	43	28	Osborne Coburg	22	4	2	16	29	66	14

SENIOR (GOLD) CUP FINAL

Newport (IoW) 3 v 1 Brading Town
Played at Cowes Sports FC   Attendance: 204

SOUTHERN FINAL LEAGUE TABLES - SATURDAY LEAGUES

PORTSMOUTH NORTH END LEAGUE

DIVISION ONE	P	W	D	L	F	A	Pts
Elite Glazing	14	12	2	0	57	17	38
George-Dragon	14	9	3	2	48	22	30
Kingston Prison Arrows	14	7	4	3	46	38	25
Havelock Rovers	14	6	2	6	35	34	20
Southside	14	4	6	4	25	28	18
Grant Thornton	14	3	3	8	28	39	12
British Red Star	14	3	1	10	26	48	10
Portsmouth Nomads	14	0	3	11	19	58	3

SOUTHAMPTON SENIOR LEAGUE

PREMIER DIVISION	P	W	D	L	F	A	Pts
Brendon	24	21	2	1	96	21	65
Ford Sports	24	13	6	5	66	34	45
Old Tauntonians	24	14	3	7	59	38	45
BTC Southampton	24	12	5	7	54	31	41
Midanbury	24	12	5	7	46	38	41
Durley	24	11	7	6	38	37	40
Nursling	24	11	6	7	57	40	39
Locksheath Res	24	11	0	13	50	59	33
Solent Youth	24	9	2	13	50	45	29
Fair Oak Linden	24	5	6	13	44	62	21
Esso Fawley Res	24	6	1	17	25	82	19
North Baddesley	24	4	6	14	30	48	18
Bishopstoke Soc Res	24	1	3	20	28	108	6

WORTHING DISTRICT LEAGUE

PREMIER DIVISION	P	W	D	L	F	A	Pts
Norwich Union Sports*	20	18	1	1	87	24	52
Tabernacle	20	13	2	5	46	34	41
Maybridge*	20	11	1	8	46	48	37
Sompting	20	10	5	5	50	35	35
AMC Athletic	20	11	2	7	40	36	35
Northbrook	20	10	2	8	53	36	32
Maple Leaf Rangers	20	9	0	11	47	38	27
St Theresa	20	7	3	10	22	47	24
Worthing United B	20	6	2	12	45	48	20
West Tarring WM	20	4	2	14	34	64	14
AFC Lion	20	1	0	19	18	78	3

WEST SUSSEX LEAGUE

PREMIER DIVISION	P	W	D	L	F	A	Pts
Rustington	22	14	7	1	60	21	49
Rogate	22	15	4	3	51	27	49
Midhurst-Easebourne	22	13	5	4	63	30	44
Southwater	22	11	5	6	47	36	38
Cowfold	22	11	2	9	48	46	35
Upper Beeding	22	10	4	8	53	43	34
Ferring	22	9	4	9	48	47	31
Henfield	22	6	3	13	42	53	21
Alfold	22	4	9	9	29	45	21
Stedham	22	6	3	13	36	57	21
South Bersted	22	6	2	14	33	54	20
Lancing United	22	2	2	18	31	82	8

WINCHESTER DISTRICT LEAGUE

DIVISION ONE	P	W	D	L	F	A	Pts
Twyford	12	10	1	1	23	10	21
Hyde United	12	8	1	3	29	13	17
Worthy Down	12	8	0	4	39	20	16
Upham	12	4	1	7	18	28	9
Winchester Castle A	12	4	1	7	19	31	9
Abbots Bourton	12	3	0	9	11	24	6
Highcliffe Corth.	12	2	2	8	26	41	6

NORTH HAMPSHIRE SENIOR LEAGUE

	P	W	D	L	F	A	Pts
Alresford Rown	22	18	2	2	63	17	56
Kings Somborne	22	18	1	3	91	26	55
AFC Basingstoke Res	21	15	2	4	55	29	47
ABC United	22	13	1	8	77	51	40
New Street A	22	12	2	8	47	57	38
Winchester Castle Res	21	10	2	9	53	35	32
Over Wallop	22	9	1	12	51	65	28
Broughton Res	22	7	3	12	40	63	24
Tadley Town Res	22	7	1	14	41	61	22
Sutton Scotney	22	6	3	13	37	60	21
King Alfred YA	22	3	2	17	26	76	11
RS Basingstoke Res	22	2	2	18	22	64	8

JEWSON WESSEX LEAGUE
FEEDER TO: Dr MARTENS FOOTBALL LEAGUE

President: Cyril Hurlock

Chairman: Norman Cook   **Vice Chairman:** Nick Spencer

Hon. Secretary: Tom Lindon, 63 Downs Road, South Wonston
Winchester, Hampshire SO21 3EW   Tel/Fax: 01962 884760

The League extended a warm welcome to the return of Andover FC, from their experience in the Southern League. In addition Newport (IW) Res and Salisbury City Res joined the Combination Division.

September 4th saw yet another round of the F.A. Cup, with some of our teams producing excellent results, but we lost Portsmouth RN, Thatcham Town (losers to Cowes Sports 6-4, some game!) and Eastleigh. As they had a bye in the F.A. Vase on 11th September, Lymington & New Milton travelled to Wroxham to defend the Jewson Champions Shield title, emerging 2-1 winners, thus having a valuable and worthwhile weekend, whilst Downton, Gosport Borough and Portsmouth RN ended their interests in this year's competition. The Second Qualifying Round of the F.A. Cup produced some excellent fixtures for our clubs, while Christchurch lost 2-3 to Worcester City, the attendance being 296, and AFC Newbury went to Hastings Town losing 3-1 in front of a crowd of 301. Result of the day had to be Wimborne Town earning a 1-1 draw at Newport County, in front of a crowd of 659, whilst Cowes Sports visited Slough Town going down 3-1 in front of 461 spectators. Having drawn with Tuffley Rovers with home advantage, Lymington & New Milton won 5-0 in the replay, and Wimborne Town went down 3-0 in their replay with Newport County. The results and attendances were a credit to our clubs. The F.A. Vase towards the end of September brought success for AFC Totton, BAT, Bournemouth, Christchurch, Cowes Sports, Fareham Town, Wimborne Town and Eastleigh.

October saw Lymington & New Milton beat Clevedon Town in the Third Qualifying Round of the F.A. Cup in front of a good gate, and hosting Aldershot Town in the F.A. Cup over 1,500 spectators attended. Success continued in the F.A. Vase for AFC Newbury, AFC Totton, Christchurch, BAT, and Cowes Sports.

AFC Newbury, AFC Totton, Lymington & New Milton, BAT and Cowes Sports progressed to the Third Round Proper of the F.A. Vase in November. Further success in the F.A. Vase came for AFC Totton and Cowes Sports and a draw for BAT at Wroxham, who went out of the competition on penalties having been on even terms 1-1 after extra time.

AFC Totton and Cowes Sports continued their runs in the F.A. Vase. Totton beat Horsham YMCA in front of 198 spectators, whilst Cowes beat Tilbury before a crowd of 248, although `extra bodies' attended the match during the second half, a great pity; some of the pride and joy in winning must have been lost.

The success in the F.A. Vase came to a sudden halt for both our remaining teams, as AFC Totton lost 5-0 to Bedlington Terriers whilst Cowes had a bad day losing 0-7 to Taunton Town, but to reach the Fifth Round of such a good competition reflects well on both teams.

March proved to be a difficult month for the League in terms of the programme, with Bournemouth FC having been placed under general suspension by their County Football Association, and matches had to be postponed yet we were unable to re-arrange fixtures for almost a month. Andover FC reached the Final of the Hampshire Senior Cup, with Eastleigh and Lymington & New Milton reaching the Final of the Russell Cotes Cup. Our own domestic cup competitions also reached their climax with the League Cup Finalists being Lymington & Wimborne Town and the Combination Cup finalists being Bashley Res and Lymington & New Milton Res. The First Division Championship proved to be very interesting with Wimborne Town and Lymington & New Milton alternating the lead. Newport (IW) Res clinched the Combination Championship in their first season.

April started well enough with the race for the First Division title `hotting up' with both Lymington & New Milton and Wimborne Town dropping points, and by the middle of the month arrangements were made for the pitches to be watered for some considerable time! Due to the hard work of our clubs very few matches were postponed; in fact we only lost twelve matches to the weather during the whole month, but it seemed like more at the time! The two Cup Finals proved to be very interesting, although played just two days apart, as the weather conditions were so different, which typified the month. I would like to thank Downton FC and Bemerton Heather Harlequins FC for staging the Cup Finals, their help, hard work and co-operation being much appreciated. The League season was extended by just two full days. The finale of the season could not have been scripted better, with two teams equal on 100 points with just five goals separating them on the final day of the First Division matches.

FIRST DIVISION FINAL LEAGUE TABLE 1999-2000

		P	W	D	L	F	A	W	D	L	F	A	Pts	GD
1	Wimborne Town	40	16	2	2	69	18	16	2	2	57	15	100	93
2	Lymington & New M.	40	16	3	1	59	15	15	4	1	56	12	100	88
3	Andover	40	13	4	3	84	25	12	3	5	63	35	82	87
4	AFC Totton	40	10	3	7	43	18	14	5	1	50	12	80	63
5	B.A.T. Sports	40	12	4	4	48	25	12	4	4	40	23	80	40
6	Moneyfields	40	11	4	5	37	29	11	5	4	39	35	75	12
7	Eastleigh	40	10	5	5	34	21	10	3	7	33	25	68	21
8	AFC Newbury	40	11	5	4	35	17	6	7	7	32	34	63	16
9	Cowes Sports	40	9	8	3	43	26	8	3	9	30	29	62	18
10	Bemerton Heath Harl.	40	11	4	5	45	36	6	5	9	30	30	60	9
11	Fareham Town	40	7	8	5	31	28	7	6	7	41	43	56	1
12	Christchurch	40	8	3	9	29	30	8	4	8	39	37	55	1
13	Thatcham Town	40	7	4	9	36	40	8	3	9	26	29	52	-7
14	Gosport Borough	40	6	3	11	22	30	2	9	9	18	40	36	-30
15	Downton	40	6	3	11	40	49	4	3	13	34	64	36	-39
16	Hamble ASSC	40	4	7	9	21	40	3	4	13	23	49	32	-45
17	Whitchurch United	40	3	5	12	27	50	4	5	11	26	39	31	-36
18	Brockenhurst	40	4	4	12	22	54	3	3	14	21	60	28	-71
19	Bournemouth*	40	4	4	12	33	58	3	4	13	21	52	27	-56
20	Portsmouth RN	40	3	5	12	31	50	2	5	13	16	64	25	-67
21	East Cowes Vics	40	5	2	13	28	51	0	3	17	15	90	20	-98

JEWSON WESSEX LEAGUE CUP 1999-2000

FIRST ROUND (Aggregate Results)

AFC Newbury	v	Bournemouth	B W/O
Gosport Borough	v	Andover	1-13
Thatcham Town	v	Moneyfields	6-2

| Fareham Town | v | Portsmouth RN | 3-3 |
| Hamble ASSC | v | Brockenhurst | 0-6 |

SECOND ROUND (Aggregate Results)

Bournemouth	v	Lymington & New M	4-6
B A T	v	Bemerton Hth Hqns	6-2
East Cowes Vics	v	Downton	6-4
Thatcham Town	v	Christchurch	6-4

AFC Totton	v	Brockenhurst	2-0
Cowes Sports	v	Eastleigh	3-3
Fareham Town	v	Andover	1-3
Wimborne Town	v	Whitchurch Utd	10-0

QUARTER FINAL (Aggregate Results)

| Lymington & New M | v | Andover | 9-0 |
| Thatcham Town | v | Eastleigh | 2-2 |

| East Cowes Vics | v | AFC Totton | 0-9 |
| Wimborne Town | v | Bemerton Hth Hqns | 8-2 |

SEMI FINAL (Aggregate Results)

| Lymington & New M | v | Thatcham Town | 4-2 |

| AFC Totton | v | Wimborne Town | 0-4 |

FINAL

| Lymington & New M | v | Wimborne Town | 0-1 | at Bemerton Heath Harlequins FC |

LEADING GOALSCORERS 1999-2000

FIRST DIVISION

61	Andrew Forbes	Andover FC
41	Leigh Phillips	Lymington & New Milton FC
36	Darren Elmes	Wimborne Town FC
28	Tommy Pegler	B A T Sports

COMBINATION DIVISION

35	Steve Wheatland	Eastleigh FC
31	Andy Nicholas	Christchurch FC
30	Dominic Taylor	Bashley FC
28	Lee Maggs	Bemerton Heath Harlequins FC
28	Rob Morant	Eastleigh FC

ROLL OF HONOUR 1999-2000

Champions, Jewson Wessex League	Wimborne Town FC
Runners Up	Lymington & New Milton FC
Winners, Jewson Wessex League Cup	Wimborne Town FC
Runners Up	Lymington & New Milton FC
Winners, Jewson Champions Shield	Lymington & New Milton FC
Champions, Combination League	Newport (IW) FC
Runners Up	Lymington & New Milton FC
Winners, Combination Cup	Lymington & New Milton FC
Runners Up	Bashley FC
Runners Up, Dorset Senior Cup	Wimborne Town FC
Runners Up, Hampshire Senior Cup	Andover FC
Winners, Russell Cotes Cup	Lymington & New Milton FC
Runners Up	Eastleigh FC
Winners, Basingstoke Senior Cup	Andover FC
Winners, Hungerford Challenge Cup	Whitchurch Utd FC
Winners, Greystone Cup	AFC Newbury
Winners, Fair Play Award	Wimborne Town FC
Winners, Best Programme Award	Portsmouth Royal Navy FC
Winners, Longest FA Vase Run	AFC Totton & Cowes Sports FC

EVENING ECHO MANAGER OF THE MONTH AWARDS

August	Derek Ohren	Cowes Sports FC
September	Steve Slade	Bemerton Heath Harlequins
October	Ken Cunningham Brown	Andover FC
November	Alex Pike	Wimborne Town FC
December	Alex Pike	Wimborne Town FC
January	Ian Robinson	AFC Totton
February	Alex Pike	Wimborne Town FC
March	Ken Cunningham Brown	Andover FC
April/May	Trevor Parker	Eastleigh FC

LEAGUE & LEAGUE CUP RECORDS

	LEAGUE CHAMPIONS	LEAGUE CUP WINNERS
1989-1990	Romsey Town	AFC Totton
1990-1991	Havant Town	Thatcham Town
1991-1992	Wimborne Town	Thatcham Town
1992-1993	AFC Lymington	Gosport Borough
1993-1994	Wimborne Town	Wimborne Town
1994-1995	Fleet Town	Thatcham Town
1995-1996	Thatcham Town	Downton
1996-1997	AFC Lymington	Thatcham Town
1997-1998	AFC Lymington	Aerostructures S & S
1998-1999	Lymington & New Milton FC	Cowes FC
1999-2000	Wimborne Town FC	Wimborne Town FC

*Leatherhead 0
Cowes Sports 1
Cowes 'keeper Joe
McCormack watches
the ball fly wide of his
goal.
Photo: Tim Edwards*

675

A.F.C. NEWBURY

Secretary: Mike Hall,17 Moores Place, Hungerford, Berks. RG17 0JS
Tel: 01488 685241 (H) 07714 953784 (W)

Ground: Faraday Road, Newbury, Berks. Tel: 01635 523222

Directions: A34 to Robin Hood roundabout, then A4 towards Reading. Right at lights after 100 yards into Faraday Road. Ground at end of road.

Previous Name: Newbury Town   **League:** Hellenic

FACT FILE
Colours: Green & white/white/green & white
Change: Red & white/red/red & white
Midweek Matches: Tuesday

CLUB PERSONNEL
Chairman: Steve Hartley Tel: 01488 683783(H) 0118 9304030 (W)
Manager: Jimmy Greenwood

A.F.C. TOTTON

Secretary: Mrs Sheila Benfield, 35 Fishers Road, Totton, Southampton SO40 9HW
Tel: 023 80865421

GROUND: Testwood Park, Testwood Place, Totton, Southampton Tel:023 80868981

Directions: Five minutes walk from Totton station. Turn off at roundabout in Totton centre into Library Road.Then first left and second right into Testwood Place.

Capacity: 2,500 **Seats:** 200 **Cover:** 250 **Floodlights:** Yes **Club Shop:** No
Clubhouse: Open for matches and training sessions. Burgers, sandwiches, tea,coffee, biscuits etc available
HONOURS : Hampshire League x2, Russlesl Cotes Cup 98-99
PREVIOUS : **League:** Hants 1886-1986 **Grounds:** Downs Park; Mayfield Park
Name: Totton FC until merger with Totton Athletic 1979
RECORD: **Gate:** 600 v Windsor & Eton, F.A. Cup 4th Qual Rd 82-83

FACT FILE
Founded: 1886
Nickname: Stags
Sponsors: Colours: Blue with white trim
Change colours: Lime/Black/Black
Midweek Matches: Tuesday
Programme: 30 pages 50p

CLUB PERSONNEL
Chairman: Bob Devoy
Vice Chairman: R.Thurston
President: D Maton
Manager: Ian Robinson
Press Officer: P Chilcott (023 80860453)

ANDOVER

Secretary: Chris Jeremy, 23 Stubbs Court, Artists Way, Andover, Hants SP10 3QR
Tel: 01264 361973
Ground: Portway Stadium, West Portway Ind. Estate, Andover SP10 3LF Tel: 01264 333052
Directions: From the Andover By-pass A303 follow signs to Portway Ind. estate. On exiting the A303 turn right at r/about & over bridge, bear off left at next mini r/about and after 150yds turn right onto estate. Straight on until you enter Hopkinson Way, ground on left 4-500 yds
Capacity: 3,000 **Cover:** 250 **Seats:** 250 **Floodlights:** Yes
Clubhouse: Open matchdays & private function **Club Shop:** No **Metal Badges:** Yes

HONOURS Wessex Lg R-up 94-95, Western Lg R-up 69-70 70-71; Hants Lg 13-14 24-25 33-34 44-45 48-49 50-51 61-62 (R-up 42-43), Northern Div 13-14, Div 2 R-up 37-38; Salisbury & Dist Lg 1894-95 95-96 96-97 99-1900 03-04 07-08 12-13; Hants Sen Cup 48-49 50-51 55-56 64-65; Russell Cotes Cup 23-24 31-32 37-38 44-45 52-53 58-59 60-61 61-62; Pickfords Cup 50-51; Hants Interm Cup 59-60 60-61; Hants Junior Cup 19-20 (R-up 1894-95 1910-11 12-13)

PREVIOUS **Leagues:** Salisbury & D.; Hants 1896-98, 1899-1901, 02-62; Southern 1898-99,1971-93 98-99; Western 1962-71; Wessex Lge 93-98

BEST SEASON **FA Cup:** 1st Rd 62-63, 0-1 v Gillingham
FA Trophy: 3rd Qual Rd 69-70, 70-71
FA Vase: 4th Rd 94-95, 1-3 v Falmouth Town (A)

FACT FILE
Founded: 1883
Nickname: The Lions
Colours: Red & black/black/red
Change cols: All Purple.
Midweek matchday: Tuesday
Reserve Team's League: None
Programme: 50 pages 50p

CLUB PERSONNEL
Chairman: John Cunningham-Brown
President: R Coleman
Manager: Ken Cunningham-Brown
Asst Manager: Mike Burford
Physio: Chris Burford

B.A.T. SPORTS

Secretary: Mike Geddes, Tel: 023 80337460(H) 0589 614158(M)
39 Pacific Close, Victoria Quay, Ocean Village,Southampton, SO14 3 TX

Ground: BAT Sports Ground, Southern Gdns, off Ringwood Road, Totton Tel: 023 8086243

Directions: Into centre of Totton, proceed up Ringwood Rd past small r'bout,2nd left into Southern Gardens. Half mile from Totton (BR), bus X2(Southampton-Bournemouth)
Capacity: 3,000 **Seats:** 150 **Cover:** 150 **Floodlights:** Yes

Clubhouse: Normal licensing hrs, all day for members' sports facilities. Hot & cold snacks

BEST SEASON **FA Vase:** 3rd Rd 99-00

FACT FILE
Founded: 1925
Colours: Blue with yellow trim/blue/blue
Change: Red & black/red/red
Midweek Matches: Tuesday
Programme: 20 pages, 30p

CLUB PERSONNEL
Chairman: Ray Roberts
Manager: Ray Light & Dave Blandford

BEMERTON HEATH HARLEQUINS

Secretary: A J Hardwick, 2 Ashley Rd, Salisbury, Wilts. SP2 7BZ Tel: 01722 333015 & mobile: 07931 284658

Ground: Western Way, Bemerton Heath, Salisbury, Wilts Tel: 01722 331925 (H) : FAX :01722 331218

Directions: Turn off A36 Salisbury-Bristol Rd at Skew Bridge (right turn if coming out of Salisbury), 1st left into Pembroke Rd for half mile, 2nd left along Western Way - ground quarter mile at end. 40 mins walk from Salisbury(BR) station. Bus 51 or 52 from city centre stops at junction of Pembroke Rd/Western Way

Capacity : 2,100   Seats: 200   Cover: 350   Floodlights: Yes   **Clubhouse:** Yes

HONOURS Wilts Snr Cup 92-93. Wilts Lg(3) as Bemerton Athletic

PREVIOUS **Names:** Bemerton Athletic, Moon FC & Bemerton Boys; all merged in 1989
Leagues: Bem. Ath.: Salisbury. & Wilts Comb.
Moon: Salisbury. & Andover Sunday   Bem.Boys: Mid Wilts

RECORD **Attendance:** 1,118 v Aldershot Town FA Cup 1st Qual Rd Aug 94
Appearances: Keith Richardson

FACT FILE
Founded: May 1989
Nickname: Quins
Colours: Black & white hoops/black/black & white hoops
Change colours: Amber/white/white
Midweek Matches: Tuesday
Programme: 32 pages, 50p

CLUB PERSONNEL
Chairman: George Parker
President: Peter Say
Manager: Steve Slade
Coah:Andy Nash
Physio: Andy Nash

BLACKFIELD & LANGLEY

Secretary: Doug Sangster, 3 Fir Tree Grove, Butts Ash Lane, Hythe, Hants SO45 3RA
Tel: 023 8084 4911 (H) 023 8031 3721 (B)

Ground: Gang Warily Rec., Newlands Rd, Blackfield, Southampton, Hants SO45 1GA
Tel: 01703 893603

Directions: A326 from Totton. At Holbury mini roundabout take right fork signposted to Lepe and Fawley. After the 1st set of lights (170m) turn left into ground.

Previous League: Hampshire League

FACT FILE
Colours: White/green/green
Change colours: Red/blue/blue
Midweek home matchday: Tuesday
CLUB PERSONNEL
Chairman: Ian Hore, 5 Foxhayes Lane,
Blackfield, Southampton, Hants SO45 2QD
Tel: 023 8089 3325 (H)   023 8084 7659 (B)

BOURNEMOUTH

Secretary: Ray Murphy, Flat 10, Richmond Court, Richmond Park Road, Bournemouth, Dorset BH8 8TH   Tel: 01202 517607 (H) 07801 638158 (W)

Ground: Victoria Park, Namu Rd., Winton, Bournemouth, Dorset Tel: 01202 515123

Directions: Any bus to Wimborne Road, Winton. 2 miles from Bournemouth Central(BR)

Capacity: 3,000   Seats: 250   Cover: 250   Floodlights: Yes

Clubhouse: Open daily 7-11pm. Sandwiches & hot snacks available.   **Club Shop:** No

HONOURS Hants Lg 13-13 21-22, B'mouth Snr Cup 66-67 89-90, Texaco F'lit Cup R-up 91-92, Hants I'mediate Cup 49-50 69-70, Hants Yth Cup 54-55 57-58 67-68

PREVIOUS **Leagues:** Hampshire **Ground:** Dene Park 1888-90
Names: Bournemouth Rovers 1875-88; Bournemouth Dene Park 1888-90

RECORD **Scorer:** B Head
Fee Received: £1,500 for Chike Onourah (Wimborne 93-94)

FACT FILE
Founded: 1875   Nickname: Poppies
Sponsors: Chapel Carpets
Colours: All red
Change colours: White/navy/white
Midweek Matches: Tuesday
Reserves' League: Jewson Wessex Comb
Programme: 58 pages, 50p
Editor: Mark Willis
Local Press: Evening Echo
CLUB PERSONNEL
Chairman: Trevor Bloor
Vice Chairman: J B Wood
President: D Nippard
Comm. Manager: Alex Pike
Press Officer: Mark Willis
Manager: Alex Pike
Asst Manager: Nick Jennings
Coach: Chris Weller
Physio: Irvin Brown

BROCKENHURST

Secretary: Peter Plowman, 6 Cherry Tree Close, Everton, Lymington, Hampshire
Tel: 01590 644535

Ground: Grigg Lane, Brockenhurst, Hants Tel: 01590 623544

Directions: M27 Junc 1, A337 to Lyndhurst, round one-way system, A337 to Brockenhurst, turn right at Carey's Manor Hotel into Grigg Lane, ground 200 yds on the right

Capacity: 2,000   Seats: 200   Cover: 300   Floodlights: Yes
Clubhouse: Every evening plus Tues, Sat & Sun lunchtimes

HONOURS HampshireIntermediate Cup 61-62; Bournemouth Senior Cup 60-61;
Hampshire Lg 75-76, R-up 73-74 79-80, Div 2 70-71 R-up 60-61, Div 3 59-60.
PREVIOUS **League:** Hampshire Lge 24-26 47-86

BEST SEASON FA Amateur Cup: 2nd Round 73-74

99-00-   Captain: Carlo Tate   P.o.Y.: Carlo Tate   Top Scorer: Lamin Dibba

FACT FILE
Founded: 1898
Nickname: The Badgers
Sponsor: Drew Smith Builders
Colours: Blue & white/blue/blue
Change colours: Red & white/red/red
Midweek Matches: Tuesday
Reserves League: Wessex Comb
Programme: 34 pages, 50p,
Editor/Press Officer: Dave Stansbridge
CLUB PERSONNEL
Chairman: Keith Collins
President: Mike Kimber
Vice Chairman: Alex Chalmers
Manager: Cliff Huxford
Asst. Mgr: M Cobb   Res Mgr: G Price
Physio: Alan Butters

AFC Totton reached the Quarter Finals of the Hampshire Senior Cup, losing to Aldershot Town. Also reached the Fifth Round of the FA Vase. Photo: Eric Marsh

Fleet Town FC. Back Row (l-r): Jocky Keir, Adam Deller-Smith, Tommy Taylor, Mark Russell, Mark Frampton, Aidan Kilner, Warren Burton, John Murphy (captain), Luke Jolly, Wayne Winklyn, Jesse Bone. Front Row: Scott Mitchell, Jon Richards, Barry McCoy, Danny Barker, Owen Shaw, Gavin Smith, Paul Burnell. Photo: Mark Sandom

Whitchurch United. Back Row (l-r): Tony Lesley, Jeremy Hayward, Steve Brown, Dan Winterbourne, Chris O'Grady, Mark Randell, Scot Elvins, Dean Maroand. Front Row: Dave Ord, Gary Shaughnessy, Mick Lonnon, Mario Nurse, Kevin Knight, Steve Dale. Photo: Andrew Chitty

CHRISTCHURCH

Secretary: Mrs Dawn Page, 87 The Albany, Manor Road, Bournemouth BH1 3EJ
Tel: 01202 551977

Ground: Hurn Bridge Sports Club, Hurn Bridge, Avon Causeway, Christchurch
Tel: 01202 473792

Directions: A338 from Ringwood, turn off signed Hurn Airport on left. Before Airport use
mini roundabout & take exit signed Sopley & ground is immed. on the right.
3 miles from Christchurch (BR)

Capacity: 2,000   **Seats:** 215   **Cover:** 265   **Floodlights:** Yes

Clubhouse: Normal pub hours. Cooked food at lunchtimes

HONOURS   Hants Jnr Cup 1892-93 1911-12 20-21; Hants Int. Cup 86-87; Pickford Cup 91;
Hants Lg Div 2 37-38 47-48 85-86 (Div 3 56-57); B'mouth Snr Cup (5) 56-57 59-
60 67-70; B'mouth Page-Croft Cup 94-95

PREVIOUS   **League:** Hampshire   **Ground:** Barrack Rd Recreation Grd (>1984)

RECORD   **Appearances :** John Haynes

Players progressing: Jody Craddock (Cambridge Utd 93), Dan West (Aston Villa 94)

FACT FILE
Founded: 1885
Nickname: Priory
Sponsors: Franklin Transport
Colours: All royal blue (white trim)
Change colours: All Red
Midweek Matches: Tuesday
Programme: 16 pages, 50p
Editor: Phil Old

CLUB PERSONNEL
Chairman: Robin Osborne
Vice Chairmen: Mick Ryan & Derek Nippard
President: Joss Jenkins
Press Officer: Robin Osborne
Manager: Colin Williams
Physio: Emma Walsh

COWES SPORTS

FACT FILE

Secretary: W (Bill) G Murray, 3 Firs Close, Cowes, Isle of Wight PO31 7NF
Tel: 01983 294445

Ground: Westwood Park, Reynolds Close, off Park Rd, Cowes, Isle of Wight PO31 7NT
Tel: 01983 293793

Directions: Take Park Road out of Cowes centre. Reynolds Close is a right turn half mile up hill

Capacity: 1695   **Seats:** Yes   **Cover:** Stand   **Floodlights:** Yes

Clubhouse: Yes   **Club Shop:** No

HONOURS   Hampshire League 93-94, Isle of Wight Gold Cup 94-95,Wessex Lg.Cup 98-9

PREVIOUS   **League:** Hampshire (pre-1994)

BEST SEASON   **FA Cup:** 4th Qual. Rd replay 57-58, 1-4 v Trowbridge (A) after 2-2
FA Vase: 5th Rd 99-00

Founded:
Colours: Blue & white stripes,black,blue
Change colours:Amber & Black
Midweek Fixtures: Wednesday
Reserves' Lge: I.O.W. Saturday Lg.
Programme Editor: Roger Hendey

CLUB PERSONNEL

President: Ada Leigh
Chairman: Ian Lee
Manager: Derek Ohren

DOWNTON

Secretary: Brian Trent 21 Fison Walk, Bishopdown, Salisbury, Wilts SP1 3JF Tel: 01722 323097

Ground: Brian Whitehead Sports Ground, Wick Lane, Downton Tel: 01725 512162

Directions: Travel south from Salisbury on A338 for about 7 miles. Turn right intoWick Lane, and
the ground is a qtr mile on left

Capacity: 1600   **Seats:** 250   **Cover:** Nil   **Floodlights:** Yes

Clubhouse: Bar with kitchen facilities   **Club Shop:** No

HONOURS   Wilts Sen Cup 79-80 80-81, (R-up 55-56 91-92 94-95); Wilts Jun Cup 49-50;
Bournemouth Sen Lge 60 61 62 64 65 67 68, Sen Lge Cup 61-62 63-64 66-67,
Cup 62-63 79-80; Wessex Lge Cup 95-96; Wessex Comb Cup (R-up 95-96);
RussellCotes Cup 95-96; Hayward Cup 64-65

PREVIOUS   **League:** Bournemouth, Hants (pre-1993)

FACT FILE

Founded: 1905
Nickname: The Robins
Sponsor: Lex Vauxhall Salisbury
Colours: Red/white/red
Change colours:Yellow/blue/yellow
Midweek Matchday: Tuesday
Programme: Yes
Editor: James Blake

CLUB PERSONNEL

Chairman: James Blake
President: R Tanner
Manager: M Savage
Coach: C Huxford
Physio: T Ship

EASTLEIGH

Secretary: Miss Andrea Vowles, 28 Franklyn Avenue, Sholing, Southampton, Hants SO19 8AP
Tel No: 01703 447802
Ground: 'Ten Acres', Stoneham Lane, North Stoneham, Eastleigh SO50 -9HT Tel: 01703 613361
Directions: M27, Jct 5, to r'bout - exit marked Stoneham Lane. Carry on to r'bout & come back
down Stoneham Lane, turning right opp. Concord Club. Ground 400 yds on left. Southampton
Parkway (BR) 3/4 mile. Bus 48 (S'hampton-Winchester) to Stoneham Church stop
Capacity: 4,300   Seats: 175   Cover: 210   Floodlights: Yes   Club Shop: No
Clubhouse: 11-11 Mon-Sat plus Sundays. Extensive function facilities. All catering undertaken

HONOURS   Wessex Lg Cup R-up 91-92, Hants Lg Div 2 69-70 (R-up 54-55 60-61 62-63
64-65(Res), Div 3(W) 50-51 53-54 70-71(Res), Comb.(Res) (3) R-up 96-Hants, Comb Cup (Res)
96-7,97-8 Midweek F'lit Cup 78-79, Soton Snr Lg(W) 49-50 (R-up 51-52(Res), Div 1 56- 57) 57-
58(Res)), Russell Cotes R-up 76-77 80-81 89-90,
PREVIOUS   **Leagues:** Southampton Jnr & Snr 46-59/ Hants 50-86
　　　　　　　　Names: Swaythling Ath. 46-73; Swaythling 73-80
　　　　　　　　Grounds: Southampton Common 46-47; Walnut Avenue, Swaythling 47-75
BEST SEASON   **FA Vase:** 4th Round 82-83,90-91, 94-95
RECORDS   **Gate:** 2,500 v Southampton, floodlight opener 30/9/75
　　　　　　Scorer : Johnny Williams, 177   **Appearances** : Ian Knight, 611
Win: 12-1 v Hythe & Dibden (H) 11/12/48   **Defeat:** 0-11 v Austin Spts (A) 1/1/47

FACT FILE

Founded: 1946
Nickname: None
Sponsors: Southern Exhaust Sedrvices
Colours: All blue
Change colours: All white
Midweek matches: Wednesday
Programme: 32 pages with admission
Editor: Richard Vowles & Tommy Whale

CLUB PERSONNEL

Chairman: Roger Sherwood
President: Clive Wilson
Manager:Derek Holloway
Asst Manager: Derek Dempsey
Physio: Bert Wyatt

FAREHAM TOWN

Secretary: Malcolm Harper, 20 Hampton Grove, Catisfield, Fareham, Hants PO15 5NL
　　Tel: 01329 8413476 (H) 01329 844074 (Fax) 0410 689939 (M)

Ground: Cams Alders, Highfield Avenue, Fareham, Hants PO14 1JA Tel: 01329 231151

Directions: M27, J11, follow A27 towards Southampton. After passing Fareham station turn left at
traffic lights (2nd left) into Redlands Ave.. Turn right at Redlands Inn then left into Highfields Ave.
　　　　　　Capacity: 5,500   Cover: 500   Seats: 450   Floodlights: Yes
Clubhouse: Open every evening except Sundays. Food available
Club Shop: Sells programmes, scarves & fanzines
HONOURS   Hants Lg (8) 59-60 62-67 72-73 74-75 (R-up 55-56 60-61 67-68 71-72 76-77 78-
79, Div 2 R-up 52-53, Eastern Div 24-25, Div 3 East 49-50), Hants Snr Cup 56-57
62-63 67-68 92-93, Russell Cotes Cup (6) 64-65 72-77, Gosport War Memorial
Cup, SW Co's Cup (2), Pickford Cup (2),
PREVIOUS   **Leagues:** Portsmouth 47-49, Hants 49-79, Southern 79-98
　　　　　　　　Name: Fareham FC   **Ground:** Bath Lane
BEST SEASON   **FA Trophy:** Semi Final 86-87   **FA Amateur Cup:** 2nd Rd 63-64 66-67 73-74
FA Vase: 1st Rd 98-99   **FA Cup:** 1st Rd replay 88-89, 2-3 v Torquay U. (H) after 2-2
RECORDS   **Attendance:** 2,650 v Wimbledon, FA Cup 1965.
　　　　　　(at Southampton F.C.) 6,035 v Kidderminster H., FAT S-F 2nd leg 86-87
　　　　　　Fee received: £43,000 for David Leworthy (Spurs)

FACT FILE
Formed: 1947
Nickname: The Town
Sponsors: Portsmouth Evening News
Colours: Red/white/red
Change colours: Whiteblack/black
Midweek matchday: Wednesday
Reserves' League: Hampshire Comb
Programme: 36 pages £1
Editor: Ian Tewson Tel. 01329 662624

CLUB PERSONNEL
Chairman: Chris Solen 01329 847784 (H)
01329 844111 (B)
Director of Football: John Green
President: Ken Atkins
General Manager: Tony Adams (01705 615931)
Press Officer: M Willis
Manager: Mark Chamberlain (01705 327527)
Physio: James McKay

FLEET TOWN

Secretary: John Goodyear, 125 Velmead Road,Fleet,Hants GU13 9LJ

Ground: Calthorpe Park, Crookham Road, Fleet, Hants Tel: 01252 623804
Directions: Leave the M3 at Junction 4A. Follow signs to Fleet via A3013.
　　　　　　At 5th roundabout (a T-junction), turn left over railway bridge.
　　　　　　Carry on past `Oatsheaf' pub on the right - ground is 1/4 mile further on right.
　　　　　　Capacity: 2,000   Seats: 200   Cover: 250   Floodlights: Yes
Clubhouse: Yes. Hot & cold food served   **Club Shop:** No

PREVIOUS   **Leagues:** Hampsire 61-77, Athenian, Combined Co's, Chiltonian,
　　　　　　　　Wessex 89-95, Southern 95-00, Wessex 00-
　　　　　　　　Names: None   **Grounds:** None

CLUB RECORDS **Win:** 15-0
　　　　　　　　Transfer fee paid: £3,000 to Aldershot Dec 99 for Mark Russell 1991
　　　　　　　　Career Goalscorer: Mark Frampton   **Career Appearances:** Mark Frampton

HONOURS   Wessex Lg 94-95 , Lg Cup R-up 92-93,
　　　　　　Hants Lg Div 2 R-up 61-62 (Div 1 R-up 60-61), Aldershot Snr Cup 92-93, 99-00
　　　　　　Simpsonair Challenge Shield 1993, Hants Yth LgDiv 3 92-93.

FACT FILE
Founded: 1890 Re-Formed: 1947
Nickname: The Blues
Sponsors: Southern Coating Contractors Ltd.
Colours: Navy & sky/sky/navy & sky
Change: Red & Black
Midweek Matches: Tuesday
Reserves' League: Suburban
Prog: Pages: 20 Price:£1.00
Editor: Stuart Reeves

CLUB PERSONNEL
Chairman: **Martn Griffiths**
President: **Tony Frost**
Vice Chairman: **Chris Reeves**
Manager: Wayne Wanklyn
Assistant Manager: Jess Bone
Coach: Andy Graves
Physio: David Keir

Bournemouth's Mark Adams makes a last ditch tackle to deny Hallen striker Steve Watts.
Photo:D Nicholson

Eastleigh's Green about to take on Sidley United's striker Steve Streeter.
Photo: Roger Turner

YMCA No 5 Matt Russell (right), with Thatcham Town's Richard Jones (left) in a mid-air challenge. Phill Fitzgerald, (No 3) YMCA, is ready to move in on the action.
Photo: Clive Turner

Niark Tryon heads home Chichester's first goal in the 2.0 victory over Wessex League side Whitchurch United.
Photo: Andrew Chitty

GOSPORT BOROUGH

Secretary: B V Cosgrave, 2 Cavanna Close, Rowner, Gosport PO13 0PE Tel: 01329314117
Ground: Privett Park, Privett Road, Gosport, Hants Tel: 01705 501042 (Office)
Directions: M27 Junct 11, A32 Fareham to Gosport. At Brockhurst r-about (about 3 miles) right into Military Rd passing thru H.M.S. Sultan, left into Privett Rd at next r-about, ground 300yds left signed `Privett Park Enclosure'. 2 miles from Portsmouth Harbour (BR) or Fareham (BR)
Capacity: 4,500   **Cover:** 500   **Seats:** 450   **Floodlights:** Yes   **Club Shop:** No
Clubhouse: Matchdays only - from 1.30 Sat., 6.30 Wed. Refreshment hut sells hot food & drinks
HONOURS Wessex Lg Cup 92-93, Southern Lg Div 1 South R-up 84-85, Hants Lg 45-46 76-77 77-78 (Div 3 (Res.) 70-71 75-76), Portsmouth Lg R-up 44-45, HantsSenior Cup 87-88, Russell Cotes Cup R-up 94-95, Hants Intermediate Cup 70-71, Portsmouth Senior Cup 61-62 69-70 70-71 94-95, South West Counties PrattenChallenge Cup 77-78
BEST SEASON   FA Trophy: 1st Rd 88-89   **FA Amateur Cup:** 3rd Rd 47-48 66-67
                     FA Vase: 6th Rd rep 77-78   **FA Cup:** 4th Qual. Rd 80-81 (lost to Windsor & Eton)
PREVIOUS   Leagues: Portsmouth 44-45; Hants 45-78; Southern 78-92
                     Name: Gosport Borough Athletic
RECORD   Attendance: 4,770 v Pegasus, FA Amtr Cup 1951
                     Scorer: Richie Coulbert 192   **Appearances:** Tony Mahoney 764
                     Win: 14-0 v Cunliffe-Owen, Hampshire Lg Div 1 45-46
                     Defeat: 0-9 twice   v Newport, Hants Lg Div 1 47-48.
                                     v Gloucester (A), SouthernLg Prem Div 89-90

FACT FILE

Founded: 1944
Nickname: The Boro'
Sponsors: Cawte & Elms
Colours: Yellow/blue/blue
Change colours: All red
Midweek matchday: Tuesday
Reserves ' League: Wessex Combination
Programme: 20 pages, 50p
Editor: Ian Hay (01329 314601)
Local Press: Portsmouth Evening News,
Southampton Evening Echo

CLUB PERSONNEL

Chairman: JohnStimpson
President: H.Mizen
Manager: Mick Marsh
Coaches: Dave Taviner
Physio: Dave Topliss

HAMBLE AEROSTRUCTURES
SPORTS & SOCIAL CLUB

Secretary: Matthew Newbold, Flat 6, 70-72 Portsmouth Road, Woolsten, Southampton, Hants. SO19 9AN   Tel: 023 803 24147 (H) 023 804 53371(W)

Ground: Folland Park, Kings Avenue, Hamble.,Southampton SO31 4NF
                     Tel: 01703 452173

Directions: M27 junction 8, then B3397 to Hamble. Half mile fromHamble (BR); turn right out of station, proceed for one mile then turn right before shops into Kings Avenue. Ground 1000 yards on right in works sports ground.

                     Capacity: 1000   **Seats:** 150   **Cover:** 150   **Floodlights:** Yes
Clubhouse: 300 capacity social club. Cricket & bowls

HONOURS: Hampshire Lg Div 3 80-81 (Div 4 79-80), Hampshire Intermediate Cup 79-90, Southampton Senior Cup 84-85 86-87 91-92
                     As Hamble AS&SC: Jewson Wessex League Cup 97-98
PREVIOUS   **Name:** Folland Sports (pre-1990), Aerostructures SSC 90-97
RECORD   **Defeat:** 1-10 v Andover (A), Wessex League 93-94

FACT FILE

Colours: Maroon & Sky Blue
Change colours: All navy blue with white trim
Midweek Matches: Tuesdays & Wednesdays
Reserves ' League: Wessex Comb
Under 18 & Under16: So'ton Youth Lgs

CLUB PERSONNEL

President: Alistair Tritten
Chairman: Peter Mence
Assistant Secretary: Matthew Newbold
Treasurer:Barry Morse
SeniorManagers: Nigel Kent &Dick Donohoe

LYMINGTON & NEW MILTON

Secretary: John Osey, 9 Samphire Close, Lymington, Hants SO41 9LR Tel: 01590 676995
Ground: Fawcett Fields,Christchurch Rd., New Milton,Hants BH25 6QF (01425 6281910
Directions: M27 Jct 1 follow A337 to Lyndhurst one way system(A35) towards Christchurch. Left in Hinton Admiral at Cat & Fiddle.Follow Ringwood road ,then left at A337 roundabout to New Milton. Ground one mile on left past Chewton Glen Hotel.
Capacity: 3,000   **Seats:** 262   **Cover:** 262   **Floodlights:** Yes
Clubhouse: Open seven days a week 11.0 am to 11.0 pm. Hot food and functions availab le
HONOURS Wessex Lg 92-93 96-97 97-98, 98-99 R-up 91-92 95-96, Wessex Lg Cup 88-89, R-up 94-95, 98-99 Wessex Comb. 92-93, Hants Snr Cup R-up 89-90, Texaco Cup 91-92, Bournemouth Snr Cup 92-93, R-up 96-97, Russell Cotes Cup 93-94 94-95, R-up91-92 92-93; Pickford Cup R-up 92-93. Jewson Champions Shield 98-99
BEST SEASON   FA Cup: 4th Qual. Rd. 99-00, 1-3 v Aldershot Town (H)
                     FA Vase: 98-99 Quarter Final, 1-3 v Taunton Town (A)
PREVIOUS   Names: Lymington Town (until 1988 merger with Wellworthy Ath.),
                     AFC Lymington 88-98 (until merger with New Milton Town)
                     Ground: Ampress Ground (Wellworthy Ath.), until 1988 merger
RECORD   Attendance: 2,900 v Karen Mills Memorial Day 12.3.95
                     Scorer: Darren Pitter 197   **Appearances:** Graham Kemp 322
                     Win: 11-1 v Romsey Town (H), Wessex League 9/11/92
                     Defeat: 0-8 v Basingstoke Town (A), Hampshire Senior Cup 10/4/90

FACT FILE

Founded as Lymington & New Milton: 1998
Nickname: Linnets
Sponsors: Sewards
Colours: Red & blue stripes/blue/red
Change colours: Yellow /green/green
Midweek Matches: Tuesday
Reserves ' League: Wessex Comb

Programme: 48 pages, £1.00
Editor/Press Officer: Richard Milbery

CLUB PERSONNEL

Chairman: Terry Morris
V - Chairmen: Richard Millbery/Bob Philpott
President: Jack Holliday & Ted Goodyer

Manager: Derek Binns
Coach: Alan Farrar

MONEYFIELDS

FACT FILE

Secretary: Peter Shires, 242 Grafton Street, Mile End, Portsmouth.
Tel: 023 9264 5813(H) 023 9261 1363 (B) 077141 76138(M)

Founded:
Colours: Yellow/blue/blue.
Change: Green & white/ green/green.
Midweek Fixtures: Wednesday

Ground: Moneyfields Sports Ground, Moneyfields Avenue, Copnor, Portsmouth,Hants.
Tel: 023 9266 5260, 023 9265 2424

Capacity: 1,500   Seats: No   Cover: 100   Floodlights: No

CLUB PERSONNEL

Chairman: David Jupe
46 Kingcote Road, Waterlooville,
Hants. PO8 8QB
Tel: 01705 359571 (H)

Directions: From Southampton & the west - travel east on M27 onto A27. Take exit marked
Southsea A2030. (From east take the same exit). Head south along A2030 exit
and turn right into Tangier Road (4th right). Follow until Tangiers' PH & take next
right into Folkestone Road. Carry on into Martin Rd & club is in front of you.

Clubhouse: No   **Club Shop:** No

PORTSMOUTH ROYAL NAVY

FACT FILE
Formed: 1962
Nickname: Sailors

Secretary: Roy Newman 8 Kimpton Close, Lee-on-Solent, Hants PO13 8JY
Tel: 02392 799198 (H)

Colours: All blue
Change colours:All red

Ground: The Navy Stadium, HMS Temeraire, Burnaby Road, Portsmouth PO1 2EJ
Tel: 0239 272 4235, (Clubhouse 023 92291660)

Midweek Matches: 1st X1 Mon., Res Tues.
Reserves ' League: Wessex Combination
Programme: 50p   Editor: Roy Newman

Directions: From Portsmouth Harbour (BR), turn right onto The Hard, pass under the rail
bridge and turn left into Park Road, after approx 200yards take 1st right into
Burnaby Road. Entrance to ground 100 mtrs on the right

1999-00
Top Scorer: Jon Wallsgrove
P.o.Y.: Steve Johnson

Capacity: 1,500   Seats: 500   Cover: 500   Floodlights: Yes   Club Shop: No

CLUB PERSONNEL
Chairman: Dave Bridger
Press Officer: Jim Molloy

Clubhouse: Open 1.5hrs before k.o. & 2hrs after game on matchdays or by arrangement only

HONOURS   Russell-Cotes Cup 67-68; Basingstoke Lg Div 2; Hants Lge Div 2 67-6877-78 80-81

Manager: Mick Marsh
Physio: A Hylands

PREVIOUS   **Leagues:** Hampshire 62-86

SWANAGE TOWN & HERSTON

FACT FILE
Colours: All white
Change colours: All yellow & sky blue
Midweek matchday: Tuesday
Programme: Yes

Secretary: Eric Webster, 24 James Day Mead, Ulwell Road, Swanage BH191NQ
Tel: 01929 423522 (H & Fax)

Ground: Days Park, off De Moulham Road, Swanage, Dorset BH19   Tel: 01929 424633

Directions: A35 to Wareham - at roundabout on the Wareham bypass take the A351 to Corfe
Castle & Swanage, bear left for the beach and town, along Victoria Avenue, until
traffic lights - cross over lights, first turning on left before the seafront, into De
Moulham Road. Carry on into North Beach car park, enter car park and turn left
into ground.

CLUB PERSONNEL

Chairman: Len Marsh
204D High Street, Swanage,
Dorset BH19 2PQ
Tel: 0129 424152

Capacity: Cover: Yes   Floodlights: Yes
Clubhouse: Yes
Previous League: Dorset Combination

President: Mayor of Swanage

THATCHAM TOWN

Football Secretary: Peter Woodage, 5 Elm Grove, Thatcham, Berks. RG18 3DJ
Tel: 01635 861937

Ground: Waterside Park, Crookham Rd, Thatcham, Berks Tel: 01635 862016

Capacity: 3,000   Seats: 300   Cover: 300   Floodlights: Yes

Directions: M4 junc 13, take A34 to Newbury, then left onto A4 towards Reading
InThatcham turn right to the railway station. The ground is on the left
beyond the station - 2 minutes walk.From South A34 to Newbury,take A339 to Basingstoke,left to
Thatcham then left again down Crookham Rd. Ground on right just before station

Clubhouse: Open every evening & lunchtimes   **Club Shop:** Yes

HONOURS Wessex Lg 95-96,R-up 98-99, Cup 90-91 91-92 94-95 96-97, (R-up twice)

PREVIOUS Ground: Station Road 46-52; Lancaster Close 52-92

BEST SEASON **FA Cup:** 4th Qual Rd 96-97

RECORD **Attendnace:** 1,400 v Aldershot, FA Vase

FACT FILE

Founded: 1895
Sponsors: Panasonic Gsm Mobile Phones
Colours: Blue & white stripes/blue/blue
Change colours:Red,black,black
Midweek Matches: Tuesday
Programme: 28 pages, 50p
Editor: Les Wiunkworth

CLUB PERSONNEL

Chairman: Phil Holdway
General Secretary: John Haines
Press Officer: Phil Holdway (*01635 867803)
Manager:Neil Baker
Coach:Jason Braidwood

WHITCHURCH UNITED

Secretary: Miss J.C.Cozzi, 39 Hartley Meadow, Whitchurch,Hants RG26 892579(H)

Ground: Longmeadow, Winchester Road, Whitchurch Tel: 01256 892493

Directions: From Whitchurch (BR) station; turn left after Railway Inn, follow road to end, turn
right into main road, arriving in town turn left alongWinchester Road. Ground three
quarters of a mile on left

Capacity: Seats: 200   Cover: Yes   Floodlights: Yes

Clubhouse: Hot food on matchdays. Sports hall with squash courts and indoor bowling green

PREVIOUS **Leagues:** Hampshire (pre-1992)

BEST SEASON **FA Vase:** Extra-Preliminary Rd 93-94, 1-3 v Peppard (H)

FACT FILE

Founded: 1903
Colours: Red &white/black/black
Change colours: White/blue/blue.
Midweek Matches: Tuesday
Programme: 24 pages

CLUB PERSONNEL

Chairman: Dave Maguire (Tel: 02380261637)

WIMBORNE TOWN

Secretary: Stephen Churchill, 40 Dales Drive, Wimborne, Dorset BH21 2JT
Tel: 01202 889806 (H), 01202 564835 (B), 07980 886607(Mob)

Ground: The Cuthbury, Cowgrove Road, Wimborne, Dorset BH21 4EL Tel: 01202 884821
Capacity: 3,250   Seats: 275   Cover: 150   Floodlights: Yes
Directions: Wimborne to Blandford Road, behind Victoria Hospital
Clubhouse: Eves 7-11, Sat noon-11, Sun 12-6 Bar & Skittle alley   **Club Shop:** Yes
HONOURS FA Vase 91-92; Wessex Lg 91-92 93-94 ,99-00(R-up 92-93 96-97), Lg Cup 93-94,99-
00 (R-up 90-91 95-96); Dorset Lg Div 1 80-81 81-82 (R-up 38-39 72-73), Div 2 31-32 34-35 36-
37(R-up 35-36), Lg Cup R-up (4) 72-74 80-82; Dorset Snr Cup 91-92 96-97, (R-up 80-82 85-86
98-99,99-00); Mark Frowde Cup 92-93 94-95; Dorset Snr Amateur Cup 36-37 63-64;Dorset Jnr
Cup 31-32 36-37 (R-up 13-14 34-35); Dorset Minor Cup 12-13; Dorset Jnr Amateur Cup (3) 34-36
38-39; Bankes Charity Cup 89-90 94-95 95-96, TexacoF/Light Cup 90-91
PREVIOUS **Leagues:** Dorset Lge, Dorset Comb, Western 81-86
BEST SEASON **FA Vase:** Winners 91-92   **FA Cup:** 1st Rd Proper 82-83
RECORDS **Attendance:** 3,250 v Bamberbridge FA Vase Semi-Final 28/3/92
Goalscorer: Jason Lovell   **Win** (Wessex Lg): 9-0 v E.Cowes V 98-99, Brockenhurst 99-00
Appearances: James Sturgess **Defeat** (Wessex Lg): 2-6 v Thatcham Town 91-92
Fee paid: £5,500 for J P Lovell (Bashley, 1992)
Fee received: £6,000; for J P Lovell (Bashley, 1989) & for Tommy Killick(Dorchester, 1993)

FACT FILE
Founded: 1878   Nickname: Magpies
Sponsors: Nicolas O'Hara
Colours: Black & white stripes/black/black
Change colours: Yellow/green/yellow
Midweek Matches: Tuesday
Reserve League: Wessex Combination
Programme: 24 pages, 50p
Editor: Secretary
1999-00 Captain: Danny Robbins
Top Scorer: Darren Elmes
P.o.Y.: Darren Powell

CLUB PERSONNEL
Chairman: Nicholas O'Hara
President: Brian Maidment
Press Officer: Secretary
Manager: Alex Pike
Asst, Mgr: Mike Buxton
Coach: Tommy Killick
Physio: Irvin Brown

HAMPSHIRE FOOTBALL LEAGUE
Established: 1896

Chairman: G Cox

Secretary: I J Craig
56 Ecton Lane, Anchorage Park, Hilsea, Portsmouth PO3 5TA
Tel/Fax: 02392 671155

League Development Officer: J Moody

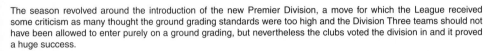

The season revolved around the introduction of the new Premier Division, a move for which the League received some criticism as many thought the ground grading standards were too high and the Division Three teams should not have been allowed to enter purely on a ground grading, but nevertheless the clubs voted the division in and it proved a huge success.

The Premier Division Championship was not decided until the last game of the season when Locks Heath threw away a chance to write their name in the history books by losing 1-0 at Hayling United despite hitting the woodwork four times and missing a penalty. Their lack of points gifted the title to Amesbury Town, who had stayed at the top of the table for three weeks waiting for the others to catch them, but the four sides below (who could all have won the Championship), Locks Heath, Pirelli General, West Wight Mayflower and Blackfield & Langley all took points off each other. The only team to take consolation from losing out on the title were third placed Blackfield & Langley, who won promotion to the Jewson Wessex League, changing places with East Cowes Victoria Athletic who dropped down to the Hampshire League.

Losing out on further Premier competition were Romsey Town who finished bottom and Hayling United, who were relegated due to the fact that the club failed to obtain the required ground grading for season 2000-01. All of the previous Division Three clubs retained their Premier status.

The Division One Championship also went to the wire with Poole Town triumphing over Vosper Thornycroft with both Fleetlands and Winchester City in with a chance of the title until the last few games of the season. The top two were promoted with Poole Town expecting to move back to their ancestral home at Poole Stadium which they left in 1994 whilst still in the Southern League.

Four sides were relegated from Division One in accordance with the League's plans to equalise the Divisions a1 and 2 and Overton United, Ordnance Survey, Bishopstoke Social and Otterbourne were the unlucky four.

Micheldever Village won the Division Three Championship in their first season in the League and AFC Portchester gained promotion to Division One as runners-up. Dropping out of the Hampshire League were Braishfield who finished bottom of Division Two, and they will compete in the Southampton Premier Division next season and Basing Rovers who withdrew from the League during the season. Alresford Town (Champions of the North Hants Senior League) and Fareham Sacred Heart (Champions of the Portsmouth Premier League) were promoted to fill the vacancies.

Colden Common Reserves won the Combination Division Championship by a mile, for the second season in succession, and nearly pulled off a League and Cup double but were unfortunately expelled from the semi-final for playing an ineligible player, a mistake brought to the League's notice by the club itself. The Combination will play as two divisions next season with the addition of another nine teams.

Division One Fleetlands caused an upset in the Trophyman League Cup by defeating Premier Division Hayling United in the final played at Petersfield Town.

With a Wiltshire based club winning the Premier Division and a Dorset based club winning Division One, the League's planned change of name for season 2001-02 to South Shires Football League will reflect more fairly the League's geographical spread.

FINAL LEAGUE TABLES 1999-2000

PREMIER DIVISION

	P	W	D	L	F	A	Pts
Amesbury Town	42	25	7	10	117	80	82
Locksheath	42	25	5	12	90	47	80
Blackfield & Langley	42	25	4	13	108	60	79
West Wight M	42	23	8	11	91	53	77
Brading Town	42	22	7	13	84	63	73
Ringwood Town	42	21	8	13	85	69	71
New Street	42	19	13	10	90	68	70
Pirelli General*	42	20	9	13	61	63	68
Hayling United*	42	19	11	12	59	50	65
Stockbridge	42	18	10	14	87	57	64
Liss Athletic	42	18	7	17	77	72	61
Hythe & Dibden	42	17	8	17	76	82	59
Lymington Town	42	16	9	17	67	75	57
Horndean	42	17	5	20	83	82	56
Bishops Walth	42	15	9	18	65	74	54
Petersfield Town	42	14	9	19	63	80	51
Colden Common	42	15	6	21	57	74	51
AFC Basingstoke*	42	14	10	18	60	67	46
Esso (Fawley)	42	9	14	19	41	74	41
Alton Town*	42	10	5	27	74	119	32
AFC Aldermaston	42	5	9	28	48	112	24
Romsey Town	42	5	7	30	36	100	22

DIVISION ONE

	P	W	D	L	F	A	Pts
Poole Town	34	27	4	3	108	41	85
Vosper Thornycroft	34	26	4	4	109	41	82
Fleetlands	34	23	5	6	88	37	74
Winchester City	34	22	3	9	93	54	69
Fleet Spurs	34	18	9	7	85	47	63
Clanfield	34	16	6	12	79	50	54
Winchester Castle	34	15	7	12	63	56	52
Paulsgrove	34	16	4	14	65	61	52
AC Delco	34	15	6	13	68	53	51
Verwood Town	34	9	8	17	54	67	35
Yateley Green	34	9	8	17	60	92	35
Hilsea	34	9	7	18	58	76	34
Co-op Sports	34	8	10	16	42	69	34
Tadley Town	34	10	4	20	51	81	34
Otterbourne	34	8	8	18	54	89	32
Bishopstoke	34	8	7	19	46	80	31
Ordnance Survey	34	8	7	19	42	84	31
Overton United	34	3	5	26	32	115	14

DIVISION TWO

	P	W	D	L	F	A	Pts
Micheldever	24	17	3	4	57	24	54
Portchester	24	15	6	3	51	21	51
Farnborough NE	24	14	2	8	69	38	44
Laverstock & Fd	24	13	4	7	66	49	43
Hedge End	24	12	5	7	64	37	41
Hamble Club	24	11	7	6	54	38	40
Hadleigh	24	12	4	8	48	38	40
Awbridge	24	8	6	10	36	44	30

	P	W	D	L	F	A	Pts
Queens Keep	24	9	3	12	47	59	30
Broughton	24	6	4	14	31	56	22
Netley Central	24	5	4	15	31	65	19
Compton	24	4	2	18	35	76	14
Braishfield	24	3	4	17	22	68	13
Basing Rovers			Resigned, record expunged				

* Points deducted

TROPHYMAN LEAGUE CUP 1999-2000

QUARTER FINALS

Hayling United	v	Lymington Town	3-0		AFC Portchester	v	Blackfield & Langley	1-3
Fleetlands	v	Horndean	1-0		Vosper Thornycroft	v	AFC Basingstoke	2-3

SEMI FINALS

Fleetlands	v	AFC Basingstoke	2-1		Hayling United	v	Blackfield & Langley	3*1

FINAL

Hayling United	v	Fleetlands	3-2		at Petersfield Town FC

TROPHYMAN COMBINATION CUP 1999-2000

QUARTER FINALS

AC Delco Res	v	Liss Athletic Res	2-1		Fleet Spurs Res	v	Pirelli General Res	1-2
Co-op Sports Res	v	Laverstock & F Rs	1-1, 3p2		Hayling United Res	v	Winchester C Rs	1-1, 3p4

SEMI FINALS

Co-op Sports Res	v	Winchester City Res	0-1		AC Delco Res	v	Pirelli General Res	2-1

FINAL

AC Delco Res	v	Winchester City Res	2-2		AC Delco Reserves won 4-3 on penalties.
					Played at Alton Town FC

AFC ALDERMASTON
Secretary: Christine Collier, 14 Brackenwood Drive, Tadley, Hants RG26 4YB (H 0118 9811947   B 01256 363344)
Ground: AWRE Aldermaston Recreation Society, Aldermaston, Reading RG7 4PR (0118 9824544)
Colours: Blue/white/white
Change: Yellow/blue/white

AFC BASINGSTOKE
Secretary: A Blenkarn, 1a Chestnut House, 2 Fairfields Rd, Basingstoke RG21 3DR (01256 332691)
Ground: Batts Meadow, Laverstoke Lane, Basingstoke, Hants
Colours: Blue & black stripes/black/black
Change: Red/white/white

ALTON TOWN
Secretary: A J M Hillman, 19a Beechwood Rd, Alton, Hants GU34 1RL (H 01420 87103   B 01420 541177 ext 2362)
Ground: Bass Spts Ground, Anstey Rd, Alton (01420 82564)
Colours: Black & white/black/black
Change: Red & black/white/white

BISHOPS WALTHAM TOWN
Secretary: J Bailey, 46 Claylands Rd., Bishops Waltham, Southampton SO32 1BH (H 01489 894888   M 07901 885673)
Ground: Priory Pk, Elizabeth Way, Bishops Waltham (01489 894269)
Colours: Red & black/black/red & black
Change: Yellow & black/yellow/yellow & black

BLACKFIELD & LANGLEY
Secretary: D Sangster, 3 Fir Trees Grove, Butts Ash Lane, Hythe, Southampton SO45 3RA (H 02380 844911   B 02380 313721)
Ground: Gang Warily Rec., Newlands Rd, Blackfield, Southampton, Hants (02380 893603)
Colours: White/green/green
Change: Red/blue/blue

BRADING TOWN
Secretary: D Munday, 67 Howgate Rd, Bembridge, Isle of Wight PO35 5QU (H 01983 875033   B 0207 4523401)
Ground: Vicarage Lane, Brading, Isle of Wight (01983 405217)
Colours: Red & white/red/red
Change: All yellow

COLDEN COMMON
Secretary: M.Budden, 44 Orchard Close, Colden Common, Winchester. SO21 1ST (H 01962 713813   B 02380 613151   M 0411 186032)
Ground: Colden Common Recreation Ground, Main Road, Colden Common, Winchester (01962 712365)
Colours: Red & white stripes/black/red
Change: All navy or green & white/green & white/green

EAST COWES VICTORIA ATHLETIC
Secretary: J Stone, 99 High Park Rd, Ryde, Isle of Wight PO33 1BZ (H 01983 565269   M 07970 009901   email: John@Stoners.demon.co.uk
Ground: Beatrice Avenue, Whippingham, East Cowes, Isle of Wight (01983 297615)
Colours: Red/black/white
Change: Tangerine/navy/green

ESSO (FAWLEY)
Secretary: S Amos, 14 Burley Down, Chandlers Ford, Southampton SO53 4NR (H 02380 255721   B 02380 895300)
Ground: Esso Recreation Club, Long Lane, Holbury, Southampton, Hants (02380 893750)
Colours: All red
Change: All blue

HORNDEAN
Secretary: M Austin, 22 Abbas Green, Havant, Hants PO9 4EP (H 02392 645335   M 07710 203302   B 02392 783556   email: michaelaustin@horndeanfc.fsnet.co.uk)
Ground: Five Heads Park, Five Heads Road, Horndean, PO8 9NZ (02392 591363)
Colours: Red & black stripes/black/red
Change: Blue & white stripes/blue/blue

HYTHE & DIBDEN
Secretary: Mr A Moyst, 105 Hobart Drive, Hythe, Southampton, Hants SO40 6FD (H 02380 847335)
Ground: Ewart Recreation Ground, Jones Lane, Hythe, Southampton (02380 845264)
Colours: Green & white/white/green
Change: All blue

LISS ATHLETIC
Secretary: N Noble, 11 Southdown View, Waterlooville, Hants PO7 6BJ (H 02392 240795   M 0778 7506086   B 01428 654941)
Ground: Newman Collard PF, Hillbrow Rd, Liss, Hants (01730 894022)
Colours: 1st XI All blue, 2nd XI All green
Change: Reverse as above

LOCKSHEATH
Secretary: P Smith, 20 Wildrose Crescent, Locksheath, Hants SO31 6TG (H 01489 602256   B 02392 337209)
Ground: Locksheath Rec, Warsash Rd, Titchfield Common, Eastleigh (01489 600932)
Colours: Red/black/red
Change: All yellow

LYMINGTON TOWN
Secretary: D Webb, Little Compton, Pless Road, Lymington, Hants SO41 0MY (01590 644629   email: DWebb47470@aol.com)
Ground: Sports Ground, Southampton Rd, Lymington, Hants (01590 671305)
Colours: Red/white/red & white
Change: Black & white/black/black

NEW STREET
Secretary: J Dunn, Foxcotte Park, Charlton, Andover SP11 0HS (Tel & Fax 01264 358358)
Ground: Foxcotte Park, Charlton Down, Andover.(01264 358358)
Colours: Green & black/black/green
Change: Orange/white/orange

PETERSFIELD TOWN
Secretary: M Nicholl, 49 Durford Rd, Petersfield, Hants GU31 4ER (H 01730 300518   B 01730 234133)
Ground: Love Lane, Petersfield, Hants GU31 4BW (01730 233416)
Colours: Red & Black/Black/Black
Change: Green/white/white

PIRELLI GENERAL
Secretary: Mrs V Tuck, 47 Gurnays Mead, West Wellow, Southampton SO51 6BP (H 01794 322168)
Ground: Jubilee Spts Ground, Chestnut Ave., Eastleigh (02380 612725)
Colours: Blue & white hoops/blue/blue
Change: Yellow & black/black/black

POOLE TOWN
Secretary: Bill Read, 15 Addison Close, Romsey, Hants SO51 7TL (01794 517969)
Ground: Haskells Rec Ground, off Ringwood Rd, Newtown, Poole
Colours: Red & white halves/red/white
Change Colours: Navy & white/white/red or white

RINGWOOD TOWN
Secretary: Mrs S Crewe, 278 Windham Rd., Bournemouth BH1 4QU (Tel & Fax: 01202 398975)
Ground: Long Lane, Ringwood BH24 3BX (01425 473448)
Colours: Red/white/red
Change: All blue

STOCKBRIDGE
Secretary: Robin Smith, Curlews Farm, Quarley, Andover, Hants (H 01980 629781   B 01264 773545)
Ground: The Recreation Ground, High Street, Stockbridge, Hants
Colours: All red
Change: Yellow & green/green/green

Premier Division continued.

VOSPER THORNYCROFT
Secretary: Peter Prinn, 454 Bursledon Road, Sholing, Southampton, Hants. SO19 8QQ (M 0589 225596)
Ground: Vosper Thornycroft Spts Ground, Portsmouth Rd, Sholing, Southampton(02380 403829)
Colours: Navy/tangerine/jade
Change: All purple with white trim

WEST WIGHT MAYFLOWER
Secretary: Mr C J Papadatos, 5 Albion Close, Portchester, Fareham, Hants PO16 9EW (H 01329 510623 B 02392 722709)
Ground: Camp Rd, Freshwater, Isle of Wight PO34 9HL (01983 754780)
Colours: Blue & black stripes/black/black
Change: Yellow/green/yellow

HAMPSHIRE LEAGUE DIVISION ONE

A.C. DELCO
Secretary: Dominic Freeman, 63 Bassett Green Rd, Southampton SO16 3DW (H 02380 559352 M 0402 211897 B 02380 375219)
Ground: AC Delco Sports Ground, Stoneham Lane, Eastleigh (02380 613334)
Colours: Orange/black/orange
Change: All blue or green & white/green/white

AFC PORTCHESTER
Secretary: C Brans, 2 Eden Rise, Fareham, Hants PO16 0UL (H 01329 311560 B 07980 799280)
Ground: Portchester Community School, White Hart Lane, Portchester (02392 364399)
Colours: Flourescent lime & black/black/blac/
Change: Black & white stripes/black/white

AMESBURY TOWN
Secretary: Peter Taylor, Virginia House, Coldharbour, Amesbury, Wilts. SP4 7AH (H 01980 623212 M 0831 241738)
Ground: Recreation Ground, Amesbury, Wilts (01980 623489)
Colours: Blue & white
Change: Yellow

CLANFIELD
Secretary: S Wallis, 42 Glamorgan Rd, Catherington, Waterlooville, Hants PO8 0TR (H 02392 570231 (T & F) M 0802 735627
B 02392 219230 email: swalliscfc@bigfoot.com)
Ground: Peel Park, Charlton Lane, Clanfield
Colours: Blue & black stripes/black/black
Change: Yellow & sky blue stripes/yellow/yellow

CO-OP SPORTS
Secretary: B R Campbell, 61 Bramshott Rd, Milton, Portsmouth, Hants PO4 8AW (H 02392 647479 B 02392 736846 F 02392 432933)
Ground: Langstone College, Furze Lane, off Locksway Rd, Milton, Portsmouth (01705 824798)
Colours: Yellow & navy/navy/navy
Change: Blue & black, black, black

FLEETLANDS
Secretary: David Bell, 72 White Hart Lane, Portchester, Hants. PO16 9BQ.(H 02392 321781 M 0772 0008262)
Ground: Lederle Lane, Gosport, Hants (01329 239723)
Colours: Red & black/black/black
Change: All white

FLEET SPURS
Secretary: S Houghton 2A The Cedars, Fleet, Hants, GU13 9YL (H 01252 815463 M 0966 225446)
Ground: Kennels Lane, Southwood, Farnborough, Hants
Colours: Red & blue/blue/red
Change: Yellow/green/yellow

HAYLING UNITED
Secretary: Mrs S Westfield, L'Ancresse, 14 Harolds Rd, Hayling Island, PO11 9LT (H 02392 463305 M 07803 881501
email: shirl-west@cwcom.net
Ground: Hayling SC, Mengham Pk, Hayling Island, Hants (02392 463359)
Colours: Black & white stripes/black/black
Change: All red

HILSEA
Secretary: S Cobb, GFF, 18 Gladys Ave, North End, Portsmouth PO2 9BE (H 02392 792825 M 0771 4042280 B 02392 286733)
Ground: Langstone Harbour Sports Ground, Eastern Rd, Portsmouth
Colours: Yellow/blue/white
Change: Sky blue/white/sky blue

PAULSGROVE
Secretary: P Lipscombe, 5 Braunston Close, Paulsgrove, Portsmouth PO6 4EN (H 07901 651435)
Ground: The Grove Club, Marsden Rd (off Allaway Ave), Paulsgrove, Portsmouth (02392 324102)
Colours: All blue
Change: Red/black/red

ROMSEY TOWN
Secretary: Andy Spreadbury, 13 Tanners Road, North Baddesley Southampton SO52 9FD (H 02380 739034 M 07940 291544)
Ground: The By-Pass Ground, South Front, Romsey (01794 512003)
Colours: Yellow & black stripes/black/yellow
Change: All red

TADLEY TOWN
Secretary: S Blackburn, 7 Bramdean Close, Tadley, Hants RG26 3RD (H 0118 9816697 M 07880 770899 B 01256 342102
email: tadley.townfc@virgin.net
Ground: The Green, Tadley, Hants
Cols: Yellow & blue/blue/yellow & blue
Change: Burgundy or blue/burgundy/burgundy

VERWOOD TOWN
Secretary: Mrs J A Fry, 19a Noon Hill Rd, Verwood, Dorset BH31 7DB (01202 822826)
Ground: Potterne Park, Potterne Way, Verwood, Dorset
Colours: White with red & black/red/red
Change: Gold or red/black/black

WINCHESTER CASTLE
Secretary: A J Rutter, 31 Whistler Close, Basingstoke, Hants RG21 3HN (J 01256 350922 B 01256 493004
email: therutters@talk21.com)
Ground: Hants County Council Spts Ground, A31, Petersfield Rd, Chilcomb, Winchester (01962 866989)
Colours: Red & black/black/red
Change: Yellow & blue/yellow/yellow

WINCHESTER CITY
Secretary: D Rattey, 21 Cozens Close, Woolston, Southampton SO19 9TU (Tel & Fax 02380 420859 M 07909 521213)
Ground: The City Ground, Hillier Way, Abbotts Barton, Winchester (01962 863553)
Colours: Red & black stripes/black/black
Change: Yellow & blue/blue/yellow

YATELEY GREEN
Secretary: Alan Baynes, 7 Borderside, Yateley, Hants GU46 6LJ (H 01252 409703 M 0780 3155890 email: askjbaynes@aol.com)
Ground: Sean Deveraux Park, Chandlers Lane Playing Fields, Chandlers Lane, Yateley Hants
Colours: Green/blue/green
Change: All blue

DIVISION TWO CLUBS
ALRESFORD TOWN, AWBRIDGE, BISHOPSTOKE SOCIAL, BROUGHTON FC, COMPTON, FAREHAM SACRED HEARTS, FARNBOROUGH NORTH END, HADLEIGH, HAMBLE CLUB, HEDGE END, LAVERSTOCK & FORD, MICHELDEVER VILLAGE, NETLEY CENTRAL SPORTS, ORDNANCE SURVEY, OTTERBOURNE, OVERTON UNITED, QK SOUTHAMPTON

KEYLINE DORSET COMBINATION LEAGUE

Founded: 1957

President: J Cruickshank   **Chairman:** R E Maidment

Secretary: Geoff Theobald, 41 South Road, Corfe Mullen
Wimborne, Dorset BH21 3HZ   Tel: 01202 697994

The chase for League Championship honours once again proved to be a two horse race, this time between Dorchester Town FC Reserves and Portland United FC. The destination of the League Trophy was not decided until the very last game of the season, and in the end it was Portland who retained the Championship by a 3 point margin from Dorchester Town Reserves, with Swanage Town & Herston and Hamworthy Engineering in third and fourth places respectively.

At the other end of the table, newcomers, Witchampton United found life in the Combination League difficult, recording only 2 League wins throughout the season. One of those being at the Avenue Stadium, Dorchester. However, Bournemouth Sports, gaining only 9 points, finished in bottom place, only retaining League membership when Swanage Town & Herston FC were accepted into the Jewson Wessex League for the 2000/01 season.

The Combination Cup Final, played at Days Park, Swanage, in front of a crowd in excess of 400 people, was contested by Gillingham Town and Portland United Football Clubs. An excellent match saw Portland United win by 4 goals to 3 after extra-time. This victory gave the 'Blues' a hat-trick of Cup wins and also a League and Cup double, a feat they also accomplished last season..

The Representative squads under managers Barry Lawley - Portland United FC (Senior) and Stuart Gill/Terry White - Swanage Town & Herston FC (Under 21) performed well. The Seniors losing to the Wiltshire League 1 - 0 at Shaftesbury, and beating the Bournemouth FA 3 - 1 at Downton. Under 21s losing to the Bournemouth FA 2 - 0 at Swanage.

Geoff Theobald, Hon Secretary

FINAL LEAGUE TABLE 1999-2000

		P	W	D	L	F	A	Pts
1	Portland United	36	27	5	4	100	30	86
2	Dorchester Town	36	27	2	7	101	38	83
3	Swanage Town & H	36	23	7	6	82	32	76
4	Hamworthy Eng.	36	23	3	10	115	67	72
5	Parley Sports*	36	23	5	8	100	59	68
6	Gillingham Town	36	17	8	11	87	70	59
7	Blandford United	36	17	7	12	65	43	58
8	Hamworthy United	36	16	8	12	63	54	56
9	Westland Sports	36	16	7	13	72	73	55
10	Flight Refuelling	36	15	9	12	84	65	54
11	Bridport	36	16	6	14	62	50	54
12	Allendale	36	14	9	13	66	55	51
13	Wareham Rangers	36	11	8	1	51	69	41
14	Sturminster Newton	36	12	4	20	61	65	40
15	Weymouth Sports	36	9	7	20	53	90	34
16	Sherborne Town	36	8	9	19	40	91	33
17	Shaftesbury	36	6	4	26	40	90	22
18	Witchampton United	36	2	5	29	26	122	11
19	Bournemouth Sports	36	2	3	3	35	140	9

* points deducted

LEADING GOALSCORERS 1999-2000

Crispin Rigler	Hamworthy Eng.	33	Kieran Campbel	Hamworthy United	13
Christian Chambers	Gillingham Town	25	Simon Hobbs	Parley Sports	13
Jamie Reeve	Portland United	25	Rick Hooley	Hamworthy Eng.	13
Darren Vye	Flight Refuelling	23	Jon Marvin	Flight Refuelling	13
Mark Gaskel	Swanage Town & H	21	Andrew Southern	Dorchester Town	13
Keith Middleton	Dorchester Town	21	Danny King	Parley Sports	12
	(includes 3 for Hamworthy Utd)			*(includes 4 for Bournemouth S)*	
Paul Honeybun	Flight Refuelling	18	Simon McClellan	Gillingham Town	12
Jamie Moores	Hamworthy Eng.	18	Ossie Onuorah	Parley Sports	12
Aaron Turner	Hamworth Eng.	16	Chris Smith	Swanage Town & Hersham	12
Alan Etherton	Sturminster Newton	15	Lee Stebbings	Weymouth Sports	12
Nick Johnson	Allendale	15		*(includes 3 for Portland Utd)*	
Wesley O'Connor	Blandford United	15	Rob Taylor	Dorchester Town	12
Mick Greeno	Portland United	14	Stacey White	Westland Sports	12
Kieron Howes	Weymouth Sports	14	David Dick	Swanage Town & Hersham	11
Gary Manson	Blandford United	14	Sam Merison	Wareham Rangers	11
Steven McDaid	Westland Sports	14	Mike Trim	Gillingham Town	11

COMBINATION LEAGUE CUP 1999-2000

FIRST ROUND

Shaftesbury	v	Allendale	3*3, 2-1	Sherborne Town	v	Blandford United	2*1
Weymouth Sports	v	Flight Refuelling	2-1				

SECOND ROUND

Bridport	v	Hamworthy United	7-0	Gillingham Town	v	Dorchester Town	5-0
Hamworthy Eng.	v	Parley Sports	2-3	Shaftesbury	v	Sherborne T	1*1, 3-1
Sturminster Newton	v	Wareham Rangers	4-1	Swanage T & H	v	Bournemouth S	S W/O
Westland Sports	v	Portland United	1-3	Witchampton Utd	v	Weymouth Sports	2-3

THIRD ROUND

Portland United	v	Sturminster Newton	1-0	Shaftesbury	v	Parley Sports	2-3
Swanage T & H	v	Bridport	0-1	Weymouth Sports	v	Gillingham Town	2-3

SEMI FINALS

Parley Sports	v	Gillingham Town	2*4	Portland United	v	Bridport	2-1

FINAL

Portland United	v	Gillingham Town	4*3

PREVIOUS RECORDS

	Combination League			Combination Cup	
	Champions	*Runners Up*		*Champions*	*Runners Up*
1999-00	Portland United	Dorchester Town Res		Portland United	Gillingham Town
1998-99	Portland United	Parley Sports		Portland United	Parley Sports
1997-98	Sturminster Marshall	Portland United		Portland United	Westland Sports
1996-97	Shaftesbury	Bournemouth Sports		Bournemouth Sports	Hamworthy Engineering
1995-96	Hamworthy Eng.	Bridport Reserves		Sturminster Newton	Sherborne Town
1994-95	Hamworthy Eng.	Bournemouth Sports		Shaftesbury	Hamworthy Engineering
1993-94	Hamworthy Eng.	Westland Sports		Westland Sports	Sherborne Town
1992-93	Westland Sports	Sherborne Town		Westland Sports	Portland United
1991-92	Blandford United	Westland Sports		Dorchester Town	Parley Sports
1990-91	Dorchester Town R	Flight Refuelling		Flight Refuelling	Dorchester Town Res.
1989-90	Weymouth Res.	Flight Refuelling		Hamworthy Utd	Wareham Rangers
1988-89	Shaftesbury	Westland Sports		Shaftesbury	Portland United
1987-88	Bridport	Flight Refuelling		Bridport	Shaftesbury
1986-87	Bridport	Parley Sports		Bridport	Parley Sports
1985-86	Bridport	Parley Sports		Parley Sports	Flight Refuelling

ALLENDALE
Chairman: E Case (01202 887920 H, 01258 857191 B)

Secretary: Rod Pope, 51 Dalkeith Road, Corfe Mullen Wimborne, BH21 3PQ (01202602922 H, 01929 424601 B)

Ground: Redcotts Recreation Ground, School Lane, Wimborne

Colours: White/blue/blue   Change Colours: All red

GILLINGHAM TOWN
Chairman: E Murphy
Secretary: David J Ayles, 37 Sylvan Way, Bay Road, Gillingham SP8 4EQ (01747822065)
Ground: Hardings Lane, Gillingham (01747 823673)
Cover: Yes
Programme: Yes   Clubhouse: Yes
Colours: Tangerine/black/tangerine
Change colours: Yellow & green/green/green

BLANDFORD UNITED
Chairman:M.Westwood
Secretary: Mrs Catherine Johnson, 37 Damory Street,Blandford Forum, Dorset DT117EU (01258 455899)
Ground: Recreation Ground, Park Road, Blandford Forum, Dorset. (HQ Tel: 01258456374)
Cover: No   Clubhouse: No   Programme: Yes
Colours: All Royal Blue
Change colours: Red/black/green

HAMWORTHY RECREATION
Chairman: M,Robson
Secretary: Ray Willis ,52 Heckford Road, Poole BH15 2LY (01202 773 290)
Ground: Hamworthy Rec. Club, Magna Rd, Canford Magna, Wimborne, Dorset BH21 3AE(01202 881922)
Cover: No   Clubhouse: Yes   Programme: No
Colours: All green.
Change colours: Blue & White stripes/blue/blue.

BOURNEMOUTH SPORTS CLUB
Chairman: I.Hansford

Secretary: Mrs June Johnson,19 Lawns Road, Wimborne,. Bh21 2JP Tel No: 01202 887195
Ground: Chapel Gate, East Parley, Christchurch, Dorset BH23 6BD (01202 581933)
Cover: No   Clubhouse: Yes   Programme: Yes
Colours: Gold/black/gold   Change colours: All blue

HAMWORTHY UNITED
Chairman: D.Manuel
Secretary: Peter Gallop, 51A Symes Road, Hamworthy, Poole, Dorset BH15 4PR(01202 670792)
Ground: The County Ground, Blandford Close, Hamworthy, Poole, Dorset (01202674974)
Cover: Yes   Floodlights: Yes
Programme: Yes   Clubhouse: Yes
Colours: Maroon & Sky Blue stripes/maroon/maroon
Change colours:Yellow & black stripes/black/black

BRIDPORT Reserves

Chairman: David Fowler
Secretary: Keith Morgan, 95 Orchard Crescent, Bridport DT6 5HA 01308 456142 (H) 01308 424 269 (W)
Ground: The Beehive, St Mary's Field, Bridport, Dorset (01308 423834)
Colours: Red & black/black/red & black
Change colours:All blue.

PARLEY SPORTS

Chairman: S.Milne
Secretary: Gail Williams, 64b Mallard Road,Strouden Park, Bournemouth BH8 9PL
Ground: Parley Sports Club, Christchurch, West Parley, Bournemouth, Dorset(01202 573345)
Cover: No   Clubhouse: Yes
Colours: Yellow/blue/blue   Change colours: Blue/white/blue.

DORCHESTER TOWN Reserves
Chairman: C E Clarke
Secretary: David Martin, 21 Diggory Crescent, Dorchester DT1 2SP
      Tel: 01305 262345 (H) 07971 172795 (M)
Ground: The Avenue Stadium, Dorchester. (01305 262451)
Cover: Yes   Floodlights: Yes   Clubhouse: Yes
Programme: Yes
Colours: Black & white stripes/black/black
Change: All red.

PORTLAND UNITED
Chairman: P.Laming
Secretary: David Naerger, 5 Three Yards Close, Portland Tel Nos: 01305 821553 (H) 01305 768888 (W)
Ground: New Grove Corner, Grove Road, Portland (01305 861489)
Cover: Yes   Clubhouse: Yes
Programme: Yes
Colours: All blue   Change colours: Red & White/black/red

FLIGHT REFUELLING
Chairman: A Miles
Secretary: Harry W Doyle, 27 Fairview Crescent, Broadstone, Poole BH18 9AL Tel: 01202 698393 (H) 07718 896211 (M)
Ground: Merley Park, Merley, Wimborne, Dorset (01202 885773)
Cover: No   Clubhouse: Yes   Programme: Yes
Colours:Sky blue/navy blue/navyblue.
Change colours: All red

SHAFTESBURY
Chairman: A.P.Humphries
Secretary: Phil Watts, 4 Willow Cottages, Compton Abbas, Shaftesbury SP70NF (01747 811037)
Ground: Cockrams, Coppice Street, Shaftesbury (01747 853990)
Cover: Yes   Floodlights: Yes   Clubhouse: Yes
Colours: Red & white striped/Red/Red
Change colours: Yellow/black/black

SHERBORNE TOWN

Chairman: F Henderson
Secretary: Mike Mock, 67 Yew TRe Close, Yeovil. BA20 2PB Tel Nos:
01935 426219 (H) 01935 703934 (W)
Ground: Raleigh Grove, The Terrace Playing Fields, Sherborne
(01935 816110)
Cover: Yes   Clubhouse: Yes   Programme: Yes
Colours: Yellow/black/yellow
Change colours: Black& white/white/black.

STOURPAINE

Chairman: C.Hardiman
Secrtary: Rob Turner, 35 Hod View, Stourpaine, BLandford DT11 8TN
Tel : 01258 451691
Ground: Dick Draper Memorial Fields, Stourpaine, Blandford Forum,
Dorset Tel: None
Previous league: Dorset County League
Colours: Navy blue & Yellow/navy blue/ yellow & navy blue.
Change Colours: Red & white stripes/red & white/red & white

STURMINSTER NEWTON UNITED

Chairman: A.Stockley
Secretary: Richard Frear 44 Green Close, Sturminster Newton DT10
1BL (01258473036)
Ground: Barnetts Field, Honeymead Lane, Sturminster Newton,
Dorset. (01258471406)
Cover: Yes   Clubhouse: No   Programme: Yes
Colours:Red & Black stripes /red/red
Change colours:Blue & Black stripes/blue/blue.

BRITAIN'S MOST POPULAR NATIONAL NON-LEAGUE FOOTBALL MONTHLY

WAREHAM RANGERS

Chairman: G.Hawkes
Secretary: Mrs Carol White, 18 Folly Lane, Wareham, Dorset BH20
4HH (01929551765)
Ground: Purbeck Sports Centre,Worgret Rd, Wareham, Dorset
Cover: No   Clubhouse: No   Programme: Yes
Colours: Amber & black/black/black
Change colours:Navy & light blue/ navy/ light blue

WESTLAND SPORTS

Chairman:A.Fisher
Secretary: Dean Vincent, 8 Whitemead, Abbey Manor Park, Yeovil.
BA21 3RX Tel NOs: 01935 479971 (H) 01935 705381 (W)
Ground: Westland Sports Ground, Westbourne Close, Yeovil (01935
703810)
Cover: No   Clubhouse: No   Programme: Yes
Colours: Red & Black/Black/Black
C hange colours: All White

WEYMOUTH SPORTS

Chairman: M.Richards
Secretary: Alan Burt, 32 Preston Road, Weymouth, DT3 6PZ
Tel Nos: 01305 833256 (H) 01305 773536 (W)
Ground: Weymouth College, Cranford Ave., Weymouth, Dorset
(01305 208859/208860)
Colours: Blue & yellow stripes/yellow/blue.
Change: Red/black/red
Prev. Lge: Dorset (champs 1993)

WINCHAMPTON UNITED

Chairman: A Wrixon
Secretary: Geoff Parnell, 28 Bovington Close, Canford Heath, Poole,
BH17 8AZ .Tel Nos: 01202 600382(H) 07976 331369 (M)
Ground: Critchell Park, Winchampton, Wimborne. Tel: 01258 840986
Colours: Yellow/green/yellow
Change Colours: Claret/navy blue/navy blue.

TeamTalk

provides comprehensive coverage of the whole spectrum of non-League football from the Nationwide Conference to County League

including extensive coverage of

§ the FA Carlsberg Vase   § the FA Umbro Trophy

§ non-League involvement in the AXA sponsored FA Cup

and the England Semi-Professional team

(Team Talk is the ONLY magazine to give such support and coverage to this England team)

SCREWFIX DIRECT
WESTERN LEAGUE

President: Rod Webber   **Chairman:** Cliff Ashton

Secretary: Ken Clarke, 32 Westmead Lane, Chippenham, Wiltshire SN15 3HZ
Tel: 01249 464467   **Fax:** 01249 652952   **Email:** westernleague@aol.com

The season was overshadowed by the sad death of League President Stan Priddle, a tireless worker for the League, and a man who was so deeply involved for many, many years.

Although the League operated with lower membership numbers – nineteen teams in the Premier Division and seventeen in the First – April showers extended the season for many clubs.

Some of the fixture backlog was caused by success, most notably that of Chippenham Town FC, who battled through to the FA Carlsberg Vase Final at Wembley. In a close encounter Chippenham Town were denied their winners' medals by a late strike from Deal.

Taunton Town again took the prestigious League Championship, but decided to forgo their chance of stepping up to the Dr Marten's Southern League, an opportunity that second placed Mangotsfield United grasped firmly. The back room staff worked as hard off the pitch, to ensure that the facilities were first class, as the team did on it.

A decision by the Management Committee not to relegate this term took some of the bite out of the last few bottom of the table skirmishes, but there was a sigh of relief from the reprieved clubs when handed the opportunity to consolidate their positions in the new campaign.

Brislington surprised some by pipping Chippenham for third place, but the majority of the other Premier Division sides ran true to form with their final placings.

The culmination of the season came at Mangotsfield's Cossham Street ground when Taunton Town met Chippenham Town in the Les Phillips (League) Cup final. Taunton could not overcome their jinx in finals, and a post Wembley Chippenham gained some comfort from their win.

In the First Division Devizes Town entered the record books by remaining unbeaten for the whole of their league run. Their impressive record attracted the attention of the media, and the modest Nursteed Road ground hosted television crews on several occasions.

Welton Rovers completed a successful season, having led Devizes for much of the campaign, finishing behind the undefeated Wiltshire side to gain promotion to the League's top flight. Keynsham Town did not live up to their early season promise and were pipped by an improving Clyst Rovers and Exmouth Town in the final placings.

With the decision not to relegate, Corsham Town and Frome Town eagerly seized the opportunity to regroup for the new season.

FINAL LEAGUE TABLES 1999-2000

PREMIER DIVISION

	P	W	D	L	F	A	Pts
Taunton Town	36	30	4	2	116	37	94
Mangotsfield United	36	23	9	4	95	31	78
Brislington	36	20	5	11	64	43	65
Chippenham Town	36	18	9	9	69	41	63
Paulton Rovers	36	16	11	9	53	34	59
Melksham Town	36	15	11	10	50	46	56
Backwell United	36	15	9	12	50	44	54
Bridport	36	12	13	11	56	56	49
Dawlish Town	36	12	11	13	51	45	47
Yeovil Town	36	11	14	11	64	63	47
Elmore	36	13	8	15	51	63	47
Bishop Sutton	36	13	4	19	51	73	43
Bideford	36	10	10	16	46	68	40
Bridgwater Town	36	10	8	18	42	53	38
Barnstaple Town	36	9	7	20	35	51	34
Westbury United	36	9	7	20	39	67	34
Bristol Manor Farm	36	8	9	19	48	78	33
Odd Down	36	9	6	21	36	82	33
Minehead	36	9	5	22	60	101	32

FIRST DIVISION

	P	W	D	L	F	A	Pts
Devizes Town	32	23	9	0	88	30	78
Welton Rovers	32	22	4	6	74	19	70
Clyst Rovers	32	19	5	8	83	38	62
Exmouth Town	32	16	9	7	67	43	57
Keynsham Town	32	16	9	7	48	34	57
Bitton	32	16	6	10	60	47	54
Torrington	32	16	6	10	62	50	54
Street	32	13	10	9	56	40	49
Larkhall Athletic	32	11	8	13	45	55	41
Wellington	32	11	7	14	46	44	40
Ilfracombe Town	32	12	2	18	59	65	38
Warminster Town	32	10	6	16	40	77	36
Calne Town	32	10	5	17	48	70	35
Pewsey Vale	32	10	2	20	50	88	32
Chard Town	32	8	7	17	31	52	31
Corsham Town	32	5	5	22	36	86	20
Frome Town	32	3	2	27	30	84	11

PREMIER DIVISION RESULTS CHART 1999-2000

		1	2	3	4	5	6	7	8	9	10	11	12	13	14	15	16	17	18	19
1	Backwell Utd	X	0-1	1-1	3-1	0-0	1-1	2-1	1-0	0-1	1-0	1-0	3-5	0-1	4-0	3-0	0-2	2-4	0-0	2-4
2	Barnstaple Town	1-2	X	1-1	1-2	2-3	1-0	1-0	2-1	0-4	0-0	0-1	0-0	1-2	5-0	0-1	1-1	0-2	4-1	3-1
3	Bideford	0-0	2-0	X	3-1	2-1	0-0	0-0	0-1	1-2	1-1	1-1	0-7	3-0	2-1	0-1	1-4	2-5	3-2	0-3
4	Bishop Sutton	1-2	1-0	2-3	X	0-0	1-0	2-0	1-3	0-4	0-3	2-2	2-3	1-1	5-2	2-0	0-2	1-2	3-2	2-2
5	Bridgwater Town	1-2	1-0	2-0	1-2	X	0-0	2-0	3-1	2-2	3-0	3-1	2-1	0-1	6-0	0-0	0-0	0-2	1-1	2-4
6	Bridport	1-1	3-2	1-1	6-2	4-1	X	4-3	5-1	0-2	2-2	3-2	0-6	3-0	3-2	3-1	2-1	2-3	2-1	1-1
7	Brislington	1-4	1-0	0-3	1-0	2-1	1-0	X	2-0	2-1	2-1	3-0	0-0	0-0	3-2	4-1	0-0	4-0	1-0	2-1
8	Bristol Manor Fm	0-0	2-3	3-2	1-2	1-0	6-1	0-4	X	2-1	0-2	3-3	1-1	1-4	4-2	5-2	1-1	1-2	1-3	0-0
9	Chippenham Tn	1-2	5-1	3-1	2-0	2-0	2-0	3-4	3-0	X	1-1	2-1	3-3	2-0	1-1	3-2	1-2	1-5	3-0	0-0
10	Dawlish Town	0-1	2-0	2-2	3-2	0-1	0-0	1-0	6-1	0-1	X	1-2	0-3	0-0	1-0	1-2	0-0	2-6	1-3	4-2
11	Elmore	3-2	1-0	0-1	3-2	4-1	0-0	0-4	0-0	1-0	0-4	X	1-1	0-0	4-2	2-0	2-1	0-4	1-2	5-2
12	Mangotsfield Utd	2-2	1-0	1-1	4-0	3-0	1-1	3-0	4-0	1-2	2-1	3-0	X	2-0	6-0	4-0	2-1	4-0	3-0	1-2
13	Melksham Town	0-3	2-2	2-0	0-2	1-0	2-1	2-1	3-0	3-3	1-1	3-1	0-2	X	2-2	2-1	0-0	1-5	4-0	4-1
14	Minehead	4-3	1-1	2-5	4-1	3-1	2-4	0-3	5-3	0-5	1-2	1-3	2-4	1-1	X	1-2	1-3	0-5	2-0	3-3
15	Odd Down	0-0	2-0	2-1	0-2	1-0	1-1	4-3	2-2	0-0	0-4	2-3	0-3	1-4		X	1-2	1-2	2-0	1-1
16	Paulton Rovers	1-0	2-1	5-1	3-2	3-1	3-0	0-2	1-1	1-1	1-0	4-1	0-0	0-2	0-2	1-0	X	1-2	4-1	2-2
17	Taunton Town	5-1	3-0	5-1	7-1	4-0	2-1	2-2	2-1	0-0	2-2	4-0	5-0	3-0	3-1	7-1	1-0	X	3-0	3-1
18	Westbury Utd	0-1	0-1	4-1	0-1	1-1	0-0	0-4	1-1	2-1	1-2	2-1	0-3	1-1	1-4	5-2	2-1	0-3	X	1-1
19	Yeovil Town	1-0	0-0	2-0	0-2	3-2	1-1	3-4	4-0	3-1	1-1	1-1	0-6	3-2	1-2	7-0	0-0	3-3	0-2	X

FIRST DIVISION RESULTS CHART 1999-2000

		1	2	3	4	5	6	7	8	9	10	11	12	13	14	15	16	17
1	Bitton	X	2-3	1-0	1-3	2-1	0-3	2-2	6-1	2-1	0-3	2-1	1-0	2-0	1-1	5-0	5-4	0-1
2	Calne Town	1-2	X	1-2	4-2	0-2	0-0	0-3	3-1	4-1	3-5	4-3	2-1	0-3	1-2	4-1	1-1	0-1
3	Chard Town	1-1	2-0	X	1-2	1-0	0-8	1-2	4-0	1-4	0-1	1-1	1-0	1-1	4-3	0-1	1-1	1-0
4	Clyst Rovers	2-2	4-1	3-0	X	9-1	2-4	2-3	3-0	4-2	0-0	1-2	6-0	3-2	0-0	4-1	0-1	0-1
5	Corsham Town	2-3	0-2	3-2	2-4	X	3-*	0-1	1-2	1-4	1-5	0-1	1-2	0-0	1-4	4-3	0-0	0-0
6	Devizes Town	3-1	2-2	4-2	1-0	4-0	X	4-1	4-3	3-2	0-0	1-1	3-0	2-2	2-1	3-1	0-0	1-0
7	Exmouth Town	2-2	7-1	3-1	0-0	3-3	1-1	X	3-0	3-1	1-2	3-1	2-3	2-1	2-2	2-2	3-2	1-0
8	Frome Town	1-2	2-2	0-0	2-3	3-0	1-2	0-4	X	1-3	2-3	0-1	0-2	0-1	0-2	0-1	0-4	1-2
9	Ilfracombe Town	1-4	1-0	2-0	3-4	3-1	1-2	1-3	3-1	X	2-2	1-0	1-1	2-3	1-2	2-3	2-1	2-4
10	Keynsham Town	1-0	2-0	1-0	0-2	2-4	1-1	0-0	2-1	2-1	X	0-1	1-3	1-2	1-1	2-1	0-1	
11	Larkhall Athletic	1-1	1-2	4-1	0-4	2-0	1-2	0-1	2-1	2-0	0-0	X	5-1	3-3	2-5	1-1	2-0	2-0
12	Pewsey Vale	0-2	1-4	2-1	0-7	4-1	1-6	1-4	2-3	3-5	2-3	4-2	X	2-2	1-3	4-1	2-1	0-2
13	Street	2-1	3-1	0-0	1-0	0-1	1-2	3-3	5-0	1-2	0-3	1-1	6-1	X	3-1	0-0	3-0	1-1
14	Torrington	2-0	2-2	0-2	0-2	2-2	2-3	1-0	3-0	3-2	1-1	4-0	3-1	1-2	X	2-1	2-0	0-4
15	Warminster Town	1-4	1-0	1-0	1-3	4-1	0-5	2-1	2-1	1-0	0-1	2-2	3-5	1-3	1-5	X	2-1	0-5
16	Wellington	1-3	3-0	2-0	2-3	2-0	0-0	2-0	5-2	0-2	0-0	0-2	3-1	0-2	2-1	1-1	X	3-1
17	Welton Rovers	2-0	7-0	0-0	1-1	2-0	0-2	2-1	4-1	3-1	3-0	7-0	3-0	1-0	6-0	7-0	3-1	X

TOP GOALSCORERS 1998-99
(League matches only)

A Lynch	Taunton Town	42
K Squire	Ilfracombe	24
N Woon	Minehead	23
L Langmead	Torrington	22
D Edwards	Mangotsfield	21
M Boyle	Mangotsfield	21
A Perrett	Welton	21
S Day	Bitton (5 for B Sutton)	17
J Babb	Clyst Rovers	17
D Kilmurray	Devizes	17
A Stansfield	Elmore	17
D Morrisey	Brislington	17

LES PHILLIPS CHALLENGE CUP 1999-2000

PRELIMINARY ROUND

Bridgwater Town	v	Welton Rovers	2-1	Melksham Town	v	Elmore	2-0
Odd Down	v	Pewsey Vale	1-2	Torrington	v	Westbury United	2-1

FIRST ROUND

Backwell United	v	Yeovil Town	3-1	Bishop Sutton	v	Bideford	0-1
Bridgwater Town	v	Minehead	0-1	Brislington	v	Bridport	4-1
Bristol Manor Farm	v	Clyst Rovers	3*3, 4p2	Chard Town	v	Frome Town	3*4
Corsham Town	v	Barnstaple Town	0-1	Devizes Town	v	Bitton	2*2, 3p2
Ilfracombe Town	v	Calne Town	3-1	Keynsham Town	v	Street	1-3
Mangotsfield United	v	Larkhall Athletic	6-0	Melksham Town	v	Torrington	3-1
Paulton Rovers	v	Chippenham Town	0-2	Pewsey Vale	v	Dawlish Town	1-6
Taunton Town	v	Exmouth Town	3-1	Warminster Town	v	Wellington	0*4

SECOND ROUND

Backwell United	v	Street	2*1	Bideford	v	Melksham Town	1-3
Brislington	v	Dawlish Town	2-1	Bristol Manor Farm	v	Chippenham Town	0-4
Ilfracombe Town	v	Barnstaple Town	3-4	Mangotsfield United	v	Devizes Town	0-3
Minehead	v	Frome Town	2-1	Taunton Town	v	Wellington	5-1

QUARTER-FINALS

Devizes Town	v	Brislington	2-4	Melksham Town	v	Backwell United	0-1
Minehead	v	Chippenham Town	0-4	Taunton Town	v	Barnstaple	3-1

SEMI-FINALS

Backwell United	v	Taunton Town	0*2	Brislington	v	Chippenham Town	1-2

FINAL

Chippenham Town	v	Taunton Town	2-1	at Mangotsfield United FC. Attendance 1,328

PREMIER DIVISION ATTENDANCES 1999-2000

	Aggregate		Average Gate		Gates over 200	
	1999-00	1998-99	1999-00	1998-99	1999-00	1998-99
Backwell United	1494	1940	83.0	102.1	-	1
Barnstaple Town	2712	3004	150.66	158.1	2	2
Bideford	2172	1692	120.66	89.05	2	2
Bishop Sutton	1292	1966	71.77	103.5	-	1
Bridgwater Town	2847	4297	158.16	226.15	1	5
Bridport	2786	2861	154.77	150.6	4	2
Brislington	1322	1768	73.44	93.05	1	1
Bristol Manor Farm	630	711	35.0	37.42	-	-
Chippenham Town	4215	5314	234.16	279.7	12	11
Dawlish Town	1465	1260	81.38	66.31	1	-
Elmore	2146	2960	81.38	155.8	1	2
Mangotsfield United	3962	3102	220.11	163.26	7	6
Melksham Town	2685	2674	149.16	140.73	2	3
Minehead Town	1137	1804	63.16	100.2	-	-
Odd Down	1181	1043	65.61	54.9	-	-
Paulton Rovers	2665	3473	148.5	182.8	2	4
Taunton Town	5892	8348	327.33	439.36	18	19
Westbury United	1513	1915	84.05	100.8	1	1
Yeovil Town	2382	2719	132.33	143.1	1	2

HIGHEST LEAGUE ATTENDANCES 1999-2000

Melksham Town	v	Chippenham	714	27.12.99
Mangotsfield Utd	v	Taunton Town	514	26.10.99
Chippenham Town	v	Melksham Town	513	24.04.00
Taunton Town	v	Mangotsfield United	451	08.04.00
Taunton Town	v	Bridgwater Town	429	18.03.00
Devizes Town	v	Welton Rovers	410	11.04.00
Mangotsfield United	v	Brislington	407	27.12.99
Taunton Town	v	Chippenham Town	406	25.09.99
Bridgwater Town	v	Taunton Town	406	25.09.99
Taunton Town	v	Yeovil Town	392	15.04.00
Taunton Town	v	Paulton Rovers	391	10.03.00

PAST RECORDS

WESTERN FOOTBALL LEAGUE CHAMPIONS

1980-81	Bridgwater Town	1990-91	Weston-super-Mare
1981-82	Bideford	1991-92	Clevedon Town
1982-83	Bideford	1992-93	Tiverton Town
1983-84	Exmouth Town	1993-94	Tiverton Town
1984-85	Saltash United	1994-95	Tiverton Town
1985-86	Exmouth Town	1995-96	Taunton Town
1986-87	Saltash United	1996-97	Tiverton Town
1987-88	Liskeard Athletic	1997-98	Tiverton Town
1988-89	Saltash United	1998-99	Taunton Town
1989-90	Taunton Town	1999-00	Taunton Town

WESTERN FOOTBALL LEAGUE FIRST DIVISION CHAMPIONS

1980-81	Chippenham Town	1990-91	Minehead
1981-82	Shepton Mallet	1991-92	Westbury United
1982-83	Bristol Manor Farm	1992-93	Odd Down
1983-84	Bristol City Reserves	1993-94	Barnstaple Town
1984-85	Portway-Bristol	1994-95	Brislington
1985-86	Portway-Bristol	1995-96	Bridgwater Town
1986-87	Swanage Town & Herston	1996-97	Melksham Town
1987-88	Welton Rovers	1997-98	Bishop Sutton
1988-89	Larkhall Athletic	1998-99	Minehead
1989-90	Ottery St Mary	1999-00	Devizes Town

WESTERN FOOTBALL LEAGUE CHALLENGE CUP WINNERS

1954-55	Poole Town	1974-75	Falmouth Town
1955-56	Salisbury City	1975-76	No competition
1956-57	Trowbridge Town	1976-77	Weston-Super-Mare
1957-58	Bridgwater Town	1977-78	Bridport
1958-59	Yeovil Town	1978-79	No competition
1959-60	Torquay United	1979-80	Frome Town
1960-61	Exeter City	1980-81	Dawlish Town
1961-62	Bristol City	1981-82	Bridgwater Town
1962-65	No competition	1982-83	Frome Town
1965-66	Glastonbury	1983-84	Dawlish Town
1966-70	No competition	1984-85	Bideford
1970-71	Bridport	1985-86	Portway-Bristol
1971-72	Bideford	1986-87	Saltash United
1972-73	Bridport	1987-88	Saltash United
1973-74	Mangotsfield United		

LES PHILLIPS CHALLENGE CUP WINNERS

1988-89	Exmouth Town	1994-95	Elmore
1989-90	Plymouth Argyle Reserves	1995-96	Tiverton Town
1990-91	Elmore	1996-97	Tiverton Town
1991-92	Plymouth Argyle Reserves	1997-98	Tiverton Town
1992-93	Tiverton Town	1998-99	Yeovil Town Reserves
1993-94	Tiverton Town	1999-00	Chippenham Town

BACKWELL UNITED

Secretary:Doug Coles, 156 Rodway Road, Patchway, Bristol BS34 5ED (0117 985 7089)

Ground: Backwell Recreation Ground, West Town Rd, Backwell, Avon Tel: 1275 462612

Directions: Near centre of Backwell on main A370 Bristol to Weston-super-Mare road. Buses from Bristol or Weston, or 20 mins walk from Nailsea & Backwell(BR) station; turn right out of station, right at traffic lights (half mile),ground quarter mile on right just past car sales

Capacity: 1,000   Seats: 60 Cover: 150   Floodlights: Yes

Clubhouse: Open 6-11pm weekdays, 12.30-11pm Sat. Snacks available   Club Shop: No

HONOURS   Somerset Snr Lg 77-78 79-80 80-81 81-82 82-83 (Lg Cup 82-83 (R-up 79-80)
Div 1 72-73); Somerset Snr Cup 81-82; SW Co.'s Sutton Transformer Cup 81-82.
Western Lge Div 1 89-90 Champions, 94-95 promoted in 3rd place
PREVIOUS   **Leagues**: Clevedon & Dist; Bristol C. of E.; Bristol Surburban (pre 1970);
Somerset Senior 70-83
Grounds: Two in Backwell prior to 1939. Club reformed in 1946
RECORD   **Attendance**: 487 v Brislington, Gt Mills Lg. 2/5/94
Goalscorer: Steve Spalding   **Appearances:** Wayne Buxton
Win: 10-1 v Dowton, F.A.Cup 1st Qualifying Round. 1998-99
Defeat: 2-6 v Tiverton Town (H), Les Phillips Cup QF 1.2.94

FACT FILE
Founded: 1911
Nickname: Stags
Club Sponsors: C W Jones Carpets
Colours: All red
Change colours: All Gold
Midweek Matches: Tuesday
Programme: 42 pages, 50p
Editor: Dick Cole (01275 463627)

CLUB PERSONNEL
Chairman: Richard Cole
Vice-Chairman: Peter Higgins
President: John Southern
Press Officer:Mike Naylor (01275 858576)
Manager:Jamie Patch
Asst Manager: Shaun Penny
Physio: Steve Tregale

BARNSTAPLE TOWN

Secretary: David Cooke, 51 Walnut Way, Whiddon Valley, Barnstaple, Devon. EX32 7RF
Tel: 01271 326088
Ground: Mill Road, Barnstaple, North Devon Tel: 01271 343469
Directions: A361 towards Ilfracombe (from M5 Jct 26), in Barnstaple follow A361Ilfracombe
signs, second left after crossing small bridge is Mill Road
Capacity: 5,000   Seats: 250   Cover: 1,000   Floodlights: Yes
Clubhouse: Full license. Bar snacks   Club Shop: Yes

HONOURS   Western Lg 52-53 79-80 (R-up 80-81 81-82, Div 1 49-50 94-95, Merit Cup74-75
83-84 84-85, Comb. 92-93), Devon Professional Cup 62-63 64-65 67-68 69-70
71-73 (X2) 74-75 76-81 (X5), Devon Youth Lg, Devon St Lukes Cup 87-88, Devon Snr
Cup 92-93, Devon Youth Cup 48-49 51-52
PREVIOUS   **Leagues**: Nth Devon, Devon & Exeter, S. Western   **Name**: Pilton Yeo Vale
Grounds: Town Wharf (> 1920); Highfield Rd, Newport (> 35), Pilton Pk, Rock Pk
RECORDS   **Attendance:** 6,200 v Bournemouth, FA Cup 1st Rd, 54   **Appearances:**
Win: 12-1 v Tavistock (H), FA Cup 3rd Qual. Rd 1954   Ian Pope
Defeat: 1-10 v Mangotsfield Utd (A), Western Lge Prem. Div. 90-91
BEST SEASON   FA Cup: 1st Rd replay 51-52   **FA Vase:** 4th Rd 94-95
Players progressing: Len Pickard (Bristol R. 51), John Neale (Exeter72), Barrie Vassallo (Torquay
77), Ian Doyle (Bristol C. 78), Ryan Souter (Swindon 94), Jason Cadie (Reading 94)

FACT FILE
Founded: 1906
Nickname: Barum
Sponsors:Witts
Colours: Red/red/white
Change colours: Yellow/black/yellow
Midweek Matches: Tuesday
Reserve League:
Programme: 60p
Programme Editor: David Cooke
Local Press: N. Devon Journal Herald
99-00- Captain: Gary Bedler
P.O.Y.: Simon Langmead
Top Scorer: Robert Gough
CLUB PERSONNEL
President: Wilf Harris
Chairman: Paul Mitchell
Manager: John Hore
General Manager: Mark Jenkins
Physio: Amanda James

BIDEFORD

Secretary: Kevin Tyrrell, 69 Laurel Ave., Bideford, devon EX39 3AZ Tel: 01237 4707747

Ground: The Sports Ground, Kingsley Road, Bideford Tel: 01237 474975

Directions: A361 for Bideford - ground on right as you enter the town
Capacity: 6,000   Seats: 120   Cover: 1,000   Floodlights: Yes
Clubhouse: `Robins Nest' - on ground. Open lunchtimes and evenings, snacks and bar menu.
Mgr: Mrs Sue Tyrell

HONOURS   Western Lg 63-64 70-7171-72 81-82 82-83, Div 1 51-52, Div 3 49-50, Lg Cup 71-
72 84-85; Alan Young Cup 64-65 69-70; Merit Cup 68-69; Subsidiary Cup 71-72;
Devon Snr Cup 79-80; Devon St Lukes Cup 81-82 83-84 85-86 95-96 (R-up 86-87 91-92 94-95)

PREVIOUS   Leagues: Devon & Exeter 47-49; Western 49-72; Southern 72-75
Name: Bideford Town   **Ground:** Hansen Ground (1 season)

BEST SEASON   FA Cup: 1st Rd 64-65(replay) 73-74 77-78 81-82. **FA Vase:**

RECORD   **Gate:** 6,000 v Gloucester C., FA Cup 4th Qual. Rd 60
Scorer: Tommy Robinson 259   **Appearances:** Derek May 527
Win: 16-0 v Soundwell 50-51   **Defeat:** 0-12 v Paulton 96-97

Players progressing: Shaun Taylor (Swindon Town) Tony Dennis (Cambridge)

FACT FILE
Founded: 1949
Nickname: Robins
Colours: All Red
Change colours: Blue/blue/white
Midweek Matchday: Tuesday
Programme: 32 pages, 50p
Editor: Ian Knight

CLUB PERSONNEL
President: C Prust
Chairman: Ian Knight
Manager:Sean Joyce
Reserve Manager: Barry Hooper

BISHOP SUTTON

Secretary: Roy Penney, 53 Ridgway Lane, Whitchurch, Bristol BS14 9PJ Tel: 01275 541392

Ground: Lakeview Football Field, Bishop Sutton Tel: 01275 333097

Directions: On A368 at rear of Butchers Arms pub - ground signposted on left entering village from the West

Capacity: 1,500   Seats: None   Cover: 200   Floodlights: yes

Clubhouse: Open matchdays. Rolls, pies and usual pub food available   Club Shop: No

HONOURS Somerset Snr Lg R-up 89-90 (Div 1 83-84 (R-up 81-82), Div 2 82-83), Bristol & Avon Lg 80-81 (Div 2 79-80), Somerset Jnr Cup 80-81, Weston Yth Lg77-78, Chew Valley KO Cup 83-84, Mid-Somerset Lg(Res) R-up 82-83 (Div 3 81-82)

PREVIOUS **Leagues:** Weston & Dist. Yth; Bristol & Avon; Somerset Snr (pre 1991)
Ground: Adjacent cricket field

BEST SEASON **FA Cup:**   **FA Vase: 3rd Rd 1998**

CLUB RECORDS **Attendance:** 400 v Bristol City, friendly
Win: 15-0 v Glastonbury Res

Players progressing: David Lee (Chelsea), S Williams (Southampton), J French(Bristol R.)

FACT FILE
Founded: 1977
Nickname: Bishops
Sponsors: Symes Off License
Colours: All blue
Change colours: All yellow
Midweek Matches: Tuesday
Youth team's League: Somerset Mid Week
Programme: Yes
Editor: G Williams

CLUB PERSONNEL
Chairman: G.Williams
Vice Chairman: Roy Penney
President: Bob Redding
Manager: Tony Corneling
Coach: Peter Wills
Physio: Chris Bailes

BRIDGWATER TOWN '84

General Secretary: Mrs Glenda Fletcher,18 Dunkery Road, Bridgwater Tel:01278 425599
Football Secretary: Miss Sally Wright, 37 Kidsbury Rd, Bridgwater, Som. TA6 7AQ
Tel: 01278 421189

Ground: Fairfax Park, College Way, Bath Road, Bridgwater Tel: 01278 446899 (matchdays and weekday mornings only)

Directions: M5 jct 23, follow signs to Glastonbury (A39), turn right for Bridgwater (A39). Look for sign to Bridgwater College via College Way
One mile from Bridgwater (BR) station

Capacity: 2,000   **Seats:** 150   **Cover:** Yes   **Floodlights**: Yes

Clubhouse: On the Ground

HONOURS Somerset Senioir Cup 93-94, Somerset Senior Lge 90-91 91-92 ,
Western Lge Div 1 95-96

PREVIOUS **League:** Somerset Snr (pre-1994)**Names:** None
BEST SEASONFA Cup: 2nd Q Rd **FA Vase:** First Round
RECORDS **Attendance:** 1,112 v Taunton Town 26.2. 97

FACT FILE
Founded: 1984
Nickname: The Robins
Sponsor: TMB Patterns
Colours: Red&white stripes/red/white
Change colours: All blue
Midweek Matchday: Tuesday
Youth Team's League: U18 Floodlight
Programme: Yes
Eds:G ordon Nelson,MarkHollidge& Andy Cole

CLUB PERSONNEL
Chairman: Keith Setter
President: Tom Pearce
Press Officer: GordonNelson
Manager: Jon Bowering
Sports Injury Therapist: Dave Callow
L.C.S.P., F.A.Dip.

BRIDPORT

Secretary: Keith Morgan, 95 Orchard Crescent, Bridport, Dorset. DT6 5HA
Tel Nos: 01308 456113 (H) 01308 862404 (W)

Ground: The Beehive, St Mary's Field, Bridport, Dorset Tel: 01308 423834

Directions: Take West Bay road from town centre, turn right just before Palmers Brewery

Capacity: 2,000   Seats: 200   Cover: 400   Floodlights: Yes   Club Shop: No

Clubhouse: Yes, open matchdays and for functions. Hot and cold snacks available

HONOURS Western Lg Cup 70-71 72-73 77-78 (R-up 76-77, Div 1 R-up 94-95, Merit Cup 69-70 71-72 73-74); Dorset Comb.(3) 85-88 (Lg Cup 86-87 87-88); Dorset Snr Cup(8) 63-64 69-71 75-76 78-81 87-88; Dorset Snr Amtr Cup(6) 48-50 54-55 56-57 70-72; W. Dorset Chal. Bowl 07-08; Perry Str. Lg 22-23; Mark Frowde Cup 76-77 88-89

PREVIOUS **Leagues:** Perry Street; Western 61-84; Dorset Combination 84-88
Grounds: Pymore (pre 1930s); Crown Field (pre 1953)
BEST SEASON **FA Cup:**   **FA Vase:**5th Round 88-89
RECORD **Attendance:** 1,150 v Exeter City, 1981; 3,000 v Chelsea, at Crown, 1950
Scorer (in a season): Ellis Hoole 36
Fee received: £2,000 for Tommy Henderson
Fee paid: £1,000 for Steve Crabb

FACT FILE
Founded: 1885
Nickname: Bees
Sponsors: ABC Blinds
Colours: Red & black/black/red & black
Change colours: Blue & black/blue/blue
Midweek Matches: Tuesday
Reserves ' League: Dorset Combination
Programme: 40pages, 50p
Editor: Ian Hallett (01308 868795)

CLUB PERSONNEL
President: B Williams
Chairman: David Fowler
Manager: David Kiteley
Asst Manager/Physio: Tony Diaz

BRISLINGTON

Secretary: David Braithwaite, 3 Ashcott,Whitchurch, Bristol BS14 0AG
Tel: 01275 542040 (H)   0794 701 2253 (M)

Ground: Ironmould Lane, Brislington, Bristol Tel: 0117 977 4030
Directions: 4 miles out of Bristol on main A4 to Bath - turn left up lane opposite Garden
Centre just before dual carriageway (500 yards past Park & Ride on right)

Capacity: 2000   Seats: 144   Cover: 1500   Floodlights: Yes

Clubhouse: Yes - on ground, open matchdays   **Club Shop:** No

HONOURS Somerset Senior Cup 92-93 R-up 93-94;
Somerset Senior League, Les Phillips Cup SF 93-94 99-00, Premier Cup 95-96

PREVIOUS **League:** Somerset Senior (pre-1991)

BEST SEASON **FA Vase:** 3rd Rd 89-90, 2-3 v Abingdon T. (A)

FACT FILE
Formed:
Nickname: Bris
Sponsors: Trade Windows
Colours: Red & black/black/black & red
Change colours: Yellow & blue/blue/blue
Midweek matches: Tuesday
Reserves ' League: Somerset Senior
Programme: £1.00
Editor: Laserset (0117 969 5487)

CLUB PERSONNEL
President: C Elston
Chairman: M.Richardson
Vice-Chairman:B.Perrott
Manager: Tony Ricketts
Asst Manager: Graham Bird
Physio: Dave Gould

BRISTOL MANOR FARM

Secretary: Mike Lawrence, 2 East Parade, Sea Mills, Bristol BS9 2JW
Tel: 0117 968 3349 (H) 0117 968 3571 (W)
Ground: `The Creek', Portway, Sea Mills, Bristol BS9 2HS Tel: 0117 968 3571

Directions: M5 jct 18 (Avonmouth Bridge), follow A4 for Bristol - U-turn on dual carriageway by
Bristol & West sports ground and return for half mile on A4- ground entrance is down narrow lane
on left (hidden entrance). Near to Sea Mills station (BR Temple Meads-Severn Beach line)

Capacity: 2,000   Seats: 84   Cover: 350   Floodlights: Yes   Club Shop: No

Clubhouse: Open every evening & lunchtime Sat & Sun. Lounge bar, skittle alley, bar meals.

HONOURS Western Lg Div 1 82-83, Glos Tphy 87-88, Glos Amtr Cup 89-90,
Somerset Snr Lg Div 1 (Lg Cup, Div 2)
PREVIOUS **Leagues:** Bristol Suburban 64-69; Somerset Snr 69-77
Name: Manor Farm O.B. 1964-68   **Grounds:** None
BEST SEASON **FA Cup:**   **FA Vase:**
RECORD **Attendance:** 500 v Portway, Western Lg 1974
Goalscorer: Chris Rex, 222   **Appearances:** Paul Williams, 821
Win: 8-2, v Frome (A), 2/9/84   **Defeat:** 1-8, v Exmouth (A), 5/5/86
Fee paid: Nil   **Fee received:** £3,000 for Nicky Dent (Yeovil Town, 1989)
Players progressing: Ian Hedges (Newport) 88-89, Gary Smart (Bristol Rovers)

FACT FILE
Formed: 1964
Nickname: The Farm
Club Sponsors: 'D & D'
Colours: Red/black/red
Change colours: All sky blue
Midweek Matchday: Tuesday
Reserve s' League: Suburban League
Programme: 28 pages, 50p
Editor: Natalie & Michelle Lawrence

CLUB PERSONNEL
Chairman: John Phillips
Vice Chairman: Brian Bartlett
President: Fred Wardle
Manager: Geoff Bryant
Assistant Manager: John Black
Physio: Rod Rutter

CHIPPENHAM TOWN

Secretary: Chris Blake, 28 Sadlers Mead, Chippenham, Wilts SN15 3PB Tel: 01249 658212

Ground: Hardenhuish Park, Bristol Road, Chippenham Tel: 01249 650400

Directions: M4 jct 17, A350 into Chippenham, follow signs for Trowbridge/Bath until r'bout,
left onto A420 into town, ground 800yds on left 15 mins walk from railway station
on main A420 Bristol Road

Capacity: 4,000   Seats: 100   Cover: 300   Floodlights: Yes

Clubhouse: Yes, open matchdays. Food available   **Club Shop:** Yes

HONOURS Western Lg 51-52 (Div 1 80-81, Div 2 52-53(Res)80-81), Wilts Shield,
Wilts Snr Cup, Wilts Snr League Les Phillips Cup(Western Lg Cup) 99-00
BEST SEASON **FA Cup:** 1st Rd 51-52   **FA Vase:** Finalists 99-00

PREVIOUS **Leagues:** Hellenic, Wiltshire Senior, Wiltshire Premier
Grounds: Westmead, Lowden, Little George Lane, Malmesbury Rd

RECORD **Gate:** 4,800 v Chippenham Utd, Western Lg, 1951
Goalscorer: Dave Ferris   **Appearances:** Ian Monnery

FACT FILE
Formed: 1873   Nickname: The Bluebirds
Club Sponsors:
Stentorfield,D.L.Windows,Costcutters,
Shoestrings
Club colours: Blue & white/blue& white/blue
Change colours: All yellow
Midweek matches: Wednesday
Programme: 32 pages,£1.00
Editor/Press Officer: TBA
Local Press: Chippenham News,
Wilts Gazette

CLUB PERSONNEL
Chairman: Malcolm Lyus
Vice-Chairman: Les Weir
President: G W Terrell
Tresurer: Richard Terrell
Commercial Manager: T.B.A.
Manager: Tommy Saunders
Physio: Barnes Sports Clinic

Chippenham Town pictured before the semi-final Vase tie with Vauxhall GM at Hardenhuish Park. Photo: Peter Barnes

Chippenham Town warming up before the second semi-final of the Vase at Hardenhuish Park. Photo: Peter Barnes

FA Carlsberg Vase Final: Chippenham Town v Deal Town. The "two Tommys", Sampson of Deal (left) and Chippenham's Saunders, lead their teams into the Wembley sunshine. Photo: Francis Short

DAWLISH TOWN

Secretary: John Wathen, Yardley, Oak Hill Cross Road,Dawlish, Devon. TQ14 8TN
Tel: 01626 776852 (H)   07801 976582(W)

Ground: Playing Fields, Sandy Lane, Exeter Road, Dawlish Tel: 01626 863110

Directions: Approx 1 mile from centre of town, off main Exeter road (A379)
Capacity: 2,000   Seats: 200   Cover: 200   Floodlights: Yes
Clubhouse: Open nightly, situated in car park opposite ground

FACT FILE
Founded: 1889
Colours: Green /black/green
Change Colours:Blue/white/white
Midweek matchday: Wednesday
Programme: 34 pages, 30p
Programme Editor: Roy Bolt

HONOURS   Western Lg Div 1 R-up 98-99, Lg Cup 80-81 83-84, Devon Premier Cup 69-70
72-73 80-81, Devon Snr Cup 57-58 67-68, Devon St Lukes Cup 82-83 (R-up 81-
82), Carlsberg Cup 96

BEST SEASON   FA Cup: FA Vase: Quarter Finals 86-87

PREVIOUS   **League:** Devon & Exeter   **Ground:** Barley Bank 1875-1900

RECORD   **Gate:** 1,500 v Heavitree Utd, Devon Prem. Cup Q-Final
Defeat: 0-18 v Clevedon (A), Western Lge Prem. Div. 92-93

CLUB PERSONNEL
President: Bob Webster
Chairman: John Wathen
Manager: Tony Bowker

DEVIZES TOWN

Secretary: Chris Dodd, 69 Broadleas Park, Devizes, Wilts. SN10 5JG. Tel: 01380 726205

Ground: Nursteed Road, Devizes. Tel: 01380 722817

Directions: Off Nursteed Road (A342 signposted Andover); leaving town ground on right
opposite Eastleigh Rd
Capacity: 2,500   Seats: 130   Cover: 400   Floodlights: Yes

FACT FILE
Founded: 1883
Colours: Red & white stripes/black/red
Change colours: All yellow
Midweek Matchday: Tuesday

HONOURS   Western League Div. 1 99-00; Wilts Snr Cup 07-08 49-50 56-57 57-58 58-59
60-61 61-62 62-63 65-66 67-68 70-71 71-72 73-74 78-79

PREVIOUS   **Leagues:** Wilts Comb.; Wilts Premier
Name: Southbroom (until early 1900s)   **Ground:** London Rd (pre 1946)

CLUB PERSONNEL
Chairman:Les Moore
Manager: Brian Newlands

ELMORE
Secretary: Neville Crocker, Flat 1, 9 Belmont Road, Tiverton, Devon
Tel: 07968 642094 (H) 07968 642094 (M) 01884 253687 (W)

Ground: Horsdon Park, Tiverton, Devon EX16 4DE Tel: 01884 252341

Directions: M5 Jct 27, A373 towards Tiverton, leave at 1st sign for Tiverton &Business Park,
ground 500yds on right
Capacity: 2,000   Seats: 200   Cover: Floodlights: Yes
Clubhouse: 11am-11pm Mon-Sat. Full canteen service - hot & cold meals & snacks
Club Shop: Yes

FACT FILE
Founded: 1947
Nickname: Eagles
Club Sponsors: Ken White Signs
Colours: All Green
Change colours: Red & black/black/black
Midweek matches: Tuesday
Reserve League: None
Programme: 12 pages, 30p
Editor: Richard Tapp(01884 252341)

HONOURS   East Devon Snr Cup 72-73 75-76, Western Lge R-up 94-95. Lge Cup 90-91,94-
95, Div 1 R-up 90-91, Prem Div Merit Cup R-up 91-92, Div 1 Merit Cup 86-87
89-90 90-91, Devon St Lukes Cup R-up 90-91, Devon Snr Cup 87-88, Devon
Intermediate Cup 60-61, Football Express Cup 60-61, Devon & Exeter Lg Div
2A 73-74 86-87(res)(Div 1A 76-77(res)), Devon Yth Cup 77-78.

PREVIOUS   **Leagues:** Devon & Exeter 47-74; South Western 74-78   Grounds: None

RECORD   **Attendance:** 1,713 v Tiverton Town Fri.April 14th 95
Appearances: P Webber   **Goalscorer:**
Win: 17-0   **Defeat:** 2-7

CLUB PERSONNEL
Chairman: Alan J Cockram
Vice Chairman: P.J.Garnsworthy
Manager: Peter Buckingham
Asst Manager: R Moore
Physio: M Crocker

Bridgwater. Back Row (l-r): Jon Bowering (Player-Manager), Scott Wheadon, Jamie Winter, Tim Dyer, Dave Clarke. Middle Row: Colin Paczoski (Physio), Richard Uffendell, Shaun Strange, Liam Bull, Ian Spence, Chris Young, Kevin Milsom (Asst. Manager). Front Row: Craig Rice, Matt Francis, Julian Stearns, Dave Pople, Leigh Hurford, Keith Graddon.

Bristol Manor Farm: John Black (Manager), Greg Welsher, Leigh Williams, Tim Cotter, Dean Smart (Captain), Ally Hines, Mark Lippiatt, Paul Bainbridge, James Barry, Mark Young, Anthony Court, Geoff Bryant (Manager). Front Row: Campball Bannerman, Mark Cherry, Joe Mogg, Mike Airs, Carl Rutter, Rod Rutter (Physio)

Melksham Town. Back Row (l-r): Gary Lewis, Matty Messenger, Justin Messenger, Darren Chitty, Steve Seals, Mike Brooks, Sam Robinson, James Lye, Kevin Bush. Middle Row: Jeremy Christopher, Adam Gingell, Robbie Lardner (Player/Manager), Mick Perrin (Chairman), David Phillips (Sec.), Russell Fishlock, Frankie Coleman. Front Row: John Scott, Adie Stagg, Jason Lunt, Matty Bown.

Paulton Rovers. Back Row (l-r): Alan Bull (coach), Glen Smart, Phil Park, Justin Cartledge, Mark Buxton, Lee Gould, John Rendell, Tony Bennett, Dean Smart, Darren Hobbs, Tony Quoi, Alan Pridham (Manager), Steve Strong (Coach). Front Row: Mark Keen, Paul Tovey, Tony Cook, Jamie Crandon, Jimmy Wring, Richard Perry, Gary Smart, Stuart Johnson, Lee Groves, Ian Eisentrager (Coach).

MELKSHAM TOWN

Secretary: David Phillips, 37 Duxford Close, Bowerhill,Melksham,Wlts. SN12 6XN
Tel: 01225 706904

Ground: The Conigre, Melksham (01225 702843)
Capacity: 3,000   Seats: 150   Cover: 1,500   Floodlights: Yes

Directions: Just off main square in grounds of Melksham House

Clubhouse: Inside ground, open every evening & weekend lunchtimes

HONOURS Wilts Lg 03-04 93-94 (R-up 24-25 29-30 59-60 67-68 68-69 71-72),
Western Lg Div 1 79-80, 96-97, Wilts Snr Cup 03-04 69-70 77-78 (R-up 57-58
67-68 68-69), Wilts Shield 80-81 81-82 84-85 ,85-86,97-98 ,99-00(R-up 86-87).

PREVIOUS **Leagues:** Wiltshire 1894-1974 93-94; Western 74-93
Grounds: Challymead; Old Broughton Road Field

BEST SEASON **FA Cup:** 2nd Q Rd 57-58   **FA Vase:** 3rd Rd 81-82,98-99
FA Amateur Cup: 1st Rd 68-69

RECORD **Attendance:** 2,821 v Trowbridge Town, FA Cup 57-58

FACT FILE

Founded: 1876
Colours:yellow/black/yellow
Change colours: All white
Midweek Matchday: Tuesday

CLUB PERSONNEL

President: Mike Harris
Chairman: Mike Perrin
Manager: Darren Perrin

MINEHEAD

Secretary: Mike Till, 6 Badger Park, Minehead, Som. TA24 6LL Tel: 01643 706309

Ground: The Recreation Ground, Irnham Road, Minehead, Somerset (01643 704989)

Directions: Entering town from east on A39 turn right into King Edward Road at Police station,
first left into Alexandra Rd and follow signs to car park;ground entrance within. Regular buses to
Minehead from Taunton, the nearestrailhead. (Steam train 'holiday route' Taunton to Minehead)

Capacity: 3,500   Seats: 350   Cover: 400   Floodlights: Yes

Clubhouse: Yes   **Club Shop:** No

HONOURS Southern Lg R-up 76-77, Div 1 Sth 75-76, Merit Cup 75-76;
Western Lg R-up 66-67 71-72, Div 1 90-91 98-99, Alan Young Cup 67-68 (jt with
Glastonbury),Somerset Premier Cup 60-61 73-74 76-77
PREVIOUS **Leagues:** Somerset Senior; Southern 72-83
RECORD **Attendance:** 3,600 v Exeter City, FA Cup 2nd Rd, 77
Defeat: 1-11 v Odd Down (A), Western Lge Prem. Div. 19/3/94
Longest unbeaten run of league games 36, May 1998- May 1999
BEST SEASON **FA Cup:** 2nd Round 76-77, 1-2 v Portsmouth (A); 77-78, 0-3 v Exeter City (H).
League clubs defeated: Swansea City 1-0 (A) 76-77
FA Vase: **FA Trophy:** Not applicable

FACT FILE
Founded: 1889
Colours: Blue & white/blue/blue
Change colours: Yellow/black/black
Midweek Matches: Tuesday
Reserves League: TBA
Programme: Yes
Editor:

CLUB PERSONNEL
Chairman: Peter Bate
Tel: 01643 704063

Manager: Chris Porter
Coach: Andy Gill

ODD DOWN ATHLETIC

Secretary: Mike Mancini, 36 Caledonian Rd., East Twerton, Bath BA2 3RD
Tel: 01225 423293 Mobile: 07788 635560

Ground: Coombe Hay Lane, Odd Down, Bath Tel: 01225 832491

Directions: On main Bath/Exeter road - leaving Bath turn left into Combe Hay Lane opposite
Lamplighters Pub.opposite Park & Ride car park. 40 mins walk from Bath (BR)

Capacity: 1,000   Seats: 160   Cover: 250   Floodlights: Yes

Clubhouse: Yes, open noon-3 & 7-11pm. Hot & cold food available
Club Shop: No

HONOURS Western Lg Div 1 92-93, Somerset Snr Cup 91-92

PREVIOUS **Leagues:** Wilts Premier, Bath & District, Somerset Senior

BEST SEASON **FA Cup:**   **FA Vase:**

RECORD **Appearances:** Steve Fuller 424
Scorer: Joe Matano 104
Win: 11-1 v Minehead (H), Western Lge Prem. Div. 19/3/94

FACT FILE

Founded: 1901
Sponsors: First Bus/Streamline
Colours: Black & white/black/black
Change :All Yellow
Midweek Matches: Tuesday (7-30)
Reserves ' League: Somerset Senior
Programme: 12 pages with admission
Editor: Secretary

CLUB PERSONNEL

President: P A L Hill
Chairman: N Fenwick
Vice Chairman: Eric Clarke
Manager: Chris Mountford

PAULTON ROVERS

Secretary: John Pool, 111 Charlton Park, Midsomer Norton,Bath BA3 4BP Tel: 0176 1415190

Ground: Athletic Ground, Winterfield Road, Paulton Tel: 01761 412907

Directions: Leave A39 at Farrington Gurney (approx 15 miles south of Bristol),follow A362 marked Radstock for two miles, left at junction B3355 to Paulton,ground on right. Bus services from Bristol and Bath

Capacity: 5,000   Seats: 138   Cover: 200   Floodlights: Yes

Club Shop: Old programmes available - contact Chairman

Clubhouse: 3 bars, lounge, skittle alley, dance hall. Capacity 300. Cateringfacilities

HONOURS   Western Lg Div 2 R-up 1900-01; Somerset Snr Cup 00-01 02-03 03-04 07-08 08-09 09-10 34-35 67-68 68-69 71-72 72-73 74-75; Somerset Snr Lg 00-01 03-04 04-05 70-71 71-72 72-73 73-74; Somerset F/Lit Youth Lge 96-97

PREVIOUS   **Leagues:** Wilts Premier; Somerset Snr
Grounds: Chapel Field; Cricket Ground; Recreation Ground 1946-48

BEST SEASON   **FA Cup:**   **FA Vase:**

RECORDS   **Attendance:** 2,000 v Crewe, FA Cup, 1906-07
Appearances: Steve Tovey   **Goalscorer:** D Clark

FACT FILE
Founded: 1881
Nickname: Rovers
Sponsors: Barons Property Centre/Bass Breweries
Colours: White/maroon/maroon
Change colours: Yellow/navy/navy
Midweek matches: Tuesday
Reserves' League: Somerset Snr
Programme: 20 pages, 50p
Editor: D Bissex (01761 412463)
Local Press: Bath Evening Chronicle, Bristol Evening Post, Western Daily Press

CLUB PERSONNEL
President: Mr T Pow
Chairman: David Bissex
Vice Chairman: Mr D Carter
Manager: Alan Pridham
Physio: Mike Brown

Taunton Town. Back Row (l-r): Kevin Matthews, Tom Kelly, Antony Lynch, Ellis Laight, Tony Harris (Chairman), Russell Musker (Manager), Des Badcock, Paul West, Martin Parker, Derek Fowler. Front Row: Paul Edwards, Liam Ford, Ian Down, Scott Legg, Leon Hapgood, Ben Rowe, Ian Bastow.

TAUNTON TOWN

Secretary: The Secretary, c/o the club, Tel: 01823 333833 (H)

Ground: Wordsworth Drive, Taunton, Somerset TA1 2HG Tel: 01823 278191

Directions: Leave M5 Jct 25, follow signs to town centre, at 2nd set of lights turn left into Wordsworth Drive; ground on left. 25 mins walk from Taunton (BR); turn left out of station and follow road right through town centre bearing left into East Reach. Follow road down and turn right into Wordsworth Drive shortly after Victoria pub

Capacity: 4,000   Seats:400   Cover: 1,000   Floodlights: Yes   Club Shop: Yes

Clubhouse: Social club to accommodate 300, full bar facilities, separate bar & hall for private functions

HONOURS FA Vase R-up 93-94, Western Lg Champions 68-69 89-90,95-6,98-9,99-00 (R-up 93-94 97-98, Les Phillips R-up 93-94 97-98, Alan Young Cup 73-74 75-76 (jt with Falmouth), Charity Chall. Cup 49-50, 50-51), Somerset Snr Lg 52-53, Som Prem.Cup R-up 82-83 89-90 92-93 98-99

PREVIOUS   **Leagues:** Western 54-77; Southern 77-83   **Grounds:** Several prior to 1953

BEST SEASON   **FA Cup:** 1st Rd Proper 81-82, 1-2 v Swindon T. (A)   **FA Trophy:** 1st Rd Proper 80-81, 1-5 v Hendon at Q.P.R   **FA Vase:** Finalists 93-94, S-F 97-98 98-99, Q-F 96-97.

RECORDS   **Attendance:** 3,284 v Tiverton Town, FA Vase Semi-Final 98-99
Appearances: Tony Payne   **Scorer** (in a season) : Reg Oram 67
Win: 12-0 v Dawlish Town (A), FA Cup Prel. Rd, 28/8/93
Defeat: 0-8 v Cheltenham Town (A), FA Cup 2nd Qual. Rd, 28/9/91

Players progressing: Charlie Rutter (Cardiff), Stuart Brace (Southend), Steve Winter (Torquay) Kevin Maloy (Exeter C.)

FACT FILE
Formed: 1947
Nickname: Peacocks
Club Sponsors: T.G.Roofing
Colours: Sky blue & claret/claret/sky blue
Change colours: Yellow/sky blue/yellow
Midweek matches: Wednesday
Reserves ' League: None
Programme: 32 pages, £1
Editor: Les Gill
Newsline: 0930 555 849

CLUB PERSONNEL
Chairman: T F Harris
Treasurer: Joan Ellis
Press Officer: Les Gill
Manager: Russell Musker
Asst Manager: Derek Fowler
Physio: Barry Wilson

WELTON ROVERS

Secretary: Michael Taylor, 31 Gryphon Close, Westbury, Wiltshire BA13 3XU
Tel Nos: 01373 865406(H) 01373 823814(W)

Ground: West Clewes, North Road, Midsomer Norton, Somerset Tel: 01761 412097

Directions: A367 Bath to Radstock ō right at lights at foot of hill onto A362,ground on right.

Capacity: 2,400   **Seats:** 300   **Cover:** 300   **Floodlights:** Yes   **Club Shop:** No

Clubhouse: 7.30-11pm daily, plus Sat matchdays 1.30-2.45pm, Sun 12-2pm

HONOURS Western Lg 11-12 64-65 65-66 66-67 73-74, Div 1 59-60 87-88,Amateur Cup 56-57
57-58 58-59 59-60, Alan Young Cup 65-66 66-67 67-68(jt); Somerset Snr Cup 06-07
11-12 12-13 13-14 19-20 24-25 25-26 60-61 61-62 62-63, Som. I'mediate Cup 77-78,   Som. Jnr
Cup 06-07(jt) 24-25 30-31, WBC Clares City of Wells Cup 78-79

PREVIOUS	**Leagues:** None	**Names:** None	**Grounds:** None
BEST SEASON	**FA Cup:**	**FA Vase:**	**FA Amateur Cup:**
RECORD	**Attendance:** 2,000 v Bromley, FA Amateur Cup 1963		
	Goalscorer: Ian Henderson, 51		

FACT FILE
Formed: 1887
Nickname: Rovers
Sponsors: Young Bros (Roofing)
Colours: Green & white/green/green
Change colours: All Yellow
Midweek matchday: Monday
Reserve s' League: Somerset Senior
Programme: 12 pages, 25p
Editor: M Brown

CLUB PERSONNEL
Chairman: Rae James
Manager: Adrian Britton
Asst Manager: Martin Finn
Physio: John Carver

WESTBURY UNITED

Secretary: Michael Taylor, 31 Gryphon Close, Westury, Wiltshire BA13 (01373 865406)

Ground: Meadow Lane, Westbury Tel: 01373 823409

Directions: In town centre, A350, follow signs for BR station, Meadow Lane on right (club signposted). Ten mins walk from railway station (on main London-South West and South Coast-Bristol lines)

Capacity: 3,500   **Seats:** 150   **Cover:** 150   **Floodlights:** Yes

Clubhouse: Evenings 7-11pm, Fri, Sat & Sun lunchtimes 12-3pm   **Club Shop:** No

HONOURS Western Lg Div 1 91-92, Wilts Senior Cup 31-32 32-33 47-48 51-52,
Wilts Combination, Wilts Lg 34-35 37-38 38-39 49-50 50-51 55-56,
Wilts Premier Shield R-up 92-93

PREVIOUS **Leagues:** Wilts Comb.; Wilts Co. (pre-1984)
Ground: Redland Lane (pre-1935)

BEST SEASON **FA Cup:**   **FA Vase:**

RECORD Gate: 4,000 - v Llanelli, FA Cup 1st Rd 37 & v Walthamstow Ave. FA Cup 37

Players progressing: John Atyeo (Bristol City)

FACT FILE
Formed: 1921
Nickname: White Horsemen
Colours: Green & white/white/green
Change colours: Sky & navy/blue/blue
Midweek Matches: Tuesday
Reserves' league: Wilts County Lg.
Programme: 16 pages, 50p
Editor: Mike Taylor (01373 865406)

CLUB PERSONNEL
Chairman: Phillip Alford
Vice Chairman: Bert Back
President: George Nicholls
Managers: Nigel Tripp & Lee Darby
Physio: Dave Prescott

YEOVIL TOWN RESERVES

Secretary: Jean Cotton, c/o Club.
Tel: 01935 428130 (H) 01935 423662 (B) Fax: 01935 473956

Ground: Huish Park, Lufton Way, Yeovil Somerset, BA22 8YF.
Tel: 01935 23662   Fax 01935 73956

Directions: Leave A303 at Cartgate roundabout and take A3088 signposted Yeovil.Take first exit at next roundabout and first exit at next roundabout intoLufton Way. Railway station - Yeovil Pen Mill (Bristol/Westbury to Weymouth)2.5 miles from ground. Yeovil Junction (Waterloo to Exeter) 4 miles.
Bus service from both stations on Saturday - matchdays

Capacity: 8,720   **Seats:** 5,212   **Terracing:** 3,508   **Floodlights:** Yes

Club Shop: Open on matchdays selling full range of souvenirs, match programmes etc

Clubhouse: Matchdays hot + cold food available. Meals can be ordered with advance notice. All weather astro turf pitch available for bookings9am-10pm

HONOURS: Western League: Champions 58-59, Div. 1 R-up 97-98

FACT FILE
Founded: 1895
Nickname: Glovers
Sponsors: Precision Publishing Papers
Colours: Green/white/green
Change colours: Navy & red/navy/navy & red
Midweek matchday: Wednesday
Programme: Yes

CLUB PERSONNEL
Chairman: John Fry
President: S N Burfield
Manager: Terry Rowles
Physio: Maurice O'Donnell

BATH CITY RESERVES

Secretary: Quentin Edwards c/o the club.
Tel: 01225 359087 (H) 01225 423087 (B) & 07785 795532 (M)

Ground: Twerton Park, Twerton, Bath Avon BA2 1DB
Tel: 01225 423087/313247 Fax: 01225 481391

Directions: Twerton Park is situated on the A4/A36 Lower Bristol Road - on the Bristol side of Bath City Centre (Approx 2.5 miles). The area is serviced by J18 on the M4. From the centre of Bath the bus route is No.5 - Twerton High Street
Capacity: 8,840   Seated: 1,017   Covered Terracing: 4,800

Clubhouse: Several bars open all week and full service with menu on match-days catering for up to 250 people   **Club Shop:** Contact MrM.Brush

FACT FILE
Founded: 1889
Nickname: Stripes & The City
Midweek matchday: Wednesday
Colours: Black & white stripes/black/b & w
Change: All yellow

CLUB PERSONNEL
Chairman: Stephen Hall
Directors: J Turner, K Loach, G Todd,
P Weaver, M Hughes.
Commercial Director: G Todd
Press Officer: P Weaver

Manager: Dave Hobbs
Tel: 01225 840619

BITTON

Secretary: Michael Hall, 14 Pillingers Road, Kingswood, Bristol BS15 8DE Tel: 0117 960 3627

Ground: The Recreation Ground, Bath Road, Bitton, Tel: 0117 932 3222
Capacity: 500   Cover: 80Seats: 48   Floodlights: No

Directions: M4 junc 18. Take A46 towards Bath, at first roundabout take A420 for Wick/ Bridgeyate. On approach to Bridgeyate turn left at mini-r'about onto A4175 and follow for 2.2 miles, then left for Bath on the A431. The ground is 100 yards on right. Nearest station: Keynsham Bristol

Clubhouse: Weekdays 7.30-11, Sat. all day, Sun 12-3 & 7.30-10.30   Club Shop: No
HONOURS   Glos. Jun Cup r-up 90; Avon Prem. Lg r-up 94, 95; Glos Sen amat Cup 95; Glos Chall Trophy r-up 97; Glos County Lg r-up 97.
PREVIOUS   **Leagues:** Avon Premier Comb., Glos County

FACT FILE
Founded: 1922
Sponsors: John Dean Builders
Colours: Red & white stripes/black/black
Change colours: Yellow/green/yellow
Midweek Matches: Wednesday 6.30 ko.
Programme: 36 pages   Editor: Paul Cater

CLUB PERSONNEL
Chairman: John Langdon (0117 9611244)
Vice Chairman: Steve Webb (0117 967 4114)
President: Roy Ewans
Commercial Man.: Paul Cater (0117 932 5205)
Manager: Martyn Dyer (0117 9323754)

CADBURY HEATH

Secretary: Colin Trotman, 51 Deanery Road, Kingswood, Bristol BS15 9JB
Tel: 0117 983 7510 (H)

Ground: Springfield, Cadbury Heath Road, Warmley, Bristol. Tel: 0117 967 5731

Directions: Situated in East Bristol on the road between Warmley & Oldeland. Tower Road (North & South) runs from Warmley to Oldland and passes Cadbury Heath road. Look for Spar shop and King William P.H.. Turn into Cadbury Heath Road. 20 yds on right entrance to Social Club.

PREVIOUS   **League:** Gloucestershire County Lge.
HONOURS   Glos. County Lge 98-99, R-up 99-00

FACT FILE
Colours: Red & white/red/red
Change Cols.: yellow/black/black
Midweek Matchday: Wednesday

CLUB PERSONNEL
Chairman: Dave Smart
1 Farm Close, Emerson Green,
Bristol BS16 7RU
Tel: 0117 956 1223

Manager: Steve Plenty
Tel: 0117 957 3053

CALNE TOWN

Secretary: Laurie Drake, 22 Falcon Rd, Calne, Wilts SN11 8PL Tel: 01249 819186
Ground: Bremhill View, Lickhill Rd., North End, Calne Tel: 01249 816716
Directions: Take the A3102 off A4 at roundabout , turn right at next roundabout and ground will be directly ahead.
Capacity: 2,500   Seats: 78   Cover: 250   Floodlights: Yes   Club Shop: No
Clubhouse: Mon-Fri 7-11pm, Sat-Sun 12-11pm. Filled rolls, hot food, tea,coffee, sweets etc
HONOURS   Western Lg Div 1 R-up 92-93; Wilts Snr Cup 12-13 34-35 84-85 (R-up1894-95 94-95 1911-12 49-50); Wilts Lg 33-34, ('Ghia' Cup 8) 1-81 85-86, Div 279-81, Div 3 85-86, Div 4 81-82
PREVIOUS   **League:** Wilts Co. (pre-1986)   **Ground:** Anchor Road Rec. 1887-1967
Names: Calne Town (1886) & Harris Utd merged; Calne & Harris Utd (1921-67)
RECORD   **Attendance:** 1,100 v Swindon, Friendly 25/7/1987
Scorer: Robbie Lardner   **Appearances:** Gary Swallow, 259
Win: 11-1 v Heavitree (H)   **Defeat:** 2-7 v Odd Down (A)

FACT FILE
Founded: 1887   Nickname: Lilywhites
Sponsors: Calne Engineering
Colours: White/black/black
Change colours: All Blue
Midweek Matchday: Tuesday 7.45
Programme: 20 pages, 50p
Editor: Kath Brindle (01249 815198)
99-00- Captain: Martin Wheeler
Top Scorer: Toby Colebourne
P.o.Y.: IBen Sammut
CLUB PERSONNEL
President: Fred Rutty
Chairman: Steve Walker
Manager: Graham Learmont

CHARD TOWN

Secretary: Michael Froom, 0 Helliers Close, Chard , Somerset TA20 1LJ (01460 63670)
Ground: Town Ground, Zembard Lane, Chard TA20 1JL Tel: 01460 61402
Capacity: 1,500   Seats: 60   Cover: 200   Floodlights: Yes

Directions: 150 yards from the town centre, off Combe Street.
8 miles from Crewkerne BR station
Clubhouse: Matchdays & most evenings. Snacks served

HONOURS   Som. Snr Lg 49-50 53-54 59-60 67-68 69-70 (Lg Cup 61-62 71-72 76-77);
Western Lg Div 1 R-up 83-84 87-88 95-96, (Merit Cup 82-83, Comb. Cup(Res) 91-92 (R-up 92-93)); Som. Snr Cup 52-53 66-67; S W Co's Cup 88-89; Western Com Lge 96-97, Cup 96-97.

BEST SEASON   FA Cup: 2nd Qual Rd. 77-78 82-83   **FA Vase:**

PREVIOUS   Leagues: Somerset Snr 20-24 48-75; Perry Street 25-48 **Grounds:** None

FACT FILE
Founded: 1920
Nickname: Robins
Colours: Scarlet/black/black
Change colours: White/white/red
Midweek matches: Wednesday
Reserves ' League: None
Programme: 24 pages with entry
Editor: Mike Froom

CLUB PERSONNEL
Chairman: Brian Beer
Manager: N.Clarke
Physio: Richard Butt

CLYST ROVERS

Secretary: Bob Chamberlain, Orchard Cottage, Clyst St George, Exeter EX3 0NZ(01392 873498)
Ground: Waterslade Park, Clyst Honiton, Devon Tel: 01392 366424
Directions: A30 following signs for Exeter Airport. Coming from Exeter take 1st right after airport
turning (ground signposted) up narrow 200yds past Duke of York Pub
Capacity: 3,000   Seats: 130   Cover: 300   Floodlights: Yes
Club Shop: Yes, Programmes, souvenirs etc
Clubhouse: Open one and a half hours before kick off and after game. Excellent food available
HONOURS   Devon St Lukes Cup R-up 92-93, Western Lg Cup SF 92-93
PREVIOUS   Leagues: Exeter & District 26-44 51-66; Exeter & District Sunday 67-82;
South Western 81-92   **Grounds:** Fair Oak 1926-44
RECORD   Gate: 768 v Tiverton, Devon St Lukes final 11/5/93
Win: 6-0 v Heavitree United, 1993
Defeat: 0-12 v Torpoint Athletic, South Western League, October 1990

FACT FILE
Founded: 1926   Reformed: 1951
Nickname: Rovers
Sponsors: Vantage Pharmacy, Paignton
Colours: All yellow
Change colours: Blue/black/black
Midweek Matches: Wednesday
Programme: 32 pages, 30p
Editor: Ray Dack (01392 215075)

CLUB PERSONNEL
President: Mr P W Brown
Chairman: Bob Chamberlain
Vice Chairman: Colin Dadson
Manager:Bill Potter
Physio: Bill Wreford

CORSHAM TOWN

Secretary: Richard Taylor, 7 Cresswells, Corsham, Wilts SN13 9NJ   Tel: 01249 714406
Internet: www.widcom.demon.co.uk

Ground: Southbank Ground, Lacock Road, Corsham, Wilts. SN13 9HS Tel: 01249 715609
Directions   From the A4 turn into Corsham at the Hare & Hounds PH roundabout, taking the
Melksham Road, B3353, past the Methuen Arms PH then straight across the next
mini-r'about into Lacock Road. The ground is situated 1/2 mile on right
Capacity:1,500Seats: No   Cover: Yes   Floodlights: No
Clubhouse: Yes   Club Shop: No

HONOURS   Wiltshire Lge. 97-98, Wiltshire FA Sen. Cup 75-76 96-97,
Wiltshire Lge. KO Cup 95-96 96-97

PREVIOUS   League: Wiltshire Co. Lge

FACT FILE
Founded: 1893
Sponsors: Hong Kong House & Addkey Print
Colours: All red
Change colours: Yellow/blue/blue
Midweek matchday: Tuesday

CLUB PERSONNEL
President:
Chairman: Colin Hudd
Manager: Rob Humphries
Assistant Manager: Mark Godley

EXMOUTH TOWN

Secretary: David Richardson J.P.,44 Whitchurch Avenue, Exeter. EX2 1NT (01392 430985)
Ground: King George V Ground, Southern Road, Exmouth Tel: 01395 263348

Directions: On right side of main Exeter to Exmouth road (A376). Half mile from Exmouth (BR)

Capacity: 2,500   Seats: 100   Cover: 250   Floodlights: Yes   Club Shop: Yes
Clubhouse: Open every night and weekend lunchtimes. Snacks available

HONOURS   Western Lg 83-84 85-86 (R-up 86-87 88-89; Lg Cup 88-89; Div 1 R-up 81-82;
Sportmanship Tphy 86-87 92-93); Devon Premier Cup 70-71 79-80; Devon St
Lukes Cup 84-85 88-89 89-90; Devon Snr Cup 50-51; East Devon Snr Cup
50-51 82-83; Harry Wood Mem. Cup 84-85; Exmouth Chal. Cup [7]
PREVIOUS   League: Devon & Exeter 1933-73
BEST SEASON   FA Vase: SF 84-85   **FA Cup:**
RECORD   Gate: 2,395 v Liverpool XI, friendly in 1987   **Scorer:** Mel Pym, 117
Appearances: Keith Sprague, Geoff Weeks 410 (Western Lg)

FACT FILE
Formed: 1933
Nickname: `Town' or `Blues'
Colours: Blue & white/blue/blue
Change cols: Red & white/black/red & white
Midweek matchday: Tuesday
Reserves' League: Devon & Exeter
Programme: 36 pages, 30p
Editor: A.Hooker

CLUB PERSONNEL
President: Brian Bradley
Chairman: Malcolm Hale
Vice Chairman: John Dibsdall
Manager:Russell Wilson

FROME TOWN

Secretary: Geoff Norris, 10 Clumber Drive, Frome, Somerset BA11 2LG (01373 464 803)
Ground: Badgers Hill, Berkeley Road, Frome Tel: 01373 453643

Directions: On the Westbury Road, 1 mile from town centre and Frome BR station
Capacity: 5,000   **Seats:** 250   **Cover:** 800   **Floodlights:** Yes   **Club Shop:** No
Clubhouse: Evenings & weekends. Cold food only

HONOURS   Wiltshire Lge 1909-10,1910-11,Western Lg 78-79 (Div 2 19-20, Div 2R-up 54-55, Lg Cup 79-80 82-83, Merit Cup 82-83, Alan Young Cup 79-80,Subsidiary Cup 59-60), Somerset Prem Cup 66-67 68-69 82-83, Wilts Prem Lg 62-63, Western Co's F'lit Cup 83-84, Somerset Snr Cup 32-33 33-34 50-51, Somerset Snr Lg 06-07 08-09 10-11

PREVIOUS   **League:** Somerset Senior, Wilts League and Wilts Premier

BEST SEASON   **FA Trophy:** 2nd Rd v Boston Utd (a) 0-4, 1984-85
    FA Cup: 1st Rd Proper v L.Orient 1954-55   **FA Vase:** 2nd Rd v Paulton R (a) 1-2

RECORD   **Attendance:** 8,000 v Leyton Orient, F.A.Cup 1st Rd. 58

FACT FILE
Founded: 1904   Nickname: Robins
Sponsors: Telewest Communications
Colours: All red
Change colours: Purple/navy/navy
Midweek matchday: Tuesday
Reserves ' League: Somerset Senior
Programme: 24 pages, 50p
Editor: Secretary

CLUB PERSONNEL
President: Mr C W M Norton
Chairman: Paul McGuinness
Vice Chairman: Steve Porter, Geoff Norris
Manager: Simon White
Physio: Bob Stokes

HALLEN

Secretary: Jonathon Rogers, 114 Wellington Hill West, Westbury on Trym, Bristol BS9 4QY
    Tel: 0117 985 6138 (H) 0117 900 1811 (B)
Ground: Hallen Playing Fields, Moorhouse Lane, Hallen, Nr Bristol Tel: 0117 950 2265
Directions: M5 jct 17, A4018 to Henbury r'bout, right, right again at junction,next right to
    Station Road, left into Avonmouth Road at r'bout. One mile to Hallen, ground first
left, then right into lane to ground
    Capacity: Unknown   **Seats:** No   **Cover:** No
Clubhouse: Yes

HONOURS   Glos County Lg 92-93, Glos Snr Trophy 92-93
PREVIOUS   **League:** Glos County (pre-1993), Hellenic 93-00
    Names: Lawrence Weston Athletic (80's), Lawrence Weston Hallen (pre-1991)
    Ground: Kings Weston (early 1980's)
RECORD   **Attendance:** 803 v Bristol Rovers 1997

FACT FILE
Founded: 1949
Colours: Royal Blue/black/black
Change Colours: Yellow & Navy/ Navy/ Yellow
Midweek Matchday: Tuesday
Programme: No

CLUB PERSONNEL
Chairman: Barrie Phillips
Tel: 0117 950 1754
President: Ken Naish
Manager: Sean Bond
Coach: D Bruno
Physio: Tammy Mullan

ILFRACOMBE TOWN

Secretary: Tony Alcock, 2 Worth Road, Ilfracombe, North Devon EX34 9JA Tel: 01271 862686.
Mobile: 07977 589199

Ground: Marlborough Park, Ilfracombe, Devon Tel: 01271 865939

Directions: A361 to Ilfracombe. Turn 1st right in town after lights and follow Marlborough Rd to
the top, ground on left
Capacity: 2,000   **Seats:** 60 **Cover:** 450   **Floodlights:** Yes   **Club Shop:** No
Clubhouse: Every night 7-11pm and weekend lunchtimes. Hot & cold meals on matchdays

HONOURS   E Devon Prem Lg 25-26 28-29 29-30, N Devon Senior Lg, N Devon Prem Lg 66-67 70-71 81-82 82-83, Western Lg Div 2 R-up 52-53, Les Phillips Cup R-up 91
PREVIOUS   **Leagues:** North Devon 04-14 20-22 60-84; East Devon Premier 22-31;Exeter & District 32-39 46-49; Western 49-59
    Names: Ilfracombe FC 02-09; Ilfracombe Utd 09-14; Ilfracombe Comrades 14-20
RECORDS   **Attendance:** 3,000 v Bristol City, Ground opening, 2/10/24
    Goalscorer: Paul Jenkins 77   **Appearances:** Bobby Hancock 458

FACT FILE
Founded: 1902   Nickname: Bluebirds
Sponsors: Park View
Colours: All Blue
Change colours: All Green
Midweek matchday: Tuesday
Reserves ' League: North Devon
Programme: The Bluebird 8 pages, 40p
Editor: Peter Bidgood (01271 864756)

CLUB PERSONNEL
Chairman: Phil Hill
Vice-Chairman:Barry Jones
President: Mrs Jo Rose
Manager: Kevin Constantine
Physio: Ray Woolf

KEYNSHAM TOWN

Secretary: Iain Anderson, 195 Mount Hill Road, Hanham, Bristol BS15 9SU Tel: 0117 961 6426
Ground: Crown Field, Bristol Road, Keynsham Tel: 0117 986 5876
Directions: A4 from Bristol to Bath, ground on left before entering village opposite Crown Inn.
Bus service every 30 mins from Bristol passes ground. 10mins walk from Keynsham BR station
Capacity: 2,000   **Seats:** 120   **Cover:** 500   **Floodlights:** Yes
Clubhouse: Evenings & before & after games. Sunday lunch. Snacks   Club Shop: No
HONOURS   Somerset Lg Div 1 77-78; Somerset Snr Cup 51-52 57-58; GFA Jnr Cup 25-26; Somerset & Avon (South) Premier Cup 79-80 (SF 93-94);
BEST SEASON   **FA Cup:** 4th Qual. Rd   **FA Vase:**
PREVIOUS   **Leagues:** Bristol District, Bristol Comb., Bristol Premier, Somerset
    Grounds: The Hams 1886-1910; Gaston 1910-25; Park Road 25-30; Charlton Rd 30-39
RECORD   **Attendance:** 3,000 v Chelsea, f'light opening 88-89.
    Competitive:2,160 v Saltash, Amateur Cup, Oct 1952
98-99 - Captain: Stuart Nethercott   Top Scorer: Wayne Norman P.o.Y.: Mark Brain

FACT FILE
Founded: 1895   Nickname: K's
Sponsors: Ace Building Services Ltd
Colours: All amber
Change colours: All white
Midweek matchday: Monday
Reserves ' League: Somerset Senior
Programme: 32 pages, 50p
Editor: Mark Brown (0117 969 5487)

CLUB PERSONNEL
Chairman: Steve Brindle
President: Lester Clements
Press Officer: D Brassington
Manager: Paul Hirons
Physio:Dave Souter

Chard Town. Back Row (l-r): Kevin Warren (Goal Coach), Malcolm Adcock (Gen. Manager), Lewis Bacon, Matt Corrick, Andy Buse, Rob Webb, David Harvey (Sponsor), Roy Lock (President), Nigel Clarke (Manager), Brian Beer (Chairman). Front Row: Kirk Broom, Paul Davies, Paul Nichols, Jason Behan (Asst. Mngr), Steve Sivell, Karl Diament, Steve Redwood, Terry Emmett, Matt Foreman.

Frome Town. Back Row (l-r): Simon White (Mngr), Terry Bull (Res Mngr), Dick Pickergill (Physio), Andrew Edwards (Physio), Matt Fricker, Aaron Cribb, James Dodd, Lloyd Chamberlain, Paul Thorpe, John Haines, Rob Trapnell, Mark Salter, Aaron Blacker, Shaun Baker (Physio), Ken Randall (Asst Mngr). Front Row: Craig Tuck, Kieron White, Paul Antell, Neil Smith, John Miller, Bob Latchem, Neil Davis, Chris Moore.

Street. Back Row (l-r): Andy Lee (Physio), Sean Bobbyer, Jed Want, Justin Lewis, Kevin Hurd, Wayne Bradshaw, Steve Thompson, Matt Harris, Neil Seymour (Jnt Mngr), Julian Thresher (Jnt Mngr), Mark Clarke (Sec.). Front Row: Adam Rizutti, Fran Dellavalle, Karl Willis, Dommy Cinicola, Chris Witcombe, Paul Hayward, Gary Brown, Mark Tolls, Rhys Helmer.

Wellington. Back Row (l-r): Roger Breveton (Asst Manager), Bill Buddle (Physio), M Breveton, Mark Jones, Simon Towler, Darren Knowline, Stuart Parris, Luke Fishlock, Marcus Vaughan, Jason Greedy, Martin Ingram (Youth Manager), Dave Sheehan (Manager). Front Row: Phil Gratton, Steve Trevelyan, Simon Ingram, Chris May, John Norman, Shane Gage.

LARKHALL ATHLETIC

Secretary: Mervyn Liles, 9 Eastbourne Ave., Claremont Rd., Bath BA1 6EW (01225319427)

Ground: "Plain Ham", Charlcombe Lane, Larkhall, Bath (01225 334952)

Directions A4 from Bath, 1 mile from city centre turn left into St Saviours Rd. In Larkhall Square fork left, and right at junction, road bears into Charlcombe Lane. Ground on right as lane narrows

Capacity: 1,000   Seats: None   Cover: 50Floodlights: No

HONOURS Somerset Senior Cup 75-76, Somerset Senior Lg,; Western Lg Div 1 88-89 93-94 94-95(Div1 Merit Cup(4) 83-86 87-88(jt with Yeovil Res)

PREVIOUS **League:** Somerset Senior

FACT FILE
Founded: 1914
Nickname: Larks
Colours: Royal & white/royal & white/royal
Change colours: Red & white/red & white/red
Midweek Matches: Tuesday
Programme: Yes

CLUB PERSONNEL
President: Tony Codd
Chairman: Jim McLay
Tel: 01373 834050
Joint Managers: Paul Rankin& Mark Jefferies

PEWSEY VALE

Secretary: Russell Goodenough, 16 Easterton Lane, Pewsey, Wiltshire SN9 5BP
Tel Nos: 01672 564694 (H) 07768 512732 (M)
Ground: Recreation Ground, Ball Rd, Pewsey Tel: 01672 562990

Directions: On entering Pewsey from A345, at the Market Place proceed to end of High Street and turn right into Ball Rd, entrance to ground on right opposite pub. BR to Pewsey station
Cover: Yes   Floodlights: No

HONOURS Wiltshire County League 92-93

PREVIOUS **League:** Wiltshire County (pre-1993)
Name: Pewsey Y.M. (until late 1940s)

FACT FILE
Colours: Black & White]/Black/Black
Change colours: Blue& white/white/white
Midweek matchday: Tuesday

CLUB PERSONNEL
Chairman: Rob Thompson
Manager: Russell Goodenough

STREET

Secretary: Mark Clarke, Ostia, Overleigh,Street,Somerset BA16
Tel Nos: 01458 447353 (H) 0800252418 (W) 07979 514181 (M)
Ground: The Tannery Ground, Middlebrooks, Street, Somerset
Tel: 01458 445987 Matchdays 01458 448227
Directions: Sign posted from both ends of A39 & B3151, Station Castle Cary
Capacity: 2,000   Seating: 120   Cover: 25   Floodlights: Yes   Club Shop: No

HONOURS: Western Lge R-up 52-53

RECORDS: **Attendance:** 4,300 v Yeovil Town FA Cup 17/11/47

PREVIOUS: **Grounds:** Victoria Field, Tunpike Ground

FACT FILE
Founded: 1880   Nickname The Cobblers
Sponsors C I C A
Colours: Green & white/white/white
Change colours: Red & black/black/black
Midweek home matchday: Tuesday
Programme: 44 pages 50p
Editor: M Clarke
CLUB PERSONNEL
Chairman: Andrew Walton
Manager: Simon White
Asst Mgr: Simon Culliford
Physios: Dick Pickersgill, Andrew Lee

TEAM BATH

Secretary: Matt Birch, Flat 4, 15 Shrubbery Road, Weston-super-Mare, Som. BS23 2JJ
Tel: 01934 418645 (H) 01225 826339 (B) 01225 826755 (F)
e-mail: adsmab@bath.ac.uk

Ground: University of Bath, Sports Training Village, Claverton Down, Bath.
Tel: 01225 826339

Directions: Follow signs to Claverton Down and Park & Ride (University). Take the Norwood Ave. entrance to the campus and as you drive towards the university you will approach two "hanger" like buildings on the right. This is the Sports Training Village. Follow signs to free car park.

FACT FILE
Formed: 2000
Colours: Gold/blue/gold
Change colours: All blue
Midweek Matchday: Monday

CLUB PERSONNEL
Chairman: Ivor Powell
c/o Univ. of Bath, Sports Development, Claverton Down, Bath BA2 7AY
Tel: 01225 826656

Manager: Ged Roddy
Tel: 01225 826339

TORRINGTON

Secretary: David Priscott, 6 Highfield Terrace, Bishops Tawton, Barnstaple EX32 0AN
Tel: 01271 328316 (H) 07713 215584 (M) e-mail AFC Torrington@ talk21.com
Ground: Vicarage Field, School Lane, Great Torrington Tel: 01805 622853 **Directions:** In town centre turn left by parish church, right at swimming pool, ground behind swimming pool. Good parking. Red Bus from Bideford & Barnstaple (nearest BR station).Bus stop 300yds from ground

Capacity: 4,000   Seats: 100   Cover: 1,000   Floodlights: Yes   Shop: No

Clubhouse: Weekdays 7-11pm, Sat 11-11 & Sun 12-3. Light snacks available on matchdays.
HONOURS Western Lg R-up 90-91; Merit Cup 91-92 93-94 95-96; South Western Lg Cup 81;
Devon St Lukes Cup R-up 95-96 96-97; Devon & Exeter Lg & Cup 73-74;
Festival of Britain Cup 96-97; Les Phillips Cup R-up 91-92; Torridge Cup (13)
Somerset Youth Floodlight League 99-00

PREVIOUS   **Leagues:** N Devon; Devon & Exeter; S Western 77-84   Grounds: None
BEST SEASON   **FA Vase:** 5th Rd 84-85   FA Cup: 2nd Qual Rd. 81-82,94-95,96-97
RECORDS:Scorer: Trevor Watkins, 254 **Apps:**Mike Gilbert 527 **Fee Rcd:** £3,000 D.Walter(Yeovil)

FACT FILE
Formed: 1908
Nickname: Torrie or Supergreens
Sponsors: R & S Ware
Colours: Green & white
Change cols: White/black/black
Midweek Matches: Wednesday
Programme: 64 pages, 50p Editor: Secretary
Local Press: North DEvon Journal

CLUB PERSONNEL
President: Keith Curtis
Chairman: Winston Martin
Manager: Jeff Evans
Coach: Paul Terry
Physio: Matt McConnachie

WARMINSTER TOWN

Secretary: Mrs Joy Brown c/o club.
Ground: Weymouth Street, Warminster, Wilts BA12 9NS, Tel: 01985 217828

Directions: Take A350 for Weymouth from lights at centre of town - ground on left at brow of hill

Capacity: 2,000   Seats: 75   Cover: 150   Floodlights: Yes

Clubhouse: Yes. Evenings & matchdays   Club Shop: No

HONOURS Wilts Snr Cup 1900-01 02-03 10-11, R-up 09-10 26-27 32-33 53-54; Wilts Prem.
Lg 56-57; Wilts Jnr Cup R-up 21-22 27-28 55-56 58-59; Central Wilts Lg 08-09

PREVIOUS   **League:** WiltshireGrounds: None

RECORD   **Attendance:** 1,500 for Ladies International, England v Wales, mid-1970s

BEST SEASON   **FA Cup:** 2nd Qual. Rd.(x5)   **FA Vase:** 2nd Qual Rd

1999-00 Captain: Mick Byrne **Player of the Year:** James Theobald **Top Scorer:** Carl Clarke.

FACT FILE
Founded: 1878
Nickname: Red & blacks
Sponsors: The Assam
Colours:Blue & Black
Change: All white
Midweek Matchday: Tuesday
Reserve League: Wiltshire
Programme: 50p
Editor: Harry Theobald

CLUB PERSONNEL
Chairman: Harry Theobald
Vice-Chairman:Glen Shuttlewood
General Manager: T.B.A.
Manager: Gerry Pearson

WELLINGTON

Secretary: Dave Grabham, 12 Drakes Park, Wellington, SomersetTA21 8TB
Tel: 01823 664946 (H), 01823 355687 (B)

Ground: Wellington Playing Field, North Street, Wellington, Somerset Tel: 01823 664810

Directions: At town centre traffic lights turn into North St., then first left by Fire Station into the public car park that adjoins the ground

Capacity: 3,000   Seats: None   Cover: 200   Floodlights: Yes

Clubhouse: Yes   **Club Shop:** No

HONOURS Western Lg Div 1 R-up 80-81, Merit Cup 91-92, Comb Lge 95-96;Comb Lge
KO Cup 95-96 98-99; Somerset Snr Lg Div 1 R-up; Rowbarton & Seward Cup, Bill Slee Trophy
PREVIOUS   **Leagues:** Taunton Saturday, Somerset Senior
RECORD   **Attendance:**   **Goalscorer:** Ken Jones
BEST SEASON   **FA Cup:** 1st Qual Rd. 81-82, 84-85   **FA Vase:** 2nd rd Prop 98-99
99-00 Captain: Stuart Parris   **P.o.Y.:** Matthew Burfield   Top Scorer: Simon Towler

FACT FILE
Founded: 1892
Sponsors: A J Shire & Wadham Fencing
Colours: All tangerine
Change cols: Blue & claret stripes/blue/blue
Midweek Matches: Wednesday
Reserve Lge: Devon & Exeter Sen Div
Programme: Yes   Editor: Jane Brown
CLUB PERSONNEL
Chairman: Selwyn Aspin
Vice-Chairman: Mike Bull
President: Alan Shire
Manager: Dave Sheehan
Reserves Manager: Adrian Gladstone Smith
Physio: Ken Pearson

WORLE ST. JOHNS

Secretary: Gail Norton, 101 Devonshire Road, Weston-super-Mare, Somerset BS23 4NY
Tel: 01934 413843 (H) 01934 621167 (B) 0794 730661 (M) 01934 420048 (F)
e-mail: jahiley@aol.com

Ground: Coleridge Road, Bournville Estate, Weston-s-Mare, Somerset
Tel: 01934 612862

Directions: Leave M5 at J21and take main road into Weston-s-Mare.
Turn left at the 4th r'about into Winterstoke Road, then take the 2nd right into
Byron Road and then 1st left into Coleridge Road.

PREVIOUS   **League:** Somerset Senior Lge.
           Names: Worle & Weston St. Johns amalgamated 2000

HONOURS   R-up Somerset Sen. Lge. 99-00 (Worle)

FACT FILE
Colours: blue & black/black/blue & black
Change Colours: Claret & blue/claret/claret
Midweek Matchday: Tuesday

CLUB PERSONNEL
Chairman: John Hiley
101 Devonshire Road, Weston-s-Mare,
Somerset BS23 4NY
Tel: 01934 413843 (H)

Manager: Martin Dancey
Tel: 01934 517792

SOUTH WEST FINAL LEAGUE TABLES - SUNDAY LEAGUES

DREW SMITH HOMES SOUTHAMPTON LEAGUE

Premier Division	P	W	D	L	F	A	Pts
Brendon	24	21	2	1	96	21	65
Ford Sports	24	13	6	5	66	34	45
Old Tauntonians	24	14	3	7	59	38	45
BTC Soton Petpax	24	12	5	7	54	31	41
Midanbury	24	12	5	7	46	38	41
Durley	24	11	7	6	38	37	40
Nursling	24	11	6	7	57	40	39
Locks Heath Res	24	11	0	13	50	59	33
Solent Youth	24	9	2	13	50	45	29
Fair Oak Linden	24	5	6	13	44	62	21
Esso Fawley Res	24	6	1	17	25	82	19
North Baddesley	24	4	6	14	30	48	18
Bishopstoke Soc Res	24	1	3	20	28	108	6

WINCHESTER DISTRICT SUNDAY LEAGUE

PREMIER DIVISION	P	W	D	L	F	A	Pts
Sportsmans	18	14	2	2	63	15	30
Rising Sun	18	12	3	3	72	29	27
Owslebury	18	9	5	4	45	24	23
King Charles	18	10	2	6	52	37	22
Romsey Printing	18	9	4	5	55	40	22
Littleton CC	18	8	1	9	41	53	17
Twyford SC	18	5	1	12	26	52	11
Winchester Castle	18	4	3	11	27	80	11
Supply Line	18	4	1	13	51	72	9
Micheldever Station	18	2	4	12	30	61	8

CHICHESTER - WEST SUSSEX SUNDAY LEAGUE

DIVISION ONE	P	W	D	L	F	A	Pts
Foresters	12	10	1	1	44	12	31
Eastergate Sun	12	7	3	2	40	21	24
Rustington Sports	12	7	1	4	48	32	22
East Preston YC88	12	5	2	5	34	44	17
Berkeley Arms	12	3	2	7	31	42	11
Iavant	12	3	1	8	37	49	10
Angmering	12	1	2	9	23	57	5

GOSPORT FAREHAM SUNDAY LEAGUE

DIVISION ONE	P	W	D	L	F	A	Pts
Cyanamid	16	14	1	1	83	14	43
Golden Lion	16	10	2	4	38	22	32
Rowner Rec	16	9	4	3	66	28	31
Salterns WMC	16	8	1	7	33	37	25
Down End	16	6	3	7	33	46	21
Junction	16	5	3	8	43	40	18
Solent Athletic	16	4	3	9	26	54	15
Pentas	16	4	0	12	32	64	12
AFC Fareham	16	3	1	12	18	67	10

CITY OF PORTSMOUTH SUNDAY LEAGUE

PREMIER DIVISION	P	W	D	L	F	A	Pts
Millennium FC	16	16	0	0	88	17	48
Havant Rovers	16	11	2	3	53	33	35
Golden Hind	16	10	2	4	51	39	32
South Coast Hire	16	9	1	6	48	36	28
Stamshaw	16	6	0	10	33	59	18
Prospect	16	5	2	9	35	38	17
Harvest Home	16	3	3	10	23	52	12
HN CC	16	3	2	11	25	54	11
Court Lane	16	2	2	12	37	65	8

SOLENT LEAGUE

DIVISION ONE	P	W	D	L	F	A	Pts
Carisbrooke Arms	12	11	1	0	53	15	22
Mould Tools	12	9	1	2	39	16	19
Alver	12	7	2	3	46	25	16
Maddies	12	4	3	5	36	32	12
Cornwall Rangers	12	4	1	7	27	44	9
BSC	12	1	2	9	21	40	4
Miramar	12	1	0	11	12	62	2

MEON VALLEY LEAGUE

DIVISION ONE	P	W	D	L	F	A	Pts
East Meon	16	13	1	2	64	38	40
Fareham Sacred Heart	16	13	0	3	78	13	39
AFC Hayling	16	10	3	3	47	24	33
Fareham Sacred H WD	16	10	1	5	61	34	31
Wickham Dynamos	16	6	2	8	41	54	20
Waterlooville BOBS	16	5	3	8	43	56	18
West Meon/Wamford	16	5	0	11	28	52	15
Inter Northain	16	1	4	11	22	57	7
Crows Nest	16	1	2	13	20	76	5

PORTSMOUTH DOCKYARD LEAGUE

PREMIER DIVISION	P	W	D	L	F	A	Pts
Co-op Dragons A	16	14	0	2	71	15	42
Riga	16	9	3	4	52	27	30
Heron	16	9	3	4	50	34	30
Farmhouse	16	8	1	7	44	40	25
Dundas	16	8	1	7	45	44	25
Harvest Home	16	7	0	9	42	37	21
Hilsea Rangers	16	6	2	8	40	49	20
Mermaid	16	3	2	11	31	83	11
A/B Motors	16	1	2	13	17	63	5

HAVANT SUNDAY LEAGUE

SENIOR DIVISION	P	W	D	L	F	A	Pts
Pop Inn	16	13	1	2	63	20	40
Works FC	16	12	2	2	66	18	38
Horndean	16	8	4	4	39	30	28
Ensinger	16	8	2	6	47	34	26
Plough	16	6	2	8	31	40	20
Kenwoods	16	6	1	9	29	50	19
Clanfield	16	5	3	8	32	50	18
SMS	16	2	3	11	24	48	9
OHAH	16	2	2	12	25	66	8

BLACKMORE VALE SUNDAY LEAGUE

Division One	P	W	D	L	F	A	Pts
Bishops Caundle	16	13	2	1	70	16	41
Zeals	16	13	1	2	66	18	40
Brickfield Terriers	16	11	2	3	87	51	35
Greyhound	16	7	3	6	51	45	24
Shaston Anarchists	16	6	3	7	50	53	21
Iwerne Minster	16	6	0	10	42	52	18
Donhead	16	4	1	11	31	46	13
British Legion	16	3	2	11	34	80	11
Pegasus	16	2	0	14	24	98	6

JEWSON SOUTH WESTERN FOOTBALL LEAGUE

President: Tristan H Scott   **Chairman:** Bob Bell

Secretary: Ray Rowe, 5 Alverton Gardens, Truro, Cornwall TR1 1JA
Press Officer: Mrs Wendy Donohue, 115 Longfield, Falmouth, Cornwall TR11 4SL
Tel: 01326 316642 **Fax:** 01326 219022 **Email:** wendyjswleague@talk21.com

Many changes took place within this season, Tristan Scott who had been chairman for 22 years was elected president of the League, Bob Bell took over as chairman and ex referee Bruce Taylor was elected vice-chairman. The new chairman wasted no time in making his mark on the League and introduced the code of conduct which hopefully would help eliminate the foul and abusive language on and off the pitch.

This season also saw the successful introduction of the ground hop, which will be held over the next three years, this is the first time the hop was staged by the Jewson League and with hard work from all involved in the organisation it was voted a great success by all who attended.

The League Championship was not decided until the final week of the season with Falmouth finally taking home the trophy, but only on goal difference of only one, St. Blazey who were runners up in the League were also successful in winning the League Cup, the Senior Cup and were voted Top Ground award which they shared with last year's winners Torpoint Athletic. The new Runners-up Shield in memory of the late Dave Donohue was presented to St. Blazey at their Annual Awards Dinner held in Newquay by his widow Wendy.

JEWSON SOUTH WESTERN LEAGUE ROLE OF HONOUR 1999-2000

League Champions	Falmouth Town	**Groundsman Trophy**	St Blazey
Runners Up	St Blazey		Torpoint Athletic
Third Place	Porthleven		
Fourth Place	Liskeard Athletic	**Sporting Trophy**	Liskeard Athletic
League Cup Winners	St Blazey	**Top Referee**	Colin Spence
Runners Up	Tavistock		
Semi-Finalists	Holsworthy	**Best Programme**	Saltash United
	Falmouth Town		

FINAL LEAGUE TABLE 1999-2000

		P	W	D	L	F	A	Pts
1	Falmouth Town	34	24	8	2	88	25	80
2	St Blazey	34	25	5	4	97	36	80
3	Porthleven	34	23	9	2	91	41	78
4	Liskeard Athletic	34	18	7	9	80	40	61
5	Millbrook	34	17	9	8	68	47	60
6	Saltash United	34	18	3	13	61	50	57
7	Wadebridge Town	34	17	4	13	66	59	55
8	Tavistock	34	14	9	11	51	46	51
9	Plymouth Parkway	34	15	6	13	57	73	51
10	Newquay	34	14	5	15	67	76	47
11	Bodmin Town	34	14	4	16	60	64	46
12	Truro City	34	10	5	19	55	71	35
13	Penzance	34	10	4	20	51	76	34
14	Torpoint Athletic	34	9	6	19	53	74	33
15	Holsworthy	34	7	10	17	51	63	31
16	Callington Town	34	7	6	21	41	85	27
17	Launceston	34	5	5	24	35	95	20
18	St Austell	34	4	5	25	31	82	17

JEWSON SOUTH WESTERN LEAGUE CHALLENGE CUP 1999-2000

PRELIMINARY ROUND

Launceston	v	St Austell	1-3	Saltash	v	St Blazey	0-1

FIRST ROUND

St Austell	v	Falmouth Town	1-3	Parkway	v	Liskeard Athletic	0-5
St Blazey	v	Porthleven	2-0	Newquay	v	Tavistock	2-3
Millbrook	v	Truro City	5-2	Wadebridge	v	Penzance	1-6
Holsworthy	v	Bodmin	3-2	Torpoint	v	Callington	0-4

QUARTER FINALS

Falmouth	v	Penzance	5-1	Liskeard	v	Tavistock	0-1
St Blazey	v	Callington	3-0	Holsworthy	v	Millbrook	1-0

SEMI FINALS

St Blazey	v	Holsworthy	1-1, 3-2	Tavistock	v	Falmouth Town	3-1

FINAL

TAVISTOCK	v	St BLAZEY	1-2

Falmouth Town: Back Row (l-r): Dave Ball, Adnrew Dyer, Dave Sweet, Dominic Pullen, Ian Stephens, Steve Taylor, Andrew Street, Luke Hodge, Wayne Brown, Keith Barker (Assistant Coach), John Thompson (Secretary). Front Row: Chris Strike, Wayne Hughes, Gavin Richardson, Jason Carwardine, Adrian Street, Gary Wheildon, Andrew Parr

Liskear Athletic: Back Row (l-r): James cole, Nancy Rawlings (President), Dave Rawlings (General Secretary), John Hillson (Assistant Manager), John Collins, Brian Glanville (Treasurer), Ellis Glassup, Jamie Ahearn, Mark Henwood, Glenn Toms, Neil Webber, Ian Pook (Sponsor), T Webber, Eddie Harrison, Chris Hill. Front Row: Brian Olver (Football Secretary), Wayne Hillson, Johnny Rylatt, Jon Dawe, Mark Skerton, Steve Williams, Chris Burchell (Manager), Graeme McMillan, Andrew Wright, Andy Sargent, Wayne Tregenza, Mike Richards, Dave Hick.

BODMIN TOWN

FACT FILE
Founded: 1889   Nickname: Black & Ambers
Sponsors: Gynn Construction
Colours: Yellow & black/black/yellow
Change colours: All white
Midweek Matchday: Wednesday
Reserves' League: East Cornwall Premier
Programme: 64pages, 40p
Programme Editor: Secretary

Secretary: Jason Truman, 1 Kinsman Estate, Bodmin, Cornwall PL31 1PG
Tel: 01208 79902 (H) 0796 8216763 (M)

Ground: Priory Park, Bodmin. Tel: 01208 78165

Directions: Just off town centre in Priory Park complex, at rear of town car park

Capacity: Cover: Grandstand   Seats: Yes   Floodlights: Yes

Clubhouse: Mon-Thu 6.30-11pm (matchdays 6-11), Fri-Sat 12-11pm,
Sun 12-3 & 7-10.30pm, unless Sky matches are on then 12 -10.30 pm
Bar snacks available most times   Club Shop: No

Honours: South Western Lg 90-91 93-94 (R-up 76-77, 92-93, 94-95, Lg Cup 93-94 ,97-98
(R-up 7-78 88-89 94-95,95-96), Cornwall Snr Cup Winners 98-99 R-up 93-94,
Cornwall Charity Cup 86-87 89-90,96-97.Cornish Guardian E.C.P.L.Supplimentary
Cup 91-92 (R-Up. 93-94)-GordonSweet Cup 90-91,92-93,98-99

CLUB PERSONNEL
Chairman: C.Hooper
Vice-Chairman: P.Lee
President: A.Gynn
Manager: Sean Hooper
Asst Manager: Phil Brown
Physio: Jim Brewer

CALLINGTON TOWN

FACT FILE
Colours: Red & black/black/red & black
Change Cols.: Blue & yellow/blue/blue & yellow
Midweek Fixtures: Wednesday

Secretary: Philip Brown, Mount Pleasant Cottage, Harrowbarrow, Callington PL17 8JL
Tel: 01822 833851 (H) 01752 307102 (B)

Ground: Marshfield Park, Callington Comm. College, Launceston Rd., Callington, Cornwall
Tel: 01579 382647   e-mail: ajlong@supanet.com

Directions Turn into Callington Community College from the A388, Callington to Launceston
road. Go to the top of the drive and bear left - the ground is 100m ahead.

CLUB PERSONNEL
Chairman: Andrew Long
10 Tamar Close, Callington
Tel: 01579 383982 (H) 01752 220881 (B)

Manager: Ian Southcott
Tel: 01579 383561 (H) 07973 109609

FALMOUTH TOWN

FACT FILE
Founded: 1949   Nickname: Town
Club Sponsors: Stralfors/ Diadora
Colours: Amber/black
Change colours: Red/white
Midweek Matchday: Tues/Wed
Reserves' League: Cornwall Comb
Programme: 16 pages, 30p
Editor/ Press Off.: Mike Odgers 01209 715766

Secretary: John E Thompson, 45 Woodland Avenue, Penryn, Cornwall TR10 8PG
Tel No: 01326 372972(H) 01326 372778 (W)

Ground: Bickland Park, Bickland Vale, Falmouth, Cornwall Tel: 01326 375156
Directions: Follow A39 to Tregoniggie Industrial Estate - will pass ground on left.
1 1/2 miles from Penmere Halt (BR) on Falmouth-Truro branch line. Bus service from town centre
Capacity: 6,000   Seats: 300   Cover: 1,200   Floodlights: Yes   Club Shop: TBA
Clubhouse: Mon-Fri 7-11pm, Sat 12-11pm, Sun 12-3 & 7-10.30pm. Meals available

HONOURS: Cornish Senior Cup x 10 R-up x 7; Western Lg x 4, Lg Cup 74-75, Alan Young
Cup x 3; South Western Lg x 12 R-up x 4, Lg Cup x 10 R-up x 5; Pratten Cup   73-74,
Cornwall Charity Cup 59-60 94-95.
BEST SEASON   FA Cup: 1st Round 62-63 & 67-68
  FA Vase: Quarter Final 86-87   **FA Trophy:** 2nd Round 77-78
PREVIOUS   Leagues: Cornish Snr 50-51; South Western 51-74; Western 74-83
RECORDS   Gate: 6,300 v Oxford United, FA Cup 1st Round 3/11/62

CLUB PERSONNEL
Chairman: Malcolm Newland
Vice Chairman: Paul Ashburn
President: Seb Coe
Manager: David Ball
Coach: Keith Barker

HOLSWORTHY

FACT FILE

Nickname: Magpies
Colours: Black & White/Black/black & red
Change colours:yellow/green/green & yellow
Programme: 28 pages, ¨2 with entry
Editor: Terry Trewin.& Bob Thomson

Secretary: Mel Goodenough, 114B New Stret, Torrington, DEvon EX38 8BT
EX22 NU
Tel Nos: 01805 625049(H) 01805 622315 (emergency W)

Ground: Upcott Field Tel: 01409 254295
Cover: Yes   Floodlights: No

Directions: Leaving town on A388 towards Bideford, 100 yards past mini-roundabout on left.

Honours: Devon Senior Cup 53-54 (Prem. Cup 71-72 78-79), Devon Junior Cup 38-39

CLUB PERSONNEL
Chairman: Mike Pett
Manager: Leigh Cooper
Assistant Manager: Alan Mayes

LAUNCESTON

Secretary: Chris Martin, 3 Tavistock Road, Launceston, Cornwall PL15 9HA
Tel: 01566 776175 (H) 01566 772277 (B)
Ground: Pennygillam, Pennygillam Industrial Estate, Launceston PL15 7ED
Tel: 01566 773279   **Web site:** www.launcestonfc.co.uk
Directions: Follow signs to Pennygillam Ind. Est., just off main A30 -ground 400yds on left

Capacity: Seats: 150   Cover: 150   Floodlights: Yes
Clubhouse: Open after every game. Bar meals available.   Club Shop: No

HONOURS South Western Lg Winners 94-95, R-up 84-85, S.W Lg.Cup Winners: 95-96
Cornish Snr Cup 1899-1900 00-01 82-83 (R-up 92-93, Charity Cup R-up 88-89)

FACT FILE
Founded: 1891 Nickname: Clarets
Colours: Claret & blue/blue/claret
Change colours: Sky/Sky/claret
Midweek matchday: Tues/Wed
Reserves' League:East Cornwall Prem.
Programme: Yes
CLUB PERSONNEL
Chairman: Keith Ellacott
President: Mr.S.Dawe
General Manager: Keith Ellacott
Joint Managers: Keith Ellacott & Gary Shirley
Physio: Mrs Wendy Allen

LISKEARD ATHLETIC

Football Secretary: Brian Olver, Windrush, Tremeddan Lane, Liskeard, Cornwall PL14 3DS
Tel: 01579 342569 (H) 01752 207653 (B) 01752 207654 (Fax) 07974 636964 (M)
Ground: Lux Park, Coldstyle Road, Liskeard, Cornwall PL14 3HZ Tel: 01579 42665
Directions: Take Tavistock Road (A390) from town centre, after 1/2 mile turn left on St
Cleer Road (follow signs to Lux Park Sports Complex) & ground is 200 yards on left.
Half mile from Liskeard BR station
Capacity: 2,000 Seats: 100   Cover: 300   Floodlights: Yes   Club Shop: No
Clubhouse: (01579 342665) Normal licensing hours. Hot & cold food available

HONOURS: South Western Lg 76-77 78-79 (R-up 75-76 77-78; Lg Cup 76-77 78-79) Western Lg 87-88 (R-up 85-86 89-90, Merit Cup 80-81); Cornwall Snr Cup 04-05 83-84 84-85 85-86 88-89 89-90 93-94 (R-up 70-71 75-76 76-77 78-79 94-95); Cornwall Charity Cup 21-22 79-80, Cornwall Jnr Cup 05-06 13-14 26-27; SWPratten Cup 78-79; E Cornwall Prem RAOB Cup 67-68, Plymouth & Dist. Lg 60-61(Div 1 59-60 (R-up 54-55 73-74), Div 2 76-77(Res)), Victory Cup 60-61, Charity Cup 59-60), E Cornl Prem. Lg (Res) 84-85 92-93 93-94 R-up: 98-99,99-00(Lg.Cup 88-89 93-94,99-00)

PREVIOUS Leagues: E. Cornwall Prem., Plymouth & Dist., South Western 66-79, Western 79-95
RECORDS   Goalscorer: T Turner 59, 60-61   **Appearances:** Brian Bunney, 500+

FACT FILE
Formed: 1889   Nickname: Blues
Sponsors: J P Leisure & Gilbert Outfitters
Colours: Blue & White/blue/blue & white
Change colours: All white
Midweek matchday: Tuesday
Programme: 40 pages, 50p
Editor:I.Pook

CLUB PERSONNEL
Chairman: David Hick
Vice Chairman: B.Harding
President: W.N.Rawlings
Gen. Secretary: D J Rawlings, Bradwood, Woodgate Rd., Liskeard PL14 6DY
Manager: Chris Burchell
Asst Manager: John Hillson
Physio: Eddie Harrison

MILLBROOK

Secretary: Martin Mul;lis, 15 Statham Road, Bodmin, Cornwall. PL31 1JL
Tel: 01208 73928 (H) 01208 72681 (W)
Ground: Mill Park, Millbrook, Cornwall (01752 822113)

Directions: From Torpoint Ferry - 3 miles to Antony on A374, fork left, after 1 mile turn left again and follow B3247 to Millbrook (3 miles), take road marked `Town Centre Southdown', right at mini-r'bout after 1/4 mile, ground clearly visible. From Tamar Bridge - follow signs for Torpoint, 2 miles after Polbathic right turning marked Millbrook, 5 miles to Millbrook then proceed as above
Capacity: Seats: None   Cover: 200   Floodlights: Yes   Club Shop: No
Clubhouse: Weekdays 7-11pm, Sat 11am-11pm, Sun noon-3 & 7.30-10.30. Hot food (chips, burgers etc) available during and after matchdays
HONOURS: South Western Lg R-up 81-82, Cornwall Snr Cup R-up 83-84 (Charity Cup 84-85, Jnr Cup 75-76), Plymouth & District Lg 80-81 (Div 1 R-up 76-77)
PREVIOUS   Leagues: Plymouth Comb.(8yrs)/ Plymouth & Dist.(6yrs)
CLUB RECORDS Scorer: Unknown   **Appearances:** John Horne 215

FACT FILE
Founded: 1973   Nickname: The Brook
Sponsors: Plymouth Boat Cruises Ltd
Colours: White & Black/black/black
Change colours: All Royal blue
Midweek matchday: Tuesday
Reserve's League: Plymouth & District
Programme: 20 pages, 10p
Editor: J Weekes (01752 822637)
CLUB PERSONNEL
President: Mrs E Weekes
Chairman: Martin Bettridge
Vice Chairman: K Townsend
Press Officer: W Linney
Managers: Ricky Cardew
Asst Manager: S Matthews

NEWQUAY

Secretary: John Hawkey, 16 Higher Tower Rd, Newquay, Cornwall.TR7 1QL (01637871884)
Ground: Mount Wise, Newquay (01637 872935)
Directions: 1/2 mile from Newquay BR, follow 1-way system for 1/2 mile - ground signed on left at Clevedon Road
Capacity: 4,000   Seats: 250   Cover: 500   Floodlights: Yes   Club Shop: No
Clubhouse: 7-11pm w/days, 12-11pm Sat, 12-10.30 Sun. Hot & cold snacks during matches
HONOURS: Cornish Snr Cup 34-35 52-53 54-55 56-57 91-92(R-up(10) 05-07 08-09 25-26 33-34 35-36 57-58 69-70 84-85 87-88), S. Western Lg(7) 58-60 77-78 79-80 81-82 83-84 87-88 (R-up 57-58 85-86 94-95, Lg Cup 55-56 88-89(R-up(4) 56-58 79-81), Cornwall Charity Cup(13) 06-07 08-09 53-56 57-59 62-63 69-70 74-75 76-78 88-89 (R-up(10) 07-08 20-21 56-57 60-61 73-74 75-76 81-82 84-87), W. Cornwall Lg 06-07 (R-up(2) 07-09), Cornish Snr Lg Herald Cup 34-35 (R-up(7) 33-34 35-36 49-51 55-57 58-59)
PREVIOUS   Leagues: West Cornwall; Plymouth & District 21-27; Cornish Senior 31-51
BEST SEASON   FA Vase: 3rd Round 90-91

FACT FILE
Founded: 1890   Nickname: Peppermints
Sponsors:Hunters Sports
Colours: Red & white stripes/white/white
Change colours: Blue & white/white/white
Midweek Matchday: Tuesday
Reserve League: Cornwall Combination
Programme: 24 pages, 50p Editor: J Hawkey

CLUB PERSONNEL
Chairman: Eric.Tummon
Vice-Chairman: M.Jago
President: A.Kendall
Manager: Conrad Robins
Physio: Ross McOnie

PENRYN ATHLETIC

Secretary: Mike Young, 1 Dunvegan Road, Penryn, Cornwall TR10 8HJ
Tel: 01326 374098 (H) 01326 212974 (B) 01326 374098 (F)

Ground: "Kernick", Kernick Road, Penryn, Cornwall   Tel: 01736 75182 (Clubhouse)
Directions: From Truro take the NEW Falmouth road at Treluswell and at the Treleiver
roundabout follow signs for Kernick Industrial Estate.
Turn left at the new Asda store.

PREVIOUS **League:** Cornwall Comb. >00

FACT FILE
Colours: Red & black stripes/black/red & black
Change colours: Light & dark blue stripes/
dark blue/dark blue
Midweek matchday: Wednesday

CLUB PERSONNEL
Chairman: Peter Young
Tel: 01326 378035 (H)
Manager: David Jenkin

PENZANCE

Secretary: John Mead, 8 Chyanclare, St Clare Street, Penzance TR18 2PG
Tel./Fax: 01736 369066 (H)

Ground: Penlee Park, Alexandra place, Penzance Tel: 01736 361964
No Floodlights

Directions: Seafront road past harbour, after amusement arcade turn right at
r'bout (Alexander Rd), ground second right.
Fifteen minutes walk from Penzance(BR); directions as above

HONOURS Cornish Snr Cup 1892-93 95-96 97-98 98-99 1903-04 07-08 47-48 60-61 72-73
80-81 (R-up 1896-97 99-1900 00-01 04-05 48-49 49-50 54-55 56-57 74-75),
South Western Lg 55-56 56-57 74-75 (Lg Cup R-up 60-61), Cornwall Charity Cup 47-48 48-49 (R-
up 21-22 63-64), Cornwall Snr Lg Div 2 57-58 (Div 2 Cup 53-54 54-55), Cornwall Comb. R-up 65-
66 (Lg Cup 69-70 (R-up 81-82)), Cornwall Jnr Cup(West) 03-04 04-05 05-06 07-08 09-10

Players progressing: Gerry Gazzard (Brentford), Tony Kellow (Exeter)

FACT FILE
Founded: 1888
Nickname: Magpies
Colours: Black & white/black/black
Change colours: All sky blue
Midweek matchday: Tuesday - no lights
Reserves' league: Cornwall Comb

CLUB PERSONNEL

President: Len Stanbury
Chairman: Nigel Jolly
Manager:Gary Marks
Trainer: Ken Prowse

PLYMOUTH PARKWAY

Secretary: Stuart Cadmore, 71 Trelawny Road, Menheniot, Liskeard, Plymouth PL14 3TS
Tel: 01579 340820 (H) 01752 304096 (B) 07776 14102 (M)

Ground: None
All games, whether shown as home or away fixtures,
will be played on their opponents ground this season.

FACT FILE
Colours: Yellow/royal blue/white
Change colours: Azure blue/black/black
CLUB PERSONNEL
Chairman: Mark Rowles
Tel: 01752 790436 (H) 01752 201918 (B)
Manager: Gez Baggott
Tel: 01752 302596 (H) 0966 542982 (M)

PORTHLEVEN

Team Secretary: Vidal James, 23 Parc-an -Bans,Camborne, TR14 7RW (01209 710618)

Ground: Gala Parc, Mill Lane, Porthleven (0208 574181) Clubhouse (01326 574754)

Directions: From Penzance on A394, B3304 into Porthleven, ground on left immediately before
town. From Helston on B3304 ground on right as you exit town. Buses from Helston & Penzance
Capacity: 1,500   Seats: None   Cover: Yes   Floodlights: Yes   Shop: No
Clubhouse: Mon-Fri 7-11pm, Sat 11am-8pm, Sun 11-3 & 7-10.30pm. Full food menu at wek-ends
PREVIOUS Grounds: Treza Downs; Sunset Farm
Leagues: West Penwith; Cornwall Snr; South Western 66-77; Cornwall Comb. 77-89
HONOURS S Western Lg R-up 72-73, 98-99 Lg Cup R-up 98-99, Cornwall Comb.(6), (Lg Cup(6),
CornwallCharity Cup 70-71, 97-98 Cornwall Snr Cup R-up 68-69, 97-98 ,99-00 George Evely
Cup 64-65 65-66 83-84 86-87, West Penwith Lg, Penzance Hosp. Cup, Penzance Charity Cup
Best Performance: F.A.Vase: Quarter Finalists 1997-98

FACT FILE
Founded: 1896
Nickname: Fishermen
Colours: Yellow & black/ black/yellow & black
Change colours: All blue
Midweek Matchday: Wednesday
Reserves' Lge: Cornwall Comb
Programme: 50p

CLUB PERSONNEL
President: Mr P F Johns
Chairman: Mr Len.Williams
Vice Chairman: Mr J.Cowles
Manager: Alan Carey
Assistant Manager: George Torrance

SALTASH UNITED

Secretary: P J Gammage, 23 Spire Hill Park, Saltash, Cornwall, PL12 4SR   Tel: 01752 844046
Ground: Kimberley Stadium, Callington Road, Saltash, Cornwall Tel: 01752 845746
Directions: First left after crossing Tamar Bridge, through town centre, at top of town fork right at
min- roundabout, ground 400 yds ahead on left.
Capacity: 3,000   Seats: 250   Cover: 250   Floodlights: Yes
Clubhouse: Club attached to stand and caters for dancing and club activities.Sapphire Lounge
caters for wedding receptions,quiz nights and private functions etc
Previous Lges: Cornwall Snr; Sth Western 51-59 62-76; E Cornwall Prem 59-62; Western 76-95
HONOURS   Cornwall Snr Lg 49-50 50-51, Western Lg 84-85 86-87 88-89 (R-up 83-84 87-
88, Lg Cup 86-87 87-88 (R-up 88-89), Div 1 76-77, Merit Cup 79-80 87-88),
Sth Western Lg 53-54 75-76 (R-up 3), Lg Cup 3, Cornwall Snr Cup 6

FACT FILE
Formed: 1945
Nickname: The Ashes
Colours: Scarlet&Black/black/black
Change: All Royal Blue with yellow trim
Midweek Matchday:Tuesday/ Wednesday
Programme: 52 pages,50p
Editor: Marian Gammage
CLUB PERSONNEL
President: P Skinnard
Chairman: Michael Howard
Manager:Mike Doel & Chris Wakeham

St. AUSTELL

FACT FILE

Secretary:	Peter Beard, 24 Alexandra Rd, St Austell, Cornwall PL25 4QP
	Tel: 01726 64138
Ground:	Poltair Park, Poltair Road, St. Austell Tel: 01726 66099
Directions:	5 mins walk north of St Austell (BR)
	Capacity: 8,000 Seats: 200 Cover: 300 Floodlights: No
Clubhouse:	Mon-Fri 7-10.30 & Sat 12-11pm Food is available
PREVIOUS	**Leagues:** Rocky Park (1890s)
RECORD	**Gate:** 15,000 v Penzance, Senior Cup 49
HONOURS	South Western Lg 68-69 (R-up 4), Lg Cup 64-65 71-73 87-88 (R-up 4), Cornish Senior Cup(11)

Founded: 1890
Sponsors: Kwik Print
Colours: White/black/red
Change colours: Blue & Yellow/Red/Black
Midweek Matchday: Tuesday
Reserves' League: East Cornwall Prem.

CLUB PERSONNEL

Chairman: B.Powell
Asst Chairman: Alan Lucas
Manager: Tony Nancarrow
Asst Manager: Keith Hosbani

St. BLAZEY

FACT FILE

Secretary: Ken Cocks, 20 North St Tywardreath, Par, Cornwall PL24 2PN Tel: 01726 815187

Ground: St Blaise Park, Station Road, St Blazey Tel: 01726 814110

Directions: A390 Liskeard-St Austell road, turn into Station Road at lights inSt Blazey village; ground 100 yards on left. One and a half miles from Par (BR)

Capacity: 3,500   Seats: 200   Cover: 700   Floodlights: Yes   Club Shop: No
Clubhouse: Mon-Thur 11-3pm & 7-11pm, Fri&Sat 11-11.45pm, Sun 12-3pm & 7-11pm. Bar snacks

HONOURS   SWestern Lg (7), R-up (10), Lg Cup 5, (R-up 5), Cornish Snr Cup (9),Cornish Charity Cup (5) Cornwall Snr Lg Cup (Herald Cup) 35-3648-49

RECORDS   Gate: 6,500 v St Austell, Cornwall Snr Cup 48-49
Goalscorer: B Tallamy   **Appearances:** W Isbell

Founded: 1896
Nickname: Saints
Sponsors: Eden Project
Colours: Green, Black & White
Change colours: Blue & white/blue/blue
Midweek matchday: Wednesday
Reserve's League: East Cornwall Premier
Programme: 24 pages,50p
Editor: Steve Paynter

CLUB PERSONNEL

Chairman: Mr H Cooke
Vice Chairman: MrA Putt
Manager: Trevor Mewton
Assistant Manager: Paul Goodwin

TAVISTOCK AFC

FACT FILE

Secretary:	Philip Lowe, 25 Hessary View, Tavistock Pl19 OEZ
	Tel: 01822 613516 (H) 01752 206700(W)
Ground:	Langsford Park, Crowndale Rd, Tavistock (01822 614447)
Directions:	A386 from Plymouth, 2nd left after Ford garage into Crowndale Road and the ground is half mile on left opposite Tavistock College

Capacity: 2,000   Seats: 200   Cover: 200   Floodlights: Yes   Club Shop: No
Clubhouse: Open all day Saturday and evenings 6.30-10.30 or 11pm. Hot & cold food
HONOURS   Devon Premier Cup R-up 94-95, Devon Snr Cup 1889-90 1968-69 77-78 81-82, South Western Lg 68-69 (R-up 76-77 83-84), Bedford Cup -numerous times; Devon Charity Cup 78-79, R-up 77-78
RECORDS   Gate: 5,000 v Calstock, Bedford Cup final 1952
Appearances: A Pethick 1,000+
Players progressing: Peter & Neil Langman (Plymouth A., 51 & 53); Robbie Pethick (Portsmouth); Mike Trebilcock (Plymouth A. 65); Harold Redmond & Danny Sullivan (Crystal Pal. 57 - £100)

Founded: 1888
Nickname: `Tavy' or `Lambs'
Sponsors: SMC / Applied Automation
Colours: Red/black/black
Change colours: All Blue
Midweek matchday: Wednesday
Reserves' Lge: Plymouth & Dist Comb. (Prem)
Programme: 32 pages, with entry
Editor: Vice Chairman

CLUB PERSONNEL

Chairman: David Rowe
Vice Chairman: Eric Pinch (Press Officer)
Manager: Steve Hart
Asst Manager: Gary Tiffany
Physio: Les Mewton

TORPOINT ATHLETIC

FACT FILE

Secretary: Vic Grimwood, 43 Hemerdon Heights, Plympton PL7 3EY Tel: 01752 344263 (H)

Ground: The Mill, Mill Lane, Torpoint, Cornwall Tel: 01752 812889

Directions: Bear left from Torpoint ferry, ground down hill on left after half a mile

Capacity: Seats: Yes   Cover: Yes   Floodlights: No
Clubhouse: Yes

PREVIOUS   League: Plymouth & District League.(Premier)

BEST SEASON   FA Vase: 4th Round 93-94, 0-3 v Diss Town (H), eventual winners

HONOURS   South Western Lg 64-65 66-67 (Lg Cup R-up 65-66), Cornish Snr Cup 8

Colours: Gold & black stripes/gold/gold
Change colours: Red/white/red
Programme: Yes

CLUB PERSONNEL

Chairman: Colin Phillips
Tel: 01752 705845 (H)

Manager: Phil Cardew
Tel: 01752 812721 (H)

TRURO CITY

Secretary: Brian Fisher, 33 Southview Road, Biscosey, Par Pl24 2HJ(01726 812238)

Ground: Treyew Road, Truro, Cornwall (01872 278853)

Capacity: 5,000   Seats: 250   Cover:Yes   Floodlights: Yes

Directions: On A39 by-pass south of city.
10 mins walk from BR station; up hill and left at junction

HONOURS   South Western Lg 60-61 69-70 92-93 95-96 97-98, (R-up 54-55 62-63 66-67
67-68 70-71 96-97), Lg Cup 59-60 66-67(jt) 92-93 (R-up 54-55 58-59 67-68 93-94 95-96 97-98);
Cornish Snr Cup x13; Cornish Charity Cup x7; Cornish Snr Lg 31-32 32-33; Cornwall Combination
94-95 98-99 League Cup: 1968,78,86,88,99

FACT FILE
Formed: 1889
Colours: Red & black/black/black
Change colours: Blue& white/white/white
Midweek Matchday: Tuesday
Programme: Yes

Reserve s' League: Cornwall Combination

CLUB PERSONNEL
Chairman: Des Coad
Manager: Chris Webb

WADEBRIDGE TOWN

Secretary: Mike Tregaskes, 10 TRezaise Close, Roche, St Austell Pl26 8HW
Tel Nos: 01726 890782 (H) 01726 890782 (W)

Ground: Bodieve Park (0208 812537)

Seats: No   Cover: Some   Floodlights: No

Directions: At junction of A39 and B3314 to east of Wadebridge

HONOURS   South Western Lg R-up 68-69 78-79 79-80 (Lg Cup 5), (R-up 3),
CornishSenior Cup 79-80, Cornish Charity Cup 8

FACT FILE

Nickname: Bridgers
Colours:All red/white
Change colours: All blue/white
Reserve s' League: East Cornwall Premier

CLUB PERSONNEL

Chairman: Dave Herring
Manager:Gary McKinnon

BRITAIN'S MOST POPULAR NATIONAL NON-LEAGUE FOOTBALL MONTHLY

TeamTalk

provides comprehensive coverage of the

whole spectrum of non-League
football from the Nationwide
Conference to County League

including extensive coverage of
- the FA Carlsberg Vase   • the FA Umbro Trophy
- non-League involvement in the AXA sponsored FA Cup
and the England Semi-Professional team

(Team Talk is the ONLY magazine to give such support and coverage to this England team)

Penryn. Back Row (l-r): Dennis Pitt (Coach), Paul Kneebone, Ryan Treloar, Gareth Pitt, Steve Coggin, Darren Burchen, David Hodges, Rob Riley, Andrew Trathan, Lee Oldfield, David Jenkin (Manager). Front Row: Bryn Wheeler, Matthew Potts, Steven Jewell, Andy Angove, Jon Perrow, Ben Way, Kevin Burleigh, Martin Ede (Physio).

Porthleven. Back Row (l-r): Jan Cowls (Vice Chair), Vidal James (Football Sec.), Graham Hart (Physio), Ian Hodges, Adrian Hart, Andy Avery, Gary Penhaligon, Ben Hayden, Dwayne Britton, Richard Triggs, Darren Holsey, Len Williams (Chairman), Alan Carey (Mngr). Front Row: Paul Ainscough, Adrian Bleasdale, Alan Roberts, Nick Medlin, John Burrows (Capt), Malcolm Gilbert (Sponsor), David Phillips, Danny Williams, George Torrance (Asst Manager)

Saltash. Back Row (l-r): Chris Howells (Coach), Chris Wakeham (Jnt Mngr), Gary Andrew, Gary Turner, Paul Sowden, Charles West, Harry Richardson, Jamie Morgan, Mike Doel (Jnt Player/Manager), Jeff Bennett (Coach). Front Row: Richard Daly, Stefan May, Nathan Blamey, Mark Conday, Darren Gilbert, Ian Symons, Nick Griffiths, Paul Adcock, Lee Harvey, Dave Williams (Physio).

St Blazey. Back Row (l-r): Terry Huddy (Trainer), Ken Cocks (President-Secretary), Harry Cooke (Chairman), Neil Burton, Dave Jones (Asst Mngr), Dave Philp, Glynn Hooper, Nigel Pugh, Paul Smith, Brian Brokenshire (Treasurer), Amos Putt (Vice Chairman). Front Row: Justin Harrington, Graham Waters, Ian Gosling, Trevor Mewton (Manager), Mark Rowe (Captain), Sam McKone, Shaun Sullivan, Chris Hawke.

WESTERN DEVELOPMENTS
DEVON COUNTY LEAGUE

President: Carl Throgmorton
Vice President: William Smale
Chairman: David Moore   **Vice Chairman:** Stephen Ware
Hon. Secretary: Philip Hiscox
19 Ivy Close, Wonford, Exeter EX2 5LX   (Tel/Fax: 01392 493995)

That was the season that was? Or was it? I really don't know what to make of the past season. Some will claim that quality was sadly lacking, that consistency was simply inconsistent and that the sheer unpredictable nature of the season meant that really nobody was able to take a firm grip. Others will point to a thrilling title race which was as open and as exciting as it is ever likely to get, that the previous "lesser" powers caught up on the bigger clubs and that it was that same unpredictability that made it all so good.

There were without doubt some notable successes and high points. For me the emergence of Ivybridge Town and Newton Abbot Spurs as title contenders, the fresh faces of Exeter Civil Service in the Cups and the restoration of Alphington, Budleigh, and Stoke & Vospers as leading lights, coupled with the hard to beat solid progress of Plymstock United, shows eight clubs with plenty to be happy about. Cullompton, Dartmouth, Newton Abbot, Ottery and Willand all were hard to beat and had their moments, but in the end analysis they all had one thing in common; they had under-achieved despite their crowing glory moments of recent seasons.

Appledore and Buckfastleigh had reasonable seasons given their exodus of managers and players last summer but, of course, for some the season provided very little to shout about. Crediton United, Elburton Villa, Heavitree United and Topsham Town all had reason to be grateful for the early season failings of Newton St Cyres. St Cyres made a late and at times uplifting fight for survival but in the end it was a case of just too little, too late. St Cyres will return to the Devon & Exeter League with a reputation as a friendly and sportsmanlike club firmly intact and I wish them well. Buckland Athletic will join us next year after another impressive season spent knocking on our door; they deserve their chance and will no doubt be looking forward to the challenge.

The title race was of course thrilling and exciting, and the early pace setters were Alphington who waltzed through August and looked as good as anything we had seen before, but suddenly Budleigh visited the Chronicles and inflicted the first of too many home defeats. Budleigh took up the mantle at the top but were chased hard, firstly by Dartmouth who won successive Manager of the Month Awards, then when the Darts slipped Newton Spurs became the main challengers, embarking on an impressive run through the winter months. The chase was joined by Ivybridge Town and Vospers Oak Villa, who both had free scoring spells in the Spring and really set the whole thing alive. As the West Devon challenge faded in the lighter evenings of April, so Stoke Gabriel came into the running, having spent so much of the season hovering around in sixth place. They put a run of twelve successive league wins together and Budleigh were pressured. The "Robins" dropped points and when the two met on May 6th the Stoke victory ensured a battle royal for the title. Budleigh responded at Crediton, Stoke won at Topsham. Dartmouth inflicted a second loss in a week on Budleigh, then Stoke won at Elburton, leaving Budleigh to have to beat Appledore to stay in the running. This they did to set up Stoke needing a win on May 15th, nine months after it had all begun, and after 90 minutes pulsating passion Dartmouth showed again that they are a match for anybody by breaking Stoke Gabriels' hearts and sending Budleigh the title by only a single point.

The strength of the league could be explained by just one fact; last season Willand collected 90 points to win the league and Teignmouth earned just seven in last place. This season Budleigh amassed 81 (one less than the previous season when they were third!) and St Cyres notched up twenty, meaning that the top to bottom spread had fallen by a remarkable 22 points. Budleigh's 81 points is the lowest in a 38 game season and the first time a club had dropped more than 30 points in a season and won. This is not to distract from Budleigh's glory, more to illustrate the nature of the season.

In the Cups Vospers Oak Villa caused a few replays and a long drawn out saga about a trip into Europe, but in the end it was all worthwhile as they landed themselves the Cup and kept up the league record of five County Cup wins in the last five years. New boys Exeter Civil Service marched through to the final to set up a second all-league affair, but on the night the firepower of Vospers was just too much.

Vospers also equalled the record for the most league goals in a season (117) and had Sean Cornish end as the league's highest scorer, and with Roger Bonaparte's goals they can claim the most lethal forward line of the season too.

The Throgmorton Cup was won under the new penalties rule by the league new boys, Exeter Civil Service, some reward for an excellent first season from the Foxhayes club. Spare a thought for Stoke Gabriel though, as the league record of nobody doing a "double" may still be intact, but it must have been hard on Stoke to be runners up in both league and cup.

Elsewhere Willand Rovers beat Hellenic League Tuffley Rovers to achieve the first FA Vase win by a league club and players from both Willand and Alphington made huge contributions to the Devon FA team that won their group only to lose in the Counties Final.

Other honours were shared around with Plymstock United being the winners of the Bass Sporting trophy, not only top marked by referees but also the only club not to have a red card all season. Ottery St Mary were second in the Sporting Award and claimed the Charity Shield back in August, and Newton Abbot Spurs notched up two claims of prize money with third place in the league and a semi-final appearance in the Throgmorton Cup too.

So that was the season that was? Yes, it certainly was!

Philip Hiscox, Secretary

FINAL LEAGUE TABLE 1999-2000

	P	W	D	L	F	A	W	D	L	F	A	Pts
Budleigh Salterton	38	13	3	3	54	25	12	3	4	48	26	81
Stoke Gabriel	38	15	1	3	42	16	11	1	7	50	32	80
Newton Abbot Spurs	38	11	4	4	37	27	12	4	3	47	18	77
Alphington	38	10	2	7	40	36	13	2	4	42	26	73
Vospers Oak Villa	38	12	1	6	62	31	11	2	6	55	39	72
Ivybridge Town	38	10	3	6	49	27	12	3	4	50	29	72
Willand Rovers	38	11	4	4	44	19	9	4	6	39	25	65
Dartmouth	38	11	1	7	42	23	9	4	6	53	35	65
Ottery St Mary	38	12	5	2	55	25	5	8	6	25	30	64
Cullompton Rangers	38	12	2	5	59	34	6	2	11	36	40	58
Newton Abbot	38	12	3	4	57	33	5	2	12	24	38	56
Exeter Civil Service	38	8	4	7	48	53	7	6	6	29	23	55
Appledore	38	8	7	4	33	23	5	5	9	30	48	51
Plymstock United	38	8	3	8	28	27	4	3	12	24	42	42
Buckfastleigh Rangers	38	7	2	10	21	32	3	4	13	22	43	36
Topsham Town	38	4	2	13	26	44	5	2	12	27	45	31
Crediton United	38	4	3	12	28	52	3	3	13	25	65	27
Heavitree United	38	2	5	12	22	57	5	1	13	28	61	27
Elburton Villa	38	2	5	12	26	58	3	2	14	32	81	22
Newton St Cyres	38	3	3	13	29	67	2	2	15	23	56	20

RESULTS CHART 1999-2000

		1	2	3	4	5	6	7	8	9	10	11	12	13	14	15	16	17	18	19	20
1	Alphington	X	2-0	3-1	3-6	1-0	1-5	5-3	2-5	0-1	3-1	2-3	1-0	0-0	2-3	1-1	6-0	0-4	2-0	3-2	3-1
2	Appledore	0-1	X	1-1	1-1	2-0	2-1	2-2	2-0	1-1	2-2	0-2	2-0	1-1	9-3	0-0	1-0	1-3	1-2	4-3	1-0
3	Buckfastleigh Rngrs	2-3	4-2	X	2-1	0-3	1-1	0-3	3-0	1-1	1-0	0-2	2-1	0-4	2-1	0-1	0-2	0-1	3-2	0-2	0-3
4	Budleigh Salterton	2-4	6-0	3-0	X	5-1	4-1	2-2	7-2	2-1	3-0	0-0	2-0	1-3	3-2	3-3	1-0	3-2	2-0	5-1	0-3
5	Crediton United	0-4	1-4	2-3	1-2	X	3-1	2-8	2-3	1-5	4-1	1-0	2-4	0-0	0-2	1-1	2-1	3-3	0-3	1-3	2-4
6	Cullompton Rngrs	4-1	1-1	1-0	2-3	2-1	X	6-0	14-2	0-3	6-0	0-4	5-3	3-0	6-4	0-3	2-1	3-2	2-2	2-1	0-3
7	Dartmouth	0-1	4-1	4-2	1-0	8-0	1-2	X	3-0	2-1	3-1	2-3	1-2	2-2	2-0	0-1	2-1	2-0	3-1	2-3	0-2
8	Elburton Villa	1-4	3-3	2-2	0-5	3-2	2-5	1-5	X	2-2	2-4	2-6	0-3	0-3	0-0	2-2	0-2	0-3	4-2	2-3	0-2
9	Exeter Civil Service	2-4	2-0	6-3	4-5	3-3	2-1	3-7	4-4	X	2-0	3-3	0-2	1-6	3-1	4-1	0-0	3-2	3-2	1-6	2-3
10	Heavitree United	1-4	0-3	2-0	0-5	1-1	1-4	0-4	3-2	1-1	X	2-4	1-3	0-1	2-2	2-2	2-5	0-4	1-1	1-7	2-4
11	Ivybridge Town	0-3	1-1	3-0	2-1	1-1	0-2	1-4	5-0	1-3	5-0	X	3-1	3-4	2-0	5-0	4-1	1-2	6-0	4-2	2-2
12	Newton Abbot	4-4	3-1	2-3	2-2	4-2	2-0	2-1	3-1	3-1	10-1	0-0	X	3-1	5-1	3-2	3-0	4-6	0-1	2-5	2-1
13	Newton Abbot Spurs	1-1	5-0	2-0	1-1	2-1	3-1	0-6	1-1	1-0	3-2	4-1	5-1	X	1-0	2-1	2-1	0-2	1-2	2-5	1-1
14	Newton St Cyres	1-2	1-3	3-2	0-5	1-2	5-2	2-5	2-3	0-2	2-3	1-8	1-1	1-10	X	1-2	2-3	2-1	1-6	2-2	0-5
15	Ottery St Mary	3-1	1-1	4-1	0-1	6-0	2-2	0-0	7-2	1-1	5-2	6-1	3-1	0-3	4-2	X	3-1	3-2	3-1	2-2	2-1
16	Plymstock United	1-2	1-1	1-0	2-3	4-2	3-2	0-2	5-0	0-1	2-1	0-2	3-1	1-3	1-0	1-1	X	0-3	1-0	1-2	1-1
17	Stoke Gabriel	0-1	4-0	0-0	2-0	5-0	2-1	2-0	2-1	3-2	3-0	1-3	1-0	1-2	5-1	1-0	2-1	X	2-0	3-2	2-1
18	Topsham Town	1-2	2-4	1-2	1-2	1-4	1-3	2-1	4-3	1-3	2-3	1-4	1-0	0-1	1-0	0-1	3-3	2-5	X	1-2	1-1
19	Vospers Oak Villa	1-0	5-2	2-1	2-4	12-2	3-2	5-0	4-3	0-0	1-3	1-2	5-1	0-3	3-1	1-2	6-1	1-3	7-0	X	3-1
20	Willand Rovers	2-0	2-3	1-1	0-1	4-0	2-0	0-0	8-0	3-0	2-4	3-2	0-0	1-0	5-0	2-1	1-1	4-2	3-2	1-2	X

LEADING GOALSCORERS 1999-2000

Sean Cornish	Vospers Oak Villa	36
Kevin Smith	Alphington	34
Richard Lennie	Crediton United	31
Justin Osborne	Stoke Gabriel	31
Mark Seatherton	Cullompton Rangers	28
Steve Blurton	Budleigh Salterton	27
Roger Bonaparte	Vospers Oak Villa	27
Rob McGahey	Alphington	26
Simon Purrington	Exeter Civil Service	25

BASS SPORTSMANSHIP CUP 1999-2000

Position	Club	Marks	Average
1	Plymstock United	293	7.71
2=	Heavitree United	291	7.65
	Ottery St Mary	291	7.65
4=	Budleigh Salterton	290	7.63
	Exeter Civil Service	290	7.63

LEAGUE ALL TIME RECORDS

		P	W	D	L	F	A	Pts	P/G
1	Stoke Gabriel	280	170	56	54	710	328	566	2.02
2	Willand Rovers	280	157	52	71	657	388	523	1.86
3	Newton Abbot	280	141	58	81	635	408	481	1.71
4	Cullompton R	280	130	45	105	539	449	435	1.55
5	Alphington	280	124	54	102	539	500	426	1.52
6	Vospers Oak V	280	121	46	113	610	542	409	1.46
7	Buckfastleigh R	280	118	48	114	540	525	402	1.43
8	Topsham Town	280	109	54	117	546	531	381	1.36

ALL TIME LEADING GOALSCORERS

Justin Osborne	132
Mark Seatherton	132
David Downing	109
Alan Clarke	102

GLOUCESTER COUNTY LEAGUE

Chairman: A C Barrett
Hon. Secretary: D J Herbert, 8 Fernhurst Road, St George, Bristol BS5 7TQ
Tel: 0117 951 7696

FINAL LEAGUE TABLE 1999-2000

	P	W	D	L	F	A	Pts		P	W	D	L	F	A	Pts
Highbridge United	34	26	5	3	68	29	83	Old Georgians	34	13	7	14	47	62	46
Cadbury Heath	34	22	6	6	81	42	72	Frampton Athletic	34	13	5	16	50	49	44
Patchway Town	34	19	6	9	70	33	63	Roman Glass St George	34	12	5	17	57	74	41
Hardwicke	34	18	5	11	62	47	59	Viney St Swithins	34	10	10	14	43	48	40
DRG	34	16	10	8	63	35	58	Broad Plain House OB	34	10	9	15	35	51	39
Henbury Old Boys	34	17	6	11	51	41	57	Pucklechurch Sports	34	11	5	18	47	70	38
Ellwood	34	16	8	10	54	37	56	Brockworth	34	7	9	18	40	61	30
Tytherington Rocks	34	17	3	14	67	60	54	Broadwell Amateurs	34	6	3	25	38	93	21
Winterbourne United	34	13	7	14	73	67	46	Dursley Town	34	4	3	27	29	76	15

RESULTS CHART 1999-2000

		1	2	3	4	5	6	7	8	9	10	11	12	13	14	15	16	17	18
1	Broad Plain House OB	X	2-0	1-4	1-4	1-2	0-0	1-0	0-1	0-1	2-2	0-0	2-1	0-0	1-2	4-2	0-2	0-0	1-2
2	Broadwell Amateurs	0-1	X	5-4	1-4	2-0	1-0	1-1	3-2	1-0	0-2	1-2	4-2	1-3	1-4	1-3	2-4	0-3	1-3
3	Brockworth	0-0	3-3	X	1-3	2-2	1-0	2-3	0-1	0-0	0-1	0-2	1-1	1-2	1-4	1-1	3-3	1-1	2-1
4	Cadbury Heath	1-1	4-2	2-1	X	1-1	5-2	2-1	2-1	1-2	2-0	2-4	1-1	0-3	4-0	7-0	5-2	0-3	3-0
5	DRG	1-2	7-0	5-1	0-2	X	3-0	1-0	1-0	4-0	0-0	0-0	1-2	0-3	6-0	3-1	1-2	3-3	3-3
6	Dursley Town	1-2	2-0	0-1	1-2	0-1	X	1-3	0-2	0-2	0-1	1-3	3-2	1-1	2-3	0-3	5-3	4-2	0-1
7	Ellwood	1-2	5-1	2-1	1-0	1-1	5-1	X	1-1	0-1	2-0	4-2	0-0	2-1	3-1	1-1	2-0	0-0	2-0
8	Frampton Athletic	0-2	3-0	2-0	1-2	0-3	3-1	3-0	X	1-1	1-3	0-1	2-3	2-4	3-3	0-1	2-3	2-0	1-1
9	Hardwicke	4-1	5-0	3-1	1-3	3-1	2-0	0-3	0-1	X	3-1	2-4	2-0	2-1	3-0	4-2	0-3	2-2	4-1
10	Henbury Old Boys	1-1	2-1	2-0	1-1	0-2	4-0	0-2	2-0	0-0	X	1-2	1-0	1-1	2-0	2-1	4-2	2-1	1-2
11	Highridge United	2-0	3-0	4-1	0-4	0-0	4-1	2-0	2-1	2-0	4-1	X	2-0	1-0	2-0	2-0	2-0	2-1	2-2
12	Old Georgians	2-1	1-1	1-0	0-3	1-1	2-1	1-0	2-4	2-0	1-0	1-0	X	1-2	2-1	2-2	4-2	1-3	6-3
13	Patchway Town	4-0	3-0	L-W	2-2	1-2	1-0	4-0	2-0	2-0	4-1	2-2	4-0	X	5-1	3-0	1-3	1-1	3-1
14	Pucklechurch Sports	2-2	3-1	2-1	0-2	1-1	1-1	1-0	0-1	2-4	2-1	2-3	2-0	4-0	X	2-4	1-1	1-2	0-3
15	Roman Glass St George	1-2	4-3	1-0	1-4	1-3	2-0	0-0	2-4	3-1	1-3	0-1	6-2	0-4	2-0	X	2-5	2-2	1-2
16	Tytherington Rocks	3-2	3-0	1-3	1-1	1-0	3-0	0-1	0-2	2-4	2-4	0-1	0-1	2-1	3-0	1-0	X	3-0	1-3
17	Viney St Swithins	1-0	1-0	1-2	0-1	0-2	2-0	1-4	1-0	2-2	1-3	0-1	2-2	2-0	0-1	2-3	1-2	X	1-1
18	Winterbourne Utd	4-0	4-1	1-1	6-1	1-2	5-1	4-4	3-3	1-4	0-2	2-4	5-0	0-2	3-1	3-4	2-4	0-1	X

CONSTITUTION FOR 2000-01

AXA Sun Life, Broad Plain House Old Boys, cBrockworth, DRG, Ellwood, Frampton Athletic Rangers, Hardwicke, Henbury Old Boys, Highridge United, Old Georgians, Patchway Town, Pucklechurch Sports, Roman Glass St George, Totterdown Port of Bristol, Tytherington Rocks, Viney St Swithens, Whitminster, Winterbourne United

Top: Witchampton United defend a Portland United corner, they survive on this occasion but lost 6-2 to visiting Portland United in the Dorset Combination League.
Photo: Tim Lancaster

Centre: Skurrays Wiltshire League Premier Division action from Shrewton United against Bradford Town. Bradford Town won 2-1.
Photo: Tim Lancaster

Bottom: SWEB South West Counties Youth League Champions: Yeovil Town Youth Team with their coach Stuart Housley on the extreme left.
Photo: Ken Gregory

SOMERSET SENIOR FOOTBALL LEAGUE

Chairman: Miss S A Wright

Hon Secretary: C R J Rose Esq.
Sutley House, Pilton, Shepton Mallet BA4 4BL   Tel: 01749 890767

FINAL LEAGUE TABLES 1999-2000

PREMIER DIVISION

	P	W	D	L	F	A	Pts
Shirehampton	36	24	6	6	99	43	78
Worle	36	24	5	7	97	45	77
Shepton Mallet	36	22	6	8	59	24	72
Brislington	36	20	7	9	77	42	67
Clevedon United	36	20	5	11	92	53	65
Burnham United	36	20	5	11	72	51	65
Portishead	36	18	6	12	55	46	60
Mangotsfield United*	36	17	5	14	74	60	55
Timsbury Athletic	36	15	9	12	66	66	54
Radstock Town	36	15	7	14	61	53	52
Nailsea United	36	14	10	12	59	58	52
Bridgwater Town	36	16	3	17	70	67	51
Robinsons	36	13	9	14	52	50	48
Wells City	36	9	10	17	50	61	37
Fry Club	36	10	4	22	59	83	34
Backwell United	36	8	10	18	47	82	34
Oldland Abbotonians	36	8	8	20	39	69	32
Glastonbury	36	4	5	27	33	121	17
Westland United	36	2	6	28	39	126	12

FIRST DIVISION

	P	W	D	L	F	A	Pts
Welton Rovers	34	25	4	5	85	37	79
Long Sutton	34	20	4	10	78	45	64
Watchet Town	34	18	10	6	65	36	64
Castle Cary	34	17	10	7	64	40	61
Stockwood Green	34	14	12	8	60	55	54
Cheddar	34	16	5	13	51	52	53
Congresbury	34	14	9	11	69	61	51
Cleeve West Town	34	11	12	11	48	39	45
Saltford	34	11	9	14	67	65	42
Peasedown Athletic	34	10	9	15	49	62	39
Hengrove Athletic	34	10	9	15	37	52	39
Winscombe	34	12	3	19	44	64	39
Clevedon United Res*	34	10	10	14	57	56	38
Paulton Rovers	34	9	11	14	52	65	38
Bishop Sutton	34	11	4	19	45	68	37
Odd Down	34	10	5	19	43	63	35
Imperial FC	34	8	10	16	42	57	34
Nailsea United Res	34	9	6	19	35	74	33

WILTSHIRE COUNTY LEAGUE

Secretary: Peter Ackrill, 3 Dallas Avenue, Swindon SN3 3NP
Tel: 01793 520334

FINAL LEAGUE TABLES 1999-2000

PREMIER DIVISION

	P	W	D	L	F	A	Pts
Malmesbury Victoria	28	22	4	2	91	25	70
Raychem S & S	28	20	5	3	77	34	65
Cricklade Town	28	20	3	5	103	24	63
Devizes Town Res	28	17	4	7	55	43	55
Melksham Town Res	28	18	0	10	60	53	54
Biddestone	28	16	4	8	73	35	52
Shrewton United	28	14	5	9	77	42	47
Bradford Town	28	14	1	13	50	43	43
Westbury Utd Res	28	9	4	15	44	51	31
Purton Res	28	9	4	15	44	72	31
Wroughton	28	6	6	16	41	60	24
Corsham Town Res	28	6	3	19	28	91	21
Warminster Town Res	28	6	2	20	35	78	20
Marlborough Town	28	4	5	19	27	81	17
Pewsey Vale Res	28	2	4	22	14	87	10

INTERMEDIATE DIVISION

	P	W	D	L	F	A	Pts
Trowbridge Town	24	20	2	2	97	28	62
Southbrook	24	19	2	3	124	28	59
Aldbourne	24	16	3	5	79	33	51
Blunsdon United	24	14	2	8	57	42	44
Burmah Castrol	24	13	3	8	64	33	42
Wanborough Utd	24	11	6	7	69	40	39
Down Ampney	24	11	4	9	63	55	37
Mitel	24	10	6	8	55	58	36
Biddestone Res	24	8	4	12	60	71	28
Raychem S & S Res	24	7	3	14	32	55	24
Wroughton Res	24	5	4	15	46	69	19
Dunbar Athletic	24	2	1	21	19	96	7
Marlboro Town Res	24	0	0	24	14	171	0

CONSTITUTION FOR 2000-01

Aldbourne, Biddestone, Bradford Tn, Chiseldon Southbrook, Corsham Tn Res, Cricklade Tn, Devizes Tn Res, Malmesbury Victoria Res, Marlborough Town, Melksham Town Res, Pewsey Vale Res, Purton Res, Stratton Crosslink, Shrewton Utd, Trowbridge Town, Warminster Town Res, Westbury Utd Res, Wroughton

CONSTITUTION FOR 2000-01

Biddestone Reserves, Blunsdon United, Burmah Castrol, Chiseldon Southbrook Reserves, Cricklade Town Reserves, Down Ampney, Dunbar Westside, Mitel, Stratton Crosslink Reserves, Wanborough United

WEST OF ENGLAND SUNDAY LEAGUE TABLES 1999-2000

BRISTOL COMMERCIAL SUNDAY LEAGUE

PREMIER DIV.

	P	W	D	L	F	A	Pts
Nailsea Glass	18	14	2	2	79	33	44
Nailsea Pats.	17	10	3	4	64	35	33
Cliftonwood Cors	17	9	2	6	34	27	29
Bridge Academs*	16	8	2	6	45	40	25
George Hotel*	15	7	3	5	41	31	23
Oracle Rapide	17	5	5	7	52	45	20
Avon Rams	13	5	4	4	30	32	19
Bellcelona	16	5	2	9	35	74	17
Broad Plain Sunday	17	4	2	11	32	54	14
Unathletico	18	2	1	15	22	62	7

TAUNTON SUNDAY LEAGUE

DIVISION ONE

	P	W	D	L	F	A	Pts
TYCC	19	16	2	1	70	24	50
Foxy Ferrets	20	12	4	4	68	40	40
Cannonsgrove	19	9	5	5	53	46	32
Spartans	17	9	4	4	46	43	31
Waggon Clavel	20	9	1	10	43	48	28
Staplegrove	18	8	2	8	57	43	26
Ash Rangers	20	7	3	10	55	49	24
Bathpool	19	6	3	10	50	52	21
Britannia Inn	19	6	1	12	55	76	19
Hamilton Athletic	20	4	3	13	24	72	15
Milverton	19	4	2	13	40	68	14

DIVISION TWO

	P	W	D	L	F	A	Pts
Perfecto	21	19	0	2	99	42	57
Inter Royal	22	14	2	6	74	44	44
Sampsford Blues	22	13	1	8	103	63	40
Cyder Press	21	12	4	5	80	51	40
Vivary Rovers	21	10	3	8	45	48	33
North Curry	22	9	3	10	45	44	30
Dolphin Inn	22	9	2	11	64	72	29
Priorswood United	22	8	1	13	42	59	25
Wiveliscombe	22	8	1	13	63	81	25
Norton Fitzwarren	22	8	1	13	50	71	25
Old Inn	21	5	3	13	42	75	18
Blackbrook	22	4	1	17	38	95	13

DIVISION THREE

	P	W	D	L	F	A	Pts
Black Horse	22	18	1	3	125	46	55
Wilton Rangers	21	14	4	3	97	37	46
Trull Rovers	22	14	4	4	88	57	46
Kings Park Rangers	21	12	4	5	71	55	40
Cross Farm Celtic	22	10	3	9	95	88	33
Eagle Taverners	22	9	6	7	66	66	33
Watchet Town BW	22	9	2	11	64	72	29
CS Mariners	22	8	4	10	81	87	28
E Reach Wanderers	22	6	4	12	48	76	22
Linden City	22	4	8	10	31	50	20
W Somerset W	22	4	1	17	31	79	13
Royal Crown	22	1	3	18	32	116	6

CHIPPENHAM & DISTRICT SUNDAY LEAGUE

PREMIER DIV

	P	W	D	L	F	A	Pts
Cooper Avon R	22	16	3	3	79	38	35
Kings Arms	22	12	3	7	72	45	27
Neston 81	22	9	7	6	45	43	24
Dog & Fox	22	10	4	8	43	42	24
Box	22	11	4	7	50	37	21
Winsley	22	8	6	8	46	37	21
Old Lane Utd 'A'	22	8	4	10	62	64	20
Westbury Rangers	22	9	2	11	50	60	20
Avon News	22	8	4	10	42	59	20
Corsham Centre	22	9	1	12	56	69	19
Goatacre	22	7	4	11	54	53	18
North Star 'A'	22	2	4	16	22	74	8

DIVISION ONE

	P	W	D	L	F	A	Pts
Melksham MS	22	15	3	4	77	30	33
Quarry Arms	22	15	0	7	101	47	30
George Lacock	22	12	5	5	73	34	29
Courthouse	22	12	2	8	74	51	26
Bromham	22	10	6	6	59	47	26
Colerne 'A'	22	10	5	7	61	48	25
Gladstone Libs	22	11	2	9	54	49	22
Hullavington	22	8	5	9	35	43	21
Chipp. Police	22	7	3	12	48	69	17
Atworth United	22	6	4	12	31	69	16
North Bradley	22	6	3	13	48	80	14
Avon Bradford	22	0	2	20	27	121	2

BRISTOL & DISTRICT SUNDAY LEAGUE

PREMIER DIV

	P	W	D	L	F	A	Pts
Lebeq Tavern	18	14	2	2	58	21	44
Autocrash	18	11	3	4	53	32	36
Hanham Sunday	18	10	2	6	49	32	32
Aidan Rangers	18	9	2	7	31	27	29
Beaufort	18	8	2	8	29	26	26
Shireway Sports	18	7	3	8	42	56	24
Hallen United	18	7	2	9	34	32	23
Golden Bottle	18	5	2	11	26	41	17
Rowles Tiling	18	4	4	10	23	53	16
Cutters Friday	18	3	2	13	29	54	11

SENIOR DIVISION

	P	W	D	L	F	A	Pts
Hawkins Insulat.	16	14	2	0	72	21	44
Backwell Sunday	16	12	1	3	56	31	37
Cross Hands	16	9	3	4	58	37	30
St Jospephs	16	9	3	4	58	37	30
Harriers	16	7	1	8	42	40	22
Chessel United	16	6	4	6	52	51	22
Sportscene	16	4	2	10	29	54	14
Shield & Dagger	16	3	0	13	34	67	9
The Robins	16	2	1	13	34	71	7

Fleet Spurs on the attack against Vosper Thornycroft. Vosper won 3-2 in this Hampshire League Division One match. Photo: Tim Lancaster

Drimpton FC of the Perry Street League Division One. Photo: Tim Lancaster

Trowbridge Town, Champions of the Wiltshire League Intermediate Division. Back Row (l-r): Wayne Miles, Chris Tucker, Steve Eade, Rob Coombes, Andy Bonsor, Neil Kirkpatrick, Adam Smith, Mark Edwards. Front Row: Ben Gardner, Neil Willcox, Chris Vaughan, Jerad O'Pray, Gary Holding. Photo: Gordon Whittington

Top: Barwell FC (Midland Football Alliance). Back Row (l-r): Dave Laing (Chairman), Viv Coleman (Physio), Adam Turner, Neil Lyne, Danny Finlay, Scott Mackay, Ken Hughes, Steve Lawson, Nick Stanborough, Mick Grwcock, Mark Rosegreen, Ron Boorman (Vice Chairman), Paul Purser (Manager). Front Row (l-r): Kevin Murray, Darren Grassby, Scott Clamp, Mark Drinkwater (Captain), Jason Weafer, Steve Markham, Spencer Truslove.

Centre: Chasetown FC (Midland Football Alliance). Back Row (l-r): Chris Marshall (Assistant Manager), Simon Hyden, John Jackson, Steve Neuchterlein, Martin Leadbeater, Ryan Young, Shaun Bradbury, Paul Haddaway, Paul Gregory, Steve Millard (Trainer). Front Row (l-r): Paul Tester, Craig Machin, David Yates, Andy Hitchcroft, Clive Gilbey, Steve Oldaker, Andy Banks, Will Tranter. Photo: Peter Barnes

Bottom: Bloxwich (Interlink Express Alliance). Back Row (l-r): Andy Richardson, Keith Hoskins, Paul Bishop, Tom Bailey, Gavin Barlow, Stephan Marshall, Scott Kaasikmae, Steve Highway, Tom Paskin, Mark Frith, Dave Bates. Front Row (l-r): Robert Jacombs, Danny Stackhouse, Paul Atthey, Norman Smith, Aslam Javed, Andip Singh, Darren Barnwell, Alan Martle. Photo: Marshalls Sports Service.

MIDLAND FOOTBALL ALLIANCE

President: N D Jeynes   **Chairman:** P Fellows

Secretary: P Dagger, 32 Drysdale Close,
Wickhamfrd, Worcestershire WR11 6RZ
Tel: 01386 831763   Fax: 01386 833488
E-mail: pdagger@talk21.com

This is the sixth annual report of the Midland Football Alliance since its inception in 1994. I am sorry to report the end of our association with our main sponsors Interlink Express Parcels, who have sponsored the League for six years. My personal thanks go in particular to Mrs Julie Roy who, as chief executive, has personally supported us on numerous occasions during the last six years. The League has continued to owe a great debt of gratitude to its main sponsors, whose support has given us the necessary resources not only to administer the League in an effective manner, but also to provide member clubs with excellent financial rewards at the end of the season.

The other sponsors to whom we are also extremely grateful are James Gilbert Limited, who supply each club with twelve match balls per season; Bernard Davis who sponsors the Midland Invitation Cup; Industrial Rewind Services who sponsor the League Challenge Cup; Baker & Joiner who sponsor the Hospitality Cup; Polymac Services who sponsor the Golden Boot Top Goalscorer Award, Best Disciplinary Award and the Manager of the Year Award; Joe McGorian who sponsors the annual match between the League Champions and the League Challenge Cup Winners; and Sportslines who sponsor the Team of the Month Award.

Oadby Town were League Champions in their first season in the League. During the campaign Stratford Town, Boldmere St Michaels, Wednesfield and Stourport Swifts looked as if they would provide a challenge to Oadby for the title. However, Oadby kept their nerve and ran out as Champions by ten points from Stratford. Sadly, Kings Norton Town resigned from the League.

The Industrial Rewinds League Challenge Cup final was a tense affair between Willenhall Town and Knypersley Victoria. Knypersley led 3-1 at half time, Willenhall then staged a remarkable comeback to score three times in the last 20 minutes through Man of the Match Lee Bullimore and two penalties from Dave Butler to lift the cup 4-3.

Malvern Town defeated Stourport Swifts 4-3 on penalties in the final of the Worcester Senior Urn, and another team involved in penalties were Rushall Olympic, who defeated Rocester 5-4 on penalties after drawing 2-2 to lift the Walsall Senior Cup. Barwell lost 4-0 to Leicester City in the final of the Westerby Cup Final.

The Davis Invitation Cup sponsored by Bernard and Irene Davis of Interlink Express is a competition for clubs in the Midland Football Alliance and its three feeder leagues; the final at Shifnal Town was between Bridgnorth Town and Darlaston Town from the West Midlands League which Bridgnorth won 3-1.

Prior to the start of the season the match for the Joe McGorian Trophy, which was competed for by the previous season's League runners-up and the League Challenge Cup winners, saw Oldbury United take the trophy after defeating Rocester, losing finalists for the second year running.

Our referees also had a good season. Mark Cooper and Phil Prosser were promoted to the Football League, Gary Chapman was appointed to the panel referees list, and further appointments include Rob Lewis to the assistant referees panel in the Premier League, whilst Kevin Friend, Phil Gibbs and Rob Steans joined the Nationwide League as assistant referees.   *P Dagger, General Secretary/Treasurer*

MIDLAND FOOTBALL ALLIANCE ANNUAL AWARDS 1999-2000

LEAGUE CHAMPIONSHIP SHIELD
Champions   Oadby Town
Runners Up   Stratford Town

GOLDEN SOVEREIGN LEAGUE CUP
Winners   Willenhall Town
Runners Up   Knypersley Victoria

DAVIS MIDLAND INVITATION CUP
Winners   Bridgnorth Town
Runners Up   Darlaston Town

BAKER & JOINER HOSPITALITY CUP
Winners   Halesowen Harriers

POLYMAC SERVICES BEST DISCIPLINARY AWARD
Winner   Boldmere St Michaels

KEVIN KEEGAN PLAYER OF THE YEAR
Winner   David Davies
(Oldbury United)

TOP GOALSCORER AWARD
Winner   Shaun Bradbury
(Chasetown FC)

PAT FELLOWS BEST PROGRAMME AWARD
Winner   Shifnal Town

**POLYMAC SERVICES
MANAGER OF THE YEAR AWARD**
Winner   A Hussey (Oadby Town)

JOE McGORIAN CUP
Winners   Oldbury United

729

FINAL LEAGUE TABLE 1999-2000

		P	W	D	L	F	A	Pts	GD
1	Oadby Town	42	27	7	8	107	48	88	59
2	Stratford Town	42	22	12	8	73	47	78	26
3	Willenhall Town	42	20	13	9	77	42	73	35
4	Wednesfield	42	21	9	12	71	56	72	15
5	Boldmere St Michaels	42	20	12	10	61	48	72	13
6	Stourport Swifts	42	19	13	10	73	57	70	16
7	Rushall Olympic	42	20	9	13	75	65	59	10
8	Shifnal Town	42	17	16	9	66	50	67	16
9	Barwell	42	18	12	12	85	57	66	28
10	Oldbury United	42	17	13	12	62	45	64	17
11	Chasetown	42	18	7	17	61	62	61	-1
12	Knypersley Victoria	42	17	10	15	75	71	60	4
13	West Midlands Police	42	15	8	19	62	71	53	-9
14	Bridgnorth Town	42	15	7	20	70	72	52	-2
15	Halesowen Harriers	42	14	8	20	63	71	50	-8
16	Sandwell Borough	42	12	13	17	53	69	49	-16
17	Bloxwich Town	42	11	13	18	57	84	46	-27
18	Kings Norton Town	42	9	16	17	60	68	43	-8
19	Cradley Town	42	10	12	20	56	87	42	-31
20	Pelsall Villa	42	9	10	23	57	88	37	-31
21	Stapenhill	42	8	6	28	42	91	30	-49
22	Pershore Town	42	7	6	29	46	103	27	-57

RESULTS CHART 1999-2000

		1	2	3	4	5	6	7	8	9	10	11	12	13	14	15	16	17	18	19	20	21	22
1	Barwell	X	5-0	2-2	2-1	4-1	3-2	0-0	1-0	3-2	1-5	1-0	6-2	2-0	1-2	7-1	4-1	3-1	1-1	5-0	0-0	2-0	0-1
2	Bloxwich T	0-3	X	0-0	3-2	5-0	2-2	1-1	2-3	1-1	0-7	2-0	3-0	3-2	1-0	1-1	2-2	4-1	0-3	1-1	1-1	2-1	1-2
3	Boldmere	2-3	0-0	X	0-1	1-3	3-2	2-1	3-1	4-2	2-1	1-1	1-0	3-2	0-3	1-0	1-1	3-0	1-1	0-0	4-2	1-1	1-0
4	Bridgnorth	1-1	2-3	0-2	X	3-2	3-0	0-3	1-0	4-2	3-2	1-1	5-1	1-2	1-3	1-1	0-6	4-1	0-1	1-1	0-3	2-3	1-1
5	Chasetown	2-1	4-1	3-1	2-1	X	1-1	1-2	3-1	0-3	1-2	3-1	0-4	2-0	3-1	2-1	2-0	3-1	1-3	0-2	3-0	2-1	1-4
6	Cradley T	2-2	0-1	0-3	4-2	1-3	X	1-2	1-1	2-2	1-6	1-2	2-0	3-0	2-7	0-0	1-1	2-1	1-3	0-1	1-2	1-1	0-6
7	Halesowen	2-0	7-2	2-0	1-1	0-1	2-2	X	4-1	0-1	0-3	0-1	3-1	3-2	3-4	0-2	2-2	3-0	0-3	0-2	2-1	1-3	0-4
8	Kings Norton	3-1	1-2	0-2	0-3	2-2	2-2	0-1	X	1-1	0-2	1-4	4-0	1-1	0-2	2-2	4-1	1-2	2-2	1-2	2-1	0-1	1-1
9	Knypersley	1-0	3-1	1-1	1-0	1-1	8-1	1-3	4-3	X	0-4	0-1	0-4	3-1	2-5	2-1	1-1	3-0	0-3	1-0	2-0	1-1	1-2
10	Oadby T	2-1	6-2	3-1	2-1	2-1	3-0	1-1	1-1	2-0	X	0-0	5-1	3-0	3-0	3-1	0-3	4-1	1-2	3-1	1-4	2-0	2-2
11	Oldbury U	0-0	2-0	1-0	1-1	0-1	1-2	3-0	0-3	1-3	0-0	X	2-2	6-0	4-2	1-1	3-2	3-0	2-0	1-1	0-2	3-1	1-2
12	Pelsall V	2-2	3-1	1-2	1-3	1-1	1-4	3-2	1-4	1-2	1-3	3-2	X	3-0	2-1	2-0	1-1	1-1	0-2	1-1	1-2	1-3	0-0
13	Pershore T	2-5	2-0	0-1	2-3	2-1	0-1	3-0	0-3	3-3	3-3	0-0	2-1	X	2-2	2-3	0-3	0-1	0-0	1-2	2-5	0-2	1-3
14	Rushall O	4-2	2-2	2-0	2-0	1-0	1-0	2-1	2-2	0-3	1-4	0-1	2-2	3-0	X	3-2	1-1	3-2	1-2	2-2	0-2	0-0	2-1
15	Sandwell B	2-2	1-0	0-0	2-1	3-2	1-3	3-2	1-1	1-1	0-1	1-0	2-0	2-3	1-2	X	0-3	3-1	1-1	0-5	0-1	3-0	2-4
16	Shifnal T	2-0	0-1	0-1	2-0	0-0	0-0	0-0	4-4	1-0	2-0	1-5	3-2	1-0	1-0	1-1	X	3-3	1-0	1-1	3-3	2-1	1-2
17	Stapenhill	0-0	2-2	0-1	0-3	1-0	0-3	4-3	1-1	3-2	0-4	4-2	1-1	4-1	0-2	2-0	0-3	X	1-2	0-3	1-2	0-2	0-3
18	Stourport	1-4	2-1	2-4	1-3	1-1	3-2	3-2	3-1	2-2	3-2	0-0	3-2	4-0	2-2	2-3	1-1	3-1	X	0-2	0-0	2-2	0-2
19	Stratford T	2-2	3-2	2-2	2-1	1-1	3-0	0-1	0-1	4-1	6-2	0-0	3-1	0-2	5-0	1-1	0-3	1-0	1-0	X	2-1	2-0	3-2
20	Wednesfield	2-1	0-0	3-0	0-4	1-0	2-0	4-1	2-1	5-3	1-1	0-1	1-1	3-1	1-1	2-1	0-1	2-1	3-1	0-2	X	3-1	2-3
21	WM Police	2-1	5-2	0-3	3-4	0-1	2-2	2-1	0-0	0-3	0-3	1-3	2-0	4-2	1-0	1-2	0-1	1-0	2-4	6-2	4-0	X	0-5
22	Willenhall T	1-1	1-0	1-1	2-1	1-0	0-1	1-1	0-0	0-2	0-3	2-2	1-2	7-0	1-2	0-0	3-0	1-0	1-1	0-1	2-2	2-2	X

POLYMAC SERVICES GOLDEN BOOT AWARD
LEADING GOALSCORERS 1999-2000

Shaun Bradbury	Chasetown	25	Lee Booth	Stourport Swifts	19
Ian Palin	Knypersley Victoria	24	Richard Walker	Oadby Town	19
Matt Cartwright	Stourport Swifts	23	Ian Aldridge	Cradley Town	18
Mark Bellingham	West Midlands Police	22	Adie Edwards	Bloxwich Town	17
Matt Boyles	Oadby Town	21	Darryl Smith	Wednesfield	17
Andy Jones	Halesowen Harriers	21	Paul Thompson	Pelsall Villa	17
Andy Tiday	Oadby Town	21	Danny Coates	Willenhall Town	16
Chris Bourton	West Midlands Police	20	John Nightingale	Oldbury United	15
John Powell	Shifnal Town	20	Peter McBean	Stratford Town	14
Jason Treharne	Shifnal Town	20			

SPORTSLINE TEAM OF THE MONTH AWARDS

August/September	Willenhall Town FC	January	Oadby Town FC
October	Stourport Swifts FC	February	Wednesfield FC
November	Stourport Swifts FC	March	West Midlands Police FC
December	Chasetown FC	April/May	Oadby Town FC

MIDLAND FOOTBALL ALLIANCE RECORDS

QUICKEST MFA LEAGUE GOAL
10 Sec   Neil Hitchman   for   Halesowen Harriers   v   Stratford Town   20.08.96

QUICKEST MFA LEAGUE HAT-TRICK
6 Mins   Mark Holdcroft   for   Wednesfield   v   Chasetown   26.08.98

HIGHEST ATTENDANCE
571   Hinckley Athletic   v   Barwell   08.04.96

LOWEST ATTENDANCE
17   Sandwell Borough   v   Stratford Town   06.12.97

FA Vase First Qualifying Round: Wednesfield v Stratford Town 1-2. Second half action from Amos Lane as Stratford's John Brant rifles in a shot which goes just wide of the post. Photo: Martin Wray

INDUSTRIAL REWINDS LEAGUE CHALLENGE CUP 1999-2000

FIRST ROUND

Boldmere St M.	v	Oadby Town	5-2	Knypersley Victoria	v	Pelsall Villa	3-2
Oldbury United	v	Stourport Swifts	2-3	Rushall Olympic	v	Willenhall T	1-1, 0-0, 3p1
Sandwell Borough	v	Bridgnorth Town	0-2	Kings Norton Town	v	Stratford T	2-2, 2-2, 3p4

SECOND ROUND

Barwell	v	Willenhall Town	0-1	Bloxwich Town	v	Stratford Town	0-3
Boldmere St M	v	Shifnal Town	4-0	Chasetown	v	West Mids Police	2-1
Cradley Town	v	Knypersley Victoria	2-6	Sandwell Borough	v	Halesowen Harriers	2-3
Stourport Swifts	v	Pershore Town	6-0	Wednesfield	v	Stapenhill	2-3

QUARTER FINALS

Halesowen Harriers	v	Willenhall Town	0-1	Knypersley Victoria	v	Stourport Swifts	2-1
Stapenhill	v	Boldmere St M	0-1	Stratford Town	v	Chasetown	1-1, 2-2, 5p6

SEMI-FINALS (Two Legs)

Boldmere St M	v	Willenhall Town	1-1, 0-3	Knypersley Victoria	v	Chasetown	4-0, 0-3

FINAL

Knypersley Victoria	v	Willenhall Town	3-2	Attendance 338	

DAVIS INVITATION CUP 1999-2000

FIRST ROUND

Alveston	v	Stratford Town	0-3	Anstey Nomads	v	Oldbury United	1-2
Aylestone Park	v	Stapenhill	1*3	Barwell	v	Oadby Town	3-2
Birstall United	v	Tividale	3-0	Blackheath Electro	v	Boldmere St Michaels	0-1
Bloxwich Town	v	Halesowen Harriers	4*5	Causeway United	v	Knypersley Vic	3-3, 3p1
Continental Star	v	Highgate United	0-1	Darlaston Town	v	Sandwell Borough	5-0
Feckenham	v	Bolehall Swifts	2-4	Gornal Athletic	v	Bustleholme	4*3
Kings Norton Town	v	Handrahan Timbers	3-2	Kirby Muxloe	v	Thurmaston Town	0-2
Little Drayton Rngrs	v	Wolverhampton Cas.	2-3	Malvern Town	v	Kenilworth Town	6-0
Pelsall Villa	v	Cheslyn Hay	0-1	Stafford Town	v	Pershore Town	3-0
St Andrews Sports	v	Bridgnorth Town	0-1	Studley BKL	v	Coalville Town	5-1
Willenhall Town	v	Bandon	1-0				

SECOND ROUND

Barwell	v	Knypersley Victoria	4-1	Birstall United	v	Brierley Hill T	1-1, 4p2
Bolehall Swifts	v	Stratford Town	1-3	Cottesmore Amat.	v	Bridgnorth Town	3-10
Cradley Town	v	Chasetown	0-4	Dudley Town	v	Malvern Town	0-2
Gornal Athletic	v	Thringstone United	1-2	Holwell United	v	Oldbury United	3-2
Ibstock Welfare	v	Highgate Utd	IW W/O	Kings Norton Town	v	Cheslyn Hay	2-0
Stafford Town	v	Halesowen Harriers	1-3	Stapenhill	v	Darlaston Town	0-1
Studley BKL	v	Boldmere St M	2-2, 2-3	Thurmaston Town	v	Stourport Swifts	0-1
Willenhall Town	v	Coventry Swifts	1-4	Wolverhampton Cas.	v	Star	3-2

THIRD ROUND

Darlaston Town	v	Barwell	2-0	Holwell Sports	v	Wolverhampton Cas.	2-0
Ibstock Welfare	v	Halesowen Harr.	0*0, 3p1	Kings Norton Town	v	Brierley Hill Town	3-2
Malvern Town	v	Thringstone United	6-1	Stourport Swifts	v	Chasetown	**2-0, 0-1
Studley BKL	v	Coventry Sphinx	0-1	Stratford Town	v	Bridgnorth Town	2-3

** Match abandoned after 38 minutes

QUARTER FINALS

Darlaston Town	v	Coventry Sphinx	2-1	Holwell Sports	v	Chasetown	2*4
Kings Norton Town	v	Ibstock Welfare	0-1	Malvern Town	v	Bridgnorth Town	2-3

SEMI FINALS

Darlaston Town	v	Chasetown	5-1	Kings Norton Town	v	Bridgnorth Town	0-1

FINAL

Darlaston Town	v	Bridgnorth Town	1-3	Attendance: 220	

BARWELL

Secretary: Mrs Shirley Brown, 101 Eskdale Road, Hinckley, LE10 0NW (01455 446048)

Ground: Kirkby Rd, Barwell, Leics (01455 843067)

Directions: M42 jct 10 (Tamworth Services), A5 towards Nuneaton. Remain on A5for approx 11 miles, go straight on at traffic lights at the Longshoot Motelthe 400 yards at r/about take 1st exit left sign A47 Earl Shilton, in 3 milesat traffic lights go straight ahead and in 1 mile at r/about, take first leftexit sign Barwell in village centre 1/2 mile go straight over mini r/about, 20yards turn right into Kirkby Rd, ground 400 yards on right.

Capacity: 2,500   Seats: 140   Cover: 750   Floodlights: Yes

Clubhouse: Evenings & lunchtimes. Snacks available.   **Club Shop:** No

HONOURS: Barwell Ath.: Leics Snr Lg Tebbutt Brown Cup 91-92, Leics Sen Cup 96-97.

PREVIOUS   Names: Barwell Athletic F.C., Hinckley F.C. - amalgamated in 1992.
          Leagues: Midland Combination 92-94
          (Barwell Ath.: Leics Senior. Hinckley: Central Midlands 86-88)
Ground: Barwell Ath.: Kirkby Road pre 1992, Hinckley: groundshare at Hinckley Ath. pre-'92

RECORDS   Goalscorer: Andy Lucas
          Appearances: Kevin Johnson.

FACT FILE

Founded: 1992.
Nickname: Kirkby Roaders
Sponsors: Cleartherm
Colours: All yellow with green trim
Change colours: All blue with white trim
Midweek matchday: Tuesday
Programme: 36 pages,70p
Editor: R Backhouse/R Boorman
99-00 Captain: Mark Drinkwater
Top Scorer: Kevin Murray
P.o.Y.: Darren Grassby

CLUB PERSONNEL

Chairman: David Laing.
Vice Chairman: Ron Boorman.
President: Derek Withers
Press Officer: Merv Nash.
Manager: Paul Purser
Asst Manager: Mark Rosegreen
Physio: Viv Coleman

BLOXWICH TOWN

Secretary: Ian Brant, 16 Westbourne Av., Cannock, Staffs Ws11 2AN Tel: 01543 570473 (H)
          01902 305446 (W)   07773 185256 (M) E mail: Bloxwichtown@supanet.com

Ground: Abbey Park, Glastonbury Crescent, Bloxwich, Walsall Tel: 01922 477640

Directions: A34 Walsall-Bloxwich, then west onto A4124. Ground 2-3 miles on right, sign-posted Mossley Estate

Capacity: 1,000   Seats: 200   Covered: 400   Floodlights: Yes

Clubhouse: Yes   **Club Shop:** No

HONOURS   Midland Alliance 97-98, League Cup R-up 97-98; Bloxwich Comb.(2), Staffs Co. Lg Div 1, Walsall Snr Cup 96-97 R-up 86-87, Invitation Cup 89-90, Midland Comb. Prem. Div. 95-96 R-Up.94-95. Div 1 89-90, Alan Peck Cup x3 Carlsberg Chall. Cup 95-96, Industrial Rewinds Lge Cup R-up 96-97

PREVIOUS   **Leagues:** Bloxwich Comb.,Midland Comb., MFA, Southern Midland, MFA.
          Names: Bloxwich AFC.

CLUB RECORDS   Atendance: 252
          Win: 8-1 v Alvechurch   **Defeat:** 9-0 v Shepshed Dynamo
          Goalscorer: Mark Holdcroft **Appearances:** Stephen Hillman

BEST SEASON   FA Vase: 3rd Rd Proper 97-98   **F.A.Trophy:** lst Q 98-99
          FA Cup: 97-98 First Season   **League Clubs Defeated:** None
Players Progressing: Martin O'Connor (C.Palace, Walsall, Birmingham City)

FACT FILE

Founded: 1977
Nickname: Kestrels
Sponsors: Home Zone
Colours: Blue & white/white/blue
Change Colours: Red & Black/Black/Black
Midweek Matches: Wednesday
Programme: 30 pages £1.00
Editor: Andy Poole

CLUB PERSONNEL

President: Noman smith,
Chairman: Michael Ross
Manager:Pul Wildei
Coach: John Pascal
Physio: Alan Mantle
99-00 Top Goalscorer: Adie Edwards (18)

BOLDMERE St. MICHAEL

Secretary: Dave Holvey, 38 Aldridge Road, Streetly, Sutton Coldfield, B743TT
          Tel: 0121 353 6321 (H & FAX)   07899 950102 (M)

Ground: Church Road, Boldmere, Sutton Coldfield
          Tel: 0121 373 4435 or 0121 384 7531

Directions: A38 & A5127 from City towards S. Coldfield, left at Yenton lights onto A452 (Chester Rd), Church Rd is 6th turning on the right.
          Nearest station: 400yds from Chester Road (BR).

Capacity: 2,500   Seats: 230   Covered: 400   Floodlights: Yes

Clubhouse: Bar & lounge, every evening and four lunchtimes.

HONOURS: Birmingham AFA 36-37; Birmingham AFA Snr Cup; Birmingham Jnr Cup, FA Amtr Cup SF 47-48; AFA Snr Cup 47-48; Central Amtr Lg 48-49; Midland Comb 85-86 88-89 89-90, Challenge Cup 77-78 89-90; Tony Allden Mem. Cup 78-79 88-89 91-92; Challenge Trophy 86-87; Sutton Charity Cup 96-97.

PREVIOUS: **Leagues:** West Mids 49-63; Midland Combination 63-94.

Players Progressing: John Barton (Everton, Derby County),Kevin Collins (Shrewsbury), Jack Lane (Birmingham City, Notts Co.), John Lewis(Walsall), Don Moss (Cardiff, C Palace), Harry Parkes (Aston Villa), Wally Soden (Coventry). Mike Griffiths (Torquay Un ited)

FACT FILE

Founded: 1883
Nickname: Mikes.
Sponsor: Swift Forwarding
Colours: White/black/black
Change Colours: Yellow/green/yellow
Midweek matches: Tuesday
Programme: 32 pages, 90p
Editor: John Smart (0121 350 6356)

CLUB PERSONNEL

Chairman: Keith Fielding
Match Secretary: as secretary
Manager: Alan Parsons

BRIDGNORTH TOWN

Secretary: Mary Boot, 68 Wellmeadow,Bridgenorth,Shropshire WV15 6DE (01746 764204)
Ground: Crown Meadow, Innage Lane, Bridgnorth, Salop WV16 6PZ (01746 762747)
Directions: Follow signs for Shrewsbury (A458) over river bridge on by-pass,turn right for town centre at island, right at T junction, 1st left into Victoria Road, right at cross-road, follow road into Innage Lane, ground on left.
Capacity: 1,600   **Shop:** Yes   **Seats:** 250   **Cover:** 700   **Floodlights:** Yes
Clubhouse: Evenings & weekend lunches, Dancehall, darts, pool, hot food on matchdays
Record Fee Recieved: £10,000 for Delwyn Humphries from Kidderminster Harriers
Players Progressing: Roger Davies (Derby county) and Paul Jones (Wolves via Kidd'ter H)

HONOURS: Midland Comb 79-80 82-83 (R-up 76-77 80-81); Lg Cup 78-79, Tony Allden Mem Cup R-up, Kidderminster & Dist Lge,Shropshire Snr Cup 85-86; Shropshire County Cup 70-71 75-76 76-77 78-79 79-80;Welsh Amt Cup 70-71; Shropshire County Jun Cup 98-99.
BEST SEASON: FA Cup: 3rd Qual Rd 64-65FA Vase: 5th Rd 75-76, 94-95
PREVIOUS   Leagues: Kidderminster & Dist until 68; Midland Comb 68-83; Southern Lge, Midland Div. 83-96   Names: St Leonards Old Boys pre 46
RECORDS   Goalscorer: Roger Davies 157   Appearances: Kevin Harris 426
Attendance: 1,600 v South Shields FA Vase 5th Rd 1976

FACT FILE
Founded: 1946
Nickname: The Town
Sponsors:
Colours: All Blue
Change colours: All red
Midweek matchday: Tuesday
Programme: 24 pages,60p
Editor: Simon Bromley
Local Press : Shropshire Star, Bridgnorth Journal, Express & Star.. Local Radio: Beacon, BBC Radio Shropshire
Youth League: West Mids Regional Regional
CLUB PERSONNEL

Chairman: Simon Bromley
Vice Chairman: Ian Thomas
President: Mike Williams
Manager:Les Bristow
Asst Manager: Paul Blakeley
Physio: Andy Perry

CHASETOWN

Secretary: Chris Harris, 38 Naden House, Stafford Rd., Cannock, Staffs. WS12 4NU
   tel; 01543 572927 (H) 01889 583306 (B)

Ground: The Scholars, Church Street, Chasetown, Walsall WS7 8QL Tel: 01543 682222/684609

Directions: Follow Motorways M5, M6 or M42 and follow signs for A5. A5 to White Horse Road/Wharf Lane, left into Highfields Rd (B5011), left into Church Street at top of hill, ground at end just beyond church. Buses 394 or 395 W Mids Travel, 94 Chase Bus,from Walsall, 860 Midland Red from Cannock.
Capacity: 2,000   **Seats:** 112   **Cover:** 250   **Floodlights:** Yes   **Club Shop:** Yes
Clubhouse: Mon-Fri 7.30-11pm, Sat 11.30am-11pm, Sun 8-10.30pm. Basic snacks

HONOURS   West Mids Lg R-up 90-91 92-93 (Lg Cup 89-90 90-91, Div 1 77-78 (R-up73-74 74-75 75-76 80-81 82-83), Div 1 Cup R-up 80-81 82-83, Div 2 R-up 87-88,Div 2 Cup R-up 86-87); Walsall Snr Cup 90-91 92-93; Staffs Snr Cup R-up 91-92.

PREVIOUS   **Name:** Chase Terrace Old Scholars 54-72 **Ground:** Burntwood Rec Cte (pre'83)
   Leagues: Cannock Yth 54-58; Lichfield & Dist. 58-61; Staffs Co. 61-72; West Mids 72-94.

RECORDS   **Attendance:** 659 v Tamworth, FA Cup 2nd Qual Rd 1/10/88.
   Appearances: A Cox 469 (+15)   **Win:** 14-1 v Hanford (H), Walsall Snr Cup 17/10/92.
   Goalscorer: T Dixon 172   **Defeat:** 1-8 v Telford U Res., West Mids (Reg.) Lge Div. 1

FACT FILE

Founded: 1954.
Nickname: Scholars
Colours: All blue
Change Colours: All Red.
Sponsors: Aynsley Windows
Midweek matchday: Tuesday
Reserves League: West Midlands
Programme: 26 pages, 50p
Editor/Press Officer: Mike Fletcher

CLUB PERSONNEL

Chairman: Brian Baker
Vice Chairman: B Simpson
President: A Scorey.
Manager: Cliff Painter
Asst Manager: Brian Fox
Physio: E Highfield.

CRADLEY TOWN

Secretary: David Attwood, 4 Birch Coppice, Quarry Bank, Brierley Hill, W Midlands DY5 1AP
   Tel: 01384 637430
Ground: Beeches View, Beeches View Ave, Cradley, Halesowen, B63 2HB. (01384 569658)

Directions: From M5 Jct 3 take A 456 towards Kdderminster.Rt at 2nd island into Hagley Rd. 3rd left into Rosemary Rd.Straight on and left at T jct..Left at next T jct into Stourbridge Rd. First left into Beeches View Avenue.Ground entrance between houses Nos 48 and 50.
Capacity: 3,000   **Seats:** 200   **Cover:** 1,500   **Floodlights:** Yes
Clubhouse: Open matchdays only. Food available   Club Shop: No

HONOURS   West Mids Lg Div 1 90-91, Midland Comb. Div 2 72-73 R-up 75-76 77-78, Presidents Cup 74-75 75-76, Invitation Cup 72-73); Metropolitan Lg 70-71, Wednesbury Charity Cup 90-91, Dudley Guest Hosp. Cup 71-72 72-73 75-76 90-91
PREVIOUS   **Leagues:** Metropolitan; Brierley Hill; Kidderminster; West Mids Amtr; Midland Comb. 71-82; West Midlands 82-99   **Name:** Albion Haden United
RECORDS   **Gate:** 1,000 v Aston Villa, friendly
   Goalscorer: Jim Nugent   **Apearances:** R J Haywood
   Win: 9-1 v Wolverhampton United (H), West Midlands Lge 1990
   Defeat: 0-9 v Paget Rangers (A) Midland Invitation Cup 97
   Transfer fee paid: £1,000 for Darren Marsh (Oldswinford, 1992)
   Received: £20,000 for John Williams (Swansea, 1991)

FACT FILE
Founded: 1948
Nickname: Lukes
Sponsors: Allen Homes/Stables & Co Solicitors
Colours: Red & black/black/black
Change colours: Yellow/blue/blue
Midweek matchday: Tuesday
Reserve's League: West Mids Lge Div One
Programme: Yes

CLUB PERSONNEL
President: Alf Hill
Chairman: Graham Taylor
Vice Chairman: Trevor Thomas
Press Officer: Trevor Thomas (01384 569658)

Manager: Trevor Thomas
Asst Mgr: Kevin Weston
Physio: Derek Cronin

HALESOWEN HARRIERS

Secretary: Mrs Christine Beasley, 43 Hawne Lane, Halesowen, West Midlands B63 3RN
Tel: 0121 550 3788 (H) 01384 896748 (B) 07788 697167 (Mobile)

Ground: Hayes Park, Park Rd, Colley Gate, Halesowen   Tel: 01384 896748

Directions: On A458 Birmingham to Stourbridge Rd (B'ham 10 miles, Stourbridge 4 miles).
M5 Jct 3 (towards Kidderminster), right at 1st island (towards Dudley),
turn left at island (towards Stourbridge), straight over next island then 3m to
ground on left side, 200yds past Park Lane.   1 mile from Lye BR

Capacity: 4,000   **Seats:** 350   **Cover:** 500   **Floodlights:** Yes   **Club Shop:** Yes

Clubhouse: Open every evening. Limited range of hot snacks, but full cold snack kitchen.

HONOURS   West Mids League Div 1 85-86 (Div 2 84-85, Div 2 Cup 84-85),
Inter City Bowl 67-68 68-69, Festival League x5, R-up x9,
FA Sunday Cup SF 79-80, Midland Sunday Cup, Birmingham Sunday Cup.

PREVIOUS   **Leagues:** Festival (Sunday)/ West Midlands (pre-1994)

Grounds: Birmingham Parks 61-70/ Halesowen Town FC 70-84 (both whilst in Sunday football).

RECORDS   **Attendance:** Friendly matches 750 v Walsall and Wolves in 1985
Competitive: 450 v Lye, Lge 1988

Defeat: 2-8 v Frickley Athletic (A), F.A. Cup 2nd Qual Rd 26/9/92.

Win: 12-1 v Lichfield & v Malvern Town, 1986. **Fee paid:** £750 to Oldswinford for L Booth, 1991.

FACT FILE

Founded: 1961
Nickname: None
Sponsors:Ludlow Coaches,Bevan Contracts
Colours: White/black/white
Change colours: Yellow/Blue/Yellow
Midweek matchday: Tuesday or Wednesday.
Programme: 28-36 pages
Editor: Rob Shinfield (01384 850819)

CLUB PERSONNEL

Chairman: Derek Beasley
Tel: 01384 896748(W) 0771 855 2337(M)

KNYPERSLEY VICTORIA

Secretary: Steve Chawner, 18 John St., Biddulph, Stoke on Trent. ST6 6BB (01782 518998)

Ground: Tunstall Road, Knypersley, Stoke-on-Trent, (01782 522737 club).

Directions: M6 Jct 15 join A500, 4th exit, pick up A527, follow through Tunstall, Chell, to
Biddulph. Ground is situated on A527 just before Biddulph. From M6 jct 18 follow signs to
Holmes Chapel then Congleton, A527 to Biddulph,continue thru lights, ground on left.

Capacity: 1,200   **Seats:** 200   **Cover:** 200   **Floodlights:** Yes **Club Shop:** Yes

Clubhouse: Open from 1pm Saturdays, 7pm weekdays. Hot snacks at tea bar

HONOURS   West Mids Lg Div 1 92-93, Staffs Snr Lg 84-85 (Lg Cup 84-85 85-86),
Staffs Co. Lg R-up 79-80, Staffs FA Vase 83-84 86-87, Sentinel Cup 86-87,   Leek &
Moorlands Lg 72-73 (Div 2 71-72). Industrial Rewinds Cup 98,
Joe McGorian Cup 88.

BEST SEASON   **FA Cup** 3rd Qual Rd 96-97 **FA Vase:**

PREVIOUS   **Leagues:** Leek & Moorlands 69-78; Staffs Co. (North) 78-83; Staffs Sen
83-90; W Midland (Reg) 90-94. **Grounds:** None

RECORDS   **Attendance:** 1,100 v Port Vale, friendly 1989
Goalscorer: J Burndred 128   **Appearances:** Terry Stanway 601
Fee paid: £1,000 M Biddle (Congleton 93) **Defeat:** 0-9 v Meir KA, Staffs Sen.
Win: 10-0 v Clancey Dudley, West Midls (Reg.) Div. 1 90-91

FACT FILE

Founded: 1969.
Nickname: The Vics.
Sponsors: Potters Packaging
Colours: Claret & sky/claret/claret & sky.
Change colours; Blue & Yelow/ Blue/Yellow
Midweek matchday: Tues/Thurs
Reserve League: Staffs Senior.
Programme: 40 pages 60p.
Editor/ Press Officer: J A Shenton
(01782 517962).

CLUB PERSONNEL

Chairman: Alan farr
President: G Quinn

Manager: Terry Stanway
Coach: Mick Biddle
Physio: T.B.A.

OADBY TOWN

Secretary: Kevin Zupp, 14 Swiftway, Lutterworth, Leics LE17 4PB Tel: 01455 550358

Ground: Invicta Park, Wigston Road, Oadby, Leics LE2 5QG   Tel: 0116 271 5728

Directions: Oadby is situated 4 miles south of Leicester on the A6. from Oadby church in
the centre of town, follow signposts for Wigston. The ground is 3/4 mile from   t h e
church on the left.

Capacity: **Cover:** 224   **Seating:** 224   **Floodlights:** Yes

Clubhouse: Yes

HONOURS   Leicestershire Senior Lge: (8) Midland Football Alliance 99-00
Div. 2 51-52; Lge Cup 77-78 93-94 94-95;
Leics Senior Cup 62-63 63-64 75-76 76-77 80-81

Charity Cups Rolleston 58-59 59-60 68-69 74-75 88-89 93-94 96-97 97-98;
Coalville 60-61 63-64 65-66 69-70; Harborough 83-84 88-89; Oadby 70-71;
Battle of Britain 93-94 94-95 96-97

PREVIOUS   **Leagues:** Leicestershire Senior League

FACT FILE

Founded:1939
Colours: red/white/black
Change colours: All Blue
Midweek matchday: Wednesday
Programme Editor: Rob Campion

CLUB PERSONNEL

Chairman: Brian Ford Powell
Vice Chairman: Stuart Blyth
President: Bob Mallet
Vice President: Alan Hussey

Manager: Alan Hussey
Asst. Manager: Steve Scott
Physio: Derek Hewitt

Top: Boldmere St Michaels FC. Back Row (l-r): Colin Burton (Reserve Team Manager), Nathan King, Myles Day, Richard Evans, Ron Green, Jon Hanson, Dave Wright (Assistant Reserve Team Manager). Middle Row: Don Marsh (C o m p a n y Secretary), Paul Welburn, Darren Owen, Guy Naraine, Andy McNair, Nad Naguthney, Alan Parsons (Club Manager), Gareth Palmer, Richard Birkin, Mick Hawkins (Coach), Steve Watson, Alan Lee (Treasurer), John Smart (Chairman). Front Row (l-r): Mark Wood, Andy Canning, Craig Feasey, Charlie Carpenter, Des Green (Secretary), Trevor Bennett (Main Sponsor), Harry Peakman (President), Dave Holvey (Assistant Secretary), Jamie Russell, Neil Watkins, Jimmy Quiggin, Gerard Eivors.

Centre: Bridgenorth FC (Interlink Alliance). Back Row (l-r): Les Bristow, Ian Smith, Matt Illingworth, Kristian Woods, Darren Jones, Neil Price, Chris Smith, Darryl Williams, Damon Russell, Shaun Williams, Paul Blakeley. Front Row (l-r): Steve Rogers, Neil Stokes, Phil Bates, Kiedran Emstock, Andy Blakely, Andy Perry. Photo: Marshalls Sports Services

Bottom: Cradley Town. Back Row (l-r): Mark Sivers, Calvin Guest, Shaun Pratt, Ian Aldridge, Paul Smith, Mark Hodges, Simon Moore, Ian Cooksey, Richard James, Kevin Weston. Front Row (l-r): Derek Cronin, David Jackson, Tony Whitehouse, Bill Morris, Trevor Thomas, Arron Roberts, Paul McColgan, Richard Cole, Jason Thomas.

OLDBURY UNITED

Secretary: Lee Tomkinson, 36 Bryan Road, Walsall,WS2 9DW
Tel. Nos: 01922-447834 (H) 0121 3034468 (W) 07790 295141 (M)

Ground: The Cricketts, York Road, Rowley Regis, Warley, West Midlands (0121 5595564)

Directions: M5 jct 2, follow Blackheath & Halesowen signs, first left at lights and fourth right into York Road (turning before motorway flyover), ground 200yds on left.
One and a half miles from Sandwell & Dudley and Rowley Regis BR stations.
Bus 404 from West Bromwich, Oldbury and Blackheath.

Capacity: 3,000   **Seats:** 300   **Cover:** 1,000   **Floodlights:** Yes

Clubhouse: Mon-Fri 7.30-11pm, Sat-Sun 12-2.30 (12-11pm Sat matchdays).
Snacks available on matchdays.   **Club Shop:** No

HONOURS West Mids Lg 92-93, Staffs Snr Cup 87-88, Midland Comb. R-up 78-79(Presidents Cup 72-73(res), Div 3 R-up 82-83(res), Chal. Vase 82-83(res)),Walsall Snr Cup 82-83, B'ham Snr Amtr Cup, Oldbury Lg Div 2 61-62, Worcs Snr Urn 86-87, Sandwell Charity Cup 86-87, Interlink Invitation Cup 96-97. Industrial Rewinds League Cup: 98-99

PREVIOUS   Leagues: Oldbury 58-62/ Warwick & W Mids All. 62-65/ Worcs (later Midland) Comb. 65-82/ Southern 82-86.**Names:** Queens Colts 58-62/ Whiteheath Utd 62-65
Grounds: Brittania Park 61-63/ Newbury Lane (Oldbury Stadium) 63-78.

RECORDS   Attendance: 2,200 v Walsall Wood, Walsall Snr Cup Final 1982.
Win: 10-1 v Blakenall   **Defeat:** 1-9 v Moor Green.

FACT FILE
Founded: 1958
Nickname: Cricketts,The Blues.
Sponsors: Beswick Paper Group, Oldbury.
Colours: Navy with sky trim/blue/blue
Change colours: All amber
Midweek matchday: Tuesday
Programme: 28 pages, 60p
Editor: Football Secretary.

CLUB PERSONNEL
Chairman: Roy Keeling.
Vice Chairman: Ken Harris.
Press Officer: Ian Whitmore

Manager: John Morris
Asst Mgr: Kevin Sweeney
Physio: Paul Millard

PELSALL VILLA

Secretary: Gareth J Evans, 72 St Pauls Crescent, Pelsall, Walsall WS3 4ET(01922 693114).

Ground: The Bush, Walsall Road, Pelsall, Walsall

Tel: 01922 682018 Club, 01922 692748 Ground

Directions: M6 jct 7 marked A34 B'ham. Take A34 towards Walsall to 1st island,turn right (marked Ring Road), cross two islands. At large island at bottom of hill take last exit marked Lichfield, up hill, cross next island to lights.Continue to next set of lights and turn left (B4154 Pelsall). Over railway bridge to Old Bush pub on right (next to Pelsall Cricket & Sports Club).

Capacity: 2,000   **Seats:** Yes   **Cover:** 624   **Floodlights:** Yes   **Club Shop:** Yes

Clubhouse: Mon-Fri 7-11pm, Sat noon-11pm, Sun noon-3 & 7-10.30pm. Hot &cold meals.

HONOURS West Mids Lg - Prem. Lge 94-95 (R-up 95-96) Div Cup 95-96, Div 1 Cup 88-89 (R-up 89-90, Div 2 Cup R-up 83-84, Walsall Snr Cup R-up 89-90 92-93, Wednesbury Charity Cup 6, (R-up 7), D Stanton Shield(2) 73-75 (R-up 75-76), Sporting Star Cup 76-77 (R-up 61-62), Prem Div Tphy(res)89-90, Rugeley Charity Cup 78-79 (R-up 69-70), Bloxwich Charity Cup(2), Edge Cup 83-84, Ike Cooper Tphy R-up 89-90. Midland Triangle Cup 95-96.

BEST SEASON   FA Cup: 3rd Qual. Rd 92-93, 2-4 V Gainsborough T. (A).
FA Vase: 5th Rd 92-93, 0-1 v Buckingham T. (A)

PREVIOUS   League: Staffs County (South) 61-81, West Midlands 82-96 **Grounds:** None
RECORDS   Attendance 2,060 v Aston Villa 29.7.98
Goalscorer: Dean Walters 231   **Appearances:** Neil Coles 588

FACT FILE
Reformed: 1961
Nickname: Villians
Sponsor: Metelec
Colours: Red & black/black/red
Change colours: Blue & white/white/white
Midweek home matchday: Tuesday
Programme: 68 pages, 80p
Editor: Secretary

CLUB PERSONNEL
Chairman: RonNew
Vice Chairman: J H Gough
President: B J Hill
Press Officer: B J Hill

Manager: Kevin Gough
Asst Manager: A.Dixon
Physio: R.Pickering

RUSHALL OLYMPIC

Secretary: Peter Athersmith, 46 Blakenall Lane, Leamore, Walsall, W Mids WS31HG
Tel: 01922 712632 (H) 0121 553 5525 (W) 07909 792422(M)

Ground: Dales Lane, off Daw End Lane, Rushall, Nr Walsall (01922 641021).

Directions: From Rushall centre (A461) take B4154 signed Aldridge. Approx., 1mile on right, directly opposite Royal Oak P.H., in Daw End Lane. Grd on right. 2 miles Walsall (BR) station.

Capacity: 2,500   **Seats:** 200   **Cover:** 200   **Floodlights:** Yes   **Club Shop:** No

Clubhouse: Bar/lounge, every night 8-11pm, Sat matchdays, Sun noon-2.30pm

HONOURS   West Mids Lge Div 1 79-80; Walsall Amtr Lge Div 1 55-56, Div 2 52-53, Snr Cup 54-55 55-56, Jabez Cliff Cup 55-56 ; Staffs Co. Lge Div 1 60-61 61-62 62-6364-65 (Div 2 56-57); Walsall Charity Cup 52-53; Walsall Chal.Cup 54-55 56-57; Walsall Mem. Charity Cup (x7) 55-62; W Preston Chal. Cup 56-57; Cannock & Dist. Charity Cup 56-57; Wednesbury Snr Cup 58-59 59-60 60-61; Sporting Star Cup 59-60 60-61(jt) 64-65 65-66 67-68; J W Edge 62-63 66-67; Walsall Snr Cup 64-65; Lichfield Charity64-65 66-67; Staffs Yth Cup 81-82.

PREVIOUS   Leagues: Walsall Amateur 52-55/ Staffs County (South) 56-78/ West Midlands (Reg) 78-94. **Grounds:** Rowley Place 51-75/ Aston University 76-79.

RECORDS   Attendance: 2,000 v Leeds Utd Old Boys **Goalscorer:** Graham Wiggin
Appearances: Alan Dawson (400+ apps) **Players progressing:** Lee Sinnott (Watford), Lee Palin (Aston Villa),Stuart Watkiss (Walsall), Steve Taylor (Crystal Palace via Bromsgrove £1,500 + £18,000 sell on-record club fee)

FACT FILE
Founded: 1951
Nickname: Pics.
Sponsors: Staus Systems
Colours: Amber with black trim/black/black
Change colours: White & Black/white/white
Midweek matchday: Tuesday
Youth League: West Mids (Reg.)
Programme: 36 pages, 50p
Editor/ Press Officer: Darren Stockall
(01922 379153).

CLUB PERSONNEL
Chairman: John Burks
Vice Chairman: Trevor Westwood
President: Brian Greenwood.
Manager: John Allen
Asst Manager:Kevin Foster
Physio: Lee Horrocks

Top: Halesowen Harriers. Back Row (l-r): Chris Busby, Darren Taylor, Andy Jones, Les Smith, Phil Walters, Giles Parry, Neil Matthewson, Alan Matthewson, Simon Ward, Alan Collett. Front Row (l-r): Lee Brown, Dave Evans, Tim Langford, Mark Clark, Jason Downing, Gavin Adams, Stuart Butler, Neil Smith, Steve Haywood. Photo: Marshall's Sports Services, Birmingham

Centre: Knypersley (Interlink Express Alliance). Back Row (l-r): Andrew Brownsord, Rick Leigh, Steve Wilkes, Rob Powner, Paul James, Paul Shenton. Front Row: Nicky Benton, Alan Thompson, Gary Stribling, Richard Poxon, Ian Palin. Photo: Marshall's Sports Services, Birmingham.

Bottom: Shifnal Town FC. Back Row (l-r): K Howells (Manager), M Kiernan, J Powell (Player/Asst Manager), G Rooney, A O'Connor, C Ashley, N Gregory, L Turton, G Owen. Front Row (l-r): J Treharne, J Hull, M Flavell, N Guy, D Jones, D Gazzillo, I Lane.

SANDWELL BOROUGH

Secretary: Joe Owen, 42 Chartwell Drive, Wolverhampton WV10 8JQ
Tel: 01902 780479 (H)   0121 520 1234 (B)

Ground: Oldbury Stadium, Newbury Lane, Oldbury Tel: 0121 544 4013
Directions: Follow A4123 B'ham-Wolverhampton Rd, past island at jnt 2 M5, after half mile turn left into Newbury Lane and stadium is on the right. 2 miles from Sandwell & Dudley (BR).
Capacity: 3,000   Seats: 200   Cover: 200   Floodlights: Yes

Clubhouse: Licensed bar overlooking pitch. Open everyday

HONOURS   Mids Comb Chall Cup R-up 49-50 51-53 67-68 74-75, Chall Tphy R-up 88-89,Pres. Cup 79-80 (R-up 76-77), Div 2 R-up 79-80; B'ham Jnr Cup;
Industrial Rewind Lge Cup 94-95.

PREVIOUS   Leagues: B'ham Suburban; Central Amtr; Worcs (Midlands Comb.) 48-88, 90-94; Southern 88-90.
Ground: Londonderry, Smethwick 18-81

BEST SEASON   FA Vase: FA Cup:

RECORDS   Attendance: 950 v Halesowen T., FA Cup 1987
Players progressing: Andy Micklewright(Bristol R.),Gary Bull (South'ton) Mick Mason(Mack'field)

FACT FILE
Founded: 1918.
Nickname: Trees
Colours: Green & White Hoops/ Green/Green
Change Colours: Red/white/red
Midweek matches: Tuesday
Programme: 16 pages 60p
Editor: Trevor Hackwood

CLUB PERSONNEL
Chairman: Joe Owen
Manager: Dave Downing

SHIFNAL TOWN

Secretary: Glyn Davies, 30 Drayton Road, Shifnal, Shropshire, TF11 8BT (01952460326 H)

Ground: Phoenix Park, Coppice Green Lane, Shifnal, Shropshire.

Directions: M54 jct 3, A41 towards Newport, 1st left for Shifnal (3 miles), in Shifnal take 1st right, and sharp right again up Coppice Green Lane, ground800yds on left past Idsall School.
Capacity: 3,000   Seats: 224   Cover: 300   Floodlights: Yes

Clubhouse: Not on ground but in Newport Rd, Shifnal.   Open Mon-Fri 7.30-11pm, Sat
7.30-11pm (matchdays 12-11pm), Sun 12-3 & 7.30-10-30
Club Shop: No

HONOURS   West Mids Lg 80-81 81-82 Div 1 78-79,
Shropshire Snr Cup 80-81 90-91 92-93.

BEST SEASON   FA Cup: 1982-83   **FA Vase:** 1983-84
PREVIOUS   **Leagues:** Wellington (Dist.) 64-69; Shropshire County 69-77 85-93;
West Midlands 77-85; Midland Combination 94-95.
Grounds: Admirals Park 80-85

RECORDS   **Attendance:** 1,002 v Bridgnorth T., FA Vase 3rd Rd 83-84 (Admirals Park)
Goalscorer: Steve Kelly 35   **Appearances:** John Powell 321
Win: 10-1 v Malvern, 82-83   **Defeat:** 1-6

FACT FILE
Founded: 1964
Nickname: None.
Sponsors: Associated Cold Stores & Transport Ltd.
Colours:All Red & white
Change cols: Blue & white/white/blue & white
Midweek matchday: Tuesday
Reserves' League: West Midlands
Programme: 32 pages, 60p
Editor: J.Wilson (01952 274855).
99-00 Player of the Year: Mick Flavell
CLUB PERSONNEL
Chairman: Mr. A.Dodd
Vice Chairman: Mr. R Owen
President: Mr.D.Millward
Press Off:K.Fullerton 01952 405274
Manager: Ken Howells
Asst Manager: John Powell
Physio: Charlott Lewis

STAFFORD TOWN

Secretary: Dave Rowley, 32 Lodge Rd, Brereton, Rugely, Staffs WS15 1HG
Tel: 01889 800779 (H) 07970 536379 (Mobile)

Ground: Stafford Rangers FC, Marston Road, Stafford
Directions: From M6 junction 14, Take 3rd left to Red Hill Roundabout and follow signs for Aston Fields Ind Est along Beaconside. Aston Fields is signposted 3rd right along Common Road, having travelled over railway bridge, Stafford Rangers FC ground is on the right

Capacity: 6,000   Cover: 3,000   Seats: 426   Floodlights: Yes   Club Shop: No

Club address: Chamley Club, Beconside, Stafford Tel: 01785 665739 (Mr N Payne)

HONOURS   WMRL Div 1 93-94, Staffs Snr Lg R-up 91-92, Midland Comb. Div 2 78-79,
Staffs Vase 84-85 92-93 (R-up 87-88), Bourne Sports Trophy 84-85, Walsall Sen Cup SF 91-92

PREVIOUS   **Leagues:** Staffs Co. (North) 74-77 82-84; Midland Comb. 77-82; StaffsSen. 84-93
Names: Stafford Town 74-90; Stafford MSHD 90-92
Grounds: Silkmore Lane 74-77; Burton Manor Spts 77-88; Riverway 88-91;
Rowley Park Stadium 91-94

RECORD   **Win:** 14-0 v Leek CSOB (H), Staffs Senior League 8/10/88

FACT FILE
Founded: 1974
Nickname: Reds or Town
Colours: All red
Change colours: Blue/navy/navy
Midweek matches: Mon/Wed
Programme: 28 pages, 50p
Editor: Chris Curtis (01785 605561)

CLUB PERSONNEL
Chairman: Mr F James
01785 254073 (H) 01785 283863 (B)
President: T Logan
Press Officer: Chris Curtis
Manager: Alan Somerville

STAPENHILL

Secretary: Peter Begent, 22 Grasmere Close, Stapenhill, Burton-on-Trent DE159DS
Tel: 01283 540583
Ground: Edge Hill, Maple Grove, Stapenhill, Burton-on-Trent (01283 562471).
Directions: 3 miles from Burton on A444 Measham Rd, turn right (coming from Burton) at Copperhearth Pub Hse into Sycamore Rd, Maple Grove is 5th left. 3miles from Burton-on-Trent (BR) buses 15, 16 from opposite station.
Capacity: 2,000   Seats: 200   Covered: 500   Floodlights: Yes
Clubhouse: In ground. Pub hours. Matchday tea bar.   **Club Shop:** No

HONOURS	Midland Combination R-up 92-93 Div 1 89-90, Challenge Cup 92-93 93-94, Leics Snr Lg 59-60 86-87 88-89 (Tebbutt Brown Cup (2) 87-89), Leics Snr Cup 69-70 86-87, Derby Snr Cup R-up 88-89 91-92.
BEST SEASON	FA Cup: FA Vase:
PREVIOUS	**League:** Leics Snr 58-89/ Midland Combination 89-94.
	Name: Stapenhill Waterside Community Centre.
RECORDS	**Attendance:** 2,000 v Gresley, Derbys Snr Cup final 88-89.
	Goalscorer: Brian Beresford 123 **Appearances:** Ian Pearsall 172.
	Win: 11-0 v Alcester Town (H), Midland Comb. Prem. Div.,1992-93.
	Defeat: 0-7 v Bridgnorth Town, FA Vase.

FACT FILE
Founded: 1947
Nickname: Swans
Sponsors: TAG Football Kits
Colours: Red & Green
Change Colours: All blue
Midweek matchday: Tuesday
Programme: 50p
Editor: Secretary
99-00- Captain: Chris Allan
Top Scorer: Philip Lonergan
P.o.Y.: Dave Clark

CLUB PERSONNEL
Chairman: Tony Smith
Vice Chairman: Ken Hulland
President: Fred Sleigh.
Press Officer: Secretary.
Manager: Steve Coburn
Asst Manager: Gary Norton

STOURBRIDGE

Secretary: Hugh Clark,10 Burnt Oak Drive, Stourbridge, W. Mids DY8 1HL   Tel: 01384 392975

Ground: War Memorial Ath. Grd, High St., Amblecote, Stourbridge DY8 4HN   (01384 394040)

Directions: Take A491, signposted Wolverhampton, from Stourbridge ring-road -ground 300yds on left immediately beyond traffic lights and opposite `RoyalOak' pub. Buses 311, 313 from Dudley, and 256 from Wolverhampton, pass ground. 1 mile from Stourbridge Town (BR)
Capacity: 2,000   Cover: 1,250   Seats: 250   Floodlights: Yes
Clubhouse: Open every evening from 8pm and Sunday lunchtimes
Club Shop: Programmes & souvenirs. Contact Nigel Gregg

PREVIOUS   Name: Stourbridge Standard   **Leagues:** West Midlands (prev. Birmingham) 1892-1939 54-71, Birmingham Comb. 45-53, Southern 71-00

HONOURS   Welsh Cup R-up 73-74; Southern Lg Midland Div 90-91 (Lg Cup 92-93), Div 1 North73-74, Merit Cup 73-74; West Mids (prev. B'ham) Lg 23-24 (R-up 4); B'ham Comb. R-up 51-52; B'ham Snr Cup 49-50 45-46 75-76 (R-up 3); Worcs Snr Cup 9, (R-up 12); Herefordshire Snr Cup 54-55; Camkin Cup R-up 69-70; Camkin Presidents Cup 70-71; Albion Shield 43-44; Keys Cup 37-38 62-63, Worcs Comb. R-up 27-28; Worcs Jnr Cup R-up 27-28; Tillotson Cup R-up 39-40, Brierley Hill Lg R-up 44-45 (Lg Cup R-up 44-45); Brierley Hill Yth Lg Coronation Cup 56-57

BEST SEASON   FA Cup: 4th Qual Rd: 67-68, 84-85 85-86 98-99   **FA Trophy:** Qtr Final 70-71

CLUB RECORDS   Career Goalscorer: Ron Page 269   **Career Appearances:** Ron Page 427

FACT FILE
Formed: 1876   Nickname: The Glassboys
Sponsors: Carlsberg
Colours: Red & white stripes
Change colours: Yellow & blue
Midweek matchday: Tuesday
Programme: Pages: 28   Price: £1
Editors: Hugh Clark & Nigel Gregg

99-00 Captain: Derek Kodua
Top scorer: C.McKenzie (8)

CLUB PERSONNEL
Chairman: Mark Serrell
Vice Chairman: David Hardie
Press Officer: as Secretary

Manager/Coach: Mark Harrison
Assistant Manager;Steve Brown
Coach: Kelvin Sukkivan
Physio: Steve Ball

STOURPORT SWIFTS

Secretary: Nigel Green, 32 Golden Hind Drive, Stourport -on-Severn,Worcs. DY13 9RJ
Tel: 01299 822993
Ground: Walshes Meadow, Harold Davis Drive, Stourport-on-Severn (01299 825188).
Directions: Follow one-way system through Stourport sign posted Sports Centre.Go over River Severn Bridge, turn left into Harold Davies Drive. Ground is at rear of Sports Centre. Nearest rail station is Kidderminster.
Capacity: 2,000Seats: 250Cover: 150Floodlights: Yes

Clubhouse: Open matchdays. Hot snacks available. Licensed bar.   **Club Shop:** No

HONOURS	West Mids Prem Div R-Up 94-95 96-97 97-98, Lg Div 1 R-up 87-88, Prem Div Cup 92-93, Div 2 Cup R-up 82-83; Worcs Snr Urn 92-93 93-94 94-95 97-98 Worcs Infirmary Cup 94-95 95-96 97-98
BEST SEASON	FA Cup FA Vase
PREVIOUS	**Leagues:** Kidderminster/ Worcester/ Midland Combination.
	Grounds: Bewdley Rd; Moor Hall Park; Feathers Farm; Olive Grove; Hawthorns.
RECORDS	**Attendancee:** 4,000 v Birmingham, charity match.
	Goalscorer: Gary Crowther **Appearances:** Ian Johnson
	Win: 10-0 **Defeat:** 1-7

FACT FILE
Founded: 1882.
Nickname: Swifts
Sponsors: M.I.P. Halesowen
Colours: Yellow & black/black/black
Change colours: White/gold/gold
Midweek matchday: Tuesday
Programme: 40 pages,80p
Editor: Malcolm Cowell

CLUB PERSONNEL
Chairman: Chris Reynolds

President: Roy Crowe.
Managers: Rod Brown
Coach: Gary Whild

STRATFORD TOWN

Secretary: Roger Liggins, 17 Hammerton way, Wellesbourne, Warwicks. CV35 9NS
Tel Nos: 01789 840755 (H) 02476 539401 (W)
Ground: Masons Road, off Alcester Road, Stratford-upon-Avon, Warks (01789 297479).
Directions: Follow the signs for Alcester/Worcester A422 from the town centre.
Masons Road is the 1st right afterthe railway bridge.
400 yards from Stratford-on-Avon (BR)station.
Local buses for West Green Drive.

Capacity: 1,100   Seating/Cover: 200   Floodlights: Yes

Clubhouse: Open every night except Sunday   **Club Shop:** No.

HONOURS Midland Comb 56-57 86-87; Chal. Cup 86-87 88-89 (R-up 55-56); Chal. Vase 81-82; Jack Mould Tphy 81-82; Tony Allden Mem. Cup 86-87; B'ham Snr Cup62-63.

BEST SEASON FAVase: **FA Cup:**

PREVIOUS **Leagues:** W Mids 57-70/ Mid Com. 70-73 75-94/ Hellenic 70-75.

RECORDS **Attendance:** 1,078 v Aston Villa, Birmingham Snr Cup, Oct 1996

Players progressing: Martin Hicks (Charlton '77), Roy Proverbs (Coventry, '56)

FACT FILE
Founded: 1944
Nickname: The Town
Sponsors: Porters Precision Products
Colours: All Blue
Change Colours: All Tangerine
Midweek Matchday: Tuesday
Reserves' League: Midland Comb. Res. Div..
Programme: 20 pages, 50p
Editor:

CLUB PERSONNEL
Chairman: Stuart Dixon
Vice-Chairman: T.B.A.
President: P Chatburn
Commercial Mgr: J Carruthers.
Manager: S Dixon
Physio: N Dixon

WEDNESFIELD

Secretary: Brian Saville, 74 Dunstall Hill, Wolverhampton WV6 0SP (01902 653266)

Ground: Cottage Ground, Amos Lane, Wednesfield, Wolverhampton (01902 735506).
Directions: From Wolverhampton on the A4124 Wednesfield Rd. Stay on road right through Wednesfield until island. Leave island at 1st exit (Wood End Rd), left after 200yds into Amos Lane. Ground on right, approx. 400yds along. 3 miles Wolverhampton BR station. Bus 559 to Wood End or 560 to Red Lion.

Capacity: 1,000   Seats: 148   Cover: 250   Floodlights: Yes

Clubhouse: Evenings 7-11pm. Food (burgers, chips etc) on 1st team matchdays.
Club Shop: No.

HONOURS West Mids Lg Div 1 76-77 (R-up 77-78).
BEST SEASON **FA Vase:**   **FA Cup:**
PREVIOUS **League:** Wolverhampton & District Amateur 61-76/West Midlands 77-97.
Ground: St Georges PF 61-76   **Name:** Wednesfield Social 61-89.
RECORDS **Attendance:** 480 v Burton Albion, FA Cup 1981.

FACT FILE
Founded: 1961.
Nickname: Cottagers.
Sponsors: Ansells
Colours: Red/black/black& white
Change colours: Black & White
Stripes/white/black & white
Midweek matchday: Tuesday
Programme: 50p
Editor: TBA

CLUB PERSONNEL
Chairman: Surinda Ghattaura
Vice Chairman: J Massey
Manager/Coach: Ken Hall
Physio: M Andrews
Commercial Mgr: D Clayton
Press Officer: J Massey (01902 781819).

WEST MIDLANDS POLICE

Secretary: John Black, 57 Grosvenor Close, Sutton Coldfield, W.Mids. B756RP. 0121 308 7673

Ground: Police Sports Ground, `Tally Ho', Pershore Road, Edgbaston, Birmingham B57RN
Tel: 0121 472 2944
Directions: 2 miles south west of city on A441 Pershore Road. Ground is on the left 50yds past Priory Road lights (Warks County Cricket Ground).
3 miles from Birmingham New Street (BR) - buses 41, 45 & 47 from city.

Capacity: 2,500   Seats: 224   Covered: 224   Floodlights: Yes

Clubhouse: Complex of 3 bars including snooker room, ballroom, kitchen.
Hot &cold food. Open all day.   **Club Shop:** No.

HONOURS Mids Comb 90-91 (R-up 94-95, Chal. Cup 74-75 (R-up 85-86)), Tony Allden Mem. Cup 75-76 (R-up 91-92), B'ham Jnr Cup, Worcs Snr Urn 84-85 90-91 91-92 (R-up 81-82 85-86), National Police Cup (12) 61-65 66-67 69-70 73-76 80-81 87-88 91-92 (R-up (7) 67-68 70-72 76-78 88-89 94-95), Aston Villa Cup 60-61 64-65 65-66.

BEST SEASON **FA Vase:** Quarter Final 91-92   **FA Cup:**

PREVIOUS Leagues: B'ham Wednesday 28-38; Mercian 46-53; B'ham Works 53-69; Midland Comb 74-94.

RECORDS **Attendance:** 1,072 v Sudbury Town, FA Vase QF 29/2/92.

FACT FILE
Founded: 1974
Colours: Red & black stripes/black/black
Change Colours: All Blue
Midweek matchday: Tues/Thurs.
Reserves' League: Midland Combination.
Programme: 16 pages, 50p
Editor: K Horrigan
(0121 626 4020x6100)

CLUB PERSONNEL
President: Chief Constable E,Crew
Chairman: Deputy Chief Constable
Anne Summers
Vice Chairman : Chief Inspector M.Rose
Manager: Jim Scott
Commercial Manager: John Black.
Press Officer: Tony Pearson.

WILLENHALL TOWN

Secretary: Malcolm Skitt, 52 Longwood Rise, Willenhall, W. Mids WV12 4AX (01902 632557)

Ground: Noose Lane, Willenhall, West Midlands (01902 605132-club, 636586-office).
Directions: M6 Jnc 10 follow 'new' Black Country route and then 'Keyway'. On leaving 'Keyway' follow signs to Wolverhampton(A454). At 'Neachells' P H house right into Neachells Lane, and first right again into Watery Lane. At island turn left onto Noose Lane, ground is 200yds on left.
Capacity: 5,000   Seats: 324   Cover: 500   Floodlights: Yes

Clubhouse: Open Mon-Thurs 12-3 & 7-11pm, Fri-Sat 11am-11pm, Sun 12-2 & 7-10.30pm.
Snacks available.   **Club Shop:** Yes

HONOURS	FA Vase R-up 80-81; West Mids Lg 78-79, Div 1 75-76, Prem. Div Cup 79-80, Div 2 Cup 78-79(res); Southern Midland 83-84; Birmingham Snr Cup R-up 82-83; J W Hunt Cup 73-74.
BEST SEASON	**FA Vase:** Runners-up 80-81 **FA Cup:**
PREVIOUS	**Leagues:** Wolverhampton Amateur/ Staffs County/ West Mids 75-82 91-94/Southern 82-91.
RECORDS	Attendance: 3,454 v Crewe Alexandra, FA Cup 1st Rd 1981. Goalscorer: Gary Matthews Appearances: Gary Matthews.
Players progressing:	Sean O'Driscoll (Fulham),Joe Jackson (Wolves), Stuart Watkiss (Wolves), Tony Moore (Sheff U), Andy Reece (Bristol R.), Wayne O'Sullivan (Swindon).

FACT FILE

Founded: 1953
Nickname: Reds
Sponsors: Aspray Transport.
Colours: All Red
Change colours: White & Blue/Blue/Blue
Midweek matchday: Tuesday.
Reserves League: Midland Comb.
Programme: 40 pages, 70p
Editor: Bill Taylor (01902 843435)

CLUB PERSONNEL

President: Jack Williams
Chairman: David Homer
Vice Chairman: Keith Badger
Manager: Kevin Hadley
Asst Manager: Paul Waddington
Physios: Mike Andrews & Garyt McHale

Top: Stapenhill FC. Back Row (l-r): Chris Hanson, Chris Brown, Neil Akers, John Warriner, Neil Davies, Brian Jones, Russell Harrison, Pete Allum, Dave Clark. Front Row (l-r): Ricky Turner, Philip Lonergan, Simon Harrison, Chris Allum, Gary Norton, Paul Kendrick, Darren Read.

Centre: Stourport Swifts. Back Row (l-r): Rod Brown (Manager), Lee Booth, Jim Conway, Lee Young, Nigel Laker, Rob Clarke, Liam Meenan, Andy Wright (now Willenhall Town), Kevin Nokes (now Pershore Town), Paul Mountford, Gary Whild (Asst Manager). Front Row (l-r): Lea Shaw, Gary Hackett (Player/Coach), Kerry Giddings, Marc Pardoe, Adam Ward (now Malvern Town), Alex Cowley, Simon Marsh.

Bottom: Willenhall Town. Back Row (l-r): Gary McHale (Physio), Kevin Hadley (Manager), Chris Homer, Alec Grice, Scott Turbutt, Gary Chadwick, Steve Grosvenor, Gary Eades, Paul Waddington, Michael Andrews (Physio). Front Row (l-r): Jamie Howe, Andy Lunt, Peter Berks, Craig Harris, Curtis Barnes, Danny Coates, David Follows, Ian Long.
Photo: Marshall's Sports Services, Birmingham

RAPIDE MIDLAND FOOTBALL COMBINATION
FEEDER TO: MIDLAND FOOTBALL ALLIANCE

Chairman & Treasurer: David Prust
Hon Secretary: Norman Harvey
115 Millfield Road, Handsworth Wood, Birmingham B20 1ED   Tel: 0121 357 4172

It was very much a season of the newcomers as the new teams more than made their presence felt. The Premier title went to the former Coventry Alliance champions, Nuneaton Griff, who fully justified their inclusion by heading the table practically from the start. Fellow Coventry side, Marconi, chased them all the way but faltered in the last few strides slipping down to fourth spot after being overtaken by Kings Heath and Studley BKL.

In the First Division, two former Sunday sides switched to Saturday and the newcomers, Brookvale Athletic, clinched the title in the penultimate game and condemned Romulus to runners up as these two teams had dominated throughout the season.

Polesworth North Warwick reformed and joined the Second Division heading the ladder until Wyre Forest put in a very late burst to snatch the championship.

Wilmcote Sports & Social had sewn up the Third Division title long before the season ended, thus leaving County Sports and Bustleholme Reserves to fight for the lesser places along with newcomer Droitwich St. Peters and Leamington Hibernian.

The Challenge Cup was won by Brookvale Athletic, who are changing their name to Sutton Town next season, after a really titanic struggle against Marconi that needed extra time. Athletic also reached the final of the Birmingham County FA Vase.

The Presidents Cup went to Brownhills Town, who overcame Romulus by the odd goal in three, and Handsaker took the Challenge Vase by the same score against West Midlands Police Reserves.

Wilmcote Sports & Social did the double by beating Chelmsley Town Reserves 2-1 after extra time in the Challenge Urn and in the Reserve Division finals Solihull Borough lost both games, by four goals to two against Shepshed Dynamo in the Challenge Bowl and 1-0 to Willenhall Town in the Challenge Trophy.

Derek Christopher collected the Fred Shepherd Memorial Trophy after clouting 52 goals for Romulus. In October, Darren Reaney broke the Meir KA record appearances total of 555 games held by Dave Preston, and on March 4th Lee Adams played his 500th game for Studley BKL.

In the programme stakes, once again the Premier clubs managed to raise their standards, whilst notable issues came from teams in the First, Second and Third Divisions as more sides are producing programmes.

The League is, yet again, losing match officials as referees Shaun Ainge and Mark Weaver have been promoted to the Midland Football Alliance and we wish them bon voyage.

To paraphrase Brian Clough, "If they are good enough, they are old enough" - twenty year old Simon Barrow

refereed the Challenge Urn final and nineteen year old Oliver Langford was in charge of the Challenge Vase final.

All in all, the Millennium season was a great success and next season promises much as twelve teams have applied to play in the Football Association Vase competition.

Paul W Vanes, Press Officer

Above: Nuneaton Griff are the first club to be placed into the Premier Division on application, and subsequently the first club to win the Premier Division title on their debut.
Back Row (l-r): James Williams, Stewart Marsden, Mick Upton, Darren Wright, Lee Bateman (captain), Mark Dunn, Ian Brain, Craig Whitmore, Chris Stanley (Physio), David Thompson (Assistant Manager). Front Row: Mark Green (Manager), Daniel Wright, Wayne Hadley, Jason Woodiwiss, Mark Whitehead, Ruban Field, Wayne Pulford. Mascots: Iain Green, Daniel Stanley. Trophies: Coventry Charity Cup, Midland Combination Premier Division Shield, Foleshill Charity Cup.

Above: Brookvale Athletic

Above: Wilmcote Sports & Social FC

Above: Marconi (Coventry)   *Photo: Alan Watson*

FINAL LEAGUE TABLES 1999-2000

PREMIER DIVISION

	P	W	D	L	F	A	Pts
Nuneaton Griff	38	25	10	3	118	41	85
Kings Heath	38	22	10	6	79	42	76
Studley BKL	38	21	7	10	85	50	70
Marconi (Coventry)	38	20	9	9	81	51	69
Meir K.A.	38	18	10	10	81	48	64
Coventry Sphinx	38	18	7	13	69	47	61
Massey Ferguson	38	17	10	11	75	59	61
Cheslyn Hay	38	17	9	12	82	60	60
Feckenham	38	16	11	11	60	47	59
Alvechurch	38	17	8	13	74	77	59
Continental Star	38	14	11	13	62	75	53
Handrahan Timbers	38	15	7	16	51	61	52
Northfield Town	38	15	6	17	57	57	51
Bolehall Swifts	38	14	8	16	90	63	50
Blackheath Electrodrive	38	13	9	16	54	73	48
Southam United	38	11	8	19	64	78	41
Alveston	38	11	5	22	52	93	38
Highgate United	38	8	7	23	53	88	31
Coleshill Town*	38	5	5	28	52	124	17
Kenilworth Town	38	3	3	32	34	139	12

DIVISION ONE

	P	W	D	L	F	A	Pts
Brookvale Athletic*	38	31	3	4	145	29	93
Romulus	38	28	6	4	121	44	90
Fairfield Villa	38	25	6	7	121	46	81
Mile Oak Rovers	38	23	7	8	95	60	76
County Sports	38	21	3	14	105	61	66
Brownhills Town	38	21	3	14	91	47	66
Holly Lane '92	38	17	10	11	79	67	61
Thimblemill R.E.C.	38	18	6	14	100	82	60
Burntwood Town	38	17	8	13	78	59	59
Shirley Town*	38	17	8	13	84	90	56
Alvis Oakwood Cov.	38	15	5	18	76	78	50
Knowle	38	13	10	15	83	74	49
Hams Hall	38	13	10	15	76	79	49
Kings Norton T Rs	38	13	7	18	66	91	46
Loughborough Ath	38	13	4	21	60	90	43
West Mids Fire Service	38	10	6	22	65	101	36
Dudley Sports	38	9	8	21	54	86	35
Wellesbourne*	38	12	2	24	65	109	35
Malvern Athletic*	38	2	4	32	35	166	4
Chelmsley Town*	38	2	4	32	31	171	4

DIVISION TWO

	P	W	D	L	F	A	Pts
Wyre Forest	28	18	6	4	82	27	60
Polesworth North Wck	28	17	5	6	69	35	56
Old Hill Town	28	17	4	7	72	47	55
Handsaker	28	14	8	6	70	38	50
M.C.L. Claines	28	14	6	8	50	31	48
Kenilworth Wardens	28	12	6	10	66	51	42
Lichfield Enots	28	12	5	11	60	58	41
Barlestone St Giles	28	11	7	10	49	52	40
West Mids Police Res	28	11	6	11	53	50	39
Cadbury Athletic	28	10	7	11	53	53	37
Archdale '73	28	9	6	13	37	58	33
Earlswood Town	28	9	6	13	36	64	33
Enville Athletic	28	6	4	18	33	62	22
Burman Hi-Ton	28	4	5	19	32	69	17
G.N.P. Sports	28	4	3	21	24	91	15

* points deducted

RESULTS CHART 1999-2000

	1	2	3	4	5	6	7	8	9	10	11	12	13	14	15	16	17	18	19	20
1 Alvechurch	X	1-2	1-3	2-1	1-1	7-2	2-0	2-1	0-3	0-1	1-1	7-3	0-3	4-0	4-2	1-1	2-1	1-6	2-3	1-0
2 Alveston	1-3	X	1-1	2-2	3-6	2-4	1-2	2-2	0-2	2-0	2-4	3-1	1-4	0-1	0-4	0-3	1-2	1-4	3-1	0-2
3 Blackheath Electro	1-1	1-3	X	1-1	0-5	2-1	3-1	0-1	1-2	3-1	2-1	2-0	2-3	2-2	2-2	0-4	0-2	0-4	6-2	2-2
4 Bolehall Swifts	6-1	0-1	5-1	X	3-2	7-2	1-0	4-1	2-2	1-1	6-1	7-0	2-2	0-1	1-1	2-3	0-1	2-5	5-1	4-1
5 Cheslyn Hay	6-1	3-1	0-2	3-1	X	1-0	5-2	1-1	1-1	2-3	1-1	4-1	3-3	3-7	4-1	1-1	0-1	2-3	3-0	0-0
6 Coleshill Town	7-1	2-2	1-1	1-3	0-2	X	2-3	1-4	2-3	1-1	5-2	4-4	0-2	0-3	1-5	1-6	1-2	1-4	0-1	1-3
7 Continental Star	4-1	0-2	2-2	2-2	0-5	3-2	X	0-0	2-0	0-0	2-1	7-3	0-2	0-4	0-2	1-0	3-0	2-2	3-3	2-1
8 Coventry Sphinx	0-2	1-1	1-2	2-0	3-0	4-0	2-0	X	0-1	4-0	3-0	8-0	0-3	2-1	2-1	3-1	1-0	0-1	0-0	1-2
9 Feckenham	1-1	3-0	0-0	0-5	0-0	7-0	1-1	4-2	X	1-2	1-0	4-0	1-3	1-2	3-1	1-3	2-0	2-2	1-0	0-1
10 Handrahan Timbers	0-3	3-0	2-0	2-1	1-2	1-0	0-2	2-3	0-2	X	3-1	2-2	0-3	2-3	2-2	1-0	5-1	0-4	2-0	2-2
11 Highgate United	0-3	3-2	1-3	0-5	1-2	0-1	2-2	0-2	3-1	0-1	X	2-5	0-1	0-0	1-1	3-0	4-0	1-1	3-3	2-3
12 Kenilworth Town	1-2	1-4	1-0	0-1	0-2	2-1	0-1	1-5	0-3	0-4	0-5	X	0-2	2-3	1-4	1-3	0-3	1-6	2-3	1-1
13 Kings Heath	0-3	6-0	1-2	1-1	3-2	1-1	7-0	1-0	2-0	2-0	1-0	4-3	X	4-3	1-1	1-1	1-1	0-4	0-4	4-0
14 Marconi (Coventry)	5-1	1-4	3-1	2-0	1-3	7-0	2-2	2-2	0-1	2-0	3-0	6-0	3-1	X	1-1	0-0	3-2	2-2	1-0	2-1
15 Massey Ferguson	3-3	1-3	4-0	2-0	3-2	7-1	1-1	2-2	1-1	3-1	2-0	4-0	2-4	1-0	X	1-0	1-0	0-3	4-2	0-2
16 Meir K.A.	2-1	4-0	2-0	5-4	1-1	1-2	7-5	4-0	4-0	1-1	0-1	3-0	0-0	4-1	3-1	X	1-0	1-1	1-1	1-2
17 Northfield Town	1-2	1-2	5-1	2-1	3-2	3-1	1-2	2-0	1-1	3-1	2-3	3-0	1-1	0-0	0-1	1-1	X	2-5	4-0	3-1
18 Nuneaton Griff	4-4	5-0	2-0	4-1	2-0	8-1	2-2	1-2	3-1	3-0	7-1	3-1	0-0	1-1	4-1	3-2	2-0	X	2-4	1-2
19 Southam United	1-1	3-0	1-2	3-2	1-2	4-1	1-2	2-1	1-1	1-2	3-2	10-0	0-3	1-2	0-1	1-5	2-2	0-4	X	1-1
20 Studley B.K.L.	0-1	6-0	2-3	2-1	4-0	5-1	3-1	1-3	1-1	1-2	7-3	6-0	3-1	3-1	4-1	5-2	3-1	0-0	2-0	X

1999-2000 CUP RESULTS

COMBINATION CUP FINAL

Brookvale Athletic v Sudley BKL 4-1

CHALLENGE URN FINAL

Chelmsley Town Res v Wilmcote S & S 1*2

PRESIDENTS CUP FINAL

Brownhills Town v Romulus 2-1

CHALLENGE TROPHY FINAL

Solihull Borough v Willenhall Town 0-1

CHALLENGE VASE FINAL

Handsaker v West Mids Police Res 2-1

CHALLENGE BOWL FINAL

Shepshed Dynamo v Solihull Borough 4-2

ALVECHURCH F.C.

Secretary: Alan Deakin, 58 Chesterfield Close, Northfield, Birmingham, B31 3TR(0121 411 1745)
Ground: Lye Meadow, Redditch Rd, Alvechurch, Worcs (0121 445 2929)
Directions: M42 jct 2, follow signs to Redditch, taking dual carriageway. At island turn right (signed Alvechurch) ground approx one mile on right. Ground is actually on Redditch Road, just south of Alvechurch village
Capacity: 3,000   **Seats:**100   **Cover:**Yes   **Floodlights:**Yes
Clubhouse: Evenings and matchdays   **Club shop:** No
HONOURS   Mid Comb Chall Cup R-up 95-96, Smedley Crooke Cup R-up 94-95
CLUB RECORDS Goalscorer: Dean Meyrick   **Appearances:** Dean Meyrick
PREVIOUS   **Leagues:** None
Name: None (predecessors, Alvechurch FC, founded 1929, folded in 1992)

Founded: 1994
Nickname: The Church
Sponsors: Centreprint
Colours: Gold/black/black
Change colours: White,blue,blue
Midweek matchday: Wednesday
Chairman: Andy Roberts
Director of Football: Lee Shaw
Patron: Roy Yardley
Manager:Mick Preece
99-00 Player of the Year: Nolan Talbot

ALVESTON

Secretary: Ken Unitt, Grafton, 47 Luddington Road, Stratford upon Avon, Warwicks. CV37 9SG (01789 205698)

Ground: Home Guard Club, Main Street, Tiddington, Stratford-upon-Avon. Tel: 01789 297718
Social Club Telephone : 01789 297718   **Floodlights:** Yes

Directions: ground is on the Stratford - Wellesbourne Road (B 40860) Home Guard Club is last building on right through Tiddington

Chairman: Martin Beese (01203 305294)

Colours: Maroon & Sky Blue/Sky Blue/ Maroon & Sky Blue

Change Colours: Black & White Stripes/ White/White

BLACKHEATH INVENSYS

Secretary: Graham.Ellison, 66 Richmond Grove,Wollaston Stourbridge, DY8 4SF
Tel: 01384 836112 (H) 0121 698 3362 (B) 07932 842787 (M)

Ground: Halesowen Harriers FC, Park Road, Halesowen B63 2RG Tel: 01384 896748

Directions: Ground is on A458 Birmingham to Stourbridge road.
From M5 J3, take A456 towards Kidderminster. Right at 1st island, then left at the island (A458 to Stourbridge). After approx. 2.5 miles ground on left 300m past Park Lane turning.   1 mile from Lye BR
Capacity: 4,000   Seats: 350   Cover: 500   Floodlights: Yes

Founded: 1920
Colours: Red & white/red/red
Change colours: All blue

Chairman: John Jones
Tel: 0121 550 1393 (H)

BOLEHALL SWIFTS

Secretary: Mal Tooley, 7 Ninefoot Lane, Belgrave, Tamworth, Staffs B77 2NA(01827 251973)
Ground: Rene Road, Bolehall, Tamworth (01827 62637)
Directions: A51 signs south to Bolebridge island, left under railway archesinto Amington Rd, 4th left into Leedham Ave, fork right into Rene Rd, ground onright by school. From Tamworth BR station walk up Victoria Road for threequarters of a mile and catch No.3 or No.6 mini-bus to Bolehall. Alight atLeedham Avenue or Rene Road and follow as above
Capacity: 2,000   Seats: 500   Cover: 600   Floodlights: Yes   Club Shop: No
Clubhouse: Large Social Club. Open evenings 7-11 & lunchtimes. Snacks available
HONOURS: Midland Comb. Div 2 84-85, F/Lit Cup R-up 96-97, Chall. Vase 84-85, Presidents Cup R-up 85-86; Fazeley Char Cup 84-85 (R-up 85-86); Ernie Brown Mem. Cup R-up 89-90 90-91 91-92 92-93 94-95 98-99, Jack Mould Cup R-up 85-86 Tony Allden Nenorial Cup 98-99

Founded: 1953   Nickname: Swifts
Colours: Yellow/black/yellow
Change Colours: All Green
Sponsors: Need -A-Skip-Hire Ltd.
Midweek matches: Tuesday
Programme: 24 pages, 70p
Editor: W Gould (01827 64530)
President: mr.L. Fitzpatrick
Chairman: James Latham
Vice-Chairman: K.Norchi
Manager: Ron Tranter Ass.Man: D.Finney
Coach: J.Capaldi
Physio: D.Crump

CHESLYN HAY

Secretary: J Rogers, 22 John Riley Dr., New Invention, Willenhall WV12 5AS (01922 860064)
Ground: Scholars Ground, Chasetown F.C., Church St., Chasetown, Walsall. 01543 682222
Directions: M6 Junct 11, A460 to Cannock, A5 to Brownhills, to Whitehouse Rd and Wharf Lane, at junction turn left into Highfield Rd., leading to Church St., ground on left.
Capacity: 2,000   Seats: 200   Cover: 300   Floodlights: Yes   Club Shop: Yes
Clubhouse: Evenings 7-11pm. Food (burgers, chips etc) on 1st team matchdays
HONOURS: Midland Comb. Prem Div. R-up 98-99, Div. 3 R-up 94-95;
Wolves Cup 86-87 87-88, Staffs. Chall. Cup 96-97; Walsall Chall. Cup 96-97;
W H Johns Mem. Cup 96-97; J W Hunt Cup R-up 96-97
CLUB RECORDS Appearances: Gary Osborne 492
Goalscorer: Ian Morgan 142 (in 113 games)

Founded: 1984
Sponsors: Pro Clean Ind. Services
Colours: Orange/white/black
Change colours: Blue & white stripes/blue/white
Programme: Yes
Editor: F Lowbridge 01543 577743

Chairman: Ivor Osborne (01922 414755)
Press Officer: C Cross
Jt. Managers: Carl Oulton & Andy Jones
Physio: M Bailey

CONTINENTAL STAR

Secretary: Barry Cole, 14 Devine Croft, Tipton, West Midlands. Dy4 8XJ (0121 557 0092)

Ground: Sandwell Borough F.C.

Directions: See S.B F.C. Page.in Midland Alliance.

Capacity: 3,000   Seats: 200   Cover: 200   Floodlights: Yes

Clubhouse: Bar open 7 nights a week. Bar manager resident

HONOURS: Midland Comb Div One R-up 96-97; Birmingham Vase

Colours: All Blue
Change Colours: Blue & Yellow/ Black/ Black

Chairman: Keith John
Tel: 0121 605 0708 (H)
Manager: Derek Stevens/ Lincoln Moses

COVENTRY MARCONI F.C.

Chairman: B Olsen   **Vice-Chairman:** D Ryan   **Press Officer:** P Scanlon

Secretary: P Scanlon, 61 Norton Hill Drive, Wyken, Coventry, West Mids CV2 3AX
           Tel: 02476 616576

Ground: Allard way, Copswood, Coventry   Tel: 01203 451361
Capacity 1,500   **Seats:** 92   **Cover:** Yes, Seats and standing   **Floodlights:**Yes

Clubhouse: 12-11 Saturdays 6.00-11.00 weekdays

HONOURS: Midland Comb Div 1 96-97, Presidents Cup 96-97.
Only winners of Coventry Evening Telegraph Cup (3 years), R-up Endslegh Comb Cup 99-00

Formed: 1923
Sponsors: Marconi
Colours: White with blue trim/white/white
Change colours: All red
Programme: 20pages Price:
Editor P.Scanlon 75p

Manager: C.Davies
Assistant Manager: J.McGinty
Physio: P.Tovey

COVENTRY SPHINX

Secretary: David Rees. 1 Pleydell Close, Willenhall Wood, Coventry CV3 3EF2 (02476 305921)

Match Secretary: Kevin Monks: Tel Nos: 02476 659249 (H) 0403 508358 (M)

Ground: Sphinx Drive, off Siddeley Avenue, Stoke Aldermoor, Coventry Tel: 01203 451361
 Social Club Telephone Number: 02476 451361

Chairman: Ron Cooper

Manager: Willie Knibbs

Colours:
Sky blue & navy/navy & sky/navy & sky
Change Colours: All White

FECKENHAM

Secretary: M G Hawkes4 Mill Lane, Feckenhamk, Redditch, Worcs B96 6HY (01527 893341)

Ground: Redditch United F.C. See details in Dr. Martens Section

Chairman: I Sprott (01527 894101)

Colours: Gren & White Hoops/Green/Green
Change Colours: Green & Yellow/yellow/yellow

HANDRAHAN TIMBERS

Secretary: Darren Mansell, 56 Windermere Drive, Kingswinford DY6 8AN (01384 830815)
Ground: Mile Flat Sports Ground, Mile Flat, Wallheath, Kingswinford, W. Mids (01381 484755)
Capacity: Cover: 200   Seats: 40   Floodlights: Yes
Clubhouse: Teas and refreshments   Club Shop: No
HONOURS   Midland Comb. Div 1 R-up 93-94, Birmingham Chall. Vase R-up 93-94,
           Wednesbury Charity Cup 91-92, J W Hunt Cup 92-93 R-up 93-94; Invitation Cup 94-95
PREVIOUS   **Leagues:** Staffs County Lg (South) 82-86   **Grounds:** None
CLUB RECORDS Goalscorer: Paul Baker   **Appearances:** Jonathan Pole
           Win: 9-0   **Defeat:** 0-6

Founded: 1982
Nickname: Timbers
Sponsors: W J Handrahan & Son
Colours: Red & black/black/black
Change colours: Sky/navy/navy
Midweek matchday: Wednesday
Programme: All games except outside cups
Chairman: E J Smith
President: W J Handrahan
Manager: Glen Taylor/Nigel Kirkham
Asst Manager: Phillip McNally
Press Officer: E J Smith (01384 295394)

HIGHGATE UNITED

Secretary: David McEvoy, 21 Bradfield House, Greenvale Avenue, Sheldon, 0788 7862549 (M)
Ground: The Coppice, Tythe Barn Lane, Shirley, Solihull B90 1PH (0121 7444194)
Directions: A34 from City through Shirley, fork right B4102 (Tanworth Lane), half mile then right into Dickens Heath Rd, then first right & ground on the left. 100yds from Whitlocks End (BR)
Capacity: 5,000   Seats: 250   Covered: 750   Floodlights: Yes
Clubhouse: Members Club open Tue to Thur, Sat & Sun. Light refreshments available weekends
HONOURS   Midland Comb (3) 72-75 (Div 2 66-67 68-69 71-72), Lg Cup (5) 72-74 75-77 84-85
(R-up 78-79 92-93); Presidents Cup 70-71 85-86); Tony Allden Mem. Cup 74-75;
Invit. Cup 68-69 71-72 85-86; West Mids All. 63-64; Birmingham Snr Cup 73-74
CLUB RECORDS Attendance: 4,000 v Enfield, FA Amateur Cup QF 1967
Players progressing: John Gayle (Wimbledon), Keith Leonard (A Villa), Geoff Scott (Leicester C.)

Founded: 1947   Nickname: The Gate
Colours: All red
Change Colours: White/blue/blue
Midweek matches: Tuesday
Programme: 28 pages, 50p
Editor: Terry Bishop (0676 22788)

Chairman: Terry Bishop
Treasurer: G Read
Press Officer: N C Sawyer
Manager: Jim Simms
Physio: Richard Flynn

KINGS HEATH

Secretary: Stuart Maddocks, 37 Rowheath Road, Cotteridge, Birmingham B30 2EP
Tel No: 0121 604 7543
Ground: Highgate Utd, The Coppice, Tythe Barn Lane, Shirley, Solihull B901PH (0121 744 4194)
Directions: A34 from City through Shirley, fork right B4102 (Tanworth Lane), half mile then right into Dickens Heath Rd, then first right & ground on the left. 100yds from Whitlocks End (BR)
Capacity: 5,000   Seats: 250   Covered: 750   Floodlights: Yes
HONOURS Midland Comb. Div 1 R-up 92-93, Div 2 R-up 82-83, Presidents Cup R-up 79-80 81-82
92-93; Birmingham Chall. Vase R-up 86-87; Worcester Sen Urn 96-97,Chall. Cup R-up 96-97
PREVIOUS   Names: Horse Shoe FC/ Kings Heath Amateur
              Ground: Shirley Town (pre-1994)
Player progressing: Geoff Scott (Stoke C.)

Founded: 1964
Nickname: The Kings
Colours: Old Gold/black/gold
Change Colours: All white
Midweek Matchday:
Programme: 12 pages
Editor: M Kite

Acting Chairman: D.Ellis
Manager: Clive Seeley

MASSEY-FERGUSON

Secretary: Terry Borras, Masey Ferguson, c/o Massey Ferguson social Club, Broad Lane, Coventry
Ground: Massey-Ferguson Sports Ground, Banner Lane, Tile Hill, Coventry   (01203 694400)
Directions: A45 to Meridan turn (B4104). Over two traffic islands, turn rightat 3rd island into Pickford Grange Lane, continue to Pickford Green Lane, &Hockley Lane, left into Broad Lane, right into Banner Lane, 3rd entrance right
       Seats: 70   Cover: 200   Clubhouse: Not on ground
HONOURS   Midland Comb. Div 1 94-95, Div 2 93-94, Chall. Vase 93-94, Chall Cup 94-95,
Presidents Cup 94-95; Coventry Evening Telegraph Cup 95-96
PREVIOUS   **League:** Coventry Alliance (pre-1993)

Colours: Red & Black,Black,Red
Change Colours: Blue / White
Programme: Yes

Chairman: Dave Malintel

Manager: John Halford, Geoff Brassington
Coach: Carl Lascelles
Physio: Joe Doolan

MEIR K.A.

Secretary: Chris Robinson , 19 Tthe Square, Meir, Stoke -on- Trent, Staffs ST3 6DW
Tel No: 01782 332152
Ground: Kings Park, Hilderstone Road, Meir Heath, Stoke-on-Trent (01782 388465)
Directions: M6 jct 14, A34 to Stone, A520 to Rough Close then Meir Heath, turnright (B5066) ground approx 1 mile on right. 3m Blythe Bridge (BR)
Capacity: 5,000 Seats: 200 Cover: 250 Floodlights: YesClub Shop: No
Clubhouse: open matchdays. Hot food
HONOURS: Staffs Snr Lg 88-89, 90-91; Staffs FA Vase 93-94; Walsall & Dist Sen Cup
89-90;Mid Comb Prem Lge R-up 96-97; Mid Comb Lge Chall Cup R-up 97-98
PREVIOUSLeagues: Staffs Alliance/ Staffs Snr 84-92
Ground: Normacot Rec   **Name:** 'The Station'&'Shoulder of Mutton.'

Founded: 1972   Nickname: Kings
Colours: Old gold/black/black
Change colours: Blue & white/blue & white/blue
Midweek matchday: Wednesday
Programme: 32 pages 50p
Editor: Kelly Reaney (01782 325624)
President: Peter Bott
Chairman: Des Reaney
Vice Chairman: Graham Lovatt
Manager: Des Reaney Coach: Bernie Bramwell
Press Officer: Mark Allen (01782 304472)
Commercial Mgr: Paul Robinson

NORTHFIELD TOWN

Secretary: Harvey Ryder, 10 Meadow Brook Road, Birmingha,m B31 1NE (0121 694 7571)

Ground: Oldbury United F.C The Cricketts, York Road, Rowley Regis, Warley, West Midlands
Tel: 0121 559 5564
Directions: M5 jct 2, follow Blackheath & Halesowen signs, first left at lights and fourth right
into York Road (turning before motorway flyover), ground 200yds on left.
One and a half miles from Sandwell & Dudley and Rowley Regis BR stations.
Bus 404 from West Bromwich, Oldbury and Blackheath.
Capacity: 3,000   Seats: 300   Cover: 1,000   Floodlights: Yes

Colours: yellow/blue/yellow
Change colours: All green

Chairman: Harvey Ryder

NUNEATON GRIFF

Secretary: Bob Archer, 27 Park Lane, Robinsons End, Nuneaton, Warwicks. CV10 8LX
Tel: 02476 375593 (H)
Ground: The Pingles Stadium, Avenue Road, Nuneaton. Tel: 024 76 37 0688
Directions: Avenue Road (A4252) leads to Cedar Tree Pub traffic lights, where you turn left into the stadium car park service road - unsuitable for coaches.
Capacity: 2,000   **Seats:** 238   **Cover:** 400   **Floodlights:** Yes
Clubhouse: Yes / Usual Licensing hours Tel: 02476 386798 (Social Club)   **Club Shop:** Yes / No
HONOURS: Coventry Alliance 97-98, Coventry Telegraph Cup 98, Cov. Charity Cup 99,
BCFA Junior Cup Winners 98-99 R-up 99-00, Midland Comb 99-00
(NB Only club to be placed in Premier Division on application and win title in
first season.)

Founded: 1972-73
Nickname: Griff
Colours: Blue & white/blue/red & blue
Change colours: All yellow
Midweek Matchday:Wednesday
Programme:16 pages £1.00

Chairman: John Gore
Manager: Mark Green

PERSHORE TOWN 88

Secretary: Don Roberts, 6 Gardens Close, Upton-on-Severn, Worcs.WRS 0LT (01684 593439)
Ground: King George V Playing Fields, King Georges Way, Pershore, Worcs (01386556902).
Directions: M5 jct 7, A44 to Pershore (8 miles) cross 1st lights in Pershore,at 2nd lights turn left & fold road round into King Georges Way, ground immediately on left.
Capacity: 4,000   **Seats:** 200   **Cover:** 200   **Floodlights:** Yes (148 lux)   Club Shop:Yes
Clubhouse: Open every evening, Sun lunch & all day Sat. Snack available during matches.
HONOURS   Midland Comb Prem 93-94, Div 2 89-90; Worcs Jnr Cup 90-91, Robert
Biggart Cup (5), R-up (3); Worcs Snr Urn 95-96, R-up 92-93, Jack Mould
Cup 90-91, Alfred Terry Cup 90-91 Martley Hosp. Cup(`A') 90-91
RECORDS   **Atttendance:** 1,356 v Yeading, FA Cup 4th Qual. Rd 23/10/93
PREVIOUS   League: Midland Comb 89-90 90-94

Founded: 1988   Nickname: The Town
Colours: Blue & White,blue,blue
Change colours:Red,black, red
Midweek matchday: Tuesday
Programme: 20 pages,60p
Editor: Terry Conway (01386 654380)
99-00 Captain: Colin Followay
P.o.Y.:Grant Beckett
Chairman: Anthony Bradstock
Manager: Colin Shepherd
Asst Mgr: Mike Pugh
Coach: Frank Concannon

ROMULUS

Secretary: Roger Evans, 34 Leam Drive, Church Farm, Burntwood, WS7 9JG
Tel: 01543 675152 (H) 0956 187016 (M)

Ground: Bolehall Swifts F.C.,Rene Rd, Bolehall, Tamworth B77 3NN
Tel: 01827 62637

Directions: A51 signs south to Bolebridge island, left under railway archesinto Amington Rd, 4th left into Leedham Ave, fork right into Rene Rd, ground onright by school. From Tamworth BR station walk up Victoria Road for threequarters of a mile and catch No.3 or No.6 mini-bus to Bolehall. Alight atLeedham Avenue or Rene Road and follow as above
Capacity: 2,000   **Seats:** 500   **Cover:** 600   **Floodlights:** Yes

Founded: 1979
Colours: Red & white stripes/red/red
Change colours: White/white/black

Chairman: John Matthews
Tel: 01827 899583 (H) 0121 327 5778 (B)

SOUTHAM UNITED

Secretary: R J Hancocks, 18 Warwick Road, Southam, Leamington Spa CV33 0HN
Tel: 01926 813483

Ground: Banbury Road Ground, Southam, Leamington Spa. Tel: 01926 812091

Directions: A423 - 12 miles south of coventry on the Banbury side of Southam
Capacity: 2000   **Seats:** 200   **Cover:** 250   **Floodlights:** Yes
Clubhouse: Yes, with food available   Club Shop: No
HONOURS   Midland Comb. Prem. Div. R-up 97-98: Birmingham County Sat. Vase 97-98;
Coventry Chall. Cup; Coventry City Cup; Coventry & N. Warwicks. Lge Pre. Div.
RECORD   **Attendance:** 1,500 v Coventry City, friendly 86-87

Founded: 1905
Colours: White & black/black/black
Change colours: red & black/white/white
Midweek Matchday: Tuesday
Programme: 10 pages 50p Editor: Ian Jowsey

Chairman: D Shanahan
Presss Officer: Vic Shepherd
Manager: Bobby Hancocks & Ashley Alexander
Physio: Bill Rutledge

STUDLEY B.K.L.

Secretary: Mark Sealey c/o club.
Ground: Beehive, BKL Sports Ground, Abbeyfields,Birmingham Rd., Studley, Warwicks
Tel: 01527 853817   **Directions:** M42 Jct.3 onto A435 to Redditch.Over island at Dog Pub on left continue towards Studley. Ground on left signposted to Abbeyfields.
Capacity : 1,500   **Seats:** 200   **Cover :** Yes   **Floodlights:**Yes   **Clubhouse:** Yes,on ground.
HONOURS   Midland Comb. Div 1 91-92, Chall Cup R-up 91-92, Presidents Cup R-up 91-
92, Div2 Cup 87-88; Smedley Crooke Char. Cup 90-91 91-92; Birmingham Vase R-up 96-97
PREVIOUS   League: Redditch & South Warwickshire Sunday Combination 71-87
Name: BKL Works
CLUB RECORDS **Appearances:** Lee Adams   **Goalscorer:** Brian Powell
Attendance: 500 v Feckenham 31.8.98 **Appearances:** Lee Adams

Founded: 1971   Nickname: Bees
Sponsors: BKL Fittings
Colours: All Skyblue & navy blue.
Change colours: All Yellow
Programme: 50p   Editor: Gordon Wilkie
Reserve's League:
Chairman: David Robinson
Vice-Chairman: Alec James
Press Officer: Dave Chiswell
Manager: John Adams
Asst Manager: Alan Scarfe & Glen Adams
Physio: Dave Middleton

749

SUTTON TOWN (formerly Brookvale Athletic)

	Founded: 1959
Secretary: Alan Fleming,28 Manor Road, Streetly, W.Mids B74 3NG	Colours: Blue/yellow/blue
Tel: 01235 39260 07970 573638 (M)	Change colours: Yellow/blue/yellow

Ground: The Central Ground. Coles Lane, Sutton Coldfield
Tel: 0121 355 5475

Directions: From M6 J5 (Spaghetti Junction), take A5127 along Gravelyy Hill. Follow into Sutton New Road then Birmingham Road. Turn right into Holland Road at junction with Odeon Cinema then 1st right into Coles lane. Ground 400m on left.

Previous: **Names:** Brookvale Athletic >00

Chairman: Ron Evans
Tel: 01543 673620 (H)
Match Secretary: Susan Fleming
Address & Tel as Secretary

MIDLAND COMBINATION DIVISION ONE

ALVIS OAKWOOD
Secretary: D A Leslie, 9 Stephenson Close, Milverton, Leamington
Spa CV32 6BS Tel: 01926 336700
Ground: Alvis Sports & Social Club, Green Lane, Finham,
Coventry. Tel: 01203 692576
Colours: Blue and White/White/Blue

BROWNHILLS TOWN
Secretary: Paul Dixon, 263 Chase Road, Burntwood, Stafafs WS7
0EA (01543 683730)
Ground: Holland `Park, The Parade, Brownhills, Walsall(0956535545)
Colours: Yellow/blue/blue

BURNTWOOD
Secretary: Mervyn Ellis, 11 Green Meadows, Heath Hayes,
Cannock, Staffs WS125YA Tel: 01543 271770
Ground: Memorial Institute, Rugeley Road, Burntwood.
Tel: 01543 675578
Colours: Red and Blue /Blue/Red

COLESHILL TOWN
Secretary: Neil Hamilton, 31 Fourfields Way, New Arley, N Warwicks,
CV7 8PX(01676 54088)
Ground: Pack Meadow, Packington Lane, Coleshill, Birmingham B46
3JQ (0167563259)
Colours: All green Change Colours: Green/white/green

COUNTY SPORTS
Secretary: Geoff Woodward, 2 Lansdowne Rd., Worcester WR1 1ST
Tel: 01905 23341
Ground: County Council Sports Ground, Claines Lane, Worcester
Tel: 0589 329771
Colours: Yellow/blue/blue

DUDLEY SPORTS
Secretary: John Lewis, 6 Hern Rd., Brieley Hill, West Mids DY5 2PW
Tel: 01384 895782
Ground: High Ercal Avenue, Brierley Hill, West Mids (01384 826420)
Colours: Red & blue/blue/red Change colours: All blue

FAIRFIELD VILLA
Secretary/Press Officer: C W Harris, 7 Churchill Road, Catshill,
Bromsgrove B610PE Tel: 01527 831049
Ground: Recreation Ground, Stourbridge Road (B4091), Fairfield,
Bromsgrove. Tel: 01527 77049
Colours: White/black/black

HAMS HALL
General Manager/Press Officer: Bob Ringrose, 6 Holly Drive, Hurley,
Atherstone,Warks CV9 2JY Tel: 0827 872747
Ground: Hams Hall Generating Station, Lea Marston,
Sutton Coldfield B76 0BG Tel: 0370 936219
Colours: White/black/black

HOLLY LANE '92
Secretary: R G Ashton, 19 Grange Road, Erdington,
Birmingham B24 0DG Tel: 0121 350 2352
Ground: Holly Sports & Social Centre, Holly Lane, Erdington,
Birmingham B249LH. tel: 01213 730979
Colours: Yellow/green/green

KENILWORTH TOWN
Secretary: R Butler, 52 Farmer Ward Road, Kenilworth, Warwicks. Tel:
01926857097
Ground: Gypsey Lane (off Rouncil Lane), Kenilworth, Warwicks. Tel:
01926 50851
Colours: All red with white trim

KNOWLE
Secretary: Roger Whittick, 149 Richmond Road, Solihull B92 7RZ
Tel No 0121 684 2753
Ground: Hampton Rd, Knowle, Solihull , W.Mid B93 0NX (01564
779807)
Colours: Red/black/black

LOUGHBOROUGH ATHLETIC
Secretary: John Belton: 51 Farndale Drive, Loughborough,
Leics.LE112RG Tel No: 01509 231583 (H) 01509 231583 (W)
Ground: The Drome, Derby Road Playing Fields, Derby Road,
Loughborough Tel: 01509 610022
Colours: All yellow

MILE OAK ROVERS
Secretary: Keith Lycett, 1 Price Avenue, Mile Oak, Tamworth, Staffs.
B78 3NL Tel Nos 018267 708735 (H)01827 89614(W)
Colours: Navy& Yellow/navy/navy

OLD HILL TOWN
Ground: Hingleys, Bluebell Road, Cradley Heath, West Midlands.
(01384 566827)

POLESWORTH NORTH WARWICK
Ground: North warwick Sports Ground, Hermitage Hill, Tamworth
Road, Polesworth, warks.

SHIRLEY TOWN
Secretary: B Fox, 26 Claines Road, Northfield, Birmingham B31 2EE
Tel: 0121 475 4465
Ground: Shirley Stadium, Tile House Lane, Shirley, Solihull
Tel: 0121 744 1560
Colours: All maroon

THIMBLEMILL R.E.C.
Secretary: Karl Young, 30 Moorpool Close, Harborne, Birmimgham
Tel: 0121 427 2807
Ground: Thimblemill Recreation, Thimblemill Road, Smethwick,
Warley. Tel: 0121 429 2459
Colours: White (blue trim)/white/navy blue

WELLESBOURNE
Secretary: Ted Forster Tel: 01926 494507
Ground: The Sports Field, Loxley Close, Wellesbourne
Tel: 01789 841878
Colours: Blue & white halves/blue/blue

BANKS'S BREWERY
WEST MIDLANDS (REGIONAL) LEAGUE

FEEDER TO: MIDLAND ALLIANCE

Hon Secretary: Neil Juggins
14 Badgers Lane, Blackwell, Bromsgrove

Stafford Town are the new champions, making for an unusual double as they ground-share with Stafford Rangers, who were also champions of their own league. Town always looked likely champions after starting their league campaign with ten consecutive victories, though they did not always head the table due to other clubs having played more games. They were pushed hardest of all by newly promoted Causeway United, who led the table on various occasions, but Stafford regained top spot in mid March and went on to clinch the title with a game to spare. For Causeway there was some consolation in the form of the Keys Cup (awarded to the runners-up), whilst mention should also be made of Darlaston Town who held second place for several weeks without really looking like championship contenders but nevertheless finished third, their highest league placing since 1967. For a change there was no club obviously out of its depth in this section and an interesting three way tussle developed to avoid the two relegation spaces, with Westfields ultimately spared the need to wait and hope for survival.

Stafford were surprisingly denied a league and cup double by Tipton Town. Tipton had belied their modest league performances by eliminating reigning double winners Kington Town and championship chasing Causeway along the way, and in a hard fought final Tipton scored twice in extra time to bring a successful conclusion to their first ever Premier Division Final. Causeway had further consolation by winning the Birmingham County FA Vase Final, whilst Bandon clinched the Shropshire Challenge Cup by defeating Shawbury United from Division One. Another mention here should go to Darlaston whose exploits in the Midland Invitation Cup saw them eliminate two Midland Alliance clubs along the way, only to lose to a third in the Final, namely Bridgnorth Town.

The restricted league programme in the regionalised divisions one (North and South) meant it took some time for patterns to develop. In the Northern section Sedgley White Lions and newcomers Shawbury United both remained unbeaten until the New Year, though at this stage the number of league fixtures fulfilled by the clubs ranged from seven to seventeen! Shawbury then began to pull away from the pack and even led the table by sixteen points at one stage, finishing their programme with a 1-1 draw at Walsall Wood Reserves in mid April. This all but ensured the championship as it left Wolverhampton United with the unlikely task of of not only winning their five remaining games, but also making up a 29 deficit in goal difference. Mathematical certainty for Shawbury was achieved on Easter Monday as Wolves lost to Sedgley, though the latter gained sufficient points from the other games to clinch the runners-up spot on goal difference from Great Wyrley, whom they beat during the final week. Corestone claimed the wooden spoon with just a single league victory to their credit all season, having avoided bottom place for much of the campaign as a consequence of being well ahead with their fixtures.

In the Southern section reigning champions Wellington were another club to benefit from being ahead with their fixtures, leading the table by as many as fourteen points at one stage, and remaining unbeaten until February 5th when they were defeated by closest challengers Bromyard Town, who had five games in hand. Bromyard whittled away at this lead to such an extent that they were allowed the luxury of a 0-5 home defeat by their main rivals in Wellington's penultimate league fixture, eventually clinching the title with victory over another Herefordshire side, Leominster, in their final game. Wellington gained some consolation in becoming the first club to retain the Division One cup. Down at the bottom Mahal endured a miserable campaign, losing all but four of their fixtures.

The days when WMRL clubs dominated the FA Vase are now just a distant memory and out of twelve member clubs just two made it as far as the competition proper. Malvern Town was the only club to reach the Second Round, holding Glossop to a 2-2 draw before going down 0-3 in a replay. Another sign of the times saw no entries at all for the FA Cup.

Top: Westfields FC. Back Row (l-r): Paul Price, Danny Phillips, Matt Morris, Carl Morgan. Middle Row: Dave Howes, Mike Ingram, Jon Pugh, Anthony Richards, Tony Richards, Dan Moon, Darren Hall, Lee Symonds (Physio). Front Row: Adrian Powell, Darrel Addis, Sean Edwards (Coach), Dave Ellis (Manager), Dave Cartwright (Coach), Andy Morris (Chief Executive), Andy Meadmore, Richard Legden.

Left: Dudley Town FC. Back Row (l-r): Steve Taylor, Luke Handley, Noel Haye, John Carmichael (captain), John Street, Keron Jackson, Ian Cornfield, Jason Attwell, Tom Botfield, Tommy Johnson. Front Row: Richard Taylor, Lee Smith, Bernie Gethins, Ian Davis (Manager), Philip Male, Adam Evans, Albert Johnson

Left: Malvern Town FC. Back Row (l-r): Nick Clayton, Ed Draper, Rob Perrins, Andy Shepherd, Simon Judge, Sean Cotterill, John Wade, Ross Sanders, Rob Bastock, Adam Higgins, Dene Whittal-Williams. Front Row: David Cannon, Joe Maidment, Steve Walker, Simon Brain, Darren Tafft, Micky Lowe.

Left: Malvern Town v Ibstock Welfare 4-2. Darren Taft equalises (2-2) with a penalty for Malvern.
Photo: Bill Wheatcroft

FINAL LEAGUE TABLES 1999-2000

PREMIER DIVISION

	P	W	D	L	F	A	Pts		P	W	D	L	F	A	Pts
Stafford Town	42	35	4	3	113	31	109	Dudley Town	42	13	13	16	53	59	52
Causeway United	42	34	2	6	88	35	104	Gornal Athletic	42	14	4	24	58	75	46
Darlaston Town	42	30	5	7	115	64	95	Tipton Town	42	12	9	21	61	87	45
Brandon	42	26	7	9	83	46	85	Smethwick Rangers	42	12	8	22	66	95	44
W'ton Casuals	42	25	6	11	99	54	81	Ettingshall H T	42	11	10	21	53	91	43
Kington Town *	42	25	3	14	88	68	72	Ludlow Town	42	10	11	21	52	75	41
Tividale	42	19	9	14	66	58	66	Brierley Hill Town	42	11	8	23	50	73	41
Heath Hayes	42	19	4	19	64	66	61	Bustleholme	42	10	9	23	69	95	39
Malvern Town	42	17	7	18	73	55	58	Westfields	42	9	9	24	56	89	36
Little Drayton Rangers	42	16	10	16	64	66	58	Walsall Wood	42	8	10	24	55	99	34
Lye Town	42	15	9	18	65	66	54	Star	42	8	9	25	37	81	33

DIVISION ONE NORTH

	P	W	D	L	F	A	Pts
Shawbury United	24	18	3	3	75	19	57
W'ton United	24	16	2	6	55	23	50
Great Wyrley	24	16	2	6	57	31	50
Sedgley White Lions	24	13	8	3	48	18	47
Cannock Chase	24	15	2	7	67	46	47
Newport	24	13	4	7	44	28	43
Lucas Flight Controls	24	8	5	11	58	50	29
Shifnal Town Res	24	8	5	11	45	55	29
Morda United	24	8	1	15	40	61	25
Walsall Wood Res	24	6	5	13	35	59	23
Borgfeld Celtic	24	4	5	15	38	75	17
Heath Hayes Res	24	3	5	16	28	71	14
Corstone Services *	24	1	7	16	28	82	9

DIVISION ONE SOUTH

	P	W	D	L	F	A	Pts
Bromyard Town	22	17	2	3	75	48	53
Wellington	22	16	4	2	65	21	52
Ledbury Town	22	14	2	6	65	35	44
Sikh Hunters	22	9	4	9	58	51	31
Hinton	22	10	1	11	40	52	31
Malvern Town Res	22	8	6	8	37	38	30
Leominster Town	22	8	3	11	41	53	27
Chaddesley Corbett	22	8	2	12	47	53	26
Bewdley Town	22	7	5	10	42	48	26
Pershore T Res	22	7	3	12	47	66	24
Cradley T Res *	22	7	3	12	40	63	21
Mahal	22	3	1	18	26	76	10

* Points deducted

PREMIER DIVISION RESULTS CHART 1999-2000

		1	2	3	4	5	6	7	8	9	10	11	12	13	14	15	16	17	18	19	20	21	22
1	Bandon	X	2-1	2-1	0-1	1-2	2-0	2-0	4-2	3-0	6-0	4-0	0-0	3-1	3-1	1-1	2-1	1-1	3-1	2-0	1-1	1-0	2-1
2	Brierley Hill	2-3	X	3-3	0-0	2-4	1-0	1-1	2-1	0-2	2-1	2-1	3-0	0-2	2-3	1-1	0-3	1-3	0-2	0-3	3-1	0-1	1-3
3	Bustleholme	1-3	1-2	X	1-4	0-1	2-0	1-1	3-4	3-3	1-0	1-2	1-2	2-4	0-2	1-0	2-3	3-1	0-3	2-0	5-2	4-1	1-2
4	Causeway U	2-0	4-2	3-2	X	1-2	0-0	1-0	5-1	2-1	2-1	3-1	1-0	1-0	2-0	2-0	1-4	3-0	2-0	3-0	1-0	1-0	2-3
5	Darlaston T	3-1	3-2	7-3	5-2	X	3-2	4-0	2-0	2-1	0-1	1-4	3-2	6-2	3-1	4-2	0-1	2-0	2-3	4-1	4-1	5-2	
6	Dudley Tn	1-4	0-2	2-1	1-4	0-1	X	4-0	2-2	2-0	0-1	1-0	0-0	1-1	2-1	3-1	0-1	1-1	2-0	0-1	2-0	4-3	0-2
7	Ettingshall	3-1	0-2	0-0	1-4	1-4	1-1	X	1-1	4-0	1-2	0-1	1-2	1-3	2-1	3-1	1-7	0-0	2-2	2-1	3-3	1-2	2-1
8	Gornal Ath	0-1	2-1	1-1	0-3	1-0	0-2	0-2	X	1-4	2-2	5-2	2-1	1-3	0-1	1-2	0-3	0-2	1-3	0-1	0-1	4-1	1-4
9	Heath Hayes	1-2	0-1	2-1	0-3	0-2	1-1	4-1	1-3	X	2-3	2-0	3-1	0-2	2-1	1-1	0-3	4-1	1-1	0-2	2-1	4-0	0-1
10	Kington Tn	3-2	1-1	3-2	0-1	3-3	3-0	9-1	3-2	2-1	X	0-1	3-1	1-5	0-3	4-2	3-4	5-2	3-0	0-1	7-1	1-0	3-1
11	L Drayton R	1-0	4-1	2-1	1-2	2-2	1-2	1-0	1-0	0-1	0-4	X	1-5	2-1	1-1	2-1	1-1	3-0	0-2	3-3	3-3	1-1	3-1
12	Ludlow Tn	1-2	1-0	1-2	0-2	4-4	4-2	3-1	0-4	1-3	1-2	1-1	X	0-0	0-3	3-1	0-4	1-1	0-0	1-2	1-1	2-0	1-2
13	Lye Town	3-3	2-3	0-1	0-2	2-0	0-0	2-3	0-3	1-0	2-2	2-3	3-1	X	1-0	1-2	2-0	0-0	2-2	0-2	3-0	4-1	0-2
14	Malvern Tn	3-1	0-0	3-1	0-1	2-3	0-0	1-4	0-1	5-0	1-2	2-1	2-2	4-2	X	1-1	1-2	2-0	1-2	1-1	3-1	4-2	1-0
15	Smethwick R	0-3	2-0	3-5	2-3	2-7	1-5	1-1	0-1	0-2	3-1	1-2	2-1	1-2	2-1	X	0-6	3-2	2-1	2-2	4-1	2-2	2-3
16	Stafford Tn	1-1	3-0	3-0	2-1	1-1	4-1	4-1	3-0	2-0	3-0	2-1	5-0	3-0	1-0	4-1	X	4-0	5-1	2-1	4-1	3-2	1-0
17	Star	1-4	2-1	0-0	0-2	1-3	0-0	1-2	1-0	0-2	1-4	0-3	0-2	2-3	1-0	1-2	1-2	X	0-5	0-1	2-0	2-5	2-2
18	Tipton Town	0-1	2-1	4-4	0-3	1-2	3-1	1-1	1-4	0-1	1-3	2-1	1-1	1-2	1-8	1-4	0-2	2-1	X	1-3	4-1	2-2	3-0
19	Tividale	2-1	3-2	3-3	1-2	1-1	1-2	1-0	0-2	2-3	0-1	1-0	3-1	1-1	2-2	1-0	0-1	6-0	X	2-1	2-2	2-4	
20	Walsall Wood	1-1	2-1	1-1	1-4	1-4	2-3	1-3	2-1	2-4	2-0	3-2	0-1	2-3	0-1	5-2	2-2	0-0	3-0	1-1	X	2-1	0-6
21	Westfields	1-2	1-1	4-1	2-0	2-4	1-1	4-0	2-3	0-4	0-1	0-4	1-1	1-6	2-4	0-2	2-1	4-1	0-1	0-0	X	0-0	
22	Wolver'ton C	1-2	0-0	8-1	1-2	4-0	2-2	6-1	2-1	3-0	6-0	1-1	3-2	1-0	1-0	2-2	2-0	1-2	3-2	5-2	4-2	3-0	X

BANKS'S BREWERY PREMIER DIVISION LEAGUE CUP 1999-2000

FIRST ROUND

Bustleholme	v	Smethwick Rangers	1*2		Dudley Town	v	Tipton Town	1-5
Ettingshall Holy Trinity	v	Gornal Athletic	5-4		Lye Town	v	Kington Town	1-2
Star	v	Darlaston Town	0-1		Tividale	v	Westfields	2-0

SECOND ROUND

Bandon	v	Stafford Town	0*1		Brierley Hill Town	v	Ettingshall H T	3*3, 3p2
Causeway United	v	Little Drayton Rangers	1-0		Darlaston Town	v	Heath Hayes	4-2
Ludlow Town	v	Wolverhampton Cas	3-2		Malvern Town	v	Tividale	1-0
Smethwick Rangers	v	Kington Town	1-4		Tipton Town	v	Walsall Wood	1-0

QUARTER FINALS

Darlaston Town	v	Causeway United	0-2		Malvern Town	v	Brierley Hill Town	2-1
Stafford Town	v	Ludlow Town	3-2		Tipton Town	v	Kington Town	2-0

SEMI-FINALS (two legs)

Causeway United	v	Tipton Town	1-2, 1-1		Stafford Town	v	Malvern Town	0-0, 4-3

FINAL

Stafford Town	v	Tipton Town	0-2	After extra time. At Tividale FC

BANKS'S BREWERY DIVISION ONE LEAGUE CUP 1999-2000

SEMI-FINALS (two legs)

Cannock Chase	v	Wellington	0-2, 1-3		Sedgley White Lions	v	Ledbury Town	3-2, 0-3

FINAL

Ledbury Town	v	Wellington	1-2	At Bromyard Town FC

BCD STEELS YOUTH LEAGUE CUP

SEMI-FINALS (two legs)

Lye Town	v	Cradley Town	0-5, 1-6		Bridgnorth Town	v	Walsall Wood	2-1, 3-5

FINAL

Cradley Town	v	Walsall Wood	4-0	At Tividale FC

Above: Tipton Town FC - West Midlands Premier Division Cup Winners. Back Row (l-r): N Hickenbottom (Tipton & Coseley Building Society), M Hudson, S Hall, N Smith, G Rhodes, D Bennett, S Mole, M Perry, M Walters, L Judson (Tipton & Coseley Building Society). Front Row (l-r): C Love, M Williams, L Smith, D Hurley, W Thornton, C Hunter, D Stanway, C Phillips.

BRIERLEY HILL TOWN

Secretary: Nick Pratt, 91 Rangeways Road, Kingswinford, West Midlands DY6 8NU
Tel: 01384 78725
Ground: The Dell Sports Stadium, Bryce Rd, Pensnett, Brierley Hill, West Mids (01384 812943)
Directions: At lights in Brierley Hill High St turn into Bank St by PoliceStation. Over bridge into Pensnett Rd, ground 3/4 mile on left Paddy's Garage.Entrance 120yds in Bryce Rd
Capacity: 5,000   Seats: 300   Cover: 300   Floodlights: Yes
Clubhouse: Open Mon, Wed & Fri. Hot foods & drinks on matchdays

HONOURS   West Mids Lg Prem. Div Cup R-up 84-85 (Div 1 80-81 (Div 1 Cup 80-81))
PREVIOUS   Leagues: Kidderminster (8 seasons); Staffs County (South)(7 seasons); West Midlands Regional (pre-94)

Founded: 1955
Nickname: Lions
Colours: Blue & white halves/blue/blue/
Change colours: White/yellow/yellow
Midweek matchday: Mon or Wed
Programme: 20 pages, 50p
Editor: Secretary
Chairman: Anthony Purchase
Vice-Chairman: Terry Baker
Manager: Richard Gwinnett
Asst Manager: Steve Scott
Coach: Chris Conway

BROMYARD TOWN

Secretary: Tony Haverfield, 16 Highwell Avenue, Bromyard, Hereford HR7 4EL
Tel: 01885 483655 (H) 01855 483655 0585 849948 (M)

Ground: Delahay Meadow, Stourport Road, Bromyard HR7 4NT Tel: 01885 483974

Directions: 1/4 mile outside Bromyard on the Stourport/Kidderminster road (B4203). The ground is on the right through iron gates, adjacent to O'Malleys Irish restaurant

Founded: 1893

Colours: Blue & black/black/black
Change colours: Yellow/red/yellow

Chairman: Tony Watkins
Tel: 01885 483509

BUSTLEHOME

Secretary: Suzanne Glover, 15 Swann Hill, Hurst Hill, Coseley, WolverhamptonWV14 9UP
Tel: 01902 659380
Ground: Darlaston Town FC, Waverley Rd, Darlaston, W Midlands (0121 526 4423)
Directions: M6 jct 10, A454 Walsall/Willenhall. Take the A454 towardsWillenhall. Turn left at traffic lights, outside the Lane Arms Public Houseinto Bentley Road North. Follow road down hill, over railway & canal bridges to lights. Cross over lights into Richard Street & along Victoria Road. Take the first right into Slater Street, ground on left
Seats: Yes   Cover: Yes   Floodlights: Yes

FACT FILE
Founded: 1975
Colours: Yellow/green/green
Change colours: White/green/green
CLUB PERSONNEL
Chairman: Geoff Fellows

CAUSEWAY UNITED

Secretary: Frank Webb, 10 Moorfield Drive, Halesowen, West Midlands B63 3TG Tel: 0121 550 5219 (H) 0121 550 9916 (B)
Ground: Halesowen Town F.C., The Grove, Old hawne Lane, Halesowen Tel: 0121 550 2179
Directions: M5 jct 3, A456 (signed Kidderminster) to 1st island turn right (signed A459 Dudley), left at next island (signed A458 Stourbridge), at next island take 3rd left into Grammar School Lane, then Old Hawne Lane - ground 400 yds on left
Capacity: 5,000   Cover: 1,420   Seats: 420   Floodlights: Yes

DARLASTON TOWN

Secretary: Mrs Kath Abley, 42 Addenbrooke Street, Darlaston (0121 531 0487)
Ground: City Ground, Waverley Rd, Darlaston (0121 526 4423) **Directions:** M6 Jct 10, A454 towards Willenhall, left at lights outside`Lane Arms' into Bentley Rd North, follow this down hill & over the railway & canal bridges to traffic lights. Cross over the lights into Richards St and along into Victoria Rd, 1st right into Slater St and ground on left but entrance is next left in Waverley Rd
Capacity: 2,000 Seats: Yes Cover: Yes Floodlights: Yes Club Shop: Yes
Clubhouse: Open matchdays. Tues/Wed/Thur evenings & Sunday Lunch. Hot/colddrinks/snacks
HONOURS West Mids Lg Div 1 89-90 (R-up 91-92 92-93, Div 1 Cup Cup 89-90), B irmingham Snr Cup 72-73, B'ham Vase 90-91 91-92, B'ham Jnr Lg 07-08, B'hamComb. 10-11 37-38 45-46 (Tillotson Cup 36-37 37-38 38-39 45-46), Keys Cup 11-12), Wednesbury Lg(5) 1896-1901
PREVIOUS Leagues:(inc Wedn'bury Lg) pre-1908/ B'gham Comb. 08-11 28-54/ WMids 11-28

Founded: 1874   Nickname: Blues
Sponsors: Rubery owen
Colours: Blue & white stripes/blue/blue
Change colours: All yellow
Midweek matchday: Tuesday
Prog. Editor: Dave Stevenson (0121 526 2465)
Chairman: John Reeves
Match Sec: Neil Arrowsmith (01902 450612)
Press Officer: 'Scotch Bob'
Manager: Jim McMorran
Assistant Manager: Colin Johnson
Physio: Michelle Cookson

DUDLEY TOWN

Secretary: Margaret Turner, 3,Straits Road, Lower Gornal, Dudley, DY3 2UY Tel: 01384 214741
Ground: The Beeches, Packwood Road, Tividale W,Mids Tel : 01384 211743
Directions: M5 Jct 2 signs to Dudley (A4123). One mile past school and playing fields under walkway to lights. Left into Regent Road.,left into Elm Terrace then left again into BirchTerrace and 2nd left into Pakewood Road. Ground is at end of cul-de-sac.
Capacity: 500   Cover: 1000   Seats: 100   Floodlights: Yes Club Shop: Yes
Clubhouse: Peacocks social club open on matchday . Snacks available from clubhouse
HONOURS   Southern Lg Midland Div 84-85, Birmingham Comb 33-34 (R-up 34-35 47-48), Midland (Worcs) Comb 31-32 (R-up 29-30 30-31), West Mids Lg Cp R-up 75-76 (Div2 Cp R-up 80-81), Birmingham Senior Cup 85-86 (R-up 64-65 83-84)

FACT FILE
Formed: 1893   Nickname: The Robins
Colours: Red/black/black
Change: Yellow/black or white/black or red
Midweek matchday: Tuesday 7.45pm
Programme: Pages:28 Price75p
Editor: Paul Hawthorne
Chairman: Nevil Jeynes
Vice Chairman: Alan Guest
President: N D Jeynes
Manager: Ian Davis
Asst Manager:Tommy Johnson

ETTINGSHALL HOLY TRINITY

Secretary: Graham Mills, 27 Ashen Close, Sedgley, Dudley, West Mids DY3 3UZ(01902 66222)
Ground: Aldersley Stadium, Aldersley Road, Tettenhal, Wolverhampton (01902 556200)
Directions: From Wolverhampton take A41 Tettenhal Road, 1.5 miles turn right into Lower Street, then right into Aldersley Road, ground on right
HONOURS West Mids Lg Div 1 Cup R-up 85-86 (Div 2 R-up 84-85), Sporting Award 85-86,Staffs Co. Lg R-up 82-83 (Lg Shield 82-83 83-84), Ike Cooper Cup 82-84 83-84,Sporting Club Award 81-82, Wolverhampton & District Amateur Lg 80-81 (Div 1 65-66, Div 2 64-65), Div 1/2 Cup 64-65 65-66, A H Oakley Cup 80-81, J W Hunt Cup 82-83 83-84 (R-up 79-80), Wolverhampton Cup 83-84 (R-up 82-83)
PREVIOUS **League:** Wednesbury Church & Chapel (early 1900s), Bilston Youth (1950s),Wolverhampton & District Amateur (1960s), Staffs County (South)

FACT FILE
Founded: 1920   Nickname: Trins
Club Sponsors: DKB Electric/ John O'Dell
Colours: All Green/white
Change colours: All Blue
Midweek matchday: Wednesday
Prog. Editor: John Edwards (01785 713458)
Chairman: John O'Dell
President: David Gadd
Manager: Graham Mills
Asst Manager:
Physio: Tony Kiddle

GORNAL ATHLETIC

Secretary: Chris Smith, 50 Redhall Road, Gornal Wood, Dudley West Midlands(01384 866688)
Ground: Garden Walk Stadium, Lower Gornal, Dudley, West Midlands (01384 358398)
Directions: From Dudley take A459 to Sedgley past the Burton Rd Hospital. 1ston left at the Green Dragon public house on the B4175 (Jews Lane). Follow theroad until you come to the Old Bull's Head, turn left into Rednall Road, 2ndleft to Garden Walk
Capacity: 3,000 **Seats:** 100 **Cover:** 500 **Floodlights:** Yes **Club Shop:** No
HONOURS West Mids Lg Div 1 R-up 83-84 (Div 1 Cup 92-93), Birmingham Vase 91-92
PREVIOUS **League:** Midland Comb. 51-63
Name: Lower Gornal Ath
RECORDS **Transfer fees received:** £1,500 for Gary Bell and for George Andrews both toCardiff City, 1965

FACT FILE
Founded: 1945   Nickname: Peacocks
Sponsors: Jasper Steels
Colours: White/blue/blue
Change colours: Blue/white/blue
Reserves' Lge: West Mids (Reg.) Lge Res. Div
Chairman: Colin Worth
Commercial Manager: Martin Wedgebury
Manager: John Gwinnell
Coach: Ian Clark/ Ross Hill
Reserves' Manager: Ian Davies

HEATH HAYES

Secretary: John Deans, 280 Hednesford Rd., Heath Hayes, Cannock, Staffs. WS12 5DS Tel: 01543 278430 (H) 01543 378181 (B)

Ground: Coppice Colliery Ground,Newlands Lane, Heath Hayes, Cannock, Staffs.

Directions: From Cannock ,take Lichfield Road. After 2.5 miles first right past Texaco garage on right
Colours: Blue & white stripes/blue/blue

KINGTON ATHLETIC

Secretary: Mrs Pauline Shaw, 9 Banley Drive, Headbrook, Kington, Hereford HR5 3NL
Tel: 01544 231777
Ground: Park Road Ground, Mill Street, Kington, Hereford (01544 231007)
Directions: Follow signs for kington Town Centre, look for left turn betweenthe Town Clock and the Burton Hotel. Carry on this road for 500 metres, groundon left as road bends

FACT FILE
Colours: Yellow & black/black/black
Change colours: All Red

CLUB PERSONNEL
Chairman: William Mayglothing

LITTLE DRAYTON RANGERS

Secretary: Brian Garratt, 4 Quarry Bank Road, Market Drayton, Shropshire TF9 1DR Tel: 01630 654618 (H)
Ground: Greenfield Sports Club, Greenfield Lane, Market Drayton. Tel: 01630 655088
Directions: A41 to Tern Hill island, turn right for Newcastle-u-Lyme. Over 1st island and turn right at next, by Gingerbread P.H. towards town centre. After 200 yds turn right, before going over bridge, into Greenfields Lane. Ground is 150 yds down lane on right.
Colours: Royal & pale blue stripes/royal/royal

LUDLOW TOWN

Secretary: Mr J Nash, 58 Hucklemarsh Road, Ludlow, Shropshire (01584 874337)
Ground: Riddings Park, Riddings Road, Ludlow, Shropshire (01584 875103)
Directions: From Kidderminster A4117; straight over r'bout into Henley Rd, 2ndleft into Sandpits Rd, follow road for 1/4 mile until road bears round to theleft into Ridding Rd - grd on right
Capacity: **Seats:** No Cover: 150Floodlights: YesClubhouse: Yes
HONOURS West Mids. Prem Lg.Cup, Finalists 94-95. Div 1 Cup 90-91; Shropshire Co.Cup: 73-7493-94, 94-95 96-97; Presteigne-Otway Cup 90-91.94-95:
PREVIOUS **League:** Kidderminster League 1961-63, Shropshire Co. Lg.: 1963-1978
BEST SEASON **F.A.Vase:** 1st Q Rd. 98-99 (1st season) **F.A.Cup:** Never Entered

FACT FILE
Formed: 1890
Colours: Red & white/black/black
Change colours: Blue & white/white/blue
Midweek Matchdays: Tuesday/Wednesday
Reserve League: Kidderminster
Programme: Yes
Chairman: P.Gwilliam
Vice Chaiman: Colin Badlan
Manager: Nigel Vaughan
Asst Manager: Bob Jones
Physio: Miss J Stretton

LYE TOWN

Secretary: Mrs Jane Pargeter, 47 St Marks Road, Lye, Stourbridge, W.Mids DY8 3LB
Tel: 01384 833890
Ground: Sports Ground, Stourbridge Road, Lye (01384 422672) **Directions:** On A458
Birmingham-Stourbridge road about 400yds afterlights/crossroads at Lye. From M5 jct 3 take road
marked Kidderminster as faras lights at bottom of Hagley Hill, right at island, 3rd turn off at nextis-
land,turn off left at crossroads/lights, ground about 400yds on left. Quarter mile from Lye (BR)
Capacity: 5,000 **Seats:** 200 **Cover:** 600 **Floodlights:** Yes **Clubhouse:** Yes (01384 822672)
HONOURS   West Mids Lg R-up 76-77 78-79 79-80 80-81 (Prem. Div Cup 75-76), Midland
          Comb.35-36 (R-up 32-33 34-35 37-38), B'ham Snr Cup R-up 80-81
PREVIOUS   **Leagues:** Midland Combination 31-39
RECORD   **Gate:** 6,000 v Brierley Alliance

FACT FILE
Founded: 1930   Nickname: Flyers
Colours: Blue & white/blue/blue
Change Colours: Red/black/red
Programme: 24 pages, 40p
Editor: J.Galloway
Chairman: Roy Pearson
President: Ian Cole
Manager: David Beasley
Coach: Alan Moore
Physio: Harry Hill

MALVERN TOWN

Secretary: Margaret Caldiott, 20 Nixon Court, Callow End, Worcester WR2 4UU(01905 831327)
Ground: Langland Stadium, Langland Avenue, Malvern, Worcs Tel: 01684 574068
Directions: From Worcester take A449o Malvern.Turn left at roundabout signposted B4208 to
Welland. Left vat traffic lights into Pickersleigh Road. Turn left at Longford Arms pub, into
Maddesfield R oad. 2nd left into Langland Ave., ground 100yds on right. 1 mile from Malvern (BR)
Capacity: 4,000 **Seats:** 140   **Cover:** 310   **Floodlights:** Yes **Shop:** No
Clubhouse: 2 bars, large dance area, teabar matchdays   **Best F.A.Vase Season:** 99-00 2nd Rd
HONOURS Worcester/ Midland Comb. 55-56 Mid Comb Cup R-up 75-76, WFA Senior Urn (7),
WFA Sat Junior Cup Winners (4) Banks's Brewery Premier League Cup R-up 87-88 WFA Nursing
Cup Winners 97-98, Robert Biggart Cup Winners 97-98, 98-99 ,Evesham Hosp Cup 99-00
PREVIOUS League: Midland Comb. 55-79   **RECORD Gate:** 1,221 v Worcester, FA Cup

FACT FILE
Founded: 1947
Sponsors: Malvern Instruments
Colours: Claret/white/sky
Change colours: White/black/maroon
Reserves League: Banks's Brewery Div 1 S
Midweek Matchday: Tuesday
Programme: 24pages 50p Editor: Brian Scott
Chairman: Geoff Brewer President: R H Mann
Manager: Joe RawleAss Man: Richard Anson
Press: Malvern Gazette Worcs Evening News
Local radio: BBC Hereford & Worcester

SHAWBURY UNITED

Secretary: Russell Thomas, 12 Alms Court, Meole Brace, Shrewsbury, Shropshire SY3 9JB
       Tel: 01743 245457 (H)
Ground: The Butler's Sports Centre, Bowen's Field, Wem. Tel: 01939 233287
Directions: Go into Wem town centre and at the Church junction turn right.
       Take the first left after pedestrian crossing, then first left with Hawkestone pub on
       corner. 2nd left into car park and ground.

Formed: 1992

Colours: Blue/yellow/blue
Change colours: Yellow/blue/yellow

Chairman: Ron Humphreys
Tel: 01939 251076

SMETHWICK RANGERS

Secretary: Mohan S Gill, 11 Middlesmoor, Wilnecote, Tamworth, Staffs B77 4PL (01827 330702)
Ground: Bilston United FC Parkfield Stadium, Rooker Ave, Parkfields,Wolverhampton
Directions: From Wolverhampton Centre, proceed along A459 to junc Parkfields Rd & Sedgley
Rd. Turn left at the main Parkfield traffic lights A4039, sign Ettingshall, travel 500yds, left into Myatt
Ave, 1st right into Lawn Rd. Ground on right

FACT FILE
Founded: 1972
Colours: Blue & white/blue/blue
Change colours: Red & black/black/black

CLUB PERSONNEL
Chairman: Sukbinder Binning

STAR

Secretary: David Rymer, 6 Callaughton, Much Wenlock, Shropshire TF13 6PT
       Tel: 01952 727542 (H) 01746 713000 (B)
Ground: Lawson Mardon Star, Stourbridge Road, Bridgnorth.

Colours: Blue/black/black

TIPTON TOWN

Secretary: Ruth Shinfield,21 Blue Rock Place, Tower Road, Tividale. B69 1PB(0777 904 3929)
Ground: Tipton Sports Acadamy, Wednesbury Oak Road, Tipton, West Midlands
Directions: M6 Jct 9 through Wednesbury taking A461 until right at island signto Tipton. At next
island - Ocker Hill - turn full right owards Bilston & Wolverhampton. After 1/3 mile turn left at traffic
lights and ground is on left.
Capacity: 1000   **Seats:** 200 **Cover:** New covered stand and dressing rooms **Floodlights**:Yes
Clubhouse: Open with excellent food available week-ends. 12noon - 7.00 p.m.**Club Shop:** no
Honours: West Mid Regional League DIv One Championship and League Cup, Wednesbury
Senior Charity Cup (5)
Record Attendance: Approx 1100 v Wolverhampton Wanderers in a pre season friendly 1.8.88

FACT FILE
Founded: 1948
Sponsors: Tipton & Cseley Building Society
Colours: Black & white stripes/black/black
Change colours: All red
Midweek Matchday: Wednesday
Reserves League:Kidderminster & District
Programme Editor: Ruth Shinfield
CLUB PERSONNEL
Chairman: Kevin Jennings
Manager:Neil Hickinbottom

TIVIDALE

Secretary: Leon Murray,59 Peel Way, Tividale, Oldbury, W.Mids B69 3JZ(0121 532 6979)
Ground: The Beeches, Packwood Rd, Tividale, Warley, W. Midlands B69 1UL tel: 01384 211743
Directions: Dudley Port Station to Burnt tree, left towards Birmingham, ground1 mile on right. Or, M5 jct 2, follow Dudley signs A4123, after approx 2 miles turn left into Regent Rd & left again into Elm Terraces, 1st left into Birch Crescent. Packwood Rd is second left - ground at end of cul-de-sac
Capacity: 3,500   **Seats:** 200   **Cover:** 1,000   **Floodlights:** Yes   **Club Shop:** No
Clubhouse: Mon-Fri 8-11pm, Sat 12-11pm, Sun 12-3 & 8-10.30. Cobs, rolls,sandwiches available
HONOURS   West Midlands Lg Div 1 72-73 (Prem. Div Cup 76-77, Div 1 Cup 72-73),
                    Wednesbury Charity Cup 76-77
PREVIOUS   Ground: City Road   **Leagues:** Handsworth & District 56-60; inactive 60-62; West Mids Alliance 62-66   **RECORD Attendance:** 2,400 v Telford United, FA Cup

Founded: 1954   Nickname: Dales
Sponsors: Midland & North Security Consultants
Colours: All Yellow
Change colours:Black & White/Black/Black
Midweek matchday: Tuesday
Programme: 40 pages, 60p Editor: c/o Club
Newsline: 0891 66 42 52
Chairman: Donald Ashton
President: Lord Peter Archer
Press Officer: T Clark
Manager: Paul Madders
Asst Manager: Ron Blackwood
Physio: John Cotton

WELLINGTON

Secretary: Michael Perkins, haworth, Wellington, Hereford HR4 8AZ
    Tel: 01432 830523 (H) 01432 345432 (B) 07974 447817 (M)

Ground: Wellington Playing Fields, Wellington. No telephone.

Directions: The ground is situated off the A49, 8 miles south of Leominster & 5 miles north of Hereford. At the end of the dual carriageway turn for Wellington. The ground is 1/4 mile from A49, on the left , behind Wellington School and opposite the Church.

Formed: 1968

Colours: tangerine/blue/tangerine
Change colours: Blue & white/blue/blue

Chairman: Philip Smith
Tel: 01432 830096 (H)
Match Secretary: Colin Williams
Tel: 01432 830620 (H) 0374 101316 (M)

WESTFIELDS

Secretary:& Chief Executive: Andrew Morris, 17 Fayre Oaks Green, Kings Acre, Hereford HR4 0QT(01432 264711)
Ground: Thorn Lighting, Holme Lacy Rd, Rotherwas, Hereford Tel: 0860410548
Directions: Proceed 1.5 mile from Hereford on A49, left in Home Lacy Rd at Broadleys Inn.One mile to Thorn Lighting Rotherwas, ground on the right on Ind. Estate. 2 miles from Hereford (BR)
Capacity: 2,000   **Seats:** 100   **Cover:** 150   **Floodlights:** Yes   **Club Shop:** Yes
Clubhouse: 'Broadleys Inn' Holme Lacey Rd. Hereford (1/2 mile from ground)
HONOURS   West Mids Lg Div 1 86-87, Div 2 R-up 83-84 (Div 2 Cup 79-80 83-84), Herefordshire Snr Cup 85-86 88-89 91-92 95-96 (Yth Cup 92-93 95-96), Kington Chall. Cup x5; Kington Invit. Cup x4; Presteigne Ottway Cup x4, Worcs Jnr Cup 79-80, Wye Guild Cup x2, Hereford Sunday Lg Prem 75-76 76-77 (Div 1 71-72, Div 2 76-77, Div 3 75-76, Prem Div Cup x2, Div 1 Cup x2, Div 3 Cup 72-73), Smart Brown Cup 67-68, Fair Play Cup 67-68. Dennis Hartland Mem Trophy 95-96,99-00 Robert Biggart Trophy 95-96,99-00

Founded: 1966
Nickname: The Fields
Sponsors: Left Bank Village
Colours: Maroon & sky/sky/sky
Change colours: Sky/white/sky & maroon
Midweek matchday: Tuesday
Programme: Yes Editor: John Blackmore
Chairman: Alan Dunsford
Vice Chairman: Neil Preece
President: Graham Preece
Manager: Sean Edwards
Coach:Clive Harris Physio: Neil Preece

WOLVERHAMPTON CASUALS

Secretary: Michael Green, 63 St Phillips Avenue, Pennfields Wolverhampton WV67ED
Tel: 01902 333677
Ground: Brinsford Lane, Coven Heath, Wolverhampton (01902 783214)
Directions: Onto M54 from M6 North, at Junc 2 turn right (A449 to Stafford).Ground half a mile, turn right into Brinsford Lane. Billbrooke (BR) 2 miles
Seats: 50Cover: 50Capacity: 2,000Floodlights: No
Clubhouse: Bar & snacks, open Tues/Wed/Thurs/Sat/Sun & alternate Mondays
HONOURS   WMRL Div 1 94-95, R-up (3) 85-88, Div 1 Cup 85-86
PREVIOUS   Name: Staffs Casuals (pre 81)
                        Ground: Aldersley Stadium

FACT FILE
Founded: 1896
Colours: White & green/green/green
Change colours: Gold/black/gold
Programme: 28pages 30p
Editor: G Smith
CLUB PERSONNEL
Chairman: Barry Austin
President: Clive Hammond
Manager: Gary Walters

EVERARDS BREWERY
LEICESTERSHIRE SENIOR FOOTBALL LEAGUE
Founded 1896

President: John M Elsom F.C.A.   **Chairman:** David Jamieson
Hon Secretary: Robert J Holmes, 8 Huntsman Close, Markfield, Leics LE67 9XE
Tel: 01530 243093
www.leicestershireseniorfootballleague.com   www.oxfordshire.demon.co.uk/leic1.htm

We couldn't quite match the excitement of the last day of last season, but there was still much to savour during the months that made up the 1999-2000 season. As we entered the year 2000 only a handful of points separated the top six clubs in the Premier Division, and the race for the title looked as open as it had done for a number of years. By the beginning of April, although Highfield Rangers were favourites, both St Andrews and Quorn were waiting for any slip that they might make. For them it was not be be, however, and Highfields made sure of their first Senior League Championship with a game to spare, St Andrews taking second place as Quorn faltered. Fourth place went to Downes Sports, after they won their last match to hold off Kirby Muxloe, who, if they had started the season in the way they finished, may have had a greater say in the title itself. At the foot Ellistown and Lutterworth struggled for most of the season and finished in the bottom two places.

In Division One, Leicester YMCA took an early lead, and were ahead as 2000 started, with Blaby and Whetstone, Fosse Imps and Huncote S & S close on their heels. YMCA slowly took a firm grip, although they were headed briefly during April, but winning their games in hand took them to the title with a bit to spare, as Blaby and Whetstone pushed them hard. Huncote, despite beating both the top two on their own patch, found consistency a problem and had to be content with third whilst Fosse Imps were a couple of wins behind in fourth.

At the foot Harborough Town finished bottom but retain their place in the League as the District League have agreed that we may keep our constitution up to the optimum 36. To complete the constitution we welcome Ratby Sports on promotion from the District League and hope they find life with us successful and enjoyable. This emphasises that the relationship we have with the District League is flourishing, although we are in discussions with the North Leicestershire League as to where they fit into the system.

The Beacon Bitter Cup final was a classic David v Goliath situation as St Andrews met Saffron Dynamo, and what a match it produced. All there will remember the thrilling climax to normal time as Saffron equalised at 3-3, to send the match into extra-time, and then, just to show lightning can strike twice, they hit the winner in the very last minute of the match. The only danger then to the win was whether or not we could get their players back onto the pitch to complete the game. Our thanks go to Anstey Nomads for the hosting of the match with their normal hospitality and efficiency.

On the wider scene the Jelson Homes Senior Cup remained with the League as Coalville Town beat Holwell Sports in the final at Holmes Park. Again there were many excellent FA Vase performances with Anstey Nomads flying the flag to the Third Round Proper, whilst Ibstock Welfare and Holwell Sports reached the quarter-finals of the Midland Football Alliance Invitation Cup.

It is again pleasing to see the ground facilities improving, although we accept there is still some further work to come. The League will start next season with 24 sets of floodlights. Ten years ago there was only Aylestone Park's pioneering set. This represents a terrific achievement, and next season our under 18 midweek floodlit league will boast two divisions of ten apiece.

Finally we would like to re-echo our grateful thanks to David Rae and Everards Brewery for their continued sponsorship of the League. Without their considerable input the cost of football in the League would be considerably higher and both the committee and the clubs would wish to thank them for their generous contributions.

Dave Lumley, Press Officer

FINAL LEAGUE TABLES 1999-2000

PREMIER DIVISION

	P	W	D	L	F	A	Pts	GD
Highfield Rangers	34	23	7	4	82	28	76	54
St Andrews	34	21	9	4	97	30	72	67
Quorn	34	19	7	8	69	44	64	25
Downes Sports	34	18	9	7	73	41	63	32
Kirby Muxloe	34	19	6	9	72	44	63	28
Ibstock Welfare	34	16	6	12	58	53	54	5
Thringstone	34	14	7	13	64	61	49	3
Friar Lane OB	34	13	8	13	71	71	47	0
Thurmaston Tn	34	12	9	13	60	56	45	4
Holwell Sports	34	11	11	12	58	65	44	-7
Coalville Town	34	11	10	13	45	48	43	-3
Barrow Town	34	10	9	15	58	64	39	-6
Birstall United	34	9	11	14	46	60	38	-14
Anstey Nomads	34	10	6	18	51	69	36	-18
Cottesmore	34	8	10	16	79	96	34	-17
Aylestone Park	34	8	9	17	48	72	33	-24
Ellistown	34	6	6	22	32	109	24	-77
Lutterworth	34	6	4	24	38	90	22	-52

DIVISION ONE

	P	W	D	L	F	A	Pts	GD
Leics YMCA	32	27	2	3	103	14	83	89
Blaby & Whetstone	32	24	5	3	97	33	77	64
Huncote S & S	32	21	6	5	82	35	69	47
Fosse Imps	32	20	3	9	82	56	63	26
Thurnby Rangers	32	17	4	11	87	48	55	39
Stoney Stanton	32	15	7	10	59	50	52	9
Anstey Town	32	14	9	9	61	42	51	19
Sileby Town	32	13	8	11	82	48	47	34
Narborough	32	14	4	14	62	56	46	6
Earl Shilton Albion	32	13	6	13	51	51	45	0
Asfordby	32	13	5	14	48	46	44	2
Constabulary	32	13	5	14	56	61	44	-5
Saffron Dynamo	32	12	4	16	66	66	40	0
Loughboro D'mo	32	4	6	22	29	85	18	-56
North Kilworth	32	4	4	24	38	110	16	-72
Bardon Hill	32	4	1	27	27	122	13	-95
Harborough Town	32	2	5	25	29	136	11	-107

PREMIER DIVISION RESULTS CHART 1999-2000

		1	2	3	4	5	6	7	8	9	10	11	12	13	14	15	16	17	18
1	Anstey Nomads	X	0-1	0-5	4-0	1-2	4-3	1-2	5-2	6-1	0-0	2-2	1-1	1-5	2-0	1-4	0-4	4-2	1-2
2	Aylestone	1-1	X	2-2	3-2	2-0	3-3	2-3	1-1	0-2	1-3	2-4	3-1	1-2	4-1	1-1	0-7	3-0	1-2
3	Barrow	1-1	5-1	X	3-3	1-1	2-3	2-4	1-2	2-1	1-4	1-1	1-0	0-1	0-1	0-3	0-4	1-1	2-1
4	Birstall	1-2	1-1	1-2	X	2-2	2-2	1-3	3-0	3-3	0-2	1-0	1-3	3-4	1-0	0-3	2-1	2-1	3-3
5	Coalville	2-1	2-3	0-3	0-1	X	6-2	0-0	2-0	2-1	0-1	3-2	3-0	1-1	0-1	0-1	0-1	2-0	2-2
6	Cottesmore	1-3	0-2	3-1	1-2	0-2	X	2-4	7-0	2-2	0-3	3-5	1-6	1-1	1-1	2-5	2-2	2-2	5-3
7	Downes	2-0	2-0	2-1	4-1	0-0	2-1	X	1-1	2-2	1-0	0-0	1-0	10-2	1-2	0-3	2-2	1-3	
8	Ellistown	1-2	2-1	0-5	1-1	0-1	2-10	0-6	X	0-0	1-5	2-1	0-1	0-4	1-4	1-5	1-1	0-6	1-6
9	Friar Lane OB	2-1	1-1	2-1	2-0	2-1	1-6	0-7	10-0	X	0-4	2-4	2-3	1-6	6-1	2-0	1-4	0-2	1-1
10	Highfield	3-0	3-0	4-1	1-1	3-0	5-0	2-2	1-1	3-2	X	2-2	0-1	3-1	2-0	1-1	0-3	4-3	4-0
11	Holwell	1-0	4-1	2-2	0-0	1-1	2-6	1-1	4-1	2-2	0-6	X	2-1	0-2	2-1	0-1	3-3	1-7	1-2
12	Ibstock	3-1	3-1	3-1	1-1	3-0	2-2	1-0	0-3	2-3	0-3	1-5	X	4-1	1-1	2-1	3-1	1-2	1-2
13	Kirby	1-2	3-2	2-2	0-0	4-3	5-0	1-0	5-1	1-3	1-2	3-1	2-2	X	3-1	0-2	1-0	1-0	5-2
14	Lutterworth	1-1	3-1	2-1	1-2	0-2	3-4	3-4	0-2	0-3	0-3	0-2	0-1	1-4	X	2-5	1-7	3-2	0-4
15	Quorn	4-2	1-1	1-2	1-0	3-3	2-2	3-1	2-0	2-3	2-4	0-1	3-1	2-0	1-0	X	2-2	2-2	2-1
16	St Andrews	5-0	0-0	5-2	2-1	4-0	7-0	1-2	2-1	1-1	3-0	3-0	3-1	0-0	2-2	3-0	X	1-1	2-0
17	Thringstone	3-1	3-1	2-3	3-2	1-1	2-0	1-0	1-2	0-7	0-1	1-1	3-4	2-1	3-1	3-1	0-5	X	1-0
18	Thurmaston	1-0	4-1	1-1	1-2	1-1	2-2	2-2	5-2	1-0	0-0	1-1	0-1	0-1	3-1	0-1	3-5	1-2	X

LEADING GOALSCORERS 1999-2000

PREMIER DIVISION

Neal	Cottesmore	33
Warner	St Andrews	32
Marsden, Phil	St Andrews	30
Budge	Downes	28
Master	Highfield	24
Emery	Ibstock	22
Munton	Cottesmore	21
Hollis	Thringstone	20

DIVISION ONE

Towers	YMCA	36
Anastasi	Blaby & Whetstone	27
Wingfield	Thurnby	25
Seal	Sileby	24
McManus	Saffron Dynamo	22
Gurney	Narborough	21
Parker	Sileby	21

Above: Anstey Nomads FC. Back Row (l-r): Richard Deeping, Chris O'Brien, Ben Boyce, Andy Greasley, Lee Connerly, Rob Poutch, Laurenstone Chambers, Gary Tebbet. Front Row (l-r): Adrian Capell (Player/Manager), Darren Warne, Lloyd Murning, Wayne McAtee (Captain), Chris Joseph, Mark Gilbert. Photo: Peter Barnes

Above: Quorn FC. The team line up before their 1-1 draw (aet) at home v Kirkby Muxloe. Photo: Martin Wray

Above: Friar Lane Old Boys FC.
Back Row (l-r): Steve Taylor (Coach), Paul Shilton, Stacey Coore, Neil Skinner, Ian Morris, Scott James, Nick Moreland, Billy Hobson, Philip Smith, Louie Carr (Asst Manager). Front Row (l-r): Danny McNulty, Reece Lester, Nicki Finney, Adie Allen, Darren Bradley, Leon Doughty, John Metcalf, Clem Dublin. Photo: Peter Barnes.

AYLESTONE PARK OLD BOYS

Secretary: Pete Burrows, 27 Cartwight Drive, Oadby, Leicester Tel: 0116 271 2682
Ground: Dorset Avenue, Fairfield Estate, Wigston, Leics (0116 277 5307)
Capacity: 2,000   **Seats:** 40**Cover:** 100   **Floodlights:**Yes
Clubhouse: Open matchdays 2pm -11pm   **Club shop:** No
Previous League : Leicester District
HONOURS: Leics. Senior League Runners-up 94-95

Founded: 1967   Nickname: The Park
Colours: Red/white/red   Change: All white
Midweek matchday: Tuesday
Programme: Yes
Hon.Chief Executive: Bob Stretton M.B.E.
President: Gary Lineker
Chairman: John Nutt
Managers: Carl Williams & Gary Franks

COTTESMORE AMATEURS

Secretary: Kevin Nimmons, 17 Redwing Close, Oakham, Rutland LE15 6DA Tel: 01572 724582
Ground: Rogues Park, Main Street, Cottesmore, Rutland (01572 813486)
Directions: Rear of Sun Inn.
Capacity: 1,000   **Seating:** Yes **Cover:** Yes   **Floodlights:**Yes
Clubhouse : Yes   **Club shop:** No
PREVIOUS Leagues: Melton & Rutland ,Leics District
HONOURS: Leics. Senior League Cup Winners 1997.

Founded: 1941
Colours: Green/black/green
Change colours: Sky Blue/navy/navy
Midweek matchday: Tuesday
Programme: Yes

ANSTEY NOMADS
Colours: Red/white/red
Secretary: Mervyn Miles,66 CharlesDrive, Anstey,Leics.LE7 7BG
Tel No: 0116 236 2909
Ground: Llimah International Park, Cropston Road, Anstey (0116 236 4868)

BARROW TOWN
Secretary: Alan Dawkins, 72 Beaumont Road, Barrow-on-Soar, Loughborough, LeicsLE12 8PJ (01509 413288)
Ground: Riverside Park, Meynell Road, Quorn, Leics (01509 620650)
Access via Quorn Lodge Drive & Barrow road. Cover: 50 Seats : No
Clubhouse :Yes Colours: Red & Black/black
Honours: Leics Sen Lg. 92-93 R-up 94-95.Loughborough Charity Cup 68-69,96-97,98-99

BIRSTALL UNITED
Colours: White/navy/navy
Secretary: Jim Lennon, 25 Allington Drive,Birstall, Leicester LE4 4FD (0116 221 6855 (H) 0421520563 (W)
Ground: Meadow Lane, Birstall (0116 267 1230)

BLABY & WHETSTONE ATHLETIC
Colours: Navy/& white/navy/navy
Secretary: Mrs S C Morris, 10 Winchester Road, Blaby, Leics LE8 3HJ (0116 2773208)
Ground: Blaby & Whetstone Boys Club, Warwick Road, Whetstone (0116 286 4852)

COALVILLE TOWN
Colours: Black&White/black/black
Secretary: Robert Brooks, 17 Ashland Drive, Coalville, Leics LE67 3NH (01530833269)
Ground: Owen Street Sports Ground, Owen Street, Coalville (01530 833365)

DOWNES SPORTS
Colours:Gold/black/Gold
Secretary: A. Jacques, 17 Merton Close, Broughton, Astley Leicester Le9 6QP Tel No: 01455 28402 (H) 01455 282028 (W)
Ground: Leicester Rd,Hinckley (01455 615062)
Directions: Off northern perimeter road.

FRIAR LANE OLD BOYS
Colours: Black & white stripes/black/black
Secretary: Kevin Brooks, 299 Milligan Rd, Leicester LE4 2RJ (0116 224 3854)
Ground: Knighton Lane East, Leicester (0116 283 3629)

HIGHFIELD RANGERS
Secretary: Maurice Christian, 18 Blanklyn Avenue, Leicester LE5 5FA (0116 2734002)
Ground: 443 Gleneagles Ave., Rushey Mead, Leicester
Tel: 0116 266 0009   Colours: Yellow/blackyellow

HOLWELL SPORTS
Colours: Green & gold/green/green
Secretary: Mrs Anne Marriott, 24 Church Lane, Croxton Kerrial, Grantham, Lincs NG32 1PZ (01476 870658)
Ground: Welby Road, Asfordby Hill, Melton Mowbray, Leics (01664 812663)

IBSTOCK WELFARE
Colours: Red/black/red
Secretary: R A Wilkinson, 6 Valley Rd, Ibstock, Leicester LE67 6NY (01530 450243) Ground: The Welfare, Leicester Road, Ibstock (01530 260656) Seating : 50 Cover 150 Clubhouse : Yes Honours: Leics Sen Cup Winners 93-94 R-Up 97-98. Leics Sen Lg Div 1 R-up 90-91. Coalville Ch Cup Winners (3) R-up (4),Loughboro ChCup (4) R-up(2)

KIRBY MUXLOE S.C.
Colours: All Blue
Secretary: Philip Moloney, 16 Church Lane, Ratby, Leics LE6 0JE (0116 239 2916)
Ground: Ratby Lane, Kirby Muxloe (0116 239 3201)

LEICESTER YMCA
Colours: Red & black/black/black
Secretary: Colin Chappell, 132 South Knighton Rd, Leicester, LE2 3LQ (0116 270 27821)
Ground: YMCA Sports Ground, Belvoir Drive, Leicester(0116 244 0740)Directions: M1 Jct21 (M69) onto A563, Soarvalley Way, Aylestone Rd. Left at lights, to city. Belvoir Drive 2nd Right after next lights.Capacity:1,500 Cover 100 Clubhouse: Yes

QUORN
Colours: Red/white/red
Secretary: Margaret Berry, 214 BarrowRd.Sileby,Leics.LE12 7LR
Tel: 01509 813259
Ground: Farley Way, Quorn, Leics (01509 620232)

St ANDREWS SOCIAL CLUB
Colours: Black & white/black/black
Secretary: L Botting, 2 Neston Road, Saffron Lane, Leicester LE2 6RD(0116 224 3961)
Ground: Canal Street, off Aylestone Rd (next to Big City Tyres)Old Aylestone,Leicester.(01162839298)
Honours: Leics Sen Lg. Premier: 89-90, 93-94, 95-96

THRINGSTONE UNITED
Colours: Sky Blue, navy blue, sky blue.
Secretary: Peter Hordley, The Willows, 9 Main Street, Thringstone,
Leics. LE67 8ND Tel: 01530 223055
Ground: Homestead Road, Thringstone (01530 223367)

THURMASTON TOWN
Colours: Black & white stripes, black,black.
Secretary: Kevin Sadler, 81 Woodgreen Road, Leicester LE4 9UD
(0116 246 0093)
Ground: Elizabeth Park, Checklands Road, Thurmaston.
Tel No: 0116 260 2519
Honours: Dist. Lg Champs 97-99, Page & Moy Junior Cup 97-98 Leics
Div One & Beacon Bitter Cup 98-99

DIVISION ONE CLUBS

ANSTEY TOWN
Colours: All blue
Secretary:Stephen Staniforth, 38 Woodgon Road, Anstey, Leicester
LE4 7EQ 0116 236 5490 (H) 0116 254 6447(W)
Ground: Leicester Road, Thurcaston (0116 236 8231)

ASFORDBY AMATEURS
Colours: red/black/black
Secretary: Stephen Hazeldine,19 Mildmay Close,Melton
Mowbray,LeicsLE13 1AH Tel No:01664 857362
Ground: Hoby Road Sports Ground, Asfordby, Melton Mowbray (01664
434545)

BARDON HILL
Colours: Red/blue/blue
Secretary: Adrian Bishop, 138 Bradgate Drive, Coalville, Leics LE67
4HG (01530815560)
Ground: Bardon Close, Coalville, Leicester (01530 815569)

EARL SHILTON ALBION
Colours: Green & gold/green/gold
Secretary: Graham Redshaw,3 Lucas Way,Earl Shilton,Leics.LE9 7GL
Tel No: 01455 847822
Ground: Stoneycroft Park, New St., Earl Shilton, Leics (01455 844277)

ELLISTOWN
Colours: Red/black/red
Secretary: John Measom, 29 Standard Hill, Coalville, Leicester LE67
3HN (01530 810941)
Ground: 1 Terrace Road, Ellistown (01455 844277)

FOSSE IMPS
Colours: All Red
Secretary: Ivan V Colbourne, 55 Harrowgate Drive, Birstall, Leics LE4
3GQ (0116267 1424)
Ground: Co-op Ground, Birstall Rd, Leicester (0116 267 4059)

HARBOROUGH TOWN
Colours: Black& white/black/white.
Secretary:JohnChambers,62 Oaklands Drive, Whetstone, Northampton
NN3 3JL . Tel No: 01604 412294
Ground: Symingtons SportsGround,St Mary's Road, Market
Harborough,Leics (Half a mile from town centre and railway styation)

HUNCOTE SPORTS & SOCIAL
Colours: Yellow & blue/blue/blue
Secretary: D Russell, 72 Sycamore Way, Littlethorpe, Leics LE9 5HU
(0116 2841952)
Ground: Enderby Lane, Thurlaston, Leics (01455 888430). Seating: No
Cover: No Clubhouse: Yes Directions: 3 miles from exit 21 on M1. Via
Enderby on B582. Thurston Lane onto Endersby Road.

LEICESTERSHIRE CONSTABULARY
Colours: Gold/black/black.
Secretary: Mick Allard, 8 Evelyn Rd., Braunstone, Leicester LE3 3BA
Tel No: 0116 289 0027
Ground: Police HQ, St Johns, Enderby (0116 248 2198)

LOUGHBOROUGH DYNAMO
Colours: Gold/black/gold
Secretary: Max Hutchinson, 3 Wythburn Close, Loughborough, Leics
LE11 3SZ(01509 266092)
Ground: Nanpanton Sport Ground, Loughborough (01509 612144)

LUTTERWORTH TOWN
Colours: White & blue/blue/blue.
Secretary:Martha Matthews, Silver Leas, Birrewell,Lutterworth,Leics.
Tel No: 01455 552613
Ground: Hall Lane, Bitteswell, Lutterworth, Leics (01455 554046)

NARBOROUGH & LITTLETHORPE
Colours: Sky Blue/Navy Blue/Navy Blue.
Secretary: Barry Garner, 7 Riverside Court, Littlethorpe, Leicester LE9
5HU (0116 286 7632)
Ground: Ray Hurd Pavilion, Leicester Road, Narborough (Near M1
bridge) (0116275 1855)

NORTH KILWORTH
Colours: Red/black/red
Secretary: Matthew Bailey, 1Holly Drive,Lutterworth,Leics.LE17 4RG
Tel No: 01455556188
Ground: Rugby Road, North Kilworth, Lutterworth, Leics (01858
880890)

RATBY SPORTS
Secretary: John Rowe, 57 Danehill, Ratby, Leicester LE6 0NG
Tel: 0116 238 6806
Ground: Ratby Sports Club, Desford Lane, Ratby (0116 239 2474)
Colours: All red

SAFFRON DYNAMO
Colours: Red/black/black
Secretary: Bob King, 14 Bramley Close, Broughton Astley, Leicester
LE9 6QU(01455 284270)
Ground: Cambridge Road, Whetstone, (0116 284 9695) Near County
on road from Whetstone to Cosby..
Honours : Many as a Sunday club in last 25 years.

SILEBY TOWN
Colours: All Red
Secretary: Ann Bettles, 6 Jubilee Avenue, Sileby, Leics LE12 7TH
(01509 813864)
Ground: Memorial Park, Seagrave Road, Sileby, Leics (01509 816104)

STONEY STANTON
Colours: All Blue
Secretary:Nigel Bradbury,144 Sketchley ,Burbage,Leics(01455
615305)
Ground: Highfields Farm, Huncote Road, Stoney Stanton,Leics.
Directions: M69 Jct 2 towards Sapcote.1st left toStoney Stanton.Right
at mini roundabout and left into Long Street.Follow road out of village
Highfield Farm on left.(Clubhouse open but no cover or seats)
Honours: Leics Sen Lg Div 1 R-Up 98

THURNBY RANGERS
Colours: All Green
Secretary: Pat Darby,69 Kinross Avenue,Thurnby,Lodge Estate, Leics
Tel No: 0116 241 4790
Ground: Dakyn Road, Thurnby Lodge, Leics

An irresistable strike force

Every month

INSIDE! MORE ACTION * MORE PHOTOS * EVERY MONTH!

NO.1 NON-LEAGUE MAGAZINE

OFFICIAL F.A. MAGAZINE

Team Talk

Every week

THE NON-LEAGUE PAPER

CONFERENCE & PYRAMID LEAGUES SOCCER / £1.00

Every day

For up to the minute news, results, fixtures,
and general facts and figures
from the world of non-league football
log on to

www.nlfootball.com

Brought to you by Non-League Media in conjunction with e-comsport

ISTHMIAN LEAGUE

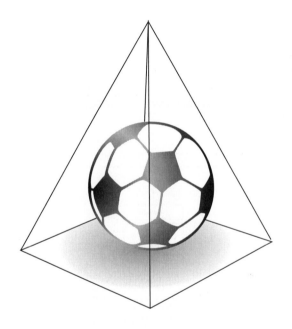

PYRAMID SECTION

Ryman
ISTHMIAN LEAGUE

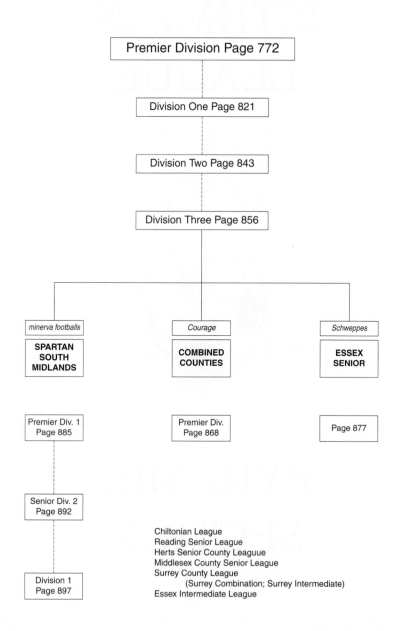

Premier Division Page 772

Division One Page 821

Division Two Page 843

Division Three Page 856

minerva footballs

SPARTAN SOUTH MIDLANDS

Courage

COMBINED COUNTIES

Schweppes

ESSEX SENIOR

Premier Div. 1 Page 885

Premier Div. Page 868

Page 877

Senior Div. 2 Page 892

Division 1 Page 897

Chiltonian League
Reading Senior League
Herts Senior County Leaguue
Middlesex County Senior League
Surrey County League
        (Surrey Combination; Surrey Intermediate)
Essex Intermediate League

RYMAN LEAGUE

Chairman: A C F Turvey, MCIM, 18 Apple Way, Old Basing, Basingstoke, Hants RG24 7HA

Tel: 01256 461789 (H)   0836 251368 (M)

Secretary & Treasurer: N R Robinson FCRArb, 226 Rye Lane, Peckham, London SE15 4NL

Tel: 0181 409 1978 (H)   0171 639 5726 (B)   Fax: 0181 409 1979 (H)   0171 277 6061 (B)

E-mail: nickrob@clara.net

A season that started with at least eight clubs appearing to be strong enough to challenge for the championship soon saw the realistic promotion race whittled down to two with Dagenham & Redbridge always very much the favourites.

St Albans City started with a flourish as did Enfield and Dulwich Hamlet, but despite wonderful support throughout their campaign, Aldershot, with regular exciting signings to keep the fans on their toes, just couldn't sustain their challenge as they battled to catch up with their fixtures.

Good F.A. Cup runs were achieved by Hendon, Aldershot and Enfield with Whyteleafe (two games with Chester City) and Worthing from Division One, really enjoying themselves.

But excitement in the glamourous Cup Competition doesn't help consistency in the league. In the F.A. Trophy only Heybridge Swifts reached the Fifth Round, although Division One club Bedford Town did well to reach Round Four, where they had no luck at all against Yeovil Town.

Dagenham & Redbridge paced their season perfectly having had no luck in the knock out competitions and, under the dedicated guidance of Garry Hill and a determined board of directors who had set their sights on a return to the Conference, they achieved their target with the minimum of fuss. At the other end of the table a thrilling battle nearly saw homeless Enfield dragged into a relegation place, but in another exciting battle Maidenhead United achieved promotion from Division One on the last day of the season to join a triumphant Croydon and yo yo club Grays Athletic back in the Premier Division.

Essex clubs dominated promotion from the lower divisions with Ford United, Great Wakering Rovers, East Thurrock United and Tilbury all moving up.

Spare a thought for Hemel Hempstead, whose excellent season was spoilt by not possessing the acceptable ground grade for promotion, and for Southall, a famous name of the past slipping out of Ryman football.

Another hectic season produced some excellent end of season excitement, but in the next campaign will Aldershot move one league nearer to a return to The Football League, by winning a place in the Conference?   *TW*

The Ryman Football League has announced the following awards following the completion of the 1999-2000 season: The Umbro Fair Play Awards recognise the clubs who have incurred the fewest disciplinary points in their League season. Each club will receive Umbro products up to the value of £1,000.

The Carlsberg Goalscoring Awards reward the team which scores the most League goals in each division. Each club receives a cash reward of £400.

	Umbro Fair Play Award	**Carlsberg Goalscoring Award**	
Premier Division	Canvey Island	Dagenham & Redbridge	97 goals
Division One	Staines Town	Croydon	85 goals
Division Two	Berkhamsted Town	Northwood	109 goals
Division Three	Camberley Town	East Thurrock United	89 goals

RYMAN LEAGUE NEWSLINE

09066 555 777

Calls cost 60p per minute

RYMAN LEAGUE FAXBACK

09068 210 290

Calls cost 60p per minute

PREMIER DIVISION FINAL LEAGUE TABLE 1999-2000

		P	HOME					AWAY					TOTAL						
			W	D	L	F	A	W	D	L	F	A	W	D	L	F	A	Pts	GD
1	Dagenham & Redbridge	42	20	1	0	58	13	12	4	5	39	22	32	5	5	97	35	101	62
2	Aldershot Town	42	13	2	6	39	23	11	3	7	32	28	24	5	13	71	51	77	20
3	Chesham United	42	11	6	4	33	21	9	4	8	31	29	20	10	12	64	50	70	14
4	Purfleet	42	10	8	3	39	22	8	7	6	31	26	18	15	9	70	48	69	22
5	Canvey Island	42	13	2	6	37	18	8	4	9	33	35	21	6	15	70	53	69	17
6	St Albans City	42	8	6	7	37	26	11	4	6	38	29	19	10	13	75	55	67	20
7	Billericay Town	42	10	6	5	36	28	8	6	7	26	34	18	12	12	62	62	66	0
8	Hendon	42	11	4	6	38	31	7	4	10	23	33	18	8	16	61	64	62	-3
9	Slough Town	42	10	3	8	37	30	7	6	8	24	29	17	9	16	61	59	60	2
10	Dulwich Hamlet	42	10	2	9	32	31	7	3	11	30	37	17	5	20	62	68	56	-6
11	Gravesend & Northfleet	42	9	6	6	36	25	6	4	11	30	42	15	10	17	66	67	55	-1
12	Farnborough Town	42	8	5	8	25	19	6	6	9	27	36	14	11	17	52	55	53	-3
13	Hampton & Richmond B	42	8	4	9	26	28	5	9	7	23	29	13	13	16	49	57	52	-8
14	Enfield	42	9	6	6	42	34	4	5	12	22	34	13	11	18	64	68	50	-4
15	Heybridge Swifts	42	7	5	9	34	33	6	6	9	23	32	13	11	18	57	65	50	-8
16	Hitchin Town	42	10	4	7	36	29	3	7	11	23	43	13	11	18	59	72	50	-13
17	Carshalton Athletic	42	6	9	6	30	30	6	3	12	25	35	12	12	18	55	65	48	-10
18	Basingstoke Town	42	10	6	5	31	24	3	3	15	25	47	13	9	20	56	71	48	-15
19	Harrow Borough	42	7	4	10	31	26	7	2	12	23	44	14	6	22	54	70	48	-16
20	Aylesbury United	42	9	4	8	38	33	4	5	12	26	48	13	9	20	64	81	48	-17
21	Boreham Wood	42	3	6	12	21	40	8	4	9	23	31	11	10	21	44	71	43	-27
22	Walton & Hersham	42	4	4	13	19	38	7	4	10	25	32	11	8	23	44	70	41	-26

PREMIER DIVISION RESULTS & ATTENDANCES 1999-2000

		1	2	3	4	5	6	7	8	9	10	11	12	13	14	15	16	17	18	19	20	21	22
1	Aldershot Town	X	1-1	5-2	0-1	1-0	3-1	4-0	4-1	1-0	3-2	0-4	1-2	2-1	1-1	1-2	2-1	0-1	5-1	0-2	0-2	2-0	3-0
		X	2018	1909	2045	1679	1802	1553	2157	2439	1696	2038	5518	1921	1280	2043	1824	2041	1712	1336	2234	2123	2100
2	Aylesbury United	3-0	X	3-0	0-1	0-1	3-3	3-2	3-2	0-2	2-3	1-0	1-2	4-1	2-2	3-1	2-3	2-2	3-1	0-3	0-2	2-2	1-0
		761	X	517	339	425	602	384	828	729	366	614	515	1232	645	534	412	804	545	457	678	662	603
3	Basingstoke Town	2-1	4-2	X	2-0	1-1	2-0	2-0	0-1	0-4	0-1	2-2	2-2	3-3	2-0	2-0	1-1	2-2	3-1	0-3	3-1	1-3	1-3
		1425	494	X	377	430	532	575	416	507	526	546	748	390	484	455	444	473	797	385	559	524	536
4	Billericay Town	3-2	5-0	1-0	X	1-0	0-0	2-0	3-1	0-4	3-5	0-0	0-3	3-3	1-0	5-0	1-1	1-2	1-1	1-1	3-1	3-1	0-3
		901	601	510	X	473	868	471	404	1182	459	527	583	519	534	469	471	558	470	556	581	456	426
5	Boreham Wood	2-5	2-2	3-4	0-2	X	3-2	0-2	1-3	0-1	0-0	1-0	1-1	3-4	0-4	0-1	0-2	0-0	0-0	1-1	2-3	1-3	1-0
		668	349	271	226	X	355	302	404	354	325	481	285	228	204	314	362	253	457	187	547	326	244
6	Canvey Island	2-1	2-3	3-1	3-0	0-1	X	1-0	3-1	3-1	0-1	1-0	2-2	4-1	1-2	2-0	0-0	6-1	0-3	0-1	0-1	1-0	1-1
		1720	540	301	1040	570	X	370	342	2003	678	1005	278	511	703	629	411	389	282	612	681	878	225
7	Carshalton Athletic	3-0	2-1	1-1	3-3	3-0	3-1	X	0-3	1-1	0-5	2-2	1-1	1-2	1-1	3-1	0-1	1-1	2-0	0-1	0-1	1-1	0-2
		941	365	281	217	224	287	X	212	462	402	420	311	223	189	234	237	318	306	290	307	332	302
8	Chesham United	2-0	1-1	1-1	1-1	5-0	2-1	0-0	X	0-0	3-0	2-1	2-1	1-1	1-0	1-2	2-1	2-0	2-1	1-0	3-4	3-0	2-1
		679	930	302	202	313	460	313	X	548	1141	397	440	273	340	405	441	286	326	290	398	401	279
9	Dagenham & R	3-2	4-1	1-0	2-1	2-0	2-0	3-1	1-1	X	3-0	4-0	3-2	2-1	5-0	4-1	4-0	2-0	4-1	3-1	1-2	2-1	2-0
		1150	838	1040	1102	1028	1722	673	907	X	1141	1200	844	1332	894	971	802	912	774	1400	1582	1540	776
10	Dulwich Hamlet	1-2	3-0	1-2	2-1	1-2	2-0	1-3	1-2	0-0	X	0-0	1-3	1-5	0-0	2-0	1-0	2-1	1-2	3-2	3-2	2-3	1-0
		1241	385	285	374	349	617	407	516	489	X	556	251	332	304	339	405	328	227	239	582	405	415
11	Enfield	1-4	3-1	3-1	1-1	1-1	1-1	3-2	2-2	1-1	3-2	X	3-0	0-1	2-3	0-3	5-3	3-2	1-2	1-2	4-0	2-3	4-1
		472	458	623	168	174	187	114	220	482	395	X	203	232	176	168	467	281	243	165	235	204	214
12	Farnborough Town	0-0	4-1	3-0	2-0	0-2	1-2	4-1	0-1	2-1	2-0	1-1	X	3-2	0-1	0-0	0-1	0-1	1-1	1-1	1-0	0-1	1-2
		1524	515	942	407	484	577	554	202	616	430	744	X	453	229	409	497	287	547	577	693	713	296
13	Gravesend & N	1-1	5-0	1-0	2-2	3-0	0-1	0-5	3-2	2-1	3-1	1-1	5-1	X	0-0	4-1	1-0	1-1	1-3	1-3	1-2	1-0	1-1
		880	438	369	401	425	639	389	347	836	886	449	444	X	362	340	374	369	458	454	405	462	355
14	Hampton	0-1	2-1	2-1	1-2	1-1	0-2	0-1	0-1	2-3	3-0	2-1	1-0	1-0	X	3-1	1-2	11-4	2-1	1-1	2-2	1-1	0-2
		1008	251	192	163	218	237	279	285	453	193	139	377	244	X	333	274	176	235	213	307	345	353
15	Harrow Borough	0-1	4-1	1-1	1-1	1-3	1-3	0-0	0-2	2-1	1-0	1-0	4-0	6-0	3-0	X	2-1	2-0	4-0	2-3	0-2	4-0	0-1
		701	245	213	235	268	221	236	285	443	182	307	405	188	220	X	231	180	278	210	190	317	165
16	Hendon	1-2	1-0	4-3	3-2	2-1	3-2	2-0	4-2	0-1	1-2	2-2	5-3	1-0	1-0	0-1	X	2-0	1-1	1-3	0-3	1-0	2-2
		1005	366	278	178	312	275	374	258	410	381	448	233	183	212	319	X	252	221	259	380	407	218
17	Heybridge Swifts	1-3	1-0	2-0	1-2	0-1	3-0	0-2	2-1	5-4	1-1	2-1	1-2	2-4	2-2	1-2	1-2	X	2-3	0-0	2-1	1-1	5-1
		633	337	245	407	190	340	248	255	604	287	403	233	202	194	201	269	X	287	304	253	213	222
18	Hitchin Town	1-2	4-3	2-0	1-2	1-3	3-3	3-2	2-1	0-2	2-0	2-1	1-2	1-0	2-2	4-0	1-0	1-2	X	2-4	3-3	1-1	2-0
		806	251	325	368	428	632	322	478	504	417	507	419	430	359	288	449	288	X	248	609	437	397
19	Purfleet	2-4	0-2	1-2	2-2	3-2	2-0	1-1	0-0	1-1	1-1	4-2	4-0	0-0	0-0	1-1	4-1	1-0	3-0	X	3-3	2-0	3-1
		562	268	163	301	215	405	203	219	1173	236	332	216	257	161	185	157	173	147	X	287	203	187
20	St Albans City	0-1	1-1	1-4	4-0	2-3	1-2	2-1	3-0	2-3	4-1	5-0	1-2	3-1	1-1	2-3	3-0	2-0	2-1	2-4	X	3-0	1-1
		1499	678	840	529	640	459	572	740	1264	829	1180	435	520	682	515	785	326	755	420	X	843	701
21	Slough Town	0-1	1-2	1-4	4-0	2-3	1-2	2-1	3-0	2-3	2-1	4-0	1-2	2-1	1-1	2-3	1-1	3-1	3-0	3-0	0-3	X	3-1
		761	556	630	612	445	663	453	551	592	548	406	707	455	504	504	480	410	463	568	610	X	488
22	Walton & Hersham	0-1	0-3	1-0	0-1	3-1	0-3	0-2	1-2	0-2	0-3	0-2	0-0	2-2	1-3	3-1	1-2	0-1	4-3	0-3	1-1	2-2	X
		1419	267	237	234	141	159	264	251	402	203	246	442	255	303	161	181	217	132	164	232	303	X

RYMAN LEAGUE CUP 1999-2000

PRELIMINARY ROUND

Hertford Town	1	v	0	Corinthian Casuals
Thame United	2	v	1	Croydon Athletic*
Molesey	1	v	2	Bedford Town
Marlow	5	v	4	Hornchurch*
Metropolitan Police	1	v	2	Abingdon Town*
Cheshunt	3	v	2	Harlow Town
Hemel Hempstead T	3	v	0	Barking
Dorking	4	v	7	Windsor & Eton*
Banstead Athletic	3	v	4	Ford United
Flackwell Heath	1	v	0	Egham Town
Northwood	0,5	v	0,0	Tilbury*
Kingsbury Town	1	v	3	Leighton Town
Southall	1	v	1	Chalfont St P*(p)
Camberley Town	1	v	0	East Thurrock Utd
Witham Town	2	v	4	Lewes*
Tooting & Mitcham U	1	v	3	Wembley
Bracknell Town	2	v	1	Berkhamsted Town
Wokingham Town	2	v	4	Gt Wakering Rvrs*
Aveley	0	v	1	Wingate & Finchley
Clapton	0	v	4	Epsom & Ewell
Wivenhoe Town	5	v	2	Horsham
Hungerford Town	5	v	3	Ware
Edgware Town	0	v	2	Tring Town

ROUND ONE

Hertford Town	3	v	4	Wealdstone
Leyton Pennant	2	v	0	Thame United
Bedford Town	0	v	2	Oxford City
Marlow	2	v	1	Leatherhead
Enfield	1	v	2	Barton Rovers*
Gravesend & N'fleet	1	v	2	Hendon*
Slough Town	1	v	0	Grays Athletic
Carshalton Athletic	0,2	v	0,0	Bognor Regis T*
Abingdon Town	2	v	1	Cheshunt
Hemel Hempstead T	1	v	3	Aldershot Town*
Uxbridge	1	v	2	Hitchin Town
Farnborough Town	2	v	0	Yeading
Heybridge Swifts	5	v	1	Harrow Borough
Windsor & Eton	2	v	1	Worthing
Canvey Island	1	v	3	Romford
Braintree	3	v	1	Aylesbury United
Ford United	2	v	1	Flackwell Heath
Northwood	3,1	v	2,3	Chesham United*
Purfleet	2	v	0	Leighton Town
Chertsey Town	5	v	3	Southall*
Camberley Town	0	v	1	Lewes
Billericay Town	3	v	2	Wembley
Hampton & Rich. B	0	v	2	St Albans City
Bracknell Town	0	v	1	Gt Wakering Rvrs
Wingate & Finchley	0	v	5	Whyteleafe
Epsom & Ewell	1,0	v	3,1	Staines Town*
Bromley	1	v	2	Maidenhead United
Basingstoke Town	3	v	1	Walton & Hersham
Dulwich Hamlet	6	v	2	Wivenhoe Town
Croydon	5	v	0	Dagenham & Red.
Boreham Wood	0	v	2	Bishop's Stortford
Hungerford Town	1	v	2	Tring Town

ROUND TWO

Wealdstone	1	v	0	Leyton Pennant
Oxford City	5	v	1	Marlow
Barton Rovers	3	v	1	Hendon
Slough Town	0	v	1	Carshalton Athletic
Abingdon Town	0	v	3	Aldershot Town
(r) Hitchin Town	3	v	3	Farnborough T*
Heybridge Swifts	2	v	1	Windsor & Eton
Romford	0,1	v	1,0	Braintree Town*(p)
Ford United	0	v	2	Chesham United
Purfleet	2	v	1	Chertsey Town
Lewes	1	v	3	Billericay Town
St Albans City	4	v	2	Gt Wakering Rvrs
Whyteleafe	3	v	2	Staines Town*
Maidenhead Utd	2	v	1	Basingstoke Town
Dulwich Hamlet	1	v	2	Croydon
Bishop's Stortford	2,2	v	1,2	Tring Town*

ROUND THREE

Wealdstone	0	v	1	Oxford City
Barton Rovers	5	v	0	Carshalton Athletic
Aldershot Town	1	v	2	Farnborough T*
Heybridge Swifts	3	v	1	Braintree Town
Chesham United	1	v	0	Purfleet
Billericay Town	1	v	2	St Albans City (r)
Whyteleafe	1	v	2	Maidenhead Utd
Croydon	0	v	2	Bishop's Stortford

ROUND FOUR

Oxford City	0,1	v	1,0	Barton Rovers(p)
Farnborough Town	2	v	7	Heybridge Swifts (r)
Chesham United	0	v	2	Billericay Town
Maidenhead Utd	2	v	1	Bishop's Stortford

SEMI-FINALS

Barton Rovers	1,0	v	2,1	Farnborough Town
Billericay Town	1,0	v	0,1	Maidenhead U (p)

FINAL

FARNBOROUGH T 1 v 0 MAIDENHEAD U

At Basingstoke Town FC

* after extra time
(r) removed from competition
(p) match decided on penalties

770

FULL MEMBERS CUP 1999-2000

ROUND ONE

Hendon	2 v 2	Wealdstone* (p)
Slough Town	4 v 1	Staines Town
(p) Croydon	1 v 1	Bognor Regis T*
Dulwich Hamlet	0 v 3	Farnborough Town
Bromley	3 v 1	Aldershot Town
Hampton & Rich. B	2 v 4	Worthing
Maidenhead Utd	2 v 0	Walton & Hersham
St Albans City	2 v 1	Chesham United
Billericay Town	0 v 2	Bedford Town
Harrow Borough	3 v 3	Chertsey Town* (p)
Barton Rovers	0 v 3	Grays Athletic
Purfleet	5 v 0	Bishop's Stortford

ROUND TWO

Braintree Town	2 v 5	Gravesend & N
Wealdstone	3 v 0	Boreham Wood
Leatherhead	4 v 1	Whyteleafe
Slough Town	2 v 1	Carshalton Athletic
Croydon	3 v 0	Farnborough Town
Aylesbury United	1 v 2	Oxford City*
Bromley	1 v 0	Worthing
Basingstoke Town	2 v 0	Maidenhead Utd
Hitchin Town	2 v 1	Enfield
St Albans City	2 v 2	Bedford Town* (p)
Yeading	3 v 2	Chertsey Town
Thame United	1 v 0	Uxbridge
Harlow Town	1 v 5	Grays Athletic
Heybridge Swifts	2 v 4	Purfleet
Leyton Pennant	2 v 1	Canvey Island
Dagenham & Red.	2 v 0	Romford

ROUND THREE

Gravesend & North.	3 v 1	Wealdstone
Leatherhead	0 v 3	Slough Town
Croydon	1 v 0	Oxford City
Bromley	1 v 0	Basingstoke Town
Hitchin Town	3 v 2	Bedford Town
Yeading	2 v 1	Thame United
Grays Athletic	3 v 4	Purfleet*
Leyton Pennant	1 v 5	Dagenham & Red.

ROUND FOUR

Gravesend & North.	3 v 2	Slough Town
Croydon	2 v 1	Bromley
Hitchin Town	1 v 3	Yeading
Purfleet	5 v 2	Dagenham & Red.

SEMI-FINALS

Gravesend & North.	1 v 2	Croydon
Yeading	2 v 3	Purfleet

FINAL

PURFLEET	0 v 2	CROYDON

VANDANEL TROPHY 1999-2000

ROUND ONE

Horsham	2 v 6	Epsom & Ewell
Molesey	1 v 2	Camberley Town
Windsor & Eton	3 v 1	Dorking
Cheshunt	0 v 2	Ware
Leighton Town	0 v 1	Northwood
Gt Wakering Rovers	1 v 1	Aveley* (p)
Wembley	1 v 2	Wivenhoe Town*
Clapton	0 v 1	Hertford Town*
Flackwell Heath	1 v 1	Chalfont St P* (p)
(p) Hungerford Tn	2 v 2	Abingdon Town*
Marlow	2 v 0	Metropolitan Police

ROUND TWO

Berkhamsted Town	2 v 0	Witham Town
Wingate & Finchley	4 v 2	Ford United
(p) East Thurrock U	1 v 1	Hornchurch
Tilbury	0 v 2	Barking
Tooting & Mitcham U	4 v 1	Epsom & Ewell
Tring Town	0 v 1	Southall
Lewes	2 v 4	Camberley Town
Corinthian Casuals	1 v 2	Windsor & Eton
Ware	5 v 1	Kingsbury Town
Northwood	4 v 1	Hemel Hempstead
Aveley	1 v 2	Wivenhoe Town
Hertford Town	2 v 1	Edgware Town
Chalfont St Peter	2 v 1	Hungerford Town
Banstead Athletic	4 v 0	Wokingham Town
Croydon Athletic	0 v 2	Marlow
Bracknell Town	5 v 1	Egham Town

ROUND THREE

Berkhamsted Town	3 v 0	Wingate & Finchley
East Thurrock Utd	1 v 5	Barking
Tooting & Mitcham U	4 v 1	Southall
Camberley Town	1 v 3	Windsor & Eton*
Ware	2 v 3	Northwood
Wivenhoe Town	3 v 0	Hertford Town
Chalfont St Peter	1 v 2	Banstead Athletic
Marlow	1 v 0	Bracknell Town

ROUND FOUR

Berkhamsted Town	1 v 1	Barking* (p)
Tooting & Mitcham U	3 v 4	Windsor & Eton*
Northwood	2 v 1	Wivenhoe Town*
Banstead Athletic	1 v 1	Marlow* (p)

SEMI-FINALS

Barking	3 v 1	Windsor & Eton
Northwood	3 v 0	Marlow

FINAL

NORTHWOOD	3 v 0	BARKING

---

* after extra time   (p) match decided on penalties

ALDERSHOT TOWN

CLUB OFFICIALS

Chairman: Karl Prentice

Vice Chairman: John McGinty

Company Secretary: Graham Brookland
c/o Aldershot Town FC, (0973 172073)

Press Officer: Nick Fryer Tel:01483 563570

FOOTBALL MANAGEMENT TEAM
Manager: George Borg
Asst Man.: Stuart Cash
Physio: Alan Mc Creanney

FACT FILE
Formed: 1992
Nickname: The Shots
Sponsors:Charters Peugeot
Colours: Red / white & red
Change : Black & white/black & red/black
Midweek matchday: Tuesday
Reserves' League: Suburban league
Club Newsline: 09066 555855

1999-2000 Captain: Ollie Adedeji
Top Scorer: Gary Abbott (45)
P.o.Y.: Ollie Adedeji

GROUND	Recreation Ground, High Street, Aldershot, Hants GU11 1TW
	Tel: 01252 320211 Fax: 01252324347

Directions: Ground situated on eastern end of High Street next to large multi-storey B.T. building. From M3 (jct 4) take A325 to Aldershot. After five milesat r'bout take 1st exit marked town centre (A323) into Wellington Ave. At Burger King r'bout take 2nd exit into High Street - ground on left, large carpark adjacent. 5 mins walk from Aldershot (BR)

Capacity: 7,500   Cover: 6,850   Seats: 1,800   Floodlights: Yes

Clubhouse:	Matchdays and special functions Steward: Wally Clarke 01252 338426
Club Shop:	Range of souvenirs, programmes, replica kits.
	Open matchdays or contact Janet Guess (01252-528007) for mail order

PREVIOUS	**Leagues:** None **Names:** None **Grounds:** None

CLUB RECORDS **Attendance:** 6,870 v Woking (F.A.Cup 4th Q) 5,9,98.
"Ground record: 19,138 Aldershot FC v CarlisleUnited, FA Cup 4th Rd replay 28/1/70
Win: 8-0 v Bishop's Stortford (a) League 5.9.98 **Defeat:** 0-6v Worthing (a) Puma Cup 2.3.99
9-1 v Andover (n) Hants Senior Cup Final 99-00
Career Goalscorer: Mark Butler 155. (92-98)   **Career Appearances:** Mark Butler 303. (92-98)
Transfer Fee Paid: £20,000 to Woking for Grant Payne (11.99)
Transfer Fee Received: £6,000 for Leon Gutzmore from Bedford Town (11.99)
BEST SEASON **FA Cup:** Second Round 99-00 v Exeter City   **FA Trophy:** Fourth Rd Replay 99-00
FA Vase: Quarter Final 93-94

HONOURS Isthmian League Prem. Div. R-up 99-2000, Div 1 97-98, Div 3 92-93; Simpsonair Trophy 92-93; Skol Invitation Trophy 92-93; Hants Senior Cup SF 92-93; 98-99, 99-00. Suburban Lge Western Div 94-95; Allied Counties Youth Lge 1994-95; Guardian Insurance Lge Cup 98-99 R-up 95-96

Pages: 44   Price: £1.50
Editors: Karl Prentice/Graham Brookland
Tel: 01256 471630

Local Press: Aldershot News, Farnham Herald
Local Radio: County Sound (96.4, 1476 khz),
BBC Southern Counties(104.6 fm)

Top Row: Grant Payne, Michael Ruffles, Toby Sumner, Richard Gell, Ian Hathaway, Jason Chewins. **Middle:** Graham Francis (kit man.), Paul Priddy (g/k coach), Gary Abbott, Mark Blake, Lee Holsgrove, Stuart Searle, Andy Pape, Mark CRossley, Ollie Adedeji, Wayne Andrews, Paul Grace & Simon Pullen (res/yth managers). **Front:** Jon Lloyd, Simon Ullathorne, Mark Bentley, Colin Fielder (player/coach), George Borg (manager), Stuart Cash (asst. man.), Alan McCreeney (physio), Owen Coll, Lee Protherow, Mark Rye. **Photo:** Eric Marsh

Match Facts 1999-00

	Date	Comp.	H/A	Opponents	Att.	Result	Goalscorers
1	14.08	RYM P	A	Hendon	1,005	W 2 - 1	Abbott 8, McGrath 87
2	17.08	RYM P	H	GRAVESEND & NORTHFLEET	1921	W 2 - 1	McGrath 42, Bentley 61
3	21.08	RYM P	H	BILLERICAY TOWN	2,045	L 0 - 1	
4	23.08	RYM P	A	Purfleet	562	W 4 - 2	Hathaway 63, McGrath 66, Gutzmore 68, Nartey 70
5	28.08	RYM P	A	Heybridge Swifts	633	W 3 - 1	Abbott 36, Gutzmore 47, Bentley 90
6	30.08	RYM P	H	ST ALBANS CITY	2,234	L 0 - 2	
7	05.09	RYM P	H	HARROW BOROUGH	2,043	L 1 - 2	Sugrue 7
8	07.09	RYM P	A	Aylesbury United	761	L 0 - 3	
9	11.09	RYM P	A	Chesham United	679	L 0 - 2	
	14.09	LC 1	A	Hemel Hempstead Town	275	W 3 - 1	Coll, Bentley, Robson
	18.09	FAC 2Q	H	LEWES	1396	W 6 - 1	Sugrue 18, Bentley 33, **Abbott 3** (38 44[p] 75,) Hathaway 63
10	25.09	FAC 3Q	H	HITCHIN TOWN	1712	W 5 - 1	**Abbott 3** (31 56 90), Sugrue 37, Cretton 37[og]
	02.10	FAC 3Q	A	Fisher Athletic	852	W 2 - 1	Gutzmore 43, Hathaway 51
	16.10	FAC 4Q	A	Lymington & New Milton	1524	W 3 - 1	Bentley 18, Abbott 75 80
	26.10	FMC 1	A	Bromley	341	L 1 - 3	Gutzmore 72
	30.10	FAC 1	H	HEDNESFORD TOWN	3269	D 1 - 1	Abbott 56
	02.11	Hants SC 2	H	WHITCHURCH UNITED	822	W 2 - 0	Abbott, Bell
11	06.11	RYM P	H	BOREHAM WOOD	1679	W 1 - 0	Bentley 23
	08.11	FAC 1 r	A	Hednesford Town	1719	W 2 - 1	Chewins 68, Abbott 87
12	13.11	RYM P	H	Enfield	472	W 4 - 1	**Payne 4** (32 63 69 85)
	20.11	FAC 2	A	Exeter City	4151	L 0 - 2	
	23.11	LC 2	A	Abingdon Town	356	W 3 - 0	**Payne 3** (43 55 88)
	27.11	FAT 2	H	BRAINTREE TOWN	1878	W 3 - 1	Abbott, Gill, Payne
13	30.11	RYM P	A	Dagenham & Redbridge	1150	L 1 - 3	Abbott 12
14	04.12	RYM P	A	Harrow Borough	701	W 1 - 0	Payne 88
	06.12	RYM Shield	H	SUTTON UNITED	691	W 2 - 1	Cash 36, Gill 39
15	11.12	RYM P	H	DULWICH HAMLET	1696	W 3 - 2	Abbott 13, Payne 27 86
16	18.12	RYM P	A	Boreham Wood	668	W 5 - 2	Adedeji 14, **Payne 3** (57 75 82), Abbott 52
	21.12	LC 3	H	FARNBOROUGH TOWN	2682	L 1 - 2	Coll 61
17	27.12	RYM P	H	FARNBOROUGH TOWN	5518	W 1 - 0	Coll 31
18	03.01	RYM P	A	Walton & Hersham	1419	W 1 - 0	Abbott 75
19	08.01	RYM P	H	HEYBRIDGE SWIFTS	2041	L 0 - 1	
20	11.01	RYM P	A	Basingstoke Town	1425	L 1 - 2	Harvey 27
	15.01	FAT 3	H	STAINES TOWN	2050	W 4 - 1	Bentley 15 57, Payne 30 75
21	22.01	RYM P	H	HENDON	1824	W 2 - 1	Abbott 20, Baker 50
	25.01	H SC 3	A	Newport IOW	367	W 2 - 0	Hutchings 51, Abbott 57
22	29.01	RYM P	A	Gravesend & Northfleet	880	D 1 - 1	Abbott 44
	05.02	FAT 4	A	Woking	4973	D 0 - 0	
23	08.02	RYM P	H	CARSHALTON ATHLETIC	1553	W 4 - 0	Abbott 39 75, Hathaway 65, Bentley 78
24	12.02	RYM P	A	St Albans City	1499	W 1 - 0	Abbott 89[p]
	15.02	FAT 4 R	H	WOKING	5307	L 0 - 1	
25	19.02	RYM P	H	AYLESBURY UNITED	2018	D 1 - 1	Abbott 22
26	26.02	RYM P	A	Canvey Island	1720	L 1 - 2	Abbott 80
27	04.03	RYM P	H	DAGENHAM & REDBRIDGE	2439	W 1 - 0	Abbott 59
28	11.03	RYM P	A	Hitchin Town	806	W 2 - 1	Abbott 8 23
	14.03	H SC SF(1)	H	BASINGSTOKE TOWN	1598	W 2 - 0	Andrews, Abbott
29	18.03	RYM P	A	CHESHAM UNITED	2157	W 4 - 1	**Abbott 3** (17 27 55), Ullathorne 45
30	25.03	RYM P	H	SLOUGH TOWN	2123	W 2 - 0	Abbott 89, 90
31	01.04	RYM P	A	Hampton & Richmond Bor.	1008	W 1 - 0	Abbott 66 (p)
32	08.04	RYM P	H	WALTON & HERSHAM	2100	W 3 - 0	Blake 2, Andrews 41, 80
33	11.04	RYM P	H	CANVEY ISLAND	1802	W 3 - 1	Abbott 16, 35, Hutchings 73
34	15.04	RYM P	A	Dulwich Hamlet	1241	W 2 - 1	Bentley 72, Abbott 90
35	18.04	RYM P	A	Billericay Town	901	L 2 - 3	Andrews 10, Hutchings 32
36	22.04	RYM P	H	ENFIELD	2038	L 0 - 4	
37	24.04	RYM P	A	Farnborough Town	1524	D 0 - 0	
38	26.04	RYM P	H	HAMPTON & RICHMOND B.	1280	D 1 - 1	Coll 88
39	29.04	RYM P	A	BASINGSTOKE TOWN	1909	W 5 - 2	Abbott 5, **Andrews 3** (13, 40, 89), Ullathorne 29
40	02.05	RYM P	A	Slough Town	761	D 0 - 0	
41	04.05	RYM P	H	PURFLEET	1336	L 0 - 2	
42	06.05	RYM P	A	Carshalton Athletic	941	L 0 - 3	
	08.05	H SC Final	N	Andover	1500	W 9 - 1	**Abbott 5** (19, 28, 54, 70, 79), **Bentley 3** (23, 26, 82(p)), Harvey 87

PLAYING SQUAD

GOALKEEPERS: Andy Pape (Sutton U)

DEFENDERS: Owen Coll (Stevenage B), Jason Chewins (Wealdstone), Mark Blake (AS Cannes), Ollie Adedeji (Bromley), Stuart Cash (Enfield), Matt Crossley (Kingstonian), Lee Protheroe (Enfield), Lee Holsgrove (Wycombe)

MIDFIELDERS: Mark Bentley (Enfield), Richard Gell (Chesham U), Mark Pye (Slough T), Colin Fielder (Yeovil T), Sam Cobbett (Youth), Toby Sumner (Reading), Ian Hathaway (Colchester)

FORWARDS: **Gary Abbott** (Slough T), Grant Payne (Woking), Wayne Andrews (St.Albans C), Simon Ullathorne (St.Albans C), Nana Achamfuur (Egham T)

BASINGSTOKE TOWN

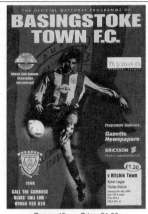

CLUB OFFICIALS
Chairman: David Knight
President: Rafi Pazzak
Secretary: Richard Trodd
5 Lehar Close, Brighton Hill,
Basingstoke RG22 4HT
Tel: 01256 413076
Press Officer: John Gray
Commercial Manager: T.B.A.

FOOTBALL MANAGEMENT TEAM

Manager: Ernie Howe
Asst Manager: Pete Peters
Coach: Steve Richardson
Physio: Mark Randall & Zoe Dempster

FACT FILE
Formed: 1896
Nickname: Stoke
Sponsors: Centerprise International & Ericsson
Colours: Blue & gold stripes/blue/blue
Change colours: Red & black stripes/black/black
Midweek home matchday: Tuesday
Reserves' League: Suburban (Prem Div)
and Capital league

1999-00
Captain & P.O.Y.: Steve Harris
Top Scorer: Tim Sills

GROUND
Camrose Road, Western Way, Basingstoke RG24 6HW
Tel: 01256 325063 or 01256 464353

Directions: Exit 6 off M3 and follow A30 west, ground off Winchester Road.
Two miles from bus and rail stations
Capacity: 6,000   Cover:2,000   Seats: 651   Floodlights: Yes

Clubhouse: Open every day (incl. lunchtime)   Steward: Cheryl Fox (01256 464353)
Club Shop: Open daily 10-5pm, selling programmes, books, scarves, shirts, badges etc.

Pages: 40   Price: £1.50
Editor: T.B.A. Tel: 01256 410103

Local Press: Basingstoke Gazette (461131)
Local Radio: Radio 210 (01189 413131),
Kestrel Radio (01256 694000)

PREVIOUS   Leagues: Hants 1900-40 45-71; Southern 71-87   Ground: Castle Field 1896-1947

CLUB RECORDS   Attendance: 5,085 v Wycombe Wanderers, FA Cup 1st Rd replay 97-98
Win: 10-0 v Chichester City (H), FA Cup 1st Qualifying Round, September 1976
Defeat: 0-8 v Aylesbury United, Southern League, April 1979.
Goalscorer: Paul Coombs 159 (Oct 91 99)   Appearances: Billy Coombs
TransferFees - Paid: £4,750 for Steve Ingham (Gosport Borough)   Received: £6,750 for Steve Ingham (Bashley)

BEST SEASON   FA Trophy: 3rd Rd 98-99, 0-2 v Yeovil T. (H)
FA Cup: 2nd Rd replay 97-98, 3-4 pens aet 0 -0 v Northampton (H) after 1-1; 2nd Rd 89-90, 2-3 v Torquay U. (H)
League clubs defeated: Wycombe Wanderers 97-98

HONOURS   Southern Lge Southern Div 85-86; Isthmian League Div 1 R-up 88-89 96-97; Hants League 67-68 69-70 70-71 (R-up 65-66 66-
67 68-69, North Div 11-12 19-20); HantsSenior Cup 70-71 89-90 95-96 96-97

Players progressing: Tony Godfrey (Southampton 58), John Neale (Exeter 72),Mike Doherty (Reading 82), Micky Cheetham (Ipswich 88),
Matt Carmichael(Lincoln), Tony Franklin (Exeter), Steve Welsh (Peterborough 90)

Basingstoke Town Squad 1999-2000

Match Facts 1999-00

	Date	Comp.	H/A	Opponents	Att.	Result	Goalscorers	Lge Pos.
1	14.08	RYM P	A	Farnborough Town	942	L 0 - 3		
2	17.08	RYM P	H	AYLESBURY UNITED	494	W 4 - 2	S T Richardson 26 55, Hurdle 76, Mancey 82	
3	21.08	RYM P	H	HEYBRIDGE SWIFTS	473	D 2 - 2	T Sills 29, Mancey 31	
4	23.08	RYM P	A	Dulwich Hamlet	260	L 2 - 3	Hurdle 10[p], Mancey 84	
5	28.08	RYM P	A	Purfleet	163	W 2 - 1	T Sills 18, J Sills 81	
6	30.08	RYM P	H	CARSHALTON ATHLETIC	575	W 2 - 0	Richardson 76, Simpson 86	
7	04.09	RYM P	H	ST ALBANS CITY	559	L 0 - 2		
8	07.09	RYM P	A	Harrow Borough	223	D 1 - 1	Killick 34	
9	11.09	RYM P	A	Enfield	623	L 0 - 2		
	14.09	LC 1	H	WALTON & HERSHAM	207	W 3 - 1		
	18.09	FAC 2Q	H	MERTHYR TYDFIL	540	D 0 - 0		
	21.09	FAC 2QR	A	Merthyr Tydfil	523	L 1 - 2	Xavier 66[p]	
10	25.09	RYM P	H	WALTON & HERSHAM	556	L 1 - 3	Wilkinson 57	
	09.10	FAT 1	H	BOGNOR REGIS TOWN	359	D 1 - 1	Dean	
	12.10	FAT 1 R	A	Bognor Regis Town	263	L 0 - 2		
11	16.10	RYM P	H	BOREHAM WOOD	430	D 1 - 1	Wilkinson 67	
12	23.10	RYM P	A	Gravesend & Northfleet	369	L 0 - 1		
13	30.10	RYM P	H	DAGENHAM & REDBRIDGE	507	L 0 - 4		
	02.11	Hants SC2	A	Cove		W 3 - 1	Harris 29, Chudy 92, Green 106	
14	06.11	RYM P	A	Hampton & Richmond Bor.	192	L 1 - 2	T Sills 52	
	09.11	LC 2	A	Maidenhead United	149	L 1 - 2		
15	14.11	RYM P	H	CHESHAM UNITED	416	L 0 - 1		
	16.11	FMC 2	H	MAIDENHEAD UNITED	132	W 2 - 0	T Sills, Simpson	
16	20.11	RYM P	A	Hitchin Town	325	L 0 - 2		
17	04.12	RYM P	H	PURFLEET	385	D 2 - 2	Winter 35 73	
18	11.12	RYM P	A	Hendon	278	L 3 - 4	Gorman 26, J Sills 64, Mancey 84	
19	18.12	RYM P	H	BILLERICAY TOWN	377	W 2 - 0	Wilkinson 11, Harris 44	
20	27.12	RYM P	A	Slough Town	630	W 4 - 1	Harris 7, T Sills 15 37, Simpson 89	
21	03.01	RYM P	H	HAMPTON & RICHMOND B.	484	W 2 - 0	Simpson 34, Gorman 49	
22	08.01	RYM P	A	St Albans City	840	L 1 - 4	Gorman 46	
23	11.01	RYM P	H	ALDERSHOT TOWN	1425	W 2 - 1	T Sills 12 73[p]	
	18.01	FMC 3	A	Bromley	176	L 0 - 1		
24	22.01	RYM P	H	FARNBOROUGH TOWN	748	D 2 - 2	T Sills 55, Gorman 90	
	26.01	H SC 3	A	Cowes Sports	117	W 2 - 0		
25	29.01	RYM P	A	Aylesbury United	517	L 0 - 3		
26	05.02	RYM P	H	DULWICH HAMLET	526	W 2 - 0	Wilkinson 8, Mancey 90	
27	08.02	RYM P	A	Canvey Island	301	L 1 - 3	Winter 25	
28	12.02	RYM P	A	Carshalton Athletic	281	D 3 - 3	Gorman 3 28, T Sills 37[p]	
	16.02	H SC QF	A	Fareham Town	143	W 4 - 0	Gorman, Mancey, Howes(2)	
29	19.02	RYM P	H	HARROW BOROUGH	455	W 2 - 0	Richardson 34, T Sills 90	
30	26.02	RYM P	A	Boreham Wood	271	W 4 - 3	McCarthy 7[og], S T Richardson 63, T Sills 79, Gorman 83	
31	04.03	RYM P	H	CANVEY ISLAND	532	L 0 - 1		
32	11.03	RYM P	A	Walton & Hersham	237	L 0 - 1		
	14.03	HSC SF(1)	A	Aldershot Town	1598	L 0 - 2		
33	18.03	RYM P	H	ENFIELD	546	W 2 - 1	Winter 13[p], T Sills 25	
34	21.03	RYM P	A	Heybridge Swifts	245	L 0 - 2		
35	25.03	RYM P	A	Dagenham & Redbridge	1040	L 0-1		
	28.03	HSC SF(2)	H	ALDERSHOT TOWN	1159	D 0-0		
36	01.04	RYM P	H	GRAVESEND & N'FLEET	390	W 2-0	T Sills 16, Winter 45	
37	08.04	RYM P	A	Billericay Town	510	L 0-1		
38	15.04	RYM P	H	HENDON	444	D 1-1	T Sills 35	
39	22.04	RYM P	A	Chesham United	302	D 1-1	Simpson 35	
40	24.04	RYM P	H	SLOUGH TOWN	524	W 1-0	Gorman 83	
41	29.04	RYM P	A	Aldershot Town	1909	L 2-5	Mancey 41, OG (Blake) 82	
42	06.05	RYM P	H	HITCHIN TOWN	797	D 1-1	Gorman 7	

PLAYING SQUAD

GOALKEEPERS: Vince Matassa (Gambia), Scott Tarr (Yeading)

DEFENDERS: Jason Bristow (Reading), Steve Baker (Farnborough T), Steve Richardson (Newbury T), Paul Hardyman (Slough T), Mark Lisk (Dorchester T), Don Forbes (Forest Green R), Chris Honor (Forest Green R), Toby Redwood (Dorchester T)

MIDFIELDERS: Paul Wilkinson (Dorchester T), Stuart Girdler (Woking), Glenn Howes (Eastleigh), Julian Sills (Camberley T), Steve Winter (Forest Green R), Rob Cook (Forest Green R)

FORWARDS: Tim Sills (Camberley T), Lee Chudy (Burnham), Richard Newbery (Carshalton Ath), Sean Gorman (Godalming & Guildford), Adie Mings (Forest Green R), Aaron Roberts (Farnham T)

BILLERICAY TOWN

CLUB OFFICIALS

Chairman: Rod Moore
Vice Chairmen: Jim Hall and John Stacey
President: T.B.A.
Secretary: Len Dewson
14 Graham Close, Billericay,
Essex CM12 0QW   Tel: 01277 622375
Press Officer: T.B.A.

FOOTBALL MANAGEMENT TEAM
Manager: Gary Calder
Asst. Man.: Chris King
Coach: Joe Dunwell
Physio: Dave Lawson

FACT FILE
Formed: 1880
Nickname: The Town
Sponsors: Entertainment for Fun Ltd.,
Colours: Royal Blue/White/ Royal Blue
Change colours: White/Royal Blue/White
Midweek Matches: Tuesday

1999-00 Captain: Dean Parratt
P.o.Y.: Dean Parratt
Top Scorer: Colin Simpson (17)

GROUND: New Lodge, Blunts Wall Road, Billericay CM12 9SA (01277 652188)
Directions: From Shenfield (A129) right at 1st lights then 2nd right. FromBasildon (A129) over 1st lights in town, then left at next lights and 2nd right. Half mile from Billericay (GER) (London Liverpool St. - Southend line). 5 mins walk from buses 222, 251, 357, 255, 551
Capacity: 3,500   Seats: 424   Cover: 800   Floodlights: Yes
Clubhouse: Open every evening 8-11pm (except Monday)(1pm-11pm Sat) and weekend-lunchtimes noon-2.30pm. Discos, live entertainment
Club Shop: Open matchdays for souvenirs, metal badges, old progs, programme swaps
Nigel Harris (01268 558114)

Pages: 48 .Price: £1.30
Editor: Mark Kettlety (01277 636149)
Local Press: Evening Echo, Billericay Gazette, Billericay Recorder
Local Radio: BBC Radio Essex, Essex Radio, Essex FM

PREVIOUS   **Leagues:** Romford & Dist. 1890-1914; Mid Essex 18-47; South Essex Comb. 47-66; Essex Olympian 66-71; Essex Snr 71-77; Athenian 77-79   **Grounds**: Laindon Road (pre-1971).

CLUB RECORDS Attendance: 3,841 v West Ham Utd, Floodlight opener 77. Comp match: 3,193 v Farnborough Tn, FA Vase SF 1st leg 76
Win: 11-0 v Stansted (A), Essex Senior League 5/5/76
Defeat: 3-10 v Chelmsford City (A), Essex Senior Cup 4/1/93
Goalscorer: (career) F Clayden 273, (season) Leon Gutmore 51 (97-98)   **Appearances:** J Pullen 418
Fees - Paid: Undisclosed   **Received:** £22,500+ increments for Steve Jones (West Ham, Nov. 1992)

BEST SEASON   **FA Cup:** 1st Rd Proper 97-98   **FA Vase:** Winners - 75-76, 76-77 & 78-79
FA Trophy: 4th Rd 99-00   **FA Amateur Cup:** 3rd Qual Rd 73-74

HONOURS: Essex Snr Lg 72-73 74-75 75-76, R-up 71-2 73-4, Lg Cup 71-72, Challenge Cup 72-73, 76-77 (R.up 74-75); Isthmian Lge Div 2 79-80, Div 1 R-up 80-81, 97-98; Athenian Lg 77-79 (Lg Cup 77-78); East Anglian Cup R-up 79-80 84-5; Essex Snr Cup 75-76 (R-up 85-6 93-4,4-5,5-6); Essex Snr Tphy 77-78 79-80; Essex Thameside Tphy 86-87 91-92 (R-up 90-1); Essex F'lit Tphy 77-78; Phillips F'lit Tphy 76-77; Rothmans Merit Award 1978
Players progressing: D Westwood (QPR) 75, A Hull, D Carter (Peterborough,Orient), D Cass (Orient) 88, D Ludden (Orient) 92, S Jones (West Ham Utd) 92

Billericay Town F.C. pictured before their F.A. Umbro Trophy Fourth Round replay. Photo: Peter Barnes

Match Facts 1999-00

	Date	Comp.	H/A	Opponents	Att.	Result	Goalscorers
1	14.08	RYM P	H	HAMPTON & RICHMOND B.	534	W 1-0	Roudette 59
2	17.08	RYM P	A	Hitchin Town	368	L 0-4	
3	21.08	RYM P	A	Aldershot Town	2045	W 1-0	Browne 76
4	24.08	RYM P	H	CHESHAM UNITED	404	W 2-1	Brett 13 43
5	28.08	RYM P	H	BOREHAM WOOD	473	W 1-0	Brett 43
6	30.08	RYM P	H	Slough Town	612	L 0-4	
7	03.09	RYM P	A	Dagenham & Redbridge	1102	L 1-2	Hammatt 44
8	07.09	RYM P	H	CANVEY ISLAND	868	D 0-0	
9	11.09	RYM P	H	GRAVESEND & NORTHFLEET	519	D 3-3	Simpson 52, Hammatt 54, Linger 89
	14.09	LC 1	A	WEMBLEY	168	W 3-2	
	18.09	FAC 2Q	A	Wisbech Town	554	W 3-1	Game 17, Gentle 32, Simpson 50
	03.10	FAC Q3	A	Enfield	358	L 0-2	
10	09.10	RYM P	H	DULWICH HAMLET	459	L 3-5	Williams 14, Simpson 34, Parratt 78
11	23.10	RYM P	H	ST ALBANS CITY	581	W 3-1	Simpson 1, Gentle 26, Browne 78
	26.10	FMC 1	H	BEDFORD TOWN	224	L 0-2	
12	30.10	RYM P	A	Gravesend & Northfleet	401	D 2-2	Browne 18 42
13	25.09	RYM P	A	Purfleet	301	D 2-2	Simpson 21, Hammatt 75
14	06.11	RYM P	H	HARROW BOROUGH	469	W 5-0	Simpson 19, Parratt 41[p], Browne 46 88, Williams 65
	09.11	LC 2	A	Lewes	118	W 3-1	
15	13.11	RYM P	A	Carshalton Athletic	218	D 3-3	Game 70, Parratt 89[p], Simpson 90
16	20.11	RYM P	H	FARNBOROUGH TOWN	583	L 0-3	
	27.11	FAT 2	A	Yate Town	142	W 2-0	Browne 11, Simpson 20
17	30.11	RYM P	A	Aylesbury United	339	W 1-0	Game 32
18	04.12	RYM P	A	Boreham Wood	226	W 2-0	Williams 72, Browne 82
19	11.12	RYM P	A	WALTON & HERSHAM	426	L 0-3	
	14.12	LC 3	H	ST ALBANS CITY	102	L 1-2	Williams St. Albans City removed from competition
20	18.12	RYM P	A	Basingstoke Town	377	L 0-2	
21	27.12	RYM P	H	HEYBRIDGE SWIFTS	558	L 1-2	Gentle 89
22	03.01	RYM P	A	Harrow Borough	235	D 1-1	Williams 23
23	08.01	RYM P	H	DAGENHAM & REDBRIDGE	1182	L 0-4	
	15.01	FAT 3	H	HEREFORD UNITED	757	W 3-1	Browne 32, Gentle 49, Simpson 70
	18.01	E SC 4	A	AVELEY	123	W 4-0	
	25.01	LC QF	A	Chesham United	161	W 2-0	
24	29.01	RYM P	H	HITCHIN TOWN	470	D 1-1	Linger 57
	05.02	FAT 4	H	RUSHDEN & DIAMONDS	2027	D 0 - 0	
	08.02	FAT 4 R	A	Rushden & Diamonds	2132	L 1 - 2	Browne 86
25	12.02	RYM P	H	SLOUGH TOWN	456	W 3 - 1	Williams 7, Gentle 17, Parratt 35
	15.02	ESC QF	H	ROMFORD	187	W 2 - 0	
26	19.02	RYM P	A	Canvey Island	1040	L 0 - 3	
27	26.02	RYM P	H	HENDON	471	D 1 - 1	Conner 70
	29.02	LC SF(1)	H	MAIDENHEAD UNITED	202	D 1 - 1	Simpson 26
28	04.03	RYM P	A	Dulwich Hamlet	374	W 2 - 1	Gentle 7, Baker 69
	07.03	LC SF(2)	A	Maidenhead United	258	D 0 - 0	Lost 3-4 after penalties
29	11.03	RYM P	H	PURFLEET	556	D 1 - 1	Simpson 44
30	14.03	RYM P	A	Enfield	168	D 1 - 1	OG (Cooper) 60 at Boreham Wood
31	25.03	RYM P	H	ENFIELD	527	D 0 - 0	
32	27.03	RYM P	A	Hendon	178	L 2 - 3	Baker 45, Parratt 57 (p)
33	01.04	RYM P	A	St. Albans City	529	W 2 - 1	Gentle 6, Simpson 75
34	04.04	RYM P	H	Hampton & Richmond Bor.	163	W 2 - 1	Culverhouse 67, Linger 69
35	08.04	RYM P	H	BASINGSTOKE TOWN	510	W 1 - 0	Blaney 64
36	11.04	RYM P	A	Chesham United	202	D 1 - 1	Baker 78
37	18.04	RYM P	H	ALDERSHOT TOWN	901	W 3 - 0	**Simpson 3** (30, 48, 56)
38	22.04	RYM P	H	CARSHALTON ATH.	471	W 2 - 0	Simpson 20, 87
39	24.04	RYM P	A	Heybridge Swifts	407	W 2 - 1	Baker 14, Woolsey 87
40	29.04	RYM P	H	AYLESBURY UNITED	601	W 5 - 0	Williams 8, Gentle 10, 33, Baker 35, Browne 55
41	01.05	RYM P	A	Walton & Hersham	234	W 1 - 0	Spencer 90
42	06.05	RYM P	A	Farnborough Town	407	L 0 - 2	

PLAYING SQUAD

GOALKEEPERS: Paul Newell (Dag & Red)

DEFENDERS: **Steve Conner** (Dag & Red), Kevin Jordan (Bishop's Stortford), Jeff Woolsey (Dag & Red), Kirk Game (Dag & Red), Dave Culverhouse (Dag & Red), Chris Moore (Canvey Is)

MIDFIELDERS: Paul Linger (Welling U), Russell Penn (Enfield), Dean Parratt (Dag & Red), Gary Henty (Barking), Glenn Southgate (Enfield), Simon Spencer (Egham T)

FORWARDS: Junior Harvey (Aldershot T), Joe Baker (Sutton U), Justin Gentle (Dag & Red), Lee Williams (Enfield), Alan Harding (Bishop's Stortford), Richard Dunwell (Enfield)

CANVEY ISLAND

CANVEY ISLAND
FOOTBALL CLUB

CLUB OFFICIALS
Chairman: **Ray Cross,** 95 Lakeside Path,
Canvey Island, Essex SS8 5PD.
Tel: 01268 684357 (H)
Secretary: **Mrs Frances Roche,** 56
Harvest Road, Canvey Island SS8 9RP.
Tel: 01268 698586 (H/Fax)
Press Officer: **Tony Roche**
Tel: 01268 698586

FOOTBALL MANAGEMENT TEAM
Manager: Jeff King. 01268 511555 (B)
0850 654321 (Mobile)
Asst Manager: Glenn Pennyfather
Physio: Harry Johnson

FACT FILE
Formed: 1926
Nickname: Gulls
Sponsors: Kings The Clubs
Colours: Yellow/blue/white
Change colours: Red & Blue/White/white
Midweek matchday: Tuesday
Reserves' League:
Essex & Herts Border Comb

1999-00 Captain & Top Scorer: Steve Tilson
Supporters P.o.Y.: Steve Ward

RYMAN LEAGUE PREMIER DIVISION
MILLENNIUM SEASON 1999 - 2000

KINGS
The Clubs
Ryman **Ryman**
CANVEY • EASTBOURNE • COPFORD

Pages: 52 Price: £1.30
Editor: Keith Johnson (01268 682991)

Local Press: Evening Echo
Local Radio: Essex FM, BBC Essex

GROUND: Park Lane, Canvey Island, Essex SS8 7PX
Tel: 01268 682991

Directions: A130 from A13 or A127 at Sadlers Farm r/about, 1 mile through town centre, 1st right past old bus garage. Bus 3 or 151 fromBenfleet (BR) to stop after Admiral Jellicoe (PH)

Capacity: 3,108   Seats: 300   Cover: 800   Floodlights: Yes

Clubhouse: Open Tues, Thurs & Sats. Full licence. Food avaiable

Club Shop: Open matchdays. Selling programmes, badges, shirts etc.
Contact Mrs J Edwards

PREVIOUS   **Leagues:** Southend & Dist.; Thurrock & Thameside Comb.; Parthenon; Metropolitan;Gtr London 64-71; Essex Senior
Grounds: None   **Names:** None

CLUB RECORDS **Attendance:** 3,250 v Brighton & Hove Albion F.A. Cup 95-96
Win: 7-1 v Bedford   **Defeat:** 7-0 v Halstead
Career Appearances: Steve Price (407)   **Career Goalscorer:** Andy Jones (200)
Fee received: £3,000 for Ian Durrant from Grays Athletic
Fee paid: £ 5,000 for Chris Duffy to Northwich Victoria

BEST SEASON   **FA Cup:** 1st Rd v Brighton (2-2) (replay 1-4) 95-96
FA Vase: Semi-final v Tiverton 27/3/93   **FA Trophy:** 3rd Rd V Cheltenham Town 98-99

HONOURS: Ryman Lge - Div 2 95-96, 97-98,R-up 98-99 Div 3 R-up 94-95; Carlton Trophy 95-96; Essex Sen Lg 86-87 92-93 (Lg Cup 79-80 92-93),Trophy R-up 93-94; Harry Fisher Mem.Tphy 93-94; Essex Thameside Trophy 93-94; Parthenon Lge Cup 58-59; Metropolian Lge 67-68 68-69, Cup 67-68 68-69; Thameside 95-96 97-98; Res. Lge 95-96, Cup 95-96, Essex Senior Cup 98-99

Players progressing: Peter Taylor (Spurs), Gary Heale (Luton T)

Canvey Island's Neil Gregory rises high to send his header powering towards the Dulwich goal.
Photo: Alan Coomes

Match Facts 1999-00

	Date	Comp.	H/A	Opponents	Att.	Result	Goalscorers
1	14.08	RYM P	A	Gravesend & Northfleet	639	W 1 - 0	Tilson 51
2	17.08	RYM P	H	HARROW BOROUGH	629	W 2 - 0	Jones 7, Tilson 75[p]
3	21.08	RYM P	H	ST ALBANS CITY	681	L 0 - 1	
4	23.08	RYM P	A	Hendon	275	L 2 - 3	Jones 34, Tilson 90
5	28.08	RYM P	A	Aylesbury United	602	D 3 - 3	Stimson 27, Davidson 59, Parmenter 88
6	30.08	RYM P	H	PURFLEET	612	W 2 - 0	Duffy 2, Jones 90
7	04.09	RYM P	H	CARSHALTON ATHLETIC	370	W 1 - 0	Wilkins 49
8	07.09	RYM P	A	Billericay Town	868	D 0 - 0	
9	11.09	RYM P	A	Slough Town	785	L 0 - 3	
	14.09	LC 1	H	ROMFORD		L 1 - 3	
	18.09	FAC 2Q	H	BOREHAM WOOD	245	W 3 - 1	Jones 35, 50, Brazier 90
10	25.09	RYM P	H	CHESHAM UNITED	342	W 2 - 1	Davidson 36, Bartley 86
	02.10	FAC Q3	A	Wembley	153	W 3 - 0	Readings 22[og], Jones 30, Bartley 62
11	09.10	RYM P	A	Farnborough Town	577	W 2 - 1	Bartley 66, Tilson 73
	16.10	FAC Q4	H	ST ALBANS CITY	711	D 3 - 3	Tilson 65 75, Jones 85
	19.10	FAC Q4R	A	St Albans City	678	L 1 - 2	Tilson 27[p]
12	23.10	RYM P	H	HITCHIN TOWN	282	L 0 - 3	
13	30.10	RYM P	A	Hampton & Richmond Bor.	237	W 2 - 0	Tilson 54 56
14	06.11	RYM P	H	ENFIELD	1005	W 1 - 0	Jones 50
15	13.11	RYM P	A	Dulwich Hamlet	617	L 0 - 2	
	16.11	FMC 2	A	Leyton Pennant	65	L 1 - 2	Parmenter 66
16	20.11	RYM P	H	WALTON & HERSHAM	225	D 1 - 1	Duffy 20
	23.11	Eastern FC	A	Burnham Ramblers	80	D 1 - 1	Britnell 90
	27.11	FAT 2	A	Uxbridge	140	W 2 - 0	Tilson, Britnell
17	04.12	RYM P	A	Carshalton Athletic	287	L 1-3	Brazier 40
18	11.12	RYM P	H	HEYBRIDGE SWIFTS	389	W 6-1	Duffy 35 80, Jones 65 75, Tilson 70 85
19	18.12	RYM P	A	Enfield	187	D 1-1	Jones 55
	21.12	Essex SC 4	H	TILBURY		W 6-0	Parmenter 43, Tilson 45, Bright 66, Duffy 71, Jones 80 85
20	27.12	RYM P	H	DAGENHAM & REDBRIDGE	2003	W 3-1	Gregory 10, Jones 32, Duffy 73
21	03.01	RYM P	A	Boreham Wood	355	L 2 - 3	Gregory 65, Jones 90
22	08.01	RYM P	H	AYLESBURY UNITED	540	L 2 - 3	Gregory 26, Tilson 55
	15.01	FAT 3	A	Sutton United	719	L 0 - 1	
23	22.01	RYM P	H	GRAVESEND & NORTHFLEET	511	W 4 - 1	Duffy 27, **Tilson 3** (37 74 89)
	25.01	E FC	H	BURNHAM RAMBLERS		W 6 - 1	Abrahams 24 27, Gregory 50 65, Brazier 75, OG 80
24	29.01	RYM P	A	Harrow Borough	221	W 3 - 1	Gregory 22, Brazier 45, Cooper 61
	01.02	E SC QF	A	Clacton Town		W 3 - 0	Parmenter(3)
25	05.02	RYM P	H	HENDON	411	D 0 - 0	
26	08.02	RYM P	H	BASINGSTOKE TOWN	301	W 3 - 1	Cooper 2, Duffy 45, Stimson 70
27	19.02	RYM P	H	BILLERICAY TOWN	1040	W 3 - 0	Abrahams 68, Tilson 73 90[p]
28	26.02	RYM P	H	ALDERSHOT TOWN	1720	W 2 - 1	Abrahams 4, Duffy 89
29	04.03	RYM P	A	Basingstoke Town	532	W 1 - 0	Tilson 75[p]
	07.03	E SC SF	H	SOUTHEND UNITED		W 2 - 1	Jones 70 81
30	11.03	RYM P	A	Chesham United	460	L 1 - 2	Parmenter 71
	14.03	E FC QF	H	BOWERS UNITED		W 2 - 1	Jones 52, Parmenter 94
31	18.03	RYM P	H	SLOUGH TOWN	878	W 2 - 0	Tilson 82, Jones 84
32	20.03	RYM P	A	St Albans City	459	W 5 - 2	**Gregory 3** (9 54 84), Jones 39 66
33	25.03	RYM P	H	HAMPTON & RICHMOND B.	705	L 1 - 2	Tilson 20
34	01.04	RYM P	A	Hitchin Town	362	D 3 - 3	Abrahams 26, Gregory 66, 87
35	03.04	RYM P	A	Purfleet	405	L 0 - 2	
36	08.04	RYM P	H	BOREHAM WOOD	570	L 0 - 1	
37	11.04	RYM P	A	Aldershot Town	1802	L 1 - 3	Gregory 51
	17.04	E SC Final	N	Purfleet	405	W 2 - 0	Jones 64, Duffy 89
38	21.04	RYM P	H	DULWICH HAMLET	678	L 0 - 1	
39	24.04	RYM P	A	Dagenham & Redbridge	1722	L 0 - 2	
40	29.04	RYM P	H	FARNBOROUGH TOWN	278	W 2 - 0	Jones 39, Parmenter 40
41	01.05	RYM P	A	Heybridge Swifts	340	L 0 - 3	
42	06.05	RYM P	A	Walton & Hersham	159	W 3 - 0	Parmenter 63, Gregory 64, Jones 66

PLAYING SQUAD

GOALKEEPERS: Ashley Harrison (Dover Ath)

DEFENDERS: Micky Bennett (Brighton), John Kennedy (Ipswich), Mark Stimson (Leyton O),
Craig Davidson (Billericay T), Peter Smith (Woking), Jeff Brazier (Leyton O),
Mick Bodley (Dag & Red), Garry Britnell (Enfield)

MIDFIELDERS: Chris Duffy (Northwich V), Steve Tilson (Southend), Sam Cooper (Billiericay T),
Paul King (Barking), Liam Bright (Tilbury), Wayne Vaughan (Spurs)

FORWARDS: Andy Jones (Billiericay T), Steve Clark (St.Albans C), Neil Gregory (Colchester),
Steve Parmenter (Dorchester T)

CARSHALTON ATHLETIC

CLUB OFFICIALS

Chairman: Andy Hay
Jt-President: W Stephenson
Vice Chairman: T.B.A.
Secretary: Vic Thompson
11 Poulton Ave, Sutton, Surrey. SM1 3PZ.
Tel: 0181 6446402 (H)
General Manager: Bob Clifford
Press Officer: Roger Fear
Comm. Man.: Roger Fear

FOOTBALL MANAGEMENT TEAM

Manager: Tony Rains
Coach: Dixon Gill
Physio: Alan McCreeney

FACT FILE

Formed: 1903

Nickname: Robins

Sponsors: CDL Exhibition Contractors

Colours: White, maroon trim/maroon/white

Change colours: Maroon/white

Midweek matchday: Monday

Reserve League: Suburban

Newsline: 0930 555 877

GROUND War Memorial Sports Ground, Colston Av, Carshalton SM5 2PW
Tel: 0181 642 8658
Directions: Turn right out of Carshalton BR Station, and Colston Avenue is first left. Entrance 150 yards on right. London Transport bus 151 from Morden to Wrythe Green Lane
Capacity: 8,000   Cover: 4,500   Seats: 240   Floodlights: Yes
Clubhouse: Open every evening and lunchtime. Licenced bar, pool, darts,machines, discos on Saturday. Separate function hall (bookings taken). Food:sandwiches, rolls, burgers, hot dogs, teas, coffees and soft drinks. (0181 642 8658)
Club Shop: Sells hats, scarves, T-shirts, badges, programmes etc

Pages: 20 Price: £1.00p
Editor: Andy Hill (0181 647 6288)

Local Press: Sutton Comet, Sutton Herald
Local Radio: BBc Southern Counties

PREVIOUS   **Leagues:** Southern Sub (pre-1911); Surrey Snr 22-23; London 23-46; Corinthian46-56; Athenian 56-73
Grounds: Wrythe Recreation Ground 1907-14; Culvers Park 19-20

CLUB RECORDS **Attendance:** 7,800 v Wimbledon, London Senior Cup
Career goalscorer: Jimmy Bolton(242)   **Career appearances:** Jon Warden (504)
Transfer fee paid: £5,000 for Junior Haynes 1998   **Transfer fee received:** £15,000 for Curtis Warmington (Enfield)
Win: 13-0 v Worthing, Loctite Cup Third Round 28/2/91
F.A.Trophy : 3rd Rd 95-96 lodst away at Hyde United (2-3)
FA Cup: 2nd Rd 82-83, lost 1-4 at Torquay. - League clubs defeated: None

HONOURS: Isthmian League Div 2 R-up 76-77, Corinthian League 52-53 53-54, Surrey Senior League R-up 22-23, Surrey Senior Cup(3) Runners-up (5) Surrey Senior Shield 75-76 Runners-up (2)), London Challenge Cup 91-92 Isthmian Lg Cup R-up 90-91

Players progressing: Roy Lunnes (Crystal Pal. 60), Les Burns (Charlton 67), Ron Walker (Watford), Nobby Warren (Exeter),Terry Stacey (Plymouth A.), Frank GeorgeILeyton Orient) ,Tommy Williams (Colchester U), Alan Eagles (Leyton Orient), Derek Razzell (Q.PR),Muray Jones Crystal Pal.) Gus Caesar (Arsenal), Darren Annon (Brentford) 94, Ian Cox (Crystal Pal.) 94, Carl Asaba (Brentford)

Back Row L-R: Ryan Denys, Gary Bowyer (player/manager), Tyrone Myton, Matt Fowler, Adrian Blake, Phil Barber, Lee Akers, Paul Sears, Dixon Gill (coach). Front Row: Richard Newbury, Orlando Hollingsworth, Junior Haynes, Curtis Johnson, Matt Elverson (capt.), Noel Frankham, Steve Battams, Neil Robson, Steve Talboys.   Photo: Kevin W Rolfe

Match Facts 1999-00

	Date	Comp.	H/A	Opponents	Att.	Result	Goalscorers
1	14.08	RYM P	H	ENFIELD	423	D 2-2	Newbery 1, Sears 51
2	17.08	RYM P	A	Dagenham & Redbridge	673	L 1-3	Newbery 87 [p]
3	21.08	RYM P	A	Boreham Wood	302	W 2-0	Bowyer 17, Dennis 19
4	23.08	RYM P	H	SLOUGH TOWN	334	D 1-1	Barber 75
5	28.08	RYM P	H	HITCHIN TOWN	306	W 2-0	Newbery 56, Fowler 89
6	30.08	RYM P	A	Basingstoke Town	575	L 0-2	
7	04.09	RYM P	A	Canvey Island	370	L 0-1	
8	06.09	RYM P	H	WALTON & HERSHAM	304	L 0-2	
9	11.09	RYM P	A	Heybridge Swifts	248	W 2-0	Sears 6, Fowler 17
	13.09	LC 1	H	BOGNOR REGIS TOWN	183	D 0-0	
	18.09	FAC 2Q	H	SITTINGBOURNE	293	D 2-2	Elverson 89, 90
	21.09	FAC 2QR	A	Sittingbourne	278	W 1-0	Newbery 48
10	25.09	RYM P	H	DULWICH HAMLET	402	L 0-5	
	29.09	LC 1R	A	Bognor Regis Town	108	W 2-0	Nareydo, Battams
	02.10	FAC Q3	A	Slough Town	620	L 0-1	
11	16.10	RYM P	A	Aylesbury United	384	L 2-3	Newbery 64, Denny 87
12	23.10	RYM P	H	HARROW BOROUGH	234	W 3-1	Nwaokola 23[og], Callaghan 77, Salako 90
13	30.10	RYM P	A	Farnborough Town	554	L 1-4	Denys 16
14	06.11	RYM P	A	St Albans City	572	L 0-4	
	09.11	LC 2	A	Slough Town	230	W 1-0	Haynes 89
15	13.11	RYM P	H	BILLERICAY TOWN	218	D 3-3	Newbery 16[p] 20, Ansell 61
	16.11	FMC 2	A	Slough Town	207	L 1-2	????
	27.11	FAT 2	A	Hampton & Richmond Borough	264	W 2-1	McKinlay[og], Newbery
16	29.11	RYM P	H	GRAVESEND & NORTHFLEET	223	L 1-2	Newbery 81
17	04.12	RYM P	H	CANVEY ISLAND	287	W 3-1	Fleming 18, Newbery 71 72
	14.12	LC 3	A	Barton Rovers	66	L 0-5	
18	18.12	RYM P	H	ST ALBANS CITY	307	L 0-1	
19	27.12	RYM P	A	Purfleet	203	D 1-1	Salako 81
20	08.01	RYM P	A	Hitchin Town	322	L 2-3	Callaghan 6, Newbery 33
21	10.01	RYM P	H	CHESHAM UNITED	212	L 0-3	
	15.01	FAT 3	H	FARNBOROUGH TOWN	392	L 0-1	
22	22.01	RYM P	A	Enfield	114	L 2-3	Elverson 12, Newbery 43
	24.01	S SC 1	H	BANSTEAD ATHLETIC	63	W 2-1	Robson, Elverson
23	29.01	RYM P	H	DAGENHAM & REDBRIDGE	482	D 1-1	Daly 81
	02.02	S SC QF	A	Croydon		L 0-4	
24	05.02	RYM P	A	Slough Town	453	L 1-2	Elverson 77
25	08.02	RYM P	A	Aldershot Town	1553	L 0-4	
26	12.02	RYM P	H	BASINGSTOKE TOWN	281	D 3-3	Salako 20, Newbery 58 82
27	14.02	RYM P	H	BOREHAM WOOD	224	W 3-0	Salako 13, Newbery 38, Thomas 54
28	19.02	RYM P	A	Walton & Hersham	264	W 2-0	Newbery 39, Salako 41
29	26.02	RYM P	H	AYLESBURY UNITED	365	W 2-1	Thomas 71, Salako 76
30	11.03	RYM P	A	Dulwich Hamlet	407	W 3-1	Salako 26, Newbery 35[p], Fleming 45
31	14.03	RYM P	A	Hampton & Richmond Bor.	279	W 1-0	Rodgers 80
32	18.03	RYM P	H	HEYBRIDGE SWIFTS	318	L 1-3	Thomas 36
33	25.03	RYM P	H	FARNBOROUGH TOWN	311	D 1-1	Salako 30
34	01.04	RYM P	A	Harrow Borough	236	D 0-0	
35	08.04	RYM P	A	Chesham United	313	D 0-0	
36	10.04	RYM P	H	HENDON	237	L 0-1	
37	18.04	RYM P	H	HAMPTON & RICHMOND B.	189	D 1-1	Salako 30
38	22.04	RYM P	A	Billericay Town	471	L 0-2	
39	24.04	RYM P	H	PURFLEET	290	D 0-0	
40	29.04	RYM P	A	Gravesend & Northfleet	389	W 5-0	Fleming 19, Elverson 21, Newberry 35, Fowler 56, Currie 90
41	01.05	RYM P	A	Hendon	374	L 0-2	
42	06.05	RYM P	H	ALDERSHOT TOWN	941	W 3-0	Newberry 1, 41, Fleming 84

PLAYING SQUAD

GOALKEEPERS:	Andy Harris (Welling U)
DEFENDERS:	Neil Robson (Molesey), Lee Akers (Dulwich Hamlet), Matt Elverson (Walton & Hersham)
MIDFIELDERS:	Simon Bassey (Aldershot T), Martin Kuhl (Farnboough T)
FORWARDS:	Dean Thomas (Kingstonian), Leon Raishbrook (Corinthian Cas), Joel Rogers (Banstead Ath)

CHESHAM UNITED

CHESHAM UNITED FOOTBALL CLUB

Ryman football league

1999/2000 SEASON

'The Community' 'Our Goal'

RYMAN LEAGUE – PREMIER DIVISION

Ryman League – Premier Division
Harrow Borough
Saturday 8th January 2000. Kick-off 3.00 p.m.

OFFICIAL PROGRAMME £1.20

CLUB OFFICIALS

President: **Bill Wells**
Chairman: **David Pembroke**
Secretary: **Jim Chambers**
c/o Chesham United FC.
Tel: 01494 774494 (H) 0181327 4016(B)
Commercial Manager: **Brian Lloyd**
Press Officer: **David Pembroke**

FOOTBALL MANAGEMENT TEAM

Manager: John Kendall
Physio: T.B.A.

FACT FILE

Formed: 1886
Nickname: The Generals
Sponsors: MFI
Colours: Claret & Blue
Quarters/Claret/Claret
Change colours: All Yellow & green
Midweek home matchday: Tuesday
Reserve Team's League: Suburban North
Match information: 0891 884580

Pages: 52   Price: £1,20
Editors: Alan Calder
(01442 230420 [H])

Local Radio: Three Counties
Local Press: Bucks Examiner, Bucks
Advertiser, Bucks Free Press

GROUND: The Meadow, Amy Lane, Amersham Road, Chesham, Bucks. HP5 1NE
Tel: 01494 783964 (ground clubhouse) Fax: 01494 794244

Directions: M25 junction 18, A404 to Amersham, A416 to Chesham - go down to r-about at foot of Amersham Hill, then sharp left. 10 mins walk from Chesham station (Metropolitan Line)
Capacity: 5,000   Cover: 2,500   Seats: 284   Floodlights: Yes

Clubhouse: Open every evening & matchdays. Bar snacks. Available for hire(business training meetings, weddings etc)
Club Shop: Open matchdays   Metal Badges: Yes

PREVIOUS   **Leagues:** Spartan 17-47; Corinthian 47-63; Athenian 63-73

CLUB RECORDS **Attendance:** 5,000 v Cambridge Utd, FA 3rd Rd 5/12/79
Goalscorer: John Willis   **Appearances:** Martin Baguley (600+)
Record Fees - Paid & Received: Undisclosed (club policy)

BEST SEASON   **FA Cup:** 3rd Rd 79-80. 1st Rd 66-67 68-69 76-77 82-83
FA Amtr Cup: R-up 67-68   **FA Trophy:** 3rd Rd 92-93 (1-3 v Sutton United [H])

HONOURS: FA Amtr Cup R-up 67-68, Isthmian Lg 92-93 (Div 1 90-91 96-97), Div 2 Nth 86-87, Associate Members Cup R-up 90-91, Charity Shield 94-95; Athenian Lg Div 1 Cup 63-64 68-69; Corinthian Lg R-up (2) 60-62 (Lg Cup 60-61); Spartan Lg(4) 21-23 24-25 32-33 (R-up 26-27 29-30 33-34); Berks & Bucks Snr Cup 21-22 25-26 28-29 33-34 47-48 50-51 64-65 66-67 75-76 92-93 (R-up 94-95)

Players progressing: Bill Shipwright & Jimmy Strain (Watford 53 & 55), StewartScullion (Charlton 65), John Pyatt (L'pool 67), Brian Carter (Brentford 68),Kerry Dixon (Spurs 78), Tony Currie (Torquay 84)

Chesham United's Paul Kelly chases
Mark Jones of Harrow Borough
Photo: Paul Carter

Match Facts 1999-00

	Date	Comp.	H/A	Opponents	Att.	Result	Goalscorers
1	14.08	RYM P	A	Purfleet	219	D	0-0	
2	17.08	RYM P	H	ST ALBANS CITY	398	L	3-4	Brackett 15 53, Lawford 52
3	21.08	RYM P	H	GRAVESEND & NORTHFLEET	273	D	1-1	Boothe 29
4	24.08	RYM P	A	Billericay Town	404	L	1-2	Boothe 63
5	28.08	RYM P	A	Harrow Borough	285	W	2-0	Lawford 45, Morrisey 87
6	30.08	RYM P	H	DULWICH HAMLET	307	L	1-2	Hippolyte 51
7	04.09	RYM P	H	HEYBRIDGE SWIFTS	286	D	1-1	Boothe 63
8	06.09	RYM P	A	Hendon	258	L	2-4	Boothe 89, Brackett 90
9	11.09	RYM P	H	ALDERSHOT TOWN	679	W	2-0	Lawford 10, 35
	14.09	LC 1	A	Northwood	125	D	*3-3	OG 31, Lawford 81, 103
	18.09	FAC 2Q	H	BALDOCK TOWN	260	L	1-3	Mitchell 75
10	25.09	RYM P	A	Canvey Island	342	L	1-2	Allen 65
	28.09	LC 1R	H	NORTHWOOD	141	W	2-1	Mitchell 54, Boothe 107
11	02.10	RYM P	H	WALTON & HERSHAM	279	W	2-1	Fox 40[p], Renner 70
	09.10	FAT 1	A	Gloucester City	513	L	2-4	Fox 56[p], Boothe 90
12	16.10	RYM P	A	Hampton & Richmond Bor.	285	W	1-0	Allen 56
13	23.10	RYM P	H	SLOUGH TOWN	401	W	3-0	Bowes 14, Allen 44 90
	25.10	FMC 1	A	St Albans City	154	L	1-2	Bowes
14	30.10	RYM P	A	Hitchin Town	478	W	2-0	Fox 36, Allen 90
	02.11	LC 2	A	Ford United	82	W	5-0	Bowes 3 (18,26, 53), Akurang 44, Renner 90
15	09.11	RYM P	H	ENFIELD	397	W	1-0	Akurang 42
16	14.11	RYM P	A	Basingstoke Town	416	W	1-0	Cannon 45
17	20.11	RYM P	H	BOREHAM WOOD	313	W	5-0	Bowes 3 (18 60 63), Renner 35 83
18	27.11	RYM P	A	Dagenham & Redbridge	907	D	1-1	Plummer 66
19	04.12	RYM P	A	Heybridge Swifts	255	L	1-2	Fox 64[p]
20	11.12	RYM P	H	FARNBOROUGH TOWN	440	W	2-1	Renner 45 81
	14.12	LC 3	H	PURFLEET	123	W	1-0	Akurang 7
21	18.12	RYM P	A	Walton & Hersham	251	W	2-1	Akurang 22, Allen 63
22	27.12	RYM P	H	AYLESBURY UNITED	930	D	1-1	Bowes 59
	04.01	B&B SC 3	A	Wycombe Wanderers	400	L	1-4	Fox 23
23	08.01	RYM P	H	HARROW BOROUGH	405	L	1-2	Nartey 69
24	10.01	RYM P	A	Carshalton Athletic	212	W	3-0	Canham 16, Plummer 22 70
25	22.01	RYM P	H	PURFLEET	290	W	1-0	Bowes 67[p]
	25.01	LC QF	H	BILLERICAY TOWN	161	L	0-2	
26	29.01	RYM P	A	St Albans City	740	D	1-1	Allen 7
27	12.02	RYM P	A	Dulwich Hamlet	516	W	2 - 1	Bowes 28, Nartey 43
28	19.02	RYM P	H	HENDON	441	W	2 - 1	Bowes 60 62
29	22.02	RYM P	A	Gravesend & Northfleet	347	L	2 - 3	Bowes 50 49
30	26.02	RYM P	H	HAMPTON & RICHMOND B.	340	W	1 - 0	Allen 89
31	04.03	RYM P	A	Enfield	220	D	2 - 2	Allen 29 68 at Boreham Wood
32	11.03	RYM P	H	CANVEY ISLAND	460	W	2 - 1	Bowes 15, Boothe 75
33	18.03	RYM P	A	Aldershot Town	2157	L	1 - 4	Boothe 45
34	25.03	RYM P	H	HITCHIN TOWN	326	W	2 - 1	Bowes 68 (p), Brown 74
35	01.04	RYM P	A	Slough Town	551	L	0 - 2	
36	08.04	RYM P	H	CARSHALTON ATHLETIC	313	D	0 - 0	
37	11.04	RYM P	H	BILLERICAY TOWN	202	D	1 - 1	Bowes 71
38	22.04	RYM P	H	BASINGSTOKE TOWN	302	D	1 - 1	Bowes 83
39	24.04	RYM P	A	Aylesbury United	828	L	2 - 3	Allen 11, Bowes 26
40	26.04	RYM P	A	Farnborough Town	202	W	1 - 0	Bowes 78
41	29.04	RYM P	H	DAGENHAM & REDBRIDGE	548	L	0 - 3	
42	06.05	RYM P	A	Boreham Wood	404	W	3 - 1	Renner 26, 75, OG (Hamley) 55

PLAYING SQUAD

GOALKEEPERS: Delroy Preddie (Walton & H), Darryl Flahavan (Woking)

DEFENDERS: Brian Statham (Gillingham), Marc Sinfield (Billericay T), Martin Fox (Grantham T), Marvin Harriott (Scarborough), Dave Stephenson (Hampton), Lee Kersey (Enfield), Chris Boothe (Farnborough T), Chris Sparks (St.Albans C), Aiden O'Brien (Woking)

MIDFIELDERS: **Dereck Brown** (Welling U), Scott Canham (Leyton O), Ross White (Barnet), Terry Bowes (Wisbech T), Lee Allen (Walton & H), Dwayne Plummer (Stevenage B), John Butterfield (Barnet), Stuart Storer (Kettering T)

FORWARDS: Victor Renner (Gravesend), Paul Abrahams (Canvey Is), Colin Simpson (Billericay T), Michael Mahoney-Johnson (QPR)

CROYDON

CLUB OFFICIALS

Chairman: Ken Jarvie
Secretary: Mrs Sally Jarvie
2 Spa Close, London SE25 6DS
Tel: 020 86537250(H),
Press Officer: Russell Chandler
26 Dartnell Rd, Croydon, Surrey. CR0 6JA
Tel: 0208 406 4573 (H) 0208 654 8555 (B)
Match Secretary: Gordon Tennant

FOOTBALL MANAGEMENT TEAM
Manager: Ken Jarvie
Coach: John Finch
Physio: Ian Fairs

FACT FILE
Formed: 1953
Nickname: The Trams
Sponsors:Bass Brewers
Colours: Sky & navy quarters/
navy & sky/navy & sky
Change colours: Red & White or Black
Midweek home matchday: Wednesday
Reserve Team's League: Suburban

1999-00
Captain: Ali Reeve
P.o.Y.: Mark Dickinson
Top Scorer: Eben Allen

CROYDON v BISHOP'S STORTFORD
Pages: 28 Price: £1.00
Editor: Russell Chandler (0181 406 4573 H)

Local Press: Whyteleafe Advertiser,
Croydon Midweek Post, Times, Guardian

GROUND Croydon Sports Arena, Albert Road, South Norwood, London. SE25 4QL
Tel: 0208 654 3462/8555
Directions: Train to East Croydon or Norwood Junction, then bus 12 to eitherBelmont or Dundee Road. Walk down either - ground at bottom. 5 mins walk fromWoodside (BR)
Capacity: 8,000   Cover: 1,000   Seats: 450   Floodlights: Yes
Clubhouse: Open every evening and lunchtime, holds 250, snacks available
Dancing, discos, bingo. Lounge bar available for private hire
Club Shop: Yes Badges £2.50, Croydon Women's F.C. Champions badges £3.00

PREVIOUS **Leagues:** Surrey Senior 53-63; Spartan 63-64; Athenian 64-74
Name: Croydon Amateurs 1953-74

CLUB RECORDS **Attendance:** 1,450 v Wycombe, FA Cup 4th Qualifying Rd 1975
Career appearances: Alec Jackson (1977-88) 452 + 111goals and Tony Luckett(1962-73) 411 appearances + 411 goals
Transfer fee paid: Steve Brown   **Transfer fee received:** Peter Evans (to Sutton Utd)

BEST SEASON **FA Cup:** 2nd Round replay 79-80, 2-3 v Millwall after 1-1
FA Trophy: 2nd Round 81-82, 82-83   **FA Amateur Cup:** 3rd round 71-72

HONOURS Isthmian Lg Div. 1 99-2000, Div 2 R-up 75-76 95-96, Lg Cup: R-up 74-75 FM Cup 99-2000; Surrey Snr Cup 81-82 (R-up 76-77 99-00), Surrey Prem Cup 86-87, Spartan Lg 63-64, Athenian Lg R-up 71-72 (Div 2 65-66 (R-up 70-71)), Surrey Snr Lg R-up 56-57 60-61 62-63 (Lg Cup 60-61, Charity Cup 53-54 62-63, Res Section 57-58), London Senior Cup R-up 77-78, Suburban Lg South 86-87(Lg Cup(2), Southern Yth Lg 85-86 (Lg Cup 85-86 87-88), Berger Yth Cup 78-79, Southern Youth Lg Cup 96-97. Womens F.A.Cup 95-6,99-00 R-up 97-98 Premier Lg 99-00

Players progressing: Alan Barnett (Plymouth 1955), Peter Bonetti (Chelsea), Leroy Ambrose (Charlton 1979), Steve Milton (Fulham - via Whyteleafe), Murray Jones (Crystal Pal. - via Carshalton)

Ryman League Division One Champions & Full Members Cup Winners 1999-2000   Photo: Dave West

Match Facts 1999-00

	Date	Comp.	H/A	Opponents	Result	Goalscorers	Att.
1	14.08	RYM 1	A	Whyteleafe	W 2-1	Allen 2	136
2	18.08	RYM 1	H	Oxford City	W 2-0	Allen, Mitchell	87
	21.08	FAC Pre	A	Egham Town	L 0-2		40
3	24.08	RYM 1	A	Bedford Town	L 0-1		561
4	28.08	RYM 1	H	Worthing	W 1-0	Dickson (p)	86
5	30.08	RYM 1	A	Bromley	L 2-3	Harper, Dickinson	304
6	04.09	RYM 1	H	Chertsey Town	W 3-2	Allen, Mitchell 2	52
7	11.09	RYM 1	A	Braintree Town	W 2-0	Mitchell, Dickson (p)	270
	15.09	LC 1	H	Dagenham & Redbridge	W 5-0	Mitchell 2, Dickson (p), Harper, Allen	57
8	25.09	RYM 1	A	Yeading	W 2-0	Mitchell, Ndah	107
9	02.10	RYM 1	H	Leyton Pennant	W 3-0	Dickinson, Judge, Dickson (p)	67
	09.10	FAT 1	H	Margate	D 0-0		150
	12.10	FAT 1 R	A	Margate	L 0-5		324
10	16.10	RYM 1	H	Maidenhead United	D 2-2	Mitchell, Dickson (p)	81
11	23.10	RYM 1	A	Thame United	D 0-0		244
	27.10	FMC 1	H	Bognor Regis Town	D *1-1	Allen won 3-2 after penalties	66
12	30.10	RYM 1	H	Harlow Town	W 1-0	Harper	81
13	06.11	RYM 1	H	Romford	D 1-1	Mitchell	96
	08.11	LC 2	A	Dulwich Hamlet	W 2-1	Allen, Mitchell	132
14	13.11	RYM 1	A	Bishop's Stortford	L 0-1		212
	16.11	FMC 2	H	Farnborough Town	W 3-0	Dickinson, Allen, Simpson	72
15	20.11	RYM 1	H	Grays Athletic	D 0-0		77
16	24.11	RYM 1	H	Bognor REgis Town	L 0-2		78
17	27.11	RYM 1	A	Chertsey Town	W 4-2	Brodrick, Reeve, Harper, Allen	124
18	30.11	RYM 1	A	Staines Town	W 6-2	Liddle, Allen 2, **Harper 3**	212
19	04.12	RYM 1	H	Worthing	W 3-2	Bower, Simpson, Allen	346
	15.12	LC 3	H	Bishop's Stortford	L 0-2		59
20	18.12	RYM 1	A	Barton Rovers	L 1-2	Dundas	157
21	27.12	RYM 1	H	Leatherhead	D 2-2	Liddle, Dickinson	76
22	08.01	RYM 1	H	Bromley	W 3-1	Liddle, Allen, Judge	326
	19.01	Surrey SC 1	H	Sutton United	W 2-0	Dickinson, Hughes	
23	22.01	RYM 1	H	Bedford Town	D 1-1	Kingford	166
	02.02	S SC 2	H	Carshalton Athletic	W 4-0	Dickson, Kingsford, McDonnell, Judge	
24	05.02	RYM 1	H	Whyteleafe	W 3-0	Dickinson, Judge, Allen	176
	09.02	FMC 3	H	Oxford City	W 1-0	Judge	71
25	12.02	RYM 1	A	Wealdstone	W 2-1	OG, Vercesi	383
	16.02	FMC 4	H	Bromley	W 2-1	Dickson (p), Judge	149
26	19.02	RYM 1	H	Braintree Town	W 6-1	Allen, Dickinson 2, Ndah 2, Harper	84
27	26.02	RYM 1	A	Bognor Regis Town	W 2-1	Ndah 2	276
28	04.03	RYM 1	H	Uxbridge	D 1-1	Allen	71
29	08.03	RYM 1	H	Wealdstone	D 2-2	Liddle 2	118
30	11.03	RYM 1	A	Leyton Pennant	W 4-1	Judge, Allen 2, Simpson	87
	14.03	FMC SF	A	Gravesend & Northfleet	W 2-1	Dickinson 2	213
31	18.03	RYM 1	H	Yeading	W 2-0	Allen, Dickson	70
32	21.03	RYM 1	A	Romford	W 2-0	Edwards, Allen	119
33	25.03	RYM 1	A	Harlow Town	W 4-1	Allen, Liddle 2, Ndah	252
	28.03	S SC SF	A	Walton & Hersham	W 2-1	Bower, Dickson (p)	131
34	01.04	RYM 1	H	Thame United	L 2-4	Simpson, Edwards	73
35	04.04	RYM 1	A	Uxbridge	W 2-1	Liddle, Dundas	85
36	08.04	RYM 1	H	Barton Rovers	L 1-2	Ndah	92
37	21.04	RYM 1	H	Bishop's Stortford	D 1-1	Liddle	151
38	24.04	RYM 1	A	Leatherhead	W 2-1	Ndah 2	125
39	29.04	RYM 1	H	Staines Town	W 2-1	Ndah, Dickson	90
40	01.05	RYM 1	A	Oxford City	W 2-0	Harper, Allen	163
41	04.05	RYM 1	A	Maidenhead United	L 0-1		305
42	06.05	RYM 1	A	Grays Athletic	W 4-3	Dickinson, **McDonnell 3**	259
	08.05	S SC Final	A	Woking	L 0-1		963
	09.05	FMC Final	A	Purfleet	W 2-0	McDonnell, Allen (p)	317

PLAYING SQUAD

GOALKEEPERS: James Wastell (Molesey)

DEFENDERS: Marc Crome (Youth), Ross Edwards (Gravesend), Mark Dickinson (Crawley T), Orlando Hollingsworth (Carshalton Ath), Andy Fisher (Kingstonian), John Finch (Dulwich Hamlet), Danny Bower (Dulwich Hamlet)

MIDFIELDERS: Ben Judge (Crystal Pal.), Graham Harper (Portsmouth), Chris Dickson (Tooting & Mitcham), Craig Dundas (Local), Barry Kingsford (Carshalton Ath)

FORWARDS: Eben Allen (Molesey), Nic McDonnell (Farnborough T), Simon Liddle (Corinthian Cas), Jamie Ndah (Dulwich Hamlet)

DULWICH HAMLET

CLUB OFFICIALS

Chairman: **Martin Eede**
President: **Tommy Jover**
Vice Chairman: **Brian Shears**
Secretary:: **Ron McLean**,60 Fawkham
Avenue,New Barn, Kent DA3 7HE Tel: (H)
01474 709495
Press Officer: **John Lawrence**
Tel: 0171 733 6385

FOOTBALL MANAGEMENT TEAM

Manager: Dave Garland
Physio: Danny Keenan

FACT FILE

Formed: 1893 Nickname: The Hamlet
Sponsors: Domino's Pizza
Colours: Navy blue & pink
stripes/navy/navy
Change colours: Green & white
stripes/white/white
Midweek matchday: Tuesday
Reserve League: Suburban

1998-99 Captain: Russell Edwards
P.o.Y.: Les Cleveley
Top Scorer: David Stevens(22)

For up to the minute news, results, fixtures, plus general facts & figures from the world of non-league football

log on to

www.nlfootball.com

GROUND: Champion Hill Stadium, Edgar Kail Way, East Dulwich, London SE22 8BD
Tel: 0171 274 8707

Directions: East Dulwich station, 200yds. Denmark Hill station, 10 mins walk. Herne Hill station then bus 37 stops near grd. Buses 40 & 176 from Elephant & Castle, 185 from Victoria

Capacity: 3,000   Cover: 1,000   Seats: 500   Floodlights: Yes

Clubhouse: Open 7 days a week, 3 bars. Function rooms and meeting room available for hire. Gymnasium, squash courts (0171 274 8707)

Club Shop: Sells programmes, pennants, badges, scarves, baseball caps, replica shirts (by order only). Contact Mishi D Morath at club

Pages: 36   Price: £1

Editor: John Lawrence

Local Press: South London Press, Southwark News

PREVIOUS

Leagues: Camberwell 1894-97; S/thern Sub 1897-1900 01-07; Dulwich 00-01; Spartan 07-08

Grounds: Woodwarde Rd 1893-95; College Farm 95-96; Sunray Avenue 96-1902; Freeman's Ground, Champion Hill 02-12; Champion Hill (old ground) 1912-92; Sandy Lane (groundshare with Tooting & Mitcham F.C.) 91-92

CLUB RECORDS

Attendance: 20,744, Kingstonian v Stockton, FA Am Cup Final 1933 (at refurbished ground): 1,850 v Southport FAC 98-99

Career Goalscorer: Edgar Kail 427 (1919-33)   **Career Appearances:** Reg Merritt 571 (50-66)

Fee Paid: T Eames (Wimbledon), G Allen (Carshalton Ath 80)   **Fee Received:** E Nwajiobi (Luton 83)

Win: 13-0 v Walton-on-Thames, 37-38   **Defeat:** 1-10 v Hendon, 63-64

BEST SEASON

FA Amateur Cup: Winners 19-20 31-2 33-4 36-7   **FA Trophy:** Quarter Final 79-80

FA Cup: 1st Rd replay 30-31 33-34. 1st Rd on 14 occasions

HONOURS:
Isthmian League 19-20 25-26 32-33 48-49, (R-up(7) 21-22 23-24 29-31 33-34 46-47 58-59, Div 1 77-78); London Senior Cup 24-25 38-39 49-50 83-84 (R-up 05-06 07-08 20-21 27-28); Surrey Senior Cup 04-06 08-10 19-20 22-23 24-25 27-28 33-34 36-37 46-47 49-50 57-59 73-75, (R-up 11-12 31-33 37-38 50-51 67-68); London Chal. Cup R-up 91-92; London Charity Cup(12) 10-11(jt) 19-21 22-23 23-24(jt) 25-26 27-29 30-31(jt) 47-48 56-58; Surrey Senior Shield 72-73; Surrey Centen. Shld 77-78; Sth of the Thames Cup (4) 56-60; Southern Comb Cup 73-74

Players progressing: W Bellamy (Spurs), A Solly (Arsenal), L Fishlock/A Gray/APardew (C Palace), J Moseley & E Toser (Millwall), R Dicks (Middlesborough), GJago/J Ryan (Charlton Ath 51/63), G Pearce (Plymouth), R Crisp (Watford 61), ENwajiobi (Luton 83), C Richards & J Glass (Bournemouth), P Coleman (Millwall86), A Perry (Portsmouth 86), N Kelly (Stoke City), C Emberson (Rotherham), CAsaba (Brentford)

Danny Carroll runs towards the Dulwich fans after scoring Hamlet's 2nd goal against Canvey Island.
Photo: Paul Dennis

Match Facts 1999-00

	Date	Comp.	H/A	Opponents	Att.	Result	Goalscorers
1	14.08	RYM P	H	BOREHAM WOOD	349	L 1 - 2	P Garland 42 [p]
2	17.08	RYM P	A	Walton & Hersham	203	W 3 - 0	Carroll 40, McEwan 72, P Garland 82
3	21.08	RYM P	A	Enfield	395	L 2 - 3	Stevens 4, Houghton 77
4	23.08	RYM P	H	BASINGSTOKE TOWN	260	W 3 - 2	Stevens 14, 27, P Garland 30 [p]
5	28.08	RYM P	H	HAMPTON & RICHMOND B.	304	W 2 - 0	Stevens 52, 75
6	30.08	RYM P	A	Chesham United	307	W 2 - 1	Carroll 16, Stevens 75
7	04.09	RYM P	A	Slough Town	548	L 1 - 2	Carroll 70
8	06.09	RYM P	H	DAGENHAM & REDBRIDGE	489	D 0 - 0	
9	11.09	RYM P	H	HARROW BOROUGH	310	W 2 - 0	Stevens 15, Green 81
	13.09	LC 1	H	WIVENHOE TOWN	97	W 6 - 2	Stevens (2), Green, McEwan, Holness, Chin
	18.09	FAC 2Q	A	Newport IOW	569	D 1 - 1	Garland 51
10	25.09	RYM P	A	Carshalton Athletic	402	W 5 - 0	Gregory 26, McGovern 40, Sears 60[og], Stevens 75, 85
	02.10	FAC Q3	H	HASTINGS TOWN	437	W 2 - 1	P Garland 41, McEwen 74
	05.10	London CC 1	A	Metropolitan Police	70	W 4 - 0	Stevens (2), Holness, Green
11	09.10	RYM P	A	Billericay Town	459	W 5 - 3	Stevens 17 87, McEwan 36 60, P Garland 72[p]
	16.10	FAC Q4	H	HAYES	830	D 0 - 0	
	19.10	FAC Q4R	A	Hayes	602	L 0 - 3	
12	23.10	RYM P	A	Aylesbury United	366	W 3 - 2	Stevens 16, Carroll 75, Garland 84
	25.10	FMC 1	H	FARNBOROUGH TOWN	161	L 0 - 3	
13	30.10	RYM P	H	HEYBRIDGE SWIFTS	328	W 2 - 1	Stevens 30, Carroll 31
14	06.11	RYM P	A	Hendon	381	W 2 - 1	P Garland 69, Houghton 81
	08.11	LC 2	H	CROYDON	132	L 1 - 2	Carroll
15	13.11	RYM P	H	CANVEY ISLAND	617	W 2 - 0	McEwen 8, Carroll 77
16	20.11	RYM P	A	St Albans City	829	L 1 - 4	Carroll 49
	27.11	FAT 2	H	BURNHAM	304	D 1 - 1	Carroll 58
	30.11	FAT 2R	A	Burnham	125	L *0 - 1	
17	04.12	RYM P	H	SLOUGH TOWN	405	L 2 - 3	P Garland 17, Stevens 28
18	11.12	RYM P	A	Aldershot Town	1696	L 2 - 3	McEwen 37 67
19	18.12	RYM P	H	PURFLEET	239	W 3 - 2	Macken 15, McEwen 40, Carroll 66
20	27.12	RYM P	A	Gravesend & Northfleet	886	L 1 - 3	McEwen 52
21	03.01	RYM P	H	HENDON	405	W 1 - 0	Bartley 36
22	15.01	RYM P	H	ENFIELD	556	D 0 - 0	
23	22.01	RYM P	A	Boreham Wood	325	D 0 - 0	
	25.01	Surrey SC 1	A	Ashford Town (Middx)	81	W 3 - 2	Houghton, Holness, Bartley
24	29.01	RYM P	H	WALTON & HERSHAM	415	W 1 - 0	Carroll 39
25	05.02	RYM P	A	Basingstoke Town	526	L 0 - 2	
26	12.02	RYM P	H	CHESHAM UNITED	516	L 1 - 2	Houghton 18
	16.02	L CC QF	A	Welling United	186	W 3 - 0	OG (Taylor) 17, McGibbon 21, Hakki 35
27	19.02	RYM P	A	Dagenham & Redbridge	1141	L 0 - 3	
	21.02	S SC QF	H	WALTON & HERSHAM	159	L 0 - 2	
28	26.02	RYM P	A	Farnborough Town	430	L 0 - 2	
	28.02	L CC SF	H	ROMFORD	105	W 3 - 1	Carroll 10, Houghton 49[p], Green 86
29	04.03	RYM P	H	BILLERICAY TOWN	374	L 1 - 2	Crouch 85
30	07.03	RYM P	A	Hampton & Richmond Bor.	193	L 0 - 3	
31	11.03	RYM P	H	CARSHALTON ATHLETIC	407	L 1 - 3	Perkins 6
32	18.03	RYM P	A	Harrow Borough	182	L 0 - 1	
33	25.03	RYM P	A	Heybridge Swifts	287	D 1 - 1	Carroll 24
34	01.04	RYM P	H	AYLESBURY UNITED	385	W 3 - 0	Green 38, Chin 45, Carroll 60
35	08.04	RYM P	A	Purfleet	236	D 1 - 1	OG (McFarlane) 83
36	10.04	RYM P	H	HITCHIN TOWN	227	L 1 - 2	Green 63
37	15.04	RYM P	A	ALDERSHOT TOWN	1241	L 1 - 2	P Garland 5
38	17.04	RYM P	H	FARNBOROUGH TOWN	251	L 1 - 3	Perkins 47
39	21.04	RYM P	A	Canvey Island	678	W 1 - 0	Green 82
40	24.04	RYM P	H	GRAVESEND & N'fleet	332	L 1 - 5	McGibbon 48
41	29.04	RYM P	A	Hitchin Town	417	L 0 - 2	
	03.05	L CC F	N	Uxbridge	264	D *2 - 2	P Garland 23 (p), Chin 99 — Lost 4-5 after penalties
42	06.05	RYM P	H	ST. ALBANS CITY	582	W 3 - 2	Carroll 45, Cobb 64, Palmer 85

PLAYING SQUAD

GOALKEEPERS: Les Cleevely (Sutton U)

DEFENDERS: Mark Garland (Crawley T), Tony Chin (Youth), Michael Ebanks (Youth), Gary Hewitt (Erith & B), Dean Palmer (Youth), Caleb Kamara-Taylor (Youth)

MIDFIELDERS: Veli Hakki (Youth), Nick White (Horsham), Phil Barber (Carshalton Ath), Declan Perkins (Braintree T), Lee Macken (Youth)

FORWARDS: Peter Garland (Crawley T), Bobby George (Whyteleafe), Matt Fowler (Carshalton Ath), Paul Scott (Hendon)

ENFIELD

CLUB OFFICIALS

Chairman: **A Lazarou**
President: **R.Prosser**
Secretary: **Roger Reed,**
16 College G/dens, Enfield, Middx EN2 0QF
Tel: 0181 350 4064
Press Officer: **John Jefferson**
Tel 01656 784550

FOOTBALL MANAGEMENT TEAM

Manager: Jim Chandler
Physio: Steve Gracie
Coaches: Eddie Jones/ Peter Hammett

FACT FILE
Formed: 1893
Nickname: The E's
Sponsors: Enfield Gazette & Advertiser
Newsline: 0930 555845
Colours: White/blue/white
Change colours: Blue/white/blue
Midweek matchday: Tuesday
Reserves' League: Middlesex Co.
1999-00: Captain Wayne Brown
P.O.Y.: Lee Protheroe
Top Scorer: Danny Jones

versus
HAMPTON FC
Saturday 6 May 2000
at Hendon FC
Kick off 3pm

Pages: 48 Price: £1.50
Editor: Steven Edwards
Local Press: Enfield Gazette,
Enfield Advertiser, Enfield Independent

GROUND: Boreham Wood FC.
Meadow Park, Broughinge Rd, Boreham Wood,Herts WD6 5AL (020 8953 5097)
Directions: A1 towards London from M25, 1st turn for Boreham Wood, head for town centre,
into Brook Rd at r'bout before town centre, Broughinge Rd is 1st right. 1 mile from Elstree &
Boreham Wood station (Thameslink),or bus 292 or107 to McDonalds (5 minutes walk)
Capacity: 4,502 **Cover:** 1,568 **Seats:** 500 **Floodlights:** Yes
Club Shop: Yes, contact Dave Hicks 01992 769156 or Alan Farmer 0181 366 6066

PREVIOUS **Leagues**: Tottenham & Dist 1894-95; Nth Middx 96-1903; London 03-13 20-21; Middx 08-12, 19-20;
Athenian 12-14 21-39 45-63; Herts & Middx Comb 39-42; Isthmian 63-81; GMV Conference 81-90
Name: Enfield Spartans 1893-1900 **Grounds:** Baileys Field 1893-96; Tuckers Field 96-1900; Cherry Orchard Lane1900-36
CLUB RECORDS Attendance: 10,000 (10/10/62) v Spurs, floodlight opener   Southerby Road 1936-1999
Win: 18-0 v Stevenage FA Cup 2nd Qual 22/10/27 (H) **Defeat:** 0-12 v Woolwich Polytechnic, London Lge Div 2 27/4/04
Fee Paid: for Gary Abbott (Barnet) **Fee Received:** for Paul Furlong (Coventry City)
Scorer: Tommy Lawrence, 191 1959-1964. **Appearances:** Steve King 617 (77-89)
BEST SEASON **FA Amateur Cup:** Winners 66-7 69-70 R-up 63-4 71-2 **FA Trophy:** Winners 81-2 87-8
FA Cup: 4th Rd replay 80-81, 0-3 v Barnsley (at Spurs), Att 35,244, after 1-1.
League clubs beaten: Wimbledon, Northampton 77-78, Hereford, Port Vale 80-81, Wimbledon 81-82, Exeter 84-85,
Orient 88-89, Aldershot 91-92, Cardiff City 94-95, Torquay Utd 94-95, Chesterfield 99-00
HONOURS: Alliance Premier Lge 82-83 85-86 (R-up 81-82), Lg Cup R-up 81-82; IsthmianLg(8) 67-70 75-78 79-80 94-95 (R-up 64-65 71-
72 74-75 80-81 90-92 95-96), LgCup(2) 78-80 (R-up 91-92 94-95); Athenian Lg(2) 61-63 (R-up 34-35); London LgDiv 1 11-12
(R-up 04-05 06-07); Middx Snr Cup 13-14 46-47 61-62 65-66 68-71 77-81 88-89 90-91 97-98, (R-up 10-11 20-21 47-48 51-52
57-60 62-63 66-67 72-73 75-76 84-85); London Snr Cup 34-35 60-61 66-67 71-73 75-76 (R-up 63-64 67-68 70-71); Middx Lg
(West) 09-10 (R-up 10-11); European Amtr Cup Winners Cup 69-70
Players progressing: Terry McQuade (Millwall 61), Roger Day (Watford 61), Jeff Harris (Orient 64), Peter Feely (Chelsea 70), Carl Richards & Jon
Bailey (B'mouth 80 & 95), Paul Furlong (Coventry 91), Andy Pape (Barnet 91), GregHeald (Peterborough 94), Lee Marshall (Norwich City 97)

Enfield visit Farnborough Town
in the Ryman Premier league.
Photo: Ian Morsman

Match Facts 1999-00

	Date	Comp.	H/A	Opponents	Att.	Result	Goalscorers	
1	14.08	RYM P	A	Carshalton Athletic	423	D 2 - 2	Jones 35(p), Brown 79	
2	17.08	RYM P	H	HEYBRIDGE SWIFTS	281	W 3 - 2	Jones 8(p), 13, Southgate 58	
3	21.08	RYM P	H	DULWICH HAMLET	395	W 3 - 2	Morris 49, Bunn 63, Jones 70(p)	
4	24.08	RYM P	A	Harrow Borough	307	W 2 - 1	Morgan 12, Morris 39	
5	28.08	RYM P	A	Farnborough Town	744	D 1 - 1	Jones 66	
6	30.08	RYM P	H	AYLESBURY UNITED	458	W 3 - 1	Bunn 7, Jones 40(p), Annon 65	
7	04.09	RYM P	H	HENDON	467	W 5 - 3	Cooper 3, Bunn 24, 50, Jones 32, Southgate 34	
8	07.09	RYM P	A	Gravesend & Northfleet	449	W 2 - 1	Dunwell 69, Jones 70	
9	11.09	RYM P	A	BASINGSTOKE TOWN	623	W 2 - 0	Bunn 14, Tomlinson 82	
	14.09	LC 1	H	BARTON ROVERS	222	L 1 - 2	Cooper	
	18.09	FAC 2Q	A	Soham Town Rangers	512	W 3 - 1	Protheroe (2), Dunwell	
10	25.09	RYM P	A	Dagenham & Redbridge	1200	L 0 - 4		
	03.10	FAC Q3	H	BILLERICAY TOWN	358	W 2 - 0	Cooper, Brown	at St. Albans City
11	09.10	RYM P	H	WALTON & HERSHAM	214	W 4 - 1	Bunn 20, Rattray 31, Dunwell 45, Cooper 62	at Hendon
	16.10	FAC Q4	H	BALDOCK TOWN	450	D 1 - 1	Jones 73	at St. Albans City
	19.10	FAC Q4 R	A	Baldock Town	610	D *2 - 2	Bunn 16, 18 Won 4-3 after penalties	
12	23.10	RYM P	A	Boreham Wood	481	L 0 - 1		
	30.10	FAC 1	A	Chesterfield	2506	W 2 - 1	Bunn 23, Brown 67	
13	06.11	RYM P	A	Canvey Island	1005	L 0 - 1		
14	09.11	RYM P	A	Chesham United	397	L 0 - 1		
15	13.11	RYM P	H	ALDERSHOT TOWN	472	L 1 - 4	Dunwell 90	at St. Albans City
	16.11	FMC 2	A	Hitchin Town	148	L 1 - 2	Deadman	
	20.11	FAC 2	A	Preston North End	11,566	D 0 - 0		
	27.11	FAT 2	H	NEWPORT IOW	273	D 2 - 2	Dunwell 19 47	at St. Albans City
	30.11	FAC 2 R	A	Preston North End	1,808	L 0 - 3		at St. Albans City
16	04.12	RYM P	H	GRAVESEND & NORTHFLEET	232	L 0 - 1		at St. Albans City
	07.12	FAT 2 R	A	Newport IOW	386	L 0 - 1		
17	14.12	RYM P	A	Hampton & Richmond Borough	139	L 1 - 2	McDonald 50	
18	18.12	RYM P	H	CANVEY ISLAND	187	D 1 - 1	Dunwell 47	at St. Albans City
19	27.12	RYM P	A	St Albans City	1780	L 0 - 5		
20	03.01	RYM P	H	HITCHIN TOWN	243	D 1 - 1	Morris 15	at St. Albans City
21	08.01	RYM P	A	Hendon	448	D 2 - 2	Cooper 40, Rattray 68	
	11.01	M SC 2	A	WEMBLEY	93	W 2 - 0	Jones (2)	at Brimsdown Rovers
22	15.01	RYM P	A	Dulwich Hamlet	556	D 0 - 0		
23	22.01	RYM P	H	CARSHALTON ATHLETIC	114	W 3 - 2	Alleyne 35, Tomlinson 65, Morgan 89	at Hendon
24	29.01	RYM P	A	Heybridge Swifts	403	L 1 - 2	Jones 90[p]	
	01.02	MSC QF	A	Harrow Borough	147	W 2 - 0	Jones(2)	
25	05.02	RYM P	H	HARROW BOROUGH	168	L 0 - 3		at Hendon
26	12.02	RYM P	H	Aylesbury United	614	L 0 - 1		
27	19.02	RYM P	H	FARNBOROUGH TOWN	203	W 3 - 0	Protheroe 31, Samuels 61, Morris 76	at Hendon
28	22.02	RYM P	H	PURFLEET	165	L 1 - 2	Dunwell 70	at Boreham Wood
29	26.02	RYM P	A	Walton & Hersham	246	W 2 - 0	Alleyne 45, Morgan 82	
30	04.03	RYM P	H	CHESHAM UNITED	220	D 2 - 2	Cooper 25, Jones 55	at Boreham Wood
31	12.03	RYM P	H	DAGENHAM & REDBRIDGE	482	D 1 - 1	Brown 72	at Boreham Wood
32	14.03	RYM P	H	BILLERICAY TOWN	168	D 1 - 1	Brown 28	at Boreham Wood
33	18.03	RYM P	A	Basingstoke Town	546	L 1 - 2	Clark 39	
34	21.03	RYM P	A	Slough Town	406	L 1 - 2	Brown 10	
35	25.03	RYM P	A	Billericay Town	527	D 0 - 0		
36	01.04	RYM P	H	BOREHAM WOOD	174	D 1 - 1	Okita 88	at Bishop's Stortford
37	08.04	RYM P	A	Hitchin Town	507	L 1 - 2	Jones 77 (p)	
38	15.04	RYM P	H	SLOUGH TOWN	204	L 1 - 3	Livett 76	at Hendon
39	22.04	RYM P	A	Aldershot Town	2038	W 4 - 0	Morgan 29, Bunn 60, 84, Rattray 67	
40	28.04	RYM P	A	Purfleet	332	L 2 - 4	Jones 37 (p), Bunn 69	
41	02.05	RYM P	H	ST. ALBANS CITY	235	W 4 - 0	Morris 4, 73, Bunn 6, 76	at Boreham Wood
42	06.05	RYM P	H	HAMPTON & RICHMOND B.	176	L 2 - 3	Bunn 5, Jones 63 (p)	at Hendon

PLAYING SQUAD

GOALKEEPERS: Jereme John (Kingstonian), Ian Mitchell (Cambridge U)

DEFENDERS: Wayne Brown (Kingstonian), David McDonald (Boreham Wood), Jay Devereux (Ford U), Lee Francis (Hertford T), John Morgan (Youth), Grant Cooper (Youth), Jamie Morris (Youth)

MIDFIELDERS: Adam Gant (Youth), Kevin Rattray (Kingstonian), Jason Geraghty (Leyton Pennant), Glen Southam (Fulham), Bryan Hammatt (Slough T)

FORWARDS: James Bunn (Spurs), David Flemming (Carshalton Ath), **Leroy May** (Hereford U), Danny Alleyne (Youth), Jean-Marie Okita (Haringey B), Danny Jones (Youth), Julian Capone (Bedford T)

FARNBOROUGH TOWN

v. Billericay Town
Ryman League Premier Division, Saturday, 6 May 2000
Official Matchday Programme £1.00

CLUB OFFICIALS

President: **Charles Mortimer**
Chairman: **Graham Westley**
Exec Directors: **Matthew Mills & Ron Berry**
Non Executive Directors : **Tony McAleese &**
John Thridgould
Football Secretary: **Vince Williams**
Tel: 01252 522161
Commercial Consultant: **Graham Willis**
Tel: 01924 266393
Press Officer: **David Hughes**
Tel: 01276 28354

FACT FILE

Founded: 1967
Nickname: The "Boro"
Club Sponsor: AMITA Corporation
Club Colours: Red & White
Change colours: Yellow & Blue
Midweek matchday: Tuesday
Reserves' League: Suburban (Premier Div.)
Club Newsline:09068 400224
1999-00
Top Goalscorer: Steve Darlington
P.o.Y.: Steve Darlington

FOOTBALL MANAGEMENT TEAM

Manager: Graham Westley   **Coach:** Graham Pearce   **Physio:** Jim Brown

GROUND   John Roberts Ground, Cherrywood Road, Farnborough, Hampshire GU14 8UD
Tel: 01252 541469 Fax: 01252 375613
Directions: M3 exit 4, A325 towards Farnborough, right into Prospect Ave. (club signposted),
2nd right into Cherrywood Rd, ground on right. 20-30 min walk fromFarnborough Main,
Farnborough North and Frimley BR stations. Whippet mini-bus 19 No12 Bus passes ground.
Capacity: 4,900   Seated: 627   Covered Terracing: 1,350
Clubhouse: Open during normal pub hours and matchdays. Hot pies, bar meals, crisps etc.
Club Shop: Boro' Leisurewear shop - all types of club leisurewear and matchballs (contact
Graham Willis - 01924 266393)
Supporters Club shop: Old programmes, scarves, badges etc (contact Paul Doe).

Pages: 40   Price: £1.00
Editor: Jane White
Other club publications:
"Simon Read's Haircut" (fanzine)

Local Press: Farnborough News
Local Radio: BBC Southern Counties
County Sound

PREVIOUS   **Leagues:** Surrey Senior 68-72; Spartan 72-76; Athenian 76-77; Isthmian 77-89; Alliance Premier (Conference) 89-90 91-93 94-99; Southern 90-91 93-94.   **Grounds:** Queens Road, Farnborough (1969-1976)

CLUB RECORDS   **Attendance:** 3,581 v Brentford 22/11/95 (FA Cup).
Win: 11-0 v Chertsey Town (H), Spartan League 72-73   **Defeat:** 2-10 v Worplesdon (H), Surrey Senior Lge Div. 1 68-69
Career Goalscorer: Simon Read 209, 1986-1994   **Career Appearances:** Brian Broome 529, 1980-1994
Season Goalscorer: Simon Read 53, 1988-89.
Transfer Fee Paid: £10,000 to Kingstonian for David Harlow December 1994.
Transfer Fee Received: £50,000 from Dover Athletic for David Leworthy, August1993

BEST SEASON   **FA Cup:** 3rd Rd Proper replay 91-92, 0-1 v West Ham U. (A) after 1-1
League clubs defeated: Torquay Utd 91-92   **FA Trophy:** Quarter Final 92-93   **FA Vase:** Semi-Final 75-76 76-77

HONOURS   Southern Lg 90-91 93-94, Isthmian Lg R-up 88-89 (Div 1 84-85, Div 2 78-79),Athenian Lg Div 2 78-79, Spartan Lg 72-73 73-74 74-75 (Lg Cup 74-75), LondonSpartan Lg 75-76 (Lg Cup 75-76), Hants Snr Cup 74-75 81-82 83-84 85-86 90-91(R-up 93-94)

Players progressing: Dennis Bailey (Crystal Palace), Paul Mortimer (Charlton Athletic), Tommy Jones (Aberdeen), Allan Cockram (Brentford), Paul Holsgrove (Millwall), Maik Taylor (Barnet), Martin Rowlands (Brentford)

Back Row: Ian Baird, Richard Horner, Mark Harper, Danny Coleman, Graham Benstead (gk coach), Stuart MacKenzie, Bruno Mendonca, Barry Laker, Keith Dublin. **Middle:** Jim Brown (physio), Michael Warner, Tony Taggert, Jordan Fastnedge, Lee Riddell, Graham Pearce (1st team coach), Scott Corbett, Scott Bennetts, Steve Darlington, Ron Berry (back room man.). **Front:** Justin Gregory, Gary Crawshaw, Jimmy Dack, Steve Watson, Graham Westley (manager/chairman), Lenny Piper, Darren Annon, Danny Yeoman, Nick Hooper. **Photo:** Eric Marsh

Match Facts 1999-00

	Date	Comp.	H/A	Opponents	Att.	Result	Goalscorers
1	14.08	RYM P	H	BASINGSTOKE TOWN	942	W 3 - 0	Darlington 61 80, Warner 90
2	17.08	RYM P	A	Boreham Wood	285	D 1 - 1	Darlington 28
3	21.08	RYM P	A	Hampton & Richmond Borough	377	L 0 - 1	
4	24.08	RYM P	H	DAGENHAM & REDBRIDGE	616	W 2 - 1	Darlington 62, Dublin 69
5	28.08	RYM P	H	ENFIELD	744	D 1 - 1	Warner 69
6	30.08	RYM P	A	Walton & Hersham	442	D 0 - 0	
7	04.09	RYM P	A	Hitchin Town	419	D 1 - 1	Darlington 59
8	07.09	RYM P	H	SLOUGH TOWN	713	L 0 - 1	
9	11.09	RYM P	H	AYLESBURY UNITED	512	W 3 - 1	Kuhl 68, Mendonca 82, Darlington 90
	14.09	LC 1	H	YEADING	265	W 2 - 0	Watson, Ansah
	18.09	FAC 2Q	A	Tonbridge Angels	606	W 2 - 0	Darlington 14, Ansah 53
10	25.09	RYM P	A	Harrow Borough	405	W 3 - 1	Kuhl 12[p], Mendonca 45, Corbett 74
	02.10	FAC Q3	A	Bath City	890	L 1 - 3	Mendonca 72
11	09.10	RYM P	H	CANVEY ISLAND	577	L 1 - 2	Ansah 58
12	19.10	RYM P	H	PURFLEET	374	D 1 - 1	Corbett 20
13	23.10	RYM P	A	Heybridge Swifts	233	W 2 - 1	Darlington 30, Dublin 47
	25.10	FMC1	A	Dulwich Hamlet	161	W 3 - 0	Endersby 19, Mendonca 25, Darlington 56
14	30.10	RYM P	H	CARSHALTON ATHLETIC	554	W 4 - 1	Mendonca 3 18, Dublin 9 89
	02.11	Hants SC2	H	BOURNEMOUTH	151	W 3 - 0	Darlington 12, Mendonca 13, Warner 48
15	06.11	RYM P	A	Gravesend & Northfleet	444	L 1 - 5	Mendonca 69
	09.11	LC 2	A	Hitchin Town		D *3 - 3	Darlington, Mendonca, Codnor
16	14.11	RYM P	H	HENDON	497	L 0 - 1	
	16.11	FMC 2	A	Croydon	72	L 0 - 3	
17	20.11	RYM P	H	Billericay Town	583	W 3 - 0	Darlington 28 85, Mendonca 88
	27.11	FAT 2	A	Tiverton Town	842	W 4 - 0	Mendonca 57 79, Darlington 59 90
18	04.12	RYM P	H	HITCHIN TOWN	547	D 1 - 1	Bennett 60
19	11.12	RYM P	A	Chesham United	440	L 1 - 2	Darlington 19
	15.12	Hants SC 3	H	WEST WIGHT MAYFLOWER	95	W 4 - 2	Ansah (3), Westley
20	18.12	RYM P	H	GRAVESEND & NORTHFLEET	453	W 3 - 2	Watson 52 88, Darlington 59
	21.12	LC 3	A	Aldershot Town	2682	W 2 - 1	Kuhl 29, Warner 110
21	27.12	RYM P	A	Aldershot Town	5518	L 0 - 1	
22	03.01	RYM P	H	ST ALBANS CITY	693	W 1 - 0	Watson 27
23	08.01	RYM P	A	Slough Town	707	W 2 - 1	Dublin 36, Omigie 51
	15.01	FAT 3	A	Carshalton Athletic	392	W 1 - 0	Warner 69
	18.01	H SC QF	H	HARTLEY WINTNEY	200	L 0 - 1	
24	22.01	RYM P	A	Basingstoke Town	748	D 2 - 2	Omigie 24, Darlington 41
	25.01	LC QF	H	HEYBRIDGE SWIFTS	198	L 2 - 7	Carruth 19, Darlington 31
25	29.01	RYM P	H	BOREHAM WOOD	484	L 0 - 2	
	05.02	FAT 4	A	Telford United	944	L 1 - 2	Darlington 59
26	15.02	RYM P	H	HAMPTON & RICHMOND B.	229	L 0 - 1	
27	19.02	RYM P	A	Enfield	203	L 0 - 3	
28	26.02	RYM P	H	DULWICH HAMLET	430	W 2 - 0	Darlington 4, Kuhl 48[p]
29	04.03	RYM P	A	Purfleet	216	L 0 - 4	
	07.03	LC SF(1)	A	Barton Rovers	152	D 1 - 1	Darlington
30	11.03	RYM P	H	HARROW BOROUGH	409	D 0 - 0	
	14.03	LC SF(2)	H	BARTON ROVERS	232	W 2 - 0	Darlington 58 80
31	18.03	RYM P	A	Aylesbury United	515	W 2 - 1	Horner 4, Darlington 18
32	22.03	RYM P	H	WALTON & HERSHAM	296	L 1 - 2	Mendonca 90[p]
33	25.03	RYM P	A	Carshalton Athletic	311	D 1 - 1	Darlington 42
34	01.04	RYM P	H	HEYBRIDGE SWIFTS	287	L 0 - 1	
35	04.04	RYM P	A	Dagenham & Redbridge	844	L 2 - 3	Jones 5, Darlington 59
36	08.04	RYM P	A	St. Albans City	425	D 0 - 0	
37	17.04	RYM P	A	Dulwich Hamlet	251	W 3 - 1	Darlington 7, Watson 25, B Mendonca 74 (p)
38	22.04	RYM P	A	Hendon	233	L 3 - 5	Darlington 1, James 41, Mendonca 66
39	24.04	RYM P	H	ALDERSHOT TOWN	1524	D 0 - 0	
40	26.04	RYM P	H	CHESHAM UNITED	202	L 0 - 1	
41	29.04	RYM P	A	Canvey Island	278	L 0 - 2	
	01.05	LC Final	A	Maidenhead United	701	W *1 - 0	Dublin 92
42	06.05	RYM P	H	BILLERICAY TOWN	407	W 2 - 0	Darlington 83, Hooper 90

PLAYING SQUAD

GOALKEEPERS: Stuart Mackenzie (Yeading), Danny Coleman (Brentford)

DEFENDERS: Barry Laker (Sutton U), Keith Dublin (Canvey Is), Justinm Gregory (Dulwich Hamlet), Tony Taggert (Brentford), Richard Horner (Wealdstone), Mark Harper (Sutton U), Tim O'Shea (Instant Dict (HK))

MIDFIELDERS: Steve Watson (Sutton U), Darran Annon (Enfield), Lennie Piper (St.Albans C), Scott Bennetts (Youth), Jimmy Dack (Sutton U), Scott Corbett (Kingstonian)

FORWARDS: **Lee Endersby** (Slough T), Steve Darlington (Enfield), Gary Crawshaw (Aylesbury U), Danny Yeoman (Northwood), Michael Warner (Northampton), Nick Hooper (Southampton)

GRAVESEND & NORTHFLEET

CLUB OFFICIALS

Chairman: Peter Dean

Secretary: Roly Edwards
c/o Football Club

Press Officer: Paul Cossom
Tel: 01474 533796

FOOTBALL MANAGEMENT TEAM
Manager: Andy Ford
Assistant Manager: Phil Handford
Physio: Martin Allen

FACT FILE

Formed: 1946
Nickname: The Fleet
Sponsors: Scartruck Ltd
Colours: Red/white/red
Change colours: All blue
Midweek matchday: Tuesday
Reserves' League : London Suburban Lg

1999-00
Captain: Scortt Lindsey
P.o.Y.: Lee Spiller
Top Scorer: Che Stadhart

Pages: 32 Price: £1.50
Editor: Paul Cossom
Local Press: Gravesend Reporter,
Kent Evening Post, Gravesend Extra,
Leader, The News Shopper
Local Radio: Invicta Radio, Radio Kent,
RTM, Medway FM

GROUND: Stonebridge Road, Northfleet, Kent DA11 9BA Tel: 01474 533796
Directions: From A2 take Northfleet/Southfleet exit (B262), follow to Northfleet then B2175 (Springhead Rd) to junc A226, turn left (The Hill, Northfleet), road becomes Stonebridge Rd, grd on right at bottom of steep hill after 1 mile - car parking for 400-500. 2 mins from Northfleet BR station
Capacity: 3,300 Cover: 2,200 Seats: 600 Floodlights: Yes
Clubhouse: Fleet Social Centre. Hot and cold food available at tea bars on matchdays
Club Shop: Sells progs, hats, scarves, badges etc, & other memorabilia.
Contact John Still or Angela Still

PREVIOUS **Leagues:** Kent (Gravesend Utd), Southern 46-79, Alliance Prem. 79-80
Names: Gravesend Utd, Northfleet Utd (merged 1946)
Ground: Central Avenue (Gravesend Utd) (Northfleet always played at Stonebridge Rd)
CLUB RECORDS Attendance: 12,036 v Sunderland, FA Cup 4th Rd 12.2.63. 26.081 v Aston Villa FA Cup 3rd Rd 95-96 at Villa Park
Goalscorer (career): Steve Portway 150+ (92-94, 97-present) **Appearances:** Ken Burrett 537
Win: 8-1 v Clacton Tn, Sth Lge 62-63, 7-0 Godalming 95-96 FAC. **Defeat:** 0-9 v Trowbridge Tn, Southern Lge Prem Div 91-92
Fee Paid: £8,000 for Richard Newbery (Wokingham 96), £8,000 for Craig Williams (Tonbridge 97)
Fee Received: £35,000 for Jimmy Bullard (West Ham 1998)
BEST SEASON FA Cup: 4th Rd Replay 1963, 2-5 v Sunderland (A), 1-1 (H) **FA Trophy:** 3rd Rd 88-89 , 99-00
HONOURS: Southern Lg 57-58, Southern Div 94-95, Div 1 Sth 74-75 (R-up 70-71 88-89), Lg Cup 77-78 (R-up 57-58), Champ Cup 77-78;
Kent Sen Cup Winners 48-49 52-53 80-81, 99-00 (R-up 47-48 76-77 90-91 97-98); Kent Floodlit Cup 69-70 (R-up 72-73); Kent
Sen Shield R-up 47-48 51-52; Kent Interm Cup R-up 87-88; Kent Midweek Lg 95-96, R-up 92-93 93-94 94-95; Kent Youth Lg
Cup 82-83 86-87 96-97; Kent Youth Lg 95-96 96-97; John Ullman Cup 82-83
Players progressing: Several incl. most recently: K Baron (Aldershot 60), R Dwight (Coventry 62), R Cameron (Southend 63),
R McNichol (Carlisle 65), A Humphreys (Mansfield 64), B Thornley (Brentford 65), P Jeavons (Lincoln 66), B Fry (Orient 66),
B Gordine (Sheffield Utd 68), T Baldwin (Brentford 77), L Smelt (Nottm Forest 80), T Warrilow (Torquay 87), J.Bullard (W.H.U.98)

Back Row: Martin Allen (physio), Darren Gowler, Craig Wilkins, Darren Smith, Scott Tarr, Micky Desborough, Paul Booth, Corey Campbell, Bruce Sewell. Middle: Nigel Donn (Res. manager0, Phil Handford (Asst. manager), Don Turner (kit), Vinny Tam, Darren Smith, Dave Powell, Justin Skinner, Paul Wilson, Kirk Dodgson, Andy Ford (manager). Front: Matt Chaplin, Simon Elliott, Nick Hegley, Luke Anderson, Ross Edwards, Mitchell Crawley, Lee Spiller, Jimmy Jackson, Scott Honeyball.

Match Facts 1999-00

	Date	Comp.	H/A	Opponents	Att.	Result	Goalscorers
1	14.08	RYM P	H	CANVEY ISLAND	639	L 0 - 1	
2	17.08	RYM P	A	Aldershot Town	1921	L 1 - 2	Powell 52
3	21.08	RYM P	A	Chesham United	273	D 1 - 1	Powell 10
4	24.08	RYM P	H	HAMPTON & RICHMOND B.	362	D 0 - 0	
5	28.08	RYM P	H	SLOUGH TOWN	462	W 1 - 0	Campbell 66
6	30.08	RYM P	A	Hitchin Town	430	L 0 - 1	
7	04.09	RYM P	H	WALTON & HERSHAM	335	D 1 - 1	Honeyball 87
8	07.09	RYM P	H	ENFIELD	449	L 1 - 2	Sewell 26
9	11.09	RYM P	A	Billericay Town	519	D 3 - 3	Hegley 6, 36, Sewell 37
	14.09	LC 1	H	HENDON	148	L 1 - 2	
	18.09	FAC 2Q	H	FISHER ATHLETIC	316	D 1 - 1	Wilkins 58
	21.09	FAC 2QR	A	Fisher Athletic	183	L 1 - 2	Cooper 53
10	25.09	RYM P	H	ST ALBANS CITY	495	L 1 - 2	Jackson 24
	09.10	FAT 1	A	Bishop's Stortford	372	W 3 - 1	Cooper (2), Powell
11	16.10	RYM P	A	Purfleet	257	D 0 - 0	
12	23.10	RYM P	H	BASINGSTOKE TOWN	369	W 1 - 0	Cooper 16
13	30.10	RYM P	H	BILLERICAY TOWN	401	D 2 - 2	Sewell 3, Wilkins 23
14	06.11	RYM P	H	FARNBOROUGH TOWN	444	W 5 - 1	**Hegley 3** (25 60 90), Powell 33, Stadhart 68
15	12.11	RYM P	A	Heybridge Swifts	202	W 4 - 2	Powell 10 74, Hegley 56 83
	16.11	FMC 2	A	Braintree Town	131	W 5 - 2	
16	20.11	RYM P	H	AYLESBURY UNITED	438	W 5 - 0	Spiller 7 53, Stadhart 11, Jackson 16, Hegley 75
	23.11	Kent SC 1	A	Erith & Belvedere	137	D 3 - 3	Stadhart 15, Driscoll 23, Spiller 65
	27.11	FAT 2	H	WORTHING	371	W 2 - 0	Campbell, Stadhart
17	29.11	RYM P	A	Carshalton Athletic	223	W 2 - 1	Hegley 39, 40
18	04.12	RYM P	A	Enfield	232	W 1 - 0	Stadhart 41
19	11.12	RYM P	H	BOREHAM WOOD	425	W 3 - 0	Restarick 13, Powell 33 80
20	14.12	RYM P	H	HARROW BOROUGH	340	W 4 - 1	Stadhart 19 33, Powell 49, Restarick 55
21	18.12	RYM P	A	Farnborough Town	453	L 2 - 3	Anderson 23, Powell 39
	21.12	K SC 1R	A	ERITH & BELVEDERE	165	W 4 - 2	Restarick 5 42, Gowler 94[p], Stadhart 107
22	27.12	RYM P	H	DULWICH HAMLET	886	W 3 - 1	Campbell 44[p] 56[p], Restarick 90
23	03.01	RYM P	A	Dagenham & Redbridge	1332	L 1 - 2	Stadhart 1
24	08.01	RYM P	A	Walton & Hersham	255	D 2 - 2	Restarick 21, Anderson 66
	15.01	FAT 3	H	DOVER ATHLETIC	1265	D 1 - 1	Restarick 57
	18.01	FAT 3R	A	Dover Athletic	1059	L 1 - 2	Stadhart 48
25	22.01	RYM P	H	Canvey Island	511	L 1 - 4	Powell 25
	25.01	FMC 3	H	WEALDSTONE	136	W 3 - 1	Powell 23 71, Stadhart 90
26	29.01	RYM P	H	ALDERSHOT TOWN	880	D 1 - 1	Jackson 85
	01.02	K SC QF	H	FISHER ATHLETIC	202	W 4 - 0	Dunwell 24, Stadhart 45 70, Saunders 90[og]
27	05.02	RYM P	A	Hampton & Richmond Borough	244	L 0 - 1	
28	07.02	RYM P	A	Hendon	183	L 0 - 2	
29	12.02	RYM P	H	HITCHIN TOWN	458	D 1 - 1	Gowler 74
30	19.02	RYM P	A	Slough Town	455	L 1 - 2	Grime 22
31	22.02	RYM P	H	CHESHAM UNITED	347	W 3 - 2	Restarick 14, Hegley 16, Jackson 42
32	26.02	RYM P	H	PURFLEET	454	L 1 - 2	Stadhart 41
33	04.03	RYM P	A	Harrow Borough	188	L 0 - 6	
	07.03	FMC QF	A	SLOUGH TOWN	156	W 3 - 2	Campbell 22, Crispin 51[p], Stadhart 79
34	11.03	RYM P	A	St Albans City	520	W 1 - 0	Hegley 37
	14.03	FMC SF	H	CROYDON	213	L 1 - 2	Restarick[p]
35	25.03	RYM P	H	HENDON	374	W 1 - 0	Stadhart 9
	29.03	K SC SF	A	Dartford	403	D 0 - 0	
36	01.04	RYM P	A	Basingstoke Town	390	L 0 - 2	
37	08.04	RYM P	H	DAGENHAM & REDBRIDGE	836	L 1 - 2	Hegley 4
	29.03	K SC SF R	H	DARTFORD	388	W 1 - 0	Hegley 16
38	22.04	RYM P	H	HEYBRIDGE SWIFTS	369	D 1 - 1	Wilkins 17
39	24.04	RYM P	A	Dulwich Hamlet	332	W 5 - 1	Spiller 11, 63, OG (Garland) 70, Stadhart 80, Jackson 82
40	26.04	RYM P	A	Boreham Wood	228	W 4 - 3	Restarick 7, 59, Powell 62, Stadhart 90
41	29.04	RYM P	H	CARSHALTON ATHLETIC	389	L 0 - 5	
	29.03	K SC Final	H	FOLKESTONE INVICTA	880	W 3 - 0	Restarick (2), Stadhart
42	06.05	RYM P	A	Aylesbury United	1232	L 1 - 4	Restarick 25

PLAYING SQUAD

GOALKEEPERS: Colin Lewington (Dartford), Jamie Turner (Erith & Belvedere)

DEFENDERS: Aaron Barnett (Erith & B), Robbie White (Youth), Stewart Watts (Welling U), Mitchell Crawley (Dartford), Craig Wilkins (Tonbridge)

MIDFIELDERS: Nick Hegley (Coventry), Scott Lindsay (Canvey Is), Lee Spiller (Margate), Paul Malcolm (Dulwich Hamlet), Jimmy Jackson (Charlton)

FORWARDS: Paul Booth (Tunbridge Wells), Ian Walford (Youth), Steve Restarick (Purfleet), Pat Gwayameadde (Youth), Che Stadhart (Hampton & R)

GRAYS ATHLETIC

CLUB OFFICIALS

Chairman: **Frank Harris**
Secretary: **Jeff Saxton**
216 Thundersley Park Road,
South Benfleet, Essex SS71HP
Tel: 01268 756964
Press Officer: **Gordon Norman**
Tel: 014024 51733

FOOTBALL MANAGEMENT TEAM
Manager: Chris Snowsill
Asst Man.:Lee MalcolmPhysio: David Guthrie
Coach: Billy Gillman

FACT FILE

Formed: 1890
Nickname: The Blues
Sponsors: Harris Commercials
Colours: Royal & white
Change colours: Red/white
Midweek matchday: Tuesday

1999-00 Captain: Rikky Hazel
P.o.Y.:Mark Risley
Top Scorer: Vinny John

> **Grays Athletic
> Football Club**
>
> The Ryman Football League
> Division One
> SEASON 1999/2000
>
> Ryman
> football league
>
> Main sponsors:
> Harris Group of Companies
>
> Pages: 48 Price: £1
> Editor: Jeremy Mason (01375 400188)
>
> Local Press: Thurrock Gazette
> Local Radio: BBC Essex, Radio Essex

GROUND   Recreation Ground, Bridge Road, Grays RM17 6BZ (01375 391649)
Directions: Seven minutes walk from Grays station - turn right round one way system, right into Clarence Road, and at end into Bridge Road. Bus No. 370. By road - A13 towards Southend from London, take Grays exit and follow signs to town centre, keep left on one-way system, continue up hill for about 1/2 mile, turn right into Bridge Road, ground 1/2 mile on right
Capacity: 4,500   Cover: 1,200   Seats: 300   Floodlights: Yes
Clubhouse: Bar, pool, darts, bar snacks available. Indoor sports hall.
          Stewardess: Sue Riley (01375 377753)
Club Shop: Sells `The First Hundred Years', sweaters, T-shirts, replica shirts, scarves, ties, etc.
          Contact Bill Grove 01375 391649

PREVIOUS   **Leagues:** Athenian 12-14, 58-83; London 14-24, 26-39; Kent 24-26; Corinthian 45-58

CLUB RECORDS **Attendance:** 9,500 v Chelmsford City, FA Cup 4th Qual. Round 1959
          Win: 12-0 v Tooting (H) London Lge 24/2/23   **Defeat:** 0-12 v Enfield (A) Athenian Lge 20/4/63
          Goalscorer: Harry Brand 269 (1944-52)   **Appearances:** Phil Sammons, 673. 1982-97
          Fee Paid: For Ian Durant (Canvey Island 85)
          Fee Received: Undisclosed for Tony Witter (C. Palace), Dwight Marshall(Plymouth 1991) and Matthew Lawrence(Wycombe W)

BEST SEASON   **FA Cup:** 1st Rd 51-52 88-89   **FA Trophy:** 3rd Rd 92-93   **FA Amateur Cup:** 3rd Rd 63-64

HONOURS   Isthmian Div 1 R-up 87-88 ,99-00(Div 2 Sth 84-85, Lg Cup 91-92); Athenian Lg R-up 82-83, Res. Sect. R-up 58-59 (Cup R-up 59-60); Corinthian Lg 45-46 (R-up 51-52 54-55 56-57), Lg Cup(2) 45-47, Mem. Shield(4) ; Essex Snr Cup 8(R-up 9; Essex SenTr 98-99; East Anglian Cup 44-45 (R-up 43-44 54-55); Essex Thameside Tphy x6 (R-up 7); Essex Elizabeth Tphy 76-77 (R-up 65-66); Claridge Tphy 87-88 88-89; Mithras Cup 79-80; Essex Int Cup(3) 56-57 58-60 (Jun Cup 19-20 R-up 58-59); Essex & Herts ,Border Comb. East 87-88 (Ancillary Cup 78-79, Comb Cup 82-83); Fred Budden Tphy 86-87; Hornchurch Charity Cup 78-79 86-87; Neale Tphy 50-51; Ford Rate Tphy 83-84 85-86 87-88 (R-up 84-85 86-87); Stan Veness Mem. Tphy (8) 87-96

Players progressing: J Jordan (Spurs 47), R Kemp (Reading 49), B Silkman & TBanfield (Orient), G O'Reilly (Spurs), W Entwhistle (Bury 83), M Welch(Wimbledon 84), T Witter (C Palace 90), D Marshall (Plymouth 91), M Lawrence(Wycombe W. 96-97)

Vinnie John of Grays
Athletic heads his second
goal against Whyteleafe.
Photo: Alan Coomes

Match Facts 1999-00

Att.

	Date	Comp.	H/A	Opponents	Result	Goalscorers	
1	14.08	RYM 1	A	Staines Town	D 1-1	John	203
2	17.08	RYM 1	H	Bromley	W 5-0	Cox 3, Wilson, Risley	214
	21.08	FAC Pre	H	basildon United	W 7-1	John 4 (1p), Hayzelden, Risley, Nesling	193
3	24.08	RYM 1	A	Maidenhead United	L 1-3	Wilson	129
4	28.08	RYM 1	H	Wealdstone	L 0-1		266
5	30.08	RYM 1	A	Whyteleafe	W 5-0	John 2, Walker, Cox, Hayzelden	101
	04.09	FAC 1Q	A	Barking	W 1-0	John	183
6	07.09	RYM 1	H	Barton Rovers	W 4-1	Hazle, John, Wallace, Reilly	139
7	11.09	RYM 1	A	Oxford City	L 1-2	Hazle	131
	14.09	LC 1	A	Slough Town	L 0-1		222
	18.09	FAC 2Q	A	Hendon	L 0-2		201
8	25.09	RYM 1	H	Romford	W 2-1	Risley, John	227
9	02.10	RYM 1	A	Bishop's Stortford	W 1-0	John	369
10	16.10	RYM 1	H	Leatherhead	D 2-2	Wallace, John	198
11	23.10	RYM 1	A	Uxbridge	D 1-1	Wilson	82
	26.10	FMC 1	A	Barton Rovers	W 3-0	Johns 2, Wilson	85
12	30.10	RYM 1	H	Bedford Town	W 3-0	Hazle, John, Wilson	284
13	06.11	RYM 1	A	Harlow Town	D 4-4	John, Reilly, Nesling, Hayzelden	176
14	09.11	RYM 1	H	Worthing	W 3-1	John 2, Reilly	165
15	13.11	RYM 1	H	Thame United	L 0-2		159
	15.11	FMC 2	A	Harlow Town	W 5-1	John, Hayzelden 2, Reilly, Dickinson	115
16	20.11	RYM 1	A	Croydon	D 0-0		77
	23.11	Essex SC 3	A	Great Wakeing Rovers	W 4-2	Mosely, John2, Reilly	88
	27.11	FAT 2	A	Hendon	L 0-1		177
17	30.11	RYM 1	H	Chertsey Town	L 1-2	Hazle	137
18	04.12	RYM 1	H	Whyteleafe	W 4-1	**Reilly 4**	165
19	18.12	RYM 1	H	Yeading	D 1-1	Wallace	147
	21.12	E SC 4	H	Stanway Rovers	W 7-0	Twidell, Wilson 3, Hazle, Reilly, Nesling	46
20	27.12	RYM 1	A	Braintree Town	W 1-0	Reilly	350
21	03.01	RYM 1	H	Harlow Town	D 2-2	Wallace 2	271
22	08.01	RYM 1	A	Wealdstone	W 2-0	Wallace, Risley	332
	11.01	FMC 3	H	Purfleet	L *3-4	Reilly, Hazle, Wilson	157
23	15.01	RYM 1	A	Bognor Regis Town	W 3-1	Reilly, Risley, Dickinson	194
24	22.01	RYM 1	H	Maidenhead United	D 2-2	Wallace 2	211
	24.01	E SC 5	A	Purfleet	L 2-3	Wilson, Dickinson	105
25	29.01	RYM 1	A	Barton Rovers	W 2-0	Hayzelden, wallace	168
26	05.02	RYM 1	H	Staines Town	W 1-0	Risley	232
27	12.02	RYM 1	A	Worthing	D 1-1	Nesling	565
28	19.02	RYM 1	H	Oxford City	W 1-0	Nesling	218
29	22.02	RYM 1	A	Leyton Pennant	W 3-0	Hayzelden, Mosely, Wright	124
30	26.02	RYM 1	A	Leatherhead	W 3-1	Nesling, Wallace, Wright	152
31	04.03	RYM 1	H	Bognor Regis Town	D 0-0		238
32	11.03	RYM 1	H	Bishop's Stortford	L 1-3	Mosely	278
33	18.03	RYM 1	A	Romford	W 1-0	Hazle	181
34	25.03	RYM 1	A	Braintree Town	D 1-1	Mosely	350
35	01.04	RYM 1	H	Uxbridge	W 1-0	Hayzelden	188
36	08.04	RYM 1	A	Yeading	D 1-1	Wilson	105
37	18.04	RYM 1	H	Leyton Pennant	W 4-0	Hazle, Dickinson, Wright, Mosely	105
38	22.04	RYM 1	A	Thame United	L 1-2	Wright	282
39	24.04	RYM 1	H	Braintree Town	W 4-0	Wilson, Hazle, Hayzelden, Dickinson	236
40	29.04	RYM 1	A	Chertsey Town	L 1-2	Wallace	131
41	01.05	RYM 1	A	Bromley	W 2-1	Mosely, D Snowsill	371
42	06.05	RYM 1	H	Croydon	L 3-4	Mosely, D Snowsill, Wallace	259

PLAYING SQUAD

GOALKEEPERS: Ian Brooks (Leyton Pennant), Craig Tucker (Deal T)

DEFENDERS: Steve Dickinson (Canvey Is), Tolo Mas (Dag & Red), Jason Walker (Enfield), Mark Risley (Enfield), Ray Taylor (Romford), Steve Mosely (Purfleet)

MIDFIELDERS: Danny Hazelden (Hornchurch), Alan Brett (Canvey Is), Danny Snowsill (Purfleet), Donovan Wilson (Royal Tigers (SA)), Daren Twidell (Billericay T), Steve Blaney (Billericay T)

FORWARDS: Aaron Wright (East Thurrock U), Jamie Wallace (Dag & Red), Ricky Hazle (Barking), Jamie Reilly (East Thurrock U), Lee Snowsill (Aveley), Danny Hazle (Canvey Is)

HAMPTON & RICHMOND BOROUGH

CLUB OFFICIALS
Chairman: Victor Searle
President: Alan Simpson
Vice Chairman: Ken Gazzard
Press Officer: Les Rance
Secretary: Adrian Mann,
30 Burniston Court, Manor Rd, Wallington,
Surrey SM6 0AD (0208 773 0858)

FOOTBALL MANAGEMENT TEAM
Manager: Steve Cordery
Assistant Manager: Tony Coombe
Coach: Paul Shrubb
Physio: Gareth Workman

FACT FILE

Formed: 1920
Nickname: Beavers/Borough
Sponsors: Richmond Comet
Colours: Red & blue/white/blue
Change Colours: Tangerine/Blue/Blue
Midweek Matchday: Tuesday
Reserve Team's League: Suburban
1999-00
Captain: Jason Shaw
Top scorer: Craig Maskell
P.o.Y.: Nick Burton

The Official Matchday Programme of
HAMPTON & RICHMOND BOROUGH FC
Ryman League Premier Division
1999-2000 Season

Pages: 28 Price: £1.20p
Editor: Tony Nash
Local Press: Middx Chronicle, Surrey Comet, Richmond & Twickenham Times, The Informer

GROUND: Beveree Stadium, Beaver Close, off Station Rd, Hampton TW12 2BX
Tel: Office 020 8979 2456(matchdays only) Club: 020 8941 4936 Boardroom: 020 8941 2838
Directions: A3 out of London, fork left (signed Staines/Esher/Sandown Pk) onto A243, A309
Staines exit to Hampton Ct at `Scilly Isles' r'bout, left at r'bout after Hampton Court Bridge
onto A308, after 1 mile right into Church St (A311), left after White Hart after 200yds into High
St, Station Rd on right just before junction with A308
Capacity: 3,000 Seats: 300 Cover: 800 Floodlights: Yes
Clubhouse: (020 8979 2456). Lounge bar and hall, open on matchdays and training nights.
Hall available for hire. Steward: Steve Penny
Club Shop: Sells various souvenirs & prog. Contact Les Rance (020 887 4682)

PREVIOUS **Leagues:** Kingston & District 21-33; South West Middx 33-59; Surrey Snr 59-64; Spartan 64-71; Athenian 71-73
Grounds: Hatherop Rec (until 1959)
CLUB RECORDS **Win:** 11-1 v Eastbourne Utd, Isthmian Lge Div 2 (S), 90-91   **Defeat:** 0-13 v Hounslow Town, Middlesex Senior Cup 62-63
Goalscorer: Peter Allen (176) 1964-73   **Appearances:** Tim Hollands (700) 1977-95
Fees - Paid: £1,500 for Danny Smith (Kingstonian) Nov 99.
Fees - Received: £25,000 for Julian Charles (Brentford) Dec 99.
BEST SEASON **FA Cup:** 4th Qual Rd 77-78 (1-2 v Barnet)   **FA Amateur Cup:** 1st Rd Prop 73-74 (2-4 v Leytonstone)
FA Trophy: 1st Rd Prop 83-84 (0-2 v Maidstone Utd)
FA Vase: 3rd Rd 91-92 (0-1 v Newport IOW), 95-96 (0-1 v Colllier Row)
HONOURS: London Snr Cup(2) 86-88; Spartan Lg(4) 64-67 69-70, (R-up 67-68), Lg Cup(4) 64-68 (R-up 2); Surrey Snr Lg 63-64 (Lg Cup
R-up 60-61); Middx Charity Cup 69-70 95-96 97-98,98-99 (R-up 68-69 71-72 89-90 94-95); Middx Snr Cup R-up 71-72 76-77
95-96; Athenian Lg Div 2 R-up 72-73; Southern Comb. Cup 68-69 71-72 76-77 81-82 83-84 85-86 96-97 (R-up 77-78 79-80 97-
98); Isthmian Lge promotion from Div 1 97-98, Div 2 95-96, Div 3 91-92
Players progressing: Andy Rogers (Southampton), Dwight Marshall (Plymouth), Paul Rogers (Sheffield Utd via Sutton Utd),
Derek Bryan (Brentford 97), Darren Powell (Brentford 98), Julian Charles (Brentford 99.)

Back Row: Steve Cordery (manager), Tony Coombe (asst. man.), Andy Walker, Nick Burton, Peter Barnsby, James Courtnage, Leroy Griffiths, Fiston Mputu, Peter Wood, Rob Frankland, Gareth Workman (physio), Malcolm Taylor (gen. asst.). Front Row: Warren Williams, Danny Smith, Dudley Gardner, Jason Shaw, Martin Carter, Craig Maskell, Colin Johnson (fitness coach)

Match Facts 1999-00

	Date	Comp.	H/A	Opponents	Att.	Result	Goalscorers
1	14.08	RYM P	A	Billericay Town	534	L	0-1	
2	17.08	RYM P	H	PURFLEET	213	D	1-1	Buglione 4
3	21.08	RYM P	H	FARNBOROUGH TOWN	377	W	1-0	Longhurst 77
4	24.08	RYM P	A	Gravesend & Northfleet	362	D	0-0	
5	28.08	RYM P	A	Dulwich Hamlet	304	L	0-2	
6	30.08	RYM P	H	HENDON	274	L	1-2	Buglione 90
7	04.09	RYM P	H	AYLESBURY UNITED	251	W	2-1	Carter 17, Buglione 49
8	06.09	RYM P	A	St Albans City	684	D	1-1	Emmerick 17
9	11.09	RYM P	A	Hitchin Town	359	D	2-2	Marshall 4, Burton 39
	14.09	LC 1	H	ST ALBANS CITY	113	L	0-2	
	18.09	FAC 2Q	H	BOGNOR REGIS TOWN	243	D	1-1	Carter 57
	21.09	FAC 2QR	A	Bognor Regis Town	306	D	0-0	Lost 4-5 after penalties
10	25.09	RYM P	H	SLOUGH TOWN	345	D	1-1	Maskell 8
	28.09	Middx SC 1	H	HENDON	220	W	4-2	Maskell (2), Shaw, Walker
11	02.10	RYM P	A	Boreham Wood	204	W	4-0	Buglione 65 82, Barnsby 69, Maskell 71
	09.10	FAT 1	A	Chertsey Town	241	W	2-1	Charles 12, Burton 72
12	16.10	RYM P	H	CHESHAM UNITED	285	L	0-1	
13	30.10	RYM P	H	CANVEY ISLAND	237	L	0-2	
	02.11	FMC 1	H	WORTHING	90	L	2-4	Mputu, Buglione
14	06.11	RYM P	H	BASINGSTOKE TOWN	192	W	2-1	Maskell 2, Rouco 69
15	12.11	RYM P	A	Dagenham & Redbridge	894	L	0-5	
16	20.11	RYM P	H	HEYBRIDGE SWIFTS	176	L	1-4	Shaw 90
	27.11	FAT 2	H	CARSHALTON ATHLETIC	264	L	1-2	Charles
17	04.12	RYM P	A	Aylesbury United	645	D	2-2	Maskell 32, Charles 66
18	14.12	RYM P	H	ENFIELD	139	W	2-1	Flitter 27, Rouco 70
19	18.12	RYM P	A	Heybridge Swifts	193	D	2-2	Adams 60 65
20	29.12	RYM P	H	WALTON & HERSHAM	353	L	0-2	
21	03.01	RYM P	A	Basingstoke Town	484	L	0-2	
22	15.01	RYM P	A	Harrow Borough	220	L	0-3	
	18.01	M SC 2	A	Northwood	200	L	1-3	Shaw 70
	26.01	S C C 2	A	Walton & Hersham	100	L	0-2	
23	29.01	RYM P	A	Purfleet	161	D	0-0	
24	05.02	RYM P	H	GRAVESEND & NORTHFLEET	244	W	1 - 0	Maskell 75
25	15.02	RYM P	A	Farnborough Town	229	W	1 - 0	Barnsby 28
26	19.02	RYM P	H	ST ALBANS CITY	307	D	2 - 2	Shaw 45, Adams 49
27	26.02	RYM P	A	Chesham United	340	L	0 - 1	
28	04.03	RYM P	H	BOREHAM WOOD	218	D	1 - 1	Adams 31
29	07.03	RYM P	H	DULWICH HAMLET	193	W	3 - 0	Griffiths 73, Burton 80, Maskell 89
30	11.03	RYM P	A	Slough Town	504	D	1 - 1	Adams 14
31	14.03	RYM P	H	CARSHALTON ATHLETIC	279	L	0 - 1	
32	18.03	RYM P	H	HITCHIN TOWN	235	W	2 - 1	Carter 9, Shaw 37
33	20.03	RYM P	A	Hendon	212	L	0 - 1	
34	25.03	RYM P	A	Canvey Island	705	W	2 - 1	Shaw 33, Williams 78
35	01.04	RYM P	A	ALDERSHOT TOWN	1008	L	0 - 1	
36	04.04	RYM P	H	BILLERICAY TOWN	163	L	1 - 2	Shaw 55 (p)
37	18.04	RYM P	A	Carshalton Athletic	189	D	1 - 1	Barnsby 43
38	22.04	RYM P	H	DAGENHAM & REDBRIDGE	453	L	2 - 3	Maskell 43, 47
39	24.04	RYM P	A	Walton & RHersham	303	W	3 - 1	Maskell 13, Griffiths 23, Williams 24
40	26.04	RYM P	A	Aldershot Town	1280	D	1 - 1	Williams 45
41	29.04	RYM P	H	HARROW BOROUGH	333	W	3 - 1	Williams 7, Maskell 59, Adams 79
42	06.05	RYM P	A	Enfield	176	W	3 - 2	Shaw 7 (p), Maskell 32, Griffiths 58

PLAYING SQUAD

GOALKEEPERS: Mark Russell (Fleet T)

DEFENDERS: Fiston Mputu (Brentford), Nick Burton (Aldershot T), Peter Wood (Malden Vale), Matt Flitter (Chesham U), Tony Houghton (Dulwich Hamlet), Simon Whall (Yeading), Peter Barnsby (Crystal Palace)

MIDFIELDERS: Danny Rouco (Viking Greenford), Jason Shaw (Chertsey T), Dudley Gardner (Slough T), Martin Carter (Chertsey T)

FORWARDS: Warren Williams (Hanwell T), Marc Coates (Walton & H), Leroy Griffiths (Corinthian Cas), Craig Maskell (Leyton O), Paul Longhurst (Brentford), Darren Adams (Welling U)

HARROW BOROUGH

CLUB OFFICIALS
Chairman: Jim Ripley
President: Jim Rogers
Secretary/Press Officer: Peter Rogers,
21 Ludlow Close, South Harrow, Middx HA2
8SR (0208 248 8003)
Commercial Manager:
Jim Hayes c/o the club

FOOTBALL MANAGEMENT TEAM
Manager: Edwin Stein
Asst Manager:T.B.A.
Physio: Chas E Cox

FACT FILE

Formed: 1933
Nickname: The Boro
Sponsors: T.B.A.
Colours: Red, white trim/white/red, white hoops
Change cols: Black & white stripes/black/black
Midweek matchday: Tuesday

1999-00
Captain: Mark Cooper
P.o.Y.: Andy Rose
Top Scorer:Damien Markman

PURFLEET
6th May, 2000

Pages: 32 Price: £1.00p
Editor: Jim Rogers (0208 248 8003)

Local Press: Harrow Observer

GROUND: Earlsmead, Carlyon Avenue, South Harrow, Middx HA2 8SS
Tel: 0208 422 5989/5221
Directions: Underground to Northolt (Central Line) then 140 bus to Northolt Park BR, 282 bus, to Eastcote Arms or to South Harrow (Piccadilly Line) then 114 or H10 to Kings Rd.Junction. By road leave A40 at Macdonalds roundabout towards Northolt station (A312 north), left at lights, right at next island (Eastcote Arms pub), ground 5th turning on right.
Capacity: 3,070 Cover: 1,000 Seats: 350 Floodlights: Yes
Clubhouse: Open daily, normal pub hours. Four bars, games room, equipped for all social
events. Hot and coldfood available, buffets by prior request
Club Shop: Sells progs, scarves, badges, T-shirts, etc. Contact Tony Trowbridge c/o club

PREVIOUS **Leagues:** Harrow & Dist 33-4; Spartan 34-40, 45-58; W Middx Comb 40-1; Middx Sen41-45; Delphian 58-63; Athenian 63-75;
Names: Roxonian 1933-8; Harrow Town 38-66 **Ground:** Northolt Road 33-4
CLUB RECORDS Attendance: 3,000 v Wealdstone, F.A. Cup 1st Qualifying Round 1946 **Fee Received:** £16,000 for Lee Endersby (Enfield 97)
Scorer: Dave Pearce, 153 **Appearances:** Steve Emmanuel 522 (1st team only), Les Currell 582, Colin Payne 557
Fee Paid: Unspecified to Dagenham for George Duck & Steve Jones, Summer 81
Win: 13-0 v Handley Page (A), Middlesex Snr Lg 18/10/41. **Defeat:** 0-8 5 times: Wood Green T. (A) Middx Lge 40,
Met Police (A) Spartan Lg 52, Briggs Spts (A) Spartan Lg 53, Hertford T. (A) Spartan Lge 53, Hendon (A) Middx Snr Cup 65
BEST SEASON FA Trophy: Semi final 82-83 **FA Cup:** 2nd Rd 83-84 (1-3 at home to Newport Co)
HONOURS: Isthmian Lg 83-84 (Div 1 R-up 78-79); Athenian Lg Div 2 R-up 63-64; Spartan Lg R-up 57-58 (Div 2 West 38-39 (R-up 37-38);
Middx Senior Cup 82-83 92-93; Harrow & Dist. Lg Div 1 R-up 33-34; Middx Charity Cup 79-80 92-93 (R-up 78-79); Middx
Intermediate Cup 55-56,R-up 75-76, Middx Premier Cup 81-82,R-up 82-83, Harrow Sen Cup 95 97, London Interm'te C 78-79
Players progressing: D.Russell (Arsenal), M.Lucas (L.Orient), R.Shaw (Torquay U), T.Eden (Raith R), T. Carpenter (Watford), M Bottoms (QPR
60), C Hutchings (Chelsea 80), R Holland (Crewe 85), J Kerr (Portsmouth 87), D Howell, A Pape & E Stein, (Barnet), D .Byrne (Gillingham),
R.Rosario (Norwich), D Kemp (Crystal Palace), M Doherty (Reading), D Bassett (Wimbledon), G Borthwick (Bournemouth), B.Shaw, Torquay
U),T.Evans (Scunthorpe U), L.Charles (Q.P.R.), P.Barrowcliff (Brentford).

Back Row L-R: Chas Cox (physio), Nelson Heldt (team asst.), Mike Bignall, Otis Roberts, Vladimar Gusavac, David Hook, Garry Hedges, Matt Pollard, Mark Cooper, Pat Gavin, Eddie Stein (asst. man.), Leroy Rhodes (res. manager). Front Row: Danny Nwaokolo, Kelechi Duru, Frank McCormack, Alan Paris (player/manager), Jon-Barrie Bates, Marvin Walker, Andy Rose. Photo: Paul Carter

Match Facts 1999-00

	Date	Comp.	H/A	Opponents	Att.	Result	Goalscorers	
1	14.08	RYM P	H	DAGENHAM & REDBRIDGE	443	D 1 - 1	Gavin 47	
2	17.08	RYM P	A	Canvey Island	629	L 0 - 2		
3	21.08	RYM P	A	Walton & Hersham	163	L 1 - 3	Jones 5[p]	
4	24.08	RYM P	H	ENFIELD	307	L 1 - 2	Markman 36	
5	28.08	RYM P	H	CHESHAM UNITED	285	L 0 - 2		
6	30.08	RYM P	A	Boreham Wood	314	W 1 - 0	Nwaokolo 6	
7	05.09	RYM P	A	Aldershot Town	2043	W 2 - 1	Thomas 21, Gavin 90	
8	07.09	RYM P	H	BASINGSTOKE TOWN	223	D 1 - 1	Bates 66	
9	11.09	RYM P	A	Dulwich Hamlet	310	L 0 - 2		
	14.09	LC 1	A	Heybridge Swifts	108	L 1 - 5		
	18.09	FAC 2Q	A	Marlow	250	W 4 - 1	Roberts (3), Bates	
10	25.09	RYM P	H	FARNBOROUGH TOWN	405	L 1 - 3	Ripley 2	
	02.10	FAC Q3	A	Worcester City	767	L 2 - 3	Barrie-Bates 70, Gavin 75	
	09.10	FAT 1	A	Hitchin Town	291	D 1 - 1	Thomas	
	12.10	FAT 1 R	H	HITCHIN TOWN	153	W 2 - 1	Gusavac, Towle	
11	16.10	RYM P	H	HEYBRIDGE SWIFTS	180	W 2 - 0	Markman 5 32	
12	23.10	RYM P	A	Carshalton Athletic	234	L 1 - 3	Nwaokola 45	
	26.10	FMC1	H	CHERTSEY TOWN	109	D *3 - 3	Markman (2), Nwaokolo	Lost 2-3 after penalties
13	30.10	RYM P	H	AYLESBURY UNITED	241	W 4 - 1	**Markman 3** (55 58 68), Gavin 80	
	02.11	Middx SC1	H	KINGSBURY TOWN	147	W 2 - 1	Markman 18 22	
14	06.11	RYM P	A	Billericay Town	469	L 0 - 5		
15	13.11	RYM P	H	ST ALBANS CITY	189	L 0 - 2		
16	20.11	RYM P	A	Purfleet	185	D 1 - 1	Harvey 85	
	27.11	FAT 2	H	OXFORD CITY	182	D 0 - 0		
17	04.12	RYM P	H	ALDERSHOT TOWN	701	L 0 - 1		
18	14.12	RYM P	A	Gravesend & Northfleet	340	L 1 - 4	Toule 89	
19	18.12	RYM P	H	SLOUGH TOWN	317	L 0 - 1		
20	03.01	RYM P	H	BILLERICAY TOWN	235	D 1 - 1	Nwaokolo 11	
21	08.01	RYM P	A	Chesham United	405	W 2 - 1	Gladdy 40, Bignall 80	
22	15.01	RYM P	H	HAMPTON & RICHMOND B.	220	W 3 - 0	Cooper 71, Burton 73[og], Roberts 90	
23	22.01	RYM P	A	Dagenham & Redbridge	971	L 1 - 4	Markman 44	
24	29.01	RYM P	H	CANVEY ISLAND	221	L 1 - 3	Bignall 73	
	01.02	MSC QF	H	ENFIELD	147	L 0 - 2		
25	05.02	RYM P	A	Enfield	168	W 3 - 0	Markman 32, Bignall 79, Roberts 84	
26	12.02	RYM P	H	BOREHAM WOOD	268	L 1 - 3	Markman 44	
27	19.02	RYM P	A	Basingstoke Town	455	L 0 - 2		
28	04.03	RYM P	H	GRAVESEND & NORTHFLEET	188	W 6 - 0	**Bignall 3** (3[p] 17 41), OG(Campbell) 50, Gavin 83, Browne 90	
29	07.03	RYM P	H	WALTON & HERSHAM	165	L 0 - 1		
30	11.03	RYM P	A	Farnborough Town	409	D 0 - 0		
31	13.03	RYM P	A	Hendon	319	W 1 - 0	Bignall 60	
32	18.03	RYM P	H	DULWICH HAMLET	182	W 1 - 0	Bignall 45	
33	21.03	RYM P	A	Hitchin Town	288	L 0 - 4		
34	25.03	RYM P	A	Aylesbury United	534	L 1 - 3	Bignall 23	
35	28.03	RYM P	A	Heybridge Swifts	201	W 2 - 1	Walker 29, Guacvic 70	
36	01.04	RYM P	H	CARSHALTON ATHLETIC	236	D 0 - 0		
37	08.04	RYM P	A	Slough Town	504	W 3 - 2	Gavin 38, Hurlock 40, Barrie-Bates 80	
38	15.04	RYM P	H	HITCHIN TOWN	278	W 4 - 0	Bignall 63, Gavin 69, Markman 83, Rose 90	
39	18.04	RYM P	H	HENDON	229	W 2 - 1	Markman 53, Gusavac 76	
40	22.04	RYM P	A	St. Albans City	515	L 2 - 3	McCormack 32, Gavin 50	
41	29.04	RYM P	A	Hampton & Richmond Bor.	333	L 1 - 3	Nwaokolo 47	
42	06.05	RYM P	H	PURFLEET	207	L 2 - 3	Hurlock 5, Roberts 30	

PLAYING SQUAD

GOALKEEPERS: David Hook (Chesham U)

DEFENDERS: Andrew Rose (Oxford U), Mark Cooper (Chalfont St.Peter), Tommy Bryson (St.Albans C),
Daniel Nwaokolo (Wokingham T), Perry Norman (Camb.C)

MIDFIELDERS: Otis Roberts (FC Hoogstraten (Belg)), Jon-Barrie Bates (Wembley),
Corey Browne (St.Albans C), Vladimir Gusavac (Youth), John Kumah (Kingsbury T),
Ishmael Dodds (Bournemouth), Joe Lyons (St.Albans C)

FORWARDS: Pat Gavin (Farnborough T), Mark Xavier (Dulwich Hamlet), Mike Bignall (Boreham Wood),
Warren Gladdy (Youth), Kelechi Duru (St.Albans C)

HENDON

CLUB OFFICIALS
Chairman: **Ivor Arbiter**

Secretary: **Graham Etchell,** c/o Hendon FC.
Tel: 020 8201 9494(Club)
Press Officer: Club Secretary

Marketingl Manager: **Jennie Cairns**

FOOTBALL MANAGEMENT TEAM
Manager: Frank Murphy
Coaches: D Anderson & Curtis Warmington
Physio: T.B.A.

FACT FILE
Formed: 1908 Nickname: Dons or Greens
Sponsors: UK Packaging
Colours: White & green,green,white & green
Green & white/green/green & white
Midweek matchday: Monday
Reserve League: Suburban (Premier))
Club Line: 09066 555 836
1999-00
Captain: Gary Fitzgerald
P.o.Y.: Jon Daly
Top Scorer: Dominic Gentle

GROUND: Claremont Road, Cricklewood, London NW2 1AE.
Tel: 020 9201 8494 Fax: 020 8905 5966
Directions: From Brent Cross station (Northern Line) to the east take first left after flyover on North Circular - Claremont Rd is then left at 3rd mini-r'bout. Buses 102, 210, 226 and C11 pass ground
Capacity: 3,029   Cover: 601   Seats: 329   Floodlights: Yes
Clubhouse: (contact Sue Damary 020 8455 9185). Two banqueting suites,conference centre, room hire, restaurant & bars open licensing hours 7 days aweek. Hot & cold food, pool, darts, bingo, members club, satelite TV,entertainments
Club Shop: Contact Derek Furmedge, 020 8459 2042 (H) Sells football souvenirs

Pages: 40 Price: £1.50p
Editor: Secretary
Local Press: Hendon Times,
Willesden & Brent Chronicle
Hampstead & Highgate Express
Local Radio: Capital, GLR, LBC

PREVIOUS   **Leagues:** Finchley & Dist. 08-11, Middx 10-11, London 11-14, Athenian 14-63.
Names: Christ Church Hampstead to 08, Hampstead Town to 26, Hampstead to 33,Golders Green to 46
Grounds: Kensal Rise 08-12; Avenue Ground, Cricklewood Lane 12-26
CLUB RECORDS Attendance: 9,000 v Northampton, FA Cup 1st Rd 1952
Goalscorer: Freddie Evans 176 (1929-35)   **Appearances:** Bill Fisher 787 (1940-
Defeat: 2-11 v Walthamstow Ave. (A), Athenian Lge 9/11/35   **Win:** 13-1 v Wingate (H), Middx Senior Cup 2/2/57
Fee Paid: Paul Whitmarsh (undisclosed)   **Fee Received:** £30,000 for Iain Dowie (Luton)
BEST SEASON   F.A. Cup: First Rd 20 times, Second Rd 5 times   **F.A.Trophy:** 5th Rd 98-99
HONOURS: European Am Champions 72-3; Isthmian Lg 64-5 72-3 (R-up 63-4 65-6 73-4) Lg Cup 76-7 (R-up 86-7), Full Members Cup 94-5 97-8 98-99, Premier Inter-Lge Cup R-up 86-7; Middx Lge 12-3 13-4; Athenian Lg 52-3 55-6 60-1 (R-up 28-9 32-3 47-8 48-9 51-2); London Lg Div 1 R-up 12-13 (Amtr Div 13-4); Finchley & Dist. Lg 10-1; London Snr Cup 63-4 68-9 (R-up 35-6 50-1 54-5 58-9 71-2); Middx Snr Cup (12) (R-up 83-4), Middx Interm 64-5 66-7 72-3, Middx Charity Cup(14); London IntermCup (4) (R-up (2); Suburban Lg 92-3 (R-up 84-5 97-8)
Players progressing: Peter Shearing (WHU 60), Iain Dowie (Luton 88), PeterAnderson (Luton), Jeff Harris (Orient), Phil Gridelet (Barnsley 90), GerrySoloman (Leyton O 91), Junior Hunter & Micah Hyde (both Cambridge 94-95),Simon Clark (Peterboro' 94-95),Junior Lewis(Gillingham 99-00)

Back Row: Frank Murphy (manager), Ron Fearon, Mavuto Sakala, jason McKoy, Jon Daly, Dominic Gentle, Paul Towler, Simon Clarke, Bontcho Guentchev, Tony Millard, Steve baker, Caroline Brouwer (physio). Front Row: Gary Fitzgerald, John Johnson (coach), Freddie Hyatt, Marvyn Watson, Paul Whitmarsh, john-Simon White, Dale Binns, Matthew Maran, Curtis warrington, Dave Anderson (coach)

Match Facts 1999-00

	Date	Comp.	H/A	Opponents	Att.	Result	Goalscorers
1	14.08	RYM P	H	ALDERSHOT TOWN	1005	L 1-2	Towler 31
2	17.08	RYM P	A	Slough Town	480	D 1-1	Hyatt 4
3	21.08	RYM P	A	Hitchin Town	449	L 0-1	
4	23.08	RYM P	H	CANVEY ISLAND	275	W 3-2	Guentchev 27, Gentle 56[p] 60
5	28.08	RYM P	H	DAGENHAM & REDBRIDGE	410	L 0-1	
6	30.08	RYM P	A	Hampton & Richmond Borough	274	W 2-1	Whitmarsh 57, Millard 90
7	04.09	RYM P	A	Enfield	467	L 3-5	Watson 35, McKay 39, Gentle 59
8	06.09	RYM P	H	CHESHAM UNITED	258	W 4-2	**Gentle 3** (5[p] 15 32), Whitmarsh 75
9	11.09	RYM P	A	St Albans City	663	W 2-1	Duffy 14, Williams 21
	14.09	**LC 1**	A	Gravesend & Northfleet	148	W 2-1	Sakala, Towler
	18.09	**FAC Q2**	H	GRAYS ATHLETIC	201	W 2-0	Whitmarsh (2)
10	25.09	RYM P	H	BOREHAM WOOD	312	W 2-1	White 8, Towler 85
	28.09	**Middx SC**	A	Hampton & Richmond Bor.	220	L 2-4	Baker 4[p], Watson 10
	02.10	**FAC Q3**	H	BLAKENALL	302	W 2-1	Hyatt 41, Gentle 87
	09.10	**FAT 1**	A	Slough Town	461	W 2-0	Hyatt, Gentle
	16.10	**FAC Q4**	H	MARGATE	531	W 1-0	Hyatt 11
11	23.10	RYM P	A	Purfleet	157	L 1-4	Gentle 6[p]
	30.10	**FAC 1**	A	Bath City	1690	W 2-0	Gentle 87, Guentchev 90
12	06.11	RYM P	H	DULWICH HAMLET	381	L 1-2	Guentchev 44
	09.11	**LC 2**	A	Barton Rovers		L 1-3	Fitzgerald 43
13	14.11	RYM P	A	Farnborough Town	497	W 1-0	Guentchev 53
	20.11	**FAC 2**	A	Blackpool	2975	L 0-2	
	22.11	**FMC 1**	H	WEALDSTONE	184	*D 2-2	Lost 6-7 after penalties
	27.11	**FAT 2**	H	GRAYS ATHLETIC	237	W 1-0	Gentle 26
14	30.11	RYM P	A	Walton & Hersham	181	W 2-1	Fitzgerald 42, Whitmarsh 90
15	04.12	RYM P	A	Dagenham & Redbridge	802	L 0-4	
16	11.12	RYM P	H	BASINGSTOKE TOWN	278	W 4-3	Whitmarsh 4, Harris 13[og], Daly 33, Binns 48
17	18.12	RYM P	A	Aylesbury United	412	W 3-2	Gentle 24, Binns 44, Whitmarsh 83
18	03.01	RYM P	A	Dulwich Hamlet	405	L 0-1	
19	08.01	RYM P	H	ENFIELD	448	W 2-2	Gentle 8[p], Cowler 81
	10.01	**M SC 2**	H	EDGWARE TOWN	76	W 3-1	Howard, Fitzgerald,Sakala
	15.01	**FAT 3**	A	Forest Green Rovers	583	L 1-4	Daly 40
20	22.01	RYM P	A	Aldershot Town	1824	L 1-2	Whitmarsh 41
21	29.01	RYM P	H	SLOUGH TOWN	407	L 1-1	White 3
	01.02	**MSC QF**		Yeading		W 3 - 2	**Gentle (3)**
22	05.02	RYM P	A	Canvey Island	411	D 0 - 0	
23	07.02	RYM P	H	GRAVESEND & NORTHFLEET	183	W 2 - 0	Watson 12, Daly 14
24	19.02	RYM P	A	Chesham United	441	L 1 - 2	Gentle 83
25	21.02	RYM P	A	HEYBRIDGE SWIFTS	252	W 2 - 0	Whitmarsh 53 72
26	26.02	RYM P	A	Billericay Town	471	D 1 - 1	Clark 43
	28.02	**M SC SF**	H	NORTHWOOD	167	L 0 - 1	
27	06.03	RYM P	H	HITCHIN TOWN	221	D 1 - 1	Gentle 15[p]
28	11.03	RYM P	A	Boreham Wood	362	W 2 - 0	Whitmarsh 45, Watson 70
29	13.03	RYM P	H	HARROW BOROUGH	319	L 0 - 1	
30	18.03	RYM P	H	ST ALBANS CITY	380	L 0 - 3	
31	20.03	RYM P	H	HAMPTON & RICHMOND B	212	W 1 - 0	Edwards 87
32	25.03	RYM P	A	Gravesend & Northfleet	374	L 0 - 1	
33	27.03	RYM P	H	BILLERICAY TOWN	178	W 3 - 2	Scott 7, Clarke 22, Gentle 67
34	01.04	RYM P	H	PURFLEET	259	L 1 - 3	Daly 34
35	08.04	RYM P	H	AYLESBURY UNITED	366	W 1 - 0	Gentle 24
36	10.04	RYM P	A	Carshalton Athletic	237	W 1 - 0	Hyatt 90 (p)
37	15.04	RYM P	A	Basingstoke Town	444	D 1 - 1	Bartholomew 73
38	18.04	RYM P	A	Harrow Borough	229	L 1 - 2	Watson 59
39	22.04	RYM P	H	FARNBOROUGH TOWN	233	W 5 - 3	Haule 24, Whitmarsh 28, 52, Fitzgerald 33, Scott 90
40	29.04	RYM P	H	WALTON & HERSHAM	218	D 2 - 2	Daly 29, Haule 45
41	01.05	RYM P	H	CARSHALTON ATHLETIC	374	W 2 - 0	Hyatt 62 (p), Towler 68
42	06.05	RYM P	A	Heybridge Swifts	269	W 2 - 1	Hyatt 19, Haule 90

PLAYING SQUAD

GOALKEEPERS: Gary McCann (Dulwich Hamlet), Andrew Iga (Chesham U)

DEFENDERS: Simon Clarke (Kettering T), Iain Duncan (Aylesbury U), Curtis Warmington (Kingstonian), Warren Kelly (St.Albans C), Alan McCarthy (Boreham Wood), Paul Towler (Met.Police), John-Simon White (Watford)

MIDFIELDERS: Jon Daly (St.Albans C), Dale Binns (Youth), Marvyn Watson (Youth), Gary Fitzgerald (Enfield), Matt Bartholomew (Youth), Paul Adolphe (Harrow B), **Phil Gridelet** (Woking)

FORWARDS: Bontcho Guentchev (CSKA Sofia (Bulg)), Davis Haule (Wembley), Ross Pickett (Walton & Hersham)

HEYBRIDGE SWIFTS

CLUB OFFICIALS

Chairman: Andrew Barber
President: Ronnie Locker
Vice Chairman: Michael Gibson
Secretary: Dennis Fenn
31 Saxon Way, Maldon, Essex CM9 7JN
(01621 854798)

Match Secretary: Terry Stowers
74 Wood Road, Heybridge, Maldon, Essex
CM9 4AW   (01621 857226)

Press Offr: Tony Foster (M 07931 330756)
Treasurer: Chris Daines

FACT FILE

Formed: 1880
Nickname: Swifts
Sponsors:
Towermaster.Lighting Towers Systems
Colours: Black & white stripes/black/black
Change colours: All Red or Amber/ white
Midweek matchday: Tuesday
Reserves' Lge: Essex & Herts Border Comb

FOOTBALL MANAGEMENT TEAM

General Manager: Robbie Nihill
Manager Liam Cutbush.   Asst M: Tony English
Coach: Keith Hull   Physio: Glenn Churchett

OFFICIAL MATCHDAY MAGAZINE SPONSOR
ROBERT E. LEE
Plastering Contractor

Ryman
football league
1999/2000 SEASON   £1.00

Pages: 40 Price: £1
Editors: Chris Daines & Tony Foster

Local Press: Maldon & Burnham Standard
Loval Radio: BBC Essex, Essex FM, Chelmer FM

GROUND: Scraley Road, Heybridge, Maldon, Essex Tel: 01621 852978
Directions: Leave Maldon on the main road to Colchester, pass through Heybridge then turn right at the sign to Tolleshunt Major (Scraley Road). The ground on the right. Six miles from nearest station (Witham). By bus via Chelmsfordand Maldon
Capacity: 3,000   **Cover:** 1,200   **Seats:** 550   **Floodlights:** Yes
Clubhouse: Two bars open every night. Games room, boardroom, kitchen (on matchdays)
Club Shop: Open matchdays, selling club sweaters, shirts, scarves, baseball hats, enamel badges, old programmes etc.   Contact Chris Daines, c/o club.

PREVIOUS   Leagues: Essex & Suffolk Border, North Essex, South Essex, Essex Senior 1971-84
CLUB RECORDS Attendance: 2,477 v Woking FA Trophy 97 and pre season v West Ham United , 3,000 +, 99-00.
      Goalscorer: Julian Lamb 115 (post war), Dave Matthews 112 (Isthmian)
      Appearances: Hec Askew 500+, Robbie Sach 358 (Isthmian)
      Fee Paid: None   **Fee Received:** £35,000, Simon Royce (Southend Utd)

BEST SEASON   FA Trophy: Qtr finals v Woking 22/3/97 (lost 0-1)
      FA Cup: First round 0-2 v Gillingham 11/11/94, 0-3 v Bournemouth 15.11.97 **League clubs defeated:** None

HONOURS: Isthmian Lg Div 1 R-up 95-96, Div 2 North 89-90; Essex Senior Lg 81-82 82-83 83-84, Lg Cup 82-83, Trophy 81-82; JT Clarke Cup 82-83; Thorn EMI National Floodlit Competition R-up 82-83; Eastern Floodlit Cup 93-94; East Anglian Cup 93-94 94-95; Essex & Suffolk Border Lge 31-32; Essex Jun Cup 31-32; North Essex Lge 46-47

Players progressing: Simon Royce (Southend United & Charlton Athletic), Peter Cawley & Ben Lewis (Colchester Utd), Alan Hull (Leyton Orient), Jonathan Hunt (Birmingham City), Dominic Naylor (Leyton Orient), Haken Hayrettin (Doncaster Rovers), Derek Payne & Tom Meredith (Peterborough Utd), Ben Barnett, Eddie Stein & Tim Alexander (Barnet), Ashley Vickers (Peterborough United), James Pullen (18 year old ,goalkeeper to Ipswich Town) 99-00.

Back Row: Chris Heasman, Ian Wiles, Mark Cranfield, Gary Waters, Chris Payne, Nicky Simpson.
Middle: Glen Churchett (physio), Nicky Haydon, Dave Streetley, Dave MacKrory, Kingsley Banks, Colin Wall, Sean Caton, Kris Lee, Christian McClean, Tony Adcock (asst. man.). **Front Row:** Keith Hull (coach), Ross Taylor, Dave Kreyling, Liam Cutbush (manager), Terry Warwick, Alex Fiddes, Simon Parker, Adam Gillespie.

Match Facts 1999-00

	Date	Comp.	H/A	Opponents	Att.	Result	Goalscorers
1	14.08	RYM P	H	HITCHIN TOWN	278	L 2 - 3	Parker 63 84
2	17.08	RYM P	A	Enfield	281	L 2 - 3	Springett 30[p], Parker 73
3	21.08	RYM P	A	Basingstoke Town	473	D 2 - 2	Springett 30, Warwick 89
4	24.08	RYM P	H	WALTON & HERSHAM	222	W 5 - 1	Gillespie 2 33, Lewis 9, 75, Springett 88
5	28.08	RYM P	H	ALDERSHOT TOWN	633	L 1 - 3	Parker 28
6	30.08	RYM P	A	Dagenham & Redbridge	912	L 0 - 2	
7	04.09	RYM P	A	Chesham United	286	D 1 - 1	McClean 33
8	07.09	RYM P	H	BOREHAM WOOD	190	L 0 - 1	
9	11.09	RYM P	H	CARSHALTON ATHLETIC	248	L 0 - 2	
	14.09	LC 1	H	HARROW BOROUGH	108	W 5 - 1	Parker (2), Simpson, Warwick, Lewis
	18.09	FAC 2Q	H	ROMFORD	288	L 1 - 2	T Adcock
10	25.09	RYM P	H	Aylesbury United	804	D 2 - 2	Parker 34, Lewis 48[p]
	09.10	FAT 1	H	WESTON-SUPER-MARE	197	W 2 - 0	McClean 16, Streetley 88
11	16.10	RYM P	A	Harrow Borough	180	L 0 - 2	
12	23.10	RYM P	H	FARNBOROUGH TOWN	233	L 1 - 2	Parker 90
13	30.10	RYM P	A	Dulwich Hamlet	328	L 1 - 2	Taylor 3
14	06.11	RYM P	A	Purfleet	173	L 0 - 1	
	09.11	LC 2	H	WINDSOR & ETON	111	W 2 - 1	Simpson, Gillespie
15	12.11	RYM P	H	GRAVESEND & NORTHFLEET	202	L 2 - 4	Gillespie 27, Lewis 89
	16.11	FMC 2	H	PURFLEET	74	L 2 - 4	McLean 12, McKrory 90
16	20.11	RYM P	A	Hampton & Richmond Bor.	176	W 4 - 1	Grice 6, Parker 65, McClean 68, Smith 75[og]
	27.11	FAT 2	H	WITNEY TOWN	204	W 3 - 2	Parker 49 90, Simpson 55
	30.11	Essex SC 3	A	Leyton Pennant	63	W 2 - 1	Warwick, David
17	04.12	RYM P	H	CHESHAM UNITED	255	W 2 - 1	Taylor 75, Parker 90
18	11.12	RYM P	A	Canvey Island	389	L 1 - 6	Parker 4
	14.12	LC 3	H	BRAINTREE TOWN	165	W 3 - 1	Parker 3 (44, 70, 90)
19	18.12	RYM P	H	HAMPTON & RICHMOND B.	193	D 2 - 2	Lewis 12 52
	21.12	E SC 4	H	SOUTHEND UNITED	117	L 1 - 4	Lewis (p)
20	27.12	RYM P	A	Billericay Town	558	W 2 - 1	Parker 10 53
21	03.01	RYM P	H	PURFLEET	304	D 0 - 0	
22	08.01	RYM P	A	Aldershot Town	2041	W 1 - 0	Gillespie 53
	16.01	FAT 3	A	Dartford	542	W 2 - 1	Simpson 35 83
23	18.01	RYM P	H	ST ALBANS CITY	253	W 2 - 1	Haydon 36, Keen 87
24	22.01	RYM P	A	Hitchin Town	288	W 2 - 1	Haydon 46, Parker 78 ... Simpson 82
	25.01	LC QF	A	Farnborough Town	198	W 7 - 2	Gillespie 11, David 23, Warwick 3 (38 59 66), Haydon 43[p],
25	29.01	RYM P	H	ENFIELD	403	W 2 - 1	Parker 26, Simpson 40
	05.02	FAT 4	H	NEWPORT IOW	420	W 1 - 0	McClean 65
26	12.02	RYM P	H	DAGENHAM & REDBRIDGE	604	W 5 - 4	Simpson 3 (5 66 76), Taylor 19, Parker 68
27	19.02	RYM P	A	Boreham Wood	253	D 0 - 0	
28	21.02	RYM P	A	Hendon	252	L 0 - 2	
	26.02	FAT 5	A	Runcorn	759	L 1 - 2	Gillespie 89
29	04.03	RYM P	A	St Albans City	326	L 0 - 2	
30	11.03	RYM P	H	AYLESBURY UNITED	337	D 0 - 0	
31	13.03	RYM P	A	Walton & Hersham	217	W 1 - 0	Heasman 55
32	18.03	RYM P	A	Carshalton Athletic	318	D 1 - 1	Warwick 58
33	21.03	RYM P	H	BASINGSTOKE TOWN	245	W 2 - 0	Caton 23, Wall 43
34	25.03	RYM P	H	DULWICH HAMLET	287	D 1 - 1	Payne 73
35	28.03	RYM P	H	HARROW BOROUGH	201	L 1 - 2	Warwick 73
36	01.04	RYM P	A	Farnborough Town	287	W 1 - 0	OG (Corbett) 90
37	18.04	RYM P	H	SLOUGH TOWN	213	D 1 - 1	Simpson 58
38	22.04	RYM P	A	Gravesend & Northfleet	369	D 1 - 1	Warwick 45
39	24.04	RYM P	H	BILLERICAY TOWN	407	L 1 - 2	Wall 33
40	29.04	RYM P	A	Slough Town	410	L 1 - 2	Parker 65
41	01.05	RYM P	H	CANVEY ISLAND	340	W 3 - 0	Wall 10, 13, Lee 82
42	06.05	RYM P	H	HENDON	269	L 1 - 2	Simpson 40

PLAYING SQUAD

GOALKEEPERS: Kingsley Banks (Witham T)

DEFENDERS: Gary Waters (Canvey Is), Ross Taylor (Stevenage B), Luke Dockwray (Edgware T), Colin Wall (Billericay T), Ian Wilde (Hayes), Mark Cranfield (Braintree T)

MIDFIELDERS: Adam Gillespie (Youth), Alex Fiddes (Maldon T), Nicky Hayden (Leyton O), Dave Streetley (Halstead T), Sean Caton (Wivenhoe T), Ashley Bond (Youth), John Pollard (St.Albans C), Glenn Moss (Youth), Mark Kane (St.Albans C)

FORWARDS: Christian McClean (Sudbury T), Wayne Adcock (Witham T), Chris Payne (Canvey Is), Simon Parker (Stowmarket T), Kris Lee (Tiptree U)

HITCHIN

CLUB OFFICIALS

Chairman: **Terry Barratt**

Secretary: **Roy Izzard**
2 Bedford Road, Ickleford, Hitchin,Herts
Tel: 01462 433171

Media Officer: **Neil Jensen**
Tel: 01462 454678/0207 5457921

FOOTBALL MANAGEMENT TEAM

Manager: Andy Melvin
Physio: Peter Prince
Asst Mgr: Robbie O'Keefe

FACT FILE

Formed: 1865
Nickname: The Canaries
Sponsors:
Colours: Yellow/green/green
Change colours: white/black/black
Midweek matchday: Tuesday
Clubcall Line: 0930 555 817
Reserves League: Suburban
1999-00
Captain: Mark Burke
P.o.Y Adam Parker
Top Scorer: Gary Dixon (22)

BILLERICAY TOWN
Tuesday 17th August 1999 (7.45pm)
Ryman League Premier Division

Pages: 48 Price: £1 Editor: Barry Swain
Local Press: Hitchin Gazette/Hitchin Comet,
Herts on Sunday
Local Radio: Chiltern, BBC Three Counties

GROUND: Top Field, Fishponds Road, Hitchin SG5 1NU (01462 459028-matchdays only)
Directions: On A505 near town centre opposite large green. 1 mile from Hitchin(BR). From A1(M) Jct 8,A602 towards Bedford into Hitchin.Over two roundabouts through lights on one way system. Turn right at next roundabout for Fishponds Road.
Capacity: 3,800 **Cover:** 1,250 **Seats:** 400 **Floodlights:** Yes
Clubhouse: (01462 434483). Members bar, Function Hall (available for hire). Open everyday.
Steward: Eamonn Watson/ Nigel Collins
Club Shop: Yes, contact Medwyn Williams (01462 817182)

PREVIOUS **Leagues:** Spartan 28-39; Hert & Middx 39-45; Athenian 39,45-63
CLUB RECORDS **Attendance:** 7,878 v Wycombe Wanderers, FA Amateur Cup 3rd Rd 18/2/56
Win: Spartan Lge 29-30 13-0 v Cowley, 13-0 v RAF
Defeat (Isthmian Lge)**:** 0-10 v Kingstonian (A) 65-66, v Slough T. (A) 79-80
Career (Isthmian Lge) **appearances:** Paul Giggle 950+ 67-88   **Career** (Isthmian Lge) **goals:** Paul Giggle, 129
Fee paid: £2,000 for Ray Seeking (Potton United, July 1989)   **Fee received:** Undisclosed
BEST SEASON **FA Trophy:** 5th Rd 98-99   **FA Amateur Cup:** Semi Final 60-61, 62-63
FA Cup: 2nd Rd on four occasions -
v Swindon 1-3 (A) 76-77, v Boston Utd, 0-1 (A) 73-74, v Wycombe Wand. 0-5 (H) 94-95, v Gillingham 0-3 (A) 95-9
HONOURS: Isthmian Lge R-up 68-69Div 1 92-93 R-up 98-99, Spartan Lge 34-35; AFA Sen Cup 30-31; Herts Snr Cup (19-record); London Sen Cup 69-70 (R-up 72-73); E Anglian Cup 72-73; Herts Charity Cup(16), Herts I'mediate Cup (8); Woolwich Trophy 82-83; Televised Sport International Cup 88-89 90-91; Southern Comb. Senior Floodlit Cup 90-91

Players progressing:

R Smith (Millwall),
L Garwood (Spurs 46),
C J Walker, W Odell,
S Foss, R Stevens,
T Clarke, G Goodyear,
L Harwood, P Burridge,
R Kitchener
(Chelsea 54),
D Bumstead, M Dixon,
D Pacey (Luton 56),
M Dixon & BWhitby
(Luton 57),
K Abiss (Brighton 57),
D Hille, G Ley,
R Morton, L Payne
(Newcastle),
M Small (Brighton),
R Nugent (Barnet),
Chris McMenamin
(Coventry &
Peterborough 96),
Z.Abbey(Camb.U 2000)

Adam Parker (left) and Jeran Meah with the Herts Charity Cup after Hitchin's 4-1 victory over Baldock Town.

Photo:
Duncan Wright

Match Facts 1999-00

	Date	Comp.	H/A	Opponents	Att.	Result	Goalscorers
1	14.08	RYM P	A	Heybridge Swifts	278	W 3-2	Abbey 26, Parker 38, Dixon 55
2	17.08	RYM P	H	BILLERICAY TOWN	368	W 4-0	**Dixon 3** (20 29 62), Abbey 77
3	21.08	RYM P	H	HENDON	449	W 1-0	Parker 4
4	23.08	RYM P	A	St Albans City	755	L 1-2	Dixon 30
5	28.08	RYM P	A	Carshalton Athletic	306	L 0-2	
6	30.08	RYM P	H	GRAVESEND & NORTHFLEET	430	W 1-0	Parker 26
7	04.09	RYM P	H	FARNBOROUGH TOWN	419	D 1-1	Parker 14
8	06.09	RYM P	A	Purfleet	147	L 0-3	
9	11.09	RYM P	H	HAMPTON & RICHMOND B.	359	D 2-2	Dixon 21, Parker 79
	14.09	LC 1	A	Uxbridge	86	W 2-1	Elad (2)
	18.09	FAC 2Q	A	Saffron Walden Town	261	W 4-1	Dixon (2), Parker (2)
10	25.09	RYM P	A	Aldershot Town	1712	L 1-5	Abbey 40
	02.10	FAC Q3	H	GRANTHAM TOWN	430	W 2-1	Meah 53, Dixon 68
	09.10	FAT 1	H	HARROW BOROUGH	291	D 1-1	Salton
	12.10	FAT 1 R	A	Harrow Borough	153	L 1-2	Dixon
	16.10	FAC Q4	A	Merthyr Tydfil	726	L 0-2	
11	19.10	RYM P	H	AYLESBURY UNITED	251	W 4-3	Fenton 42 63, Burke 52, Parker 79
12	23.10	RYM P	A	Canvey Island	282	W 3-0	Dixon 36 69, Parker 67
13	30.10	RYM P	H	CHESHAM UNITED	478	L 0-2	
	02.11	Herts SC2	H	LONDON COLNEY	158	W 3-2	Fenton (3)
14	06.11	RYM P	H	DAGENHAM & REDBRIDGE	504	L 0-2	
	09.11	LC 2	H	FARNBOROUGH TOWN	124	D *3-3	Bates(2), Dixon - Hitchin eliminated for fielding an ineligible player
15	13.11	RYM P	A	Walton & Hersham	131	L 3-4	Parker 25, Lawes 65, Fenton 75
	16.11	FMC 2	H	ENFIELD	148	W 2-1	Abbey, Own-Goal
16	20.11	RYM P	H	BASINGSTOKE TOWN	325	W 2-0	Abbey 52, Marshall 58
	23.11	Herts CC SF	H	HEMEL HEMPSTEAD TOWN	129	W 4-2	Parker 30, Ryder 35[og], Abbey 61, Dixon 80
17	04.12	RYM P	A	Farnborough Town	547	D 1-1	Abbey 27
	07.12	H SC QF	H	ST ALBANS CITY	141	L 1-5	Burke
18	18.12	RYM P	A	Dagenham & Redbridge	774	L 1-4	Dixon 3
19	27.12	RYM P	H	BOREHAM WOOD	428	L 1-3	Kean 84
20	03.01	RYM P	A	Enfield	243	D 1-1	Kean 51
21	08.01	RYM P	H	CARSHALTON ATHLETIC	322	W 3-2	Abbey 53, Kean 79, Hall 87
	11.01	FMC 3	H	BEDFORD TOWN	261	W 3-2	Fenton 14[p] 75, Parker 25
22	15.01	RYM P	A	Slough Town	463	L 0-3	
23	22.01	RYM P	H	HEYBRIDGE SWIFTS	288	L 1-2	Abbey 80
24	29.01	RYM P	A	Billericay Town	470	D 1-1	Abbey 10
25	05.02	RYM P	H	ST ALBANS CITY	609	D 2-2	Abbey 42, Parker 80
26	12.02	RYM P	A	Gravesend & Northfleet	458	D 1-1	Williams 27
	15.02	FMC QF	H	YEADING	123	L 1-3	Marshall
27	19.02	RYM P	H	PURFLEET	248	W 1-0	Parker 80
28	26.02	RYM P	H	SLOUGH TOWN	437	L 1-2	Parker 16
29	04.03	RYM P	A	Aylesbury United	545	L 1-3	Lamey 24
30	06.03	RYM P	A	Hendon	221	D 1-1	Fenton 37[p]
31	11.03	RYM P	H	ALDERSHOT TOWN	806	L 1-2	Lamey 39
32	18.03	RYM P	A	Hampton & Richmond Bor.	235	L 1-2	Fenton 82[p]
33	21.03	RYM P	H	HARROW BOROUGH	288	W 4-0	Dixon 33 83, Burke 36, Lamey 84
34	25.03	RYM P	A	Chesham United	326	L 1-2	Scott 90
	29.03	H CC F	N	Baldock Town		W 4-1	Dixon, Parker (2), Fenton
35	01.04	RYM P	H	CANVEY ISLAND	362	D 3-3	Fenton 2, Parker 17, Dixon 51
36	08.04	RYM P	H	ENFIELD	507	W 2-1	Fenton 7, 69 (p)
37	10.04	RYM P	A	Dulwich Hamlet	227	W 2-1	Parker 65, Ougham 70
38	15.04	RYM P	A	Harrow Borough	278	L 0-4	
39	22.04	RYM P	H	WALTON & HERSHAM	397	L 0-2	
40	24.04	RYM P	A	Boreham Wood	457	D 0-0	
41	29.04	RYM P	H	DULWICH HAMLET	417	W 2-0	Fenton 50, Dixon 52
42	06.05	RYM P	A	Basingstoke Town	797	D 1-1	Parker 12

PLAYING SQUAD

GOALKEEPERS: Darren Bonfield (Wealdstone), Richard Wilmot (Aylesbury U)

DEFENDERS: James Dillnut (Stevenage B), Tim Allpress (St.Albans C), Jon Bone (Bedford T), Nick Grime (Boreham Wood), Mark Burke (Luton), Scott Cretton (Stevenage B), Sam Turner (Luton)

MIDFIELDERS: Ian Scott (St.Albans C), Carl Williams (Carshalton Ath), Jamie Ougham (Stevenage B), Stuart Beevor (Aylesbury U), Robbie Kean (Stevenage B), Delroy McKoy (Bedford U), Adam Parker (Stevenage B), Jeran Meah (Stevenage B)

FORWARDS: Gary Dixon (Stevenage B), Shaun Marshall (Boreham Wood), Matthew Nolan (Youth)

MAIDENHEAD UNITED

"The Magpie 2000"
the official MILLENNIUM PROGRAMME
MAIDENHEAD UNITED F.C.
Sponsored by TradeMark WINDOWS

Ryman football league
RYMAN LEAGUE CUP – 4ᵀᴴ ROUND
v
BISHOP'S STORTFORD
THURSDAY 17ᵀᴴ FEBRUARY 2000
PRICE £1.20

CLUB OFFICIALS

Chairman: **Roger Coombs**
Vice Chairman: **Jon Swan**
President: **Jim Parsons**
Secretary: **Ken Chandler**
c/o Maidenhead United
Press Off .: **Jon Swan** (01189 349410)

FOOTBALL MANAGEMENT TEAM
Manager: Alan Devonshire
Asst. Man. & Coaches: Carl Taylor,Phil Parkes & Dave Harrison
Physios:Jon Urry & Bryan Clements

GROUND   York Road, Maidenhead, Berks SL6 1SQ Tel: 01628 624739/636314

FACT FILE

Formed: 1870
Nickname: Magpies
Sponsors: Trademark Windows
Colours: Black & white stripes/black/black
Change colours: Red/white/white
Midweek matchday: Tuesday
Reserve League: Suburban
Local Press: Maidenhead Advertiser,
Reading Evening Post, Slough Observer

Pages: 36   Price: £1
Editor: J Swan/R Jackson Tel: 01344 723750

Local Radio: 2-Ten FM, Star FM,
Thames Valley FM

Directions: From Maidenhead BR station proceed eastwards down Bell St - grd 300yds.
Ground in Town Centre five minutes from M4
Capacity: 4,000   Cover: 1,500   Seats: 400   Floodlights: Yes
Clubhouse: Open evenings & matchdays. Some hot food
Club Shop: Wide range of programmes and club souvenirs.
Contact Mark Smith (01753 854674)

PREVIOUS   Leagues: Southern 1894-1902; West Berks 02-04; Grt West Sub 04-22; Spartan 22-39; Grt West Comb 39-45; Corinthian 45-63; Athenian 63-73, Isthmian 1973-
Names: Maidenhead FC, Maidenhead Norfolkians. **Grounds:** None
CLUB RECORDS Attendance: 7,920 v Southall, FA Amat Cup Q/F 7/3/36   **Season's goalscorer:** Jack Palethorpe 66, 1929-30
Career appearances: Bert Randall 532, 1950-64   **Career goalscorer:** George Copas 270, 1924-35
Win: 14-1 v Buckingham Town (H), FA Amat. Cup 6/9/52   **Defeat:** 0-14 v Chesham United (A), Spartan Lge 31/3/23
Transfer fee paid: Undisclosed   **Transfer fee received:** £5,000 from Norwich for Alan Cordice, 79
BEST SEASON   FA Cup: Qtr Finals 1873-74 74-75 75-76   **F A Trophy:** 3rd Qual Rd   **FA Amateur Cup:** Semi Final 35-36
HONOURS   Isthmian Lg Div 2 Sth R-up 90-91,Promotion to Premier Division 99-00 Full Members Cup 96-97; Spartan Lg x3 R-upx2;
Corinthian Lg 57-58 60-61 61-62 R-up 58-59 59-60, Mem. Shield 56-57 61-62,R-up x4, Neale Cup 48-49 57-58 60-61; Gt Western Suburban Lg
19-20 R-up 20-21; Berks & Bucks Snr Cup x17, Berks & Bucks Benev. Cup x6 R-up x2; Mithras Cup R-up x4; Southern Comb. Cup R-up 81-82;
Sub Lge West 97-98; Allied Counties Champ 97-98
Players progressing: A Cordice (Norwich 79), P Priddy (Brentford 72), D Kemp (Plymouth), L Sanchez (Reading),E Kelsey, J Palethorpe (Reading
30), B Laryea(Torquay), R Davies (Torquay), Mark Harris (C.Palace & Swansea C 1985),Ben Abbey (Oxford U via Crawley 99)

Back Row: Richie Goddard (Res. Manager), Chris Ferdinand, Billy Cove, Jon Urry (Physio), Garath Ormshaw, Mickey Creighton, Barry Rake, Tim Cook, Kieran Draice, Tom Hickey, Tyrone Houston. **Front:** Brian Connor, Craig Webster, Steve Brown, Shane Small, Steve Croxford, Obi Ulasi, Dave Harrison (Coach). Seated: Chuk Agudosi.   **Photo** courtesy of The Windsor & Maidenhead Observer

Match Facts 1999-00

	Date	Comp.	H/A	Opponents	Result	Goalscorers	Att.
1	14.08	RYM 1	H	Leyton Pennant	L 1-3	Ferdinand	171
2	17.08	RYM 1	A	Uxbridge	W 4-0	Channell 2, Webster, Cook	137
	21.08	FAC Pre	A	Whitehawk	W 1-0	Agudosi	125
3	24.08	RYM 1	H	Grays Athletic	W 3-1	Croxford, Agudosi 2	129
4	28.08	RYM 1	A	Harlow Town	D 1-1	Agudosi	148
5	30.08	RYM 1	H	Yeading	W 2-1	Cook, Channell	172
	04.09	FAC 1Q	H	Viking Greenford	W 5-0	Clark, Channell, Agudosi 2, Nesbeth	121
6	07.09	RYM 1	A	Bishop's Stortford	D 1-1	Agudosi	317
7	11.09	RYM 1	H	Leatherhead	D 1-1	Creighton	162
	14.09	LC 1	A	Bromley	W 2-1	Channell, Rake	1125
	18.09	FAC 2Q	A	Walton & Hersham	W 2-0	Agudosi 2	258
8	25.09	RYM 1	A	Barton Rovers	D 1-1	Agudosi	143
	02.10	FAC 3Q	H	Salisbury City	L 0-1		345
	09.10	FAT 1	A	Raunds Town	D 0-0		104
	12.10	FAT 1R	H	Raunds Town	L 0-1		154
9	16.10	RYM 1	A	Croydon	D 2-2	Cove, Ulasi	81
10	23.10	RYM 1	H	Staines Town	W 3-2	Cove, Rake, Cook	162
	26.10	FMC 1	H	Walton & Hersham	W 2-0	Agudosi, Rake	144
11	30.10	RYM 1	A	Leatherhead	W 3-1	Cove 2, Croxford	132
12	06.11	RYM 1	H	Braintree Town	D 2-2	Cove, OG	352
	09.11	LC 2	H	Basingstoke Town	W 2-1	Robertson, Creighton	149
13	12.11	RYM 1	H	Bedford Town	W 2-1	Cook 2	222
	16.11	FMC 2	A	Basingstoke Town	L 0-2		132
14	20.11	RYM 1	A	Thame United	L 0-1		182
15	23.11	RYM 1	A	Worthing	D 1-1	Agudosi	264
16	27.11	RYM 1	A	Romford	W 3-1	Cove, Agudosi, Ferdinand	183
17	30.11	RYM 1	H	Whyteleafe	L 0-1		152
18	04.12	RYM 1	H	Harlow Town	W 2-0	Connor, Agudosi	179
19	18.12	RYM 1	H	Bognor Regis Town	D 1-1	Creighton	188
20	03.01	RYM 1	H	Braintree Town	W 4-3	Ferdinand, Agudosi, Croxford 2	198
21	08.01	RYM 1	A	Yeading	W 2-1	Agudosi, Creighton	188
	11.01	B & B SC 1	H	Slough Town	D *1-1	Croxford	282
	18.01	B & B SC 1R	A	Slough Town	L 0-1		332
22	22.01	RYM 1	A	Grays Athletic	D 2-2	Channell, Creighton	211
23	29.01	RYM 1	H	Bishop's Stortford	L 0-1		211
24	01.02	RYM 1	H	Bromley	W 3-2	Creighton 2, Rake	205
	03.02	LC 3	A	Whyteleafe	W 2-1	Cove, Agudosi	92
25	05.02	RYM 1	A	Leyton Pennant	W 3-0	Croxford, Ferdinand 2	110
26	15.02	RYM 1	A	Chertsey Town	W 2-1	Croxford, OG	160
	17.02	LC 4	H	Bishop's Stortford	W 2-1	Agudosi, Rake	143
27	22.02	RYM 1	A	Oxford City	W 3-1	Agudosi 2, Cove	171
28	26.02	RYM 1	H	Worthing	D 1-1	Lockwood	295
	29.02	LC SF1	A	Billericay Town	D 1-1	Cove	202
29	04.03	RYM 1	H	Wealdstone	W 1-0	Creighton	343
	07.03	LC SF2	H	Billericay Town	D *0-0	Won 4-3 after penalties	258
30	11.03	RYM 1	A	Bromley	D 0-0		289
31	18.03	RYM 1	H	Barton Rovers	D 2-2	Allen, Ferdinand	232
32	25.03	RYM 1	H	Oxford City	L 0-1		208
33	28.03	RYM 1	H	Uxbridge	D 2-2	Agudosi 2	205
34	01.04	RYM 1	A	Staines Town	L 0-1		275
35	08.04	RYM 1	A	Bognor Regis Town	W 2-1	Cove, Creighton	225
36	19.04	RYM 1	A	Wealdstoen	W 2-0	Webster, Agudosi	182
37	22.04	RYM 1	H	Bedford Town	D 2-2	Brown, Agudosi	500
38	24.04	RYM 1	H	Chertsey Town	W 2-0	Agudosi, Terry	215
39	29.04	RYM 1	A	Whyteleafe	D 1-1	Allen	278
	01.05	LC Final	N	Farnborough Town	L *0-1		701
40	03.05	RYM 1	H	Romford	W 4-0	Brown, Creighton, Terry, OG	225
41	04.05	RYM 1	H	Croydon	W 1-0	Ferdinand	305
42	06.05	RYM 1	H	Thame United	L 0-1		310

PLAYING SQUAD

GOALKEEPERS: Gareth Ormshaw (Crystal Palace), Kieran Drake (Oxford C)

DEFENDERS: Obinna Ulasi (Hayes), Tyrone Houston (Chalfont St.Peter), Michael Beaton (Youth), Steve Croxford (Hampton & R), Craig Webster (Youth), Andy Morley (Basingstoke T), Rob Clark (Youth)

MIDFIELDERS: Tim Cook (Thame U), Chris Ferdinand (Oxford C), Barry Rake (Walton & H), Andy Driscoll (St.Albans C), Tom Hickey (Youth), Andy Robertson (Reading), Matthew Glynn (Windsor & Eton), Steve Brown (Feltham)

FORWARDS: Chuk Agudosi (Osterley), Adrian Allen (Leyton Pennant), Billy Cove (Leyton Pennant), Lee Channell (Feltham), Micky Creighton (Uxbridge)

PURFLEET

CLUB OFFICIALS
Chairman: **Grant Beglan**
V/Chairman/Chief Executive: **Tommy Smith**
Secretary: **Tony Perkins** 48 Saltash Road,
Hainault, Essex IG6 2NL
(0181 500 3092)
Match Secretary/Press Officer:
Norman Posner
Comm Mger: **Tony Joy** (01375 392906)

FOOTBALL MANAGEMENT TEAM
Manager: Colin McBride
Asst Manager: David Crown
Coach: George Cook
Physio: Bob Johnson

FACT FILE

Founded: 1985
Nickname: Fleet
Colours:
Green & yellow/green/green & yellow
Change colours: All white
Midweek home matchday: Monday
Reserve's League: None

Pages: 44   Price: £1
Editor: Norman Posner (01708 458301 H)
Local Press: Romford, Thurrock Recorder,
Thurrock Gazette
Local Radio: Essex Radio, BBC Radio Essex

GROUND: Thurrock Hotel, Ship Lane, Grays, Essex
Tel: 01708 868901 Fax: 01708 866703
Directions: M25 or A13 to Dartford tunnel r'bout. Ground is fifty yards on right down Ship Lane. Nearest station is Purfleet, two miles from ground
Capacity: 4,500   Cover: 1,000   Seats: 300   Floodlights: Yes
Clubhouse: 10am-11pm every day. Snooker, squash, weights room, aerobics, a-lacarte restaurant, steam room. Three Bars. 56 Bedroom Hotel. Steward: Tommy South
Club Shop: Selling programmes & magazines. Contact Tommy South (01708 868901)

PREVIOUS   League: Essex Senior 85-89.   **Grounds:** None

CLUB RECORDS Attendance: 1,578 v West Ham United, friendly 1997
Goalscorer: Paul Cobb, 101.   **Appearances:** John Rees, 286
Win: 10-0 v Stansted (H) 86-87, v East Ham Utd (A) 87-88 (both Essex SeniorLeague)
Defeat: 0-6 v St Leonards Stamco (A), FA Trophy 96-97. 0-6 v Sutton United (H)Isthmian Lge 97-98

BEST SEASON   FA Cup: Fourth Qual Rd 95-96 (lost 1-3 away to Rushden & D)
FA Trophy: Second Rd Prop 95-96 (lost 1-2 away to Macclesfield Tn)

HONOURS: Isthmian Lg Div 2 91-92 (Div 1 R-up 93-94), Div 2 Nth R-up 88-89, Associate Members Tphy 91-92; Essex Snr Lg 87-88 (Lg Cup (2) 86-88, R-up 97-98), Stanford Charity Cup 87-88 (R-up 85-86); Essex Thames-Side Trophy 94-95; Loctite Trophy 91-92; Essex Bus Houses Sen L/Cup 93-94; F Budden Trophy 94-95; Essex & HertsBorder Comb R-up 94-95

Players progressing to Football League: Paul Cobb & Lee Williams (Leyton O.)

Purfleet F.C. 21.07.00   **Photo:** Peter Singh

Match Facts 1999-00

	Date	Comp.	H/A	Opponents	Att.	Result	Goalscorers
1	14.08	RYM P	H	CHESHAM UNITED	219	D 0 - 0	
2	17.08	RYM P	A	Hampton & Richmond Borough	213	D 1 - 1	Coombs 39
3	21.08	RYM P	A	Slough Town	567	L 0 - 3	
4	23.08	RYM P	H	ALDERSHOT TOWN	562	L 2 - 4	Georgiou 15, 35[p]
5	28.08	RYM P	H	BASINGSTOKE TOWN	163	L 1 - 2	Keeling 30
6	30.08	RYM P	A	Canvey Island	612	L 0 - 2	
7	04.09	RYM P	A	Boreham Wood	187	L 1 - 1	Coombs 46
8	06.09	RYM P	H	HITCHIN TOWN	147	W 3 - 0	McFarlane 15, Berry 56, Perkins 86
9	11.09	RYM P	A	Walton & Hersham	164	W 3 - 0	Berry 4, Coombes 49, Keeling 84
	13.09	LC 1	H	LEIGHTON TOWN	85	W 2 - 0	Carthy, Marsden
	18.09	FAC 2Q	H	BANBURY UNITED	176	D 0 - 0	
	21.09	FAC 2QR	A	Banbury United	405	W 1 - 0	Carthy 83
10	25.09	RYM P	H	BILLERICAY TOWN	301	D 2 - 2	Carthy 11, Georgiou 55
	02.10	FAC Q3	A	Boston United	1024	L 0 - 4	
	09.10	FAT 1	H	DAGENHAM & REDBRIDGE	532	W 2 - 0	Coombs, Georgiou
11	16.10	RYM P	H	GRAVESEND & NORTHFLEET	257	D 0 - 0	
12	19.10	RYM P	A	Farnborough Town	374	D 1 - 1	Barry 90[p]
13	23.10	RYM P	A	HENDON	157	W 4 - 1	Berry 42 51, Coombs 45, Georgiou 90
	25.10	FMC1	A	BISHOP'S STORTFORD	124	W 5 - 0	Coombs 11, Georgiou 4 (40 60 74 88)
	01.11	Essex SC3	H	BURNHAM RAMBLERS	106	W 4 - 1	Berry 25, Georgiou 42, Southon 66, Barry 90
14	06.11	RYM P	H	HEYBRIDGE SWIFTS	173	W 1 - 0	Keeling 1
	08.11	LC 2	H	CHERTSEY TOWN	102	W 2 - 1	Coombs, Berry
15	12.11	RYM P	A	Aylesbury United	457	W 3 - 0	Georgiou 3 (30 76 86)
	16.11	FMC 2	A	Heybridge Swifts	74	W 4 - 2	Coombs, Barry, Georgiou (2)
16	20.11	RYM P	H	HARROW BOROUGH	185	D 1 - 1	Berry 25
	27.11	FAT 2	H	RAUNDS TOWN	113	W 5 - 0	Keeling 12, Coombs 21 80, Georgiou 32, Dorrell 81
17	04.12	RYM P	A	Basingstoke Town	385	D 2 - 2	Berry 21, Georgiou 80
	14.12	LC 3	A	Chesham United	123	L 0 - 1	
18	18.12	RYM P	H	Dulwich Hamlet	239	L 2 - 3	Coombs 10 68
	21.12	E SC 4	A	Southend Manor	72	W 4 - 2	Georgiou 3 (21 40 63), Keeling 53
19	27.12	RYM P	H	CARSHALTON ATHLETIC	203	D 1 - 1	Keeling 74
20	03.01	RYM P	A	Heybridge Swifts	304	D 0 - 0	
21	08.01	RYM P	H	BOREHAM WOOD	215	W 3 - 2	McFarlane 35, Marsden 67, Georgiou 77
	11.01	FMC 3	A	Grays Athletic	100	W 4 - 3	Curran (2), Coombs (2)
	15.01	FAT 3	H	NEWPORT IOW	203	D 1 - 1	Georgiou 87
	18.01	FAT 3R	A	Newport IOW	404	L 1 - 2	Marsden 58
22	22.01	RYM P	A	Chesham United	290	L 0 - 1	
	24.01	E SC QF	H	GRAYS ATHLETIC	105	W 3 - 2	Southon, Georgiou, Marsden
23	29.01	RYM P	H	HAMPTON & RICHMOND B.	161	D 0 - 0	
24	04.02	RYM P	H	DAGENHAM & REDBRIDGE	1173	W 2 - 0	Georgiou 17 86
25	07.02	RYM P	H	St Albans City	420	W 4 - 2	Coombs 36, Georgiou 45, Southon 54, Carthy 67
	14.02	FMC QF	H	DAGENHAM & REDBRIDGE	206	W 5 - 2	Coombs (2), McFarlane, Keeling, Curran
26	19.02	RYM P	A	Hitchin Town	248	L 0 - 1	
27	22.02	RYM P	A	Enfield	165	W 2 - 1	Keeling 4, Berry 85[og]
28	26.02	RYM P	A	Gravesend & Northfleet	454	W 2 - 1	Coombs 22, Southon 65
29	04.03	RYM P	H	FARNBOROUGH TOWN	216	W 4 - 0	McFarlane 10, Georgiou 71[p], Curran 86 89
30	11.03	RYM P	A	Billericay Town	556	D 1 - 1	McFarlane 53
	14.03	FMC SF	A	Yeading	110	W 3 - 2	Coombs, Georgiou (2)
31	18.03	RYM P	H	WALTON & HERSHAM	187	W 3 - 1	Coombs 24, McFarlane 36, Curran 49
	22.03	E SC SF	H	BILLERICAY TOWN	276	W 4 - 2	Coombs (3), Georgiou
32	25.03	RYM P	H	ST. ALBANS CITY	287	D 3 - 3	Marsden 21, Coombs 22, Georgiou 45
33	01.04	RYM P	A	Hendon	259	W 3 - 1	Georgiou 1, Keeling 10, Southon 44
34	03.04	RYM P	H	CANVEY ISLAND	405	W 2 - 0	Georgiou 38, Webb 85
35	08.04	RYM P	H	DULWICH HAMLET	236	D 1 - 1	Georgiou 22 (p)
36	10.04	RYM P	H	SLOUGH TOWN	203	W 2 - 0	Coombs 19, 83
37	15.04	RYM P	A	Dagenham & Redbridge	1440	L 1 - 3	Barry 83
	17.04	E SC Final	N	Canvey Island	405	L 0 - 2	
38	22.04	RYM P	H	AYLESBURY UNITED	268	L 0 - 2	
39	24.04	RYM P	A	Carshalton Athletic	290	D 0 - 0	
40	28.04	RYM P	H	ENFIELD	332	W 4 - 2	Georgiou 23, Coombs 55, Webb 63, McFarlane 70
41	04.05	RYM P	A	Aldershot Town	1336	W 2 - 0	Webb 58, Coombs 77
42	06.05	RYM P	A	Harrow Borough	207	W 3 - 2	Coombs 18, Georgiou 40, 85
	09.05	FMC Final	N	Croydon	317	L 0 - 2	

PLAYING SQUAD

GOALKEEPERS: Steve Mead (Concord R)

DEFENDERS: Jamie Southon (Chelmsford C), Gary Howard (Dag & Red), Steve Pashley (Hornchurch), John Purdie (Billericay T), Kevin Marsden (Romford), Micky Engwell (Hertford M), Jim McFarlane (Concord R)

MIDFIELDERS: Martin Carthy (Erith & B), Mark Barry (Canvey Is), Graham Dorrell (Burnham Ramblers), Jon Keeling (Tilbury)

FORWARDS: Martyn Lawrence (Concord R), George Georgiou (Paralimon (Cyp)), Paul Coombs (Basingstoke T), Danny Curran (Leyton O)

SLOUGH TOWN

CLUB OFFICIALS

Chairman: Jonathon Freese

Secretary / Press Off.: Roy Merryweather
Tel: 01753 554833 (Ground)
01735 534033(W)
01189 722871(H)

FOOTBALL MANAGEMENT TEAM
Manager: Steve Browne
Physio: Kevin McGoldrick
Kit Man: Brian Burke

FACT FILE

Formed: 1890
Nickname: The Rebels
Sponsor: T.B.A.
Colours: Amber/navy blue/amber
Change colours: All white
Midweek home matchday: Tuesdays

Pages: 36 Price: £1.50
Editor: John Tebbit
Local Press: Slough Observer Slough Express
Local Radio: Thames Valley FM, Star FM
Radio Berkshire

GROUND: Wexham Park Stadium, Wexham Road, Slough, Berkshire. SL2 5QR.
Tel: 01753 554833 Fax: 01753 533949
Directions: From North : M25 J16 East London M40 J1 - South A412 through Iver Heath to George Green. 2nd set lights turn right by George PH, George Green.Church Lane 1 mile to end, then small roundabout, turn left, ground 1/4 mile onright
Capacity: 5,000   Cover: 1,890   Seats: 450   Floodlights: Yes
Clubhouse: Lounge bar open weekdays 7pm-11pm, weekends, lunchtimes, evenings.
Banqueting hall for all types of functions
Club Shop: Contact: Graham Gowland 01252 873620

PREVIOUS **Leagues:** Southern Alliance 1892-93; Berks & Bucks 1901-05; Gt Western Suburban1906-19; Spartan 1920-39; Herts & Middx 1940-45; Corinthian 1946-63; Athenian1963-73; Isthmian 1973-90, 94-95; Alliance Prem. (GMVC) 90-94
Grounds: Dolphin Playing Fields & Stadium, Chalvey Rd Sports Grd, YorkRd Maidenhead 1920, Centre Sports Ground 36-42

CLUB RECORDS **Attendance:** 8,000 - Schoolboys u15 Final Slough v Liverpool - 1976
Win: 17-0 v Railway Clearing House - 1921-22   **Defeat:** 1-11 v Chesham Town 1909/10
Transfer fee paid: £18,000 for Colin Fielder from Farnborough - 1991   **Career appearances:** Terry Reardon 458 - 64/81
Received: £22,000 from Wycombe Wanderers for Steve Thompson   **Career goalscorer:** E.J.C. Tory Norris 84 - 25/26

BEST SEASON **FA Cup:** 2nd Round Proper, 79-80 (Yeovil T), 82-83 (Bishop's Stortford), 85-86 (Leyton O.), 86-87 (Swansea C.).
League clubs defeated: Millwall, 1-0 (H) Jan. 1983
FA Trophy: Semi-Final 1976-77, 2-6(agg) v Dagenham; 97-98, 1-2(agg) v Southport

HONOURS: FA Amateur Cup R-up 72-73; Great Western Suburban League R-up 19-20: Spartan League R-up 20-21 21-22 31-32 32-33 38-39; Herts & Middx League R-up 43-44; Corinthian League 50-51 (R-up 45-46 46-47 57-58); Athenian League 67-68 71-72 72-73 (R-up 68-69),LgCup 71-2 72-3 Div 1 64-65, Memorial Shield 64-65 71-72 72-73); Isthmian League 80-81 89-90 R-up 94-95, (Div 2 R-up 73-74),Lg Cup 75-76 80-81 R-up 94-95 Lge Shield 89-90 ; Berks & Bucks Sen Cup (10) 02-03 19-20 23-24 26-27 35-36 54-55 70-72 76-77 80-81

Players progressing:
Bill McConnell,
Peter Angell,
Dennis Edwards,
Ralph Miller,
John Delaney,
Paul Barron,
Dave Kemp,
Roy Davies,
Mickey Droy,
Eric Young,
Alan Paris,
Tony Dennis,
Lloyd Owusu
(Brentford 98)

Slough Town's
David Adekola
holds off Gravesend's
Ross Edwards

Photo: Alan
Coomes

Match Facts 1999-00

	Date	Comp.	H/A	Opponents	Att.	Result	Goalscorers
1	14.08	RYM P	A	St Albans City	843	W 1 - 0	Hawthorne 82
2	17.08	RYM P	H	HENDON	480	D 1 - 1	Barrowcliff 19
3	21.08	RYM P	H	PURFLEET	567	W 3 - 0	Hall 11, Hawthorne 15, Townley 35
4	23.08	RYM P	A	Carshalton Athletic	334	D 1 - 1	Denton 90
5	28.08	RYM P	A	Gravesend & Northfleet	462	L 0 - 1	
6	30.08	RYM P	H	BILLERICAY TOWN	612	W 4 - 0	Hall 29, Townley 66, Nabil 81, Adekola 89
7	04.09	RYM P	H	DULWICH HAMLET	548	W 2 - 1	White 29, Deaner 57
8	07.09	RYM P	A	Farnborough Town	713	W 1 - 0	Rainford 24
9	11.09	RYM P	H	CANVEY ISLAND	663	L 1 - 2	Hawthorne 61 (p)
	14.09	LC 1	H	GRAYS ATHLETIC	222	W 1 - 0	Hannigan
	18.09	FAC 2Q	H	COWES SPORTS	461	W 3 - 1	Hall 45, Deaner 72, Rainford 75
10	25.09	RYM P	A	Hampton & Richmond Borough	345	D 1 - 1	Pye 58
	02.10	FAC Q3	H	CARSHALTON ATHLETIC	620	W 1 - 0	Deaner 25
11	05.10	RYM P	A	Walton & Hersham	303	D 2 - 2	Adekola, Deaner
	09.10	FAT 1	H	HENDON	461	L 0 - 2	
	16.10	FAC Q4	H	CAMBRIDGE CITY	771	D 1 - 1	Deaner 39
	19.10	FAC Q4 R	A	Cambridge City	650	L 2 - 3	Deaner 44, Hawthorne 62
12	23.10	RYM P	A	Chesham United	401	L 0 - 3	
	26.10	FMC 1	H	STAINES TOWN	282	W 4 - 1	Pye, Deaner, Hammatt (2)
13	06.11	RYM P	H	AYLESBURY UNITED	556	L 1 - 2	Deaner 49
	09.11	LC 2	H	CARSHALTON ATHLETIC		L 0 - 1	
14	13.11	RYM P	A	Boreham Wood	326	W 3 - 1	Deaner 54, Hammatt 66, Hall 90
	16.11	FMC 2	H	CARSHALTON ATHLETIC	207	W 2 - 1	Townley, Hall (p)
15	20.11	RYM P	H	DAGENHAM & REDBRIDGE	592	L 2 - 3	Hall 2, Adekola 81
16	04.12	RYM P	A	Dulwich Hamlet	405	W 3 - 2	Rainford 35, Hall 52, Marshall 65
17	18.12	RYM P	A	Harrow Borough	317	W 1 - 0	Richardson 45
18	27.12	RYM P	H	BASINGSTOKE TOWN	630	L 1 - 4	Adekola 53
19	03.01	RYM P	A	Aylesbury United	662	D 2 - 2	Marshall 6, Richardson 45
20	08.01	RYM P	H	FARNBOROUGH TOWN	707	L 1 - 2	Hawthorne 65
	11.01	B&B SC 3	A	Maidenhead United	325	D 1 - 1	Dyer (B&B SC - Berks & Bucks Sen. Cup)
21	15.01	RYM P	H	HITCHIN TOWN	463	W 3 - 0	Gladhill 9, Hall 28, Hawthorne 64
	18.01	B&B SC 3R	H	MAIDENHEAD UNITED	416	W 1 - 0	Hall
22	22.01	RYM P	H	ST ALBANS CITY	610	L 0 - 3	
23	29.01	RYM P	A	Hendon	407	D 1 - 1	Hawthorne 32[p]
24	05.02	RYM P	H	CARSHALTON ATHLETIC	453	W 2 - 1	Stevens 24 28
25	12.02	RYM P	A	Billericay Town	456	L 1 - 3	Hall 4
	15.02	FMC 3	A	Leatherhead	124	W 3 - 0	Richardson, Hammatt, Adekola
26	19.02	RYM P	H	GRAVESEND & NORTHFLEET	455	W 2 - 1	Marshall 30, Richardson 61
	22.02	B&B SC QF	A	Hungerford Town	253	W 3 - 0	Townley, Hammatt, Daly
27	26.02	RYM P	A	Hitchin Town	437	W 2 - 1	Richardson 3, Hammatt 70[p]
28	04.03	RYM P	H	WALTON & HERSHAM	488	W 3 - 1	Haynes 30, Marshall 74, Rainford 78
	07.03	FMC QF	A	Gravesend & Northfleet	156	L 2 - 3	Daly 45, Marshall 87
29	11.03	RYM P	H	HAMPTON & RICHMOND B	504	D 1 - 1	Haynes 86
30	18.03	RYM P	A	Canvey Island	878	L 0 - 2	
31	21.03	RYM P	H	ENFIELD	406	W 2 - 1	Marshall 25, Hawthorne 45
32	25.03	RYM P	A	Aldershot Town	2123	L 0 - 2	
	28.03	B&B SC SF	A	Aylesbury United	390	L 2 - 4	OG (Maqrshall) 8, Richardson 34
33	01.04	RYM P	H	CHESHAM UNITED	551	W 2 - 0	Marshall 17, Patton 37
34	08.04	RYM P	H	HARROW BOROUGH	504	L 2 - 3	Richardson 51, 76
35	10.04	RYM P	A	Purfleet	203	L 0 - 2	
36	15.04	RYM P	A	Enfield	204	W 3 - 1	Richardson 6, 17, Hawthorne 42
37	18.04	RYM P	A	Heybridge Swifts	213	D 1 - 1	Haynes 67
38	22.04	RYM P	A	BOREHAM WOOD	445	L 2 - 3	Haynes 6, Hawthorne 33 (p)
39	24.04	RYM P	A	Basingstoke Town	524	L 0 - 1	
40	29.04	RYM P	H	HEYBRIDGE SWIFTS	410	W 2 - 1	Haynes 26, Marshall 39
41	02.05	RYM P	H	ALDERSHOT TOWN	761	D 0 - 0	
42	06.05	RYM P	A	Dagenham & Redbridge	1530	L 1 - 2	OG (Heffer) 75

PLAYING SQUAD

GOALKEEPERS: Danny Honey (Yeading), Steve Mautone (Reading)

DEFENDERS: Steve Daly (Boreham Wood), Chris White (Farnborough T), David Timothy (Woking), Keith McPherson (Brighton), Leon Townley (Brentford)

MIDFIELDERS: Mark Hawthorne (Crawley T), David Rainford (Colchester), Graham Kemp (Chesham U), Aaron Patton (Hayes), Paul Barrowcliff (Chesham U)

FORWARDS: Marcus Richardson (Burnham), Clement James (Brentford), Damian Markman (Harrow B), Junior Haynes (Carshalton Ath), Dwight Marshall (Kingstonian), Mark Hall (Hayes), Chris Allen (Stockport)

St ALBANS CITY

CLUB OFFICIALS

Chairman: **Lee Harding**
President: **Cllr Malcolm MacMillan**
Vice Chairman: **Gary Elliott**
Secretary: **Steve Eames** c/o Club
Safety Officer: **Rex Winn** 0966 175124 (M)
Comm. Man: **Roberta Rolland**

FOOTBALL MANAGEMENT TEAM

Manager: Kevin Mudd
Consultant Physio: Jude Monteath

FACT FILE

Formed: 1908
Nickname: The Saints
Colours: Yellow with blue trim/blue/whitel
Change colours: Sky Blue with red trim
Midweek home matchday: Monday
Newsline: 0930 555822
Internet: http://www.andyzad.demon.co.uk
E-Mail: andy@andyzad.demon.co.uk

For up to the minute news,
results, fixtures,
plus general facts & figures
from the world of
non-league football

log on to

www.nlfootball.com

GROUND: Clarence Park, York Rd, St Albans, Herts AL1 4PL Tel: 01727 864296
Directions: Left out of St Albans station - Clarence Pk 200yds ahead acrossHatfield Rd. M25, jct 21 to Noke Hotel island, straight on thru Chiswell Green towards St Albans, straight over 2 mini-r'bouts and one larger island, thru 2sets of lights and right at island at far end of city centre (St Peters St.) into Hatfield Rd, over mini-r'bout, left at 2nd lights into Clarence Rd, ground on left
Capacity: 6,000   Cover: 1,900   Seats: 904   Floodlights: Yes
Clubhouse: Open matchdays and available for functions. Manager: Ray McCord (01727 837956). Tea bar within ground serves hot food
Club Shop: Club merchandise & League & non-League progs,magazines, videos etc
Managers: Lee Woods and Rob Fenn c/o club

Programme: Pages: 32   Price: £1.50
Published by Queensway Publishing

Local Press: St Albans & District Observer,
Herts Advertiser
Local Radio: BBC Three Counties,
Chiltern Radio, Oasis

PREVIOUS   **Leagues:** Herts County 08-10; Spartan 08-20; Athenian 20-23
CLUB RECORDS   **Attendance:** 9,757 v Ferryhill Ath., FA Amtr Cup QF 27/2/26
Appearances: Phil Wood 900 (62-85)Goalscorer: W H (Billy) Minter 356 (top scorer for 12 consecutive seasons 1920-32)
Win: 14-0 v Aylesbury United (H) Spartan Lge 19/10/12   **Defeat:** 0-11 v Wimbledon (H), Isthmian Lge 9/11/46.
Fee Paid: £6,000 for Paul Turner (Yeovil Town Aug 97)   **Fee Received:** £92,750 for Dean Austin (Southend 90/Spurs 92)

BEST SEASON   **FA Amateur Cup:** Semi final 22-23 24-25 25-26 69-70.   **FA Trophy:** Semi-Final 1998-99 1-2 & 2-3 v Forest Green Rovers
FA Cup: 2nd Rd replay 68-69 (1-3 at Walsall after 1-1 draw), 80-81 (1-4 atTorquay after 1-1 draw), 96-97 (9-2 at Bristol City)

HONOURS: Isthmian Lg 23-24 26-27 27-28 (R-up 54-55 92-93); Div 1 85-86, Div 2 R-up 83-84, Lg Cup R-up 89-90, Res. Sect. R-up 48-49 60-61 61-62; Athenian Lg 20-21 21-22 (R-up 22-23); Spartan Lg 11-12 (R-up 12-13), East Div 09-10); Herts Co. Lg 09-10 (West Div 08-09, Aubrey Cup(res) 61-62); London Snr Cup 70-71 (R-up 69-70); AFA Snr Cup 33-34 (R-up 30-31 32-33 34-35); E Anglian Cup 92-93; Herts SnrCup(12) (R-up 10); Herts Snr Tphy 86-87, Herts Charity Cup(25) (R-up(18);Mithras Cup 64-65 71-72 (R-up 76-77); Wycombe F'lit Cup(2) 68-70; St AlbansHosp Cup 45-46; Hitchin Centenary Cup 70-71 (R-up 71-72); Victory Cup 25-26 27-28, Liege Cup 26-27; Billy Minter Invit. Cup (3) 90-93

Players progressing: A Grimsdell (Spurs 11), G Edmonds (Watford 14), R Burke(Man Utd 46), J Meadows (Watford 51), M Rose (Charlton 63), J Kinnear (Spurs 65), J Mitchell (Fulham 72), A Cockram (Brentford 88), D Austin (Southend 90),T Kelly (Stoke 90), M Danzey (Cambridge 92), D Williams (Brentford 93),

St. Albans
Ashley Vickers
gets in a
successful tackle
on Pat Gavin of
Harrow Borough

Photo:
Paul Carter

Match Facts 1999-00

	Date	Comp.	H/A	Opponents	Att.	Result	Goalscorers
1	14.08	RYM P	H	SLOUGH TOWN	843	L 0 - 1	
2	17.08	RYM P	A	Chesham United	398	W 4 - 3	Haworth 41, 85, Turner 81, Clark 88
3	21.08	RYM P	A	Canvey Island	681	W 1 - 0	Pratt 39
4	23.08	RYM P	H	HITCHIN TOWN	755	W 2 - 1	Turner 74, Clark 81
5	28.08	RYM P	H	WALTON & HERSHAM	701	D 1 - 1	Piper 90
6	30.08	RYM P	A	Aldershot Town	2234	W 2 - 0	Turner 19, Piper 87
7	04.09	RYM P	A	Basingstoke Town	559	W 2 - 0	Andrews 90, 90
8	06.09	RYM P	H	HAMPTON & RICHMOND B.	684	D 1 - 1	Hunter 90
9	11.09	RYM P	H	HENDON	785	W 3 - 0	Hunter 36, McCormack 47, Andrews 69
	14.09	LC 1	A	Hampton & Richmond Bor.	113	W 2 - 0	Clark, Duru
	18.09	FAC 2Q	A	Bedford Town	851	W 2 - 0	Piper 31, 75
10	25.09	RYM P	A	Gravesend & Northfleet	495	W 2 - 1	Adams 29, Hunter 54
	02.10	FAC Q3	H	NANTWICH TOWN	504	W 4 - 2	Clark(3), Andrews
	09.10	FAT 1	H	THAME UNITED	373	L 1 - 2	Pratt
	16.10	FAC Q4	A	Canvey Island	711	D 3 - 3	McMenamin 17, Clark 37 74
	19.10	FAC Q4 R	H	CANVEY ISLAND	678	W 2 - 1	Randall 48, Pollard 51
11	23.10	RYM P	A	Billericay Town	581	L 1 - 3	Andrews 38
	25.10	FMC1	H	CHESHAM UNITED	154	W 2 - 1	Randall, Duru
	30.10	FAC 1	H	BAMBER BRIDGE	1127	L 0 - 2	
	01.11	Herts SC2	H	HODDESDON TOWN	41	W 1 - 0	Duru
12	06.11	RYM P	H	CARSHALTON ATHLETIC	572	W 4 - 0	Butler 12, Clark 33 82, Randall 75
	08.11	LC 2	H	GREAT WAKERING TOWN	81	W 4 - 2	Andrews (2), OG (Randall)
13	13.11	RYM P	A	Harrow Borough	189	W 2 - 0	Clark 79, Piper 90
	15.11	FMC 2	A	BEDFORD TOWN	146	D 2 - 2	Andrews 66 72 Lost 3-4 after penalties
14	20.11	RYM P	H	DULWICH HAMLET	829	W 4 - 1	**Clark 3** (30 54 58), Piper 53
15	27.11	RYM P	A	Boreham Wood	547	W 3 - 2	McCormack 28 54, Piper 73
16	04.12	RYM P	A	Walton & Hersham	232	D 1 - 1	Piper 83
	07.12	Herts SC QF	A	Hitchin Town	141	W 5 - 1	Clark (2), Rutherford (2), Randall
17	11.12	RYM P	H	AYLESBURY UNITED	678	D 1 - 1	Piper 75
	14.12	LC 3	A	Billericay Town	102	W *2 - 1	Randall 18, Haworth 99 St. Albans removed from competition
18	18.12	RYM P	A	Carshalton Athletic	307	W 1 - 0	Randall 90
19	27.12	RYM P	H	ENFIELD	1780	W 5 - 0	Protheroe 13[og], Randall 45, Andrews 47, Piper 57, Haworth 90
20	03.01	RYM P	A	Farnborough Town	693	L 0 - 1	
21	08.01	RYM P	H	BASINGSTOKE TOWN	840	W 4 - 1	Andrews 7, Randall 39 79, Piper 75
22	18.01	RYM P	A	Heybridge Swifts	253	L 1 - 2	Turner 40
23	22.01	RYM P	A	Slough Town	610	W 3 - 0	Harvey 65, Haworth 76, Piper 82
24	24.01	RYM P	H	DAGENHAM & REDBRIDGE	1264	L 1 - 3	Clark 43
25	29.01	RYM P	H	CHESHAM UNITED	740	D 1 - 1	Piper 90
26	05.02	RYM P	A	Hitchin Town	609	D 2 - 2	Piper 25, Haworth 57
27	07.02	RYM P	H	PURFLEET	420	L 2 - 4	Andrews 44, Piper 53[p]
28	12.02	RYM P	H	ALDERSHOT TOWN	1499	L 0 - 1	
29	19.02	RYM P	A	Hampton & Richmond Bor.	307	D 2 - 2	C Piper 62, Randall 75
30	26.02	RYM P	A	Dagenham & Redbridge	1582	L 1 - 2	L Piper 49
31	04.03	RYM P	H	HEYBRIDGE SWIFTS	326	W 2 - 0	Clark 16, C Piper 57
	07.03	HSC SF	A	Boreham Wood	213	D 3 - 3	L Piper (2), C Piper
32	11.03	RYM P	H	GRAVESEND & NORTHFLEET	520	L 0 - 1	
33	18.03	RYM P	A	Hendon	380	W 3 - 0	C Piper 73, Clark 83 90
34	20.03	RYM P	H	CANVEY ISLAND	459	L 2 - 5	C Piper 8, Vickers 86
35	25.03	RYM P	A	Purfleet	287	D 3 - 3	C Piper 50, Pollard 69, L Piper 74 (p)
36	01.04	RYM P	H	BILLERICAY TOWN	529	L 1 - 2	C Piper 51
	03.04	H SC SF R	H	BOREHAM WOOD	161	W 5 - 1	Randall, **Clark (3)**, OG
37	08.04	RYM P	H	FARNBOROUGH TOWN	425	D 0 - 0	
	11.04	H SC Final	N	Baldock Town	345	W 3 - 1	Lyons, Randall, L Piper
38	15.04	RYM P	A	Aylesbury United	678	W 2 - 0	James 66, Randall 75
39	22.04	RYM P	H	HARROW BOROUGH	515	W 3 - 2	C Piper 60, 90, Clark 88
40	29.04	RYM P	H	BOREHAM WOOD	640	D 0 - 0	
41	02.05	RYM P	A	Enfield	235	L 0 - 4	
42	06.05	RYM P	A	Dulwich Hamlet	582	L 2 - 3	Simpson 12, Randall 52

PLAYING SQUAD

GOALKEEPERS: Laurence Batty (Woking)

DEFENDERS: Andy Futcher (Ware), Lee Harvey (Aylesbury U), Al-James Hannigan (Slough T),
Corey Campbell (Grabesend), Mark Rooney (Aylesbury U), Peter Risley (Bishop's Stortford)

MIDFIELDERS: Dwain Clarke (Harro B), Michael Mison (Rushden & D), Paul Turner (Yeovil T),
Tom Meredith (Bury T), David Pratt (Dag & Red)

FORWARDS: Martin Randall (Hayes), Tony Samuels (Stevenage B), Gary Ansell (Barnet),
Chris Piper (Charlton), Francis McCormack (Harrow B)

SUTTON UNITED

CLUB OFFICIALS
Chairman: Bruce Elliott
President: Andrew W Letts
Secretary: Dave Farebrother, 38 Plevna Rd
Hampton.TW12 2BP(0771 2682415-M)
Press Officer: Tony Dolbear
Tel: 0207 782 8644 (daytime)
Mobile 07966 507023

FOOTBALL MANAGEMENT TEAM
Manager: John Rains
Assistant Manager: TBA
Coach: Micky Cook **Physio:** Dennis Rose
Youth& Res Team Manager: Phil Dunne

FACT FILE
Formed: 1898
Nickname: The U's
Sponsors: Securicor
Colours: Amber & chocolate/chocolate/
amber & chocolate
Change colours: Green & white/black/black
Midweek matchday: Tuesday
Reserve League: Suburban League
Season 99-00
Leading Scorer: Sam Winston 16
Player of the Year: Barry Laker
Captain: Dave Harlow

GROUND: Borough Sports Ground, Gander Green Lane, Sutton, Surrey SM1 2EY
Tel:0181 644 4440 Fax: 0181 644 5120
Directions: Gander Green Lane runs between A232 (Cheam Road - turn by Sutton Cricket Club) and A217 (Oldfields Road - turn at`Goose & Granite' PH lights). Ground opposite `The Plough' 50 yards from West Sutton BR station. Bus 413 passes ground
Capacity: 7,032   **Seated:** 765   **Terracing - Covered:** 1,250 **Uncovered:** 5,000
Clubhouse: Open every day, food. Available for hire with five function rooms
Club Shop: Open matchdays selling a full range of souvenirs, etc, contact Tony Cove via club

Pages: 48   **Price:** £1.50
Editor: Tony Dolbear Tel: 0966 507023
Other club publications:
'Touchliner' (Supporters' Club)
Local Press: Sutton Advertiser, Sutton Guardian, Sutton Independent, Sutton Comet
Local Radio: Thames Radio, County Sound

PREVIOUS Leagues: Sutton Junior, Southern Sub 10-21, Athenian 21-63, Isthmian 63-86, 91-99, GMVC 86-91, 99-00
Names: Sutton Association, Sutton Guild Rovers   **Grounds:** Western Road, Manor Lane, London Road, The Find.
CLUB RECORDS Attendance: 14,000 v Leeds United,FA Cup 4th Rd 24/1/70
Victory: 11-1 v Clapton 66, & leatherhead 82-83   **Defeat:** 13-0 v Barking 25-26
Scorer: Paul McKinnon (279)   **Appearances:** Larry Pritchard 781 (65-84)
Fee Paid: to Malmo FF for Paul McKinnon 83   **Fee Received:** £100,000 for Efan Ekoku (Bournemouth 90)
BEST SEASON FA Amateur Cup: Runners-up 62-63 68-69; SF 28-29 36-37 67-68   **FA Trophy:** Runners-up 80-81; SF 92-93,99-00
FA Cup: 4th Round - 69-70, 0-6 v Leeds Utd (H); 88-89, 0-8 v Norwich C. (A) ,3rd Rd 87-88 v Middlesbrough 1-1,0-1.
HONOURS Bob Lord Trophy 90-91; **Isthmian League** 66-67 84-86 98-99 R-up 67-68 70-71 81-82, Lge Cup (3) 82-84 85-86 97-98 R-up 79-80; Loctite Cup 91-92; Carlton Cup 95-96; **Athenian Lge** 27-28 45-46 57-58 R-up 46-47, Lg Cup 45-46 55-56 61-62 62-63, Res Sec 61-62 R-up 32-33; Anglo Italian Semi-Pro Cup 79 R-up 80 82; London Snr Cup 57-58 82-83; London Charity Cup 69-70 R-up 67-68 68-69 72-73; Surrey Snr Cup x14 R-up x9; Surrey Interm. Cup x4 R-up x6; Surrey Jnr Cup R-up 09-10; Surrey Snr Char. Sh. x3 R-up x6; Surrey Interm Char. Cup 31-32 R-up 34-35 38-39; Dylon Char. Sh. 84 R-up 80 82 83 85; Groningen Yth tournament 83 85 R-up 79 81 89 91; John Ullman Invit. Cup 88-89
Past Players progressing: Numerous including the following since 1980 - S Galloway (C Palace 84), P McKinnon (Blackburn 86), R Fearon (Ipswich 87), PHarding (Notts Co), E Ekoku (Bournemouth 91), M Golley (Maidstone), A Barnes (C Palace 91), P Rogers (Sheff U 92), S Massey (C Palace 92), A & R Scott (Sheff U 93), O Morah (Cambridge 94), M Watson (West Ham 95)

Back Row: Tony Rains (now Carshalton A.), Mark Watson, Colin Simpson, Andy Little, Gareth Howells, Paul Harford, John Mackie, John Rains.
Front : Geoff Moxy, Richard Skelly, Keith Rowlands, Danny Brooker, Dave Harlow, Andy Salako, Jimmy Dack, Gwynne Berry, Sammy Winston, Micky Cook.   Photo: Garry Letts

Match Facts 1999-00

	Date	Comp.	H/A	Opponents	Gate	Result & Score	Goalscorers	League Position
1	14.08	N.C.	H	Hereford United	1,386	D 1-1	Harford 58	
2	21.08	N.C.	A	Hednesford Town	1,062	L 0-1		17
3	24.08	N.C.	H	Stevenage Borough	1,152	L 0-2		
4	28.08	N.C.	H	Rushden & Diamonds	1,083	L 0-4		22
5	30.08	N.C.	A	Dover Athletic	1,226	D 1-1	Winston 79	22
6	04.09	N.C.	A	Kettering Town	1,328	L 0-1		22
7	11.09	N.C.	H	Altrincham	805	W 3-0	Watson 26, 58 Dack 80	20
8	18.09	N.C.	A	Yeovil Town	2,839	W 2-1	Watson 65, Laker 76	19
9	21.09	N.C.	H	Welling United	814	L 2-3	Dack 6, 8	
10	25.09	N.C.	A	Southport	1,122	D 1-1	Winston 11	20
11	02.10	N.C.	H	Telford United	825	W 2-1	Winston 38, 70 (2 pens)	17
	05.10	NMT 1	A	Hereford United	625	L 0-2		
12	09.10	N.C.	H	Northwich Victoria	803	D 2-2	Watson 55, Laker 73	17
	16.10	FAC 4Q	A	Rushden & D	2,525	L 1-4	Rowlands 53	
13	23.10	N.C.	A	Nuneaton Borough	1,799	L 0-2		19
14	02.11	N.C.	H	Kingstonian	1,422	D 2-2	Dack 69, Winston 88	19
15	06.11	N.C.	A	Doncaster Rovers	1,097	W 1-0	Watson 20	19
16	12.11	N.C.	A	Welling United	704	W 3-2	Harlow 45, Watson 47, Harford 72	15
17	20.11	N.C.	H	Yeovil Town	1,010	L 0-1		16
	27.11	FAT 2	A	Salisbury City	643	W 5-2	Winston 6, 33, Ekoku 61, Rowlands 87, Harlow 88	
18	04.12	N.C.	A	Morecambe	1,460	L 2-6	Watson 48, Riley 63	17
19	11.12	N.C.	H	Kettering Town	716	D 1-1	Newhouse 57	16
20	15.12	N.C.	A	Forest Green Rovers	586	W 2-1	Watson 21, Newhouse 34	
21	18.12	N.C.	H	Nuneaton Borough	749	L 1-2	Skelly 66	16
22	27.12	N.C.	A	Hayes	1,006	L 0-1		18
23	03.01	N.C.	H	Hayes	1,058	D 2-2	Hutchinson 6, Newhouse 22	19
24	08.01	N.C.	A	Doncaster Rovers	2447	L 0-1		19
	15.01	FAT 3	A	Canvey Island	719	W 1-0	Winston	
25	22.01	N.C.	A	Kidderminster Harriers	2818	L 0-1		20
26	29.01	N.C.	H	Southport	850	D 1-1	Hutchinson 58	20
	05.02	FAT 4	H	Forest Green Rovers	711	W 3-0	Brooker 25, Newberry 41, Winston 62	
27	12.02	N.C.	A	Kingstonian	1,527	L 2-4	Winston 3, 31	22
28	19.02	N.C.	A	Scarborough	1,395	L 0-3		22
	26.02	FAT 5	H	Dover Athletic	1,207	W 2-1	Winston 13, Newhouse 84	
29	04.03	N.C.	A	Altrincham	889	L 0-3		22
	11.03	FAT 6	H	Rushden & Diamonds	1,586	D 1-1	Winston 12	
	14.03	FAT 6R	A	Rushden & Diamonds	2,703	W 3-1	Winston 35, Newhouse 51, Ekoku 67	
30	18.03	N.C.	A	Rushden & Diamonds	2,749	L 0-4		22
31	25.03	N.C.	A	Woking	2,065	W 2-1	Winston 51 (p), Watson 53	22
32	28.03	N.C.	H	Hednesford Town	642	D 0-0		21
	01.04	FAT SF1	H	Kingstonian	2,384	D 1-1	Winston 4	
33	05.04	N.C.	A	Woking	935	D 1-1	Forrester 75	22
34	08.04	N.C.	A	Telford United	1,011	L 0-2		22
35	11.04	N.C.	H	Forest Green Rovers	607	W 3-2	Watson 36, 81, Hutchinson 38	22
	18.04	FAT SF2	A	Kingstonian	2,309	L 0-6		
36	20.04	N.C.	H	Scarborough	463	L 1-2	Hutchinson 75	22
37	22.04	N.C.	H	Morecambe	659	L 0-1		22
38	24.04	N.C.	A	Stevenage Borough	1,485	L 0-1		22
39	29.04	N.C.	A	Northwich Victoria	805	L 0-2		22
40	01.05	N.C.	H	Dover Athletic	601	L 0-1		22
41	03.05	N.C.	H	Kidderminster Harriers	579	L 0-3		22
42	06.05	N.C.	A	Hereford United	1,432	L 1-4	Rowlands 63	22

PLAYING SQUAD

GOALKEEPERS: Gareth Howells (St.Albans C), Tommy Dunn (Youth)

DEFENDERS: Gwynne Berry (Welling U), Danny Brooker (Kingstonian), Andy Walker (Hampton & R), Ryan Palmer (Brighton), Andy Riley (Dulwich Hamlet), Stuart Hammonds (Lincoln U)

MIDFIELDERS: Paul Harford (Welling U), John Westcott (Brighton), Danny Bolt (Woking), Paul Sears (Carshalton Ath), **David Harlow** (Farnborough T)

FORWARDS: Andy Salako (Carshalton Ath), Jimmy Sugrue (Aldershot T), Jamie Pace (Leatherhead), Nko Ekoku (Harrow B), Aiden Newhouse (Wimbledon), Joe Nartey (Chesham U)

AYLESBURY UNITED

Match Facts 1999-00

	Date	Comp.	H/A	Opponents	Att.	Result		Goalscorers
1	14.08	RYM P	H	WALTON & HERSHAM	603	W	1-0	Browne 16
2	17.08	RYM P	A	Basingstoke Town	494	L	2-4	Browne 29, Beevor 31
3	21.08	RYM P	A	Dagenham & Redbridge	838	L	1-4	Beevor 66
4	24.08	RYM P	H	BOREHAM WOOD	425	L	0-1	
5	28.08	RYM P	H	CANVEY ISLAND	602	D	3-3	Hercules 6, Crawshaw 33, Gallagher 86
6	30.08	RYM P	A	Enfield	458	L	1-3	Selby 46
7	04.09	RYM P	A	Hampton & Richmond Borough	251	L	1-2	Selby 19
8	07.09	RYM P	H	ALDERSHOT TOWN	761	W	3-0	Hercules 64, Selby 65, Baker 86[og]
9	11.09	RYM P	A	Farnborough Town	512	L	1-3	King 8
	14.09	LC 1	A	Braintree Town		L	1-3	?????
	18.09	FAC 2Q	H	CHELMSFORD CITY	602	L	1-3	Hercules 7
10	25.09	RYM P	H	HEYBRIDGE SWIFTS	804	D	2-2	King 23, Selby 69
	09.10	FAT 1	A	Havant & Waterlooville	289	D	0-0	
	12.10	FAT 1R	H	HAVANT & WATERLOOVILLE	250	L	2-4	Gallagher 51, King 79
11	16.10	RYM P	H	CARSHALTON ATHLETIC	384	W	3-2	Cook 31 83, Catlin 47
12	19.10	RYM P	A	Hitchin Town	251	L	3-4	Selby 25, Gallagher 69 82
13	23.10	RYM P	H	DULWICH HAMLET	366	L	2-3	Selby 41 55
14	30.10	RYM P	A	Harrow Borough	241	L	1-4	Gallagher 87[p]
15	06.11	RYM P	A	Slough Town	556	W	2-1	Heard 9, Stanbridge 84
16	12.11	RYM P	H	PURFLEET	457	L	0-3	
17	20.11	RYM P	A	Gravesend & Northfleet	438	L	0-5	
18	30.11	RYM P	H	BILLERICAY TOWN	339	L	0-1	
19	04.12	RYM P	H	HAMPTON & RICHMOND B.	645	D	2-2	Gallagher 80, Selby 86
20	11.12	RYM P	A	St Albans City	678	D	1-1	Crawshaw 21
21	18.12	RYM P	H	HENDON	412	L	2-3	Crawshaw 48, Davies 87
	21.12	FMC 2	H	OXFORD CITY		L	1-2	Heard
22	27.12	RYM P	A	Chesham United	930	D	1-1	Crawshaw 11
23	03.01	RYM P	H	SLOUGH TOWN	662	D	2-2	Squires 43, Stanbridge 46
24	08.01	RYM P	A	Canvey Island	540	W	3-2	Honeyball 50, Mason 78, Hutchings 81
	11.01	B&B SC 3	A	Marlow		W	2-1	Davies, Crawshaw
25	15.01	RYM P	H	DAGENHAM & REDBRIDGE	729	L	0-2	
26	22.01	RYM P	A	Walton & Hersham	267	W	3-0	Armstrong 17, Hercules 50, Crawshaw 85[p]
27	29.01	RYM P	H	BASINGSTOKE TOWN	517	W	3-0	Crawshaw 13, Armstrong 61, Grieves 73
28	05.02	RYM P	A	Boreham Wood	349	D	2 - 2	Crawshaw 21 31
29	12.02	RYM P	H	ENFIELD	614	W	1 - 0	Hercules 45
	15.02	B&B SCQF	H	CHALFONT ST PETER		W	5 - 0	Highton, Heard, Grieves, Honeyball, Crawshaw
30	19.02	RYM P	A	Aldershot Town	2018	D	1 - 1	Mason 90
31	26.02	RYM P	H	Carshalton Athletic	365	L	1 - 2	Hercules 19
32	04.03	RYM P	H	HITCHIN TOWN	545	W	3 - 1	Grieves 23 78, Crawshaw 47
33	11.03	RYM P	A	Heybridge Swifts	337	D	0 - 0	
34	18.03	RYM P	H	FARNBOROUGH TOWN	515	L	1 - 2	Stanbridge 22
35	25.03	RYM P	H	HARROW BOROUGH	534	W	3 - 1	Armstrong 44, 56, Squires 88
	28.03	B&B SC SF	H	SLOUGH TOWN	390	W	4-2	Honey 12, Grieves 29, Matthew 40, Crawshaw 65
36	01.04	RYM P	A	Dulwich Hamlet	385	L	0 - 3	
37	08.04	RYM P	A	Hendon	366	L	0 - 1	
38	15.04	RYM P	H	ST. ALBANS CITY	678	L	0 - 2	
39	22.04	RYM P	A	Purfleet	268	W	2 - 0	Grieves 46, 80
40	24.04	RYM P	H	CHESHAM UNITED	828	W	3 - 2	Mason 32, Crawshaw 47, Grieves 70
41	29.04	RYM P	A	Billericay Town	601	L	0 - 5	
	01.05	B&B SC F	H	READING	1239	W	2-0	OG (Williams) 3, Hercules 7
42	06.05	RYM P	H	GRAVESEND & N'FLEET	1232	W	4 - 1	Hill 42, Grieves 46, 82, Crawshaw 66

BOREHAM WOOD

Match Facts 1999-00

	Date	Comp.	H/A	Opponents	Att.	Result	Goalscorers
1	14.08	RYM P	A	Dulwich Hamlet	349	W 2 - 1	N Grime 13, Lamine 41
2	17.08	RYM P	H	FARNBOROUGH TOWN	285	D 1 - 1	P Jordan 26
3	21.08	RYM P	H	CARSHALTON ATHLETIC	302	L 0 - 2	
4	24.08	RYM P	A	Aylesbury United	425	W 1 - 0	Hatchett 39
5	28.08	RYM P	A	Billericay Town	473	L 0 - 1	
6	30.08	RYM P	H	HARROW BOROUGH	314	L 0 - 1	
7	04.09	RYM P	H	PURFLEET	187	D 1 - 1	Collins 89
8	07.09	RYM P	A	Heybridge Swifts	190	W 1 - 0	Delisser 53
9	11.09	RYM P	H	DAGENHAM & REDBRIDGE	354	L 0 - 1	
	14.09	LC 1	H	BISHOP'S STORTFORD	81	L 0 - 2	
	18.09	FAC 2Q	A	Canvey Island	245	L 1 - 3	Lamine 53
10	25.09	RYM P	A	Hendon	312	L 1 - 2	Rutherford 72
11	02.10	RYM P	H	HAMPTON & RICHMOND B.	204	L 0 - 4	
	09.10	FAT 1	A	Rothwell Town	217	D 0 - 0	
	12.10	FAT 1 R	H	ROTHWELL TOWN	63	L 3 - 5	Howard 75, Lamine 85 89
12	16.10	RYM P	A	Basingstoke Town	430	D 1 - 1	Bignall 63
13	23.10	RYM P	H	ENFIELD	481	W 1 - 0	Lawford 50
14	30.10	RYM P	A	Walton & Hersham	141	L 1 - 3	Lawford 18
	02.11	Herts SC2	H	HERTFORD TOWN	72	W 4 - 0	Delisser, Kelly, Marshall(2)
15	06.11	RYM P	A	Aldershot Town	1679	L 0 - 1	
16	13.11	RYM P	H	SLOUGH TOWN	326	L 1 - 3	Lawford 48
17	20.11	RYM P	A	Chesham United	313	L 0 - 5	
18	27.11	RYM P	H	ST ALBANS CITY	547	L 2 - 3	Lawford 63, Bignall 64
19	04.12	RYM P	H	BILLERICAY TOWN	226	L 0-2	
20	11.12	RYM P	A	Gravesend & Northfleet	425	L 0-3	
21	18.12	RYM P	H	ALDERSHOT TOWN	668	L 2 - 5	Lawford 10, Hutchings 26
22	27.12	RYM P	A	Hitchin Town	428	W 3-1	Robson 31, Lawford 70 88
23	03.01	RYM P	H	CANVEY ISLAND	355	W 3 - 2	Lawford 16, Meredith 39, Buglione 80
24	08.01	RYM P	A	Purfleet	215	L 2 - 3	Buglione 72, Selby 79
	17.01	HSC QF	H	WATFORD	215	W 4 - 2	**Buglione (3)**, Robson
25	22.01	RYM P	H	DULWICH HAMLET	325	D 0 - 0	
26	29.01	RYM P	A	Farnborough Town	484	W 2 - 0	Selby 86 90
27	05.02	RYM P	H	AYLESBURY UNITED	349	D 2 - 2	Samuels 64, Selby 72
28	12.02	RYM P	A	Harrow Borough	268	W 3 - 1	Selby 23[p] 67, Samuels 75
29	14.02	RYM P	A	Carshalton Athletic	224	L 0 - 3	
30	19.02	RYM P	H	HEYBRIDGE SWIFTS	253	D 0 - 0	
31	26.02	RYM P	H	BASINGSTOKE TOWN	271	L 3 - 4	McCarthy 26, Adams 38, Selby 65[p]
32	04.03	RYM P	A	Hampton & Richmond Bor.	218	D 1 - 1	Hamlet 2
	07.03	HSC SF	H	ST ALBANS CITY	213	D 3 - 3	Delisser, Lawford, Selby
33	11.03	RYM P	H	HENDON	362	L 0 - 2	
34	18.03	RYM P	A	Dagenham & Redbridge	1028	L 0 - 2	
35	25.03	RYM P	H	WALTON & HERSHAM	244	W 1 - 0	Lawford 79
36	01.04	RYM P	A	Enfield	174	D 1 - 1	Adams 49
	07.03	HSC SF R	A	St Albans City	161	L 1 - 5	Grime
37	08.04	RYM P	A	Canvey Island	570	W 1 - 0	Robson 24
38	22.04	RYM P	A	Slough Town	445	W 3 - 2	Lawford 17 (p), Delisser 22, Selby 77
39	24.04	RYM P	H	HITCHIN TOWN	457	D 0 - 0	
40	26.04	RYM P	H	GRAVESEND & N'FLEET	228	L 3 - 4	Delisser 52, Shafer 90, Harvey 90
41	29.04	RYM P	A	St. Albans City	640	D 0 - 0	
42	06.05	RYM P	H	CHESHAM UNITED	404	L 1 - 3	Lawford 81 (p)

WALTON & HERSHAM

Match Facts 1999-00

	Date	Comp.	H/A	Opponents	Att.	Result	Goalscorers
1	14.08	RYM P	A	Aylesbury United	603	L 0 - 1	
2	17.08	RYM P	H	DULWICH HAMLET	203	L 0 - 3	
3	21.08	RYM P	H	HARROW BOROUGH	163	W 3 - 1	Dowling 14, Allen 66, Bartley 84
4	24.08	RYM P	A	Heybridge Swifts	222	L 1 - 5	Rose 22
5	28.08	RYM P	A	St Albans City	701	D 1 - 1	Jones 25
6	30.08	RYM P	H	FARNBOROUGH TOWN	442	D 0 - 0	
7	04.09	RYM P	A	Gravesend & Northfleet	335	D 1 - 1	Bartley 10
8	06.09	RYM P	A	Carshalton Athletic	304	W 2 - 0	Pickett 57, Allen 90
9	11.09	RYM P	H	PURFLEET	164	L 0 - 3	
	14.09	LC 1	A	Basingstoke Town	207	L 1 - 3	Craker
	18.09	FAC 2Q	H	MAIDENHEAD UNITED	209	L 0 - 2	
10	25.09	RYM P	H	Basingstoke Town	556	W 3 - 1	Pickett 12, Coates 45, Whelan 54
11	02.10	RYM P	A	Chesham United	279	L 1 - 2	Coates 65
12	05.10	RYM P	H	SLOUGH TOWN	303	D 2 - 2	Tilbury, Dowling[p]
13	09.10	RYM P	A	Enfield	214	L 1 - 4	Coates 70
14	23.10	RYM P	A	Dagenham & Redbridge	776	L 0 - 2	
	26.10	FMC1	A	Maidenhead United	144	L 0 - 2	
15	30.10	RYM P	H	BOREHAM WOOD	141	W 3 - 1	Craker 27, Killick 68, Coates 69
16	13.11	RYM P	H	HITCHIN TOWN	131	W 4 - 3	Killick 15 74, Coates 27, Rose 86
17	20.11	RYM P	A	Canvey Island	225	D 1 - 1	Tilbury 38
	27.11	FAT 2	A	Bognor Regis Town	379	W 2 - 1	Blackman, Coates
18	29.11	RYM P	H	HENDON	181	L 1 - 2	Coates 38
19	04.12	RYM P	H	ST ALBANS CITY	232	D 1 - 1	Tilbury 60
20	11.12	RYM P	A	Billericay Town	426	W 3 - 0	Tilbury 12, Dowling 59, Coates 64
21	18.12	RYM P	H	CHESHAM UNITED	251	L 1 - 2	Coates 81
22	29.12	RYM P	A	Hampton & Richmond Bor.	353	W 2 - 0	Moat 8, Pickett 33
23	03.01	RYM P	H	ALDERSHOT TOWN	1419	L 0 - 1	
24	08.01	RYM P	H	GRAVESEND & NORTHFLEET	255	D 2 - 2	Rose 26 28
	12.01	Surrey SC 1	H	MOLESEY	103	W 3 - 1	Blackman, Whelan, Pickett
	15.01	FAT 3	A	Rothwell Town	207	D 1 - 1	Cowling 34
	18.01	FAT 3R	H	ROTHWELL TOWN	208	W 1 - 0	Pickett 38
25	22.01	RYM P	H	AYLESBURY UNITED	267	L 0 - 3	
26	29.01	RYM P	A	Dulwich Hamlet	415	L 0 - 1	
	05.02	FAT 4	A	Kettering Town	1128	D 2 - 2	Dowling 46[p], Blackmam 65
	08.02	FAT 4 R	H	KETTERING TOWN	490	L 0 - 2	
27	19.02	RYM P	H	CARSHALTON ATHLETIC	264	L 0 - 2	
	21.02	S SC QF	A	Dulwich Hamlet	159	W 2 - 0	Coates 45, Pickett 75
28	26.02	RYM P	H	ENFIELD	246	L 0 - 2	
29	04.03	RYM P	A	Slough Town	488	L 1 - 3	Blackman 23
30	07.03	RYM P	A	Harrow Borough	165	W 1 - 0	Adekola 80
31	11.03	RYM P	H	BASINGSTOKE TOWN	237	W 1 - 0	Coates 9
32	13.03	RYM P	H	HEYBRIDGE SWIFTS	217	L 0 - 1	
33	18.03	RYM P	A	Purfleet	187	L 1 - 3	Pickett 88
34	21.03	RYM P	A	Farnborough Town	296	W 2 - 1	Tilbury 58, Pickett 66
35	25.03	RYM P	A	Boreham Wood	244	L 0 - 1	
36	28.03	S SC SF	H	CROYDON	131	L 1 - 2	Pickett 50
	01.04	RYM P	H	DAGENHAM & REDBRIDGE	402	L 0 - 2	
37	08.04	RYM P	A	Aldershot Town	2100	L 0 - 3	
38	22.04	RYM P	A	Hitchin Town	397	W 2 - 0	Ball 19, 70
39	24.04	RYM P	H	HAMPTON & RICHMOND B.	303	L 1 - 3	White 31
40	29.04	RYM P	A	Hendon	218	D 2 - 2	Coates 58 (p), Adekola 74
41	01.05	RYM P	H	BILLERICAY TOWN	234	L 0 - 1	
42	06.05	RYM P	H	CANVEY ISLAND	159	L 0 - 3	

DIVISION ONE FINAL LEAGUE TABLE 1999-2000

		Home					Away					Total						
	P	W	D	L	F	A	W	D	L	F	A	W	D	L	F	A	Pts	GD
Croydon	42	10	8	3	39	23	15	1	5	46	24	25	9	8	85	47	84	38
Grays Athletic	42	11	5	5	44	23	10	7	4	36	21	21	12	9	80	44	75	36
Maidenhead Utd	42	11	5	5	36	24	9	10	2	36	21	20	15	7	72	45	75	27
Thame United	42	10	8	3	31	16	10	5	6	30	22	20	13	9	61	38	73	23
Worthing	42	9	6	6	45	34	10	6	5	35	26	19	12	11	80	60	69	20
Staines Town	42	10	7	4	36	30	9	5	7	27	22	19	12	11	63	52	69	11
Whyteleafe	42	10	5	6	31	23	10	4	7	29	26	20	9	13	60	49	69	11
Bedford Town	42	9	6	6	27	22	8	6	7	32	30	17	12	13	59	52	63	7
Bromley	42	10	4	7	36	31	7	5	9	26	34	17	9	16	62	65	60	-3
Uxbridge	42	10	4	7	41	23	5	9	7	19	21	15	13	14	60	44	58	16
Bishop's Stortford	42	6	6	9	26	29	10	4	7	31	33	16	10	16	57	62	58	-5
Barton Rovers	42	9	4	8	29	30	7	4	10	35	53	16	8	18	64	83	56	-19
Oxford City	42	10	2	9	30	24	7	2	12	27	31	17	4	21	57	55	55	2
Braintree Town	42	11	6	4	40	26	4	4	13	25	48	15	10	17	65	74	55	-9
Yeading	42	7	8	6	30	28	5	10	6	23	26	12	18	12	53	54	54	-1
Wealdstone	42	8	5	8	27	26	5	7	9	24	32	13	12	17	51	58	51	-7
Bognor Regis Town	42	3	7	11	19	30	9	6	6	28	23	12	13	17	47	53	49	-6
Harlow Town	42	3	9	9	26	39	8	4	9	36	37	11	13	18	62	76	46	-14
Romford	42	5	3	13	21	36	7	6	8	30	34	12	9	21	51	70	45	-19
Leatherhead	42	4	4	13	22	36	5	9	7	25	34	9	13	20	47	70	40	-23
Chertsey Town	42	5	3	13	28	43	4	2	15	22	41	9	5	28	50	84	32	-34
Leyton Pennant	42	4	5	12	17	43	3	9	14	17	42	7	9	26	34	85	30	-51

DIVISION ONE RESULTS CHART 1999-2000

		1	2	3	4	5	6	7	8	9	10	11	12	13	14	15	16	17	18	19	20	21	22
1	Barton R	X	0-1	2-3	3-1	1-1	1-2	0-3	2-1	0-2	0-3	2-1	0-2	1-1	3-1	3-2	0-1	1-0	1-1	2-1	1-0	2-2	4-1
2	Bedford T	1-0	X	1-0	2-1	1-1	1-2	2-2	1-0	1-1	3-3	1-1	1-0	2-2	2-0	0-1	0-2	0-2	1-0	4-0	0-1	2-3	1-0
3	Bishop's S	1-2	2-3	X	0-0	0-0	0-3	3-1	1-0	0-1	2-1	0-1	3-0	1-1	0-3	0-0	2-3	0-3	1-2	3-0	4-2	4-4	0-0
4	Bognor R T	2-2	1-1	0-1	X	0-1	0-0	1-0	1-2	1-3	0-1	1-3	2-2	1-2	2-1	1-2	0-1	1-2	2-1	1-1	0-0	1-3	1-1
5	Braintree T	2-2	3-1	3-0	4-0	X	2-2	2-1	0-2	0-1	2-1	2-1	3-2	2-1	1-3	3-3	1-1	0-0	1-0	2-1	2-1	1-2	4-0
6	Bromley	4-1	0-2	0-2	3-2	1-3	X	2-0	3-2	1-2	1-1	1-1	1-0	0-0	2-1	2-1	1-2	0-1	4-1	4-1	3-2	1-4	2-2
7	Chertsey T	2-1	2-1	3-5	1-1	4-1	0-0	X	2-4	2-1	1-3	0-1	1-2	1-2	2-0	2-5	0-4	2-2	0-1	1-3	0-2	2-3	0-1
8	Croydon	1-2	1-1	1-1	0-2	6-1	3-1	3-2	X	0-0	1-0	2-2	3-0	2-2	0-1	2-1	2-1	2-4	1-1	2-2	3-0	1-0	2-0
9	Grays Ath	4-1	3-0	1-3	0-0	4-0	5-0	1-2	3-4	X	2-2	2-2	4-0	2-2	1-0	2-1	1-0	0-2	1-0	0-1	4-1	3-1	1-1
10	Harlow T	2-3	0-5	2-2	0-3	1-1	2-2	5-2	1-4	4-4	X	0-1	1-0	1-1	0-1	0-1	1-1	3-2	1-3	0-0	0-1	1-1	1-1
11	Leatherh'd	1-2	2-0	0-2	0-2	4-1	0-2	1-1	1-2	1-3	2-5	X	3-1	1-3	1-2	1-1	1-2	2-2	1-1	0-2	0-0	1-2	0-1
12	Leyton P	0-3	1-0	2-2	0-1	1-5	2-0	1-0	1-4	0-3	2-2	1-1	X	0-3	1-5	2-1	0-0	1-2	0-1	0-2	0-4	0-2	2-2
13	M'head U	2-2	2-1	0-1	1-1	4-3	3-2	2-0	1-0	3-1	2-0	1-1	1-3	X	0-1	4-0	3-2	0-1	2-2	2-0	0-1	1-1	2-1
14	Oxford C	2-0	1-2	5-0	0-1	2-0	3-1	1-0	0-2	2-1	0-2	5-0	1-1	1-3	X	0-3	1-0	2-4	1-1	2-1	0-1	0-1	1-0
15	Romford	1-2	2-2	0-1	1-2	2-1	2-1	3-2	0-2	0-1	0-2	2-1	2-1	1-3	1-2	X	1-1	1-1	0-2	1-3	1-2	0-3	0-1
16	Staines T	2-2	1-1	0-0	1-4	3-2	4-1	4-0	2-6	1-1	2-1	0-2	1-0	1-0	2-2	3-1	X	3-1	0-0	3-1	1-3	1-0	3-2
17	Thame U	2-0	0-1	3-2	1-2	3-0	1-0	0-2	0-0	2-1	3-0	2-2	5-1	1-0	3-1	1-1	1-1	X	1-0	1-1	1-1	0-0	0-0
18	Uxbridge	5-1	0-1	5-1	3-2	3-1	2-0	1-0	1-2	1-1	6-0	5-0	3-0	0-4	1-0	1-3	0-1	0-0	X	1-1	2-3	0-1	1-1
19	Wealdstone	4-1	1-1	0-2	0-0	2-0	1-3	0-1	1-2	0-2	3-1	1-1	2-2	0-1	2-1	2-0	0-2	1-2	1-1	X	3-1	2-1	1-3
20	Whyteleafe	4-2	2-1	0-1	1-0	1-2	1-1	4-1	1-2	0-5	3-1	2-1	4-0	1-2	2-1	0-1	2-0	0-1	0-0	2-1	X	1-1	0-0
21	Worthing	8-2	3-4	3-2	1-2	2-0	0-2	3-1	2-3	1-1	1-5	3-1	3-0	1-1	1-1	4-0	3-1	2-0	1-1	1-1	1-1	X	0-0
22	Yeading	3-4	3-3	2-0	1-1	3-1	1-2	2-1	0-2	1-1	1-2	1-1	0-0	1-2	2-1	2-2	2-1	1-0	1-1	1-1	0-2	2-0	X

AYLESBURY UNITED

CLUB OFFICIALS

Chairman: **Bill Carroll**
Vice Chairman: **Roger Payne**

Secretary: **Tony Graham**
c/o the club.
Press Officer: **Tony Graham**

FOOTBALL MANAGEMENT TEAM

Manager: Gary Phillips
Assistant Manager: T.B.A.
Physio: T.B.A.

FACT FILE

Formed: 1897
Nickname: The Ducks
Sponsors: Driftgate Press
Colours: White with Green trim/green/green
Change colours: Yellow & black, black,black
Midweek home matchday: Tuesday
Reserve Team's League: None
Newsline: 0891 446 824

For up to the minute news,
results, fixtures,
plus general facts & figures
from the world of
non-league football

log on to

www.nlfootball.com

GROUND The Stadium, Buckingham Road, Aylesbury HP20 2AQ Tel: 01296 436350/436891
Fax: 01296 395667
Directions: On A413 to Buckingham, just off ring road opposite Horse & Jockey PH. Arriving
from Buckingham ground is on left - from all other directions follow Buckingham signs and
ground on right. Half hour walk from Aylesbury rail and bus stations
Capacity 4,000   Cover: 1000   Seats: 500   Floodlights: Yes
Clubhouse: Pub hours, but shut during matches. Bar snacks available
          Function room available for hire(01296 436891).
Club Shop: Sells programmes, magazines, leisurewear, badges etc.
          Contact DebbieGamage c/o The Club

Programme
Pages: 36 Price: £1.50
Editor: Dave Gamage (01296 434006)

Local Press: Bucks Herald, Bucks Advertiser
Local Radio: Three Counties Radio,
Chiltern Radio, Mix 96

PREVIOUS **Leagues:** Bucks Contiguous 1897-1903, South Eastern 03-07, Spartan 07-51, Delphian 51-63, Athenian 63-76,
Southern 76-88, GMV Conference 88-89
Grounds: Printing Works Ground 1897-1935, Sports Stadium, Wendover Rd (ground name changed to The Stadium,
Turnfurlong Lane) 35-85, shared grounds 85-86   **Name:** Night School, Printing Works (merged in 1897)

CLUB RECORDS **Attendance:** 6,000 v England 1988 (at old ground; 7,500 v Watford, FA Cup 1st Rd1951)
Career goalscorer: Cliff Hercules   **Career appearances:** Cliff Hercules
Transfer fee paid: £15,000 for Glenville Donegal (Northampton, 1990)
Transfer fee received: £35,000 for Glenville Donegal (Maidstone Utd, 1991)

BEST SEASON **FA Trophy:** Quarter-Final replay 80-81   **FA Cup:** 3rd Rd 95. League clubs defeated: Southend Utd 89-90

HONOURS Southern Lg 87-88 (Mids Div R-up 84-85, Sth Div R-up 79-80); Athenian Lg Div 2 R-up 67-68; Delphian Lg 53-54 (R-up 52-53,
Lg Cup 59-60); Spartan Lg 08-09 (R-up 52-53), West Div 28-29 (R-up 45-46), Div 1 38-39 (R-up 34-35); Berks & Bucks Snr
Cup 13-14 85-86 96-97; Isthmian League Cup 94-95, Isthmian Charity Shield 95-96 Isthmian League R-up 98-99

Players progressing: Ray Mabbutt (Bristol Rovers), Phil Barber (Crystal Palace 1986), Jermaine Darlington (Q.P.R. 99)

This season's Aylesbury United
player/manager, Gary Phillips,
foils last season's Harrow
Borough player/manager Alan
Paris.
Photo: Paul Carter

BARTON ROVERS

CLUB OFFICIALS
Chairman: **John Milton**
President: **P Howarth**
Vice Chairman: **Ken Burr**
Secretary: **Owen Clark,** 108 Manor Road,
Barton-le-Clay, Bedford MK45 4NS
Tel: 01582 882398
Press Officer: **Nick Rhodes**
Tel: 01582 881865

FOOTBALL MANAGEMENT TEAM

Manager: Ian Donnelly
Asst Manager: Matt Walker
Physio: Mark Boulding

FACT FILE
Formed: 1898
Nickname: Rovers
Sponsors: SRC Contractors
Colours: All royal blue
Change colours: All yellow
Midweek Matchday: Tuesday
Reserves' League: None

1999-00
Captain: Danny Turner
P.o.Y. Gordon Guile
Top Scorer: Gordon Guile (44)

GROUND Sharpenhoe Road, Barton-le-Clay, Bedford MK45 4SD (01582 707772)

Directions: M1 Jct 12, from London exit turn right, take 2nd right through Harlington and Sharpenhoe. Entrance to ground 44 yds on right down concrete drive entering village. 41/2 miles from Harlington (BR), 6 miles from Luton (BR), good bus or taxis service from Luton
Capacity: 4,000 Seats: 160 Cover: 1,120 Floodlights: Yes

Clubhouse: Noon-3pm weekends (no football), noon-11pm (matchdays), 7-11pm weekdays. Real ale, hot & cold snacks, pool, darts, gaming machines
Club Shop: Yes (contact 01582 751013)

Pages: 64 Price: £1
Editor: Nick Rhodes (01582 881865)
Local Press: Luton News, Herald, Beds on Sunday
Local Radio: Radio Chiltern, Radio Beds
Three Counties Radio

PREVIOUS **Leagues:** Luton & Dist. 47-54; Sth Midlands 54-79
Grounds: Church Pitch 1898-1912; Barton Cutting 1912; Sharpenhoe Rd 12-33;Faldo Rd 33-38; Barton Rec. 46-75

CLUB RECORDS **Attendance:** 1,900 v Nuneaton, FA Cup 4th Qual. Rd 1976
Win: 17-1 v Flitwick Athletic (H), S Midlands Lge Div 1 55-56
Defeat: 1-11 v Leighton United (H), S Midlands Lge Prem Div 62-63
Scorer: Richard Camp 152, 1989-98   **Appearances:** Tony McNally 514 (1988-2000)
Fees - Paid: £1,000 for B Baldry (Hitchin Town, 1980)   **Received:** £1,000 for BBaldry (Bishop's Stortford, 1981)

BEST SEASON **FA Cup:** 1st Round 1980-81, 0-2 v Torquay United (A)
FA Vase: Runners-up 77-78 (SF 76-77 81-82, QF 75-76 78-79)   **FA Trophy:** 2nd Rd 98-99,99-00

HONOURS: Sth Mids Lg(8) 70-73 74-79 (R-up 67-68), Div 1 64-65 (R-up 55-56), Div 2 54-55,Lg Shield 57-58 60-61 68-69, Chal. Tphy 71-72 74-75 77-78 78-79; Beds Snr Cup(7), R-up (5); Beds Premier Cup 95-96, R-up 81-82 83-84 88-89, 99-00Beds Intermediate Cup 53-54; Luton & Dist. Lg Div 3 47-48; North BedsCharity Cup 72-73 74-75 76-77 77-78 79-80 80-81 (R-up 70-71); Isthmian Lg Associate Members Tphy R-up 92-93; Isthmian Div 2 R-up 94-95, South Midlands Floodlight Cup 98-99. Hinchingbroke Cup R-up: 98-99,99-00

Players progressing: Kevin Blackwell (Huddersfield T.)

Barton Rovers at the start of the 1999-2000 season - **Back Row:** Carl Drew*, Jason Downey, Gareth Grant, Wesley Jean, Gordon Guile, Bright Dartnos, Brad Gillham, Kevin Wheeler, Tony McNally, Tony Fontenelle, Jay Thomas, Mark Whelan, Steve Hunt. **Front:** Anthony Rhodes (Mascot), Mick Clark (Physio), Scott Turner, Stuart Postanick, Danny Turner (capt.), Ian Allinson (Manager)*, Martin Young*, Richard Fisher, Dave Cook*, Owen Clark (Hon. Sec.), Lee Allinson.   * now Harlow Town
Missing from photo: Ian Donnelly (Asst. Man.), Negus Johnson, Keith Coughlin, Neil Yates, Aaron Powell, Neil Lewis, Mark Oakley, Pete Jennings

BEDFORD TOWN

CLUB OFFICIALS

Chairman: **Paul Brown**

Vice Chairman: **Nic Meaney**

President: **Allen J Sturgess**

Secretary: **Barry Stephenson**
9 Aspen Ave., Bedford, Beds MK41 8BX
Tel: 01234 342276

FOOTBALL MANAGEMENT TEAM
Manager: Roger Ashby
Asst. Managers: Kenny Mist & Andy Lomas
Physio: Mick Dilley

FACT FILE
Founded: 1908   Reformed: 1989
Nickname: Eagles
Sponsors: Allen Sturges Travel
Colours: Blue, white trim/blue/blue
Change Colours: White
Midweek Matchday: Tuesday
Reserves' League: Capital
99-00- Captain: Tony Joyce
Top Scorer:Gavin Jaggard
P.o.Y.: Gavin Jaggar

GROUND   The New Eyrie, Meadow Lane, Cardington, Bedford MK44 3SB
Fax: 01234 831990 Tel: 01234 838448
Directions: BR station Bedford Midland 3miles from ground. Bus station 5 minutes walk from station.Service 171 & 172 stop outside ground(Canvins stop). Trains from London Thameslink run every half hour to Bedford.By road: north up M1 to jct 13 onto A421 (right), follow on to bypass at Sandy exit.A603 to Sandy, ground on left just before layby.

Capacity: 3,000   Seats: 300   Cover: 1000   Floodlights: Yes

Clubhouse: Natchdays bar snacks

Club Shop: Good range of merchandise incl. programmes. Mick Spavins (01234 402822)

Pages: 40 Price: £1
Editor: Adrian Brown(01234 300242)

Local Press:Beds Times, Beds on Sunday
Local Radio: Chiltern Radio,Three Counties

PREVIOUS   **Leagues:** South Midlands 91-94 (predecessors: Utd Co's 08-39; Southern 46-82)
Grounds: Allen Park, Queens Park, Bedford (park pitch) 1991-93
(predecessors: London Rd; Gasworks; Queens Pk; The Eyrie, Raleigh Street)

CLUB RECORDS **Attendance:** 3,000 v Peterborough Utd, ground opening 6/8/93.
At Allen Park: 1,227 v Bedford Utd, South Midlands Lge Div. One, 26/12/91
(predecessors: 18,407 v Everton, FA Cup 4th Round 12/2/66)
Career scorer: Jason Reed   **Career appearances:** Jason Reed
Win: 9-0 v Ickleford, and Caddington   **Defeat:** 1-5 v Toddington

BEST SEASON   **FA Cup:** 2nd Q 98-99 , 99-00 **FA Vase:** 5th Round 1998-99, 1-2 v Tiverton Town (H) **F.A.Trophy:** 4th Rd v Yeovil Town 99-00

HONOURS: Isthmian League Div. 2 98-99; South Midlands Lg 94-95 (Div 1 92-93, F'lit Cup 94-95); Hinchingbrook Cup 94-95 94-95;
Beds Sen Cup 94-95.   (Predecessors: Southern Lg 58-59 (Div 1 69-70), Utd Co's Lg 30-31 32-33 33-34 (R-up 7 Times)
Vandanal Cup 97-8 Beds Prem , Beds Premier Cup 97-98 **FA Cup** 4th Rd 63-64 65-66. **FA Trophy** Semi-Final 74-75.
Players progressing: Bill Garner (Southend 69), Nicky Platnaeur (Bristol Rovers 77). Ray Bailey/Derek Bellotti/Billy Brown/Bert
Carberry/PeterHall/Dave Quirke/Bobby Fold (Gillingham 56-67), Phil Driver (Wimbledon 78), Joe Dubois (Grimsby T 53), Ted Duggan (Luton T 56),
Harry Duke (Noprwich C 46),John Fahy (Oxford U 64), Ken Flint (Spurs 47), Joe Hooley (Accrington 61), Joe Kirkup (Reading 55), Graham Moxon
(Exeter C 75), Bela Olah (Northampton 58),Gary Sergeant (Peterborough U 77), Neil Townsend (Southend U 73)

Back Row L-R: Kenny Mist (Asst. Man.), Adam Hancock, Chris Payne, Paul Daniels, Paul Covington, Gary Williams, James Heeps, Andy Lomas (Asst. Man.), Chris Tubb, Paul Sherlock, Gavin Jaggard, Jon Bone, Mick Dilly (physio). **Front Row:** Kevin Slinn, Steve Searle, Tony Joyce, Gary Cobb, Roger Ashby (manager), Eddie Lawley, Gavin Covington, Julian Capone

BISHOPS STORTFORD

CLUB OFFICIALS

Chairman: **John Goodwin**
President: **B W A Bayford**
Vice-Chairman: **Mick Hooker**
Secretary: **Martin Stone**
15 Thornbera Gardens, Bishop's Stortford, Herts. CM23 3NP
01279 466931 (H) 0207 653 4858 (B)
Press Officer: **Martin Stone**

FOOTBALL MANAGEMENT TEAM
Team Manager: Martin Hayes
Coach: Perry Suckling & Billy Gillman
Physio: Peter Fox & Brian Curtis

FACT FILE

Formed: 1874
Nickname: Blues or Bishops
Colours: White & blue stripes/blue/blue
Change colours: Yellow/yellow/yellow
Midweek matchday: Tuesday
Local Press: B.Stortford Citizen,
Herts & Essex Observer, Herald
Local Radio: BBC Essex, Essex FM,
Breeze AM, TEN17

Pages: 72 Price: £1.50
Editor: Dave Ryan
Tel: 01279 833995

GROUND   Woodside Park, Dunmow Road, Bishop 's Stortford (01279 306456)
Directions: M11 jct 8, A1250 towards town centre, left at first roundabout. Woodside is first on right opposite Golf Club. Entrance is between industrial units on right. By rail: British Rail: W. Anglia Line (London, Liverpool Str.-Cambridge)
Capacity: 4,000   Cover: 700   Seats: 298   Floodlights: Yes
Clubhouse: Open lunchtimes,evenings and matchdays.Function room(seating 250) available for hire .
Club Shop: Full stock inc. scarves,badges and other souvenirs.Massive stock of pro-grammes and books etc. Contact Mark Pulfervia club.

PREVIOUS   **Leagues:** East Herts 1896-97, 02-06, 19-21; Stansted & Dist. Lg 06-19; HertsCounty 21-25 27-29; Herts & Essex Border 25-27; Spartan 29-51; Delphian 51-63;Athenian 63-73
CLUB RECORDS **Attendance:** 6,000 v Peterborough Utd, FA Cup 2nd Rd 1972 & v Middlesbrough FACup 3rd Rd replay, 1983
Win: 11-0: Nettleswell & Butntmill, Herts Jun Cup 2nd Rd 1911   **Defeat:** 0-13 v Cheshunt (H), Herts Sen. Cup 1st Rd 9/1/26
Fee Paid: For Vinnie John to Grays Athletic (1999)   **Fee Received:** £10,000 for Carl Hoddle (Leyton O., 89)
Scorer: (Since 29) Jimmy Badcock 123   **Appearances:** Phil Hopkins 543
BEST SEASON   **FA Amateur Cup:** Winners 73-74   **FA Trophy:** Winners 80-81
FA Cup: 3rd Rd rep. 82-83 (above) - League clubs beaten: Reading 82-83
HONOURS   Isthmian Lg Div 1 80-1 94-5 (Lg Cup 88-9, Full Mem. Cup 90-1); Prem. Inter Lg Cup 89-90; Athenian Lg 69-70 (R-up 66-7, Div 1 65-6, Div 2 R-up 64-5); Delphian Lg 54-5; London Snr Cup 73-4; Herts Snr Cup 58-9 59-0 63-4 70-1 72-3 73-4 75-686-7; E Anglian Cup 81-2; Herts Charity Cup 62-3 65-6 73-4 81-2 82-3 84-5 87-896-7; Herts Charity Shield 54-5; Herts I'mediate Cup (res) 94-95; Eastern F'lit Cup 84-5; Essex F'lit Cup 67-8; Essex & Herts Border Comb 81-2 88-9 R-up (2) 92-4; Fred Budden Tphy R-up 78-9 90-1 92-3
Players progressing: P Phelan (Southend 61), M Hollow (Orient 62), P Phillips(Luton 69), T Baker (Colchester 86), T Sorrell (Maidstone, Colchester, Barnet 88), C Hoddle (Leyton O., Barnet 89), T English (Colchester 89), L Fortune-West (Gillingham 95), L Braithwaite (Exeter City 96)

The stand at Woodside Park

BOGNOR REGIS TOWN

CLUB OFFICIALS

Chairman: **Jack Pearce**
President: **S Rowlands**
Secretary: **Peter Helsby,** c/o The Club.
01243 587421 (H)
Press Officer: Jack Pearce
Comm. Manager: **Maurice Warner**

FOOTBALL MANAGEMENT TEAM
Manager: Jack Pearce
Asst Manager: Neil Hider
Physio: Steve Robinson/Clair Eastland

FACT FILE

Founded: 1883
Nickname: The Rocks
Sponsors: Butlins South Coast World
Colours: White (green trim)/green/white
Change colours: Blue/white/red
Midweek home matchday: Tuesday
Reserves ' League: None

For up to the minute news,
results, fixtures,
plus general facts & figures
from the world of
non-league football

log on to

www.nlfootball.com

GROUND

Nyewood Lane, Bognor Regis PO21 2TY
Tel: 01243 822325
Directions: West along sea front from pier, past Aldwick shopping centre then turn right into
Nyewood Lane
Capacity: 6,000   Cover: 3,800   Seats: 243   Floodlights: Yes
Clubhouse: Open every night, matchdays and Sunday lunchtimes. Hot food available
Club Shop: Selling programmes and normal club items

Programme
Pages: 36 Price: £1
Editor: Maurice Warner Tel: 01243 822325

Local Press: Bognor Regis Journal &
Guardian, Bognor Observer, Brighton Argus,
Portsmouth News
Local Radio: Radio Sussex, Ocean Sound,
Radio Solent, Southern Sound, Spirit FM

PREVIOUS   **Leagues:** W Sussex Lge 1896-1926; Brighton, Hove & District Lge 26-27; Sussex County Lge 27-72; Southern Lge 72-81
CLUB RECORDS **Attendance:** 3,642 v Swansea FA Cup 1st Rd replay, '84
Goalscorer: Kevin Clements (206)   **Appearances:** Mick Pullen, 967 (20 seasons)
Transfer Fee Paid: £2,200 Guy Rutherford 95-96
Fee Received: £10,500 for John Crumplin & Geoff Cooper (Brighton & Hove Alb, 87) & Simon Rodger (C Palace 89)
BEST SEASON   **FA Amateur Cup:** 1st Round 71-72   **F A Trophy:** 3rd Round 95-96
F A Cup: 2nd Rd on four occasions -   League clubs beaten: Swansea 84-85, Exeter 88-89
84-85 2-6 v Reading (A), 85-86 1-6 v Gillingham (A), 88-89 0-1 v Cambridge (H), 95-96 0-4 v Peterborough (A)
HONOURS: Isthmian Lg Div 1 R-up 81-82, (Lg Cup 86-87); Southern Lg R-up 80-81 (Lg Cup R-up 80-81), Merit Cup 80-81; Sussex Lg 48-
49 71-72 (R-up 38-39 51-52), Div 2 70-71, Invitation Cup 40-41 49-50 62-63 71-72; Brighton Lg R-up 26-27; W Sussex Lg (5)
20-25 (R-up 1896-97, 25-26), Jnr Lg 10-11 13-14; Southern Co's Comb 78-79; Sussex Snr Cup(9) 54-56 79-84 86-87 94-95
(R-up 51-52 58-59 84-85); Sussex Prof. Cup 73-74, Sussex RUR Cup 71-72; Sussex I'mediate Cup 52-53, Littlehampton
Hosp. Cup 29-30 33-34; Bognor Charity Cup(8) 28-29 30-31 32-33 37-38 47-48 58-59 71-73; Gosport War Mem. Cup (2) 81-83
(R-up 86-87); Snr Midweek F'lit Cup R-up 74-75
Players progressing: E Randall (Chelsea 50), J Standing (Brighton 61), A Woon (Brentford 72), J Crumplin & G Cooper (Brighton 87),
Simon Rodger (C Palace 89)

Bognor's Roy Young seen here
trying to gain possession from
Didcot's David Beaven in last
season's Axa sponsored FA Cup.
Photo: Andrew Chitty

BOREHAM WOOD

CLUB OFFICIALS

Chairman: **Danny Hunter**
President: **W F O'Neill**
Secretary:**Peter Smith**,26 Briarwood Road,Stoneleigh,Epsom, Surrey KT19 2LYTel: 020 8393 2902(H) 07711745987(W)
Press Officer: **John D Gill** (020 8723 6407)

FOOTBALL MANAGEMENT TEAM

Manager: Colin Payne
Asst Manager: Alan Carrington
Coach: Mark Robson
Physio: Dave Dickens

FACT FILE

Formed: 1948
Nickname: The Wood
Sponsors: One 2 One
Colours: All white
Change colours: Alll yellow
Midweek matchday: Tuesday

GROUND: Meadow Park, Broughinge Rd, Boreham Wood,Herts WD6 5AL (020 8953 5097)
Directions: A1 towards London from M25, 1st turn for Boreham Wood, head for town centre, into Brook Rd at r'bout before town centre, Broughinge Rd is 1st right. 1 mile from Elstree & Boreham Wood station (Thameslink),or bus 292 or107 to McDonalds (5 minutes walk)
Capacity: 4,502   Cover: 1,568   Seats: 500   Floodlights: Yes
Clubhouse: (0181 953 5097). Open during normal licensing hours. Snacks available.
Function room (250) available for hire
Club Shop: Sells good selection of souvenirs & programmes.
Contact: Dell Ward (020 8363 7345)

v CHESHAM UNITED
SATURDAY 6th MAY 2000 - Kick Off 3.00pm
Ryman Football League Premier Division

Pages: 44 Price: £1.50
Editor: John Gill
(020 8723 6407)
Local Radio: Chiltern Radio
Local Press: Boreham Wood Times, Watford Observer, Herts Advertiser

PREVIOUS   Leagues: Mid Herts 48-52, Parthenon 52-57, Spartan 56-66, Athenian 66-74
Ground: Eldon Avenue 1948-63   **Names:** Boreham Wood Rovers and Royal Retournez, amalgamated in 1948
CLUB RECORDS Attendance: 3,892 v Arsenal , 9 July 99 (friendly)   **Goalscorer:** Micky Jackson, 208
Appearances: Dave Hatchett, 714
BEST SEASON   FA Amateur Cup: 3rd Rd. replay 70-71   **FA Trophy:** 3rd Rd 1995-96. Replay at Chorley 3-4, 3rd Rd replay 97-98
FA Cup: 2nd Round v Luton Town 1996-97. v Cheltenham Town 97-98
HONOURS: Isthmian Lg.Prem Div R-Up 97-98 Div I 94-95, Isthmian Lg Div 2 76-77 (Yth Cup R-up 80-81), Isthmian Lge. Cup 96-97; R-Up 94-95,95-96 ,98-99 Athenian Lg 73-74 (Div 2 68-69, Div 1 R-up 69-70), Spartan Lg R-up 65-66, Herts Senior Cup 71-72 ,98-99 (R-up 66-67 74-75 79-80 87-88,96-97,97-98), Herts Junior Cup   51-52, Parthenon Lg 55-56 (R-up(2) 53-55 56-57, Herts Charity Shield 64-65, Herts Interm Cup 69-70, Herts Charity Cup (5) 80-81 83-84 85-86 88-90 (R-up 71-72 84-85 86-87 90-91 91-92 92-93), London Senior Cup R-up89-90, London Intermediate Cup 70-71, Neale Trophy 69-70, Essex & Herts BorderComb 72-73 (Lg Cup 72-73, Western Div R-up 82-83 89-90), Mithras Cup 76-77, Middx Border Lg 81-82 (Lg Cup 79-80), Wallspan Floodlit 86-87, London Challenge Cup 97-98

Players progressing: Colin Franks (Watford & Sheff Utd), Charles Ntamark (Walsall), Dean Samuels (Barnet 96)

THE NON-LEAGUE PAPER
CONFERENCE & PYRAMID LEAGUES SOCCER / £1.00
AVAILABLE AT A NEWSAGENT NEAR YOU EVERY SUNDAY

BRAINTREE TOWN

CLUB OFFICIALS
Chairman: **George Rosling**
Vice Chairman: **Ivan Kibble**
President: **Ron Webb**
Secretary: **T A Woodley**, 19a Bailey Bridge
Rd., Braintree, Essex CM7 5TT
(01376 326234)
Press Officer: **Ron Webb** (01376 325338)

FOOTBALL MANAGEMENT TEAM
Manager:John Embery
Assistant Manager Steve Jackson
Physio: Tony Brightwell

FACT FILE
Founded: 1898
Nickname: The Iron
Sponsors: T.B.A.
Colours:Yellow with navy side panel
Change colours: White/navy
Midweek matches: Tuesday
Reserves' Lg: Essex/Herts Border Comb
1999-00 Captain: Nicky Smith
P.o.Y.: Nicky Smith
Top Goalscorer: Robbie Reinelt

For up to the minute news,
results, fixtures,
plus general facts & figures
from the world of
non-league football

log on to

www.nlfootball.com

GROUND   **C** ressing Road Stadium, Clockhouse Way, Braintree, Essex (01376 345617)
Directions: From Braintree by-pass, turn into Braintree at the McDonalds r'bout, follow signs
for East Braintree Ind. Est. - floodlights on left 3/4 mile into town just past. Orange Tree Pub.
Entrance next left in Clockhouse Way, then left again. 1 mile from Braintree & Bocking (BR).
Bus 353 from Witham or town centre Town centre 20 mins walk
Capacity: 4,000   Cover 1,500   Seats 250   Floodlights:Yes
Clubhouse: Open evenings 7-30-11, Sun 12-3, Sat matchday 12.00- 11.00 Full bar facilities
Club shop: Contact Jon Weaver 01376 347920 (75 year History of Braintree £15.99)

Programme
Pages: 40 Price: £1
Editor: Len Llewellyn (01277 363103 T/Fax)

Local Radio: BBC Essex (103.5 fm),
Essex Radio (102.6 fm)

PREVIOUS   **Leagues:** North Essex 1898-1925; Essex & Suffolk Border 25-28 55-64; Spartan 28-35; Eastern Co's 35-37 38-39 52-55 70-91;
Essex Co. 37-38; London 45-52; GtrLondon 64-66; Metropolitan 66-70; Southern 91-96
          Names: Manor Works 1898-1921; Crittall Ath. 21-68; Braintree & Crittall Ath. 68-81; Braintree FC 81-82
          Grounds: The Fair Field 1898-1903; Spaldings Meadow, Panfield Lane 03-23
CLUB RECORDS Attendance: 4,000 v Spurs, charity challenge match, May 1952
          Career Goalscorer: Chris Guy 211, 63-90.   **Seasonal Record Scorer:** Gary Bennett 57, 97-98
          Career Appearances: Paul Young 524, 66-77   **Fee Paid:** £2,000 for Shane Bailey (Sudbury Town)
          Fee Received: £10,000 Matt Metcalf (Brentford 93) & John Cheesewright(Colchester 93)
          Win: 15-3 v Hopes (Birmingham Friendly 39), 12-0 v Thetford Tn (Eastern Lge 35-36)
          Defeat: 0-14 v Chelmsford City A (Nth Essex Lge 23)
BEST SEASON **FA Cup:** 4th Qual. Rd 69-70 85-86 94-95 97-98
HONOURS: Isthmian Lge Div 2 R-up 97-98, Div 3 R-up 96-97; Guardian Insurance Cup R-up 96-97; Eastern Counties Lg 36-37 83-84 84-85 (R-up
          86-87 87-88 88-89 90-91), Lg Cup 87-88 (R-up 35-36 74-75); Essex County Lg R-up 37-38; London Lg (East) R-up 45-46, Lg Cup 47-
          48(jt) 48-49 51-52 (R-up 49-50); Metropolitan Lg Cup 69-70; Essex Elizabethan Tphy R-up 68-69; E. Anglian Cup 46-47 68-69 95-96;
          Essex Sen.Tphy 86-87 (R-up 90-91); Essex & Suffolk Border Lg 59-60 84-85 (Lg Cup 59-60); Nth Essex Lg 05-06 10-11 11-12; Essex
          Sen Cup 95-96 R-up 96-97; Essex Jnr Cup R-up 04-05 05-06 22-23; RAFA Cup 56-57; Gtr Lon. Ben. Cup 65-66; Worthington Evans
          Cup (3) R-up (4); Eastern F'lit Cup 85-86 96-97 (R-up 94-95 97-98); Anglian F'lit Lg 69-70; Jan Havanaar Inter. Tour. 94-95 (R-up 92-93)
Players progressing: J Dick (West Ham 53), S Wright (Wrexham 83), J Cheesewright (Birmingham C. 91), G Bennett, M Metcalf (Brentford 93),
R Reinhelt (Gillingham 93), M de Souza (Birmingham C.), G Culling (Colchester U94)

Back Row: Peter Catchpole, Declan Perkins, Ian Brown, Russell Tanner, Paul Knight, Mark Keen, Nicky Rust, Gavin Cowan, Trevor
Gunn, Shane Bailey, Ian Renshaw, Tony Brightwell, Graham Daniels, Richie Dowling. **Front Row:** Richard Philp, Lee Hunter, Lee
Owen, Ben Woolnough, Nicky Smith, Mark Adams, Robbie Reinelt, Andy Polston, Simon Milton, Scott Forbes.   **Photo:** Jon Weaver

BROMLEY

CLUB OFFICIALS

Chairman: **Glyn Beverly**

Secretary: **John de Palma**,39 Moorfield
Road, Orpington, Kent BR6 0HG
Tel: 01689 819418

FOOTBALL MANAGEMENT TEAM

Manager: Frank Coles
Coach: Martin Coates
Physio: T.B.A.

GROUND

Directions: One mile from Bromley South (BR). Buses 316, 146 and 119 pass ground.
Junction 4 off M25, then A21 towards London
Capacity: 5,000   Cover: 2,500   Seats: 1,300   Floodlights: Yes
Clubhouse: Open matchdays. Food available
Club Shop: Yes. contact Jim Brown

FACT FILE
Formed: 1892
Nickname: The Lilywhites
Colours: White/black/black
Change colours: All red
Midweek home matchday: Tuesday
Reserve's League: None
Youth League: Southern Youth
Newsline: 0930 555 838
1999-00
Captain: Frank Coles
Ps.o.Y.: Ian Rawlings,Billy Goldstone and
Mark Tompkins
Top Scorer: Matt Woolf

Hayes Lane, Bromley, Kent BR2 9EF
Tel: 0181 460 5291 or 0181 313 3992

Ryman
Football
League
Division
One

**Match Day
Magazine**
Season 1999/2000   £1.20

Pages: 32 Price: £1.20
Editor: Colin Russell(020 8405 0738)

Local Press: Bromley Times
Local Radio: Radio Kent,
Bromley Local Radio

PREVIOUS   **Leagues:** South London - 1894; Southern 94-96; London 96-98 99-1901; West Kent 01-04; Southern Suburban 04-07;
Kent 1898-99, 11-14; Spartan 07-08; Isthmian 08-11; Athenian 19-52
Grounds: White Hart Field Cricket Ground, Widmore Rd (pre-1904); Plaistow Cricket Field 1904-37; Hayes Lane 06-37

RECORDS   **Attendance:** 12,000 v Nigeria, 1950
Goalscorer: George Brown 570 (1938-61)   **Appearances:** George Brown
Win: 12-1 v Chertsey FA Cup 75   **Defeat:** 1-11 v Cray Wands 33
Fee Paid: Unknown   **Fee Received:** £50,000 for Jon Goodman (from Millwall 90)

BEST SEASON   **FA Amateur Cup:** Winners 10-11, 37-38, 48-49
FA Trophy: Second Round 91-92   **FA Cup:** 2nd Rd replay v Scarborough 37-38, Lincoln 38-39, Watford 45-46

HONOURS: Isthmian League(4) 08-10 53-54 60-61 (R-up 52-53 55-56 87-88), Div 1 R-up 79-80 5-86 90-91, Prince Phillip 5-a-side Cup
1979; Athenian League 22-23 48-49 50-51 (R-up 35-36); London League Div 2 1896-97; Spartan League 07-08; London
Snr Cup 09-10 45-46 50-51; Kent Senior Cup 49-50 76-77 91-92 96-97; Kent AmateurCup (12) 07-08 31-32 35-37 38-39 46-47
48-49 50-51 52-53 53-55 59-60; LondonChallenge Cup 1995-96.
Players progressing: Roy Merryfield (Chelsea), Stan Charlton (Arsenal 52), RonHeckman (Orient 55), John Gregory (West Ham 51), Bill Lloyd
(Millwall 56), Brian Kinsey (Charlton 56), Harold Hobbs (Charlton & England), Matt Carmichael (Lincoln 90), Leslie Locke (QPR 56), Jon Goodman
(Millwall 90), Dean Wordsworth (Crystal Palace 97), Landry Zahana-ONI (Luton Town 98)

Back Row: Paul Selway, Joe Odegbami, Darren White, Danny Harwood, Ian Rawlings, Andy Constable, Lee Goodwin.
Front: Aaron Day, Jamie Kyte, Matt Woolf, Ernie Cooksey, John Myatt, Kirk Watts, Dean Francis.   **Photo** courtesy of Kentish Newspapers

FORD UNITED

CLUB OFFICIALS

Secretary: Colin Mynott, 11 Rantree Fold,
Basildon, Essex SS16 5TG
(01268 452965 H, 01268 404624 B)
Chairman: Jimmy Chapman
Vice-Chairman: George Adams
President: Nick Scheele

FOOTBALL MANAGEMENT TEAM
Manager: Denis Elliott
Coaches:
Steve Brice, Les Witton & Hilroy Emaneus
Physio.: Alan Jeyes

FACT FILE

Founded: 1934
Nickname: Motormen
Sponsor: Sky Sports
Colours: All blue
Change: All red
Midweek home matchday: Tuesday
Reserves' League:
Essex & Herts Border Comb

Pages: 72   Price: £1
Editor: Michael Ewen
Tel: 01708 724178 (H)

GROUND   Ford Sports & Soc. Club, Rush Green Rd., Romford. Tel: 01708 745678

Directions: On the A124 (Rush Green road) on left going towards Hornchurch.
2 miles from Romford (BR). Buses 173, 175 87, 106, 23

Capacity: 3,000   Seats: 354   Cover: Yes   Floodlights: Yes

Clubhouse: 4 bars, 2 dance halls, tea bar. ??Opening hours & is food available??
Club Shop: No

HONOURS: London Snr Cup 55-56 56-57 94-95 97-98; Essex Snr Lge 91-92 96-97,R-up 94-95,Trophy 90-91 91-92, Cup 39-40 49-50 50-51 51-52 85-86, R-up Spartan Lg 49-50 50-51 55-56 56-57 57-58; London Lg 36-37 38-39; Essex Elizabethan 59-60 60-61 70-71; Gtr London Lg 70-71; Sportsmanship Award 77-78 79-80 80-81; Essex & Herts Border Comb.(res) 94-95 (Lg Cup 94-95); Isthmian League Div 3 98-99

RECORDS: **Attendance:** 58,000 Briggs Sports v Bishop Auckland, at St James Park, Newcastle, FA Amateur Cup
Appearances: Roger Bond   **Goalscorer:** Unknown
Win: Unknown   **Defeat:** Unknown

PREVIOUS: **Leagues:** Spartan, Aetolian, Metropolitan, Essex Senior
Names: Brigg Sports (1934) & Ford Sports (1934) amalgamated in 1958   **Grounds:** None

BEST SEASON: **FA Vase:** 98-99, 5th Round, 1-2 v Bedlington Terriers (H)
FA Amateur Cup: Semi-Final 53-54

Players progressing: Les Allen (Spurs), Mick Flanagan (QPR, Charlton, Crystal Palace), Jim Stannard (Fulham, Southend, Millwall), Nicky Hammond (Arsenal,Swindon), Laurie Abrahams (Charlton), Doug Barton (Reading, Newport)

Ford United's Jeff Wood scored with this header against Wingate & Finchley last season.
Photo: Alan Coomes

HARLOW TOWN

Established 1879

HARLOW TOWN *Football Club*

CLUB OFFICIALS

Chairman: **Jeff Bothwell**

President: **Ron Bruce**

Press Officer: **Gavin McWilliams**
Tel: 01279 441894

Secretary: **Graeme Auger**
58 Braziers Quey, South Street,Bishop's
Stortford, Herts (01279 465998)

FOOTBALL MANAGEMENT TEAM
Manager: Ian Allinson
Asst. Manager: Geoff Livingstone
Physio: Mickey Stevens

FACT FILE
Founded: 1879
Nickname: Hawks
Sponsors: BritSec Int. Ltd
Colours: Red & white/white/white
Change: White & yellow/yellow/yellow
Midweek matches: Wednesday
Reserves' Lge: Essex & Herts Border Comb

99-00- Captain: Neil Moore
P.o.Y.: Marvin Samuel
Top Scorer: Wade Falana

GROUND
Harlow Sports Centre, Hammarskjold Rd, Harlow CM20 2JF
Tel: 01279 445319

Directions: Near town centre, 10 mins walk from Harlow Town (BR) station

Capacity: 10,000   Cover: 500   Seats: 400   Floodlights: Yes

Club Shop: Yes

Clubhouse: Open daily 11-11 (10.30 Sundays). Hot & cold food available

36 pages £1.00
Editor: Phil Tuson (01279 416743)
Local Press: Harlow Citizen, Harlow Star,
Harlow Herald & Post
Local Radio: Essex Radio, BBC Essex, Ten 17

PREVIOUS   **Leagues:** East Herts (pre-1932); Spartan 32-39 46-54; London 54-61; Delphian 61-63; Athenian 63-73; Isthmian 73-92;
Inactive 92-93
Grounds: Marigolds 1919-22; Green Man Field 22-60

CLUB RECORDS   **A**ttendance: 9,723 v Leicester, FA Cup 3rd Rd replay 8/1/80
Goalscorer: Jeff Wood (45 in 88-89)   **Appearances:** Norman Gladwin 646 (1949-70)
Win: 12-0 v Hertford Ath. (H), E. Herts Lge 5/10/29   **Defeat:** 0-11 v Ware (A), Spartan Lge Div. One (East) 6/3/48

BEST SEASON   **FA Amateur Cup:** 2nd Rd 72-73   **FA Trophy:** 2nd Rd(2) 80-82   **FA Vase:** 3rd Rd 88-89
FA Cup: 4th Rd 79-80 (lost 3-4 at Watford). Also 1st Rd 80-81 81-82   League clubs defeated: Southend, Leicester 79-80

HONOURS   Isthmian Lg Div 1 78-79 (R-up 82-83, Div 2 Nth 88-89, Yth Cup 77-78), Ath'n LgDiv 1 71-72, E Angl. Cup 89-90, Knight F'lit
Cup R-up 87-88, Essex Snr Cup 78-79, Essex F'lit Competition R-up 71-72, London Lg Chal. Cup 59-60, Spartan LgCup 52-
53, Epping Hosp. Cup (3) 46-49, Essex & Herts Border Comb Cup 75-76, Fred Budden Trophy 88-89 89-90,
Chelmsford Yth Lg 86-87 (Lg Cup 86-87 87-88)

Players progressing: Jeff Wood (Charlton 75), Neil Prosser (B'mouth 80)

Back Row: John Alderton (dressing room attendant), Lee Claridge, Paul Walton (coach), Darryl Trigg, Wade Falana, Shaun
O'Neill, Greg Howell, Tony Kelly, Geoff Livingstone (coach), Malcolm Roddy (physio), Ian Allinson (Manager).
Front: Marc Salmon, John Nicholson, Roy Parkyn, Phil Leggatt, Danny Cowley, John Ridout, Martin Young, Leon Ettienne,
Dave Cook, James Chrysanthou, Marvin Samuel

LEATHERHEAD

CLUB OFFICIALS

Chairman: **David Zackheim**
President: **Gerald Darby**
General Manager: **Keith Wenham** (at club)
Secretary: **Gerald Darby**
Ranmore, Harriots Lane, Ashtead,
Surrey, KT21 2QG
Press Office/Comm. Director: **Keith Wenham**

FOOTBALL MANAGEMENT TEAM
Manager: Clive House
Asst. Manager:"Chick' Botley
Youth Team Manager: Alex Inglethorpe
Physio: Steve Young

FACT FILE

Founded: 1946
Nickname: Tanners
Sponsors: The Beer Seller
Colours: Green and White
Change colours: Blue & white
Midweek Matchday: Tuesday

For up to the minute news,
results, fixtures,
plus general facts & figures
from the world of
non-league football

log on to

www.nlfootball.com

GROUND   Fetcham Grove, Guildford Rd, Leatherhead, Surrey KT22 9AS
Tel: 01372 360151, Fax: 01372 362705
Directions: M25 jct 9 to Leatherhead; follow signs to Leisure Centre, ground adjacent. Half
mile from Leatherhead (BR)
London Country Buses 479 and 408 - ground opposite bus garage
Capacity: 3,400   Seats: 200   Cover: 445   Floodlights: Yes
Clubhouse: (01372 360151) Bar open 12-11pm matchdays. Full catering.
Club Shop: Yes. 01372 362705

Programme
Pages: 24 Price: £1
Edito: Robert Wooldridge (0208 669 3824)
Local Press: Leatherhead Advertiser,
Surrey Advertiser
Local Radio: County Sound

PREVIOUS   **Leagues:** Surrey Snr 46-50; Metropolitan 50-51; Delphian 51-58; Corinthian 58-63; Athenian 63-72
                  Names: None   **Grounds:** None

CLUB RECORDS   **Attendance:** 5,500 v Wimbledon, 1976
                  Win: 13-1 v Leyland Motors 46-47 Surrey Sen Lge   **Defeat:** 1-11 v Sutton United
                  Career goalscorer: Steve Lunn 96-97 (46)   **Career appearances:** P Caswell
                  Fee paid: £1,500 to Croydon (B Salkeld)   **Fee received:** £1,500 from Croydon (B Salkeld)

BEST SEASON   **FA Amateur Cup:** Semi finalists 70-71 73-74   **FA Trophy:** Runners-up 77-78
                  F A Cup: 4th Round 74-75, 2-3 v Leicester C.(A). Also 2nd Rd 75-76 76-77 78-79,1st Rd 77-78 80-81
                  League clubs defeated: Colchester, Brighton 74-75, Cambridge Utd 75-76,Northampton 76-77

HONOURS   FA Trophy R-up 77-78; Isthmian Lg Cup 77-78; Corinthian Lg 62-63; Athenian Lg Div 1 63-64;
                  Surrey Snr Cup 68-69 (R-up 64-65 66-67 74-75 78-79); Surrey Snr Lg 46-47 47-48 48-49 49-50(Lg Cup 49-50),
                  Snr Shield 68-69, Charity Cup 46-47 49-50); E. Surrey Charity Cup 68-69 (R-up 67-68); London Snr Cup R-up 74-75 77-78;
                  Surrey Inter Cup 89-90; Southern Comb. Cup 89-90

Players progressing: Chris Kelly (Millwall), B Friend (Fulham), L Harwood (Port Vale), John Humphrey (Millwall)

NORTHWOOD

CLUB OFFICIALS

Secretary: Steve Williams, 35 Evelyn Drive
Hatch End, Pinner, Middx HA5 4RL
Tel: (02088 428 1533 - H & fax)
Chairman: Andy Johnson
Vice Chairman: Geoff Foster
President: Lothar Hahn
Press Off: M Russell (01923 827690)

FOOTBALL MANAGEMENT TEAM
Manager: Tony Choules
Asst. Man: **Bob Webster**
Physio: George Price

FACT FILE
Founded: 1902
Nickname: Woods
Sponsors: IFS Freight Forwarding
Colours: All red
Change colours: All yellow
Midweek Matches: Tuesday
Reserve League: Suburban

99-00 Captain: Chris Gell
Ps.o.Y: L.Yaku, Paul Riordan
Top Scorer: Lawrence Yaku(61)

NORTHWOOD FOOTBALL CLUB
OFFICIAL MATCH-DAY PROGRAMME
Price £1.00
Tuesday 2nd May 2000
CHESHUNT
Ryman League Division Two
Kick-Off: 7.45 p.m.
Ryman Football League

SEASON 1999/2000

Pages: 52   Price: 80p
Editor: A Evans (0208 8566 2880)
Local Press: Ruislip & Northwood Gazette,
Watford Observer

GROUND   Northwood Park, Chestnut Avenue, Northwood (01923 827148)
Directions: A404 (Pinner-Rickmansworth) - Chestnut Ave. on left by large grey iron rail
way bridge. Third of a mile from Northwood Hills station (Metropolitan Line) -
turn right out of station to r'bout, left into Pinner Road, left into Chestnut
Avenue after 300yds. Buses 282 and H11 to Northwood Hills
Capacity: 2,580   Seats: 200   Cover: 500   Floodlights: Yes
Club Shop: No
Clubhouse: Weekends & most eves from 6pm. Bar. Hot and cold food. Pool, juke-box

HONOURS: Isthmian Lg Associate Members Cup 92-93,99-00; London Spartan Lg 91-92 (R-up 89-90), Lg Cup 89-90 91-92;
Hellenic Lg Div 1 78-79 (Prem Div Cup R-up 81-82); Middx Lg 77-78 (R-up 72-73 76-77), Div 1 R-up 71-72,
Challenge Cup 74-75 76-77 77-78; Middx Snr Charity Cup R-up 93-94; Middx Snr Cup SF 91-92 92-93 98-99; R-up 99-00
Jnr Cup 46-47 47-48 48-49; Harrow & Wembley Lg (9); Middlesex Premier Cup 94-95.Isthmian Div 2 R-up 99-00

PREVIOUS: **Leagues:** Harrow & Wembley 32-69; Middlesex 69-78; Hellenic 79-84; London Spartan 84-92
Names: Northwood Town   **Grounds:** None

CLUB RECORDS: **Attendance:** 1,642 v Chelsea Friendly July 1997
Goal Scorerin Season: Lawrence Yaku 61 (99-00) **Career Appearances:** Norman Heslop
Win: 15-0 v Dateline (H) Middlesex Inter Cup 1973   **Defeat:** 0-8 v Bedfont (Middlesex Lg.1975)

BEST SEASON: **FA Cup:** 2nd Qual Rd 94-95, 99-00
FA Vase: Qtr finals 96-97

Players progressing: Gavin Maguire, Derek Payne (Barnet), Warren Patmore (Cambridge United)

Gerry Henry (Coach), George Price (Physio), Dave Nolan, Paul Watkins, Rene Strett, Danny Butler, Paul Riordan,
Danny Gladman, Gary Williams, Andy Sherry, Dave Sargent, Ryan Ambler, Bob Webster (asst. Man.), Tony Choules
(Manager). Front: Lawrence Yaku, Gavin Hart, Craig McIntosh, James Burgess, Chris Gell, Steve Hale, Andy
Draper, Gary Issott, Scott Fitzgerald.

OXFORD CITY

CLUB OFFICIALS

Chairman: **M Woodley**
President:
Vice Chairman: **R Holt**

Press Officer/Secretary: **John Shepperd**
20 Howe Close, Wheatley, Oxford OX33 1SS
Tel: 01865 872181 (& Fax)

FOOTBALL MANAGEMENT TEAM

Manager: Paul Lee
Asst Manager:
Physio: C. Perkins

FACT FILE

Formed: 1882
Nickname: City
Sponsors: Unipart D.C.M
Colours: Blue & white hoops/blue/blue
Change colours: yellow,black,black
Midweek Matchday: Tuesday
Reserve's Lge: Suburban Lge Prem Div.

99-00: Captain Andy Smith
Top Scorer: Andy Smith
P.o.Y.: Julian Dark

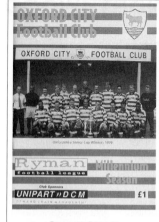

GROUND Court Place Farm, Marsh Lane, Marston, Oxford. OX3 0NQ.
Tel: 01865 744493.01865 742394 (Clubhouse)

Directions: From London M40/A40, ring-road to North, take 1st slip road, follow signs to John Radcliffe hospital and Court Place Farm Stadium, ground on left after leaving flyover. From the north same ring-road.
Capacity: 3,000   Seats: 300   Cover: 400   Floodlights: Yes
Clubhouse: Open matchdays, most refreshments available
Club Shop: Yes, open matchdays, selling souvenirs. Contact Paul Cotterell

Pages: 60 Price: £1
Editor: John Sheppard
Local Press: Oxford Mail
Local Radio: Radio Oxford FM, Fox FM

PREVIOUS   **Leagues:** Isthmian 07-88; South Midlands 90-93
Grounds: The White House 1882-1988; Cuttleslowe Pk 90-91; Pressed Steel,Romanway 91-93

CLUB RECORDS **Attendance:** 9,500 v Leytonstone, FA Amateur Cup 50
Win: 9-0 v Harlow Town, Isthmian League 9/10/76
Defeat: 0-8 v Wycombe Wanderers, Isthmian League - date unknown
Scorer: John Woodley   **Appearances:** John Woodley
Fee Paid: £3,000 for S Adams (Woking)   **Fee Received:** £17,500 for Howard Forinton (Yeovil T. 1.97)

BEST SEASON **FA Amateur Cup:** Winners 05-06 Runners-up 02-03 12-13   **FA Vase:** Runners-up 94-95
FA Cup: Second Round 69-70, 1-5 v Swansea City (H)   **FA Trophy:** 1st Rd Prop 96 v Merthyr Tydfil

HONOURS   FA Amateur Cup 05-06 (R-up 02-03 12-13); F.A.Vase R-Up 94-95; Isthmian Lg R-up 34-35 45-46, Div 1 95-96 R-up 77-78
South MidlandsLg 92-93; Oxon Senior Cup - 28 times

Players progressing: A Blakeman (Brentford 46), C Holton (Arsenal 50), K Savin(Derby 50), R Adams (Blackpool 48), A Jeffries (Brentford 49), P James (Luton 49), D Gordon/E Wilcox (WBA 47/48), V Mobley (Sheffield Wed 63), J Varney (Hull 50), P Lee (Hereford 73), H Poole (Port Vale 55), G Parker (Luton 81), M Keown(Arsenal 84), D Meeson (Wolves 52)

Back Row: Danny Wise, Michael Thorp, Richard Pierson, Andy Smith, Alan Foster, Dwaine Strong, Matty Whitehead, Stewart McCleary, Matt Hayward. **Front:** Justin Lee, Gary Smart, Julian Dark, Terry Sweeney, Chris Potter, Richard Twine, Shaun Wimble.

ROMFORD

CLUB OFFICIALS

President: **Dave Howie**
Chairman: **Mark Corr**

Vice-Chairman: **Steve Gardener**
Secretary:**Derek Robinson**Tel: 01708 507803
Press Officer: **Steve Gardener**

FOOTBALL MANAGEMENT TEAM

Team Manager: Amin Levitt
Physios: Don Calder & Allen Hyde

FACT FILE

Reformed: 1992
Nickname: The Boro
Sponsors: TBA
Colours: Blue & old gold/blue/blue
Change colours: Red & black/black/black
Midweek home matchday: Tuesday (7.45)
Reserves' League: Essex & Herts Border Prem
Club Call: 0930 555 841
1999-00 - Captain: mal Grayburn
P.o.Y.: Jason White
Top Scorer: Chris Rose (15)

ROMFORD
Football Club
1999-2000

TODAY'S
MATCH BALL
SPONSORS

SEAN BUTLER
ROBERT FROST
STEVE FROST
DAVE WRIGHT

Ryman
Football League
vol. 8 no. 33

YEADING
RYMAN LEAGUE DIVISION ONE
Saturday 6th May 2000
Kick-off 3.00 pm

Pages: 40 Price: £1.20
Editor: Derek RobinsonTel: 01708 507803
Local Press: Romford Recorder
Local Radio:Active FM

GROUND   `Sungate', Collier Row Road, Collier Row, Romford, Essex. Tel: 01708 722766

Directions: Take the A12 from London as far as the Moby Dick junction. Turn left and then right at the 1st roundabout into Collier Row Road. The ground entrance is signposted 200 yards on the right. Nearest station is Romford (BR). From directly outside the station the London bus 247 passes the ground.
Capacity: 2,500   Cover: 300   Seats: 175   Floodlights: Yes

Clubhouse: Open seven days a week 11am - 11pm
Club Shop: Open matchdays, selling replica shirts, programmes etc.
                   Contact Barry Quantrill 01708 705755

PREVIOUS   **Names:** Romford FC, formed 1876, folded in the Great War. Reformed 1929 until78.
                 Restarted in 1992 & in 96 merged with Collier Row - both names being used for that season only.
                 Name changed to Romford in 1997
                 Leagues: Essex Senior 92-96   **Grounds:** Hornchurch 92-95, Ford United 95-96

CLUB RECORDS **Attendance:** 820 v Leatherhead (IL2) 15/4/97
                 Career Goalscorer: Micky Ross 57   **Season goalscorer:** Vinny John 45 (97-98)
                 Career Appearances: Danny Benstock 197
                 Win: 9-0 v Hullbridge (H) ESL 21/10/95   **Defeat:** 1-7 v St Albans (A) EAC 29/10/96
                 Transfer fee paid: £1,500 for Wade Falana (Braintree) June 97
                 Fee received: £4,000 for Vinny John from Grays A.July 98

BEST SEASON **FA Cup:** 4th Qual Rd 97-98 v Bromsgrove Rovers (A), 1999-2000 v Ilkeston Town (A)
                 FA Vase: 5th Rd 96-97 v Bedlington Terriers 2-1
                 FA Trophy: 2nd Round v Worthing 98-99
HONOURS   Essex Senior Lge Champ 95-96, Lge Cup 95-96; Isthmian Div 2 Champ 96-97; East Anglian Cup 97-98

Back Row: Ken Horne (Commercial Manager), Ron May, Keith Preston (Kit Managers), Mark Jones, Danny Winney, John Ray, Chris Rose, Steve Good, Ken Roudette, Tommy Lee, Mal Grayburn, Tony Kinnear, Allen Hyde (Physio), Ken Smith (Reserve Team Manager), Enrico Tiritera (Reserve Team Coach), Mark Corr (Chairman). **Front:** Gary Price, Bryan Page, Jason White, Amin Levitt (First Team Manager), Larry Whitmore (First Team Assistant Manager), Paul Rogan, Mervin Abraham

STAINES TOWN

CLUB OFFICIALS

Chairman: **Alan Boon**
President: **Nigel Iggulden**
Vice Chairman: **Ken Williams**
Secretary: **Steve Parsons**
3 Birch Green, Staines, Middx TW18 4HA Tel:
01784 450420
Commercial Mgr: **Ken Williams**
Press Officer: **Stuart Moore** (01784 421118)

FOOTBALL MANAGEMENT TEAM

Manager: Ken Ballardr
Asst Manager: Danny Pipe
Physios: Dave Beard & Mike Critchall

FACT FILE

Formed: 1892
Nickname: The Swans
Sponsors: The Exchange Nightclub
Colours: Old gold (blue trim)/royal/royal
Change colours: All white
Midweek matchday: Tuesday
Reserve league: Suburban (since 72)

1999-00
Capt: Mark Costello
P.o.Y: Matthew Lovett
Top Scorer: Mark Butler (32)

GROUNDWheatsheaf Park, Wheatsheafe Lane,Staines,Middlesex TW18 2PD(01784 455988)
Directions: M25 Jct13 to A30 Staines by-pass to Crooked Billet roundabout.Take town centre
exit(A308) and left into South St, at iron bridge.Pass bus staion and bear left into Laleham
Rd. Wheatsheafe Lane is 1km on right Buses 481,570,and 573 pass Wheatsheaf Lane.
Capacity: 2,500 **Cover:** 850 **Seats:** 250 **Floodlights:**Yes **Food:** Rolls and snacks available
Club HQ & Clubhouse: Staines Town FC, Wheatsheaf Lane, Staines (01784 455988).
Fully furnished clubhouse & function hall, open 7-11 matchdays and every evening.s
Rolls and other snacks available
Club Shop: Souvenirs available from Ray Moore c/o STFC.

Pages: 44   Price: £1
Editor: Sec. & Stuart Moore (01784 421118)
Local Press: Staines & Ashford News,
Middx Chronicle, Informer,Staines Gaurdian
Local Radio: County Sound, GLR, Capital,
Star FM, Radio Wey.

PREVIOUS   **Leagues:** W London All (pre-1900), W London, W Middx (pre-1905), Gt WesternSuburban 05-13 20-24, Gt Western Comb,
Munitions Lg (World War 1), London Works(World War 1), Hounslow & Dist 19-20, Spartan 24-35 58-71, Middx Sen 43-52;
Parthenon 52-53, Hellenic 53-58, Athenian 71-73
Names: Staines Albany and St Peters Institute (merged) in 1895, Staines 05-18,Staines Lagonda 18-25, Staines Vale (2nd World War)
Grounds: Edgell Rd (St Peters Inst); The Lammas, Shortwood Common, Mill Mead(Hammonds/Wicks/Pursers Farm); Shepperton Road (to 51);
Wheatsheaf Lane (51-96) ,Alwyns Lane Chertsey (1996-8)
CLUB RECORDS Attendance: 2,750 v Banco di Roma (Barassi Cup) 1975 (70,000 saw 1st leg inRome)
Goalscorer: Alan Gregory 122   **Appearances:** Dickie Watmore 840
Win: 14-0 v Croydon (A), Isthmian League Div. 1 19/3/94   **Defeat:** 1-18 v Wycombe Wanderers (A), G West Sub Lge 1909
Fee Paid: For R Teale (Slough 81)   **Fee Received:** For Scott Taylor (Millwall 95-96)
BEST SEASON   FA Amateur Cup: 3rd Rd 23-24   **FA Trophy:** 2nd Rd 2nd Replay 76-77I (Last 32)
FA Cup: 1st Rd 84-85, 0-2 v Burton Alb (A) & 1879-80 & 80-81 (as St PetersInstitute)
HONOURS   Isthmian Lg Div 1 74-75 88-89 (Div 2 74-75); Athenian Lg Div 2 71-72 (Div 1 R-up 72-73); Spartan Lg 59-60 (R-up 70-71), Lg
Cup 68-69 (R-up 60-61 70-71); Hellenic Lg R-up 55-56 (Lg Cup R-up 53-54 55-56); Gt Western Suburban Lg Div 1R-up 11-12 22-24 (Div 2
(Middx) 20-21); W London All Div 1 1899-1900; W LondonLg Div 1 00-01; W Middx Lg 04-05 (R-up 03-04); London Snr Cup R-up 76-77 80-81;
Middx Snr Cup(7), (R-up 09-10 32-33 79-80), Snr Charity Cup 94-95; Barassi Cup76; Southern Comb. Chall. Cup 64-65 66-67 68-69 94-95 96-
97,(R-up 67-68 94-95,99-00);W Middx Cup 23-24; Staines Cottage Hosp Cup 24-25; Merthyr Middx Charity Shield 90-91,(R-up 94-95); El Canuelo
Trophy 92-93 94-95 94-95; Carlsberg Cup 94-95; Melksham Middx Charity Shield 96-97 Jim Lawford Memorial Cup 99-00

The Staines Town
defence about to be
tested by Aldershot's
Ian Hathaway.
Photo: Ian Morsman

THAME UNITED

CLUB OFFICIALS

Chairman: **Jim Tite**

Vice Chairman: **Mike Dyer**

Secretary: **Sally Hunt**
c/o Thame United.

FOOTBALL MANAGEMENT TEAM

Joint Managers:
Andy Sinnott and Alan Thorne

FACT FILE

Founded: 1883
Sponsors:F.M.C.G.
Nickname: United
Colours: Red & black hoops/black/red & black.
Change colours: Green & white
Midweek Matchday: Tuesday
Reserves' League: Suburban
1999-00
Top Scorer: Mark West
P.o.Y.:Andy Williams
Captain: Martin Brown

GROUND: Windmill Road, Thame, Oxon OX9 2DR (01844 213017)

Directions: Into Nelson Street from Market Square. 3 miles from Haddenham &Thame Parkway (BR). Nearest bus stop at Town Hall (half mile away)

Capacity: 3,600   Seats: 284   Cover: 850   Floodlights: Yes

Clubhouse: Open every evening and weekend lunch times
Banqueting facilities for 200 (weddings, dinners, dances etc)

Club Shop: No -

Pages: 24 Price: £1
Editor: Sally Turner (c/o Club)
Local Press: Oxford Mail, Thame Gazette,
Bucks Free Press
Local Radio: Radio Oxford, Fox FM, Mix 96

PREVIOUS **Leagues:** Oxon Senior; Hellenic 1959-87; South Midlands 1987-91
Name: Thame FC   **Ground:** None

CLUB RECORDS **Attendance:** 1,035 v Aldershot, Isthmian Div 2 4/4/94
Win: 9-0 v Bracknell, 31/10/92   **Defeat:** 2-11 v Hungerford, FA Cup Prelim. Rd 1984
Career Goalscorer: Not known   **Career Appearances:** Steve Mayhew
Transfer Fee received: **Fee paid:**

BEST SEASON **FA Cup:** Third Qualifying Round 91-92, 0-4 v Salisbury   **FA Amateur Cup:** if applicable
FA Vase: Semi Final 1998/99

HONOURS Isthmian Lg Div 2 94-95, Div 2 R-up 98-99 Div 3 R-up 92-93; Hellenic Lg 61-62 69-70, Premier Div Cup (4); Sth Mids Lg 90-91; Oxon Snr Cup 1894-95 05-06 08-09 09-10 75-76 80-81 92-93; Oxon Interm Cup 76-77 78-79 91-92,99-00; Oxon Charity Cup
Players progressing to the Football League: None

Back Row: Alan Thorne & Andy Sinnott (Jt. managers), Nando Perna, Chris Fontaine, Andy Williams, Ronnie Joe, Ian Moores, Wayne Cort, Martin Brown (capt.), Dave Tregurtha, Jefferson Louis, Pete Lamont (coach). **Front Row:** Neil Greig (physio), Paul Sherwood, Nigel Emsden, Mark Jones, Greg Williams, John Mitchell, Mark West   **Photo:** Oxford & County Newspapers

UXBRIDGE

CLUB OFFICIALS
Chairman: Alan Holloway
President: Alan Odell
Secretary: Roger Stevens
9 Bourne Ave, Hillingdon, Middx UB8 3AR
Tel: 01895 236879
Match Sec: Mick Burrell Tel: 01895 443094
Res & Youth Sec: Bob Clayton
Tel: 01895 857001
Press Officer: Andy Peart Tel: 01895 443094
Commercial Manager: Trevor Birch
Tel: 0208 813 7291

FACT FILE
Formed: 1871
Nickname: The Reds
Sponsor: Dagenham Motors
Colours: Red/white/red
Change: Sky & navy blueOR White and black
Midweek matchday: Tuesday
Reserves' League: Suburban (Prem Div)
1999-00
Captain: Mark Gill
P.o.Y Awards:Chris Moore & Lee Tunnell (2)
Top Scorer: Chris Moore (15)

FOOTBALL MANAGEMENT TEAM
Manager: George Talbot
Coaches: Mike Nicks & Sean Dawson
Res Manager: Andy Everley
Physio:Catherine Horne
Youth Manager: Bob Hill

GROUND Honeycroft, Horton Road, West Drayton, Middx UB7 8HX Tel: 01895 443557
Directions: From West Drayton (BR) turn right then 1st right (Horton Road).Ground 1 mile on left. From Uxbridge (LT) take 222 or U3 bus to West Draytonstation, then follow as above. By road, ground 1 mile north of M4 jct 4 takingroad to Uxbridge and leaving by first junction and turning left into Horton Rd- ground 500yds on right
Capacity: 3,770   Cover: 760   Seats: 339   Floodlights: Yes
Club Shop: Good selection of souvenirs & programmes. Contact Averill Hinde
Clubhouse: Open every evening and weekend/bank holiday lunchtimes. (01895 443557)
Hot & cold snacks available on matchdays
Large clubhouse with bar and function room availablefor hire.

Pages: 44 Price: £1.00
Editor: A Peart (01895 443094) & Roy Green (01895 254784)
Local Press: Uxbridge Gazette & Leader, Uxbridge Recorder
Local Radio: Capital, G L R, Star FM

PREVIOUS **Leagues:** Southern 1894-99; Gt Western Suburban 1906-19, 20-23; Athenian 1919-20, 24-37, 63-82; Spartan 37-38; London 38-46; Gt Western Comb. 39-45;Corinthian 46-63
Name: Uxbridge Town 23-45   **Grounds:** RAF Stadium 23-48, Cleveland Rd 48-78
CLUB RECORDS **Attendance:** 1,000 v Arsenal, opening of floodlights 1981
Career Scorer: Phil Duff, 153   **Career Appearances:** Roger Nicholls, 1054
BEST SEASON **FA Trophy:** 2nd Rd.1998-99   **FA Vase:** 4th Rd 83-84
FA Cup: 2nd Rd 1873-74. Also 1st Rd 1883-84 84-85 85-86   **FA Amateur Cup:** Runners-up 1897-98
HONOURS FA Amateur Cup R-up 1897-98; London Chall. Cup 93-94 96-97 98-99, R-up 97-98; IsthLge Div 2 S. R-up 84-85; Athenian Lge Cup R-up 81-82, Res. Sect. 69-70, Res. Cup R-up 68-69; Corinthian Lge 59-60 (R-up 48-49), Lge Mem. Shield 50-51 52-53; Middx Sen.Cup 1893-94 95-96 1950-51, R-up 97-98; Middx Sen. Charity Cup 07-08 12-13 35-36 81-82 (R-up 69-70 82-83 85-86); Middx PremCup 95-96; Allied Counties Yth Lge [East] 92-93 (Lge Cup R-up 86-87), Lge Shield 88-89 92-93, R-up 97-98; AC Delco Cup R-up 85-86; Suburban Lge North Div 95-96 97-98, R-up 96-97; Middx Sen Yth Cup 96-97
Players progressing: William Hill (QPR 51), Lee Stapleton (Fulham 52), Gary Churchouse (Charlton A.), Tony Witter (QPR), Guy Butters (Spurs), Michael Meaker (QPR)

Back Row L-R: Mike Nicks (coach), Mark Weedon, Gavin Bamford, Stuart Bamford, Simon Poulter, Kevin Cleary, Mark Gill (capt.), Phil Glanville, Sean Dawson, Dean Clark, George Talbot (manager). **Front Row:** Catherine Horne (physio), Leyton Brooks, Paul Mills, Jamie Cleary, Nicky Ryder, Lee Tunnell, Chris Moore.
Photo: Roy Green

WALTON & HERSHAM

CLUB OFFICIALS

Chairman: **A.Smith**
President: TBA
Secretary: **Mark Massingham,** 7b Sidney
Rd., Walton-on-Thames, Surrey. KT12 2NP
Tel: 01932 885814
Press Officer: **Mervyn Rees**
Tel: 01932 245756

FOOTBALL MANAGEMENT TEAM

Manager: Kevin Hinge
Asst Manager: John Humphrey
Physio: Stuart Smith

FACT FILE

Formed: 1896
Nickname: Swans
Sponsors: T.B.A
Colours: White with red band/white/red
Change colours: Yellow/Blue/yellow
Midweek home matchday: Tuesday
Reserve Team's League: Suburban

1999-00 Captain: Chris Whelan
P.o.Y.: Garfield Blackman
Top Scorer: Marc Coates

GROUND: Sports Ground, Stompond Lane, Walton-on-Thames Tel: 01932 245263 (club)

Directions: From North: Over Walton Bridge & along New Zealand Ave., down 1-way street and up A244 Hersham Rd - grd 2nd right. From Esher: Down Lammas Lane then Esher Rd, straight over 1st r'bout, 4th exit at next r'bout (WestGrove) 2nd left at end of Hersham Rd and Stompond Lane 1/2 mile on left.Ten min walk Walton-on-Thames (BR). Bus 218 passes grd

Capacity: 6,500   Cover: 2,500   Seats: 500   Floodlights: Yes
Clubhouse: (01932 245263). Open most nights. TV, darts, pool, refreshments on matchdays
Club Shop: Open matchdays. Contact Richard Old, c/o the club

Pages: 36 Price: £1.20
Editor: Mark Massingham Tel: 01932 885814

Local Press: Surrey Herald, Surrey Comet
Local Radio: County Sound,
BBC Southern Counties

PREVIOUS **Leagues:** Surrey Senior; Corinthian 45-50; Athenian 50-71
CLUB RECORDS **Attendance:** 6,500 v Brighton, FA Cup First Round 73-74
Scorer: Reg Sentance 220 in 11 seasons
Win: 10-0 v Clevedon, FA Amateur Cup 1960
Transfer fee paid: £6,000

Appearances: Terry Keen 449 in 11 seasons
Defeat: 11-3 v Kingstonian Surrey Sen Shield 58
Transfer fee received: £150,000 for Nathan Ellington 99

BEST SEASON **FA Trophy:** 4th Round 99-00   **FA Amateur Cup:** Winners 72-73, (SF 51-52, 52-53)
FA Cup: 2nd Rd 72-73 (v Margate), 73-74 (v Hereford). League clubs defeated: Exeter 72-73, Brighton 73-74

HONOURS: Isthmian Lg R-up 72-73, Barassi Cup 73-74; Athenian Lg 68-69 (R-up 50-51 69-70 70-71, Lg Cup 69-70); Corinthian Lg 46-49 (R-up 49-50), Premier Midweek F'litLg 67-69 70-71 (R-up 71-72); Surrey Snr Cup 47-48 50-51 60-61 61-62 70-71 72-73(R-up 46-47 51-52 59-60 69-70 71-72 73-74); London Snr Cup R-up 73-74; SouthernComb. Cup 82-83 88-89 91-92; 99-00 Surrey Comb.Cup 49-50 91-92; John Livey Memorial Trophy 91-92

Players progressing: Andy McCulloch (QPR 1970), Mick Heath (Brentford 1971),Paul Priddy (Brentford 1972), Richard Teale (Q.P.R. 1973), SteveParsons (Wimbledon 1977), Stuart Massey (Crystal Palace), Ross Davidson(Sheffield Utd), Nathan Ellington (Bristol Rovers), Tommy Williams (West Ham United)

Despite the anxious looks on the Walton & Hersham defence, no Rothwell player was on hand to punish them in this 3rd Round FA Umbro Trophy tie.
Photo: Gordon Whittington

WEALDSTONE

CLUB OFFICIALS
Chairman: **Paul Rumens**
Vice Chairman: **Nick Dugard**
Secretary: **Roger Slater,** c/o 31 Jersey
Avenue,Stanmore,Middlesex HA7 2JG
Tel: 0208 552 3595
Commercial Director: **Nick Dugard**
Press Officer: **Graham Sharpe**
Company Secretary: **Graham Clark**

FOOTBALL MANAGEMENT TEAM
Manager: Gordon Bartlett
Asst Mgr: Leo Morris Coach: Chris Walton
Physio: Ian Pickens

FACT FILE
Formed: 1899
Nickname: The Stones
Sponsors: Warwick & Wright
Colours: Blue & white quarters
Change colours: Yellow
Midweek matches: Tuesday
Reserves' League: None

1999-00
Captain: Paul Lamb
P.o.Y: Paul McKay
Top Scorer: Rocky Baptists (23)

GROUND: (Sharing with Edgware FC)

White Lion Ground, High Street,Edgware,Middlesex
(Ground Tel No: 020 8952 6799)
Directions: Left out of Edgware station(Northern Line), left again at crossroads and ground
is on right , 300 yards down Edgware High Street behind White Lion pub.
Clubhouse: Open nightly and Friday, Saturday and Sunday lunch time. Hot and cold food on
matchdays.

main club sponsor:
Warwick Wright

wealdstone
football club
founded
1899
ryman
league
div 1

the royal
blue review
centenary season 2nd club day programme 1999-2000

Pages: 36 Price: £1.50
Editor: Roy Couch (0208 907 4421)
Local Press: Harrow Observer, Harrow Times
Local Radio: Capital, G.L.R., L.B.C.
Stones Soccerline: 09003 800 160

PREVIOUS **Leagues:** Willesden & Dist. 1899-1906 08-13; London 1911-22; Middx 13-22; Spartan 22-28; Athenian 28-64; Isthmian 64-71;
Southern 71-79 81-82,88-95; GMVConference 79-81 82-88
Grounds: College Farm 03-10; Belmont Rd 10-22; Lower Mead Stad 22-91; Vicarage Rd (Watford FC) 91-93; The Warren (Yeading F.C.) 93-95

CLUB RECORDS **Attendance:** 13,504 v Leytonstone FA Amateur Cup Fourth Round replay 5/3/49
Goalscorer: George Duck, 251 **Appearances:** Charlie Townsend, 514
Win: 22-0 v The 12th London Regiment (The Rangers)(H), FA Amateur Cup 13/10/23
Defeat: 0-14 v Edgware Town (A), London Senior Cup 9/12/44
Fees Paid: £15,000 for David Gipp (Barnet, 90) **Received:** £25,000 for Stuart Pearce (Coventry City 83); for Sean Norman (Chesham, 1989)

BEST SEASON **FA Amateur Cup:** Winners 1965-66 **FA Trophy:** Winners 1984-85
FA Cup: Third Round 77-78, 0-4 v Q.P.R. (A). 1st Rd on 13 occasions. League clubs defeated: Hereford Utd and Reading, 77-78
HONOURS: FA Trophy 84-85; FA Amateur Cup 65-66; GMV Conference 84-85; Isthmian Lge - Div3 96-97; Southern Lg Southern Div 81-82,
Div 1 South 73-74, Lg Cup 81-82; Athenian Lg 51-52 (R-up 52-53 58-59 60-61); Spartan Lg R-up 22-23; London LgDiv 2 12-13 (R-up 11-12);
London Snr Cup 61-62 (jt) (R-up 39-40 51-52 60-61); Middx Snr Cup (11); Middx Senior Charity Cup (11); Capital League 84-85 86-87

Players progressing: Stuart Pearce (Coventry City 83), Vinnie Jones(Wimbledon 86), Danny Bailey (Exeter 89), Phil White (Orient 53), Tom
McGhee & John Ashworth (Portsmouth 54 & 62), Charlie Sells (Exeter City 62), Eddie Dilsworth (LincolnCity 67), Colin Franks (Watford 69)

Back Row: Barry Tarrant, Leo Morris (Asst. Man.), Vincent Cooper, Dominic Sterling, Dave Tilbury, Mark Campbell, Brian Jones,
Lee Walker, Marvin Morgan, Mick Swaysland, Michael Roche, Paul Benning, Simon Robinson, Ian Pickens (Physio), Gordon
Bartlett (Manager). **Front:** Chris Walton (Coach), Carl Holmes, Paul Lamb, Darren Watts, Paul McKay, Mitchell Murphy, Andy
Peaks, Graham Smith (Kit Man.). **Photo:** James Smith

WHYTELEAFE

CLUB OFFICIALS	**FACT FILE**	

Chairman: **Paul Owens**
President: **A F Lidbury**
Secretary: **Ian Robertson**
253 Godstone Road, Whyteleafe,
Surrey. CR3 0BD
Tel: 01883 622096 (H&B)
Press Officer: **Peter Stimpson**
Tel: 01883 348310 (H)
Commercial Manager: T Dounce
Tel: 01883 343450

Formed: 1946
Nickname: Leafe
Sponsors: Sunday Sport
Colours: Green & white/white/white
Change colours: Yellow & black/black/black
Midweek matchday: Tuesday
Reserve Team's League: Suburban

For up to the minute news,
results, fixtures,
plus general facts & figures
from the world of
non-league football

log on to

www.nlfootball.com

FOOTBALL MANAGEMENT TEAM

Manager: Lee Richardson   Assistant Man.: Bernie Donnelly
Coach: Mark Coote   Physio: John Knapton

GROUND   15 Church Road, Whyteleafe, Surrey CR3 0AR
Tel: 0181 660 5491 (Ground) 0181645 0422 (Boardroom)
Directions: Five minutes walk from Whyteleafe (BR) - turn right from station, and left
into Church Road

Capacity: 5,000   Cover: 600   Seats:400   Floodlights: Yes

Clubhouse: Open every lunchtime & evening. Hot & cold food, pool, darts, gaming machines
Clubshop: No

PREVIOUS   **Leagues:** Caterham & Edenbridge, Croydon, Thornton Heath & Dist., SurreyIntermediate (East) 54-58, Surrey Senior 58-75, Spartan 75-81, Athenian 81-84
Names: None   **Grounds:** None

CLUB RECORDS **Attendance:** 2,210 v Chester City F.A.Cup 1st Rd 99-00.
Transfer fee paid: £1,000 for Gary Bowyer (Carshalton)**Transfer fee received:** £25,000 for Steve Milton

BEST SEASON **FA Vase:** 5th Rd 80-81 85-86
FA Trophy: 3rd Qualifying Rd 89-90   **FA Cup:** First Round proper, 99-00 v Chester City (H)

HONOURS   Isthmian Lge Div 2 South R-up 88-89; Surrey Senior Lge 68-69 (Lge Cup R-up 68-69, Lge Charity Cup 71-72, Res Sect 62-63 (Chall. Cup 62-63 (R-up 59-60); Surrey Sen. Cup 68-69 (R-up 87-88); Surrey Prem. Cup R-up 84-85; E. Surrey Charity Cup 79-80 (R-up 76-77 77-78); Thornton Heath & Dist Lge 51-52(Lge Cup 51-52) Div 4 R-up 51-52; Edenbridge Charity Cup 51-52; Caterham & Purley Hospital Cup 51-52; Surrey County Interm Lge East Sect 1 55-56; Surrey Jun. Cup R-up 51-52; Caterham & Edenbridge Lge Div 3 51-52; Borough of Croydon Charity Cup 56-57; Southern Yth Lge 89-90 (R-up 88-89), Lge Cup 88-89 89-90; Southern Counties M'week F'lit Cup 95-96

Players progressing: Steve Milton (Fulham)

Programme
Pages: 36 Price: £1.00
Editor: Warren Filmer (0181 660 3255)

Local Press: Croydon Advertiser
Local Radio: Mercury

Back Row: Bobby George, Gani Ahmet, Duncan Alger, Leion Dillon, Scott Thornton.
Middle: Gary Elliott, Gary Fisher, Danny Rose, Danny Arkwright, Nigel Golley, Matt Martin, Les Boswell, David Boswell.
Front: Lee Richardson, Steve Lunn, Graham Douce, Phil Dawson, Paul Owens, Stuart Massey, Bernie Donnelly

WORTHING

CLUB OFFICIALS

Chairman: **Beau Reynolds**
President: **Morty Hollis**
Vice Chairman: **Ray Smith**

Secretary/Press Off.: **Paul Damper**
19 Fletcher Road, Worthing,
West Sussex BN14 8EX
Tel: 01903 210290

FACT FILE

Formed: 1886
Nickname: The Rebels
Sponsors: Lionvest Trading
Colours: Red, with white trim/red/red
Change colours: Blue with white
trim/blue/blue
Midweek matches: Tuesday

FOOTBALL MANAGEMENT TEAM

Manager: Brian Donnelly
Assistant Manager:Jason Rutherford
Physio: Alan Robertson

1999-00

Captain: Mark Burt
P.o.Y: Simon Funnell
Top Scorer: Simon Funnell & Lee Weston

GROUND   Woodside Road, Worthing, West Sussex BN14 7HQ (01903 239575)

Directions: Follow A24 to town, at end of Broadwater Rd having gone over railway bridge,
1st right into Teville Rd, right into South Farm RD, 2nd left into Pavilion Rd,
Woodside Rd is first right. Half a mile fromWorthing (BR)
Capacity: 4,500   Seats: 450   Cover: 1,000   Floodlights: Yes
Clubhouse: Open 2 hrs before kick-off & closes 11pm. Hot & cold food available
Club Shop: Yes

Pages: 48 Price: £1
Editor: Ian Fowler
Local Press: Evening Argus, Worthing Herald
Local Radio: Southern FM,
Southern Counties Radio

PREVIOUS   **Leagues:** West Sussex Sen 1896-04, 05-14, 19-20; Brighton, Hove & Dist 19-20; Sussex County 20-40, 45-48;
Corinthian 48-63; Athenian 63-77   **Names:** None   **Grounds:** Homefield Park, Beach House Park
CLUB RECORDS Attendance: 4,500 v Depot Battalion Royal Engineers, FA Amtr Cup 07-08
Transfer fee paid: Undisclosed fee forMarc Rice (Havant & Waterlooville1998)
Transfer fee received: £7,500 for Tim Read (Woking, 1990)
Win: 25-0 v Littlehampton (H) West Sussex Lge 1911-12   **Defeat:** 0-14 v Southwick (A), Sussex County Lge 1946-47
Career Goalscorer: Mick Edmonds 275   **Career Appearances:** Geoff Raynsford
BEST SEASON   FA Vase: 5th Rd 78-79   **FA Trophy:** 4th rd Replay 85-86   **FA Amateur Cup:** Quarter-Final replay 07-08
FA Cup: 2nd Rd 82-83, 0-4 v Oxford Utd; 1st Rd 36-37, 94-95 (1-3 v AFC Bournemouth), 99-00 (0-3 v Rotherham United)
HONOURS   Isthmian Lg R-up(2) 83-85 (Div 1 82-83, Div 2 81-82 92-93);Isth Full members Cup r-up98-99, Athenian Lg Div 1 R-up 63-64,
Div 2 R-up 71-72, Lg Cup R-up 72-73, Mem. Shield R-up 63-64; SussexSnr Cup (21); Sussex RUR Char. Cup (13); Sussex Co. Lg(8) 20-22 26-27
28-29 30-31 33-34 38-40; W Sussex Lg (7); Brighton Char. Cup(9) 29-31 34-35 62-63 69-7173-74(jt) 80-82; Worthing Char. Cup (11); AFA Invit. Cup
63-64 68-69 73-74 75-76 (Snr Cup R-up 36-37 46-47 48-49); Corinth. Lg Mem. Shield R-up 49-50 (NealeTphy 58-59); Roy Hayden Mem. Tphy
75(jt), 77 78,79. Don Morecraft Tphy 72 73 76 8182; Sussex F'lit Cup(3) 88-90 97-98; Sussex I'mediate Cup 34-35 64-65; BrightonChal. Shield 29-
30 31-32
Players progressing: Ken Suttle (Chelsea 48), Alan Arnell & Fred Perry (Liverpool 54), Craig Whitington (Scarborough, via Crawley Town) 93,
Darren Freeman (Gillingham), Paul Musselwhite (Scunthorpe), Trevor Wood (Port Vale), Richard Tiltman (Brighton)

Back: Beau Reynolds (chairman), Jason Rutherford (asst. man.), Simon James, Lee Weston, Mark Burt (capt.), Lee Bray, Ben Carrington,
Paul Kennett, Danny Smith, Neil Francis, Alan Robertson (physio), Sammy Donnelly (manager), Chris Tinker (former sponsor).
Front: Adie Miles (now Bognor Regis T.), Guy Rutherford, Lee Cox, Mark Knee, Marc Rice, Tony Holden (no longer at club), Simon Funnell,
Miles Rutherford, Paul Thomas (now Chichester C.U.)   **Photo:** Roy Fowler, courtesy of the Worthing Guardian

YEADING

CLUB OFFICIALS

Chairman: **Philip Spurden**
President: **Mr R Carter**
Vice Chairman: **Steve Perryman**
Secretary: **Colin Stupack**
24 Nower Hill,Pinner,Middlesex HA5 5QS
Tel: 0208 868 9311
Press Officer: **Tim Fuell** (020 8842 4612)

FOOTBALL MANAGEMENT TEAM
Manager: Jon Turner
Assistants: Paul Sweales & Jon Denton
Physios: Eddie Cole & Denis Collins

FACT FILE

Formed: 1965
Nickname: The Ding
Sponsors: T.B.A.
Colours: Red & black stripes/black/black
Change colours: yellow/blue/white
Midweek matchday: Tuesday
Reserve League: Suburban Lge
Youth League: Harrow

Programme - Pages: 32   Price: £1
Editor: Tim Fuell
Local Newspapers: Hayes Gazette

For up to the minute news, results, fixtures, plus general facts & figures from the world of non-league football

log on to

www.nlfootball.com

GROUND The Warren,Beaconsfield Rd.Hayes,Middx.(0208 848 7362/7369.Fx:0181 561 1063)
Directions: 2 miles from Hayes (BR) - take Uxbridge Road and turn right towards Southall, right into Springfield Rd and then left into Beaconsfield Rd. Bus 207 stops 1/2 mile from ground
Capacity: 3,500   Cover: 1,000   Seats: 250   Floodlights: Yes
Clubhouse: Open normal pub hours.' The Warren' Conference & Banquetting suite available for hire .(Social Secretary: William Gritt)
Club Shop: Planned   Metal Badges: Yes
Well stocked football bookshop at internet site: http://welcome.to/yeadingfc

PREVIOUS **Leagues:** Hayes & District Yth; Uxbridge; S W Middx 1967-74; Middx 74-84;Spartan 1984-87
CLUB RECORDS Attendance: 3,000; v Hythe Town, FA Vase SF 1990; v Tottenham Hotspur,friendly
Career Goalscorer: Dave Burt 327   **Career Appearances:** Norman Frape
Fee Paid: Unknown   **Fee Received:** £45,000 for Andrew Impey (QPR)
BEST SEASON **FA Cup:** Furst Round Proper (93-94 & 94-95)
FA Vase: Winners 89-90
F.A.Trophy: 2ndRd (97-98 & 98-99)
HONOURS FA Vase 89-90; Isthmian League Div 2 Sth 89-90 (Div 1 R-up 91-92); SpartanLeague 86-87 (R-up 85-86, Senior Div R-up 84-85, League Cup 85-86 86-87); Middlesex Snr League (6) 71-73 74-76 81-82 83-84 (R-up 73-74 74-75 78-79, LeagueCup (6) 72-73 75-76 79-83); South West Middlesex League (2) 69-71; Middlesex SnrCup 89-90 91-92, Middlesex Prem. Cup 80-81, Middlesex I'mediate Cup (5) 70-7274-76 77-78, Middlesex Jnr Cup (4) 68-69 70-72 74-75; Uxbridge League 66-67; Middlesex Border League Cup 86-87 (AJA Cup 86-87); Suburban League Nth 87-88; Allied Counties Yth League 89-90 (Lge Cup 89-90)
Players progressing: Andrew Impey (Leicester City ,West Ham United , QPR and England U 21) and Lee Charles (Q.P.R.via Chertsey Town)

An irresistable strike force

Every month

INSIDE! *MORE ACTION* ✸ *MORE PHOTOS* ✸ *EVERY MONTH!*

NO.1 NON-LEAGUE MAGAZINE

OFFICIAL F.A. MAGAZINE

Team Talk

Every week

THE NON-LEAGUE PAPER

CONFERENCE & PYRAMID LEAGUES SOCCER / £1.00

Every day

For up to the minute news, results, fixtures, and general facts and figures from the world of non-league football log on to

www.nlfootball.com

Brought to you by Non-League Media in conjunction with e-comsport

DIVISION TWO FINAL LEAGUE TABLE 1999-2000

	P	Home					Away					Total						
		W	D	L	F	A	W	D	L	F	A	W	D	L	F	A	Pts	GD
Hemel Hempstead T	42	18	3	0	66	15	13	5	3	32	12	31	8	3	98	27	101	71
Northwood	42	18	1	2	64	17	11	8	2	45	23	29	9	4	109	40	96	69
Ford United	42	17	3	1	59	13	11	5	5	49	28	28	8	6	108	41	92	67
Berkhamsted T	42	15	3	3	47	25	7	5	9	28	27	22	8	12	75	52	74	23
Windsor & Eton	42	10	6	5	43	32	10	7	4	30	21	20	13	9	73	53	73	20
Wivenhoe Town	42	11	6	4	32	20	9	3	9	29	27	20	9	13	61	47	69	14
Barking	42	8	7	6	35	24	10	6	5	35	27	18	13	11	70	51	67	19
Marlow	42	12	2	7	42	22	8	2	11	44	44	20	4	18	86	66	64	20
Met Police	42	14	3	4	45	27	4	4	13	30	44	18	7	17	75	71	61	4
Banstead Ath	42	11	5	5	32	17	5	6	10	23	39	16	11	15	55	56	59	-1
Tooting & Mitcham U	42	10	5	6	38	28	6	2	13	34	46	16	7	19	72	74	55	-2
Wokingham Town	42	8	3	10	30	42	7	6	8	28	38	15	9	18	58	80	54	-22
Wembley	42	8	4	9	23	26	6	7	8	24	27	14	11	17	47	53	53	-6
Edgware Town	42	7	8	6	37	35	6	3	12	35	36	13	11	18	72	71	50	1
Hungerford Town	42	9	4	8	38	34	4	6	11	23	44	13	10	19	61	78	49	-17
Cheshunt	42	5	8	8	25	32	7	4	10	28	33	12	12	18	53	65	48	-12
Horsham	42	8	6	7	45	37	5	2	14	21	44	13	8	21	66	81	47	-15
Leighton Town	42	6	3	12	33	39	7	5	9	32	45	13	8	21	65	84	47	-19
Molesey	42	5	7	9	24	28	5	5	11	30	41	10	12	20	54	69	42	-15
Wingate & Finchley	42	8	5	8	33	39	3	2	16	21	58	11	7	24	54	97	40	-43
Witham Town	42	6	5	10	23	49	1	4	16	16	61	7	9	26	39	110	30	-71
Chalfont St Peter	42	2	4	15	22	53	0	4	17	17	71	2	8	32	39	124	14	-85

DIVISION TWO RESULTS CHART 1999-2000

		1	2	3	4	5	6	7	8	9	10	11	12	13	14	15	16	17	18	19	20	21	22
1	Banstead A	X	0-1	3-1	4-1	3-0	2-0	0-0	1-2	1-0	1-1	0-0	3-2	1-0	2-1	1-3	0-0	0-2	1-0	1-0	7-1	0-1	1-1
2	Barking	1-1	X	2-2	0-0	0-0	1-1	1-3	0-1	3-1	2-0	2-4	6-0	1-0	3-0	3-1	2-2	0-1	1-2	3-1	2-0	1-1	3-1
3	Berk'sted T	3-1	1-3	X	0-0	2-1	3-1	2-0	0-2	4-1	3-2	4-0	3-1	1-0	1-0	1-1	4-3	4-1	4-4	2-1	1-0	3-0	1-3
4	Chalfont SP	1-1	2-2	1-3	X	1-2	0-3	0-6	0-1	2-3	2-3	2-3	3-0	3-3	2-4	0-3	0-6	1-0	1-2	0-2	0-0	0-2	1-4
5	Cheshunt	1-1	1-4	0-2	2-1	X	3-1	2-2	0-0	1-2	1-1	3-2	0-1	0-2	1-4	2-3	2-0	0-0	1-1	0-1	0-0	3-3	2-1
6	Edgware T	1-2	0-0	2-2	4-0	1-1	X	1-1	0-3	3-0	2-1	5-1	2-4	3-0	2-2	1-1	4-3	1-1	0-0	2-3	2-1	1-3	0-1
7	Ford Utd	2-0	1-1	3-1	3-1	2-0	2-1	X	0-0	4-0	6-0	3-1	2-0	2-0	4-2	1-1	1-0	2-1	3-1	6-1	4-0	3-1	0-1
8	Hemel H T	3-0	3-0	3-1	2-1	3-0	3-0	1-0	X	3-1	1-1	4-1	1-0	7-1	3-0	2-2	5-2	2-0	0-0	2-1	4-1	4-2	5-1
9	Horsham	4-0	1-2	1-2	5-2	2-2	0-2	2-5	2-3	X	2-1	1-1	1-1	5-2	0-0	2-5	3-0	4-1	1-2	2-2	5-3	2-1	0-0
10	Hungerford	3-0	0-2	0-4	3-2	0-2	1-1	1-4	0-0	2-1	X	5-0	3-2	2-0	1-4	3-2	1-1	1-3	2-1	1-1	1-2	4-0	6-2
11	Leighton T	2-2	2-0	0-1	5-0	1-1	2-3	1-3	0-1	1-2	2-1	X	2-5	1-3	3-3	0-5	0-1	1-0	0-2	4-1	1-0	0-2	5-1
12	Marlow	2-1	3-0	1-0	1-0	2-1	1-0	0-1	1-2	3-0	1-2	2-0	X	2-2	4-1	0-0	3-0	0-3	0-2	3-1	0-0	0-3	5-1
13	Met Police	1-2	2-0	2-0	2-0	3-0	3-1	1-5	1-3	4-2	3-2	3-2	2-0	X	4-2	1-2	5-2	0-0	0-0	2-2	2-0	1-0	3-2
14	Molesey	0-0	0-3	2-0	1-1	0-1	2-3	2-3	2-2	1-2	1-2	1-1	1-3	1-1	X	0-3	3-0	0-2	2-1	4-0	0-0	1-0	1-1
15	Northwood	2-0	6-2	1-0	7-2	4-0	1-0	7-2	4-0	1-0	0-3	0-0	2-0	7-1	2-3	X	4-2	2-1	3-0	7-2	5-0	2-1	4-0
16	Tooting & M	1-2	1-1	0-0	2-0	3-2	2-1	2-2	0-1	3-1	1-2	2-2	3-0	6-5	3-2	0-1	X	1-2	0-2	3-1	3-0	1-0	1-1
17	Wembley	0-1	2-2	0-1	2-1	1-4	2-0	1-6	0-1	3-1	2-0	0-1	2-1	2-1	1-1	0-0	0-1	X	0-1	1-0	3-0	0-2	1-1
18	W & Eton	2-1	1-1	1-1	3-3	2-1	3-2	4-0	1-1	2-1	3-1	3-5	3-4	0-0	3-0	3-2	1-4	1-1	X	2-0	4-0	1-2	1-2
19	Wingate & F	2-1	1-2	1-1	4-1	0-1	0-9	4-2	3-1	0-0	2-1	1-1	2-5	0-3	1-2	1-1	1-2	1-1	0-2	X	5-2	0-1	3-1
20	Witham T	2-1	0-4	0-5	2-1	2-7	0-4	1-3	1-0	2-2	0-0	2-1	0-6	1-0	0-2	1-3	1-3	2-2	1-1	4-2	X	0-1	1-1
21	Wivenhoe T	1-1	0-3	1-0	3-0	1-0	1-1	0-1	1-0	2-0	0-0	0-2	1-1	4-2	2-0	2-2	0-1	3-1	3-3	2-0	2-1	X	5-2
22	Wokingham	0-5	0-2	3-1	2-0	2-3	3-1	0-3	1-2	1-0	1-1	0-1	2-6	0-5	0-0	1-3	4-2	2-1	0-3	4-0	2-2	2-1	X

BANSTEAD ATHLETIC

GROUND
Address: Merland Rise, Tadworth, Surrey KT20 5JG (01737 350982)

Directions: Follow signs to Tattenham Corner (Epsom racecourse), then to Banstead Sports Centre. Ground adjacent to swimming pool. Half a mile fromTattenham Corner (BR) Bus 420 from Sutton stops outside ground. Also buses 406 & 727 from Epsom

Capacity: 3,500 **Seats:** 250 **Cover:** 800 **Floodlights:** Yes

Clubhouse: All week 11am-11pm. 2 bars, real ale, bar snacks Club Shop: Yes

HONOURS: Surrey Snr Lg(6) 50-54 56-57 64-65, R-up(5) 49-50 54-56 57-59, Lg Cup 57-58, Charity Cup 52-53 58-59; London Spartan Lg R-up 77-78 (Lg Cup(2) 65-67);Surrey Prem. Cup R-up 91-92, 95-96; Surrey Snr Shield 55-56; Gilbert Rice F'lit Cup 81-82 86-87 (R-up(4) 82-86); Athenian Lg Cup(2) 80-82 (R-up 82-83 (SF 79-80); Surrey Int. Lg(2) 47-49, Cup 46-47 54-55; E. Surrey Charity Cup (4) 59-6066-67 76-78, R-up 79-80, I'mediate Sect. 75-76 (R-up 76-77), Jnr Sect. 81-82;Southern Comb. Cup R-up 69-70; Suburban Lg R-up 86-87; Carlton T.V. Trophy R-Up 95-96

PREVIOUS **Leagues:** Surrey Int., Surrey Snr 49-65, Spartan 65-75, London Spartan 75-79, Athenian 79-84

CLUB RECORDS **Attendance:** 1,400 v Leytonstone, FA Amateur 1953
Win: 11-0 **Defeat:** 0-11
Career goalscorer: Harry Clark **Career appearances:** Dennis Wall
Transfer fee received: None **Transfer fee paid:** None

BEST SEASON **FA Cup:** 3rd Qual.Rd. 86-87. FA Vase: Semi - finals 96-97

Players progressing : W Chesney & B Robinson (Crystal Palace)

FACT FILE

Founded: 1944
Nickname: A's
Sponsors: PDM Marketing
Colours: Amber/black/black
Change colours: Red & white
Programme : Pages: 38 Price: £1.00
Editor: Colin Darby (0181 643 5437)
Midweek Matchday: Tuesday

99-00- Captain: Kristian Sorensen
Jt P.o.Y.: Mark Leahy & Matt York
Top scorer: Kevin Webb

CLUB PERSONNEL

Secretary: Gordon Taylor
116 Kingston Avenue, North Cheam,
Surrey SM3 9UF
TEL: 0181 641 2957

Chairman: Terry Molloy
President: E C Winser MBE
Press Officer: Colin Darby
Manager: Bob Langford
Coaches: Ray Best & Michael Stratford
Physio: John Steerwood

BARKING

GROUND Address: Mayesbrook Park, Lodge Avenue, Dagenham RM8 2JR (020 8595 6900).
Directions: Off A13 on A1153 (Lodge Ave), and groud 1 mile on left. Bus 162 from Barking station. Nearest tube Becontree.
Capacity: 2,500 **Cover:** 600 **Seats:** 200 **Floodlights:** Yes
Clubhouse: 2 large bars, open daily 11am-11pm (Sundays Noon-11pm). Hot & cold food and drinks. Club Shop: No

PREVIOUS **Grounds:** Eastbury Field, Kennedy Estate,Movers Lane,Barking Recreation Ground Merry Fiddlers,Vicarage Field (until 1973)
Names: Barking Rovers, Barking Institute, Barking Woodville,Barking Town.
Leagues: London 1896-98 09-23, South Essex 1898-21, Leyton & Dist 1899-1900,Athenian 23-52

CLUB RECORDS **Attendance:** (At Mayesbrook) 1,972 v Aldershot FA Cup 2nd Rd 78
Win: 14-0 v Sheppey Utd Mithras Cup 69-70 **Defeat:** 0-8 v Marlow.
Fee received: £6,000 for Alan Hull (Orient) **Fee paid:** None over £1,000
Goal scorer: Neville Fox 241 (65-73) **Appearances:** Bob Makin 566

BEST SEASON **FA Vase:** 96-97 **FA Amateur Cup:** Runners-up 26-27
FA Cup: 2nd Rd rep. 81-82 1-3v Gillingham (A) after 1-1. Also 2nd Rd 78-79 79-80 83-84, and 1st Rd 26-27 28-29 78-80. - League clubs defeated: Oxford Utd 79-80.
HONOURS FA Amateur Cup R-up 26-27; Isthmian Lg 78-79 (Lg Cup R-up 76-77); Athenian Lg 34-35 (R-up 24-25); London Lg 20-21 (Div 1 (A) 09-10); South Essex Lg Div 1 1898-99,R-up (2), Div 2 (4); London Senior Cup (4), R-up (3); Essex Senior Cup (7), R-up (8); Dylon Shield 79-80; Eastern Floodlit R-up (3); Essex Elizabethan 66-67, R-up (2); Essex Thameside (4), R-up (4); London Charity Cup61-62 R-up 21-22; London Intermediate Cup 85-86; East Anglian Cup 37-38 53-54;Mithras Cup (3), R-up (2); Premier Midweek (2). Vandenel Trophy R-up 99-00
Players progressing: 21 players since 1908 - 1956; Peter Carey (Orient 57), Lawrie Abrahams (Charlton 77), Kevin Hitchcock (Nottm Forest83), Dennis Bailey (Fulham 86), Alan Hull (Orient 87) Joe Sibley1939, Hedley Sheppard 1932, Paul Wilson (Barnet) John Still(Manager Barnet),

FACT FILE

Founded: 1880
Nickname: The Blues
Sponsors: Capital Coin Ltd
Colours: Blue & white
Change colours: Yellow/red/white
Midweek matchday: Tuesday
Reserves' League: None
PROGRAMME
Pages: 16 Price: 80p
Editor: Roger Chilvers
99-00Captain: Andy Sussex
P.o.Y.: Nathan Thomas
Top Scorer: Nathan Thomas

CLUB PERSONNEL

Secretary: Roger Chilvers
50 Harrow Rd, Barking, Essex IG11 7RA
Tel:020 8591 5313

Chairman: John Edgeworth
Vice-Chairman: Paul Lovell
President: Terry Lovell
Press Officer: Derek Pedder
Tel: 020 8592483
Manager: Craig Edwards
Asst Manager .Paul Downes
Coach: Martin Stevens
Physio: Martin stevens

BERKHAMSTED TOWN

GROUND:
Address: Broadwater, Lower Kings Road, Berkhamsted, Herts HP4 2AA Tel: 01442 862815

Directions: Adjacent to Berkhamsted station (Euston-Birmingham line). A41 to Berkhamsted town centre traffic lights, left into Lower Kings Road

Capacity: 2,500   Seats: 170   Cover: 350   Floodlights: Yes

Clubhouse: Open 7 days a week. Pool & darts - Big screen

Club Shop: Contact Lee Whybrow

PREVIOUS   **Leagues:** Herts Co. 1895-1922; Herts Co: 1921 ,Spartan 22-51, 66-75;
Delphian 51-63; Athenian 63-66,83-84; London Spartan 75-83
Grounds: Sunnyside Enclosure 1895-1919, Sports Ground 1919-83
Name: Bekhamsted Comrades 1919-22

CLUB RECORDS   **Attendance:** 1,163 v Barnet, FA Cup 3rd Qual. Rd 1987
Career appearances: Ray Jeffrey (612)
Victory: 14-0   **Defeat:** 2-12
BEST SEASON   **FA Cup:** 3rd Qual Rd v Barnet 87-88, v Slough 91-92, v Chesham U. 92-93
FA Vase: 4th Rd v Collier Row 84-85, Ramsgate 99-00
FA Trophy: 1st Rd v Kidderminster Harriers 97-98

HONOURS   Herts Senior Cup 52-53; London Spartan Lge 79-80 (Div 2 26-27);
Herts Charity Shield 50-51(jt) 73-74 79-80 84-85 90-91; Herts Senior County
Lge Aubrey Cup 52-53; St Marys Cup(13); Apsley Senior Charity Cup (9);
Southern Comb 84-85(F/lit Cup 84-85)

Players progressing: Frank Broome(Aston Villa & England), Maurice Cook (Fulham), Keith
Ryan(Wycombe), Maurice Telling (Millwall)

1999-00   Captain: Paul Lowe   Top scorer: Terry Nightingale (14)   P.o.Y.: Paul Lowe

FACT FILE
Formed: 1919
Nickname: Lilywhites
Sponsors: C D Wright Elect Wholesalers
Colours: Yellow/Blue/Blue
Change Colours: Red/blue
Midweek Matchday: Tuesday
Reserves' Lge: Suburban League Premier
PROGRAMME
Pages: 64   Price: £1
Editor: Frank Hastie (0208 374 2175)

Local Press: Berkhamsted Herald,
Berkhamsted Gazette
Local Radio: Chiltern Radio, Mix '96',
Three Counties Radio

CLUB PERSONNEL
Secretary: Keith Bayliss
56 St Edmunds, Berkhamsted, Herts.
tel: 01442 384937

Chairman: Danny Jennings
President: Dennis Wright
Press Off.: Bob Sear (01442 864547 H & B)
Match Sec: Bob McGregor

Manager: Steve Bateman
Coach: Mark Pearson
Physio: Brian Harding

CHERTSEY TOWN

GROUND
Address: Alwyns Lane, Chertsey, Surrey KT16 9DW Tel: 01932 561774

Directions: Alwyns Lane is off Windsor Street at north end of shopping centre.
10 mins walk from Chertsey (BR). London Country bus
Capacity: 3,000   Seats: 250   Cover: 1000   Floodlights: Yes

Clubhouse: Open weekday evenings and weekend lunchtimes
Club Shop: Open matchdays, selling club & football souvenirs. Contact Blake Robias

HONOURS   Isthmian Lge Cup 94-95 (Assoc. Members Trophy 94-95), Div 2 R-up 94-95, Div 3
R-up 91-92; Surrey Snr Lge 59-60 61-62 62-63 (Lge Cup 59-60 61-62); Combined Co's Lge R-up
85-86 (Concours Tphy 85-86); Surrey Snr Cup R-up 85-86; Spartan Lge & Lge Cup R-up 74-75

PREVIOUS Leagues: West Surrey (pre-1899); Surrey Jnr 1899-1920; Surrey Intermediate 20-46;
Surrey Snr 46-63; Metropolitan 63-66; Gtr London 66-67; Spartan 67-75;
London Spartan 75-76; Athenian 76-84; Isthmian 84-85; Combined Counties 85-86.
Grounds: The Grange (pre-World War 1), The Hollows (pre-1929)

CLUB RECORDS   **Attendance:** 2,150 v Aldershot, Isthmian Lge Div. 2 4/12/93
Goalscorer: Alan Brown 54, 1962-63
Win: 10-1 v Clapton (H), Isthmian Lge Div. 3, 91-92
Defeat: 1-12 v Bromley (H), FA Cup Preliminary Rd, 82-83
Transfer fee received: £67,500. Paid: Nil

BEST SEASON   **FA Vase:** Quarter Final 87-88 91-92
FA Cup: 3rd Qual. Rd 92-93, 1-3 v Kingstonian (H)
FA Trophy: 2nd Qual Rd 95-96   **FA Amateur Cup:** 3rd Qual Rd 61-62

Players progressing: Rachid Harkouk (Crystal Palace), Peter Cawley (Wimbledon 87),
Lee Charles (Q.P.R. 95)

FACT FILE
Formed: 1890
Nickname: Curfews
Sponsors: Holly Tree
Colours: Blue & white stripes/white/white
Change colours: Yellow & Black
Midweek Matchday: Tuesday
PROGRAMME: Pages: 36 Price: £1
Editor: Chris Gay (01276 20745)
Local Press: Surrey Herald
Local Radio: BBC Southern Counties,
County Sound

1999-00 Captain: Richard Evans
P.o.Y.: Warren Bayliss
Top Scorer: Rob French

CLUB PERSONNEL
Chairman: Nick Keel
President: Cllr Chris Norman
Vice Chairman: Steve Powers
Press Officer/Secretary: Chris Gay
23 Richmond Close, Frimley,
Camberley,Surrey GU16 5NR
Tel: 01276 20745

FOOTBALL MANAGEMENT TEAM
Manager: Paul Walker
Asst Manager: T.B.A.
Coach: T.B.A.
Physio: T.B.A.

CHESHUNT

FACT FILE
Founded: 1946
Nickname: Ambers
Sponsors: None
Colours: Gold & black/Black/Black
Change colours: All blue
Midweek matchday: Tuesday
Reserves' Lge: Essex & Herts Border Comb
Programme: Pages: 28 Price: £1
Editor: Derek Bird

GROUND Address: The Stadium, Theobalds Lane, Cheshunt, Herts . Tel: 01992 626752

Directions: M25 to junction 25, A10 north towards Hertford, next roundaboutthird exit to next roundabout, turn left proceed under railway bridge, turnleft, ground approx 400 yards on right. 400yds from Theobalds Grove BR station,Buses 310, 242, 311 & 363 to Theobalds Grove station

Seats: 285　　Cover: 600　　Capacity: 2,500　　Floodlights: Yes
Clubhouse: Yes　　Club Shop: No

HONOURS:
Athenian Lg 75-76 (R-up 73-74), Div 1 67-68, Div 2 R-up 65-66, Lg Cup74-75 75-76; Spartan Lg 62-63, Lg Cup 63-64 92-93, (R-up 89-90); London Lg 49-50 (R-up 56-57), Div 1 47-48 48-49 (R-up 46-47), Div 1 Cup 46-47, Lg Cup R-up58-59, Park Royal Cup 46-47; Isthmian Lg Div 2 R-up 81-82 (Div 3 R-up 94-95);Herts Snr Cup 23-24 (R-up 48-49 49-50 68-69 69-70 71-72 73-74); Herts CharityCup 00-01 05-06 (R-up 70-71 74-75 80-81); Herts Charity Shield 46-47 65-66 (52-53 53-54 54-55 63-64 64-65); Herts Snr Centenary Tphy 91-92; East Anglian Cup74-75 (R-up 75-76); Mithras Floodlit Cup 69-70 (R-up 75-76); London Charity Cup73-74; Roy Bailey Tphy 90-91 94-95 97-98

PREVIOUS:　　**Leagues:** Athenian 19-20 21-31 64-77; London 20-21 24-25 46-51 55-59; Delphian51-55; Aetolian 59-62; Spartan 62-64; Isthmian 77-87
Name: None　　**Ground:** None

RECORDS:　　Attendance: 7,000 v Bromley, London Senior Cup 1947

BEST SEASON:　FA Vase: Quarter Final 81-82
FA Cup: 4th Qual. Rd(4)

Players progressing: Ian Dowie, Ruben Abgula, SteveSedgeley, Lee Hodges, Paul Marquis, Steve Terry, Neil Prosser, Mario Walsh

CLUB PERSONNEL
Secretary:
Mr Keith Hughes, 28 Peace Close,
Rosedale, Cheshunt, Herts EN7 5EQ

Chairman:Vince Satori
Vice Chairman: Paul Cully
President: Paul Philips
Press Officer: Neil Harrison

Manager: Tom Loizou
Asst Manager: Kevin O'Dell
Physio: Lou Dedman

EAST THURROCK UNITED

FACT FILE
Founded: 1969
Nickname: Rocks
Colours: Amber/black/black
Change: Blue/white/white
Midweek Matchday: Tuesday
Reserves' Lge: Essex/Herts Border Com
Programme: 24 pages, 50p
Editor: Tony Smith (01375 892888)
Local Press:
Thurrock Gazette/ Thurrock Recorder
Local Radio: BBC Essex

Ground: Rookery Hill, Corringham, Essex (01375 644166-club)
Directions: A13 London-Southend, take 1014 at Stanford-le-Hope for two and ahalf miles - ground on left. Two miles from Stanford-le-Hope and Basildon BR stations
Capacity: 3,000　　Seats: 160　　Cover: 360　　Floodlights: Yes　　Club Shop: No
Clubhouse: Open all day seven days a week. Hot and cold snacks

HONOURS: Metropolitan Lg Div 2 72-73, Essex Snr Lg R-up 88-89 (Lg Cup 88-89 91-92, Harry Fisher Mem. Tphy 83-84 90-91, Sportsmanship Award 81-82 86-87 89-89), Essex SnrTphy R-up 91-92 95-96, Fred Budden Tphy R-up 89-90, Essex & Herts Border Comb.89-90 (Lg Cup 89-90) , Isthmian League Div. Three 99-00

PREVIOUS　　**Leagues:** Sth Essex Comb.; Gtr London; Metropolitan 72-75; London Spartan 75-79; Essex Snr 79-92
Grounds: Billet, Stanford-le-Hope 70-73 74-76; Grays Athletic 73-74; Tilbury FC 77-82; New Thames Club 82-84
Name: Corringham Social (pre-1969 Sunday side)

CLUB RECORDS　Attendance: 947 v Trevor Brooking XI, May 1987.
Competitive: 845 v Bashley, FA Vase 1989
Goalscorer: Graham Stewart 102　　**Appearances:** Glen Case 600+
Win: 7-0 v Coggeshall (H) 1984
Defeat: 0-9 v Eton Manor (A) 1982, both Essex Snr League
Transfer Fee Paid: £2,000 + 10% of future fee for Greg Berry (Orient, 1989)

BEST SEASON　FA Cup: 3rd Qual 93-94　　　**FA Vase:** 5th Rd 84-85

Players progressing to Football League: Greg Berry (Leyton Orient)

1999-00　　Leading Goalscorer:Mark Cox
Player of the Year: Tony Pizzey
Captain: Tony Pizzey

CLUB PERSONNEL
Secretary: Malcolm Harris
14 Colne Valley, Upminster,
Essex RM14 1QA
Tel: 01708 228818
Chairman: Harry Caine
Vice Chairman: Alan Gower
President: Alan Gower
Press Officer: Secretary
Manager: Lee Patterson
Asst. Man.: Dave Card
Physio: Richard Mainwaring

EDGWARE TOWN

GROUND
Address: White Lion Ground, High Street, Edgware HA8 5AQ. Tel: 0181 9526799

Directions: Turn left out of Edgware tube station (Northern Line), turn left again at crossroads and ground 300yds on right in Edgware High Street behindWhite Lion pub. Buses 32, 288 142

Capacity: 5,000   Seats: 220   Cover: 1,500   Floodlights: Yes   Club Shop: No

Clubhouse: Open nightly and Fri, Sat, Sun lunchtimes.
Hot & cold food matchdays, cold food lunchtimes

HONOURS: Isthmian Lg Div 3 91-92; London Spartan Lg 87-88 89-90 (Lg Cup 87-88); Corinthian Lg R-up 53-54, Memorial Shield 52-53 61-62; Athenian Lge R-up 81-82;Middx Snr Lg 40-41 41-42 42-43 43-44 44-45, Cup 47-48 (R-up 73-74 94-95);London Snr Cup R-up 47-48; Middx Border Lg Cup 79-80; Suburban Lg Div R-up 89-90

PREVIOUS **Leagues:** Corinthian 46-63; Athenian 64-84; London Spartan 84-90
Names: Edgware F.C.   **Grounds:** None

CLUB RECORDS **Attendance:** 8,500 v Wealdstone, FA Cup 1948
Career Appearances: John Mangan
Career Goalscorer: Steve Newing

BEST SEASON **FA Vase:** 5th Round, 1991-92
FA Cup:

Players progressing: Brian Stein (Luton), Dave Beasant (Wimbledon), Scott McGleish (Charlton 94)

FACT FILE

Founded: 1939
Nickname: Wares
Colours: Green & white Quarters/Green/Green
Change colours: All yellow
Midweek Matchday: Tuesday
Reserve League: Suburban
Sponsor: Philiam Construction

Programme: Pages: 16   Price: 50p
Editor: Paul Gregory (0181 959 2535)

CLUB PERSONNEL

Secretary: Pan Symeou,21Church Hill, Walthamstowe,London E17 3AD
Tel: 020-8520 7392 (W) 01494 476605 (M)

Chairman: George Karaiskos
President: Mr V Deritis
Patron: Russell Grant

Manager: Gary Had
Asst Manager:
Physio: Sarah Gow

GREAT WAKERING ROVERS

Ground: Borroughs Park,Little Wakering Hall Lane, Gt.Wakering, Souithend SS3 OHQ
Tel: 01702 217812

Directions: 4a bus from Shoeburyness (BR), 4a or 4b from Southend - alight at British Legion in Gt Wakering alongside which runs Little Wakering Hall Lane. A127 past Southend signposted Gt Wakering. In Gt Wakering, half mile past large Esso garage along High Street is Little Wakering Hall Lane, ground 250 yds along on left

Capacity: 2,100   Cover: 300   Seats: 150   Floodlights: Yes

Clubhouse: Every eve., Sat 11-11, Sun 12-3 & 7.30-10.30. Hot meals, snacks etc matchdays only
Club Shop: No

HONOURS Isthmian League div. 3 R-iup 99-00; Essex I'mediate Cup 91-92, Essex I'mediate Lg Div 2 91-92, Div 3 90-91, Lg Cup 91-92, Southend Charity Shld 90-91 91-92, Essex Snr Lg. 94-95, Lg Res. Sect. 94-95 (Wirral Programme Essex Sen. Lg. Award 92-93 94-95)

PREVIOUS **Leagues:** Southend & Dist. 19-81, Southend All. 81-89, Essex I'mediate 89-92
Ground: Gt Wakering Rec   **Names:**

BEST SEASON **FA Cup:** 2nd Qual 98-99
FA Vase: 5th Round 97-98

RECORDS **Attendance:** 659 v Potters Bar FA Vase 5th Rd 7-2-98
Win (in Senior Football): 9-0 v Eton Manor 27/12/93
Defeat (in Senior Football): 1-7 v Bowers Utd, Essex Snr Lge 1-4-98

Players progressing: Les Stubbs (Southend, Chelsea) 1947, Jackie Bridge(Southend Utd) 1948, Kevin Maddocks (Maidstone Utd)

FACT FILE
Founded: 1919
Nickname: Rovers
Sponsors: E.C.O.
ColoursGreen & white stripes/whte/green
Change Coours: All Red
Midweek Matchday: Tuesday
Reserves' Lge: Essex & Herts Border Comb
Programme: 24-32 pages, £1.00
Editor: Keith Perryman 01245 354084

1999-00 Captain:John Heffer
P.o.Y.: Mick Munro
Leading Goalscorers: Paul Flack & Mark Hampshire (26)

CLUB PERSONNEL

Secretary: Roger Sampson
37 Lee Lotts, Gt. Wakering, Southend SS3 0HA
Tel: 01702 217812

Chairman: Fred Smith
Vice-Chairman: Barry Beadle
President: Eddie Ellis
Manager: Eddie Nash
Physio: Phil Hunteer
Press Officer: Nobby Johnson
Tel: 01702 297840

Ashford Town (Middx) FC - Back: Gary Cambridge (Asst Man.), Dave Kent (Manager), Jim Heggarty, Tony Nolan, Lee Holman, Paul Burgess, Lee Bardini, Stefan Elekes, Anthony Eggington, Ian Yates, Pat Munns (Physio). Front: Darren Smith, Andy Sherwood, Ian Miles, Jason Zazzera, Vince O'Sullivan, Andy Frost, Des Vertannes, Kwame Ossei

Epsom & Ewell after their 5-2 victory in the FA Vase tie at Ash United. Photo: Eric Marsh

Croydon Athletic FC - Back: Jon Thorpe, Tommy Wright, Stewart Vaughan, Jamie Gibson, Chris Desbrow, Mick Reed (Physio). Middle: Paul Hicks (Chief Scout), Leon Maxwell (Chief Coach), Dave Finch (Manager's Asst), Brian Baker (Res. Team Man.). Front: Marc Hudson, James Evans, Simon Ray, Dean Davenport (Team Capt.), Hayden Bird (Manager), John Fowler (Club Capt.), Leon Johnson, Danny Stassinos

HEMEL HEMPSTEAD TOWN

FACT FILE

Ground: Vauxhall Ground, Adeyfield Rd, Hemel Hempstead HP2 4HW Tel: 01442 259777

Directions: Euston to Hemel Hempstead Station. H2 or H3 bus to Windmill Rd,Longlands

Capacity: 3,000   Seats: 175   Cover: Yes   Floodlights: Yes

Clubhouse: Tel: 01442 259777. Open 7-11pm weekdays, 12-11pm w/ends & Bank Hols.
Tea bar open matchdays
Club Shop: No

HONOURS   Ryman Lge Div 3 98-99; Herts Snr Cup 05-06 07-08 08-09 25-26 61-62
65-66 91-92, Herts Charity Cup/Shield 25-26 34-35 51-52 63-64 76-77 83-
84 (R-up 90-91), Spartan Lg 33-34, Herts Intermediate Cup 54-55 65-66 83-
84, West Herts St Mary Cup 70-71 75-76 82-83 85-86 90-91 91-92 93-94,
Athenian Lg Div 1 R-up 64-65 (Res Cup 65-66), Delphian Lg (res) 54-55
(Res Cup 54-55 61-62)

PREVIOUS   **Leagues:** Spartan 22-52; Delphian 52-63; Athenian 63-77
Names: Apsley 1885-1947; Hemel Hempstead Town (merged with Hemel
Hempstead Utd in1947)   **Grounds:** Crabtree Lane (til '71)

CLUB RECORDS Attendance: 2,000 v Watford 1985
(at Crabtree Lane: 3,500 v Tooting, FA AmtrCup 1st Rd 1962)
Goalscorer: Dai Price   **Appearances:** John Wallace, 1012

BEST SEASON   FA Cup: Never past Qualifying Rounds
FA Vase: 4th Rd 98-99 v Taunton Town

FACT FILE

Founded: 1885
Nickname: Hemel
Sponsors: Barling
Colours: All red with white trim
Change colours: Green/white trim
Midweek Matches: Tuesday

Programme: 48 pages, 80p
Editor/Press Off.: Paul Bullen
Local Press: Hemel Gazette, Herald
Local Radio: Beds Radio, Chiltern,
Three Counties Radio

CLUB PERSONNEL

Secretary: Leo Glynn
4 Little Catherells, Gadebridge, Hemel
Hempstead, Herts HP1 3QB

Chairman: David Boggins
President:
Vice President: Dave Lloyd

Manager: Neil Price
Asst Manager: Roy Butler
Physio: Zoey

HORSHAM

FACT FILE

GROUND: Queen Street, Horsham RH12 5AD (01403 252310)

Directions: From the station turn left into North Street. Pass the Arts Centreto the traffic
lights and turn left. At the next set of lights (200 yards) turn left again into
East Street. East Street becomes Queen Street after the IronBridge and the
ground lies opposite Queens Head public house

Capacity: 4,500   Seats: 300   Cover: 3,000   Floodlights: Yes
Clubhouse: Matchdays only. Hot and cold snacks. Dancehall
Club Shop: Yes

HONOURS   Sussex Snr Cup 33-34 38-39 49-50 53-54 71-72 73-74 75-76;
Sussex RUR Cup (13); Sussex Floodlight Cup 77-78;
Sussex County Lg (7), R-up (4), Lg Cup 45-46 46-47;
Metropolitan Lg 51-52;
Athenian Lg Div 1 72-73, Div 2 69-70 72-73;
West Sussex Sen Lge (4); ICIS Div 3 95-96

CLUB RECORDS Attendance: 8,000 v Swindon, FA Cup 1st Rd, November 1966
Victory: 16-1 v Southwick Sususex Co Lg 1945-46
Defeat: 1-11 v Worthing Sussex Sen Cup 1913-14
BEST SEASON   FA Cup: 1st Rd 47-48 (lost 1-9 at Notts County), 66-67 (lost 0-3 v Swindon)
F.A. Trophy: 1st Rd Proper Replay 76-77   **F.A.Vase:** 4th Rd Replay 85-86
PREVIOUS   **Leagues:** W Sussex Sen County 26-51; Metropolitan 51-57;
Corinthian 57-63; Athenian 63-77
Grounds: Horsham Park, Hurst Park, Springfield Park
Players progressing: Jamie Ndah (Barnet), Darren Freeman (Fulham)

1999-00 Captain: Matt Smart   **P.o.Y.:** John Kirby   **Top scorer:** Steve Flain (21)

FACT FILE

Founded: 1885
Nickname: Hornets
Club Sponsors: Sunley Homes
Colours: All Amber
Change colours: All white
Midweek Matches: Tuesday
Reserves' League: Suburban

Programme: 40 pages, £1.20
Editor:Adam Hammond (01403 217316)
Local Press: West Sussex County Times;
Market Square, Horsham (01403 253371)

CLUB PERSONNEL

Secretary: Jef Barrett, 3Bunting Close,
Horsham, West Sussex RH13 5PA.
Tel No 01403 267730

Chairman: Frank King
Vice Chairman: Tim Hewlett
President: Geoff Holtom
Press Officer: Jeff Barrett (01403 267730)

Manager: John Maggs
Asst Mgr/Coach:Ali Rennie
Physio: Geoff Brittain

HUNGERFORD TOWN

FACT FILE
Founded: 1886
Nickname: Crusaders
Club Sponsors: Kerridge Insurance
Colours: White/navy blue/blue
Change colours: All yeoow
Midweek Matchday: Tuesday
Reserves' League: Suburban (North)
Programme: 24 pages, 50p
Editor:Martyn Leach (01488 683682)
Local Press: Newbury Weekly News,
Newbury Evening Post
Local Radio: Radio Berkshire , Radio 210
Kick F.M.
99-00 - Captain: Andy Wollen
P.o.Y.: Gary Horgan
Top scorer: Micky Durkin (21)

CLUB PERSONNEL

Chairman: Alan Holland
Vice Chairman: Ron Tarry
President: Sir Seton Wills
Press Officer: Ron Tarry (01488 682539)
Manager: Richard Evans
Physio: Gerald Smith

Secretary: Ken Holmes
35 Queens Court, St Johns Road, Newbury
Berkshire RG147PX
Tel: 01635 523632

GROUND
Address: Town Ground, Bulpit Lane, Hungerford RG17 0AY
Tel: 01488 682939 (club) 01488 684597 (boardroom) 01488 684597 (Fax)

Directions: M4 jct 14 to A4, right and left at Bear Hotel, through town centre on A338, left into Priory Rd, second left into Bulpit Lane, over crossroads, ground on left. 3/4 mile from Hungerford BR station

Capacity: 3,000   Seats: 172   Cover: 200   Floodlights: Yes   Club Shop: Yes

Clubhouse: Open every evening and lunchtimes including Sunday. 2 bars,dancehall, boardroom/committee room, darts, pool, fruit machines. Hot & coldsnacks. Steward: Dianne Tanner (01488 682939)

HONOURS: Berks & Bucks Snr Cup 81-82 (R-up 75-76 76-77); Hellenic Lg Div 1 70-71, PremDiv Cup 77-78, Div 1 Cup 70-71, Benevolent Cup 60-61; Hungerford Cup 96-97, Isthmian Lge Representatives in Anglo-Italian Tournament 81.

PREVIOUS   **Leagues:** Newbury & D.; Swindon & D.; Hellenic 58-78
Names: None   **Grounds:** None

CLUB RECORDS **Attendance:** 1,684 v Sudbury Town, FA Vase SF 1st leg 88-89
(20,000 v Modena inItaly 1981)
Scorer: Ian Farr (268)   **Appearances:** Dean Bailey (approx 400)
Transfer Fee Paid: £4,000 for Joe Scott (Yeovil Town)
Received: £3,800 for Joe Scott (Barnstaple Town)

BEST SEASON   **FA Cup:** 1st Rd 79-80, 1-3 v Slough T. (A)
FA Vase: Semi-Final 77-78 79-80 88-89

Players progressing to Football League: Steve Hetzke (Reading, Blackpool,Sunderland), Bruce Walker (Swindon, Blackpool), Des McMahon (Reading), BrianMundee (Bournemouth, Northampton), Darren Anderson

LEIGHTON TOWN

FACT FILE
Founded: 1885
Nickname: Reds
Sponsors: Camden Motors
Colours: Red & white
Change colours: Orange & black
Midweek Matchday: Tuesday
Reserve's League: Suburban
Programme: £1.00
Editor: David Friend(01525 375931)
Local Press: Leighton Buzzard Observer,
The Citizen
Local Radio: Three Counties Radio,
Radio Chiltern, Mix 96
99-00 Captain:Ken Hollis
P.o.Y.: Damien Matthews
Top scorer: Steve Callinan

CLUB PERSONNEL
Secretary: Jim Whitaker,2 Winstone Close,
12 Rowley Furrows, Linslade,
Leighton Buzzard, Beds LU7 8DL
Tel: 01525 377006

Chairman: Iain S McGregor
President: M.Hide
Press Officer: Iain S McGregor
Tel: 01525 370142

Manager: Craig Johnstone
Physio: Dawn Thomas

GROUND:
Address: Bell Close, Lake Street, Leighton Buzzard, Beds Tel: 01525 373311

Directions: From bypass (A505) take A4146 (Billington Rd) towards Leighton Buzzard, straight overfirst roundabout then straight over mini-r'bout & 1st left into car park - ground behindCamden Motors just before town centre. Half mile from Leighton Buzzard (BR)station. Buses from Luton, Aylesbury and Milton Keynes

Capacity: 2,800   Seats: 155   Cover: 300   Floodlights: Yes   Club Shop: Yes

Clubhouse: Normal licensing hours.
Snack/refreshment bar on matchdays - full range of hot snacks & drinks

HONOURS Isthmian Lge Div 3 R-up 95-96; Sth Midlands Lg 66-67 91-92, Lg Cup 90-91, O'Brien Tphy 90-91, Reserve Div 1 87-88 91-92 94-95, Res Div 2 76-77, ResChallenge Cup 93-94 94-95; Beds Snr Cup 26-27 67-68 68-69 69-70 92-93; BucksCharity Cup 94-95;98-99 Spartan Lg Div 2 23-24 27-28;
Leighton & District Lg, Beds Intermediate Cup (res) 90-91; Beds Yth Cup 91-92 92-93,94-95 94-95; Chiltern Youth Lg94-95, Lg Cup 93-94; East Anglian Yth.Cup 94-95; Assoc Mem Cup 96-97.98-99

PREVIOUS   **Leagues:** Leighton & District; South Midlands 22-24 26-29 46-54 55-56 76-92;Spartan 22-53 67-74; United Counties 74-76
Name: Leighton United   **Ground:** None

CLUB RECORDS **Attendance:** 1,522 v Aldershot T., Isthmian Lg Div 3, 30/1/93
Win: 7-2   **Defeat:** 1-6

BEST SEASON   **FA Cup:** Third Qual. Round 70-71, 1-2 v St Albans City (A)

LEYTON PENNANT

GROUND   Wadham Lodge Sports Ground, Kitchener Rd, Walthamstow, London. E17 4JP
Tel:0208 527 2444

Directions: North Circular Road to Crooked Billet,turn into Chingford Road,then into Brookscroft Road, first on left. Walthamstow Central (Victoria Line tube) 1 mile away, then buses W21 or 256

Capacity: 2,000   Cover: 600   Seats: 200   Floodlights: Yes

Clubhouse: (0208 527 2444). Open 11-11 Mon-Sat, 12-3 & 7-10.30 Sun. No hot food.
Hot snacks from tea bar on matchdays
Club Shop: Sells progs, pennants, scarves, badges etc. Contact Ian Ansell c/o the club

HONOURS   Isthmian Lg Div 1 R-up 86-87 (Div 2 North 84-85); Essex Snr Tphy R-up 84-85; National Floodlight Cup 84-85; London Sen. Cup 03-04 (R-up 33-34 37-38 45-46); London Charity Cup 34-35 36-37 R-up (4) London Lg 23-24 24-25 25-26 (R-up 26-27), Lg Cup 56-57; Athenian Lge 28-29 65-66 66-67 76-77 81-82 ,R-up (3), Div 2 Cup R-up 69-70; London Chall. Cup R-up 09-10 27-28 95-96; East Anglian Cup R-up 45-46 72-73; Essex Thameside Trophy 64-65 66-67 81-2 (R-up 63-64); Leyton & Dist. All 1892-93 94-95; Eastern F'lit Comp 97-98, 99-00

PREVIOUS   **Name:** Leyton FC, Leyton Wingate (75-92), Walthamstow Pennant (64-92)
Leagues: Leyton & Dist. Alliance, South Essex, Southern 05-11, London 20-26, Athenian 27-82, Spartan (Walthamstow Pennant)
Grounds: Brisbane Rd (Home of Leyton Orient), Hare & Hounds Leabridge Rd

CLUB RECORDS Attendance: 676 v Aldershot, Isthmian Lge 10/2/96
(100,000, Leyton v Walthamstow Ave., FA Amateur Cup final, Wembley, April 26th 1952)
Win: 10-2 v Horsham 1982   **Career goalscorer:** Steve Lane 118
Defeat: 1-11 v Barnet 1946   **Career appearances:** Steve Hamberger 387
Transfer fee paid: £200 for Dwight Marshall (Hampton)
Transfer fee received: £6,000 for T Williams (Redbridge Forest)

BEST SEASON   **FA Amateur Cup:** Winners 26-27 27-28, R-up x6
FA Vase: Sixth Rd 83-84   **FA Trophy:** 3rd Rd 86-87
FA Cup: 3rd Rd 09-10 League clubs defeated: None

Players progressing: C Buchan (Sunderland 10), Casey (Chelsea 52), K Facey (Orient 52), M Costello (Aldershot 56), D Clark (Orient 61), D Marshall (Luton)

FACT FILE
Formed: 1868
Nickname: Lilywhites
Sponsors: Kay Sports
Colours: White/navy/navy
Change colours: All navy
Midweek home matchday: Tuesday
Reserves' Lge: Essex & Herts Border Comb
PROGRAMME: Pages: 32 Price: £1
Editor: Ian Ansell
Local Press: Waltham Forest Guardian,
Hackney Gazette
Local Radio: LBC

99-00 Captain: Andy Silk
P.O.Y.: Andy Silk
Top Scorer: Billy Read

CLUB PERSONNEL
Chairman: Dave Crabb
Vice-Chairman: Dave Salmon
President: George Cross
Secretary: Andy Perkins, 4 Chestnut Drive,
Wanstead, London E11 2TA,
Tel: 0208 530 4551
Web site: www.btinternet.com/~andy.perkins
Gen. Manager: Kevin Moran
Press Officer: Andy Perkins

FOOTBALL MANAGEMENT TEAM
Team Manager/Coach:Martin Busson
Physio: Christie Keene

MARLOW

GROUND:
Address: Alfred Davis Memorial Ground, Oak Tree Road, Marlow SL7 3ED (01628 483970)

Directions: A404 to Marlow (from M4 or M40), then A4155 towards town centre.Turn right into Maple Rise (by ESSO garage), ground in road opposite (Oak TreeRd). 1/2 mile from Marlow (BR). 1/4 mile from Chapel Street bus stops

Capacity: 3,000   Cover: 600   Seats: 250   Floodlights: Yes
Clubhouse: Open matchdays & most evenings. Snack bar open matchdays
Club Shop: Sells programmes, badges, ties, pens, videos etc

HONOURS: Isthmian Lg Div 1 87-88, Div 2 South R-up 86-87, Lg Cup 92-93; SpartanLg Div 1 37-38 (Div 2 West 29-30); Berks & Bucks Sen Cup (11)

PREVIOUS: **Leagues:** Reading & Dist.; Spartan 1908-10 28-65; Great Western Suburban;Athenian 65-84
Name: Great Marlow
Grounds: Crown Ground 1870-1919); Star Meadow 19-24

CLUB RECORDS: **Attendance:** 3,000 v Oxford United, FA Cup 1st Rd 1994. (Ground - 8,000 SloughT. v Wycombe W., Berks & Bucks Snr Cup Final, 1972)
Goalscorer: Kevin Stone 31
Appearances: Mick McKeown 500+
Fees - Paid: £5,000 for Richard Evans (Sutton Utd. 94)
Received: £8,000 for David Lay from Slought Town 94

BEST SEASON: **FA Cup:** Semi-Finals 1882; 3rd Rd 94-95 (0-2 v Swindon) 92-93 (1-5 v Tottenham); 1st Rd on   19 times -1871-85 86-88 92-93 1991-92 94-95
FA Trophy: 1st Rd 1987-88, 91-92
FA Vase: 5th Rd replay 74-75

Players progressing: Leo Markham (Watford 1972), NaseemBashir (Reading)

FACT FILE
Formed: 1870
Nickname: The Blues
Sponsors: The Marlow Building Company
Colours: Royal, white trim/royal/royal
Change colours: Orange & black
Midweek matchday: Tuesday
Reserves' League: Suburban Premier
Programme: Pages: 40 Price: £1
Editor: Terry Staines
Local Press: Bucks Free Press, Maidenhead
Advertiser, Evening Post
Local Radio: Eleven 70, Radio 210, Thames
Valley Radio
Information Line (normal call rates):
01932 710215
99-00- Captain: Lee Carroll
P.O.Y.: Jim Bradley
Top scorer:Matt McDonnell (23)

CLUB PERSONNEL
Secretary; Paul Burdell, 69 Wycombe Rd.,
Marlow. (01628 483722)
Chairman: Terry Staines
President:
Vice-Chairman:

Press Off./Comm. Man.: Terry Staines
Manager: Graham Pritchard
Coach: Derek Sweetman
Physio: Mark Skoyles

METROPOLITAN POLICE

GROUND:
Metropolitan Police Sports Ground, Imber Court, East Molesey (0181 3987358)
Directions: From London: A3 then A309 to Scilly Isles r'bout, right into Hampton Court Way, left at 1st r'bout into Ember Court Rd - ground faces in 300yds. From M25 jct 10: A3 towards London for 1 mile, A307 through Cobham, left immediately after Sandown Park into Station Rd - ground 1 mile on left. Half mile from either Thames Ditton or Esher BR stations

Capacity: 3,000   Seats: 297   Cover: 1,800   Floodlights: Yes   Club Shop: No

Clubhouse: (0181 398 1267). Four bars, dancehall, cafeteria open 9am-11pm. Hot & cold food

HONOURS: Isthmian Lg Div 2 R-up 77-78 87-88; Spartan Lg 28-29 29-30 36-37 38-39 45-46 53-54 54-55, (R-up 47-48), Lg Cup 59-60 (R-up 57-58); Middx Snr Cup 27-28;Surrey Snr Cup 32-33, Charity Shield 38-39; Metropolitan Lg Cup 68-69 (Amtr Cup 68-69 69-70); London Snr Cup R-up 34-35 40-41; Herts & Middx Comb. 39-40;Diadora Lg Carlsberg Trophy 94-95

PREVIOUS: **Leagues:** Spartan 28-60; Metropolitan 60-71; Southern 71-78
Grounds: None
Name: None

CLUB RECORDS: **Attendance:** 4,500 v Kingstonian, FA Cup 1934
Goal Scorer: Mario Russo
Appearances: Pat Robert
Win: 10-1 v Tilbury 1995
Defeat: 1-11 v Wimbledon, 1956

BEST SEASON   **FA Cup:** 1st Rd - 32-33, 0-9 v Northampton T. (A);
84-85, 0-3 v Dartford (H); 94-95, 0-3 v Crawley T. (H)

FACT FILE
Founded: 1919
Nickname: Blues
Club Sponsors: McDonalds
Colours: All blue
Change colours: Black & White stripes
Midweek Matches: Tuesday
Reserves' League: Suburban

Programme: 10 pages, 50p
Editor/ Press Officer:
Cliff Travis (01932 782215)

Local Press: Surrey Comet, Surrey Herald
Local Radio: County Sounds

CLUB PERSONNEL

Secretary: Tony Brooking,
15 Westmoreland Ave, Hornchurch, Essex.
RM112EJ. Tel: (01708 450715)

Chairman: Des Flanders QPM
Vice Chairman:Dave Smith
President: Sir John Stevens QPM

Manager: Ian Fleming
Physio: Dick Pierce

MOLESEY

GROUND   **Address:** 412 Walton Road, West Molesey, Surrey KT8 0JG
Tel: 0181 941 7989 (Boardroom)   0181 979 4823 (Clubhouse)

Directions: A3 from London to Hook, thenA309 to Marquis of Granby pub, right to Hampton Court station, turn left forWest Molesey, ground one mile on left

Capacity: 4,000   Cover: 600   Seats: 400   Floodlights: Yes
Clubhouse: Open every evening and weekend lunchtimes
2 bars, discos, live artists, darts, bingo, pool. Steward: TBA
Club Shop: Contact John Chambers

PREVIOUS   **Name:** Molesey St Pauls 1950-53.   **Grounds:** None
Leagues: Surrey Intermediate 53-56; Surrey Snr 56-59; Spartan 59-72; Athenian72-77

CLUB RECORDS   Attendance: 1,255 v Sutton United, Surrey Senior Cup Semi-Final 1966
CareerGoalscorer: Michael Rose, 139
Career Appearances: Frank Hanley, 453
Transfer fee paid: £500 for Chris Vidal (Leatherhead 88)
Transfer fee received: £5,000 for Chris Vidal (Hythe Town 89)

BEST SEASON   **FA Vase:** 6th Rd 81-82.   **FA Trophy:** 1st Rd replay 90-91
FA Cup: First Round Proper 94-95, 0-4 v Bath City (H)

HONOURS   Isthmian Lg Div 1 R-up 92-93 (Div 2 South R-up 89-90, Lg Cup R-up 92-93), Surrey Senior Lg 57-58, (Lg Charity Cup 56-57), Spartan Lg R-up 59-60 (Lg Cup 61-62 (R-up 63-64)), Surrey Senior Shield R-up 74-75, Southern Combination Cup 90-91 94-95

Players progressing: John Finch (Fulham), Cyrille Regis (WBA, Coventry &England)

1999-00 -   Captain:Neil Musgrove   P.o.Y.: AdamGray   Top Scorer: Neil Musgrove (10)

FACT FILE
Formed: 1950
Nickname: The Moles
Colours: White/black/black
Change colours: Yellow/royal
Midweek home matchday: Tuesday
Reserve Team's League: Suburban
Youth Team: Southern Yth Lge

Programme - Pages:16 Price: £1
Editor: Simon Carthew
c/o the club
Local Press: Surrey Comet, Surrey Herald,
Molesey News
Local Radio: Thames 107.8 FM
Hospital Radio, County Sound, Three
Counties, Star FM.

CLUB PERSONNEL

Secretary/Press Officer:
Ben O'Connor (c/o the club)

Chairman: Norman Clark
President: Fred Maynard

Manager: John Harding
Coach: Peter Burdett
Reserve Manager: Dave Wellar

TILBURY

GROUND: Chadfields, St Chad's Rd, Tilbury, Essex RM18 8NL Tel: 01375 843093
Directions: BR from Fenchurch Street to Tilbury Town then bus 20
By road: M25 (jct 30 or 31) - A13 Southend bound, Tilbury Docks turn off after 4 miles, Chadwell St Mary turn off (left) after another 1.5 miles, right after 400 metres, rt at r'bout (signed Tilbury), right into St Chad's Rd after .5 mile, 1st rt into Chadfields for ground.

Capacity: 4,000   **Seats:** 350   **Cover:** 1,000   **Floodlights:** Yes   **Club Shop:** No
Clubhouse: Open evening, all day Fri. & Sat. and Sun. lunchtimes. Hot &cold food

HONOURS: Isthmian Lg Div 1 75-76, (Div 1 Cup 74-75), Div 3 Prom.: 91-92, 99-00; Athenian Lg 68-69 (Div 2 62-63); London Lg 58-59 59-60 60-61 61-62, Lg Cup 58-59 60-61 61-62, R-up (3); DelphianLg 67-68 (Div 2 62-63); Essex Snr Cup 60-61 63-64 72-73 74-75 (R-up 46-47 47-48 69-70 71-72 78-79);

PREVIOUS   Leagues: Grays & Dist.& Sth Essex (simultaneously); Kent 27-31; London 31-39 46-50 57-62; Sth Essex Comb. (war-time); Corinthian 50-57; Delphian 62-63; Athenian 63-73   **Names:** None
Grounds: Green & Silley Weir Ground 1900-11; Orient Field 19-38

RECORDS   Attendance: 5,500 v Gorleston, FA Cup 4th Q Rd 19/11/49
Goalscorer: Ross Livermore 305 (in 282 games, 1958-66)
Appearances: Nicky Smith 424 (1975-85)
Fee received: £2,000, Tony Macklin to Grays A. 1990 &
for Steve Conner to Dartford, 1985
Win: 17-0 v No.9 Coy Royal Artillery (H), South Essex Lg 4/10/02.
In Senior Football; 13-2 v Chalfont National (A), London Lg 28/4/92
Defeat: 1-10 v Maidstone U. (A), Corinthian Lge 4.9.62
v Met. Police (A), Isthmian Lg. 6.5.95

BEST SEASON   FA Cup: 3rd Rd 77-78, 0-4 v Stoke City (A)
FA Amateur Cup: Quarter Final v Wimbledon 46-7
FA Vase: Round 4 v Cowes Sports (a) 99-00
Players progressing to Football League: L Le May, T Scannell, T Oakley, JEvans

FACT FILE
Founded: 1900
Nickname: Dockers
Colours: Black& white stripes,black,black
Change colours: All red
Midweek Matches: Tuesday
Reserves' League:
Essex & Herts Border Comb
Programme: 32 pages, 50p
Editor: Lloyd Brown
Local Press:
Thurrock Gazette, Thurrock Recorder
Local Radio: Essex Radio, BBC Essex

CLUB PERSONNEL
Secretary: Lloyd Brown
52 Lionel Oxley House, New Road,
Grays, Essex RM17 6PP
Tel: 01375 409938

Chairman: R Nash
Vice Chairman: Daniel Nash
President: T.B.A.
Press Officer: Lloyd Brown
(01375 409938)
Manager: Tony Cross
Physio: Roger Hutton

TOOTING & MITCHAM

GROUND:
Address: Sandy Lane, Mitcham, Surrey CR4 2HD Tel: 0181 648 3248
Directions: Tooting (BR) quarter mile.
Sandy Lane is off Streatham Road near the Swan Hotel

Capacity: 8,000   **Cover:** 1,990   **Seats:** 1,990   **Floodlights:** Yes
Clubhouse: Open every evening and weekend lunchtimes. Wide variety of food available
Club Shop: Sells souvenirs & confectionary

HONOURS: Isthmian League 57-58 59-60 (Full Members Cup 92-93); Athenian League 49-50 54-55; London Challenge Cup R-up 59-60; Surrey Senior Cup 37-38 43-44 44-45 52-53 59-60 75-76 76-77 77-78; London Senior Cup 42-43 48-49 58-59 59-60 (R-up 43-44 44-45); South Thames Cup 69-70; Surrey Senior Shield 51-52 60-61 61-62 65-66

PREVIOUS: **Leagues:** London 32-37, Athenian 37-56   **Ground:** None   **Name:** None

CLUB RECORDS: Attendance: 17,500 v QPR, FA Cup 2nd Rd 56-57
Goalscorer: Alan Ives 92 (1972-78)   **Appearances:** Danny Godwin 470
Win: 11-0 v Welton Rovers, FA Amateur Cup 62-63
Defeat: 1-8 v Kingstonian, Surrey Snr Cup 66-67
v Redbridge Forest (H), LoctiteCup 3rd Rd 19/2/91
Fee Paid: £9,000 for Dave Flint (Enfield)
Fee Received: £10,000 for Herbie Smith (Luton)

BEST SEASON: FA Trophy: 2nd Qualifying Rd Replay 71-72 81-82
FA Amateur Cup: 1st Rd replay 22-23   **FA Vase:**
FA Cup: 4th Rd 75-76, 1-3 v Bradford C. (A)
3rd Rd 58-59; 2nd Rd 56-57 76-77;1st Rd 5 other occasions
League clubs defeated: Bournemouth & Boscombe Ath, Northampton 58-59, Swindon 75-76

Players progressing: Trevor Owen (Orient 58), Dave Bumpstead (Millwall 58), Paddy Hasty (Aldersot 58), Walter Pearson(Aldershot), Richie Ward & Alex Stepney (Millwall 62 & 63), Vic Akers(Watford 75), Paul Priddy (Wimbledon 78), Carlton Fairweather & Brian Gayle(Wimbledon 84)

FACT FILE
Formed: 1932
Nickname: Terrors
Sponsors: Claremont Coaches
Colours: Black & white stripes/black/white
Change colours: All red
Midweek matchday: Tuesday
Reserve League: Suburban

Local Press: Mitcham News, South London
Press, South London Guardian
Local Radio: Capital
Programme: Pages: 24 Price: 80p Editor:
Jim Silvey

CLUB PERSONNEL

Secretary: Les Roberts, 91 Fernlea Road,
Mitcham, Surrey CR4 2HG (01816 465275)

Chairman: John Buffoni
President: Cliff Bilham
Vice Chairman: Alan Simpson

Commercial Manager: John Pollard
Press Officer: Jim Silvey 0181 640 5678 (H)

Manager: Keith Boanes
Coach: Peter Shaw
Physio: Danny Keenan

WEMBLEY

FACT FILE
Formed: 1946
Nickname: The Lions
Sponsors: G & B Builders
Colours: Red & white/red/red
Change colours: All gold
Midweek matchday: Tuesday
Reserves' League: Suburban
Programme - Pages: 28 Price: £1
Editor: Richard Markiewicz
(0181 902 0541 - before 9pm)
Local Press: Wembley & Harrow Observer
Local Radio: Capital, G.L.R

GROUND **Address:** Vale Farm, Watford Road, Sudbury, Wembley HA0 4UR
Tel: 0181 908 8169
Directions: Sudbury Town station (Underground) 400 yds, or 10 mins walk
from North Wembley (BR) station. Buses 18, 92, 245 & 182
Capacity: 2,000   Cover: 350   Seats: 350   Floodlights: Yes
Clubhouse: Open every night & weekend lunchtimes.
Hot food on matchdays (0181 904 8169).   Club Shop: No

PREVIOUS **Leagues:** Middx 46-49; Spartan 49-51; Delphian 51-56; Corinthian 56-63;
Athenian 63-75

CLUB RECORDS Attendance: 2,654 v Wealdstone, FA Amateur Cup 52-53
Career goalscorer: Bill Handrahan 105 (1946-52)
Career appearances: Spud Murphy 505 (78-88)
Win: 11-1 v Hermes, London Senior Cup 1963
Defeat: 0-16 v Chelsea, London Challenge Cup 59-60
Transfer Fee paid: Nil
Fee received: £10,000 for Gary Roberts (Brentford, 1981)

BEST SEASON FA Trophy: 1st Round proper 91-92
FA Amateur Cup: 2nd Round 66-67, 68-69
FA Cup: 1st Round Proper 1980-81, 0-3 v Enfield (A)

HONOURS Middx Sen Cup 83-84 86-87 (R-up 55-56 68-69 78-79 87-88 91-92 92-93
98-99);Middx Lge 47-48 (Lge Cup 46-47), Middx Charity Cup 67-68 (jnt) 80-
81(jnt) 82-83 86-87 94-95,(R-up 83-84 87-88 96-97); Middx Invitation Cup
56-57; Athenian Lge R-up 74-75 (Div 1 R-up 67-68); Corinthian Lge Mem
Shield R- up 58-59; Delphian Lge R-up 55-56; Spartan Lge Div 1 West 50-
51 (Dunkel Trophy 50-51 jnt); London Sen Cup R-up 55-56; Hitachi Cup SF
83-84; Suburban Lge North 85-86, Lge Cup 84-85 (R-up 83-84)

Players progressing: Keith Cassells (Watford 1977), MikeO'Donague (Southampton 1979), A
McGonigle (Olympiakos), Gary Roberts (Brentford1980), Richard Cadette (Orient 1984)

CLUB PERSONNEL

Secretary: Mrs Jean Gumm, 14 Woodfield
Avenue, North Wembley, Middx HA0
3NR(0181 908 3353)

Chairman: Brian Gumm
President: Eric Stringer
Vice Chairman:
Press Officer: Richard Markiewicz
(0181 902 0541 before 9pm)
Commercial Manager: Nick Bennett

Manager:Ben Laryea
Asst. Manager: Roger Linton

WINDSOR & ETON

FACT FILE
Founded: 1892
Nickname: Royalists
Sponsors: Murex Welding Products
Colours: All red with green trim
Change colours: White/black/black
Midweek matches: Tuesday
Reserves' League: Suburban (North)
Programme: 28 pages Editor: Eric Richford

Local Press: Windsor & Eton Express,
Windsor & East Berks Observer,
Evening Post

GROUND
Address: Stag Meadow, St Leonards Road, Windsor, Berkshire SL4 3DR (01753860656)
Directions: A332 from M4 junct 6. Left at r'bout (B3173), left into St LeonardsRd at lights on T-
junction, ground 500 yards on right on B3022 opposite Stag &Hounds PH. 1 mile from town cen-
tre - pass available to St Leonards Rd. BR toWindsor Central station (from) Slough or Windsor
Riverside (change at Stainesfrom Waterloo)
Capacity: 4,500   Cover: 650   Seats: 400   Floodlights: Yes
Clubhouse: Yes   Club Shop: Yes

HONOURS Isthmian Lg Div 1 83-84 (Div 2 R-up 82-83), Athenian Lg 79-80 80-81 (Lg Cup
79-80 (R-up 78-79 80-81), Div 2 Cup 63-64 (R-up 68-69)), Spartan Lg R-up 36-37
37-38 (Div 1 30-31), Metropolitan Lg R-up 53-54 (Lg Amtr Cup 51-52 52-53, Lg
Cup 52-53 (R-up 53-54 54-55)), Gt Western Suburban Lg R-up 21-22, Berks &
Bucks SnrCup(11) 10-11 36-38 40-45 61-62 87-89 (R-up 07-08 24-25 26-27 38-39
46-47 62-63), Berks & Bucks Benev. Cup 35-36 37-38 46-47 62-63 (R-up 38-39
47-48 49-50)

PREVIOUS **Leagues:** Southern 1895-96; West Berks; Great Western Suburban 1907-22;
Athenian 22-29 63-81; Spartan 29-32; Great Western Comb; Corinthian 45-50;
Metropolitan 50-60; Delphian 60-63   **Ground:** Ballon Meadow 1892-1912

CLUB RECORDS Attendance: 8,500 (Charity match) Appearances: Kevin Mitchell
Fee Paid: £9,000 for Keith White (Slough Town)
Fee Received: £45,000 for Michael Banton & Michael Barnes (Barnet)

BEST SEASON FA Amateur Cup: 4th Rd 21-22 FA Vase: Semi-Final 80-81 (QF 79-80)
FA Cup: 2nd Rd replay 83-84. 1st Rd 7 times 25-26 80-81 82-86 91-92.
League clubs defeated: None   **FA Trophy:** 3rd Rd 88-89

Players progressing: Reg Dare (Southampton 1949), Steve Adams (Charlton 1979), Dave
Barnett (Colchester 1988), Vic Woodley (Chelsea & England), Billy Coward (QPR, Walsall), Ken
Groves (Preston), Dave Regis (Notts County)

CLUB PERSONNEL

Secretary: Steve Rowland,
91 Duke Street, Windsor, Berks SL4 1SJ
Tel: 01753 774528 (H, emergency only)

Chairman: Peter Simpson/Kevin Stott
President: Sir David Hill-Wood, Bt
Press Officer: Secretary

Manager: Byron Walton
Asst Manager: Alan Rowe
Physio: Des Hunt

WIVENHOE TOWN

FACT FILE

GROUND: Broad Lane Ground, Elmstead Road, Wivenhoe CO7 7HA Tel: 01206 825380
Directions: Coming out of Colchester towards Clacton take first turning (right) towards Wivenhoe, 1st left and ground clearly visible on right at cross-roads. 1 mile from Wivenhoe (BR)
Capacity: 3,000   Cover: 1,300   Seats: 250   Floodlights: Yes
Clubhouse: (01206 825380) Open normal pub hours   Club Shop: A full range of souvenirs etc

PREVIOUS: **Leagues:** Brighlingsea & District 1927-50; Colchester & East Essex 50-71; Essex & Suffolk Border 71-79; Essex Senior 79-86   **Name:** Wivenhoe Rangers
Grounds: Spion Kop; Broomfield; Claude Watcham's Meadow; Vine Farm; Spion Kop; Broomfield; King George V Playing Fields; Essex University

CLUB RECORD **Attendance:** 1,912 v Runcorn, FA Trophy 1st Rd, Feb 1990
Transfer fee received: £5,875 for Bobby Mayes (Redbridge Forest)
Win: 18-0 v Nayland. **Defeat:** 0-8 v Carshalton A. (H), Isthmian Lg 28/8/93
Career goalscorer: Paul Harrison, 258 in 350 games
Career appearances: Keith Bain, 536

BEST SEASON **FA Cup:** 4th Qual Rd 89-90 2-3 v Halesowen Tn (A), 94-95 1-2 v Enfield (H)
FA Trophy: 2nd Rd replay 89-90   **FA Vase:** 5th Rd 82-83;

HONOURS Isthmian Lg Div 1 89-90 (Div 2 Nth 87-88); Essex Snr Lg R-up 79-80 81-82 85-86(Harry Fisher Tphy 83-84 85-86); Essex & Suffolk Border 78-79, Div 1 72-73,Div 2 71-72, Lg Cup R-up(2); Colchester & East Essex Lg 52-53 55-56 (R-up 70-71), Div 1 59-60 69-70, Div 2 R-up 68-69, Lg KO Cup 51-52 52-53 54-55 55-56 (R-up 59-60), Challenge Cup 52-53); Brighlingsea & Dist Lg Div 1 35-36 36-37 47-48(R-up 37-38), Lg KO Cup 36-37 37-38 47-48, Challenge Cup 36-37; Essex Snr Tphy87-88 Essex Jnr Cup R-up 55-56 78-79; Amos Charity Cup(7) (R-up 72-73); StokesCup(3); Wivenhoe Charity Cup (4), (R-up [4]); Cristal Monopole Cup (5), (R-up 2); Sidney James Mem. Tphy 69-70 (R-up 72-73), Tolleshunt D'Arcy Mem. Cup(3)(R-up 2); Walton & District Charity Cup 73-74 78-79; Coggeshall Brotherhood Cup80-81; Brantham Charity Cup R-up 82-83; Worthington Evans Cup 81-82 (R-up 80-8185-86); Harwich Snr Cup R-up 84-85; Woodbridge Chal. Cup 91-92; Mat FowlerShield 92-93 94-95

Players progressing: Robert Reinelt (Gillingham) 1993

Formed: 1925
Nickname: The Dragons
Colours: Royal blue/yellow
Change colours: Red/black
Reserves' League: Essex & Suffolk Border
Midweek matchday: Tuesday
Programme: 36 pages £1.00
Editor: P Reeve
Local Press: East Anglian Daily Times, Colchester Evening Gazette
Local Radio: BBC Radio Essex, S.G.R.

CLUB PERSONNEL

Secretary//Press Officer: Mike Boyle, 15 Daniell Drive, Colchester, Essex (01206 573223)

Chairman: Kevin Foskett
Vice Chairman: Mike Boyle
Manager: Julian Hazel
Asst Manager: Steve Pitt
Physio: Barry Wreford

WOKINGHAM TOWN

FACT FILE
Formed: 1875
Sponsors: Trademark Windows
Nickname: The Town
Colours: Amber & black/black/black
Change colours: All w hite
Midweek matchday: Tuesday
Programme: Pages: 32 Price: £1
Editor: Alan Glenny
Local Press: Wokingham Times, Wokingham News, Reading Evening Post
Local Radio: 210 FM
99-00- Captain: Simon Turner
P.O.Y.: Nathan Freeman
Top scorer: Dave Puckett (18)

GROUND
Address: c/o Windsor & Eton FC, Stag Meadow, St Leonards Road, Windsor, Berks SL4 3DR
Tel: 01753 860656
Directions: A332 from M4 junct 6. Left at r'bout (B3173), left into St Leonards Rd at lights on T-junction, ground 500 yards on right on B3022 opposite Stag & Hounds PH. 1 mile from town centre - pass available to St Leonards Rd.
BR to Windsor Central station (from) Slough or Windsor Riverside (change at Staines from Waterloo)
Capacity: 4,500   Cover: 650   Seats: 400   Floodlights: Yes
Clubhouse: Yes   Club Shop: No

HONOURS Isthmian Lg R-up 89-90 (Div 1 81-82, Full Members Cup R-up 94-95), Berks & Bucks Snr Cup 68-69 82-83 84-85 95-96, Berks & Bucks I'mediate Cup 52-53

PREVIOUS **Leagues:** Reading & Dist.; Great Western Comb 07-54; Metropolitan 54-57; Delphian 57-59; Corinthian 59-63; Athenian 63-73.
Grounds: Oxford Road 1875-1883; Wellington Road 83-96; Langborough Rd 96-1906, Finchampstead Road 06-99

CLUB RECORDS **Attendance:** 3,474 v Norton Woodseats, FA Amateur Cup 57-58
Career Goalscorer: Terry Brown 91
Career Appearances: Dave Cox, 533
Fee paid: £5,000 for Fred Hyatt (Burnham, 1990)
Fee received: £25,000 for Mark Harris (C Palace 88)

BEST SEASON **FA Trophy:** Semi finals 87-88   **FA Amateur Cup:** 4th Rd 57-58
FA Cup: 1st Rd replay 82-83, 0-3 v Cardiff (A) after 1-1
League clubs defeated: None

Players progressing: Ian Kirkwood (Reading 53), John Harley (Hartlepool 76), Kirk Corbin (Cambridge 78), Phil Alexander (Norwich 81), DougHatcher (Aldershot 83), Steven Butler & George Torrance (Brentford 84), MarkHarris (C Palace 88), Gary Smart (Oxford 88), Darren Barnard (Chelsea 90), PaulHolsgrove (Luton Town 91), Darron Wilkinson (Brighton) 92

CLUB PERSONNEL
Secretary: John Aulsberry, 8 Paice Green, Wokingham RG40 1YN (01189 790441)

Chairman: Richard Brown
President: G Gale
Vice Chairman:
Commercial Manager:

Manager: Steve Mellor
Assistant Manager: Dave Wakefield
Physio: Melanie Garratt

DIVISION THREE FINAL LEAGUE TABLE 1999-2000

	P	Home					Away					Total						
		W	D	L	F	A	W	D	L	F	A	W	D	L	F	A	Pts	GD
East Thurrock Utd	40	16	2	2	54	18	10	5	5	35	24	26	7	7	89	42	85	47
Gt Wakering Rovers	40	13	5	2	48	21	12	2	6	33	20	25	7	8	81	41	82	40
Tilbury	40	13	5	2	41	15	8	7	5	26	24	21	12	7	67	39	75	28
Hornchurch	40	14	4	2	47	22	5	8	7	25	35	19	12	9	72	57	69	15
Croydon Athletic	40	11	5	4	52	26	8	6	6	33	26	19	11	10	85	52	68	33
Epsom & Ewell	40	9	10	1	40	22	9	2	9	27	24	18	12	10	67	46	66	21
Lewes	40	10	6	4	34	20	8	4	8	39	31	18	10	12	73	51	64	22
Bracknell Town	40	9	7	4	40	29	6	9	5	41	35	15	16	9	81	64	61	17
Aveley	40	9	6	5	42	25	8	4	8	31	39	17	10	13	73	64	61	9
Corinthian Casuals	40	9	3	8	32	27	7	7	6	27	24	16	10	14	59	51	58	8
Flackwell Heath	40	12	2	6	47	35	5	4	11	27	41	17	6	17	74	76	57	-2
Ware	40	9	5	6	42	28	7	3	10	32	34	16	8	16	74	62	56	12
Egham Town	40	9	5	6	27	19	5	8	7	21	24	14	13	13	48	43	55	5
Hertford Town	40	6	6	8	28	31	9	4	7	35	29	15	10	15	63	60	55	3
Abingdon Town	40	5	5	10	18	31	5	7	8	30	33	10	12	18	48	64	42	-16
Kingsbury Town	40	6	5	9	29	32	5	3	12	26	54	11	8	21	55	86	41	-31
Camberley Town	40	7	5	8	25	29	4	2	14	19	50	11	7	22	44	79	40	-35
Tring Town	40	6	4	10	20	29	4	5	11	17	35	10	9	21	37	64	39	-27
Dorking	40	7	5	8	33	27	2	5	13	20	42	9	10	21	53	69	37	-16
Clapton	40	6	3	11	25	37	3	4	13	25	56	9	7	24	50	93	34	-43
Southall	40	1	3	16	21	58	2	2	16	12	65	3	5	32	33	123	14	-90

DIVISION THREE RESULTS CHART 1999-2000

		1	2	3	4	5	6	7	8	9	10	11	12	13	14	15	16	17	18	19	20	21
1	Abingdon Town	X	1-2	0-1	0-1	1-1	0-0	1-3	0-4	2-2	1-0	1-2	0-1	1-0	1-2	1-1	2-2	1-5	0-2	2-1	2-1	1-0
2	Aveley	1-2	X	1-1	5-1	4-0	0-3	1-1	2-0	0-1	2-2	0-1	2-1	2-1	2-2	4-1	5-1	0-1	3-0	4-3	0-0	3-3
3	Bracknell Town	1-1	3-3	X	3-1	5-1	1-1	2-0	1-1	0-2	5-2	1-3	3-1	2-3	1-2	2-1	3-3	2-1	1-1	1-0	2-2	1-0
4	Camberley Town	0-0	0-2	2-2	X	2-0	3-1	0-3	0-2	0-1	1-2	1-0	2-2	1-2	1-4	2-1	3-4	1-1	2-0	2-2	1-0	1-0
5	Clapton	1-2	1-2	0-6	3-2	X	3-1	2-4	1-0	0-1	1-1	1-2	3-3	0-4	0-1	0-0	3-1	0-2	4-0	1-2	1-0	0-3
6	Corinthian Cas	1-1	5-1	2-2	0-1	3-0	X	3-1	0-0	0-2	1-0	0-3	1-2	1-2	1-0	3-1	1-3	4-1	3-1	0-3	1-2	2-1
7	Croydon Athletic	1-1	5-1	5-3	3-0	6-0	0-1	X	1-1	3-4	2-1	4-1	1-2	0-0	4-2	2-2	2-1	1-1	4-0	1-2	3-0	4-3
8	Dorking	1-0	1-2	4-4	5-1	1-2	0-0	3-2	X	2-2	1-0	2-1	1-1	0-1	1-5	0-0	0-1	1-2	4-0	0-1	5-0	1-2
9	East Thurrock U	2-1	4-1	1-1	3-0	3-2	2-0	1-2	5-0	X	2-0	0-4	3-0	2-1	2-1	3-0	6-2	1-0	6-0	3-0	2-2	3-1
10	Egham Town	0-5	2-4	1-1	3-1	3-0	3-1	3-0	3-1	0-0	X	1-0	3-0	1-2	0-1	0-1	2-0	1-0	1-1	0-1	0-0	0-0
11	Epsom & Ewell	1-1	0-0	1-1	2-1	2-2	1-1	1-0	3-2	2-1	0-0	X	2-1	3-1	2-2	0-1	1-1	3-3	4-0	6-1	3-3	3-0
12	Flackwell Heath	3-1	6-2	4-2	3-0	3-5	1-4	0-3	2-1	1-0	1-1	2-1	X	1-0	1-1	6-2	5-0	1-6	2-1	0-1	3-0	2-4
13	Gt Wakering R	3-3	2-0	2-2	1-0	5-0	2-2	1-1	3-1	0-3	0-1	3-1	2-1	X	3-1	4-1	4-0	2-1	5-0	1-1	3-1	2-1
14	Hertford Town	2-1	1-3	1-1	4-1	1-1	0-1	3-3	2-1	2-1	2-2	0-0	0-1	0-3	X	1-3	2-0	1-2	4-1	0-0	0-2	2-4
15	Hornchurch	2-1	2-0	2-3	2-2	3-3	3-1	1-1	3-2	2-1	0-1	3-0	3-2	1-0	3-1	X	4-0	3-2	3-0	0-0	4-1	3-1
16	Kingsbury Town	2-0	0-3	1-3	3-0	2-0	0-2	0-3	2-2	3-3	0-1	2-1	3-1	1-3	0-1	1-1	X	1-1	7-2	0-2	0-2	1-1
17	Lewes	4-1	1-0	4-1	1-1	2-1	1-1	0-2	1-1	5-2	1-1	0-2	2-1	1-3	3-1	1-1	4-0	X	2-0	0-0	1-0	0-1
18	Southall	2-3	2-3	1-5	1-2	4-5	0-3	1-1	3-1	0-3	1-1	0-3	3-1	1-1	1-4	1-3	0-3	1-6	X	1-4	0-1	0-3
19	Tilbury	4-2	0-0	1-0	3-0	1-0	2-1	2-1	5-0	1-1	2-0	1-1	2-1	1-2	2-2	1-1	2-0	2-0	5-0	X	2-0	2-3
20	Tring Town	1-1	2-1	1-0	1-3	2-1	0-1	0-1	2-0	0-3	0-4	0-1	2-2	0-1	1-0	0-0	0-2	2-3	2-3	1-1	X	3-1
21	Ware	1-3	1-1	1-2	3-1	3-1	2-2	1-1	3-0	1-2	1-1	2-0	5-1	1-3	0-2	3-4	5-2	3-1	3-0	1-1	2-0	X

ABINGDON TOWN

Secretary: Ted Quail, 107 Park Lane, Thatcham, Newbury, Berks RG18 3BZ (01635868967)
GROUND Address: Culham Road, Abingdon OX14 3BT (01235 521684)
Directions: On A415 road to Dorchester-on-Thames half a mile south of town centre. Nearest rail station is Culham. Main line: Didcot Parkway or Oxford. Bus service from Didcot & London
Capacity: 3,000   Cover: 1,771   Seats: 271   Floodlights: Yes
Clubhouse: (01235 521684). 7.30-11pm. 6pm matchdays. 12.30-2.30, 4-11 Sat. Hot food on matchdays. Pool, darts, jukebox, canteen
Club Shop: Selling programmes, magazines, scarves. Metal Badges: £2
HONOURS Berks & Bucks Sen Cup 58-59 (R-up 88-89 92-93); Isthmian League Div 2 (Sth) 90-91 (Assoc. Mem. Tphy R-up 90-91); London Spartan Lg 88-89 Hellenic Lge(4) 56-57 58-60 86-87, R-up(3) 70-72 87-88,Lg Cup 57-58 70-71 81-82 (R-up 83-84 86-87), Div 1 75-76, Div 1 Cup 75-76,Res. Div(3) 69-71 86-87, Res. Div Cup 70-71 85-86, Res. Div Suppl. Cup 74-75;Oxford & Dist. Lg (3) 1898-1901; Reading & Dist. Lg 47-48; Berks & Bucks Jnr Cup 06-07; Abingdon Centenary Cup 58-59; Joan Lee Mem. Cup 69-70 70-71 86-87
PREVIOUS   Leagues: Oxford & Dist.; West Berks; Reading Temperance; North Berks; Reading & Dist. 1927-50; Spartan 50-53; Hellenic 53-88; London Spartan 88-89
RECORDS   Attendance: 1,400 v Oxford City, FA Cup September 1960
BEST SEASON FA Vase: Fifth Round, replay, 199-90. **FA Cup:** 4th Qual. Rd 60-61 0-2 v Hitchin, 89-90 1-3 v Slough(H), 92-93 1-2 v Merthyr T.(A) after 0-0

FACT FILE
Formed: 1870   Nickname: The Abbotts
Sponsors: Morlands
Colours: Yellow & green/green/yellow
Change colours: Black & white
Programme: Pages: 40 Price:£1.00
Editor: Rick Gray (01235 527345)
Midweek Matchday: Wednesday
Reserves ' League: Suburban (West)
Local Press: Oxford Mail, Oxford Times,
Abingdon Herald, South Oxon Guardian

CLUB PERSONNEL
Chairman: Phil Evans
President: Dr Tim Reynolds
Vice Chairman: Craig Norcliffe
Press Officer: Simon Element (01235 202164)
Manager: Bob Raynor
Asst Manager:T.B.A.
Physio:T.B.A.
Coach: T.B.A.

ARLESEY TOWN

Secretary: John Albon, 13 St Johns Rd, Arlesey, Beds SG15 6ST.
Tel: 01462 731318 (H & B), Mob 0711 566044

GROUND: Hitchin Rd, Arlesey,Beds SG15 6RS Tel: 01462 734504

Directions: A1 take A507 to Shefford, at 3rd roundabout turn left, 1st left follow road through village, ground 1.5 miles on left
Capacity: 2,096   Seats: 150   Cover: 300   Floodlights: Yes   **Club Shop:** Yes
Clubhouse: Members bar & function suite Open daily 11.30, Sat 12-11.30, Sun12-2.30 6-11.30

HONOURS: FA Vase Winners 1994-5; Beds Sen Cup 65-66 78-79 96-97, Prem Cup 83-84, Interm Cup 57-58; S Mids Lge Prem Div 51-52 52-53 94-95 95-96.99-00, Div 2 29-30 31-32 35-36, Chall Trophy 79-80, Prem Shield 64-65, O'Brien Prem Cup 93-94, Flood-LitCup 90-91; Utd Co Lge Prem Div 84-85, KO Cup 87-88; Hinchingbrooke Cup 77-78 79-80 81-82 96-97; Biggleswade KO Cup 77-78 80-81
PREVIOUS   Leagues: Biggleswade & Dist.; Beds. Co. (S. Mids) 22-26 ,27-28; Parthenon; London 58-60; Utd Co's 33-36 82-92. Spartan South Midlands 92-99
RECORDS: **Attendance:** 2,000 v Luton Res, Beds Snr Cup 1906
Appearances: Gary Marshall
BEST SEASON: FA Vase: Winners 94-95   **FA Cup:** ????
Players progressing to Football League: Roland Legate (Luton), Pat Kruse(Brentford, Leicester)

FACT FILE
Founded: 1891
Nickname: Blues
Colours: Sky & navy/navy/navy
Change Colours: All white.
Midweek matchday: Tuesday
Reserves' Lge: S. Midlands Lge Res Div 1
Programme: £1.00
Editor: Pete Brennan (01462 834455)

CLUB PERSONNEL
Chairman: Eddie Haetzman (01462 816836)
Vice-Chairman: Scott Geekie (01462 732396)
President: Maurice Crouch
Manager: Nicky Ironton
Asst Man:Alan Dawson   Physio: Eric Turner

ASHFORD TOWN (MIDDX)

Secretary: Alan B J Constable,3 Craigwell Close, Chertsey Lane, Staines, Middx. TW18 3NP
Tel: 01784 440613 (H) 0956 930719 (M)
Ground: Short Lane, Stanwell, Staines, Middx Tel: 01784 245908
Directions: M25 jct 13, A30 towards London, 3rd left at footbridge after Ashford Hospital crossroads - ground signposted after 1/4 a mile on right down Short Lane. 2 miles from Ashford (BR) & Hatton Cross (tube) stations.
Bus route - Westlink 116
Capacity: 2,000   Seats: 100   Cover: 100   Floodlights: Yes
Clubhouse: Open 7 days a week. Refreshments always available - hot food on matchdays
Club Shop: No
HONOURS: Combined Co's Lg Champions 94-95, 95-96, 96-97, 97-8, 99-00; Chall Cup R-up 92-93 94-95, Lg Vase Cup R-up 91-92 94-95; Surrey I'mediate Lg, Surrey Prem. Cup 89-90; Middx Prem. Cup R-up 89-90; Southern Comb Cup 95-96, World Wide Carpets Prem Ch Cup 98-99
PREVIOUS   Ground: Clockhouse Lane Rec
Leagues: Hounslow & Dist. 64-68; Surrey Intermediate 68-82; Surrey Premier 82-90 Combined Counties League 90-00
RECORD   Appearances: Alan Constable 650
Attendance: 750 v Brentford, friendly 29/7/8
Goalscorer: Andy Smith

FACT FILE
Formed: 1964
Nickname: Ash Trees
Colours: Tangerine & white/white/tangerine
Change colours:Blue/Black/Blue
Midweek matchday: Tuesday
Programme: 24 pages, £1
Editor: Secretary

99-00- Captain: Jim Heggarty
Top Scorer:Tony Nolan (43)
P.o.Y .Tonu Nolan

CLUB PERSONNEL
Chairman: Robert Parker
Vice Chairman: Des Vertannes
President: T.B.A.
Press Secretary: Kerry Vertannes
Manager: Dave Kent

AVELEY

Secretary: Craig Johnston,62 Brimfield Rd., Watts Wood,Purfleet, Essex RM19 1RG (01708 864313)
GROUND: `Mill Field', Mill Road, Aveley, Essex RM15 4TR (01708 865940)
Directions: London - Southend A13, turn into Sandy Lane at Aveley.
Rainham or Purfleet BR stations then bus No. 723 to the ground
Capacity: 4,000   Cover: 400   Seats: 400   Floodlights: Yes
Clubhouse: Normal pub hours. Bar snacks and hot food available   Club Shop: No
HONOURS: Isthmian Lg Div 2 (North) R-up 89-90, Lg (AC Delco) Cup 89-90; London Lg 51-5254-55 (R-up 55-56, Lg Cup 53-54); Delphian Lg R-up 57-58 (Lg Cup 61-62);Athenian Lg 70-71 (Div 2 R-up 68-69); Essex Junior Cup 47-48 48-49; Essex Thameside Trophy 79-80 R-up 97-98; Hornchurch Charity Cup 81-82 (R-up 83-84); East Anglian Cup 88-89, R-up 97-98
PREVIOUS Leagues: Thurrock Com 46-49; London 49-57; Delphian 57-63; Athenian 63-73
RECORDS   Attendance: 3,741 v Slough T., FA Amateur Cup 27.2.71
Goalscorer: Jotty Wilks, 214   **Appearances:** Ken Riley, 422
Win: 11-1 v Histon, 24/8/63
Defeat: v Orient, Essex Thameside Trophy, 11/4/85
BEST SEASON FA Cup: 1st Rd 70-71, 0-1 v Yeovil   League clubs defeated: None
FA Amateur Cup QF 70-71 **FA Trophy** 3rd Qual Rd replay 74-75 **F.A.Vase** 3rd Rd 89-90
1999-00 Captain: Lee Double   P.o.Y.: Robbie Bird   Top Scorer: tony Rogers

FACT FILE

Founded: 1927
Sponsors: Dagenham Motors
Colours: All Royal blue
Change: All Red
Midweek matches: Tuesday
Reserves' Lge: Essex & Herts Border Comb
Programme: 30 pages Price: £1
Editor: Terry King
Local Press: Thurrock Gazette
Recorder
Local Radio: Radio Essex, Essex Radio

CLUB PERSONNEL

Chairman: David Patient
President: Ken Clay
Press Officer: Terry King
Manager: Paul Joynes
Asst Mgr/Coach: Douggie Quinnell
Physio: Phil Hunter

BRACKNELL TOWN

Ground: Larges Lane, Bracknell RG12 9AN. Tel: 01344 412305 (club), 01344 300933 (office)
Directions: Off A329 just before Met Office r'bout by Bracknell College, ground 200 yards. From Bracknell (BR)/bus station - right out of station, follow pathover bridge, left down steps and follow cycle path ahead, after 300yds follow curve over footbridge, right and follow lane to end, left and ground on leftafter bend
Capacity: 2,500   Seats: 190   Cover: 400   Floodlights: Yes
Clubhouse: Members' bar open 11am-11pm Mon-Sat, 12-3 & 7-10.30pm Sun.
Club Shop: Yes, selling metal badges, programmes, scarves, club sweaters, club ties

PREVIOUS   Leagues: Great Western Comb.; Surrey Snr 63-70; London Spartan 70-75
Grounds: None   **Names:** None
CLUB RECORDS Attendance: 2,500 v Newquay, FA Amateur Cup 1971
Career Goalscorer: Richard Whitty   **Career Appearances:** James Woodcock
BEST SEASON   FA Cup: 4th Qual Rd - 88, 1-2 v Cheltenham T., 96, 1-3 v Burton A
HONOURS: Isthmian Lg Div 3 93-94; Berks & Bucks Snr Cup R-up; Spartan Lg 74-75, (Lg Cup 81-82 82-83); Surrey Snr Lg 68-69 (Lg Cup 68-69 69-70)
Players progressing: Willie Graham (Brentford)
99-00 - Captain: M Parker   P.o.Y: Dave Osgood   Top Scorer: John Smith

FACT FILE

Founded: 1896   Nickname: Robins
Reserve's League: Suburban (west)
Colours: Red & white quarters
Change colours: Blue & white stripes/blue/blue
Midweek Matchday: Tuesday
Programme: Pages: 32 Price: £1.00
Editor/Press Off.: Robert Scully 01344 640721

CLUB PERSONNEL

Secretary: Cliff McFaden
15 Goodways Drive, Bracknell,
Berks RG12 9AU Tel: 07801 843333 (M)

Chairman: Dave Mihell
Vice Chairman: Chris Nixon
President: Jack Quinton

Manager: Clive Tallentire
Asst Manager:Mark Tallentire
Physio: Geoff Jones

CAMBERLEY TOWN

Secretary: David Clifford 63 Unglewood Ave, Camberley, Surrey. GU15 1RS
Tel & Fax: 01276 20732
Ground: Krooner Park, Krooner Road, off Frimley Rd, Camberley, Surrey GU15 2QP
Tel: 01276 65392   **Directions:** M3 Jct 4, follow signs to Frimley, then B3411 towards Camberley, ground on left opp. `The Standard' pub
Capacity: 3,000   Seats: 195 Cover: 280   Floodlights: Yes   Club Shop: Yes
Clubhouse: Open matchdays & 2 evenings. Food available from burger bar matchdays

HONOURS: Isthmian Lg Div 2 R-up 78-79; Surrey Snr Lg 30-31 31-32 32-33 (R-up 46-47 61-62), Lg Charity Cup 37-38 51-52 (R-up 31-32 36-37 54-55 72-73); Surrey Snr Cup 78-79 (R-up 35-36); W. Surrey Lg 13-14 (R-up 12-13); Ascot & Dist Lg 03-04; Surrey Jnr Charity Cup R-up 08-09; Surrey Jnr Cup 1897-98 1909-10 (R-up 07-08); Aldershot Snr Lg 12-13 (Lg Charity Cup R-up 21-22); Southern Comb. Cup 80-81 (R-up 78-79 85-86 87-88); Aldershot Sen Cup 96-97 97-98

PREVIOUS   Leagues: Ascot & District; West Surrey; Aldershot Snr; Surrey Snr 22-73 Spartan 73-75; Athenian 75-77 82-84; Isthmian 77-82
CLUB RECORDS   Attendance:3,500 v Crystal Pal. friendly 14.10.74
Competitive: 2,066 v Aldershot T., Isthmian Lge Div. 3, 10.11.92
BEST SEASON   FA Vase: Quarter Final 85-86, 98-99 v Woodbridge
FA Cup: 1st Rd Prop 98-99 v Brentwood 4th Qual. 32-33 33-34 97-98

FACT FILE

Founded: 1896
Nickname: Krooners, Reds or Town
Colours:Red & White Stripes/ Red/Red
Change colours: L & D Blue strips
Midweek Matches: Tuesday
Reserve's League: Suburban
Programme: 24 pages, £1
Local Press: Camberley News
Bracknell News

CLUB PERSONNEL

Chairman: Ian Waldren
Press Officer: Andy Vaughan
Manager: Trevor Norris
Physio: Ken Weaver

CHALFONT ST PETER

Secretary: Dave Ward, 3 Greenfield End, Chalfont St Perters, Bucks SL9 0DW
Tel: 01494 482208 (H) 0378 144475 (W)
Ground: The Playing Fields, Amersham Road, Chalfont St Peter SL9 7BQ Tel: 01753 885797
Directions: A413 from Uxbridge (London) to Chalfont. Turn left 100 yds after2nd major round-
about (between Ambulance station and Community Centre. Two miles from Gerrards Cross
(BR), regular buses from Slough & Uxbridge
Capacity: 4,500   Cover: 120   Seats: 220   Floodlights: Yes   Club Shop: Yes
Clubhouse: Open every evening, Saturday afternoons and Sunday lunchtimes
PREVIOUS   **Leagues:** Great Western Combination 1948-58; Parthenon 58-59; London
60-62;Spartan 62-75; London Spartan 75-76; Athenian 76-84
BEST SEASON   **FA Trophy:** 3rd Qual Rd 89-90 91-92   **FA Vase:** 4th Rd 87-88
FA Cup: 3rd Qual Rd85-86 (wins over Banbury, King's Lynn and Barking)
HONOURS   Isthmian Lg Div 2 87-88; Athenian Lg R-up 83-84 (Lg Cup 76-77 82-83);
London Spartan Lg Div 2 75-76; Berks & Bucks Intermediate Cup 52-53;
Berks & Bucks Benevolent Cup 64-65
CLUB RECORDS   **Attendance:** 2,550 v Watford, benefit match 85
Career Goalscorer: Unknown **Career Appearances:** Colin Davies
Transfer Fee Paid: £750 to Chertsey (Steve Church, March 1989)
Players progressing to Football League: Paul Barrowcliff (Brentford), Dean Hooper (Swindon)

FACT FILE
Founded: 1926
Nickname: Saints
Colours: Red, green trim/green/green & red
Change colours: Yellow/black/black
Midweek matchday: Tuesday
Reserves' League:
Programme: Pages: 30 Price: 50p
Editor: Mal Keenan
Local Press: Bucks Advertiser,
Bucks Examiner, Bucks Free Press,
Wycombe Midweek
Local Radio: Chiltern Radio

CLUB PERSONNEL
Chairman: Peter Manson
Press Officer: Nick Simon
Manager: Sean West
Physio:

CLAPTON

Secretary: Bill Robertson, 2Humphrey Close, Clayhell, Ilford, Essex IG5 0RW
Ground: The Old Spotted Dog, Upton Lane, Forest Gate, London E7 9NP
Tel: 0181 472 0822
Directions: BR to Forest Gate,Tube to Plaistow (District Line). Official entrance in Upton
Lane. Docklands Light Railway to Prince Regent then 325 bus to ground
Capacity: 2,000 Seats: 100   Cover: 180   Floodlights: Yes   Club Shop: No
Clubhouse: Most eves & match day. Light snacks available. To hire please contact club
HONOURS: FA Amateur Cup: 06-07 08-09 14-15 23-24 24-25 (R-up 04-05);
Isthmian Lg 10-11 22-23 (R-up 05-06 07-08 09-10 24-25), Div 2 82-
83; Essex Thames-side Tphy(2); A.F.A.Invitation Cup (2); London
Snr Cup (2); London Charity Cup; Essex Snr Cup (4);Middlx Snr
Cup; Essex Sen Trophy; First English team to play on the continent,
beating a Belgian Select XI over Easter 1890
PREVIOUS   **Leagues:** Southern 1894-96 (founder members); London 1896-97
CLUB RECORDS **Attendance:** 12,000 v Tottenham Hotspur, FA Cup 1898-99
BEST SEASON   **FA Cup:** 3rd Rd Proper 25-26 (lost 2-3 to Swindon at Upton Park)
League clubs defeated Norwich City 25-26.
FA Amateur Cup: 06-07 08-09 14-15 23-24 24-25 (R-up 04-05);

FACT FILE
Founded: 1878
Nickname: Tons
Sponsors: T.B.A.
Colours: Red & white stripes/black/black
Change colours: All blue
Midweek Matchday: Tuesday

Programme: 12-16 pages £1.00
Editor: Match Secretary

CLUB PERSONNEL
Chairman: Ken Harris
Chief Executive: Vince McBean
Press Officer:Ian Hollowell
Manager: Micky Welch

CORINTHIAN CASUALS

Secretary: Brian Wakefield, 5 Martingales Close, Richmond, Surrey Tel: 020 8940 9208
Ground: King George's Field, Hook Rise South, Tolworth, Surrey KT6 7NA
Tel: 020 8397 3368
Directions: A3 to Tolworth r'bout (The Toby Jug). Hook Rise is slip road immediately
after the Toby Jug pub. Turn left under railway bridge after a 1/4mile - grd on right. Half
mile from Tolworth (BR); turn left, continue to Toby Jug, then as above. K2 Hoppa bus
from Kingston passes ground
Capacity: 1,700 Seats: 126   Cover: 500   Floodlights: Yes Club Shop: Yes
Clubhouse: Evenings, matchdays, Sunday lunchtimes. Darts, pool, hot & coldsnacks on
matchdays
HONOURS   FA Amateur Cup R-up 55-56 (SF 56-57), London Spartan Lg R-up 92-
93 (Lg Cup R-up 91-92); Combined Counties Lg R-up 96-97
PREVIOUS   **Leagues:** Isthmian 39-84, Spartan 84-96; Combined Counties 96-97
BEST SEASON   **FA Cup:** 1st Rd 65-66 1st Rd replay 85-86   **FA Vase:** 5th Rd 83-84
FA Amateur Cup: Runners-up 55-56
Career Records: Goals Cliff West 219   **Appearances** Bruce Martin 472
Players progressing: Peter Phillips (Luton Town),Andy Gray, Tony Finnegan, Alan
Pardew to Crystal Palace

FACT FILE
Founded: 1939
Sponsors: London Catering Services
Colours: Chocalte & Pink/sky/sky
Change colours: White/navy/white Midweek
Matchday: Tuesday
Reserves' League: Suburban
Programme: 24-48 pages, £1
Editor: Rob Cavallini

CLUB PERSONNEL
Chairman: David Harrison
President: Jimmy Hill
Team Manager: Trevor Waller
Press Officer: Rob Cavallini (0181 404
2763)
Match Secretary:
Rob Cavallini(020 8404 2763)

CROYDON ATHLETIC

Secretary: Dean Fisher, 153 Chipstead Valley Road, Coulsdon, Surry CR5 3BQ
Tel: 020 84073296 (H & Fax) 020 7556 6092
Ground: Mayfields, off Mayfield Road, Thornton Heath, Surrey CR7 6DN (0181-664-8343)
Directions: Follow A23 from London & continue on A23 into Thornton Road. After roundabout take !st on right into Silverleigh Road, left fork into Trafford Road which continues into Mayfield Road. To end and turn left and follow narrow road to ground. 1 mile from Norbury (BR). Buses 109, 154
Capacity: 3,000   Seats: 163   Cover: 300   Floodlights: Yes
Clubhouse: Open every evening & weekends   Club Shop: Yes
HONOURS: London Spartan Lg winners 94-95, R-up 88-89 93-94, (Reserve Div 88-89, R-up 88-89); London Snr Cup R-up 91-92; Southern Youth Lg 92-93; Bearman Harber MemTrophy 87-88; Wirral Prog 86-87 96-97; Umbro Fair Play Winners 97-98
PREVIOUS   Leagues: None
RECORDS   Attendance: 550   **Goalscorer:** Graham Edginton
Appearances: Graham Edginton/ Paul Gall/Leon Maxwell
BEST SEASON   FA Vase: 3rd Rd 94-95   **FA Cup:** 2nd Qual. Rd 94-95
Players progressing to Football League: Jamie Ndah (Torquay Utd)

FACT FILE
Founded: 1990   Sponsors: T.C.S. Media
Colours: Maroon & white/maroon/maroon
Change colours: Yellow/royal/royal/royal
Midweek matches: Tuesday
Reserve League: Suburban (S)
Programme: 52 pages, £1
Editor: Secretary
99-00 - P.o.Y.: Jamie Gibson
Top Scorer: Jamie Fowler
CLUB PERSONNEL

Chairman: Keith Tuckey
V Chairman/ Press Officer: Clive Thompson
Manager: Haydon Bird
Asst Man.: Peter Thomas
1st Team Coach: Leon Maxwell
Chief Scout: John Langford
Managers Asst: Dave Finch
Physio: Mick Reed

DORKING

Secretary: Ray Collins,11 Richmond Way, Fetcham, Surrey KT22 9NP (01372 453867)
Ground: Meadowbank, Mill Lane, Dorking, Surrey RH4 1DX (01306 884112)
Directions: Mill Lane is off Dorking High St. next to Woolworths and Marks &Spencers opposite the White Horse pub. Fork right in Mill Lane past theMalthouse pub. 1/2 mile from both Dorking and Deepdene (BR) stations
Capacity: 3,600   Cover: 800   Seats: 200   Floodlights: Yes   Club Shop: Yes
Clubhouse: All week &Sun. 4-11 p.m. Sats 12-11pm Hot & cold food on matchdays
HONOURS Isthmian Lge Div 2 Sth 88-89, (Full Members Cup R-up 92-93); Surrey Sen Cup R-up 1885-86 1989-90; Surrey Senior Shield (2), R-up (3); Surrey Sen Lge (4), R-up (2), Lge Cup (3); Lge Charity Cup (4), R-up (5); Gilbert Rice F'lit Cup 87-88 (R-up 89-90); Surrey I'mediate Cup 56-57 (R-up 54-55); Southern Comb.Challenge Cup 92-93
PREVIOUS Leagues: Surrey Senior 22-56 77-78; Corinthian 56-63; Athenian 63-74 78-80;Surrey 74-77Ground: Prixham Lane (until 1953)
CLUB RECORDS Attendance: 4,500 v Folkestone Town, FA Cup 1st Qual. Rd 1955 and v Plymouth argyle 1st Rd F.A.Cup 92-93
BEST SEASON FA Cup: 1st Round Proper 92-93, 2-3 v Plymouth A. (H) **FA Vase:** 3rd Rd (3) 83-84 86-88 **FA Trophy:** 2nd Rd 91-92
1998-99 Captain: Nick Torpey   **P.o.Y.:** Stephen Gillet   **Top Scorer:** Stuart White

FACT FILE
Formed: 1880   Nickname: The Chicks
Colours: Green & white hoops/green/green
Change colours: All navy blue
Midweek matches: Tuesday
Reserve League: Suburban
Programme: 48 pages £1 Editor: Paul Mason
Press: Dorking Advertiser, Surrey Mirror
Surrey Advertiser
Local Radio: County Sound, Radio Surrey, Radio Mercury
CLUB PERSONNEL
Chairman: Jack Collins
President: Ingram Whittingham
Vice-Chairman: Ray Collins
Co. Sec.: Martin Collins
Press Officer: Bryan Bletso
Manager: Ian Dawes
Asst Manager: Chick Banes
Physio: Bennie Fishlock

EGHAM TOWN

Club Administrator: Alison Thompson, 138A Thorpe Lea Rd, Egham, Surrey. TW20 8BL
Tel: 01784 463562
GROUND: Runnymeade Stadium, Tempest Road, Egham, Surrey TW20 8HX (01784 435226)
Directions: M25 jct 13, follow signs to Egham, under M25 at r'bout, left to end, left at mini-r'bout, over railway crossing, left in past (Pooley Green Rd), right, Tempest Rd 2nd right.
Bus 41 43 441 from Staines to Pooley Green Rd. 30 mins Egham or Staines (BR)
Capacity: 5,635   Seats: 335   Cover: 1,120   Floodlights: Yes   Club Shop: No
Clubhouse: (01784 435226) 7-11pm daily & weekend lunchtimes. Function hall
HONOURS Isthmian Lg Assoc Members Tphy R-up 91-92; Spartan Lg 71-72 (Lg Cup R-up 67-68); Athenian Lg R-up 75-76 (Div 2 74-75); Surrey Snr Cup R-up 91-92, Surrey Snr Lg 22-23, Lg Charity Cup 22-23 (R-up 26-27 34-35); Surrey Intermediate Lg20-21, Charity Cup 19-20 20-21 (R-up 26-27); North West Surrey Charity Cup 20-21; Egham Twinning Tournament 67-68 71-72 74-75 75-76 76-77 80-81; SouthernComb. Floodlit Cup 77-78 (R-up 83-84)
RECORD   Attendance: 1,400 v Wycombe Wanderers, FA Cup 2ndQual Rd 72
Scorer: Mark Butler 50 (91-92) Career record scorer as well
Appearances: Dave Jones 850+   **Win:** 10-1 v Camberley, 81-82
PREVIOUS   Leagues: Hounslow & District 1896-1914; Surrey Intermediate 19-22; Surrey Senior 22-28 65-67; Spartan 29-33 67-74; Parthenon 64-65; Athenian 74-77
BEST SEASON FA Cup: 4th Qual Rd 90-91, 0-2 v Telford Utd (A)

FACT FILE
Founded: 1877
Nickname: Sarnies/Town
Colours: Yellow & Green/yellow/yellow
Change colours: All white
Midweek Matches: Tuesday
Reserves' League: Suburban
Programme: 40 pages, £1
Editor: A lisonThompson (01784 463562 H)
Local Press: Herald & News
Local Radio: County Sound

CLUB PERSONNEL
Chairman: Patrick Bennett
Vice Chairman: Peter Barnes
President: Peter Barnes
Press Officer: Steve Kell
(01784 449368)
Coaches: Glynn Stephens & Adam Dale
Physio: Ken Weaver

EPSOM & EWELL

Secretary: D Wilson, 33 Delaporte Close, Epsom, Surrey KT17 4AF (01372 729817)
GROUND: Share with Banstead A. Merland Rise, Tadworth, Surrey KT20 5JG(01737 350982)
Directions: Follow signs to Tattenham Corner (Epsom racecourse), then toBanstead Sports Centre. Ground adjacent to swimming pool. Half a mile fromTattenham Corner (BR). Bus 420 from Sutton stops outside ground. Also buses 406& 727 from Epsom
Capacity: 3,500   **Seats:** 250   **Cover:** 800   **Floodlights:** Yes   **Club Shop:** No
Clubhouse: Normal licensing hours, food available
HONOURS FA Vase R-up 74-75; London Lg 27-28, R-up (5); Corinthian Lg Memorial Shield 59-60 (R-up 51-52 56-57); Athenian Lg Div 2 R-up 75-76 (Lg Cup R-up 76-77, Div2 Cup R-up 67-68); Isthmian Lg Div 2 77-78 (Div 1 R-up 83-84), Vanranel Ass Members Trophy R-up 97-98; Surrey Snr Lg 25-26 26-27 74-75 (R-up 73-74), Lg Cup73-74 74-75, Charity Cup 26-27 (R-up 73-74), Surrey Snr Cup 80-81 (R-up 3); Surrey Snr Shield 32-33 54-55; Surrey Intermediate Cup 29-30,Charity Cup 57-58; Southern Comb. Cup 79-80 (R-up 82-83 92-93)
PREVIOUS Leagues: Surrey Snr 24-27 73-75; London 27-49; Corinthian 49-63; Athenian 63-73 75-77
CLUB RECORDS Attendance: 5,000 v Kingstonian, F.A. Cup 2nd Qual. Rd, 15/10/49
BEST SEASON FA Cup: 1st Rd 33-34, **FA Vase:** R-up 74-75 **FA Trophy:** 2nd Rd 81-82
Players progressing: Matt Elliott (Leicester), Chris Powell(Derby), Paul Harding (Notts County, Birmingham), Murray Jones (Grimsby), Alan Pardew (Charlton), Mick Leonard (Chesterfield)

FACT FILE
Founded: 1917   Nickname: E's
Colours: Royal & white
Change: All yellow
Midweek Matches: Tuesday
Reserves' League: Suburban
Programme: 28/32 pages, 50p
Editor: Stella Lamont (01737 356245)
99-00 - Captain:Graham Morris
Top Scorer:Barry Stevens (130)
P.o.Y.: James Hall
Record Goalscorer: Tommy Tuite

CLUB PERSONNEL
Chairman: Peter Atkins
Vice Chairman: Stella Lamont
Press Officer: Sec
Manager: Adrian Hill
Coaches: John Wood & Barry Barnes
Physio: Kevin Taylor

FLACKWELL HEATH

Secretary: Mrs Christine Hobbs, 23 Southfield Rd., Flackwell Heath, Bucks. HP10 9BT
Tel: 01628 521051
GROUND: Wilks Park, Heath End Rd, Flackwell Heath, High Wycombe. HP10 9EA
Tel: 01628 523892
Directions: M40 jct 3 Wycombe East, follow signs for F/Heath left up Treadway Hill & right at top of hill at roundabout. Wilks park 800yds on right, grd at rear of Magpie (PH). Bus 301 either from bus station or High Street near bottom of Crendon Street which comes from BR station. Ask for Oakland Way
Capacity: 2,000   **Seats:** 150   **Cover:** Yes   **Floodlights:** Yes   **Club Shop:** No
Clubhouse: Open every night 6.30-11pm & before & after matches. Hot food in tea bar

HONOURS:	Gt Western Combination 57-58 62-63; Hellenic Lg Div 1 R-up 76-77; Berks & Bucks Snr Cup SF 85-86
PREVIOUS:	**Leagues:** Wycombe & District; Gt Western Comb.; Hellenic 76-82; Athenian 82-84
RECORDS:	**Attendance:** 4,500 v Oxford U., charity game 1986 (competitive: 700 v Aldershot Town, 27/10/92)
	Goalscorer: Tony Wood **Appearamces:** Ben Richards
	Win: 6-0 v Clapton & v Petersfield (both away) **Defeat:** 0-7 v Aveley (H)
BEST SEASON:	**FA Cup:** 2nd Qual. Rd replay 90-91, 0-3 v Grays A (A) after 2-2

FACT FILE
Founded: 1907
Colours: Red/black
Change colours: Yellow/black/black
Midweek Matches: Tuesday
Reserves' League: Suburban
Programme: 18 pages £1

CLUB PERSONNEL
Chairman: T Glynn
Vice Chairman: J.Driscoll
President: Ken Crook

HERTFORD TOWN

Ground: Hertingfordbury Park, West Street, Hertford Tel: 01992 583716

Directions: Rail to Hertford Nth (from Moorgate) or Hertford East (LiverpoolStr.); both 15 mins walk. Green Line bus to town centre then 10 mins walk.
By road; off bypass heading east, turn off at Ford garage
Capacity: 6,500   **Seats:** 200   **Cover:** 1,500   **Floodlights:** Yes
Club Shop: Souvenirs   **Clubhouse:** Yes   **Sponsors:** Atlantic Tiger Corporation
HONOURS Herts Char. Cup 72-73, 89-90, Herts Snr Cup 66-67, Hertford Char.Shd 19-20 20-21 35-36 49-50 55-56 59-60, Eastern Co's Lg Cup 72-73, East Anglian Cup 62-63 69-70, Southern Co's Comb. F-lit Cup 94-95, Mithras Cup SF 85-86, Ryman Div 3 R-up 97-98

PREVIOUS   **Leagues:** Herts Co.; Spartan 21-47 48-59; Delphian 59-63; Athenian 63-72; Eastern Co's 72-73   **Names:** None   **Grounds:** None

BEST SEASON   **FA Cup:** 4th Qual. Rd. 73-74 (lost 1-2 at Hillingdon Borough)

CLUB RECORDS Gate: 5,000 v Kingstonian, F.A. Amateur Cup 2nd Rd 55-56
Appearances: Robbie Burns
Players progressing to Football League: G Mazzon (Aldershot), J.Hooker (Brentford)

FACT FILE
Founded: 1908   Nickname: The Blues
Colours: Blue & yellow/blue/blue
Change colours: Orange & Black
Midweek Matches: Tuesday
Reserves' Lge: Essex & Herts Border Comb
Programme: 28 pages, £1.00
Editor: Martin Climpson:(01992 589972)
Local Newspapers: Hertfordshire Mercury

CLUB PERSONNEL
Secretary: Stephen Hedley,
29 Upper field Road,Wewyn Garden City,
Herts AL7 3LP(01707 333712)
President: John Hedley
Chairman: Mike Schulze
Vice Chairman:David Thomas
Manager: Graham Roberts
Physio: Ray Price

Great Wakering Rovers at Camberley Town on the day they gained promotion. Photo: Eric Marsh

Ford United's Paul Salmon outjumps Wingate & Finchley 'keeper, Michael Kalli, to score the first of Ford's six goals.
Photo: Alan Coomes

HORNCHURCH

Secretary: Rob Monger,1 PIcknick Close,Laindon,Basildon Essex SS15 5SW(01268 490847)

GROUND: The Stadium, Bridge Avenue, Upminster, Essex RM14 2LX (01708 220080)
Directions: Fenchurch Street to Upminster (BR) then 10 mins walk. Or tube toUpminster Bridge (LT), right outside station, 2nd right into Bridge Ave. ground 150yds on right. By road Bridge Avenue is off A124 between Hornchurch and Upminster. Buses 248, 348, 370, 373 from Romford or Upminster BR stations
Capacity: 3,000   **Seats:** 300   **Cover:** 350   **Floodlights:** Yes   **Club Shop:** Yes,
Clubhouse: Mon-Fri 7.30-11, Sat 12-11, Sun 12-3. Cafeteria open matchdays
Club Shop: Yes, selling programmes, handbooks, scarves, hats, souvenirs etc.
Contact : Peter Harris(01268 544151)
HONOURS: Athenian Lg 66-67, Romford Lg(2), Essex Snr Trophy R-up 86-87, Essex Jnr Cup Essex Thameside Tphy 84-85, Isthmian Yth Cup, CarlsbergTrophy R-up 93-94
PREVIOUS: **Leagues:** Romford 25-38; Spartan 38-52; Delphian 52-59; Athenian 59-75
   Names: Hornchurch & Upminster (Upminster FC pre-1950s) merged with UpminsterWanderers in 1961
RECORDS: **Attendance:** 3,000 v Chelmsford, FA Cup 66-67
BEST SEASON: **FA Cup:** 4th Qual Rd 66-67, lost 0-4 at home to Chelmsford City
   F.A. Vase: 5th Rd 74-75

FACT FILE

Founded: 1923   Nickname: Urchins
Sponsors: Premier Snacks
Colours: Red & white/red/red
Change Colours: White/Blue

Midweek Matches: Tuesday
Reserve Lge: Essex & Herts Border Comb
Programme: 16-20 pages with admission
Editor: Peter Harris (01268 544151)
Local Press: Romford Recorder
Local Radio: Essex Radio, Active FM

CLUB PERSONNEL
Chairman: Tom Wallace
Vice Chairman: Brian Davie
Manager: Mick Marsden
Physio: D Edkins

KINGSBURY TOWN

Secretary: David Thomas, 9 Hillview Gardens, Kingsbury, NW9 0DE
GROUND: Silver Jubilee Park, Townsend Lane, Kingsbury, London NW9 7NE (0181 2051645)
Directions: Underground to Kingsbury, cross road and take bus 183 to TownsendLane (2 miles) - ground in far left-hand corner of Silver Jubilee Park
Capacity: 2,500   Seats: 165   Cover: 400   Floodlights: Yes   Club Shop: Yes
Clubhouse: Mon-Fri 7-11, Sat 12-11, Sun 12-2.30 & 7-10.30. Food on matchdays

HONOURS: Isthmian Lg Div 2 Nth R-up 85-86; Spartan Lg Cup R-up 59-60 64-65; Parthenon Lg 51-52 (Prem Charity Cup 52-53 53-54; Snr Charity Cup 53-54); Middx Snr Cup R-up 88-89; Middx Charity Cup 85-86 (R-up 88-89); Middx Lg Charity Cup (3) 44-47; Willsden & Dist. Lg R-up 30-31 (Div 2 34-35)

PREVIOUS: **Leagues:** Hellenic 27-30 (as Davis Sports); Willesden & District 30-43; MiddxSnr 44-47; Parthenon 47-59; Spartan 59-76 78-81; Athenian 76-78 81-84

RECORDS: **Attendance:** 1 ,300 v Wealdstone, FA Amateur Cup 1971

BEST SEASON: FA Vase: 4th Rd 74-75
         FA Cup: 3rd Qual. Rd. 87-88, 0-1 v Leytonstone-Ilford (H)

FACT FILE

Founded: 1927   Nickname: Kings
Sponsors: VPA Entertainment Technology
Colours: Royal blue & White/white/royal
Change colours: Yellow/navy/yellow
Midweek Matches: Tuesday
Reserves' League: Suburban
Programme: 16-20 pages, 50p
Editor: Dave Thomas
Local Press: Harrow Observer, Willesden Chronicle, Allsport Weekly, Edgware &Finchley Times

CLUB PERSONNEL

Chairman: Mark Harrt
Press Officer: Allan Davies (01895 443761)
Manager: Peter Blain
Physio: Margaret Romer

LEWES

Secretary: Steve Kitchener, 8 Malling Down, Lewes, E Sussex BN7 2BN (01273 475228)
GROUND: The Dripping Pan, Mountfield Road, Lewes BN7 1XN (01273 472100)
Directions: Two minute walk from Lewes (BR) - turn left out of station and left into Mountfield Road. Ground 100 yards on right
Capacity: 2,600   Cover: 400   Seats: 400   Floodlights: Yes   Club Shop: Yes
Clubhouse: (01273 472100). Bar, tea bar, pool.

HONOURS: Isthmian Lg Div 2 R-up 79-80 91-92; Ath'n Lg Div 1 69-70 (Div 2 67-68); Sussex Co. Lg 64-65 (R-up 24-25 33-34 58-59 63-64, Lg Cup 39-40); Mid Sussex Lg 10-11 13-14; Sussex Snr Cup 64-65 70-71 84-85 (R-up 79-80 82-83 87-88); Sussex Royal Ulster Rifles Charity Cup(3) 61-63 64-65; Gilbert Rice F'lit Cup 82-83 88-89; Neale Tphy 68-69; Sussex F'lit Cup 76-77 (SF 83-84); Southern Counties Comb Div1 80-81

PREVIOUS: **Leagues:** Mid Sussex 1886-1920; Sussex Co 20-65; Athenian 65-77

RECORDS: **Attendance:** 2,500 v Newhaven, Sussex County Lg 26/12/47

BEST SEASON: FA Cup: 4th Qual. Rd, lost to Harwich & Parkeston
         FA Trophy: 1st Rd 82-83   **FA Amateur Cup:** 2nd Rd 67-68
         FA Vase: 1st Rd 79-80

FACT FILE

Founded: 1885   Nickname: Rooks
Colours: Red & Black stripes/black/black
Change colours: All white
Midweek matches: Tuesday
Reserves' League: Sussex Co. Res. Sect
Programme: 32 pages, £1 Editor: Martin Burke
Local Press: Evening Argus, Sussex Express
Local Radio: Southern F.M.,B.B.C. Southern Counties

CLUB PERSONNEL

President: T.Carr
Chairman: T.Parris
Manager: Jimmy Quinn
Asst Man.:

TRING TOWN

Secretary: Laurie McParland, 125 Bennetts End Rd, Hemel Hempstead, Herts HP3 8DX
         Tel Nos:01442 263902 (H) 07836 265105 (M)

GROUND: Pendley Sports Centre, Cow Lane, Tring, Herts HP23 5NS (01442 824018)

Directions: One mile from Tring centre on A41 - direct connection to M25 (jct20) via new A41 bypass. One and a half miles from Tring (BR). Numerous busesfrom station and Watford-Aylesbury routes serve ground

Capacity: 2,500   Seats: 150   Cover: 250   Floodlights: Yes   Club Shop: No
Clubhouse: All licensing hours. Dancehall, pool, darts, kitchen.

HONOURS: Spartan Lg 67-68, R-up 68-69. Herts Charity Shield winners 4, R-up 2. Athenian Lg Div 2 R-up 76-77, Herts Snr Cup R-up 77-78

PREVIOUS: **Leagues:** Gt Western Combination; Spartan 53-75; Athenian 75-77
         Names: None   Ground: Tring Cricket Ground (40 yrs)

RECORD: **Attendance:** 2,500 v West Ham, friendly
         Goalscorer & Appearances: Gary Harthill

BEST SEASON: FA Cup: 3rd Qual. Rd replay 84-85, 0-5 v Fisher(A) after 1-1

FACT FILE

Founded: 1904
Nickname: T's
Colours: White & red stripewhite/red
Change: Yellow & blue stripes/blue/yellow
Midweek Matchday: Tuesday
Reserves' Lge: Suburban Lge
Programme: 24 pages £1
Editor/Press Officer:
Alan Lee (01702 216063)
Local Radio: Chiltern, Mix 96
BBC Three Counties Radio

CLUB PERSONNEL

Chairman: Harry Bowden
Manager: Mick Vipond
Asst Manager: Danny Johnson
Physio: Keith Hardy

WARE

FACT FILE

Secretary: I Bush, 42 Burnett Squ, Hertford, Herts SG14 2HD (01992 587334)

GROUND: Wodson Park, Wadesmill Road, Ware Herts SG12 0HZ (01920 463247)

Directions: A10 off at junction A602 & B1001 (Ware North), turn right at roundabout 300yds, and follow Ware sign, past Rank factory, turn left at main roundabout onto A1170 (Wadesmill Rd). After 3/4 mile stadium on right

Capacity: 3,300   Seats: 312   Cover: 500   Floodlights: Yes   Club Shop: Yes

Clubhouse: Licensed bar open matchdays. Light snacks at refreshment bar

HONOURS: Herts Snr Cup 1898-99 03-04 06-07 21-22 53-54, Herts Char. Shield 26-27 56-57 58-59 62-63 85-86, Herts Char. Cup R-up 64-65 65-66 78-79 89-90, Spartan Lg 52-53 (Div 1 Sect.B 51-52, Div 2 Sect.A 26-27), Athenian Lg Div 2 Cup 65-66 72-73,East Anglian Cup 73-74, Herts Co. Lg 08-09 21-22, East Herts Lg 04-05 06-07 (LgCup 06-07), Perry Cup 26-27 28-29 37-38 51-52 52-53 53-54 55-56, Dunkels Cup 52-53, Rolleston Cup 39-40 51-52

PREVIOUS: Leagues: East Herts; North Middx 07-08; Herts County 08-25; Spartan 25-55;Delphian 55-63; Athenian 63-75

RECORDS Attendance: 3,800 v Hendon Amt Cup 56-57

BEST SEASON: FA Cup: First Round Proper 68-69 (lost 6-1 to Luton Town)

Founded: 1892   Nickname: Blues
Sponsors: Charvill Bros Ltd
Colours: Blue & white stripes/blue/red
Change colours: Amber/black
Midweek Matchday: Tuesday
Reserves' Lge:
Essex & Herts Border Comb
Programme: 24 pages, 50p
Editor/Press Officer: Tony Raisborough
(01707 656568)
Local Press: Herts Mercury, Herts Star, Herald & Post

CLUB PERSONNEL

Chairman: W J Luck
Manager: Dave Edwards
Coach: Dermot Drummy
Physio: Frank Roberts

WINGATE & FINCHLEY

FACT FILE

Secretary: Richard Cooper, c/o Club Tel: 0208 446 2217 Fax 0208 343 8194

GROUND: The Abrahams Stadium, Summers Lane, Finchley, London N12 0PD 0208 446 2217

Directions: North Circular (A406) to jct with High Road Finchley (A1000), go north and Summers Lane is 200 yds on rt - parking 80 cars.

Tube to East Finchley (Northern Line) and then 263 bus to Summers Lane towards North Finchley

Capacity: 8,500   **Seats:** 500   **Cover:** 500   **Floodlights:** Yes

Clubhouse: Open during matches. Also tea-bar selling most refreshments   **Club Shop:** No

HONOURS: Isthmian League Div. 3 R-up 98-99, London Senior Cup Winners 94-95

CLUB RECORDS: **Attendance:** 9,555 - Finchley v Bishop Auckland, F.A. Amat Cup QF 49-50
Career Goalscorer: Marc Morris 578
Career Appearances: Marc Morris 587(1975-93)
Win: 9-0, Wingate v Sarratt, Herts Co. Lge Div. 1, 20/4/85
Defeat: 0-9 v Edgware,Ryman League Division Two. 15.0.2000

BEST SEASON **FA Vase:** 74-75 Quarter Final (Wingate)
FA Amateur Cup: Semi-Final (Finchley)

PREVIOUS: **Names:** Wingate (founded 46), Finchley (founded late 1800s) merged in 91
Leagues: (as Wingate & Finchley) South Mids 89-95

Founded: 1991
Nickname: Blues
Colours: Blue/white/blue
Change Colours: All yellow
Midweek matches: Tuesday
Reserve's Lge: Sub Lge U18
Programme: 32pages, £1.00
Editor: Peter Rebak (0181 371 6001)

CLUB PERSONNEL

Chairman: StevenAstaire
Vice Chairman: Peter Rebak
President: Kenneth Aston
Press Off.: Harvey Ackerrman
(Tel No: 0208 349 0160)
Manager: Martin Burt
Player/Coach: Clive Wilson
Coach: Physio: Jim Connolly

WITHAM TOWN

FACT FILE

Secretary: Jim Claydon, 58 Silver Street, Silver End, Witham, Essex CM8 3QG
Tel: 01376 584086 H, 01376 583241 x 426 B

Ground: Spa Road, Witham, Essex CM8 1UN
Tel: 01376 511198 (lounge) 500146 (reception) 520996 (boardroom)

Directions: From Witham BR (network S.E.) station; through pub car park and follow road to Faulkbourne, at main r'bout turn left and ground is on the right.
By road: Off A12 at Witham sign, left at 1st lights (Spinks Lane), right at end of road, follow road under railway bridge - ground 100yds on left

Capacity: 2,500   Seats: 150   Cover: 300   Floodlights: Yes

Clubhouse: Open every night and weekend lunctimes.Hot bar snacks. **Club Shop:** No

HONOURS: Essex Snr Lg 70-71 85-86 (R-up 84-85 86-87), Tphy 85-86 (R-up 88-89); Essex Thameside Trophy R-up 95-96; Loctite Tphy SF 90-91

PREVIOUS: Leagues: Mid Essex; Essex & Suffolk Border; Essex Senior 71-87
CLUB RECORDS Attendance: 800 v Billericay Town, Essex Senior League, May 1976
Win: 7-0 v Banstead 27/9/94   **Defeat:** 0-9 v Collier Row 21/10/95
Goalscorer: Colin Mitchell   **Appearances:** Keith Dent (16 years)
Fee received: for Steve Tilson (Southend)

BEST SEASON: **FA Vase:** 5th Round, 85-86
FA Cup: 2nd Qual. Rd 87-88 (v Gravesend), 88-89 (v B. Stortford), 89-90 (v Dartford)

FACT FILE
Founded: 1947
Nickname: Town
Colours: Red & black stripes/white/white
Change colour: Blue & white
Midweek Matchday: Tuesday
Reserve's League:
Essex & Herts Border Comb
Programme: 24 pages, 60p
Editor: Nigel Dudley

CLUB PERSONNEL
Chairman: Reg Wright
Vice Chairman:
President: B Olley
Press Officer: G Vale (01376 513861)
Manager: George Young
Asst Mgr: Pat Garrett
Physio: John Barwick

COMBINED COUNTIES LEAGUE

President: Ron Monkley   **Chairman:** John Bennett   020 8568 9047
Secretary: Clive Tidey, 22 Silo Road, Farncombe, Godalming, Surrey GU7 3PA
Tel: 01483 428453 Fax: 01483 426117

As the season edged towards its climax, the pursuit of the Combined Counties League championship became a two horse race between Ashford Town (Middlesex), and holders Ash United. Both clubs were virtually unstoppable during the final run-in but in the end it was Ashford who just managed to come out on top and thus clinched their fifth championship in six seasons, a record that will be hard to beat.

With Ashford Chairman, Bob Parker, pulling out all the stops to ensure the ground was acceptable to the Ryman League inspectors, promotion was duly achieved and the club will take their place in Division Three of the Ryman League for season 2000-01 and the best wishes of the Combined Counties League go with them.

Earlier in the season, Ashford's local rivals, Bedfont, looked as if they would be serious challengers as well but they slipped towards the end, as indeed did AFC Wallingford and Chipstead, both in contention at Christmas. A feature of the season was the change around in fortunes of both Walton Casuals and Cove, previously perennial strugglers, but both now forces to be reckoned with.

At the wrong end of the table, it was Cranleigh who finished with the wooden spoon but, with an influx of youth due for next season, the club seem to be on a firmer footing and will hopefully improve their situation. Newcomers Chessington United also found the going tough at times but a year's experience of senior football should stand them in good stead.

The Premier Challenge Cup was notable for a number of shock results, resulting in most of the top teams making an early exit. In the end it was Walton Casuals who won an entertaining final at Farnborough Town FC, beating Viking Greenford by four goals to two, all six goals coming in the second period.

In national competitions, Bedfont and Farnham Town made the Second Qualifying Round of the FA Cup, before going out to Burgess Hill (after a replay) and Herne Bay respectively. Farnham's eventual departure was something of a sore point, with Herne Bay allowed to remain in the competition after being permitted to put four substitutes on the field in one of the matches.

In the FA Carlsberg Vase, Bedfont were the last Combined Counties team to leave the competition after making the long trip to Porthleven in Cornwall, losing by the only goal of the game in the Third Round. To get to that point Bedfont had seen off the challenges of Wantage Town, Southwick and Hythe.

In County competitions there was greater success, with Ashford winning the coveted Middlesex Charity Cup at Northwood FC, a goal by Tony Nolan, his 43rd of the season, being good enough to beat Hanwell Town from the Spartan South Midlands League.

Bedfont, who had reached the Final in the previous year, went one better as they really comprehensively won the prestigious London Senior Cup, beating Kent League Erith Town by five goals to one in this year's final at Wingate & Finchley.

In the meantime, Hartley Wintney did superbly well to reach the semi-finals of the Hampshire Senior Cup, beating Farnborough Town on the way before going out to Andover.

The sportsmanship trophy for the season went to Feltham FC, whilst the Programme of the Season award went to Farnham Town.

With the League losing one of its main feeder leagues when the Chiltonian League was allowed to cross the pyramid, it was determined that the League should endeavour to form a further division and this will be one of the main objectives in the forthcoming future.

The constitution for season 2000-01 sees Southall, relegated from the Ryman League, coming in to take Ashford's place whilst the addition of Withdean 2000, if approved by the Management Committee at a special meeting, will allow for 22 clubs.

The League was sorry to lose the sponsorship of Courage Thames Valley at the end of the season after three years successful partnership and hopes to be able to announce fresh sponsors shortly.

A Constable

FINAL LEAGUE TABLES 1999-2000

PREMIER DIVISION

	P	W	D	L	F	A	Pts
Ashford Town (Mx)^	40	31	6	3	123	37	102
Ash United	40	31	6	3	132	50	99
Bedfont	40	23	8	9	100	55	77
Chipstead	40	21	10	9	88	49	73
Walton Casuals^	40	20	10	10	80	64	73
AFC Wallingford	40	20	11	9	77	50	71
Godalming & G'ford	40	18	7	15	89	69	61
Cove	40	17	9	14	68	61	60
Westfield	40	15	13	12	60	47	58
Farnham Town	40	15	10	15	51	60	55
Cobham	40	15	8	17	74	65	53
Reading Town	40	14	10	16	64	74	52
Merstham	40	14	10	16	76	95	52
Chessington & Hook	40	11	13	16	57	66	46
Feltham	40	13	4	23	54	83	43
Raynes Park Vale	40	13	4	23	59	90	43
Sandhurst Town	40	9	9	22	70	96	36
Viking Greenford*	40	11	6	23	55	104	36
Chessington United*	40	9	9	22	45	92	33
Hartley Wintney	40	7	10	23	59	95	31
Cranleigh	40	4	5	31	35	114	17

DIVISION ONE

	P	W	D	L	F	A	Pts
Bedfont	34	25	4	5	112	30	79
Ash United	34	23	6	5	119	46	75
Cobham	34	23	6	5	87	44	75
Ashford Town (MX)	34	21	4	9	81	31	67
Chessington United	34	17	9	8	88	58	60
Walton Casuals	34	14	9	11	74	57	51
Farnham Town^	34	14	7	13	75	62	51
Raynes Park Vale	34	15	3	16	55	60	48
Westfield	34	13	7	14	74	70	46
Sandhurst Town	34	13	6	15	82	85	45
Merstham	34	14	3	17	80	90	45
Godalming & G'ford	34	13	4	17	63	69	43
Chessington & Hook	34	12	6	16	67	61	42
Reading Town	34	11	8	15	53	88	41
Viking Greenford	34	10	4	20	40	108	34
Cove	34	9	6	19	59	78	33
AFC Wallingford*	34	8	6	20	69	108	29
Cranleigh	34	0	4	30	18	151	4

^ points awarded
* points deducted

PREMIER DIVISION RESULTS CHART 1999-2000

		1	2	3	4	5	6	7	8	9	10	11	12	13	14	15	16	17	18	19	20	21
1	AFC Wallingford	X	0-4	1-2	3-1	2-1	1-3	1-4	1-1	2-0	6-0	4-0	4-1	2-2	2-1	2-3	2-0	2-0	2-1	2-1	1-1	0-3
2	Ashford	3-1	X	1-1	3-1	2-2	1-2	2-1	2-1	3-3	4-0	1-0	4-0	3-2	5-2	7-2	6-0	3-1	6-0	7-0	3-0	3-1
3	Ash United	1-1	1-2	X	8-0	4-2	6-1	3-2	4-2	2-1	5-1	2-2	2-1	1-2	5-2	2-2	4-0	7-1	4-1	1-0	4-2	2-1
4	Bedfont	2-1	2-2	3-5	X	1-1	1-2	1-1	1-1	3-0	7-0	3-0	0-3	3-1	3-1	4-2	5-1	3-0	3-0	4-0	2-0	2-0
5	Chess. & Hook	0-2	2-2	3-2	1-0	X	1-2	1-1	2-2	0-2	4-0	2-0	2-0	2-4	0-0	1-1	0-1	2-2	3-1	4-2	0-1	0-0
6	Chessington U	1-7	0-3	1-6	1-5	0-3	X	0-3	0-2	0-1	1-2	1-1	1-1	2-1	0-0	3-4	1-3	1-2	1-1	4-3	3-3	1-1
7	Chipstead	1-2	1-2	0-3	1-1	4-1	3-0	X	0-0	4-0	1-3	3-1	3-0	4-1	3-1	2-2	3-1	2-0	6-1	1-2	3-2	1-5
8	Cobham	2-2	2-2	0-4	2-3	1-3	3-0	0-1	X	3-2	3-0	0-1	1-2	2-1	5-3	1-2	2-0	0-1	2-0	2-4	1-1	0-2
9	Cove	2-2	0-0	1-4	1-3	3-2	1-2	0-3	0-0	X	3-1	3-0	3-0	6-2	1-3	2-2	2-0	4-1	2-2	2-0	2-2	0-3
10	Cranleigh	0-2	0-4	1-3	1-2	2-2	0-1	1-4	1-6	2-3	X	1-2	1-2	1-3	1-2	0-1	3-1	1-3	4-3	0-1	0-4	0-0
11	Farnham T	1-3	0-0	2-2	3-1	1-1	1-0	1-3	3-1	1-2	1-1	X	1-2	0-1	1-0	0-2	3-1	3-1	1-0	3-1	2-2	0-2
12	Feltham	1-3	0-2	0-2	0-6	5-1	2-2	1-2	6-3	0-2	2-1	0-2	X	0-6	3-1	0-4	3-0	2-0	2-1	8-1	0-1	1-1
13	Godalming & G	2-1	1-3	1-3	2-2	1-1	2-1	3-1	0-3	1-2	4-1	1-0	4-0	X	2-2	7-1	3-0	6-2	0-1	4-2	2-1	1-1
14	Hartley W	1-2	0-2	2-5	1-2	0-0	1-1	1-1	2-2	0-3	2-2	0-3	1-2	3-4	X	2-3	1-4	2-0	4-6	4-2	0-6	1-2
15	Merstham	0-0	1-4	1-2	0-8	2-0	4-2	0-4	1-4	0-3	2-0	2-2	2-0	0-0	4-2	X	3-5	1-4	1-1	5-0	3-4	2-2
16	RP Vale	1-1	1-2	0-3	0-3	2-3	3-4	0-0	1-4	1-1	1-0	5-0	4-3	2-1	2-3	2-1	X	2-1	1-1	6-1	0-1	1-0
17	Reading Town	1-1	1-3	0-0	3-1	1-2	3-0	0-2	2-1	2-2	2-1	1-1	1-0	1-1	3-3	6-1	X	2-0	2-1	3-3	0-1	0-1
18	Sandhurst Tn	1-3	2-5	3-5	1-2	3-1	5-0	1-2	san	1-1	9-1	2-2	1-2	1-4	0-4	1-3	5-2	2-2	X	3-2	3-3	3-1
19	Viking Sports	1-1	1-4	1-8	2-2	3-1	1-0	1-1	3-2	2-1	2-0	2-4	1-0	1-4	0-1	4-2	1-3	0-3	1-1	X	0-1	0-1
20	Walton Cas	0-2	3-2	0-2	1-1	2-1	3-0	2-2	0-4	1-0	2-0	2-0	3-0	3-1	2-2	3-2	3-1	4-2	2-1	1-3	X	1-4
21	Westfield	0-0	0-4	0-2	1-3	0-1	0-0	2-2	1-4	1-2	4-0	0-0	3-0	2-2	3-0	2-0	1-0	2-2	4-1	1-1	2-4	X

LEADING GOALSCORERS 1999-2000

PREMIER DIVISION

36	S Mitchell	Ash United
33	I Concannon	AFC Wallingford
33	T Nolan	Ashford Town (Mx)
28	S Christophe	Feltham
27	J Horton	Ash United
27	A Wood	Sandhurst Town
25	S Robinson	Cobham
23	S Willies	Cove
23	S Gorman	Godalming & Guildford

DIVISION ONE

33	S Joyce	Ash United
24	G Ellis	Sandhurst Town
21	B Campbell	Walton Casuals
20	K Annetts	Farnham Town
19	C Haddington	Chessington United
19	D Martin	Chessington United
18	A Clark	Farnham Town
18	R Watson	Bedfont
17	K Ossei	Ashford Town (Mx)

PREMIER CHALLENGE CUP 1999-2000

FIRST ROUND

Ashford Town (Mx)	v merstham	3-1	
Cranleigh	v Cobham	3*1	
Walton Casuals	v Cove	3-2	

Chipstead	v Bedfont	1-4
Hartley Wintney	v Feltham	1*3

SECOND ROUND

AFC Wallingford	v Farnham Town	1-2	Ash United	v Bedfont	1-3
Cranleigh	v Chessington Utd	2*2, 3*4	Raynes Park Vale	v Feltham	2-0
Reading Town	v Chess. & Hook	2*2, 0-3	Sandhurst Town	v Ashford Town (Mx)	1-0
Viking Greenford	v Westfield	2-0	Walton Casuals	v Godalming & G'ford	2-0

THIRD ROUND

Bedfont	v Farnham Town	1*3	Chessington Utd	v Walton Casuals	0-3
Raynes Park Vale	v Sandhurst Town	1-5	Viking Greenford	v Chess. & Hook	4-4, 1-2

SEMI-FINALS

Farnham Town	v Viking Greenford	1-5	Walton Casuals	v Sandhurst Town	3-1

FINAL

Walton Casuals	v Viking Greenford	4-2	at Farnborough Town FC

DIVISION ONE CHALLENGE CUP 1999-2000

FIRST ROUND

Ash United	v Ashford Town (Mx)	5-2^	Chessington Utd	v Reading Town	3-1

^ awarded to Ashford Town

SECOND ROUND

Bedfont	v AFC Wallingford	6*2	Cobham	v Sandhurst Town	3*2
Cove	v Walton Casuals	2-4	Cranleigh	v Farnham Town	0-4
Godalming & G'ford	v Chessington Utd	0-4	Raynes Park Vale	v Merstham	2-3
Viking Greenford	v Chessington & Hook	4-3	Westfield	v Ashford Town (Mx)	3-2^

^awarded to Ashford Town

THIRD ROUND

Chessington Utd	v Bedfont	3-5	Cobham	v Viking Greenford	4-0
Merstham	v Ashford Town (Mx)	0-3	Walton Casuals	v Farnham Town	2-0

SEMI-FINALS

Ashford Town (Mx)	v Cobham	2-1	Bedfont	v Walton Casuals	1-0

FINAL

Bedfont	v Ashford Town (Mx)	6-1	at Farnborough Town FC

FAIR PLAY TABLE 1999-2000

PREMIER DIVISION	Points		DIVISION ONE	Points
Feltham	38		Ash United	24
Westfield	40		Chessington & Hook	24
Sandhurst Town	43		Westfield	25
Godlaming & Guildford	43		Godalming & Guildford	28
Raynes Park Vale	47		Reading Town	29
Reading Town	48		Ashford Town	31
Bedfont	51		Cranleigh	31
Chipstead	52		Walton Casuals	32
Farnham Town	55		Merstham	35
Ash United	56		Raynes Park Vale	35

AFC WALLINGFORD

Secretary: Eddie Gniadek, 17 Offas Close, Benson, Wallingford, Oxon OX10 6NR
Tel: 01491 838540 (H) 01491 838308 (B)

Ground: Wallingford Sports Park, Hithercroft Road, Wallingford, Oxon. Tel: 01491 835044
Directions:
Nearest Railway station: Cholsey & Moulsford. Bus - Thames Transit.
Capacity: 1,500 **Cover:** 100 **Seats:** 40 **Floodlights:** Yes
Clubhouse: Open evenings 7.30-11.00, Sat & Sun Tea & snacks available 01491 835044
Club Shop: Yes

HONOURS: Chiltonian Prem Lge 97-98; Bon Accord Trophy 95-96

RECORDS: **Attendance:** 280 v Reading Town 98-99
Goalscorere: Carl Henry 68 97-98 **Appearances:** Anthony Hill 240

PREVIOUS: **Leagues:** Chiltonian Lge 95-98

FACT FILE
Founded: 1995
Colours: Red & black hoops/black/red & black
Change colours: Blue & white
Midweek matchday: Tuesday
Programme: 20 pages; price 50p
Editor: Andy Ham (01491 837608)

CLUB PERSONNEL
President: K Lester
Chairman: E L Townsend
Tel: 01491 839103 (H)
Match Secretary: G Lee
21 Orchard Close, Brightwell, Wallingford,
Oxon. Tel: 01491 836921 (H)
Manager: Dave Crowdy Coach: Gary Elkins

ASH UNITED

Secretary: Alex Smith-Gander, 41 Ash Street,Ash,Surrey
Tel: 01252 345221 (H & Fax) Email: alex@smith-gander.freeserve.co.uk

Ground: Youngs Drive, off Shawfield Rd, Ash, Nr Aldershot Tel: 01252 320385
Directions: A323 towards Ash, left into Shawfield Rd, left into Youngs Drive
1 mile from both Ash and Ash Vale BR stations. Bus - Stagecoach 20A, 550
Capacity: 1,500 **Seats:** None **Cover:** Yes **Floodlights:** Yes

HONOURS: Prem Chall Cup 97-98; Comb Co Lge 98-99; Aldershot Sen Cup 98-99
CLUB RECORDS **Attendance;** 650 v Tiverton Town FA Vase
Goalscorer: Scott Joyce 40 **Appearances:** Tommy Burton 540
BEST SEASON **FA Cup:** 2nd Qual Rd v Walton & Hersham 98-99
FA Vase: 4th Rd v Tiverton Town 98-99
PREVIOUS **Ground:** Ash Common Rec. 70-71 **Leagues:** Surrey Snr, Aldershot Snr

FACT FILE
Founded: 1911
Colours: Red & green/green/green
Change colours: All blue
Midweek Matchday: Tuesday
Admission: £2
Programme: 36 pages, 50p
Editor: Garth Watmore

CLUB PERSONNEL
President; Mr E Britzman
Chairman: Robert J Atkins
Vice Chairman: Cliff Foster
General Manager: Alex Smith-Gander
Manager: Jamie Horton
Asst. Manager: Angelo Barbato

BEDFONT

Secretary: Leslie King, 16 Sidney Road, St Margarets, Twickenham, Middlesex. TW1 1JR
Tel No: 0181 891 1985
Ground: The Orchard, Hatton Rd, Bedfont, Middx. Tel: 0208 8907264
Directions: Turn down Faggs Rd opposite Hatton Cross (Picadilly Line) station on Great
South Western Rd (A30), then sharp right into Hatton Rd. Ground opposite
Duke of Wellington pub. Bus - Westlink 203
Capacity: 2,000 **Seats:** 100 **Cover:** 50Floodlights: Yes Clubhouse: Yes

HONOURS Comb. Co's Chal. Vase 92-93 (Res. Div R-up 88-89, Res. Cup R-up 89-90,
Grant McClennan Yth Cup 91-92), Middx Lg 73-74 76-77 (Div 1 (Res) & Div 1 Cup 71-72 78-79
79-80, Surrey Prem. Lg 84-85 86-87, Middx l'mediate Cup 69-70 76-77, Inter. Contois Tour. 1992,
Liege Euromann Tour. 89, Harold Clayton Cup 90-91, Hounslow & Dist. Div 1 (Res) 86-87

PREVIOUS Names: Bedfont Inst.(1900), Bedfont Rangers(1950) & Fairholme Utd(1953) merged
1968. Club later merged with Interharvester(1973) & Bedfont Eagles(1988). **Ground:** Bedfont Rec.

FACT FILE
Founded: 1968
Colours: Yellow & blue stripes/blue/blue
Change colours: All red or White/navy/navy
Midweek matches: Tuesday
Programme: 20 pages, 50p. Editors: Les King
(020 8891 1985)

CLUB PERSONNEL
President: Roger Cooper
Chairman: John Dollimore
Vice Chairman: Mick Carroll
Manager: John Morris
Coach: Ron Griffin
Asst. Man.: Mark Wilson

CHESSINGTON & HOOK UNITED

Secretary: Alan Warwick, 38 Hartfield Road, Chessington, Surrey. KT9 2PW
Tel:020 8397 1843(H)
Ground: Chalky Lane, Chessington, Surrey. Tel: 01372 729892

Directions: Turn off A243 into Chalky Lane opposite Chessington World of Adventure
Theme Park Railway - Chessington South. Bus - London Transport 71.
Capacity: **Seats:** **Cover:** **Floodlights:** Yes

HONOURS: Combined Counties Lge Prem Cup R-up 97-98, Surrey County Lge Prem Div
R-up 96-97, Div 1 70-71,

PREVIOUS **Leagues:** Middx Lge 68-69, Surrey County 69-72, Home Counties 72-78
Comb Co 78-81, Surrey Prem, Surrey Comb, Surrey Prem.

FACT FILE
Founded: 1968
Colours: All blue
Change colours: Yellow/black/yellow
Midweek Matchday:
Programme: Yes

CLUB PERSONNEL
Chairman: Graham Ellis
63 Stormont Way, Chessington,
Surrey. KT9 2QW
Tel: 020 8391 4829(H)
Manager: Paul Ellis 020 8397 8499 (H)

CHESSINGTON UNITED

Secretary: Michael Smith, 34 Sopwith Avenue, Chessington, Surrey KT9 1QE
Tel: 020 8255 8847 (H) 0797 9606125 (M)

Ground: Fetcham Park Utd., Riverlane, Leatherhead, Surrey. Tel: 01737 363995
Nearest Railway Station: Leatherhead
Buses: London Country 465 & 479

FACT FILE
Colours: All Green
CLUB PERSONNEL
President: J F Curran
Chairman: Richard Jaramillo
19 Purbeck Close, Merstham, Redhill
Surrey RH1 1PG
Tel: 01737 644588

CHIPSTEAD

Secretary: Geoff Corner, 20 Sunnymede Avenue, Carshalton Beeches, Surrey SM54JF
Tel: 0181 642 0827 (H)

Ground: High Road, Chipstead, Surrey. Tel: 01737 553250
Directions: Brighton Road northbound, left into Church Lane, left into HogcrossLane, right into High Road. 1 1/2/ miles from Chipstead (BR). Bus -London County 405, 407
Capacity: 2,000   Seats: 30   Cover: 100   Floodlights: Yes

HONOURS Surrey Premier Lg R-up 82-83 83-84 85-86 (Lg Cup 82-83 84-85 85-86),
Combined Co's Lg 89-90 (R-up 90-91 92-93, Lg Cup 86-87 90-91 92-93, Elite Class Cup R-up 89-90, Reserve Section Cup 92-93)
BEST SEASON **FA Cup:** 1998-99   **FA Vase:** 1998-99
CLUB RECORDS Attendance: 903
Goalscorer: Appearances:
PREVIOUS **Leagues:** Surrey Intermediate 62-82; Surrey Premier 82-86

FACT FILE
Founded: 1906
Nickname: Chips
Colours: Green & white/black/black
Change colours: Purple/yellow/yellow
Midweek matchday: Tuesday
Programme: 44 pages

CLUB PERSONNEL
President: Clive Wood
Chairman:D.Faircloth, 156 St Andrews Road,
Coulsdon,Surrey CR5 3HF(0208 668 8348)
Manager: S Bangs
Coach:M.Ford

Top: Bedfont FC. The last Combined Counties club to be knocked out of the FA Carlsberg Vase last season.

Centre: Hartley Wintney FC. Back Row (l-r): Paul Cenci, Michael Collins, Paul Gallager, Kevin Valance, Nigel Taylor, Warren Hopkins, Jon Flannagan, James Taplin, Michael Bradley (Chairman). Front Row: Bob Lucas (Asst Manager), Ian McCoubrie (Manager), Paul Duncan, Brian Cenci, Richard McCoubrie, Erol McCauchlin, Mark Stimpson, Roger Campion (Captain). Photo: Eric Marsh

Bottom: Reading Town. Back Row (l-r): Simon Monaghan, Gary Clifford, Alan Campbell (Asst Manager), James Murray, Damien Massarella, Danny Campbell, Paul Bolger, Duncan Geraldes, Alex Kington, Paul Barham. Front Row: James McKinney, Bradley Ward, Ryan Willmott, Bobby Wilkinson, Steve Dale, Craig Rutherford, Paul Evans (Manager). Photo: Roger Turner

COBHAM

Secretary: Ken Reed, 29 Waterer Gardens, Tadworth, Surrey. KT20 5PB
Tel: 01737352641 (H) Fax: 01737 352259
Ground: Leg O'Mutton Field, Anvil Lane, Downside Bridge Rd, Cobham, Surrey
Tel: 01932 865959
Directions: A3 turnoff A245, A307 (Portsmouth) towards Leatherhead, right intoBetween Streets, rt into Downside Rd then rt opposite car park. Cobham & StokeD'Abernon (BR) 2 miles. Bus - Green Line 715, London Country 501, 513

Capacity: 2,000   Seats: None   Cover: Yes   Floodlights: Yes   Club Shop: No
Clubhouse: Yes

HONOURS   Combined Co's Lge Cup, Res Lge (3)

BEST SEASON   **FA Cup:**   **FA Vase:** 1998-99 3rd Rd.

CLUB RECORDS   **Attendance:** 2,000 v Showbiz XI, charity game 1975

PREVIOUS   **League:** Surrey Senior   **Grounds:** Cobham Rec

FACT FILE
Founded: 1892
Nickname: Hammers
Sponsor: PeterHaworth Consultancy
Colours: Red & navy/navy/navy
Change colours:Black & White stripes
Midweek matchday: Tuesday
Programme: Yes

CLUB PERSONNEL
Chairman: Peter Haworth
President: E D Strange
Manager: Gary Block
Coach: Tony Wilson
Physio: C Bird

COVE

Secretary: Graham Brown, 6 Longfield Close,Haley Estate, Farnborough. GU14 8HQ
Tel: 01252 650920
Ground: 7 Squirrels Lane, Farnborough, Hants GU14 8PB. Tel.: 01252 543615
Directions: Farnborough (BR) 2 miles; right into Union Street, right at lights into Prospect Rd, left into West Heath Rd, right into Romayne Close and follow signs to Cove FC. Or, M3 jct 4, follow A325 signed Aldershot & Farnham, right into Prospect Rd. (signed Cove FC & Farnborough Town FC), then as above
Capacity: 3,500   Seats: 75   Cover: 475   Floodlights: Yes   Club Shop: No
Clubhouse: Mon-Fri 7-11, Sat 12-11, Sunday 12-3 & 7-11. Hot food on matchdays
HONOURS   Surrey I'mediate Lg; Surrey Prem. Lg x5, R-up x3, Lg Cup x3, Res.Section x4, R-up x4, Res. Cup x2; Combined Co's Lg Cup 81-82; Hants Lg Div 3,Div 4, Div 2 R-up; Aldershot - Snr Cup x5, R-up, Snr Shield x4, Snr Lg, Div 2x3, Div 2 Cup, Div 4 Cup
PREVIOUS   **Leagues:** AldershotJnr; Aldershot I'mediate 45-48; Surrey I'mediate 48-71; Surrey Snr 71-73; Hants 74-81; Combined Counties 81-90; Isthmian 90-95; Comb. Cos. 95-
CLUB RECORDS   Attendance: 1,798 v Aldershot, Isthmian Lg Div 3, 1/5/93
BEST SEASON   FA Cup: 1st Qual. Rd replay 91-92, 0-4 v Burgess Hill Town (A)

FACT FILE
Founded: 1897
Sponsors: Sunnyside Removals
Colours: Yellow & black stripes/black/yellow
Change colours: Red & white stripes/red/red
Midweek Matches: Tuesday
Reserves' League: Comb. Cos. 1st Div
Programme: 30 pages, 50p
Editor: Graham Brown (01252 650920)

CLUB PERSONNEL
Chairman: T.Bannister,'Kelvinside',Ridgway, Camberley,Surrey (01276 507132)
,President: Ron Brown
Manager:
Asst. Manager:

CRANLEIGH

Secretary: Steve Dawe,2 Seltops Close,Cranleigh, Surrey GU6 7JW (01483 427100)
Match Secretary: Alan Pavia Tel: 01483 271233 (H) 01483 894248 (B)
Ground: Snoxall Playing Fields, Knowle Lane, Cranleigh Tel: 01483 275295
Directions: A281 from Guildford towards Horsham, at Shalford take B2128 to Cranleigh High St., right opposite Onslow Arms into Knowle Lane, ground half mile on left. Public transport: Guildford (BR) then bus (Alder Valley) 273 or 283
Capacity: 450   Seats: None   Cover: 50Floodlights: No
Clubhouse: Licensed bar. Hot food on matchdays   Club Shop: No
HONOURS   W Sussex County Times Cup 92-93
BEST SEASON   FA Vase 3rd Rd 92-93   **FA Cup:**
CLUB RECORDS   Attendance: 450 v C Palace, friendly 1989
Competitive: 285 v Hailsham,FA Vase 3rd Rd 12/12/92
PREVIOUS   **League:** Surrey Intermediate

FACT FILE
Founded: 1893
Nickname: Cranes
Sponsors: Roger Coupe, Est. Agents
Colours: All Blue
Change colours: Yellow/green/yellow
Midweek matchday: Tuesday
Programme: £1.50
Editor: Peter Slater (01483 894245)
CLUB PERSONNEL
Chairman: Roy Kelsey (01483 427100)
President: Alan Pavia
Manager: Roy Kelsey
Asst Manager: Paul Jones
Coach: Andy Clements

FARNHAM TOWN

Secretary: Mrs Barbara Fripp, 70 Lower Farnham Rd., Aldershot. GU12 4EA   (01252 657184)

Ground: Memorial Ground, Babbs Mead, West Street, Farnham, Surrey   (01252 715305)

Directions: From A31, direction Winchester, take 2nd turning into town at Coxbridge roundabout. Follow West Street until you come to new mini roundabout - the Memorial Ground is on the right.

Capacity: 2,000   Seats: None   Cover: 150   Floodlights: Yes
Clubhouse: Open every evening and match daysClub Shop: No

HONOURS   Combined Counties Lg 90-91 91-92, Challenge Cup Prem Div 95-96, Challenge Tphy 91-92 (R-up 89-90).
CLUB RECORDS   Attendance: 500 v Kingstonian, Surrey Snr Cup 1960.
PREVIOUS   **Leagues:** Surrey Intermediate; Surrey Snr 47-71: Spartan 71-75: London Spartan 75-80: Combined Counties 80-92.
BEST SEASON   FA Cup: Never past Qualifying Rounds

FACT FILE
Founded: 1921   Nickname: The Town
Sponsors: Frazer Freight.
Colours: All claret & blue.
Change: White, pale blue & claret/claret/claret
Midweek Matchday: Tuesday
Reserve League: Comb Counties Res Div
Programme: 32 pages 50p
Editor: Ann Butters
CLUB PERSONNEL
Chairman: Steve Hopper(01252 794659)
President; Paul Cooper
Press Officer: Charlie White
Manager: Peter Browning
Asst Manager: Roy Atkin
Coach: A Wyciechowski/A Metcalfe

FELTHAM

Secretary: John Cronk,Flat 8 Wyvern Court, 24 Gordon Rd, Ashford, Middsx TW15 3EZ
Tel: 01784 243122 (H) 0208 839 2104 (B)
Ground: Feltham Arena(All weather surface), Shakespeare Ave., Feltham, Middx.Tel: 0208 890 6164 (club), 0208 890 6905 (ground)**Directions:** BR to Feltham & 5 mins walk thro' Glebelands Park. Buses 90, 285,117, 237, H24 or H25 to Feltham station, or 116 to top of Shakespeare Ave. By car: M3, M4, A312 Staines road towards Bedfont, 2nd left is Shakespeare Ave
Capacity: 10,000   Seats: 650   Cover: 1,500   Floodlights: Yes
Clubhouse: Open 7 days a week. 2 bars, dancehall available for hire Club Shop: No
HONOURS   Surrey Snr Lg R-up 65-66 (Lg Cup 65-66), Charity Cup 63-64 65-66),Southern Comb. Cup(2)(R-up(2)), Middx Summer Cup, Isthmian Div 2 80-81, Comb.Cos. Lge Co. 96-97
PREVIOUS   **Leagues:** Feltham: West Middx Sunday; Staines & Dist.; Hounslow & Dist.; Surrey Snr 63-68; Spartan 68-73; Athenian 74-77; Isthmian 78-95
CLUB RECORDS **Attendance:** 1,9 38 v Hampton,Middlesex Senior Cup 1968
Goalscorer: Paul Clarke 130**Appearances:** Paul Clarke 326
BEST SEASON   **FA Cup:** 3rd Qual.Rd.77-78, 1-4 v Tilbury; 82-83, 0-1 v Chesham U

FACT FILE
Founded: 1946
Colours: Royal blue & white halves/blue/blue
Change colours: Red /White or Blue/White
Midweek Matches: Wednesday
Programme: 20 pages, 50p
Editor: Richard Sevice
Sponsors: Feltham first
CLUB PERSONNEL
Chairman: Willi F P Seuke 0181296 9630 (H)
Press Off.: Richard Seuke
01932 - 761544(Tel) 761744 (Fax)
Managers: Sammy Boyd & Dave Patience
Players progressing:Rachid Harkouk,Tony Witter(CrystalP) Andy Pape (QPR), Pat Gavin (Gillingham) Bobby Wilson (Brentford)

GODALMING & GUILDFORD

Secretary: Eddie Russell, 31 Harts Gardens, Guildford, Surrey GU2 9QB. 01483 535287 (H & B)
Ground: Wey Court, Meadrow, Godalming, Surrey (01483 417520)
Directions: A3100 from Guildford - past Beefeater Hotel on left, then 'Save' petrol station on right, then 1st right 50 yards on. From Godalming on A3100, grd on left by Leather Bottle pub. Three quarters of a mile from Farncombe BR station
Capacity: 3,000   Seats: 200   Cover: 200   Floodlights: Yes   Club Shop: No
Clubhouse: Open Tues, Wed, Thurs eves, matchdays. Hot & cold snacks available
HONOURS   Combined Co's Lg 83-84, Lge Chall. Trophy 82-83, Res Lge 95-96 96-97, Res Chall Cup 92-93 97-98, Chall Shield 96-97: Southern Comb Chall Cup 97-98
PREVIOUS   **Leagues:** Guildford & Dist 50-71; Surrey Intermediate 71-78; Surrey Co. Senior 78-79
RECORDS   **Attendance:** 600+ ex-Guildford City XI v ex-Football Lg XI. Tony Burge benefit 91
Goalscorer: Sean Gorman 127 **Appearances:** Paul Monger 356
BEST SEASON FA Cup: 1st Q.Rd.   **FA Vase:** 2nd Rd.
Players progressing: John Humphreys (MIllwall)

FACT FILE
Founded: 1950
Nickname: The Gees
Colours: Green & yellow/green/green
Change colours: Red & blue/blue/blue
Midweek matchday: Tuesday
Programme: Yes

CLUB PERSONNEL
Chairman: Jane Phillips
President: W F Kyte
Press Officer: Secretary
Manager: Roger Steer
Asst Managers: Andy Deer & Phil George
Coach: Duncan Falconer

HARTLEY WINTNEY

Secretary: Mick Bradley, 8 Dairy Walk, High St., Hartley Wintney, Hampshire RG27 8XX Tel No: 01252 845745(H/Fax)
Ground: Memorial Playing Fields, Green Lane, Hartley Wintney, Hants Tel: 01252 843586
Directions: A30 west through Camberley, left at parade of shops at beginning of village then sharp right - ground on right. Two miles from Winchfield (BR) Buses: Stagecoach 200, Bee Line 111, 112
Capacity:4,000   Seats: None   Cover: No   Floodlights: Yes
HONOURS: Aldershot Senior League winners: 73-74,74-75,75-76. Alderhot Senior Cup Winners 76-77,80-81 CoCo.League Winners 82-83,R-up 80-81
BEST SEASON   **FA Cup:** Do not compete   **FA Vase:** Do not compete
PREVIOUS   **Leagues:** Basingstoke/ Aldershot

FACT FILE
Founded: 1897
Nickname: The Row
Colours: Orange/black/black
Change colours: All white or Red/black/black
Midweek matchday: Tuesday
Programme: Yes

CLUB PERSONNEL
Chairman: as Secretary
President: W A Mitchell
Treasurer: D.Willoughby

MERSTHAM

Secretary: Richard Baxter, 2 Wood Street, Merstham, Surrey. RH1 3PF
Tel: 01737 645748 (H) 01293 450890 (B) Email: the.baxters@virgin.net
Ground: Merstham Rec., Weldon Way, Merstham, Redhill, Surrey RH1 3QB (01737 644046)
Directions: Leave Merstham village (A23) by School Hill, take 5th right (WeldonWay), clubhouse and car park 100m on right. 10 mins walk from Merstham (BR);down School Hill, under railway bridge, then 5th turning on right into WeldonWay. Bu98-99s - London Country 430, 432 & 435
Capacity: 2,000   Seats: 100   Cover: 100   Floodlights: Yes   Club Shop: No
Clubhouse: Across adjacent footpath. Open daily (am & pm). Snacks available
HONOURS   Combined Co's Lg R-up 87-88 89-90 (Elite Class Cup 89-90 (R-up 90-91), Res. Sect. 90-91), Spartan Lg 79-89 (Lg Cup 79-80), Surrey Snr Lg 71-72, Surrey Snr Char. Cup 79-80, E. Surrey Char. Cup 80-8 98-99, Surrey I'mediate Lg 52-3
CLUB RECORDS Attendance: 532
BEST SEASON   FA Cup: 3rd Q Rd   **FA Vase:** 4th Rd.
PREVIOUS   **Leagues:** Redhill & Dist.; Surrey Co.S.E. I'mediate; Surrey Snr 64-78; London Spartan 78-85   **Grounds:**None

FACT FILE
Founded: 1892
Club Sponsors: Merstham Glass
Colours: Amber & black stripes/black/amber
Change colours: All red
Midweek matches: Tuesday/Thursday
Programme: Yes Editor:Andy Wheeler

CLUB PERSONNEL
Chairman: M.Morley
President: Bill Lawton
Press Officer: Roger Peerless
Manager:Alan Gallagher
Asst Manager: Graeme Crawford

RAYNES PARK VALE

FACT FILE

Secretary: Alan Salmon, 229 Sutton Common Road, Sutton, Surrey SM3 9PY
Tel Nos: 0208 644 4046 (H 7 F)01372 364006 (W)

Ground: Grand Drive, Raynes Park. SW20 9NB Tel: 07714 339747
Directions: Bus - London Transport 131 & 152
Nearest railway station - Raynes Park.

HONOURS: None

Colours:Claret & blue stripes/blue/red
Change colours: Green & white
hoops/green/white

CLUB PERSONNEL

President: Robert Hallett

Chairman: Dave Brenen
22 The Crescent, Belmont, Surrey. SM2 0BJ.
Tel: 0181 2968626

READING TOWN

FACT FILE

Secretary: Richard Grey, 6 Milestone View Court, Lowfield Road, Caversham Park,
Reading RG4 6ND   Tel: 0118 948 2006   Email: rgrey.cia@talk21.com
Ground: Reading Town Spts Ground, Scours Lane, Tilehurst, Reading, Berks (0118 945 3555)

Directions: Out of Reading on Oxford road (A329), past Battle Hosp. Scours Lane1st right after
r'bout. Nearest station - Tilehurst or Reading (General). Bus -Reading Bus 17

Capacity: 2,000   Seats: No   Cover: Yes   Floodlights: Yes   Clubhouse: Yes

PREVIOUS   Leagues: Chiltonian 89-95, Reading 66-89
Names: Lower Burghfield, XL United, Vincents Utd, Reading Garage, ITS Reading Town
CLUB RECORDS Attendance: 253 v Banstead Ath FA Vase 96-97
Defeat: 0-10 v Feltham(A) 96-97
Win: 7-0 v Cranleigh/Viking Spts/AFC Wallingford all Home 97-98
BEST SEASON   FA Cup: Prelim Rd 97-98   **FA Vase:** 4th Rd 96-97
HONOURS   Comb Counties Lge R-up 97-98; Chiltonian Lge Champions 94-95,
Berks &Bucks Sen. Trophy 95-96, R-up 96-97

Founded: 1968
Colours: Red & black stripes/black/black
Change colours: Navy/navy/red
Midweek Matchday: Tuesday
Programme: 20 pages 50p
Editor: Richard Grey
CLUB PERSONNEL
Chairman: Roland Ford, 103 Little Heath
Road, Tilehurst, Berkshire RG31 5TG
Tel: 0118 941 2270
Fixture Sec.: Mrs Pauline Semple, 278
Hemdean Rd., Caversham, Reading RG4 7QT
Tel: 0118 947 9394
Manager:T.B.A.

SANDHURST TOWN

FACT FILE

Secretary: Tony Ford, Pennings Cottage, Aldershot Road, Guildford, Surrey GU3 3AA
Tel Nos: 01483 567284 (H) 0378 628547 (M)
Ground: Bottom Meadow, Memorial Ground, Yorktown Rd, Sandhurst (01252 873767)

Directions: A30 westwards through Camberley, right at r-bout with traffic lights onto A321, past
superstore turning left the 3rd set of traffic lights onA321 towards Wokingham. Ground situated
near to Town & Council offices & Community Centre. Nearest station - Sandhurst. Bus - Bee Line
193, 194

Capacity: 2,000   Seats: None   Cover: Yes Floodlights: Yes   Clubhouse: open 6 days
PREVIOUS   Leagues: Reading & Dist.; Aldershot Snr 79-84; Chiltonian84-90
CLUB RECORDS Attendance: 353 v Aldershot Town (Friendly)
Win: 6-2 v Viking Sports   **Defeat:** 8-2 v Ashford Town (Middx)
Goalscorer: Glenn Price   **Appearances:** John Parker
BEST SEASON   FA Vase: 1st Rd 93-94   **FA Cup:** 1st Rd Qualifying
HONOURS   Combined Co's Lge Chal. Vase R-up 92-93 (Reserve Chal. Cup R-up 91-92),
Chiltonian Lg R-up 86-87, Aldershot Snr Lg R-up 83-84; Berks & Bucks Sen.Trophy R-up 92-93

Founded: 1910
Nickname: Fizzers
Colours: Red/black/black
Change colours: Blue & white hoops,blue,blue
Midweek matchday: Wednesday
Programme: Yes
Editor: Paul Varndell

CLUB PERSONNEL
Chairman:Phil Sigley (01276 37242)
President: Malcolm Watts
Match Sec.: as Secretary
Manager:Peter Hayward
Coach: Paul McKinnon

SOUTHALL

FACT FILE

Secretary: Andy Fitzsimons, PR Office, PO Box 110, Feltham, Middx. TW13 4YA
Tel: 0208 751 3107 (H & Fax)   Email: freespace@musicbase@virgin.net
Ground: Ground share with Chalfont St. Peter FC, The Playing Fields, Amersham Road, Chalfont
St Peter SL9 7BQ Tel: 01753 885797 **Directions:** A413 from Uxbridge (London) to Chalfont. Turn
left 100 yds after2nd major roundabout (between Ambulance station and Community Centre. 2
miles from Gerrards Cross (BR), regular buses from Slough & Uxbridge
Capacity: 4,500   Cover: 120   Seats: 220   Floodlights: Yes
PREVIOUS: Leagues: Southern 1896-1905; Gt Western Suburban; Herts & Middx;
Athenian 19-73, Ryman 73-00
BEST SEASON   FA Cup: 3rd Round 35-36, 1-4 v Watford (H)
FA Vase: Runners-up 85-86   **FA Amateur Cup:** Runners-up 24-25
HONOURS   FA Amtr Cup R-up 24-25, FA Vase R-up 85-86, Isthmian Lg Div 2 R-up 74-75,
Gt Western Suburban Lg 12-13, Athenian Lg 26-27 R-up 54-55,
Middx Snr Cup x12, Middx Charity Cup x9

Founded: 1871   Nickname: Fowlers
Colours: Red & white stripes/white/rwhite
Change: Yellow & black
Midweek Matchday: Wednesday
Res' Lge: Middx County
Programme: 6 pages, 50p
Editor: Steve Hawkins
99-00 - Captain: Nicholas Caiger
P.o.Y.: NicholasCaiger
Top Scorer: Andrew Moy
CLUB PERSONNEL
Chairman: B T Wadlow
Manager: Keith Chamberlin
Physio: Keith Chamberlin

VIKING GREENFORD

Secretary: Stephen Hosmer, 27 St Georges Rd., Hanworth, Middlesex. TW13 6RD
Tel. & Fax: 0208 894 1244 (M) 0831 393559
Ground: Avenue Park, Western Avenue, Greenford, Middx (020 8578 2706)

Directions: On London-bound carriageway of A40, 300 yds before Greenford flyover and slip road to A4127. 12 mins walk from Greenford (Central Line) station - turn right out of station to A40, turn right - grd 1/4 mile on rght

Capacity: 450   Seats: 50   Cover: 100   Floodlights: Yes   Club Shop: No
Clubhouse: Open every evening except Sunday. Hot & cold snacks on matchdays

HONOURS   Hellenic Lg Div 1 85-86 (Div 1 Cup R-up 90-91).Co.Counties Lg.(R-Up.94-95)
CLUB RECORDS Att: 180 v Wealdstone,Middx.SenCup,Sept.96 **Goalscorer:** Frank Healy, 43
PREVIOUS   Leagues: Middlesex 70-80; Hellenic 80-91
BEST SEASON   FA Cup: 1st Q Rd 96 F,A.Vase: 2nd Rd v Diss Town 1991
1999-00 Captain: Tom Hupe   **P.o.Y.:** Tom Hupe **Top Scorer:** Marc Smith

FACT FILE
Founded: 1945   Nickname: Vikings
Sponsors: Measham Self-Drive/ Greeene King
Colours: All tangerine, black trim
Change colours: Sky blue & maroon/sky/sky
Midweek matchday: Tuesday
Programme: 12 pages, 50p
Editor: John Bennett

CLUB PERSONNEL
Chairman: Terry Cross
President: Roy Bartlett
Press Officer: T.B.A.
Manager: Wayne Haley
Asst Man.:Steve Parsons
Physio: Ernie Stockwell

WALTON CASUALS

Secretary: Stuart Roberts, 47 Foxholes, Weybridge, Surrey. KT13 0BN. Tel: 01932845923

Ground: Franklyn Road Sports Ground, Waterside Drive, Walton-on-Thames, Surrey KT12 2JG
Tel: 01932 787749 (24hrs ansaphone).
Directions: Next to Elmbridge Leisure Centre, left off Terrace Rd at first roundabout out of Walton centre. Hersham (BR), then bus 564 to Elmbridge Leisure Centre.

Capacity: 1,500   Seats: None   Cover: 80Floodlights: Yes
Clubhouse: Matchdays only. Hot food available from Tea Bar   Club Shop: No

HONOURS   Suburban Lge (South) 82-83, (R-up 83-84); Surrey Prem Lge R-up 94-95,
S.P.L. Chall Cup 93-94, (R-up 94-95); Surrey Premier Cup R-up 86-87
BEST SEASON   FA Vase: 1Q 96-97(only Game)   **FA Cup:** Never entered
PREVIOUS   Leagues: Surrey Premier, Surrey Senior, Surrey Intermediate, Suburban.
CLUB RECORDS Attendance: 178 v Pagham FA Vase 96/97

FACT FILE
Founded: 1948
Nickname: The Stags
Sponsors: Tallents Bar
Colours: Tangerine/black/tangerine
Change colours: Red & black/white/red
Midweek Matchday: Tuesday
Programme: 36 pages 50p
Editor/Press Officer: Stuart Roberts

CLUB PERSONNEL
Chairman:Graham James (01932 227921)
General Manager: David Symonds
President: Grahan James
Managers: Mick Sullivan & Garry Clark

WESTFIELD

Secretary: Michael Lawrence, 19 Ash Road, Barnsbury Estate, Woking, Surrey. GU22 0BJ
Tel/Fax: 01483 722184 (H)

GROUND   Woking Park, Kingfield, Woking, Surrey Tel: 01483 771106

Directions: (Adjacent to Woking FC.)
M25 J10 or 11, signposted from outskirts of Town.Ground 1 mile.
Woking B.R.Station & buses from Woking
Capacity: 1,000   Seats: None   Cover: Yes   Floodlights: Yes
Clubhouse   Yes - open matchdays when snacks are available.
Club Shop   No

PREVIOUS   League: Surrey County Senior League

FACT FILE
Founded: 1953
Colours: All yellow
Change colours:Yellow/Black/Yellow
Midweek Matchday:Tuesday
Programme: No

CLUB PERSONNEL
President: R Hill
Chairman: S P Perkins
160 Coleford Bridge Road, Mytchett,
Camberley, Surrey
Tel: 01252 547900 (B)
Manager: John Cassidy
Asst. Managers:
Alan Morton & Brian Hennessy

WITHDEAN 2000

Secretary: Brian Davies, 119 Church Road, Hove BN3 2AF
Tel: 01272 272776 (H) 01273 764874 (B) Email: briand@bdinsurance.demon.co.uk
Ground: Withdean Stadium, Tongdean Lane, Brighton BN3 2AF
Tel: 01273 542100
Capacity: 10,000   Seats: 6,000   Cover: 1,000   Floodlights: No

Directions: Off main London - Brighton road
Clubhouse: Pub on ground   **Club Shop:** No

HONOURS   Sussex Co. Lg Div 3 92-93 (Div 3 Cup 91-92)

PREVIOUS   **Leagues:** Brighton Hove & District
Ground: Council pitch

FACT FILE
Founded: 1984
Colours: White with black trim/white/white
Programme Editor: Gary Arnold
Local Newspaper: Brighton Evening Argus

CLUB PERSONNEL
Chairman: Desmond Ralfe
President: Stan Hunt
Manager: Dave Cole

*Top: First half action from Bottom Meadow as Bedfont attack the Sandhurst goal.
Photo: Martin Wray*

*Centre: Chessington United. Back Row (l-r): David Joslyn (Manager), Arun Carl St Pier, Paul O'Sullivan, Richard Bryant, Chris West, Tommy Duffell, John McGettigan, Ricky Dymond. Front Row: Wesley Field, Darren Smith, Darren Barnes, David Sutton, Danny Heath.
Photo: Gordon Whittington*

*Bottom: The lights go on. Hartley Wintney v Ash United.
Photo: Eric Marsh*

SCHWEPPES
ESSEX SENIOR LEAGUE

President: Arthur Dimond   **Chairman & Publicity:** Robert Errington
Secretary: David Walls, 77 Thorpedene Gardens, Shoeburyness, Essex SS3 9JE
Tel: 07071 201639   Fax: 01702 294047   Email: EssexSenior@wallsd.freeserve.co.uk

Saffron Walden Town emerged as League and Cup double champions in the closest finish that the League has ever witnessed. The top three clubs all attaining the same points total but separated on goal difference. In fact, Southend Manor knew they had to reach double figures in their final match with Woodford Town but only managed seven. They were also beaten finalists in the Ancient Order of Foresters sponsored League Cup Final, held at one of the grand old grounds of Non-League football, the Hare & Hounds in Lea Bridge Road, now seeing a new lease of life as home of newcomers Leyton FC. The most disappointed club was Burnham Ramblers who, in the year that saw their most beloved member, Gordon Brasted, pass away, lost out on promotion to the Ryman League as the third placed side of the top three.

The season started with the addition of Bury Academy but, after eight League and League Cup games found the pace too hot to handle and resigned in October. The Charity Cup saw last season's double winners Bowers United add another trophy to their cabinet with a win over Saffron Walden Town then, although the end was close, both at home and away, in the League Brentwood and Leyton. After the League season was completed, they even went on to win the South Midlands Floodlight Cup, the first ESL side ever to do so and then, by default, the Eastern Floodlight Competition. Their priority is now to level their pitch and upgrade their most picturesque Catons Lane home to make themselves eligible for the Ryman League if they can repeat their success on the field.

The Harry Fisher Trophy went to Concord Rangers, after extra time at Barking FC, the losers being the most unfortunate Burnham Ramblers. One young man that thoroughly enjoyed his season was Ben Barnett of Southend Manor who, in winning the Don Douglas Trophy as leading goalscorer had a number of League clubs showing interest and is sound in the knowledge that the jump from the ESL to the Football League can be achieved with Stuart Wardley of Saffron Walden ending the season as leading scorer and Player of the Year at Queens Park Rangers.

Hullbridge Sports, a club not normally associated with national publicity received well-deserved plaudits when their Youth team went further than any previous ESL club in the FA Youth Cup and met Blackburn Rovers at their Lower Road home. Over 800 turned out on a crisp December evening to watch the club who were great ambassadors for the League. A club that joined us during the summer, Leyton, were yet another example of how the transition from Intermediate to Senior football can be made through the pyramid system. Their administration and hosting of the League Cup Final was first class and culminated in the Secretary of the Year Award going to Tony Hampford. Another ex-Intermediate side, Great Wakering Rovers, having been promoted last season to the Ryman League achieved another promotion to their Division Two at the first attempt, joining East Thurrock United, another ex-ESL club who won the Division under manager Lee Patterson. He guided Concord Rangers to similar honours in 1998. The promotion of Ford United from Division Two to One was another success for an "old boy" and the continuing success of Purfleet and Canvey Island in the Premier Division is even more to be cheerful about as an important feeder league. We now welcome Barkingside FC to the League and this brings the constitution back to 16 for the coming season.

Robert A Errington, Chairman

FINAL LEAGUE TABLE 1999-2000

	P	W	D	L	F	A	Pts		P	W	D	L	F	A	Pts
Saffron Walden Town	28	19	5	4	85	33	62	Leyton	28	9	5	14	45	55	32
Southend Manor	28	19	5	4	81	33	62	Hullbridge Sports	28	8	3	17	44	63	27
Burnham Ramblers	28	19	5	4	68	32	62	East Ham Utd	28	5	8	15	30	65	23
Ilford	28	18	4	6	70	34	58	Eton Manor*	28	6	8	14	41	61	22
Brentwood	28	17	2	9	49	40	53	Basildon Utd*	28	6	6	16	37	61	22
Bowers United	28	14	6	8	51	42	48	Woodford Town*	28	5	3	20	46	99	15
Sawbridgeworth T	28	11	10	7	65	48	43	Stansted	28	2	3	23	35	86	9
Concord Rangers	28	11	9	8	46	41	42	* points deducted							

LEADING GOALSCORERS 1999-2000

38	Ben Barnett	Southend Manor	24	Chris Stevens	Ilford
27	Marc Das	Saffron Walden Town	20	Kris Down	Burnham Ramblers
24	Damon Miles	Saffron Walden Town			

RESULTS CHART 1999-2000

		1	2	3	4	5	6	7	8	9	10	11	12	13	14	15
1	Basildon Utd	X	1-5	0-1	1-4	1-5	3-3	2-1	1-2	2-5	2-2	1-2	1-2	0-3	4-0	2-1
2	Bowers Utd	0-0	X	0-1	1-2	1-1	3-1	4-1	0-2	1-0	1-0	0-4	0-0	2-7	3-2	4-3
3	Brentwood	2-1	1-2	X	1-4	1-2	3-0	4-1	1-0	1-3	1-0	4-2	1-1	2-1	1-3	4-3
4	Burnham R	5-0	3-1	5-2	X	1-1	3-3	5-1	2-1	0-1	3-1	1-3	3-0	0-3	1-0	3-0
5	Concord R	2-1	1-1	2-0	1-1	X	1-1	1-1	1-2	1-4	3-0	1-1	0-2	2-3	3-0	3-0
6	East Ham U	0-0	0-2	0-2	0-2	0-0	X	0-2	2-3	0-0	2-2	0-3	0-0	0-3	1-0	2-4
7	Eton Manor	0-1	2-2	3-0	3-3	1-3	0-1	X	6-1	1-3	0-0	0-5	3-3	0-0	1-0	1-3
8	Hullbridge S	3-2	0-1	1-2	1-1	0-1	0-2	2-3	X	1-2	2-3	0-2	0-3	0-4	4-1	8-0
9	Ilford	1-1	1-2	3-0	0-2	3-0	4-1	3-2	2-2	X	5-1	1-2	3-0	3-0	3-1	6-1
10	Leyton	1-2	2-1	0-1	2-3	1-2	5-0	0-0	4-2	0-3	X	2-1	2-2	0-5	5-2	0-1
11	Saffron Walden	3-2	2-1	1-2	1-0	4-1	8-0	3-1	8-0	4-1	1-3	X	1-1	1-0	1-1	4-3
12	Sawbridgeworth	2-0	3-4	0-6	0-1	5-1	3-4	6-2	2-1	1-1	2-1	2-2	X	1-1	3-1	10-0
13	Southend M	3-2	1-1	1-1	2-4	3-2	3-1	2-0	4-0	4-0	5-1	3-3	4-3	X	2-0	1-0
14	Stansted	2-3	1-5	1-3	1-3	2-2	4-2	1-1	0-3	0-4	0-3	1-5	4-7	3-6	X	1-2
15	Woodford T	1-1	0-3	0-1	1-3	1-3	2-4	3-4	3-3	3-5	3-4	1-8	1-1	1-7	5-3	X

LEAGUE CHALLENGE CUP 1999-2000

FINAL

Saffron Walden Town   v   Southend Manor   2-1   at Leyton FC, attendance 235

HARRY FISHER MEMORIAL TROPHY 1998-99

FINAL

Burnham Ramblers   v   Concord Rangers   2-3   aet, at Barking FC, attendance 156

Concord Rangers celebrating their Harry Fisher Trophy win.   Photo: Robert Errington

876

BARKINGSIDE

Secretary: Phil O'Reilly, 102 Luxborough Lane, Chigwell, Essex IG7 5AA
Tel: 020 8559 0709 (H) 020 8504 9618 (B) 07946 317148 (M) Email:PR.O'Reilly@virgin.net
Ground: Oakside, Station Road, Barkingside, Ilford, Essex Tel: 020 8550 3611
Directions: From London A12 Eastern Ave to Green Gate, left into Hurns Rd to Barkingside, right into Craven Gardens, right Carlton Drive to Station Rd, under bridge and grd on right. Next to Barkingside station (Central Line). From Ilford station (BR) take 169 Bus to Craven Gardens
Capacity: 2,500 Seats: 140 Cover: 240 Floodlights: Yes Club Shop: No
Clubhouse: Saturdays 1pm-12. midweeek matchnights 6.30-11pm. Rolls, hotdogs,hamburgers
HONOURS: Spartan Lge. Prem. Div. 96-97, R-up 90-91 (Harry Sunderland Shld 83-84 (R-up 84-85); London Sen. Cup 96-97; S. Essex Lge R-up 46-47, L'don Lg R-up 49-50 (Lg Cup 55-56 (R-up 52-53 62-63)), Gtr L'don Lg 64-65,Spartan S.Mids Premier Champions 98-99
PREVIOUS: Leagues: Ilford & Dist. 1898-1925 44-47; Ilford Minor 25-44; Sth Essex 47-48; Walthamstow 48-50; London 50-64; Gtr London 64-71; Metropolitan-London 71-75; Spartan 76- South Midlands 1996-99

FACT FILE
Founded: 1898

Colours: Blue & yellow/blue/blue
Change colours: All yellow
Midweek matchday: Tuesday
Programme: Yes

CLUB PERSONNEL
President: A Smith
Chairman: Michael Woodward
Manager: John Bennett

BASILDON UNITED

Secretary: C.A.Thomas, 52 Conway Gardens, Grays, Essex RM17 6HG
Tel: 01375 390231 (H) Email: clivekaren@bun.co.uk
Ground: Gardiners Close, Gardiners Lane, Basildon, Essex SS14 3AW Tel: 01268 520268
Directions: A176 off Southend arterial (A127), left at r'bout into Cranes FarmRoad, proceed to end of duel carriageway, left at lights, Gardiners Close is 1st left (Football Club signed). Two and a half miles from Basildon BR station
Capacity: 2,000 Seats: 400 Cover: 1,000 Floodlights: Yes
Clubhouse: Open lunchtimes, evenings, weekends. Hot food sold Club Shop: No
HONOURS Isthmian Lge Div 2 83-83; Essex Senior Lge (5) 76-80 94-95, Lg Cup 77-78 94-95 97-98, Res. Cup 92-93; Essex Senior Trophy 78-79; Res. Lge &Shield 94-95
PREVIOUS Leagues: Grays & Thurrock; Gtr London 68-70; Essex Snr 70-80; Athenian 80-81; Isthmian 81-91 Name: Armada Sports Ground: Grosvenor Park 63-69
CLUB RECORDS Attendance: 4,000 v West Ham, ground opening 11/8/70

FACT FILE
Founded: 1963
Sponsors: T.B.A.
Colours: Amber & black stripes
Change: Green & white squares/white/white
Midweek Matches: Wednesday
Programme: 16 pages, 50p Editor: T.B.A.

1999-00 Top Scorer: Michael Gore

CLUB PERSONNEL
President: J Oakes
Chairman: John Strange
Press Officer: Frank Ford (01268 552994)
Manager:Steve Wheeler

BOWERS UNITED

Secretary: Stephen Bond, 42 Brundish, Pitsea, Basildon, Essex SS13 3EU 01268 478035 (H)
Ground: Crown Avenue, off Kenneth Rd, Pitsea, Basildon (01268 452068)
Directions: Turn into Rectory Rd from Old London Rd (B1464) at Pitsea Broadway into Kenneth Rd, right at top Crown Ave. 1.25 miles Pitsea (BR). Bus 5& 42 toRectory Rd, Bowers Gifford
Capacity: 2,000 Seats: 200 Stand: Yes Floodlights: Yes
Clubhouse: Open every night Club Shop: No
PREVIOUS Leagues: Thurrock & Thameside Comb.; Olympian
Ground: Gun Meadow, Pitsea
HONOURS Thurrock & Thameside Comb. 58-59; Essex Snr Lg 80-81,98-99 R-up 83-84 Div 1 Cup 90-91,Lg Cup Winners 81-82,98-99 R-up (3) Harry Fisher mem Trophy 91-92 R-up (3)
BEST SEASON FA Cup: 1st Rd Q 98-99 FA Vase: 4th Rd 98-99
CLUB RECORDS Attendance: 1,800 v Billericay F.A.Vase
Players progressing: Steve Tilson (Southend Utd)
99-00 P.o.Y.: Steven Chambers Captain: Steven Chambers Top Scorer: David Hope

FACT FILE
Founded: 1946
Colours: Red & white/red/red
Change colours:Yellow/Black/Yellow
Midweek Matches: Wednesday 7.30
Res League; Essex & Herts Border Comb
Programme: 30pages 50p
Editor: Dennis Osborne

CLUB PERSONNEL
Chairman: Dennis Osborne
Vice Chairman: Dick Dallison
Manager: Tom Harris(01268 511608)

BRENTWOOD

Secretary: Colin Harris, 56 Viking Way, Pilgrims Hatch, Brentwood, Essex CM15 9HY
Tel: 01277 219564 (H)
Ground: Brentwood Centre, Doddinghurst Rd, Brentwood, Essex. 01277 215151 Ext.713
Directions: From east end High St (Wilsons Corner) turn north into Ongar Rd. 3rd mini-round-about take right fork into Doddinghurst Rd, Centre half mile on right after A12 Bridge, ground far right corner.
Capacity: !,000 Cover: 100 Seats: Floodlights: Yes
Clubhouse: Open Tues & Thur evening & matchdays Club Shop: No
PREVIOUS Names: Manor Ath. 55-70, Brentwood Ath. 70-72
Grounds: King George, Hartswood, `Larkins', Ongar (pre-92), East Thurrock 92/93
Leagues: Romford & Dist., Sth Essex Comb., London & Essex Border,Olympian
HONOURS Olympian Lg Cup 67-68, Essex Inter. Cup 76-77, Essex Lg Cup 75-76 78-79 90-91; Harry Fisher Mem. Trophy 95-96
BEST SEASON FA Vase: 3rd Rd Prop 95-96

FACT FILE
Founded: 1955 Sponsor: T.B.A.
Nickname: Blues
Colours: All sky blue
Change colours: Pink with blue stripe
Midweek Matches: Tuesday
Programme: 50p

CLUB PERSONNEL
Chairman: K J O'Neale
Manager: Paul Delea (H) 01708 550630
99-00 Top Scorer: David Stittle

BURNHAM RAMBLERS

Secretary: Chris Dobson, 13 Chapel Rd, Burnham-on-Crouch, Essex CM10 8JB(01621 786334)

Ground: Leslie Field, Springfield Rd, Burnham-on-Crouch CM0 8QL (01621 784383)

Directions: On B1010 from South Woodham Ferrers, trt,1/2 mile before town.
15 mins -Burnham (BR)

Capacity: 2,000   Seats:132   Stand: Yes   Floodlights: Yes   Club Shop: No

Clubhouse: Mon-Fri 7-11pm, Sat 12noon -11pm, Sun 12-3 & 7-9.30pm. Hot meals & snacks available

HONOURS   Olympian Lg 65-66; Essex I'mediate Cup R-up 81-82; Essex Snr Lg Cup R-up 86-87 89-90 97-98, (Reserve Cup R-up 92-93), Reserve Shield R-up 90-91; Harry Fisher Mem. Trophy 96-97, R-up 97-98 99-00; Sportsmanship Award 96-97

PREVIOUS   Leagues: N Essex, Mid-Essex, Olympian, S.E. Essex
Grounds: Wick Rd ,Millfields and Saltcourts
BEST SEASON   FA Vase: 5th Rd 88-89
CLUB RECORDS   Gate: 1,500 v Arsenal at opening of new stand

FACT FILE
Founded: 1900   Nickname: Ramblers
Colours: Royal blue & yellow
Change colours: All yellow
Midweek matches: Tuesday
Reserves' Lge: Essex & Herts Comb.
Programme: 36 pages, 50p   Editor: T.B.A.

CLUB PERSONNEL
Chairman: Ron Hatcher(acting)
Vice-Chairman: Chris Brown (acting)
President: R J Cole, Esq
Press Officer: Nigel Radcliffe, 01621 783774
Manager: Grant Gordon
Physios: Cyril Tennant & Maxine Joyce
1999-00:Top Scorer: Kristian Down

CONCORD RANGERS

Secretary: Mick Stephens, 39 New Park Rd, Benfleet, Essex SS7 5UR
Tel: 01268 458571 or 07979 214350

Ground: Thames Road, Canvey Island, Essex. SS8 0HP (01268 691780/515750)

Directions: Follow A130 onto Canvey Island and turn right into Thorney Bay Road, then right again into Thames Road.

Capacity: 1,500   Cover: Yes   Seats: No   Floodlights: Yes

HONOURS   Southend & Dist. Lge - Lge & Cup 84-85; Southend Alliance - Lge & Cup 87-88; Essex Intermediate Lg Div 2 90-91; Essex Sen Lge 97-98, Cup 96-97; Wirral Programme Award 93-94, Harry Fisher Trophy 99-00

PREVIOUS   Leagues: Southend & Dist. All., Essex I'mediate (pre-1991)   **Ground:** Waterside

CLUB RECORDS   Gate: 1,500 v Lee Chapel North, FA Sunday Cup 89-90
Win: 9-0 v Eton Manor, Essex Snr Lge 96-97

FACT FILE
Founded: 1967
Colours:Yellow & Blue/blue/yellow
Change colours: white/black/black
Midweek Matches: Tuesday
Clubhouse: Evenings & weekends
Programme: 20 pages, 50p
Editor: Mike Stephenson (01268 684638)

CLUB PERSONNEL
President: Albert Lant
Chairman: Eddie Brown
Manager: Steve Knott
1999-00 Top Scorer: Danny Heale

EAST HAM UNITED

Secretary: Reuben Gane, 108 Beccles Drive, Barking, Essex IG11 9HZ.
020 8594 7861 (H & B)   020 8507 1099 (Fax)   Email: reubengane@yahoo.com

Ground: Groundshare with Barking F.C.Capacity: 2,500   Seats: 150 Cover: 300 Floodlights: Yes
Clubhouse: Open Evenings & weekends   Club Shop: Yes/No   Programme: Yes
HONOURS   Metropolitan Lg; Essex Snr Tphy 76-77, Sportsmanship Trophy 97-98; Gtr London Lg Cup 69-70; London Jnr Cup 46-47; Ron Murrant Memorial Trophy 94-95; Carpathian Charity Cup 94-95; Harry Fisher Memorial Trophy 97-98,(R-u 94-95), Stepney Charity Cup 47-48,87-88
PREVIOUS   **Leagues:** Spartan, Metropolitan   **Name:** Storey Ath. 1933-55
BEST SEASON   FA Vase: Quarter finals   FA Cup:
CLUB RECORDS   Gate: 4,250 - East Ham XI v West Ham, friendly 15/2/76 at Terrance McMillanStadium. 2,400 v Sutton United, FA Amateur Cup 14/11/53
Goalscorer : David Norris   **Appearances:** Ken Bowhill, 1964-84
PREVIOUS Ground: Whitebarn Lane (previous East Ham Utd, formed 1880 and played in Sth Essex Lge) 1892-1914; Tilletts Farm 33-46

FACT FILE
Founded: 1933   Nickname: Hammers
Sponsors: Stereolab Rock Band
Colours: Green/white/gold
Change : Red & White hoops/black/white
Midweek Matchday: Tuesday & Wednesday
99-00 Top Scorer:
Steve Grant (Barbados Trialist) 28

CLUB PERSONNEL
Chairman: Ted Whatmough 0181 599 4542
Press Officer: Roland Clooge
Manager: Reuben Gane
Assistant Manager/ Coach: Dorian West
Head of Coaching: Reuben Gane

ETON MANOR

Secretary: Mrs Jackie Jones, 31 Greenleafe Drive, Barkingside, Essex (020 8550 9618(H)0956 547220(M)

Ground: Waltham Lodge Sports Ground,Kitchener Rd.,Walthamstowe London E17 4JP(020 8527 2444)
Directions: Sharing with Leyton Pennant (Ryman League).
Capacity: 1,000   Seats: 60   Cover: 60Floodlights: Yes   Clubhouse: Yes

HONOURS   Essex Snr Cup R-up 37-38, London Lg 33-34 37-38 52-53 53-54 (R-up 48-49 57-58, Lg Cup 55-56 (R-up 46-47 54-55)), Greater London Lg 64-65, Essex Intermediate Cup 64-65, London Intermediate Cup R-up 33-34 66-67, Essex Snr Lg Sportsmanship Award 75-76   (Div 1 Cup 90-91, Res. Div 76-77, Res. Div Cup 91-92).
PREVIOUS   Leagues: London 33-59; Aetolian 59-64; Greater London 64-69; Metropolitan 69-75.
Grounds: Wildness, Hackney; GUS Sports Ground, Clapton; Walthamstow Ave. FC; Norwegian Ground, Barking; Roding Lane, Buckhurst Hill, ThurrockHotel   **Name:** Wilderness Leyton.
CLUB RECORDS   Gate: 600 v Leyton Orient, opening of floodlights at Roding Lane.
Goalscorer: Dave Sams

FACT FILE
Founded: 1901
Nickname: The Manor
Colours: Sky/navy/navy
Change colours: Maroon &
green/maroon/maroon
Midweek Matches: Tuesday
Programme: 12 pages with entry Editor:
Secretary

CLUB PERSONNEL
Chairman: Reg Curtis
Manager:Tony Jones
Physio: Alf Jones
Top Scorer: Jamie Everton

HULLBRIDGE SPORTS

Secretary: Beryl Petre, 58 Grasmere Ave., Hullbridge, Essex SS5 6LF
Tel: 01702 230630 (H) 01702 552211 (B)
Ground: Lower Road, Hullbridge, Hockley, Essex SS5 6BJ Tel: 01702 230420
Directions: Turn into Rawreth Lane from A130 (left if arriving fromChelmsford), down to
mini-r'bout, left, across next mini-r'bout, up hill, ground signed on right just past garage
Capacity: 1,500   Seats: No   Cover: Yes   Floodlights: Yes   Club Shop: No
Clubhouse: Lounge bar, function hall with bar & changing rooms - set in 16 acres

HONOURS   Essex Intermediate Snr Div Cup 87-88, Southend & District Lg Div 1 65-66 (Div 2
51-52, Div 3 56-57), French Cup 51-52, Essex Snr Lg Sportsmanship Award 91-92 92-93 94-95

PREVIOUS   **Leagues:** Southend & Dist., Alliance, Essex I'mediate
Grounds: Pooles Lane Rec

RECORD ATTENDANCE: 800 v Blackburn Rovers F.A.Youth Cup 99-00

FACT FILE

Founded: 1945
Sponsor: Thermo Shield
Colours: Royal Blue & white/blue/blue
Change colours: All yellow
Midweek matches: Tues/Thursday
Programme Editor: T.B.A.

CLUB PERSONNEL

Chairman: Terry Scourfield
Manager: Andy Dixon

ILFORD

Secretary: Kevin Wilmot, 83 Mandeville Court, Lower Hall Lane, Chingford, London E4 8JD
Tel: 0181 529 9475 (H), 0956 902456 (Club Mobile)
Ground: Cricklefield Stadium, High Road, Ilford, Essex. IG1 1UB Tel: 0181 514 0019
Directions: 5 min walk from Seven Kings Station. Opposite 'TheCauliflower' publ, Or 86 Bus
Capacity: 5,000   Seats - 216   Cover - Yes   Floodlights - Yes
Clubhouse: No, but snackbar available on matchdays
HONOURS   FA Amateur Cup: 28-29 29-30, R-up 35-36 57-58 1973-74 Isthmian Lge Champ.
06-07 20-21 21-22 R-up 11-12 26-27 31-32 37-38 38-39 Essex Senior Cup x13 (record nos. of
wins), R-up x5; London Sen. Cup: x7 R-up x 5; London Charity Cup: x 6 R-up x 7: Essex I'mediate
Cup R-up x1; London I'mediate Cup R-up x1; Eastern F'lit Comp. Group Winners 96-97
PREVIOUS   League: Spartan 87-95
BEST SEASON   **FA Cup:** 73-74 2nd Rd, 0-2 v Southend Utd. (H)
FA Vase: 99-00 2nd Rd 1-2 v Watton United (a)
CLUB RECORDS Attendance: 17,000 Ilford Boys v Swansea Boys (Schools Trophy Final)

FACT FILE
Founded: 1881   Re-Formed: 1987
Sponsor: Kelvin Hughes
Colours: Blue & white hoops/white/blue & white
Change colours: Red & white qtrs/red/red
Midweek matches: Monday
Programme Editor: L Llewellyn
CLUB PERSONNEL
Chairman: George Hogarth
Vice Chairman: Melvin Attwell
President: Lord John Taylor of Warwick
Fixture Secretary: D Quinlan, 25 Burwood
Gardens, Rainham, Essex. RM13 8JS
Tel: 01708 526323
Manager: Alan Bailey (0208 5173852)

LEYTON

Secretary: Tony Hampford, 282 Lea Bridge Road, Leyton, London E10 7LD
Tel: 0208 556 2665 (H) 0208 539 5405 (B)

Ground: Wingate Leyton Stadium, 282 Lea Bridge Road, Leyton, London E10 7LD
Tel: 0208 539 5405   Email: enquiries@leytonfc.co.uk
Directions: Lea Bridge Rd. is A104, ground next to Hare & Hounds PH.
Leyton (Central Line) thence bus 58 or 158 to Lea Bridge Road.
Clapton (BR) Walk 100 yds to Lea Bridge Rd. roundabout, buses 48, 55, 56 to
ground. Bus 48 runs direct to ground from London Bridge (BR) station
Capacity: 2,500   Seats: Yes   Cover: Yes   Floodlights: Yes

PREVIOUS   **Leagues:** Essex Intermediate; Spartan

FACT FILE
Founded: 1868   Nickname: Lilywhite
Colours: Blue & white stripes/blue/blue
Change colours: Red & black halves/red/red
Midweek Matches: Tuesday
Programme Editor: Tony Hampford

CLUB PERSONNEL
Chairman: Phil Foster
Vice Chairman: Doug Digby
President: Peter Lewis
Fixture Sec.: as Secretary
Manager: Rowley Cray
99-00 Top Scorer:Mark Sophoclevs

SAFFRON WALDEN TOWN

Secretary: Peter Rule, 48 Church Street, Saffron Walden, Essex, CB10 1VQ (Tel 01799 522417)
Ground: Catons Lane, Saffron Walden, Essex CB10 2DU (01799 522789)
Directions: In Saffron Walden High St turn into Castle St, left at T-junction, 1st left by Victory pub
Capacity: 5,000   Seats: 500 Cover: 2,000 Floodlights: Yes   Club Shop: Yes Clubhouse: Yes -
PREVIOUS   Leagues: Haverhill & Dist.; Stansted & Dist.; Cambridgeshire; Nth Essex; Herts Co.;
Spartan 33-49 50-54; Parthenon 49-50; Essex Snr 71-74; Eastern Co's 74-84
HONOURS   Essex Snr Lg 73-74, 99-00Lg.Cup 99-00 Eastern Co's Lg 82-83, Spartan Lg
Eastern Div 2 36-37,Essex Snr Tphy 82-83 83-84 84-85, Eastern F'lit Comp. 91-92 (R-up 88-
89,Nth Thames Group B 82-83), Essex Jnr Cup 1896-97 (R-up 25-26), Cambs Lg R-up 22-23,
Essex & Herts Border R-up 25-26(jt), Stansted & Dist. x 7, Haverhill & Dist. x 5 ,Harry Fisher
Mem& Uttlesford Ch Cup 98-99,S.Mids Floodlit Cup 99-00 Spoertsmanship Cup: 98-99.99-00
CLUB RECORDS Scorer: John Tipputt   **Appearances:** Les Page, 700+
Attendance: 6,000 v Rainham Ath., Essex Jun. Cup Final 1926 (played at Crittals, Braintree)
BEST SEASON   FA Cup: 2nd Qual. Rd replay 84-85, 1-2 v King's Lynn (A)

FACT FILE
Founded: 1872
Nickname: Bloods
Club Sponsors: Tolly Cobbold
Colours: Red & black/black/black
Change cols: Blue & yellow/yellow/yellow
Midweek Matchday: Tuesday
Reserves' League: Essex & Herts Comb
Programme: 24 pages, 40p
Editor: R Smith (01799 500061)
CLUB PERSONNEL
Chairman: Steve Cox
Press Officer: Secretary
Manager: Tim Moylette
99-00 Top Scorer: Mark Das

SAWBRIDGEWORTH TOWN

Secretary: Barrie Mutimer, 'Ebenezer, 18 Forebury Avenue, Sawbridgeworth, Herts CM21 9BG

Ground: Crofters End, West Road, Sawbridgeworth, Herts. CM21 0DE (01279 722039)

Directions: Three quarters of a mile from the station; up Station Road then into West Road.

Capacity: 1,500   Seats: None   Cover: 250   Floodlights: Yes   Club Shop: No
Clubhouse: Yes/No - when is it open ??? is food available ???

HONOURS   Essex Olympian Lg 71-72; Essex Snr Lg R-up 92-93 94-95; Harry FisherMem.
Cup 87-88; Lg Cup 94-95 R-up 92-93 93-94, Res. Div 91-92 92-93 (R-up 93-94), Res. Shield R-up
92-93); Herts Snr Tphy 90-91 93-94 (R-up 92-93);Herts Charity Shield 92-93 94-95 95-96;
Uttlesford Charity Cup 92-93; Herts Intermediate Cup R-up 93-93(res); S. Midlands F'lit Cup R.up
94-95; Res. Sect S.M Lge & Lg.Cup R-Up 94-95
PREVIOUS   Leagues: Essex Olympian, Spartan 36-53
CLUB RECORDS Attendance: 610 v Bishop's Stortford.
PREVIOUS GROUNDS: Hyde Hall, Pishiobury, Hand & Crown.

FACT FILE
Founded: 1890
Nickname: Robins
Colours: Red & black stripes/black/black
Change colours: All blue
Midweek Matchday;
Prog Editor:Gary Bennett (01279 830306)
Wirral programme Award 99-00
CLUB PERSONNEL
Chairman: Anton johnson
President: Ron Alder
Press Officer: Gary Bennett
Manager: John Higley
Physio: Brian Latchford
1999-00 Top Scorer: Roy Smith

SOUTHEND MANOR

Secretary: Dave Kittle, 15 Seymour Rd, Hadleigh, Benfleet, Essex SS7 2HB
     Tel: 01702 559581 (H) 01268 752811 (B) 01268 793416 (Fax)
Ground: Southchurch Park Arena, Lifstan Way, Southend-on-Sea. Tel: 01702 615577
Directions: A127 then A1159 for 1 mile turn right at second roundabout by Invisible Man PH,
     then due south for 1 mile, ground on right near sea front
Capacity: 2,000   Seats: 500   Cover: Yes   Floodlights: Yes
Clubhouse: Open every evening   Club Shop: No
HONOURS Essex Snr Trophy 92-93; Essex Intermediate Cup 78-79; Essex Snr Lg 90-91, R-Up:
99-00 Cup 87-88,R-Up: 99-00 Challenge Cup 89-90; Harry Fisher Mem. Tphy 90-91 92-93 (R-up
91-92)
PREVIOUS   Leagues: Southend Borough Combination, Southend Alliance
     Grounds: Victory Spts/ Oakwood Rec
RECORDS   Attendance: 1,521 v Southend Utd, 22/7/91, floodlight opener
BEST SEASON   FA Vase: 1996-97

FACT FILE
Founded: 1955   Nickname: The Manor
Sponsors: Davlaw
Colours: Yellow/black/black
Change colours: All white
Midweek Matchday: Tuesday
Reserves Lge: Essex & Herts Border Comb
Programme: 10 pages, 50p
Editor/Press Officer: Harry Cooper
Tel: 01702 308482

CLUB PERSONNEL
Chairman: Robert Westley
Vice-Chairman: John Hughes
Manager: Mark Jenkins
Coach: Peter Heathcote

STANSTED

Secretary: Mrs Denise Murnane,   01279 815404 (H&B) 07957 855023 (M) 01279 815780 (F)
     Appletree House, Fullers End, Elsenham, Bishops Stortford. CM22 6DU.
Ground: Hargrave Park, Cambridge Road, Stansted, Essex. (01279 812897)
Directions: B1383 north of Bishops Stortford on west side of Cambridge Rd.
     Stansted (BR) - 1/2 mile
Capacity: 2,000   Seats: 200   Cover: Yes   Floodlights: Yes
Clubhouse: Matchdays till 11pm. Sandwiches available.   Club Shop: No

HONOURS FA Vase Winners 83-84; Essex Snr Lg R-up 82-83; Essex Snr Lg Cup 83-84, (R-up
72-73 94-95); Harry Fisher Mem Cup 82-83 84-85 (R-up 92-93 93-94); E. Anglian
     Cup 83-84; Eastern F/lit Cup 83-84; Uttlesford Char. Cup 93-84 86-87 88-89 94-95 97-98
PREVIOUS   Leagues: Spartan; London; Herts Co. **Grounds:** Greens Meadow; ChapelHill
RECORDS   Attendance: 828 v Whickham (FA Vase 83-84)
BEST SEASON   FA Cup: 97-98   **FA Vase:** Winners 83-84

FACT FILE
Founded: 1902
Nickname: The blues
Sponsor: D C Poultons
Colours: Blue & white/blue/blue
Change: Green & red/green/red
Midweek matches: Tuesday
Reserves League: Cambridgeshire League
Programme Editor: D Murnane

CLUB PERSONNEL
Chairman: Terry Shoebridge
President: Percy Heal
Manager: Tony Mercer

WOODFORD TOWN

Secretary: Bill Robertson, 2 Humphrey Close, Clayhall, Ilford, Essex IG5 0RW
     0181 550 6680 (H) 07930 104076 (B&M)

Ground: Clapton FC ground share
     Old Spotted Dog Ground, Upton Lane, Forest Gate, London E7
     Tel: 0181 472 0822
Directions: BR to Forest Gate,Tube to Plaistow (District Line).
     Official entrance in Upton Lane.
     Docklands Light Railway to Prince Regent then 325 bus to ground
     Buses: Any bus fron Forest Gate station
Capacity: 2,000 Seats: 100   Cover: 180   Floodlights: Yes

FACT FILE

Founded: 1937
Colours: Red, black & white/red/red
Change colours: Blue & white/white/white
Programme Editor: T.B.A.

CLUB PERSONNEL

Chairman: Mick Wakeling
Fixture Sec. as Secretary
Manager: John Burns
99-00 Top Scorer: Solomon Torson

CHERRY RED BOOKS TROPHY
(CAPITAL COUNTIES FEEDER LEAGUES TROPHY)

THIRD ROUND

Bedmond Sports	v	RS Basingstoke	2-1	Colney Heath	v	Risborough Rangers	3-0
Eton Manor	v	Finchampstead	2-1	Greenacres	v	Kings Langley	5-3
Hartley Wintney	v	Wormley Rovers	0-3	Henley Town	v	Peppard	1*0
Leyton	v	Bushey Rangers	6-0	Met Police Bushey	v	Tring Athletic	0-2

QUARTER FINALS

Bedmond Sports	v	Greenacres	1-0	Colney Heath	v	Wormley Rovers	2*2, 0-3
Eton Manor	v	Leyton	1-2	Tring Athletic	v	Henley Town	1*1, 1-0

SEMI-FINALS

Bedmond Sports	v	Leyton	3*2	Tring Athletic	v	Wormley Rovers	2-0

FINAL

Bedmond Sports	v	Tring Athletic		at Arlesey Town FC

SOUTHERN YOUTH LEAGUE

OVERALL LEAGUE CHAMPIONS
Aldershot Town FC
Runners Up Faygate Falcons FC

FAIRPLAY TROPHY Colliers Wood FC

SOUTHERN YOUTH LEAGUE CUP
Winners Tooting & Mitcham United FC
Runners Up Sutton United FC

PLAYER OF THE SEASON
Liam Collins (Walton & Hersham FC)

SECRETARY OF THE YEAR
Derek York (Hailsham Town FC)

LEADING GOALSCORER
23 Greg Ball *(Walton & Hersham FC)*
Damien Mulgrew *(Ashford Town FC)*
James Smith *(Ashford Town FC)*
Shaun Lyden *(Godalming & Guildford FC)*
Damien Philips *(Molesey FC)*

FINAL LEAGUE TABLES (Top 5)

CENTRAL SECTION	P	W	D	L	F	A	Pts
Sutton United	20	13	2	5	51	23	41
Tooting & Mitcham	20	11	4	5	50	23	37
Kingstonian	20	12	1	7	58	39	37
Walton & Hersham	20	10	4	6	60	38	34
Croydon FC	20	9	3	8	40	41	30

WESTERN SECTION	P	W	D	L	F	A	Pts
Aldershot Town	18	15	1	2	68	17	46
Ashford Town	18	14	2	2	80	15	44
Cobham	18	10	3	5	59	39	33
Godalming & G'ford	18	9	3	6	44	28	30
Bedfont	18	9	2	7	46	36	29

SOUTHERN SECTION	P	W	D	L	F	A	Pts
Faygate Falcons	16	10	3	3	45	26	33
Leatherhead	16	10	2	4	44	20	32
Dorking	16	10	1	5	47	42	31
Hailsham Town	16	8	2	6	49	32	26
Lewisham	16	6	4	6	26	28	22

SOUTHERN COUNTIES FLOODLIT YOUTH LEAGUE

CORINTHIAN DIV	P	W	D	L	F	A	Pts
Leighton Town	14	11	3	0	26	7	36
Bedford Town	14	8	4	2	31	10	28
Hemel Hempstead T	14	7	4	3	40	12	25
Royston Town	14	6	4	4	28	16	22
Welwyn Garden City	14	4	4	6	18	21	16

DELPHIAN DIV	P	W	D	L	F	A	Pts
Stevenage Borough	14	11	1	2	44	15	29
Bishops Stortford	14	8	5	1	25	13	29
Hitchin Town	14	5	5	4	20	20	20
Hayes	14	5	2	7	25	23	17
Ware	14	3	7	4	24	25	16

NEMEAN DIV	P	W	D	L	F	A	Pts
Hoddesdon Town	14	13	1	0	47	11	40
Clapton	14	9	3	2	44	15	30
Wingate & Finchley	14	8	1	5	29	14	25
Tilbury	14	5	2	7	23	29	17
Somersett A V & E	14	4	3	7	14	21	15

LEAGUE CHAMPIONSHIP PLAY-OFFS

Hoddesdon Town	5	v 1	Leighton Town
Leighton Town	1	v 1	Stevenage Borough
Stevenage Borough	3	v 0	Hoddesdon Town

LEAGUE SHIELD FINAL

Enfield	3	v 1	Hemel Hempstead T

Above: Arlesey Town. Back Row (l-r): Nicky Ironton (Manager), Richard Donner, Rob McClelland, Darren Turpin, Junior George, Gregg Pike, Michael Jarrett, Spencer Knight, Gary Smith, Russell Ball (Coach). Front Row: Helen Bardell (Physio), Steve Justin, Matt Turnbull, Tony Ward, Danny Driscoll, Danny Gibb, Kevin Culverhouse, Adrian Campbell. Photo: Gordon Whittington

Above: Beaconsfield SYCOB. Back Row (l-r): Matt Chandler (Coach), Gavin Mernagh, Francis Arquez, Simon Sweeney, Steve Hale, Julian Taylor, Kevin Brown, Mark Keadell, Steve Clements. Front Row: Simon Delahunty (Manager), Steve Small, Kevin Cotton, Keith Bedwell, Steve Jones, Steve Small, Stuart Walsh, Peter Scott. Photo: Eric Marsh

Above: Brache Sparta. Back Row (l-r): Shaun Sutcliffe, Paul Mullings, Lee Dagnall, Brendan Healy, Steve Brinkman (Manager), John Tipper, Gary Dowling, Steve Farrell, Jon Cook, Iain Temple. Front Row: Paul Sheridan, Mark Little, Jason Campbell, Paddy Walsh, Mark Smith (Asst Manager), Grey Toyer, Colin Massie.

SPARTAN SOUTH MIDLANDS FOOTBALL LEAGUE

President: B F Smith **Chairman:** Pat Burns

Hon. Press Secretary: Jim Bean, 224 The Hide, Netherfield, Milton Keynes MK6 4JE

Tel/Fax: 01908 696059

Arlesey Town became Premier Division champions, finishing four points clear of second-placed Brook House. Considering that Arlesey were second from bottom midway through the previous season, their transformation was complete. Arlesey started the season with nine straight wins, and after a slight hiccup in early March, finished their League season with seven wins. They first topped the table in September, and, after brief top-spot spells by both Brache Sparta and Brook House, they regained the lead on 20th November and maintained their position for the rest of the season. They finished with 93 points from 40 games, compared to last season's champion Barkingside, who gained 96 points from 44 games. Second placed Brook House, with games in hand at one time, looked like they could take the lead, but they too had a bad March and could not compete with Arlesey's successful finishing run. Third place went to Beaconsfield SYCOB, who started with five straight wins, but by mid-November had slumped to ninth place. In contrast, fourth placed Potters Bar Town started with only seven points from nine games, but between 6th November and 4th March had twelve successive victories which saw them rapidly climb the table. For the second successive season Potters Bar scored over 100 goals, with 105 from their 40 games, compared with last season's 109 from 44 games. Brook House scored 102 goals. London Colney had the best defensive record, conceding 38 goals. Harpenden Town finished bottom of the Premier with only fifteen points, the same number as last season's bottom club Brimsdown Rovers. Harpenden won just two of their first five games, but gained only two points from their next 21 games and moved into bottom position on 11th March. Of the four clubs fighting to avoid rthe elegation positions, Harpenden were unable to make any headway, and finished eleven points behind second bottom Somersett Amebury V & E who, despite winning three successive games in the closing weeks, finally finished three points behind Welwyn Garden City. Welwyn, who started the season with only one point from eight games, won six and drew ten of their last 32.

Two clubs reached the third round of the FA Vase, Letchworth for the second successive season, and London Colney. In the Middlesex Senior Charity Cup Hanwell Town, who had knocked out Isthmian clubs Kingsbury Town, Edgware Town and Staines Town, lost 1-0 in the Final to Combined Counties League champions Ashford. In the all-SSML Berks & Bucks Senior Trophy final, New Bradwell St Peter beat Milton Keynes City 3-1 on penalties after a 1-1 draw. In Bedfordshire, Dunstable Town "98" retained the Intermediate Cup for the SSML, whilst Ampthill Town Reserves won the Junior Cup. Hopes of a clean sweep were dashed when Arlesey Town lost 1-2 to United Counties League side Stotfold in the final of the Senior Cup. Biggleswade Town reached the finals of the Huntingdonshire Premier Cup and North Beds Charity Cup, yet to be played.

The most successful cup side was Tring Athletic, who won the inaugural Cherry Red Books Trophy, beating Herts County League side Bedmond Sports in a penalty shoot-out after a 0-0 draw. This is a new competition for clubs in the Lower Pyramid and was Tring's third final in five days. Tring had previously beaten Potters Bar Town 2-1 in the Herts Charity Shield final, and two days earlier Senior had won the Herts Senior Centenary Trophy, beating Herts Senior League side Wormley Rovers 2-0 in the final. In addition, Tring have reached the final of the St Mary's Cup, a trophy competed for by local teams including Isthmian sides, which they won last year.

Stan Eaton

PREMIER DIVISION FINAL LEAGUE TABLE 1999-2000

	P	W	D	L	F	A	GD	Pts		P	W	D	L	F	A	GD	Pts
Arlesey Town	40	30	3	7	98	45	53	93	Holmer Green	40	12	10	18	56	92	-36	46
Brook House^	40	27	6	7	102	33	69	89	St Margaretsbury	40	10	9	21	67	93	-26	39
Beaconsfield *	40	26	4	10	87	42	45	81	Biggleswade T	40	9	7	24	49	73	-24	34
Potters Bar T	40	26	2	12	105	66	39	80	Haringey Boro	40	10	2	28	56	99	-43	32
London Colney	40	22	12	6	87	38	49	78	Welwyn Garden C	40	6	11	23	49	98	-49	29
Waltham Abbey	40	23	4	13	78	64	14	73	Somersett A V & E	40	7	5	28	48	102	-54	26
Brache Sparta	40	19	13	8	85	48	37	70	Harpenden Town	40	4	3	33	41	155	-114	15
Hoddesdon T	40	21	7	12	85	55	30	70									
Milton Keynes C	40	21	5	14	80	53	27	68									

^ points awarded * points deducted

Hanwell Town	40	20	6	14	73	52	21	66
Royston Town	40	15	8	17	53	54	-1	53
Ruislip Manor	40	16	4	20	61	81	-20	52
New Bradwell SP	40	12	13	15	65	75	-10	49
Hillingdon Boro	40	14	6	20	56	63	-7	48

PREMIER DIVISION LEADING GOALSCORERS

	LG	CT	PC	TL
Greg Pike (Arlesey Town)	39	2	1	42
Darren Lynch (Milton Keynes C)	32	7	1	40
Lee Talbot (Potters Bar Town)	27	-	2	29
Allan Collins (Milton Keynes C)	24	4	-	28

FINAL LEAGUE TABLES 1999-2000

SENIOR DIVISION

	P	W	D	L	F	A	GD	Pts
Tring Athletic	36	27	5	4	103	29	74	86
Ampthill Town	36	23	6	7	86	46	40	75
Bedford United	36	22	5	9	106	48	58	71
Biggleswade Utd	36	18	10	8	71	55	16	64
Letchworth	36	17	10	9	74	57	17	61
Cockfosters	36	17	9	10	79	55	24	60
Bridger Pack.	36	19	3	14	74	63	11	60
Brimsdown Rvrs^	36	17	5	14	74	52	22	58
Amersham Town	36	15	11	10	63	48	15	56
Totternhoe	36	15	11	10	56	46	10	56
Langford	36	14	9	13	59	60	-1	51
Leverstock Green	36	12	10	14	61	59	2	46
Greenacres (Hml)	36	11	9	16	56	66	-10	42
Stony Stratford T	36	11	6	19	60	86	-26	39
Harefield Utd*	36	8	13	15	40	49	-9	36
Risborough Rngrs	36	6	7	23	44	73	-29	25
Caddington	36	6	6	24	40	127	-87	24
Luton Old Boys	36	5	7	24	35	89	-54	22
Shillington	36	6	4	26	46	119	-73	22

DIVISION ONE

	P	W	D	L	F	A	GD	Pts
Dunstable T 98	32	26	6	0	115	17	98	84
de Havilland	32	24	4	4	113	31	82	76
Pitstone & Iving.	32	22	7	3	97	28	69	73
Winslow Utd	32	21	5	6	84	34	50	68
Scot*	32	19	1	12	92	64	28	55
Mursley United	32	16	6	10	62	42	20	54
Old Dunstablians	32	15	3	14	51	53	-2	48
Crawley Green	32	14	5	13	67	47	20	47
Kent Athletic	32	14	1	17	55	60	-5	43
Buckingham Ath	32	12	5	15	50	55	-5	41
Flamstead	32	12	5	15	53	59	-6	41
Abbey National MK	32	10	6	16	46	75	-29	36
The 61 FC (Luton)	32	9	7	16	52	72	-20	34
Newport Ath	32	8	5	19	49	91	-42	29
Leighton Ath	32	6	7	19	45	98	-53	25
Old Bradwell Utd^	32	3	4	25	26	101	-75	16
Markyate	32	1	3	28	18	148	-130	6

^ points awarded   * points deducted

SENIOR DIVISION LEADING GOALSCORERS

	LG	CT	PC	TL
Paul Sloley (Stoney Stratford T)	28	-	7	35
Andy Humphreys (Tring Athletic)	22	-	5	27
Danny Hollis (Ampthill Town)	21	4	1	26

DIVISION ONE LEADING GOALSCORERS

	LG	CT	PC	TL
Steve Castleman (Dunstable Town)	37	-	5	42
Ikeme Ojulah (Dunstable Town)	25	-	-	25
Paul Talbot (Winslow United)	22	-	-	22
Roy Henney (Pitstone & Ivinghoe)	19	-	3	22

PREMIER DIVISION RESULTS CHART 1999-2000

	1	2	3	4	5	6	7	8	9	10	11	12	13	14	15	16	17	18	19	20	21
Arlesey Town	X	2-1	2-1	2-0	4-0	5-2	6-2	7-1	2-1	3-1	1-2	0-0	2-1	3-1	3-1	1-0	3-0	3-0	4-1	2-1	5-1
Beaconsfield	2-1	X	3-0	2-1	0-0	1-0	6-0	6-2	5-2	1-1	6-0	2-2	2-0	3-6	0-2	1-0	2-1	3-0	3-0	1-3	2-0
Biggleswade T	2-3	2-3	X	0-1	0-3	2-1	0-3	2-3	1-1	0-1	1-1	1-3	0-1	2-2	2-3	1-1	2-1	3-1	2-0	1-2	1-1
Brache Sparta	1-1	1-2	2-0	X	0-0	2-2	1-3	9-0	3-1	1-1	2-0	2-2	0-0	1-0	1-0	0-4	1-0	1-3	5-1	3-0	3-0
Brook House	3-0	1-3	1-0	1-2	X	5-0	1-0	6-0	1-0	2-0	3-1	3-0	0-2	3-2	5-3	2-0	6-1	1-1	4-2	2-3	6-0
Hanwell Town	3-0	1-0	4-0	2-2	0-2	X	1-0	4-4	0-1	2-1	6-0	0-3	3-0	6-0	2-0	1-0	4-0	3-0	4-0	0-3	0-0
Haringey Borough	2-0	1-4	0-1	3-6	0-3	3-0	X	2-1	0-1	1-5	1-3	0-0	1-3	2-1	1-3	0-1	3-4	1-5	1-4	0-3	3-4
Harpenden Town	0-2	0-2	2-3	1-5	0-6	1-2	0-4	X	0-3	2-7	2-4	0-1	0-6	0-4	1-5	2-3	1-4	6-5	2-2	1-5	0-2
Hillingdon Boro	1-1	0-5	0-2	1-2	1-0	0-2	1-1	4-1	X	0-2	1-2	0-0	1-3	1-1	5-1	1-2	0-1	1-2	4-1	2-0	2-1
Hoddesdon T	1-2	2-0	5-3	2-2	0-2	1-2	4-2	2-0	2-1	X	8-3	0-1	3-2	1-1	2-1	2-1	2-3	3-1	1-2	2-2	3-1
Holmer Green	3-1	1-5	2-1	1-1	1-1	0-2	1-5	2-1	2-0	0-4	X	0-0	1-1	1-1	3-4	1-1	0-2	2-2	2-1	3-3	3-1
London Colney	1-2	3-0	1-0	1-1	0-2	4-2	2-0	7-0	2-2	2-2	5-1	X	3-3	3-2	2-0	6-0	0-0	2-1	5-1	6-2
Milton Keynes C	0-2	0-1	3-0	2-4	0-2	0-1	3-1	6-1	0-2	1-0	1-3	0-2	X	3-0	2-0	1-1	2-1	4-2	7-3	2-0	3-1
New Bradwell St P	0-3	1-2	1-1	1-1	0-3	2-2	1-0	3-0	2-0	0-1	1-1	2-0	0-5	2-3	X	1-2	1-1	3-2	2-1	4-1	0-1	3-3
Potters Bar Town	2-3	0-3	4-3	2-0	1-0	1-1	1-2	7-0	5-3	2-4	5-2	2-1	2-1	2-2	X	3-0	5-1	5-2	6-0	5-1	6-2
Royston Town	1-4	2-0	2-1	0-3	0-0	2-0	3-1	2-0	1-2	1-0	2-0	0-3	1-4	2-2	4-0	X	3-2	1-1	2-0	1-2	1-2
Ruislip Manor	2-1	1-0	2-0	2-2	1-1	1-3	2-1	6-0	2-0	0-1	1-0	0-2	0-2	1-3	1-3	2-1	X	2-3	5-4	2-4	1-1
St Margaretsbury	1-2	1-1	1-4	1-9	2-3	2-1	3-1	0-2	4-2	0-1	6-1	1-2	0-3	1-1	1-2	2-1	1-1	X	3-3	1-4	2-2
Somersett A V&E	1-3	0-1	1-0	1-1	1-4	1-3	1-2	1-1	0-3	0-4	1-0	0-2	1-2	3-0	1-3	0-2	4-0	2-3	X	1-4	0-2
Waltham Abbey	2-3	3-1	1-3	2-1	0-4	2-1	1-0	4-1	1-2	3-1	1-0	2-1	1-0	1-3	5-2	1-2	1-0	1-1	X	5-1
Welwyn Garden C	04	0-2	1-1	1-2	1-7	1-0	5-2	1-2	0-3	1-2	0-2	2-2	3-3	2-3	0-2	1-1	0-1	2-2	0-1	1-1	X

CHALLENGE TROPHY 1999-2000

FOURTH ROUND

Brook House	v	Royston Town	2-0
Old Dunstablians	v	Tring Athletic	1-0
London Colney	v	Arlesey Town	3-0
Milton Keynes City	v	Harpenden Town	3-0

SEMI-FINALS

Brook House	v	London Colney	0-2
Milton Keynes City	v	Old Dunstablians	1-0

FINAL (two legs)

London Colney   v   Milton Keynes City 1-1, 1*1
Milton Keynes City won 4-1 on penalties

PREMIER DIVISION CUP 1999-2000

FINAL   (Holders: Barkingside)

Brook House   v   London Colney   0*0, 5p3

SENIOR DIVISION CUP 1999-2000

FINAL   (Holders: Tring Athletic)

Letchworth   v   Tring Athletic   1-0

DIVISION ONE CUP 1999-2000

FINAL   (Holders: de Havilland)

Dunstable Town   v   de Havilland   1*0

BEACONSFIELD SYCOB

Secretary: Ken Barrett, 31 Stockey End, Abingdon, Oxon OX14 2NF. Tel: 01235202058 (H), 01235 537080 (B)

GROUND: Holloway Park, Slough Road, Beaconsfield, Bucks (01494 676868).
Directions: M40 (Jct 2), 1st exit to A355. Club 100yds on right. 1.5 miles from Beaconsfield BR Bus 441 Slough/ High Wycombe
Capacity: 3,000   **Cover:** 400   **Seats::** 250   **Floodlights:** Yes   C lub Shop: Clu
Clubhouse: Open eves & matchdays. Bar, Committee Room, Hall, Kitchen, Changing Room I
HONOURS: As Slough : Chilt.Lg R-up: 93-4,Lg Cup 92-3 Slough T Cup R-up 91-2
PREVIOUS: **Names:** Slough YCOB & Beaconsfield Utd merged 1994
Leagues: Beaconsfield Utd: Wycombe & District; Maidenhead. Slough YCOB: Windsor, Slough & District; East Berks; Chiltonian (pre 1994) **Previous Grounds:** As Slough: Haymill Community Centre,Burnham Lane,slough (pre 1944)
Record Gate: 300 Beaconsfield Utd v Chesham Utd, Berks & Bucks Sen Cup 1985
BEST SEASON: **FA Cup:** 3rd Q Rd 98-998 **FA Vase:** Beaconsfield: 1st Rd 83-84 85-86 87-88

FACT FILE
Founded: 1994   Nickname: SYCOB
Colours:Red & white quarters/black/red & white
Change colours: Blue with grey stripe
Midweek Matches: Monday or Tuesday
Reserves' League: Suburban
Programme: Yes, £1
Editor: Andy Jackson, 17 Boundary Cottages, Chipperfield Rd., Bovingdon, Herts.HP3 0JT

CLUB PERSONNEL
President: D Piercy
Chairman: Fred Deanus
Manager: Simon Delahunty

BEDFORD UNITED

Secretary: Geoff Seagrave, 16 Riverview Way, Kempston, Bedford MK42 7BB. 01234 402369

GROUND: McMullen Park, Meadow Lane, Cardington, Bedford MK45 3SB (01234 831024)

Directions: M1 jct 13, A421 to Bedford by-pass. Third exit, A603 ground 500 yards on left
Capacity: 5,000   **Seats:** 25   **Cover:** 100   **Floodlights:** Yes
Clubhouse: Open matchdays. Hot & cold snacks and drinks available

HONOURS: Bedford & Dist Lg Premier Division & Division One, County Junior Cup,
Biggleswade KO Cup, Butchers Cup(2), Britania Cup, Bedford Charity Cup
PREVIOUS: **Leagues:** Bedford & Dist. Lge (57-70 & 80-89); United Cos. Lge 70-80
Name: Printers Diemer-Reynolds (pre'72)
Grounds: Allen Park (57-80); Fairhill, Clapham Road (80-93); Hillgrounds, Kempston 93-96)

RECORD: Attendance: (at Fairhill) 1500 v Bedford Town, South Midlands Lge Div. 1 26/12/92
Scorer: Neil Tysoe 220   **Appearances:** Simon Fordham 418

Founded: 1957   Nickname: United
Club Sponsors: JDP Finance
Colours: Blue & White/blue/blue
Change colours: All red
Midweek matches: Wednesday
Reserves' League: S. Mids Lge Res. sect
Programme: 24 pages, £1
Editor: Robin King (01234 364654)

Chairman: John Cleverley
Vice Chairman/Press Off Jim McMullen
President: D Rostron

Manager: S Ackroyd
Asst. Man.: M Ackroyd
Coach/Physio: Dave Petrie

BIGGLESWADE TOWN

Secretary: Graham Arkwright, 21 Willsheres Rd, Biggleswade, Beds SG18 0BU
Tel: 01767 221574
GROUND: `Fairfield', Fairfield Road, Biggleswade, Beds (01767 312374).
Directions: A1 North r'bout, left immediately after bridge into car park.
10 mins walk from Biggleswade (BR).
Capacity: 2,400   **Seats:** 50   **Cover:** 100   **Floodlights:** Yes   Club Shop: No.
Clubhouse: Open all matchdays. , teas, coffees, snacks.
HONOURS: South Mids Lge: Res Div 2 87-88, Res Chall Trophy 88-89, S.M. Floodlit Cup 95-96; Beds Snr Cup 02-03 07-08 46-47 51-52 61-62 62-63 66-67 73-74; Beds Premier Cup 22-23 27-28; N. Beds Charity Cup x13; Utd Co's Lg Cup 73-74; Hinchingbrooke Cup 03-04 12-13 92-93 Hunts Premier Cup 92-93 93-94(joint) 94-95 97-98; Jess Piggott Trophy 87-88 89-90 91-92 92-93
PREVIOUS: Leagues: Biggleswade & Dist. 02-20; Bedford & Dist. 09-12; Utd Co's   (prev. Northants Lg) 20-39 51-55 63-80; Spartan 46-51; Eastern Co's 55-63 **Name:** Biggleswade F.C.
RECORD: **Attendance:** 2,000

FACT FILE
Founded: 1874   Nickname: Waders
Club Sponsors: Mantles Ford
Colours: green/black/black
Change: green & yellow stripes
Midweek Matchday: Tuesday
Programme: 32 pages, admission
Editor: Brian Doggett (01767 318307 (H).

CLUB PERSONNEL
Chairman: Maurice Dorrington
Vice Chairman: M Jarvis
President: R Dorrington
Manager: David Northfield
Physio: A.Wellings

BRACHE SPARTA

Secretary: Roy Standring, 37 Taunton Avenue, Luton, Beds. LU2 0LN. Tel: 01582 736574

GROUND: Foxdell Sports Ground, Dallow Rd, Luton LU1 1UP (01582 720751).
Directions: From M1 jct11, take A505 towards Luton. Right at Chaul End roundabout. Across A505 keep B&Q on left, into Dallow Rd. Ground 50 yds on right by Foxdell junior school.
Capacity: 400   **Cover:** 100   **Seats:** 25   **Floodlights:** Yes   Club Shop: No
Clubhouse: Open daily 12-3 & 7.30-11. Light snacks & refreshments etc available

HONOURS: South Mids Lg R-up 92-93, 96-97 (Div 1 R-up 83-84 87-88), Lg Cup R-up 75-76 80-81 92-93 97-98, Premier Div Cup Winners 97-98 R-up 91-92, Res Div 2 R-up 75-76, Res Cup R-up 87-88; Luton & Dist. Lg 67-68 69-70 70-71 71-72; William Pease Trophy 66-67 67-68 70-71 71-72; Beds Interm Cup 71-72 (R-up 68-69 70-71), BedsJnr Cup 82-83; Leighton Challenge Cup R-up 69-70 South Mids Lg Prem Div 1 North Champions 97-98, Beds Premier Cup R-up. 97-98

PREVIOUS: **League:** Luton & Dist   **Grounds:** Crawley Green Rd, (public park); Hitchin Town FC (share 93-94)   **RECORD Attendance :**320

FACT FILE
Founded: 1960
Nickname: The Foxes
Club Sponsors: A & E Engineering
Colours: White/navy/white
Change Colours: All royal
Midweek matches: Tuesday
Prog: 32 pages, £2.50 (incl. admission)
Career Record Goalscorer: Keith Denness

CLUB PERSONNEL
Chairman: Roy Standring
President: Doug Smith
Manager: Steve Brinkman
Physio: T.B.A.

BROOK HOUSE

Secretary: Barry Crump, 19 Bradenham Road, Hayes, Middlesex UB4 8LP.
Tel: 0208 841 3959 (H), 0966 468029 (B)

Ground: Farm Park, Kingshill Avenue, Hayes, Middlesex (0208 842 1448)
Directions: From North Circular road: A40 Western Ave. to Target r'about, left towards Hayes (A312), over White Hart r'about towards Yeading/Hayes, right at traffic lights in to Kingshill Ave, ground 1 mile on right. Nearest BR stationis Hayes & Harlington, then bus 90 or 195 to Brook House pub. Nearest tube is Northolt (central line), then bus to ground
Capacity: 2,000   **Cover:** 100   **Seats:** 120   **Floodlights:** Yes   **Club Shop:** No
Clubhouse: Open weekdays 7-11pm, Sat noon-11pm, Sun noon-11.00pm

HONOURS: SSM Prem South 97-98, Prem Div R-Up 99-00, Lge Cup 99-00 R-up 91-92.
BEST SEASON: **FA Vase:** 3rd Round Proper 97-98   **FA Cup:** 1st Qual Rd 93-94
Players progressing: Neil Shipperley (Crystal Palace), MarkHyde (Orient), Mark Perry (QPR)
David Warner (To Watford for £10,000) and Anthony Charles (To Crewe Alexandrafor £6,000)

FACT FILE
Founded: 1974
Colours: Blue & white stripes/blue/blue
Change colours: All yellow
Midweek matchday: Tuesday
Reserve League: Midd'sex Co Lg
Programme: 28 pages, £3 with entry
Editor: Andrew Gavin
CLUB PERSONNEL
President: Victor Kirby
Chairman: Mick Ralph
Vice-Chairman: JohnHandell
Press Officer: Lawrie Watts
Manager: Mickey Harvey Ass Man: B Strutton
Coach: R Leather

HANWELL TOWN

Secretary: John A Wake, 38 Warwick Ave., South Harrow, Middx. HA2 8RD.
Tel/Fax: 0181 422 1048 (H)
GROUND: Reynolds Field, Perivale Lane, Perivale, Greenford, Middx (0181 998 1701)

Directions: A40(M) west from London, leave opp Hoover building (B456 for Ealing), turn left into Argyle Rd, left into Perivale Lane. Grd on left. 500 yards from Perivale tube station (Central line)

Capacity: 2,000   **Seats:** 90   **Cover:** 200   **Floodlights:** Yes   **Club Shop:** No
Clubhouse: Saturday matchdays 2-11pm, Tuesdays 6-11pm, Non-matchdays 7.30-11pm

HONOURS: Spartan Sen Lg R-up 98-99 83-84 (Lg Cup R-up 93-94, London Snr Cup 91-92 92-93 (R-up 93-94), Middx Charity Cup R-up 92-93, 99-00
PREVIOUS: **Leagues:** Dauntless Lge, Harrow, Wembley & District and Middlesex County
RECORDS: **Attendance:** 600 v Spurs, Floodlight opening October 1989
Scorer: Trevor Canoville **Appearances:** Phil Player, 20 seasons, 617 games
BEST SEASON: **FA Cup:** 3rd Rd Qual 97-98

FACT FILE
Founded: 1948   Nickname: The Town
Colours: Black & white stripes/black/black & white
Change colours: White with red trim
Midweek matchday: Tuesday
Reserves' League: S.S.M.Res Lg
Programme: 16 pages, with entry
Editor: Bob Fisher as below

CLUB PERSONNEL
Chairman/Press Officer: Bob Fisher
Tel: 0181 952 4142 (H) 0181 519 7511 (B)
President: Dave Iddiols
Patron: Stephen Pound MP
Manager: Ray Duffy

HARINGEY BOROUGH

Secretary: George Kilikita, 44 Hatley Close, Friern Barnet, London N11 3LN,
Tel Nos: 020 8368 2783 (H) 020 7272 9242 (W)

GROUND: Coles Park, White Hart Lane, Tottenham N17 (020 88891415)
Directions: From M1 take North Circular Road (A406). Leave A406 turning right into Bounds Green Road (A109), proceed to end then turn left into Wood Green High Rd (A105) and then first right into White Hart Lane. Ground is on right 300 yds past New River Sports Centre. Wood Green (Picadilly Line). BR (EasternRegion) to White Hart Lane, W3 bus passes ground A105 or A10 from Nth. Circularto Wood Green
Capacity: 2,500   **Seats:** 280   **Cover:** Yes   **Floodlights:** Yes
Clubhouse: Open 7 days a week
HONOURS: None
PREVIOUS: **Leagues:** London 07-14; Isthmian 19-52 84-88; Spartan 52-54; Delphian 54-63; Athenian 63-84
Names: Edmonton; Tufnell Park; Tufnell Park Edmonton; Edmonton & Haringey

FACT FILE

Colours: Green/white/green
Change colours: All Yellow
Programme Editor: John Bacon
Tel: 01707 646797

CLUB PERSONNEL
Chairman: Peter Lawlor
Tel: 0181 889 2726
Vice-Chairman: T O'Connell
Match Secretary: John Bacon
Tel: 01707 646797

Manager: Paul Phelan

HILLINGDON BOROUGH

Secretary: Garry Grant, 19 Leveret Close,Leavesden, Watford, herts WD2 7AX
Tel Nos: 01923 463602 (H) 0958 409678 (W)

GROUND: Middlesex Stadium, Breakspear Road, Ruislip, Middx HA4 7SB (01895 639544)

Directions: From A40 take B467 (signed Ickenham), left at 2nd r'bout into Breakspear Rd South, right after 1 mile by Breakspear pub - ground half mile on left. Nearest station is Ruislip. Bus U1 passes ground
Capacity: 1,500   **Seats:** 150   **Cover:** 150   **Floodlights:** Yes   **Club Shop:** No
Clubhouse: Mon-Fri 7.30-11pm, Sat & Sun lunchtime & 7.30-10.30pm

RECORDS: **Win:** 12-0 v Hanwell T. (H), S.S.M. Prem 97/98
Defeat: 1-11 v St. Albans City (A), FA Cup 2nd Qual. Rd. 24.9.94
Transfer Fee Received: ¨1,000 for Craig Johnson (Wealdstone)

FACT FILE
Founded: 1990   Nickname: Boro
Sponsors: Airport Motor Radiator Co
Colours: White/blue/blue
Change colours: All red
Midweek Matches: Tuesday
Reserves' League: Suburban
Programme: 20 pages Editor/Press Off:
Alan Taylor (0181 581 0981)
CLUB PERSONNEL
Chairman: Dhally Dhaliwall
Commercial Mgr: Gamdoor Dhaliwal
Manager: Steve Hawkins
Asst Man.: Ian Lancaster
Physio: Dave Pook

HODDESDON TOWN

Secretary: Brenda Timpson, 82 Tolmers Rd, Potters Bar, Herts EN6 4JY (01707 874028)
GROUND: `Lowfield', Park View, Hoddesdon, Herts (01992 463133)
Directions: A10, A1170 into Hoddesdon, over 1st r'about, right at 2nd r'aboutand follow signs to Broxbourne, keeping to the left. Turn right at 1st @mini r-about into Cock Lane and 1st right is Park View. Ground 200yds on the left,entrance opposite Park Rd. BR station is Broxbourne
Capacity: 3,000 Seats: 100 Cover: 250 Floodlights: Yes Club Shop: Scarves,badges,hats &pens
Clubhouse: Bar and well-stocked Tea Bar with hot food. Open at every home game
HONOURS: FA Vase 74-75 (1st winners); S.S.M. Lg Prem Div Plate 97-98 (R-up 96-97, SthMids Lge Cup 85-86 86-87 91-92 (Prem Div Tphy R-up 92-93); Spartan Lg 70-71(R-up(3 71-74), Div 1 35-36, Div 2 `B' 27-28, Lg Cup(2) 70-72;
PREVIOUS: Lges: East Herts 1896-1908, 11-21; Herts Co. 08-25; N Middx Dist 10-22; Spartan 25-75; London Spartan 75-77; Athenian 77-84; South Midlands 84-97
RECORDS: **Attendance:** 3,500 v West Ham, (Floodlight opening friendly), 1975
BEST SEASON: **FA Vase:** Winners 74-75

FACT FILE
Founded: 1879
Nickname: Lilywhites/ Lowfielders
Colours: White/black/black
Change Colours: All yellow
Midweek matchday: Tuesday
Reserves' Lge: Essex/Herts Border Com
Programme: 100 + pages £1.00
Editor: Mrs Jane Sinden Tel: 01767 631297Fax: 01767 631562

CLUB PERSONNEL
President: Peter Haynes
Chairman: Roger Merton
Manager: Paul Surridge Gen Man: Jim Briggs
Coach: Don Nicholson

HOLMER GREEN

Secretary: Bill Scholes, The Brambles, Penfold Lane, Holmer Green, High Wycombe, Bucks HP15 6XS 01494 713867 (H) 01494 556185 (W)
GROUND: Watchet Lane, Holmer Green, High Wycombe (01494 711485)
Directions: From Amersham on A404 High Wycombe Road, after approx 2 miles turn right into Sheepcote Dell Road. Continue until end of road by Bat & Ball PH.Turn right then immediate left, continue approx 1/2 mile until 2 mini roundabouts, turn left in front of the Mandarin Duck into Watchet Lane. The ground is 150 yards on the right
Capacity: 1,000 Seats: 25 Cover:Yes Floodlights:Yes Club Shop:No
Clubhouse: Saturdays 12pm -11 pm midweek 7pm 11pm Badges: Yes (£3)
HONOURS: Berks & Bucks Sen Tr.Finalists 98-99, BB Jun Cup Winners 52-53, 63-64 B&B Inter-mediate Cup Winners 76-77; S.Mid Sen Div Winners (2), S.Mid Sen Cup Winners 96-97
PREVIOUS **Leagues:** 1908-34 Chesham & Dist. 34-84 Wycombe Comb. & Lge 84-95 Chiltonian 95-98 South Midlands

FACT FILE
Founded: 1908
Colours: Green & White/ Green/Green
Change colours: All blue
Midweek Matchday: Tuesday (7.45)
Programme: Yes - Inc.Admission
Editor: Bill Scholes (Chairman)

CLUB PERSONNEL
Chairman: Bill Scholes 01494 713867 (H)
Match Secretary: T.B.A.
Manager: Jez Hodges

LONDON COLNEY

Secretary: Dave Brock, 50 Seymour Rd., St Albans, Herts. AL3 5HW. Tel: 01727 761644 (H)
Ground: Cotslandswick, London Colney (01727 822132)
Directions: From London Colney r'bout (junction of A414/A1081) take A414 towards Watford, after layby (300yds) turn left (hidden turning marked `SportsGround') and follow around to gates.
Capacity: 1,000 Cover: 100 Seats: 30 Floodlights: Yes Club Shop:
Clubhouse: Open after games. Hot food available
HONOURS Sth Mids Lg Sen Div 94-95 R-up 93-94 (Chall. Tphy 93-94, Div 1 R-up 92-93, Res.Div 1 92-93), Herts Co. Lg 56-57 59-60 86-87 88-89 (R-up 57-58 58-59). Aubrey Cup 21-22 22-23 56-57 58-59 81-82, Res. Div 1 87-88 88-89 89-90 91-92, Res. Cup 62-63 89-90 91-92 (R-up 70-71)
PREVIOUS **Leagues:** Mid Herts 1907-54; Herts Co. 07-92
Ground: Whitehorse Lane 07-75
Record Attendance: 300 v St Albans City. Herts Senior Cup 98-99

FACT FILE
Founded: 1907 Nickname: Blueboys
Sponsors: City Glass
Colours: All Royal blue
Change Colours: Yellow/black/yellow
Midweek Matchday: Tuesday
Programme: £1 with entry
Editor: Bill Gash (01727 767556)

CLUB PERSONNEL
Chairman: Bill Gash
Vice Chairman: P Light
President: K.Parsons
Manager: Mick Wright
Physio: J Burt

MILTON KEYNES CITY

Secretary: Peter Baldwin,1 Wantage Close, Hackleton,Nirthants NN7 2AG (01604 870457 (H) 01908 245408 (W) FAX 01908 245088 (Fax at Work)
Ground: Wolverton Park,Old Wolverton Rd.,Wolverton,Milton Keynes MK12 5QH(01908 318317)
Directions: From A5 trunk road exit at Milton Keynes North onto Great Monks Way (V5). Continue over two oundabouts onto Old Wolverton Road. Ground is 1 milwe on right, between two railway arches and next to Wolverton BR station.p
Capacity: 3000 Cover: Yes Seats: 150 Floodlights: Yes Club Shop: No
Clubhouse: On ground and open normal opening hours.Closed Mondays
HONOURS: North Bucks Lge - Div 1 90-91, Prem. Div Cup 92-93, I'mediate Tphy 91-92; Daimler-Benz Austrian International Tournament R-up 1990 S.S.M.Lg Trophy Winners 99-00 **Previous Name:** Mercedes - Benz F.C.
PREVIOUS **Leagues:** Milton Keynes Sunday/ North Bucks & District (pre'93)
RECORD **Scorer:** Stuart Collard 132 **Appearances:** Stuart Collard 206 **Win:** 24-2 v Milton Keynes Saints, Berks & Bucks Jun Cup 1st Rd 16/10/93 **Defeat:** 1-8 v Greenleys, Milton Keynes Sun Lge Cup 1st Rd 22/11/87

FACT FILE
Founded: 1967 Nickname: Blues or City
Sponsors: P.B.I. International
Colours: All Royal Blue
Change Colours: Old Gold/Black/Old Gold
Midweek matches: Tuesday
Reserves' league: S.S.M. Reserve Div
Programme: 25 pages,£1.00
Editor: Stuart Collard, 01908 505042 (H), 01908 600394 (B)

CLUB PERSONNEL
Chairman: Bob Flight. President: T.B.A.
Manager: Terry Shrieves
Asst Man.: Zane Flanagan
Coach: Steve White Physio: Jackson Ryan

Right: Bridger Packaging FC.
Back Row (l-r): Jason Kitchener, Gareth Grant, Jason Gornall, Paul Starling, Craig Reynolds, John Furness, Perry Phillips. Next Row: Paul King, Tony Heath. Next Row: Mick Page, Mick Everitt, Graham Kinchin, Paul Gittings, Alan Gittings, Stuart Potasnick. Front Row: Kevin Higlett. Photo: Gordon Whittington

Below: Hoddesdon Town FC. Back Row (l-r): Paul Surridge (Manager), Ritchie Simmonds, Ian Barnes, Tony Dalli, Mark Foster, Richard Evans, Alex Clark, Matt Norman, Leon Hughton, Don Nicholson (Coach), Neil Conner, Jim Briggs (General Manager). Front Row: Darren White, Paul Evitt, Paul Mann, Barry White, Richard Howard, Matt Negus, Jeff Cross (Club Captain).

Above: Milton Keynes City FC. Back Row (l-r): Jason Hirst, Trevor Hopps, Darren Lynch. Middle Row: Zane Flanagan (Asst Manager), Simon Bloomfield, Seppi Lagioia, Andy Nichols (Physio), Dave Fenton, Gary Hartwell, Lee Broughton, Mark McCarthy, Tony Aluko, John Byrne, Wayne Calder, Abdul Aziz, Keith Brady, Steve White (Coach). Front Row: Gary Flynn, Maz Lagioia, Matt Quinn, James Kidd, Terry Shrieves (Manager), Paul Dart, Scott Watson, Lee Powell

NEW BRADWELL St PETER

Secretary: Les Smith,25 Bishopstone,Bradville, Milton Keynes. MK13 7OQ (01908 315736)
Ground: Recreation Ground, Bradwell Road, New Bradwell, Milton Keynes MK13 7AT
Tel.: 01908 313835
Directions: From M1 Jnt 14 go towards Newport Pagnell, left at 1st r-about into H3 (A422 Monks Way). Over 5 r-abouts, right at 6th island into V6 (GraftonSt.), At 1st roundabout go right the way round (back on yourself) then take 1st left at mini-r'about into Bradwell Rd. Go straight over next mini r'about. Ground immediately on left.
Capacity: Seats: 30   Cover: 100   Floodlights: Yes
Clubhouse: Members only (member can sign in 2 guests). Evenings & w/e mid day. No food.
HONOURS: Sth Mids Lg Div 1 76-77 83-84 Sen Div Champs 97-98, (Res Div 2 R-up 76-7), Berks& Bucks Senior Trophy Winners 1999-2000
PREVIOUS: **League:** North Bucks
    Names: Stantonbury St James (predecessors were New Bradwell St James); Stantonbury St Peters (until merger with New Bradwell Corinthians in 1946)

FACT FILE
Founded: 1902
Nickname: Peters
Colours: Maroon & blue stripes/maroon/maroon
Change: Amber/black/black.
Midweek matches: Tuesday
Programme: 32 pages, £2 with entry
Editor: Paul Smith 01908 550211 (H)
CLUB PERSONNEL
Chairman: John Haynes
President: J P Booden
Vice-Chairman: R.Creasey
Press Officer: P Smith
Manager: A Milne

POTTERS BAR TOWN

Secretary: Carole Waller, 26 Queen Annes Grove, Bush Hill Park, Enfield, Middx EN1 2JR
Tel: 020 8360 7859
GROUND: Parkfield, The Walk, Potters Bar, Herts EN6 1QN, 01707 654833
Directions: M25 jct 24, enter Potters Bar along Southgate Rd (A111), at 1st lights right into the High St (A1000), half mile left into The Walk, grd 200yds on right (opp. Potters Bar Cricket Club)
Capacity: 2,000   Seats: 25   Cover: 100   Floodlights: Yes   Club Shop: No Contact Jeff Barnes(01707 662399) for details of pennants,badges, car stickers and hangers etc.
Clubhouse: Sat 12.30-11pm, Sun noon-5pm, Tues & Thurs 7.30-11pm, midweek matchnights
HONOURS: South Midlands Lge. - Prem. Div. 96-97, Plate 96-97; Herts. Sen. Co. Lge. -Prem. Div. 90-91, Div. 1 73-74, 81-82, Div. 2 68-69; North London Comb. - Prem.Div. 67-68, Div. 1 67-68, Div. 2 R-up 65-66;SSMLg R-up 98-99 Prem Div North R-up 97-98 ,SML Floodlight Cup 99-00
PREVIOUS: **Leagues:** Barnet & Dist. 60-65/ N London Comb. 65-68/ Herts Snr Co. 68-91
RECORD: **Attendance:** 4000 v Eastenders XI, 20.4.97. 387 v Barnet, f/light open93
    Competitive: 268 v Wealdstone ,F.A.Cup 1998
BEST SEASON: FA Vase: 6th Rd 97-98

FACT FILE
Founded: 1960
Nickname: The Grace or The Scholars
Sponsors: T.B.A.
Colours: Red & royal stripes/royal/royal Blue & Yellow stripes/ryellow/yellow
Midweek matchday: Tuesday or Wednesday
Programme: 20pages, £1
Editor/PRO Jeff Barnes (01707 660445 Fax)
CLUB PERSONNEL
Chairman: Peter Waller
Vice Chairman: Alan Bolt
President: B Wright General Mger: L Eason
Manager:DaveWhitehead.Coach:JohnMeakes
Physio: Brian Goymer

ROYSTON TOWN

Secretary/Press Officer: Elaine Phillips, 14 Roan walk, Royston, Herts SG8 9HT
Tel No: 01763 241041 (H)
GROUND: Garden Walk, Royston, Herts SG8 7HP (01763 241204).
Directions: FromBaldock, A505 to Royston bypass, right at 2nd island onto A10 towards London, 2nd left is Garden Walk; ground 100 yds on left.
Capacity: 4,000   Seats: 300   Cover: 300   Floodlights: Yes   Club Shop: Yes
Clubhouse: Mon-Thurs 7-11, Fri 11-3 & 7-11, Sat 11-3 & 4-11, Sun 12-3.

HONOURS   Herts Co. Lg 76-77 (Div 1 69-70 76-77); Sth Mids Lg R-up 79-80 (Div 1 78-79,Chall. Cup R-up 78-79
PREVIOUS   **Leagues:** Buntingford & Dist. 18-28; Cambs 28-50; Herts Co. 50-59 62-77; SthMids 59-62 77-84; Isthmian 84-94
RECORDS   **Attendance:** 876 v Aldershot, 13/2/93
    Scorer: Trevor Glasscock 289 (1968-82)   **Appearances:** Fred Bradley 713
BEST SEASON   FA Cup: 2nd Qual. Rnd 59-60, 0-9 v Barnet (A), 89-90, 0-3 V Bromley (A)

FACT FILE
Founded: 1875   Nickname: Crows
Res League: Essex & Herts Border Comb
Sponsors: ABA Consultants
Colours: White/black/black& white
Change colours: Red/white/white
Midweek Matches: Tuesday
Programme: 16 pages, 30p
Editor: Secretary
CLUB PERSONNEL
Chairman: Tony Moulding
Vice-Chairman: Bernard Brown
President: Alan Barlow
Manager: Kevin Pugh
Asst Mgr: S Salomone   Physio: C Mardell

RUISLIP MANOR

Secretary: John Price, 1 Filey Way, Ruislip,Middlesex (01895 631933)
Ground: Grosvenor Vale, off West End Rd, Ruislip, Middx 01895 637487-office,676168-boardroom
Directions: A40 to Ruislip, turn off on A4180, right at r'bout into West EndRd, right into Grosvenor Vale after a 1 1/2 miles - ground at end. From RuislipManor station (Metropolitan Line) turn left out of station, then 1st right intoShenley Ave, 3rd left into Cranley Dr - ground 150 yds on left
Capacity: 3,000   Seats: 250   Cover: 600   Floodlights: Yes   Club Shop: Yes
Clubhouse: Mon-Fri 12-3.30 & 5.30-11pm, Sat & Sun 12-3 & 7.30-10.30
HONOURS   London Lg R-up 51-52 (Div 1 R-up 47-48), Isthmian Lg Div 2 R-up 92-93 (Associate Members Tphy 90-91), Athenian Lg Div 2 72-73, Middx Snr Cup SF (6), Middx Charity Cup R-up 90-91 95-96
PREVIOUS   **Leagues:** Uxbridge 38-39; Middx Snr 39-46; London 46-58; Spartan 58-65; Athenian65-84; Isthmian 84-96
RECORDS   **Attendance:** 2,000 v Tooting & Mitcham United, F.A. Amateur Cup 1962
    Appearances: Chris Balls, 350 **Goalscorer:** Kevin Quinn, 76
BEST SEASON   FA Cup: 4th Q Rd 90-91, 2-5 v Halesowen T (A) F.A.Am.Cup: 1st Rd 73-74

FACT FILE
Founded: 1938   Nickname: The Manor
Sponsors: Golf Course Management
Colours: Black & White/black/black
Change colours: Yellow & blue/yellow/yellow
Midweek Matches: Monday
Reserve League: Suburban Lge (North)
Programme: 24 Price: 50p
Editor/ Press Off.: Tom O'Shea
01895 625458

CLUB PERSONNEL
Chairman: Tom O'Shea
Vice Chairman: Craig Smith
Manager:Keith Chamberlain
Physio: Gary Strudwick

St MARGARETSBURY

Secretary: Christine O'Driscoll.114 Winchester Road,Edmonton,LondonN9 9EE(020 8803 9744)

GROUND: Station Road, Stanstead St Margarets, Nr Ware, Herts (01920 870473)

Directions: Harlow/Chelmsford exit from A10 to A414, take B181 at Amwell roundabout after 300yds towards Stanstead Abotts, ground quarter mile on right. 300yds from St Margaretsbury BR station (Liverpool Str.-Hertford East line)

Capacity: 1,000   **Seats**: 60   **Cover**: 60   **Floodlights**: Yes   **Club Shop**: No

Clubhouse: Bar open every evening 7.30-11, plus Sat 12-2, Sun 12-3. Bar snacks available

HONOURS: Herts Snr Cent Tphy 92-93; Herts Co. Lg Div 2 48-49, Div 3 78-79; Aubrey Cup 48-49 71-72; Res. Div 1 82-83 86-87; Res. Cup 84-85 86-87 87-88); Waltham &Dist Lg 46-47; Spartan Lge 95-96; Roy Bailey Mem Trophy 95-96, Herts Charity Shield 97-98.

PREVIOUS: Lges: East Herts; Hertford & Dist.; Waltham & District 47-48; Herts Co. 48-92

RECORD: Attendance: 327 v Wisbech Town, FA Vase 3rd Round 14/12/85

BEST SEASON   FA Vase: 3 Rd 1985

FACT FILE

Founded: 1894   Nickname: The Bury
Sponsors: Lawfords Building Supplies
Colours: Red & black/black/red & black
Change colours: All white
Midweek matchday: Tuesday
Reserve Lg: Essex & Herts Border Comb.
Programme: £3.00 with entry
Editor/Match Sec.: Lyn Groulott
Tel: 01992 424639

CLUB PERSONNEL
Chairman: Dave Stock
President: R L Groucott
Manager: Bill O'Driscoll Asst Mng:Nick Wood
Physio: John Elliott

SOMERSETT AMBURY V & E

Secretary: Peter Harris, 30 Lordship Road, Cheshunt, Herts. EN7 5DP
Tel : 01992 429297 (H) 0208 345 1133(W)

Ground: V & E Club, Goffs lane, Cheshunt, Herts. Tel: 01992 624281

Capacity: 500   **Seats:** 20   **Cover:** Yes   **Floodlights:** Yes   **Club Shop:** No

Directions: M25 junct. 25, A10 towards Cheshunt. Take the first left at the first roundabout onto the B198 (Cuffley & Goffs Oak). At the end of the road turn right off roundabout into Goffs lane. Clubhouse on immediate right.

Previous League: Herts County

FACT FILE
Founded: 1959
Colours: White & blue/blue/blue
Change Colours: Orange/white/orange
Midweek Matchday: Tuesday
Reserves League; Essex ,Herts Border
Programme Editor: Peter Harris
01992 429297 (H) 0181 345 1133 (B)

CLUB PERSONNEL
Chairman:Dave Bidwell
Tel: 01992 428187 (H)
Vice Chairman:Mario Persico
President: Doug Bacon
Manager: T.B.A.

WALTHAM ABBEY

Secretary: Alex Myers, 88 The Weymarks, Weir Hall Road, Tottenham N17 8LD.
Tel/Fax: 0181 808 2706 (H)

GROUND: `Capershotts', Sewardstone Road, Waltham Abbey, Essex (01992 711287)
Directions: Just off M25 jct 26. Waltham Cross (BR Eastern Region) station three miles distant. 242 Bus

Capacity: 2,000   **Seats**: 100   **Cover**: 400   **Floodlights**: Yes   **Club Shop**: No
Clubhouse: 7-11pm Mon-Fri, 11am-11pm Sat, noon-3pm Sun. Cold snacks, pool, darts

HONOURS: Middx Sen Charity Cup R-up 97-98; London Sen Cup 98-99; SSM Lge Chall Trophy 98-99

PREVIOUS: Leagues: Northen Suburban
RECORDS: Attendance: 1,800 v Spurs, charity game
   Scorer: Paul Holloway   **Appearances**: Colin Winter
BEST SEASON   **FA Cup**: Prel. Rd 90-91
   FA Vase: Prel. Rd 87-88 88-89 89-90

FACT FILE
Founded: 1948
Nickname: The Abbey
Colours: All green and white
Change colours: Al White with green trim
Midweek matches: Tuesday
Reserves' Lge: Essex & Herts Border Comb
Programme: 8 pages 50p
Editor: John Thorpe 01992 892653 (H)

CLUB PERSONNEL
Chairman: Joe Collins
President: Dennis Cordell
Manager: T.B.A.

WELWYN GARDEN CITY

Secretary: James Bruce, 6 Autumn Grove, Welwyn G.C., Herts AL7 4DB. Tel: 01707331048 (H)

GROUND: Herns Lane, Welwyn Garden City (01707 328470)
Directions: From A1 follow signs for industrial area. Take one-way systemopposite Avdel Ltd (signed Hertford B195), take 2nd exit off one-way system.Ground 400 yards on left. One and a half miles from Welwyn GC (BR)

Capacity: 1,500   **Seats**: 40   **Cover**: 120   **Floodlights**: Yes   **Club Shop**: Yes
Clubhouse: Open every night and weekend lunchtimes. Members Bar, Hall. Steward:D Parham

HONOURS: Herts Snr Centenary Tphy 84-85 (R-up 88-89), Herts Charity Shield 27-28 86-8787-88 94-95 (R-up 48-49), Sth Mids Lg 73-74 (R-up 85-86, Div 1 69-70 81-82, LgCup R-up 74-75 81-82 88-89, Reserve Cup 85-86)

PREVIOUS: Leagues: Spartan; Metropolitan; Gtr London. **Ground**: Springfields
RECORD: Attendance: 600 v Welwyn Garden United
BEST SEASON: FA Vase: 1st Rd 86-87   **FA Cup**: First Qual.Rd. 94-95

FACT FILE
Founded: 1921   Nickname: Citzens
Colours: Maroon & blue/blue/maroon
Change Colours: Yellow/blue/yellow
Midweek Matches: Tuesday
Programme: 24 pages, 50p
Editor: Tina Debenham(01707 892940)
Local Press: Welwyn & Hatfield Times,
Welwyn & Hatfield Herald & Post

CLUB PERSONNEL
Chairman: Terry Hazel
Manager: David Steedman
Physio: Arthur Wood

GET ALL THE LATEST NEWS ON THE

THE FOOTBALL ASSOCIATION

COMPETITIONS
NEWSLINE

Updated daily with Draws, Match Dates, Change of Venues, Kick-off Times and Midweek Results for the F.A. Cup sponsored by AXA, F.A. Umbro Trophy, F.A. Carlsberg Vase, AXA F.A. Youth Cup, AXA F.A. Women's Cup and F.A. Umbro Sunday Cup. Saturday and Sunday results will be on the Newsline after 6.30pm - Midweek results available after 10.00pm - Cup draws on Monday after 1.00pm.

PHONE NOW
09066 555 888

Presented by Tony Incenzo

Marketed by Sportslines, Scrutton Street, London EC2A 4PJ   Tel: 01386 550204

Calls cost 60p per minute at all times.

OR FAX-BACK ON
09065 511 051

Weekend results, Monday draws and midweek fixtures and results service

Calls cost £1.00 per minute at all times.
Call costing correct at time of going to press (June 2000)

AMERSHAM TOWN

FACT FILE

Secretary: Michael Gahagan, 7 Ely Close, Lincoln Pk,Amersham,Bucks.HP7 9HS (01494 24798)
GROUND: Spratley's Meadow, School Lane, Old Amersham, Bucks. (01494 727428)
Directions: From London A413 to Amersham Old town, in front of market hall, right into Church St., first left into School Lane, ground on left past Mill Lane. 1 mile from Amersham Station - BR & underground Metropolitan Line
Capacity: 1,500   **Seats:** 50   **Cover:** 100   **Floodlights:** Yes   **Club Shop:** No
Clubhouse: Open matchdays. Bar facilities. Teas, coffees and light snacks
HONOURS: Hellenic Lg 63-64 (R-up 64-65 65-66, Div 1 62-63, Cup 53-54), Ldn Spartan Lg R-up 79-80, St Marys Cup 89-90 96-97 (R-up 90-91,96-97), B & Bucks Jnr Cup 22-23 (Snr Cup SF 79-80 80-81), Wycombe Chal. Cup 23-24
1998-99 Leading Scorer& P.o.Y.: Satoshi Otani.   Manager's P.o.Y. John Smyth

Founded: 1890   **Nickname:** Magpies
Colours: Black & white stripes/black/black
Change colours: All Red
Midweek matches: Tuesday
Reserve's League: Middx Co
Prog. Editor: Michael Gahagan
CLUB PERSONNEL
Chairman: David Holdcroft
President: Graham Taylor
Manager: Paul Pitfield   **Coach:** Richard Mount

AMPTHILL TOWN

Secretary: Eric Turner, 34 Dunstable Street, Ampthill, Beds MK45 2JT.
Tel:01525 403128 (H & B)

Ground: Ampthill Park, Woburn Road, Ampthill, Beds. Tel: 01525 404440

Directions: From Ampthill Town Centre follow signs to Woburn then take the first right into Ampthill Park

Chairman: Michael Lomax
Tel: 01525 755343 (H)

Manager: Nicholas Burton

Programme Editor: Graham Ford
Tel:01234 346806

Colours: Yellow & navy blue/navy/navy
Change Colours: Green/black/black

BIGGLESWADE UNITED

Secretary: Tracey James, 17 Havelock Road, Biggleswade, Beds SG18 0DB.
Tel: 01767 316270 (H), 020 7270 6045(B), 0771 466 1827(M)
GROUND: Second Meadow, Fairfield Road, Biggleswade, Beds. (01767 600408)
Directions: From A1 Sainsbury's roundabout, cross over iron bridge and take 2nd left into Sun Street.(before Peugot Garage) Take first left into Fairfield Road ground at bottom of road in lane
Capacity: 2,000   **Seats:** 30   **Cover:** 130   **Floodlights:** Yes   **Club Shop:** No
Clubhouse: Open all matchdays, rolls available. Also refreshment hut with hot snacks
HONOURS: Hunts F.A. Prem Cup : 98-99,S.Mids Lg Div 1 96-97 Cup Winners 96-97Beds & District Prtem Div.94-95, 95-96, Div 1. 91-92, Div2 90-91,Div3 88-89 Beds F.A. Inter Cup (2)
Record Crowd: 250 v Biggleswade Town 28.12.98 **Previous Name:**Biggleswade F.C.
Best Season in F.A.Vase: 1st Rd Proper 95-96

Founded: 1959 (original club 1935)
Colours: Red/navy/navy
Change : Yellow & Black
Midweek Matchday: Tuesday /Thursday
Prog-With admission Editor: Secretary

Chairman: David McCormick.(01767 316018)
Match Sec.: Mick Brown, (01767 221512)
Manager: 'Snowy' Wright
Physio: Phil Lunceford

BRIDGER PACKAGING

Secretary: Laurence Jack, 17 Curlew Close, Letchworth, Herts. SG6 4TG.
Tel: 01462 625936 (H), 0181 905 1992 (B)

Ground: Letchworth Corner Sports Club, Muddy Lane, Letchworth, Herts. SG6 3TB.
Tel: 01462 486459

Directions: A1(M) junc 9 towards Letchworth, over large roundabout, turn left at next roundabout A505 Hitchin, through lights, turn left at pelican crossing into Muddy Lane

Colours: Sky blue & yellow stripes/sky blue/ sky blue & yellow

Programme Editor: John Furness
Tel: 01462 627279 (H)

Chairman: Lawrence Bridger

Manager: Paul Starling
Tel: 01483 227520 (H)

BRIMSDOWN ROVERS

FACT FILE

Secretary: Mrs Lorraine Winter, 5 Sunnyside Road East, Edmonton, London N9 0SP (Tel & Fax: 020 8807 3666 and Mobile: 07747 681044)
GROUND: Brimsdown Sports & Social Club, Goldsdown Road, Enfield, Middlesex Tel: 0181 804 5491 **Directions:** BR from Liverpool Street to Brimsdown (half mile away) or Southbury Road. By road off Green Street, itself off Hertford Road (A1010). Buses 191 or307
Capacity: 1,000   **Seats:** 25**Cover:** 50**Floodlights:** Yes   Club Shop:
Clubhouse: Large lounge & clubroom, games room & stage. 3 bars (300 capacity)
HONOURS: Spartan Lg 92-93. Spartan Lg Cup 95-96
RECORD: **Gate:** 412 v Chesham Utd, FA Cup 3rd Qual. Rd 12/10/91
BEST SEASON: **FA Vase:** 3rd Rd 93-94   **FA Cup:** 3rd Qual. replay 91-92
PREVIOUS: **Leagues:** Northern Suburban   **Names:** Durham Rovers; Brimsdown FC

Founded: 1947
Colours: Black & white stripes/black/black
Change colours: Yellow/Blue/Yellow
Midweek Matchday: Tuesday
Programme: With admission
Editor: Peter Wade
Chairman: Tony Ashall
Match Secretary: Peter Wade.
5 Goldsdown Rd., Enfield Middlesex EN3
Tel: 0208 804 7053
Manager: Kelvin Hart

COCKFOSTERS

Secretary: Graham Bint, 15 Chigwell Park, Chigwell, Essex IG7 5BE (0181 500 7369)
GROUND: Cockfosters Sports Ground, Chalk Lane, Cockfosters, Barnet (0181 449 5833)
Directions: M25 Jct 24 (Potters Bar), take A111 signed Cockfosters - ground 2 miles on right.
Adjacent to Cockfosters underground station (Picadilly Line). Bus 298 to Cockfosters station
Capacity: 1,000   Seats: None   Cover: 50   Floodlights: Yes   Club Shop: No
Clubhouse: 7-11pm Tues & Thurs, 4-11pm Sat, 12-3pm Sun. Hot & cold food onmatchdays
HONOURS: London Interm Cup 70-71 89-90, Herts Snr Co. Lg 78-79 80-81 83-84 R-up
82-83 84-85, Aubrey Cup 78-79 84-85 R-up 70-71 77-78, Herts Interm Cup 78-79 R-up x3
Previous Leagues: Wood Green & Dist. 21-46/ Northern Suburban 46-66/ Herts Snr Co.66-91
BEST SEASON: FA Vase: 2nd Round 91-92
RECORDS: Gate: 408 v Saffron Walden, Herts Senior County Lg 68-69

Founded: 1921   Nickname: Fosters
Colours: All Red
Change colours: All White
Midweek matches: Tuesday
Reserve League: SSM Res Sect
Programme: 12 pages with entry
Editor: A Simmons (0181 440 7998)

Chairman/Press Off.: Frank Brownlie
(0181 500 5930)
President: Vic Bates
Manager: Tony Faulkner
Physio: John Walsh

COLNEY HEATH

Secretary: Michael Wright, 5 Grove Lea, Hatfield, Herts. AL10 8LA
Tel: 01707 880825 (H) 0956 937895 (M)

Ground: The Pavillion Recreaton Ground, High St., Colney Heath, St. Albans, Herts.
Tel: 01727 826188

Directions: Turn off the A414 (was A405) into Colney Heath village and the ground is
behind the school on the left.

DE HAVILLAND

Secretary: Roy Ridgway, 85 Garden Ave., Hatfield, Herts AL10 8LH.
Tel: 01707 267327 (H)

Ground: De Havilland (Hatfield) Sports & Social Club, Comet Way, Hatfield
Tel: 01707 263204

Directions: From south leave A1(M) at Hatfield turn, A1001 to Birchwood
r'bout,1st exit into car park.
From north leave A1(M) at Welwyn G.C., A1001 to Birchwood
r'bout and 4th exit into car park

DUNSTABLE TOWN

Secretary: Colin Howes, 3 Rotherwood Close, Dunstable, Beds LU6 1UA
Tel: 01582 478395

Ground: Creasey Park, Brewers Hill Rd, Dunstable

Directions: Travel north on A5, Through centre Dunstable, left at 1st r/about
into Brewers Hill Rd, str over mini r/about, grd on right

GREENACRES (Hemel Hempstead)

Secretary: Rebecca Pass, 85 Northend, H. Hempstead, Herts HP3 8TW
Tel: 01442 390260 (H)

Ground: Hemel Hempstead FC, Vauxhall Rd., Adeyfield, Hemel Hempstead.
Tel: 01442 259777

Directions: M1 J8; over two roundabouts, then first right off dual carriageway.
First left and then right at roundabout

Capacity: 3,000   **Seats:** 100   **Cover:** Yes   **Floodlight:** Yes   **Club Shop:** No

Clubhouse: as for Hemel Hempstead F.C.

Colours: All Green & white
Change Colours;Red & White
Midweek Matchday: Wednesday
Programme: £1.00
Editor: Rebecca Pass (Sec.)

Chairman: David Boggins 01442 264300 (H)
Match Sec. David Lloyd 01442 259721 (H)
Manager: T.B.A.

HAREFIELD UNITED

Secretary: Terry Devereux, 72 Williamson Way, Rickmansworth, Herts WD3 2GL.
Tel: 01923 711451 (H/B)
GROUND: Preston Park, Breakespeare Rd North, Harefield, Middx UB9 6DG (01895 823474)
Directions: M25 jct 16 to M40 East, left at 1st roundabout, then 2nd left into Harvill Rd. Follow road up the Church Hill into village, right at mini roundabout, ground on right. Denham (BR)
Capacity: 2,000   **Seats:** 100   **Cover:** Yes   **Floodlights:** Yes   **Club Shop:** No
Clubhouse: (01895 823474) Lunchtimes and evenings. Cold snacks (hot on matchdays)
HONOURS: Middx Premier Cup 85-86, Athenian Lg R-up 83-84, Parthenon Lg 64-65
(Div 1 Cup 65-66), Middx Lg 66-67 68-71 (Lg Cup 66-67 68-69)
BEST SEASON: **FA Cup:** 2nd Qual. Rd replay 80-81, 86-87 **F.A.Vase:** 6th Rd 1989-90
RECORD: **Gate:** 430 v Bashley, FA Vase

Founded: 1868   Nickname: Hares
Colours: Red & white stripes/black/red
Change colours: Yellow /red/black
Midweek Matches: Tuesday
Reserves' League: Suburban
Programme: 12-40 pages, 30p
Editor: Terry Deveraux (Sec.)

Chairman: Keith Ronald. Tel: 01895 824287
President: Dave West
Manager: Stuart Levy

HARPENDEN TOWN

Secretary: Neil Ludlow, 93 RussellSt.,Luton,Beds LU1 5EB 01582 486802(H) 01582 424233(W)
GROUND: Rothamsted Park, Amenbury Lane, Harpenden (01582 715724)
Directions: A1081 to Harpenden. Turn left/right at George Hotel into Leyton Rd.Turn left into Amenbury Rd, then left again (50yds) into `Pay and Display' carpark - entrance is signposted thru car park to opposite corner
Capacity: 1,500   **Seats:** 25   **Cover:** 100   **Floodlights:** Yes   **Club Shop:** No
Clubhouse: Open matchdays
HONOURS: Sth Mids Lg 61-62 64-65, Ch'ship Shield 67-68, Lg Cup 70-71, Div 1 89-90, Prem Div Tphy 89-90; Mid-Herts Lg 09-10 20-21, Div 1 99-00; Herts Co. Lg 11-12 49-50 51-52 53-54
PREVIOUS: **Leagues:** Mid-Herts; Herts County   **Best Seasons:** F.A.Cup: 1st Rd Q
Name: Harpenden FC 1891-1908   F.A.Vase: 2nd Rd

FACT FILE
Founded: 1891
Nickname: The Town
Colours: Yellow/blue/blue
Change:Red & Black Hoops/Black/Black
Midweek matches: Tuesday
Programme: 50p
Editor: Chairman

CLUB PERSONNEL
Chairman: Stephen Whiting (01582 761606)
Manager: Mike Oleseinde (01582 765598)

LANGFORD

Secretary: Frank Woodward, 4 West View, Langford, Biggleswade. Beds. SG18 9RT
Tel: 01462 701015 (H)
GROUND: Forde Park, Langford Road, Henlow SG16 6AF (01462 816106).
Directions: Halfway between Langford and Henlow on A6001 Hitchin to Biggleswade road. Bus 177 on main Hitchin-Biggleswade route stops right outside ground
Capacity: 4,000   **Seats:** 50   **Cover:** 250   **Floodlights:** Yes   **Club Shop:** Yes
Clubhouse: Weekday evenings, matchdays 11am-11pm, Sun 12-3pm. Hot food on matchdays
HONOURS: S Mids Lg 88-89 (Lg Cup 73-74 75-76, Prem. Div Tphy 88-89,94-95.O'Brien Div 1Tphy 84-85), N Beds Charity Cup 27-28 30-31 69-70 75-76 86-87 92-93 94-95 98-99 Bedford & Dist. Lg 30-31 31-32 32-33, Bedford I'mediate Cup 68-69, Hinchingbrooke Cup 72-73
RECORD: **Gate:** 450 v Q.P.R., 75th Anniversary and clubhouse opening, 22/8/85

Founded: 1910   Nickname: Reds
Sponsors: B.B & E.A. (Sandy); `The Boot' Pub & Rest
Colours: All red with white trim
Change Colours: Blue & white
Midweek matches: Tuesday
Programme: With admission.
Editors: Bob Reed 01462 700155 (H)
Chairman: Mick Quinlan
President: Ted Rutt
Commercial Manager: Diane Woodward
Manager: Jim Burke

LETCHWORTH

Secretary: Paul Hopkins, 5 Chatterton, Letchworth, Herts (01462 674036)
Ground: Baldock Road, Letchworth, Herts SG6 2GN (01462 637979)
Directions: Jct 9 (A6141) off A1M straight over large r-about, right at next r-about, ground on right. From Luton (A505) thru Hitchin, ground 3 miles afterHitchin. 2 miles from Letchworth (BR)
Capacity: 3,200   **Cover:** 400 **Seats:** 200   **Floodlights:** Yes   **Clubhouse:** No:
HONOURS: Herts Lg 11-12, Spartan Lg 29-30 35-36 51-52, Delphian Lg 57-58, Athenian Lg 74-75 (Mem. Shield 65-66 66-67), Herts Snr Cup 12-13 35-36 51-52, Herts Charity Shield 22-23 47-48 87-88 91-92, East Anglian Cup 76-77, Woolwich Cup 81-82, Hitchin Cup 81-82 Senior DivisionTrophy Winners: 99-00
PREVIOUS: Leagues: Herts Co. 06-07; Biggleswade 07-08; Nth Herts 08-22 ,S Mids 22-23 24-29; Spartan 29-56; Athenian 63-77; Isthmian 77-90

FACT FILE
Founded: 1906
Nickname: Bluebirds
Colours: All Blue
Change Colours: Red & white stripes/red/red
Midweek matchday: Tuesday
Programme: 24 pages, 50p Editor: Keith Brown 0385 338584
CLUB PERSONNEL
Chairman: Graham Hopkins
Match Sec.: T.B.A.
Manager: Kerry Dixon

LEVERSTOCK GREEN

Secretary: Brian Barter, 11 Curlew Close, Berkhamsted, Herts HP4 2HZ (01442 862322)
GROUND: Pancake Lane, Leverstock Green, Hemel Hempstead. Tel: 01442 246280.
Directions: From M1 leave at A4147 to 2nd r-about. 1st exit to LeverstockGreen, Pancake Lane is on left 300 yrds past the `Leather Bottle' pub
Capacity: **Seats:** 25   **Cover:** 100   **Floodlights:** Yes **Club Shop:** Yes   **Clubhouse:** Yes, one hour before kick-off but no food

HONOURS: South Midlands Lge - Sen. Div 96-97, Sen Div Cup R-up 93-94, Herts CentenaryTphy R-up 91-92, Herts Charity Shield R-up 91-92, Frank Major Tphy 1991
PREVIOUS: Leagues: West Herts (pre-1950); Herts County 50-91
Players progressing to Football League: Dean Austin (Tottenham Hotspur)

Founded: 1895 Nickname: The Green
Sponsor: Sunshine Cabs
Colours: Yellow/Blue/Blue
Change Colours: Green & black/white/black
Midweek Matchday: Tuesday
Programme: 24 pages, 50p
Editor: Bill Dawes (Chairman)
Chairman: Bill Dawes, 01442 395748 (H)
Match Sec: Brian Pollard 01442 256720 (H)
Press Officer: Brian Pollard
Manager: Brian Jackson
Coach: Brian Howard

LUTON OLD BOYS

Secretary Terry Owen, 29 Elm Park Close, Houghton Regis, Dunstable, Beds. LU5 5PN
Tel: 01582 863273 (H) 01582 664264 (B)

Ground Luton Old Boys Association , Dunstable Road, Luton.
Tel: 01582 582060

Directions On the A505 Luton to Dunstable Road towards Luton, between J 11 of the M1 and Chaul End Lane. **NB** - there is **NO** right turn approaching from Dunstable direction.

Chairman: Terry McCabe

Manager: Guillermo Garnet

Programme Editor: Secretary

Colours: Red /Black/Black
Change Colours: White/ Red/ red

RISBOROUGH RANGERS

Secretary: Derrick J Wallace, 42 Ash Road, Princes Risborough, Bucks, HP27 0BQ
Tel: 01844 345179 (H), 01844 345435 (B)
GROUND: `Windsor', Horsenden Lane, Princes Risborough. (01844 274176)
Directions: Rear of Princes Risborough BR Station (Chiltern Line). A4010 fromAylesbury thru Princes Risborough, fork right onto A4009, left by thatched cottage, over railway bridge, immediate right ground 150 yds on right
Capacity: 2,000 **Seats:** 25 **Cover:** 100 **Floodlights:** No **Club Shop:** No
Clubhouse: Yes. Snacks available matchdays
HONOURS: Berks & Bucks Jnr Cup 85-86, Wycombe & Dist Lg D 2 85-86 D 3 84-85
PREVIOUS: **League:** Wycombe & Dist. 71 -
RECORD: **Gate:** 1,200 v Showbiz XI **Scorer:** Craig Smith

Founded: 1971
Club Sponsors: Systems 3R
Colours: Red & white/red/red&white
Change Colours: Blue & white/blue/white
Midweek matches: Tuesday
Programme: 20+ pages, £1 with entry
Chairman: Trevor Taylor
Tel: 01844 342202 (H)
Manager: Jon Franklyn

STONY STRATFORD TOWN

Secretary: Maurice J Barber, 26 Boundary Cres., Stony Stratford, Milton Keynes MK11 1DF
Tel: 01908 567930 (H)
GROUND: Sports Ground, Ostlers Lane, Stony Stratford (01908 562267).
Directions: From Dunstable use old A5, Watling Street. Approaching Bletchley continue on A5 loop road (Hinkley) to end of dual c'way to A422/A508 r'bout. First exit, thru lights, 2nd right into Ostlers Lane.
Capacity: 2000 **Seats:** 30 **Cover:** 120 **Floodlights:** Yes **Club Shop:** No
Clubhouse: Open evenings & weekends
HONOURS: Sth Mids Lg R-up 70-71 71-72 (Div 1 93-94, Div 1 Cup 93-94)
PREVIOUS: **Leagues:** North Bucks & Dist.; Northampton Combination
RECORD: **Attendance:** 476 v Aston Villa u21, floodlight opening 12.11.96

Reformed: 1953
Sponsor: BILDOR Transport & BUSIPRINT
Colours: Sky blue/navy/navy
Change Colours: All yellow
Midweek matches: Tuesday
Reserves' League: SSM Res. Div. One
Programme: 28 pages, 50p
Editor: Maurice Barber (Sec.)
Chairman: Glyn Horwood
Match Sec.: Robin Gustafson
Manager: Perry Mercer

TOTTERNHOE

Secretary: Jim Basterfield, 41 Park Avenue, Totternhoe, Dunstable, Beds LU6 1QF.
Tel: 01582 667941 (H)
GROUND: Totternhoe Recreation Ground, Dunstable (01582 606738)
Directions: Turn off the main Dunstable to Tring Road B489. Ground on right as you enter Totternhoe. Five miles from Leighton Buzzard (BR), 7 miles fromLuton. Bus 61 Luton-Aylesbury
Capacity: 1,000 **Seats:** 30 **Cover:** 200 **Floodlights:** No **Club Shop:** No
Clubhouse: Evenings 8pm, Saturday after games, Sunday lunch. Tea,coffee, soups at matches
HONOURS: S. Mids Lg Div 1 61-2 (R/u 68-9 85-6), Beds Sen Cup R/u 69-70 86-7 91-2, Beds I'mediate Cup 77-8 (R/u 81-2), Luton & Dist. Lg 57-8
PREVIOUS: **League:** Luton & Dist. (pre-1958)
RECORDS: **Gate:** 300 v Luton Town, clubhouse opening 13/10/82

Founded: 1906 Nickname: Totts
Sponsors: Sovereign Coaches
Colours: All red
Change Colours: All Blue
Midweek matchday: Tuesday
Programme: 16 pages with entry
Editor: Steve Massey 01908 392313 (H)
Chairman: Jim Basterfield
Vice Chairman: Gifford Kelly
President: Alf Joyce
Manager:Alex Butler
Physio: Roy Mackerness

TRING ATHLETIC

Secretary: Ralph Griffiths, 42 Bedgrove, Aylesbury, Bucks HP21 7BD.
Tel: 0129626425 (H), 01296 393363 x 278 (B)
Ground: Miswell Lane, Tring, Herts. (01442 828331) **Directions:** Through Tring on main rd towards Aylesbury, right after Anchor PH into Miswell Lane, grd 500yds on right opposite Beaconsfield Rd. Tring station is several miles outside town, grd by bus ortaxi
Capacity: **Seats:** 25+ **Cover:** 100+ **Floodlights:** No **Club Shop:** No
Clubhouse: Bar, open matchdays, training nights & Sunday lunchtimes
HONOURS: West Herts Lg R-up 72-73 (Lg Cup 65-66, Div 1 61-62 64-65 65-66 (R-up 71-72 85-86), Div 2 (res) 71-72 (R-up 62-63), Div 3 R-up 83-84, Reserve Cup 72-73,
PREVIOUS: **League:** West Herts 58-88
RECORD **Scorer:** Ian Butler **Appearances:** Alan Sheppard

Founded: 1958 Nickname: Athletic
Sponsors: Heygates
Colours: Red & black/black/black
Change colours: yellow/green/yellow
Midweek matchday: Wednesnay
Programme: 36 pages, 50p Editor: Sec
President: Paul Nichols
Chairman: S Thomas Tel: 01442 381633 (H)
Manager: Mick Eldridge
Asst Manager: Ray Brimson
Physio: Jean Adams

Left: Tring Athletic
Back Row: Mick Eldridge (Joint Manager), Keith Eldridge, Jeb Stewart, Jamie McBeath, Ian Ranger, Grant Mosley, John Perry, Will Saintey, Tom Vincent, Marc Boniface, Richard Vincent (Joint Manager). Front Row: Ray Brimson, Richard Shirley, Matt Ruscoe, Danny Robbins, Gary Langdale, Paul Lewis, Andy Humphreys, Ben Chesters.
Photo: Gordon Whittington

Above: Dunstable Town FC. Back Row (l-r): Lyndon Moore, Tony Lang, Steve Howarth, Simon Gooding, Micky Benham, Shane Blackett, Steve Castleman, Paul Reeves (Manager), John Bell (Physio), Dave Healey (Committee). Front Row: Ikeme Ojulah, Martin Large, Darren Croft (Manager), Paul Taylor, Dave Morgan, Scott Harvey, Clive Douglas. Photo: Gordon Whittington

Above: Leverstock Green FC. Back Row (l-r): Bill Dawes (Chairman), Brian Jackson (Manager), Antony Perry, Kevin Godbold, Robert Mooney, Dave Hindle, Matt Griffin, Gary Woolf, Bernie Chapman (Physio), Brian Howard (Coach). Front Row: Andy Still, Steve Kempson, Paul Jackson, James Bates, Lewis Saville, Martin Hollick.

ABBEY NATIONAL (M.K.)
Secretary: kerry McGregor, 25a Cruickshank Grove, Crownhill, Milton Keynes MK8 OEW (01908 265969)
Ground: Loughton Sports & Social Club, Lincesdale Grove, loughton, Milton Keynes. Tel: 01908 690668
Directions: From M1 Jct 14 follow H6, Childs Way for 5 miles until V4 Watling Way (Knowlhill r-about), right to Loughton r-about, right along H5 Portway 1st right Linceslade Grove

BUCKINGHAM ATHLETIC
Secretary: Colin Howkins, 13 Poplars Road, Buckingham, Bucks Mk18 1BQ (01280 817498)
Ground: Stratford Fields, Stratford Rd, Buckingham Tel: 01280 816945
Directions: From Milton Keynes take the A422 Stony Stratford-Buckingham road -ground on left just before town centre. From Oxford, Aylesbury or Bletchley, take the ring road to the A422 Stony Stratford roundabout, turn left, theground is situated at the bottom of the hill on the left

CADDINGTON
Secretary: Dave Mark, 7 Heathfield Close, Caddington, Luton, Beds. LU1 4HD Tel: 01582 421404 (H) 01797 147968 (B)
Ground: Caddington Recreation Club, Manor Road, Caddington (01582 450151)
Directions: On entering village turn into Manor Road (adjacent to shops andvillage green), proceed 500 metres: Clubhouse and ground on left side next to Catholic Church

CRAWLEY GREEN
Secretary: Alan Burgess, 23 Higham Drive, Luton LU2 9SP (01582 483172)
Ground: Crawley Green Recreation Ground, Crawley Green Road, Luton, Beds. 01582 451058
Directions: From M1 jct 10 , to roundabout at end of motorway slip road into Airport Way. At fourth roundabout turn right into Crawley Green Road. Ground is 1/2 mile on left past Ashcroft High School.

FLAMSTEAD
Secretary: Mark McGreevy, 3 Whitehill, Flamstead, Herts AL3 8DN (01582 841481)
Ground: Flamstead Sports Assoc., Friendless Lane, Flamstead, St Albans, Herts(0582 841307)
Directions: From Dunstable Town Centre travel south on A5 Trunk Roadtowards the M1. Follow for approximately 3 miles then turn right oppositeHertfordshire Moat House Hotel. Ground and parking approximately half a mile onthe corner of the first right turn

HAYW00D UNITED
Secretary: Lynne Nappin, 6 Evesham Green, Aylesbury, Bucks. HP19 9RX (01296 486924)
Ground: Stocklake Sports & Social Club, Haywards Way, Aylesbury, Bucks. Tel: 01296 423324
Directions: Follow signs to Bicester from Aylesbury ring road . At fifth road island, with Aylesbury Duck Public House on right ,turn right into Jackson Road and then second left into Haywood Way. Club is at bottom of the road.
Previous Leagues: Chiltonian

KENT ATHLETIC
Secretary: Irene Oodian, 9 Gafield Court, Handcross Road,Luton, Beds. LU2 8JZ (01582 483090)
Ground: Kent Social Club, Tenby Drive, Leagrave, Luton (01582 582723)
Directions: M1 jct 11 take A505 towards Luton. Take the first turning on theleft (Stoneygate Road), straight over at the roundabout and turn right attraffic lights into Beechwood Road. Take the first road on the left and then the first right into Tenby Drive. Ground and car park 100 yards on left

LEIGHTON ATHLETIC --- WITHDRAWN
Secretary: Salvatore Leotta, 28 Ashburnham Crescent, Linslade, LeightonBuzzard, Beds. LU7 7PB. Tel: 01525 382396 (H)
Ground: Memorial Playing Fields, Mentmore Road, Linslade, Leighton Buzzard,Beds (01525 370469)
Directions: On A5 north of Dunstable travelling towards Hockliffe turn left onto A505 Leighton Buzzard bypass. At end of bypass turn right towartds LeightonBuzzard and take the first right immediately after the railway bridge intoCedars Way. At 'T' Junction turn left into Mentmore Road, ground 300 yards on right

MARKYATE
Secretary: John Dephley, 121 Burges Close, Dunstable, Beds LU6 3EU (01582 656325)
Ground: The Playing Fields, Cavendish Rd, Markyate (01582 841731)
Directions: M1 Junc 9, take A5 north towards Dunstable. After 2 miles left intovillage after footbridge. Right into High Street, 5th left Cavendish Rd, grd onright before school

MILLCUTT ROVERS

Secretary: Graham Watson, 107 Bedford Road, Barton-le-Clay, Beds MK45 4LP (01582 883109)
Ground: Barton Rovers FC, Sharpenhoe Road, Barton-le-Clay, Beds. Tel: 01582 707772 Fax: 01582 882398
Directions: Jct 12 M1,turn right. Then second right through Harlington and Sharpenhoe into Barton-le-Clay. Right at Royal Oak Public House onto A6. Ground is 400 yrds on right down concrete drive.

MURSLEY UNITED

Secretary: Roger Gurnett, 20 Tweedale Close, Mursley, Milton Keynes MK17 0SB.Tel: 01296 720505 (H)
Ground: Station Road, Mursley, Milton Keynes
Directions: A421 Bletchley to Buckingham Road, first right in village

NORTH CRAWLEY UNITED (previously Newport Athletic)

Secretary: Sharon Stanley, The Chequers , High Street, North Crawley MK16 9LH (01234 391224)
Ground: Willen Rd Sports Ground, Willen Rd, Newport Pagnell
Directions: M1 Junc 14, A509 to Newport Pagnell. 1st r/about turn left A422.1st r/about right into Willen Rd. 1st right Sports Ground 100 yds right

OLD BRADWELL UNITED

Secretary: Paul Mills,36 Craddocks Close, Bradwell, Milton Keynes MK13 9DX (01908 227520)
Ground: Abbey Road, Bradwell, Milton Keynes (01908 312355)
Directions: M1 junction 14 go towards Newport Pagnell. Turn left at firstroundabout into H3 Honks Way. Go six r'abouts then left onto V6 Grafton Street.Take 1st right at mini-r'about into Rawlins Road and then 2nd left intoLoughton Road. Take 1st right into Primrose Road and at the 'T' junction turnright into Abbey Road

OLD DUNSTABLIANS

Secretary: Craig Renfrew, 75B Princes Street. Dunstable. LU6 3AS. Tel: 01582471794 (H), 01234 265444 (B)
Ground: Lancot Park. Dunstable Road, Totternhoe (01582 663735)
Directions: From Dunstable Town Centre take the B489 Tring Road. At the 4throundabout turn right, signposted Totternhoe. The pitch is located withinDunstable Town Cricket Club which is on the right just before entering thevillage of Totternhoe

PITSTONE & IVINGHOE

Secretary: Jay Adlem, 22 Maud Janes Close, Ivinghoe, Leighton Buzzard. LU7 9ED.Tel: 01296 668663 (H)
Ground: Pitstone Recreation Ground, Vicarage Road, Pitstone, Bucks (01296661271)
Directions: Tring Rd (B489) from Dunstable, turn right for Ivinghoe, andcontinue through to Pitstone r-about; ground left then right. From Aylesbury -left at `Rising Sun' in Aston Clinton, keep on that road to Pitstone r'bout;ground right then right. Bus 61 from Luton or Aylesbury. Nearest BR stationsare Tring or Cheddington

SCOT

Secretary: George Egerton, 10 Saffron Street, Bletchley, Milton Keynes MK2 3AH (07940 737298)
Ground: Selbourne Avenue, Bletchley, Milton Keynes (01908 368881)
Directions: Main roads to Bletchley then A421 Buckingham road, at Glen Garageright into Newton Rd, 2nd left into Selbourne Ave., through railway bridge tobottom of road

THE 61 FC (LUTON)

Secretary: Richard Everitt, 44 Somersby Close, Luton LU1 3XB. 0 1582485095 (H)
Ground: Kingsway, Beverley Road, Luton, Beds. (01582 582965)
Directions: M1 jct 11, A505 to Luton centre, right at 1st island, 1st left,Beverley Rd is 3rd left, entrance in Beverley Rd, exactly 1 mile junction 11.All Luton to Dunstable buses pass ground - alight at Beech Hill Bowling Club. 1mile from both Leagrave & Luton BR stations

WINSLOW UNITED

Secretary: David F Ward, 28 Park Road, Winslow, Buckingham MK18 3DL.
Tel: 01296713202 (H), 01865 781210 (B)
Ground: Recreation Ground, Elmfields Gate, Winslow, Bucks. (01296 713057)
Directions: A413 from Aylesbury to Winslow, in High Street turn right into ElmfieldsGate, ground on left opp. car park.A421 from Milton Keynes to Buck'ham then thro 'Gt Horwood

HERTS SENIOR COUNTY LEAGUE

President: William J R Venneear Esq.   **Chairman:** Cecil T Husdon Esq.
Secretary: Kevin Folds, 6 Lanthony Court, High Street, Arlesey, Beds SG15 6TU
Tel/Fax: 01462 834084

To coin that well worn phrase; "It's a funny old game". On Saturday evening 12th February 2000 Wormley Rovers sat fifteen points clear at the top of the Premier Division with their principle rivals in second spot albeit with three games in hand. If you were a betting man you would have been considered mad to bet against the East Herts club winning the League and pursuing their ambition of moving to a more Senior level of the game. The outcome of the race for the Premier Division title is now history, Colney Heath triumphing by a nine point margin and thus being able to follow their own selected route up the Pyramid. After 47 consecutive seasons in membership of the League, Colney Heath will be playing their soccer in the Spartan South Midlands League in 2000-01. Spare a thought though for Wormley Rovers. By any standards they have had a superb season: Runners-up in both the Premier Division and Reserve Division One; Runners-up in the Herts Senior Centenary Trophy; and semi-finalists in the Cherry Red Books Trophy.

The turning point in the race for the Premier Division crown seemed to come when three sides declared their desire to move up the Pyramid - should they qualify. From that time on a three horse race for the title ensued with Kings Langley the third contenders coming from nowhere actually to lead the division during the run-in.

At the foot of the table Bushey Rangers found the division too tough to cope with and rapidly fell adrift of the rest. Happily for the club they have a strong crop of youngsters coming through the Reserves who will doubtless bring success to the club in the coming years.

Hatfield Town and Whitewebbs filled the other relegation spots although the latter have won a reprieve from the drop due to Colney Heath's evaluation.

Division One also produced a close title race. Four clubs were close contenders for the three promotion places for most of the season. As the final matches were played it was London Lions who emerged as Champions with Old Parmiterians runners-up and Chipperfield Corinthians taking the final promotion spot. St Peters were the unlucky side who fell away at the vital time.

In the Senior Section one club were forced to call it a day, Walkern-Castle dropping out just a few weeks into the season due to a shortage of players.

At the foot of the Division One table three clubs fought out a battle to avoid the wooden spoon. Two wins and a draw in their final three games ensured that Kimpton Rovers missed the unwanted prize and left Standon & Puckeridge propping up the rest. It is to both clubs' credit that despite their lean times on the pitch they completed their season with both First and Reserve sides.

In the Aubrey Cup there was success, after a nineteen year gap, for Bedmond Sports & Social. As is often the case, the game wasn't spectacular but the goal which won it - from a free kick twenty yards out - was worth the admission price on its own. Baldock Town hosted the Final and, despite fears that the West Herts public wouldn't travel to the far flung north, a crowd of over 300 watched the game.

One new club is joining the League. The Cheshunt club have been playing in the Southern Olympian League and will step up to Herts Senior County League soccer with just a first team.

Herts Police, having played for most of last season at the Welwyn Sports & Social Club ground, are switching permanently and will change their name to Welwyn Police. Sadly, through, they will withdraw their Reserves, feeling unable to field two competitive sides.

Several clubs will be switching grounds. At long last Oxhey Jets' move to a superb purpose built ground is happening as they wave goodbye to Chilwell Gardens and move in to Little Oxhey Lane and the Altham Centre. In order to take up their places in the Premier Division, London Lions are moving to the Copthall Athletics Stadium in Hendon whilst Old Parmiterians have brought the old Bricket Wood facilities up to scratch at Lye Lane - switching from Parmiters School.

One highly contentious issue over the new season will the the Management Committee's decision that all Premier Division clubs must produce match programmes for all First team games. Acknowledging the extra workload for hard pressed club officials it was still felt important that the League progressed its standards in order to safeguard its Senior status.

Kevin Folds, General Secretary

FINAL LEAGUE TABLES 1999-2000

PREMIER DIVISION

	P	W	D	L	F	A	Pts
Colney Heath	30	23	2	5	93	33	71
Wormley Rovers	30	20	2	8	78	38	62
Sun Postal Sports	30	17	6	7	73	35	57
Kings Langley	30	17	6	7	74	50	57
Bedmond S & S	30	12	11	7	65	49	47
Elliott Star	30	13	4	13	83	75	43
Oxhey Jets	30	13	4	13	65	60	43
Sandridge Rovers	30	12	5	13	51	56	41
Cuffley	30	11	6	13	53	60	39
Metro Police (Bushey)	30	10	8	12	58	57	38
Agrevo Sports	30	10	8	12	46	65	38
Benington	30	10	6	14	57	69	36
Bovingdon	30	11	3	16	41	62	36
Whitewebbs	30	9	4	17	56	72	31
Hatfield Town	30	8	4	18	54	75	28
Bushey Rangers	4	1	25	37	37	132	13

DIVISION ONE

	P	W	D	L	F	A	Pts
London Lions	26	18	5	3	68	23	59
Old Parmiterians	26	16	7	3	64	35	55
Chipperfield Corinth.	26	16	5	5	67	34	53
St Peters	26	15	3	8	61	46	48
North Mymms	26	13	6	7	68	54	45
Hadley	26	12	6	8	46	43	42
Evergreen	26	8	9	9	51	47	33
Mill End S & S	26	10	3	13	55	54	33
Codicote	26	8	5	13	41	48	29
Croxley Guild	26	8	3	15	39	56	27
Herts Police Athletic	26	7	6	13	32	53	27
Sarratt	26	6	4	16	39	73	22
Kimpton Rovers	26	6	2	18	51	73	20
Standon & Puckeridge	26	6	2	18	29	71	20

AUBREY CUP 1999-2000

SEMI-FINALS

London Lions	v	Bedmond Sports	1-2	Agrevo Sports	v	Sun Postal Sports	0-2

FINAL

Bedmond Sports	v	Sun Postal Sports	1-0	at Baldock Town FC

RESERVE CUP 1999-2000

SEMI-FINALS

Codicote	v	Colney Heath	3-2	Sun Postal Sports	v	Oxhey Jets	3-2

FINAL

Codicote	v	Sun Postal Sports	5-1	After extra time. At Whitewebbs FC

LEADING GOALSCORERS

Agrevo Sports	R Beatie	15	London Lions	J Zneimer	14
Bedmond Sports & Social	R Johnson	22	Met Police Bushey	R Grant	24
Benington	S Casha	11	Mill End Sports & Social	P Element	14
Bovingdon	R Atkins	11	North Mymms	L Field	18
Bushey Rangers	M Salim	9	Old Parmiterians	D Perman	16
Chipperfield Corinthians	T Purser	17	Oxhey Jets	G Page	22
Codicote	D Steer	12	St Peters	M Tilney	30
Colney Heath	E Richardson	19	Sandridge Rovers	D Smith	15
Croxley Guild	G Coniam	11	Sarratt	A Kemp	14
Cuffley	P Wackett	12	Standon & Puckeridge	C Dieguez	7
Elliott Star	K Cooper	40	Sun Postal Sports	M Woolner	29
Evergreen	L Smith	14	Whitewebbs	J Hoy	24
Hadley	S Goddard	18	Wormley Rovers	L Munt	32
Hatfield Town	P Clarke	17			
Herts Police Athletic	E Reyner	17			
Kimpton Rovers	P Barnes	26			
Kings Langley	S Stratford	26			

CONSTITUTION FOR 2000-01

PREMIER DIVISION: Agrevo Sports, Bedmond Sports & Social, Benington, Bovingdon, Chipperfield Corinthians, Cuffley, Elliott Star, Kings Langley, London Lions, Metropolitan Police Bushey, Old Parmiterians, Oxhey Jets, Sandridge Rovers, Sun Postal Sports, Whitewebbs, Wormley Rovers.

DIVISION ONE: Bushey Rangers, Codicote, Croxley Guild, Evergreen, Hadley, Hatfield Town, Kimpton Rovers, Mill End Sports & Social Athletic, North Mymms, St Peters, Sarratt, Standon & Puckeridge, The Cheshunt Club, Welwyn FC (Police)

A QUOTE INSURANCE
READING FOOTBALL LEAGUE

President: Leon Summers   **Chairman:** John Dell
Secretary: David Jeanes, 6 Hawkesbury Drive, Fords Farm, Calcot, Reading RG31 5ZP
Tel: 01734 413926 (H)
http://www.rdgleague.mcmail.com

FINAL LEAGUE TABLES 1999-2000

SENIOR DIVISION

	P	W	D	L	F	A	Pts
Forest Old Boys	22	15	3	4	59	28	48
Westwood United	22	15	2	5	46	22	47
Mortimer	22	10	6	6	49	33	36
Cookham Dean	22	10	5	7	46	48	35
Checkendon Sports	22	10	4	8	42	32	34
West Reading	22	9	6	7	46	33	33
Unity	22	9	4	9	46	48	31
Emmbrook Sports	22	7	5	10	27	43	26
Reading Exiles	22	6	6	10	33	42	24
Sonning Common	22	7	2	13	32	45	23
Highmoor	22	5	4	13	37	50	19
South End	22	5	1	16	30	69	16

PREMIER DIVISION

	P	W	D	L	F	A	Pts
Marlow United	22	15	2	5	68	43	47
Roundhead	22	14	2	6	80	48	44
Goring United	22	13	3	6	71	30	42
Royal Mail	22	11	4	7	45	25	37
Finchampstead 'A'	22	11	4	7	53	61	37
Forest Old Boys Res	22	10	4	8	48	48	34
Reading Old Blues	22	9	3	10	40	45	30
REME Arborfield	22	8	5	9	42	47	29
Ibis	22	6	8	8	38	48	26
Reading Exiles Res	22	5	5	12	27	53	20
Frilsham/Yattendon	22	4	3	15	41	57	15
Whitley Rovers	22	3	3	16	28	76	12

SENIOR DIVISION RESULTS CHART 1999-2000

		1	2	3	4	5	6	7	8	9	10	11	12
1	Checkendon Sports	X	0-2	4-1	2-3	2-2	1-1	1-0	2-3	4-1	2-1	0-2	1-3
2	Cookham Dean	0-7	X	2-2	2-2	3-0	1-3	5-1	4-2	4-1	0-5	2-2	0-2
3	Emmbrook Sports	0-3	1-1	X	1-4	0-1	1-0	1-1	1-0	3-1	1-1	0-2	1-5
4	Forest Old Boys	1-1	2-0	5-1	X	4-2	0-1	2-1	2-0	4-2	2-4	2-0	0-1
5	Highmoor	0-1	1-2	0-2	1-2	X	2-4	3-1	1-3	7-1	4-6	1-1	1-2
6	Mortimer	1-1	1-3	4-0	1-3	5-6	X	1-1	2-2	3-1	7-0	2-5	2-0
7	Reading Exiles	3-1	7-1	3-3	2-4	1-1	0-1	X	0-3	3-2	0-4	2-0	0-3
8	Sonning Common	1-0	0-1	0-2	1-5	6-2	2-2	0-3	X	3-1	2-3	0-3	0-3
9	South End	1-2	3-6	3-2	0-7	1-0	0-5	1-2	3-1	X	2-1	0-1	2-3
10	Unity	1-5	1-4	1-3	2-2	2-0	2-0	0-0	1-3	1-1	X	1-3	4-3
11	West Reading	5-1	3-3	0-1	1-3	0-1	2-2	2-2	3-0	6-1	1-3	X	2-2
12	Westwood United	0-1	2-0	2-0	2-0	1-1	0-1	3-0	1-0	1-2	3-2	4-2	X

PREMIER DIVISION RESULTS CHART 1999-2000

		1	2	3	4	5	6	7	8	9	10	11	12
1	Finchampstead 'A'	X	2-2	W-L	3-1	W-L	1-6	3-7	2-2	5-4	7-1	1-0	3-1
2	Forest Old Boys Reserves	3-3	X	4-3	1-0	2-2	5-2	1-3	1-0	3-1	0-3	0-4	1-4
3	Frilsham/Yattendon	3-5	1-3	X	1-2	0-2	2-3	2-2	4-1	8-1	1-3	0-4	3-2
4	Goring United	6-0	2-2	2-0	X	6-0	3-5	6-0	1-0	1-2	4-2	2-4	8-0
5	Ibis	3-5	2-0	2-1	1-3	X	0-5	2-2	3-0	1-1	3-7	0-0	4-2
6	Marlow United	2-1	3-1	1-4	2-2	2-2	X	3-2	6-1	1-5	4-2	1-3	2-1
7	REME Arborfield	2-3	4-3	2-1	1-1	2-1	0-2	X	3-0	1-3	2-5	3-2	5-2
8	Reading Exiles Reserves	2-2	0-3	2-2	1-11	2-2	0-2	2-0	X	0-0	1-3	1-4	6-2
9	Reading Old Blues	2-3	2-4	4-2	2-1	1-3	0-2	3-0	0-1	X	1-3	0-3	3-1
10	Roundhead	6-3	5-1	9-1	1-3	3-3	6-3	0-0	2-1	1-3	X	1-4	4-2
11	Royal Mail	5-0	1-2	1-1	0-2	3-1	2-5	1-0	0-2	0-0	1-3	X	0-0
12	Whitley Rovers	3-1	1-6	2-1	2-4	1-1	0-6	1-1	0-2	1-2	0-10	0-3	X

SENIOR CUP 1999-2000

SEMI-FINALS

Marlow United   v   Highmoor   3-1   Sonning Common   v   Checkendon Sports   1-3

FINAL

Checkendon Sports   v   Marlow United   1*1, 4p3   at Reading FC

CONSTITUTION FOR 2000-01

SENIOR DIVISION

Checkendon Sports, Cookham Dean, Emmbrook Sports, Forest Old Boys, Highmoor, Marlow United, Mortimer, Reading Exiles, Roundhead United, Sonning Common, Unity, West Reading, Westwood United.

PREMIER DIVISION

Finchampstead 'A', Forest Old Boys Reserves, Goring United, Ibis, Newtown Henley, RBC, Reme Arborfield, Reading Exiles Reserves, Reading Old Blues, Reading YMCA, Royal Mail, South End, Westwood United Reserves.

For up to the minute news, results, fixtures,
and general facts and figures
from the world of non-league football
log on to

www.nlfootball.com

Brought to you by The Non-League Newspaper in conjunction with e-comsport

SURREY COUNTY SENIOR LEAGUE

FINAL LEAGUE TABLE 1999-2000

	P	W	D	L	F	A	Pts
Worcester Park	30	20	5	5	73	35	65
Colliers Wood	30	18	4	8	68	41	58
Virginia Water	30	17	5	8	63	44	56
Frimley Green	30	16	6	8	63	41	54
Chobham & Ottershaw	30	16	5	9	66	52	53
Ditton	30	16	4	10	56	32	52
Crescent Rovers	30	15	5	10	59	40	50
Croydon Mun. Off.	30	13	7	10	54	50	46
Holmesdale	30	14	2	14	56	49	44
Guildford	30	10	6	14	40	55	36
Bookham	30	10	5	15	32	44	35
Shottermill	30	9	7	14	53	63	34
Sheerwater	30	9	5	16	35	49	32
Netherne Village	30	9	1	20	32	59	28
Bisley Sports	30	6	7	17	46	81	25
Farleigh Rovers	30	3	4	23	38	99	13

RESULTS CHART 1999-2000

		1	2	3	4	5	6	7	8	9	10	11	12	13	14	15	16
1	Bisley Sports	X	0-0	2-3	2-2	1-2	0-1	1-3	4-1	0-0	3-2	0-5	2-3	3-2	4-1	1-1	2-3
2	Bookham	2-1	X	2-0	0-2	0-2	1-1	0-2	3-2	2-0	2-3	3-2	3-0	1-0	0-1	0-1	1-1
3	Chobham & Ottershaw	0-2	2-1	X	3-4	4-1	2-1	0-2	4-2	2-3	1-0	3-1	2-1	2-1	2-2	1-5	4-1
4	Colliers Wood	4-1	W-L	3-3	X	0-1	1-0	1-2	2-1	0-2	5-0	5-2	3-2	2-3	3-1	3-0	1-1
5	Crescent Rovers	4-3	2-0	2-0	1-3	X	0-2	1-2	5-0	1-1	2-1	1-2	4-0	1-0	2-2	2-2	0-1
6	Croydon Mun. Off.	2-1	3-1	2-2	4-3	1-1	X	3-1	2-1	2-5	3-2	2-1	1-2	1-1	2-1	3-5	2-4
7	Ditton	6-0	2-1	1-1	0-2	0-1	1-2	X	1-1	2-0	4-0	1-2	1-2	0-1	4-1	3-0	0-1
8	Farleigh Rovers	4-4	0-1	0-5	2-6	1-2	0-7	1-6	X	1-3	2-2	3-1	2-2	2-3	1-2	3-1	1-5
9	Frimley Green	5-0	2-0	2-5	L-W	3-1	3-1	0-0	4-2	X	0-2	3-0	2-0	2-0	3-0	2-3	1-7
10	Guildford	1-1	2-3	2-2	2-1	3-1	1-1	1-2	1-0	1-3	X	3-1	1-0	1-1	0-1	2-1	1-0
11	Holmesdale	5-1	1-2	0-2	0-4	3-1	0-0	3-0	5-2	1-1	3-1	X	5-1	1-0	4-0	0-1	0-1
12	Netherne Village	4-0	1-0	0-1	0-1	0-8	0-1	0-1	0-1	2-1	2-0	4-2	X	0-1	2-1	1-4	0-2
13	Sheerwater	1-1	1-1	3-4	2-1	0-2	3-2	0-1	2-1	0-4	0-1	0-1	3-2	X	1-1	0-1	3-2
14	Shottermill	0-4	2-2	2-4	3-3	4-2	2-2	3-1	10-0	2-4	2-1	1-3	1-0	2-1	X	2-3	2-2
15	Virginia Water	6-0	2-0	2-1	0-2	0-5	3-0	2-2	3-1	2-2	3-3	3-1	3-0	4-1	1-0	X	0-1
16	Worcester Park	8-2	6-0	2-1	3-1	1-1	2-0	1-5	3-0	2-2	5-0	0-1	2-1	2-1	2-1	2-1	X

LEAGUE CUP 2000-01

FIRST ROUND

Bisley Sports	v	Worcester Park	1-0	Bookham	v	Ditton	1-0, 0-2
Crescent Rovers	v	Shottermill	4-1	Croydon Mun. Off.	v	Colliers Wood Utd	0-5
Farleigh Rovers	v	Frimley Green	0-5	Guildford	v	Chobham & Otter.	3-0
Holmesdale	v	Sheerwater	3-0	Netherne Village	v	Virginia Water	2-1

QUARTER-FINALS

Bisley Sports	v	Colliers Wood Utd	4-2	Crescent Rovers	v	Guildford	4-3
Ditton	v	Netherne Village	1-4	Holmesdale	v	Frimley Green	1*3

SEMI-FINALS

Bisley Sports	v	Frimley Green	1-0	Netherne Village	v	Crescent Rovers	1*2

FINAL

Bisley Sports	v	Crescent Rovers	0-2

CONSTITUTION FOR 2000-01

Bisley Sports, Bookham, Chobham & Ottershaw, Colliers Wood, Crescent Rovers, Croydon Municipal Officers, Ditton, Farleigh Rovers, Frimley Green, Guildford, Hersham RBL, Netherne Village, Sheerwater, Shottermill, Virginia Water, Worcester Park

SUBURBAN FOOTBALL LEAGUE
Chairman: David Stanley
Chief Executive/Hon. Secretary: Michale Bidmead
55 Grange Road, Chessington, Surrey KT9 1EZ
Tel/Fax: 020 8397 4834

HONOURS LIST 1999-2000

PREMIER DIVISION
Champions   Dulwich Hamlet
Runners Up   Basingstoke Town

SOUTH DIVISION
Champions   Croydon
Runners Up   Walton & Hersham

NORTH DIVISION
Champions   Chesham United
Runners Up   Berkhamsted

LEAGUE CUP
Winners   Hayes
Finalists   Kingstonian

SHIELD
Winners   Uxbridge
Finalists   Basingstoke Town

CHAMPIONS CUP
Winners   Hayes
Finalists   Kingstonian

COUNTY CUPS

MIDDLESEX PREMIER CUP
Winners
Hampton & Richmond Borough

OXFORDSHIRE INTERMEDIATE CUP
Winners
Thame United

SURREY PREMIER CUP
Winners
Tooting & Mitcham United

*Suburban League Premier Division Champions Dulwich Hamlet FC
are presented with the trophy by League Chairman, Mr David Stanley (Centre)*

FINAL LEAGUE TABLES 1999-2000
PREMIER DIVISION

	P	W	D	L	F	A	Pts		P	W	D	L	F	A	Pts
Dulwich Hamlet	34	22	6	6	88	42	72	Whyteleafe	34	12	7	15	43	65	43
Basingstoke T	34	19	5	10	89	35	62	Oxford City	34	12	6	16	63	66	42
Hayes	34	17	9	8	80	48	60	Farnborough T	34	10	11	13	70	83	41
Met Police	34	16	8	10	56	59	56	Hampton & Rich.	34	11	8	15	66	79	41
Maidenhead Utd	34	16	7	11	72	53	55	Thame United	34	11	8	15	47	71	41
Uxbridge	34	16	7	11	62	48	55	Hendon	34	12	4	18	63	78	40
Kingstonian	34	15	8	11	63	43	53	Fisher Athletic	34	11	6	17	62	73	39
Woking	34	14	8	12	53	45	50	Hungerford T	34	11	3	20	56	96	36
Gravesend & N.	34	13	8	13	58	53	47	Marlow	34	7	3	24	41	95	24

PREMIER DIVISION LEADING GOALSCORERS 1999-2000

21	C Bassett	Basingstoke Town
18	A Green	Basingstoke Town
17	D Green	Dulwich Hamlet
14	A Nesbeth	Maidenhead United
14	M Redfern	Whyteleafe

SOUTH DIVISION

	P	W	D	L	F	A	Pts
Croydon	34	23	4	7	120	44	73
Walton & Hersh.	34	23	4	7	106	40	73
Chertsey Town	34	22	4	8	100	40	70
Staines Town	34	22	3	9	117	53	69
Tooting & M Utd	34	21	5	8	110	47	68
Crawley Town	34	18	7	9	101	49	61
Croydon Athletic	34	18	6	10	73	49	60
Tonbridge Angels	34	15	8	11	86	59	53
Carshalton Ath	34	14	9	11	93	61	51
Corinthian Cas	34	15	6	13	67	67	51
Chipstead	34	13	9	12	50	45	48
Molesey	34	13	7	14	69	66	46
Bracknell Town	34	12	6	16	55	68	42
Epsom & Ewell	34	9	8	17	49	64	35
Camberley T	34	7	5	22	44	104	26
Fleet Town	34	5	4	25	40	125	19
Horsham	34	5	3	26	34	147	18
Alton Town	34	1	2	31	16	202	5

NORTH DIVISION

	P	W	D	L	F	A	Pts
Chesham Utd	34	24	3	7	127	45	75
Berkhamsted T	34	21	7	6	85	41	70
Leighton Town	34	18	7	9	75	46	61
Yeading	34	18	6	10	83	44	60
Flackwell Heath	34	18	5	11	62	49	59
Northwood	34	16	9	9	74	47	57
Hillingdon Boro	34	16	7	11	76	54	55
Burnham	34	14	12	8	65	48	54
Beaconsfield	34	16	6	12	56	59	54
Wingate & Finch.	34	15	8	11	69	54	53
Kingsbury Town	34	15	5	14	61	74	50
Abingdon United	34	11	8	15	50	64	41
Thatcham Town	34	11	6	17	61	77	39
Wembley	34	11	5	18	76	74	38
Ruislip Manor	34	11	3	20	54	100	36
Tring Town	34	6	6	22	58	96	24
Abingdon Town	34	5	4	25	29	117	19
Chalfont St Peter	34	4	5	25	46	118	17

SOUTH DIVISION LEADING GOALSCORERS

25	D Cory	Walton & Hersham
23	N Flint	Crawley Town
20	D Tanner	Croydon
20	N McDonnell	Croydon
18	K Phillips	Staines Town
18	J Cummins	Staines Town
18	D Hall	Croydon

NORTH DIVISION LEADING GOALSCORERS

23	O Boujettif	Chesham United
23	D Campbell	Chesham United
21	B O'Brien	Yeading
17	D Robinson	Hillingdon Borough
16	A Kingsley	Tring Town

SUBURBAN LEAGUE CHALLENGE CUP 1999-2000

FOURTH ROUND

Staines Town	v	Carshalton Athletic	4-1	Corinthian Casuals	v	Basingstoke Town	4-2
Northwood	v	Hayes	0-3	Kingstonian	v	Gravesend & N'fleet	3-0

SEMI-FINALS

Corinthian Casuals	v	Kingstonian	1-2	Hayes	v	Staines Town	5-1

FINAL

Hayes	v	Kingstonian	2-1	at Metropolitan Police FC

ESSEX & HERTS
BORDER COMBINATION

HONOURS LIST 1999-2000

BORDER COMBINATION	Champions	Dagenham & Redbridge	Runners Up	Potters Bar Town
DIVISION ONE EAST	Champions	Aveley	Runners Up	Hornchurch
DIVISION ONE WEST	Champions	Harlow Town	Runners Up	Ford United
COMBINATION CUP	Winners	St Margaretsbury	Runners Up	Harlow Town
FRED BUDDEN TROPHY	Winners	Braintree Town	Runners Up	Baldock Town
PREMIER DIVISION CUP	Winners	Ware	Runners Up	Leyton Pennant
DIVISION ONE CUP	Winners	Ford United	Runners Up	St Margaretsbury

FINAL LEAGUE TABLES 1999-2000
PREMIER DIVISION

	P	Home			Away			Totals			F	A	Pts	GD
		W	D	L	W	D	L	W	D	L				
Dagenham & Redbridge	20	6	2	2	5	3	2	11	5	4	66	30	38	36
Potters Bar Town	20	8	1	1	2	5	3	10	6	4	42	31	36	11
Canvey Island*	20	7	1	2	4	2	4	11	3	6	47	32	33	15
Heybridge Swifts	20	6	3	1	4	0	6	10	3	7	49	38	33	11
Ware	20	6	2	2	3	3	4	9	5	6	46	37	32	9
Leyton Pennant	20	6	2	2	3	2	5	9	4	7	46	35	31	11
East Thurrock United	20	4	3	3	2	3	5	6	6	8	39	37	24	2
Romford	20	4	3	3	3	0	7	7	3	10	33	40	24	-7
Braintree Town	20	6	1	3	1	2	7	7	3	10	35	56	24	-21
Witham Town	20	1	6	3	1	4	5	2	10	8	22	45	16	-23
Sawbridgeworth Town	20	2	2	6	0	2	8	2	4	14	22	66	10	-44

DIVISION ONE EAST

	P	W	D	L	W	D	L	W	D	L	F	A	Pts	GD
Aveley	22	8	1	2	11	0	0	19	1	2	72	22	58	50
Hornchurch	22	6	2	3	6	2	3	12	4	6	52	38	40	14
Brentwood	22	7	0	4	6	0	5	13	0	9	50	31	39	19
Southend Manor	22	7	0	4	4	4	3	11	4	7	61	32	37	29
Tilbury	22	5	2	4	6	0	5	11	2	9	49	39	35	10
Great Wakering Rovers	22	4	3	4	4	2	5	8	5	9	34	27	29	7
Hullbridge Sports	22	3	2	6	5	1	5	8	3	11	37	47	27	-10
Concord Rangers	22	4	2	5	3	2	6	7	4	11	30	52	25	-22
Burnham Ramblers	22	3	4	4	2	3	6	5	7	10	33	42	22	-9
Maldon Town	22	4	2	5	1	4	6	5	6	11	34	60	21	-26
Bowers United	22	3	3	5	2	3	6	5	6	11	32	60	21	-28
Basildon United*	22	3	1	7	3	1	7	6	2	14	26	60	17	-34

DIVISION ONE WEST

	P	W	D	L	W	D	L	W	D	L	F	A	Pts	GD
Harlow Town	20	8	0	2	6	4	0	14	4	2	70	23	46	47
Ford United	20	6	3	1	6	2	2	12	5	3	51	22	41	29
Baldock Town	20	6	2	2	6	2	2	12	4	4	61	27	40	34
Bishops Stortford	20	4	6	0	3	5	2	7	11	2	40	17	32	23
St Margaretsbury	20	6	1	3	3	4	3	9	5	6	43	28	32	15
Waltham Abbey	20	4	4	2	3	3	4	7	7	6	25	24	28	1
Saffron Walden Town	20	1	5	4	4	2	4	5	7	8	23	45	22	-22
Halstead Town	20	3	1	6	2	2	6	5	3	12	35	52	18	-17
Hertford Town	20	3	3	4	1	3	6	4	6	10	21	42	18	-21
Hoddesdon Town	20	2	1	7	1	1	8	3	2	15	15	54	11	-39
Somersett Ambury*	20	3	2	5	1	0	9	4	2	14	21	71	11	-50

* points deducted

RESULTS CHARTS 1999-2-000

PREMIER DIVISION

		1	2	3	4	5	6	7	8	9	10	11
1	Braintree Town	X	2-4	4-1	3-1	3-2	3-1	0-2	2-0	4-1	1-6	0-0
2	Canvey Island	2-1	X	1-4	3-1	2-3	4-4	4-0	3-1	3-0	5-1	3-0
3	Dagenham & Red.	9-2	3-2	X	3-3	2-0	2-3	2-3	4-0	2-0	3-3	13-1
4	East Thurrock	3-3	0-3	0-2	X	6-1	3-1	4-0	1-2	2-1	3-3	2-2
5	Heybridge Swifts	1-1	6-0	1-6	1-0	X	3-0	2-2	2-0	11-2	5-0	1-1
6	Leyton Pennant	6-1	3-0	1-3	3-1	3-1	X	2-2	0-2	2-2	2-1	3-1
7	Potters Bar Town	3-0	3-2	3-3	3-0	0-2	1-0	X	4-0	3-0	4-1	2-1
8	Romford	6-0	0-2	2-1	1-1	2-0	2-6	1-1	X	7-1	0-4	2-2
9	Sawbridgeworth Town	5-1	0-4	0-0	0-4	3-4	0-4	2-2	2-0	X	0-1	0-2
10	Ware	0-3	0-0	1-1	1-3	4-0	2-1	2-1	4-1	9-2	X	1-0
11	Witham Town	3-1	0-0	0-2	1-1	1-3	1-1	3-3	0-4	1-1	2-2	X

DIVISION ONE EAST

		1	2	3	4	5	6	7	8	9	10	11	12
1	Aveley	X	6-1	5-1	1-2	2-0	5-2	2-1	2-0	0-1	1-1	1-0	5-1
2	Basildon United	0-6	X	1-1	0-1	3-1	0-1	1-0	3-2	2-4	0-1	1-10	1-4
3	Bowers United	0-2	3-0	X	3-1	1-1	2-2	2-0	2-10	1-2	1-1	0-3	2-4
4	Brentwood	2-4	1-2	1-2	X	2-1	5-1	0-1	2-0	3-1	9-0	5-2	2-0
5	Burnham Ramblers	1-3	2-3	4-4	1-2	X	3-1	1-3	1-1	3-1	1-1	0-0	2-1
6	Concord Rangers	2-4	2-0	2-1	0-3	1-0	X	0-0	0-3	4-4	3-2	2-5	1-3
7	Gt Wakering Rovers	0-2	2-2	4-1	4-1	1-1	2-0	X	2-3	0-1	4-1	2-2	2-3
8	Hornchurch	0-6	1-0	3-3	0-2	2-3	0-0	1-0	X	4-2	5-1	3-2	4-2
9	Hullbridge Sports	2-7	1-2	3-1	1-3	4-1	5-1	0-3	0-2	X	0-0	1-1	1-2
10	Maldon Town	3-4	4-3	0-1	3-2	4-3	4-2	1-3	1-1	1-2	X	1-1	3-6
11	Southend Manor	1-2	4-1	4-0	2-0	1-2	1-2	2-0	3-5	4-1	5-0	X	5-1
12	Tilbury	1-2	3-0	7-0	2-1	1-1	0-1	0-0	1-2	2-0	3-1	2-3	X

DIVISION ONE WEST

		1	2	3	4	5	6	7	8	9	10	11
1	Baldock Town	X	1-1	4-1	1-2	1-2	4-1	2-0	4-0	11-3	0-0	2-0
2	Bishop's Stortford	0-0	X	1-1	3-1	1-1	0-0	9-0	4-0	8-0	0-0	0-0
3	Ford United	4-1	2-0	X	2-0	5-5	4-2	4-1	1-1	1-2	5-0	1-1
4	Halstead Town	0-9	2-2	0-4	X	0-7	6-1	5-0	0-2	12-0	1-2	1-2
5	Harlow Town	4-1	2-3	2-1	5-0	X	4-0	4-0	0-2	3-2	5-1	2-1
6	Hertford Town	3-5	0-0	0-2	2-0	2-2	X	2-1	0-0	4-1	0-4	1-2
7	Hoddesdon Town	1-2	1-1	0-2	1-0	1-6	0-1	X	1-2	4-0	0-3	1-2
8	Saffron Walden	1-3	0-3	1-5	2-2	0-8	1-1	0-0	X	3-0	2-2	1-1
9	Somersett Am.	3-7	0-2	0-0	0-0	1-6	3-0	0-2	1-2	X	3-0	2-0
10	St Margaretsbury	0-2	4-1	1-4	6-1	0-1	0-0	4-0	7-2	5-0	X	4-1
11	Waltham Abbey	1-1	1-1	0-2	1-2	1-1	3-1	5-0	2-1	1-0	0-0	X

PREMIER DIVISION CUP

SEMI-FINALS

Leyton Pennant	v	Romford	3-0
Ware	v	East Thurrock Utd	4-3

FINAL

Leyton Pennant	v	Ware	0-3

COMBINATION CUP

SEMI-FINALS

Tilbury	v	Harlow Town	1*3
St Margaretsbury	v	Dagenham & Red.	2*1

FINAL

St Margaretsbury	v	Harlow Town	2*0

DIVISION ONE CUP

SEMI FINALS

Ford United	v	Great Wakering Rvrs	2-0
St Margaretsbury	v	Hoddesdon Town	3-2

FINAL

St Margaretsbury	v	Ford United	1-2

FRED BUDDEN TROPHY

SEMI-FINALS (2 legs)

Brentwood	v	Braintree Town	0-0, 0-1
Baldock Town	v	Ford United	2-0, 1-0

FINAL

Braintree Town	v	Baldock Town	2-0

Above: Arthur Evans, our roving reporter, with Chippenham Town manager, Tommy Saunders
Photo: Eric Marsh

A new squad member of the Team Talk photographers, Paul Carter from Harrow.   Photo: Darren C Thomas

COUNTY
FOOTBALL
ASSOCIATIONS

BEDFORDSHIRE F.A.

Tel: 01582 476163 (H)   01582 565111 (B)   Fax: 01582 565222
Century House, Skimpot Road, Dunstable LU5 4JU
Secretary: Peter D Brown
Executives (Responsibility)   Century House for
Coaching Exams/Courses, Referees, Womens Football
Number of Affiliated Clubs: Senior: 385   U.18:   110   **President:** R Berridge
Number of Affiliated Leagues: Senior: 12   Junior: 4
County Representative Teams: Senior, U18, U16, Intermediate, Womens
Inter County Competitions: East Anglia Counties Intermediate, U18, U16 & Womens, FA County Youth Cup

BEDFORDSHIRE PREMIER CUP 1999-2000
(14 entries)   (FOUNDED 1894-95)

LAST SEASON'S FINAL: Stotfold v Luton Town 2-1
MOST WINS: Waterlows 10   Dunstable 9   Luton Clarence 8

FIRST ROUND (6 matches)

Shillington	v	Barton Rovers	0-3		Wootton Blue Cross	v	Biggleswade Town	1-2
Bedford Town	v	Stotfold	4p3 3*3		Biggleswade United	v	Leighton Town	1-2
Brache Sparta	v	Langford	4-1		Bedford United	v	Potton United	5-0

SECOND ROUND (4 matches)

Kempston Rovers	v	Bedford Town	1-2		Barton Rovers	v	Leighton Town	3-0
Biggleswade Town	v	Arlesey Town	0-1		Bedford United	v	Brache Sparta	1-4

SEMI-FINALS

Bedford Town	v	Brache Sparta	4-2		Arlesey Town	v	Barton Rovers	2-6

FINAL

BARTON ROVERS	v	BEDFORD TOWN	0-3		at Leighton Town FC

BEDFORDSHIRE SENIOR CUP 1999-2000
(18 entries)

LAST SEASON'S FINAL: Barton Rovers v Bedford Town 3-0

PRELIMINARY ROUND (2 matches)

Biggleswade United	v	Stotfold	0*0 1*4		Totternhoe	v	Caddington	2*4

FIRST ROUND (8 matches)

Potton United	v	Brache Sparta	0-2		Leighton Town	v	Kempston Rovers	3-1
Langford	v	Bedford Town	0-4		Biggleswade Town	v	Stotfold	1-2
Wootton Blue Cr	v	Ampthill T 4*4 3A0 f/f	2-1		Caddington	v	Barton Rovers	0-6
Bedford United	v	Shillington	6-1		Luton Old Boys	v	Arlesey Town	1-5

SECOND ROUND (4 matches)

Arlesey Town	v	Bedford United	5-0		Bedford Town	v	Barton Rovers**	4V2
Stotfold	v	Brache Sparta	3-1		Leighton Town	v	Wootton Blue Cross	2-4

(** fielded an ineligible player opponents re-instated,void)

SEMI-FINALS

Wootton Blue Cross	v	Stotfold	1-2		Barton Rovers	v	Arlesey Town	2-3

FINAL

ARLESEY TOWN	v	STOTFOLD	1-2		at Arlesey Town

BERKS & BUCKS F.A. LIMITED

Tel: 01367 242099 Fax: 01367 242158

15a London Street, Faringdon, Oxon SN7 7HD

Secretary: Brian Moore   **Press Officer:** R G Woolman

Responsibilities   J Kelman (Coaching Exams/Courses)

                                     R J Claridge (Referees)

                                     A Glenny (Womens Football)

Number of Affiliated Leagues: Senior: 17   Junior: 10   **President:** D J Frost

County Representative Teams: U18, U16 Girls, U14 Girls   **Chairman:** J A Christopher

Inter County Competitions: South/South West Counties Championship Youth

BERKS & BUCKS SENIOR CUP 1999-2000
(18 entries)   (FOUNDED 1878-79)

LAST SEASON'S FINAL: Maidenhead United v Wycombe Wanderers 4*1

MOST WINS: Wycombe 24   Maidenhead United 16   Marlow 13

SECOND QUALIFYING ROUND (2 matches)

Wokingham Town	v	Burnham	3-1	Thatcham Town	v	Buckingham Town	5-0

FIRST ROUND (8 matches)

Reading	v	Flackwell Heath	2-1	Thatcham Town	v	Abingdon Town	4-3
Chalfont St Peter	v	Beaconsfield SYCOB	3-2	Windsor & Eton	v	Bracknell Town	4-1
Wokingham Town	v	Hungerford Town	2*6	Marlow	v	Aylesbury United	1-2
Wycombe Wanderers	v	Chesham United	4-1	Maidenhead United	v	Slough Town	1*1 0-1

SECOND ROUND (4 matches)

Reading	v	Windsor & Eton	3-0	Slough Town	v	Hungerford Town	3-0
Aylesbury United	v	Chalfont St Peter	5-0	Thatcham Town	v	Wycombe Wanderers	0-2

SEMI-FINALS

Aylesbury United	v	Slough Town	4-2	Wycombe Wanderers	v	Reading	2-4

FINAL

AYLESBURY UTD	v	READING	2-0	at Aylesbury United FC

Gary Crawshaw of Aylesbury in the close presence of Reading defenders, Aylesbury ran out 2-0 winners in this Berks & Bucks Senior Cup Final in front of a large and very vocal crowd.   *Photo: Steve Ayre*

BERKS & BUCKS SENIOR TROPHY 1999-2000

(24 entries)

LAST SEASON'S FINAL: Eton Wick v Holmer Green 1-0

SECOND QUALIFYING ROUND (No First Round, 8 matches)

Finchampsted	v	Olney Town	3-0	Penn & Tylers Green	v	Stocklake S & SC	0-2
Amersham Town	v	Abingdon United	1-3	New Bradwell St Peter	v	Risborough Rangers	4-1
Milton United	v	Reading Town	2-1	Stony Stratford Tn	v	Kintbury Rangers	0*0 2-1
Wantage Town	v	Newport Pagnell Town	3-1	Prestwood	v	Newbury	0-2

THIRD ROUND (8 matches)

Newbury	v	Milton Keynes City	0-1	Stocklake S&S	v	New Bradwell St Peter	0-2
Wantage Town	v	Finchampstead	2-1	Holmer Green	v	Kintbury Rangers	3-2
Wallingford	v	Sandhurst T 5p6 4V1	2*2	Didcot Town	v	Taplow United	5-2
Milton United	v	Eton Wick	2*2 1-2	Abingdon United	v	Binfield	3-0

(Match 5 void, tie ordered to be re-played)

QUARTER-FINALS

Holmer Green	v	Eton Wick	1-0	New Bradwell St Peter	v	Abingdon United	2-1
Wantage Town	v	Milton Keynes City	1*2	Sandhurst Town	v	Didcot Town	0-2

SEMI-FINALS

Didcot Town	v	Milton Keynes City	1-2	New Bradwell St Peter	v	Holmer Green	2-0

FINAL

NEW BRADWELL ST P v   MILTON KEYNES C 3p1 1*1   at Beaconsfield & Slough YC OBFC

BRITAIN'S MOST POPULAR NATIONAL NON-LEAGUE FOOTBALL MONTHLY

TEAM TALK

Team Talk is published by Non League Media Plc, c/o Helland, North Curry, Taunton, TA3 6DU
Tel: 01823 490080 Fax: 01823 490281 e-mail: tony.williams12@virgin.net

BIRMINGHAM COUNTY F.A.

Tel: 0121 357 4278   Fax: 0121 358 1661
Ray Hall Lane, Great Barr, Birmingham B43 6JF
Secretary & Press Officer: M Pennick F.F.A.
Executives (Responsibility)   T Stack (Coaching Exams/Courses, Womens Football)
G J Southall (Referees)
Number of Affiliated Clubs   Senior: 1,685   U.18:   349   **President:** E P Smith
Number of Affiliated Leagues: Senior: 54   Junior: 8   **Chairman:** R J Wood
County Representative Teams: Senior, U18, U15, Womens, U18, U15
Inter County Competitions: FA County Youth, Midland County Youth (including Mitre Trophy)

BIRMINGHAM SENIOR CUP 1999-2000
(43 entries)   (FOUNDED 1875-76)

LAST SEASON'S FINAL: Birmingham City v Wolverhampton Wanderers 4-1

MOST WINS: Aston Villa 19   Birmingham City 8
Kidderminster Harriers 7   Wolverhampton Wanderers 7

FIRST ROUND (15 matches)

West Midland Police	v	Banbury United @B	0-2	Oldbury United	v	Sandwell Borough	3-1
Stourbridge	v	Evesham United	1*3	VS Rugby	v	Brierley Hill Town	3*1
Sutton Coldfield Tn	v	Stratford Town	5-1	Gornal Athletic	v	Cradley Town	0-1
Darlaston Town	v	Paget Rangers	5-1	Dudley Town	v	Studley BKL	1-4
Wednesfield	v	Tividale	5*2	Halesowen Harriers	v	Handrahan Timbers	5-1
Willenhall Town	v	Boldmere St Michaels	0-1	Kings Heath	v	Racing Club Warwick	3-1
Lye Town	v	Bedworth United	0-4	Highgate United	v	Kings Norton Tn	1A1 1-2
Bolehall Swifts	v	Coleshill Town	4-0				

SECOND ROUND (12 matches)

Boldmere St Michaels	v	Halesowen Town	2*1	Burton Albion	v	Banbury United	2-1
Tamworth	v	V S Rugby	5-2	Oldbury United	v	Evesham United	0-2
Nuneaton Borough	v	Bedworth United	1-2	Redditch United	v	Sutton Coldfield Town	1-3
Kings Heath	v	Hednesford Town	1*2	Cradley Town	v	Darlaston Town	1-3
Bolehall Swifts	v	Studley BKL	0-3	Wednesfield	v	Halesowen Harriers	0-2
Solihull Borough	v	Kings Norton Town	1-0	Atherstone United	v	Moor Green	3-1

THIRD ROUND (8 matches)

Boldmere St Michaels	v	Walsall	1-2	Burton Albion	v	Tamworth	0-2
Evesham United	v	West Bromwich Albion	2-0	Bedworth United	v	Sutton Coldfield T	0*0 0-1
Hednesford Town	v	Wolverhampton W 4p2	2*2	Darlaston Town	v	Studley BKL	5*5 2-4
Halesowen Harriers	v	Solihull Borough	1-5	Atherstone United	v	Birmingham City	0-2

QUARTER-FINALS

Evesham United	v	Walsall	2-3	Studley BKL	v	Tamworth	0-5
Hednesford Town	v	Sutton Coldfield Tn	4-0	Birmingham City	v	Solihull Borough	5-0

SEMI-FINALS

Birmingham City	v	Hednesford Town	4-0	Tamworth	v	Walsall	1-2

FINAL

BIRMINGHAM CITY v WALSALL   5th August 2000 at 3.00pm at Birmingham

CAMBRIDGESHIRE F.A.

Tel: 01223 576770   Fax: 01223 576780
3 Signet Court, Swanns Road, Cambridge CB5 8LA
Secretary: Roger Pawley
Executives (Responsibility)   B G Manley (Coaching Exams/Courses
                                              Referees, Womens Football)
Number of Affiliated Clubs   Senior: 350   U.18:   50   **President:** W W Ashton
Number of Affiliated Leagues: Senior: 1   Junior: 6   **Chairman:** J W Coad
County Representative Teams: Senior, U18, U16, Womens
Inter County Competitions: East Anglian Counties

CAMBRIDGESHIRE INVITATION CUP 1999-2000
(12 entries)   (FOUNDED 1950-51)

LAST SEASON'S FINAL: Soham Town Rangers v Newmarket Town 3-2
MOST WINS: Wisbech Town 9   Cambridge City 9   Chatteris Town 7

PRELIMINARY ROUND (4 matches)

Chatteris Town	v	Warboys Town	1-3	Histon	v	Cambridge City	1-2
March Town United	v	Sawston United	1-2	Mildenhall Town	v	Over Sports	2-1

QUARTER-FINALS

Ely City	v	Cambridge City	1-4	Sawston	v	Newmarket Town@ NT	1-2
Mildenhall Town	v	Wisbech Town	3-0	Soham Town Rngrs	v	Warboys Town	2-1

SEMI-FINALS

Newmarket Town	v	Cambridge City	1*1 2*4	Soham Town Rngrs	v	Mildenhall Town	0-1

FINAL
CAMBRIDGE CITY v MILDENHALL TOWN 3-0   at Cambridge City FC

An irresistable strike force

Every month

Team Talk

OFFICIAL F.A. MAGAZINE

THE NON-LEAGUE PAPER
CONFERENCE & PYRAMID LEAGUES SOCCER / £1.00

Every week

Every day

For up to the minute news, results, fixtures,
and general facts and figures
from the world of non-league football
log on to

www.nlfootball.com

Brought to you by Non-League Media in conjunction with e-comsport

CHESHIRE F.A.

Tel: 01606 871166   Fax: 01606 871292
The Cottage, Moss Farm Recreation Centre, Winnington, Northwich CW8 4BG
Secretary & Press Officer: Maureen J Dunford
Executives (Responsibility)   Sheila Goulden (Coaching Exams/Courses)
Bob Cooper (Referees)
Anita Gore (Women's Football)

Number of Affiliated Clubs	Senior:	816	U.18:	271	**President:** Alan Burbidge
Number of Affiliated Leagues:	Senior:	27	Junior:	13	

County Representative Teams: U18 (Womens/Girls teams for 1999-2000)
Inter County Competitions: FA County Youth, Northern Counties Youth Cup, Northern Counties Ladies Cup

CHESHIRE SENIOR CUP 1999-2000
(17 entries)   (FOUNDED 1879-80)

LAST SEASON'S FINAL: Altrincham v Northwich Victoria 1-0

MOST WINS: Macclesfield Town 20   Northwich Victoria 16   Crewe Alexandra 12   Runcorn 12

PRELIMINARY ROUND (1 match)

Witton Albion	v	Vauxhall Motors	1-2

FIRST ROUND (8 matches)

Cheadle Town	v	Altrincham	1*1 0-2	Crewe Alexandra	v	Congleton Town	5-0
Chester City	v	Tranmere Rovers	3-2	Nantwich Town	v	Hyde United	3*4
Runcorn	v	Warrington Town	3-4	Woodley Sports	v	Stalybridge Celtic	2-3
Winsford United	v	Macclesfield Town	1-3	Northwich Victoria	v	Vauxhall	2A0 2-0

SECOND ROUND (4 matches)

Hyde United	v	Crewe Alexandra	1-3	Macclesfield Town	v	Chester City	2-1
Northwich Victoria	v	Altrincham	1-3	Stalybridge Celtic	v	Warrington Town	2-0

SEMI-FINALS

Altrincham	v	Stalybridge Celtic	2-1	Macclesfield Town	v	Crewe Alexandra	2-1

FINAL

ALTRINCHAM	v	MACCLESFIELD TN	1-2	at Witton Albion FC

BUREAU of NON-LEAGUE FOOTBALL MONTHLY RESULTS MAGAZINE

Subscription ONLY £21.00

Send your Chx/p.p. with name and address to Mike Ford
THE BUREAU OF NON-LEAGUE FOOTBALL (BNLF)
173, LEYTONSTONE ROAD, LONDON, E15 1LH

CHESHIRE AMATEUR CUP 1999-2000
(FOUNDED 1886-87)

LAST SEASON'S FINAL: Poulton Victoria v Barnton 1-0
MOST WINS: ICI Alkali 9 Cammell Laird 6 Poulton Victoria 6

SECOND ROUND (16 matches)

Barnton	v	Willaston	4-0	Bollington	v	Poulton Victoria	0-4
Castrol Social	v	Mersey Royal	2-1	Cheadle Heath N	v	Cammell Laird	1-4
Chester Nomads	v	Dukinfield Town	0-2	Christleton	v	Blacon YC	3-2
Heswall	v	Shaftesbury	4-2	Lymm MSA	v	West Kirby	3-5
Partington Village	v	St Werburgh's	5-2	Poynton	v	Shell	4-3
Stockport Georgians	v	Ashville	1-5	Stork	v	Cheadle Hulme	2-0
Styal	v	Linotype	0-3	Upton AA	v	Knutsford	0-2
Warrington Borough	v	BICC Helsby	0-4	Wilmslow Albion	v	Middlewich Town	2-2,1-2

THIRD ROUND (8 matches)

Ashville	v	Linotye	2-1	Barton	v	Partington Village	6-0
Cammell Laird	v	Knutsford	1-2	Castrol Social	v	BICC Helsby	2-2,2-3
Heswall	v	Stork	0-1	Middlewich Town	v	Dukinfield Town	1-5
Poyton	v	Christleton	2-3	West Kirby	v	Poulton Victoria	2-3

FOURTH ROUND (4 matches)

BICC Helsby	v	Dukinfield Town	2-0	Christleton	v	Knutsford	2-1
Poulton Victoria	v	Asfville	1-0	Stork	v	Barton	1-2

SEMI FINALS

Barnton	v	Poulton Victoria	3-2	BICC Helsby	v	Christleton	5-1

FINAL

BICC HELSBY	v	BARNTON	3-1	at Vauxhall Motors FC.

Action from a Cheshire Amateur Cup First Round tie. Manchester League side Dukinfield Town defeat Manor Athletic of the West Cheshire League 5-2.
Photo: Colin Stevens

WIRRAL SENIOR CUP 1999-2000
(FOUNDED 1885-86)
LAST SEASON'S FINAL: Heswall v Stork 3*2
MOST WINS: Cammell Laird 10   Tranmere Rovers 9   Heswall 7   Poulton Victoria 7

SECOND ROUND (4 matches)

Mersey Royal	v	New Brighton	3-2	Poulton Victoria	v	Cammell Laird	2-3
Shell	v	Vauxhall	1-2	Stork	v	Heswall	1-1,1p3

SEMI FINALS

Mersy Royals	v	Cammell Laird	1-4	Vauxhall	v	Heswall	3-0

FINAL

Cammell Laird	v	Vauxhall	2*1	at Heswell FC

ADDITIONAL 1999-2000 CUP FINALS

WIRRAL AMATEUR CUP

Cammell Laird Res	v	Charing Cross	3-2

WIRRAL JUNIOR CUP

North Star	v	Seven Stiles Youth	3-1

RUNCORN SENIOR CUP

BICC Helsby	v	Pavillians	4-0

CHESTER SENIOR CUP

Christleton	v	St Teresa's	4-2

NORTHERN COUNTIES CHAMPIONSHIP

East Riding FA	v	Cheshire FA	1*0

Lee Martin (Macclesfield) gathers safely, Richard Landon (Altrincham) can only look on in the Cheshire Senior Cup Final.   *Photo: Keith Clayton*

CORNWALL F.A.

Tel: 01726 74080   Fax: 01726 76174   E-mail: cfa@btclick.com
1 High Cross Street, St Austell, Cornwall PL25 4AB
Secretary: Barry Cudmore
Executives (Responsibility)   John Riley (Coaching Exams/Courses)
Ian Anear (Referees)
Phil Cardew (Football Development Officer)

Number of Affiliated Clubs	Senior:	311	U.18:	84	**President:** R C Roberts
Number of Affiliated Leagues:	Senior:	18	Junior:	3	**Chairman:** D G Champion

County Representative Teams: Senior, Youth U18
Inter County Competitions: South West Counties Senior & Youth, FA County Youth Cup

CORNWALL SENIOR CUP 1999-2000
(42 entries)   (FOUNDED 1892-93)

LAST SEASON'S FINAL: Bodmin Town v Millbrook 2-1

MOST WINS: Truro City 12   St Austell 11
St Blazey 11   Penzance 10   Torpoint Athletic 10

FIRST ROUND (10 matches)

Foxhole Stars	v	Marazion Blues	3-2		Goonhaven	v	Troon	2-2 1-0
Penryn Athletic	v	Camelford	0-1		RNAS Culdrose	v	Illogan RBL	0-2
St Agnes	v	Nanpean Rovers	1-1 0-6		St Breward	v	Helston Athletic	0-4
St Cleer	v	Padstow United	2-3		St Dennis	v	St Ives Town	1-1 1-1 1-2
St Just	v	Roche	3-0		Wendron	v	Bude Town	0-3

SECOND ROUND (16 matches)

Bodmin Town	v	Kelly Bray Athletic	5-1		Bude Town	v	Millbrook	1-3
Callington Town	v	Torpoint Athletic	2-1		Camelford	v	Ludgvan	4-0
Foxhole Stars	v	Sticker	1-4		Helston Athletic	v	Illogan RBL	2-2 8-1
Launceston	v	Goonhavern Athletic	3-1		Mousehole	v	Padstow United	2-1
Mullion	v	Porthleven	0-6		Perranwell	v	Wadebridge Town	3-1
Saltash United	v	Newquay	3-1		Nanpean Rovers	v	St Blazey	1-5
St Austell	v	Penzance	2-1		St Ives Town	v	Falmouth Town	0-1
St Just	v	Liskeard Athletic	0-3		Truro City	v	Probus	5-0

THIRD ROUND (8 matches)

Bodmin Town	v	Truro City	2-2 0-4		Falmouth Town	v	Porthleven	1-2
Launceston	v	Saltash United	0-3		Liskeard Athletic	v	Callington Town	2-0
Mousehole	v	Camelford	2-3		Perranwell	v	Millbrook	0-4
St Austell	v	Helston Athletic	1-2		Sticker	v	St Blazey	0-9

QUARTER-FINALS

Camelford	v	St Blazey	0-0 0-3		Liskeard Athletic	v	Porth Leven	3-4
Saltash United	v	Millbrook	2-2 0-2		Truro City	v	Helston Athletic	2-1

SEMI-FINALS

Porthleven	v	Truro City	5-1	at Falmouth Town FC
St Blazey	v	Millbrook	1-0	at Newquay FC

FINAL

PORTHLEVEN	v	ST BLAZEY	1*1 1-2	at Newquay FC also Replay

CUMBERLAND F.A.

Tel: 01900 872310   Fax: 01900 872310
17 Oxford Street, Workington, Cumbria CA14 2AL
Secretary & Press Officer: Albert Murphy
Executives (Responsibility)   Peter Hampton & Keith Hunton (Coaching Exams/Courses)
Harry Upton & Thomas Jackson (Referees)

Number of Affiliated Clubs	Senior: 187	U.18: 162	**President:** Brian Taylor
Number of Affiliated Leagues:	Senior: 8	Junior: 4	**Chairman:** Maurice Perkins

County Representative Teams: Senior, Youth, Womens
Inter County Competitions: FA County Youth

CUMBERLAND SENIOR CUP 1999-2000
(39 entries)   (FOUNDED 1960-61)

LAST SEASON'S FINAL: Cleator Moor Celtic v Carlisle City 1*1, 4-2

MOST WINS: Penrith 10   Gretna 9   Haig Colliery 3

FIRST ROUND (7 matches)

Kirkoswald	v	Emperors Palace	0-8	Workington	v	Carleton Rovers	7-0
Parton United	v	Carlisle United	1-4	Wetheriggs United	v	Frizington White Star	2-0
Langwathby	v	Cockermouth	3-6	Portland	v	Windscale(w)	3-5
Whitehaven M.(wc)	v	Windscale Res(wc)	1-3				

SECOND ROUND (16 matches)

British Steel	v	Wigton Harriers	1-2	Northbank(na)	v	Keswick	3-0
Silloth	v	Carlisle United	0-1	North Lakeland	v	Penrith	0-10
Cleator Moor C R(wc)	v	Netherhall	0-3	Mirehouse Comm	v	Whitehaven AFC Rs(wc)	6-4
Egremont St Mary's	v	Cleator Moor Celtic(cd)	1-4	Greystoke	v	Windscale Res (wc)	2-5
Harraby Catholic Club	v	Gretna	1*2	St Bees	v	Emperors Palace	2-6
Workington	v	Whitehaven AFC(w)	5-0	Penrith Rangers	v	Northbank Res(cd)	1-3
Wetheriggs United	v	Carlisle City(na)	0*2	Hearts of Liddlesdale	v	Abbeytown	4-1
Longtown	v	Braithewaite	7-1	Cockermouth	v	Windscale (w)	W W-O

THIRD ROUND (8 matches)

Mirehouse	v	Longtown	2*3	Workington	v	Northbank Res(cd)	5-0
Northbank(na)	v	Gretna	2-1	Carlisle City(na)	v	Penrith	1-2
Wigton Harriers	v	Carlisle United	0-1	Windscale(w)	v	Hearts of Liddlesdale	4-0
Windscale Res(wc)	v	Cleator Moor Celtic(cd)	1-3	Netherall	v	Emperors Palace	3p4 4*4

FOURTH ROUND (4 matches)

Longtown	v	Northbank	0-5	Workington	v	Cleator Moor Celtic	2-0
Windscale	v	Emperors Palace	8-1	Penrith	v	Carlisle United	0-4

SEMI-FINALS

Workington	v	Northbank	5-1	Windscale	v	Carlisle United	0-2

FINAL

WORKINGTON	v	CARLISLE UNITED	2-0	at Workington FC

Cumberland Senior Cup: Harraby Catholic Club 1   Gretna 2 (a.e.t.)
Harraby keeper Gareth Edwards saves under pressure from Gretna's Martin Horsfield
Photo: Alan Watson

DERBYSHIRE F.A.

Tel: 01332 361422   Fax: 01332 360130
The Grandstand, Moorways Stadium, Moor Lane, Derby DE24 9HY
Secretary & Press Officer: K Compton
Executives (Responsibility)   County Secretary
(Coaching Exams/Courses, Referees, Womens Football)
Number of Affiliated Clubs   Senior: 620   U.18:   220
Number of Affiliated Leagues: Senior: 15   Junior: 5   **Chairman:** R F Johnson
County Representative Teams: U16
Inter County Competitions: East Midlands Youth Football Combination

DERBYSHIRE SENIOR CUP 1999-2000
(24 entries)   (FOUNDED 1883-84)

LAST SEASON'S FINAL: Ilkeston Town   v   Belper Town

MOST WINS: Derby County 15   Ilkeston Town 13
Buxton 8   Chesterfield 8   Heanor Town 8

FIRST ROUND (4 matches)

Blackwell M W	v	Heanor Town	1-3	Holbrook	v	Mickleover RBL	1-2
Shirebrook Town	v	Stanton Ilkeston	7-2	South Normanton A	v	Shardlow St James	3-1

SECOND ROUND (4 matches)

Shirebrook Town	v	Ripley Town	4-0	Long Eaton United	v	Graham St Prims	0-2
Sandiacre Town	v	Mickleover RBL	4-0	South Normanton A	v	Heanor Town	0-3

THIRD ROUND (8 matches)

Staveley MW	v	Glossop North End	3-4	Buxton	v	Heanor Town	1-2
Graham Street Prims	v	Matlock Tn @BV	1-3	Mickleover RBL	v	Gresley Rovers	1-2
Mickleover Sports	v	Glapwell	3-1	Ilkeston Town	v	Borrowash Victoria	3p0 1*1
Alfreton Town	v	Shirebrook Town	1-0	Belper Town	v	Stapenhill	5-1

QUARTER-FINALS

Belper Town	v	Ilkeston Town	1-2	Matlock Town	v	Alfreton Town	1-2
Heanor Town	v	Gresley Rovers	0-2	Glossop North End	v	Mickleover Sports	1-2

SEMI-FINALS

Gresley Rovers	v	Alfreton Town	4-3	Mickleover Sports	v	Ilkeston Town	0-6

FINAL 2 legs

GRESLEY ROVERS	v	ILKESTON TOWN	0-1		
ILKESTON TOWN	v	GRESLEY ROVERS	3-0	= 4-0	

DEVON F.A.

Tel: 01626 332077   Fax: 01626 336814
County Headquarters, Coach Road, Newton Abbot, Devon TQ12 1EJ
Secretary & Press Officer: Chris J Davidson
Executives (Responsibility) R Soper (Coaching Exams) C Cox (Referees)
M Lawrence (Womens Football) C Davey (Coaching Courses)
Number of Affiliated Clubs Senior: 161   U.18:   252
Number of Affiliated Leagues: Senior: 50   Junior: 10   **Chairman:** Brian Williams
County Representative Teams: Senior, U18, Womens
Inter County Competitions: South West Counties Championship
County Publications: "Kick Off" - bi-monthly Newsletter

DEVON ST LUKES BOWL 1999-2000
(12 entries)

LAST SEASON'S FINAL: Plymouth Argyle v Exeter City 1-0

MOST WINS: Tiverton Town 8   Bideford 3   Exmouth Town 3

FIRST ROUND (4 matches)

Exmouth Town	v	Tiverton Town	1-5	Ilfracombe Town	v	Exeter City	4-3
Elmore	v	Plymouth Argyle	2-1	Clyst Rovers	v	Torquay United	1-2

SECOND ROUND (4 matches)

Barnstaple Town	v	Tiverton Town	1*2	Dawlish Town	v	Ilfracombe Town	3-1
Torrington Town	v	Elmore	1-3	Bideford	v	Torquay United	0*1

SEMI-FINALS

Tiverton Town	v	Dawlish Town	4-0	Elmore	v	Torquay United	0-5

FINAL

TIVERTON TOWN	v	TORQUAY UTD	3p2,3*3	at Tiverton TownFC

BRITAIN'S MOST POPULAR NATIONAL
NON-LEAGUE
FOOTBALL MONTHLY

TEAM TALK

Team Talk is published by Non League Media Plc, c/o Helland, North Curry, Taunton, TA3 6DU
Tel: 01823 490080 Fax: 01823 490281 e-mail: tony.williams12@virgin.net

DEVON PREMIER CUP 1999-2000
(71 entries)

HOLDERS Cullompton Rangers

FIRST ROUND (7 matches)

Dolton Rangers	v	Upton Athletic	2-1	Brixham Villa	v	Newton Abbot 66	3-5
Hatherleigh Town	v	Exeter Civil Service	0-2	Elburton Villa	v	Heavitree	0-1
Feniton	v	Topsham Town	5-2	Dartington Sports	v	Holsworthy	0-1
Newton Abbot Spurs	v	Exeter St Thomas	1-1 1-2				

SECOND ROUND (32 matches)

Georgeham & Croyde	v	Newton Abbot	1-3	Prince Rock	v	Civil Service S & L	1-4
Plymouth Parkway	v	Exmouth Amateurs	6-0	Fremington	v	Appledore	2-6
Budleigh Salterton	v	Heavitree	4-0	Tavistock	v	Buckfastleigh Rangers	3-1
Culm United	v	Combe Martin	CM W-O	St Martins Jersey	v	Torrington Admirals	5-1
Galmpton United	v	Dartmouth AFC	3-2	Plymstock United	v	Willand Rovers	1-0
Pinhoe	v	St Peters Jersey	1-4	Brealwater B PD	v	Newton St Cyres	0-1
Braunton	v	Watts Blake Bearne	1-5	Feniton	v	Alphington	2-3
Plymouth Civil Serv	v	Ottery St Mary	3-2	Holsworthy	v	Bridgerule	6-1
St Martins	v	Vospers Oak Villa	1-3	Shamwickshire Rvrs	v	Exeter St Thomas	6-5
Bishopsteignton U	v	Mount Gould BP	0-2	Mainstone Sports	v	Okehampton Argyle	1-3
Sidmouth Town	v	Crediton United	1-6	Cullompton Rangers	v	Helle Rovers	3-2
Dolton Rangers	v	Bradworthy United	3-0	Plympton United	v	Dawlish Town	3-1
British Aerospace	v	Chagford	0-1	Chudleigh Athletic	v	Ivybridge Town	7*5
Witheridge	v	Putford	1-0	Exeter Civil Service	v	Buckland Athletic	4-3
Seaton Town	v	Liverton United	4-1	Ernesettle AFC	v	Stoke Gabriel	1-4
Newton Abbot 66	v	Teignmouth	3-1	Boca Seniors	v	Kingskerswell	0-3

THIRD ROUND (16 matches)

C Service S & L	v	Budleigh Salterton	3-2	Okehampton Argyle	v	Chudleigh Athletic	1-3
Newton St Cyres	v	Alphington	2-3	Galmpton United	v	Watts Blake Bearne	6-2
Plymstock United	v	Mount Gould BP	0-2	Kingskerswell	v	Plymouth Parkway	2-5
Newton Abbot	v	St Peters Jersey	3*3 1-3	Appledore	v	Newton Abbot 66	6-2
Plymouth Civil Serv	v	Plympton United	2-0	Tavistock	v	Shamwickshire Rvrs	1-0
Seaton Town	v	Vospers Oak Villa	0-3	Stoke Gabriel	v	Crediton United	2-3
Combe Martin	v	Chagford	1-2	Holsworthy	v	Cullompton Rangers	2-1
St Martins Jersey	v	Witheridge	2*2 3-0	Dolton Rangers	v	Exeter Civil Service	2-3

FOURTH ROUND (8 matches)

St Martins Jersey	v	St Peters Jersey	0-1	Civil Service S&L	v	Vospers Oak Villa	3-4
Chudleigh Athletic	v	Dartmouth AFC	2-3	Plymouth Parkway	v	Alphington	4-2
Plymouth Civil Serv	v	Holsworthy	1-5	Exeter Civil Service	v	Chagford	5-0
Crediton United	v	Mount Gould BP	1-3	Appledore	v	Tavistock	3-0

QUARTER-FINALS

Vospers Oak Villa	v	Mount Gold BP	2*2 4-3	Dartmouth	v	Plymouth Parkway	0-3
St Peters Jersey	v	Holsworthy	2-0	Exeter Civil Service	v	Appledore	5p4 2*2

SEMI-FINALS

Plymouth Parkway	v	Exeter Civil Service	2*3	St Peters Jersey	v	Vospers Oak Villa	1-5

FINAL

EXETER C SERV.	v	VOSPERS OAK V.	0-5	at Torquay United FC	

DORSET F.A.

Tel: 01202 682375   Fax: 01202 666577

County Ground, Blandford Close, Hamworthy, Poole BH15 4BF

Secretary: P S Hough   **Press Officer:** I Hallett

Executives (Responsibility)   S N Whittle (Referees)

County Representative Teams: Senior, Womens, Under 18   **President:** S D Miles

Inter County Competitions: South West Championship U21, Womens, Youth   **Chairman:** G Pike

DORSET SENIOR CUP 1999-2000
(37 entries)   (FOUNDED 1887-88)

LAST SEASON'S FINAL: Weymouth v Wimborne Town 4-1

MOST WINS: Weymouth 26   Poole Town 10   Portland United 10   Bridport 9

FIRST ROUND (8 matches)

Dorset Knob	v	Dorchester United	5-4	Beaminster	v	Verwood Town	3-3 0-2
Badger Sports	v	Weymouth United	1-1 3-2	Trinidad Green Bdg	v	Poole Borough	0-5
Okeford United	v	Lytchett Red Triangle	5-2	Dorchester YMCA	v	St Mary's RC	3-3 2-5
Stourpaine	v	Moreton	9-2	Poole Town	v	Chickerell United	3-0

SECOND ROUND (13 matches)

Allendale	v	Portland United	1-0	Blandford United	v	Badger Sports	1-3
Bournemouth Sports	v	Stourpaine	1-8	Dorset Knob	v	Poole Borough	1-8
Flight Refuelling	v	Shaftsbury	5-1	Hamworthy Eng	v	Hamworthy Utd	1-2
Northerners Athletic	v	Witchampton Utd	4-0	Poole Town	v	Gillingham Town	2-1
Sherborne Town	v	Parley Sports	1-3	Swanage T & Herston	v	St Pauls Jersey	3-1
Verwood Tn	v	Sturminster N Utd	1-1 3-2	Wareham Rangers	v	Okeford United	2-2 2-4
St Marys RC	v	Weymouth Sports	2-1				

THIRD ROUND (8 matches)

Wimborne Town	v	Swanage T & Herston	4-0	Weymouth	v	Poole Borough	1-1 3-1
Hamworthy United	v	Verwood Tn	3p4 0-0 0*0	Northerners Athletic	v	Bridport	0-4
Okeford United	v	Allendale	1-2	Parley Sports	v	St Mary R C	4-1
Poole Town	v	Flight Refuelling	3-1	Stourpaine	v	Badger Sports	0-1

QUARTER-FINALS

Wimborne Town	v	Allendale	5-1	Weymouth	v	Bridport	1-0
Parley Sports	v	Hamworthy U/Verwood T	0-1	Badger Sports	v	Poole Town	0-7

SEMI-FINALS

Poole Town	v	Weymouth	3-3 0-1	at Bridport FC	
Wimborne Town	v	Verwood Town	2-0	at Dorchester Town FC	

FINAL

WEYMOUTH	v	WIMBORNE TOWN	2-1	at Dorchester Town FC

DURHAM F.A.

Tel: 0191 384 8653   Fax: 0191 384 3234
"Codeslaw', Ferens Park, Durham DH1 1JZ
Secretary: John Topping
Executives (Responsibility)   A Philliskirk (Coaching Exams/Courses)
                                  J C Topping (Referees)

Number of Affiliated Clubs	Senior: 1040	Junior: 5	**President:** F D Patterson
Number of Affiliated Leagues:	Senior: 45	Junior: 5	**Chairman:** F D Patterson

County Representative Teams: U18
Inter County Competitions: Association of Northern Counties, FA County Youth

DURHAM CHALLENGE CUP 1999-2000
(44 entries)   (FOUNDED 1883-84)

LAST SEASON'S FINAL: Bishop Auckland v Durham City 3*2

MOST WINS: Sunderland 21   Spennymoor United 15   Bishop Auckland 14

PRELIMINARY ROUND (12 matches)

Harton & Westoe	v	Simonside S C	1-4	Jarrow Roofing BCA	v	Hebburn	2-0
Annfield Plain	v	Ryhope CW	0-1	Whickham	v	Shotton Comrades	0-1
Seaham Red Star	v	Sunderland K Roker	2-0	Billingham Town	v	Washington Nissan	0-0 2-1
Stanley United	v	Horden C W Athletic	1-0	Esh Winning	v	Eppleton C W	EW W-O
Darlington	v	Cockfield	5-0	Sunderland R H WMC	v	Jarrow	2-0
Crook Town	v	Wolviston	3-0	Cleadon SC	v	Willington	2-4

FIRST ROUND (16 matches)

Dunston F B	v	Birtley Town	2-1	Shildon	v	Seaham Red Star	0-4
Simonside S C	v	Ryhope C W	1-2	Easington Colliery	v	Billingham Synthonia	3-4
Consett	v	Willington	3-1	Darlington	v	Norton & Stockton Anc	2-0
West Auckland Tn	v	Stanley United	4-0	Boldon CA	v	Billingham Town	0-1
South Shields	v	Washington I Hoover	3-2	Durham City	v	Sunderland R H WMC	2*1
Peterlee	v	Hartlepool United	1-3	Crook Town	v	Tow Law Town	0-1
Jarrow Roofing BCA	v	Shotton Comrades	2-0	Brandon United	v	Esh Winning	3-2
Murton	v	Bishop Auckland	0-7	Evenwood Town	v	Chester le Street Tn	2-3

SECOND ROUND (8 matches)

Brandon United	v	South Shields	6-2	Hartlepool United	v	Darlington	0-2
Tow Law Town	v	Durham City	5-2	Billingham Synthonia	v	Consett	2-1
Chester le Street Tn	v	Ryhope C W	6-0	Bishop Auckland	v	Dunston F B	3-0
Seaham Red Star	v	West Auckland Town	1-0	Billingham Town	v	Jarrow Roofing BCA	3-1

THIRD ROUND (4 matches)

Seaham Red Star	v	Billingham Synthonia	Chester le Street Tn	v	Brandon United
Darlington	v	Bishop Auckland	Billingham Town	v	Tow Law Town

SEMI-FINALS

Darlington	v	Seaham Red Star	2-1	Brandon United	v	Tow Law Town	1-1 3-1

FINAL

BRANDON UNITED	v	DARLINGTON	1-3	at County Ground Durham City FC

EAST RIDING F.A.

Tel: 01482 221158   Fax: 01482 221159   E.Mail: ERCFA@DIAL.PIPEX.COM.
50 Boulevard, Hull HU3 2TB
Secretary & Press Officer: Dennis R Johnson
Executives (Responsibility)   T Mason (Coaching Exams/Courses)
                                    A Youngs (Referees)
                                    M Edge (Womens Football)

Number of Affiliated Clubs   Senior: 450   U.18:   110   **President:** Denis Grout
Number of Affiliated Leagues: Senior: 5   Junior: 2   **Chairman:** M Rawding
County Representative Teams: Senior, U18, Womens
Inter County Competitions: Association of Northern Counties, FA County Youth, East Midlands U18,

EAST RIDING SENIOR CUP 1999-2000
(22 entries)   (FOUNDED 1903-04)

LAST SEASON'S FINAL: North Ferriby United v Filey Town 5-1

MOST WINS: Hull City 25   Bridlington Town 12   North Ferriby United 8

FIRST ROUND (7 matches)

Walkington Wndrs	v	Hedon & Saltend	6-0	Ideal Standard	v	Savoy Wanderers	3-1
Sculcoates Amateurs	v	Westella & Willerby	7-3	Cottingham Sports	v	Kelvin Hall	KH W-O
Malet Lambert YC	v	Hider Foods	3-5	Tamerek Swiss Cott	v	Charleston AFC	2-1

SECOND ROUND (8 matches)

Hull City	v	Sculcoates Amateurs	4-0	Kenmar	v	Reckitts	0-4
Tamerek Swiss Cott	v	Hider Foods	3-4	Ideal Standard	v	Walkington Wndrs	5-3
Discount Carpets	v	Bridlington Town	1-5	Hall Road Rngrs Rs	v	East Hull Amateurs	4-3
Hall Road Rangers	v	Chisholms	3-2	North Ferriby United	v	Kelvin Hall	10-1

THIRD ROUND (4 matches)

Hull City AFC	v	Bridlington T	3p1 1*1 1*1	Hall Road Rangers	v	Reckitts	1-1 2-1
Hall Road Rngrs Rs	v	Hider Foods	1-2	North Ferriby United	v	Ideal Standard	2-0

SEMI-FINALS

Hall Road Rangers	v	Hull City	1-0	North Ferriby United	v	Hider Foods	4-0

FINAL

HALL ROAD RNGRS v NORTH FERRIBY UTD 1-2   at Hull City AFC

EAST RIDING COUNTRY CUP 1999-2000
(28 entries)

LAST SEASON'S FINAL: Ward v Withernsea 6-0

FIRST ROUND (12 matches)

North Cave	v	Middleton Rovers	7-0		Holme Rovers	v	Hornsea Town	6-2
Hunmanby United	v	Bridlington Rovers	3-1		Hutton Cranswick U	v	Nags Head Brid'ton	3-3 0-3
Bridlington S C	v	Nags Hd Brid 2nd	9-0		Ward	v	Crown	9-0
Full measure	v	Stirling Castle	8-0		Sledmere	v	Dunnington	D W-O
North Ferrriby U Rs	v	Easington Utd	7-2		Beverley O Gram's	v	Hooters FC	2-1
Filey Town	v	Driffield Town	5-3		Hilderthorpe	v	Wold Newton	2-0

SECOND ROUND (8 matches)

Pocklington Town	v	North Cave Utd Res	0-2		Bridlington Sports	v	North Cave	3-2
Full Measure	v	Mermaid	3-1		Ward FC	v	Holme Rovers	3-2
Nags Head Brid'ton	v	Hilderthorpe	1-2		Hutton C'wick SRA	v	Hunmanby United	1-5
Beverley OG	v	Dunnington	6-0		Withernsea	v	Filey Town	3-5

THIRD ROUND (4 matches)

Ward	v	Beverley Old Gram's	2-0		Filey Town	v	Bridlington Sports	2-0
North Ferriby Utd Rs	v	Hunmanby United	1-1 3-1		Hilderthorpe	v	Full Measure	1-2

SEMI-FINALS

Filey Town	v	North Ferriby U Rs	2-2 1-3	at Hutton Cranswick FC
Ward	v	Full Measure	4-3	at Rudston Fc

FINAL

NTH FERRIBY U RS	v	WARD	1-4	at Bridlington Town FC

BUREAU of NON-LEAGUE FOOTBALL
MONTHLY RESULTS MAGAZINE

Subscription ONLY £21.00

Send your Chx/p.p. with name and address to Mike Ford
THE BUREAU OF NON-LEAGUE FOOTBALL (BNLF)
173, LEYTONSTONE ROAD, LONDON, E15 1LH

ESSEX F.A.

Tel: 01245 357727   Fax: 01245 344430
31 Mildmay Road, Chelmsford CM2 0DN
Chief Executive: Philip Sammons
Executives (Responsibility)   Steve Goodsell (Coaching Exams/Course, Womens Football)
                                   Les Ives (Referees)
Number of Affiliated Clubs   Senior: 1604   U.18:   350   **Chairman:** R Brooks
Number of Affiliated Leagues: Senior: 40   Junior: 15   **Vice -Chairman:** E Fairchild
County Representative Teams: Senior, Intermediate, U18, U16, Womens
Inter County Competitions: East Anglian, Southern Counties

ESSEX SENIOR CUP 1999-2000
(44 entries) (FOUNDED 1883-84)

LAST SEASON'S FINAL: Canvey Island v Leyton Orient 2-1

MOST WINS: Ilford 13   Walthamstow Avenue 12   Grays Athletic 8   Leyton 8

FIRST ROUND (2 matches)
| Brentwood | v | Great Wakering Rvrs | 0-3 | | Clapton | v | Waltham Abbey | 1-2 |

SECOND ROUND (10 matches)
East Ham United	v	Southend Manor	4-6		Saffron Walden Tn	v	Ilford	1-3
Basildon United	v	Bowers United	1-2		Leyton	v	Waltham Abbey	2*3
Aveley	v	Hornchurch	1-0		Barkingside	v	Great Wakering Rvrs	2-3
Hullbridge Sports	v	Concord Rangers	1-2		Brightlingsea Utd	v	Burnham Ramblers	0-8
East Thurrock Utd	v	Stansted	2-0		Stanway Rovers	v	Tiptree United	4-1

THIRD ROUND (16 matches)
Waltham Abbey	v	Billericay Town	1-3		Harwich & Parkeston	v	Wivenhoe Town	4p3 0*0
Aveley	v	Chelmsford City	2*1		Southend United	v	Ford United	2-0
Braintree Town	v	Dagenham & Redb'dge	2-0		Purfleet	v	Burnham Ramblers	4-1
Great Wakering Rvrs	v	Grays Athletic	2-4		Witham Town	v	Harlow Town	2-3
Halstead Town	v	Stanway Rovers	1-2		Leyton Pennant	v	Heybridge Swifts	1-2
Tilbury	v	Concord Rangers	5-0		Maldon Town	v	Romford	1-3
Barking	v	Ilford	3-2		Canvey Island	v	Bowers United	4-0
Clacton Town	v	Leyton Orient	3*2		Southend Manor	v	East Thurrock United	2-0

FOURTH ROUND (8 matches)
Canvey Island	v	Tilbury	6-0		Southend Manor	v	Purfleet	2-4
Billericay Town	v	Aveley	4-0		Grays Athletic	v	Stanway Rovers	7-0
Harlow Town	v	Clacton Town	0-3		Braintree Town	v	Romford	1-2
Harwich & Parkeston	v	Barking	0*1		Heybridge Swifts	v	Southend United	1-4

QUARTER-FINALS
| Billericay Town | v | Romford | 2-0 | | Purfleet | v | Grays Athletic | 3-2 |
| Clacton Town | v | Canvey Island | 0-3 | | Southend United | v | Barking | 4p3 1*1 |

SEMI-FINALS
| Purfleet | v | Billericay Town | 4-2 | | Canvey Island | v | Southend United | 2-1 |

FINAL
| CANVEY ISLAND | v | PURFLEET | 2-0 | | at Southend United FC | | | |

ESSEX THAMES-SIDE TROPHY 1999-2000
(25 entries) (FOUNDED 1945-46)

LAST SEASON'S FINAL: Ford United v Southend United 2-1

MOST WINS: Ilford 13 Walthamstow Avenue 12 Grays Athletic 8 Leyton 8

FIRST ROUND (9 matches)

Grays Athletic	v	Barking	1-2	Barkingside	v	Tilbury	1-4
Romford	v	Concord Rangers	4-1	Hullbridge Sports	v	Aveley	2-5
Leyton Pennant	v	Brentwood	4-1	Burnham Ramblers	v	Clapton	0-1
Hornchurch	v	Southend Manor @ SM	2-0	Bowers United	v	Maldon Town	2-1
Gt Wakering Rovers	v	East Thurrock Utd	4-2				

SECOND ROUND (8 matches)

Romford	v	Ford United**	1V3 T-A	Aveley	v	Ilford	2-0
Barking	v	Witham Town	6-2	Hornchurch	v	Bowers United	6-0
Tilbury	v	Clapton	3-0	Waltham Abbey	v	Leyton Pennant @ LP	3-1
Basildon United	v	Canvey Island	0-3	Purfleet	v	Great Wakering Rvrs	3-0

(** fielded an ineligible player,opponents re-instated,void)

QUARTER-FINALS

Canvey Island	v	Aveley	8-0	Tilbury	v	Waltham Abbey	0-2
Purfleet	v	Barking	2-1	Hornchurch	v	Romford	1-3

SEMI-FINALS

Waltham Abbey	v	Canvey Island	tba	Purfleet	v	Romford	3-0

FINAL

PURFLEET	v	WALTHAM/CANVEY

BRITAIN'S MOST POPULAR NATIONAL NON-LEAGUE FOOTBALL MONTHLY

TEAM TALK

Team Talk is published by Non League Media Plc, c/o Helland, North Curry, Taunton, TA3 6DU
Tel: 01823 490080 Fax: 01823 490281 e-mail: tony.williams12@virgin.net

GLOUCESTERSHIRE F.A. LIMITED

Tel: 01454 615888   Fax: 01454 618088
Oaklands Park, Almondsbury, Bristol BS32 4AG
Company Sec. & Press Officer: Paul Britton
Executives (Responsibility)   Paul Britton (Coaching Exams/Courses, Womens Football)
                                    J W Hawkins (Referees)
Number of Affiliated Clubs   Senior: 868   U.18:   189   **President:** S T Rummins
Number of Affiliated Leagues: Senior: 21   Junior: 10   **Chairman:** CH Willcox MBE JP
County Representative Teams: Senior, U18, Womens, Womens U18
Inter County Competitions: South & South West Counties Championship, FA County Youth Cup

GLOUCESTERSHIRE SENIOR CUP 1999-2000
(8 entries)   (FOUNDED 1936-37)
LAST SEASON'S FINAL: Cheltenham Town v Gloucester City 2-0
MOST WINS: Cheltenham Town 32   Gloucester City 18   Forest Green Rovers 3

FIRST ROUND (4 matches)

Forest Green Rvrs	v	Gloucester City	5-0		Cirencester Town	v	Yate Town	3-0
Cinderford Town	v	Cheltenham Town	0-7		Bristol City	v	Bristol Rovers	1*0

SEMI-FINALS

Forest Green Rvrs	v	Bristol City	1-0		Cheltenham Town	v	Cirencester Town	1-0

FINAL
FOREST GREEN R v CHELTENHAM T   at Forest Green Rovers FC

GLOUCESTERSHIRE SENIOR TROPHY 1999-2000
(33 entries)   (FOUNDED 1978-79)
LAST SEASON'S FINAL: Fairford Town v Patchway Town 1-0
MOST WINS: Mangotsfield United 6   Moreton Town 3   Shortwood United 2

PRELIMINARY ROUND (1 match)
Bristol Manor Farm   v   Shirehampton   5p4 3*3

FIRST ROUND (16 matches)

Pucklechurch Sp	v	Hardwicke	1p3 3*3		Winterbourne Utd	v	Ellwood	1-2
Patchway Town	v	Broadwell Amateurs	4-1		Oldland Abbotonians	v	Roman Glass St G.	4-3
Tuffley Rovers	v	Viney St Swithens	4p3 2*2		Bishops Cleeve	v	Cadbury Heath	4-1
Shortwood United	v	Tytherington Rocks	3-1		Old Georgians	v	Cirencester Academy	2-4
Bristol Manor Farm	v	Almondsbury Town	3-0		Frampton Athletic	v	Hallen	0-2
Cheltenham Saracens	v	Harrow Hill	3*2		Fairford Town	v	D R G	2-1
Dursley Town	v	Highridge United	2-4		Henbury Old Boys	v	Brockworth	2-1
Broad Plain House	v	Mangotsfield United	1-6		Cirencester United	v	Bitton	0-1

SECOND ROUND (8 matches)

Henbury O B	v	Oldland Abbotonians	3-1		Ellwood	v	Tuffley Rovers	2-1
Bitton	v	Shortwood	3-1		Mangotsfield United	v	Hallen	3-0
Cirencester Academy	v	Bishops Cleeve	1-2		Cheltenham Saracens	v	Highridge United	1*3
Fairford Town	v	Hardwicke	2-1		Bristol Manor Farm	v	Patchway Town	1-2

QUARTER-FINALS

Fairford Town	v	Patchway Town	2-3		Highridge United	v	Bitton	0-3
Ellwood	v	Bishops Cleeve	2-1		Mangotsfield United	v	Henbury O B	4-1

SEMI-FINALS

Bitton	v	Mangotsfield United	0-4		Ellwood	v	Patchway Town	2*3

FINAL
MANGOTSFIELD U v PATCHWAY TOWN   2-0   at Glos FA HQ, Almondsbury.

HAMPSHIRE F.A.

Tel: 02380 791110   Fax: 02380 788340
William Pickford House, 8 Ashwood Gardens, off Winchester Road, Southampton SO16 7PW
Secretary: R G Barnes JP
Executives (Responsibility)   Ms S M Lopez (Coaching Exams/Courses, Womens Football)
R G Barnes (Referees)
Number of Affiliated Clubs   Senior: 2000   U.18:   450   **President:** M E Turner
County Representative Teams: Adult, Womens, U21, Girls U16, Boys U18, Girls U18   **Chairman:** E J Ward
Inter County Competitions: South West Counties, Hants & Dorset Cup

HAMPSHIRE SENIOR CUP 1999-2000
sponsored by Planet Logo
(47 entries)   (FOUNDED 1887-88)

LAST SEASON'S FINAL: Aldershot Town v Basingstoke Town   1-0

MOST WINS: Southampton 13   Newport 7   Cowes 6

FIRST ROUND (15 matches)

Basingstoke	v	Locksheath	2-0	Blackfield & Langley	v	Hayling United	1-3
Cove	v	Colden Common	2-1	Hamble ASSC	v	Hythe & Dibden	2-0
Hartley Wintney	v	B A T Sports	3-2	Horndean	v	Whitchurch United	1-2
Liss Athletic	v	Esseo Fawley	5-1	Lymington Town	v	Mayflower West Wight	1-2
Moneyfields	v	Alton Town	5-1	New Street	v	Ringwood Town	1-0
Petersfield Town	v	Brading Town	1-3	Pirelli General	v	Bishops Waltham Tn	2-0
Portsmouth R N	v	East Cowes Vic Ath	5-1	Romsey Town	v	R S Basingstoke	1-4
Stockbridge	v	Bournemouth	2-3				

SECOND ROUND (16 matches)

AFC Totton	v	New Street	5-1	Aldershot Town	v	Whitchurch United	2-0
Bashley	v	Sylvans Sports	1-2	Brockenhurst	v	Portsmouth R N	3-0
Cove	v	Basingstoke Town	1*3	Eastleigh	v	Liss Athletic	2-0
Fareham Town	v	Hamble ASSC	2*1	Farnborough Town	v	Bournemouth	3-0
Fleet Town	v	Moneyfields	4-2	Gosport Borough	v	AFC Basingstoke	1-0
Hartley Wintney	v	Hayling United	4p2 0*0	Havant & W'looville	v	Cowes Sports	0-3
Lymington & New M	v	Andover	0-3	Newport IOW	v	Brading Town	3-0
Pirelli General	v	Christchurch	1-2	Mayflower W Wight	v	RS Basingstoke	W-O

THIRD ROUND (8 matches)

Totton	v	Fleet Town	1-0	Brockenhurst	v	Sylvans Sports	2-1
Christchurch	v	Fareham Town	0-1	Cowes Sports	v	Basingstoke Town	0-2
Eastleigh	v	Andover	1-3	Farnborough Town	v	Mayflower West Wight	4-2
Gosport Borough	v	Hartley Wintney	0-1	Newport IOW	v	Aldershot Town	0-2

QUARTER-FINALS

Brockenhurst	v	Andover	0-5	Fareham Town	v	Basingstoke Town	0-4
Farnborough Town	v	Hartley Witney	0-1	Aldershot Town	v	Totton	2-0

SEMI-FINALS Two Legs)

Aldershot Town	v	Basingstoke T	2-0 0-0	= 2-0	
Andover	v	Hartley Witney	2-0 4-0	= 6-0	

FINAL

ALDERSHOT TOWN v		ANDOVER	9-1	at Basingstoke Town FC. Att: 1,445

Top: Hampshire Senior Cup: The Winning Team, Aldershot Town   Photo: Ian Morsman

Bottom: Gary "The Predator" Abbot scores 5, Mark Bentley scores 3 in the Hampshire Senior Cup Final. Both players are given a ball to commemmorate their 'hat-tricks'.   Photo: Ian Morsman

HEREFORDSHIRE F.A.

Tel: 01432 270308 (H)
1 Muirfield Close, Holmer, Hereford HR1 1QB
Secretary & Press Officer: Jim Lambert
Executives (Responsibility)   J Layton (Coaching Exams/Courses)
                                   A Jenkins (Referees)
                                   R J Perks (Womens Football)
Number of Affiliated Clubs   Senior: 125   U.18:   114   **President:** Sir Colin Shepherd
Number of Affiliated Leagues: Senior: 1   Junior: 1   **Chairman:** E G Powell
County Representative Teams: Under 18, Under 16
Inter County Competitions: Midland Counties U18, East Midland U16

HEREFORDSHIRE SENIOR CUP 1999-2000
(18 entries)   (FOUNDED 1973-74)

LAST SEASON'S FINAL: Pegasus Juniors v Ross Town 3-1

FIRST ROUND (2 matches)

Woofferton	v	Weston u Penyard	2-3	Sutton United	v	Westfields	0-2

SECOND ROUND (8 matches)

Golden Valley Ath	v	Fownhope	1-3	Bromyard Town	v	Ross United Services	6-0
Ross Town	v	Hinton	3-1	Wellington	v	Leominster Town	4*2
Pegasus Juniors	v	Ledbury Town	4*4 2-3	Weston U Penyard	v	Hereford Civil Service	3-2
Ewyas Harold	v	Hearts	10-1	Hereford Lads Club	v	Westfields	1-7

THIRD ROUND (4 matches)

Ross Town	v	Ewyas Harold	4*4 1-2	Bromyard Town	v	Westfields	3-0
Fownhope	v	Wellington	2-1	Ledbury Town	v	Weston under Penyard	6-0

SEMI-FINALS

Ewyas Harold	v	Fownhope	2-1	Bromyard Town	v	Ledbury Town	2-0

FINAL

BROMYARD TOWN	v	EWYAS HAROLD	4*1	at Hereford United FC	

HERTFORDSHIRE F.A.

Tel: 01462 677622   Fax: 01462 677624   E.Mail: HERTSFA@Compuserve.Com
County Ground, Baldock Road, Letchworth, Herts S96 2EN

Secretary: R G Kibble   **Press Officer:** County HQ
Executives (Responsibility)   R Dowie (Coaching Exams/Courses)
                                       R G Dowden (Referees)
                                       G Phillips (Womens Football)

Number of Affiliated Clubs   Senior: 860   U.18:   190   **President:** B W A Bayford
Number of Affiliated Leagues: Senior: 24   Junior: 11   **Chairman:** E C Hand
County Representative Teams: Senior, U18, U16
Inter County Competitions: East Anglian, EMYFC

HERTFORDSHIRE SENIOR CUP 1999-2000
(23 entries)   (FOUNDED 1886-87)

LAST SEASON'S FINAL: Boreham Wood v Watford 3-2
MOST WINS: Hitchin Town 21   Barnet 16   Watford 14

FIRST ROUND (7 matches)

Berkhamsted Town	v	Baldock Town	2-3	Stevenage Borough	v	Hemel Hempstead T	3-1
St Margaretsbury	v	Sawbridgeworth Tn	2-0	Bishops Stortford	v	Harpenden Town	8-0
Welwyn Garden C	v	Hoddesdon Town	1-2	Ware	v	Royston Town	3-1
Tring Town	v	Barnet	TT W-O				

SECOND ROUND (8 matches)

St Margaretsbury	v	Somersett Ambury V&E	3-1	Hitchin Town	v	London Colney	3-2
Cheshunt	v	Ware	3-0	Potters Bar Town	v	Baldock Town	2-4
Watford	v	Bishops S @BS	2*2 2-1	Tring Town	v	Stevenage Borough	3-2
St Albans City	v	Hoddesdon Town	1-0	Boreham Wood	v	Hertford Town	4-0

THIRD ROUND (4 matches)

Watford	v	Boreham Wood @ BW 2*4		Cheshunt	v	Tring Town	2-0
Hitchin Town	v	St Albans City	1-5	St Margaretsbury	v	Baldock Town	@ BT 1*2

SEMI-FINALS

Boreham Wood	v	St Albans City	3*3 1-5	Baldock Town	v	Cheshunt	3*2

FINAL

BALDOCK TOWN	v	ST ALBANS CITY	1-4	at Herts FA County Ground	

HERTFORDSHIRE SENIOR TROPHY 1999-2000
(21 entries)

LAST SEASON'S FINAL: Benington v Elliott Star 0-1

FIRST ROUND (5 matches)

Bushey Rangers	v	Kings Langley	2*1	Sandridge Rovers	v	Bedmond Sports	0-1
Whitewebbs	v	Tring Athletic	1-2	Letchworth	v	Bovingdon	3-1
Colney Heath	v	Agrevo Sports	5-0				

SECOND ROUND (8 matches)

Elliott Star	v	Bushey Rangers	4-2	Oxhey Jets	v	Sun Postal Sports	0-4
Wormley Rovers	v	Bridger Packaging FC	2-1	Leverstock Green	v	Hatfield Town	7-3
Tring Athletic	v	Greenacres	3-0	Cuffley	v	Letchworth	2*2 0*2
Bedmond Sports	v	Benington	4-3	Met Police Bushey	v	Colney Heath	4-5

THIRD ROUND (4 matches)

Bedmond Sports	v	Leverstock Green	3-0	Sun Postal Sports	v	Tring Athletic	0-1
Elliott Star	v	Colney Heath	3-2	Wormley Rovers	v	Letchworth	1-0

SEMI-FINALS

Bedmond Sports	v	Tring Athletic	1-3	Elliott Star	v	Wormley Rovers	0*1

FINAL

WORMLEY ROVERS	v	TRING ATHLETIC	0-2	at Herts FA County Ground	

HUNTINGDONSHIRE F.A.

Tel: 01480414422   Fax: 01480 412691

Cromwell Chambers, 8 St Johns Street, Huntingdon, Cambs. PE29 3DD

Secretary & Press Officer: Maurice Armstrong
Executives (Responsibility)   K J Oldham (Coaching Exams/Courses)
                              E K Heads (Referees)
                              M M Armstrong (Womens Football)

Number of Affiliated Clubs	Senior:	130	U.18:	30
Number of Affiliated Leagues:	Senior:	1	Junior:	1

President: D A Roberts

Chairman: R H Carter

County Representative Teams: Senior, Under 18, Under 16, Colts
Inter County Competitions: East Midlands Youth U18 & U16, East Anglian Championship Senior

HUNTINGDONSHIRE SENIOR CUP 1999-2000
(17 entries)   (FOUNDED 1888-89)

LAST SEASON'S FINAL: St Neots Town v Yaxley 3p4 1*1
MOST WINS: St Neots 34   Eynesbury Rovers 13   Huntingdon Town 12

FIRST ROUND (1 match)
Somersham Town   v   Bluntisham Rangers   8-1

SECOND ROUND (8 matches)

Warboys Town	v	Great Paxton	1*1 1-2	Brampton	v	ICA Juventus	0-3
Ortonians	v	Somersham Tn	0*0 3*4	Eynesbury Rovers	v	Stilton United	3-2
St Ives Town	v	Hemingford United	4-0	Godmanchester Rvrs	v	St Neots Town	0-2
Ramsey Town	v	Alconbury United	2-4	Hotpoint	v	Yaxley	0-1

THIRD ROUND (4 matches)

Eynesbury Rovers	v	St Neots Town	3*1	St Ives Town	v	Somersham Town	0-2
Yaxley	v	ICA Juventus	3-2	Alconbury United	v	Great Paxton	0-3

SEMI-FINALS

Great Paxton	v	Somersham Town	1*1 0-4	Yaxley	v	Eynesbury Rovers	1-3

FINAL
EYNESBURY RVRS v   SOMERSHAM TN   2-1   at Warboys Town FC

Eynesbury Rovers captain Neil Morris receives the Huntingdonshire Senior Cup from John Rignall (local district councillor and Chairman of Warboys Social Club). Eric Heads (Vice Chairman of the Huntingdonshire F.A. is on the left.   Photo: Gordon Whittington

935

Huntingdon Senior Cup Final: This 'goal' from Jamie Donald was disallowed for off-side and although he did put Somersham ahead, Eynesbury hit back to win 2-1
Photo: Gordon Whittington

KENT F.A.

Tel: 01634 843824   Fax: 01634 815369
E.Mail: KCFA.Chatham@btinternet.com
69 Maidstone Road, Chatham, Kent ME4 6DT
Secretary: K T Masters   **Press Officer:** Tony Hudd
Executives (Responsibility)   Alan Walker (Coaching)
                                  Keith Masters (Referees)
                                  Nici Dice (Womens Football)
Number of Affiliated Clubs   Senior: 1161   U.18:   211   **President:** E H Bennett
Number of Affiliated Leagues: Senior: 3   Junior: 39   **Chairman:** B W Bright
County Representative Teams: U18, U16, Womens, Girls

KENT FACIT SENIOR CUP 1999-2000
(13 entries)   (FOUNDED 1888-89)

LAST SEASON'S FINAL: Gravesend & Northfleet v Folkestone Invicta   1-0
MOST WINS: Maidstone United 15   Dartford 9   Northfleet United 9

FIRST ROUND (5 matches)

Sittingbourne	v	Dartford	1*1 0-6	Margate	v	Tonbridge Angels	3-2
Bromley	v	Fisher Ath London	0-1	Erith & Belvedere	v	Gravesend & N	3-3 2-4
Ashford Town	v	Ramsgate	4-2			

QUARTER-FINALS

Dartford	v	Ashford Town	2-1	Dover Athletic	v	Welling United	2-0
Margate	v	Folkestone Invicta	2-3	Gravesend & N'fleet	v	Fisher Athletic	4-0

SEMI-FINALS

Dover Athletic	v	Folkestone Invicta	1-4	Dartford	v	Gravesend & N	0-0 0-1

FINAL

GRAVESEND & N.	v	FOLKESTONE INV.	3-0	at Gravesend & Northfleet FC

KENT PLAAYA SENIOR TROPHY 1999-2000
(23 entries)   (FOUNDED 1874-75)

LAST SEASON'S FINAL: Ramsgate v Sheppey United 8p7 2*2
MOST WINS: Ramsgate 3   Alma Swanley 2   Corinthian 2   Faversham Town 2   Fisher Athletic 2

FIRST ROUND (7 matches)

Cray Wanderers	v	Hythe United	3-2	Canterbury City	v	Crockenhill	2-1
West Wickham	v	Faversham Town	0-2	V.C D Athletic	v	Erith Town	2-0
Beckenham Town	v	Thames Poly	3-1	Bearsted	v	Herne Bay	2-0
Milton Athletic	v	Knatchbull	2-1			

SECOND ROUND (8 matches)

Tunbridge Wells	v	Thamesmead Town	0-1	Deal Town	v	Faversham Town	8-3
V.C D Athletic	v	Beckenham Town	4-2	Bearsted	v	Sheppey United	3-1
Canterbury City	v	Lordswood	@L 5-0	Slade Green	v	Milton Athletic	1-2
Cray Wanderers	v	Whitstable Town	5-4	Chatham Town	v	Greenwich Borough	1-0

THIRD ROUND (4 matches)

Bearsted	v	VCD Athletic	1-0	Canterbury City	v	Deal Town**	0-3
Chatham Town	v	Milton Athletic	5-1	Thamesmead Town	v	Cray Wanderers	3-0
** at Whitstable Town FC						

SEMI-FINALS

Deal Town	v	Bearsted	1-0	Thamesmead Town	v	Chatham Town	1-1 1-2

FINAL

CHATHAM TOWN	v	DEAL TOWN	1-5	at Sittingbourne FC

Marine celebrate winning the Marsden Lancashire Challenge Trophy at Chorley in April. Marine thrashed Bamber Bridge 5-0 after being 3-0 up after 12 minutes.
Photo: Michael Morgan

LANCASHIRE F.A.

Tel: 01772 624000   Fax: 01772 624700
The County Ground, Thurston Road, Leyland PR5 1LF
Secretary & Press Officer   J Kenyon, ACIS
Executives (Responsibility)   D Egan (Development Officer)
J Kenyon (Referees)
Miss J Ashworth (Womens Football Development Officer)
Number of Affiliated Clubs   Senior: 1600   U.18:   300   **President:** D J Lewin
County Representative Teams: Senior, U18, Womens
Inter County Competitions: FA County Youth, Northern Counties Senior, U18 & Womens

MARSDEN LANCASHIRE TROPHY 1999-2000
(25 entries)   (FOUNDED 1885-86)
LAST SEASON'S FINAL: Morecambe v Darwen 4p2 2*2

FIRST ROUND (9 matches)

Atherton Laburnum R	v	Marine	0-6	Bacup Borough	v	Burscough	0-4
Barrow	v	Skelmersdale United	3-1	Clitheroe	v	Atherton Collieries	2*0
Great Harwood Tn	v	Colne	3-1	Fleetwood Freeport	v	Holker O B	2-1
Nelson	v	Leigh RMI	1-2	Ramsbottom United	v	Squires Gate	2-1
Rossendale United	v	Radcliffe Borough	4-1				

SECOND ROUND (8 matches)

Chorley	v	Clitheroe	1-3	Bamber Bridge	v	Lancaster City	2-1
Southport	v	Leigh RMI	1*2	Burscough	v	Marine	1-2
Fleetwood Freeport	v	Rossendale United	0-1	Morecambe	v	Barrow	0-2
Accrington Stanley	v	Ramsbottom United	4*2	Great Harwood Tn	v	Darwen	1*3

QUARTER-FINALS

Darwen	v	Marine	0-1	Accrington Stanley	v	Leigh RMI	1-2
Clitheroe	v	Bamber Bridge	0*2	Barrow	v	Rossendale United	3-2

SEMI-FINALS

Leigh RMI	v	Marine	2-4	Bamber Bridge	v	Barrow	2-1

FINAL

BAMBER BRIDGE	v	MARINE	0-5	at Chorley FC

WHITBREAD LANCASHIRE AMATEUR CUP 1999-2000
(FOUNDED 1893-94)
LAST SEASON'S FINAL: St Dominics v Aigburth PH   1-0
MOST WINS: Liverpool/Merseyside Police   11   St Dominics 6   Marine 5

FINAL

SPEKE	v	ST DOMINICS	3-2	at Leyland Motors Athletic FC

HOLLANDS LANCASHIRE AMATEUR CHALLENGE SHIELD 1999-2000

FINAL

GARSTAND	v	STAND ATHLETIC	4-1	at Leyland Motors Athletic FC

LEICESTERSHIRE & RUTLAND F.A.

Tel: 0116 286 7828   Fax: 0116 286 4858

Holmes Park, Dog & Gun Lane, Whetstone LE8 3LJ

Secretary & Press Officer: Paul Morrison

Executives (Responsibility)   John Ball (Coaching Courses)

J Ward (Referees)

Mrs G F Wait (Womens Football)

Number of Affiliated Clubs	Senior:	650	U.18:	150	**President:** G E Cooper
Number of Affiliated Leagues:	Senior:	12	Junior:	6	**Chairman:** J E Bray

County Representative Teams: Under 18, Under 16, Under 16 Girls

Inter County Competitions: East Midlands Youth Combination U18 & U16

LEICESTERSHIRE 'JELSON HOMES' SENIOR CUP 1999-2000
(39 entries)   (FOUNDED 1887-88)

LAST SEASON'S FINAL: Birstall United v Oadby Town 2p0 2*2

MOST WINS: Leicester City 27   Enderby Town 6   Shepshed Dynamo 6

FIRST ROUND (19 matches)

Coalville Town	v	Blaby & Whet. Ath.	2*1	Loughboro Dynamo	v	Downes Sports	3-1
Harborough T Imps	v	Birstall Utd	BU W-O	Earl Shilton Albion	v	Quorn	1-4
Anstey Town	v	St Andrews	0-3	Cottesmore Ams	v	Ibstock Welfare	3-4
Friar Lane O B	v	Sileby Town	6-2	Thurnby Rangers	v	Leic's Constabulary	4-0
Aylestone Park OB	v	Bardon Hill Sports	11-0	Slack & Parr	v	Castle Donington T	4-0
Loughborough Ath	v	Ellistown	7-0	Saffron Dynamo	v	Barlestone St Giles	2-0
Highfield Rangers	v	Fosse Imps	4-1	Lutterworth Town	v	Thringstone United	4-3
North Kilworth	v	Stoney Stanton	0-3	Holwell Sports	v	Asfordby Amateurs	4-0
Anstey Nomads	v	Kirby Muxloe	2-1	Thurmaston Town	v	Huncote Sports	3-0
Leicester YMCA	v	Barrow Town	4-1				

SECOND ROUND (4 matches)

Quorn	v	Loughborough D'mo	4-0	Highfield Rangers	v	Friar Lane Old Boys	2-0
Stoney Stanton	v	Slack & Parr	0-3	Thurnby Rangers	v	Thurmaston Tn	4p5 3*3

THIRD ROUND (8 matches)

Thurmaston Town	v	Anstey Nomads	0-3	St Andrews	v	Leicester YMCA	2*4
Lutterworth Town	v	Slack & Parr	3-2	Coalville Town	v	Saffron Dynamo	5*2
Birstall United	v	Quorn	4p3 4*4	Narborough-L'thorpe	v	Aylestone Park	5p4 1*1
Highfield Rangers	v	Holwell Sports	3p4 2*2	Ibstock Welfare	v	Loughborough Ath	2-4

QUARTER-FINALS

Birstall United	v	Leicester YMCA	2V1 0-3	Narboro & L'thorpe	v	Loughborough Ath	1-3
Anstey Nomads	v	Coalville Town	0-7	Lutterworth Town	v	Holwell Sports	0-6
(Match 1 tie ordered to be re-played)							

SEMI-FINALS

Coalville Town	v	Loughborough Ath	3-0	Leicester YMCA	v	Holwell Sports	0-3

FINAL

COALVILLE TOWN	v	HOLWELL SPORTS	2-1	at County FA Ground	

LEICESTERSHIRE WESTERBY CHALLENGE CUP 1999-2000
(12 entries)

LAST SEASON'S FINAL: Leicester City v Oadby Town 10-1

FIRST ROUND (4 matches)

Hinckley United	v	Quorn	3-1	Holwell Sports	v	St Andrews	5-0
Shepshed Dynamo	v	Kirby Muxloe	0-1	Barwell	v	Highfield Rangers	3-1

SECOND ROUND (4 matches)

Barwell	v	Birstall United	3-2	Leicester City	v	Ibstock Welfare	2-0
Holwell Sports	v	Oadby Town	1-3	Kirkby Muxloe	v	Hinckley United	0-2

SEMI-FINALS

Barwell	v	Oadby Town	1-0	at Holmes Park, Leics & Rutland County FA Ground.
Hinckley United	v	Leicester City	0-2	at Holmes Park, Leics & Rutland County FA Ground.

FINAL

LEICESTER CITY	v	BARWELL	4-0	at Leicester City FC

NOW IN ITS RECORD 10TH YEAR OF PUBLICATION

BRITAIN'S MOST POPULAR NATIONAL NON-LEAGUE FOOTBALL MONTHLY

TEAM TALK

Team Talk should be available from your local non-League football club or your local newsagent and is available by subscription from the publishers.

Team Talk is published by Non League Media Plc, c/o Helland, North Curry, Taunton, Somerset TA3 6DU
Tel: 01823 490080 Fax: 01823 490281 e-mail: tony.williams12@virgin.net

LINCOLNSHIRE F.A.

Tel: 01522 524917   Fax: 01522 528859
PO Box 26, 12 Dean Road, Lincoln LN2 4DP
Secretary: J Griffin   **Press Officer:** K Weaver
Executives (Responsibility)   Council of the Association:
(Coaching Exams, Referees, Womens Football)
K Leedham & W Ward (Coaching Courses)
Number of Affiliated Clubs   Senior: 930   U.18:   201   **President:** N A Saywell
Number of Affiliated Leagues: Senior: 20   Junior: 14   **Chairman:** R D Teanby
County Representative Teams: U18, U16
Inter County Competitions: East Midlands Youth Combination, FA County Youth

LINCOLNSHIRE SENIOR CUP 1999-2000
(7 entries)   (FOUNDED 1935-36)
LAST SEASON'S FINAL: Scunthorpe United v Stamford 2-0
MOST WINS: Grimsby Town 14   Lincoln City 12   Boston United 5

FIRST ROUND (3 matches)

Stamford	v	Boston United	0-1	Grantham Town	v	Scunthorpe United	0-5
Gainsborough Trinity	v	Grimsby Town	1p4 0*0				

SEMI-FINALS

Lincoln United	v	Scunthorpe United	2-1	Boston United	v	Grimsby Town	1-2

FINAL

GRIMSBY TOWN	v	LINCOLN UTD	4p2 3*3	at Grimsby Town FC

LINCOLNSHIRE SENIOR 'A' CUP 1999-2000
(10 entries)   (FOUNDED 1968-69)
LAST SEASON'S FINAL: Spalding United v Louth United 5-1
MOST WINS: Boston Town 6   Holbeach United 4   Skegness Town 4

PRELIMINARY ROUND (2 matches)

Brigg Town	v	Nettleham	2-1	Louth United	v	Winterton Rangers	0-1

FIRST ROUND (4 matches)

Brigg Town	v	Spalding United	2-0	Winterton Rangers	v	Holbeach United	2*1
Lincoln Moorlands	v	Blackstone	4-0	Bourne Town	v	Boston Town	1-5

SEMI-FINALS

Brigg Town	v	Boston Town	3-2	Lincoln Moorlands	v	Winterton Rangers	1-0

FINAL

BRIGG TOWN	v	LINCOLN M'LANDS	2-0	at Lincoln City FC

LINCOLNSHIRE SENIOR 'B' CUP 1999-2000
(16 entries)   (FOUNDED 1949-50)
LAST SEASON'S FINAL: Barton Town v Lincoln Moorlands 2-0
MOST WINS: Brigg Town 5   Appleby Frodingham Athletic 4

FIRST ROUND (8 matches)

Deeping Rangers	v	Appleby F'ham	4p2 2*2	Barrowby	v	Hykeham Town	2-1
Harrowby United	v	Bottesford Town	3V1 T-A	Grimsby Immi. Amt	v	Alston Sports	3-1
Grantham Rangers	v	Epworth Town	0-1	Sleaford Town	v	Barton Town O B	3-2
Skegness Town	v	Lymestone Rangers	1-3	Horncastle Town	v	Wyberton	1-0

(Bottesford Town were awarded the tie after it was found Harrrowby United had fielded an ineligible player)

SECOND ROUND (4 matches)

Limestone Rangers	v	Horncastle Town	4-1	Bottesford Town	v	Grimsby Imm. Amt	0-4
Deeping Rangers	v	Sleaford Town	0-1	Barrowby	v	Epworth Town	0-2

SEMI-FINALS

Sleaford Town	v	Limestone Rangers	2-1	Epworth Town	v	Grimsby Imm. Amt	1-3

FINAL

GRIMSBY I. AMT	v	SLEAFORD TOWN	1-4	at Lincoln City FC

LIVERPOOL F.A.

Tel: 0151 5234488   Fax: 0151 523 4477
Liverpool Soccer Centre, Walton Hall Park, Walton Hall Avenue, Liverpool L4 9XP
Secretary: F L Hunter   **Press Officer:** S Catterall
Executives (Responsibility)   M McGlyn (Coaching Exams/Courses)
                                   K R Naylor (Referees)
                                   Ms S Gore (Womens Football)
Number of Affiliated Clubs   Senior: 900   U.18:   600   **President:** J Lawson
Number of Affiliated Leagues: Senior: 18   Junior: 25
Inter County Competitions: All FA Competitions

LIVERPOOL SENIOR CUP 1999-2000
(11 entries) (FOUNDED 1977-78)

LAST SEASON'S FINAL: Southport v Burscough
MOST WINS: Marine 5   Liverpool 3   South Liverpool 3

FIRST ROUND (3 matches)
Bootle   v   Prescot Cables f/f 0A0 0-2   Skelmersdale United v   St Helens Town   2p4 3*3
Warrington Town   v   Marine   1-4

SECOND ROUND (4 matches)
Prescot Cables   v   St Helens Town   5-1   Southport   v   Marine   2*4
Burscough   v   Liverpool   2p4 2*2   Tranmere Rovers   v   Everton   3p2 0*0

SEMI-FINALS
Marine   v   Liverpool   2-1   Tranmere Rovers   v   Prescot Cables   @ PC 1-0

FINAL
TRANMERE RVRS   v   MARINE   0*1   at Tranmere Rovers FC

ADDITIONAL 1999-2000 CUP FINALS

LIVERPOOL JUNIOR CUP
Child   v   Sefton & District Rs   5-3   at Liverpool FA Soccer Centre

LIVERPOOL INTERMEDIATE CUP
Leyfield Reserves   v   Hill Athletic   4-0   at Liverpool FA Soccer Centre

LIVERPOOL SUNDAY PREMIER CUP
Freehouse   v   Whiston Carrs   4-1   at Liverpool FA Soccer Centre

LIVERPOOL SUNDAY JUNIOR CUP
R.A.F.A. Kirkby   v   D.O.W.   5-1   at Liverpool FA Soccer Centre

LIVERPOOL SUNDAY INTERMEDIATE CUP
Swan Signs   v   Yate's Addisons   2-1   at Liverpool FA Soccer Centre

LIVERPOOL YOUTH CUP
Burscough   v   Bootle   2-0   at Liverpool FA Soccer Centre

LIVERPOOL CHALLENGE CUP 1999-2000

(40 entries)   (FOUNDED 1908-09)

LAST SEASON'S FINAL: Waterloo Dock v St Dominics 3-2

MOST WINS: Skelmersdale United 8   Prescot Cables 6   New Brighton 5   St Dominics 5

FIRST ROUND (8 matches)

Alsop Old Boys	v	Collegiate OB	1-3	Ashton Town	v	Burscough	1-2
BRNESC	v	Southport Trinity	2-3	Manweb	v	Essemmay OB	W.O.
Marconi	v	Warbreck	2-4	Mossley Hill Athletic	v	Old Holts	1-1,4p2
ROMA	v	Sefton & District	7-0	Yorkshire CT	v	Rylands	6-0

SECOND ROUND (16 matches)

Aigburth PH	v	Waterloo Dock	3-4	Ayone	v	ROMA	3-1
Cheshire Lines	v	Marine Reserve	0-3	Collegiate OB	v	Crawfords OB	0-2
East Ville	v	Bottle Reserves	3-1	Ford Motors	v	Mossley Hill Athletic	3-2
Manweb	v	Maghull	1-2	Old Cathinians	v	Aintree Ville	0-7
Old Xaverians	v	Lucas Sports	2-4	Quarry Bank OB	v	Royal Seaforth	4-4,8p9
REMYCA Uniyed	v	Speke	0-7	St Dominics	v	Yorkshire CT	0-3
South Liverpool	v	Burscough Res	1-5	Southport Trinity	v	Merseyside Police	
Warbreck	v	Stoneycroft	1-5	Waterloo GSOB	v	Skelmersdale U. Res	0-7

THIRD ROUND (8 matches)

Aintree Ville	v	Speke	1-2	Crawfords UB	v	Marine Reserves	1-3
Ford Motors	v	East Ville	4-0	Lucas Sports	v	Ayone	2-1
Maghull	v	Skelmersdale U Res	1-2	Royal Seaforth	v	Burscough Res	2-2.3p4
Stonycroft	v	Waterloo Dock	1-3	Yorkshire CT	v	Southport Trinty	4-2

FOURTH ROUND (4 matches)

Burscough Reserves	v	Ford Motors	3-0	Lucas Sports	v	Speke	1-0
Marine Reserves	v	Yorkshire CT	2-4	Waterloo Dock	v	Skelmersdale U Rs	4-0

SEMI-FINALS

Lucas Sports	v	Burscough Reserves	2-0	Waterloo Dock	v	Yorkshire CT	1-3

FINAL

YORKSHIRE CT	v	LUCAS SPORTS 2-2, 5p4		at Liverpool FA Soccer Centre, Walton Hall Park

LONDON F.A.

Tel: 0208 690 9626   Fax: 0208 690 9471
6 Aldworth Grove, Lewisham, London SE13 6HY
Secretary: D G Fowkes
Executives (Responsibility)   A Welsh (Coaching Exams)   B Jenkins (Referees)
                                  C Arundale (Womens Football)   D Morrison (Coaching Courses)

Number of Affiliated Clubs Senior: 2360	U.18: 510	**President:** L A M Mackay
Number of Affiliated Leagues: Senior: 165	Junior: 43	**Chairman:** B M Gibbons

County Representative Teams: Senior, Womens, U16
Inter County Competitions: Southern Counties Cup, Southern Counties Womens Cup, FA County Youth Cup

---

LONDON CHALLENGE CUP 1999-2000
(16 entries)   (Original competition founded 1908)

LAST SEASON'S FINAL: Dulwich Hamlet v Uxbridge 2*1

FIRST ROUND (8 matches)

Wingate & Finchley	v	Erith & Belvedere	1-3		Tooting & Mitcham U	v	Croydon	1-2
Clapton	v	Barking	0-3		Romford	v	Bromley	4-3
Welling United	v	Leyton Pennant	3-1		Metropolitan Police	v	Dulwich Hamlet	0-4
Ford United	v	Corinthian Casuals	3-2		Uxbridge	v	Fisher Athletic	3-0

QUARTER-FINALS

Ford United	v	Barking	0-2		Welling United	v	Dulwich Hamlet	0-3
Uxbridge	v	Croydon	2-1		Erith & Belvedere	v	Romford	8p9 3*3

SEMI-FINALS

Barking	v	Uxbridge	0-4		Dulwich Hamlet	v	Romford	3-1

FINAL

DULWICH HAMLET	v	UXBRIDGE	4p52*2	at Dagenham & Redbridge FC

LONDON SENIOR CUP 1999-2000
(20 entries)   (FOUNDED 1882)

LAST SEASON'S FINAL: Waltham Abbey v Bedfont 3-2

FIRST ROUND (4 matches)

Cray Wanderers	v	Haringey Borough	0-5		East Ham United	v	Crown & Manor	2-0
Brimsdown Rovers	v	Croydon Athletic	0-2		Cockfosters	v	Southall	1-3

SECOND ROUND (8 matches)

Southall	v	Bedfont	0-5		Waltham Abbey	v	Haringey Borough	0-1
Woodford Town	v	Kingsbury Town	0-1		Hanwell Town	v	Ilford	3-1
Civil Service	v	Thames Poly	0-1		Erith Town	v	Islington St Mary's	ET W-O
Thamesmead Tn	v	Barkingside	1-2		Croydon Athletic	v	East Ham United	1-2

QUARTER-FINALS

Bedfont	v	Hanwell Town	2-1		Barkingside	v	Kingsbury Town	1-3
Haringey Borough	v	East Ham United	0-2		Thames Poly	v	Erith Town	1-4

SEMI-FINALS

Bedfont	v	Kingsbury Town	6-0		Erith Town	v	East Ham United	3*2

FINAL

BEDFONT	v	ERITH TOWN	5-1	at Wingate & Finchley FC

OTHER CUP COMPETITIONS

LFA INTERMEDIATE CUP FINAL
Metrogas   v   Old Roan   3-2   at Metropolitan Police FC

LFA JUNIOR CUP FINAL
TC Sports   v   Brampton Park   5-2   at Croydon Athletic FC

LFA MIDWEEK CUP FINAL
Crown & Manor   v   LITA Sports   3-0   at Corinthian Casuals FC

LFA SUNDAY CHALLENGE CUP FINAL
Convoys   v   Omonia   2-0   at Wingate & Finchley FC

LFA SUNDAY INTERMEDIATE CUP FINAL
Yesilada   v   Yalova   2*1   at Dulwich Hamlet FC

LFA SUNDAY JUNIOR CUP FINAL
Star Anchor   v   Heatwave   6-0   at Wingate & Finchley FC

LFA WOMEN'S CUP FINAL
Arsenal Ladies   v   Wimbledon Ladies   3-0   at Dulwich Hamlet FC

Top: Dulwich Hamlet clear their lines in the London Challenge Cup final against Uxbridge at Dagenham & Redbridge. Bottom: Uxbridge Football Club, winners of the London Challenge Cup.

Bedfont win the London Senior Cup at Ash United
Photo: Eric Marsh

MANCHESTER F.A.

Tel: 0161 881 0299 Fax: 0161 881 6833 E-mail: mancfa@cs.com
Brantingham Road, Chorlton, Manchester M21 0TT

Secretary & Press Officer: Jon Dutton
Executives (Responsibility)   Alan Keeling (Coaching Exams/Courses)
                                  Phil Morris (Referees)
                                  Jon Dutton (Womens Football)

Number of Affiliated Clubs   Senior: 383   U.18:   159   **President:** Frank Hannah
Number of Affiliated Leagues: Senior: 30   Junior: 10
County Representative Teams: U18, Womens
Inter County Competitions: FA County Youth, Association of Northern Counties Youth Competition

MANCHESTER PREMIER CUP 1999-2000
(11 entries) (FOUNDED1979-80)

LAST SEASON'S FINAL: Hyde United v Maine Road   1-0

MOST WINS: Curzon Ashton 5   Ashton United 3   Hyde United 3
                Droylsden 3   Mossley 2

PRELIMINARY ROUND (3 matches)

Abbey Hey	v	Maine Road	3-2	Salford City	v	Flixton	3-0
Oldham Town	v	Mossley	1-8				

QUARTER-FINALS

Droylsden	v	Abbey Hey	0*0 2*1	Mossley	v	Trafford	2*2 1-2
Ashton United	v	Chadderton	2-0	Salford City	v	Curzon Ashton	4-2

SEMI-FINALS

Mossley	v	Salford City	3-1	Ashton United	v	Droyslden	1-2

FINAL

DROYLSDEN	v	MOSSLEY	2-1	at Oldham Athletic FC

MIDDLESEX COUNTY F.A.

Tel: 0208 424 8524   Fax: 0181 863 0627   E.Mail: association.office@middxfa.org
39 Roxborough Road, Harrow, Middlesex HA1 1NS
Secretary: Peter Clayton
Executives (Responsibility)   P Clayton (Coaching Exams/Courses,
Womens Football, Referees)

Number of Affiliated Clubs	Senior: 30	Intermediate 11	U18 205	Junior 472	**President:** John Wake
Number of Affiliated Leagues:	Adult: 30	Youth: 8			**Chairman:** Derek Mennell

County Representative Teams: Senior, Intermediate, U18, U16, Womens, U16, Womens U16
Inter County Competitions: FA County Yth, Home Counties Yth, Southern Counties (Intermediate, Women)

MIDDLESEX SENIOR CUP 1999-2000

(23 entries)   (FOUNDED 1888-89)

LAST SEASON'S FINAL: Hendon v Wembley 4p2 2*2

MOST WINS: Enfield 13   Southall 12   Wealdstone 11

FIRST ROUND (7 matches)

Hanwell Town	v	Viking Greenford	3-1	Southall	v	Ashford Town	0-3
Wealdstone	v	Harefield United	3-1	Edgware Town	v	Feltham	4-2
Harrow Borough	v	Kingsbury Town	2-1	Ruislip Manor	v	Brook House	0-3
Northwood	v	Bedfont	3-2				

SECOND ROUND (8 matches)

Ashford Town	v	Brook House	0-4	Hendon	v	Edgware Town	3-1
Enfield	v	Wembley	2-0	Uxbridge	v	Wealdstone	3-2
Hillingdon Borough	v	Hayes	2-5	Harrow Borough	v	Staines Town	4-0
Hampton & R Boro	v	Northwood	@ N 1-3	Yeading	v	Hanwell Town	6-3

QUARTER-FINALS

Uxbridge	v	Hayes	1-2	Harrow Borough	v	Enfield	0-2
Northwood	v	Brook House	5-2	Yeading	v	Hendon	2-3

SEMI-FINALS

Hayes	v	Enfield	3-2	Hendon	v	Northwood	0-1

FINAL

HAYES	v	NORTHWOOD	2-0	at Harrow Borough FC

MIDDLESEX SENIOR CHARITY CUP 1999-2000
(17 entries)   (FOUNDED 1901-02)

LAST SEASON'S FINAL: Hampton v Southall 3-0
MOST WINS: Wealdstone 11   Hayes 10   Southall 10

FIRST ROUND (1 match)

Wealdstone   v   Waltham Abbey   2-0

SECOND ROUND (8 matches)

Wealdstone	v	Brook House	5-0	Harefield United	v	Edgware Town	0-6
Ashford Town	v	Southall	1*0	Staines Town	v	Feltham	5-0
Hillingdon Borough	v	Bedfont	4-2	Cockfosters	v	Northwood	2*4
Kingsbury Town	v	Hanwell Town	0-1	Wembley	v	Ruislip Manor	2-1

THIRD ROUND (4 matches)

Hillingdon Borough	v	Ashford Town	1-2	Wealdstone	v	Wembley	0p3 0*0
Hanwell Town	v	Edgware Town	2-0	Northwood	v	Staines Town	2p4 2*2

SEMI-FINALS

Staines Town	v	Hanwell Town	0-1	Wembley	v	Ashford Town	0-1

FINAL

ASHFORD TOWN   v   HANWELL TOWN   1-0   at Northwood FC

Middlesex FA at the Military Stadium (Aldershot) v Army   *Photo: Eric Marsh*

NORFOLK F.A.

Tel: 01603 717177   Fax: 01603 717187
Plantation Park, Blofield, Norwich NR13 4PL
Secretary & Press Officer: Roger J Howlett
Executives (Responsibility)   Through County Office
(Coaching Exams/Courses, Referees, Womens Football)
Number of Affiliated Clubs   Senior: 487   U.18:   167   **President:** R W Kiddell
Number of Affiliated Leagues: Senior: 16   Junior: 9   **Chairman:** A Williams
County Representative Teams: U18, Womens
Inter County Competitions: FA County Youth, East Anglian Counties

NORFOLK SENIOR CUP 1999-2000
(31 entries)   (FOUNDED 1881-82)

LAST SEASON'S FINAL: Fakenham Town v Swaffham Town   4-2

MOST WINS: King's Lynn   19   Great Yarmouth Town   14   Gorleston   13

FIRST ROUND (5 matches)

St Andrews	v	Hempnall	1-0	Coltishall HV	v	Wymondham Town	1-3
Mattishall	v	Anglian Windows	2*2 2-1	North Walsham Tn	v	Sprowston Athletic	2-0
Loddon United	v	Poringland Wndrs	1-5				

SECOND ROUND (10 matches)

Poringland Wndrs	v	Mattishall	1-2	Wells Town	v	Attleborough Town	2-0
North Walsham Tn	v	Thetford Town	1-0	Dereham Town	v	Wymondham Town	4-1
Mulbarton United	v	Blofield United	2*1	Cromer United	v	Thorpe Village	2*1
Swaffham Town	v	Stalham Town	4-3	Acle United	v	St Andrews	2*2 2-0
Downham Town	v	Lakeford	8-1	Scole United	v	Norwich United	2-3

THIRD ROUND (8 matches)

Acle United	v	Gorleston	1-2	Watton United	v	North Walsham Tn	2-0
Downham Town	v	Diss Town	3*5	Mulbarton United	v	Dereham Town	0*0 2-3
Cromer United	v	Norwich United	3*3 2*3	Swaffham Town	v	Fakenham Town	4-1
Great Yarmouth Tn	v	Mattishall	6-0	Wells Town	v	Wroxham	2*2 1-3

FOURTH ROUND (4 matches)

Diss Town	v	Swaffham Town	2-3	Great Yarmouth Tn	v	Gorleston	2*2 0-1
Dereham Town	v	Wroxham	1-3	Norwich United	v	Watton United	0-3

SEMI-FINALS

Gorleston	v	Watton United	3-0	Swaffham Town	v	Wroxham	1-5

FINAL

GORLESTON	v	WROXHAM	0-4	at Norwich City FC	

NORTHAMPTONSHIRE F.A.

Tel: 01604 670741   Fax: 01604 670741

2 Duncan Close, Moulton Park, Northampton

Secretary & Press Officer:	B Walden
Executives (Responsibility)	T Clifton (Coaching Exams/Courses)
	B Walden (Referees)
	Mrs J Jeffrey (Womens Football)

Number of Affiliated Clubs   Senior: 460   U.18:   84   **President:** D Vernum

Number of Affiliated Leagues: Senior: 12   Junior: 7   **Chairman:** L Homer

County Representative Teams: U18

Inter County Competitions: East Midland Youth Combination

NORTHAMPTONSHIRE 'HILLIER' SENIOR CUP 1999-2000
(14 entries)   (FOUNDED 1883-84)

LAST SEASON'S FINAL: Rushden & Diamonds v Raunds Town 2-0

MOST WINS: Kettering Town 30   Northampton Town 11   Peterborough United 11

FIRST ROUND (6 matches)

Rothwell Town	v	Long Buckby	3-1		Bugbrook St Michael	v	Wellingborough Town	1-3
Cogenhoe United	v	Brackley Town	1*2		Northampton Spncr	v	S & L Corby	4-1
Ford Sports	v	Corby Town	2-0		Desborough Town	v	Raunds Town	3-2

SECOND ROUND (4 matches)

Brackley Town	v	Desborough Town	2-3		Kettering Town	v	Rushden & Diamonds	3-1
Wellingborough Tn	v	Ford Sports Daventry	0-1		Northampton Spncr	v	Rothwell Town	4-5

SEMI-FINALS

Rothwell Town	v	Kettering Town	0-1		Ford Sports Daventry	v	Desborough Town	0-1

FINAL

DESBOROUGH T	v	KETTERING T	1*1		at Desborough Town FC

REPLAY

KETTERING T	v	DESBOROUGH T	4p3 3*3		at Kettering Town FC

BRITAIN'S MOST POPULAR NATIONAL NON-LEAGUE FOOTBALL MONTHLY

TEAM TALK

Team Talk should be available from your local non-League football club or your local newsagent and is available by subscription from the publishers.

Team Talk is published by Non League Media Plc, c/o Helland, North Curry, Taunton, Somerset TA3 6DU
Tel: 01823 490080 Fax: 01823 490281 e-mail: tony.williams12@virgin.net

NORTH RIDING F.A.

Tel: 01642 318603   Fax: 01642 318604
Southlands Centre, Ormesby Road, Middlesbrough TS3 0HB
Secretary: Mark Jarvis
Executives (Responsibility)   Contact County Office for
Coaching Exams/Courses, Referees, Womens Football
Number of Affiliated Clubs   Senior: 500   U.18:   120
Number of Affiliated Leagues: Senior: 20   Junior: 10   **President:** K Boyer
County Representative Teams: Senior, U18, Ladies
Inter County Competitions: Northern Counties Competitions, FA Youth Competition

NORTH RIDING SENIOR CUP 1999-2000
(14 entries)   (FOUNDED 1881-82)

LAST SEASON'S FINAL: Whitby Town   v   York City   1-4

MOST WINS: Middlesbrough 46   Scarborough 17   South Bank 8   Stockton 8   York City 8

FIRST ROUND (1 match)

Northallerton	v	Pickering Town	2-0

SECOND ROUND (3 matches)

Carlin How WMC	v	York Railway Inst	2*1	Northallerton	v	Fishburn Park	1-0
New Marske S C	v	Stokesley SC	6-2				

THIRD ROUND (3 matches)

Guisborough Town	v	New Marske SC	1-0	Marske United	v	Northallerton	2-0
Thornaby on Tees	v	Carlin How WMC	3-2				

FOURTH ROUND (2 matches)

Guisborough Town	v	Thornaby on Tees	2-1	Whitby Town	v	Marske United	2-3

FIFTH/FINAL qualifier/eliminator

Marske United	v	Guisborough Town	2-1

SEMI-FINALS

York City	v	Marske United	20th July 2000
Scarborough	v	Middlesbrough	21st July 2000

NORTHUMBERLAND F.A.

Tel: 0191 236 8020
10 Brenkley Way, Seaton Burn, Newcastle upon Tyne NE13 6DT
Chief Executive: R E Maughan **Press Officer:** Bill Gardner
Executives (Responsibility)   B Jones (Coaching Exams/Courses)
   L Hayden (Referees)
   G Watson (Mini Soccer & Womens Football)
Number of Affiliated Clubs   Senior: 531   U.18:   363   **President:** E A Wright
Number of Affiliated Leagues: Senior: 11   Junior: 7
County Representative Teams: Senior, U18
Inter County Competitions: Northern Counties Senior & Youth Cups, FA County Youth Cup
County Publications: "The Far Corner" - Bi-monthly Newsletter

NORTHUMBERLAND SENIOR CUP 1999-2000
Sponsored by " Albany Insurance"
(12 entries)   (FOUNDED 1883-84)

LAST SEASON'S FINAL: Newcastle United Reserves v Blyth Spartans 2-1
MOST WINS: Blyth Spartans 21   Newcastle United 21   North Shields 12

FIRST ROUND (4 matches)

Bedlington Terriers	v	West Allotment Celtic	3-0	Morpeth Town	v	Alnwick Town	1-2
Ashington	v	Whitley Bay	1-0	Prudhoe Town	v	North Shields Ath	3-1

SECOND ROUND (4 matches)

Blyth Spartans	v	Ponteland Utd	0-0 0-1	Newcastle Blue Star	v	Ashington	1-0
Alnwick Town	v	Bedlington Terriers	0-1	Newcastle Utd Res	v	Prudhoe Town	5-0

SEMI-FINALS

Bedlington Terriers	v	Newcastle Utd R	2-2 2-3	Newcastle Blue Star	v	Ponteland United	2-1

FINAL
NEWCASTLE U Rs v NEWCASTLE B STAR 4-1   at Kingston Park, United Res FC

NORTHUMBERLAND BENEVOLENT BOWL 1999-2000
Sponsored by "Brother"
(12 entries)   (FOUNDED 1975-76)

LAST SEASON'S FINAL: Seaton Delaval Am v N/C Benfield Park 4-2 aet
MOST WINS: Morpeth Town 2   Stobswood Welfare 2

FIRST ROUND (4 matches)

Seaton Delaval Amt	v	Walker Central	3*2	Heaton Stannington	v	Newbiggin C W	1-3
Proctor & Gamble	v	N/c Benfield Park	1-2	Walker Ledwood F	v	Amble Town	4*1

SECOND ROUND (4 matches)

Walker Ledwood	v	Seaton Delaval Amt	3-0	Coxlodge SC	v	Percy Main	4-2
Benfield Park	v	Newbiggin C Welfare	2-0	Shankhouse	v	Spittal Rovers	4-0

SEMI-FINALS

Walker Ledwood**	v	Benfield Park	3V1 T-A	Coxlodge	v	Shankhouse	3-4

(** fielded an ineligible player, opponents re-instated, void)

FINAL
BENFIELD PARK v SHANKHOUSE   1-3   at Blyth Spartans FC

NOTTINGHAMSHIRE F.A. LIMITED

Tel: 0115 941 8954   Fax: 0115 941 5254
7 Clarendon Street, Nottingham NG1 5HS
Secretary: Mike Kilbee
Executives (Responsibility)   Tom Goodwin (Referees)
Helen Bennett (Womens Football)

Number of Affiliated Clubs	Senior:	681	U.18:	202
Number of Affiliated Leagues:	Senior:	11	Junior:	4

President: D K Ridyard
Chairman: J J Waterall

County Representative Teams: U18
Inter County Competitions: FA County Youth Cup, East Midlands Youth Combination

NOTTINGHAMSHIRE SENIOR CUP 1999-2000
(34 entries)   (FOUNDED 1883-84)

LAST SEASON'S FINAL: Arnold Town v Hucknall Town   2-1

MOST WINS: Nottingham Forest   17   Sutton Town   17   Notts County   11

FIRST ROUND (12 matches)

Nott'shire Police	v	Welbeck Colliery	0-2		Basford United	v	Rainworth M W	2-5
Selston	v	Ruddington United	1-3		I D P Newark	v	Teversal Grange	3-0
Attenborough	v	Siemens	2-1		Ollerton Town	v	B R S A Retford	2-1
Kimberley Town	v	Cotgrave C W	2-1		Boots Athletic	v	Linby C W	6-3
Southwell City	v	Bilsthorpe C W	4-1		Keyworth United	v	Retford United	2-1
Greenwood Meadows	v	Wollaton	2-3		Radford	v	Pelican	4-2

SECOND ROUND (6 matches)

Keyworth United	v	Southwell City	5-2		IDP Newark	v	Rainworth M W	4-0
Radford	v	Ruddington United	4-0		Ollerton Town	v	Welbeck Colliery	3p1 2*2
Boots Athletic	v	Kimberley Town	5p4 2*2		Wollaton	v	Attenborough	2-1

THIRD ROUND (8 matches)

Sneinton	v	Wollaton	1-2		Keyworth United	v	Collingham	2-7
IDP Newark	v	Dunkirk	2-5		Radford	v	Eastwood Town	0-5
Hucknall Rolls Royce	v	Clipstone Welfare	5-1		Hucknall Town	v	Gedling Town	3-0
Boots Athletic	v	Blidworth Welfare	2-1		Ollerton Town	v	Arnold Town	3-8

QUARTER-FINALS

Wollaton	v	Boots Athletic	5-3		Collingham	v	Dunkirk	3-4
Eastwood Town	v	Hucknall Rolls Royce	3-1		Hucknall Town	v	Arnold Town	2-1

SEMI-FINALS

Wollaton	v	Eastwood Town	1*4		Hucknall Town	v	Dunkirk	2-1

FINAL

EASTWOOD TOWN v HUCKNALL TOWN   1-2   at Notts County FC

OXFORDSHIRE F.A.

Tel: 01865 331360   Fax: 01865 331360
Rondamician, West End Lane, Merton, Bicester, Oxon OX6 0NG
Secretary: Ron Leaver
Executives (Responsibility)   Trevor Spindler (Coaching Exams/Courses)
John Abrams (Referees)
R T Watts (Womens Football)
Number of Affiliated Clubs   350
Number of Affiliated Leagues: 12
County Representative Teams: Under 18
Inter County Competitions: Under 18

President: J W Roughton
Chairman: G R Mills

OXFORDSHIRE SENIOR CUP 1999-2000
(32 entries)   (FOUNDED 1884-85)

LAST SEASON'S FINAL: Oxford City v Carterton Town 3*0

MOST WINS: Oxford City 31   Witney Town 9   Oxford United 8

FIRST ROUND (10 matches)

Adderbury Park	v	Headington Amat	7-2	Quarry Nomads	v	Hook Norton		1-2
Goring	v	Marston Saints	0-1	Ruscote Sports	v	Yarnton		2-1
Watlington Town			Bye	Old Woodstock T	v	Checkenden Sports		3-2
Middle Barton	v	Sonning Common	3-4	Worcester Coll. OB	v	Charlton United		2-0
Chinnor	v	Garsington	2-0	Clanfield	v	Launton Sports		5-0

SECOND ROUND (10 matches)

Clanfield	v	Old Woodstock T	1-2	Eynsham	v	Ardley United		1-3
Marston Saints	v	Kidlington	4p3 2*2	Easington Sports	v	Carterton Town		3-1
Sonning Common	v	Watlington Town	5-1	Peppard	v	North Leigh		0-4
Chinnor	v	Banbury United	2-5	Henley Town	v	Abberbury Park		2*1
Ruscote Sports	v	Worcester Coll. OB	2-3	Bicester Town	v	Hook Norton		4-2

THIRD ROUND (5 matches)

Bicester Town	v	North Leigh	2-3	Ardley United	v	Henley Town	3-1
Old Woodstock T	v	Banbury United	1*2	Worcester Coll OB	v	Easington Sports	4p2 3*3
Sonning Common	v	Marston Saints	1-3				

QUARTER-FINALS

Witney Town	v	North Leigh	3-1	Banbury United	v	Thame United	3-4
Oxford City	v	Worcester Coll OB	4-1	Ardley United	v	Marston Saints	1-0

SEMI-FINALS

Ardley United	v	Thame United	1-6	at Oxford City FC
Witney Town	v	Oxford City	0-1	at Thame United FC

FINAL

THAME UNITED	v	OXFORD CITY	0-2	at Oxford United FC

SHEFFIELD & HALLAMSHIRE F.A.

Tel: 0114 267 0068   Fax: 0114 268 3348
5 Onslow Road, Sheffield S11 7AF
Secretary: G Thompson   **Press Officer:** J P Hope-Gill
Executives (Responsibility)   John Warnock (Coaching Exams/Courses)
                        Peter Jackson (Referees)
                        Julie Callaghan (Womens Football)
Number of Affiliated Clubs   Senior: 888   U.18:   243   **President:** C L Milner
Number of Affiliated Leagues: Senior: 17   Junior: 7   **Chairman:** M Matthews
County Representative Teams: Under 18
Inter County Competitions: East Midlands Youth Combination, FA County Youth Cup

SHEFFIELD & HALLAMSHIRE CUP 1999-2000
(50 entries)   (FOUNDED 1876-77)

LAST SEASON'S FINAL: Stocksbridge Park Steels v Emley 1-0

MOST WINS: Sheffield 10   Frickley Athletic 10   Sheffield Wednesday 9

QUALIFYING ROUND (18 matches)

Frecheville C A	v	Kiveton Park	4-2	Mexborough Mn St	v	Sheffield Centralians	2-0
Queens Hotel	v	Avesta Sheffield	3-2	Sheffield Bankers	v	Wombwell Town	0-4
Wombwell Main	v	Grapes Roy H	W W-O	Mexborough T Ath	v	Penistone Church	0-2
Phoenix	v	Yorkshire Main	4-1	ABS Kilnhurst	v	High Green Villa	1*1 4-2
South Kirkby Coll	v	NCB Maltby MW	4-0	Parramore Sports	v	Sheffield Lane Top	3-2
Wickersley	v	Athersley Recreation	1-0	Caribbean Sports	v	Grimethorpe MW	2-4
Hemsworth MW	v	Swinton Athletic	7-1	Oughtibridge WMSC	v	Woodhouse West End	0-3
Ecclesfield Red R	v	Old Edwardians	4*2	Groves Social	v	Harworth C I	4-3
The Wetherby	v	Thorpe Hesley	2-3	Hare & Hounds	v	Treeton Welfare	3-2

FIRST ROUND PROPER (16 matches)

Sheffield	v	Groves Social	5-2	Thorpe Hesley	v	Emley	3-6
Parkgate	v	Frecheville CA	4-2	South Kirkby Coll	v	Phoenix	0-6
Hemsworth M W	v	Queens Hotel	4-1	Rossington Main	v	Penistone Church	1-0
Brodsworth Welfare	v	Doncaster Rovers	0-5	Hallam	v	Grimesthorpe M W	2-0
Wickersley	v	Hare & Hounds	1-2	Woodhouse WE	v	Denaby United	1-8
Maltby Main	v	ABS Kilnhurst	1*1 1-0	Wombwell Town	v	Worsebrough Bridge	3-1
Worksop Town	v	Stocksbridge P S	4*3	Wombwll Main	v	Mexborough Main St	4-2
Parramore Sports	v	Ecclesfield Red R	2-4	Davy	v	Frickley Athletic @FA	1-3

SECOND ROUND (8 matches)

Emley	v	Maltby Main	3*1	Hemsworth M W	v	Wombwell Town	4-1
Rossington Main	v	Parkgate	1-2	Doncaster Rovers	v	Wombwell Main	1-0
Worksop Town	v	Ecclesfield Red Rose	5-0	Hare & Hounds	v	Hallam	0-1
Sheffield	v	Denaby United	2-5	Phoenix	v	Frickley Athletic	1-4

QUARTER-FINALS

Worksop Town	v	Denaby United	7-0	Parkgate	v	Emley	1-3
Frickley Athletic	v	Doncaster Rovers	2-0	Hallam	v	Hemsworth M W	3-3 3-1

SEMI-FINALS

Worksop Town	v	Emley	1-2	Hallam	v	Frickley Athletic	3*6

FINAL

EMLEY	v	FRICKLEY ATHLETIC 0-3		at Sheffield Wednesday FC	

SHROPSHIRE F.A.

Tel: 01743 362769   Fax: 01743 240474

Gay Meadow, Abbey Foregate, Shrewsbury, Shropshire SY2 6AB

Secretary: David Rowe   **Press Officer:** Neil Sambrook

County Reps: Alan Penton (Coaching Exams/Courses)

                                 Eric Adams (Referees)

Number of Affiliated Clubs   Senior: 330   U.18:   95   **President:** J S Constable

Number of Affiliated Leagues: Senior: 9   Junior: 5   **Chairman:** S T Farmer

County Representative Teams: U18, Womens, U16

Inter County Competitions: FA County Youth, Midland County Youth, Gilbert Trophy

SHROPSHIRE SENIOR CUP 1999-2000
(4 entries)   (FOUNDED1877-88)

LAST SEASON'S FINAL: Shrewsbury Town v Telford United   1-0

MOST WINS: Shrewsbury Town 54   Telford United 34   Oswestry Town 11

SEMI-FINALS

Bridgnorth Town	v Shrewsbury Town	2-3	Shifnal Town v Telford United 2-1

FINAL

SHREWSBURY T   v   SHIFNAL TOWN   3-0   at Gay Meadow, Shrewsbury Town FC

SHROPSHIRE COUNTY CUP 1999-2000
(23 entries)

LAST SEASON'S FINAL: Bandon v Star 3p0 1*1

FIRST ROUND (7 matches)

Little Drayton Rngrs	v	Belle Vue OB	2-0	Bandon	v	Shifnal United	3-0
Star	v	Newport Town	4p5 2*2	Wem Town	v	Weston Rhyn	0-1
Clee Hill United	v	Meole Brace	5-1	Morda United	v	Tibberton United	2-0
Wellington Amat	v	Shawbury United	1-2				

SECOND ROUND (8 matches)

Clee Hill United	v	Shawbury United	1*3	Weston Rhyn	v	Oakengates Town	4-1
Newport Town	v	Whitchurch Alport	3*1	Hanwood United	v	Shifnal Town Res	0-3
Broseley Town	v	Ludlow Town	0-4	Belvidere Colts	v	Bandon	0-1
Morda United	v	Belvidere	2-1	Little Drayton Rngrs	v	Ironbridge Town	4-2

THIRD ROUND (4 matches)

Shawbury United	v	Weston Rhyn	1-0	Newport Town	v	Morda United	0-3
Shifnal Town Res	v	Bandon	1-7	Ludlow Town	v	Little Drayton Rngrs	3-4

SEMI-FINALS

Shawbury United	v	Little Drayton Rngrs	1-0	at Newport Town FC
Morda United	v	Bandon	1-4	at Wem Town FC

FINAL

BANDON   v   SHAWBURY UTD   4*3   at Shrewsbury Town FC

SOMERSET F.A.

Tel: 01761 410280   Fax: 01761 410477
30 North Road, Midsomer Norton, Bath, Somerset BA3 2QQ
Secretary: Mrs H Marchment
Executives (Responsibility)   I Tincknell (Coaching Courses/Exams)
J H Day (Referees), L Clements (Womens Football)

Number of Affiliated Clubs	Senior:	78	U.18:	407	**President:** F P Hillier
Number of Affiliated Leagues:	Senior:	1	Junior:	22	**Chairman:** A J Hobbs

County Representative Teams: Senior, U18, Womens
Inter County Competitions: FA County Youth, South West Counties Championship (Senior, Youth & Womens)

SOMERSET PREMIER CUP 1999-2000

(22 entries)   (FOUNDED 1948-49)

LAST SEASON'S FINAL: Clevedon Town v Taunton Town 5p4 3*3

MOST WINS: Bath City 17   Yeovil Town 15   Bristol City 6

FIRST ROUND (6 matches)

Bridgwater Town	v	Glastonbury	BT W-O	Bishop Sutton	v	Bristol City	1-4
Wellington	v	Minehead Town	6-3	Clevedon Town	v	Odd Down	3-0
Frome Town	v	Street	2-1	Bristol Manor Farm	v	Chard Town	2-1

SECOND ROUND (8 matches)

Bridgwater Town	v	Bath City	0-3	Backwell United	v	Frome Town	6-3
Taunton Town	v	Wellington	2-1	Keynsham Town	v	Mangotsfield United	1-2
Clevedon Town	v	Weston super Mare	0-1	Paulton Rovers	v	Yeovil Town	2-1
Bristol Manor Farm	v	Welton Rovers	9p8 5*5	Brislington	v	Bristol City	1-2

THIRD ROUND (4 matches)

Bath City	v	Mangotsfield United	3*2	Backwell United	v	Bristol City	0-1
Weston super Mare	v	Bristol Manor Farm	1-2	Taunton Town	v	Yeovil Town	5-1

SEMI-FINALS

Bristol Manor Farm	v	Bath City	0-4	Taunton Town	v	Bristol City	1-2

FINAL

BATH CITY	v	BRISTOL CITY	2-3	at Clevedon Town FC

SOMERSET SENIOR CUP 1999-2000
(50 entries)   (FOUNDED 1895-96)

LAST SEASON'S FINAL: Fry Club v Backwell United Reserves 2-0

MOST WINS: Paulton Rovers 12   Radstock Town 12   Welton Rovers 9

FIRST ROUND (18 matches)

Long Ashton	v	Bishop Sutton Res	2-0	Westland United	v	Frome Collegians	2-3
Saltford	v	Portishead	0-4	Hartcliffe O B	v	Glastonbury Res	1-3
Wells City	v	Castle Cary	0-3	Keynsham Tn Rs	v	Wellington Res	2-1
Westland Sports	v	Dundry Athletic	3-1	Backwell Utd Rs	v	Clevedon United	3-2
Cleeve West Town	v	Brislington Res	1*2	Fry's Club	v	Radstock Town	1-2
Long Sutton	v	First Tower United	3*2	Watchet Town	v	Tunley Athletic	3-1
Shepton Mallet	v	Cutters Friday	5-1	Timsbury Athletic	v	Hengrove Athletic	3-2
Street Res	v	Welton Rvrs Rs 4p1	2*2	Winscombe	v	Congresbury	2-0
Peasedown Athletic	v	Teyfant Athletic	4-0	Bridgwater Tn Rs	v	Nailsea United 2p4	1*1

SECOND ROUND (16 matches)

Radstock Town	v	Kewstoke	3-0	Peasedown Athletic	v	Brislington Res	1-4
Temple Cloud	v	Nailsea United	1-5	Robinsons	v	St George E in G	4-2
Frome Town Res	v	Long Sutton	2-3	Timsbury Athletic	v	Imperial	2-0
Worle	v	Glastonbury	5-2	Watchet Town	v	Westland Sports	1-0
Ilminster Town	v	Backwell United Rs	2-5	Long Ashton	v	Cheddar	0-3
Odd Down Res	v	Winscombe	3-0	Portishead	v	Frome Collegians	1-0
Paulton Rovers Rs	v	Clutton	0-2	Wrington-Redhill	v	Keynsham Town Rs	3-5
Larkhall Athletic	v	Street Res	1-0	Castle Cary	v	Shepton Mallet	1-0

THIRD ROUND (8 matches)

Long Sutton	v	Timsbury Athletic	2-0	Cheddar	v	Nailsea United	3-0
Watchet Town	v	Larkhall Athletic	1-2	Worle	v	Brislington Res	3-1
Portishead	v	Backwell United Res	3-0	Robinsons	v	Odd Down Bath	4-2
Radstock Town	v	Clutton	4-0	Keynsham Tn Rs	v	Castle Cary	1-0

QUARTER-FINALS

Cheddar	v	Keynsham T Rs 2p4	1*1	Larkhall Athletic	v	Portishead	2-3
Long Sutton	v	Radstock Town	0-1	Worle	v	Robinsons	5-1

SEMI-FINALS

Portishead	v	Worle	2-0	Radstock Town	v	Keynsham Town Res	3-0

FINAL

PORTISHEAD	v	RADSTOCK TOWN	2-1	at Paulton Rovers FC

STAFFORDSHIRE F.A.

Tel: 01785 256994   Fax: 01785 224334
County Showground, Weston Road, Stafford ST18 0DB
Secretary: Brian Adshead   **Press Officer:** David Shelton
Executives (Responsibility)   I Cooper (Coaching Exams), N Broad (Referees)
S Eccleston (Coaching Courses), D Blairs (Womens Football)
Number of Affiliated Clubs   Senior: 609   U.18:   556
Number of Affiliated Leagues: Senior: 16   Junior: 13   **Chairman:** Robert Heath
County Representative Teams: Under 18 Boys, Ladies, Under 16 Girls
Inter County Competitions: FA County Youth Challenge Cup, Midland Counties Youth Championships

STAFFORDSHIRE SENIOR CUP 1999-2000
(25 entries)   (FOUNDED 1877-78)

LAST SEASON'S FINAL: Stoke City   v   Leek Town   3-1

MOST WINS: Stoke City   18   Aston Villa   16   West Bromwich Albion   13

FIRST ROUND (4 matches)

Blakenall	v	Knypersley Victoria	3-1	Chasetown	v	Pelsall Villa	5-3
Hednesford Town	v	Leek CSOB	5-1	Newcastle Town	v	Halesowen Harriers	2-0

SECOND ROUND (8 matches)

Bloxwich Town	v	Stoke City	0-2	Chasetown	v	Blakenall	1-6
Hednesford Town	v	Shifnal Town	3-1	Leek Town	v	Kidsgrove Athletic	2-0
Newcastle Town	v	Tamworth	0-2	Rocester	v	Port Vale	1-0
Rushall Olympic	v	Stafford Rangers	1-3	Stourbridge	v	Bilston Town	0-3

QUARTER-FINALS

Stafford Rangers	v	Leek Town	2-2 1-2	Rocester	v	Blakenall	0-1
Bilston Town	v	Hednesford Town	1-1 4*2	Tamworth	v	Stoke City	5-3

SEMI-FINALS

Leek Town	v	Blakenall	1-1 0*2	Tamworth	v	Bilston Town	2-1

FINAL First Leg

TAMWORTH	v	BLAKENALL	2-1	at Tamworth FC

FINAL Second Leg

BLAKENALL	v	TAMWORTH	3*2 = 4*4	at Blakenall FC

SUFFOLK F.A.

Tel: 01449 673481 Fax: 01449 770983

2 Millfields, Haughley, Stowmarket IP14 3PU

Secretary: William Steward

Executives (Responsibility) C Rowe (Coaching Exams/Courses), Brian Thompson (Referees)
Angela Locke (Womens Football)

Number of Affiliated Clubs Senior: 450 U.18: 200 **President:** Ernest Brown

Number of Affiliated Leagues: Senior: 13 Junior: 7 **Chairman:** Gordon Rayner

County Representative Teams: Intermediate (adult), U18, U16, Womens

Inter County Competitions: All in East Anglian Counties Championships

SUFFOLK PREMIER CUP 1999-2000
(9 entries) (FOUNDED 1958-59)

LAST SEASON'S FINAL: Newmarket Town v Sudbury Town 1-0

MOST WINS: Sudbury Town 12 Bury Town 10 Lowestoft Town 6

PRELIMINARY ROUND (1 match)

Woodbridge Town v Ipswich Wanderers 6-1

FIRST ROUND (4 matches)

Mildenhall Town	v	Sudbury	3*1	Newmarket Town	v	Woodbridge Town	2-0
Lowestoft Town	v	Bury Town	3-1	Felixstowe Port & T	v	Stowmarket Town	0-2

SEMI-FINALS

Lowestoft Town	v	Stowmarket Town	4-1	at Woodbridge Town FC
Newmarket Town	v	Mildenhall Town	1*2	at Newmarket Town FC

FINAL

LOWESTOFT TOWN v MILDENHALL TOWN 1-0 at Lowestoft Town FC

Lowestoft Town's victorious squad after winning the Suffolk Premier Cup with a 1-0 victory over Mildenhall Town.
Back Row (l-r): Stuart Youngman, Ady Gallagher (Coach), Micky Chapman (Manager), Justyn Chenery, Gary Andrews, Carl Chenery, Ian Smith, Andy Read, Jamie Stokeld, Micky Shade, Jon Holmes, Pongo Thompson, Micky Tacon, Nigel Wilson (Physio).
Front Row: James Clements (Mascot), Chick Crowe, Lee Pike, Grant Pierpoint, Mark Hitcham, Lee Durrant, Sean Norman.

SUFFOLK SENIOR CUP 1999-2000
(33 entries)   (FOUNDED 1885-86)

LAST SEASON'S FINAL: Walton United v Needham Market 0-1

MOST WINS: Ipswich Town 16   Lowestoft Town 10   Stowmarket Town 8

PRELIMINARY ROUND (1 match)

East Bergholt Utd   v   Kirkley   2-1

FIRST ROUND (16 matches)

Leiston	v	Walsham Le Willows	4-1		Beccles Town	v	Grundisburgh	1-4
SudburyAthletic	v	Brandon Town	4-1		Westerfield United	v	Stonham Aspal	1-0
Needham Market	v	East Bergholt	1*0		Woodbridge Athletic	v	Haverhill Rovers	0-3
Leiston St Margarets	v	Lowestoft T Rs	4p5 0*0		Whitton United	v	Ipswich Wndrs Res	4-1
Long Melford	v	Bungay Town	0-5		Hadleigh United	v	Haughley United	3*2
BS Fonnereau	v	Bury Academy	BS W-O		Brantham Athletic	v	Capel Plough	1*4
Framlingham Town	v	Cornard United	1-2		Ipswich Athletic	v	Walton United	1-4
Stowmarket Tn Res	v	Ashlea	0-3		Achilles	v	Sudbury Res	2-1

SECOND ROUND (8 matches)

British Sugar	v	Ashlea	3-0		Grundisburgh	v	Haverhill Rovers	5-1
Cornard United	v	Lowestoft Town Res	3*0		Walton United	v	Bungay Town	5-0
Hadleigh United	v	Whitton United	0-3		Achilles	v	Leiston	1-2
Sudbury Athletic	v	Capel Plough	1-0		Needham Market	v	Westerfield United	3-0

THIRD ROUND (4 matches)

Sudbury Athletic	v	Whitton United	1-2		Needham Market	v	British Sugar	3-0
Grundisburgh	v	Leiston	5-1		Walton United	v	Cornard United	1-2

SEMI-FINALS

Grundisburgh	v	Cornard United	1-0		Needham Market	v	Whitton United	4-3

FINAL

GRUNDISBURGH   v   NEEDHAM MARKET 3-1   at Ipswich Town FC

Surrey Senior Cup: Ashford Town (Middex) v Dulwich Hamlet 2-3.
Note new stand in background, hoping to join Ryman League next season. They contest both Middlesex and Surrey Cups!
Photo: Eric Marsh

SURREY F.A.

Tel: 01372 373543   Fax: 01372 361310   Website: www.surreyfa.co.uk
321 Kingston Road, Leatherhead, Surrey KT22 7TU
Secretary: Ray Ward
Executives (Responsibility)   David Bromley (Coaching Exams/Courses)
Ray Lewis (Referees)
Peter Adams (Womens Football)

Number of Affiliated Clubs Senior: 38			**President:** A P Adams
Number of Affiliated Leagues: Senior: 2	Junior: 20		**Chairman:** J A Crook

County Representative Teams: Under 18, Womens
Inter County Competitions: Home Counties Womens Competition, FA County Youth Cup

SURREY SENIOR CUP 1999-2000
(36 entries)   (FOUNDED 1882-83)

LAST SEASON'S FINAL: Sutton United v Carshalton Athletic 3-0

FIRST QUALIFYING ROUND (6 matches)

Merstham	v	Egham Town	3-2	Lingfield	v	Walton Casuals @WC	0-8
Chessington United	v	Godalming & G'ford	2-1	Dorking	v	Cranleigh	6-0
Redhill	v	Cobham	12p13 3*3	Farnham Town	v	Raynes Park Vale	6-4

SECOND QUALIFYING ROUND (8 matches)

Epsom & Ewell	v	Croydon Athletic	1-3	Corinthian Casuals	v	Chessington United	3-1
Ash United	v	Farnham Town	3-0	Dorking	v	Chessington & Hook U	5*1
Mersham	v	Westfield	0-3	Metropolitan Police	v	Ashford Town (Mx)	1-3
Cobham	v	Walton Casuals	1-0	Chipstead	v	Camberley Town	3-1

THIRD QUALIFYING ROUND (4 matches)

Ash United	v	Croydon Athletic	1p4 4*4	Ashford Town (Mx)	v	Cobham	3-0
Chipstead	v	Corinthian Casuals	1-10	Dorking	v	Westfield	4p5 1-1

FOURTH QUALIFYING ROUND (2 matches)

Westfield	v	Ashford Town	1-3	Corinthian Casuals	v	Croydon Athletic	2-3

FIRST ROUND PROPER (8 matches)

Walton & Hersham	v	Molesey	3-1	Kingstonian	v	Croydon Athletic	5-2
Carshalton Athletic	v	Banstead Athletic	2-1	Croydon	v	Sutton United	2-0
Woking	v	Whyteleafe	4-1	Tooting & Mitcham	v	Crystal Palace	0-2
Ashford Town	v	Dulwich Hamlet	2-3	Chertsey Town	v	Leatherhead	0-1

QUARTER-FINALS

Leatherhead	v	Kingstonian	3p4 1*1	Dulwich Hamlet	v	Walton & Hersham	0-2
Woking	v	Crystal Palace	2-0	Croydon	v	Carshalton Athletic	4-0

SEMI-FINALS

Croydon	v	Walton & Hersham	2-1	Kingstonian	v	Woking	0-2

FINAL

WOKING	v	CROYDON	1-0	at Woking FC	

SUSSEX F.A.

Tel: 01903 753547 Fax: 01903 761608 E-mail: sussexfa@dial.pipex.co.uk
Culver Road, Lancing, West Sussex BN15 9AX

Chief Executive   Ken Benham
Executives (Responsibility)   L Thompson (Coaching Exams) T West (Referees)
                          J Hemsley (Womens Football) H Millington (Coaching Courses)
Number of Affiliated Clubs   Senior: 951   U.18:   246
Number of Affiliated Leagues: Senior: 18   Junior: 10   **President:** John Davey
County Representative Teams: Senior, U18, U15, Womens, U18, U15   **Chairman:** Ron Pavey
Inter County Competitions: FA County Youth, Home Counties Youth,
                          South West Counties Senior & Womens, Southern Counties Intermediate

SUSSEX SENIOR CUP 1999-2000
(44 entries) (FOUNDED 1882-83)

LAST SEASON'S FINAL: Worthing v Hastings Town 3-0

MOST WINS: Worthing 20   Eastbourne Town 12   Southwick 10

FIRST ROUND (12 matches)

Sidley United	v	Withdean	1-0		Westfield	v	Lewes	3-4
Oakwood	v	Chichester City	0-3		Sidlesham	v	Hailsham Town	3-1
Broadbridge Heath	v	Peacehaven & Tels.	1-2		Ringmer	v	Crawley Down V	0-3 0-1
Littlehampton Town	v	Southwick	0*0 5*1		Three Bridges	v	Lancing	2*2 1-3
Worhing United	v	Shinewater Assn	1-2		Arundel	v	Oving	3-0
Storrington	v	Mile Oak	4-2		Selsey	v	East Grinstead Town	3-1

SECOND ROUND (16 matches)

Storrington	v	Portfield	2*1		Horsham	v	Crawley Down	4-2
Worthing	v	Lewes	4-0		Crawley Town	v	Wick	2-1
Whitehawk	v	Shoreham	2-0		East Preston	v	Hastings Town	1-5
Horsham YMCA	v	Chichester City	2-0		Bognor Regis Tn	v	Selsey	4-0
Lancing	v	Sidley United	0*4		Shinewater	v	Sidlesham	0*4
Pagham	v	Saltdean United	0-3		Burgess Hill Tn	v	Brighton & Hove Alb	0-2
St Leonards	v	Eastbourne Town	3-2		Eastbourne United	v	Peacehaven & Tels	2-0
Hassocks	v	Langney Sports	2-3		Littlehampton Town	v	Arundel	0-1

THIRD ROUND (8 matches)

Horsham	v	Horsham YMCA	4-0		Storrington	v	Hastings Town	@ HT 2-4
Arundel	v	Sidley United	1-5		Langney Sports	v	Saltdean United	2-1
Whitehawk	v	Eastbourne United	0-2		Bognor Regis Town	v	Sidlesham	2*1
Worthing	v	St Leonards	4-0		Brighton & Hove	v	Crawley Tn	@CT 0A0 2-1

QUARTER-FINALS

Eastbourne United	v	Hastings Town	1-3		Bognor Regis Town	v	Horsham YMCA	0*2
Langney Sports	v	Worthing	3-0		Sidley United	v	Brighton & Hove Alb	0-2

SEMI-FINALS

Langney Sports	v	Brighton & Hove	0-4		at Langney Sports FC
Horsham YMCA	v	Hastings Town	0-2		at Lancing FC

FINAL

BRIGHTON & H A	v	HASTINGS T	4p3 1*1		at Langney Sports FC

Top: Shinewater AFC goalkeeper Michael West saves a Sidlesham free kick during the Sussex Senior Cup. Shinewater 0 Sidlesham 4.   *Photo: Roger Turner*

Bottom: Steve Yates, Hastings Town (White) about to have his shot kicked off the line by No 4, Ryan Palmer, Brighton & Hove Albion in the Sussex Senior Cup Final.   *Photo: Roger Turner*

Hastings Town line up before the Sussex Senior Cup Final
Photo: Roger Turner

SUSSEX ROYAL ULSTER RIFLES CHARITY CUP 1999-2000
(38 entries)   (FOUNDED 1896-97)

LAST SEASON'S FINAL: Wick   v   Burgess Hill Town   1*0

MOST WINS: Horsham   13   Worthing   12   Southwick   10

PRELIMINARY ROUND (6 matches)

Crawley Down Village	v	Three Bridges	1-1 4-2	Eastbourne Town	v	Redhill	4-1
Sidley United	v	Peacehaven & Tels	4-0	Broadbridge Heath	v	Southwick	1-2
East Preston	v	Pagham	3-0	Sidlesham	v	Oving	0-4

FIRST ROUND (8 matches)

Eastbourne Town	v	Hailsham Town	4-1	Shinewater Assn	v	Whitehawk	0-1
Burgess Hill Town	v	East Grinstead Town	1-0	Sidley United	v	Lingfield	2-1
Oakwood	v	Eastbourne United	1-0	Langney Sports	v	Westfield	1-0
Saltdean United	v	Crawley Down	6-3	Ringmer	v	Withdean	3-2
East Preston	v	Horsham YMCA	4*3	Shoreham	v	Wick	0-2
Arundel	v	Chichester City	2-1	Oving	v	Littlehampton Town	2-3
Mile Oak	v	Hassocks	0-4	Lancing	v	Storrington	3-0
Selsey	v	Southwick	4-1	Portfield	v	Worthing United	7-1

SECOND ROUND (8 matches)

Eastbourne Town	v	Whitehawk	3-1	Saltdean United	v	Ringmer	4-0
Langney Sports	v	Sidley United	2-0	Burgess Hill Town	v	Oakwood	4-1
East Preston	v	Wick	2-3	Selsey	v	Portfield	1*1 5-2
Lancing	v	Littlehampton Town	2-1	Arundel	v	Hassocks	2-4

THIRD ROUND (4 matches)

Burgess Hill Town	v	Langney Sports	1*1 3-2	Selsey	v	Wick	2-1
Hassocks	v	Lancing	1-0	Saltdean United	v	Eastbourne Town	2-1

SEMI-FINALS

Burgess Hill Town	v	Hassocks	4-1	at Haywards Heath FC
Saltdean United	v	Selsey	2-1	

FINAL

BURGESS HILL T	v	SALTDEAN UNITED	3-0	at Sussex County FA Ground,Lancing

WESTMORLAND F.A.

Tel: 01539 730946 Fax: 01539 730946 E-mail: westfa@dialpipex.com
Unit 1, Angel Court, 21 Highgate, Kendal, Cumbria LA9 4DA
Secretary: P G Ducksbury
Executives (Responsibility) County Office (Coaching Exams/Courses,
                                     Womens Football, Referees)

Number of Affiliated Clubs	Senior:	54	U.18:	18	**President:** J B Fleming
Number of Affiliated Leagues:	Senior:	3	Junior:	1	**Chairman:** G Aplin

County Representative Teams: Senior, U18
Inter County Competitions: FA County Youth, Association of Northern Counties Senior & Youth Competitions

'SPRINGER' WESTMORLAND SENIOR CUP 1999-2000

(FOUNDED 1896-97)

(22 entries)

LAST SEASON'S FINAL: Kendal County v Appleby 5-2

MOST WINS: Corinthians 14   Netherfield 12   Burneside 7   Windermere 7

FIRST ROUND (6 matches)

Ambleside United	v	Greystoke	1-3	Victoria S Club	v	Sedburgh Wndrs		1-3
Windermere S C	v	Milnthorpe Corinth's	0-4	Wetheriggs United	v	Staveley United	0-0	1-0
Esthwaite Vale Utd	v	Ullswater United	1-5	Carvetti United	v	Lunesdale United		6-0

SECOND ROUND (8 matches)

Carvetti United	v	Dent	11-0	Kirkby Lonsdale	v	Wetheriggs United	1-3
Burneside	v	Coniston	4-1	Appleby	v	Netherfield Kendal	2-1
Kendal County	v	Burton Thistle	2-0	Keswick	v	Endmoor KGR	5-2
Sedbergh Wndrs	v	Greystoke	3-1	Ullswater United	v	Milnthorpe Corinth's	0-15

QUARTER-FINALS

Wetheriggs United	v	Sedburgh Wndrs	4-0	Milnthorpe Corinth's	v	Appleby	4-2
Kendal County	v	Carvetti United	2-3	Burneside	v	Keswick	0-4

SEMI-FINALS

Milnthorpe Corinth's	v	Keswick	1-0	Carvetti United	v	Wetheriggs United	0-1

FINAL

MILNTHORPE C	v	WETHERIGGS UTD	1-0	at Netherfield Kendal FC	

WEST RIDING F.A.

Tel: 01132 821222   Fax: 01132 821525
Fleet Lane, Woodlesford, Leeds LS26 8NX
Secretary & Press Officer: G R Carter
Executives (Responsibility)   Contact Secretary for:
Coaching Exams/Courses, Referees, Womens Football

Number of Affiliated Clubs	Senior:	950	U.18:	300	**President:** A C Taylor
Number of Affiliated Leagues:	Senior:	40	Junior:	12	**Chairman:** G Pawson

County Representative Teams: Senior, Junior U18, Womens
Inter County Competitions: Association of Northern Counties Senior, Junior U18 & Womens, FA County Youth

WEST RIDING COUNTY CUP 1999-2000

(18 entries)   (FOUNDED 1924-25)

LAST SEASON'S FINAL: Ossett Albion   v   Bradford Park Avenue   2-0

MOST WINS: Goole Town   11   Farsley Celtic   9   Guiseley   5

FIRST ROUND (2 matches)

Ossett Town	v	Glasshoughton W	2*2 0-2	Yorkshire Amateur	v	Guiseley	2-1

SECOND ROUND (8 matches)

Bradford Park Ave	v	Hatfield Main	4-1	Harrogate Railway	v	Armthorpe Welfare	3-2
Tadcaster Albion	v	Yorkshire Amateur	TA T-A	Thackley	v	Goole AFC	0-3
Harrogate Town	v	Liversedge	3-0	Garforth Town	v	Ossett Albion	2-0
Eccleshill United	v	Selby Town	3-0	Glasshoughton	v	Farsley Celtic	2-1

QUARTER-FINALS

Goole	v	Harrogate Town	0-2	Glasshoughton W	v	Garforth Town	0-4
Tadcaster Albion	v	Harrogate Railway	2-0	Eccleshill United	v	Bradford Park Ave	3-0

SEMI-FINALS

Eccleshill United	v	Harrogate Town	2-0	Tadcaster Albion	v	Garforth Town	1-4

FINAL

ECCLESHILL UTD	v	GARFORTH TOWN	0-2	at West Riding County FA Ground

WILTSHIRE F.A.
Tel: 01793 525245   Fax: 01793 692699
16 Robins Green, Covingham, Swindon, Wilts SN3 5AY

Secretary: Michael Benson

Executives (Responsibility)   Ian Whitehouse (Referees)
Kelly Simmons (Womens Football)

Chairman: R Gardiner

WILTSHIRE PREMIER SHIELD 1999-2000
(12 entries) (FOUNDED 1926-27)
LAST SEASON'S FINAL: Salisbury City v Swindon Supermarine 2-1
MOST WINS: Swindon Town 26   Salisbury City 11   Trowbridge Town 9

FIRST ROUND (4 matches)

Calne Town	v	Swindon Town	1-3	Warminster Town	v	Swindon Supermarine 1-2
Devizes Town	v	Salisbury City	2-1	Downton	v	Chippenham Town 1-2

SECOND ROUND (4 matches)

Devizes Town	v	Chippenham Tn	3p4 0*0	Highworth Town	v	Swindon S'm 0A0 4-0
Bemerton H Harl	v	Melksham Town	1-2	Westbury United	v	Swindon Town 1-6

SEMI-FINALS

Melksham Town	v	Chippenham Town	2-0
Highworth Town	v	Swindon Town	0-1

FINAL
SWINDON TOWN   v   MELKSHAM TOWN   0-1
at Swindon Town FC

*Right: Melksham Town celebrate after their success
in winning the Wiltshire Premier Shield 1-0 against
Swindon Town at the County Ground, Swindon.
Photo: Wiltshire Publications Ltd*

WILTSHIRE SENIOR CUP 1999-2000
(13 entries) (FOUNDED 1886-87)

LAST SEASON'S FINAL:
Wootton Bassett Town v Pewsey Vale 3-2
MOST WINS:
Devizes Town   14   Swindon Town   10   Chippenham Town   8

FIRST ROUND (5 matches)

Amesbury Town	v	Marlborough Town	5-0	Purton	v	Shrewton United 3-1
Wootton Bassett Tn	v	Cricklade Town	3-2	Malmesbury Victoria	v	Raychem Mowlem 5-0
Pewsey Vale	v	Wroughton	4-1			

SECOND ROUND (4 matches)

Pewsey Vale	v	Malmesbury Victoria	3-2	Bradford Town	v	Purton 2-4
Corsham	v	Biddestone	3*2	Amesbury Town	v	Wootton Bassett Tn 1-2

SEMI-FINALS

Corsham Town	v	Purton	0-1	Wootton Bassett Tn	v	Pewsey Vale 4p5 2*2

FINAL
PEWSEY VALE   v   PURTON   3p2 0*0   at Melksham Town FC

WORCESTERSHIRE F.A.

Tel: 01386 443215 (H)   01905 612336 (B)   Fax: 01905 729229 (B)
Fermain, 12 Worcester Road, Evesham, Worcestershire WR11 4JU
Secretary & Press Officer: M R Leggett
Executives (Responsibility)   M J Ford (Coaching Exams/Courses)
    W A Allsopp (Referees)
    Dawn Scott (Womens Football)
Number of Affiliated Clubs   Senior: 17   Junior: 270   Youth: 96
Number of Affiliated Leagues: Senior: 6   Junior: 3
County Representative Teams: U18, U16 Girls
Inter County Competitions: FA County Youth, Midland Counties Youth

President: P Rushton
Chairman: K J Clifford

WORCESTERSHIRE SENIOR CUP 1999-2000
(9 entries)   (FOUNDED 1893-94)

LAST SEASON'S FINAL: Kidderminster Harriers v Worcester City 4-3

FIRST ROUND (1 match)
Moor Green   v   Solihull Borough   0-3

SECOND ROUND (4 matches)
Bromsgrove Rovers v   Redditch United   4-3   Solihull Borough   v   Halesowen Town   1-0
Stourbridge   v   Kidderminster Harriers 2-5   Evesham United   v   Worcester City   1-2

SEMI-FINALS
Kidderminster Harriers v   Bromsgrove Rovers   1-0   Solihull Borough   v   Worcester City   3-0

FINAL
KIDDERMINSTER H v   SOLIHULL BORO   3-0   at Kidderminster Harriers FC

WORCESTERSHIRE SENIOR URN 1999-2000

LAST SEASON'S FINAL: Kings Norton Town v Kidderminster Harriers Reserves 2-1

FIRST ROUND (2 matches)
Bromsgrove Rvrs Rs v   Alvechurch   A W-O   Studley BKL   v   Kidderminster H Res   4-0

SECOND ROUND (4 matches)
Alvechurch   v   Studley BKL   0A1 1-2   Malvern Town   v   Kings Norton Town   2-1
Stourport Swifts   v   Pegasus Juniors   6-2   Feckenham   v   Pershore Town   1-4

SEMI-FINALS
Malvern Town   v   Pershore Town   3-1   Studley BKL   v   Stourport Swifts   2-3

FINAL
MALVERN TOWN   v   STOURPORT S   4p3 1*1   at Worcester City FC

DAVIES
MIDLAND INVITATION CUP 1999-2000
(55 entries)

LAST SEASON'S FINAL: Atherstone United v Bandon 2-1

FIRST ROUND (23 matches)

Alveston	v	Stratford Town	0-3		Anstey Nomads	v	Oldbury United	1-2
Aylestone Park	v	Stapenhill	1*3		Barwell	v	Oadby Town	3-2
Birstall United	v	Tividale	3-0		Blackheath Electro	v	Boldmere St Michaels	0-1
Bloxwich Town	v	Halesowen Harriers	4*5		Causeway United	v	Knypersley Vic	1p3 3*3
Continental Star	v	Highgate United	0-1		Coventry Sphinx	v	West Midlands Police	3-2
Cradley Town	v	Wednesfield	4-1		Darlaston Town	v	Sandwell Borough	5-0
Feckenham	v	Bolehall Swifts	2-4		Gornal Athletic	v	Bustleholme	4*3
Kings Norton Town	v	Handrahan Timbers	3-2		Kirby Muxloe	v	Thurmaston Town	0-2
Little Drayton Rngrs	v	W'ton Casuals	0A0 2-3		Malvern Town	v	Kenilworth Town	6-0
Pelsall Villa	v	Cheslyn Hay	0-1		St Andrews	v	Bridgnorth Town	0-1
Stafford Town	v	Pershore Town	3-0		Studley BKL	v	Coalville Town	5-1
Willenhall Town	v	Bandon	1-0					

SECOND ROUND (16 matches)

Barwell	v	Knypersley Victoria	4-1		Birstall United	v	Brierley Hill Town	1p3 1*1
Bolehall Swifts	v	Stratford Town	1-3		Cottesmore Amat	v	Bridgnorth Town	3-10
Cradley Town	v	Chasetown	0-4		Dudley Town	v	Malvern Town	0-2
Gornal Athletic	v	Thringstone United	1-2		Holwell Sports	v	Oldbury United	3-2
Ibstock Welfare	v	Highgate United	IW W-O		Kings Norton Town	v	Cheslyn Hay	2-0
Thurmaston Town	v	Stourport Swifts	0-1		Wolverhampton Cas	v	Star	3-2
Stafford Town	v	Halesowen Harriers	1-3		Stapenhill	v	Darlaston Town	0-1
Studley BKL	v	Boldmer St M's	3p2 2*2		Willenhall Town	v	Coventry Sphinx	1-4

THIRD ROUND (8 matches)

Darlaston Town	v	Barwell	2-0		Malvern Town	v	Thringstone United	6-1
Holwell Sports	v	Wolverhampton Cas	2-0		Ibstock Welfare	v	Halesowen H	3p1 0*0
Kings Norton Town	v	Brierley Hill Town	3-2		Stourport Swifts	v	Chasetown	2A0 f/f 0-1
Stratford Town	v	Bridgnorth Town	3-5		Studley BKL	v	Coventry Sphinx	0-1

QUARTER-FINALS

Darlaston Town	v	Coventry Sphinx	2*1		Malvern Town	v	Bridgnorth Town	2-3
Holwel Sports	v	Chasetown	2*4		Kings Norton Town	v	Ibstock Welfare	2-0

SEMI-FINALS

Kings Norton Town	v	Bridgnorth Town	0-1		Darlaston Town	v	Chasetown	5-1

FINAL

BRIDGNORTH T	v	DARLASTON T	3-1		at Shifnal Town FC

BUREAU of NON-LEAGUE FOOTBALL MONTHLY RESULTS MAGAZINE

BNLF (1981) still, simply produces the best Monthly Round Up of Non-League **Tables, Cup Results & Draws** an absolute avalanche of results, ties and tables each month

ALL COUNTY F A SENIOR CUPS

Stay on the Ball with The Professionals of the Amateur game
Nationwide CONFERENCE
to National & Regional LEAGUE TABLES
& LEAGUE CUP COMPETITIONS

with regular up-dates & news snippets.
INCLUDING ALL THE F A CUP, TROPHY & VASE,
WELSH CUP & TROPHY

BNLF The Country's Longest Running National Non-League Football Monthly Results Magazine
Delivered to your door for less than £2.00 per month

Subscription ONLY £21.00
Season 2000-2001 or Year 2001

(Free back issues available to new subscribers)
January, February, March, April, May, June/July, (Summer issue)
August, September, October, November, December.

Send your Chx/p.p. with name and address to Mike Ford
THE BUREAU OF NON-LEAGUE FOOTBALL (BNLF)
173, LEYTONSTONE ROAD, LONDON, E15 1LH

MIKE FORD EAST ANGLIAN CUP 1999-2000
(47 entries)

LAST SEASON'S FINAL: Ipswich Wanderers v St Neots Town 2-0

FIRST ROUND (15 matches)

Sudbury AFC	v	Soham Town Rngrs	3-1	Spalding United	v	March Town United	10-0
Wroxham	v	Fakenham Town	1*2	Lowestoft Town	v	Mulbarton United	3-0
Ware	v	Royston Town	3-1	Saffron Walden Tn	v	Stansted	4*2
Somersham Town	v	Biggleswade Town	4-3	Biggleswade Utd	v	St Neots Town	0-1
Barton Rovers	v	Eynesbury Rovers	11-1	Romford	v	Hertford Town	3-1
Basildon United	v	Concord Rangers	1-2	Great Wakering Rvrs	v	Southend Manor	2-1
Burnham Ramblers	v	Maldon Town	1-4	Wivenhoe Town	v	Harwich & Parkeston	3-1
Ipswich Wanderers	v	Tiptree United	3p4 1*1				

SECOND ROUND (16 matches)

Thetford Town	v	Cornard United	1-2	Diss Town	v	Sudbury AFC	5-1
Holbeach United	v	Bourne Town	2-0	Chatteris Town	v	Spalding United	0-3
Dereham Town	v	Downham town	2-1	Lowestoft Town	v	Fakenham Town	3-0
Harlow Town	v	Letchworth	6-1	Saffron Walden Town	v	Ware	2-3
Ely City	v	Barton Rovers	EC W-O	St Neots Town	v	Somersham Town	3-0
Halstead Town	v	Aveley	3-2	Braintree Town	v	Romford	1-2
Hullbridge Sports	v	Maldon Town	2-3	Great Wakering Rvrs	v	Concord Rangers	5-0
Felixstowe Pt & Tn	v	Clacton Town	0-2	Tiptree United	v	Wivenhoe Town	0-1

THIRD ROUND (Area Finals)

Cornard United	v	Diss Town	1*2	Holbeach United	v	Spalding United	2*1
Dereham Town	v	Lowestoft Town	4*3	Harlow Town	v	Ware	3p0 3*3
Ely City	v	St Neots Town	4p3 1*1	Halstead Town	v	Romford	3-1
Maldon Town	v	Great Wakering Rvrs	2-3	Clacton Town	v	Wivenhoe Town	1-3

QUARTER-FINALS

Great Wakering Rvrs	v	Halstead Town	4-0	Ely City	v	Diss Town	0-3
Clacton Town	v	Dereham Town	4*2	Holbeach United	v	Harlow Town	0-1

SEMI-FINALS

Harlow Town	v	Gt Wakering Rvrs 5p4 1*1			Clacton Town	v	Diss Town	5-1

FINAL

CLACTON TOWN	v	HARLOW TOWN	3-1	at Clacton Town FC

Above: If you see any of these at your ground, move them on!
Photo: Jan Turner

Left: "Uncle" Eric Marsh celebrates a team picture in a Wembley programme after 50 years trying.
Photo: Ian Morsman

Below: They do work sometimes: On duty at Wembley Stadium
Photo: Alan Coomes

Combined Services XI pictured at their match agains the F.A. XI at Worcester

Back Row (l-r): Mike Healey, Lenny Brayshaw, Sean Cooper, Pete Tagg, Fraser Quick, Daisy May

Front Row (l-r): Alfie Alford, Nigel Thwaites, Allan Pluckrise (capt), Darren Bray, Brian Kayle

THE SERVICES REPRESENTATIVE MATCHES

Every season a series of representative matches see many non-League club regulars in the shirts of their employers! The Services play each other for their own championship; the scores last season being:-

Royal Navy 0 - Royal Air Force 4
British Army 1 - Royal Navy 0
Royal Air Force 0 - British Army 0

Thus giving the Royal Air Force the title on goal difference. The Combined Services also contest The Kentish Cup with their counterpart from Belgium and this year's winner Holland.

The Civil Service and the Prison Service also play representative matches and, of course, The Amateur Football Alliance XI play against all these teams.

The general attitude to the games and indeed the social side is second to none and I recommend a visit to any of these fixtures. TW

The Army keeper clears v H.M. Prisons XI at the Military Stadium. Photo: Eric Marsh

Prison Officers at the Military Stadium, Aldershot. Photo: Eric Marsh

OPTIMUM INTERIORS CAPITAL FOOTBALL LEAGUE

Chairman: David Free
Secretary: Geoff Ellis, 69 Old Woking Road, West Byfleet, Surrey KT14 6LF
Tel: 01932 345844   Fax: 01932 342585

FINAL LEAGUE TABLE 1999-2000

		P	Home W	D	L	F	A	Away W	D	L	F	A	Pts	GD
1	Rushden & Dia.	18	9	0	0	33	9	8	0	1	33	6	51	51
2	Harrow Borough	18	6	1	2	25	12	3	1	5	18	12	29	10
3	St Albans City	18	3	0	6	12	17	4	2	3	25	18	23	2
4	Aylesbury Utd	18	3	0	6	12	33	4	2	3	15	14	23	-20
5	Boreham Wood	18	4	3	2	12	9	2	1	6	10	24	22	-11
6	Stevenage Borough	18	4	1	4	15	17	2	1	6	15	16	20	-3
7	Aldershot Town	18	3	3	3	17	24	0	1	8	5	27	13	-29

OPTIMUM INTERIORS CENTRAL CONFERENCE

Chairman: David Free
Secretary: Jason Mills, 25 Hewlett Road, Cheltenham, Glos GL52 6AD
Tel: 01242 700496

FINAL LEAGUE TABLE 1999-2000

		P	Home W	D	L	F	A	Away W	D	L	F	A	GD	Pts
1	Cheltenham Town	20	7	0	3	20	10	9	1	0	25	10	25	49
2	Rushden & Diamonds	20	7	2	1	22	5	6	3	1	26	13	30	44
3	Hednesford Town	20	3	4	3	23	18	6	1	3	25	14	16	32
4	Nuneaton Borough	20	2	1	7	24	30	7	3	0	23	6	11	31
5	Hereford United	20	3	2	5	15	16	5	2	3	19	14	4	28
6	Burton Albion	20	3	0	7	12	19	6	1	3	17	17	-7	28
7	Kidderminster Harriers	20	5	2	3	19	14	3	1	6	18	28	-5	27
8	Worcester City	20	3	3	4	15	16	2	3	5	12	23	-12	21
9	Gloucester City	20	3	1	6	16	17	3	1	6	9	20	-12	19
10	Telford United	20	4	2	4	12	19	0	3	7	8	25	-24	17
11	Tamworth	20	2	2	6	19	27	2	0	8	9	27	-26	14

LANCASHIRE FOOTBALL LEAGUE

Chairman: Neil Marsdin
Secretary: Barbara Howarth, 86 Windsor Rd, Great Harwood, Blackburn Lancs BB6 7RR
Tel: 01254 886267   Fax: 01254 877289

FINAL LEAGUE TABLE 1999-2000

		P	W	D	L	F	A	Pts
1	Southport Reserves	22	15	3	4	73	28	48
2	Morecambe Reserves	22	14	1	7	60	36	43
3	Northwich Victoria Reserves	22	12	5	5	54	32	41
4	Guiseley Reserves	22	12	3	7	44	26	39
5	Marine Reserves	22	11	5	6	44	22	38
6	Runcorn Reserves	22	11	4	7	44	31	37
7	Lancaster City Reserves	22	11	1	10	37	50	34
8	Altrincham Reserves	22	9	1	12	47	46	28
9	Bamber Bridge Reserves	22	6	4	12	26	53	22
10	Macclesfield Town Reserves	22	5	5	12	26	44	20
11	Leek Town FC Reserves	22	4	2	16	24	66	14
12	Ashton United Reserves	22	4	2	16	23	68	14

Non-League Media plc

Aims to give non-League football the very best media coverage it has ever received

Through:-

⚽ The daily use of our Website - **www.nlfootball.com**

⚽ The weekly paper **THE NON-LEAGUE PAPER** (already over 40,000 weekly sales), published nationally on Sundays.

⚽ The monthly magazine **'ON THE BALL'** which promotes Womens Football

⚽ The monthly magazine **TEAM TALK** (over 100 editions), published nationally each month
(12 months subscription £29.00 - 6 months subscription £15.00)

⚽ The best selling **F.A. NON LEAGUE CLUB DIRECTORY** (now in its 23rd year)

For subscription enquiries only please contact the
Subscribers Hotline - 0800 424 567
(For the Non-League Paper, On The Ball or Team Talk)

Any general enquiries regarding Team Talk or the Directory contact
01823 490080 or Email: tony.williams12@virgin.net

Any general enquiries regarding The Non-League Paper or On the Ball to -
Non-League Media Plc., Elvin House, Stadium Way, Wembley, Middlesex, HA9 0DW.
Tel: 0208 900 9021

TEAM TALK's
100th Birthday

Above: You can't keep them away - and they found the bar! What a surprise! The photographic team: (l-r) Gary Letts, Gordon Whittington, Roger Turner, Alan Coomes, Neil Thaler, and sitting (as usual) 'Uncle' Eric Marsh.

Right: Brian Talbot, Barry Fry and Max Griggs are certainly enjoying themselves.

Below: The bar did good business.

Photos: Andrew Chitty

LEAGUE OF WALES

Chief Executive: D G Collins
Secretary: J C Deakin
Plymouth Chambers, 3 Westgate Street, Cardiff CF1 1DD
Tel: 01222 372325   Fax: 01222 343961

FINAL LEAGUE TABLES 1999-2000

THE STRUCTURE OF WELSH FOOTBALL

Champions of Cymru Alliance and CC Sports Welsh League Division One promoted to the League of Wales

North Wales
Champions of Welsh Alliance and Welsh National League Premier Division promoted to Cymru Alliance
Champions of Gwynedd League and Clwyd League promoted to Welsh Alliance
Champions of Vale of Conwy and Caernarfon & District League promoted to Gwynedd/Clwyd League

Central Wales
Champions of Spar Mid Wales League promoted to Cymru Alliance
Champions of Mid Wales South, Ffigar and Montgomeryshire Leagues promoted to Spar Mid Wales Leagues

South Wales
Champions of Highadmit Projects Amateur League, Swansea Senior League, Neath League, and Gwent County League can seek promotion to the CC Sports Welsh League Division Three.

Other Football
Below this are a number of more local leagues. One more senior league established during the 1999-2000 season was a North Wales Floodlit League which aimed to provide opportunities for young players to make the step up from youth football to UniBond/League of Wales Cymru Alliance/Welsh National League level.

LEAGUE OF WALES

	P	W	D	L	F	A	Pts		P	W	D	L	F	A	Pts
TNS Llan'ffraid	34	24	2	6	69	37	76	Afan Lido	34	12	10	12	44	42	46
Barry Town	34	23	5	6	98	34	74	Rhyl	34	13	5	16	40	60	44
Cwmbran T	34	21	6	7	71	37	69	Caersws	34	11	8	15	49	50	41
Carmarthen T	34	22	3	9	68	42	69	F Cefn Druids	34	13	2	19	44	63	41
Llanelli	34	21	3	10	76	46	66	Rhayader T	34	9	7	18	34	47	34
Aberystyth T	34	19	4	11	70	46	61	Haverfordwest	34	6	11	17	37	65	29
Connah's Q N	34	17	6	11	57	35	57	Inter Cardiff	34	8	6	20	30	62	29
Newtown	34	14	6	14	49	41	48	Conwy Utd	34	6	5	23	33	97	20
Bangor City	34	15	3	16	56	61	48	Caernarfon T	34	1	8	25	21	81	11

HUWS GRAY FITLOCK CYMRU ALLIANCE FEEDER TO LEAGUE OF WALES						
	P	W	D	L	GD	Pts
Oswestry T	32	21	4	7	21	64
Glantraeth	32	18	7	7	43	61
Cemaes Bay	32	17	8	7	30	59
Welshpool T	32	17	6	9	19	57
CPD Porthmadog	32	17	5	10	24	56
Flint Tn Utd	32	16	8	8	22	56
Llandudno	32	16	5	11	13	53
Rhydymwyn	32	15	5	12	1	50
Llangefni T	32	13	10	9	17	49
Buckley T	32	13	8	11	9	47
Ruthin T	32	13	7	12	10	46
Holyhead Htspr	32	9	6	17	-18	33
Lex XI	32	9	3	20	-35	30
Brymbo Broughton	32	7	2	17	-19	29
Denbigh T	32	8	5	19	-43	26
Holywell T	32	7	4	21	-28	25
Corwen Amts	32	5	3	24	-66	18

CC SPORTS WELSH LEAGUE DIVISION ONE FEEDER TO LEAGUE OF WALES						
	P	W	D	L	GD	Pts
Ton Pentre	34	25	5	4	75	80
Port Talbot	34	22	9	3	52	75
Maesteg Park	34	18	11	5	26	65
BP	34	17	5	12	39	56
Cardiff C Serv	34	15	9	10	21	54
AFC Rhondda	34	17	3	14	6	54
Bridgend T	34	15	5	14	-5	50
Briton Ferry	34	14	6	14	-8	48
Gwinfi Utd	34	14	5	15	-6	47
Penrhiwceiber	34	13	6	15	-4	45
Goytre	34	13	6	15	-6	45
Porth Tywyn	34	12	7	15	-10	43
Treowen	34	12	6	16	-13	42
Pontardawe	34	11	8	15	-7	41
UWIC	34	10	8	16	-32	38
Ammanford	34	10	6	18	-13	36
Cardiff Corries	34	9	7	18	-26	34
Aberaman	34	2	2	30	-91	8

WELSH NATIONAL LEAGUE PREMIER DIV.
FEEDER TO CYMRU ALLIANCE

	P	W	D	L	GD	Pt
British Aero	30	21	4	5	47	67
Ruthin Town	30	19	6	5	25	63
Penycae	30	19	5	6	48	62
Gresford Ath	30	18	7	5	48	61
Chirk AAA	30	14	8	8	17	50
Llangollen	30	13	6	11	24	45
Brymbo Br'ton	30	12	7	11	-6	43
Mold Aex	30	12	4	14	3	40
Bradley Villa	30	11	4	15	-15	37
F Cefn Druids	30	10	6	14	-17	36
Penley	30	9	8	13	-5	35
Rhos Aelwyd	30	9	8	13	-16	35
Castell AC	30	8	7	15	-8	31
Bala Town	30	8	6	16	-32	30
Llay Welfare	30	9	2	19	-30	29
Rhostyllen Utd	30	2	4	24	-83	4

WELSH NATIONAL LEAGUE DIVISION ONE
FEEDER TO WELSH NAT. LEAGUE PREM

	P	W	D	L	GD	Pt
Hand Hotel	30	23	4	3	67	73
Brickfield*	30	23	4	3	64	70
Borras PA	30	14	8	8	14	50
Acrefair	30	15	5	10	9	50
Llanuwchllyn	30	14	7	9	12	49
Penycae Res	30	13	5	12	-9	44
Brit Aero Res	30	11	10	9	4	43
Gresford A Res	30	13	4	13	-5	43
Ruthin T Colts	30	11	7	12	-1	40
Buckley Town	30	10	5	15	-10	35
Llay Wel Res	30	10	5	15	-15	35
Corwen Res	30	9	7	14	-1	34
Mynydd Isa*	30	11	4	15	-14	34
Glyn Ceiriog	30	10	4	16	-16	34
Hightown	30	6	2	22	-50	20
Rhos Aelwyd Res	30	5	3	22	-48	18

WELSH NATIONAL LEAGUE DIV 2
FEEDER TO WELSH NAT. LEAGUE DIV 1

	P	W	D	L	GD	Pt
Cefn Utd	30	28	2	0	167	86
Led Mills FC	30	21	3	6	63	66
Summerhill Utd	30	19	2	9	53	59
Coedpoeth	30	19	2	9	47	59
Llangollen Res	30	14	3	13	-8	45
Castell AC Res	30	13	2	15	23	41
New Brighton	30	11	8	11	-3	41
Bala Town*	30	12	8	10	-14	41
Borrar Pk Res	30	12	5	13	-15	41
Brymbo Brghton	30	11	6	13	-21	39
Acrefair Res	30	11	2	17	-30	35
Llay Welfare C	30	10	5	15	-34	35
Overton Rec	30	8	9	13	-29	33
Mold Alexandra	30	7	6	17	-46	24
Johnstown Sen	30	7	3	20	-60	24
Johnstown Jun	30	2	4	24	-93	10

TYN LON ROVER WELSH ALLIANCE
FEEDER TO CYMRU ALLIANCE

	P	W	D	L	GD	Pt
Halkyn Utd	24	19	56	0	47	62
Colwyn B YMCA	24	15	6	3	23	51
Llanfairpwll	24	14	6	4	-16	24
Glan Conwy	24	13	4	7	41	40
Llandudno Jcn	24	11	4	9	16	37
Bangor City	24	10	6	8	13	36
Prestatyn Town	24	11	2	11	-6	35
Loco Llanberis	24	10	4	10	12	34
Amlwch Town	24	10	2	12	23	33
Rhyl Athletic	24	8	4	12	-8	28
Rhyl Delta	24	6	4	14	-26	22
Penmaenmawr P	24	2	8	14	-35	14
Llandyrnog Utd	24	1	1	22	-125	14

GWYNEDD LEAGUE
FEEDER TO WELSH ALLIANCE

	P	W	D	L	GD	Pt
Bethseda Ath	28	24	4	0	62	76
Llangefni T	28	21	2	5	61	65
Bodedern	28	19	2	7	37	59
Caernarfon T	28	16	7	5	39	55
Llanrug Utd	28	17	3	8	33	54
Penrhyn'draeth	28	14	4	10	5	46
Pwllheli	28	12	5	11	2	41
Blaenau Amts	28	13	2	13	-8	41
Felinheli	28	10	4	14	-11	34
Llanrwst Utd	28	10	3	15	-30	33
Holyhead Htspr	28	10	0	18	-30	30
Barmouth & D	28	7	5	16	-22	26
Deiniolen	28	6	1	21	-47	19
Bangor Univ	28	4	3	21	-34	15
Llandegfan	28	2	3	21	-57	9

TALACRE BEACH PARK CLWYD LEAGUE
FEEDER TO WELSH ALLIANCE

	P	W	D	L	GD	Pt
Abergele T	22	15	2	5	33	47
Caerwys	22	15	2	5	12	47
Pilkingtons	22	14	4	4	51	46
Prestatyn T	22	9	8	5	26	35
Mostyn Lodge	22	10	3	9	11	33
Holywell Res	22	9	4	9	5	31
Hawarden Rgs	22	9	4	9	2	31
Flint Res	22	7	5	10	-14	26
Llansannan	22	6	6	10	4	24
Rhydymwyn Rs	22	6	4	12	-22	22
Denbigh T Res	22	4	5	13	-22	17
Llandyrnog Res	22	3	3	16	-66	12

THREEWAYS VALE OF CONWY LEAGUE
FEEDER TO CWYNEDD/CLYDD LEAGUE

	P	W	D	L	GD	Pt
Betws y Coed	18	13	3	2	21	39
Penrhyn Utd	18	11	2	5	29	35
Cricketers	18	10	4	4	26	34
Glan Conwy Res	18	8	5	5	14	29
Machno Utd	18	8	4	6	14	28
Bro Cernyw	18	8	3	7	20	27
Llanfairfchan T	18	6	6	6	8	24
Mochdre Sports	18	6	0	12	-22	18
Betws yn Rhos	18	5	2	11	-22	18
Llanrwst Utd Rs	18	0	2	16	-84	2

CAERNARFON & DISTRICT LEAGUE
FEEDER TO CWYNEDD/CLYDD LEAGUE

	P	W	D	L	GD	Pt
Nefyn Utd	18	14	2	2	47	44
Talysarn Celts	18	10	4	4	31	34
Llanystundwy	18	10	3	5	22	33
Nantlle Vale	18	9	4	5	23	31
Porthmadog	18	8	4	6	10	28
Pwllheli T	18	6	4	8	0	22
Deinolen	18	5	5	8	-16	20
Pwllheli Res	18	5	5	8	-16	20
Llanrug Utd	18	5	2	11	-35	17
Harlech T	18	2	1	15	-50	7

CC SPORTS WELSH LEAGUE DIVISION 2
FEEDER TO WELSH LEAGUE DIV 1

	P	W	D	L	GD	Pt
Fields Pk/Ptfraith	30	20	5	5	73	65
Milford Utd	30	19	5	6	34	62
Caerleon	30	17	9	4	35	60
Porthcawl	30	16	7	7	26	55
Chepstow T	30	15	8	7	23	53
Hoover Sports	30	15	6	9	26	51
Taffs Well	30	15	5	10	13	50
Tredegar T	30	17	3	10	38	48
Risca Utd	30	12	4	14	-8	40
Llanwern	30	9	8	13	-8	35
Caldicot	30	9	6	15	-1	33
Portos G Q	30	9	5	16	-13	32
Albion Rovers	30	8	7	15	-24	31
Blaenrhondda	30	5	8	17	-26	23
Morriston T	30	5	4	21	-81	19
Abergavenny Th	30	2	4	24	-123	10

CC SPORTS WELSH LEAGUE DIV THREE
FEEDER TO WELSH LEAGUE DIV 2

	P	W	D	L	GD	Pt
Garw	28	24	2	2	76	74
Ely Rangers	28	23	4	1	67	73
Garden Village	28	17	4	7	25	55
AFC Llwydcoed	28	17	3	8	16	54
Seven Sisters	28	14	5	9	6	47
Treharris Ath	28	14	3	11	16	45
Skewen Ath	28	13	2	13	6	41
Caerau	28	11	7	10	7	40
Caerau Ely	28	10	4	14	-8	34
Newport YMCA	28	11	0	17	-30	33
Pontyclun	28	9	3	16	-16	30
Pontypridd	28	6	10	12	-8	28
Abercynon	28	6	3	19	-39	21
Monkton Swifts	28	4	3	21	-64	15
Pontlottyn	28	3	3	22	-54	12

HIGHADMIT AMATEUR LEAGUE DIV 1 (Top 10)
FEEDER TO WELSH LEAGUE DIV 3

Dinas Powys	30	19	8	3	48	65
Cambrian SBs	30	19	7	4	28	64
FC Cwmaman	30	17	7	6	23	58
Barry Athletic	30	13	8	9	15	47
Troedyrhiw FC	30	15	5	10	0	47
Trefelin BCG	30	12	12	6	17	43
Bryntirion Ath	30	11	7	12	3	40
Llangeinor	30	11	4	15	-5	37
Llantwit Major	30	9	10	11	-4	37
British Steel	30	11	2	17	-11	35

SPAR MID WALES LEAGUE
FEEDER TO CYMRU ALLIANCE

	P	W	D	L	GD	Pt
Carno	30	22	3	5	44	69
Penrhyncoch	30	19	8	3	46	65
Newtown	30	19	6	5	43	63
Kerry	30	15	10	5	31	55
Guilsfield	30	15	6	9	31	51
Waterloo	30	15	5	10	30	50
Rhayader	30	16	5	9	-1	53
Presteigne	30	14	3	13	-4	45
Llanidloes	30	13	6	11	-3	45
Knighton	30	10	4	16	-20	34
Aberystwyth	30	10	7	13	-11	37
Meifod	30	8	7	15	-17	31
Caersws	30	6	8	16	-23	26
UWA	30	6	5	19	-27	23
Builth Wells	30	4	5	21	-48	17
Llandrindod	30	3	5	22	-79	14

J V LIKE MID WALES LEAGUE (SOUTH)
FEEDER TO SPAR MID WALES LEAGUE

	P	W	D	L	GD	Pt
Sennybridge	28	23	3	2	82	72
Vale of Arrow	28	23	3	2	66	72
Rhosgoch	28	19	3	6	42	60
Newcastle	28	15	3	15	24	48
Llanidloes Res	28	13	2	13	-8	41
Newbridge	28	11	7	10	-4	37
Radnor Valley	28	11	4	13	-1	37
Bucknell	28	10	2	16	-21	35
Llyswen/Boroc	28	9	7	12	2	34
Builth Wells Rs	28	9	5	14	-14	29
Penybont	28	9	5	14	-23	29
Presteigne Res	28	8	4	16	-19	28
Gwernyfed	28	8	7	13	-13	24
Llandod Res	28	6	5	17	-35	20
Knighton Res	28	4	2	22	-78	11

JT HUGHES MONTGOMERYSHIRE LEAGUE
FEEDER TO SPAR MID WALES LEAGUE

DIV ONE	P	W	D	L	GD	Pt
Llangedwyn	20	18	0	2	57	54
Llanrhaeadr	20	14	2	4	21	44
Bettws	20	9	4	7	10	31
Bishops Castle	20	8	6	6	9	30
Forden Utd	20	9	2	9	-11	29
Dyffryn Banw	20	7	6	7	2	27
Llanfair Caereinion	20	8	3	9	2	27
Llanwddyn	20	8	3	9	-6	27
Llanfyllin	20	8	2	10	-3	26
Berriew	20	1	7	12	-36	10
Llanfechain	20	1	3	16	-45	6

PEMBROKESHIRE LEAGUE DIV 1 (Top 10)   FEEDER TO WELSH LEAGUE DIV 3

Hakin Utd	26	25	0	1	111	75	Milford Ath	26	11	3	12	-26	36
Goodwick Utd	26	24	0	2	70	72	Tenby	26	11	2	13	4	35
Narberth	26	16	4	6	32	52	Pennar Robins	26	10	1	15	-12	31
Camrose	26	13	8	5	39	47	Merlins Bridge	26	8	5	13	-1	29
Carew	26	14	5	7	12	47	Milford United	26	8	3	15	-29	27

GWENT COUNTY LEAGUE DIV 1 (Top 10)
FEEDER TO WELSH LEAGUE DIV 3

Spencer Y & B	30	21	7	2	47	70
Cwmtillery AFC	30	19	4	7	42	61
Newport Civ S	30	18	7	5	23	61
Abertillery T	30	18	5	7	47	59
Lucas Cwmbran	30	16	2	12	8	50
Fairfield Utd	30	15	4	11	18	49
Abercarn Utd	30	13	4	13	6	43
Croesyceiliog	30	12	6	12	12	42
RTB Ebbw Vale	30	10	12	8	8	42
Pill AFC	30	11	9	10	-2	42

SWANSEA SENIOR LEAGUE DIV 1 (Top 10)
FEEDER TO WELSH LEAGUE DIV 3

Ragged School	22	18	3	1		57
West End	22	17	2	3		53
PT Colts	22	12	4	6		40
St Joseph's	22	12	3	7		39
North End	22	10	3	9		33
Farmers Arms	22	8	8	6		32
Maltsters Spts	22	9	2	11		29
South Gower	22	8	1	13		25
Mumbles Rngrs	22	8	0	14		24
Bonymaen Colts	22	5	7	10		22

Wales Semi-Professional Squad 2000. Photo: Keith Clayton

The Skippers lead their teams out, but why do officials (who did very well on the night) have to come out first at nearly all games these days? No one has paid to see them, and in the old days the sight of the emerging captains was one of the highlights, especially for the young supporters - ed.
Photo: Keith Clayton

The main stand at Llanelli. Photo: Keith Clayton

Regionalisation of clubs

Group A (North)
Bangor City
Connah's Quay
Flexys Cefn Druids
Oswestry Town
Rhyl

Group B (Mid)
Aberystwyth Town
Caersws
Rhayader Town
Total Network Solutions
Newtown

Group C (South)
Afan Lido
Barry Town
Carmarthen Town
Cwmbran Town
Haverfordwest County
Inter Cardiff
Llanelli
Port Talbot Athletic

ABERYSTWYTH TOWN

Secretary: Rhun Owens, 31 Maesgogerddan, Aberystwyth.
Tel: 01970 623520 (H) 0777 323 0894 (M)
Ground: Park Avenue, Aberystwyth, Ceredigion. Tel: 01970 612122
Directions: From south: A487, 1st right at Trefachan Bridge to r'bout, 1st right with Park Ave.
being 3rd right. From north: A487 and follow one-way system to railway station, at r'bout 1st
left with Park Avenue being 3rd right. 5 mins walk from Aberystwyth (BR) - follow as above

Capacity: 4,500   Seats: 300   Cover: 1,200   Floodlights: Yes
Clubhouse: Open daily noon-3 & 7-12pm. Snacks available   **Club Shop:** Yes

HONOURS   Welsh Cup 1899-1900; Welsh I'mediate Cup 85-86 87-88; Mid Wales Lg (11)
(Lg Cup(7); Welsh Amtr Cup (3); Welsh Lg Div 2 Sth 51-52; Cambrian Coast Lg
(8) Central Wales Chal. Cup(6)

PREVIOUS   **League:** Welsh 1896-97; Nth Wales Comb. 99-1900; Montgomeryshire & Dist.
04-20; Central Wales 21-25 81-87; Mid-Wales 26-32 51-81; Cambrian Coast
32-51; Welsh Lg South 51-63; Abacus 87-92

RECORD   **Attendance:** 4,500 v Hereford, Welsh Cup 1971
Goalscorer: David Williams 476, 66-83
Appearances: David P Whitney 572, 62-81

FACT FILE
Founded: 1884
Nickname: Seasiders
Sponsors: Continental Cambria Tyres
Colours: Black & green/white/black
Change colours: Yellow/white/white
Midweek Matchday: Wednesday
Reserves League: Mid-Wales
Programme: 24 pages, 60p
Editor: Steve Moore (01970 617705)

CLUB PERSONNEL

Chairman: Donald Kane
President: D Jones
Press Officer: David Thomas
Manager: Barry Ivor Powell

AFAN LIDO

Secretary: Mr P Robinson, 56 Abbeyville Avenue, Sandfields Estate, Port Talbot SA12 6PY
Tel: 01639 892960 (H) 0411 832169 (M)

Ground: Princess Margaret Way, Aberavon Beach, Port Talbot.
Tel: 01639 892960

Honours: League of Wales R-up 94-95, League of Wales Cup 92-93 93-94

FACT FILE
Colours: All red
Change colours: All white
Midweek Rixtures: Tuesday

CLUB PERSONNEL
Chairman: David Dale
Tel: 01639 895524 (H)
Manager: Mark Robinson
Tel: 01639 822026 (H) 0973 638059(M)

BANGOR CITY

Secretary: Alun Griffiths, 12 Lon-Y-Bryn, Menai Bridge, Anglesey, Gwynedd LL575NM
Tel: 01248 712820
Ground: The Stadium, Farrar Road, Bangor, Gwynedd (01248 355852)
Directions: Old A5 into Bangor, 1st left before railway station, ground on leftby garage
Seats: 700   Cover: 1,200   Capacity: 5,000   Floodlights: Yes
Clubhouse: Not on ground   **Club Shop:** Yes
HONOURS   FA Tphy R-up 83-84; Northern Prem. Lg 81-82 (R-up 86-87, Lg Cup 68-69, Presidents Cup 88-89, Chal. Shield 87-88), Cheshire Co. Lg R-up 53-54 58-59,Lancs Comb. R-up 30-31, League of Wales 94-95 (Lg Cup R-up 94-95), WelshNational Lg 27-28 (R-up 26-27), Nth Wales Coast Lg 1895-96, Welsh Cup 1888-89 95-96 1961-62 (R-up 27-28 60-61 63-64 72-73 77-78 84-85), Nth Wales Chal. Cup 26-27 35-36 36-37 37-38 46-47 51-52 57-58 64-65 67-68, Welsh Amtr Cup 1894-9596-96 97-98 98-99 1900-01 02-03 04-05 05-06 11-12, Welsh Jnr Cup 1995-96 97-981919-20, Welsh All. Alves Cup 49-50 59-60 (Cookson Cup 61-62 68-69 84-85 86-87)
RECORD   **Attendance:** 10,000 v Wrexham, Welsh Cup final 78-79
PREVIOUS   **Leagues:** N Wales Coast 1893-98 1911-12; The Comb 1898-1910; N Wales Comb 30-33; WMids 32-38; Lancs Comb 38-39 46-50; Ches Co 50-68; NPL 68-79 81-82 84-92; AlliancePrem 79-81 82-84, Welsh Cup 97-98,North Wales Challenge Cup 1998-99

FACT FILE
Founded: 1876
Nickname: Citizens
Sponsors: Pentraeth Group
Colours: All blue
Change colours: All white
Midweek Matchedays: Tuesday
Reserve League: Welsh Alliance
Programme: 32 pages, 70p
Editor: Alan Monument

CLUB PERSONNEL
President: Gwyn Pierce Owen
Chief Executive: Major M.Maund
Chairman: Ken Jones
Vice Chairman: David Gareth Jones
Press Officer: Jon Jessop
Manager: Meirion Appleton
Coach: Terry Boyle
Physio: Arwel Jones

Barry Town AFC. Back Row (l-r): Terry Evans, Jamie Ince, Justin Perry, Lee Barrow (Capt.), Jody Jenkins. Centre Row: Jamie Jenkins, Paul Evans, Dave Wells, Ian Loveless, Lawrence Davies, Chris Fry. Front Row: Darren Davies, Andrew York, Richard Jones (Player/Coach), Paul Mitchell, Gary Lloyd.

BARRY TOWN

Secretary:	Alan Whelan, 132 Westward Rise, Barry, South Glam. CF62 6NQ
	Tel: 01446 412938
Ground:	Jenner Park, Barry Tel: 01446 735858
Directions:	M4 jct 33 via Wenvoe (A4050) to Barry. Left at 1st 2 r'bouts to Jenner Park.
	Nearest rail station is Cadoxton

Capacity: 3,000   Seats: 3,000   Cover: Yes   Floodlights: Yes

Clubhouse: Open normal licensing hours, 11.00-11.00 daily

HONOURS Welsh Cup (3); Welsh Trophy 94-95; Southern Lg R-up 20-21;
Western Lg R-up 11-12, Welsh Lg (7), Lg Cup (4); South Wales Senior Cup (13);
SA Brain Cup (3); League of Wales 95-96 96-97 97-98 98-99;
UEFA Cup 2 Qual Rds 96-97, Prel Rd 97-98 Champs Lg. Prelim Rd 98-99,99-00

PREVIOUS   **Leagues:** Western 08-13; Southern 13-82 89-93; Welsh 82-89 94-95

BEST SEASON   **FA Cup:** 2nd Rd 29-30   **FA Trophy** 3rd Qualifying Rd replay 90-91

RECORD   **Attendance:** 7,400 v Queens Park Rangers, FA Cup 1st Rd 1961
Goalscorer: Clive Ayres   **Appearances:** Basil Bright
Players progressing Chris Simmonds (Millwall) 47, Derek Tapscott/Dai Ward(Arsenal) 53/54, Laurie
Sheffield/Gordon Fazer/Phil Green (Newport) 62/66/84,Chris Pike (Fulham) 85, Ian Love (Swansea)
86, Tony Bird/Dave O'Gorman (SwanseaCity) 97, Mark Ovendale (Bournemouth) 98 Eifion Williams
(Torquay United) 99

FACT FILE

Founded: 1923
Nickname: Dragons
Sponsors: Tango
Colours: Yellow/yellow/blue
Change: Blue&white
Midweek Matchdays: Tuesday
Programme: Yes

CLUB PERSONNEL

Chairman: Paula O'Halloran
Player Manager: Peter Nicholas

1999-00 Captain: Lee Barrow
Top Scorer:Paul Evans
Player of the Year: Richard Jones

CAERSWS

Secretary:	T M B Jones, 3 Hafren Terrace, Caersws, Powys SY17 5ES
	Tel: 01686 688103 (H/Fax)
Ground:	The Recreation Ground, Caersws, Powys. Tel: 01686 688753
Directions:	Entering Caersws, which lies between Newtown & Llanidloes on the A470, the
	ground entrance is on the left by bridge

Capacity: 3,250   Seats: 250   Cover: 300   Floodlights: Yes   **Club Shop:** No

Clubhouse: Not on ground, but in village centre. Normal licensing hours. Food available

HONOURS Welsh Amtr Cup 60-61, I'mediate Cup 88-89 (R-up 91-92); Mid-Wales Lg (9) 59-
61 62-63 77-78 82-83 85-86 88-90 96-97 (Lg Cup 79-80 82-83 87-88 89-90);
Cent. Wales Chall. Cup 77-78 82-83 87-88 89-90 (Yth Cup 69-70 72-73);
Montgomeryshire Chall. Cup (18) 52-53 59-60 62-63 69-72 74-75 76-78 83-89
90-91 94-95 94-95 96-97 97-98 98-99; Montgomeryshire Lg 77-78

PREVIOUS   **Leagues:** Mid-Wales (pre-1989)/Cymru Alliance 90-92

RECORD   **Attendance:** 2,795 v Swansea City, Welsh Cup 1990
Goalscorer: Gareth Davies

Players progressing: P Woosnam (Leyton O.), M Evans (Wolverhampton W.), KLloyd (Hereford U)
Graham Evans (Aston Villa)

FACT FILE
Founded: 1887
Nickname: Bluebirds
Sponsor: Dave Smith
Colours: Blue & white/white/blue
Change colours: Orange/black/black
Midweek Matchday: Tuesday
Reserve League: Mid-Wales
Programme: 44 pages, 50p
Editor: Graham Burrows

CLUB PERSONNEL
Chairman: Garth Williams
Vice Chairman: John Baker
President: Phil Woosnam
Press Officer: Ivor Williams
Manager: Mickey Evans
Asst Manager: Barry Harding
Physio: Wynne Jones

CARMARTHEN TOWN

Secretary:	Alan Latham, 3 Maes Dolau, Idole, Carmarthen SA32 8DQ
	Tel: 01267 232432 (H), Fax 01267 222851
Ground:	Richmond Park, Priory Street, Carmarthen Dyfed
	Tel: 01267 232101 Fax: 01267 222851
Directions:	Proceed into Carmarthen on A48, pick up 440 to Llandilo at the 1st rounabout
	and follow signs for 800 meters. The ground is on left in PrioryStreet

Capacity: 3,000   Seats: 120   Cover: 750   Floodlights: Yes

Clubhouse: Yes   **Club Shop:** Yes

HONOURS   Welsh Lge Div 2 59-60, Div 1 95-96, Cup Winners 95-96

RECORD   **Attendance:** 3,000

PREVIOUS   **Leagues:** Welsh League

FACT FILE
Founded: 1948
Nickname: The Town
Sponsors: Jewson Carmarthen
Colours: Old gold/black/black
Change colours: navy blue/yellow/navy blue
Midweek Matchday: Wednesday
Reserve League: C C Sports Welsh Lge
Programme: Yes
Editor: Alun Charles

CLUB PERSONNEL
Chairman: Jeff Thomas
President: Anthony Jenkins
Manager : Tommi Morgan
Physio: T Poynton/A Underwood

CONNAH'S QUAY NOMADS

Secretary/ Press Officer: Robert Hunter, 40 Brookdale Ave., Connah's Quay, Deeside, Clywd CH5 4LU
Tel: 01244 831212 (H) 01244 520299 (B)

Ground: Deeside Stadium Connah's Quay

Directions: On main coast road (A548) from Chester to Rhyl west end of Connah's Quay Deeside College.

Capacity: 3,500   Seats: 500   Cover: 500   Floodlights: Yes
Clubhouse: Yes, in college.   **Club Shop:** No

HONOURS: Welsh Amtr Cup 52-53 54-55, Nth Wales FA Amtr Cup 52-53 54-55, North Wales Coast Challenge Cup, Welsh Intermediate Cup 80-81, Welsh Alliance CooksonCup 87-88, Welsh Youth Cup 47-48

PREVIOUS: Leagues: Clywd; Welsh Alliance; Cymru Alliance 90-92

RECORD: Attendance: 1,500 v Rhyl, Welsh Cup SF 29/3/93

FACT FILE
Founded: 1946
Nickname: Advantage Mortgages
Sponsors: Hallows Associatres Solicitors
Colours: White/black/black&white
Change colours: Maroon/white/maroon
Midweek Matchday: Tuesday
Reserve League: Sealink Welsh Alliance
Programme: 26 pages, £1.00
Editor: G.Thelwell

CLUB PERSONNEL
Chairman: Mr R Morris
President: Mr R Jones
Manager s: Neville Powell
Asst Manager: Gary Wynne
Physio: Mr M Latter

CYMBRAN TOWN

Secretary: Mr R L Langley, 9 Duffryn Close, Roath Park, Cardiff CF23 6HT
Tel: 029 20764381 (H/Fax) 0771 892 3142 (M)

Ground: Cwmbran Stadium, Henllys Way, Cwmbran, Gwent
Tel: 01633 866192 Fax 01633 863324

Directions: M4 jct 26, follow signs for Cwmbran. At 1st r/about (approx 1.5miles) take 1st exit & proceed along Cwmbran Drive umtil passing Stadium onright. At r/about take 1st exit, then immediately at next r/about take 3rdexit. Ground entrance 150 yardson right. One and a half miles from Cwmbran(BR)

Capacity: 8,201   Seats: 2,201   Cover: 1,857   Floodlights: Yes Club Shop: Yes
Clubhouse: Pub hours, on ground. Catering facilities

HONOURS: Lg of W. 92-93; Welsh Lg Div 1 66-67, Welsh Lg Cup 85-86 90-91
PREVIOUS: Leagues: Monmouthshire Snr 51-59/ Welsh 60-92
RECORD: Attendance: 8,148 v Manchester Utd Aug 1994
Goalscorer : Graham Reynolds   Appearances: Mostyn Lewis

Players progressing: Simon King (Newport 1984), Mark Waite (Bristol Rovers1984), Nathan Wigg (Cardiff 1993), Chris Watkins (Swansea 1993)

FACT FILE
Founded: 1951
Nickname: The Town
Sponsors: Exide Batteries Ltd
Colours: Blue-white trim/blue/blue
Change colours: Red & black stripes/black/black
Midweek Matches: Wednesday
Reserves League: Welsh Lge Res Div East
Programme: 28 pages, 50p
Programme Editor/Press Off: Andrew Havelot

CLUB PERSONNEL
Chairman: J C Colley
Vice Chairman: K M McCarthy
President: John Colley
Manager: Tony Willcox
Coach: Mark Aizelwood
Physio: Terry Cutlan

FLEXSYS CEFN DRUIDS

Secretary: Mr R Davies, 7 Lancaster Terrace, Acrefair, Wrexham LL14 3HP
Tel: 01978 823027 (H) 01978 292931 (B)

Ground: Plas Kynaston lane, Plas Kynaston, Cefn Mawr, Wrexham

FACT FILE
Colours: Black & white/black/black
Change colours: Blue/red/red
Midweek Fixtures: Tuesday

CLUB PERSONNEL
Chairman: Mr M Pritchard (01978 812100-H)
Manager: Gareth Powell (01978 755744-H)

HAVERFORDWEST COUNTY

Secretary: Barry Vaughan   Tel: 01437 710805 (H) 01437 764331 (B)
Trem y Gorwel, Chapel Lane, Keston, Haverfordwest, Pembs SA62 6HL

Ground: Bridge Meadow Stadium, Haverfordwest, Pembs.
Tel: 01437 769048 Fax: 01437 762082

Directions: Off the Safeway roundabout near town centre

Capacity: 4,000   Covered Seats: 500   Floodlights: Yes   Club Shop: Yes

HONOURS: West Wales Sen Cup 81-82 88-89 91-92 92-93 97-98 98-99, R-up 37-38 49-50 56-57 60-61 80-81; Welsh Lge 56-57, R-up 67-70 70-71, Prem Div 80-81, National Div 89-90, Div 1 96-97, R-up 94-95 95-96; SA Brains Cup 88-89 R-up 84-85

FACT FILE
Nickname: Bluebirds
Sponsor: Preseli Taxis
Colours: All Blue
Change cols: Orange & black/black/orange & black
Midweek Matchday: Wednesday
Programme: 28 Pages £1.00
Editor: JohnThomas

CLUB PERSONNEL
Chairman: Roger Cottrell
Press Officer: Robert Nesbitt
Manager: Jason Jones

UWIC INTER CARDIFF

Secretary: Mr M F Salway, 10 Hafod Road, Ponthir, Newport NP6 1GT
Tel: 01633 430065 (H/Fax)

Ground: Cardiff Athletic Stadium, Leckwith Road, Cardiff Tel: 01222 225345

Directions: M4 Junc 33 towards Penarth, A4232 past Culverhouse Cross turn off onto Leckwith Road, ground on right
Capacity: 5,000   Covered: 2,500   Seats: 2,500   Floodlights: Yes

Club Shop: Yes

HONOURS   League of Wales R-up 92-93 93-94 96-97 98-99, Abacus Lg Div 1 86-87, Sth Wales Amtr Lg 84-85 85-86. As Sully: Sth Wales Amtr Lg Coronation Cup 69-70Corinthian Cup 78-79, Abacus Lg Div 1 83-84 85-86 89-90 (Div 2 80-81), SthWales Snr Cup 80-81 81-82 , Welsh Cup Winners 98-99

PREVIOUS   **Leagues:** Barry & District; South Wales Amateur; Abacus

RECORD   **Attendance:** 1,500 v Everton August 1996

FACT FILE

Founded: 1990
Nickname: Seagulls
Sponsors: Cabletel
Colours: Black & white/black/black
Change colours: Yellow/blue or yellow/yellow
Midweek Matchdays: Tuesday
Programme: 24 pages, £1
Editor: Maurice Salway

CLUB PERSONNEL

Chairman: Mr A Warren
Commercial Manager: Peter Hunt
Press Officer: Clive Harry
Manager: Dr Jonathon Magee
Physio: Roy Langley

LLANELLI

Secretary: Mr R Davies, 29 Pemberton Park, Llanelli, Carmartenshire SA14 8NN
Tel: 01554 756176 (H) 01554 772973 (B) 01554 772973 (Fax)

Ground: Stebonheath Park, Llanelli, Carmarthenshire SA15 1HF
Tel: 01554 756216

FACT FILE
Colours: All red
Change colours: All blue
Midweek Fixtures: Wednesday

CLUB PERSONNEL
Chairman: Mr R Jones
Tel: 01792 405301 (H)
Manager: John Lewis
Tel: 01495 755229 (H) 07970 300432 (M)

NEWTOWN

Team Secretary: Howard Ellis, 30Court Close, Abermull, Montgomery, Powys (01686 630372 (H) 01686 626121 (W))

Ground: Latham Park, Newtown, Powys Tel: 01686 622666/623120, Fax: 623813
Directions: A43 to Newtown, right at 1st lights into Back Lane & town centre -400yds left into Park St., 500yds right (at Library) into Park Lane - ground at end
Capacity: 5,000   Seats:1,100   Cover: 850   Floodlights: Yes
Clubhouse: Open every evening & matchday afternoons. Hot/cold snacks, pool,darts
Club Shop: Yes

HONOURS   League of Wales R-up 95-96 97-98; Welsh Cup 1878-79 94-95 (R-up 85-65 87-88 96-97), Welsh Amtr Cup 1954-55, Central Wales Lg 75-76 78-79 81-82 86-87 87-88 (R-up 51-52 52-53 55-56 56-57 74-75 82-83, Lg Cup 54-55 56-57 74-75 75-76 81-82 83-84), Arthur Barritt Cup 86-87, Central Wales Cup 74-75 80-81 92-93, Emrys Morgan Cup 80-81

PREVIOUS   **Leagues:** The Combination/ Central Wales/ Northern Premier

RECORD   **Attendance:** 5,002 v Swansea City, Welsh Cup 1954

BEST SEASON   **FA Trophy:** 3rd Qual. 89-90
FA Cup: 2nd Rd 1884-85. Also 1st Rd 1885-86

FACT FILE
Founded: 1875
Nickname: Robins
Sponsors: ControlTechniques & Elliott Presco
Colours: All red
Change : Blue & yellow/blue/blue & yellow
Midweek Matchdays: Tuesday
Reserves League:Spar Mid Wales
Programme: 36 pages, £1
Editor: Keith Harding/ Nigel Bevan & Barry Gardiner

CLUB PERSONNEL
President: Richard Edwards
Chairman: Keith Harding
Exec Co-Ordinator: Mrs Lyn Barnett
Match Sec/Press Officer: John Annereau
Manager: Brian Coyne
Asst Manager: Richard Pike
Physio: Elwyn Morgan
Res.Team Manager: Jack Watkins

OSWESTRY TOWN

Secretary: Mr C M Lashbrook, 22 Victoria Road, Oswestry, Shropshire SY11 4DS
Tel: 01691 653786 (H) 01952 291359 (B)

Ground: Park Hall Stadium, Burma Road, Park Hall, Oswestry, Shropshire
Tel: 01691 679499

FACT FILE
Colours: Blue & white/blue/blue
Change colours: Green & whire/green/green
Midweek Fixtures: TBA

CLUB PERSONNEL
Chairman: Mr W Jerman
Tel: 01691 661297 (H)
Manager: Ken Swinnerton
Tel: 01978 352301 (H) 01978 310923 (Fax)

PORT TALBOT ATHLETIC

Secretary: Mr J Dawkins, 28 Morrison Road, Port Talbot SA12 6TG
Tel: 01639 791172 (H)

Ground: Victoria Road, Port Talbot

FACT FILE
Colours: Blue & white/blue/blue
Change colours: Yellow & green/green/green
Midweek Fixtures: TBA

CLUB PERSONNEL
Chairman: Andrew Edwards
Tel: 01639 888515 (H)
Manager: David Rees
Tel: 01639 890171 (H)

RHAYADER TOWN

Secretary: Paul Rowe, 9 Glangwy, Rhayader, Powys LD6 5BW
Tel: 01597 810185

Ground: The Weirglodd, Bridge Street, Rhayader, Powys
Tel/Fax: 01597 810067

FACT FILE
Colours: Red & white/red/white
Change Colours: Yellow/yellow & red/yellow
Midweek Matchday: Wednesday

CLUB PERSONNEL
Chairman: M A Pugh (MBE)
Tel: 01597 810234 (H)
Manager: Gary Procter
Tel: 029207 94552 (H) 07974 373311 (M)

RHYL

Secretary: Dennis McNamee, 3 Maes Rhosyn, Rhuddlan. Tel: 01745 591287 (H)
Ground: Belle Vue, Grange Road, Rhyl, Clwyd Tel: 01745 338327
Directions: Leave A55 at the St Asaph/Rhyl turn off and take A525 to Rhuddlan.At roundabout take 2nd turn for Rhyl, then left at next roundabout and over next two roundabouts .After 1mile urn right into Pendyffryn Rd, then left at junction and ground is 300yds on left.

| Capacity: 3,800 | Cover: 1,200 | Seats:150 | Floodlights: Yes |

Club Shop: Yes   Clubhouse: No

HONOURS Welsh Cup 51-52 52-53 (R-up 29-30 36-37 92-93), Welsh Amateur Cup 72-73, Northern Premier Lg Presidents Cup 84-85, North West Counties Lg R-up 82-83,North Wales Coast Challenge Cup, Cheshire County Lg 47-48 50-51 71-72 (R-up 48-49 49-50 51-52 55-56, Div 2 R-up 81-82, Lg Cup 48-49 51-52 70-71, Div 2 Shield 81-82), Cyrmu Alliance 93-94 (R-up 92-93, Lg Cup 92-93)

PREVIOUS LEAGUES: North Wales Coast League, Cheshire County; North West Counties; Northern Premier; Cymru Alliance 92-94
BEST SEASON FA Cup : 4th Rd Proper 56-57 (lost 0-3 at Bristol City)
RECORD Attendance: 10,000 v Cardiff City, Welsh Cup 1953
Goalscorer: Don Spendlove   Appearances: Not known
Players progressing: Ian Edwards, Grenville Millington, Brian Lloyd, Andy Holden, Barry Horne, Andy Jones

FACT FILE
Founded: 1870 (as Rhyl Skull & Crossbones)
Nickname: Lilywhites
Sponsors: Webber Office Solutions of Rhyl
Colours: All White
Change: Blue/white/white
Midweek matches: Tuesday
Programme: 40 pages £1
Editor: Ian Johnson (01745 353976)
1999-00 Top Scorer: Danny Barton (22)
Players of the Year: Mark Antrobus
(Players`),Danny Barton (Supporters) and
James Brewerton (Junior P.O.Y)

CLUB PERSONNEL
Managing Director; P.Parry
Chairman: David Simmons
Vice Chairmen: N.C.Jones & J.Evans
President: R B G Webster
Company Secretary:/ Press Officer D.Williams

TOTAL NETWORK SOLUTIONS

Secretary: Gwynfor Hughes, Birch Lea, Porthywaen, Oswestry, Shrops SY10 8LY
Tel: 01691 828645 (H) Fax: 01691 828862

Ground: Recreation Park, Treflan, Llansantffraid Tel: 01691 828112 & Fax 01691 828862
Directions: A483 between Oswestry and Welshpool, right for Llansantffraid (A495) at Llyclys When from North Follow signs to village. Turn opposite Mill silos towards Community Centre. Ground is behind housing estate.

Capacity: 1,500   Seats: 500   Cover:650   Floodlights: Yes Shop: no
Clubhouse: Open every evening except Sunday, plus weekend afternoons.
HONOURS League of Wales Champions 99-00,Welsh Cup 95-96; Welsh Intermediate Cup 92-93; League of Wales Cup 94-95;Cymru Alliance Lge 92-93, R-up 91-92; Central Wales Sen Cup 98-99,R-up 92-93 97-98;Central Wales Lg R-up 90-91 94-95 95-96, Lge Cup 95-96; Montgomeryshire Amtr Lg (7), Village Cup (17); European Champions League 00-01, European Cup Winners Cup Preliminary Rd 96-97

PREVIOUS League: Mid-Wales; Cymru Alliance (pre-1993)

RECORD Attendance: 2,100 v KS Ruch Chorzow Euro Cup Winners 96(at Wrexham F.C.)
Goalscorer: Adrian Jones   Appearances: Andy Mulliner

FACT FILE
Founded: 1959
Nickname: The Saints
Sponsors: Total Network Solutions
Colours: Green/white/green
Change: All Blue
Midweek Matchdays: Tuesday
Reserves League: Montgomeryshire Lge
Programme: 40 pages, £1
Editor:Tony Williams
CLUB PERSONNEL
Chairman: Edgar Jones
President: Mike Hughes
Vice-Chairman: Tony Williams
Manager: Dr Andy Cale
Asst Manager: Ken McKenna
Physio: Gordon Evans
1999-00 Captain & P.o.Y.: Tim Edwards
Top Scorer: John Toner

SCOTTISH FOOTBALL

Thanks again to Stewart Davidson, editor and publisher of the Scottish Non-League Review, from whom most of these statistics were received

Six regions make up the structure of Scottish Junior Football:

AYRSHIRE   CENTRAL
EAST   FIFE
NORTH   TAYSIDE

OVD SCOTTISH JUNIOR CUP 1999-2000

Fifth Round

Benburb 3 Larkhall Thistle 0
Cumnock 3 Kilbirnie Lakeside 1
Johnstone Borough 2 Glenafton Athletic 1
Lanark United 2 Thornton Hibs 0
Maybole 0 Arbroath SC 3
Neilston 2 Whitburn 3
Newtongrange 2 Sunnybank 0
Shotts Bon Accord 2 Carnoustie P. 2
(Shotts win 2-1 after pens)

Quarter-finals

Benburb 2 Newtongrange Star 1
Johnstone Borough 2 Cumnock 1
Lanark United 0 Shotts Bon Accors 2
Whitburn 2 Arbroath Sports Club 1.

Semi-finals

(at St Mirren FC.)

Johnstone Borough   2 - 2   Shotts Bon Accord
Fraser, Brolly   McGuinness, McHarg

Johnstone Borough won 3-0 on penalties)

(at Airdrie FC.)

Whitburn   1 v 1   Benburb
Campbell   Magee

Whitburn won 3-2 on penalties

FINAL

Sunday, 28th May 2000.
At Partick Thistle FC, Firhill Park, Glasgow

WHITBURN   2 - 2   JOHNSTONE BOROUGH
Milne pen,Campbell   Lindsay, McLay

Score at half-time: 1-1
After 90 minutes and extra-time: 2-2
Whitburn won 4-3 on penalies.

This is the first time the Scottish Junior Cup Semi-finals and the Final itself have all been decided on penalties

OVD SCOTTISH JUNIOR CUP FINAL 1999-2000

The defining moment of this thriller came when the respective penalty takers came up for the fifth round. James McGuire of Johnstone Borough shot wide and then Whitburn's captain, Steven Prior, ended a lengthy run-up by blasting the ball of Donohoe's desperate hands and into the net to give his club its first Junior Cup success and deny a third to the Renfrewshire team - a cruel way to settle matters, but is there a better way? It was also sad for the superb losing goalkeeper.

Recent Junior Finals have been patchy, but this one was a nail-biter from the start and a relief after the turgid senior event at Hampden Park the previous afternoon. Everyone gave 100 per cent even during extra time when tired legs saw several episodes of cramp. Six players were booked during the match, but this proved more the total commitment involved and some rash tackling devoid of malice.

Borough were ahead after only three minutes when Frater's swift approach to goal was foiled by Bruce Clouston's clumsy intervention. This brought the first yellow card - should it have been red? - but justice was done when the resulting free kick from just outside the penalty area was touched to Hendren, whose perfect lob beat the West Lothian defence to open the scoring.

A wobbly Whitburn gradually found some feet and Alan Donahue saved well from a Hume header and drive from Clouston before a mazy run by Callum Milne ended with the full back falling over an unlucky Martin tackle. After treatment Milne took the penalty himself and scored comfortably on 38 minutes. Was the otherwise good referee, I Brines, too generous?

Half-time's 1-1 scoreline changed dramatically immediately after the break. Gilmour's header was brilliantly saved by Donohoe, but Hannah's corner from the left was poorly marked and Colin L Cunningham's free header put Whitburn ahead.

But not for long! Borough went straight upfield, the ball bounced nicely for McLay and his drive was deflected off Clouston for the equaliser and there was no more scoring for the rest of the match and extra-time, although the luckless Lee Martin hit Whitburn's woodwork and Gilmour had one of his specials turned onto the crossbar by the splendid Donohue.

Extra-time was hectic and brave, but also notable for numerous injury and cramp stoppages. Colin L Campbell did have a chance on 98 minutes to wrap it up for Whitburn, but after beating Donohue's attempted intervention his shot was cleared.

And so we had the penalties and more drama. Skipper Colin Lindsay (Johnstone Borough) and Callum Milne scored (1-1), then cramp victim Martin and substitute Taylor had shots saved (no change). Substitute Connie and Gilmour netted well (2-2), followed by Millar and Clouston (3-3) before the climax.

There was an attendance of 7,000 and all had their money's worth on a mostly fine afternoon interspersed by a heavy shower or two. We had skills from Ryan, skipper Lindsay, Brolly and McLay for Johnstone Borough with Whitburn's Hannah, Bonnar and Gilmour also shining. Brave defending was epitomised by Borough's Heaton and Hendren and Whitburn captain Steven Prior.

Junior football in Scotland, played ironically by numerous veterans, can be extremely entertaining, and this was a fine example of that virtue.

OVD Scottish Junior Cup Action
Top left: Second Round:
Troon v Crossgates Primrose.

Top right: Second Round Replay:
Auchinleck Talbot v Vale of Clyde

Centre left: Third Round:
Troon v Lanark United

Centre right: Fifth Round:
Maybole v Arbroath Sporting Club

Bottom left: Second Round:
Troon v Crossgates Primrose

Photos: John B Vass

AYRSHIRE REGION

Division One	P	W	D	L	F	A	Ots
Kilwinning Rangers	20	15	1	4	45	17	46
Auchinleck Talbot	20	14	3	3	47	22	45
Glenafton Athletic	20	13	2	5	43	25	41
Irvine Meadow	20	12	3	5	45	22	39
Cumnock	20	10	5	5	43	27	35
Kilbirnie Ladeside	20	9	5	6	29	26	32
Beith	20	4	6	10	22	36	18
Irvine Victoria	20	4	6	10	25	49	18
Largs Thistle	20	3	4	13	25	40	13
Dalry Thistle	20	2	4	14	19	57	10
Troon	20	3	3	14	21	41	9

Division Two	P	W	D	L	F	A	Pts
Lugar Boswell This	22	15	5	2	57	20	50
Craigmark Burnton'n	22	14	4	4	54	20	48
Hurlford United	22	13	6	3	47	20	45

Lugar Boswell Thistle and Craigmark Burntonians promoted.
Hurlford United beat Largs Thistle on aggregate (4-2) in play-off.

Other league positions: Kello Rovers (44 points), Ardrossan Winton Rovers (41), Ardeer Thistle (36), Muirkirk (33), Maybole (31), Saltcoats Vistoria (22), Darvel (12), Annbank United (70, Whitletts Victoria (5).

Ayrshire League Play-off:
Largs Thistle 0 Hurlford United 2
Hurlford United 2 Largs Thistle 2

SCARLETT LEAGUE CUP
Quarter-finals:
Dalry Thistle 2 Troon 3
Glenafton Athletic 4 Craigmark Burntonians 1
Hurlford United 5 Auchinleck Talbot 3 (after extra-time - 3-3 at 90 minutes)
Kilwinning Rangers 3 Kilbirnie Ladeside 1

Semi-finals:
Glenafton Athletic 4 Hurlford United 0
Kilwinning Rangers 3 Troon 1

FINAL (Monday, 25th October 1999. At Somerset Park, Aur).
GLENAFTON ATHLETIC 4-1 KILWINNING RANGERS

IRVINE TIMES AYRSHIRE DISTRICT CUP
Quarter-finals:
Hurlford United 0 Kilbirnie Ladeside 1
Maybole 3 Ardrossan Winton Rovers 0
Saltcoats Victoria 2 Cumnock 7
Troon 0 Dalry Thistle 2

Semi-finals:
Cumnock 0 Dalry Thistle 0 (Cumnock won 5-4 on penalties)
Kilbirnie Ladeside 3 Maybole 0

FINAL (Sunday, 2nd April 2000. At Irvine Meadow FC)
KILBIRNIE LADESIDE 3-1 CUMNOCK

'ARDROSSAN & SALTCOATS' HERALD AYRSHIRE CUP
Quarter-finals:
Kello Rovers 1 Auchinleck Talbot 4
Kilbirnie Ladeside 7 Maybole 4
Saltcoats Victoria 1 Cumnock 2
Troon 1 Kilwinning Rangers 4

Semi-finals:
Cumnock 1 Kilwinning Rangers 2
Kilbirnie Ladeside 1 Auchinleck Talbot 2

FINAL (Thursday, 15th June 2000. At Auchinleck Talbot FC)
AUCHINLECK TALBOT 2-3 KILWINNING RANGERS

EAST AYRSHIRE CUP
Semi-finals:
Hurlford United 0 Auchinleck Talbot 3
Kello Rovers 0 Lugar Boswell Thistle 0 (Lugar won 4-1 on pens)

FINAL (Wednesday, 24th May 2000. At Cumnock FC)
AUCHINLECK TALBOT 2-0 LUGAR BOSWELL THISTLE

NORTH AYRSHIRE CUP
Semi-finals:
Ardrossan Winton Rovers 2 Kilwinning Rangers 4
Irvine Meadow 0 Largs Thistle 1

FINAL (Sunday, 14th May 2000. At Ardrossan Winton Rovers FC)
KILWINNING RANGERS 4-0 LARGS THISTLE

SOUTH AYRSHIRE CUP
Semi-finals:
Maybole 4 Whitletts Victoria 1
Troon 3 Annbank United 1

FINAL (Tuesday, 23rd May 2000. At Maybole FC)
MAYBOLE 1-2 TROON

AYRSHIRE SUPER CUP
Semi-finals:
Auchinleck Talbot 2 Troon 2 (Auchinleck won 5-4 on pens)
Lugar Boswell Thistle 1 Kilwinning Rangers 4

FINAL (Wednesday, 7th June 2000. At Kilwinning Rangers FC
KILWINNING RANGERS 2-3 AUCHINLECH TALBOT

WEST OF SCOTLAND CUP (for Ayrshire & Central Region clubs)
Quarter-finals:
Arthurlie 1 Auchinleck Talbot 0
Glenafton Athletic 2 Shotts Bon Accord 1
Irvine Victoria 2 Pollok 6
Neilston 0 Benburb 1

Semi-finals:
Glenafton Athletic 2 Benburb 2 (at Pollok FC)
Arthurlie 1 Pollok 1 (at Cambuslang Rangers FC - Pollok won 5-4 on pens)

FINAL
(Wed., 14th June 2000. At Cambuslang Rangers FC - Att: 600)
POLLOK 2-1 GLENAFTON ATHLETIC

Top:
Cumnock Juniors
Ayrshire Region
Division One

Centre:
Troon FC
Winners of South
Ayrshire Cup but
relegated to Division
Two after three
seasons in Division
One

Bottom:
Craigmark
Burntonians
celebrate promotion
to Ayrshire Region
Division One.

Photos: John B Vass

CENTRAL REGION

Premier Division	P	W	D	L	F	A	Pts
Benburb	22	13	6	3	36	17	46
Pollok	22	12	6	4	36	21	42
Shotts Bon Accord	22	10	7	5	36	27	37
Arthurlie	22	10	4	8	39	33	34
Maryhill	22	9	7	6	40	36	34
Petershill	22	9	4	9	35	30	31
Johnstone Borough	22	9	3	10	37	41	30
Blantyre Victoria	22	7	7	8	30	24	28
Neilston	22	6	10	6	34	31	28
Lanark United	22	8	4	10	36	39	28
Shettleston	22	6	3	13	28	41	21
Lesmehagow	22	1	3	18	10	57	6

Division One	P	W	D	L	F	A	Pts
Larkhall Thistle	26	17	4	5	41	21	55
Ruherglen Glencairn	26	16	6	4	66	33	54
Renfrew	26	15	4	7	43	32	49

The above were promoted. Other positions: Kirkintilloch Rob Roy (48 points), Vale of Leven (47), Cambuslang Rangers (42), Kilsyth Rangers (41), Greenock (34), Vale of Clyde (30), Dunipace (29), Carluke Rovers (22), plus relegated Baillieston (21), St Anthony (21), East Kilbride Thistle (20).

Divison Two	P	W	D	L	F	A	Pts
Port Glasgow	24	20	2	2	78	30	62
Glasgow Perthshire	24	16	2	6	79	27	50
Cumbernauld United	24	15	5	4	57	28	50

The above were promoted. Other positions: Thorniewood United (45 points), St Roch's (38), Bellshill Athletic (37), Ashfield (37), Royal Albert (30), Stonehouse Violet (24), Yoker Athletic (21), Forth Wanderers (2), Coltness United (16), Wishaw (12).

EVENING TIMES CUP WINNERS CUP
Preliminary Round:
Port Glasgow 5 Larkhall Thistle 2

Semi-finals:
Benburb 0 Shettleston 0 (Shettleston won 5-3 on penalties)
Port Glasgow 4 Pollok 1

FINAL (Saturday, 10th June 2000 at Cambuslang Rangers FC)
PORT GLASGOW 3-1 SHETTLESTON

BEATONS LEAGUE CUP Play-offs
Banburb 3 Larkhall Thistle 1
Kilsyth rangers 1 Shotts Bon Accord 2

Quarter-finals:
Pollok 3 Benburb 0
Port Glasgow 1 Rutherglen Glencairn 1 (Rutherglen Glencairn won 5-3 on penalties)
Shotts Bon Accord 4 Shettleston 1
Thorniewood 1 Petershill 1 (Petershill won 4-3 on penalties)

Semi-finals:
Petershill 0 Pollok 1
Shotts Bon Accord 4 Rutherglen Glencairn 3

FINAL (Monday, 25th October 1999. At Firhill Park, Glasgow)
POLLOK 4-1 SHOTTS BON ACCORD

CENTRAL LEAGUE CUP
Quarter-finals:
Rutherglen Glencairn 0 Neilston 0 (Rutherglen won 3-2 on pens)
Pollok 0 Shettleston 1
Port Glasgow 1 Lanark United 0
Vale of Clye 1 Benburb 1 (Benburb won 3-2 on pens)

Semi-finals:
Benburb 2 Rutherglen Glencairn 1
Port Glasgow 1 Shettleston 2

FINAL (Friday, 19th May 2000 at Pollok FC)
BENBURB 2-1 SHETTLESTON

FIFE REGION

	P	W	D	L	F	A	Pts
Hill of Beath Hawt	28	21	6	1	83	20	69
Kelty Hearts	28	21	3	4	96	28	66
Thornton Hibs	28	19	7	2	87	20	64
Lochore Welfare	28	17	5	6	81	43	53*
Newburgh	28	16	5	7	65	44	53
Oakley United	28	16	3	9	65	45	51
Glenrothes	28	14	5	9	62	42	47
St Andrews United	28	11	4	13	65	57	37
Crossgates Primrose	28	8	6	14	45	47	30
Rosyth Recreation	28	7	6	15	46	55	30@
Dundonald Bluebell	28	8	5	15	38	59	29
Lochgelly Albert	28	7	5	16	45	91	26
Tulliallan Thistle	28	6	7	15	62	86	25
Kirkcaldy YM	28	4	1	23	31	110	13
Steelend Victoria	28	0	2	26	21	145	2

* Denotes three points and five goals deducted
@ Denotes three points added and five goals against deducted

PSM FIFE CUP
Quarter-finals:
Glenrothes 1 Newburgh 0
Kelty Hearts 1 Crossgates Primrose 0
Oakley United 0 Hill of Beath Hawthorn 2
Thornton Hibs 4 Rosyth Recreation 3

Semi-finals:
Glenrothes 2 Hill of Beath Hawthorn 0
Kelty Hearts 2 Thornton Hibs 1

FINAL (Sun., 26th September 1999 at Moorside Park, Dundonald)
GLENROTHES 4-2 KELTY HEARTS

WHITBREAD CUP
Semi-finals:
Hill of Beath Hawthorn 4 Oakley United 4 (H O B H won 7-6 on pens)
Kelty Hearts 0 Glenrothes 1

FINAL (Saturday, 13th May 2000 at Moorside Park, Dundonald)
Hill of Beath Hawthorn 4 - 0 Glenrothes

BARDON AGGREGATES CUP
Semi-finals:
Kelty Hearts 3 St Andrews United 0
Thornton Hibs 3 Lochore Welfare 2

FINAL (Friday, 26th May 2000 at Moorside Park, Dundonald)
(Previously known as the Cowdenbeath Cup)
KELTY HEARTS 2 - 0 THORNTON HIBS

EAST REGION

Division One	P	W	D	L	F	A	Pts
Linlithgow Rose	22	16	2	4	59	26	50
Newtongrange Star	22	16	1	5	48	22	49
Bonnyrigg Rose	22	12	5	5	44	30	41
Bo'ness United	22	12	3	7	43	28	39
Whitburn	22	11	5	6	40	31	38
Haddington Athletic	22	7	7	8	35	38	28
Camelon	22	6	8	8	32	36	26
Arniston Rangers	22	5	9	8	21	31	24
Fauldhouse United	22	5	9	8	28	39	24
Bathgate Thistle	22	5	8	9	39	43	23
Bonnybridge	22	3	6	13	25	35	15
Stoneyburn	22	1	3	18	17	62	6

Division Two	P	W	D	L	F	A	Pts
Harthill Royal	24	16	4	4	49	91	52
Edinburgh United	24	17	1	6	53	24	52

The above two clubs were promoted. Other positions: Armadale Thistle (50 points), Dunbar United (49), Dalkeith Thistle (41), Musselburgh Athletic (36), Sauchie (34), Trenant (32), Pumpherston (28), Broxburn Athletic (270, Blackburn United (23), West Calder United (13), Livingston United (7).

CARLSBERG LEAGUE CUP
Quarter-finals:
Arniston Rangers 3 Stoneburn 2
Bo'ness United 2 Linlithgow Rose 2 (Linlithgow won 4-2 on pens)
Harthill Royal 1 Armadale Thistle 1 (Harthill won 8-7 on pens)
Whitburn 0 Bonnyrigg Rose 0 (Bonnyrigg Rose won 3-1 on pens)

Semi-finals:
Arniston Rangers 0 Harthill Royal 2 (at Newtongrange Star FC)
Linlithgow Rose 0 Bonnyrigg Rose 0 (at Bathgate Thistle FC -
Linlithgow Rose won 2-0 on pens)

FINAL (Wed., 22nd September 1999 at Creamery Park, Bathgate)
HARTHILL ROYAL 0-0 LINLITHGOW ROSE (Harthill Royal won 4-3 on pens)

CALDERS EAST OF SCOTLAND CUP
Quarter-finals:
Dunbar United 0 Linlithgow Rose 2
Fauldhouse United 0 Harthill Royal 0
Newtongrange Star 1 Bonnyrigg Rose 0
Trenant 1 Bo'ness United 5
Replay:
Harthill Royal 1 Fauldhouse United 0

Semi-finals:
Linlithgow Rose 2 Harthill Royal 1
Bo'ness United 3 Newtongrange Star 0

FINAL (Saturday, 13th May 2000 at Camelon FC. Att.: 1,000)
LINLITHGOW ROSE 2-1 BO'NESS UNITED

BROWN CUP
Quarter-finals:
Dunbar United 1 Blackburn United 0
Fauldhouse United 5 Whitburn 1
Haddington 2 Edinburgh United 2 (Haddington won 3-2 on pens)
Tranent 2 Harthill Royal 1

Semi-finals:
Dunbar United 4 Tranent 1
Haddington Athletic 1 Fauldhouse United 1
(Haddington Athletic won 6-5 on pens)

FINAL (Wednesday, 14th June 2000 at Bonnyrigg Rose FC)
DUNBAR UNITED 2-1 HADDINGTON ATHLETIC

ST MICHAELS CUP
Quarter-finals:
Armadale Thistle 1 Linlithgow Rose 1 (Armadale won 3-2 on pens)
Bonnyrigg Rose 1 Bo'ness United 2
Harthill Royal 3 Whitburn 1
Newtongrange Star 1 Arniston Rangers 1
(Arniston won 5-4 on pens)

Semi-finals
Armadale Thistle 5 Arniston Rangers 1
Bo'ness United 1 Harthill Royal 0

FINAL (Saturday, 10th June 2000 at Pumpherston FC)
ARMADALE THISTLE 2-1 BO'NESS UNITED

MILLENNIUN CUP
Quarter-finals
Armadale Thistle 1 Harthill Royal 2
Bathgate Thistle 0 Blackburn United 3
Stoneyburn 2 Fauldhouse United 2 (Fauldhouse won 5-4 on pens)
Whitburn 1 Pumpherston 0

Semi-finals:
Blackburn United 3 Harthill Royal 3 (Blackburn won 3-1 on pens)
Whitburn 1 Fauldhouse United 2

FINAL (Sunday, 7th May 2000 at Livingston FC)
FAULDHOUSE UNITED. 2 - 0 BLACKBURN UNITED

HEINEKEN FIFE & LOTHIANS CUP
Quarter-finals:
Fauldhouse United 0 Camelon 2
Linlithgow Rose 2 Pumpherston 0
Lochore Welfare 3 WEitburn 3 (Lochore Welfare
won 4-3 on penalties)
Stoneyburn 0 Harthill Royal 0 (Stoneyburn
won 4-0 on pens)

Semi-finals:
Linlithgow Rose 4 Camelon 1
Stoneyburn 1 Lochore Welfare 0

FINAL (Saturday, 3rd June 2000 at Camelon FC)
LINLITHGOW ROSE 4-1 STONEYBURN

NORTH REGION

East Section

Premier Div

	P	W	D	L	F	A	Pts
Longside	22	16	5	1	53	19	53
Sunnybank	22	15	4	3	55	27	49
FC Stoneywood	22	14	5	3	46	25	47
Formartine United	22	10	8	4	46	29	38
East End	22	9	2	11	39	47	29
Inveruries Loco Wks	22	8	4	10	44	46	28
Stonehaven	22	8	3	11	30	36	27
Banks o'Dee	22	6	7	9	37	38	25
Turriff United	22	5	7	10	26	43	22
Hermes	22	5	5	12	29	47	20
Lewis United	22	4	5	13	26	41	17
Culter	22	4	1	17	29	62	13

Division One

	P	W	D	L	F	A	Pts
Cruden Bay	20	14	1	5	65	32	43
Buchanhaven Hearts	20	13	3	4	33	17	42

The above two clubs were promoted. Other positions: Hall Russell United (38 points), Glentanar (34), Lads Club (30), Parkvale (25), Maud (22), Ellon United (22), Fraserburgh United (22), Banchory St Ternan (17), Dyce (14).

GRILL LEAGUE CUP
Semi-finals:
Cruden Bay 1 Sunnybank 3
Formartine United 3 Parkvale 1

FINAL (Sunday, 3rd October 1999 at Inverurie Loco works FC)
SUNNYBANK 4-3 FORMARTINE UNITED

GREAT NORTHERN TROPHIES REGIONAL CUP
Quarter-finals
Bishopmill United 2 Culter 6
Buchanhaven Hearts 1 Stonehaven 0
Formartine United 3 KLongside 1
Hall Russell United 1 Hermes 1
Replay:
Hermes 1 Hall Russell United 3

Semi-finals:
Buchanhaven Hearts 1 Culter 3
Formartine United 4 Hall Russell United 2

FINAL (Saturday, 29th April 2000 at Sunnybank FC)
CULTER 2-1 FORMARTINE UNITED

ACORN HEATING CUP
Quarter-finals:
Hall Russell United 2 Sunnybank 5
Longside 4 Buchanhaven Hearts 1
Parkvale 0 Cruden Bay 8
Stonehaven 1 Hermes 2

Semi-finals:
Cruden Bay 7 Hermes 3
Sunnybank 1 Longside 0

FINAL (Thursday, 8th June 2000 at Ellon United FC)
CRUDEN BAY 2-0 SUNNYBANK

CONSTRUCTION TROPHY
Quarter-finals:
Cruden Bay 2 FC Stoneywood 2 (FC Stoneywood
Won 5-4 on pens)
East End 2 Banks o'Dee 0
Hermes 2 Formartine United 3
Inveruries Loco works 2 Sunnybank 3

Semi-finals:
East End 2 FC Stoneywood 1
Formartine United 0 Sunnybank 1

FINAL (Tuesday, 2nd May 2000 at Pittodrie Stadium, Aberdeen)
SUNNYBANK 2-1 EAST END

ROLLSTUD ARCHIBALD CUP
Quarter-finals:
Banks o'Dee 1 Inverurie Loco Works 6
Cruden Bay 3 FC Stoneywood 6 (after extra-time)
Formartine United 1 Stonehaven 0
Sunnybank 5 Turriff United 2 (after extra-time)

Semi-finals:
FC Stoneywood 4 Formartine United 2
Sunnybank 0 Inverurie Loco works 1

FINAL (Monday, 12th June at Formartine United FC)
INVERURIE LOCO WORKS 3-1 FC STONEYWOOD

MORRISON TROPHY
Semi-finals:
Buchanhaven Hearts 1 Hall Russell United 0
Cruden Bay 3 Parkvale 1

FINAL (Thursday, 25th May 2000 at Longside FC)
CRUDEN BAY 4-1 BUCHANHAVEN HEARTS

JIMMY GIBB TROPHY
(Tuesday, 13th June 2000 at Sunnybank FC)
LONGSIDE 2-1 CRUDEN BAY

North Section

	P	W	D	L	F	A	Pts
Deveronside	26	21	4	1	82	25	67
Forres Thistle	26	20	1	5	73	32	61
Strathspey Thistle	26	14	8	4	70	36	50
New Elgin	26	15	4	7	65	39	49
Buckie Rovers	26	16	1	9	69	48	49
Islavale	26	15	3	8	72	33	48
Bishopmill United	26	12	4	10	48	50	40
Nairn St Ninian	26	8	5	13	40	52	29
Kinloss	26	8	5	13	45	59	29
Lossiemouth United	26	7	4	15	48	64	25
Burghead Thistle	26	8	0	18	41	87	24
Portgordon United	26	6	3	17	31	67	18
Fochabers	26	3	6	17	33	64	15
RAF Lossiemouth	26	3	4	19	32	93	13

ROBERSTON CUP
Semi-finals:
Deveronside 2 Buckie Rovers 1
New Elgin 1 Islavale 2

FINAL (Sunday, 26th September 1999 at Islavale FC)
ISLAVALE 2-1 DEVERONSIDE

STEWART MEMORIAL CUP
Semi-finals:
Forres Thistle 3 Nairn St Ninian 1
Lossiemouth United 3 Strathspey Thistle 8

FINAL
(Saturday, 17th December 1999 at Grant Park, Lossiemouth FC)
FORRES THISTLE 4-0 STRATHSPEY THISTLE

NICHOLSON CUP
Semi-finals:
Burghead Thistle 4 Kinloss 3
Fochabers 3 RAF Lossiemouth 5

FINAL
BURGHEAD THISTLE 7-2 RAF LOSSIEMOUTH

GORDON WILLIAMSON CUP
Quarter-finals:
Deveronside 3 Fochabers 1
Forres Thistle 2 New Elgin 2 (Forres won 7-6 on pens)
Islavale 4 Lossiemouth United 1
Nairn St Ninian 1 Bishopmill United 0

Semi-finals:
Islavale 2 Deveronside 0
Nairn St Ninian 1 Forres Thistle 1 (Nairn won 4-2 on pens)

FINAL (Sunday, 30th April 2000 at Forres Mechanics FC)
NAIRN ST. NINIAN 1 - 0 ISLAVALE

MORAYSHIRE ROSEBOWL
Quarter-finals:
Bishopmill United 2 Lossiemouth United 3
Buckie Rovers 3 New Elgin 3 (Buckie Rovers won
   3-1 on pens - after extra-time)
Forres Thistle 1 Kinloss 0
Islavale 9 Portgordon United 1

Semi-finals:
Lossiemouth United 0 Buckie Rovers 3
Forres Thistle beat Islavale (no score recorded)

FINAL (Saturday, 10th June 2000 at Burghead Thistle FC)
FORRES THISTLE 4-1 BUCKIE ROVERS

ROBBIE NICOL TROPHY
Quarter-finals:
Forres Thistle 4 Bishopmill United 0
Islavale 1 Deveronside 2
Lossiemouth United 1 Buckie Rovers 5
RAF Lossiemouth 1 Strathspey Thistle 3

Semi-finals:
Deveronside 5 Buckie Rovers 0
Strathspey Thistle 2 Forres Thistle 1

FINAL (Wednesday 14th June 2000 at New elgin FC)

CLIVE WILLIAMS TROPHY
Quarter-finals:
Buckie Rovers 1 Islavale 4 (after extra-time)
Bucghead Thistle 1 Fochabers 2
Deveronside 3 Lossiemouth United 2
Strathspey Thistle walk over Portgordon United (scratched)

Semi-finals:
Fochabers 0 Deveronside 2
Islavale 7 Strathspey Thistle 3

FINAL (Saturday, 10th June 2000 at Strathspey Thistle FC)
ISLAVALE 3-1 DEVERONSIDE

MATTHEW CUP
Semi-finals:
Forres Thistle 2 New Elgin 3
Islavale 2 Fochabers United 3 (after extra-time)

FINAL (Sunday, 4th June 2000 at Burghead Thistle FC)
NEW ELGIN 3-1 FOCHABERS

WICK ALLAN SHIELD (North Region Championship Play-off)
(Saturday, 3rd June 2000 at Deveronside FC)
DEVERONSIDE 5-2 LONGSIDE

Awards:
White Horse Cup (least goals conceded):   Deveronside
Chisholm Cup (top league goalscorers):   Deveronside
Connon Cup (league runners-up):   Forres Thistle
Top league goalscorer: Brian Minty (Forres Thistle) 29 goals

Twin Town match (Sunday, 19th March 2000):
Strathspey Thistle 11 Notre Dames de Monts (France) 1

Representative Match (Sunday, 26th March 2000 at Inverurie)
North Region 0 Central Region 1

TAYSIDE REGION

Premier Division	P	W	D	L	F	A	Pts
Tayport	22	14	4	0	57	10	58
North End	22	13	3	6	48	35	42
Kirrie Thistle	22	13	1	8	53	44	40
Arbroath SC	22	12	2	8	51	36	38
Downfield	22	9	7	6	36	32	34
Violet	22	9	5	8	40	35	32
Elmwood	22	7	8	7	33	40	29
Carnoustie Panmure	22	7	6	9	50	42	27
Lochee United	22	6	6	10	36	41	24
Forfar West end	22	4	4	14	31	56	16
Bankfoot Athletic	22	5	1	16	31	60	16
MonTrose RoseleA	22	5	1	16	23	58	16

Division One	P	W	D	L	F	A	Pts
Jeanfield Swifts	22	16	4	2	57	22	52
Forfar Albion	22	14	5	3	56	25	47

The above two clubs are promoted. Other positions: East Craigie (45 points), Broughty Athletic (42), Kinnoul (40), Blaigowrie (34), Lochee Harp (33), Coupar Angus (25), Scone Thistle (22), Brechin Victoria (17), Arbroath Victoria (10), Luncarty (4).

TAYCARS TROPHY
Quarter-finals:
Bankfoot Athletic 3 Newburgh 2
Kelty Hearts 1 Glenrothes 0
Lochgelly Albert 0 Thornton Hibs 3
Lochore Welfare 1 Tayport 3

Semi-finals:
Kelty Hearts 1 Tayport 1 (Tayport won 3-2 on penaltuies)
Thornton Hibs 0 Bankfoot Athletic 3

FINAL (Sat., 10th June 2000 at Dundee Violet FC. Att: 500)
TAYPORT 1-1 BANKFOOR ATHLETIC
(AET Tayport won 5-4 on pens)

CONCEPT GROUP TROPHY
Quarter-finals:
Brechin Victoria 0 Lochee United 6
Carnoustie Panmure 2 Dundee Violet 1
Montrose Roselea 2 Downfield 1
North End 1 Tayport 3

Semi-finals:
Carnoustie Panmure 1 Tayport 3
Montrose Roselea 0 Lochee United 1

FINAL (Saturday, 13th May 2000 at North End FC. Att: 600)
TAYPORT 1-0 LOCHEE UNITED

NORTH END CHALLENGE CUP
Quarter-finals:
East Craigie 1 Elmwood 3
Dundee Violet 2 Arbroath Sports Club 1
Montrose Roselea 4 Bankfoot Athletic 3
Tayport 2 Downfield 0

Semi-finals:
Dundee Violet 3 Elmwood 2 (after extra-time)
Tayport 3 Montroselea 0

FINAL (Tuesday, 6th June 2000 at North End FC)
TAYPORT 6-3 DUNDEE VIOLET

FINDLAY & COMPANY TROPHY
Quarter-finals:
Downfield 0 Tayport 1
Morth End 3 Kirrie Thistle 2
Loche United 3 Broughty Athletic 0
Lochee Harp 2 Elmwood 5 (after extra-time)

Semi-finals:
North End 2 Elmwood 0
Tayport 0 Lochee United 1

FINAL (Saturday, 3rd June 2000 at Downfield FC)
Formerly the Currie Cup and before that the Whyte & McKay Cup)
DUNDEE NORTH END 0-3 LOCHEE UNITED

D J LAING HOMES TROPHY
Quarter-finals:
Arbroath FC 5 Lochee United 1
East Craigie 2 Elmwood 0
North End 1 Kirrie Thistle 0
Forfar West End 0 Tayport 3

Semi-finals:
East Craigie 2 Arbroath Sports Club 3
North End 0 Tayport 2

FINAL (Friday, 18th June 2000 at Carnoustie Panmure FC)
ARBROATH SPORTS CLUB 3-1 TAYPORT

ROSEBANK CAR CENTRE CUP
Semi-finals:
Blairgoqrie 2 Jeanfield Swifts 0
Lochee Harp 0 East Craigie 3

FINAL (Tuesday, 23rd may 2000 at Coupar Angus FC)
BLAIRGOWRIE 2-1 DUNDEE EAST CRAIGIE

DOWNFIELD LEAGUE CUP
Semi-finals:
Lochee Harp 32 Jeanfield Swufts 1 (Jeanfield Swifts awarded tie after protest)
Kinnoul 2 East Craigie 2 (AET - East Craigie won 4-3 on pens)

FINAL (Monday, 5th June 2000 at Downfield FC)
DUNDEE EAST CRAIGIE 3-2 JEANFIELD SWIFTS

NON-LEAGUE CLUBS IN SCOTTISH CUP

First Round:
Huntly 0 East Stirling 1
Threave Rovers 1 Stenhousemuir 7

Second Round:
Albion Rovers 0 Dalbeattie Star 0
Brechin City 2 Annan Athletic 2
Peterhaed 2 Forfar Athletic 1
Stranraer 1 Clachnacuddin 0
Whithill Welfare 2 Alloa Athletic w

Replays:
Alloa Athletic 2 Whitehill Welfare 0
Annan Athletic 2 Brechin City 3
Dalbeattie Star 1 Albion Rovers 5
Fraserburgh 1 Arbroath 3

Third Round:
Falkirk 3 Peterhead 1

SCOTTISH QUALIFYING CUP

NORTH

First Round:
Peterhead 6 Rothes 0

Second Round:
Deveronvale 0 Clachnacuddin 0
Forres Mechanics 1 Cove Rangers 1
Fraserburgh 4 Fort William 2
Huntly 1 Buckie Thistle 0
Lossiemouth 0 Brora Rangers 3
Nairn County 0 Elgin City 1
Peterhead 5 Keith 0
Wick Academy 3 Golspie Sutherland 3
Replays:
Clachnacuddin 3 Deveronvale 2
Cove Rangers 0 Forres Mechanics 1
Golspie Sutherland 5 Wick Academy 6 (after extra-time)

Quarter-finals:
Brora Rangers 1 Clachnacuddin 2
Fraserburgh 4 Forres Mechanics 1
Huntly 4 Elgin City 2
Peterhead 4 Golspie Sutherland 1

Semi-finals:
Fraserburgh 2 Peterhead 0
Huntly 1 Clachnacuddin 1
Replay:
Clachnacuddin 0 Huntly 3

FINAL (Sat., 6th Nov. 1999. At Boroughbriggs, Elgin City FC)
HUNTLY 2-0 FRASERBURGH

SOUTH

First Round:
Annan Athletic 2 Tarff Rovers 0
Burntisland Shipyard 0 Civil Service Strollers 4
Gala Fairydean 3 Glasgow University 2
Girvan 0 Threave Rovers 5
Selkirk 1 Coldstream 4

Second Round:
Dalbeattie Star 2 Edinburgh University 1
Hawick Royal Albert 2 Gala Fairydean 1
Preston Athletic 0 Coldstream 1
St Cuthbert Wanderers 0 Anna Athletic 3
Spartans 1 Whitehill Welfare 2
Threave Rovers 4 Newton Stewart 3
Vale of Leithen 2 Edinburgh City 1
Wigtown & Bladnoch 0 Civil Service Strollers 2

Quarter-finals:
Civil Service Strollers 0 Whitehill Wekfare 1
Coldstream 1 Annan Athletic 3
Dalbeattie Star 3 Vale of Leithen 2
Hawick Royal Albert 1 Threave Rovers 2

Semi-finals:
Dalbeattie Star 0 Whitehill Welfare 3
Threave Rovers 2 Annan Athletic 1

FINAL (Saturday, 20th November 1999. At Stirling Albion FC)
WHITEHILL WELFARE 4-0 THREAVE ROVERS

Lugar Boswell Thistle v Craigmark Burntonians. Ayrshire Region Division Two top of the table battle. Photo: John B Vass

Hurlford United v Kellow Rovers 4-0
Ayrshire League Division Two
Kello's Rab Naismith heads away from Hurlford's Jim
Morrison (stripes) in this top of the table clash.
Photo: Alan Watson

Cumnock v Irvine Victoria 1-1
Ayrshire League Division One
Vics' keeper Eric Phillips saves from Cumnock's David
Pew.
Photo: Alan Watson

Troon v Kilwinning Rangers
Ayrshire League Division One
Photo: John B Vass

Annbank United v Ardeer Thistle
Ayrshire League Division Two
Photo: John B Vass

HIGHLAND LEAGUE

	P	W	D	L	F	A	Pts
Keith	30	21	3	6	76	38	66
Fraserburgh	30	17	10	3	75	32	61
Buckie Thistle	30	18	7	5	58	31	61
Peterhead	30	18	4	8	66	39	58
Huntly	30	16	6	8	69	45	54
Forres Mechanics	30	15	7	8	60	42	52
Clachnacuddin	30	14	6	10	55	37	48
Cove Rangers	30	12	6	12	81	54	42
Elgin City	30	12	6	12	45	44	42
Lossiemouth	30	12	6	12	51	54	42
Deveronvale	30	11	5	14	51	63	38
Brora Rangers	30	9	6	15	53	61	33
Rothes	30	8	5	17	41	52	29
Wick Academy	30	6	4	20	35	84	22
Nairn County	30	3	8	19	24	91	17
Fort William	30	1	5	24	34	107	8

HIGHLAND LEAGUE CUP
Semi-finals (Saturday, 29th April 2000)

Cove Rangers 6 Fraserburgh 2 (AET score at 90 mins 2-2)
Inverness Clachnacuddin 0 Elgin City 1

FINAL (Saturday, 13th May 2000)
COVE RANGERS 4-3 ELGIN CITY

McEWANS NORTH OF SCOTLAND CUP
Quarter-finals:
Elgin City 0 Ross County 'A' 2
Lossiemouth 3 Brora Rangers 0
Nairn County 0 Forres Mechanics 3
Wick Academy 0 Inverness Caledonian Thistle 'A' 2

Semi-finals:
Forres Mechanics 1 Inverness Caledonian Thistle 'A' 2
Lossiemouth 3 Ross County 'A' 1

FINAL (Sunday. 12th September 1999. At Forres Mechanics FC)
INVERNESS CALEDONIAN THISTLE 'A' 3-0 LOSSIEMOUTH

ABERDEENSHIRE CUP
First Round:
Cove Rangers wo Aberdeen 'A'
Deveronvale 2 Fraserburgh 0
Huntly 4 Keith 3
Peterhead 4 Buckie Thistle 1

Semi-finals:
Deveronvale 5 Cove Rangers 0
Huntly 1 Peterhead 0

FINAL (Saturday, 11th September 1999. At Christe Park, Huntly)
HUNTLY 2-0 DEVERONVALE

ABERDEENSHIRE SHIELD
First Round:
Cove Rangers 6 Huntly 2
Deveronvale 2 Buckie Thistle 3
Peterhead 1 Keith 2

Semi-finals:
Buckie Thistle 1 Fraserburgh 4
Keith 4 Cove rangers 2

FINAL (Wednesday, 24th November 1999. At Kynoch Park, Keith)
KEITH 1-2 FRASERBURGH

INVERNESS CUP
Quarter-finals:
Brora Rangers 0 Inverness Caledonian Thistle 'A' 12
Elgin City 4 Fort William 2 (after extra-time)
Nairn County 1 Clachnacuddin 4
Ross County 0 Forres Mechanics 2

Semi-finals:
Inverness Caledonian Thistle 'A' 4 Clachnacuddin 1
Forres Mechanics 2 Elgin City 0

FINAL (Wed., 24th November 1999. At Forres Mechanics FC)
FORRES MECHANICS 0-5 INVERNESS CALEDONIAN THISTLE 'A'

EAST OF SCOTLAND LEAGUE

Premier Division	P	W	D	L	F	A	Pts
Annan Athletic	22	15	6	1	62	21	51
Whitehill Welfare	22	15	5	2	59	13	50
Spartans	22	14	5	3	62	31	47
Lothian Thistle	22	11	4	7	45	32	37
Vale of Leithen	22	11	3	8	50	42	36
Edinburgh City	22	9	5	8	42	39	32
Civil Service Strol	22	9	3	10	42	47	30
Coldstream	22	7	4	11	34	40	25
Craigroyston	22	8	1	13	29	53	25
Easthouses Lily	22	6	2	14	27	50	20
Peebles Rovers	22	6	1	15	29	56	19
Tollcross United	22	1	1	20	19	76	4

Division One							
Threave Rovers	20	15	3	2	55	26	48
Gala Fairydean	20	13	3	4	41	21	42

Above teams promoted to repalce Peebles Rovers and Tollcross United. Remaining positions:
Preston Athletic (38 points), Edinburgh University (35), Kelso United (33), Eyemouth United (27), Pencaitland-Ormiston (25), Hawick Royal Albert (22), Heriot Watt University (16), Edinburgh Athletic (16), Selkirk (12).

EAST LEAGUE CUP
FINAL (Sunday, 23dr January 2000. At Gala Fairydean FC).
ANNAN ATHLETIC 2-1 COLDSTREAM

ALEX JACK CUP
Semi-finals:
Easthouses Lily 1 Tollcross United 0
Peebles Rovers 3 Lothian Thistle 2

FINAL (Sunday, 21st November 1999. At Whitehill Welfare FC)
EASTHOUSES LILY 1-1 PEEBLES ROVERS
(After extra-time. Peebles Rovers won 5-4 on pens)

EAST OF SCOTLAND QUALIFYING 'IMAGE PRINTERS' CUP

Quarter-finals:
Coldstream 4 Eyemouth United 2
Edinburgh University 0 Lothian Thistle 2
Spartans 1 Edinburgh City 2
Whitehill Welfare 2 Hawick Royal Albert 1

Semi-finals:
Lothian Thistle 1 Coldstraem 1
Whitehill Welfare 5 Edinburgh City 0
Replay: Coldstream 1 Lothian Thistle 0

FINAL (Sunday, 7th May 2000. At Vale of Leithen FC)
WHITEHILL WELFARE 4-2 COLDSTREAM

KING CUP

Quarter-finals:
Civil Service Strollers 0 Whitehill Welfare 1
Craigroyston 4 Hawick Royal Albert 2
Edinburgh City 4 Vale of Leithen 0
Preston Athletic 1 Gala Fairydean 3

Semi-finals:
Craigroyston 0 Whitehill Welfare 1
Edinburgh City 2 Gala Fairydean 1

FINAL (Tuesday, 23rd May 2000. At Whitehill Welfare FC)
WHITEHILL WELFARE 1-2 EDINBURGH CITY

CITY CUP

Semi-finals:
Coldstream 0 Livingston 2
Whitehill Welfare 2 Berwick Rangers Reserves 2 (Whitehill Welfare won 3-0 on pens)

FINAL (Thursday, 11th May 2000. At Whitehill Weklfare FC)
WHITEHILL WELFARE 1-0 LIVINGSTON

SOUTH OF SCOTLAND LEAGUE

	P	W	D	L	F	A	Pts
Tarff Rovers	24	22	1	1	121	27	67
Dalbeattie Star	24	19	2	3	98	22	59
Newton Stewart	24	14	2	8	80	42	44
St Cuthbert Wands	24	13	5	6	69	46	44
Annan Athletic	24	12	5	7	56	42	41
Stranraer Athletic	24	11	5	8	51	40	38
Chrichton Royal	24	11	4	9	61	59	37
Creetown	24	10	3	11	58	66	33
Threave Rovers	24	6	3	15	36	65	21
Maxwelltown HSFP	24	5	5	14	48	95	20
Girvan	24	5	3	16	47	88	18
Wigtown & Bladnoch	24	4	3	17	33	84	15
Dumfries HSFP	24	3	1	20	26	108	10

SOUTH OF SCOTLAND LEAGUE CUP

Semi-finals:
Tarff Rovers 1 Stranrear Athletic 0
Threave Rovers 4 Dalbeattie Star 2

FINAL (Monday, 23rd August 1999. At Tarff Rovers FC)
TARFF ROVERS 2-0 THREAVE ROVERS

SOUTH CHALLENGE CUP

Quarter-finals:
Annan Athletic 4 Wigtown & Bladnoch 1
Creetown 1 Stranraer Athletic 2
Crichton Royal 0 Tarff Rovers 3
Dalbeattie Star 2 Queen of the South 'A' 3
Semi-finals:
Annan Athletic 1 Queen of the South 'A' 2
Stranraer Athletic 0 Tarff Rovers 1

FINAL (Wed., 3rd May 2000. At Palmerston Park, Dumfries)
QUEEN OF THE SOUTH 'A' 5-2 TARFF ROVERS
(after extra-time - score at 90 mins - 2-2)

Annbank United v St Rochs. Whyte & McKay Cup First Round. Photo: John B Vass

CREE LODGE CUP

Quarter-finals:
Annan Athletic 1 St Cuthbert Wanderers 2
Dalbeattie Star 5 Newton Stewart 0
Girvan 2 Creetown 5
Maxwelltown HSFP) Tarff Rovers 6

Semi-finals:
Creetown 2 Dalbeattie Star 1
St Cuthbert Wanderers 0 Tarff Rovers 10

FINAL (Saturday, 15th April 2000. At Tarff Rovers FC)
TARFF ROVERS 3-1 CREETOWN

HAIG GORDON TROPHY

Quarter-finals:
Annan Athletic 5 Stranraer Athletic 1
Dalbeattie Star 0 Tarff Rovers 2
Maxwelltown HSFP 2 St Cuthbert Wanderers 3
Newton Stewart 5 Crichton Royal 3 (after extra-time)

Semi-finals:
Newton Stewart 0 Tarff Rovers 3
St Cuthbert wanderers 3 Anna Athletic 1

FINAL (Saturday, 29th April 2000. At Tarff Rovers FC)
TARFF ROVERS 3-1 ST CUTHBERT WANDERERS
(after extra-time - score at 90 mins 1-1)

POTTS CUP

Quarter-finals:
Newton Stewart 2 Creetwon 4
Stranraer Athletic 0 Threave Rovers 3
St Cuthbert wanderers 2 Dalbeattie Star 4
Tarff Rovers 7 Wigtown & Bladnoch 0

Semi-finals:
Creetown 3 Tarff Rovers 0
Threave Rovers 0 Dalbeattie Star 3

FINAL (Saturday, 6th May 2000. At Creetown FC)
CREETOWN 1-5 DALBEATTIE STAR

TWEEDIE CUP

Quarter-finals:
Dalbeattie Star 3 Annan Athletic 0
Girban 0 Tarff Rovers 5
Maxwelltown HSFP 1 stranraer Athletic 3
Newton Stewart 3 Crichton Royal 4

Semi-finals:
Crichton Royal 1 dalbeattie Star 3
Tarff Rovers 4 Stranraer Athletic 1

FINAL (Saturday, 22nd April 2000. At Tarff Rovers FC)
TARFF ROVERS 0-3 DALBEATTIE STAR

Other winners:
Detroit Trophy (overall championship and cup results)
- Tarff Rover
James Brown Fair Play Trophy - Dumfries High School FP
Leading goalscorer - Scott Reid (Tarff Rovers)

Craigmark Burntonians v Glenafton Athletic
Whyte & McKay Cup Third Round. Photo: John B Vass

OTHER WINNERS:

Scottish Amateur League Premier Division Champions:	Campbelltown Pupils
West of Scotland Amateur League Premier Division Champions:	Kelvin Athletic
Central Scottish League Champions (Amateur Premier Division):	Harestane
Aberdeenshire Amateur League Division One Champions:	Hilton
Highland Amateur Cup:	Conton
Lewis & Harris League Champions:	Ness
Highland Amateur Jock Stein Cup:	Ness
Co-op Cup (for teams from Lewis, Harris, Uist, Narra and West Highland League):	Point
West Highland League Champions:	Portree
West Highland League Second Division:	Dunvegan
Caithness County League Champions:	Pentland United
Caledonian Amateur League Champions:	Bannockburn Arms
East Fife Amateur League Champions:	Auchtermuchty Bell
Border Amateur League Champions:	Gala Rovers
Ayrshire Amateur League Champions Premier League:	Newmilns
Ayrshire Amateur Cup:	Maybole Amateurs
Greater Glasgow League Champions Division One:	St Joseph

AMATEUR FOOBALL ALLIANCE

President: C R Sharp **Chairman:** R B Rowe
Director (AFA Ltd): W P Goss
General & Company Secretary: Mike Brown, 55 Islington Park Street, London N1 1QB
Tel: 0171 3593493 Fax: 0171 359 5027

A F A SENIOR CUP 2000

FIRST ROUND PROPER

Old Salopians	v	Nat West Bank	3-2	Cardinal Manning OB	v	Kew Association	3-4
Carshalton	v	Mill Hill Village	3-3, 5-3*	Old Wilsonians	v	HSBC	1-2
Nottsborough	v	Old Owens	1-3	Old Reptonians	v	Old Danes	1-5
Broomfield	v	Old Esthameians	0-1	Old Hamptonians	v	Merton	0-2
Fulham Compton OB	v	West Wickham	1-3	Old Actonians Assn	v	Old Aloysians	5-1*
Alexandra Park	v	Polytechnic	1-2	East Barnet O Grms	v	Old Minchendenians	2-1
Civil Service	v	Old Southallians	7-1	Crouch End Vampires	v	Old Cholmeleians	1-0
Old Parmiterians	v	Old Manorians	4-4*, 4p3	Old Challoners	v	Old Finchleians	3-5*
Old Ignatians	v	Hon Artillery Co	2-1	Old Woodhouseians	v	Wandsworth Borough	5-4
Silhill	v	Old Salesians	1-2	Old Bromleians	v	Old Meadonians	2-5
Lloyds TSB Bank	v	Old Tenisonians	1-1*, 4p3	Old Chigwellians	v	Southgate County	2-3
Old Vaughanians	v	Old Sedcopians	3-0	St. Mary's College	v	Old Salvatorians	2-0
Alleyn Old Boys	v	Old Tiffinians	2-1	Old Buckwellians	v	Shene Old Gram's	4-2
UCL Academicals	v	Southgate Olympic	6-0	Old Grammarians	v	Old Isleworthians	2-1
Old Parkonians	v	Barclays Bank	2-4	Old Foresters	v	Norsemen	2-2*, 1p3
Bank of England	v	CGU Cuaco Club	4-0				

SECOND ROUND PROPER

Old Salopians	v	Kew Association	1-4	Carshalton	v	South Bank	1-0
HSBC (ex Mid Bank)	v	Old Owens	3-3*, 3p4	Old Danes	v	Old Esthameians	2-5
Merton	v	West Wickham	2-2*, 3p4	Old Actonians Ass'n	v	Polytechnic	0-0*, 2p4
East Barnet O Grm's	v	Civil Service	1-2	Crouch End V'pires	v	Old Parmiterians	5-1
Old Finchleians	v	Old Ignatians	3-0	Old Woodhouseians	v	Old Salesians	2-1
Old Meadonians	v	Lloyds TSB Bank	3-2	Southgate County	v	Old Vaughanians	3-0
St Mary's College	v	Alleyn Old Boys	3-1	Old Buckwellians	v	UCL Academicals	1-2
Old Grammarians	v	Barclays Bank	1-3	Norsemen	v	Bank of England	0-3

THIRD ROUND PROPER

Kew Association	v	Carshalton	3-1*	Old Owens	v	Old Esthameians	1-2
West Wickham	v	Polytechnic	2-3	Civil Service	v	Crouch End V's	1-1*, 3p5
Old Finchleians	v	Old Woodhouseians	4-1*	Old Meadonians	v	Southgate County	2-3
UCL Academicals	v	St Mary's College	2-1	Barclays Bank	v	Bank of England	2-1

FOURTH ROUND PROPER

Kew Association	v	Old Esthameians	3-3*, 1p4	Polytechnic	v	Crouch End V's	3-3*, 0p3
Old Finchleians	v	Southgate County	1-2	UCL Academicals	v	Barclays Bank	3-3

SEMI FINALS

Old Esthameians	v	Crouch End Vampires	0-2	Southgate Count	v	UCL Academicals	1-2

FINAL

Crouch End Vampires v   UCL Academicals 1-1*, 2p4   (* after extra time   p: kicks from penalty mark)

OTHER A.F.A. CUP RESULTS

INTERMEDIATE
Bank of England Rs   v   O Woodhouseians Rs   4-1

JUNIOR
East Barnet O G Rs   v   Globe Rangers 1st   0-2*

MINOR
HSBC 4th   v   Old Actonians 4th   2-1

SENIOR NOVETS
Old Aloysians 5th   v   Old Suttonians 5th   6-0

INTERMEDIATE NOVETS
Nat West Bank 6th   v   Old Actonians 6th   2-0

JUNIOR NOVETS
Old Actonians 7th   v   Polytechnic 7th   1-2

VETERANS
Winchmore Hill   v   Old Buckwellians Vets   1-2

OPEN VETERANS
Old Parmiterians   v   Port of London Ath'y   2-0*

YOUTH
Norsemen Youth   v   Old Parmiterians Yth   8-0

ESSEX DIVISIONAL SENIOR
Hale End Athletic   v   Old Brentwoods   1-0

MIDDLESEX DIVISIONAL SENIOR
Old Actonians Assn   v   Old Isleworthians   2-1*

SURREY DIVISIONAL SENIOR
Lloyds TSB Bank   v   Merton   2-1

ESSEX DIVISIONAL INTERMEDIATE
Old Egbertians 1st   v   Hale End Athletic Rs   2-3

KENT DIVISIONAL INTERMEDIATE
West Wickham Rs   v   Morgan Guaranty 1st   3-1

MIDDLESEX DIVISIONAL INTERMEDIATE
Old Hamptonians Rs   v   Old Vaughanians   3-4

SURREY DIVISIONAL INTERMEDIATE
Royal Sun Allce 1st   v   Carshalton Res   4-1

W E GREENLAND MEMORIAL
Old Ignatians   v   Old Actonians   2-1

AFA REPRESENTATIVE MATCH RESULTS

v	Civil Service National XI (Trial)	Lost	1-2
v	Oxford University	Lost	3-5
v	Army F A	Won	2-0
v	Royal Navy F A	Won	2-1
v	Royal Air Force F A	Lost	2-4
v	Cambridge University	Lost	1-4
v	London F A	Won	3-2
v	London University	Canc	Rain

ARTHUR DUNN CUP

Lancing Old Boys   v   Old Foresters   3-0

ARTHURIAN LEAGUE

PREMIER DIVISION	P	W	D	L	F	A	Pts
Old Brentwoods	16	10	2	4	42	26	22
Old Carthusians	16	7	4	5	35	27	18
Old Chigwellians	16	6	6	4	33	31	18
Old Cholmeleians	16	8	2	6	28	27	18
Old Reptonians	16	5	7	4	25	22	17
Old Salopians	16	8	1	7	32	33	17
Lancing Old Boys	16	5	6	5	30	32	16
Old Foresters **	16	7	2	7	32	26	13
Old Malvernians	16	0	2	14	17	50	2

DIVISION ONE	P	W	D	L	F	A	Pts
Old Harrovians	14	13	0	1	56	19	26
Old Etonians	14	10	0	4	40	21	20
Old Haberdashers	14	7	2	5	36	30	16
Old Bradfieldians	14	6	1	7	33	27	13
Old Wellingburians	14	6	0	8	25	42	12
Old Witleians	14	4	2	8	22	35	10
Old Wykehamists	14	4	1	9	31	43	9
Old Aldenhamians	14	3	0	11	21	47	6

DIVISION TWO	P	W	D	L	F	A	Pts
Old Etonians Res	16	14	2	0	50	12	30
Old Brentwoods Res	16	8	5	3	39	21	21
Old Chigwellians Res	16	7	3	6	29	32	17
Old Salopians Res	16	7	2	7	30	32	16
Lancing Old Boys Rs	16	4	6	6	32	32	14
Old Cholmeleians Rs	16	5	4	7	21	33	14
Old Etonians 3rd	16	5	4	7	27	40	14
Old Carthusians Res	16	3	5	8	26	32	11
Old Millhillians **	16	2	3	11	24	44	3

DIVISION THREE	P	W	D	L	F	A	Pts
Old Westminsters	14	12	1	1	66	13	25
Old Haberdashers Rs	14	11	0	3	45	23	22
Old Foresters Res	14	6	2	6	34	33	14
Old Aldenhamians Rs	14	6	1	7	34	25	13
Old Foresters 3rd	14	5	2	7	33	34	12
Old Harrovians Res	14	5	1	8	28	34	11
Old Reptonians Res	14	5	0	9	27	48	10
Old Cholmeleians 3rd	14	2	1	11	17	49	5

DIVISION FOUR	P	W	D	L	F	A	Pts
Old Carthusians 3rd	14	9	2	3	40	33	20
Old Bradfieldians Res	14	8	3	3	24	9	19
Old Eastbournians	14	7	2	5	42	29	16
Old Haileyburians	14	6	4	4	44	38	16
Old Cholmeleians 4th	14	6	1	7	25	30	13
Old Malvernians Rs**	14	6	2	6	35	32	12
Old Brentwoods 3rd	14	4	1	9	28	38	9
Old Cholmeleians 5th	13	1	2	10	27	56	4

DIVISION FIVE		
	8 Teams	
Won by	Old Brentwoods 4th	

*(** Points deducted - breach of Rule)*

LONDON FINANCIAL F.A.

DIVISION ONE

	P	W	D	L	F	A	Pts
Morgan Guaranty	16	13	2	1	56	23	41
Coutts	16	10	1	5	41	29	31
Royal Sun Alliance	16	8	1	7	46	33	25
Granby	16	7	4	7	32	29	25
Citibank	16	7	4	5	29	27	25
Bank of America	16	6	3	7	32	40	21
Dresdner Kleinwort B	16	7	1	12	28	40	19
Royal Bank Scotland	16	3	1	9	26	43	10
Eagle Star	16	2	3	11	37	63	6

DIVISION TWO

	P	W	D	L	F	A	Pts
Mount Pleasant P O	14	13	1	0	68	17	40
Foreign & Cmnwealth	14	8	4	2	44	22	28
Chase Manhattan B	14	7	2	5	45	26	23
Marsh	14	6	2	6	42	38	20
Standard Chartered B	14	4	4	6	23	30	16
Temple Bar	14	4	2	8	33	44	14
Abbey National	14	4	1	9	26	50	13
Customs and Excise	14	0	4	10	14	68	3

DIVISION THREE

	P	W	D	L	F	A	Pts
Royal Sun Alliance Rs	16	14	2	0	46	18	44
Chelsea Exiles	16	10	5	2	88	37	34
Bank America Res	16	9	4	4	39	28	30
Eagle Star Res	16	8	4	5	40	35	27
Cabinet Office & Trsy	16	6	4	7	39	41	21
C. Hoare & Co.	16	5	1	10	43	60	16
Salomon Smith Brny	16	4	2	10	33	44	14
ANZ Banking Group	16	3	2	11	28	51	11
Royal Bk Scotland R	16	1	4	11	13	55	7

DIVISION FOUR

	P	W	D	L	F	A	Pts
British Gas (Bromley)	16	12	3	1	73	30	39
Marsh Res.	16	9	3	4	58	32	30
Coutts Res	16	5	7	4	28	25	22
Royal Sun Alliance Rs	16	6	4	6	36	39	22
Granby Res	16	5	6	5	34	27	21
Citibank Res	16	5	5	6	38	44	20
Bank of Ireland	16	3	9	4	27	34	18
Credit Suisse F Boston	16	4	2	10	23	46	14
Noble Lowndes	16	1	5	10	21	61	18

DIVISION FIVE

	P	W	D	L	F	A	Pts
UCB Home Loans	21	15	4	2	73	24	49
Marsh 3rd	21	13	4	5	54	38	42
Standard Chrtd Rs	21	11	3	7	57	59	36
Eagle Star 3rd	21	7	5	9	49	52	26
Granby 3rd	21	6	7	8	35	42	25
CGU Cuaco 5th	21	7	3	11	62	71	24
Temple Bar Res	21	4	7	10	33	49	19
Royal B Scotland 3rd	21	2	6	13	42	70	12
Noble Lowndes Rs.						Withdrawn	

CHALLENGE CUP
HSBC v Dresdner Kleinwort B 4-1

SENIOR CUP
Morgan Guaranty v Dresdner Kleinwort B 3-0

JUNIOR CUP
Chelsea Exiles v Granby Res 7-1

MINOR CUP
UCB Home Loans v Temple Bar Res 3-1

VETERANS' CUP
Lensbury v Bank of England 1-0

W A JEWELL MEMORIAL V-A-S
Won by Mount Pleasant P O

SAUNDERS SHIELD V-A-S
Won by Temple Bar

SPORTSMANSHIP SHIELD
Won by Gaflac

REPRESENTATIVE MATCHES

LFFA v	Stock Exchange F A	Lost	2-3
	(1999 Daily Telegraph Cup)		
LFFA v	Southern Olympian League	Lost	1-8
LFFA v	Royal Marines	Lost	0-9
LFFA v	Southern Amateur League	Lost	1-5
LFFA v	Old Boys' League	Won	4-3
LFFA v	Bristol Insurance Institute	Lost	0-3
LFFA v	Stock Exchange F A	Won	2-0
	(2000 Daily Telegraph Cup)		

LONDON LEGAL LEAGUE

DIVISION ONE

	P	W	D	L	F	A	Pts
Denton Wilde S "A"	18	14	1	3	64	22	43
K.P.M.G.	18	12	3	3	42	22	39
Slaughter & May**	18	12	1	5	59	24	36
Lovell White Durrant	18	10	4	4	43	34	34
Gray's Inn**	18	10	1	7	47	31	30
Clifford Chance**	18	8	3	7	37	41	26
Linklaters & Paines**	18	7	3	8	45	46	23
Cameron Markby Hwt	18	3	2	13	20	32	11
Rosling King	18	2	1	15	18	55	7
Taylor Joynson Grt**	18	1	3	14	18	66	5

DIVISION TWO

	P	W	D	L	F	A	Pts
Norton Rose	18	10	6	2	44	21	36
Nabarro Nathanson	18	11	3	4	36	18	36
Pegasus (Inner Temple)	18	10	3	5	51	34	33
Simmons & Simmons	18	8	7	3	39	21	31
Nicholson Graham & J	18	8	2	8	30	33	26
Freshfields	18	5	5	8	27	33	20
Watson Farley & Wlms	18	5	3	10	28	33	18
Herbert Smith	18	6	0	12	28	50	18
Stephenson Harwood**	18	5	3	10	28	39	16
Denton Wilde S "B"	18	4	4	10	18	47	16

DIVISION THREE

	P	W	D	L	F	A	Pts
Eversheds	18	13	3	2	63	23	42
Baker & McKenzie	18	13	1	4	71	40	40
S.J. Berwin	18	11	1	6	38	24	34
Edge Ellison	18	8	3	7	27	43	27
Titmuss Sainer Dechert**	18	8	2	8	35	32	25
Barlow Lyde & Gilbert	18	6	6	6	42	38	24
Allen & Overy	18	6	3	9	41	59	21
Richards Butler	18	6	1	11	25	40	19
Stock Exchange	18	5	3	10	38	44	18
Macfarlanes**	18	1	3	14	30	57	4

*(** Points deducted - Breach of Rule)*

LONDON LEGAL LEAGUE cont.

LEAGUE CHALLENGE CUP
Gray's Inn   v   Slaughter & May   5-1

WEAVERS ARMS CUP
Norton Rose   v   Linklaters & Paines   5-2

LONDON OLD BOYS' CUPS

SENIOR
Old Wilsonians   v   Old Ignatians   1-0

INTERMEDIATE
Queen Mary Cg OB   v   Latymer Old Boys Rs   2-1

JUNIOR
Old Actonians 3rd   v   Old Tollingtonians Rs   2-1

MINOR
Clapham O Xavs 4th   v   Old Aloysians 4th   3-1

NOVETS
Old Suttonians 5th   v   Old Edmontonians 4th   2-1

DRUMMOND
Old Actonians A. 6th   v   Old Wilsonians 6th   2-0

NEMEAN
Old Aloysians 7th   v   Old Actonians 7th   5-3

VETERANS'
Old Tenisonians Vets   v   Old Salvatorians Vets   3-0

OLD BOYS' INVITATION CUPS

SENIOR
Old Bromleians   v   Old Owens   2-1

JUNIOR
Old Tenisonians Res   v   Old Finchleians Res   0-3

MINOR
Old Salesians 3rd   v   Old Tenisonians 3rd   1-2

4th XIs
Old Wilsonians 4th   v   Old Finchleians 4th   2-7

5th XIs
O Wminster Ctzns 5th   v   Old Suttonians 5th   3-4

6th XIs
Old Finchleians 6th   v   Old Statioers 6th   9-2

7th XIs
Old Finchleians 7th   v   Old Finchleians 8th   3-1

VETERANS'
O Tenisonians Vets   v   O Wminster Ctzns Vets   1-0

MIDLAND AMATEUR ALLIANCE

PREMIER DIVISION	P	W	D	L	F	A	Pts
A S C Dayncourt	20	14	5	1	70	25	47
Old Elizabethans	20	14	0	6	64	34	42
Bassingfield	20	11	4	5	53	27	37
Caribbean Cavaliers	20	12	1	7	53	51	37
Nottingham Irish Cntr	20	10	4	6	71	48	34
Kirton Brick Works	20	9	0	11	48	47	27
Lady Bay	20	6	5	8	51	49	26
Horse & Jockey	20	6	4	10	54	74	22
Pannell Kerr Foster S	20	6	2	12	29	54	20
Parkhead Academ's	20	4	1	15	29	75	13
Beeston O B Assn	20	3	2	15	20	58	11

DIVISION ONE	P	W	D	L	F	A	Pts
Woodborough Utd	28	20	1	7	96	47	61
A S C Dayncourt Rs	28	19	3	6	83	48	60
Hucknall Sports Y C	28	16	5	7	74	35	53
Wollaton 3rd	28	17	2	9	77	41	53
Old Elizabethans Rs	28	15	4	9	67	51	49
City & Sherwood Rs	28	13	6	9	63	49	45
Clifton Res	28	12	6	10	54	53	42
Magdala Amat's Rs	28	12	3	13	51	54	39
Radcliffe Olympic Rs	28	11	5	12	56	55	38
Nottinghamshire	28	11	3	14	57	54	36
Derbyshire Amat's Rs	28	10	4	14	53	66	34
Tibshelf Old Boys	28	8	6	14	57	76	30
Bassingfield Res	28	7	3	18	63	101	24
Dynamo Baptist	28	5	6	17	36	77	21
Edwinstowe	28	4	3	21	33	113	15

DIVISION TWO	P	W	D	L	F	A	Pts
Chaffoteaux Rs	26	23	2	1	99	18	71
Old Bemrosians	26	20	2	4	95	34	62
Linby Colliery Rs	26	19	4	3	102	28	61
Fleet Cars	26	16	4	6	80	33	52
Southwell Amateurs	26	11	3	12	65	52	36
Wollaton 4th	26	9	6	11	54	53	33
Ilkeston Rangers	26	9	5	12	66	76	32
Brunts Old Boys	26	10	2	14	33	79	32
Magdala Amat's 3rd	26	8	3	15	56	79	27
Nottinghamshire Rs	26	7	5	14	40	64	26
Cadland Chilwell	26	6	6	14	42	86	24
Horse & Jockey Rs	26	7	3	16	38	86	24
Lady Bay Res.	26	6	4	16	62	107	22
Old Elizabethans 3rd	26	5	3	18	45	83	18

DIVISION THREE	P	W	D	L	F	A	Pts
Ashland Rovers	26	23	2	1	115	33	71
County Nalgo	26	16	4	6	88	48	52
A S C Dayncourt 3rd	26	16	4	6	80	40	52
Sherwood Forest	26	14	3	9	68	59	45
Derbyshire Amat's 3rd	26	14	1	11	99	91	43
Beeston Old Boys Rs	26	11	6	9	69	59	39
E M T E C	26	12	2	12	83	84	38
West Bridgford United	26	11	3	12	60	64	36
Wollaton 5th	26	10	6	10	65	78	36
Horse & Jockey 3rd	26	11	2	13	74	63	35
Nottinghamshire 3rd	26	6	7	13	69	76	25
Ilkeston Rangers Res	26	7	3	16	47	72	24
Old Bemrosians Res	26	4	4	18	36	100	16
Tibshelf Old Boys Res	.26	2	3	21	30	116	9

LEAGUE CUPS

SENIOR
Caribbean Cavaliers v Woodborough United 3-1

INTERMEDIATE
A S C Dayncourt Rs v O Bemrosians R 0-0*, 0p4

MINOR
Ashland Rovers v Sherwood Forest 3-1

H.B. POOLE TROPHY Now ceased

OLD BOYS' AMATEUR FOOTBALL LEAGUE

PREMIER DIVISION	P	W	D	L	F	A	Pts
Old Ignatians	20	10	7	3	44	25	27
Old Aloysians	20	9	6	5	43	35	24
Old Vaughanians	20	10	4	6	36	28	24
Phoenix Old Boys	20	10	3	7	41	31	23
Old Wilsonians	20	9	4	7	36	30	22
Old Meadonians	20	9	3	8	30	24	21
Cardinal Manning OB	20	9	3	8	19	29	21
Old Tenisonians	20	6	4	10	22	27	16
Old Hamptonians	20	4	7	9	25	31	15
Old Salvatorians	20	6	3	11	29	51	15
Old Buckwellians	20	5	2	13	32	46	12

SNR DIVISION ONE	P	W	D	L	F	A	Pts
Glyn Old Boys	20	14	1	5	52	21	29
Shene Old Gramms	20	13	2	5	55	27	28
Latymer Old Boys	20	12	3	5	53	25	27
Old Dorkinians	20	9	5	6	41	32	23
Old Minchendenians	20	10	1	9	44	39	21
Old Isleworthians	20	9	3	8	39	38	21
Old Suttonians	20	6	7	7	33	41	19
Old Manorians	20	7	4	9	45	39	18
Enfield Old Gramms	20	7	4	9	28	30	18
Old Vaughanians Rs	20	4	2	14	28	69	10
Old Kingsburians	20	2	2	16	28	85	6

SNR DIVISION TWO	P	W	D	L	F	A	Pts
Old Danes	20	13	4	3	45	17	30
Old Sinjuns	20	14	2	4	57	34	30
Old Tiffinians	20	10	4	6	37	21	24
John Fisher Old Boys	20	6	8	6	39	35	20
Old Reigatians	20	7	6	7	33	40	20
Clapham O Xaverians	20	7	5	8	49	40	19
Phoenix Old Boys Rs	20	7	5	8	31	35	19
Chertsey O Salesians	20	7	3	10	44	45	17
Latymer Old Boys Rs	20	5	7	8	34	41	17
Old Meadonians Rs	20	4	5	11	30	56	13
Old Tenisonians Rs	20	4	3	13	19	54	11

SNR DIVISION THREE	P	W	D	L	F	A	Pts
Q. Mary College OB*	20	16	2	2	60	16	34
Old Sedcopians	20	11	5	4	55	29	27
Old Wokingians	20	9	6	5	49	29	24
Old Hamptonians Rs.	20	11	1	8	42	35	23
Old Wilsonians Rs.	20	8	6	6	48	43	22
Old Aloysians Rs	20	8	5	7	44	43	21
Old Manorians Rs	20	9	1	10	38	43	19
Old Tenisonians 3rd	20	8	3	9	34	42	19
Old Salvatorians Rs*	20	7	3	10	35	37	17
Old Uffingtonians	20	5	0	15	36	70	10
Old Southallians	20	1	2	17	20	74	4

final unplayed game entered as a 0-0 draw

INTERMEDIATE DIVISION NORTH
12 Teams won by Wood Green Old Boys

INTERMEDIATE DIVISION SOUTH
11 Teams won by Old Wokingians Res

DIVISION ONE NORTH
10 Teams won by Old Tollingtonians Res

DIVISION ONE SOUTH
10 Teams won by Fitzwilliam Old Boys

DIVISION ONE WEST
10 Teams won by Old Salvatorians 3rd

DIVISION TWO NORTH
12 Teams won by Old Tollingtonians 3rd

DIVISION TWO SOUTH
10 Teams won by John Fisher Old Boys Res

DIVISION TWO WEST
12 Teams won by Old Challoners Res

DIVISION THREE NORTH
11 Teams won by Old Aloysians 5th

DIVISION THREE SOUTH
11 Teams won by Old Suttonians 5th

DIVISION THREE WEST
9 Teams won by Old Salvatorians 5th

DIVISION FOUR NORTH
12 Teams won by Old Egbertians 4th

DIVISION FOUR SOUTH
12 Teams won by Fitzwilliam Old Boys Res

DIVISION FOUR WEST
11 Teams won by Old Manorians 5th

DIVISION FIVE NORTH
9 Teams won by Old Minchendenians 5th

DIVISION FIVE SOUTH
11 Teams won by Old Thorntonians Res

DIVISION FIVE WEST
10 Teams won by Old Hendonians 3rd

DIVISION SIX NORTH
10 Teams won by Ravenscroft Old Boys 3rd

DIVISION SIX SOUTH
11 Teams won by Chertsey Old Salesians 4th

DIVISION SIX WEST
9 Teams won by Phoenix Old Boys 6th

DIVISION SEVEN SOUTH
11 Teams won by Old Paulines 3rd

DIVISION EIGHT SOUTH
10 Teams won by Glyn Old Boys 8th

DIVISION NINE SOUTH
10 Teams won by Glyn Old Boys 8th

SOUTHERN AMATEUR LEAGUE

SENIOR SECTION

FIRST DIVISION

	P	W	D	L	F	A	Pts
Old Actonians Assn	22	15	2	5	51	23	47
Polytechnic	22	11	7	4	54	32	40
Crouch End Vampires	22	12	2	8	49	34	38
Norsemen	22	10	6	6	41	34	36
Old Owens	22	9	5	8	44	37	32
Carshalton	22	9	4	9	29	32	31
Barclays Bank	22	9	3	10	43	41	30
East Barnet O Grams	22	9	2	11	39	43	29
Old Bromleians**	22	8	5	9	40	49	27
Nat West Bank	22	6	5	11	39	53	23
Lloyds TSB Bank	22	6	5	11	36	52	23
Old Parmiterians	22	3	4	15	26	61	13

SECOND DIVISION

	P	W	D	L	F	A	Pts
Alleyn Old Boys	22	14	3	5	54	33	45
Old Esthameians	22	12	6	4	49	23	42
West Wickham	22	11	8	3	45	21	41
Old Salesians	22	11	4	7	56	38	37
HSBC	22	8	7	7	51	32	31
Old Stationers	22	7	7	8	38	38	28
Alexandra Park	22	9	1	12	38	55	28
Lensbury	22	8	4	10	37	64	28
Civil Service	22	7	6	9	43	40	27
Old Finchleians	22	8	2	12	55	60	26
Old Parkonians	22	5	6	11	27	32	21
South Bank	22	3	4	15	29	86	13

THIRD DIVISION

	P	W	D	L	F	A	Pts
Broomfield	22	17	1	4	54	29	52
Winchmore Hill	22	16	3	3	40	16	51
Kew Association	22	14	2	6	51	31	44
Bank of England	22	14	1	7	42	21	43
Old Lyonians	22	11	4	7	50	39	37
Southgate Olympic	22	10	5	7	47	42	35
Merton	22	8	5	9	45	45	29
O Westminster Ctzns	22	9	2	11	34	40	29
Ibis**	22	5	4	13	32	43	16
CGU Cuaco	22	3	5	14	25	49	14
Old Latymerians	22	4	2	16	24	56	14
Brentham	22	3	2	17	22	55	11

*(** Points deducted for breach of League Rule)*

RESERVE TEAMS SECTION

FIRST DIVISION
12 Teams   Won by   East Barnet Old Grams Res
SECOND DIVISION
12 Teams   Won by   Old Finchleians Res
THIRD DIVISION
12 Teams   Won by   Bank of England Res

THIRD TEAMS SECTION

FIRST DIVISION
12 Teams   Won by   East Barnet Old Gramms 3rd
SECOND DIVISION
12 Teams   Won by   Alleyn Old Boys 3rd
THIRD DIVISION
12 Teams   Won by   Old Parmiterians 3rd

FOURTH TEAMS SECTION

FIRST DIVISION
12 Teams   Won by   Norsemen 4th
SECOND DIVISION
11 Teams   Won by   Old Finchleians 4th
THIRD DIVISION
10 Teams   Won by   Kew Association 4th

FIFTH TEAMS SECTION

FIRST DIVISION
11 Teams   Won by   Polytechnic 5th
SECOND DIVISION
10 Teams   Won by   Old Stationers 5th
THIRD DIVISION
9 Teams   Won by   Old Bromleians 5th

SIXTH TEAMS SECTION

FIRST DIVISION
8 Teams   Won by   Old Actonians Association 6th
SECOND DIVISION
8 Teams   Won by   OLd Finchleians 5th
THIRD DIVISION
8 Teams   Won by   Old Salesians 6th

MINOR SECTION

FIRST DIVISION
9 Teams   Won by   Nat Westminster Bank 7th
SECOND DIVISION
9 Teams   Won by   Old Finchleians 7th
THIRD DIVISION
9 Teams   Won by   Civil Service 8th
FOURTH DIVISION
10 Teams   Won by   Kew Association 8th

CHALLENGE CUPS

JUNIOR
Bank of England 3rd   v   Old Parmiterians 3rd   3-1
MINOR
HSBC 4th   v   Polytechnic 4th   4-1
SENIOR NOVETS
Norsemen 5th   v   Polytechnic 5th   1-1*, 7p6
INTERMEDIATE NOVETS
O Actonians Assn 6th v   Old Finchleians 6th   3-1
JUNIOR NOVETS
Old Parmiterians 7th   v   Barclays Bank 8th   1-0

HAMILTON TROPHY
for Hospitality & Sportsmanship   Old Owens

WILKINSON SWORD
for Disciplinary Conduct   Not Awarded

SOUTHERN OLYMPIAN LEAGUE

SENIOR SECTION

DIVISION ONE

	P	W	D	L	F	A	Pts
Hon Artillery Co'y	18	14	1	3	62	17	29
Hale End Athletic	18	12	4	2	56	27	28
UCL Academicals	18	11	4	3	52	22	26
Nottsborough	18	9	4	5	43	25	22
Old Grammarians	18	9	3	6	44	38	21
Mill Hill Village	18	7	3	8	30	43	17
Old Woodhouseians	18	5	3	10	31	46	13
Ulysses	18	3	5	10	24	42	11
Parkfield	18	2	3	13	23	52	7
City of London	18	2	2	14	27	80	6

DIVISION TWO

	P	W	D	L	F	A	Pts
Albanian	18	14	3	1	51	16	31
Wandsworth Borough	18	12	4	2	52	25	28
Southgate County	18	11	3	4	56	22	25
St. Mary's College	18	7	5	6	28	29	19
Old Colfeians	18	6	5	7	39	39	17
Old Bealonians	18	4	7	7	27	33	15
Pegasus	18	3	7	8	26	46	13
University of Hertford	18	5	2	11	33	34	12
Fulham Compton OB**	18	3	6	9	34	56	10
Ealing Association	18	3	2	13	20	66	8

DIVISION THREE

	P	W	D	L	F	A	Pts
Duncombe Sports	16	13	1	2	59	21	27
Kings Old Boys	16	11	1	4	53	33	23
B.B.C.	16	9	4	3	54	32	22
Mayfield Athletic	16	7	4	5	40	34	18
Brent	16	7	3	6	30	24	17
Hampstead Heathens	16	8	1	7	43	41	17
London Welsh	16	3	2	11	20	41	8
The Comets	16	2	3	11	24	63	7
Inland Revenue	16	1	3	12	27	61	5
Tesco Country Club				Withdrawn			

DIVISION FOUR

	P	W	D	L	F	A	Pts
The Cheshunt Club**	21	17	0	3	72	31	32
Centymca	21	13	4	4	72	43	28
The Rugby Clubs**	21	14	3	3	78	36	30
Economicals	21	11	4	6	84	43	26
Witan	21	9	4	8	43	43	22
Westerns	21	4	4	13	35	68	10
London Airways	21	3	3	15	38	63	9
Birkbeck College	21	0	2	19	17	112	2

*(** Points deducted - breach of rule)*

INTERMEDIATE SECTION

DIVISION ONE
10 Teams   won by   Old Woodhouseians Res.

DIVISION TWO
10 Teams   won by   Albanian 3rd.

DIVISION THREE
10 Teams   won by   Centymca Res.

DIVISION FOUR
Section Deleted

JUNIOR SECTION

DIVISION ONE NORTH
11 Teams   won by   Albanian 5th

DIVISION TWO NORTH
11 Teams   won by   Mill Hill Village 4th

DIVISION THREE NORTH
10 Teams   won by   Southgate County 5th

DIVISION FOUR NORTH
Section Deleted

DIVISION ONE S&W
10 Teams   won by   Old Grammarians 3rd

DIVISION TWO S&W
9 Teams   won by   Witan 3rd

DIVISION THREE S&W
10 Teams   won by   Brent 3rd

SENIOR CHALLENGE BOWL
won by Nottsborough

SENIOR CHALLENGE SHIELD
won by Old Woodhouseians

INTERMEDIATE CHALLENGE CUP
won by Albanian Res

INTERMEDIATE CHALLENGE SHIELD
won by Nottsborough Res

JUNIOR CHALLENGE CUP
won by Old Bealonians 3rd

JUNIOR CHALLENGE SHIELD
won by Old Woodhouseians 3rd

MANDER CUP
won by Old Woodhouseians 4th

MANDER SHIELD
won by Albanian 4th

BURNTWOOD TROPHY
won by Albanian 5th

BURNTWOOD SHIELD
won by Old Grammarians 5th

VETERANS' CHALLENGE CUP
won by The Cheshunt Club Vets

VETERANS' CHALLENGE SHIELD
won by Albanian Vets

UNIVERSITY OF LONDON

MENS LEAGUE

PREMIER DIVISION	P	W	D	L	F	A	Pts
King's College	14	9	3	2	26	15	30
R Holloway College	14	9	2	3	33	16	29
Goldsmiths' College	14	9	1	4	28	22	28
Q. Mary Westfield Clg	14	7	2	5	32	26	23
Imperial College	14	5	1	8	30	31	16
GKT (formerly UMDS)	14	4	2	8	19	27	14
University College	14	3	3	8	12	24	12
Lon. School Econ	14	2	2	10	25	44	8

DIVISION ONE	P	W	D	L	F	A	Pts
Imperial Clge Med S	18	15	3	0	62	17	48
R Sch Mines (IC)	18	9	5	4	46	35	32
Goldsmiths' College R	18	8	2	8	35	47	26
St Bart's & R Lon'n MS	18	7	4	7	39	40	25
R Free UC & Mx H M S	18	8	0	10	34	26	24
Royal Holloway Clge R	18	6	4	8	49	49	22
Imperial College Res	18	7	1	10	33	42	22
Q Mary Westfield C R	18	6	3	9	36	47	21
London School Econ R	18	5	5	8	26	37	20
University College Rs	18	4	3	11	23	43	15

DIVISION TWO	P	W	D	L	F	A	Pts
St George's Hosp MS	18	13	3	2	50	20	42
King's College Res	18	9	2	7	47	42	29
Imperial Clge M S Rs	18	9	1	8	33	32	28
King's College 3rd	18	9	1	8	33	34	28
London Sch Econ 3rd	18	7	5	6	36	31	26
University College 3rd	18	8	2	8	31	35	26
Royal Veterinary Clge	18	7	4	7	45	40	25
Royal Holloway C 3rd**	18	8	4	6	38	37	25
Sch.Orien'l African S	18	6	1	11	36	42	19
R.Free UC & Mx Hp R	18	2	1	15	17	53	7

*(** 3 pts deducted - breaches of Rule)*

DIVISION THREE	P	W	D	L	F	A	Pts
King's College 4th	17	12	2	3	58	21	38
London Sch Econ 4th	18	12	2	4	45	28	38
Imperial College 3rd	18	10	2	6	41	34	32
University College 4th	17	9	0	8	40	44	27
Q. Mary Westf'd C 3rd	18	8	3	7	40	44	27
Q. Mary Westf'd C 4th	18	8	2	8	32	36	26
Imperial College 4th	18	7	2	9	39	48	23
Wye College	18	5	4	9	29	27	19
GKT Res	18	4	6	8	31	39	18
R Free, UC & Mdx H 3rd	18	2	1	15	13	47	7

DIVISION FOUR
9 Teams   won by   University College 5th

DIVISION FIVE
10 Teams   won by   Won by Imperial College 5th

DIVISION SIX
6 Teams   won by   King's College 6th

DIVISION SEVEN
7 Teams   won by   Heythrop College

CHALLENGE CUP
Imperial College v London School of Economics   4-0

UPPER RESERVES CUP
IC Medical School Res v Goldsmiths' College Res   4-0

LOWER RESERVES CUP
Q Mary Westfield 6th v University College 5th   2-1

UNITED HOSPITALS CUPS
Senior Cup   No results advised
Junior Cup   No results advised

UNIVERSITY OF LONDON

WOMENS LEAGUE

PREMIER DIVISION	P	W	D	L	F	A	Pts
Royal Holloway Clge	16	16	0	0	77	18	48
Q Mary Westf'd Clge	16	12	0	4	54	17	36
University College	16	11	0	5	88	29	33
GKT	16	11	0	5	59	30	33
Imperial College	16	5	2	9	27	61	17
London Schl of Econ	15	4	2	9	20	44	14
SOAS	14	2	4	8	35	62	10
King's College	16	2	2	12	31	80	8
Goldsmiths' College	15	2	0	13	12	62	6

DIVISION ONE	P	W	D	L	F	A	Pts
Royal Free Hospital	12	7	5	0	49	9	26
St. George's Hospital	12	7	2	3	42	10	23
R. Holloway Clge Res	12	6	4	2	23	13	22
Royal Veterinary	11	4	2	5	17	2	14
G K T Res	12	4	2	6	12	32	14
Royal Free Hosp Res	11	2	2	7	8	32	8
Wye College	12	2	1	9	5	58	7
Royal Free Hosp 3rd				Withdrawn	11th March		
University Clge Res				Withdrawn	2nd February		

WOMENS' CHALLENGE CUP
Q Mary Westfield   v   Royal Holloway 1-1*, 2p3

ENGLISH SCHOOLS' FOOTBALL ASSOCIATION

Publicity: Mike Simmonds, 19 The Spinney, Bulcote, Burton Joyce, Nottingham NG14 5GX
Tel: 0115 931 3299   Fax: 0115 931 2758

THE INTERNATIONAL SEASON

THE E.S.F.A. UNDER 18 SQUAD

High hopes were expressed of the English Schools' Under 18 international squad after the summer coaching course at Keele and the selection weekends but the season proved a disappointing one. Horrendous weather conditions for three of the games and a series of injuries (even the Team Manager broke his leg during the season!) were partly to blame for those hopes not being realised.

After an opening friendly against Republic of Ireland in which England were saved by a last minute equaliser from Callum Willcock, the side opened their programme in the Centenary Shield, the Home International Championship, when they met the holders, Northern Ireland at Armagh. A poor performance on a heavily sanded wet surface resulted in a 2-0 defeat but the side regained the lost ground by beating Wales 2-1 at Newtown. England's hero was Robyn Onions who, coincidentally, plays for the host club in the Welsh League; he scored both goals and led the line well with admirable help from his striking partner Neil Barrett. After this boost, the deciding Shield match against Scotland was a huge disappointment with a dreadful first half performance culminating in a 'gift-wrapped goal' for the visitors which was sufficient for them to take the title.

The squad's other two matches were invitation games against continental opposition in Hungary and Austria. The former were the opponents for the annual schools' international at Wembley Stadium and, although the England defence was excellent throughout, Hungary will remember their visit to the national stadium, for the first time at schoolboy level, with pride as Zsolt Szabo's goal after 30 minutes proved the match winner. England's season ended on a high note with a 4-0 win over Austria at Plainmoor, Torquay, but it was, unfortunately, a case of 'too little, too late'.

RESULTS

v	Republic of Ireland at Galway City	1-1	Willcock
v	Northern Ireland at Armagh	0-2	
v	Wales at Newtown	2-1	Onions (2)
v	Hungary at Wembley	0-1	
v	Scotland at Bradford City	0-1	
v	Austria at Torquay United	4-0	Borley, Ward, Thompson (2 pens)

Front Row (L-R): Lee Thompson (South Yorkshire), Gary Burke (Durham), Oliver Rowland (Sussex), Dave Cook (Team Manager), Geoff Lee (Chairman), Malcolm Hird (Assistant Team Manager), David Schofield (Lancashire), Martin Rhodes (Essex), Billy Sobey (Devon). Middle Row: Alan Gallafant (Physio), Mark Ward (South Yorkshire), Stephen Windegard (Surrey), Jack Potter (Merseyside), Ben Williams (Greater Manchester), Michael Feely (Warwickshire), Mark Wallington (Goalkeeping Coach). Back Row: Ashley Nicholls (Suffolk), Nick Coyle, captain (Lancashire), Calum Willcock (Inner London), Peter Barkley (Essex), Robyn Onions (Shropshire), David Borley (Northumberland)

THE INTER-ASSOCIATION COMPETITIONS

ENGLISH SCHOOLS F.A. HEINZ KETCHUP TROPHY

FINAL   (1st Leg)   Cardiff   v   Salford   0-1   at Ninian Park, Cardiff
             (2nd Leg)   Salford   v   Cardiff   2-1   at Old Trafford

The first leg, which was played in brilliant sunshine, saw Cardiff dominate the first half driven on by a strong midfield led by captain Nicky Fish and led well up front by Josh Blenman, who three times went close to opening the scoring. It was much against the run of play when Salford went ahead on the stroke of half-time, substitute Stuart Heath scoring with a strong header. Salford's superior strength saw them on top after the interval, but they could not add to their score and Cardiff had a golden opportunity to level the scores in the last minute when Blenman was brought down in the penalty area only for the resulting spot kick to be missed.

The pattern of the second leg at Old Trafford replicated that of the earlier game with Cardiff on top for most of the first half. Blenham and Calliste both went close and Huggins shot wide from four yards before Salford stunned the Welsh side by taking the lead three minutes prior to the break. Striker Greg Traynor chased a long ball over the top of the defence and rounded the keeper to put his side in front. Within a minute, however, Cardiff were on level terms when Ryan Cachia shot in from eight yards following a long throw and a flick on by Calliste. It was Salford's long ball game which finally settled the tie when David Moore outpaced the visitors' defence on to a deep pass to score the goal that brought the Trophy to Salford for the first time since 1947.

Above: Former England schoolboy international Ryan Giggs presents the Heinz Ketchup Trophy to Salford's captain Danny Livesey.

Salford Squad: Ben Power, Chris Jones, Gary McInally, Danny Livesey (captain), Mark Ayres, James Fillingham, Shaun Holden, Stuart Heath, Joe Warmington, Simon Lawrence, Chris Lynch, David Moore, Wayne Owen, Greg Traynor, Mark Platt, Philip Hardman, Martin Henzell, Tim Deasy, Craig Corfield.

Cardiff Squad: David Wheadon, Lee Jones, Callum Hart, Nicky Fish (captain), Michael Porton, Joshua Dupres, Ryan Cachia, Michael Parkins, Ramon Calliste, Josh Blenman, Kirk Huggins, John Kift, Kieran Lock, Paul Byrne, Gareth Clarke, Michael Hayward, Adam Davies, Luke Brazier, Michael Lewis, Daniel Kerslake.

Salford's Victory Run

Round 1	v	Preston	2-0	Round 5 Rep	v	Coalville (H)	2-0
Round 2	v	St Helens	3-2	Round 6	v	Wirral (A)	0-0 aet
Round 3	v	East Northumberland	1-0	Round 6 Rep	v	Wirral (H)	3-0
Round 4	v	Spen Valley (W Yorks)	2-0	Semi-final	v	Liverpool (A)	0-0
Round 5	v	Coalville (A)	1-1 aet	Semi-final Rep	v	Liverpool (H)	2-0

E.S.F.A./F.A. PREMIER LEAGUE UNDER 19 COUNTY CHAMPIONSHIP

SEMI-FINALS

Northumberland   2   v   1   Merseyside
Middlesex   0,1   v   1,1   Suffolk

FINAL

Suffolk   2   v   0   Northumberland
At the Baseball Ground, Derby

Suffolk celebrated their 50th anniversary season in the best possible manner with a well deserved victory in the final. Well led by the outstanding Ashley Nicholls, who played throughout the season for the Under 18 international squad and has been offered a contract by Ipswich Town after having originally been released, Suffolk were strong all round with four of their players already having played in the Premier Division of the Jewson League. One of them, striker Paul Stokes, had scored eleven times in twelve games which Suffolk had played en route to the final and he made it twelve in the 36th minute at the Baseball Ground after collecting a pass from Shaun Hewlett. Suffolk made it 2-0 just before half time when a superb run from Nicholls took him 50 yards up and set up Robert Ford to score from close range. Suffolk could well have added to their lead in the second period but held on comfortably to win their first ever national title.

Suffolk Schools' Under 19 squad, winners of the E.S.F.A./F.A. Premier League County Championship.

Back Row (L-R): Jon Warnock (Assistant Manager), Danny Laws (Coach), Mark Debenham, Michael Steward, Paul Snowdon, Mark Hitcham, Robert Ford, Lochlann Brown, Barry Allard, Paul Wilkinson (Manager).
Front Row: Gary Hancock, Jay Denniss, Shaun Howlett, Mark Andrews, Chris Wright, Tom Edwards, Mark Goldfinch, Ashley Nicholls, Paul Stokes.

E.S.F.A./F.A. PREMIER LEAGUE UNDER 16 COUNTY CHAMPIONSHIP

SEMI-FINALS

Sussex	1	v	0	Hampshire
West Midlands	2	v	1	Staffordshire

FINAL

Sussex	1	v	0	West Midlands

at the Baseball Ground, Derby

E.S.F.A. UNITED NORWEST CO-OP UNDER 16 GIRLS' COUNTY CHAMPIONSHIP

SEMI-FINALS

Cheshire	2	v	0	Nottinghamshire
Surrey	2	v	3	Hampshire

FINAL

Cheshire	0	v	1	Hampshire

at Ewood Park, Blackburn

E.S.F.A. ADIDAS PREDATOR PREMIER UNDER 11 7-A-SIDE CHAMPIONSHIP

SEMI-FINALS
Rothrhithe and Bermondsey v Chester-le-Street   0-0
(Chester-le-Street won on corners)
Oxford v Nottingham   1-0

FINAL
Chester-le-Street v Oxford   0-0
Trophy shared
Semi-Finals and Final played at Wembley Stadium

Left: Oxford Primary Schools' F.A., joint winners of the E.S.F.A. Under 11 7-a-side Championship

THE INDIVIDUAL SCHOOLS' COMPETITIONS

E.S.F.A. HEINZ KETCHUP CUP

FINAL

Barking Abbey School   3   v   1   Ernest Bevin School
(Barking, Essex)   (Tooting)
At Highbury Stadium, Arsenal FC

With over a thousand schools entering the second season of the Heinz Ketchup Cup it was remarkable that two from the London area should meet in the final and fitting that the game should be played at the home of the leading London club. Over 3,000 spectators saw history made when Ernest Bevin's Owen Price scored what is believed to be the fastest ever goal in British football, recorded at an astonishing 4.07 seconds.

Price's goal came with the third touch of the match as the kick-off was touched forwards and then back to Price just inside his own half and, spotting the Barking keeper off his line and perhaps not concentrating so early in the match, he cheekily hit the ball over Danny Arnold's head for his remarkable record breaking goal.

Chris Cox (Arnold Hill) shoots from 30 yards despite the challenge of two St Aloysius defenders in the E.S.F.A. Schoolsnet Final at Molineux.

This shock was not sufficient to 'derail' a Barking Abbey side which had scored 63 goals in their progress to the final and they were level in the fourth minute. Bob Thanda swung a corner to the far post, his captain Tom Laws nodded the ball back across goal and Darren Blewitt headed firmly into the net. This exciting opening set the tone for the first half with Thanda, scorer of 29 goals in the competition, Jegede and Muasi a potent attacking force for Barking and Okafor, Faulkner and Hinze outstanding in defence for Ernest Bevin.

The second half was badly disrupted by injuries but it was the Barking school who looked more threatening and it was no surprise when they went ahead early in the second half through J.J. Jegede. Despite some near misses from Ernest Bevin, Barking Abbey clinched their victory in the first minute of injury time when a fine ball by Laws was met by Morrison who ran on to beat Akporotu with a low drive.

ROUTES TO THE FINAL

Barking Abbey High School				Ernest Bevin School		
Round 1	v	Axton Chase School (Longfield)	10-0	Round 1	v	Salesian College (Battersea)	8-1
Round 2	v	William Edwards School (Grays)	3-0	Round 2	v	St Thomas the Apostle (London)	2-0
Round 3	v	Simon Langton G.S. (Canterbury)	6-2	Round 3	v	Walworth School (London)	3-2
Round 4	v	St Bonaventure's School (London)	9-1	Round 4	v	Emerson Park School (Hornchurch)	3-2
Round 5	v	Sir John Leman School (Eccles)	8-0	Round 5	v	Geoffrey Chaucer School (London)	3-0
Round 6	v	King Alfred's School (Wantage)	4-0	Round 6	v	Friesland School (Sandiacre)	5-2
Round 7	v	Carshalton High School (Surrey)	5-2	Round 7	v	Aston Park School (Bristol)	4-3
Round 8	v	Mosslands School (Liverpool)	9-2	Round 8	v	Cardinal Heenan School (Liverpool)	5-4
Semi-final	v	Nailsea School (Bristol)	7-2	Semi-final	v	Cramlington H S (Northumberland)	3-2

E.S.F.A. SCHOOLSNET UNDER 16 INDIVIDUAL SCHOOLS CHAMPIONSHIP

FINAL

Arnold Hill School   1   v   2   St Aloysius College
(Nottinghamshire)   aet   (Inner London)
At Molineux, Wolverhampton Wanderers FC

Probably the most exciting of all the English Schools' F.A. competition finals last season saw St Aloysius College take the Under 16 title with an extra time winner against a brave Arnold Hill side. The game was eventually settled by a fine goal from the game's outstanding player, James Allen, who received the ball on the left of the penalty box after a fine run from substitute Chima Obiji. Allen dragged the ball further to his left and drove home the winner low into the far corner.

It was Allen who had given St Aloysius the lead in the 36th minute when his burst through the middle was stopped illegally and he calmly netted the resulting penalty. Arnold Hill were level within a minute as they broke quickly from defence and two passes put Scott Pickard clear on the left. His cross was a good one under pressure and Carl Westcarr rose impressively to head a classic equaliser. 1-1 was a fair score at the break as St Aloysius perhaps had more pressure, but Arnold looked more dangerous with Pickard twice going close and Cox hitting a 30 yard drive just over.

Arnold Hill dominated the first fifteen minutes of the second half but failed to make their advantage pay and, with several injuries and further visits from the trainers to deal with cramp, it was no surprise that normal time ended with the score still at 1-1. Both sides were very tired, but it was Allen's piece of magic that won the game.

Arnold Hill School: David Wadd, Matthew Wheat, James Leivers, James Harrison-Fletcher, Adam Simpson, John Hickling, Chris Cox, Jared Kelly, Carl Westcarr, Scott Pickard, Adam Francis, Adam Laurie, Daniel Nicholls, Stewart Schofield, Ben Hines.

St Aloysius College: Daniel Anfossy, Chrissy Theodule, Sammy Adebayo, Ashley Sandford, Marc Charles Smith, Steven Ward, Declan Scully, Duncan Byrne, Julian Ramirez, James Allen, Anthony Fisher, Chima Obiji, Williams Higgins, Anthony Balseiro, Panayotis Christofi, Dayo Pitan.

ROUTES TO THE FINAL

St Aloysius College				Arnold Hill School		
Won five games to become Inner London champions. National Competition:				Won five games to become Nottinghamshire champions. National Competition:		
Round 1	v	Royal Docks Community College	3-0	Round 1	v	Swanwick Hall School (Derbyshire)	3-2
Round 2	v	Bexley Grammer School (Kent)	2-0	Round 2	v	Toll Bar School (Humberside)	3-2
Round 3	v	St Thomas More School (Surrey)	1-0	Round 3	v	City School (South Yorkshire)	3-3, 3-0
Round 4	v	Barclay School	2-1	Round 4	v	Heworth Grange School (Durham)	3-1
Semi-final	v	Windsor Boys School (Berks)	1*1, 2-1	Semi-final	v	Woodlands School (Warwickshire)	2-0

E.S.F.A. UNITED NORWEST CO-OP UNDER 16 GIRLS' INDIVIDUAL SCHOOLS' CHAMPIONSHIP

SEMI-FINALS

Brooksbank School (South Yorkshire)	2	v	4	Helsby School (Cheshire)
Guildford County School (Surrey)	1,1	v	0,1	Castle Manor (Suffolk)

FINAL

Helsby School	4	v	1	Guildford County High School

Helsby took a tenth minute lead in the final at Chester City's Deva Stadium through Sarah Hollyhead and Karen Randles added a second just before the break. The Cheshire school continued to dominate the game in the second half, Kate Bradley scoring their third and Randles making it four before Guildford's late consolation.

E.S.F.A. UNDER 19 SCHOOLS AND COLLEGES CHAMPIONSHIP

FINAL

Cirencester College (Gloucestershire)	2	v	1	Lancaster and Morecambe College (Lancashire)

at The Hawthorns, West Bromwich Albion

Cirencester became the first side ever to win an English Schools' competition in three successive seasons with this tense victory over Lancaster and Morecambe. The Gloucestershire side seemed to be coasting to success when early goals from Wayne Turk and vince MacMackin put them two ahead, but Ryan Black's free kick on the stroke of half time brought Lancaster back into the game. Defences were generally on top in the second half, but Cirencester had some narrow escapes before confirming their record breaking achievement.

E.S.F.A. UNDER 19 INDIVIDUAL SCHOOLS' CHAMPIONSHIP

FINAL

Kingsway High School (Cheshire)	1	v	0	Maidstone Grammar School (Kent)

at The Hawthorns, West Bromwich Albion FC

E.S.F.A. ADIDAS PREDATOR UNDER 11 6-A-SIDE CHAMPIONSHIP

SEMI-FINALS

Clifton Without Primary School (York)	1	v	0	Cantrell Primary School (Nottingham)
Headington Middle School (Oxford)	0	v	0	Wallands Primary School (Lewes)

FINAL

Headington Middle School	0	v	0	Clifton Without Primary School

Trophy shared

Semi-Finals and Final played at Old Trafford

THE E.S.F.A. WAGON WHEELS UNDER 12 INDOOR 5-A-SIDE CHAMPIONSHIP

BOY'S FINAL

St Thomas the Apostle School (South London)	3	v	1	Crawshaw School (Leeds)

GIRL'S FINAL

Cottingham School (East Riding)	4	v	0	Bishop Johnston School (Bishop Auckland)

THE TIMES F.A. YOUTH CUP

featuring non-League club involvement from the Second Qualifying Round to the Third Round Proper

SECOND QUALIFYING ROUND

Home	Score	Away	
Brigg Town	1 v 5	Runcorn	60
Gretna	0 v 1	Stocksbridge P S	52
Emley	7 v 3	Worksop Town	60
Morecambe	1 v 2	Scarborough	156
Harrogate Town	1 v 3	Guiseley	24
Doncaster Rovers	6 v 1	Selby Town	228
Leigh RMI	0 v 2	Burscough	75
Ashton United	A W/O	Flixton	
Frickley Athletic	1 v 6	Crook Town	70
Gornal Athletic	4 v 2	Malvern Town	33
Ilkeston Town	10 v 0	Racing Club Warwick	108
Stratford Town	0 v 11	Glossop North End	
Holwell Sports	0 v 3	Kidderminster Harriers	65
Bilston Town	0 v 3	Lincoln United	30
Hinckley United	2 v 0	Redditch United	55
Belper Town	7 v 1	Bromsgrove Rovers	82
Bugbrooke St M	1 v 3	Newcastle Town	62
Walsall Wood	1,1 v 1,2	Long Buckby	44, 50
Birstall United	1 v 0	Hednesford Town	45
Rushden & Dia.	2 v 3	Burton Albion	77
Canvey Island	6 v 0	Somersett Ambury V&E	35
Ilford	6,0 v 0,3	Kempston Rovers	52, 34
Hornchurch	1 v 4	Hullbridge Sports	51
Cheshunt	4,2 v 2,2	Ruislip Manor	44, 53
Thetford Town	0 v 3	Wingate & Finchley	48
Stevenage Borough	4 v 0	Lowestoft Town	88
Hampton & Rich. B	0,1 v 1,5	Bedford Town	74, 50
Soham Town Rngrs	0 v 4	Histon	53
Banbury United	0 v 2	Clapton	45
Hayes	5 v 0	Wisbech Town	
Basildon United	4 v 1	Wembley	70
Gt Wakering Rvrs	3,2 v 2,1	Kingsbury Town	55
Chesham United	0 v 6	Staines Town	67
Barkingside	2 v 5	Cambridge City	41
Braintree Town	1,2 v 2,5	Southend Manor	58, 47
Stowmarket Town	0 v 2	Ipswich Wanderers	92
East Thurrock Utd	2 v 3	Potters Bar Town	46
Witham Town	2 v 3	Hitchin Town	45
Brentwood	2 v 0	Maldon Town	73
Bromley	6 v 1	Peacehaven & Tels.	38
Margate	1 v 3	Maidenhead United	80
Chipstead	4 v 2	Whyteleafe	56
Tonbridge Angels	6 v 0	Hillingdon Borough	54
North Leigh	2 v 3	Dover Athletic	40
Sandhurst Town	4 v 3	Whitstable Town	55
Oakwood	0 v 3	Woking	41
Greenwich Borough	5 v 3	Bedfont	
Burgess Hill Town	2 v 1	Reading Town	39
Didcot Town	1 v 4	Folkestone Invicta	60
Thamesmead Town	4 v 2	Cobham	39
Kingstonian	1 v 2	Welling United	70
Banstead Athletic	5 v 2	Oxford City	67
Carshalton Athletic	1,4 * 4,1	Lordswood	57, 65
Thatcham Town	2 v 3	Sutton United	69
Abingdon United	0 v 5	Aldershot Town	65
Dorking	0 v 5	Hailsham Town	28
Lewisham	0,2 v 2,1	Walton & Hersham	50
Salisbury City	1 v 2	Yeovil Town	44
Weston Super Mare	1 v 2	Brislington	42
Worcester City	11 v 2	Gloucester City	80
Pershore Town	1 v 5	Eastleigh	43
Cirencester Town	4 v 1	Bashley	63
Warminster Town	0,3 v 3,4	Forest Green Rvrs	73, 119
Mangotsfield United	0 v 4	Bath City	87

THIRD QUALIFYING ROUND

Home	Score	Away	
Doncaster Rovers	3 v 2	Emley	213
Scarborough	2,2 * 2,3	Burscough	94, 79
Stocksbrige P S	4 v 0	Ashton United	115
Crook Town	1,0 * 0,0	Guiseley	108, 83
Newcastle Town	4 v 0	Long Buckby	100
Runcorn	1,0 v 0,3	Lincoln United	72, 107
Kidderminster Harriers	2 v 0	Burton Albion	77
Birstall United	0 v 3	Ilkeston Town	76
Belper Town	1 v 0	Gornal Athletic	94
Hinckley Town	4 v 1	Glossop North End	66
Chesham	2 v 0	Canvey Island	65
Staines Town	4 v 2	Ilford	67
Bedford Town	1 v 3	Ipswich Wanderers	93
Hayes	0 v 1	Histon	
Hullbridge Sports	2 v 1	Brentwood	59
Hitchin Town	3 v 1	Basildon United	82
Stevenage Borough	3 v 0	Gt Wakering Rovers	105
Southend Manor	1 v 0	Wingate & Finchley	38
Cambridge City	1 v 0	Clapton	102
Tonbridge Angels	9 v 2	Bromley	72
Banstead Athletic	0 v 3	42	
Woking	3,2 v 2,3	Hailsham Town	101, 140
(Hailsham Town won 6-5 on penalties)			
Folkestone Invicta	3 v 1	Greenwich Borough	65
Chipstead	5 v 0	Potters Bar Town	60
Walton & Hersham	4 v 1	Thamesmead Town	66
Sandhurst Town	0 v 4	Welling United	63
Sutton United	9 v 0	Dover Athletic	85
Lordswood	4 v 0	Burgess Hill Town	75
Eastleigh	0 v 1	Yeovil Town	58
Brislington	0 v 3	Cirencester Town	38
Aldershot Town	1 v 4	Forest Green Rovers	110
Bath City	5 v 2	Worcester City	99

FIRST ROUND PROPER

Home	Score	Away	
Blackpool	2 v 0	Stocksbridge P S	166
Burscough	1 v 3	Rotherham United	125
Darlington	3,1 * 1,0	Crook Town	275, 199
Lincoln United	4,1 v 1,1	Lincoln City	302, 252
Wigan Athletic	0 v 2	Doncaster Rovers	374
Hitchin Town	4 v 3	Ipswich Wanderers	55
Barnet	3 v 0	Staines Town	85
Southend Manor	0 v 1	Newcastle Town	41
Belper Town	1 v 7	Cambridge United	163
Reading	2 v 1	Histon	285
Hinckley United	0 v 2	Colchester United	77
Hullbridge Sports	3,2 v 2,2	Cheshunt	63, 58
Northampton Town	0 v 2	Stevenage Borough	175
Kidderminster Harriers	2 v 4	Cambridge City	106
Ilkeston Town	1,1 v 1,3	Peterborough Utd	111, 257
Chipstead	1 v 3	Welling United	53
Maidenhead United	2 v 1	Romford	38
Wycombe Wanderers	3,2 v 2,0	Tonbridge Angels	144,152
Bath City	0 v 6	Brentford	128
Luton Town	2 v 0	Sutton United	101
Brighton & Hove Alb.	5 v 0	Yeovil Town	94
Lordswood	0 v 2	Folkestone Invicta	60
Hailsham Town	1 v 3	Cirencester Town	140
Leyton Orient	7 v 1	Walton & Hersham	126
Bristol City	4 v 0	Forest Green Rovers	117

SECOND ROUND PROPER

Home	Score	Away	
Chesterfield	2 v 1	Lincoln United	226
Chester City	2 v 1	Doncaster Rovers	152
Cambridge City	0,1 v 1,2	Brentford	182, 158
Stevenage Borough	0,1 v 1,2	Hullbridge Sports	184, 167
Newcastle Town	2 v 3	Hitchin Town	71
Lincoln Town	5 v 0	Maidenhead United	149
Peterborough United	1,2 v 2,3	Welling United	252, 303
Cirencester Town	0,1 v 1,4	Reading	120, 86
Millwall	6 v 0	Folkestone Invicta	186

THIRD ROUND PROPER

Home	Score	Away	
Hitchin Town	1 v 6	Leicester City	116
Welling United	1 v 3	Luton Town	346
Hullbridge Sports	0 v 6	Blackburn Rovers	202

CHANNEL ISLANDS REVIEW

THE JERSEY REVIEW
by Rob Batiste

St Paul's won the Jersey European Combination Division One title for the first time since 1988. On the night of the penultimate matches of the season, St Paul's recorded a comfortable 4-1 victory at Le Couvent against Rozel Rovers while title challengers St Peter failed to maintain their challenge after drawing 3-3 against First Tower at La Hague Manor. The points lifted St Paul's into an unassailable five point lead over St Peter and the clash between the clubs a few days later purely academic.

St Paul's Paul Duffy said after his first title success as manager: "We thoroughly deserved to win the game and I'm glad it's all settled. It's a great feeling and I'm delighted for everyone in the club. We were really up for it and considering the number of players we had missing through injury and being away it was really pleasing. We were superb in the second half."

It was a vintage performance from another former Jersey captain, which inspired St Paul's to their win. Andy Barker was involved in the build-up to three of his team's goals and scored the other himself. St Paul's other strike, the first of the game, came just 90 seconds in from Jason O'Prey.

St Paul's players and officials had to endure a tense fourteen minutes before they knew they were champions. After defeating Rozel 4-1, in a game which was reduced to 40 minutes each way because of a possibility of bad light, St Paul's players huddled around a radio to listen to the final minutes of challengers St Peter's game against First Tower at La Hague Manor. With St Paul's three points won, St Peter now had to win their game to retain an interest in the title race, and they were 3-2 behind when St Paul's game finished. St Peter were awarded a late penalty, in the third of the game, and Tower goalkeeper Sean McDonald saved it. The St Paul's contingent leapt for joy - but their happiness was short-lived because in their excitement and shouting they hadn't heard that St Peter had equalised from the rebound. Worried looks quickly replaced grinning faces until, after several more nail-biting minutes, the final whistle went and St Paul's were champions for the first time since 1988. Back came the happy faces, handshakes of congratulations and the sound of popping champagne bottles.

St Peter's championship hopes had been dashed in a match packed with drama and controversy. It was a heartbreaking end to the title campaign for Peter Vincenti's side as they were condemned to runners-up spot for the third consecutive year.

But Tower were seething with referee Chris Gouyette who awarded three penalties against them after they had built a seemingly unassailable 3-0 lead. The Saints players, too, were unhappy with the referee over one of Tower's goals. The official waved aside their offside appeals, 'keeper John McCulloch thought the whistle had gone and threw the ball outside of the penalty area for a free kick - only for Tower striker Colin Roworth to race in and hit the ball into the unguarded net. Peter Vincenti said: "St Paul's didn't win the league, we gave it away. I'm extremely disappointed for the players and the club, everyone has put a lot of hard work in. At the end of the day it wasn't about last night but over the season. We didn't get enough points earlier in the season to be in strong enough contention. We have dominated so many games this season but it's an inherent problem we've got, we press the self-destruct button. The first goal we conceded we didn't clear our lines while the second was a total farce and it effectively ended our title hopes. I'm not being critical of the ref. He didn't signal an infringement so you can't expect him to go back and give offside just because a team goes on to score a goal."

JERSEY EUROPEAN FOOTBALL COMBINATION
FINAL LEAGUE TABLES 1999-2000

DIVISION ONE

	P	W	D	L	F	A	Pts
St Paul's	18	14	1	3	47	21	43
St Peter	18	13	2	3	54	20	41
Scottish	18	10	2	6	39	24	32
First Tower	18	9	4	5	40	23	31
Rozel Rovers	18	8	3	7	43	33	27
Wanderers	18	8	3	7	25	26	27
Magpies	18	7	3	8	16	24	24
St Martin	18	4	3	11	19	44	15
Portuguese	18	4	1	13	21	48	13
St John	18	1	2	15	14	53	5

DIVISION TWO

	P	W	D	L	F	A	Pts
Trinity	18	16	2	0	84	13	50
Sporting Acs	18	11	4	3	55	21	37
Oaklands SS	18	10	4	4	60	28	34
St Clement	18	10	2	6	40	36	32
Grouville	18	8	5	5	31	19	29
St Ouen	18	8	1	9	36	30	25
St Brelade	18	5	3	10	25	51	18
St Lawrence	18	4	5	9	33	40	17
Beeches OB	18	3	4	11	22	46	13
Sporting Club	18	0	0	18	14	116	0

St Paul's won a hard-fought Junior Upton against Guernsey's St Martin's with Paul Aitken's goal settling the issue with just three minutes of extra-time remaining.

At a balmy Springfield, Jersey's under-18s champions, who missed a penalty in normal time, appeared to be heading for a replay in Guernsey when Aitken struck his decisive blow. Racing up St Paul's left, Aitken danced his way past a couple of sliding tackles before then cutting inside. He made further ground and from 25 yards his low shot beat goalkeeper Nathan Pattimore inside his right-hand post.

"I just hit and I thought the goalkeeper had it covered," said Aitken. "But he then let it go and it hit the net. I was delighted."

St Paul's joint-manager Bill Begbie said: "I though we just about deserved in the end. We got stronger as the game went on, especially in extra time. St Martin's tired before us and that surprised me because we had a lot of younger players than them. Both teams worked extremely hard and Andy Chevalier was my man-of-the-match because he didn't stop running."

St Martin joint coach Nigel Gavey said: "We're all very disappointed, it was a big game. We prepared well but on the day three or four of our players didn't perform. Full credit to St Paul's; they are a very young side and they played some good football. For the goal Nathan thought the ball was going wide. When he realised it wasn't it was too late for him to do anything about it. Nobody is blaming him because he kept us in the game with the penalty save. If it wouldn't have been for him we wouldn't have got to extra-time."

St Paul's Portsmouth Trophy success was their fourth in nine appearances. The club has now won two Upton's this season after the first-team's 2-1 success against Sylvans in Guernsey.

Late saves from goalkeeper Steve Carlyon helped Jersey to regain the Muratti Vase at Springfield in May. With Jersey leading 1-0 in the 84th Muratti final by captain Ricky Muddyman's 28th minute penalty kick, Carlyon produced two excellent saves in the closing three minutes to prevent Guernsey forcing extra time.

Carlyon, who was making a Channel Islands record 21st appearances for a goalkeeper, came good at the death after a nervous opening period when Jersey were fortunate Guernsey didn't capitalise on three excellent opportunities in the opening ten minutes.

Jersey weathered Guernsey's early storm and for the latter part of the first half they gained the upperhand - Muddyman striking the apex of the crossbar and upright with a thunderous shot from 35 yards. Just before the half-hour Jersey, who were playing well and full of inventiveness and running, got what turned out to be the match-winning goal. Yazalde Santos, later named man-of-the-match, picked up a loose ball in midfield. He produced a fantastic weaving run and after beating three defenders he was upended by Stuart Polson's foul tackle. Muddyman stepped up to crash the ball wide to Ian Drillot's left for his second Muratti penalty goal in three years at Springfield.

It was an excellent game and both goalkeepers pulled off fine saves. The match was the best seen at the level in the Islands for over a decade and Jersey's victory puts them 43-39 ahead in the series.

THE GUERNSEY SEASON
by Nigel Baudains

Sylvans clinched their seventh successive Barclays Priaulx League title with a strong finish to the season. Former Guernsey manager Alan Le Prevost began his second spell in charge of the club in January and from then on they won all ten of their remaining games. Le Provost's side is now just two wins away from St Martin's all-time record of nine consecutive Priaulx League titles.

Sylvans won the title by eleven points from North whom they met in the Barclays Stranger Cup Final that turned out to be one of the best games of the season. Having beaten North 5-0 at their St Peter's ground just four days earlier, it looked to be all over again when Sylvans raced into a 3-0 lead after only 30 minutes. But North pulled one back by half-time and were rampant in the second half, launching the comeback of the season to win 4-3. Ross Cameron, who scored twice and was named man-of-the-match, and Mark Ogier were both outstanding for the winners.

Sylvans striker Aide Exall finished as top scorer in Guernsey football with 23 goals for the season.

Meanwhile Kevin Le Tissier, the greatest goalscorer in the history of Guernsey football and brother of Southampton's Matt, announced he had hung up his boots at the end of the season. In a senior career that began in 1978 he made a total of 437 appearances for four different clubs scoring 445 goals. In 62 appearances for Guernsey he scored 58 times.

In the Channel Island club championship for the Upton Park Trophy, Sylvans met Jersey's St Paul's at the Track. Torrential rain in the 24 hours before the match threatened it with postponement, and the Guernsey Fire Brigade had to pump water from the pitch during the morning.

Goals either side of the break from wing-back Gerard Meadows gave the Jersey side a 2-0 lead before Martin Gauvain curled a free-keck into the top left corner to pull one back for Sylvans. Inspired by former Jersey captain Andy Barker, St Paul's were worthy 2-1 winners with their first success in the competition since 1987.

In representative football, Guernsey lost 1-0 to Jersey in the Muratti Vase Final at Springfield Stadium. The game is the premier fixture of Channel Island football and Guernsey and Jersey play Alderney, whose only victory came in 1920, in the semi-final in alternate years.

Jersey went into this year's game on the back of a 10-0 semi-final victory over Alderney, the most northern of the Channel Islands. Recent Murattis have been tentative affairs, but the first final of the new millennium was in stark contrast with open football and chances at both ends.

Both sides could have won comfortably had chances been converted but it was a penalty from Jersey skipper Ricky Muddyman, given after Stuart Polson had felled Ali Santos, that clinched it for the home side. Jersey now hold a 43-49 advantage in the competition that will celebrate its centenary in 2005.

Guernsey fortunes took a turn of the better in their second season in the South-West Counties Championship when they beat Somerset and Cornwall away on consecutive days. A goal from Matt Le Cras and an own goal from the home skipper, Mangotsfield United's Nigel Gillard, earned Guernsey a 2-0 win over Somerset at Paulton Rovers' Athletic Ground. The following day at Blaise Park, St Blazey, Tom Duff equalised for Guernsey after Falmouth Town's Justin Ashburn had given Cornwall the lead. The match appeared to be heading for a draw until Dale Garland, a student at Bath University, hit a late winner for Guernsey.

Guernsey disappointed in their last match of the season in the competition when they lost 1-0 at home to Gloucestershire, with John Meadows scoring the winner for the visitors. Guernsey finished fourth in Group B of the championship, which, though not good enough to reach the final,was a vast improvement on the previous season when they finished bottom of their group.

KEVIN LE TISSIER FACTFILE

Club	Season	App.	Goals
Vale Rec	1978-83	73	84
Rovers	1982-83	17	19
North	1983-89	105	93
Vale Rec.	1988-89	17	22
North	1989-95	133	140
Belgraves	1995-00	92	87
TOTAL		437	445

Guernsey appearances: 62 with 58 goals, including 20 Muratti caps and 19 goals

BARCLAYS PRIAULX LEAGUE
FINAL LEAGUE TABLE 1999-2000

	P	W	D	L	F	A	Pts
Sylvans	18	15	1	2	77	16	46
North	18	11	2	5	34	24	35
St Martin's	18	10	2	6	43	28	32
Vale Rec	18	8	4	6	35	23	28
Rovers	18	5	0	13	27	41	15
Belgraves	18	3	5	10	26	54	14
Rangers	18	3	2	13	15	71	11

SOUTH WEST COUNTIES CHAMPIONSHIP 1999-2000

GROUP A

	P	W	D	L	F	A	Pts
Sussex	5	4	1	0	13	2	13
Hampshire	5	4	0	1	12	4	12
Dorset	5	2	1	2	7	7	7
Royal Navy	5	1	2	2	7	10	5
Army	5	1	1	3	8	14	4
Gwent	5	0	1	4	2	12	1

GROUP B

	P	W	D	L	F	A	Pts
Devon	5	4	0	1	11	1	12
Wiltshire	5	3	1	1	6	4	10
Cornwall	5	3	0	2	9	4	9
Guernsey	5	2	0	3	5	8	6
Gloucestershire	5	1	2	2	2	7	5
Somerset	5	0	1	4	1	10	1

ISLE OF MAN FOOTBALL REVIEW 1999-2000

After one of the closest Championship campaigns for a number of years Peel regained the Isle of Man Division One Championship title, but only by goal difference from Douglas High School Old Boys. It was the first title for the Westerners since 1984 but they had to wait until their last game of the season to confirm it. They scored double figures against the Police also to take their season's tally to over 100 goals. They were the first team to reach that target for a number of years.

At one time it looked as if Douglas High School Old Boys would dominate the season as they challenged for all four major awards. The Douglas side started well by winning the Railway Cup, the competition for the top four at halfway. The Old Boys beat Peel in a penalty shoot out when it looked like no one would miss.

As the season progressed Peel, with the guidance of former League man Rick Holden, took the major honour despite a number of critical late injuries. Peel captain Steve Corkill just edged Old Boys' striker Brian Gartland for the Player of the Year Award.

The F.A. Cup was not worthy for its shock results with the eventual win going to Gymns who defeated the Police, who competed in their first Final to add to their relegation. St Mary's took the final trophy, The Hospital Cup, when they edged out newly promoted Laxey. For once neither promoted side, Union Mills or Ayre went back down to join the rest of the North of the Island Clubs in Division Two.

Pulrose United dominated Division Two scoring freely in the process. They also won the Paul Henry Cup, while Colby were successful in the Woods Cup. Corinthians from Douglas were the second promoted side and all three teams have based their success on their Youth Policy.

The Isle of Man national side has had a good year, as they followed their medal at the Nat West Island Games with the winning of the Guinness Cup against Semi Pro and Amateur International sides from Scotland, Northern Ireland and the Irish Republic. The final success was followed by a first ever win over a League side in the Summer Tournament. They beat Burnley 1-0 with the goal coming from Kevin McGarvey from Peel. Kevin, 18, is one of two players who have started at the Academy at Morecambe, and there are also Isle of Man players now at Stockport, Halifax, Runcorn and Newport Isle of Wight.

All this has come about in the last two years helped by an international set up run by Kevin Manning and Rick Holden. For the first time the Island entered the Under 18 County Cup beating Lincolnshire before losing in extra time to Durham 4-3.

Finally, at this time last year there was no Women's Football on the Isle of Man. Now there are fourteen clubs, and a two division league starts this autumn.

Dave Phillips

FINAL LEAGUE TABLES 1999-2000

DIVISION ONE

	P	W	D	L	F	A	Pts
Peel	24	20	2	2	104	21	62
DHSOB	24	20	2	2	92	33	62
St Mary's	24	19	1	4	97	33	58
Marown	24	12	4	8	53	46	40
Rushen	24	10	5	9	49	52	35
Castletown	24	8	7	9	50	54	31
Laxey	24	8	6	10	54	62	30
St George's	24	9	3	12	48	64	30
Union Mills	24	9	3	12	38	62	30
Gymnasium	24	7	0	17	41	55	21
Douglas Royal	24	5	6	13	36	68	21
Ayre	24	4	1	19	36	90	13
Police	24	2	6	16	49	107	12

DIVISION TWO

	P	W	D	L	F	A	Pts
Pulrose	26	22	2	2	122	30	68
Corinthians*	26	20	3	3	101	35	60
Colby	26	18	2	6	118	35	56
Ramsey	26	17	4	5	68	44	55
Bradden	26	14	6	6	84	40	48
Malow	26	10	7	9	75	78	37
RYCOB	26	10	5	11	56	56	35
Michael Utd	26	10	4	12	53	70	34
Foxdale	26	8	5	13	65	83	29
Barclays	26	8	3	15	65	82	27
Ronaldsway	26	7	4	15	45	71	25
Ondian	26	7	3	16	45	68	24
St Johns	26	5	4	17	60	83	19
Jurby	26	0	0	26	24	198	0

* points deducted

Above: Isle of Man Division One Champions, Peel

Above: Isle of Man Division Two Champions, Pulrose, pictured here after also winning the Paul Henry Cup

WOMEN'S FOOTBALL

Compiled by Tina Lightning

INTRODUCTION Women's football in this country and around the world is growing at a phenomenal rate at all levels. The participation rate is increasing and the amount of money being ploughed into the game is more than ever before. Women's football is attracting more top sponsorship deals due to increased television coverage. The sport is in the best position it has ever been in and future progression is inevitable.

DEVELOPMENT AT GRASS ROOTS There are now 31 licensed FA CENTRE OF EXCELLENCE programmes around the country. All centres are linked to professional clubs. Each Centre has a twenty-week programme covering all aspects of the game. At the end of the twenty weeks the girls get a chance to show off their skills at the One-day National Festival. This year the festival was held in May at Warwick University. Over 1,000 players took part and the standard was extremely good. Season 2000-2001 will see the start of the first SOUTH EAST FA CENTRE OF EXCELLENCE LEAGUE for girls. Nine centres will be participating. The league should improve the girls to a greater level because they will be playing good competition every week.

There are 2,500 school teams participating in the English Schools FA/Football in the Community competitions. There are over 1,150 girl's teams outside of school and now 41,000 registered players (compared to 36,000 last year). An increase in player's means there needs to be more coaches and there has been a 60 per cent increase in the number of female coaches this season, reaching nearly 6,500.

There is a continuing coordinated system of development work throughout England run by the FA (in partnership with many agencies) to ensure the long-term success of football for girls and women.

DOMESTICALLY The Women's AXA FA Premier League and the Women's AFA FA League Cup are becoming very high profile. This is due to extensive media coverage. This season there will be a minimum of six games televised live. The coverage will start with the first Charity Shield for women. The other games televised will include the FA Cup Semi-Finals and Final, and the League Cup Final. A number of International games will also be shown.

INTERNATIONALLY Hope Powell, Women's National Team coach, has been working extremely hard over the past year with the Senior Squad, Under 18's and Under 16's Squad. The senior squad have earned a qualifying position for the European Championships. The Under 18's will start their UEFA European qualifiers and the Under 16, who are still undefeated, will continue playing friendly matches.

PROFESSIONALISM Over the last year professionalism has entered the game. The United States are starting their professional League in April 2001 luring some of the best players in the world. The FA announces a commitment to establish a woman's professional league within three years and Fulham Football Club have taken on sixteen players on full-time professional contracts. This trend will definitely continue over the next few years, as the profile of women's football becomes still even higher.

AROUND THE WORLD Women's football is the fasting growing sport around the world. The 1999 Women World Cup created an exceptional atmosphere that has put women's football in the limelight ever since. With the backing of FIFA and UEFA the game will continue to grow at this phenomenal rate.

BUDGET The budget for women's football is forever expanding due to excellent sponsors. AXA continue with their support as do Nationwide and Umbro.

GRANTS This season the Active Sports Programme will begin where ten million pounds will be invested in the development of girl s football. Awards for All scheme is still very active, funding new projects with up to £5000.

AFA FA PREMIER LEAGUE CUP

QUARTER-FINALS
Arsenal   6   v   1   Bangor City
Bangor City was under pressure right from the start and it didn't take Arsenal very long to get on the goal sheet. Arsenal were far too strong for the City side.

Croydon   4   v   0   Wembley Mill Hill
Croydon had their eyes firmly set on the Semi's and they were not letting Wembley stand in their way. Wembley tried hard but could not stop the mighty Croydon.

Everton   2   v   1   Doncaster Belles
This was a tough match for both teams, but it was the Merseysiders that came out best on the day. The Belles fought right to the end for a place in the semi-finals but it wasn't to be.

Southampton   1   v   8   Tranmere Rovers
Well you would have expected this game to be a lot closer, but instead Tranmere went on a rampage with a great performance putting eight past the Saints.

SEMI-FINALS
Arsenal   2   v   1   Everton
A good competitive game between the South and the North. On this particular day, after a great tussle, it was the Southerners that came out on top.

Croydon   5   v   0   Tramner Rovers
It was now Tranmere's turn to suffer at the hands of a goal hungry side. Croydon came out really strong and dominated the whole game earning themselves a place in the Final.

FINAL
Arsenal   4   v   1   Croydon
The League Cup Final took place at the Underhill Stadium, Barnet F.C. on the Saturday 1st April. The game between the two London teams was likely to provide a first rate battle of strength, tenancity, and masterly skills. Fortunately, Arsenal didn't let the enthusiastic crowd down. The game was dominated by the lady Gunners right from the kick off, providing an assortment of classy goals along the way.

The first came from Arsenal's Irish International Ciara Grant, a stunning shot from outside the box right into the top corner. Croydon's England International goalkeeper, Pauline Cope had no chance. Arsenal, after goal number one, were overbearing for the South London girls.

The second of the four Arsenal goals came in the 47th minute, when Marieanne Spacey's superb cross met the head of Kirsty Pealling, who coolly knocked it past the keeper. Arsenal went from strength to strength, and only seven-minutes later goal number three appeared. This time it was Clare Wheatley's turn to get onto the score sheet. After a powerful run down the left flank she linked up with Sian Williams from a sweet back heel, took on the Croydon defender and elevated the ball over Cope.

Spacey finally got her chance to join the goalscoring trio, when teammate Anglia Banks was brought down in the box four minutes later. Spacey confidently struck home the penalty kick. A consolation goal come Croydon's way towards the end of the game but it was far to late to make any kind of comeback. So Arsenal lifted the AXA F.A. Women's Premier League Cup for the third consecutive season.

AFA FA WOMENS CUP

QUARTER FINALS
Everton   1   v   2   Croydon
This was a real competitive game between the North and the South but it was the Southerners that came out best on the day. Attendance: 150

Doncaster   3   v   0   Wembley Mill Hill
Wembley started off well enough although it didn't take long for the Belles to show why they have been a dominant force in the women's game for so long. Attendance: 450

Fulham   0   v   7   Arsenal
Fulham had done extremely well to get this far, but Arsenal put on a spectacular show and showed the South London team how big the gap was from the top flight. Attendance: 150

Wolverhampton Wanderers   0   v   1   Leeds United
A really tight game with some great attemps at goal. It was Leeds that converted a chance and that was enough to put them in the semi-final. Attendance: 400

SEMI-FINALS
Doncaster Belles   3   v   2   Arsenal

The game took place at Mansfield Town F.C. It was a superb atmosphere with a crowd of 1300 in attendence. The Belles that went in front with a goal from Micky Jackson. It didn't take the Ladies Gunners long to equalise with a strike from Ciara Grant.Doncaster's Karen Walker put them in front again but it was Marieanne Spacey that put Arsenal level. It was a second half winner that finally put the Belles through.

Leeds United   1   v   2   Croydon

The game took place at Ossett Town F.C. - 600 fans watched the game from the stands. It was Joanne Broadhurst who put Croydon ahead from the spot. Leeds equalised soon after. The deciding factor was when Bampton's deflected cross went past the Leeds keeper.

FINAL
Croydon   2   v   1   Doncaster Belles

Sheffield United F.C. was the venue for this year's Final. It was Doncaster who started off the game best. However, it was the London side that got on the score sheet first. Player-manager Debbie Bampton crossed the ball in from the right and Charmaine Walker (24 mins) headed the ball in.

The equalizer came soon after with much the some move as Croydon's. This time it was Karen Walker who crossed it in for the on-coming Vicky Exley (38 mins). At 1-1 the game was becoming more intense with a lot of missed opportunities. This included a Doncaster penalty taken by Karen Walker. It was the England goalkeeper, Pauline Cope, that came out on top when she pushed the spot kick wide of the post.

The game stayed a draw until the 68th minute when the young Gemma Hunt beat the Belles keeper after a tidy Croydon move. The London side was determined not to let go of this exciting lead and after 90 minutes had the Cup safely in their hands.

1999-2000 AFA WOMEN'S FOOTBALL AWARDS Sponsored by AXA

The second FA Women's Football Awards Sponsored by AXA took place in April 2000. Below are the Winners:

AXA PLAYERS PLAYER OF THE YEAR

National Division	Karen Walker	Doncaster Belles
Northern Division	Rachel Mander	Sheffield Wed
Southern Division	Trudy Williams	Barry Town

NATIONWIDE INTERNATIONAL PLAYER OF THE YEAR
Becky Easton   Everton

THE TIMES SPECIAL ACHIEVEMENT AWARD
Gillian Coultard   Captain of England and Doncaster Belles

WALKERS YOUNG PLAYER OF THE YEAR
Carly Hunt   Croydon and England

AXA MANAGER OF THE YEAR AWARD
Julie Chipchase   Doncaster Belles

AXA FA WOMEN'S PREMIER LEAGUE TOP SCORER

National Division	Karen Walker	Doncaster Belles
Northern Division	Melanie Reay	BS Krestrels
Southern Division	Trudy Williams	Barry Town

UMBRO MOST IMPROVED TEAM
BS Kestrels

LEADING GOALSCORERS
(League Only)

National Division			Northern Division			Southern Division		
21	K Walker	Doncaster	23	M Reay	BS Kestrels	40	T Williams	Barry Town
18	M Spacey	Arsenal	16	A Wilson	BS Kestrels	28	S Flint	Barking
17	M Garside	Doncaster	15	D Lanaghan	BS Kestrels	24	E Mead	Brighton
16	A Banks	Arsenal	14	S Newbould	Sheffield W	19	S Stanbury	Wimbledon
16	R Yankey	Arsenal	13	C Foster	Bangor City			

AXA F.A WOMEN'S PREMIER LEAGUE

The AXA FA Women's Premier League produced another great season and some exceptional talent was on show. The National Division remained at ten teams while the Northern and Southern Divisions were extended to twelve apiece bringing the total number of clubs in the Premier League to 34.

In the National Division the top three teams battled all the way through the season, but it was Croydon who had the edge over Doncaster Belles and Arsenal. The Belles topped the Division for the majority of the season, but Croydon plugged away with extra games to play and pipped Doncaster at the post. However, it took them to their last game of the season to secure the title, and they only did it by one point.

In the Northern Division BS Kestrels won the league very convincingly - claiming the title in early April by winning twenty games out of their 22. They also won the Umbro Most Improved Team Award 1999/2000 for their outstanding performance. In the Southern Division it was Barry Town that won the League title. They also made history for being the first Welsh team to get promoted into the National Division. It wasn't an easy task for them - Brighton & Hove Albion fought them all the way to the end. Barry Town ended up winning the title and promotion on goal difference.

FINAL LEAGUE TABLES 1999-2000

NATIONAL DIVISION

	Pld	GD	Pts		Pld	GD	Pts
Croydon	18	45	47	Southampton Saints	18	-9	18
Doncaster Belles	18	52	46	Millwall Lionesses	18	-24	18
Arsenal	18	60	41	Liverpool	18	-23	16
Everton	18	32	33	Reading	18	-64	11
Tranmere Rovers	18	7	28	Aston Villa	18	-75	1

NORTHERN DIVISION

	Pld	GD	Pts
BS Kestrels	18	69	61
Bangor City	18	25	48
Wolverhampton Wanderers	18	30	42
Leeds United	18	18	39
Sheffield Wednesday	18	2	35
Garswood Saints	18	6	34
Ilkeston Town	18	-7	25
Birmingham City	18	-15	23
Coventry City	18	-24	19
Huddersfield Town	18	-28	19
Bradford City	18	-29	17
Arnold Town	18	-47	11

SOUTHERN DIVISION

	Pld	GD	Pts
Barry Town	18	48	49
Brighton & Hove Albion	18	37	49
Wembley Mill Hill	18	36	44
Ipswich Town	18	13	42
Langford	18	17	37
Berkhamstead Town	18	-5	32
Wimbledon	18	14	30
Barnet	18	-10	28
Barking	18	10	27
Cardiff City	18	-32	21
Three Bridges	18	-18	18
Whitehawk	18	-110	0

FA PREMIER RESERVES SECTION SOUTH

		Pts
Arsenal Reserves	12	36
Brighton & Hove Albion Reserves	12	31
Southampton Saints Reserves	12	28
Langford Reserves	13	16
Wimbledon Reserves	9	13
Millwall Lionesses Reserves	10	13
Ipswich Town Reserves	13	12
Barnet Reserves	9	6
Barking Reserves	10	4
Berkhamsted Town Reserves	9	3

FA PREMIER RESERVES SECTION MIDS/NORTH

		Pts
Everton Reserves	14	42
Doncaster Reserves	12	31
Sheffield Wednesday Reserves	15	21
Aston Villa Reserves	16	19
Wolverhampton Reserves	16	19
Leeds United Reserves	13	16
Bradford City Reserves	14	0

COMBINATION LEAGUES

NORTHERN

	P	Pts
Oldham Curzon	22	58
Blackpool Wren Rovers	22	49
Leeds City Vixens	21	48
Manchester United	22	47
Middlesbrough	22	37
Stockport	22	35
Newcastle	22	24
Doncaster Rovers	22	20
Blackburn Rovers	22	18
Chester-le-Street	22	17
Preston North End	21	6
Sunderland	22	-2

MIDLANDS

	P	Pts
Newcastle Town	21	57
Telford United	21	47
Kinhurst	22	42
Chesterfield	21	39
Shrewsbury Town	20	30
Wyrley Rangers	21	29
Derby County	21	28
Mansfield Town	20	24
Highfield Rangers	21	23
Peterborough United	20	18
Worksop Town	20	15
Rea Valley Rovers	22	7

COMBINATION LEAGUES

SOUTH EAST			SOUTH WEST		
Chelsea	21	63	Newport Strikers	22	55
Charlton	22	47	Bristol Rovers	22	53
Enfield	22	38	Swindon Town	22	48
Racers	22	38	Cheltenham	22	43
Stowmarket	22	35	Saltash Pilgrims	22	36
Hampton	22	35	Denham United	21	32
Watford	22	32	Portsmouth	22	29
Bedford Town Bells	22	26	Yeovil Town	22	26
Northampton Town	22	22	Oxford United	22	22
Crowborough Athletic	21	21	Bristol City	21	21
Clapton	22	14	Southampton WFC	22	9
Abbey Rangers	22	6	Bath City	22	4

WOMEN'S PYRAMID OF FOOTBALL

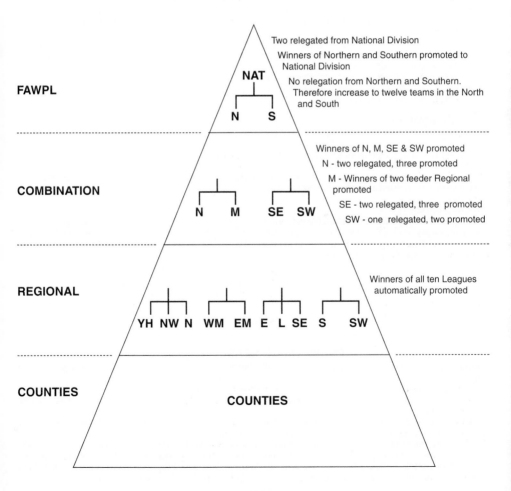

FAWPL

NAT

N   S

Two relegated from National Division

Winners of Northern and Southern promoted to National Division

No relegation from Northern and Southern. Therefore increase to twelve teams in the North and South

COMBINATION

N   M   SE   SW

Winners of N, M, SE & SW promoted

N - two relegated, three promoted

M - Winners of two feeder Regional promoted

SE - two relegated, three promoted

SW - one relegated, two promoted

REGIONAL

YH NW N   WM EM E L SE S   SW

Winners of all ten Leagues automatically promoted

COUNTIES

COUNTIES

THE FIFTH EUROPEAN CHAMPIONSHIP FOR WOMEN

ENGLAND'S 1999-2001 QUALIFYING GROUP

Group 2	P	W	D	L	F	A	Pts
Norway	6	6	0	0	30	0	15
England	6	3	1	2	8	13	10
Portugal	6	1	1	4	4	14	4
Switzerland	6	1	0	5	1	15	3

Norway	v	Switzerland	4-0	Portugal	v	England	2-2
Switzerland	v	England	0-3	Norway	v	Portugal	5-0
Portugal	v	Norway	0-4	England	v	Switzerland	1-0
Portugal	v	Switzerland	1-0	Norway	v	England	8-0
England	v	Portugal	2-0	Portugal	v	Norway	0-5
England	v	Norway	0-3	Switzerland	v	Norway	0-6
Switzerland	v	Portugal	0-2				

INTERNATIONAL FOOTBALL

SENIOR ENGLAND SQUAD

The England National Coach, Hope Powell, and her team will be playing on their biggest stage yet. Set the scene - France versus England women in September this year play at the exceptional Vellodrome Stadium in Marseille, just before France (World and European Champions) take on the FIFA All-star team. England were invited to take part in this event as a fine reward for the great work the Football Association have done to promote the women's game in this country.

Even though the game will be of a friendly nature, it will be a great opportunity for Hope to prepare her squad for the play-off games against Iceland. Defeating the girls from across the Channel will secure their place in the European Championships in the summer of 2001.

England competed well during the qualifying rounds having victories over Portugal and Sweden; but it was the strong and powerful Norwegians that prevented them from qualifying automatically. England finished second in their group earning them the qualifying position.

ENGLAND UNDER 18's

The England Under 18's squad was established in 1997 to develop young players at international level, to give them a taste of what it is like to put on an England shirt. They have done exceptionally well in the UEFA Under 18's Tournament for the last three years especially in 1998 when they reached the quarter-finals. Outstanding players in the Under 18 squad have been Carly Hunt (Croydon), Katie Chapman (Millwall Lionesses), and Fara Williams (Chelsea). You can be sure that these young players will be filling the boots of the senior players very soon. Katie has already made her full debut for the Senior England side.

ENGLAND UNDER 16's

The England Under 16 squad has done extremely well over the last year. They remain unbeaten in four games. Their first was a friendly against Scotland when they played at Wembley in front of a crowd of 14,000. They won the match 5-0. The squad then hosted a Mini Four-Team tournament where they beat Scotland for a second time and added the Republic of Ireland and the USA to their hit list.

	P	W	D	L	F	A	Pts
England	3	3	0	0	5	0	9
Republic of Ireland	3	1	1	1	5	3	4
USA	3	0	2	1	2	3	2
Scotland	3	0	1	2	3	9	1

PREVIEW FOR SEASON 2000-01

Making history is a great way to start any season. For the first time in women's football a Charity Shield game will be played to kick start the National Premiership.

The game will be between League Cup Winners Arsenal and Double Winners Croydon. It will be a great indication to other teams what to expect for next season. The game will be played at Craven Cottage and will be televised by Sky.

Predictions for the coming season have always been difficult but as in men's football you will always expect your top five teams to shine through. This is just the same for women's game.

The top three teams for next season will be very much the same as last. Croydon, Doncaster Belles and Arsenal. However, Arsenal will not be content with third place again next season. They will be pushing to win the League championship as they did in 1997 and in 1998. However, don't expect the other teams in the league to be a walk over. There is some exceptional talent throughout the Premiership to keep your eye on.

PREVIEW FOR SEASON 2000-01

CROYDON
Expect another strong season from the South London team. Not only are they in talks with Charlton for a take-over but also a couple more England internationals may be heading their way.
One to watch - Carly Hunt "Walkers Young Player of the Year" will be expected to have another outstanding season.

DONCASTER
Look to be the only stand-alone club next season and look set to challenge for pole position once again. Great developments off the pitch looking set to have their own ground built very soon.
One to watch - Karen Walker will want to regain the title of top goal scorer again this season. She is odds on to do it as well. No one has yet matched her goal scoring talent.

ARSENAL
The name itself attracts some of the best talent in this country and from around the globe. Don't be surprised if they pip Croydon to the post this season, as well as winning one of the two cups.
One to watch - Marie Anne Spacey will play to the standard she has been accustomed to for so many years.

EVERTON
Expect a solid season from the girls in blue. Although it looks like a couple of their top players are heading to join a top London side.
One to watch - Kelly Shimmin a definite star for the future.

TRANMERE
Well, the Merseysiders will be really pleased to hold on to their star player Sue Smith. She was offered a big contact to play in the pro-league but declined the offer to show her loyalty to Tranmere.
One to watch - Definitely Sue Smith will shine again this season.

SOUTHAMPTON
Will look to push the top teams with their young vibrant side again this season. However, they may have lost their star midfielder Jayne Ludlow to a top London side. This will hurt but be sure they have what it takes to compete with the top sides.
One to watch - Gemma Ritchie, a sparky youngster, will show her potential once again at the top flight.

MILLWALL
Over the years have benefited from the development of their young talent. They had a quiet season last year but their spirit and determination always makes them a force to be reckoned with. A team to watch this season.
One to watch - Leanne Champ, a smart young defender, will look to give even the top strikers a run for their money.

LIVERPOOL
Not the best of seasons for them last year but they always do enough to stay in the top flight.
One to watch - Clare Taylor should help them survive at the top level. A good all round athlete - also part of the England cricket team.

BARRY TOWN
Making history as they are the first Welsh team to break into the National Division. Let's hope the Premiership doesn't prove too tough for them.
One to watch - The club's top goalscorer Trudy Williams with a tally of 40 goals should hopefully net a few more for the newcomers.

B.S. KESTRELS
Promoted from the Northern Division will be strengthening their existence by linking up with Sunderland Football Club. Having the backing from a professional outfit will hopefully help them in their journey to survive in the top flight.
Two to watch - Striking duo Melanie Reay and Donna Lanaghan netted 38 goals between them last season. Let's hope they can find the same form again.

With the continuing support and influence of Sky Sports, AXA, Umbro, The Times, and Nationwide, the National Premier League looks set to have the biggest season yet. Media exposure is the key to success and with a minimum of five games on Sky this coming season should definitely create interest amongst football fans in general.

THE FOOTBALL ASSOCIATION

FIXTURE LIST 2000-01

SEPTEMBER 2000

02 Sat	International (World Cup Qualifier) - no England fixture
	F.A. Cup sponsored by AXA Preliminary Round
	AXA F.A. Youth Cup 1Q*
06 Wed	Football League Cup 1 (2)
09 Sat	F.A. Carlsberg Vase 1Q
10 Sun	AXA F.A. Women's Cup Extra Preliminary Round
12/13 Tue/Wed	UEFA Champions League - Group 1, Match Day 1
14 Thu	UEFA Cup 1 (1)
16 Sat	F.A. Cup sponsored by AXA 1Q
19/20 Tue/Wed	UEFA Champions League - Group 1, Match Day 2
20 Wed	Football League Cup 2 (1)
23 Sat	F.A. Carlsberg Vase 2Q
	AXA F.A. Youth Cup 2Q*
24 Sun	AXA F.A. Women's Cup Preliminary Round
26/27 Tue/Wed	UEFA Champions League - Group 1, Match Day 3
27 Wed	Football League Cup 2 (2)
28 Thu	UEFA Cup 1 (2)
30 Sat	F.A. Cup sponsored by AXA 2Q

OCTOBER 2000

01 Sun	F.A. Umbro Sunday Cup 1
07 Sat	England v Germany - FIFA World Cup Qualifier
	AXA F.A. Youth Cup 3Q*
	F.A. County Youth Cup 1*
11 Wed	Finland v England - FIFA World Cup Qualifier
14 Sat	F.A. Cup sponsored by AXA 3Q
17/18 Tue/Wed	UEFA Champions League - Group 1, Match Day 4
20 Fri	U15 Victory Shield - Northern Ireland v England - venue tbc
21 Sat	F.A. Carlsberg Vase 1P
24/25 Tue/Wed	UEFA Champions League - Group 1, Match Day 5
26 Thu	UEFA Cup 2 (1)
28 Sat	F.A. Cup sponsored by AXA 4Q
	AXA F.A. Youth Cup 1P*
29 Sun	AXA F.A. Women's Cup 1

NOVEMBER 2000

01 Wed	Football League Cup 3
03 Fri	U15 Victory Shield - Wales v England - venue tbc
04 Sat	F.A. Umbro Trophy 1
05 Sun	F.A. Umbro Sunday Cup 2
07/08 Tue/Wed	UEFA Champions League - Group 1, Match Day 6
09 Thu	UEFA Cup 2 (2)
11 Sat	F.A. Carlsberg Vase 2P
	AXA F.A. Youth Cup 2P*
	F.A. County Youth Cup 2*
15 Wed	International Friendly
18 Sat	F.A. Cup sponsored by AXA 1P
19 Sun	AXA F.A. Women's Cup 2
20 Mon	F.A. XI v Northern Premier League
21 Tue	F.A. XI v Southern League
21/22 Tue/Wed	UEFA Champions League - Group 2, Match Day 1
22 Wed	F.A. XI v Isthmian League
23 Thu	UEFA Cup 3 (1)
28 Tue	Inter-Continental Cup
29 Wed	F.A. Cup sponsored by AXA 1P replays
	Football League Cup 4

DECEMBER 2000

01 Fri	U15 Victory Shield - England v Scotland - venue tbc
02 Sat	F.A. Umbro Trophy 2
03 Sun	F.A. Umbro Sunday Cup 3
05/06 Tue/Wed	UEFA Champions League - Group 2, Match Day 2
07 Thu	UEFA Cup 3 (2)
09 Sat	F.A. Cup sponsored by AXA 2P
	F.A. Carlsberg Vase 3P
	AXA F.A. Youth Cup 3P*
10 Sun	AXA F.A. Women's Cup 3
13 Wed	Football League Cup 5
16 Sat	F.A. County Youth Cup 3*
20 Wed	F.A. Cup sponsored by AXA 2P replays

JANUARY 2001

06 Sat	F.A. Cup sponsored by AXA 3P
07 Sun	AXA F.A. Women's Cup 4
08 Mon	F.A. XI v British Universities
10 Wed	Football League Cup SF1

JANUARY 2001 cont.

13 Sat	F.A. Umbro Trophy 3
14 Sun	F.A. Umbro Sunday Cup 4
17 Wed	F.A. Cup sponsored by AXA 3P replays
20 Sat	F.A. Carlsberg Vase 4P
	AXA F.A. Youth Cup 4P*
24 Wed	Football League Cup SF2
27 Sat	F.A. Cup sponsored by AXA 4P
	F.A. County Youth Cup 4*
28 Sun	AXA F.A. Women's Cup 5
30 Mon	F.A. XI v Combined Services

FEBRUARY 2001

03 Sat	F.A. Umbro Trophy 4
04 Sun	F.A. Umbro Sunday Cup 5
07 Wed	F.A. Cup sponsored by AXA 4P replays
10 Sat	F.A. Carlsberg Vase 5P
	AXA F.A. Youth Cup 5P*
13 Tue	England Semi-Professional International
13/14 Tue/Wed	UEFA Champions League - Group 2, Match Day 3
14 Wed	International Friendly
15 Thu	UEFA Cup 4 (1)
17 Sat	F.A. Cup sponsored by AXA 5P
18 Sun	AXA F.A. Women's Cup 6
20/21 Tue/Wed	UEFA Champions League - Group 2, Match Day 4
22 Thu	UEFA Cup 4 (2)
24 Sat	F.A. Umbro Trophy 5
25 Sun	F.A. Umbro Sunday Cup SF
28 Wed	F.A. Cup sponsored by AXA 5P replays
	International Friendly

MARCH 2001

03 Sat	F.A. Carlsberg Vase 6P
	AXA F.A. Youth Cup 6P*
04 Sun	Football League Cup Final
06/07 Tue/Wed	UEFA Champions League - Group 2, Match Day 5
08 Thu	UEFA Cup QF (1)
10 Sat	F.A. Cup sponsored by AXA 6P
	F.A. Umbro Trophy 6
	F.A. County Youth Cup SF*
13/14 Tue/Wed	UEFA Champions League - Group 2, Match Day 6
15 Thu	UEFA Cup QF (2)
17 Sat	F.A. Carlsberg Vase SF 1
20 Tue	England Semi-Professional International
21 Wed	F.A. Cup sponsored by AXA 6P replays
24 Sat	England v Finland - FIFA World Cup Qualifier

MARCH 2001 cont.

24 Sat cont.	F.A. Carlsberg VAse SF 2
	AXA F.A. Youth Cup SF 1*
25 Sun	AXA F.A. Women's Cup SF
28 Wed	Albania v England - FIFA World Cup Qualifier
31 Sat	F.A. Umbro Trophy SF 1

APRIL 2001

03/04 Tue/Wed	UEFA Champions League QF (1)
05 Thu	UEFA Cup SF (1)
07 Sat	F.A. Umbro Trophy SF 2
08 Sun	F.A. Cup sponsored by AXA SF
14 Sat	AXA F.A. Youth Cup SF2*
17/18 Tue/Wed	UEFA Champions League QF (2)
19 Thu	UEFA Cup SF (2)
25 Wed	International Friendly
28 Sat	F.A. County Youth Cup Final (fixed date)

MAY 2001

01/02 Tue/Wed	UEFA Champions League SF (1)
04 Fri	AXA F.A. Youth Cup Final (1)
05 Sat	Football League ends
07 Mon	AXA F.A. Women's Cup Final
09 Wed	UEFA Champions League SF (2)
11 Fri	AXA F.A. Youth Cup Final (2)
12 Sat	F.A. Cup sponsored by AXA Final
13 Sun	Football League Play-Off SF (1)
16 Wed	UEFA Cup Final
	Football League Play-Off SF (2)
19 Sat	Premier League ends
23 Wed	UEFA Champions League Final
26 Sat	Football League Division 3 Play-Off Final
27 Sun	Football League Division 2 Play-Off Final
28 Mon	Football League Division 1 Play-Off Final

JUNE 2001

02 Sat	International (World Cup Qualifier) - no England fixture
06 Wed	Greece v England - FIFA World Cup Qualifier
to be decided:	F.A. Carlsberg Vase Final
	F.A. Umbro Trophy Final
	F.A. Umbro Sunday Cup Final
	Football League Cup Final

AXA F.A. Women's Cup dates - to be confirmed
* closing date of Round

WIRRAL PROGRAMME CLUB

The non-profit making Club formed in March 1967
Secretary: I.R.W. Runham
3 Tansley Close, Newton, West Kirby, Wirral CH48 9XH   Tel: 0151 625 9554

25th NON-LEAGUE FOOTBALL PROGRAMME OF THE YEAR SURVEY 1999-2000

There were entries from 1011 clubs, 109 down on the previous season. With reserve and youth programmes there were 1107 places.

Again there were many superb programmes with numerous clubs showing an improvement on last season. It is again pleasing to see clubs issuing for the first time plus some after a gap of many seasons. All clubs that issue a programme are to be congratulated, AS a single sheet is better than nothing. There would be no programmes without the hard work of the editors, plus any helpers they can find, put in, and I'm sure that most supporters and many committee members do not realise the time and effort needed to produce a programme, so our special thanks go to all these people. Our thanks are also due to all those who sent in programmes for the survey and to those who helped spread the word, the clubs themselves, their supporters, our members, other collectors, the Football Association, all the League Secretaries, the Non League Directory, Team Talk, the Football Traveller, Welsh Football, Programme Monthly, and all those who lent us programmes for the survey. Sincere apologies go to anyone inadvertently omitted.

Some clubs only issue for a Saturday game, some for special games, some change the style, content, price, editor, etc, during the season; some have special connections with printers, etc., and often we are not aware of these circumstances. Obviously we can only survey the programmes we receive. Some are from early in the season, others from just before the closing date, most from in between. The results always create a lot of interest with varying points being expressed; some of these we hear often second or third hand, but most miss our ears, so if you have any comments on the survey please let us know. I am sure the day will never come when there is complete agreement over the results, but the more discussion there is over the survey the better, as it will keep programmes to the forefront and hopefully encourage clubs at least to maintain or even improve the standards, or better still it may encourage more clubs to issue next season.

The club with the overall winning programme will receive a framed certificate; the winners of each league will also receive a certificate. Please note the programmes have been surveyed, not as many assume voted upon. Marks were awarded to each programme as follows (the maximum marks available in each section are given):
Cover 15 (design 10, match details 5),   **Page size** 10,   **Team layout and position** within the programme 10,
Results 10, **League tables** 10,   **Price** 15,   **Pictures** 15,   **Printing and paper quality** 20, **Frequency of issue** 20,
Value for money 20 (this takes into account the ratio of adverts to content, the club's league etc),
Contents 245 (other than those listed) taking into account their relevance to the club, its league, environs etc, the size of the print used, the spacing between the lines, the size of the margins, and if all the contents are original or reproduced (from League Bulletins, newspapers, magazines etc).
To gain full marks in the Frequency of issue section we needed to receive programmes from ten different current season matches for each team entered (allowances were made if ten home games were not played by the closing date and we were informed of this). The minimum entry was one programme.
As many programmes varied from issue to issue all were surveyed, the marks in each section being totalled and divided by the number of issues to get the final mark for each section, and the marks from each section were then being added up to get the final score.
A new standard of marks is set each season so this campaign's totals should not be compared with those of earlier seasons, as the comparison will almost certainly be inaccurate; a programme identical to last season's will almost certainly have gained different marks.

We have already received many entries for the Specials section of the survey (for one-offs, big cup ties, friendlies, testimonials, charity matches, first/last at a ground, etc), and the closing date for receiving these is 30th June 2001. To receive the results, expected by the end of July, we would appreciate it if you could send a stamped sae. Thank you.

The results of this season's survey are as follows:

Best Non-League Programme Nationally 1999-2000	**1st**	Newton Abbot Spurs	260 points
	2nd	Hoddesdon Town	210 points
	3rd	Langney Sports	195 points

NATIONAL TOP 30: 1 Newton Abbot Spurs 260;   **2** Hoddesdon Town 210;   **3** Langney Sports 195;
4 Denaby United 193;   **5** Northwood 189;   **6** Hayes 184;   **7** Lancing 183;   **8** Aldershot Town 177;
9= Dagenham & Redbridge 177; Portishead 177;   **11** Hucknall Town 172;   **12** Uxbridge 171;
13 Evans & Williams Sports 170;   **14=** Sutton United 167; Cwmtillery 167; Kings Field Casuals 167;
17= Torrington 166; Langford Ladies 166;   **19=** Coalville Town 164; Hemsworth MW 164;
21 Amesbury Town 163;   **22** Poole Town 162;   **23=** AFC Sudbury 161; Barrow 161;
25= Rushden & Diamonds 160; Northampton Spencer 160;   **27=** St Leonards 158; Redhill 158;
Blackfield & Langley 158; Colden Common Reserves 158; Penn & Tylers Green Reserves 158; St Andrews U15 158

INDIVIDUAL LEAGUE RESULTS The first number after the club"s name is the number of programmes received - 10 shows ten or more different programmes were received, or every programme if less than ten matches were played, the second number is the total points gained. The leagues are in no particular order.

LEAGUE + No of entries		Entries	FIRST		SECOND		THIRD	
Football Conference		22	Hayes	10-184	Sutton Utd	10-167	Rushden & Dia	6-160
Dr Martens	Overall	63	St Leonards	10-158	Witney Town	10-156	Worcester City	10-154
	Prem Div	20	Worcester C	10-154	Bath City	10-149	Weymouth	1-143
	West Div	22	Hinckley Utd	1-15	Stourbridge	10-149	Tiverton Town	10-139
	East Div	21	St Leonards	10-158	Witney Town	10-156	Folkestone Inv	10-142
Rymans	Overall	78	Northwood	10-189	Aldershot Town	10-177	Dagenham &Redb	10-176
	Prem Div	22	Aldershot Town	10-177	Dagenham & Red	10-176	Hitchin Town	10-157
	Div.1.	20	Uxbridge	10-171	Wealdstone	10-156	Bishops Stortford	10-149
	Div.2.	19	Northwood	10-189	Berkhamsted T	10-145	Wivenhoe Town	1-144
	Div.3.	17	Lewes	10-156	Croydon Athletic	10-151	Bracknell Town	1-142
Unibond	Overall	39	Hucknall Town	10-172	Barrow	10-161	Leek Town	1-150
	Prem Div	20	Hucknall Town	10-172	Barrow	10-161	Leek Town	1-150
	Div.1.	19	Bradford Pk Av	=10-130			Workington	6-129
			Harrogate Town	=10-130				
Minerva	Overall	46	Hoddeson Town	10-210	Arlesey Town	10-154	Holmer Green	1-151
Spartan	Prem Div	19	Hoddeson Town	10-210	Arlesey Town	10-154	Holmer Green	1-151
South	Sen Div	18	Cockfosters	10-146	Bridger Packing	1-121	Leverstock Gr'n	10-117
Midlands	Div 1	9	Crawley Green	1-108	Old Dunstablians	9-100	Old Bradwell Utd	1-94
Courage Combined Co		14	Ash United	10-132	Walton Casuals	10-128	Farnham Town	10-122
Bass	Overall	16	Erith Town	10-141	Gray Wanderers	10-135	Deal Town	10-128
Brewers	Div 1	10	Erith Town	10-141	Gray Wanderers	10-135	Deal Town	10-128
Kent	Reserves	3	Dartford	3-89	Erith Town	3-87	Ramsgate	1-62
Schweppes Essex Senior		6	Sawbridgeworth T	10-101	Bury Football Acd	4-100	Saffron Walden T	1-89
Jewson Wessex		16	Brockenhurst	10-129	Andover	10-124	Lym'ton & N Milton	4-123
Unijet	Overall	30	Langney Sports	10-195	Lancing	10-183	Redhill	10-158
Sussex	Div 1	14	Langney Sports	10-195	Redhill	10-158	Ringmer	10-144
County	Div 2	7	Lancing	10-183	Oving	10-144	Crawley Down	1-108
	Div 3	9	Ifield	10-147	Haywards Heath	10-111	Seaford Town	1-89
Screwfix	Overall	14	Torrington	10-166	Magotsfield Utd	10-141	Street	7-122
Direct	Prem Div	7	Magotsfield Utd	10-141	Backwell United	3-117	Taunton Town	1-104
	Div 1	7	Torrington	10-166	Street	7-122	Calne Town	10-112
Jewson	Overall	25	AFC Sudbury	10-161	Lowestoft Town	10-154	Gt Yarmouth T	10-141
Eastern	Prem Div	18	AFC Sudbury	10-161	Lowestoft T	10-154	Gt Yarmouth T	10-141
	Div 1	7	Downham Town	1-130	Haverhill Rovers	1-101	Swaffham T	10-96
United	Overall	16	N'ampton Spen	10-160	Eynesbury Rovers	10-146	Bourne Town	10-125
Counties	Prem Div	11	N'ampton Spen	10-160	Eynesbury Rovers	10-146	Bourne Town	10-125
	Div 1	5	Daventry Town	10-124	Woodford United	10-116	Higham Town	1-85
Complete	Overall	34	Swindon S'mar	10-144	Brackley Town	10-133	Wantage Town	10-123
Music	Prem Div	19	Swindon S'mar	10-144	Brackley Town	10-133	Wantage Town	10-123
Hellenic	Div 1	15	Old Woodst' T	10-120	Ardley United	10-112	Cirencester U	10-111
Interlink Exp Mid All		19	Shifnal Town	10-152	Pelsall Villa	10-148	Boldmere St M	10-147
North	Overall	34	Atherton Lr	10-157	Curzon Ashton	10-145	Skelmersdale U	10-142
Western	Div 1	21	Atherton	10-157	Skelmersdale U	10-142	St Helens Town	10-132
Trains	Div 2	13	Curzon Ashton	10-145	Warrington Town	1-125	Woodley Sports	2-119
Northern	Overall	32	Denaby United	10-193	Arnold Town	10-155	Pontefract Coll	10-149
Counties	Prem Div	17	Denaby United	10-193	Arnold Town	10-155	Ossett Albion	10-137
East	Div 1	15	Pontefract Coll	10-149	Mickleover Sp	10-145	Glapwell	10141
Arnott	Overall	20	Chester Le St T	10-115	Brandon United	1-112	Morpeth Town	1-108
Insurance	Div 1	8	Chester Le St T	10-115	Morpeth Town	1-108	Thornaby on T	1-98
Northern	Div 2	12	Brandon United	1-112	Penrith	1-100	Wash'ton Ikeda H	1-98
Middlesex		4	Willesden Con	1-69	Deportivo Gal	1-67	Northolt Saints	1-57
Essex Intermediate		5	Great Baddow	10-97	Epping	1-85	Barston	1-82
Kent County		6	Maidstone United	10-113	Snodland	7-110	Phoenix Sports	1-89
Hampshire	Overall	11	Amesbury Town	10-163	Poole Town	10-162	Blackfd & Lang	10-158
	Prem Div	4	Amesbury Town	10-163	Blackfd & Lang	10-158	Colden Common	10-153
	Div 1	4	Poole Town	10-162	Yateley Green	10-156	Winchester Cas	10-156
	Div 2	3	Farnborough NE	10-115	Queens Keep	10-104	AFC Portchester	1-51
Keyline Dorset Comb		3	Witchampton U	1-106	Blandford U	5-82	Weymouth Sports	1-80
Westwards Dev Devon		6	Newton A Spurs	10-260	Stoke Gabriel	10-123	Cullompton Rangers	1-115
Jewson South Western		4	Saltash United	10-157	St Blazey	1-87	Porthleven	1-65
Longwell Blake Angian C		4	Blofield United	1-94	Sprowston Ath	1-86	Wells Town	1-85
PJ Miginty	Overall	11	Walton United	10-135	Framlingham Town	1-119	Old Newton U	1-101
& Sons	Sen Div	7	Walton United	10-135	Framlingham Town	1-119	Woodbridge Ath	1-86
Suffolk / Ips	Other Divs	4	Old Newton U	1-101	Martlesham Ath	1-74	Bramford United	1-52
Kershaw Cambridgeshire		5	Debden	=1-125			Bluntisham Ran	1-88
County			Lakenheath	=2-125				
Herts Senior County		4	Bedmond Sp & S	1-84	Bovingdon	8-83	Bushey Rangers	=1-64
							Kings Langley	=1-64
Cherry Red Chiltonian		14	Penn & Tylers Gre	10-156	Peppard	1-126	Eton Wick	10-124
Gloucestershire County		6	Tytherington Roc	10-128	Cadbury Heath	1-114	Roman Glass St G	1-100
Somerset Senior		3	Portishead	7-176	Timsbury Ath	1-97	Clevedon United	1-91
Skurrays Wiltshire		3	Minety	9-130	Purton Res	9-83	Purton 'A'	1-67
Springvale Vend Midland		5	Eccleshall	10-121	Brocton	10-118	Stone Dominoes	10-99
Redfern	Overall	32	Hucknall Rolls	1-150	Blackwell M W	10-144	Selston	10-133

Internet	Sup Div	18
Cent Mids	Prem Div	14
Banks	Overall	16
Brewery	Prem Div	10
	Div 1 Nth	3
	Div 1 Sth	3
Rapide	Overall	40
Midland	Prem Div	20
Combination	Div 1	10
	Div 2	7
	Div 3	3
Everards	Overall	11
Brewery	Prem Div	8
Leicestershire		
Senior	Div 1	3
Powerleague Notts All		3
Nissan Wearside		4
Carlsberg West Cheshire		3
Green CS Mid Cheshire		4
Finnair	Overall	6
Manchester		
	Prem Div	3
	Other Divs	3
SGL Seat	Overall	7
Cars West	Prem Div	3
Lancashire	Other Divs	4
West Yorkshire		3
West Ridding Co Amateur		4
Other Leagues		29
Youth Clubs / Schools		10
Club Youth X1's		8
F.A. Youth Cup		34
Reserves		27
Wales	Overall	73
League of Wales		15
Fitlock Cymru Alliance		9
C.C. Sports	Overall	24
Welsh	Div 1	12
League	Div 2	5
	Div 3	7
Clwyd		3
Tyn Lon Rover Welsh All		6
Spar Mid Wales		3
Highadmit Projects Amat		3
Carmarthenshire		3
Other Welsh Leagues		6
Scotland	Overall	52
Highland League		8
East of Scotland		5
Ayrshire Region		5
Central	Overall	16
Region	Prem Div	9
	Div 1	7
Eastern	Overall	8
Region	Div 1	4
	Div 2	4
Tayside Region		3
North Region		3
Other Scottish Leagues		1
Ladies	Overall	36
F.A. Premier	Overall	18
	Prem Div	4
	North Div	6
	Sth Div	8
North West		3
Other Leagues		15
F.A. Womens Cup		40
Sunday Leagues		10
F.A. Sunday Cup		43

Hucknall Rolls	1-150
Stanton Ilkeston	1-121
Star	10-151
Star	10-151
Shifnal T Res	8-104
Chaddesley Cor	1-86
Loughborough Ath	10-130
Blackheath Elec	9-126
Loughborough Ath	10-130
Lichfield Enots	3-88
Droitwich st Peters	9-92
Coalville Town	10-164
Coalville Town	10-164
Loughb'ough Dy	10-153
Rainworth M W	10-134
North Shields	10-135
New Brighton	10-144
Middlewich Town	10-149
Prestwich Heys	10-145
Prestwich Heys	10-146
New Mills	7-106
Norcross & Warbk	10-147
Norcross & Warbk	10-147
Barrow Rangers	1-109
Knares'bough T	10-120
Hemsworth M W	10-164
Dag'ham & Red R	10-152
St Andrews U15	10-158
Wo'ton Bassett T	4-114
Staines Town	1-110
Colden Common	10-158=
Penn & Tylers Gr	10-158=
Evans/WilliamSp	3-170
Flexys Cefn Dru	1-152
Holyhead Hotspur	10-137
Pontardawe Town	1-106
Pontardawe Town	1-106
Portos Grange Har	1-64
Pontyclun	1-73
Prestatyn Nova	8-118
Rhyl Delta	10-123
Penrhyncoch	1-83
Cwmaman	8-157
Evans/WilliamSp	3-170
Cwmtillery	10-167
Haddington Ath	=10-146
Kirkintilloch RR	=10-146
Forres Mechan's	10-121
Edinburgh City	1-77
Kilbirnie Ladeside	7-104
Kirkintilloch RR	10-146
Shotts Bon Acc	1-128
Kirkintilloch RR	10-146
Haddington Ath	10-146
Haddington Ath	10-146
Blackburn Utd	10-126
Tayport	10-127
Forres Thistle	2-76
Crichton	1-45
Langford	6-166
Langford	6-166
Tranmere Rovers	7-132
Huddersfield T	8-149
Langford	6-166
Greyhound Gun	10-141
Telford United	10-130
Huddersfield T	1-155
Kings Field Cas	10-167
Leicester City B	1-113

Blackwell M W	10-144
Ripley Town	1-109
Westfields	10-107
Westfields	10-107
Sedgely Wh Lions	=1-70
Shawbury Utd	=10-70
Bromyard Town	1-66
Blackheath Elec	9-126
Studley BLK	10-125
Alvis Oakwood C	10-114
Burman Hi-ton	1-86
Barnt Green Spar	4-84
Loughb'ough Dy	10-113
Thurmaston Town	1-92
Blaby & Whetst A	1-97
IDP Newark	1-78
Ferryhill Ath	10-107
New Brighton Res	10-113
Whitchurch Alport	1-86
Dukinfield Town	=1-106
New Mills	=7-106
Dukinfield Town	1-106
East Manchester R	1-68
Barrow Rangers	1-109
Dalton United	1-73
Hesketh Bank	1-108
Tadcaster Mag sp	1-99
Golcar United	8-122
Ifield Res	10-147
St Andrews U18	10-142
Hendon	=6-103
AFC Sudbury	=2-103
Belper Town	1-98
Cwmtillery	10-167
Caersws	10-151
Porthmadog	1-122
Cardiff Civil Ser	10-102
Cardiff Civil Ser	10-102
Caerleon	1-57
Monkton Swifts	1-69
Prestatyn Nova R	7-107
Llanfairpwll	1-104
Quilsfield	1-73
Llangeinor	10-126
Llanelli Steel	1-155
Gresford Ath	10-147
Buckie Thistle	10-112
Gala Fairydean	1-76
Largs Thistle	1-80
Shotts Bon Acc	1-128
Shettleston	1-107
Renfrew	10-97
Blackburn Utd	10-126
Newtongrange St	1-97
Dunbar United	6-110
Stone Thistle	10-88
Glentanar	1-68
Huddersfield T	8-149
Huddersfield T	8-149
Liverpool	1-100
Wolverh'pton Wndrs	1-120
Barking	7-141
Stockport Celtic	10-134
Colchester Girls	10-109
Cardiff City	1-121
Anglians	10-139
Oakview	1-85

Selston	10-133
Askern Walfare	10-104
Shifnal T Res	8-104
Malvern Town	1-92
Bewdley Town	1-60
Studley BKL	10-125
Bolehall Swifts	10-116
Hams Hall	10-102
Kenilworth Ward	5-73
Kenilworth Tw Re	1-77
Blaby & Whetstone A	1-97
Quorn	=1-75
St Andrews	=1-75
Harborough T Imp	1-57
Linby CW	1-71
Wolviston	1-85
Capenhurst Villa	2-88
Warrington Bor	2-67
East Manchester	1-54
Wythenshawe T	1-61
Hesketh Bank	1-108
Burnley United	1-70
Milnthorp Corins	1-79
Nostell M W	1-91
Phoenix	1-117
Buckland Ath	10-137
Askern Spa T 'B'	10-140
Runcorn	1-78
Dag'ham & Redbr	10-152
Cwmaman	8-157
Llanelli	10-142
Flint Town U	1-103
Cardiff Corin	10-98
Cardiff Corin	10-98
Hoover Sports	1-53
Garden Village	1-68
Caerwys	1-99
Llandudno Junc	10-100
Meifod	1-50
Llantwit Major	1-69
Llanelli Steel Res	1-100
Penrhyndeudra'	10-102
Shotts Bon Acc	1-128
Fraserburgh	3-111
Eyemouth United	1-75
Cumnock	1-70
Shettleston	1-107
Pollok	1-104
Carluke Rovers	1-88
Dunbar Utd	6-110
Camelon	1-71
Tranent	1-74
Luncarty	1-82
Inverurie Loco Wk	1-67
Barking	=7-141
Greyhound Gu	=10-141
Barking	7-141
Aston Villa	1-69
Leeds Utd	1-95
Cardiff City	1-101
Chester City	1-68
Chelmsford	7-101
West Ham U	1-94
Research Mac	10-131
Aidan Rangers	1-83

KIDDERMINSTER HARRIERS
Nationwide Conference Champions 1999-2000

Kidderminster fans welcome their team out for the last game of the season at Altrincham. Photo: Colin Stevens

Two Happy Harriers: Stewart Hadley (left) and Ian Foster (right). Photos: Peter Barnes

KIDDERMINSTER HARRIERS

Match Facts 1999-00

	Date	Comp.	H/A	Opponents	Gate	Result & Score	Goalscorers	League Position
1	14.08	N.C.	H	Dover Athletic	2,175	L 1-2	Skovbjerg 53	
2	17.08	N.C.	A	Yeovil Town	2,473	L 0-1		
3	21.08	N.C.	A	Rushden & Diamonds	2,728	L 3-5	King 7, Petersen 53, Foster 46	21
4	28.08	N.C.	H	Woking	1,729	W 3-2	Taylor 21, Foster 62 (pen), Bennett 90	19
5	30.08	N.C.	A	Forest Green Rovers	919	L 2-3	Foster 75 (pen), Bennett 80	19
6	04.09	N.C.	A	Stevenage Borough	2,894	W 2-0	Bennett 60, Brownrigg 78	18
7	11.09	N.C.	H	Scarborough	1,784	L 0-2		16
8	13.09	N.C.	H	Nuneaton Borough	3,152	L 1-2	Brownrigg 8	16
9	18.09	N.C.	A	Morecambe	1,411	W 1-0	Bennett 84	12
10	25.09	N.C.	H	Doncaster Rovers	2,382	W 1-0	Pope 30	11
11	02.10	N.C.	A	Hayes	635	L 0-2		13
12	09.10	N.C.	H	Yeovil Town	1,769	W 4-0	Druce 26, Hinton 64, Foster 71, Webb 78	10
13	23.10	N.C.	H	Kettering Town	1,708	W 1-0	Druce 55	8
14	01.11	N.C.	A	Hednesford Town	1,522	W 2-0	Stamps 20, Skovbjerg	5
15	06.11	N.C.	A	Telford United	1,409	L 2-3	Bennett 34, Hadley 76	6
16	13.11	N.C.	H	Southport	1,404	W 5-0	Druce 3 (22, 73, 84), Petersen 34p, 63	5
17	20.11	N.C.	A	Northwich Victoria	1,310	D 1-1	Hadley 66	5
18	04.12	N.C.	H	Kingstonian	1,933	W 2-0	Druce 61, Bennett 80.	6
19	11.12	N.C.	A	Scarborough	1,125	D 0-0		6
20	18.12	N.C.	H	Morecambe	2,189	W 2-1	Stamps 70, Hadley 72	4
21	27.12	N.C.	A	Hereford United	4,437	D 1-1	Hadley 69	3
22	03.01	N.C.	H	Hereford United	4,606	D 1-1	Foster 65	4
23	08.01	N.C.	A	Nuneaton Borough	2596	W 3-2	Foster 3 (6, 42, 51)	1
24	15.01	N.C.	H	Hayes	2636	W 2-1	Foster 13, 46	1
25	22.01	N.C.	H	Sutton United	2818	W 1-0	Hinton 48	1
26	29.01	N.C.	A	Kingstonian	1523	W 1-0	Foster 50	1
27	12.02	N.C.	H	Hednesford Town	2,964	W 3-0	Hadley 33, 76, Smith 49	1
28	19.02	N.C.	A	Kettering Town	1,815	L 1-3	Bennett 49	2
29	26.02	N.C.	H	Welling United	2,673	W 4-0	Marsh 45, Foster 60, Bennett 71, Skovbjerg 80	1
30	04.03	N.C.	H	Stevenage Borough	2,832	W 3-1	Foster 77, OG (Smith) 85, Hadley 90	1
31	07.03	N.C.	A	Doncaster Rovers	2,723	W 2-1	Bennett 86, Hadley 89.	1
32	11.03	N.C.	H	Altrincham	3.054	D 1-1	Marsh 55	1
33	18.03	N.C.	A	Welling United	867	W 2-1	Foster 27, King 56	1
34	25.03	N.C.	H	Telford United	3,138	W 2-0	Hadley 28, Bennett 65	1
35	08.04	N.C.	H	Rushden & Diamonds	6,250	W 2-0	Foster 61(p), Brownrigg 85	1
36	15.04	N.C.	A	Southport	2,033	W 1-0	Midgley 9	1
37	22.04	N.C.	H	Northwich Victoria	3,443	W 3-1	Midgley 19, Hadley 25, Marsh 41	1
38	24.04	N.C.	A	Dover Athletic	1,314	W 1-0	Foster 90 (p)	1
39	29.04	N.C.	A	Woking	3,210	L 0-1		1
40	01.05	N.C.	H	Forest Green Rovers	5,301	D 3-3	Hadley 13, Hinton 56, Barnett 68	1
41	03.05	N.C.	A	Sutton United	579	W 3-0	Barnett 10, Marsh 31, Hadley 82	1
42	06.05	N.C.	A	Altrincham	1,761	D 0-0		1

CUP COMPETITIONS

F.A. Cup

16.10	4Q	A	Welling United	760	L	0-2	

Nationwide McMillan Trophy

05.10	1	A	Altrincham	370	L	0-1	

F.A. Trophy

27.11	2	H	Telford United	1,618	L	2-4	Pope 11, Clarkson 67

1	2	3	4	5	6	7	8	9	10	11	Substitutes Used	
Brock	Hinton	Hines	Webb	Weir	Smith	Collins	Peterson	Bennett	Hadley	Skovbjerg	Foster (9), King (5)	1
Brock	Hinton	King	Webb	Brownrigg	Smith	Collins	Petersen	Taylor	Hadley	Skovbjerg	Hines (3), Foster (11), Barnett (10)	2
Brock	Hinton	King	Webb	Brownrigg	Smith	Collins	Petersen	Taylor	Foster	Skovbjerg	Hadley (11), Hines (3), Barnett (7)	3
Williams	Hinton	King	Webb	Brownrigg	Smith	Collins	Petersen	Taylor	Foster	Cunnington	Hines (3), Barnet (7), Bennett (10)	4
Williams	Hinton	Hines	Webb	Brownrigg	Smith	Collins	Barnett	Taylor	Foster	Cunnington	Pope (20, Skovbjerg (8), Bennett (7)	5
Clark	Brownrigg	Stamps	Webb	Pope	Smith	Bennett	Skovbjerg	Druce	Foster	Cunnington	Brock (8), Hadley (9), Hinton (3)	6
Clark	Brownrigg	Stamps	Webb	Pope	Smith	Bennett	Skovbjerg	Druce	Foster	Cunnington	Barnett (11), Hadley (8), Hinton (7)	7
Clark	Hinton	Stamps	Webb	Pope	Smith	Bennett	Skovbjerg	Druce	Foster	Brownrigg	Barnett (8), Hadley (7)	8
Brock	Hinton	Stamps	Webb	Pope	Smith	Bennett	Skovbjerg	Druce	Foster	Brownrigg	Hadley (9)	9
Clark	Hinton	Stamps	Webb	Pope	Smith	Bennett	Skovbjerg	Druce	Foster	Brownrigg	Petersen (8), Hadley (9)	10
Clark	Hinton	Stamps	Webb	Pope	Smith	Bennett	Skovbjerg	Druce	Foster	Brownrigg	Petersen (7), Cunnington (3), Hadley (8)	11
Clark	Hinton	Hines	Webb	Pope	Smith	Bennett	Skovbjerg	Druce	Foster	Brownrigg	Cunnington (11), Hadley (9)	12
Clark	Hinton	Hines	Webb	Pope	Smith	Bennett	Skovbjerg	Druce	Foster	Cunnington	Stamps (10)	13
Clark	Hinton	Hines	Webb	Pope	Smith	Bennett	Skovbjerg	Druce	Stamps	Petersen	Hadley (9)	14
Clark	Hinton	Hines	Webb	Pope	Smith	Bennett	Skovbjerg	Druce	Stamps	Petersen	Clarkson (5), Hadley (10)	15
Clark	Clarkson	Stamps	Webb	Pope	Smith	Bennett	Skovbjerg	Druce	Hadley	Petersen	King (7), Hinton (9)	16
Clark	Clarkson	Stamps	Webb	Pope	Smith	Bennett	Skovbjerg	Druce	Hadley	Petersen	Marsh (11), King (8)	17
Clark	Clarkson	Stamps	Petersen	Hinton	Smith	Bennett	Skovbjerg	Druce	Foster	Marsh	Taylor (9)	18
Clark	Clarkson	Stamps	Webb	Hinton	Smith	Bennett	Skovbjerg	Druce	Foster	Marsh	Hadley (9)	19
Clark	Clarkson	Stamps	Petersen	Hinton	Smith	Bennett	Skovbjerg	Hadley	Foster	Marsh		20
Clark	Clarkson	Stamps	Webb	Hinton	Smith	Bennett	Skovbjerg	Hadley	Foster	Petersen	Druce (10)	21
Clark	Clarkson	Stamps	Petersen	Hinton	Smith	Bennett	Skovbjerg	Hadley	Foster	Marsh	Webb (4), Taylor (10)	22
Clark	Clarkson	Stamps	Petersen	Hinton	Smith	Bennett	Skovbjerg	Hadley	Foster	Marsh	Webb (10)	23
Clark	Clarkson	Stamps	Webb	Hinton	Smith	Bennett	Skovbjerg	Hadley	Foster	Marsh	Brownrigg (7), Druce (9)	24
Clark	Clarkson	Stamps	Webb	Hinton	Smith	Petersen	Skovbjerg	Hadley	Foster	Brownrigg		25
Clark	Clarkson	Stamps	Webb	Hinton	Smith	Bennett	Skovbjerg	Hadley	Foster	Marsh	Brownrigg (4), Druce (9)	26
Clark	Clarkson	Stamps	Petersen	Hinton	Smith	Bennett	Skovbjerg	Hadley	Foster	Marsh	Brownrigg (8), King (7), Druce (10)	27
Clark	Clarkson	Stamps	Petersen	Hinton	Smith	Bennett	Skovbjerg	Hadley	Foster	Marsh	Druce (10)	28
Clark	Clarkson	Stamps	Webb	Hinton	Smith	Bennett	Skovbjerg	Hadley	Foster	Marsh	Burgess (10), Cunnington (11)	29
Clark	Clarkson	Stamps	Webb	Hinton	Smith	Bennett	Skovbjerg	Hadley	Druce	Marsh	Burgess (8), Foster (10)	30
Clark	Clarkson	Stamps	Webb	Hinton	Smith	Bennett	Skovbjerg	Hadley	Foster	Marsh	Druce (8)	31
Clark	Clarkson	Brownrigg	Webb	Hinton	Smith	Bennett	Skovbjerg	Hadley	Foster	Marsh	Druce (8), King (4), Burgess (9)	32
Clark	Clarkson	Stamps	Webb	Hinton	Smith	King	Brownrigg	Hadley	Foster	Marsh	Bennett ((7), Pope (8)	33
Brock	Clarkson	Stamps	Webb	Hinton	Smith	Bennett	Brownrigg	Hadley	Foster	Marsh	Pope (6)	34
Clark	Clarkson	Stamps	Webb	Hinton	Smith	Bennett	King	Hadley	Foster	Marsh	Brownrigg (8), Midgley (9)	35
Clark	Clarkson	Stamps	Webb	Hinton	Smith	Bennett	King	Midgley	Foster	Marsh	Brownrigg (8),Hadley (10)	36
Brock	Clarkson	Stamps	Webb	Hinton	Smith	Brownrigg	King	Midgley	Hadley	Marsh	Bennett (8), Pope (3), Taylor (10)	37
Brock	Clarkson	Stamps	Webb	Hinton	Smith	Bennett	Hadley	Midgley	Foster	Marsh		38
Brock	Clarkson	Stamps	Webb	Hinton	Smith	Bennett	Hadley	Midgley	Foster	Marsh	Druce (9), Pope (4)	39
Brock	Clarkson	Stamps	Pope	Hinton	Smith	Bennett	Hadley	Barnett	Foster	Marsh	Clark (1), Cunnington (2), Taylor (11)	40
Brock	Clarkson	Stamps	Pope	Hinton	Smith	Bennett	Hadley	Barnett	Foster	Marsh	Taylor (10), Hines (3), Davies (6)	41
Brock	Clarkson	Stamps	Pope	Hinton	Smith	Bennett	Hadley	Barnett	Foster	Marsh	Cunnington ((9), Taylor (10), King (11)	42

Sutton United congratulate Kidderminster on winning the Nationwide Conference League. Photo: Garry Letts

Paul Webb fires in a terrific shot against Rushden & Diamonds. Photo: Peter Barnes

Jubilation after a mobile phone message confirming Harriers' promotion to the Football League. Photos: Eric Marsh

LEAGUE INDEX

Leagues are listed alphabetically below with their relevant page numbers. Where a league entry runs to more than one page, the number indicated is that of the first page of the section.
As in previous years, sponsors names have been omitted to ease reference.
League sponsors, however, get their deserved recognition in the appropriate sections.

VASE & TROPHY CLUBS' INDEX

CLUB	F.A. Competitions	League	County F.A.
Abbey Hey FC	Cup/Vase	N.W.C. Div. 1	Manchester FA
Abingdon Town FC	Cup/Vase	Isthmian Div.3	Berks & Bucks FA
Abingdon United FC	Cup/Vase	Hellenic Prem. Div.	Berks & Bucks FA
Accrington Stanley FC	Cup/Trophy	N.P.L. Prem. Div.	Lancashire FA
AFC Newbury	Cup/Vase	Wessex Div. 1	Berks & Bucks FA
AFC Sudbury	Cup/Vase	Eastern Prem. Div.	Suffolk FA
AFC Totton	Cup/Vase	Wessex Div. 1	Hampshire FA
AFC Wallingford	Cup/Vase	Comb. Counties Prem. Div.	Berks & Bucks FA
Aldershot Town FC	Cup/Trophy	Isthmian Prem. Div.	Hampshire FA
Alfreton Town FC	Cup/Vase	N.C.E. Prem. Div.	Derbyshire FA
Almondsbury Town FC	Vase	Hellenic Prem. Div.	Gloucestershire FA
Altrincham FC	Cup/Trophy	N.P.L. Prem. Div.	Cheshire FA
Alvechurch FC	Vase	Mid. Comb. Prem. Div.	Birmingham FA
Andover FC	Cup/Vase	Wessex/	Hampshire FA
Anstey Nomads FC	Vase	Leics. Sen. Prem. Div.	Leicestershire & Rutland FA
Arlesey Town FC	Cup/Vase	Isthmian Div.3	Bedfordshire FA
Armthorpe Welfare FC	Cup/Vase	N.C.E. Prem. Div.	West Riding FA
Arnold Town FC	Cup/Vase	N.C.E. Prem. Div.	Nottinghamshire FA
Arundel FC	Cup/Vase	Sussex Div. 1	Sussex FA
Ash United FC	Cup/Vase	Comb. Counties Prem. Div.	Surrey FA
Ashford Town FC (Middx)	Cup/Vase	Isthmian Div.3	Middlesex FA
Ashford Town FC	Cup/Trophy	Southern - Eastern Div.	Kent FA
Ashington FC	Cup/Vase	Northern Div. 2	Northumberland FA
Ashton United FC	Cup/Trophy	N.P.L. Div. 1	Manchester FA
Atherstone United FC	Cup/Trophy	Southern - Western Div.	Birmingham FA
Atherton Collieries FC	Cup/Vase	N.W.C. Div. 1	Lancashire FA
Atherton LR FC	Cup/Vase	N.W.C. Div. 2	Lancashire FA
Aveley FC	Cup/Vase	Isthmian Div.3	Essex FA
Aylesbury United FC	Cup/Trophy	Isthmian Div. 1	Berks & Bucks FA
Backwell United FC	Cup/Vase	Western Prem. Div.	Somerset FA
Bacup Borough FC	Cup/Vase	N.W.C. Div. 2	Lancashire FA
Baldock Town FC	Cup/Trophy	Southern - Eastern Div.	Hertfordshire FA
Bamber Bridge FC	Cup/Trophy	N.P.L. Prem. Div.	Lancashire FA
Banbury United FC	Cup/Trophy	Southern - Eastern Div.	Oxfordshire FA
Banstead Athletic FC	Cup/Vase	Isthmian Div. 2	Surrey FA
Barking FC	Cup/Vase	Isthmian Div. 2	London FA
Barnstaple Town FC	Cup/Vase	Western Prem. Div.	Devon FA
Barrow FC	Cup/Trophy	N.P.L. Prem. Div.	Lancashire FA
Barrow Town FC	Vase	Leics. Sen. Prem. Div.	Leicestershire & Rutland FA
Barton Rovers FC	Cup/Trophy	Isthmian Div. 1	Bedfordshire FA
Barwell FC	Cup/Vase	Mid. Football All.	Leicestershire & Rutland FA
Bashley FC	Cup/Trophy	Southern - Eastern Div.	Hampshire FA

Basildon United FC	Cup/Vase	Essex Sen.	Essex FA
Basingstoke Town FC	Cup/Trophy	Isthmian Prem. Div.	Hampshire FA
BAT Sports FC	Cup/Vase	Wessex Div. 1	Hampshire FA
Bath City FC	Cup/Trophy	Southern Prem. Div.	Somerset FA
Beaconsfield SYCOB FC	Cup/Vase	Spartan South Mids. Prem. Div.	Berks & Bucks FA
Beckenham Town FC	Cup/Vase	Kent Div. 1	Kent FA
Bedfont FC	Cup/Vase	Comb. Counties Prem. Div.	Middlesex FA
Bedford Town FC	Cup/Trophy	Isthmian Div. 1	Bedfordshire FA
Bedford United FC	Cup/Vase	Spartan South Mids. Prem. Div.	Bedfordshire FA
Bedlington Terriers FC	Cup/Vase	Northern Div. 1	Northumberland FA
Bedworth United FC	Cup/Trophy	Southern - Western Div.	Birmingham FA
Belper Town FC	Cup/Trophy	N.P.L. Div. 1	Derbyshire FA
Bemerton Heath Harlequins FC	Cup/Vase	Wessex Div. 1	Wiltshire FA
Berkhamsted Town FC	Cup/Vase	Isthmian Div. 2	Hertfordshire FA
Bicester Town FC	Vase	Hellenic Prem. Div.	Oxfordshire FA
Bideford FC	Cup/Vase	Western Prem. Div.	Devon FA
Biggleswade Town FC	Vase	Spartan South Mids. Prem. Div.	Bedfordshire FA
Billericay Town FC	Cup/Trophy	Isthmian Prem. Div.	Essex FA
Billingham Synthonia FC	Cup/Vase	Northern Div. 1	Durham FA
Billingham Town FC	Cup/Vase	Northern Div. 1	Durham FA
Bilston Town FC	Cup/Trophy	Southern - Western Div.	Staffordshire FA
Birstall United FC	Vase	Leics. Sen. Prem. Div.	Leicestershire & Rutland FA
Bishop Auckland FC	Cup/Trophy	N.P.L. Prem. Div.	Durham FA
Bishop Sutton FC	Cup/Vase	Western Prem. Div.	Somerset FA
Bishop's Stortford FC	Cup/Trophy	Isthmian Div. 1	Hertfordshire FA
Blackfield & Langley FC	Vase	Wessex Div. 1	Hampshire FA
Blackpool Mechanics FC	Cup/Vase	N.W.C. Div. 2	Lancashire FA
Blackstone FC	Cup/Vase	Utd. Counties Prem. Div.	Lincolnshire FA
Blakenall FC	Cup/Trophy	Southern - Western Div.	Staffordshire FA
Bloxwich Town FC	Vase	Mid. Football All.	Staffordshire FA
Blyth Spartans FC	Cup/Trophy	N.P.L. Prem. Div.	Northumberland FA
Bognor Regis Town FC	Cup/Trophy	Isthmian Div. 1	Sussex FA
Boldmere St Michaels FC	Cup/Vase	Mid. Football All.	Birmingham FA
Bolehall Swifts FC	Vase	Mid. Comb. Prem. Div.	Birmingham FA
Boreham Wood FC	Cup/Trophy	Isthmian Div. 1	Hertfordshire FA
Borrowash Victoria FC	Cup/Vase	N.C.E. Div. 1	Derbyshire FA
Boston Town FC	Cup/Vase	Utd. Counties Prem. Div.	Lincolnshire FA
Bourne Town FC	Cup/Vase	Utd. Counties Prem. Div.	Lincolnshire FA
Bournemouth FC	Cup/Vase	Wessex Div. 1	Hampshire FA
Bowers United FC	Cup/Vase	Essex Sen.	Essex FA
Brache Sparta FC	Vase	Spartan South Mids. Prem. Div.	Bedfordshire FA
Brackley Town FC	Cup/Vase	Hellenic Prem. Div.	Northamptonshire FA
Bracknell Town FC	Cup/Vase	Isthmian Div.3	Berks & Bucks FA
Bradford (Park Avenue) FC	Cup/Trophy	N.P.L. Div. 1	West Riding FA
Braintree Town FC	Cup/Trophy	Isthmian Div. 1	Essex FA
Brandon United FC	Cup/Vase	Northern Div. 1	Durham FA
Brentwood FC	Cup/Vase	Essex Sen.	Essex FA

Bridgnorth Town FC	Cup/Vase	Mid. Football All.	Shropshire FA
Bridgwater Town FC	Cup/Vase	Western Prem. Div.	Somerset FA
Bridlington Town FC	Cup/Vase	N.C.E. Div. 1	EAST RIDING FA
Bridport FC	Cup/Vase	Western Prem. Div.	Dorset FA
Brigg Town FC	Cup/Vase	N.C.E. Prem. Div.	Lincolnshire FA
Brightlingsea United FC	Vase	Eastern Div. 1	Essex FA
Brimsdown Rovers FC	Vase	Spartan South Mids./S	London FA
Brislington FC	Cup/Vase	Western Prem. Div.	Somerset FA
Bristol Manor Farm FC	Cup/Vase	Western Prem. Div.	Gloucestershire FA
Brockenhurst FC	Cup/Vase	Wessex Div. 1	Hampshire FA
Brodsworth FC	Cup/Vase	N.C.E. Prem. Div.	Sheffield & Hallamshire FA
Bromley FC	Cup/Trophy	Isthmian Div. 1	Kent FA
Bromsgrove Rovers FC	Cup/Trophy	Southern - Western Div.	Worcestershire FA
Brook House FC	Cup/Vase	Spartan South Mids. Prem. Div.	Middlesex FA
Buckingham Town FC	Cup/Vase	Utd. Counties Prem. Div.	Berks & Bucks FA
Bugbrooke St Michaels	Cup/Vase	Utd. Counties Prem. Div.	Northamptonshire FA
Burgess Hill Town FC	Cup/Vase	Sussex Div. 1	Sussex FA
Burnham FC	Cup/Trophy	Southern - Eastern Div.	Berks & Bucks FA
Burnham Ramblers FC	Cup/Vase	Essex Sen.	Essex FA
Burscough FC	Cup/Trophy	N.P.L. Prem. Div.	Liverpool FA
Burton Albion FC	Cup/Trophy	Southern Prem. Div.	Birmingham FA
Bury Town FC	Cup/Vase	Eastern Prem. Div.	Suffolk FA
Buxton FC	Cup/Vase	N.C.E. Prem. Div.	Derbyshire FA
Calne Town FC	Cup/Vase	Western Div. 1	Wiltshire FA
Camberley Town FC	Cup/Vase	Isthmian Div.3	Surrey FA
Cambridge City FC	Cup/Trophy	Southern Prem. Div.	Cambridgeshire FA
Canvey Island FC	Cup/Trophy	Isthmian Prem. Div.	Essex FA
Carshalton Athletic FC	Cup/Trophy	Isthmian Prem. Div.	Surrey FA
Carterton Town FC	Cup/Vase	Hellenic Prem. Div.	Oxfordshire FA
Castleton Gabriels FC	Cup/Vase	N.W.C. Div. 2	Lancashire FA
Causeway United FC	Vase	West Mids. Prem. Div.	Birmingham FA
Chadderton FC	Cup/Vase	N.W.C. Div. 2	Manchester FA
Chalfont St Peter FC	Cup/Vase	Isthmian Div.3	Berks & Bucks FA
Chard Town FC	Vase	Western Div. 1	Somerset FA
Chasetown FC	Cup/Vase	Mid. Football All.	Staffordshire FA
Chatham Town FC	Cup/Vase	Kent Prem. Div.	Kent FA
Chatteris Town FC	Vase	Eastern Div. 1	Cambridgeshire FA
Cheadle Town FC	Cup/Vase	N.W.C. Div. 1	Cheshire FA
Chelmsford City FC	Cup/Trophy	Southern - Eastern Div.	Essex FA
Chertsey Town FC	Cup/Vase	Isthmian Div. 2	Surrey FA
Chesham United FC	Cup/Trophy	Isthmian Prem. Div.	Berks & Bucks FA
Cheshunt FC	Cup/Vase	Isthmian Div. 2	Hertfordshire FA
Cheslyn Hay FC	Vase	Mid. Comb. Prem. Div.	Staffordshire FA
Chessington & Hook United FC	Cup/Vase	Comb. Counties Prem. Div.	Surrey FA
Chessington United FC	Vase	Comb. Counties Prem. Div.	Surrey FA
Chester-le-Street Town FC	Cup/Vase	Northern Div. 1	Durham FA
Chichester City United FC	Cup/Vase	Sussex Div. 1	Sussex FA

Chippenham Town FC	Cup/Vase	Western Prem. Div.	Wiltshire FA
Chipstead FC	Cup/Vase	Comb. Counties Prem. Div.	Surrey FA
Chorley FC	Cup/Trophy	N.P.L. Div. 1	Lancashire FA
Christchurch FC	Cup/Vase	Wessex Div. 1	Hampshire FA
Cinderford Town FC	Cup/Trophy	Southern - Western Div.	Gloucestershire FA
Cirencester Academy FC	Vase	Hellenic Prem. Div.	Gloucestershire FA
Cirencester Town FC	Cup/Trophy	Southern - Western Div.	Gloucestershire FA
Clacton Town FC	Cup/Vase	Eastern Prem. Div.	Essex FA
Clapton FC	Cup/Vase	Isthmian Div.3	London FA
Clevedon Town FC	Cup/Trophy	Southern Prem. Div.	Somerset FA
Clevedon United FC	Vase	Somerset Prem. Div.	Somerset FA
Clitheroe FC	Cup/Vase	N.W.C. Div. 1	Lancashire FA
Cobham FC	Cup/Vase	Comb. Counties	Surrey FA
Cockfosters FC	Vase	Spartan South Mids.	London FA
Cogenhoe United FC	Cup/Vase	Utd. Counties Prem. Div.	Northamptonshire FA
Colwyn Bay FC	Cup/Trophy	N.P.L. Prem. Div.	F.A. of Wales
Concord Rangers FC	Cup/Vase	Essex Sen.	Essex FA
Congleton Town FC	Cup/Trophy	N.P.L. Div. 1	Cheshire FA
Consett FC	Cup/Vase	Northern Div. 1	Durham FA
Corby Town FC	Cup/Trophy	Southern - Eastern Div.	Northamptonshire FA
Corinthian Casuals FC	Cup/Vase	Isthmian Div.3	London FA
Cornard United FC	Vase	Eastern Div. 1	Suffolk FA
Cove FC	Cup/Vase	Comb. Counties Prem. Div.	Hampshire FA
Cowes Sports FC	Cup/Vase	Wessex Div. 1	Hampshire FA
Cradley Town FC	Cup/Vase	Mid. Football All.	Birmingham FA
Crawley Town FC	Cup/Trophy	Southern Prem. Div.	Sussex FA
Cray Wanderers FC	Cup/Vase	Kent Prem. Div.	Kent FA
Crook Town FC	Cup/Vase	Northern Div. 1	Durham FA
Crowborough Athletic FC	Vase	Sussex Div. 2	Sussex FA
Croydon FC	Cup/Trophy	Isthmian Prem. Div.	Surrey FA
Croydon Athletic FC	Cup/Vase	Isthmian Div.3	London FA
Cullompton Rangers FC	Vase	Devon	Devon FA
Curzon Ashton FC	Cup/Vase	N.W.C. Div. 1	Manchester FA
Dartford FC	Cup/Trophy	Southern - Eastern Div.	Kent FA
Darwen FC	Cup/Vase	N.W.C. Div. 2	Lancashire FA
Dawlish Town FC	Vase	Western Prem. Div.	Devon FA
Deal Town FC	Cup/Vase	Kent Prem. Div.	Kent FA
Denaby United FC	Cup/Vase	N.C.E. Prem. Div.	Sheffield & Hallamshire FA
Dereham Town FC	Vase	Eastern Div. 1	Norfolk FA
Desborough Town FC	Cup/Vase	Utd. Counties Prem. Div.	Northamptonshire FA
Devizes Town FC	Cup/Vase	Western Prem. Div.	Wiltshire FA
Didcot Town FC	Cup/Vase	Hellenic Prem. Div.	Berks & Bucks FA
Diss Town FC	Cup/Vase	Eastern Prem. Div.	Norfolk FA
Dorchester Town FC	Cup/Trophy	Southern Prem. Div.	Dorset FA
Dorking FC	Cup/Vase	Isthmian Div.3	Surrey FA
Downes Sports FC	Vase	Leics. Sen. Prem. Div.	Leicestershire & Rutland FA
Downham Town FC	Vase	Eastern Div. 1	Norfolk FA

Downton FC	Cup/Vase	Wessex Div. 1	Wiltshire FA
Droylsden FC	Cup/Trophy	N.P.L. Prem. Div.	Manchester FA
Dudley Town FC	Vase	West Mids. Prem. Div.	Birmingham FA
Dulwich Hamlet FC	Cup/Trophy	Isthmian Prem. Div.	London FA
Dunstable Town FC	Vase	Spartan South Mids./S	Bedfordshire FA
Dunston Federation Brewery FC	Cup/Vase	Northern Div. 1	Durham FA
Durham City FC	Cup/Vase	Northern Div. 1	Durham FA
Easington Colliery FC	Cup/Vase	Northern Div. 1	Durham FA
East Ham United FC	Vase	Essex Sen.	London FA
East Preston FC	Cup/Vase	Sussex Div. 1	Sussex FA
East Thurrock United FC	Cup/Vase	Isthmian Div. 2	Essex FA
Eastbourne Town FC	Cup/Vase	Sussex Div. 1	Sussex FA
Eastbourne United FC	Cup/Vase	Sussex Div. 1	Sussex FA
Eastleigh FC	Cup/Vase	Wessex Div. 1	Hampshire FA
Eastwood Town FC	Cup/Trophy	N.P.L. Div. 1	Nottinghamshire FA
Eccleshill United FC	Cup/Vase	N.C.E. Prem. Div.	West Riding FA
Edgware Town FC	Cup/Vase	Isthmian Div. 2	Middlesex FA
Egham Town FC	Cup/Vase	Isthmian Div.3	Surrey FA
Elmore FC	Cup/Vase	Western Prem. Div.	Devon FA
Ely City FC	Cup/Vase	Eastern Prem. Div.	Cambridgeshire FA
Emley AFC	Cup/Trophy	N.P.L. Prem. Div.	Sheffield & Hallamshire FA
Enfield FC	Cup/Trophy	Isthmian Prem. Div.	Middlesex FA
Epsom & Ewell FC	Cup/Vase	Isthmian Div.3	Surrey FA
Erith & Belvedere FC	Cup/Trophy	Southern - Eastern Div.	Kent FA
Erith Town FC	Cup/Vase	Kent Prem. Div.	London FA
Esh Winning FC	Cup/Vase	Northern Div. 2	Durham FA
Evenwood Town FC	Cup/Vase	Northern Div. 2	Durham FA
Evesham United FC	Cup/Trophy	Southern - Western Div.	Worcestershire FA
Eynesbury Rovers FC	Cup/Vase	Utd. Counties Prem. Div.	Huntingdonshire FA
Fairford Town FC	Vase	Hellenic Prem. Div.	Gloucestershire FA
Fakenham Town FC	Cup/Vase	Eastern Prem. Div.	Norfolk FA
Falmouth Town AFC	Cup/Vase	South Western	Cornwall FA
Fareham Town FC	Cup/Vase	Wessex Div. 1	Hampshire FA
Farnborough Town FC	Cup/Trophy	Isthmian Prem. Div.	Hampshire FA
Farnham Town FC	Cup/Vase	Comb. Counties Prem. Div.	Surrey FA
Farsley Celtic FC	Cup/Trophy	N.P.L. Div. 1	West Riding FA
Felixstowe & Walton FC	Cup/Vase	Eastern Prem. Div.	Suffolk FA
Fisher Athletic FC	Cup/Trophy	Southern Prem. Div.	London FA
Flackwell Heath FC	Cup/Vase	Isthmian Div.3	Berks & Bucks FA
Fleet Town FC	Cup/Vase	Wessex Div. 1	Hampshire FA
Fleetwood Freeport FC	Cup/Vase	N.W.C. Div. 1	Lancashire FA
Flixton FC	Cup/Vase	N.W.C. Div. 1	Manchester FA
Folkestone Invicta FC	Cup/Trophy	Southern Prem. Div.	Kent FA
Ford Sports Daventry FC	Cup/Vase	Utd. Counties Prem. Div.	Northamptonshire FA
Ford United FC	Cup/Trophy	Isthmian Div. 1	London FA
Friar Lane OB FC	Vase	Leics. Sen. Prem. Div.	Leicestershire & Rutland FA
Frickley Athletic FC	Cup/Trophy	N.P.L. Prem. Div.	Sheffield & Hallamshire FA

Frome Town FC	Cup/Vase	Western Div. 1	Somerset FA
Gainsborough Trinity FC	Cup/Trophy	N.P.L. Prem. Div.	Lincolnshire FA
Garforth Town FC	Cup/Vase	N.C.E. Prem. Div.	West Riding FA
Gateshead FC	Cup/Trophy	N.P.L. Prem. Div.	Durham FA
Gedling Town FC	Cup/Vase	N.C.E. Div. 1	Nottinghamshire FA
Glapwell FC	Cup/Vase	N.C.E. Prem. Div.	Derbyshire FA
Glasshoughton Welfare FC	Cup/Vase	N.C.E. Prem. Div.	West Riding FA
Glossop North End FC	Cup/Vase	N.W.C. Div. 1	Derbyshire FA
Gloucester City FC	Cup/Trophy	Southern - Western Div.	Gloucestershire FA
Godalming & Guildford FC	Cup/Vase	Comb. Counties Prem. Div.	Surrey FA
Goole AFC	Cup/Vase	N.C.E. Prem. Div.	West Riding FA
Gorleston FC	Cup/Vase	Eastern Prem. Div.	Norfolk FA
Gornal Athletic FC	Vase	West Mids. Prem. Div.	Birmingham FA
Gosport Borough FC	Cup/Vase	Wessex Div. 1	Hampshire FA
Grantham Town FC	Cup/Trophy	Southern - Eastern Div.	Lincolnshire FA
Gravesend & Northfleet FC	Cup/Trophy	Isthmian Prem. Div.	Kent FA
Grays Athletic FC	Cup/Trophy	Isthmian Prem. Div.	Essex FA
Great Harwood Town FC	Cup/Vase	N.W.C. Div. 1	Lancashire FA
Great Wakering Rovers FC	Cup/Vase	Isthmian Div. 2	Essex FA
Great Yarmouth Town FC	Cup/Vase	Eastern Prem. Div.	Norfolk FA
Greenwich Borough FC	Cup/Vase	Kent Div. 1	Kent FA
Gresley Rovers FC	Cup/Trophy	Southern - Western Div.	Derbyshire FA
Gretna FC	Cup/Trophy	N.P.L. Div. 1	Cumberland FA
Guisborough Town FC	Cup/Vase	Northern Div. 1	North Riding FA
Guiseley FC	Cup/Trophy	N.P.L. Div. 1	West Riding FA
Hadleigh United FC	Vase	Eastern Div. 1	Suffolk FA
Hailsham Town FC	Cup/Vase	Sussex Div. 2	Sussex FA
Halesowen Harriers FC	Cup/Vase	Mid. Football All.	Birmingham FA
Halesowen Town FC	Cup/Trophy	Southern Prem. Div.	Birmingham FA
Hall Road Rangers FC	Vase	N.C.E. Div. 1	East Riding FA
Hallam FC	Cup/Vase	N.C.E. Prem. Div.	Sheffield & Hallamshire FA
Hallen FC	Vase	Western Div. 1	Gloucestershire FA
Halstead Town FC	Cup/Vase	Eastern Prem. Div.	Essex FA
Hampton & Richmond Borough FC	Cup/Trophy	Isthmian Prem. Div.	Middlesex FA
Handrahan Timbers FC	Vase	Mid. Comb. Prem. Div.	Birmingham FA
Hanwell Town FC	Cup/Vase	Spartan South Mids. Prem. Div.	Middlesex FA
Harefield United FC	Vase	Spartan South Mids./S	Middlesex FA
Haringey Borough FC	Cup/Vase	Spartan South Mids. Prem. Div.	London FA
Harlow Town FC	Cup/Trophy	Isthmian Div. 1	Essex FA
Harpenden Town FC	Vase	Spartan South Mids./S	Hertfordshire FA
Harrogate Railway FC	Cup/Vase	N.C.E. Prem. Div.	West Riding FA
Harrogate Town FC	Cup/Trophy	N.P.L. Div. 1	West Riding FA
Harrow Borough FC	Cup/Trophy	Isthmian Prem. Div.	Middlesex FA
Harrow Hill FC	Vase	Hellenic Prem. Div.	Gloucestershire FA
Harwich & Parkeston FC	Cup/Vase	Eastern Prem. Div.	Essex FA
Hassocks FC	Cup/Vase	Sussex Div. 1	Sussex FA
Hastings Town FC	Cup/Trophy	Southern - Eastern Div.	Sussex FA

Hatfield Main FC	Cup/Vase	N.C.E. Div. 1	West Riding FA
Havant & Waterlooville FC	Cup/Trophy	Southern Prem. Div.	Hampshire FA
Haverhill Rovers FC	Vase	Eastern Div. 1	Suffolk FA
Heanor Town FC	Vase	Central Mids. Supreme Div.	Derbyshire FA
Heath Hayes FC	Vase	West Mids. Prem. Div.	Staffordshire FA
Hebburn FC	Cup/Vase	Northern Div. 1	Durham FA
Hemel Hempstead Town FC	Cup/Vase	Isthmian Div. 2	Hertfordshire FA
Hendon FC	Cup/Trophy	Isthmian Prem. Div.	Middlesex FA
Herne Bay FC	Cup/Vase	Kent Prem. Div.	Kent FA
Hertford Town FC	Cup/Vase	Isthmian Div.3	Hertfordshire FA
Heybridge Swifts FC	Cup/Trophy	Isthmian Prem. Div.	Essex FA
Highfield Rangers FC	Vase	Leics. Sen. Prem. Div.	Leicestershire & Rutland FA
Highgate United FC	Vase	Mid. Comb. Prem. Div.	Birmingham FA
Highworth Town FC	Vase	Hellenic Prem. Div.	Wiltshire FA
Hillingdon Borough FC	Cup/Vase	Spartan South Mids. Prem. Div.	Middlesex FA
Hinckley United FC	Cup/Trophy	Southern - Western Div.	Leicestershire & Rutland FA
Histon FC	Cup/Trophy	Southern - Eastern Div.	Cambridgeshire FA
Hitchin Town FC	Cup/Trophy	Isthmian Prem. Div.	Hertfordshire FA
Hoddesdon Town FC	Cup/Vase	Spartan South Mids. Prem. Div.	Hertfordshire FA
Holbeach United FC	Cup/Vase	Utd. Counties Prem. Div.	Lincolnshire FA
Holker Old Boys FC	Vase	N.W.C. Div. 2	Lancashire FA
Holmer Green FC	Cup/Vase	Spartan South Mids. Prem. Div.	Berks & Bucks FA
Holwell Sports FC	Vase	Leics. Sen. Prem. Div.	Leicestershire & Rutland FA
Horden CW FC	Cup/Vase	Northern Div. 2	Durham FA
Hornchurch FC	Cup/Vase	Isthmian Div.3	Essex FA
Horsham FC	Cup/Vase	Isthmian Div. 2	Sussex FA
Horsham YMCA FC	Cup/Vase	Sussex Div. 1	Sussex FA
Hucknall Town FC	Cup/Trophy	N.P.L. Prem. Div.	Nottinghamshire FA
Hullbridge Sports FC	Cup/Vase	Essex Sen.	Essex FA
Hungerford Town FC	Cup/Vase	Isthmian Div. 2	Berks & Bucks FA
Hyde United FC	Cup/Trophy	N.P.L. Prem. Div.	Cheshire FA
Hythe United FC	Cup/Vase	Kent Prem. Div.	Kent FA
Ibstock Welfare FC	Vase	Leics. Sen. Prem. Div.	Leicestershire & Rutland FA
Ilford FC	Cup/Vase	Essex Sen.	Essex FA
Ilfracombe Town FC	Vase	Western Div. 1	Devon FA
Ilkeston Town FC	Cup/Trophy	Southern Prem. Div.	Derbyshire FA
Ipswich Wanderers FC	Cup/Vase	Eastern Prem. Div.	Suffolk FA
Jarrow Roofing Boldon CA FC	Cup/Vase	Northern Div. 1	Durham FA
Kempston Rovers FC	Cup/Vase	Utd. Counties Prem. Div.	Bedfordshire FA
Kendal Town FC	Cup/Trophy	N.P.L. Div. 1	Westmorland FA
Kennek Ryhope CA FC	Cup/Vase	Northern Div. 2	Durham FA
Keynsham Town FC	Vase	Western Div. 1	Somerset FA
Kidsgrove Athletic FC	Cup/Vase	N.W.C. Div. 1	Staffordshire FA
Kimberley Town FC	Vase	Central Mids. Supreme Div.	Nottinghamshire FA
Kings Heath FC	Vase	Mid. Comb. Prem. Div.	Birmingham FA
Kings Lynn FC	Cup/Trophy	Southern Prem. Div.	Norfolk FA
Kingsbury Town FC	Cup/Vase	Isthmian Div.3	Middlesex FA

Kington Town FC	Vase	West Mids. Prem. Div.	Herefordshire FA
Kirby Muxloe FC	Vase	Leics. Sen. Prem. Div.	Leicestershire & Rutland FA
Knypersley Victoria FC	Cup/Vase	Mid. Football All.	Staffordshire FA
Lancaster City FC	Cup/Trophy	N.P.L. Prem. Div.	Lancashire FA
Lancing FC	Cup/Vase	Sussex Div. 1	Sussex FA
Langford FC	Vase	Spartan South Mids./S	Bedfordshire FA
Langney Sports FC	Cup/Trophy	Southern - Eastern Div.	Sussex FA
Leatherhead FC	Cup/Trophy	Isthmian Div. 1	Surrey FA
Leek CSOB FC	Cup/Vase	N.W.C. Div. 1	Staffordshire FA
Leek Town FC	Cup/Trophy	N.P.L. Prem. Div.	Staffordshire FA
Leighton Town FC	Cup/Vase	Isthmian Div. 2	Bedfordshire FA
Letchworth FC	Vase	Spartan South Mids./S	Hertfordshire FA
Leverstock Green FC	Vase	Spartan South Mids./S	Hertfordshire FA
Lewes FC	Cup/Vase	Isthmian Div.3	Sussex FA
Leyton FC	Vase	Essex Sen.	London FA
Leyton Pennant FC	Cup/Vase	Isthmian Div. 2	Essex FA
Lincoln United FC	Cup/Trophy	N.P.L. Div. 1	Lincolnshire FA
Littlehampton Town FC	Cup/Vase	Sussex Div. 1	Sussex FA
Liversedge FC	Cup/Vase	N.C.E. Prem. Div.	West Riding FA
London Colney FC	Cup/Vase	Spartan South Mids. Prem. Div.	Hertfordshire FA
Long Buckby FC	Cup/Vase	Utd. Counties Prem. Div.	Northamptonshire FA
Long Eaton United FC	Vase	Central Mids. Supreme Div.	Derbyshire FA
Lordswood FC	Cup/Vase	Kent Div. 1	Kent FA
Louth United FC	Cup/Vase	N.C.E. Div. 1	Lincolnshire FA
Lowestoft Town FC	Cup/Vase	Eastern Prem. Div.	Suffolk FA
Ludlow Town FC	Vase	West Mids. Prem. Div.	Shropshire FA
Lye Town FC	Vase	West Mids. Prem. Div.	Birmingham FA
Lymington & New Milton FC	Cup/Vase	Wessex Div. 1	Hampshire FA
Maidenhead United FC	Cup/Trophy	Isthmian Prem. Div.	Berks & Bucks FA
Maine Road FC	Cup/Vase	N.W.C. Div. 1	Manchester FA
Maldon Town FC	Cup/Vase	Eastern Prem. Div.	Essex FA
Maltby Main FC	Vase	N.C.E. Div. 1	Sheffield & Hallamshire FA
Malvern Town FC	Vase	West Mids. Prem. Div.	Worcestershire FA
Mangotsfield United FC	Cup/Trophy	Southern - Western Div.	Gloucestershire FA
March Town United FC	Vase	Eastern Div. 1	Cambridgeshire FA
Marconi FC	Vase	Mid. Comb. Prem. Div.	Birmingham FA
Margate FC	Cup/Trophy	Southern Prem. Div.	Kent FA
Marine FC	Cup/Trophy	N.P.L. Prem. Div.	Liverpool FA
Marlow FC	Cup/Vase	Isthmian Div. 2	Berks & Bucks FA
Marske United FC	Cup/Vase	Northern Div. 1	North Riding FA
Matlock Town FC	Cup/Trophy	N.P.L. Div. 1	Derbyshire FA
Meir KA FC	Vase	Mid. Comb. Prem. Div.	Staffordshire FA
Melksham Town FC	Cup/Vase	Western Prem. Div.	Wiltshire FA
Merstham FC	Cup/Vase	Comb. Counties Prem. Div.	Surrey FA
Merthyr Tydfil FC	Cup/Trophy	Southern Prem. Div.	F.A. of Wales
Metropolitan Police FC	Cup/Vase	Isthmian Div. 2	London FA
Mickleover Sports FC	Cup/Vase	N.C.E. Div. 1	Derbyshire FA

Mildenhall Town FC	Cup/Vase	Eastern Prem. Div.	Suffolk FA
Milton Keynes City FC	Cup/Vase	Spartan South Mids. Prem. Div.	Berks & Bucks FA
Milton United FC	Vase	Hellenic Prem. Div.	Berks & Bucks FA
Minehead Town FC	Cup/Vase	Western Prem. Div.	Somerset FA
Molesey FC	Cup/Vase	Isthmian Div. 2	Surrey FA
Moneyfields FC	Cup/Vase	Wessex Div. 1	Hampshire FA
Moor Green FC	Cup/Trophy	Southern Prem. Div.	Birmingham FA
Morpeth Town FC	Cup/Vase	Northern Div. 1	Northumberland FA
Mossley FC	Cup/Vase	N.W.C. Div. 1	Manchester FA
Nantwich Town FC	Cup/Vase	N.W.C. Div. 1	Cheshire FA
Needham Market FC	Vase	Eastern Div. 1	Suffolk FA
Nelson FC	Vase	N.W.C. Div. 2	Lancashire FA
Nettleham FC	Vase	Central Mids. Supreme Div.	Lincolnshire FA
Newcastle Benfield Saints FC	Vase	Notts. All. Prem. Div.	Northumberland FA
Newcastle Blue Star FC	Cup/Vase	Northern Div. 1	Northumberland FA
Newcastle Town FC	Cup/Vase	N.W.C. Div. 1	Staffordshire FA
Newmarket Town FC	Cup/Vase	Eastern Prem. Div.	Suffolk FA
Newport County FC	Cup/Trophy	Southern Prem. Div.	F.A. of Wales
Newport(IW) FC	Cup/Trophy	Southern - Eastern Div.	Hampshire FA
North Ferriby United FC	Cup/Trophy	N.P.L. Div. 1	East Riding FA
North Leigh FC	Cup/Vase	Hellenic Prem. Div.	Oxfordshire FA
Northallerton Town FC	Cup/Vase	Northern Div. 2	North Riding FA
Northampton Spencer FC	Cup/Vase	Utd. Counties Prem. Div.	Northamptonshire FA
Northwood FC	Cup/Trophy	Isthmian Div. 1	Middlesex FA
Norwich United FC	Vase	Eastern Div. 1	Norfolk FA
Oadby Town FC	Cup/Vase	Mid. Football All.	Leicestershire & Rutland FA
Oakwood FC	Vase	Sussex Div. 2	Sussex FA
Odd Down FC	Cup/Vase	Western Prem. Div.	Somerset FA
Oldbury United FC	Cup/Vase	Mid. Football All.	Birmingham FA
Oldham Town FC	Cup/Vase	N.W.C. Div. 2	Manchester FA
Ossett Albion FC	Cup/Vase	N.C.E. Prem. Div.	West Riding FA
Ossett Town FC	Cup/Trophy	N.P.L. Div. 1	West Riding FA
Oxford City FC	Cup/Trophy	Isthmian Div. 1	Oxfordshire FA
Paget Rangers FC	Cup/Trophy	Southern - Western Div.	Birmingham FA
Pagham FC	Vase	Sussex Div. 1	Sussex FA
Parkgate FC	Cup/Vase	N.C.E. Div. 1	Sheffield & Hallamshire FA
Paulton Rovers FC	Cup/Vase	Western Prem. Div.	Somerset FA
Peacehaven & Telscombe FC	Cup/Vase	Sussex Div. 2	Sussex FA
Pelsall Villa FC	Cup/Vase	Mid. Football All.	Staffordshire FA
Penrith FC	Cup/Vase	Northern Div. 2	Cumberland FA
Pershore Town FC	Vase	Mid. Comb. Prem. Div.	Worcestershire FA
Peterlee Newtown FC	Cup/Vase	Northern Div. 1	Durham FA
Pickering Town FC	Cup/Vase	N.C.E. Div. 1	North Riding FA
Pontefract Collieries FC	Cup/Vase	N.C.E. Div. 1	West Riding FA
Porthleven FC	Vase	South Western	Cornwall FA
Portsmouth Royal Navy FC	Cup/Vase	Wessex Div. 1	Royal Navy FA
Potters Bar Town FC	Cup/Vase	Spartan South Mids. Prem. Div.	Hertfordshire FA

Potton United FC	Cup/Vase	Utd. Counties Prem. Div.	Bedfordshire FA
Poulton Victoria FC	Vase	West Cheshire Div. 1	Cheshire FA
Prescot Cables FC	Cup/Vase	N.W.C. Div. 1	Liverpool FA
Prudhoe Town FC	Vase	Northern Div. 2	Northumberland FA
Purfleet FC	Cup/Trophy	Isthmian Prem. Div.	Essex FA
Quorn FC	Vase	Leics. Sen. Prem. Div.	Leicestershire & Rutland FA
Racing Club Warwick FC	Cup/Trophy	Southern - Western Div.	Birmingham FA
Radcliffe Borough FC	Cup/Trophy	N.P.L. Div. 1	Lancashire FA
Rainworth MW FC	Vase	Notts. All. Premier Div.	Nottinghamshire FA
Ramsbottom United FC	Cup/Vase	N.W.C. Div. 1	Lancashire FA
Ramsgate FC	Cup/Vase	Kent Prem. Div.	Kent FA
Raunds Town FC	Cup/Vase	Utd. Counties Prem. Div.	Northamptonshire FA
Reading Town FC	Cup/Vase	Comb. Counties Prem. Div.	Berks & Bucks FA
Redditch United FC	Cup/Trophy	Southern - Western Div.	Birmingham FA
Redhill FC	Cup/Vase	Sussex Div. 1	Surrey FA
Ringmer FC	Cup/Vase	Sussex Div. 1	Sussex FA
Rocester FC	Cup/Trophy	Southern - Western Div.	Staffordshire FA
Romford FC	Cup/Trophy	Isthmian Div. 1	Essex FA
Ross Town FC	Vase	Hellenic Div. 1W	Herefordshire FA
Rossendale United FC	Cup/Vase	N.W.C. Div. 1	Lancashire FA
Rossington Main FC	Cup/Vase	N.C.E. Div. 1	Sheffield & Hallamshire FA
Rothwell Town FC	Cup/Trophy	Southern - Eastern Div.	Northamptonshire FA
Royston Town FC	Cup/Vase	Spartan South Mids. Prem. Div.	Hertfordshire FA
Rugby United FC	Cup/Trophy	Southern - Western Div.	Birmingham FA
Ruislip Manor FC	Cup/Vase	Spartan South Mids. Prem. Div.	Middlesex FA
Runcorn FC	Cup/Trophy	N.P.L. Prem. Div.	Cheshire FA
Rushall Olympic FC	Cup/Vase	Mid. Football All.	Staffordshire FA
Saffron Walden Town FC	Cup/Vase	Essex Sen.	Essex FA
Salford City FC	Cup/Vase	N.W.C. Div. 1	Manchester FA
Salisbury City FC	Cup/Trophy	Southern Prem. Div.	Wiltshire FA
Saltdean United FC	Cup/Vase	Sussex Div. 1	Sussex FA
Sandhurst Town FC	Cup/Vase	Comb. Counties Prem. Div.	Berks & Bucks FA
Sandiacre Town FC	Vase	Central Mids. Supreme Div.	Derbyshire FA
Sandwell Borough FC	Cup/Vase	Mid. Football All.	Birmingham FA
Sawbridgeworth Town FC	Cup/Vase	Essex Sen.	Hertfordshire FA
Seaham Red Star FC	Cup/Vase	Northern Div. 1	Durham FA
Selby Town FC	Cup/Vase	N.C.E. Prem. Div.	West Riding FA
Selsey FC	Cup/Vase	Sussex Div. 1	Sussex FA
Selston FC	Vase	Central Mids. Supreme Div.	Nottinghamshire FA
Sheffield FC	Cup/Vase	N.C.E. Prem. Div.	Sheffield & Hallamshire FA
Sheppey United FC	Cup/Vase	Kent Div. 1	Kent FA
Shepshed Dynamo FC	Cup/Trophy	Southern - Western Div.	Leicestershire & Rutland FA
Shepton Mallet AFC	Vase	Somerset Prem. Prem. Div.	Somerset FA
Shifnal Town FC	Cup/Vase	Mid. Football All.	Shropshire FA
Shildon FC	Cup/Vase	Northern Div. 2	Durham FA
Shirebrook Town FC	Vase	Central Mids. Supreme Div.	Derbyshire FA
Shoreham FC	Cup/Vase	Sussex Div. 2	Sussex FA

Shortwood United FC	Cup/Vase	Hellenic Prem. Div.	Gloucestershire FA
Shotton Comrades FC	Cup/Vase	Northern Div. 2	Durham FA
Sidley United FC	Vase	Sussex Div. 1	Sussex FA
Sittingbourne FC	Cup/Trophy	Southern - Eastern Div.	Kent FA
Skelmersdale United FC	Cup/Vase	N.W.C. Div. 1	Liverpool FA
Slade Green FC	Cup/Vase	Kent Div. 1	Kent FA
Slough Town FC	Cup/Trophy	Isthmian Prem. Div.	Berks & Bucks FA
Soham Town Rangers FC	Cup/Vase	Eastern Prem. Div.	Cambridgeshire FA
Solihull Borough FC	Cup/Trophy	Southern - Western Div.	Birmingham FA
Somersett Ambury V&E FC	Vase	Spartan South Mids. Prem. Div.	Hertfordshire FA
Somersham Town FC	Vase	Eastern Div. 1	Huntingdonshire FA
South Shields FC	Cup/Vase	Northern Div. 2	Durham FA
Southall FC	Cup/Vase	Comb. Counties Prem. Div.	Middlesex FA
Southam United FC	Vase	Mid. Comb. Prem. Div.	Birmingham FA
Southend Manor FC	Cup/Vase	Essex Sen.	Essex FA
Southwick FC	Cup/Vase	Sussex Div. 2	Sussex FA
Spalding United FC	Cup/Trophy	Southern - Eastern Div.	Lincolnshire FA
Spennymoor United FC	Cup/Trophy	N.P.L. Prem. Div.	Durham FA
Squires Gate FC	Cup/Vase	N.W.C. Div. 2	Lancashire FA
St Albans City FC	Cup/Trophy	Isthmian Prem. Div.	Hertfordshire FA
St Andrews FC	Vase	Leics. Sen. Prem. Div.	Leicestershire & Rutland FA
St Blazey FC	Cup/Vase	South Western	Cornwall FA
St Helens Town FC	Cup/Vase	N.W.C. Div. 1	Liverpool FA
St Leonards FC	Cup/Trophy	Southern - Eastern Div.	Sussex FA
St Margaretsbury FC	Cup/Vase	Spartan South Mids. Prem. Div.	Hertfordshire FA
St Neots Town FC	Cup/Vase	Utd. Counties Prem. Div.	Huntingdonshire FA
Stafford Rangers FC	Cup/Trophy	Southern Prem. Div.	Staffordshire FA
Stafford Town FC	Cup/Vase	Mid. Football All.	Staffordshire FA
Staines Town FC	Cup/Trophy	Isthmian Div. 1	Middlesex FA
Stalybridge Celtic FC	Cup/Trophy	N.P.L. Prem. Div.	Cheshire FA
Stamford AFC	Cup/Trophy	Southern - Eastern Div.	Lincolnshire FA
Stansted FC	Vase	Essex Sen.	Essex FA
Stanway Rovers FC	Vase	Eastern Div. 1	Essex FA
Stapenhill FC	Cup/Vase	Mid. Football All.	Derbyshire FA
Star FC	Vase	West Mids. Prem. Div.	Shropshire FA
Staveley MW FC	Cup/Vase	N.C.E. Prem. Div.	Derbyshire FA
Stewarts & Lloyds FC	Cup/Vase	Utd. Counties Prem. Div.	Northamptonshire FA
Stocksbridge Park Steels FC	Cup/Trophy	N.P.L. Div. 1	Sheffield & Hallamshire FA
Stotfold FC	Cup/Vase	Utd. Counties Prem. Div.	Bedfordshire FA
Stourbridge FC	Cup/Vase	West Mids./	Birmingham FA
Stourport Swifts FC	Cup/Vase	Mid. Football All.	Worcestershire FA
Stowmarket Town FC	Cup/Vase	Eastern Prem. Div.	Suffolk FA
Stratford Town FC	Cup/Vase	Mid. Football All.	Birmingham FA
Street FC	Cup/Vase	Western Div. 1	Somerset FA
Studley BKL FC	Vase	Mid. Comb. Prem. Div.	Birmingham FA
Sutton Coldfield Town FC	Cup/Trophy	Southern - Western Div.	Birmingham FA
Sutton Town FC	Vase	Mid. Comb. Prem. Div.	Birmingham FA

Sutton United FC	Cup/Trophy	Isthmian Prem. Div.	Surrey FA
Swaffham Town FC	Vase	Eastern Div. 1	Norfolk FA
Swindon Supermarine FC	Vase	Hellenic Prem. Div.	Wiltshire FA
Tadcaster Albion FC	Cup/Vase	N.C.E. Div. 1	West Riding FA
Tamworth FC	Cup/Trophy	Southern Prem. Div.	Birmingham FA
Taunton Town FC	Cup/Vase	Western Prem. Div.	Somerset FA
Thackley FC	Cup/Vase	N.C.E. Prem. Div.	West Riding FA
Thame United FC	Cup/Trophy	Isthmian Div. 1	Oxfordshire FA
Thamesmead Town FC	Cup/Vase	Kent Prem. Div.	London FA
Thatcham Town FC	Cup/Vase	Wessex Div. 1	Berks & Bucks FA
Thetford Town FC	Vase	Eastern Div. 1	Norfolk FA
Thornaby-On-Tees FC	Cup/Vase	Northern Div. 2	North Riding FA
Three Bridges FC	Cup/Vase	Sussex Div. 1	Sussex FA
Tilbury FC	Cup/Vase	Isthmian Div. 2	Essex FA
Tiptree United FC	Cup/Vase	Eastern Prem. Div.	Essex FA
Tiverton Town FC	Cup/Trophy	Southern - Western Div.	Devon FA
Tividale FC	Vase	West Mids. Prem. Div.	Birmingham FA
Tonbridge Angels FC	Cup/Trophy	Southern - Eastern Div.	Kent FA
Tooting & Mitcham United FC	Cup/Vase	Isthmian Div. 2	Surrey FA
Torrington FC	Cup/Vase	Western Div. 1	Devon FA
Tow Law Town FC	Cup/Vase	Northern Div. 1	Durham FA
Trafford FC	Cup/Trophy	N.P.L. Div. 1	Manchester FA
Tring Town FC	Cup/Vase	Isthmian Div.3	Hertfordshire FA
Tuffley Rovers FC	Cup/Vase	Hellenic Prem. Div.	Gloucestershire FA
Tunbridge Wells FC	Cup/Vase	Kent Div. 1	Kent FA
Uxbridge FC	Cup/Trophy	Isthmian Div. 1	Middlesex FA
Vauxhall Motors FC	Trophy	N.P.L. Div. 1	Cheshire FA
VCD Athletic FC	Cup/Vase	Kent	Kent FA
Viking Greenford FC	Cup/Vase	Comb. Counties Prem. Div.	Middlesex FA
Waltham Abbey FC	Cup/Vase	Spartan South Mids. Prem. Div.	Essex FA
Walton & Hersham FC	Cup/Trophy	Isthmian Div. 1	Surrey FA
Walton Casuals FC	Cup/Vase	Comb. Counties Prem. Div.	Surrey FA
Wantage Town FC	Vase	Hellenic Prem. Div.	Berks & Bucks FA
Warboys Town FC	Cup/Vase	Eastern Prem. Div.	Huntingdonshire FA
Ware FC	Cup/Vase	Isthmian Div.3	Hertfordshire FA
Warminster Town FC	Vase	Western Div. 1	Wiltshire FA
Warrington Town FC	Cup/Vase	N.W.C. Div. 2	Cheshire FA
Washington Ikeda Hoover FC	Vase	Northern Div. 2	Durham FA
Wealdstone FC	Cup/Trophy	Isthmian Div. 1	Middlesex FA
Wednesfield FC	Cup/Vase	Mid. Football All.	Birmingham FA
Welling United FC	Cup/Trophy	Southern Prem. Div.	London FA
Wellingborough Town FC	Cup/Vase	Utd. Counties Prem. Div.	Northamptonshire FA
Wellington Town FC	Vase	Western Div. 1	Somerset FA
Welton Rovers FC	Cup/Vase	Western Prem. Div.	Somerset FA
Welwyn Garden City FC	Cup/Vase	Spartan South Mids. Prem. Div.	Hertfordshire FA
Wembley FC	Cup/Vase	Isthmian Div. 2	Middlesex FA
West Allotment Celtic FC	Vase	Northern All. Prem. Div.	Northumberland FA

West Auckland Town FC	Cup/Vase	Northern Div. 1	Durham FA
West Midlands Police FC	Cup/Vase	Mid. Football All.	Birmingham FA
Westbury United FC	Cup/Vase	Western Prem. Div.	Wiltshire FA
Westfield FC	Vase	Comb. Counties Prem. Div.	Surrey FA
Westfields FC	Vase	West Mids. Prem. Div.	Herefordshire FA
Weston Super Mare FC	Cup/Trophy	Southern - Western Div.	Somerset FA
Weymouth FC	Cup/Trophy	Southern Prem. Div.	Dorset FA
Whickham FC	Vase	Northern Div. 2	Durham FA
Whitby Town FC	Cup/Trophy	N.P.L. Prem. Div.	North Riding FA
Whitchurch United FC	Cup/Vase	Wessex Div. 1	Hampshire FA
Whitehawk FC	Cup/Vase	Sussex Div. 1	Sussex FA
Whitley Bay FC	Cup/Vase	Northern Div. 1	Northumberland FA
Whitstable Town FC	Cup/Vase	Kent Div. 1	Kent FA
Whitton United FC	Vase	Eastern Div. 1	Suffolk FA
Whyteleafe FC	Cup/Trophy	Isthmian Div. 1	Surrey FA
Wick FC	Cup/Vase	Sussex Div. 1	Sussex FA
Willand Rovers FC	Vase	Devon	Devon FA
Willenhall Town FC	Cup/Vase	Mid. Football All.	Birmingham FA
Willington FC	Cup/Vase	Northern Div. 2	Durham FA
Wimborne Town FC	Cup/Vase	Wessex Div. 1	Dorset FA
Windsor & Eton FC	Cup/Vase	Isthmian Div. 2	Berks & Bucks FA
Wingate & Finchley FC	Cup/Vase	Isthmian Div.3	London FA
Winsford United FC	Cup/Trophy	N.P.L. Div. 1	Cheshire FA
Winterton Rangers FC	Vase	N.C.E. Div. 1	Lincolnshire FA
Wisbech Town FC	Cup/Trophy	Southern - Eastern Div.	Cambridgeshire FA
Witham Town FC	Cup/Vase	Isthmian Div.3	Essex FA
Witney Town FC	Cup/Trophy	Southern - Eastern Div.	Oxfordshire FA
Witton Albion FC	Cup/Trophy	N.P.L. Div. 1	Cheshire FA
Wivenhoe Town FC	Cup/Vase	Isthmian Div. 2	Essex FA
Wokingham Town FC	Cup/Vase	Isthmian Div. 2	Berks & Bucks FA
Wolverhampton Casuals FC	Vase	West Mids. Prem. Div.	Staffordshire FA
Woodbridge Town FC	Cup/Vase	Eastern Prem. Div.	Suffolk FA
Woodley Sports FC	Cup/Vase	N.W.C. Div. 1	Cheshire FA
Wootton Blue Cross FC	Cup/Vase	Utd. Counties Prem. Div.	Bedfordshire FA
Worcester City FC	Cup/Trophy	Southern Prem. Div.	Worcestershire FA
Workington FC	Cup/Trophy	N.P.L. Div. 1	Cumberland FA
Worksop Town FC	Cup/Trophy	N.P.L. Prem. Div.	Sheffield & Hallamshire FA
Worsbrough Bridge MW FC	Vase	N.C.E. Div. 1	Sheffield & Hallamshire FA
Worthing FC	Cup/Trophy	Isthmian Div. 1	Sussex FA
Wroxham FC	Cup/Vase	Eastern Prem. Div.	Norfolk FA
Yate Town FC	Cup/Vase	Hellenic Prem. Div.	Gloucestershire FA
Yaxley FC	Cup/Vase	Utd. Counties Prem. Div.	Huntingdonshire FA
Yeading FC	Cup/Trophy	Isthmian Div. 1	Middlesex FA
Yorkshire Amateur FC	Cup/Vase	N.C.E. Div. 1	West Riding FA